THE
CANCER
HANDBOOK

THE
CANCER
HANDBOOK

Editor-in-Chief

Malcolm Alison, PhD, FRC Path, DSc
Professor of Experimental Pathology
Faculty of Medicine
Imperial College of Science, Technology and Medicine,
London, UK

VOLUME 1

  nature publishing group

London, New York and Tokyo

Nature Publishing Group © 2002 Macmillan Publishers Ltd

Published by
Nature Publishing Group, 2002
The Macmillan Building, 4 Crinan Street,
London, N1 9XW, UK.

Associated companies and representatives throughout the world

www.cancerhandbook.net
www.nature.com

ISBN: 0-333-77659-3   vol. 1

Distributed on behalf of the Nature Publishing Group in the United States and Canada by
Grove's Dictionaries, Inc.
345 Park Avenue South, New York, NY 10010-1707, USA

ISBN: 1-56159-289-7   vol 2

British Library Cataloguing in Publication Data
A catalogue record for this book is available from the British Library

Library of Congress Cataloguing in Publication Data
A catalogue record for this book is available from the Library of Congress

Typeset by Newgen Imaging Systems (P) Ltd., India
Printed and bound in the UK by Bath Press, Bath.

CONTENTS

VOLUME 1

VOLUME 2

PREFACE

We perceived that there is too little communication between basic researchers and clinicians, and often researchers are unaware of the wider implications of their work across the whole cancer field. Thus, we have endeavoured to make this 'horizontal' connection by the production of a major new reference work, *The Cancer Handbook*. As we know, cancer is a potentially fatal disease caused mainly by environmental factors that mutate genes encoding critical cell-regulatory proteins. The resultant aberrant cell behaviour leads to expansive masses of abnormal cells that destroy surrounding normal tissue and can spread to vital organs resulting in disseminated disease (metastasis), commonly a harbinger of imminent patient death. *The Cancer Handbook* provides a comprehensive overview of scientific and clinical information in cancer research and medicine (oncology). It is aimed at a wide variety of readers wishing to readily access information on all major aspects of cancer biology, without an over-emphasis on clinical detail or very specialised research material.

The hallmarks of the cancer cell phenotype are a disregard for signals to stop proliferating and of signals to differentiate, a capacity for sustained proliferation, evasion of apoptosis, and an ability to invade and to induce angiogenesis. The section 'The Molecular Basis of Cell and Tissue Organisation' in Volume 1 of *The Cancer Handbook* covers these pathways that are so often subverted in cancer cells. The 'carcinogenic advantage' (properties that allow a mutated clone to preferentially expand) is likely to be complex involving not only continued proliferation, but also apoptosis bypass, enhanced motility, changes in cell–cell and cell–matrix adhesion and avoidance of cell cycle checkpoints. Such phenotypic changes are mostly due to genetic mutations fuelled by genetic instability; indeed, spontaneous mutations are insufficient to explain lifetime cancer risk and now there is good evidence that acquired and inherited faulty genome guardians result in a 'mutator' phenotype. Cancer is in fact a rare disease on a cell to cell basis, occurring in about 1 in 3 lifetimes amongst about 10^{14} target cells in the average human, a fact highlighting the key role of DNA protection systems in tumour prevention.

The causes of serious ill health in the world are changing, with infection as a major cause giving way to non-communicable diseases such as cardiovascular disease and cancer. Cancer is largely caused by the environment, and thus (theoretically), largely preventable by the adoption of a more healthy lifestyle. Cancer-causing agents (carcinogens) include physical factors, chemicals and in some cases, infectious agents. The incidence of cancer is rising with a doubling in new cancer cases and cancer-related deaths expected over the next 20 years. Part of the reason for this rise is that life expectancy is steadily rising and most cancers are more common in an ageing population. More significantly, a globalisation of unhealthy lifestyles, particularly cigarette smoking and the adoption of many features of the modern western diet will increase cancer incidence. It has often been said that an individual's chance of getting cancer depends on *nurture*, *nature* and *luck*. The section 'The Causation and Prevention of Cancer' explores at least the first two of these. The environment as the major factor in cancer causation is irrefutable; the incidence of many cancers vary greatly from one part of the globe to another, but a convergence towards local cancer rates among immigrants excludes an in-built genetic explanation of these differences. Most of the important causes of cancer have been identified for at least 20 years, but only now are we beginning to understand the way these carcinogens act at a molecular level. Moreover, vulnerability (*nature*) to potentially genotoxic insult varies from individual to individual, and chapters in this section make reference to molecular epidemiology.

In this new age of molecular biology it is perhaps unfashionable to take too much stock of purely morphological studies, nevertheless at present they are still absolutely essential, being the basis for the present clinical management of patients with cancer. The chapters in the section 'Systemic Oncology' illustrate the common cancers in the major tissues and organs, including information on aetiology, genetic alterations and present clinical management. It is expected that the 'new biology' of robotic microarrays, proteomic technologies and bio-informatics *etc.* will challenge some of our present concepts regarding pathogenesis and classifications.

In Volume 2 of *The Cancer Handbook*, the section 'Pre-Clinical Models for Human Cancer' provides an authoritative review of the many models that are used to dissect the basic processes common to many cancers, as well as organ-specific cancers and common methodologies such as tissue culture and transgenic technology. Insights into how cancer is imaged and how these same techniques can assist in treatment are presented in the section 'Diagnostic Imaging and Image-Guided Intervention'. Finally, particular emphasis has been given to emerging technologies in the treatment of cancer in the section 'The Treatment of Human Cancer'. While acknowledging that surgery, chemotherapy and irradiation continue to represent the most effective tools in the anti-cancer armamentarium, these are exhaustively reviewed in other texts. Since we particularly wished to be relevant to researchers in the oncology field, we have chosen to look ahead to the next generation of molecular therapeutics that specifically target the deregulated pathways that typify neoplastic growth. The completion of the human genome project, the efforts of the Cancer Genome Anatomy Project (CGAP; http://cgap.nci.nih.gov) and others will soon give us molecular profiles of cancer cells, and hopefully lead to individualised, genome-based cancer therapies.

Many people have worked very hard to bring this project to fruition, not least the section editors who have chosen and 'encouraged' their contributing authors from across the globe. Bill Gullick, David Saloman, Nigel Gooderham, Larry Weiss, Michael Bettmann, Joerg Haier, Garth Nicolson, Nick Lemoine and James Abbruzzese – thank you. I am particularly indebted to the staff at Nature Publishing Group who have been so patient and helpful during the gestation of this project: Andrew Diggle who began as Commissioning Editor but left for fields anew, replaced by Roheena Anand and ably assisted by Fozia Khan, Darren Smith who oversaw production of the Handbook, and Gina Fullerlove, Publisher for the department.

Malcolm Alison
September 2001

LIST OF EDITORS

Section Editors

The Molecular Basis of Cell and Tissue Organisation

William J. Gullick
The University of Kent at Canterbury, Department of Biosciences, Canterbury, Kent, UK

David. S. Salomon
National Cancer Institute, Laboratory of Tumour Immunology and Biology, Division of Basic Sciences, National Institutes of Health, Bethesda, Maryland, USA

The Causation and Prevention of Cancer

Nigel Gooderham
Imperial College School of Medicine, Molecular Toxicology Section, Division of Biomedical Sciences, South Kensington, London, UK

Diagnostic Imaging and Image-guided Intervention

Michael A. Bettmann
Dartmouth-Hitchcock Medical Center, Department of Radiology, Lebanon, New Hampshire, USA

Systemic Oncology

Lawrence M. Weiss
City of Hope National Medical Center, Division of Pathology, Duarte, California, USA

Pre-Clinical Models for Human Cancer

Garth L. Nicolson
Institute of Molecular Medicine, Huntington Beach, California, USA

Jörg Haier
Free University of Berlin, Department of Surgery 1, Berlin, Germany

The Treatment of Human Cancer

Nick Lemoine
Imperial College School of Medicine, ICRF Molecular Oncology Unit, Department of Cancer Medicine, London, UK

James Abbruzzese
University of Texas MD Anderson Cancer Center, Department of Gasterointestinal and Digestive Diseases, Houston, Texas, USA

Advisory Editors

Robert Weinberg
MIT, Whitehead Institute for Biomedical Research, Cambridge, Massachusetts, USA

Jerry Shay
University of Texas, Southwestern Medical Center, Dallas, Texas, USA

Lance Liotta
National Cancer Institute, Division of Clinical Sciences, National Institutes of Health, Bethesda, Maryland, USA

LIST OF CONTRIBUTORS

Hans-Olav Adami
Karolinska Institute
Stockholm, Sweden

Mahul Amin
Emory University Hospital
Atlanta, GA, USA

Peter P. Anthony
Royal Devon & Exeter Hospitals and
University of Exeter, Exeter
Devon, UK

Gary E. Archer
Duke University Medical Center
Durham, NC, USA

Sylvia Asa
University Health Network
Toronto, Canada

Paul L. Auclair
Maine Medical Center
Portland, ME, USA

Christopher B. Ballas
University Hospitals of Cleveland and Case Western
Reserve University
Cleveland, OH, USA

Menash Bar-Eli
University of Texas M.D. Anderson Cancer Center
Houston, TX, USA

Vilhelm A. Bhor
National Institute on Aging
National Institutes of Health
Baltimore, MD, USA

Roy Bicknell
University of Oxford
John Radcliffe Hospital
Oxford, UK

Darrell D. Bigner
Duke University Medical Center
Durham, NC, USA

Jacqeline S. Biscardi
University of Virginia
Charlottesville, VA, USA

Mina Bissell
Ernest Orlando Lawrence Berkeley National Laboratory,
Berkeley, CA, USA

Gregory E. Blackman
Dartmouth-Hitchcock Medical Center
Lebanon, NH, USA

Mikhail V. Blagosklonny
National Cancer Institute
National Institutes of Health
Bethesda, MD, USA

Julie L. Boerner
University of Virginia
Charlottesville, VA, USA

Paolo Boffetta
International Agency for Research on Cancer
Lyon, France

Catherine Booth
Paterson Institute for Cancer Research
Manchester, UK

Nancy Boudreau
University of California San Francisco
San Francisco, CA, USA

Janice E. Bowman
University Hospitals of Cleveland and
Case Western Reserve University
Cleveland, OH, USA

Allen Burke
Armed Forces Institute of Pathology
Washington, DC, USA

Catherine Camputaro
Yale University Medical Center
New Haven, CT, USA

Wilson Caparros-Wanderley
Imperial College of Medicine
London, UK

David P. Carbone
Vanderbilt-Ingram Cancer Center
Nashville, TN, USA

Paul L. Carmichael
Imperial College School of Medicine
London, UK

Kermit L. Carraway
University of Miami School of Medicine
Miami, FL, USA

Coralie A. Carothers Carraway
University of Miami School of Medicine
Miami, FL, USA

Thomas Casciani
Dartmouth-Hitchcock Medical Center
Lebanon, NH, USA

Phil Cavanaugh
Institute for Molecular Medicine
Huntington Beach, CA, USA

Tai-Tsung Chang
Kaohsiung Medical University
Kaohsiung, Taiwan

Mark A. Chaplain
University of Dundee
Dundee, UK

Ting-Chao Chou
Memorial Sloan-Kettering Cancer Center
New York, NY, USA

Robert Clarke
Georgetown University School of Medicine
Washington, DC, USA

Joseph F. Contrera
US Food and Drug Administration
Center for Drug Evaluation and Research (CDER)
Rockville, MD, USA

Laura E. Crotty
Duke University Medical Center
Durham, NC, USA

Ara Darzi
Imperial College School of Medicine
London, UK

Thomas Davis
National Cancer Institute
National Institutes of Health
Rockville, MD, USA

Joseph J. Degeorge
US Food and Drug Administration
Center for Drug Evaluation and Research (CDER)
Rockville, MD, USA

Rick Derynck
University of California at San Francisco
San Francisco, CA, USA

Howard Doong
National Cancer Institute
National Institutes of Health
Bethesda, MD, USA

Graeme J. Dougherty
University of California
Los Angeles, CA, USA

Colin Duckett
National Cancer Institute
National Institutes of Health
Bethesda, MD, USA

Suzanne A. Eccles
Institute of Cancer Research
Sutton, Surrey, UK

Beth Euscher
Ohio State University Medical Center
Columbus, OH, USA

Gareth Evans
St Mary's Hospital
Manchester, UK

Shereen Ezzat
Freeman Centre in Endocrine Oncology
Mount Sinai Hospital
Toronto, Canada

William Farrar
National Cancer Institute
National Institutes of Health
Frederick, MD, USA

Cecilia Fenoglio-Preiser
University of Cincinnati School of Medicine
Cincinnati, OH, USA

Tony Fletcher
London School of Hygiene and Tropical Medicine
London, UK

Jonathan A. Fletcher
Harvard Medical School
Brigham and Women's Hospital
Boston, MA, USA

Kar-Ming Fung
Children's Hospital of Philadelphia
Philadelphia, PA, USA

Suzanne Fuqua
Breast Center at Baylor College of Medicine
Houston, TX, USA

David Gatehouse
GlaxoWellcome Research & Development Ltd
Ware, Hertfordshire, UK
Present address: Covance Laboratories Ltd
Harrogate, UK

Stanton Gerson
University Hospitals of Cleveland and
Case Western Reserve University
Cleveland, OH, USA

Debra A. Gervais
Massachusetts General Hospital
Boston, MA, USA

Raffaella Giavazzi
Mario Negri Institute for Pharmacological Research
Bergamo, Italy

Michael Goggins
John Hopkins Medical Institutions
Baltimore, MD, USA

William J. Gradishar
Robert H. Lurie Comprehensive Cancer Center
Northwestern University Medical School
Chicago, IL, USA

Susan F. Grammer
Biotechwrite: Biomedical and Science Communications
Houston, TX, USA

Jean L. Grem
National Cancer Institute
National Naval Medical Center
Bethesda, MD, USA

Beverly Griffin
Imperial College School of Medicine at St Mary's
London, UK

Andy Grove
National Cancer Institute
National Institutes of Health
Bethesda, MD, USA

Lucy Hann
Memorial-Sloan Kettering Cancer Center
New York, NY, USA

Andrew Harbottle
University of Newcastle Upon Tyne
Newcastle upon Tyne, UK

Adrian L. Harris
Imperial Cancer Research Fund
Institute of Molecular Medicine
John Radcliffe Hospital
Oxford, UK

Philip Hasleton
Wythenshawe Hospital
Manchester, UK

Ernie Hawk
National Cancer Institute
National Institutes of Health
Bethesda, MD, USA

Stephen S. Hecht
University of Minnesota Cancer Center
Minneapolis, MN, USA

Matthew H. Herynk
University of Texas M. D. Anderson Cancer Center
Houston, TX, USA

Richard Hill
Princess Margaret Hospital
Ontario Cancer Institute
Toronto, Canada

Torsten Hopp
Breast Center at Baylor College of Medicine
Houston, TX, USA

O. M. Zack Howard
National Cancer Institute
National Institutes of Health
Frederick, MD, USA

Ralph H. Hruban
John Hopkins Medical Institutions
Baltimore, MD, USA

Arun Jain
Massachusetts Eye and Ear Infirmary
Boston, MA, USA

Frederick A. Jakobiec
Massachusetts Eye and Ear Infirmary
Boston, MA, USA

Jeremy R. Jass
University of Queensland
Brisbane, Australia

Rafael Jimenez
Emory University Hospital
Atlanta, GA, USA

Randy Jirtle
Duke University Medical Center
Durham, NC, USA

V. Craig Jordan
Robert H. Lurie Comprehensive Cancer Center
Northwestern University Medical School
Chicago, IL, USA

Sanjeeva Kalva
Massachusetts General Hospital
Boston, MA, USA

Darian Kameh
University of Florida Health Science Center
Jacksonville, FL, USA

Mohammed Kashani-Sabet
University of California at San Francisco
San Francisco, CA, USA

Stanley B. Kaye
Institute of Cancer Research and Royal Marsden Hospital
Sutton, Surrey, UK

Bruce Keith
National Cancer Institute
National Naval Medical Center
Bethesda, MD, USA

Gary J. Kelloff
National Cancer Institute
National Institutes of Health
Rockville, MD, USA

Eugenie S. Kleinerman
University of Texas M. D. Anderson Cancer Center
Houston, TX, USA

Yasuhiro Koh
National Cancer Research Institute
Tokyo, Japan

Kurt Kohn
National Cancer Institute
National Institutes of Health
Bethesda, MD, USA

Elise C. Kohn
National Cancer Institute
National Institutes of Health
Bethesda, MD, USA

Samantha Kubaska
Massachusetts General Hospital
Boston, MA, USA

Pagona Lagiou
University of Athens Medical School
Goudi, Athens, Greece

Karen Lapidos
National Cancer Institute
National Institutes of Health
Bethesda, MD, USA

Julia Lawrence
Louisiana State University Health Science Center
New Orleans, LA, USA

Michael Lev
Massachusetts General Hospital
Boston, MA, USA

Elsie Levin
Boston University School of Medicine
Boston, MA, USA

Petra Lewis
Dartmouth-Hitchcock Medical Center
Lebanon, NH, USA

Nancy L. Lewis
Fox Chase Cancer Center
Philadelphia, PA, USA

Esther van Lieshout
St Radboud University Hospital
Nijmegen, The Netherlands

Matthias Lindner
German Cancer Research Center
Heidelberg, Germany

Lance Liotta
National Cancer Institute
National Institutes of Health
Bethesda, MD, USA

Reuben Lotan
University of Texas M. D. Anderson Cancer Center
Houston, TX, USA

Brian C. Lucey
Massachusetts General Hospital
Boston, MA, USA

Michael M. Maher
Massachusetts General Hospital
Boston, MA, USA

Emma Marshman
Paterson Institute for Cancer Research
Manchester, UK

Shahla Masood
University of Florida Health Science Center
Jacksonville, FL, USA

William McBride
University of California
Los Angeles, CA, USA

Iain A. McNeish
Imperial College School of Medicine
London, UK

Taha Merghoub
Memorial Sloan-Kettering Cancer Center
New York, NY, USA

Luka Milas
M. D. Anderson Hospital and Tumour Institute
Houston, TX, USA

Jeffrey Miller
University of Minnesota
Minneapolis, MN, USA

Fred Miller
Barbara Ann Karmanos Cancer Institute and
Wayne State University School of Medicine
Detroit, MI, USA

Ute Modlich
University of Oxford
John Radcliffe Hospital
Oxford, UK

Carmela Morales
University of Texas Southwestern Medical Center
Dallas, TX, USA

Carl Morisson
Ohio State University Medical Center
Columbus, OH, USA

Peter Mueller
Massachusetts General Hospital
Boston, MA, USA

Hans-Konrad Mueller-Hermelink
Universitat Wurzburg
Wurzburg, Germany

Susanne Muerkoster
German Cancer Research Center
Heidelberg, Germany

Rolf Muller
Phillips University of Marburg Medical School
Marburg, Germany

Susan K. Murphy
Duke University Medical Center
Durham, NC, USA

George F. Murphy
Jefferson Medical College
Philadelphia, PA, USA

Minako Nagao
Tokyo University of Agriculture
Tokyo, Japan

Arnon Nagler
Chaim Sheba Medical Center
Tel Hashomer, Israel

Antonio G. Nascimento
Mayo Clinic
Mayo Medical School
Rochester, MN, USA

Marwan Y. Nasralla
Institute for Molecular Medicine
Huntington Beach, CA, USA

Retha Newbold
National Institute of Environmental Health Science
Research Triangle Park, NC, USA

Robert Newton
ICRF Radcliffe Infirmary
Oxford, UK

Kazuto Nishio
National Cancer Center Research Institute
Tokyo, Japan

Amy E. Noffsinger
University of Cincinnati School of Medicine
Cincinnati, OH, USA

Kees Nooter
Rotterdam Cancer Institute (Daniel den Hoed Kliniek) and
University Hospital Rotterdam
Rotterdam, The Netherlands

Gerard Nuovo
Ohio State University Medical Center
Columbus, OH, USA

Andre Oliveira
Mayo Graduate School of Medicine
Rochester, MN, USA

Christopher N. Otis
Tufts University School of Medicine
Baystate Medical Center
Springfield, MA, USA

German Ott
Universitat Wurzburg
Wurzburg, Germany

Pier P. Pandolfi
Memorial Sloan Kettering Cancer Center
New York, NY, USA

Arthur B. Pardee
Dana-Farber Cancer Institute
Boston, MA, USA

Sarah Parsons
University of Virginia
Charlottesville, VA, USA

Cloud P. Paweletz
National Cancer Institute
National Institutes of Health
Bethesda, MD, USA

Wilbert H. M. Peters
St Radboud University Hospital
Nijmegen, The Netherlands

David H. Phillips
Institute of Cancer Research
Sutton, Surrey, UK

J. Marc Pipas
Dartmouth-Hitchcock Medical Center
Lebanon, NH, USA

Chris Potten
Paterson Institute for Cancer Research
Manchester, UK

Jing Qing
University of California at San Francisco
San Francisco, CA, USA

Robert Radinsky
AMGEN, Inc.
Thousand Oaks, CA, USA

Manfred F. Rajewsky
University of Essen Medical School and
West German Cancer Center
Essen, Germany

Karen Rasmussen
Maine Center for Cancer Medicine
Scarborough, ME, USA

John C. Reed
The Burnham Institute
La Jolla, CA, USA

Jane S. Reese
University Hospitals of Cleveland and Case Western
Reserve University
Cleveland, OH, USA

Ellen Richmond
National Cancer Institute
National Institutes of Health
Bethesda, MD, USA

Heimo Riedel
Wayne State University
Detroit, MI, USA

Marian Rocha
German Cancer Research Center
Heidelberg, Germany

Arthur T. Rosenfield
Yale University Medical Center
New Haven, CT, USA

Justin C. Roth
University Hospitals of Cleveland and Case Western
Reserve University
Cleveland, OH, USA

Jack A. Roth
University of Texas M. D. Anderson Cancer Center
Houston, TX, USA

Vania P. Rudolf
Jefferson Medical College
Philadelphia, PA, USA

Jose Russo
Fox Chase Cancer Center
Philadephia, PA, USA

Irma Russo
Fox Chase Cancer Center
Philadelphia, PA, USA

Dushyant Sahani
Massachusetts General Hospital
Boston, MA, USA

Nagahiro Saijo
National Cancer Center Hospital
Tokyo, Japan

Sanjay Saini
Massachussetts General Hospital
Boston, MA, USA

John H. Sampson
Duke University Medical Center
Durham, NC, USA

Kevin J. Scanlon
Keck Graduate Institute
Claremont, CA, USA

Volker Schirrmacher
German Cancer Research Center
Heidelberg, Germany

Jeffrey L. Schwartz
University of Washington
Seattle, WA, USA

Jerry W. Shay
University of Texas Southwestern Medical Center
Dallas, TX, USA

Marissa Shrader
University of Texas M. D. Anderson Cancer Center
Houston, TX, USA

Zahid Siddik
University of Texas M. D. Anderson Cancer Center
Houston, TX, USA

Alan Siegel
Dartmouth-Hitchcock Medical Center
Lebanon, NH, USA

Caroline Sigman
CCS Associates
Mountain View, CA, USA

Anne Silas
Dartmouth-Hitchcock Medical Center
Lebanon, NH, USA

Alex Sparreboom
Rotterdam Cancer Institute (Daniel den Hoed Kliniek) and
University Hospital Rotterdam
Rotterdam, The Netherlands

Grant N. Stemmerman
University of Cincinnati School of Medicine
Cincinnati, OH, USA

Takashi Sugimura
National Cancer Center Research Institute
Tokyo, Japan

Mario Sznol
Vion Pharmaceuticals
New Haven, CT, USA

Pheroze Tamboli
University of Texas M. D. Anderson Cancer Center
Houston, TX, USA

Giulia Taraboletti
Mario Negri Insitutute for Pharmacological Research
Bergamo, Italy

Dimitrios Trichopoulos
Harvard School of Public Health
Boston, MA, USA

John Trojanowski
University of Pennsylvania
Philadelphia, PA, USA

Kevin J. Turner
Imperial Cancer Research Fund
Institute of Molecular Medicine
John Radcliffe Hospital
Oxford, UK

Thomas Ulbright
Indiana University School of Medicine
Indianapolis, IN, USA

Victor Umansky
German Cancer Research Center
Heidelberg, Germany

Harri Vainio
International Agency for Research on Cancer
Lyon, France

Jaap Verweij
Rotterdam Cancer Institute (Daniel den Hoed Kliniek) and
University Hospital Rotterdam
Rotterdam, The Netherlands

Paolo Vineis
Institute for Scientific Interchange and
University of Turin
Turin, Italy

Jayne L. Viner
National Cancer Institute
National Institutes of Health
Bethesda, MD, USA

Renu Virmani
Armed Forces Institute of Pathology
Washington, DC, USA

Punit D. Wadhwa
University Hospitals of Cleveland and Case Western
Reserve University
Cleveland, OH, USA

Keiji Wakabayashi
National Cancer Center Research Institute
Tokyo, Japan

Lihua Wang
National Cancer Institute
National Institutes of Health
Frederick, MD, USA

Louis M. Weiner
Fox Chase Cancer Center
Philadelphia
PA, USA

Bruce Wenig
The Albert Einstein College of Medicine/
Montefiore Medical Center
Bronx, NY, USA

Sharon P. Wilczynski
City of Hope National Medical Center
Duarte, CA, USA

Robb E. Wilentz
John Hopkins Medical Institutions
Baltimore, MD, USA

Paul Workman
Institute of Cancer Research and
Royal Marsden Hospital
Sutton, Surrey, UK

Laura L. Worth
University of Texas M. D. Anderson Cancer Center
Houston, TX, USA

Woodring E. Wright
University of Texas Southwestern Medical Center
Dallas, TX, USA

Nicholas A. Wright
Imperial Cancer Research Fund and
University of London
London, UK

Anthony Wynshaw-Boris
University of California, San Diego School of Medicine
La Jolla, CA, USA

Weihua Xiao
National Cancer Institute
National Institutes of Health
Frederick, MD, USA

Xiaoyi Yang
National Cancer Institute
National Institutes of Health
Frederick, MD, USA

Li Yang
Vanderbilt-Ingram Cancer Center
Nashville, TN, USA

Mitsuyaki Yoshida
Banyu Tsukuba Research Institute
Tsukuba, Ibaraki, Japan

Marlene Zawin
Yale University Medical Center
New Haven, CT, USA

Steven P. Zielske
University Hospitals of Cleveland and
Case Western Reserve University
Cleveland, OH, USA

Paul Ziprin
Imperial College School of Medicine
London, UK

Part A
The Molecular Basis of Cell and Tissue Organisation

Chapter 1
Cell and Tissue Organisation

Emma Marshman, Catherine Booth and Christopher S. Potten
Paterson Institute for Cancer Research, Manchester, UK

CONTENTS

- Tissue Classification
- Cell Proliferation and its Control
- Cellular Hierarchies
- Cell Organisation in Specific Tissues
- Control of Tissue Organisation in Development
- Cancer Development and Tissue Organisation
- Conclusions

To understand the changes that take place during cancer development, it is important to understand the basic principles of cell and tissue organisation and the mechanisms that control growth and structure.

TISSUE CLASSIFICATION

Groups of cells that are similar in structure, function and embryonic origin are referred to as tissues. The tissues of the body can be divided into four main groups as follows:

Epithelial Tissue

Epithelial tissue covers most of the free surfaces of the body, both internal and external, and often invaginates to form specialized structures such as glands. For example, it forms the outer layer of skin and the lining of the gastrointestinal tract and breast ducts. In addition to providing physical protection, epithelial cells control permeability, provide sensation and produce specialized secretions from glands, e.g. mucus, hormones and enzymes. Taking all the surface linings and their associated glands and structures together, epithelial tissues make up the major part of total body mass.

Connective Tissue

Connective tissue, or mesenchyme, protects and supports the body and its organs. Types of mesenchymal tissue include cartilage, bone and adipose tissue. The reticuloendothelial system is often considered a type of connective tissue. Reticuloendothelial cells are the defensive and oxygen-supplying cells of the body and are mostly derived from bone marrow precursor cells. The reticuloendothelial cells or haematopoietic cells are distributed throughout the body as free cells in blood and lymph or make up organs such as the spleen and lymph nodes.

Muscle Tissue

Muscle tissue is responsible for movement, such as skeletal movement, but also movement of food, blood and secretions. To carry out this function, muscle cells possess organelles and properties distinct from those of other cells which makes them capable of powerful contractions that shorten the cell along the longitudinal axis. There are three types of muscle tissue: skeletal, cardiac and smooth muscle. The contraction mechanism is similar in all three, but they differ in their internal organisation.

Nervous Tissue

Nervous tissue is specialized for the conduction of electrical impulses from one region of the body to another. Neural tissue consists of two basic cell types, neurons and supporting cells called glial cells. About 98% of the neural tissue in the body is concentrated in the brain and spinal chord with the rest making up the peripheral nervous system.

Since each tissue is made up of a number of specialized cell types that maintain tissue structure and function, there must be exquisite control over cell numbers to maintain the integrity of the tissue. The ability to respond to cell loss (via damage or senescence) varies in the different tissues, since not all cells have the same capacity for regeneration. Tissues can therefore be classified into three groups depending on this cell replacement capability, as follows:

Rapidly Self-renewing Tissues

In tissues such as the skin, the intestine and the haematopoietic system, there is continuous cell loss either by surface abrasion, by damage or because the cell has aged. This cell loss has to be compensated for by cell production (proliferation), otherwise the tissue would begin to shrink (or expand if proliferation exceeds cell loss). Thus, the number of cells produced by cell division precisely balances cell loss in order for the tissue to maintain its size and mass.

Conditionally Renewing Tissues

In tissues such as the liver, breast, prostate and connective tissue, there is little or no replacement under normal circumstances. However, there is potential for regenerative proliferation under conditions in which the tissue's integrity is significantly compromised, e.g. damage or disease, or in response to hormonal influences.

Essentially Non-renewing Tissues

In some tissues, e.g. the female germ line and the central nervous system, there is little or no cell replacement or capacity for regeneration in the adult.

CELL PROLIFERATION AND ITS CONTROL

Control of cell division within a tissue is particularly important in rapidly self-renewing tissues when proliferation must balance cell loss. Although the exact mechanisms used by tissues to sense the need to increase or decrease cell division are unclear, it is obvious that proliferation must be regulated by a complex network of signals and messages including growth factors, cytokines and hormones. These messages can be produced by the cells themselves (autocrine regulation), may be produced by neighbouring cells of either similar or unrelated cell types (paracrine regulation, e.g. epithelial–mesenchymal interactions), and by circulating hormones (systemic endocrine regulation) as illustrated in **Figure 1**.

Some of the network of signals that control tissue homeostasis may prevent overproduction where necessary or arrest the cell cycle if a cell is damaged. In the latter scenario DNA damage is detected and the cell cycle arrested as it reaches specific checkpoints. These checkpoints will be discussed in more detail in the chapter Regulation of the Cell Cycle. At the checkpoint, the defective DNA can either be repaired or, if too severe, the cell may commit suicide in a process referred to as

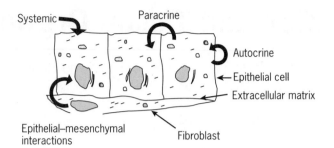

Figure 1 Signal mechanisms involved in cellular communication.

apoptosis. Apoptosis will be discussed in detail in the chapter *Apoptosis*.

Malfunctions of Control

The first stages of cancer formation are associated with malfunctions in the control mechanisms described above, in such a way that the critical balance between cell proliferation and cell loss by differentiation or apoptosis is disturbed or deregulated. If this balance is shifted in favour of proliferation, the tissue will expand in a progressive and eventually uncontrolled manner, distorting the tissue structure and function. The balance may only need to be shifted slightly in favour of proliferation for a cancer to develop. Cancer development will be further described towards the end of this chapter.

CELLULAR HIERARCHIES

At the bottom of all the hierarchies in the body are the embryonic stem cells. Embryonic stem cells are referred to as totipotent, i.e. they are capable of differentiating into all types of tissue. Embryonic cells may separate and each form complete embryos, e.g. twins. Human embryonic stem cells have recently been isolated from embryonic tissue and can be maintained as undifferentiated cells in laboratory cultures under certain carefully controlled conditions. Even after 4–5 months in culture, these cells are still able to form types of cells from all three embryonic germ layers; including gut epithelium (endoderm), cartilage, bone, smooth muscle and striated muscle (mesoderm) and neural epithelium and embryonic ganglia (ectoderm) (Thomson *et al.*, 1998). Studies with embryonic stem cells will give valuable information about the mechanisms controlling differentiation and organisation and may ultimately allow us to grow replacements for tissues or even organs that have been damaged by disease.

In development, these embryonic stem cells are abundant; however, as the animal ages the cellular potency becomes more and more restricted (the capability for wide gene expression becomes more restricted) until ultimately stem cells only remain in tissues capable of regeneration.

Such stem cells are found at the point of origin of cell production within an adult tissue and can produce a steady stream of cells (Potten, 1992). These daughter cells, termed dividing transit cells, can expand their numbers via further cell divisions and mature into functional differentiated cells, called simple transit cells. Simple transit cells are eventually lost from the tissue at the end of their functional lifespan. The linear evolution in the adult animal tissue is therefore organized into a hierarchy or 'family tree' with the cells responsible for cell production at the bottom and the functional cells at the top. The specialization process involved in the progression from the bottom to the top of the hierarchy, termed differentiation, represents a change in the pattern of gene expression which may be the consequence of changes either in the internal programming of the cell or of the external stimuli that affect the cell.

At the bottom of the adult hierarchy, and ultimately responsible for cell replacement in renewing tissues, are the pluripotent stem cells (capable of producing many but not all differentiated cell lineages, i.e. they are not totipotent). In many cases, these cells cannot be identified by a common marker or a single property. Instead, cells are classed as stem cells if they exhibit or have the potential to exhibit the following properties:

1. stem cells are undifferentiated (relative to the cells in the tissue);
2. stem cells are capable of proliferation;
3. stem cells are capable of self-maintenance;
4. stem cells can produce differentiated progeny;
5. stem cells can regenerate the tissue after damage.

When a stem cell divides, under normal circumstances, it is thought to generate a daughter that is another stem cell (thereby maintaining itself) and one daughter that will move up the hierarchy towards differentiation. Although this situation remains to be conclusively proven, it is certainly the average situation that must occur in an adult tissue. Whether the determinants of such division are intrinsic to the stem cell itself or are influenced by the surrounding environment also remains to be determined.

If stem cell numbers need to increase or decrease in response to external stimuli, this asymmetric form of cell division will switch to symmetrical division in which either two stem cell daughter or two nonstem cell daughters are produced. Stem cell expansion will inevitably increase cellular production (i.e. speed up regeneration, generate hyperplasia), whereas stem cell removal will reduce or remove cellular production (depending on how many stem cells remain in the tissue), e.g. generate aplasia or hypoplasia.

The next steps in the life of a nonstem cell daughter, particularly in a rapidly renewing tissue, are the amplification of cell numbers. The daughter cells divide a number of times and are known as transit amplifying cells. During this time the cells gradually appear to lose their stem cell properties and acquire a more mature phenotype until, after a given number of divisions, they are fully differentiated cells. These transit amplifying cells are therefore generally a short-lived phenotype, although during the early cell generations they may be called upon to behave as stem cells in a trauma situation in some tissues. With successive divisions they eventually lose this ability. The later-generation differentiated cells then perform the function for which they were generated, gradually senesce and die. This is also therefore a form of programmed cell death.

The advantage of such an organisation is that only a few stem cells are needed to maintain a whole tissue. Generally, these stem cells have a slow cell cycle time which allows for genetic housekeeping, i.e. time to repair any genetic damage. Small numbers of stem cells followed by around five generations of transit amplifying cells create an environment in which the greatest risk of introducing a mutation (during division) is in the transit cells (which are ultimately lost from the tissue) rather than in the long-lived stem cells. In conditionally renewing tissues the organisation is less clear. Although stem cells must exist, it is possible that they are normally quiescent or are cycling very slowly, and are only activated by trauma or hormonal stimuli.

The progression from stem cell to differentiated cell could be preprogrammed but is more likely to be controlled by extrinsic factors. An organized hierarchy obviously experiences (and/or is able to respond to) different control signals at different stages. This can be aided by a physical organisation, such that there is a spatial distribution within the hierarchy controlled by a series of microenvironments or niches. A gradient of controlling factors probably exists along the maturation axis.

Particularly important in the microenvironment is the basement membrane upon which epithelial cells sit. This basement membrane is a highly organized extracellular matrix (ECM) made up of proteins such as collagen and laminins. The effects of the matrix are primarily mediated by cell adhesion molecules such as integrins and cadherins which are families of cell surface receptors. Cell adhesion molecules help to connect the exterior of the cell with the interior of the cell in two ways: by transducing signals initiating from the extracellular interactions and by mediating structural linkages between the cytoskeleton and the ECM of other cells (Horwitz and Werb, 1998). These processes will be further described in the chapters *Wnt Signal Transduction* and *Extracellular Matrix: The Networking Solution.*

CELL ORGANISATION IN SPECIFIC TISSUES

To illustrate the points made in the previous section, the stem cells and hierarchies of a number of tissues will be described in more detail.

Haematopoietic System

The hierarchical organisation of the continually renewing cells in the bone marrow has been extensively studied. All mature blood cells in the body are derived from a small number of stem cells that reside in the bone marrow in a process called haematopoiesis. Over 10^{11} new cells are produced daily to maintain homeostasis since the majority of mature blood cells are short-lived. In addition, normal daily cell replacement must also be sporadically increased to fight infection or to compensate for blood loss.

The haematopoietic lineage is shown in **Figure 2**. The most primitive stem cell of the bone marrow is the pluripotent stem cell which has the capability to produce all the different cell types of the blood. To add another level of complexity, this pluripotent stem cell may itself be part of a stem cell hierarchy. Myeloid and lymphoid stem cells are produced from the pluripotent stem cell population. The myeloid stem cell then goes on to produce a number of progenitor cells which are the precursors of the six types of mature functional myeloid cells: erythrocytes, thrombocytes, eosinophils, macrophages, mast cells and neutrophils. These cells have different functions within the immune system and in the blood. There may be further as yet unknown subdivisions in the stem cell hierarchy. The lymphoid stem cell produces a number of lymphoid progenitors which mature into B and T lymphocytes to provide defence against pathogens or toxins.

Although mature blood cells can be distinguished from each other, stem cells and progenitor cells have no specific distinguishing features under the microscope. Identification of early progenitor cells and stem cells is also made difficult by the low incidence of these cells in blood. For example, pluripotent stem cells are thought to make up only 0.01–0.1% of total bone marrow cells (Heyworth *et al.*, 1997). Functional assays have been devised, the first of which was described by Till and McCullogh (1961). This method involves transplantation of some healthy bone marrow cells into mice whose own bone marrow has been destroyed by irradiation. The transplanted cells produce colonies of differentiated haematopoietic cells in the spleen which can be counted. In addition to functional assays, external markers have been used to identify progenitor cells. Myeloid and lymphoid stem cells and early progenitor cells can be separated from blood by antibodies that react to specific antigens only present on these cell types, e.g. CD34 antigen which is expressed on 0.5–5% of human bone marrow cells. Methods for separation of pluripotent stem cells using specific markers are under development.

In the bone marrow, stem cells and their progeny are exposed to a number of different stimuli including physical interactions with other cells mediated by cell adhesion molecules, interactions with extracellular matrix molecules such as collagen and fibronectin and exposure to growth-stimulatory and growth-inhibitory chemicals called cytokines. There are over 15 cytokines involved in haematopoiesis and these are produced by a number of cell types including the mature cells themselves, e.g. neutrophils, B and T cells, as well as by fibroblasts and bone marrow stromal cells providing autocrine and paracrine regulation (Heyworth *et al.*, 1997). All these signals coordinate the self-renewal and differentiation of the stem cells and the formation of the mature cell types.

The role of cytokines in determining which type of cell (e.g. mast cell or neutrophil) an early progenitor cell differentiates into is highly complex. Some cytokines have many target cells, whereas others are much more restricted. Interleukin (IL-3), for example, can stimulate stem cells

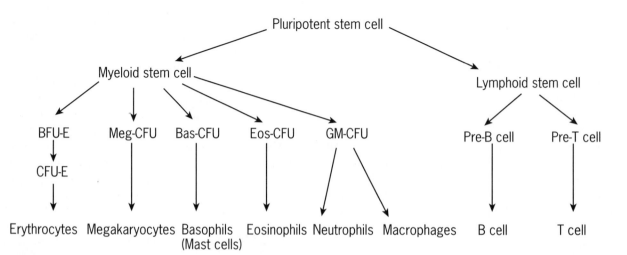

Figure 2 Haematopoietic cell lineage.
Abbreviations: BFU-E, erythroid burst-forming unit; CFU-E, erythroid colony-forming unit; Meg-CFU, megakaryocytic colony-forming unit; Bas-CFU, basophilic colony-forming unit; Eos-CFU, eosinophilic colony-forming unit; GM-CFU, granulocyte macrophage colony-forming unit.

to produce myeloid progenitor cells and can also stimulate myeloid progenitor cells to produce a number of mature cell types (Dexter, 1993). Another example is granulocyte–macrophage colony-stimulating factor (GM-CSF) which acts on the granulocyte–macrophage progenitor cell and the eosinophil progenitor cell to produce neutrophils, macrophages and eosinophils. In contrast, some growth factors have direct effects on only one cell population, e.g. erythropoietin, which acts only on the erythroid progenitor cell to produce erythrocytes. Other cytokines mainly influence the maturation of cells rather than the proliferation of progenitor cells, e.g. IL-5 and eosinophil development.

Originally it was thought that haematopoiesis was regulated solely by modulation of the production of these directly acting cytokines, e.g. stem cells would be acted upon by IL-3 to produce progenitor cells and then specific cytokines would be made to induce maturation of the progenitor cells into whichever specific cells were required by the bone marrow. It is now known that control is exerted at a more complex level such that a certain growth factor alone will not have effects on a particular cell type; however, when it is combined with another factor proliferation or maturation can be induced. For example, lymphoid stem cells will not respond to macrophage colony-stimulating factor or IL-1 alone, but are stimulated in the presence of a combination of these two growth factors.

The haematopoietic cell lineage has illustrated the complex communication network required for the differentiation of relatively unknown stem cells into the specific cells of the blood.

Small Intestine

The epithelium of the small intestine provides another example of a self-renewing tissue which has been studied for many years. The tissue organisation of the small intestine is different from that described for the haematopoietic system, being highly polarized and structured. However, the regulation mechanisms are equally complicated and largely unknown at present.

In the small intestine, epithelium covers finger-like projections called villi and flask-shaped crypts located at the base of the villi which are embedded in the connective tissue (see **Figure 3**). Epithelial cells are produced in the lower part of the crypt and migrate up the crypt on to the villi and are continuously shed from the villus tip. In common with the haematopoietic system, migration from the early precursor cells is accompanied by differentiation and specialization. Cells differentiate into three functional cell types as they move up the crypt: the predominant enterocyte, the mucus-secreting goblet cell and the peptide hormone-secreting enteroendocrine cells. In addition, a number of cells migrate down to the base of the crypt to become the fourth cell type, the Paneth cells. Paneth cells secrete a number of proteins including lysozyme, which is thought to play a role in fighting bacterial infection.

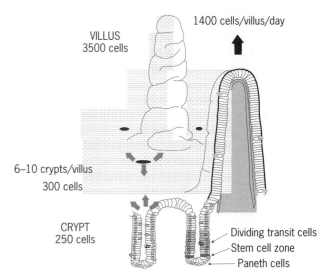

Figure 3   Organisation of small intestinal epithelium.

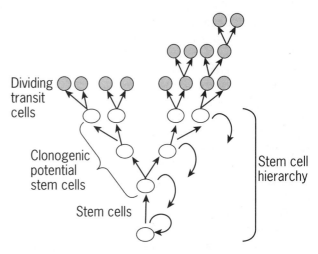

Figure 4   Proposed stem cell model for the small intestine.

Replacement of cells shed at the villus tip must be balanced by cell production in the crypt, at a rate of about 10^{10} cells per day in humans (**Figure 3**) (Potten, 1992). Cell replacement is achieved by stem cells located amongst or just above the Paneth cells at the base of the crypt. Unfortunately, there are no markers for intestinal stem cells and at present, characterization studies can only be carried out by disturbing the system and observing the outcome. A stem cell model has been proposed based on clonal regeneration studies following radiation or drug exposure (**Figure 4**). The proposed model suggests that there are 4–6 ancestor or functioning stem cells per crypt (Potten, 1998). These stem cells are very sensitive to toxic insults (e.g. radiation and some chemotherapeutic agents) and are unable to repair damaged DNA. If damaged they readily initiate apoptosis and die. This sensitivity may reflect the need to avoid repopulation of the crypt with cells containing damaged DNA, and thereby preserves the integrity of the tissue. Stem cells that die, however, are easily replaced by the other surviving stem cell members or by their immediate daughter cells, which make up the second tier of the hierarchy. The second tier stem cells have a better repair capacity and, if not required to regenerate the first tier (such as in a normal situation), they are displaced into the transit compartment. If this second tier is destroyed, a third tier may also exist that contains about 20 even more resistant stem cells with the best repair capacity. These three tiers therefore make up a population of around 30–40 potential stem cells–cells that are acting as stem cells or retain the ability to act as a stem cell if required. Since each of these cells can regenerate a clonal population (a crypt), they are also termed clonogenic cells. Above the level of clonogenic stem cells there are about 124 dividing transit cells which have no stem-cell attributes. These proliferative cells move or are displaced at a rate of 1–2 cell positions per hour from the crypt on to the villus (Potten, 1992, 1998).

Regulation of cell proliferation in the gut is not fully understood. However, a large number of factors are known to be involved, including growth factors, cytokines and ECM molecules. The epidermal growth factor (EGF) family is one group of substances known to stimulate proliferation and includes epidermal growth factor itself and TGF-α (Potten *et al.*, 1997). In contrast, the TGF-β family of growth factors have been associated with negative regulation or inhibition of crypt cell proliferation (see also the chapter *Signalling by TGF-β*). In common with growth factors, *in vitro* studies suggest that some interleukins have stimulatory effects (e.g. IL-4) and some have inhibitory effects (e.g. IL-11 and IL-6).

The ECM underlying the epithelium plays a role in a number of key processes, one of which is cell migration. The process of migration is not fully understood and it was initially thought that cells moved in tandem with underlying connective tissue. More recent studies suggest that cells 'walk' over stationary ECM which contains a number of adhesion molecules such as E-cadherin, laminin, fibronectin, tenascin and collagen. Migration is thought to involve decreased cell attachment to one or more of these adhesion molecules, since adhesion molecule expression patterns vary along the crypt/villus axis. The stationary nature of stem cells may be due to their strong anchorage to the stroma. For example, fibronectin, which is a particularly 'sticky' adhesion molecule, is abundant in the crypt whereas tenascin which is less adhesive is predominant on the villus. In addition, movement is controlled by the expression/availability of integrins, epithelial cell receptors for these adhesion molecules – a cell can only be influenced by adhesion molecule levels within the basement membrane if it expresses the appropriate receptors.

Epidermis

The outermost layer of the skin, the epidermis, is another example of a self-renewing tissue. The epidermis is predominantly made up of keratinocytes (about 80% of the total). Other epidermal cell types exist with specific functions: melanocytes give the skin its pigmentation and afford some protection against ultraviolet light, Merkel cells sense fine mechanical events and Langerhans cells form part of the body's immune system.

The outer surface of the epidermis is called the stratum corneum and is composed of a layer of thin, dead keratinocytes. These cells bear little resemblance to normal keratinocytes, since by the time they reach the surface their nucleus and internal organelles have disappeared and they are reduced to thin plates of keratin. Keratins are a family of insoluble proteins that form intermediate filaments within cells and confer mechanical strength. Surface keratinocytes represent the final mature functional differentiated cells of the skin. These cells are continually being shed or lost and therefore perpetual cell replacement is required to maintain epidermal function.

Below the stratum corneum are three other epidermal cell layers: the granular layer, the spinous layer and the basal layer. These epidermal regions are depicted in **Figure 5**, although there are many more layers of cells than are shown in the diagram. In common with the small intestine and the haematopoietic system, stem cells are responsible for the regenerative potential of skin. These stem cells are located within the basal layer (Lavkar and Sun, 1983). Studies carried out on mouse epidermis suggest that 5–12% of cells in the basal layer are stem cells (Potten, 1992). Transitory dividing cells produced from these stem cells make up about 50% of the basal layer with the remaining basal layer cells being postmitotic and having no proliferative characteristics. These cells are committed to terminal differentiation and achieve this as they slip out of the basal layer and migrate into the spinous layer, where they flatten. From the spinous layer, cells progress up into the granular layer until they reach the stratum corneum where they are eventually shed. The stem-cell progeny generate a discrete column of cells, from basal cell to keratinized cell, arranged in a hexagonal pattern and called an epidermal proliferative unit (Potten, 1981). It has been estimated that it takes the human keratinocyte between 26 and 42 days to travel from the basal layer to the outermost cornified layer and therefore it takes 1–2 months for the epidermis to replace itself completely.

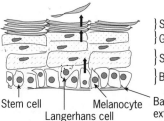

Stem cell   Melanocyte   Basal membrane containing
     Langerhans cell   extracellular matrix, integrins etc.

} Stratum corneum
} Granular layer
} Spinous layer
} Basal layer

Figure 5   The murine epidermal proliferative unit.

In common with the small intestine, the underlying ECM plays a key role in basal layer processes. It has been suggested that the ECM mediates adhesion, regulates terminal differentiation and aids cell movement upward from the basal layer. When basal keratinocytes become committed to undergo terminal differentiation, their ability to adhere to components of the ECM decreases and upward cell migration occurs (Jones and Watt, 1993). Populations of putative stem cells that are greater than 90% pure have been isolated on the basis of their adhesive properties.

The epithelial cells of the skin, and indeed other sites of the body, are able to form a barrier due to a number of functionally and structurally distinct epithelial cell junctions, including tight junctions, gap junctions, desmosomes and hemidesmosomes. Tight junctions seal neighbouring cells together to stop water-soluble molecules leaking between the cells and confine transport proteins either to the outward-facing membrane (apical) or to the inner membranes (basolateral) to control the passage of certain chemicals (e.g. glucose transport in the small intestine). In contrast, gap junctions are involved in cell–cell signalling. Gap junctions are intercellular channels made up of connexin proteins that allow inorganic ions and other small water-soluble molecules to pass directly from the cytoplasm of one cell to the cytoplasm of another, thereby coupling the cells both metabolically and electrically. To maintain mechanical strength, cells are linked together with desmosomes. Desmosomes consist of a dense plaque of intracellular attachment proteins (including plakoglobin and desmoplakins) which are associated with rope-like intermediate keratin filaments that form a continuous network throughout the tissue. Hemidesmosomes, or half-desmosomes, connect the basal surface of epithelial cells to the underlying basement membrane such as that which separates the epidermis and the dermis. In addition to aiding attachment, hemidesmosomes have also been found to be important in modulating the organisation of the cytoskeleton, proliferation and differentiation. These effects are mediated by integrins which transduce signals from the ECM to the interior of the cell as described earlier. Absence or defects of hemidesmosomal proteins can result in devastating blistering skin diseases.

Breast

The breast or mammary gland is an example of a conditionally renewing tissue in that cell replacement is generally limited except under certain conditions, e.g. pregnancy.

The organisation of the breast changes during three developmental phases. The first stage occurs in the foetus where mammary glands arise as buds from the epidermis which elongate to form simple, branched ducts. At puberty, there is rapid extension and branching of the ducts which terminate in globular structures called terminal end buds. These terminal end buds and terminal ducts then go on to form lobules of alveolar buds.

The third phase of mammary development occurs during pregnancy and lactation and at this stage the breast can be considered to be morphologically mature and functionally active. The alveolar buds and lobes subdivide further, giving rise to large clusters of alveolar lobes. During lactation, the clusters of alveolar lobes become distended and form secretory alveoli lined with alveolar cells which produce milk. After cessation of lactation, involution of the breast occurs where the secretory cells of the alveoli degenerate and disappear. Similarly, after the menopause, there is progressive involution of the ductal and glandular components of the breast. The connective tissue supporting the breast also degenerates with loss of stromal cells and collagen fibres.

In the normal breast, the ducts and lobes of the mammary gland are separated from the stroma by a basement membrane. This basement membrane is lined with two cell types, an outer lining of myoepithelial cells containing myofilaments and an inner lining of epithelial cells. As described in the section regarding the epidermis, the epithelial cells of the breast are connected together with desmosomes whereas myoepithelial cells connect to the basement membrane with hemidesmosomes.

Studies in rodent mammary glands indicate that epithelial cell types and alveolar cells arise from stem cell populations capable of generating the fully differentiated lactating mammary gland. These stem cells are thought to be present in the basal cell layer of ducts and end buds, although little more is known about their identity (Rudland et al., 1997). It has been suggested that stem cells can give rise to either ductal epithelial cells in a reversible manner or myoepithelial cells in an irreversible manner. Alveolar cells are thought to be derived from ductal epithelial cells.

As with the other tissues described, the differentiation of cells produced by breast stem cells is strictly controlled. Unlike the haematopoietic system where differentiation is controlled mainly by paracrine and autocrine secretions, the breast is also subject to control by circulating hormones secreted by the pituitary, ovary and adrenal glands. For example, during each menstrual cycle at about the time of ovulation, there is an increase in lobular size and epithelial cell vacuolization under the influence of oestrogens and rising progesterone. When menstruation occurs, the fall in hormone levels causes lobular regression. Similarly in pregnancy, oestrogens and progesterone stimulate proliferation and development, and prolactin released by the pituitary gland activates the production of alveolar cells. Additionally, lactation is triggered by the release of oxytocin, which causes contraction of the smooth muscle components of the myoepithelial cells surrounding the alveoli leading to milk expulsion.

Local growth hormones are also important since the growth promoting effects of oestrogen are believed to be mediated by TGF-α and insulin-like growth factor-1 (IGF-1) which increase epithelial cell growth and inhibit myoepithelial cell differentiation (Rudland *et al.*, 1997). Additionally, production of basic fibroblast growth factor (bFGF) by breast stem cells may regulate their own growth and that of myoepithelial cells in an autocrine/paracrine fashion.

Liver

The liver is another example of a conditionally renewing tissue. Epithelial cells make up the majority of the liver, particularly hepatocytes and also biliary duct epithelium. The hierarchial organisation of the liver, however, is not fully understood. Unlike the tissues mentioned above, where one population of stem cells is responsible for cell replacement, it seems likely that a two-compartment system is operative in this tissue (Alison, 1998). First, in the event of damage, hepatocytes are able to regenerate themselves very efficiently. This is unusual because the ability to regenerate is normally characteristic of undifferentiated stem cells, and hepatocytes are thought to be fully differentiated. A second compartment is activated if the function of surviving hepatocytes is drastically impaired and involves generation of new hepatocytes from stem cells. Liver stem cells, believed to be located in biliary ductules, produce oval cells. Oval cells are then thought to differentiate into the functional cell types, e.g. hepatocytes. The proposed model is illustrated in **Figure 6**.

Others

As indicated above, knowledge about the organisation of tissues ranges from the haematopoietic system and small intestine, which have been extensively studied, to the liver and breast, where information is more limited. Recently, a number of developments have been made in understanding the hierarchy of other tissue types. For example, mesenchymal stem cells have been isolated from human bone marrow. These cells replicate as undifferentiated cells and have the potential to differentiate into lineages of mesenchymal tissues including bone, cartilage, fat, tendon, muscle and marrow stroma (Pittenger *et al.*, 1999). Neuronal stem cells have also been discovered in foetal brain which can develop into neurons and glial cells if certain growth factors are present *in vitro* (Vogel, 1999).

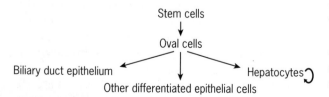

Figure 6 A proposed model for liver cell generation and regeneration.

CONTROL OF TISSUE ORGANISATION IN DEVELOPMENT

Regulation of tissue organisation in development is likely to involve a number of highly complicated mechanisms; however, one group of genes called homeobox genes has already been found to play a significant role in this process. Homeobox genes are a family of regulatory genes encoding transcription factors (homeoproteins) that can activate or repress the expression of a large number of target genes and so determine cell fate and general pattern formation. One major family of homeobox genes termed Hox genes control the identity of various regions along the body axis. These Hox genes are activated in sequence such that early Hox genes that control hindbrain development, followed by activation of Hox genes that control the thoracic region and late genes that control the lumbo-sacral region. Perturbing the expression of these factors can induce gross changes in tissue, organ and even limb development. For example, synpolydactyly, an inherited disease characterized by hand and foot malformation, is caused by expansions of the *HOXD13* gene.

In addition to developmental regulation, certain homeobox genes are also involved in inducing differentiation in renewing tissues. For example, the *cdx* genes are involved in controlling intestinal epithelial cell differentiation, possibly by transducing signals from laminin-1 in the underlying mesenchyme, and *HOXA9* and *PBX1* are some of the many genes involved in the control of haematopoietic differentiation. Altered expression of any of these can suppress differentiation and ultimately lead to tumour formation.

CANCER DEVELOPMENT AND TISSUE ORGANISATION

The chapter *Overview of Oncogenesis* will discuss the mechanisms involved in carcinogenesis in detail, but briefly the process is thought to involve a number of steps. First, a cell experiences a mutation that may or may not influence its immediate behaviour. This cell may then be more susceptible to subsequent mutations and, over time, gradually accumulate enough damage such that the normal control or 'braking' mechanisms is perturbed. This gradual accumulation of mutations is therefore known as the multistage model of carcinogenesis and explains why cancer is generally a disease of old age unless, for example, the primary mutation is an inherited disorder.

Within a tissue experiencing this process, the first observable histological stage is hyperplasia or cellular overgrowth, although this term must be used carefully since tissue regeneration in response to wounding is itself a form of hyperplasia. Hyperplasia can therefore be benign in addition to cancerous. Since in the adult hyperplasia can only occur in proliferating tissues it is not surprising that almost all cancers arise in rapidly renewing or conditionally renewing tissues. In each case there is a malfunction in cellular homeostasis and cell production exceeds cell loss.

The origin of cell production, and the only permanent resident of a renewing tissue, is the stem cell. Cancers can therefore be thought of as stem cell diseases (transformation of a maturing cell would have no long-term effect since even if it divides a few times, each cell is ultimately lost from the tissue in a relatively short time frame). An expansion of stem cell numbers can therefore lead to hyperplasia. Normally such an expansion would be detected by the tissue and the excess stem cell removed, via apoptosis. However, if this does not occur, cellular output will be dramatically increased. For example, in the colon expression of the anti-apoptotic gene *bcl-2* may allow the survival of a single extra stem cell in an intestinal crypt (Potten *et al.*, 1997). This alone can lead to 128 extra cells being produced by that one crypt (owing to the expansion by the transit amplifying cells). As the animal ages these excess stem cells persist and may experience further mutations (e.g. in apoptosis regulation such as by *p53*, growth factor signal transduction such as in *SMAD* and *ras*, DNA repair by mismatch repair enzymes such as MSH2, or in cellular adhesion such as changed integrin or E-cadherin expression), thereby increasing cancer risk. These mutations generally occur in three vital areas – regulation of cell division in the renewing population (restraint), DNA repair (such that the normal DNA is not maintained) and interactions with the extracellular environment (cells or matrix). Together these will subvert the normal differentiation process and allow unrestrained tissue growth without the accompanying levels of cell death, followed by invasion and metastasis into other tissue sites.

CONCLUSIONS

The organisation of cells and tissues has been discussed in development and in the normal adult and we have attempted to highlight the complex nature of the regulation processes that control cell proliferation, differentiation and regeneration. Cancer development provides us with an excellent example of the devastating effects observed when these processes are subverted and emphasizes the need for such exquisitely controlled mechanisms.

REFERENCES

Alison, M. (1998). Liver stem cells: a two compartment system. *Current Opinion in Cell Biology*, **10**, 710–715.

Dexter, T. M. (1993). Synergistic interactions in haemopoiesis: biological implications and clinical use. *European Journal of Cancer*, **29A**, S6–S9.

Graham, G. J. and Pagnell, I. B. (1992). The haematopoietic stem cell: properties and control mechanisms. *Seminars in Cellular Biology*, **3**, 423–434.

Heyworth, C. M., *et al.* (1997). Growth factors and the regulation of haematopoietic stem cells. In: Potten, C. S. (ed.), *Stem Cells*. 423–446 (Academic Press, London).

Horwitz, A. R. and Werb, Z. (1998). Cell adhesion and the extracellular matrix: recent progress and emerging themes. *Current Opinion in Cell Biology*, **10**, 563–565.

Jones, P. H. and Watt, F. M. (1993). Separation of human epidermal stem cells from transit amplifying cells on the basis of differences in integrin function and expression. *Cell*, **73**, 713–724.

Lavker, R. M. and Sun, T.-T. (1983). Epidermal stem cells. *Journal of Investigative Dermatology*, **81**(1S), 121–127.

Pittenger, M. F., *et al.* (1999). Multilineage potential of adult human mesenchymal stem cells. *Science*, **284**, 143–147.

Potten, C. S. (1981). Cell replacement in epidermis (keratopoiesis) via discrete units of proliferation. *International Review of Cytology*, **69**, 271–317.

Potten, C. S. (1992). Cell lineages. In: McGee, J. O'D., *et al.* (eds), *Oxford Textbook of Pathology*, Vol. 1, 43–52 (Oxford University Press, Oxford).

Potten, C. S. (1998). Stem cells in gastrointestinal epithelium: numbers, characteristics and death. *Philosophical Transactions of the Royal Society of London*, **353**, 821–830.

Potten, C. S., *et al.* (1997). The intestinal epithelial stem cell: the mucosal governor. *International Journal of Experimental Pathology*, **78**, 219–243.

Rudland, P. S., *et al.* (1997). Mammary stem cells in normal development and cancer. In: Potten, C. S. (ed.), *Stem Cells*. 147–232 (Academic Press, London).

Thomson, J. A., *et al.* (1998). Embryonic stem cell lines derived from human blastocysts. *Science*, **282**, 1145–1147.

Till, J. E. and McCulloch, E. A (1961). A direct measurement of the radiation sensitivity of normal mouse bone marrow cells. *Radiation Research*, **14**, 213–222.

Vogel, G. (1999). Harnessing the power of stem cells. *Science*, **283**, 1432–1134.

FURTHER READING

Cillo, C., Faiella, A., Cantile, M., and Boncinelli, E. (1999). Homeobox genes and cancer. *Experimental Cell Research*, **248(1)**, 1–9.

D'Andrea, A. D. (1994). Haematopoietic growth factors and the regulation of differentiative decisions. *Current Opinion in Cell Biology*, **6**, 804–808.

Loeffler, M. and Potten, C. S. (1997). Stem cells and cellular pedigrees – a conceptual introduction. In: Potten, C. S. (ed.), *Stem Cells*. 423–446 (Academic Press Ltd., London).

Schwarzbauer, J. (1999). Basement membrane: putting up the barrier. *Current Biology*, **9**, R242–244.

Stappenbeck, T. S., Wong, M. H., Saam, J. R., Mysorekar, I. U. and Gordon, J. I. (1998). Notes from some crypt watchers: regulation of renewal in the mouse intestinal epithelium. *Current Opinion in Cell Biology*, **10**, 702–709.

Chapter 2

Regulation of the Cell Cycle

Arthur B. Pardee

Dana-Farber Cancer Institute, Boston, MA, USA

CONTENTS

OVERVIEW

In each of us are about 50 trillion living cells, all of which originated from only one cell, a fertilized egg. As we developed into adults this cell divided into two cells, these into four, and so forth, at least 45 times. The orderly process by which one cell becomes two is named the cell cycle. This cycle is fundamental not only for understanding cell growth, but also for replacement of cells lost by damage, as in wound healing and from the normal wear and tear of our bodies. The cell cycle is evidently tightly regulated, because we usually make new cells only when they are needed. Indeed, cancers arise when cell growth control is defective. 'Cancer is a wound that does not heal.'

One should remember that cells in most tissues are not usually progressing through the cycle, but are at rest, happily performing their specialized functions in support of the whole organism. But as exceptions, bone marrow, intestinal epithelial and some other cells are constantly dividing. A cell has a life cycle. It is formed, eventually becomes worn and dies by a programmed cell-death mechanism called apoptosis. Thereafter, nearby cells grow and divide to replace it. Cell numbers are balanced by proliferation versus apoptosis. After a cell becomes cancerous the balance is perturbed in favour of proliferation. These facts can be overlooked because much research is performed with cells put into culture and under conditions that permit proliferation.

THE NORMAL CELL CYCLE

History of Cell Cycle Biology

Before the cell cycle, microscopy revealed an interval of about 1 day between successive divisions of one cell into two cells. Until about 50 years ago, no changes could be observed during most of this interval, until about 1 hour before division when chromosomes which contain the hereditary material become visible and are equally partitioned between the two daughter cells, a complex process termed mitosis that takes place through M phase.

Production of two cells from one requires duplication of all of the myriad molecules that compose each cell. The most evidently duplicated molecules are deoxyribonucleic acid (DNA), the heredity-containing material in chromosomes. DNA does not duplicate throughout the cycle, but only during several hours in mid-cycle. This period is named the S phase, for DNA synthesis. Other molecules are duplicated at different times throughout the cycle. These findings about DNA synthesis (Howard and Pelc, 1951) showed that the cycle is organized as a series of events, and created the present framework of its four phases: a 'gap' (G_1 phase) during which a cell prepares for DNA synthesis, DNA synthesis (S phase), preparation for mitosis (G_2 phase) and the mitotic M phase, after which the cell divides and two new cycles commence (**Figure 1**). For a historical summary of biology of the cycle, see Baserga (1985).

Quiescence

Commencing by considering normal animal cells, most of the cells within us are in a quiescent state (G_0 phase). They have left their cycling during the G_1 state, so in quiescent cells DNA has not yet duplicated. But quiescent cells differ from G_1 cells in many other properties, in particular lacking molecules required for growth. This fact told us that the molecular switch that controls growth versus quiescence, and that is defective in cancers, is to be found in G_1 phase (Pardee, 1989).

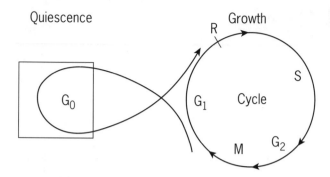

Figure 1   The basic cell cycle. The consecutive phases of the cycle, entry from G_0 and exit from G_1 to quiescence and differentiation are indicated.

G_1 Phase

When cells are activated to proliferate they advance from G_0 to G_1 phase, during several hours after several growth factor proteins are provided in their environment. These include epidermal growth factor (EGF) and insulin-like growth factor (IGF-1), which must overcome inhibitions by crowding of cells and the negative factor TGF-β. Growth factors and nutrients must be supplied from the blood in an organism. To grow cells outside the body, in tissue culture, a nutrient medium is required, in which growth factors are usually supplied by adding blood serum. Cells complete their cycle and then become quiescent after growth factors have been removed.

The length of time that cells in a culture spend in G_1 phase is highly variable, e.g. from 6 to 24 h, unlike the fairly uniform time they spend in the other phases. Many other synthetic biochemical processes take place in G_1 phase (see below).

S Phase

The requirement for growth factors to pass through G_1 phase is lost at the restriction point (R), located shortly before cells start to synthesize DNA. At the beginning of S phase, enzymes involved in DNA duplication increase, and they move into the nucleus where DNA is duplicated, from the surrounding cytoplasm where proteins are synthesized. Then at specific times during the next 6–8 h the DNAs of the perhaps 40 000 genes located on 23 pairs of chromosomes are replicated, each according to a timed program. For example the dihyrofolate reductase gene replicates quickly in very early S phase, but other genes are duplicated at other specific times throughout S phase.

G_2 Phase

After DNA synthesis is completed, several hours are required before initiation of mitosis, presumably to produce needed enzymatic machinery. Many G_2 products are unknown; a terminal one is the maturation promoting factor (MPF).

M Phase and Cell Division

Mitosis requires less than 1 h, and is subdivided into four main stages, in which the duplicate chromosomes pair and condense, and a mitotic 'machinery' consisting mainly of microtubule proteins segregates them equally between the two daughter cells. At completion of M phase, proteins of the mitotic apparatus are destroyed. The daughter cells then become separated, and each can repeat the cycle processes.

MOLECULAR BIOLOGY OF THE CYCLE

Signalling Molecules

Comparisons of growth of mammalian cancer and normal cells in culture revealed in 1974 that the basis of cancer's deranged growth control is located in G_1 phase, shortly before initiation of DNA synthesis (Pardee, 1989). In the same year, genetic studies of the cycle were intiated; research with cycle-controlling yeast mutants led to the discovery of numerous cycle-regulatory genes (Hartwell and Kastan, 1994). Biochemistry and molecular biology soon followed, with the identification of new genes and key enzymes; in particular proteins named cyclins that activate these kinases were discovered by Hunt and Ruderman (see review by Murray and Hunt). These rise and fall during the cycle because of periodic changes in their synthesis and destruction (Minshull *et al.*, 1989). Cyclin-dependent kinases (cdks) that phosphorylate proteins required for cell cycle progression were identified (Nurse *et al.*, 1998). Several proteins that inhibit these kinases and that vary during the cycle were discovered later. This involvement of both positively and negatively acting molecules illustrates the Ying–Yang principle of dynamic opposing actions, frequently seen in biology.

G_1 Phase Kinases, Cyclins and Inhibitors

We will outline the main steps of growth activation and control in G_1 phase, but this process is too complex to describe here fully (**Figure 2**) (see Murray and Hunt; Andreef). In summary, a biochemical network regulates the critical process of controlling cell growth during G_1 phase. Numerous nutrients including sugars, salts, vitamins and essential amino acids are required for cell growth (Baserga, 1985). Externally supplied growth factors start the cell cycle, from G_0 into G_1 phase. They initiate a multi-step cascade of signals that ultimately

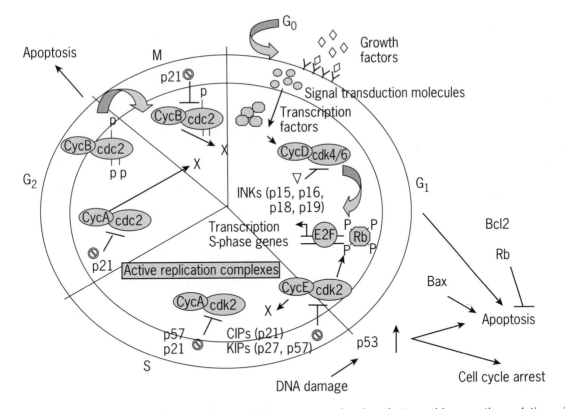

Figure 2 Cell-cycle control molecules. Some of the many molecules that provide growth-regulating signals throughout the cycle are shown, and are discussed throughout this chapter. (Adapted from Ford and Pardee, 1999.)

activates genes to produce their messenger RNAs and proteins, and which culminates in the starting up of DNA synthesis.

The growth factors bind extracellulary to their specific receptor proteins that traverse the membrane surrounding each cell (**Figure 3**). These receptors conduct the external signal to the interior of the cell, and there they activate the receptor's special kinase. These then turn on a cascade of signals involving other proteins including Ras, Fos, Myc and MAP kinases. The Ying–Yang principle is again involved, as illustrated by phosphorylations catalysed by PI-3 kinase that are balanced by dephosphorylations catalysed by the PTEN phosphatase enzyme. The activation of G_1 phase results in expression of at least 100 genes.

The discovery of cyclins, which are the key proteins regulating transition through the cycle (Roberts, 1999), was soon followed by discoveries of multiple cdks. Their complexes with cyclins catalyse stages of cell cycle progression (**Figure 4**). As cells proceed through the cycle, four major cyclins are produced sequentially (D, E, A and B), and they activate several cyclin-dependent kinases. Central is cyclin D which increases in early to mid G_1 phase and regulates cyclin-dependent kinases cdk4 and cdk6 (Sherr, 1996). Cyclin D/cdk triggers the synthesis of cyclin E in late G_1 phase, which in turn activates cdk2, cyclin A production and DNA synthesis.

Phosphorylations are also regulatory, in addition to the synthesis of cyclins. Yet another kinase, CAK, activates the cyclin-dependent kinases. Furthermore, a major role is played by relocalization of cyclin–cdk to the active nuclear compartment within a cell during the cell cycle.

Further investigations revealed yet other proteins whose role is to block activities by binding to cyclin–cdk complexes. These are a family named inhibitors of kinases (INKs). They counterbalance the cyclin's activation of cdks, to affect cycling, development and tumorigenesis (Sherr, 1996). The inhibitory proteins block cyclin D–cdk activities. p27 blocks cell progression, is high in quiescent cells and decreases during late G_1 to release cdk–cyclin activities. Inhibition of cyclins by the cdk inhibitor p21 has often been demonstrated to be induced under various growth-arresting conditions.

In the next step, activated cdks phosphorylate proteins that are essential for progression of the cell cycle. The retinoblastoma tumour suppressor (pRb), absent in retinoblastomas, releases a gene-activating protein named E2F when it is phosphorylated. If this is prevented, E2F is not active, cyclin E is not synthesized, and cells cannot pass through the R point. Additionally, proteasomes' activity of destruction of key inhibitory proteins is vital for passing each checkpoint in the cycle (Koepp *et al.*, 1999). The proteasome is a biochemical machine, composed of protein subunits, that chews up proteins including cyclins

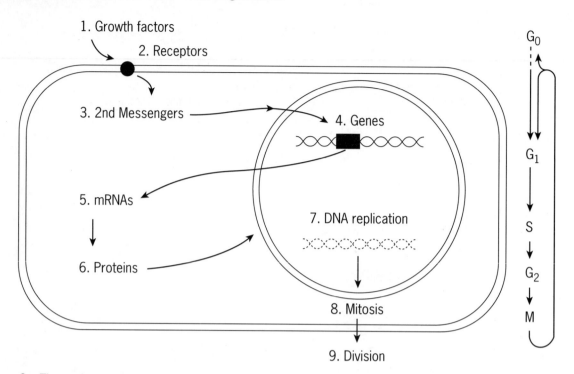

Figure 3   The path to cell proliferation. Growth factors initiate a signalling cascade that takes a cell through the cycle, indicated at the right.

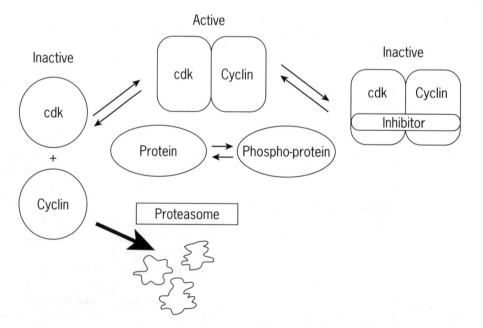

Figure 4   Interactions of cdk with cyclin and inhibitory protein. A cyclin-dependent kinase (cdk) acquires the enzymatic activity to phosphorylate substrate proteins when it binds a cyclin, and this protein complex is inactivated by binding of an inhibitory protein. These reactions are readily reversible and they depend upon phosphorylation of cdk. Cyclins are irreversibly degraded by proteasomes after they are no longer needed.

after they become chemically labelled and targeted for removal.

Unlike peptide growth factors, steroid hormones do not initiate cytoplasmic signalling pathways, but move directly to the nucleus where they activate genes. The sex hormone oestrogen binds to its receptor protein in the nucleus of breast cells, and this in turn binds to and activates growth-stimulating target genes.

Entry into S Phase

Increased cyclin D and E overcome inhibition of cdk activity, and pRb is phosphorylated. This releases E2F and activates genes involved in initiating S phase, including enzymes of DNA synthesis. An example is DNA polymerase, whose transcription is regulated at G_1/S phase by a complex of proteins that contains pRb-like p107, cyclin A and kinase. It is worth noting that most major cell cycle processes are catalysed by large complexes composed of many proteins.

Progression through S phase depends upon cyclin A kinase. Early in S phase, cyclins D and E are degraded by proteasomes. Degradation also removes E2F, which is necessary to prevent programmed cell death (apoptosis) of S phase cells (Lees and Weinberg, 1999).

G_2 Phase and Entry into Mitosis

Mitosis depends upon completion of S phase, and events in G_2 phase are preparatory for it. The complex molecular basis for onset of mitosis was explosively discovered in the early 1980s. Ruderman found that fertilization of oocytes triggers activation of cyclin mRNAs. Hunt discovered that the amounts of cyclin proteins oscillate during the cell cycle, rising during DNA replication and early mitosis and falling at the end of mitosis. Injection of isolated cyclin A into quiescent oocytes drove the cells into M phase. At this time also, Nurse identified the cdk kinase cdc2 as essential for entry into M phase. Unbound cdc2 by itself was inactive. Newly formed cyclin B was shown to bind to and activate cdc2, establishing the first molecular mechanism to explain cell-cycle progression. Then destruction of cyclin B, involving a specialized multi-subunit anaphase-promoting complex, is essential for completion of the cycle.

Research with cell free systems has permitted detailed biochemical investigations of mitosis, showing for example that cyclin B binds to cdc2 (**Figure 2**). This activation of cdc2 kinase is necessary for progression into and through mitosis. The kinase is regulated by a variety of proteins that include cyclin B, phosphatases and kinases and by its subcellular localization. Cyclin B1 begins to accumulate in S phase and increases through G_2. It forms a complex with cdc2, which primes cdc2 phosphorylation. The complex is, however, still inactive, owing to other phosphorylations on cdc2. During G_2 phase, a kinase's

(wee1) activity is greater than that of the phosphatase cdc25, and this imbalance keeps cyclin B–cdc2 inactive. At the G_2–M boundary, wee1 is degraded, allowing cdc25 to activate the complex. Furthermore, during G_2 the cyclin B–cdc2 complex resides in the cytoplasm, and at the G_2–M boundary it is rapidly relocated to the nucleus, where it phosphorylates the nuclear membrane protein laminin, which causes the nuclear membrane to break down. Thereafter, chromosomes condense and mitosis proceeds. These many phosphorylations are important for the massive morphological changes that are necessary for a cell to divide.

The Next Cycle – Licensing for DNA Synthesis

A process named licensing permits only one DNA replication per cycle. DNA synthesis cannot be reinitiated until after mitosis is completed. pRb is a critical determinant in preventing DNA reduplication. Perhaps related is the breakdown and reformation during mitosis of the membrane around the nucleus. This permits interaction of molecules from the nucleus and cytoplasm. Degradation of cyclin B by proteasomes is necessary for the start of S phase in the following cycle. Licensing can be disrupted: cells that have lost the cdk inhibitor p21 undergo multiple rounds of DNA synthesis without mitosis, and this process is also activated by anticancer agents. Staurosporin can eliminate the dependence of DNA synthesis on the prior M phase.

Cell Ageing

The normal cell cycle outlined above is modified by various conditions. One of these is cell age. The cycle in early embryo cells is very rapid. It lacks G_1 phase and the corresponding growth-controlling G_1 checkpoint. Mature human cells slow their cycle as they become older, and they cease growing, in G0 or G_1 phase, after about 50 cycles, as initially shown by Hayflick (Baserga). A cdk inhibitor was first discovered in ageing cells by its increase before final arrest of cycling. A progressive shortening of the telomeric DNA, located at the ends of chromosomes, after each cycle is proposed to provide a biological 'clock' for cell ageing. (See chapter on *Telomerase*.)

REGULATION OF CYCLE PHASES

Checkpoints

Entry into and exit from S and M phases are very carefully regulated events. Checkpoint is a name given (Hartwell and Kastan, 1994) to the set of identified cycle-regulatory steps: G_1 restriction point (and the similar START in yeast) and the G_1/S and G_2/M blocks resulting from DNA damage. Cell-cycle checkpoints are based upon pathways and feedback mechanisms ensuring that a phase of cell cycle does not begin until the preceding phase has been completed with high fidelity. If a checkpoint fails, programmed cell death (apoptosis) or genomic instability ensues. Such failures are important steps in the progression from normal to cancerous cells.

A surveillance system is engaged to make the choice between cell growth and quiescence (Pardee, 1989). When extracellular stimulation by growth factors or nutrients is inadequate, cells cannot pass beyond a specific point in late G_1 phase, in mammalian cells named the restriction point (R). Instead they revert to quiescence (G_0). The final steps that are needed to pass R require synthesis of an unstable protein, proposed to be cyclin E. Under inadequate conditions, synthesis does not keep up with loss, and so this protein cannot be accumulated to an amount sufficient to move the cell into S phase. Once beyond the R point, cells are committed to divide and they no longer require the extracellular growth factors during the remainder of the cell cycle. Restriction point control is defective in cancer cells, and this independence releases cancer cells to continue growing under conditions that keep normal cells in the quiescent state (Pardee, 1989).

The DNA Damage-induced G_1 Checkpoint

After DNA is damaged, other checkpoint controls delay entry into the next phase of the cell cycle. One such major checkpoint is at the G_1 to S transition, which prevents cells from beginning DNA synthesis until the damaged DNA is repaired. Several proteins, in particular p53, have been implicated in this checkpoint mechanism (**Figure 5**). Individuals who are mutated in the ataxia telangiectasia gene, *ATM*, are very sensitive to X-rays and have a high incidence of tumorigenesis. In response to DNA damage, ATM phosphorylates and increases the level of the p53 protein, a tumour suppressor that is mutated in more than 50% of cancers (Levine, 1997). p53 causes cells to arrest at the G_1–S boundary, which is at least partly due to its production of p21, one of the proteins that inhibits cyclin–cdk complexes.

The DNA Damage-induced S and G_2–M Checkpoints

Within several minutes of exposure to DNA-damaging agents, such as X-rays, mammalian cells in S phase exhibit a dose-dependent reduction in DNA synthesis. Less is known about the mechanism of this S phase checkpoint than about those in G_1 and G_2.

DNA damage also induces a G_2–M checkpoint, as described by Tolmach. This checkpoint delay gives time

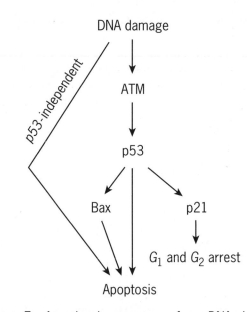

Figure 5 A molecular sequence from DNA damage to apoptosis. A variety of conditions that make a cell unnecessary, such as irreversible damage to it, initiate p53-dependent and independent signalling pathways that lead to apoptosis.

for DNA repair before the cell goes through mitosis. If repair is not completed in this interval, the cells progress into mitosis without repairing all the DNA damage (Fingert *et al.*, 1988), and this results in death or mutations of surviving daughter cells which can thereby become cancerous. This molecular G_2–M checkpoint mechanism is a complex network of phosphorylations and dephosphorylations catalysed by several enzymes and proteins that are moved between cytoplasm and nucleus. Basically, a block in activation of cyclin B–cdc2 prevents the movement of cells into mitosis.

M phase Checkpoints

Mitosis properly segregates chromosomes into the daughter cells. Accurate segregation depends on proper chromosome alignments on and attachment to the mitotic spindle, which is composed of microtubule proteins. A checkpoint ensures that this segregation process occurs correctly. As little as one double strand break in DNA, or depletion of deoxynucleotide building blocks, activates the checkpoint control and stops cells at the G_2–M boundary. This control mechanism delays completion of mitosis until all the chromosomes are attached to the mitotic spindle. The mechanism blocks progression through mitosis if chromosomes are misaligned, and assembly of the microtubules that guide the chromosomes can be inhibited by anticancer drugs such as taxol. Mutations of mitotic checkpoint genes are found in human cancers.

Checkpoints and Programmed Cell Death (Apoptosis)

Apoptosis is a highly regulated process that eliminates physiologically unneeded cells and those that are damaged beyond repair (see the chapter *Apoptosis*). Activated checkpoints give time for a cell to repair its damaged DNA, but if the damage is not soon corrected the cells will initiate apoptosis. This mechanism therefore may prevent the mutations that cause cancer (Sellers and Fisher, 1999). Checkpoint genes, including *p53*, called 'the guardian of the genome,' are involved in causing apoptosis, as is *bax* and other members of the *bcl-2* family (**Figure 5**). Different cells show various responses to damage and drugs, partly because they express different members of the Bcl-2 family (see the chapter *Apoptosis*).

The cyclin A–kinase complex necessary for S phase progression is inhibited when cells are treated with X-rays, and this can result in apoptosis because of the inability of this complex to remove the apoptotic G_1–S factor E2F (Lees and Weinberg, 1999).

Cell Ageing and the Cycle

The elimination of cell ageing is named immortalization. It is an important step in cancer progression, although it does not cause cancer-associated changes (see Hanahan and Weinberg). One way in which human cells can be immortalized is by inserting the gene for the enzyme telomerase, which restores the ageing cell's telomere lengths. Telomerase is also involved in the G_2–M checkpoint.

Cancer is a major cause of death in the elderly. Its incidence increases rapidly, killing about 10% of people between ages 75 and 85 versus 1% between ages 45 and 55. Yet in spite of these epidemiological facts, there is 60% under-representation of cancer patients 65 years or older in treatment trials, few studies have specifically focused on persons over age 65 and many pathological and molecular investigations do not include age as a determinant variable.

CHECKPOINTS, MUTATIONS AND CANCER

The general sequential organisation and duration of the cycle are preserved in cancer, but checkpoint controls are defective (Pardee, 1989; Hartwell and Kastan, 1994). Modifications in cancers are found at many levels of growth regulation, some of which have already been mentioned. The main defect is misregulation of growth initiation at the R point. Furthermore, since checkpoints ensure that mutations are kept low in normal cells, defective checkpoints increase the mutation rate in cancer cells and result in progressive loss of control and emergence of neoplastic disease.

Mutations are causal for cancer; the disease is based upon them. Mutations are found in many genes in advanced cancers. Some of these change cell-cycle controls, including creating a supply of nutrients through angiogenesis, modulating DNA repair, apoptosis, immortalization and metastatic capability (see Hanahan and Weinberg).

The minority of cancer-prone mutations are hereditary. In these cases, a mutated gene on one of a pair of chromosomes is inherited. If, later in life, a mutation occurs of this gene in its partner chromosome, a cancer cell can be produced. Several inherited diseases that are associated with cancer susceptibility have defective checkpoint control. Li-Fraumeni syndrome is a hereditary disease characterized by cancers arising in close relatives. It is a result of a germline mutation in the *p53* gene that abrogates the G_1 checkpoint. Ataxia telangiectasia is characterized by acute cancer predisposition and also other major dysfunctions. Cells from AT patients in culture exhibit severely impaired G_1, S and G_2 checkpoint functions. As mentioned, the *ATM* gene is activated in response to DNA damage and is necessary for activating p53. Another cancer, retinoblastoma, involves mutations in the *Rb* gene, and produces childhood retinal tumours. Survivors have a high risk of developing secondary cancers, particularly osteosarcoma. The BRCA-1 and -2 mutations are associated with hereditary breast cancer; they modify cell cycling and DNA repair. Several other genetic diseases, including Bloom's syndrome, Fanconi anaemia and Nijmegen breakage syndrome, are associated with defects in cell cycle checkpoints and cancer susceptibility.

The majority of cancer-related mutations arise throughout life. For example, cyclin A levels often become abnormally high in cancer cells, and contribute to tumorigenesis. The cyclin D1 and E genes are amplified and over-expressed in many human cancers.

Carcinogenesis can also be caused by viruses such as SV40 and papillomavirus. They introduce their genes that produce proteins that bind to and eliminate the functions of p53 and Rb, thereby bypassing G_1–S, and to a lesser extent G_2, checkpoint controls.

Cancers are often associated with environmental mutagens, such as are produced by smoking. Repeated exposures can produce the several different mutations that are required to cause a cancer. Master mutations can activate growth-promoting oncogenes or loss or inactivation of the tumour-suppressor genes that limit growth. As an example, many cancers have lost or mutated the *p53* gene. One consequence of this mutation is survival of the cancer cell, because p53-dependent checkpoints are eliminated and the programmed cell death mechanism is diminished. Another consequence is that the mutation rate is increased, termed genomic instability (see the chapter *Genomic Instability and DNA Repair*).

The mutations of a half-dozen or more cellular genes is required for tumour formation (Kinzler and Vogelstein, 1996). This number of events is very unlikely in normal cells, whose rate of mutation is approximately 10^{-7} per gene per cell duplication. Therefore, mutations of genes that increase the overall mutation rate are frequent early events in tumorigenesis. Defects of checkpoint controls in cancers, including hereditary ones, create mutations which are likely to be misrepaired and are progressive because of error-prone repair mechanisms in cancer cells. For example, mutations of BRCA1 or BRCA2 cause *p53* abnormality, which leads to breast cancer (Tseng *et al.*, 1997). Other good examples are mutations in colon cancer that cause defective repair of damaged DNA and thereby create genomic instability.

Substances that modify checkpoint controls can change the rate of appearance of mutations, and therefore the progression of cancer. For cells in tissue culture, very high doses of caffeine or related compounds bypass the G_2–M checkpoint, and as a consequence most damaged cells die. These results demonstrate the protective role of the G_2–M checkpoint against damage-induced chromosomal aberrations (Fingert *et al.*, 1988). However, chromosomal abnormalities may appear in the few surviving cells.

CANCER THERAPY AND THE CYCLE

Classical Chemotherapies

Currently applied therapies are aimed at killing cancer cells with cytotoxic agents that are applied in combinations. They can prolong the lives of patient with some kinds of cancer but have little effect against others, and all too often

the cancer reappears within a few years. One drug provided alone is generally ineffective, because some cancer cells survive this treatment and so the cancer reappears. Multiple drugs are necessary for effectiveness, but this multitargeting is limited by toxicity to normal cells.

Molecular differences between cancer and normal cells are subtle (see Hanahan and Weinberg). They are mainly related to defective controls of cell growth and survival. Many clinically applied drugs preferentially kill the cycling cancer cells relative to the generally quiescent normal cells, which are essential for survival of the individual. But some kinds of normal cells are cycling, and so the drugs are toxic to the patient. Several cell cycle events provide targets for therapy (**Figure 6**). (See the section on *The Treatment of Human Cancer.*)

Antagonists of Growth Factors

Sex hormones stimulate the growth of some breast, ovarian and prostate cancer cells. Blocking these hormones' action can kill these cells. Tamoxifen is chemically related to the sex hormone oestrogen, with which it competes for binding to oestrogen receptors in a cell. Since tamoxifen blocks the stimulation by oestrogen and does not activate growth, it is in fact inhibitory.

Blocking S Phase

Cornerstones of standard chemotherapy are inhibitors of DNA synthesis. These are small molecule antagonists

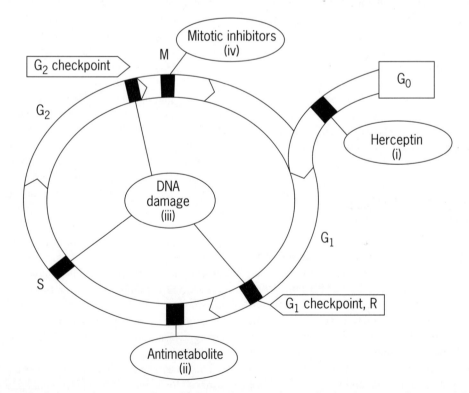

Figure 6 Current therapeutic approaches. Various therapeutic methods that are discussed in the text are summarized here.

structurally similar to metabolic compounds required in the synthesis of DNA and cell survival. As examples, fluorouracil is structurally very similar to uracil, which is needed for DNA synthesis, and methotrexate is an analogue of the vitamin folic acid, also essential for DNA synthesis.

DNA-damaging Agents

Agents that damage DNA are lethal. Examples are X-rays and clinically applied alkylating compounds such as cytoxan and cisplatin. They are more effective against cancer versus noncancer cells because the latter generally are not growing. Also, the normal cells more effectively repair damage during checkpoint delays, before the lethal event of passage of the damaged cell through mitosis and consequent partitioning of damaged DNA between the daughter cells.

Mitotic Inhibitors

Several clinically applied drugs upset the mitotic mechanism in cycling cells, and thereby are lethal. These include taxol from the yew tree and alkaloid toxins from the vinca plant. These currently used compounds, and also experimental epothilones derived from microorganisms, cause lethal mitotic arrest of cycling cells. Their targets are the microtubule proteins, which guide chromosomes through their mitotic separation. Purified plant and microbial products such as these very frequently are starting points for finding anticancer drugs.

A novel drug such as epothilone enters the clinic every few years. Another current example is the antimetabolite gemcytabine, which during S phase is incorporated into newly forming DNA where it arrests continuation of lengthening of the molecule. Difficulties in introducing novel drugs have roots not only in drug discovery, but to a great extent in complex legal requirements for meeting safety standards. These require extremely extensive clinical trials, which with the many costs of doing business, require hundreds of millions of dollars to develop one drug.

Cycle Activators as New Targets

Discovery in cancer cells of over-activated growth-signalling pathways provides possibilities for chemotherapy at every step. Drugs targeted against these reactions are being applied clinically and are in clinical trials.

Tuning Down External Stimuli

Some tumours secrete self-stimulating growth factors into their environment, which also can affect nearby cells. A fascinating example is stimulation by a tumour of the production of new blood vessels, angiogenesis. This process creates the blood supply essential for nourishment of the tumour. Secretion by the tumour of a growth factor VEGF stimulates this production of blood vessel cells, and

of blood vessels from their assembly. Both antiangiogenic drugs and also antibodies that neutralize VEGF are being developed as anticancer agents (Boehm-Viswanathan, 2000).

About one third of breast tumour cells lack oestrogen receptors. Unlike those discussed above these are not stimulated by oestrogen or inhibited by tamoxifen, and so they are generally treated with classical anticancer agents following surgery. They are stimulated to grow by EGF, because too many EGF family receptors are on their surface. The monoclonal antibody (herceptin) made against these receptors is effective against some of these cancers, especially when applied in combination with the drugs taxol and doxorubicin.

Targets in the G_1 Phase Signal Transduction Pathway

The molecules that transmit growth signals from a cell's membrane receptors to its nucleus during G_1 phase (**Figure 2**) provide numerous targets for cancer treatment, now under investigation (Adams and Kaelin, 1998; Kaelin, 1999). One major participant is Ras, a small protein that must be positioned against the inner surface of the cell membrane to interact with growth factor receptors. Enzymes must chemically modify Ras for it to occupy this position, and so drugs are being developed that prevent this modification and thereby block the signalling pathway.

Signalling events require numerous kinases that modify the activities of other proteins by addition of phosphates to them. Kinase inhibitors can arrest cell growth and cause death of tumour cells (Shapiro and Harper, 1999). Specific inhibitors of critical cyclin-dependent kinases are being developed. An inhibitor has already demonstrated high efficacy in the treatment of chronic myelogenous leukaemia, a malignancy characterized by the activation of Abl kinase (Drucker and Lydon, 2000).

S Phase Lethality

A cell initiates a sequence of molecular events culminating in apoptosis during S phase unless certain molecules that initiated DNA synthesis are first inactivated. Applying a molecular analogue of part of the G_1–S factor E2F blocks the degradation of E2F and causes apoptosis (Lees and Weinberg, 1999).

Modulating Checkpoints

Several novel potential therapies are being developed (**Figure 7**).

Mitotic catastrophe

The loss of G_2 cell cycle checkpoints can increase tumour-cell sensitivity to chemotherapy. Furthermore, these cells often cannot take refuge at the G_1 checkpoint owing to the loss of p53 or other G_1 checkpoint molecules, whereas

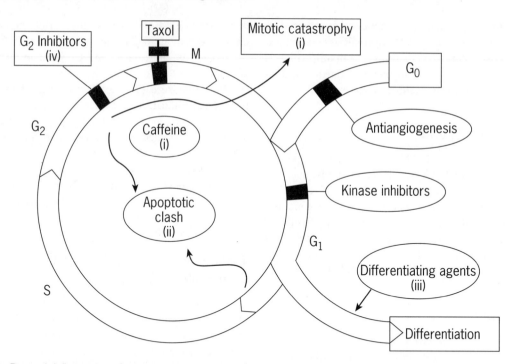

Figure 7   Potential therapies. Several potential therapies described in the text are illustrated.

cells with the normal checkpoint may still recover. Following DNA damage and the arrest at the G_2 checkpoint, some compounds can cause cycling cancer cells to move on through a lethal mitotic cell division. This process was recently aptly renamed 'mitotic catastrophe'. Post-treatment with a caffeine analogue enhanced cytotoxicity of drugs to cancer cells implanted in mice, but not to the mice (Fingert *et al.*, 1988). These agents, however, proved to be toxic to humans at doses that abrogate the G_2 checkpoint, which limits their therapeutic use. Other inhibitors that can eliminate the G_2 checkpoint such as the inhibitors of cyclin-dependent kinases, flavopiridol and UCN-0101, are currently undergoing clinical trials (Shapiro and Harper, 1999).

Clash Hypothesis

Remarkably effective synergistic killing of a variety of human cancer cells was found with the combined application together of two molecules derived from plant sources, β-lapachone and taxol (Li *et al.*, 1999). These combined drugs killed nearly all of several kinds of cancer cells in culture, at concentrations that did not show major lethality when the drugs were applied singly. Several kinds of human cancer cells growing in mice were destroyed when the drugs were applied together but not if they were applied separately. The tumours did not reappear for at least 2 months. Very importantly, the mice showed no signs of toxicity under these conditions, so there was a very high therapeutic index. Hence there are strong indications of clinical utility of this drug combination.

The mechanism of this powerful synergistic and tumour-specific lethality is being investigated. One hypothesis is based upon the proposal of 'clashing' checkpoint signals; apoptosis is caused by the production of two simultaneous molecular checkpoint signals created by growth conditions (Evan and Littlewood, 1998; Blagosklonny, 1999). Since β-lapachone causes G_1 arrest whereas taxol gives a G_2–M arrest, such clashes of conflicting molecular signals might also be created by this combination of drugs. They could selectively cause apoptotic death of cancer cells which already have defective checkpoint and apoptotic mechanisms.

Differentiation Therapy

An alternative to toxic cancer therapies is to restore the normal cell's properties. Cells in the blood are created by growth and then differentiation of precursor stem cells, followed by R point arrest of the matured cells and their eventual death. Leukaemic cells are mutated blood cells that do not undergo this terminal differentiation and death, and instead they continue to proliferate. Drugs have been discovered that recreate this differentiation-growth arrest process. Retinoids (vitamin A derivatives) are used in this way to treat promyelocytic leukaemia.

Newer drugs such as Saha show potential to inhibit leukaemias through differentiation therapy (Richon *et al.*, 1999). This approach is being generalized to make solid tumours differentiate as well. The drugs function by turning on differentiation-related genes, a process that is activated by addition of acetyl groups to the histone

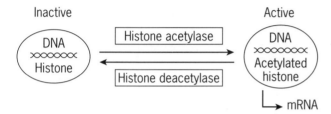

Figure 8   Control by histone acetylation. Histones that surround the DNA in chromatin block activities of genes. Acetylation of the histones permits them to produce their messenger RNAs.

proteins associated with DNA in chromatin (**Figure 8**). This process is catalysed by the enzyme histone acetylase, and it is reversed by deacetylase enzymes, which produce an inactive structure. These changes from the acetylated to the deacetylated state function as an on–off switch for regulation of gene expression. The differentiating drugs shift this balance by blocking deacetylase, thereby the activating acetylation dominates. Thus, drugs that permit histone acetylation, or that decrease the closely connected DNA methylation, are approaches for re-expression of tumour-suppressor genes such as *BRCA1*, *p16* and *p21* that are silenced in cancers by these processes.

Selective Protection of Normal Cells

Chemotherapy of cancer is limited by toxicity to normal cells. With traditional chemotherapy, dose-limiting side effects emerge, including toxicity to bone marrow and gastrointestinal tract, dermatological toxicity and cardiotoxicity. Therefore, selective protection of normal cells against chemotherapeutic drugs could improve the therapeutic index (the ratio of doses that affect cancer versus host), permitting the application of higher drug concentrations (see Blagosklonny and Pardee). Defective checkpoint mechanisms in cancer cells can be the basis of such a selective survival of normal cells (**Figure 6**).

Until recently, the mainstream approach for cancer treatment was directed to finding synergistic combinations in which all the drugs are toxic against cancer cells, and so combinations with an independently inactive drug were considered inappropriate. However, a high therapeutic index, with less toxicity to normal cells, was found in clinical trials when drugs that blocked entry of normal cells into M phase were administered before subsequently adding taxol. This prevented taxol lethality in M phase. This antagonism was translated in the clinic as a decrease in side effects to normal cells.

G_1 checkpoint arrest in normal but not in cancer cells is produced by low, nonlethal concentrations of compounds such as cycloheximide that slow protein synthesis. Later addition of a toxic S-phase-specific agent cannot kill them. In contrast, independence of cancer cells from this cycle arrest causes them to enter S phase, where they are killed while they are synthesizing DNA. This idea, proposed in 1975, has been revived in a new form. Low doses of doxorubicin or etoposide induce p53- and p21-dependent growth arrest of normal cells without cell death, but these drugs do not arrest cancer cells. This pretreatment thereby abolished the cytotoxicity otherwise caused by later addition of microtubule-active drugs (paclitaxel, vincristine, epothilones). Protection of cells with normal checkpoint was achieved, whereas no protection was observed in cancer cells lacking p53 or p21 (see Blagosklonny and Pardee).

Novel inhibitors of the cell cycle are being developed as lethal drugs against solid cancers and leukaemia cells. However, these are active also against normal cells; proliferating bone marrow and epithelial cells are particularly vulnerable. Thus, searches for compounds that reversibly inhibit proliferation of these normal cells will be especially valuable to protect the individual. For example, although two compounds similarly inhibited protein kinase C, UCN-01 was selected as the drug to develop because it had higher cytotoxicity to cancer. For a selective growth arrest of normal cells, dependent on protein kinase C, one would choose the less toxic inhibitor GF109203X. Other strategies utilizing the retention of checkpoints in normal cells to protect them versus tumour cells are discussed (see Blagosklonny and Pardee). Since proliferation of normal cells is highly regulated, the search for such inhibitors should produce surprises.

In summary, defects in cancers of various molecular mechanisms that control cell growth, differentiation and apoptosis have recently been discovered. These differences from normal cells provide novel targets for therapy, some of which are being developed and tested.

ACKNOWLEDGEMENT

This work was supported by NIH Grant CA RO1 61253.

REFERENCES

Adams, P. D. and Kaelin, W. G., Jr (1998). Negative control elements of the cell cycle in human tumors. *Current Opinion in Cell Biology*, **10**, 791–797.

Blagosklonny, M. V. (1999). A node between proliferation, apoptosis, and growth arrest. *Bioessays*, **21**, 704–709.

Boehm-Viswanathan, T. (2000). Is angiogenesis inhibition the Holy Grail of cancer therapy? *Current Opinion in Oncology*, **12**, 89–94.

Druker, B. J. and Lydon, N. B. (2000). Lessons learned from the development of an Abl tyrosine inhibitor for chronic myelogenous leukemia. *Journal of Clinical Investigation*, **105**, 3–7.

Evan, G. and Littlewood, T. (1998). A matter of life and cell death. *Science*, **281**, 1317–1322.

Fingert, H. J., *et al.* (1988). *In vivo* and *in vitro* enhanced anti-tumor effects by pentoxifylline in human cancer cells treated with thiotepa. *Cancer Research*, **48**, 4375–4381.

Hartwell, L. H. and Kastan, M. B. (1994). Cell cycle control and cancer. *Science*, **266**, 1821–1828.

Howard, A. and Pelc, S. R. (1951). Nuclear Incorporation of P32 as demonstrated by autoradiography. *Experimental Cell Research*, **2**, 178–187.

Kaelin, W. G., Jr (1999). Choosing anticancer drug targets in the postgenomic era. *Journal of Clinical Investigation*, **104**, 1503–1506.

Kinzler, K. W. and Vogelstein, B. (1996). Lessons from hereditary colorectal cancer. *Cell*, **87**, 159–170.

Koepp, D. M., *et al.* (1999). How the cyclin became a cyclin: regulated proteolysis in the cell cycle. *Cell*, **97**, 431–434.

Lees, J. A. and Weinberg, R. A. (1999). Tossing monkey wrenches into the clock: new ways of treating cancer. *Proceedings of the National Academy of Sciences of the USA*, **96**, 4221–4223.

Levine, A. J. (1997). p53, the cellular gatekeeper for growth and division. *Cell*, **88**, 323–331.

Li, C. J., *et al.* (1999). Potent inhibition of tumor survival *in vivo* by β-lapachone plus taxol: combining drugs imposes different artifical checkpoints. *Proceedings of the National Academy of Sciences of the USA*, **96**, 13369–13374.

Minshull, J., *et al.* (1989). The role of cyclin synthesis, modification and destruction in the control of cell division. *Journal of Cell Science, Supplement*, **12**, 77–97.

Nurse, P., *et al.* (1998). Understanding the cell cycle. *Nature Medicine*, **4**, 11030–1106.

Pardee, A. B. (1989). G_1 events and regulation of cell proliferation. *Science*, **246**, 603–608.

Richon, V. M., *et al.* (1999). A class of hybrid polar inducers of transformed cell differentiation inhibits histone deactylase. *Proceedings of the National Academy of Sciences of the USA*, **95**, 3003–3007.

Roberts, J. M. (1999). Evolving ideas about cyclins. *Cell*, **97**, 129–132.

Shapiro, G. I. and Harper, J. W. (1999). Anticancer drug targets: cell cycle and checkpoint control. *Journal of Clinical Investigation*, **104**, 1645–1653.

Sherr, C. J. (1996). Cancer cell cycles. *Science*, **274**, 1672–1677.

Tseng, S. L., *et al.* (1997). Allelic loss at BRCA1, BRCA2, and adjacent loci in relation to TP53 abnormality in breast cancer. *Genes Chromosomes Cancer*, **20**, 377–382.

FURTHER READING

Andreeff, M., *et al.* (2000). Cell proliferation, differentiation and apoptosis. In: Holland, J., *et al.* (eds), *Cancer Medicine*, 5th edn. 17–32. (B. C. Decker, Hamilton, Ontario).

Baserga, R. (1985). *The Biology of Cell Reproduction.* (Harvard University Press, Cambridge, MA).

Blagosklonny, M. V. and Pardee, A. B. (2001). Exploiting cancer cell cycling for selective protection of normal cells. *Cancer Research*, **11**, 4301–4305.

Ford, H. L. and Pardee, A. B. (1999). Cancer and the cell cycle. *Journal of Cellular Biochemistry*, **75**, 166–172.

Hanahan, D. and Weinberg, R. A. (2000). The hallmarks of cancer. *Cell*, **100**, 57–70.

Murray, A. W. and Hunt, T. (1993). *The Cell Cycle, an Introduction.* (Freeman, San Francisco).

Sellers, W. R. and Fisher, D. E. (1999). Apoptosis and cancer drug targeting. *Journal of Clinical Investigation*, **104**, 1655–1661.

Chapter 3

Overview of Oncogenesis

Julie L. Boerner, Jacqueline S. Biscardi and Sarah J. Parsons
University of Virginia, Charlottesville, VA, USA

CONTENTS

PROPERTIES OF NEOPLASTIC CELLS

Normal cells are exquisitely attuned to their environment and respond to external cues via tightly regulated signalling pathways that either trigger or repress growth. In order for a cell to undergo mitogenesis, a growth-promoting signal from the extracellular environment must first initiate a cascade of events within the cell that results in activation of genes that stimulate cell division. With few exceptions, most of the cell populations within an adult organism are terminally differentiated and no longer proliferate. Cancer arises when a cell, for a variety of reasons, escapes the normal constraints placed on its growth and begins to divide in an unregulated fashion.

Factors that Promote Growth

Extracellular factors that stimulate growth include peptide growth factors such as epidermal growth factor (EGF) and platelet-derived growth factor (PDGF), which bind tyrosine kinase receptors located on the cell surface. Cytokines such as growth hormone, interleukins and prolactin also bind cell surface receptors which are not kinases themselves but are able to transduce their signals via interaction with separate tyrosine kinase molecules. Another class of growth factors bind serpentine receptors that couple to intracellular pathways via heterotrimeric G proteins. Lastly, steroid hormones such as oestrogen, which bind intracellular receptors, also have mitotic activity. All classes of receptors are capable of triggering a cascade of signalling events culminating in mitotic activity, or proliferation, of the target cell.

Mutation of Growth Regulatory Genes in Cancer

In tumour cells, molecules that regulate signalling pathways which stimulate growth are often mutated, resulting in a constant 'on' signal to the cell. These molecules can be positive for growth regulation, as cancer-causing oncogenes, or negative for growth regulation, as protective tumour-suppressor genes. In addition, tumour cells often develop their own autocrine loops for growth, wherein a growth factor required for the activation of a pro-growth signalling pathway is constantly produced and secreted into the extracellular milieu. One example of such an autocrine loop is found in breast tumour cells, which are able to produce the growth factor TGF-α. TGF-α binds and activates the EGF receptor, thereby triggering mitotic pathways within the cell.

Cell Death

Apoptosis, or programmed cell death, is yet another process that is subverted by a tumour cell (Jacotot *et al.*, 2000). In a normal cell, a series of 'checkpoints' must be met before the cell permits itself to divide. If irreparable damage to its DNA is present, the cell undergoes apoptosis, thus ensuring that its mutated DNA is not transmitted to progeny cells. The molecules that regulate this process of apoptosis are often themselves mutated in cancer cells, which are then able to escape the checks and balances that a normal cell must undergo before it can divide. (See chapter on *Apoptosis*.)

Cell–Cell Interaction

Cells can also respond mitogenically to cues from other cells. Normal cells are growth-inhibited by contact with other cells and form a monolayer when grown in culture. Cancer cells, on the other hand, form foci, or piled-up accumulations of constantly dividing cells; foci result as a consequence of loss of contact inhibition. Molecules called cellular adhesion molecules (CAMs) and cadherins are expressed on the surface of cells and negatively regulate growth. Cadherin molecules on adjacent cells bind one another in a calcium-dependent manner; this binding prevents cells from entering the mitotic cycle (Christofiori and Semb, 1999). Further intracellular signalling occurs via the catenin family of molecules, which link the cadherins to the cytoskeleton and to the transcription machinery. The negative regulation normally provided by the interaction of these molecules is frequently lost in tumour cells. For example, epithelial cell cadherin (E-cadherin) is mutated, absent, or reduced in expression in a variety of human tumours. In cell culture systems, loss of the E-cadherin gene leads to loss of cell–cell contacts and increases in cell motility and invasiveness. Aberrant phosphorylation of the catenins can lead to loss of proper cell–cell contacts, which is thought to be a step in the acquisition of invasive properties of the cancer cell. Moreover, the *APC* tumour-suppressor gene, which is mutated in human cancer, is known to associate with β-catenin. Cancer-causing mutations in *APC* involve the portion of the molecule that binds β-catenin. Thus, loss of these tumour-suppressor genes and their appropriate interactions with cadherins and catenins relieves the constraints of contact inhibition, a hallmark of tumour cells.

Cell–Substratum Interactions

Pro-growth cues can also come from the extracellular matrix or substratum (such as the basement membrane) on which cells grow (Miyamoto *et al.*, 1998). Proteins such as fibronectin, a component of the ECM, bind integrin receptors on the cell surface. The integrin receptors then cooperate with growth factor receptors to trigger mitogenic pathways via activation of signalling cascades involving several different kinase molecules. Alternative, tumour-specific isoforms and unique combinations of integrins are often present in tumour cells, thereby providing additional means by which growth signals can be initiated. (See also chapter *Extracellular Matrix: The Networking Solution*.)

Angiogenesis

Tumours also exhibit extensive vascularization which increases as the tumour grows (Folkman, 1992). This outgrowth of new blood vessels is termed angiogenesis and is not seen in normal adult animals except in the cases of wound healing and pregnancy, where new tissues such as placenta are formed. In the absence of new blood vessels, a tumour is able to grow to a maximum size of approximately 1 mm in diameter, the distance that oxygen and nutrients are able to diffuse into the tumour (Kurschat and Mauch, 2000). Vascularization thus allows the tumour to grow larger. (See also chapter on *Angiogenesis*.)

Migration and Metastasis

Tumour cells often have the ability to migrate away from the original tumour site and grow in distant parts of the body (Kurschat and Mauch, 2000). This ability to

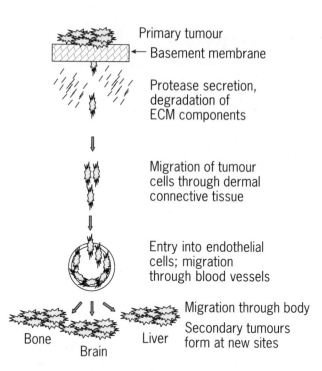

Figure 1   Metastatic progression. Individual cells within the primary tumour upregulate production of specific proteases, which gives the cell the ability to degrade ECM or basement membrane. Cells then break away from the primary tumour and begin to migrate. Migrating cells adhere to connective tissue and invade dermal tissue. Cells thus enter the vascular system by migrating between endothelial cells and moving through blood vessels. Lastly, tumour cells reach secondary sites where conditions are favourable for their continued growth.

metastasize requires that the tumour cells produce proteases that degrade the basement membrane of blood vessels through which the tumour cells will travel. Metastatic tumour cells are also able to escape immune surveillance of the host organism and then to grow again in another part of the body. Factors produced at these distal sites are thought to provide a favourable environment for the continued proliferation of the tumour cells. Evidence for this comes from the finding that specific types of tumours have a propensity to metastasize to the same sites, e.g. prostate cancer commonly targets bone. Moreover, tumour cells also have the ability to affect the underlying layer of stroma, or fibroblast cells, stimulating them to produce growth factors and cytokines that enhance tumour growth. **Figure 1** depicts how a cell breaks away from the primary tumour and generates a secondary neoplasm within the organism. (See also chapter on *Invasion and Metastasis*.)

Conversion of a Normal Cell to a Tumour Cell

A cell becomes converted from a normal to a neoplastic cancer cell when the regulation of one or more of the above processes is lost. Loss of regulation occurs when mutations arise in two broad families of genes that regulate growth: oncogenes, which act as positive signals for growth, and tumour-suppressor genes, which act as brakes or checkpoints on a cell's progression through the cell cycle. These mutations may be caused by environmental, chemical or biological agents or events that result in irreversible alterations in the genome of a cell, so that progeny cells also carry the same mutations that allow for uncontrolled growth. This is the first step on a pathway that can eventually lead to an aggressive, meta-static tumour. Fortunately, organisms possess several means of dealing with environmental insults and genetic alterations. More than one genetic 'hit,' or error, is required before an actual tumour is able to arise, as will be discussed later.

ONCOGENES

Historical Perspective

In 1911, Peyton Rous laid the groundwork for the onco-gene theory of cancer, a theory that became the basis for all modern cellular signalling and genetic research. He iden-tified a spindle-celled sarcoma in chickens that was transplantable from one bird to another, using a filtrate of the tumour (Rous, 1911; Weiss *et al*., 1985). The infectious agent responsible for the tumours was later found to be the Rous sarcoma virus (RSV). Thus, a cancer causing agent had been discovered, but the means by which the virus induced tumours was still unclear.

Further insight into the process of oncogenesis was provided in 1914, by Theodor Boveri who hypothesized that cells in cancer tissue contain defective chromosomes. Working with double-fertilized sea urchin embryos, Boveri observed that the resulting aberrant chromosomes were passed on to progeny cells (Boveri, 1925). This finding led him to believe that cells of malignant tumours have damaged chromosomes and that a neoplastic cell can arise from a normal cell and pass its altered genome on to progeny cells. Thus, a tumour cell is in some way defective and has lost the properties of a normal cell. Environmental insults were also implicated in causing cancers. In 1918, Yamagiwa and Ichikawa showed that continual irritation of the normal epithelium of rabbit ears caused papilloma-like growths and metastasis.

Building on the early work of Rous, Shope provided further evidence for the viral basis of oncogenesis by his demonstration that a papilloma-like growth was trans-missible from animal to animal (Weiss *et al*., 1985). In 1951, Gross showed that mice inoculated with leukaemic extracts developed neoplasms. From these extracts, the Gross murine leukaemia virus was isolated (Weiss *et al*., 1985). Seven years later, Temin and Rubin showed that infection of cultured chicken fibroblasts with the Rous sarcoma virus caused neoplastic transformation of the cells (Weiss *et al*., 1985). Martin and others later identified the oncogenic portion of the RSV genome as v-*src*, the viral *src* oncogene. These early results suggested a transmissible mechanism for tumour initiation. Thus, as early as the beginning of the twentieth century, a cellular/genetic model of oncogenesis had been postulated.

The Oncogene Hypothesis

The best-known theory of oncogenesis, however, is a relatively recent one. In 1982, Bishop and Varmus hypo-thesized that cancer-causing genes, or oncogenes, that are carried by tumour-inducing viruses have normal counter-parts that are present in the genomes of all vertebrate cells (Bishop, 1982). These normal genes are termed proto-oncogenes. Evidence for this hypothesis came from hybridization studies, where radiolabelled v-*src* DNA was found to bind, or hybridize, to its complementary coun-terpart (c-*src*) in normal avian cellular DNA. The v-*src* and c-*src* genes encode a tyrosine kinase, an enzyme that transfers phosphate from ATP to the amino acid tyrosine found in cellular proteins. These phosphorylations have profound effects on cell growth. Similar studies eventually led to the identification of a family of viral oncogenes, which can be transmitted by either DNA or RNA viruses. DNA viruses either can cause lytic infection leading to the death of the cellular host, or can replicate their DNA along with that of the host genome and promote neoplastic transformation of the cell. DNA viruses encode various proteins which, along with environmental and genetic factors, help to initiate and maintain the neoplastic state. RNA tumour viruses, on the other hand, integrate DNA copies of their RNA genomes into the genome of the host cell. Since the viral genomes contain transforming oncogenes, they induce cancerous transformation of the host cell.

Mechanism of Acquisition of Cellular Sequences by RNA Tumour Viruses

Multiple lines of evidence indicate that viral oncogenes arise when an RNA virus integrates its genome near the coding sequence for a proto-oncogene and incorporates the proto-oncogene's DNA into its own genetic material during the virus replication cycle. Through multiple rounds of infection and genome replication, deletions and other mutations occur in the proto-oncogene, conferring on the gene tumorigenic properties. Ensuing infection of a normal cell by an RNA tumour virus carrying such an oncogene causes malignant transformation of that cell. Although this process rarely occurs in human tumours, many of the same

Table 1 Examples of human oncogenes

Oncogene	Originally identified in	Mechanism of activation in human tumours	Location	Associated human cancers
src	Rous sarcoma virus	Overexpression, C-terminal deletion	Cytoplasmic	Breast, colon, lung carcinomas
myc	Avian myelocytomatosis virus	Translocation	Nuclear	Burkitt lymphoma
abl	Abelson murine leukaemia virus	Translocation	Cytoplasmic	Chronic myeloid leukaemia
Ha-*ras*	Harvey murine sarcoma virus	Point mutation	Cytoplasmic	Bladder cancer
K-*ras*	Kirsten murine sarcoma virus	Point mutation	Cytoplasmic	Colon, lung carcinomas
erbB (EGFR)	Avian erythroblastosis virus	Overexpression, deletion	Cytoplasmic	Breast carcinoma, glioblastoma

genes 'captured' by animal retroviruses are altered in human cancers. These alterations take the form of base pair changes, insertions, amplifications and translocations, which result in a protein product that no longer responds normally to growth-regulatory cues. Only one allele of the gene needs to be mutated for the oncogenic effect. Thus, oncogenes are described as carrying dominant mutations. For example, Ras in human tumours is often found to be mutated at a single amino acid residue (Wittinghofer, 1998), whereas the oncogene *abl* is activated by chromosomal translocation (Heisterkamp *et al.*, 1985). In the case of c-Src, a negative regulatory site present in normal c-*src* is mutated in a small subset of colon cancers, thus rendering the protein constitutively active (Irby *et al.*, 1999), whereas in human breast cancer, overexpression of the normal c-Src protein appears to play a role in the deregulation of cell growth (Biscardi *et al.*, 1999).

Proto-oncogenes can be classified as either cytoplasmic or nuclear, depending on where in the cell they are localized. Many of the cytoplasmic proto-oncogenes code for tyrosine kinase molecules, enzymes that are able to phosphorylate substrate proteins on tyrosine residues and that are known to be essential for controlling the signalling cascades that regulate mitosis. Others, such as Ras, transmit cellular growth signals by binding guanine nucleotides in the form of GTP or GDP. Ras is often found mutated at single sites such that it is constantly bound to GTP, which causes the molecule to be constitutively active. Mutations in Ras are found in approximately 30% of human cancers (Wittinghofer, 1998). Serine–threonine kinases, such as the Raf family of kinases, are the targets of Ras and constitute another family of proto-oncogenes that regulate proliferation. Nuclear oncogenes such as *myc* regulate gene transcription. **Table 1** lists a few examples of the better-known oncogenes, their subcellular localization and mechanism of oncogenic activation. Although these oncogenes are defined as cancer causing genes, it is important to note that the introduction of a single activated oncogene into a cell does not result in neoplastic transformation. At least two active oncogenes, or an activated oncogene and an inactivated tumour suppressor, are required for tumour formation.

TUMOUR SUPPRESSORS

Tumour-suppressor genes are defined as recessive genes, i.e. they must sustain mutations or deletions of both alleles in order to contribute to cancer formation and progression. This definition implies that one functional allele of the tumour-suppressor gene is sufficient for normal cell function. Patients with familial cancers frequently inherit one normal and one abnormal allele of the tumour-suppressor gene from their parents. If the second, normal allele is lost, the protective effect of the gene product no longer exists. Therefore, introduction of a wild-type copy of the gene back into the tumour should inhibit further tumour growth. Unfortunately, putative tumour-suppressor genes shown to be inactivated in cancer are not sufficient by themselves to restore normal cell function. Thus, whether such genes are actually tumour suppressors remains a debated question.

Discovery and Identification

The origin of the concept of tumour-suppressor genes (or anti-oncogenes) came from cell fusion studies dating back to the early 1900s. These studies revealed that when one tumour cell is fused with another and the fused product is introduced into mice, tumour formation results (Sager, 1989). However, when a tumour cell is fused with a normal cell and introduced into mice, the fusion blocks tumour formation. These observations suggested that some activity must be present in the normal cell that inhibits transformation.

Retinoblastoma (Rb) Gene

The first tumour-suppressor gene identified was the *Rb* gene, which is associated with the childhood illness of retinoblastoma (Knudson, 1971). In an epidemiological study, Knudson and colleagues noticed that bilateral retinoblastoma occurred frequently within the same family, whereas unilateral retinoblastoma did not appear to be a genetically inherited disease. In families with bilateral retinoblastoma, karyotyping techniques were used to detect homozygous loss of chromosome 13q, a defect that was transmitted to offspring. Homozygous loss was found to be necessary but not sufficient for the formation of retinoblastoma, since not every family member with the loss of both alleles developed the disease. Later, the gene responsible for development of the disease was cloned and termed *Rb* for retinoblastoma. Reintroduction of this gene into cultured retinoblastoma tumour cells reversed the malignant phenotype, suggesting that the gene was indeed a tumour suppressor (Bookstein *et al.*, 1989).

Tumour Suppressors in Colon Cancer

Since the cloning of *Rb*, many other tumour-suppressor genes have been identified (**Table 2**). Several of the most notable are a group of tumour-suppressor genes that were identified by studying progressive stages of colon cancer. They include the 'adenomatous polyposis coli' (*APC*) gene, the 'deleted in colon cancer' (*DCC*) gene and the 'mutated in colon cancer' (*MCC*) gene (Peddanna *et al.*, 1996). *APC* maps to chromosome 5q21 and is mutated in 70% of patients with a hereditary form of colon cancer, termed familial adenomatous polyposis (FAP). Also mapping to chromosome 5q is the *MCC* gene, which was found to be mutated in 55% of all colon cancers studied. *DCC* was mapped to chromosome 18 and is deleted in 73% of colon cancers. *APC* and *DCC* code for proteins that play roles in regulating cell adhesion in normal cells. It is speculated that loss of these genes can lead to increases in cell motility, a key characteristic of metastasis.

p53

The p53 protein is involved in sensing DNA damage and regulating cell death (Marx, 1993). In normal cells, when DNA damage is sensed by p53, the cell cycle is arrested to permit DNA repair. Upon completion of this process, the cell progresses through the mitotic cycle. If repair fails to occur, p53 initiates the process of apoptosis, or programmed cell death. Thus, normal cells with genetic defects die. If p53 is not present in the cell (via gene deletion) or is mutated to be nonfunctional, DNA damage is not repaired, and the cell progresses through the cell cycle, transmitting its damaged DNA to its progeny. p53 is so important to the maintenance of 'healthy' DNA that it is mutated or deleted in over 70% of human cancers, including osteosarcomas, rhabdomyosarcomas and carcinomas of the breast, colon, lung and prostate.

BRCA1 and *BRCA2*

Another more recently identified tumour-suppressor gene, *BRCA1*, was found to be linked to an increased risk of hereditary breast cancer (Zheng *et al.*, 2000). Loss of chromosome 17q had long been known to occur in familial breast cancer. The *BRCA1* gene mapped to chromosome 17q, but it was not until 1993 that it was identified and cloned. Many heritable mutations were identified in *BRCA1* from breast cancer patients and include an 11-bp deletion, a 1-bp insertion, a stop codon and a missense substitution. However, this may be an underestimation of its involvement in oncogenesis, as mutations and inactivating events, such as promoter methylation, also may regulate *BRCA1*

Table 2 Tumour-suppressor genes and their function and associated cancers

Name	Function in normal cells	Associated cancers
p53	Cell cycle regulator	Colon and others
BRCA1	Cell cycle regulator, genomic integrity and chromatin structure	Breast, ovarian, prostate and others
BRCA2	Genomic integrity	Breast, ovarian, prostate and others
PTEN	Tyrosine and lipid phosphatase	Prostate, glioblastomas
APC	Cell adhesion	Colon
DCC	Cell adhesion	Colon
MCC	Undetermined	Colon
p16-INK4A	Cell cycle regulator	Colon and others
MLH1	Mismatch repair	Colon and gastric cancers
MSH2	Mismatch repair	Colon and gastric cancers
DPC4	Cell death regulator	Pancreatic
Wt1	Cell death regulator	Wilms' tumour
NF1	Regulator of GTPases	Astrocytomas
NF2	Cell adhesion	Astrocytomas
VHL	Ubiquitination	Renal
PTC	Regulator of hedgehog signalling	Thyroid
TSC2	Cell cycle regulator	Breast and renal
TSG101	Cell cycle regulator	Renal and leukaemia

expression. Such gene regulation events are still being defined and are difficult to identify by screening techniques. Another *BRCA* family member, *BRCA2*, also has been cloned. This gene localizes to 13p12–13, and mutations within it correlate with breast cancer occurrence. *BRCA1* and 2 also are mutated or deleted in about 33 and 34% of sporadic breast tumours, respectively.

PTEN

PTEN, a gene encoding a phosphoprotein and phospholipid phosphatase, was first identified in glioblastoma patients who had sustained deletions of chromosome 10q23 (Li *et al.*, 1997). *PTEN* is mutated in 31% of glioblastomas, 100% of prostate cancers and 6% of breast cancers. Interestingly, deletion of *PTEN* in gliomas segregates independently of mutations in p53, i.e. tumours containing *PTEN* mutations do not contain p53 mutations (Liu *et al.*, 1997). However, *PTEN* deletions/mutations do correlate with amplification of the EGF receptor, a known oncogene. In normal cells, it is thought that PTEN downregulates phosphorylation events that promote cell growth. Its loss, therefore, allows for unregulated and unhindered proliferation.

Other Tumour-suppressor Genes

Another tumour-suppressor gene is the *p16-INK4A* gene, which negatively regulates cell cycle events. It is lost from chromosome 9 in a wide range of cancers (Kamb *et al.*, 1994). Genes involved in the efficacy of DNA replication, *MLH1* and *MSH2*, are found deleted in 50% of hereditary non-polyposis colorectal cancers (Konishi *et al.*, 1996). *DPC4* (deleted in pancreatic cancer) is lost from chromosome 18q in pancreatic cancer (Hahn *et al.*, 1996). Still other tumour-suppressor genes include the Wilms' tumour-associated tumour suppressor *Wt1*, the human astrocytoma-associated tumour suppressors *NF1* and *NF2*, the von Hippel–Lindau syndrome tumour suppressor *VHL*, the papillary thyroid cancer tumour-suppressor gene *PTC* and tumour-suppressor genes associated with breast and renal cancer, *TSG101* and *TSC2*, respectively. Each of these genes encode protein products that negatively regulate the acquisition of a malignant phenotype by a normal cell.

Tumour-suppressor Genes, Normal Cellular Function and Carcinogenesis

In normal cells, products of tumour-suppressor genes have been shown to regulate negatively cell growth and proliferation. For example, the *Rb* gene product sequesters transcription factors that are required for normal cell cycle progression. The ability of Rb to function as a block to cell cycle progression is regulated by phosphorylation of the Rb protein on multiple serine residues (Harbour and Dean,

2000). In quiescence, Rb is hypo- or under-phosphorylated and binds members of the E2F transcription factor family. Upon growth factor stimulation of the cell, Rb becomes phosphorylated by cyclin-regulated kinases and releases E2F, which then induces gene transcription events necessary for cell division. In cancers, deletion or inactivation of Rb results in constitutively 'free' E2F, which in turn leads to unfettered gene transcription and oncogenic transformation. Similarly, as described above, p53 has been shown to sense DNA damage, cause cell cycle arrest, regulate transcription and stimulate apoptotic cell death pathways in normal cells (Marx, 1993). Loss of this function increases the chance of damaged DNA being transmitted to subsequent generations of cells. The exact role of BRCA1 is still unclear, but studies using mice that lack the *BRCA1* gene show that it is essential for cellular proliferation during early embryonic development (Zheng *et al.*, 2000). BRCA1 may also regulate transcriptional events, since it is capable of acting as a coactivator of p53 and a corepressor of c-Myc. Recent studies also implicate a role for BRCA1 in chromatin remodelling, which is required for DNA transcriptional and replication events. PTEN regulates the phosphorylation status of phospholipids that are involved in regulating apoptotic pathways within the cell (Di Cristofano and Pandolfi, 2000). Taken together, these findings indicate that tumour-suppressor gene products act by negatively controlling cell growth in normal cells and that their loss contributes to the unregulated cell growth seen in tumour cells.

Mismatch Repair Genes

Critical regulators of genomic integrity, as exemplified by mismatch repair genes, also have been implicated as tumour-suppressor genes. The microsatellite instability genes described above, *MLH1* and *MSH2*, are important to the maintenance of genomic integrity by repairing mismatched base pairs that arise with a stable frequency during DNA replication (Kolodner and Marsischky, 1999). Mismatched base pairs are recognized and cleared by mismatch repair enzymes, and new bases are added in their place. Without such genes, repairs are not made and mutations are introduced into newly synthesized DNA. Alternatively, the stress of the mismatch structure may fragment the DNA. Both of these possibilities can lead to changes in the sequence of genes critical to cell growth or death. Although the alteration of mismatch repair genes may seem like a key event for all cancers, it has been determined that only 13% of gastric/colorectal cancers and less than 2% of other cancers have mutations in mismatch repair genes. Furthermore, the 2% occurrence is thought to reflect the normal rate of DNA mutation. These considerations therefore suggest that mismatch repair defects may be more specific for gastric cancers and not a general phenomenon associated with cancer development.

New Techniques for Identification of Tumour-suppressor Genes

RFLP

Knudson's original method of analysing karyotypes of tumour cells is still in use today for examining large, consistent chromosomal alterations, but new methods have evolved in the last 20 years. One such technique, restriction fragment length polymorphism (RFLP), utilizes bacterial restriction enzymes that cleave DNA at specific sites. DNA encoding a normal gene has a characteristic DNA fragment pattern, while tumour DNA shows an abnormal pattern. RFLP DNA fragments have been linked together to span an entire normal human genome. At a frequency of approximately every 10 million base pairs, a known gene has been mapped to specific RFLP fragments. This approach has yielded a crude map of the genome, which is more sensitive than karyotyping methods and allows one to map a loss of specific regions of a chromosome.

Comparative Genomic Hybridization (CGH)

Comparative genomic hybridization compares the ability of tumour RNA labelled with one fluorophore (i.e. green) and normal RNA labelled with another fluorophore (i.e. red) to hybridize to a chromosome spread from a given tissue type. The spread is analysed by fluorescence microscopy after hybridization of the RNAs. Losses (or gains) in a chromosome can be observed by the colour of the fluorophore hybridized to the region on the chromosome. For example, if a region of chromosome 13 is deleted in the tumour DNA, chromosome 13 will appear red since there would be no green-labelled (tumour-derived) RNA to hybridize with that region. Gains in the tumour DNA score green whereas equal expression in both normal and tumour cells scores yellow (a merging of red and green). Thus a complete genomic map of genetic changes that occur in a tumour cell can be obtained. Other more sensitive techniques, such as DNA microarrays, are currently being perfected to identify additional tumour-suppressor genes. It should be noted that in comparison with oncogenes, a very small number of tumour-suppressor genes have been discovered. The techniques that detect tumour-suppressor genes are somewhat insensitive, since even the most accurate screening approaches localize the region of loss only to a megabase or more.

Methylation

The techniques described above tend to identify tumour-suppressor genes that are grossly mutated in cancer. However, there are other mechanisms of tumour-suppressor gene inactivation, including point substitutions, small insertions and deletions. Almost half of all tumour-suppressor genes are also methylated in their promoter regions, preventing gene transcription (Baylin, 1997). Abnormally high levels of methylation appear in cancer cells that have a loss in the $p21/WAF1$ gene. In normal cells, $p21^{WAF1}$ protein negatively regulates the ability of DNA-methyltransferase to add a methyl group to CpG islands, thereby protecting these sites in the DNA from methylation. Inactivation or loss of $p21^{WAF1}$ allows these sites to be methylated and transcriptionally silenced. Some tumour-suppressor genes shown to be methylated in tumours include $BRCA1$, VHL, and $p16INK4A$.

MOLECULAR MECHANISMS OF CANCER

Tumorigenesis *in vivo* is actually a multistep process requiring the alterations of two or more genes (Knudson, 1971). **Figure 2** depicts a single cell bearing a mutation or genetic 'hit' in gene A. This mutation is passed on to progeny cells, which, at a defined probability, sustain a second 'hit' in gene B. The figure depicts the mutation in gene A as a dominant 'oncogene-like' mutation and the mutations in both alleles of gene B as a recessive 'tumour-suppressor-like' mutation. Such alterations provide the initial steps in tumour formation. Every cell in the tumour carries the identical mutations that initiated tumour development.

The Two-hit Hypothesis of Knudson and Hereditary Cancers

One of the first concepts to arise regarding the molecular mechanism of tumours was suggested by Knudson and colleagues, who developed the two-hit hypothesis (Knudson, 1985). The assumptions of this hypothesis are threefold: malignant transformation of a single cell is sufficient to give rise to a tumour; any cell in a specific tissue is as likely to be transformed as any other of the same type; and once a malignant cell is generated, the mean time to tumour detection is generally constant. Once these assumptions are met, the model suggests that at least two events are necessary for carcinogenesis and that the cell with the first event must survive in the tissue long enough to sustain a second event.

Multistep Carcinogenesis Models

Land and Weinberg Model

At about the same time that Knudson proposed the two-hit hypothesis, Weinberg and Barrett independently suggested models of carcinogenesis based on the activation of a series of oncogenes. Weinberg suggested that the activation of two or more oncogenes is required for tumorigenesis and that the right combination must be activated in

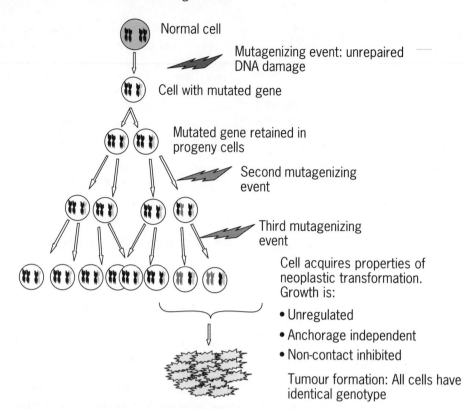

Figure 2   Acquisition of tumorigenic phenotype and clonality. Once a cell has acquired a mutation in an oncogene (depicted as the chromosome in light grey), that mutation is passed on to subsequent generations of progeny cells. These cells are still phenotypically normal, however. Cellular transformation occurs when a second and third mutation arise in a tumour-suppressor gene, e.g. in one of the previously mutated cells (depicted in dark grey). This cell now harbours three mutations in at least two different genes, and displays the hallmarks of neoplastic growth in culture.

the right context (Weinberg, 1983). Which oncogenes are activated is dependent on the signalling events each regulates. For example, Ras (a cytoplasmic oncoprotein) was shown to cooperate with Myc (a nuclear oncoprotein) to form tumours. Other combinations of cytoplasmic and nuclear oncoproteins also cause tumours to form, but one oncoprotein from each group must be activated.

Barrett's Model

Barrett's model further divides the process into tumour initiation vs tumour-promotion events (Boyd and Barrett, 1990). These investigators suggested that initiation is most often a mutational event, including mutations in a proto-oncogene, such as *ras*. Promotion, on the other hand, can be a mutational or an epigenetic change, and is defined as a series of '... qualitative, heritable changes in a sub-population of initiated cells, resulting in malignancy or an increased potential to progress to malignancy.' In this model, morphological transformation (or initiation) occurs upon treatment with a mutagen or carcinogen. This event is followed by a loss or inactivation of a gene controlling cell senescence along with activation of immortalizing genes. With such changes, an immortal cell line is generated. The subsequent loss or inactivation of a tumour-suppressor

gene or activation of a transforming oncogene then leads to the formation of a tumorigenic cell.

Vogelstein's Model

Studies by Vogelstein and colleagues led to a progression model in colon cancer which includes both the activation of oncogenes and the loss of tumour suppressors (Vogelstein and Kinzler, 1993). This model, dubbed the Vogelgram, is based on several observations. The first is that cancer cells contain 3–7 somatic mutations per cell. Second, benign tissue surrounding the malignant tissue frequently contains many of the same set of mutations found in the tumour but lacks at least one mutation that is found in tumour tissue. Third, certain genes have a high probability of mutating at each definable stage of colon cancer progression. Based on these and other genetic data, a model for colon cancer progression was formulated. **Figure 3** suggests that the loss of the tumour-suppressor gene *APC* occurs early in the process of transformation, converting colonic epithelial cells to a hyperproliferative state. Hypomethylation of DNA then occurs in the early ademona stage, followed by activation of the oncogene Ki-*ras* in carcinoma *in situ*. The tumour-suppressor genes *DCC* and *p53* are lost later in the disease,

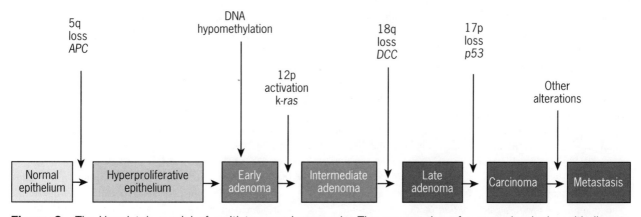

Figure 3 The Vogelstein model of multistep carcinogenesis. The progression of a normal colonic epithelium to metastatic colon cancer can be observed as it passes through several distinct stages. Chromosomal loss can be noted at different steps of progression. For example, chromosomal loss at 5q appears to occur prior to development of hyperproliferative epithelium whereas loss at 17p does not occur until the late adenoma transitions to a full carcinoma.

with the eventual development of a metastatic colon cancer.

CLINICAL CORRELATIONS

There are many ways in which mutations in cancer-promoting genes can occur. The predisposition to cancer can be inherited, as in patients with Li–Fraumeni syndrome, whose cells contain a germ-line mutation of *p53*, one of the cell cycle checkpoint regulators described above. Cells from patients with chronic myelogenous leukaemia often contain an abnormal chromosome resulting from a translocation between chromosomes 9 and 22, the so-called Philadelphia chromosome (Rowley, 1973). This abnormal fusion juxtaposes two genes, which code for the proteins BCR and the Abl tyrosine kinase, and results in aberrant activity and subcellular localization of the Abl protein. In breast cancer, *BRCA1* is mutated at specific sites in the gene. Such mutations are largely inherited.

In contrast to germ-line or inherited mutations, 'sporadic' cancers also can arise when a mutation occurs in a previously normal somatic cell. In this regard, environmental factors are thought to play major roles as mutagens or carcinogenic agents. For example, the relationship between tobacco smoke and lung cancer is well documented (Henderson *et al.*, 1991). Anilines used in rubber tyre production are linked to the development of bladder cancer, while exposure to solar ultraviolet rays can cause melanoma (Case *et al.*, 1993; Armstrong *et al.*, 1997). Hundreds of chemical carcinogens that exist in food and products in daily use can either directly or through the production of secondary metabolites irreversibly alter a normal cell's DNA. So-called 'lifestyle' factors can also play a role. A link has been made between consumption of a diet high in animal fats and prostate cancer (Tzonou

et al., 1999). In women, reproductive history and the resulting cumulative lifetime exposure to oestrogen correlate with an increased risk of breast cancer (Hankinson *et al.*, 1995). How environmental factors trigger the activation and mutation of cancer-causing genes is, in many cases, still unclear. Subsequent chapters will detail what is known about a very complicated and intricate process.

REFERENCES

Armstrong, B. K., *et al.* (1997). Sun exposure and skin cancer. *Australasian Journal of Dermatology*, **38**, S1–S6.

Baylin, S. B. (1997). Tying it all together: epigenetics, genetics, cell cycle, and cancer. *Science*, **277**, 1948–1949.

Biscardi, J. S., *et al.* (1999). c-Src, receptor tyrosine kinases, and human cancer. *Advances in Cancer Research*, **76**, 61–119.

Bishop, J. M. (1982). Oncogenes. *Scientific American*, **246**, 80–92.

Bookstein, R., *et al.* (1989). Human retinoblastoma gene: long-range mapping and analysis of its deletion in a breast cancer cell line. *Molecular and Cellular Biology*, **9**, 1628–1634.

Boveri, T. (1929). The Origin of Malignant Tumors. Williams Wilkins, Baltimore, pp. 1–119.

Boyd, J. A. and Barrett, J. C. (1990). Genetic and cellular basis of multistep carcinogenesis. *Pharmacology and Therapeutics*, **46**, 469–486.

Case, R. A., *et al.* (1993). Tumours of the urinary bladder in workmen engaged in the manufacture and use of certain dyestuff intermediates in the British chemical industry. Part I. The role of aniline, benzidine, alpha-naphthylamine, and beta-naphthylamine. 1954. *British Journal of Industrial Medicine*, **50**, 389–411.

Christofiori, G. and Semb, H. (1999). The role of the cell adhesion molecule E-cadherin as a tumor-suppressor gene. *Trends in Biochemical Sciences*, **217**, 801–806.

Di Cristofano, A. and Pandolfi, P. P. (2000). The multiple roles of PTEN in tumor suppression. *Cell*, **100**, 387–390.

Folkman, J. (1992). The role of angiogenesis in tumor growth. *Seminars in Cancer Biology*, **3**, 65–71.

Hahn, S. A., *et al.* (1996). DPC4, a candidate tumor suppressor gene at human chromosome 18q21.1. *Science*, **271**, 350–353.

Hankinson, S. E., *et al.* (1995). Reproductive factors and family history of breast cancer in relation to plasma estrogen and prolactin levels in postmenopausal women in the Nurses' Health Study (United States). *Cancer Causes and Control*, **6**, 217–224.

Harbour, J. W. and Dean, D. C. (2000). Rb function in cell-cycle regulation and apoptosis. *Nature Cell Biology*, **2**, E65–E67.

Heisterkamp, N., *et al.* (1985). Structural organization of the bcr gene and its role in the Ph' translocation. *Nature*, **315**, 758–761.

Henderson, B. E., *et al.* (1991). Toward the primary prevention of cancer. *Science*, **254**, 1131–1138.

Irby, R. B., *et al.* (1999). Activating SRC mutation in a subset of advanced human colon cancers. *Nature Genetics*, **21**, 187–190.

Jacotot, E., *et al.* (2000). Apoptosis and cell cycle: distinct checkpoints with overlapping upstream control. *Pathologie et Biologie*, **48**, 271–279.

Kamb, A., *et al.* (1994). Analysis of the p16 gene (CDKN2) as a candidate for the chromosome 9p melanoma susceptibility locus. *Nature Genetics*, **8**, 23–26.

Knudson, A. G., Jr (1971). Mutation and cancer: statistical study of retinoblastoma. *Proceedings of the National Academy of Sciences of the USA*, **68**, 820–823.

Knudson, A. G., Jr (1985). Hereditary cancer, oncogenes, and antioncogenes. *Cancer Research*, **45**, 1437–1443.

Kolodner, R. D. and Marsischky, G. T. (1999). Eukaryotic DNA mismatch repair. *Current Opinions in Genetics and Development*, **9**, 89–96.

Konishi, M., *et al.* (1996). Molecular nature of colon tumors in hereditary nonpolyposis colon cancer, familial polyposis, and sporadic colon cancer. *Gastroenterology*, **111**, 307–317.

Kurschat, P. and Mauch, C. (2000). Mechanisms of metastasis. *Clinical and Experimental Dermatology*, **25**, 482–489.

Li, J., *et al.* (1997). PTEN, a putative protein tyrosine phosphatase gene mutated in human brain, breast, and prostate cancer. *Science*, **275**, 1943–1947.

Liu, W., *et al.* (1997). PTEN/MMAC1 mutations and EGFR amplification in glioblastomas. *Cancer Research*, **57**, 5254–5257.

Marx, J. (1993). How p53 suppresses cell growth. *Science*, **262**, 1644–1645.

Miyamoto, S., *et al.* (1998). Fibronectin and integrins in cell adhesion, signaling, and morphogenesis. *Annals of the New York Academy of Sciences*, **857**, 119–129.

Peddanna, N., *et al.* (1996) Genetics of colorectal cancer. *International Journal of Oncology*, **9**, 327–335.

Rous, P. (1911). A sarcoma of the fowl transmissible by an agent separable from the tumor cells. *Journal of Experimental Medicine*, **13**, 397–411.

Rowley, J. D. (1973). A new consistent chromosomal abnormality in chronic myelogenous leukaemia identified by quinacrine fluorescence and Giemsa staining. *Nature*, **243**, 290–293.

Sager, R. (1989). Tumor suppressor genes: the puzzle and the promise. *Science*, **246**, 1406–1412.

Tzonou, A., *et al.* (1999). Diet and cancer of the prostate: a case-control study in Greece. *International Journal of Cancer*, **80**, 704–708.

Vogelstein, B. and Kinzler, K. W. (1993). The multistep nature of cancer. *Trends in Genetics*, **9**, 138–141.

Weinberg, R. A. (1983). Alteration of the genomes of tumor cells. *Cancer*, **51**, 1971–1975.

Weiss, R., *et al.* (eds) (1985). *RNA Tumor Viruses*, 2nd edn (Cold Spring Harbor Laboratory Press, Cold Spring Harbor, NY).

Wittinghofer, F. (1998). Ras signalling. Caught in the act of the switch-on. *Nature*, **394**, 317, 319–320.

Zheng, L., *et al.* (2000). Lessons learned from BRCA1 and BRCA2. *Oncogene*, **19**, 6159–6175.

FURTHER READING

Bishop, J. M. (1992). Oncogenes. *Scientific American*, **246**, 80–92.

Knudson, A. G. (1985). Hereditary cancer, oncogenes, and anti-oncogenesis. *Cancer Research*, **48**, 1437–1442.

Land, H., *et al.* (1983) Cellular oncogenes and multistep carcinogenesis. *Science*, **222**, 771–778.

Sager, R. (1989). Tumor suppressor genes: the puzzle and the promise. *Science*, **246**, 1406–1412.

Vogelstein, B. and Kinzler, K. W. (1993). The multistep nature of cancer. *Trends in Genetics*, **9**, 138–141.

Weiss, R., *et al.* (eds) (1985). *RNA Tumor Viruses*, 2nd edn (Cold Spring Harbor Laboratory Press, Cold Spring Harbor, NY).

Chapter 4

Inherited Predispositions to Cancer

Gareth Evans
St. Mary's Hospital, Manchester, UK

C O N T E N T S

- Introduction
- Retinoblastoma
- Genetic Syndromes
- Common Cancer Predisposition
- Conclusions

INTRODUCTION

There has been increasing evidence of familial predisposition to cancer since the classic model of hereditary
retinoblastoma was outlined (Knudson, 1971). The notion
that some cancer is hereditary has long been held by more
than just a few diehard clinicians. The earliest reports of
cancer families date back more than 180 years to a large
cluster of breast cancer in the wife and family of a French
physician named Broca and the cluster of gastric cancer
in Napoleon's family. Despite the pioneering work of
clinicians and researchers such as Henry Lynch and Mary-
Claire King in the USA in the 1960s to 1980s, demonstrating the hereditary nature of at least a proportion of
cancers such as those affecting the breast and colon, the
hereditary element was not proven until the advent of
molecular biology when abnormalities were demonstrated
in cancer-predisposing genes. It is, therefore, only since
1987 that developments in molecular biology have proven
the hereditary nature of a small proportion of certain
common cancers. That cancer is now indisputably
'genetic' at the cellular level is beyond dispute. All
tumours result from mutations or deletions of two types
of gene (Eeles *et al.*, 1996): the tumour suppressor gene,
which needs to be inactivated to allow growth (like the
brakes on a car), and the oncogene, which requires activation to promote growth (like the accelerator pedal of a
car being stuck down). The great majority of these events
are acquired whether through replication error (simple
copying of DNA during cell division) or due to external
agents (chemical mutagens, radiation, viruses). Occasionally, mutations in tumour suppressor genes can be inherited rather than acquired. Identifying the genes which
cause hereditary disease has given an insight into many
cancers. The role of cancer-predisposing genes in the
causation of sporadic cancer is still the subject of much
research, and we can still learn from the more obscure
cancer-prone syndromes.

Broadly, the predisposition can be subdivided into rare
genetic syndromes which have malignancy as a high-risk
side effect and a larger group which cannot be easily
identified clinically, and which have a strong family history
of one or more common malignancies.

RETINOBLASTOMA

Retinoblastoma has been the model from which much of
our current knowledge of tumour suppressor genes was
fashioned. This early childhood eye malignancy was
recognized as having a familial tendency in the nineteenth
century. About 50% of cases are due to the inheritance of a
gene defect in one copy of the retinoblastoma gene (*RB* on
chromosome 13), and over 90% of individuals who carry a
mutation will develop retinoblastoma, usually bilaterally.
In 1971, Knudson (1971) proposed that the disorder was
caused by mutational events in both copies of the gene.
Those cases that inherited a mutated copy, only need one
further mutation and are far more likely to develop the
malignancy, which occurs at a younger age and is usually
bilateral. The sporadic cases require two mutations ('hits')
in a retinal cell as opposed to one in the familial case
(**Figure 1**) and so bilateral tumours are extremely unlikely
to occur and the unilateral tumours present later. This
hypothesis, which has since been proven to be true, now
bears the conceiver's name. Familial retinoblastoma may
even be present in foetal life, as can be seen in **Figure 2
(see colour plate section)**. This case had a 13q deletion
as a result of a maternal chromosomal translocation.

The discovery of retinoblastoma cases with cytogenetically visible constitutional deletions in the long arm of
chromosome 13 (Francke and King, 1976; Knudson *et al.*,
1976) concentrated research on that region. One of the
genes deleted in these cases, esterase D, then acted as a
marker for further studies. One study showed that although

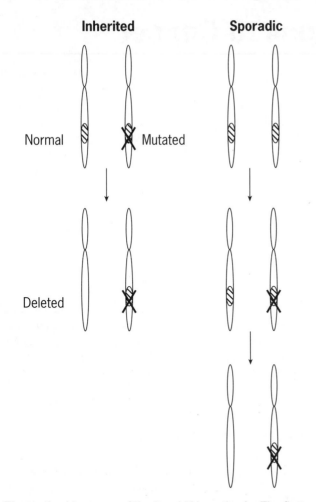

Inherited   **Sporadic**

Normal   Mutated

Deleted

Figure 1 Ideogram of the 'two-hit' hypothesis. The first hit is usually a mutation (represented by a cross) which causes disruption of the protein product. The second hit is often loss of the whole gene by deletion of part or all of the chromosome on which the gene resides.

an individual was heterozygous for esterase D their tumour was hemizygous, suggesting loss of material by deletion or monosomy (Godbout *et al.*, 1983). The introduction of restriction fragment length polymorphisms (RFLPs) led to further studies showing loss of constitutional heterozygosity. RFLPs rely on the differences in large portions of DNA between individuals and therefore between the two equivalent chromosomal regions in any one individual. This difference means that enzymes (endonucleases) which cut at specific gene codes will cut at different sites on the chromosome. There is therefore a good chance that a gene or genetic marker will end up on two different lengths of DNA when a particular endonuclease is used. If an individual is shown to have two lengths (heterozygous) on constitutional testing, but only one in their tumour, then loss of constitutional heterozygosity has occurred. These RFLPs were used to localize the gene further until it was eventually cloned (Friend *et al.*, 1986). Since the isolation of the *RB* gene, many groups have tried to isolate the

underlying defects that cause retinoblastoma and that make the gene important in cell regulation. These studies have confirmed that *RB* acts as a typical tumour suppressor gene with an initial mutational event consisting of small changes in nucleotides resulting in truncation of the resultant protein product. These are usually nonsense mutations leading to an early stop codon or small frameshift deletions or insertions with a similar downstream effect. Nonetheless, pathogenic missense mutations do occur although they are more difficult to prove. Simple cosegregation of a missense mutation in a small family is not enough, although the presence of an amino acid change in a functional domain with cross-species conservation does add credence. In the final estimation it is only with functional assays that a pathogenic effect can be proven. Initial studies showed a relatively low rate of mutation identification in the *RB* gene (Liu *et al.*, 1995), but with a combination of strategies including a coding sequence analysis taking in intron/exon boundaries (for splicing mutations) and a deletion strategy such as fluorescent *in situ* hybridization (FISH) and Southern blotting, the great majority of aberrations of the *RB* gene can be identified (Lohmann *et al.*, 1996).

The retinoblastoma gene also predisposes to osteosarcoma. An individual who has had an enucleation and irradiation for retinoblastoma is 500 times more likely to develop the bone tumour. As the gene is involved in many common carcinomas such as that of the breast, it is likely that survivors will be at risk of these tumours also.

GENETIC SYNDROMES

These are usually readily identifiable by a clinical phenotype or by laboratory tests. The syndromes may be autosomal dominant or recessive or X linked (**Tables 1** and **2**). Of these it is the dominant conditions which are of most interest as they are likely to represent the inheritance of a faulty copy of a tumour suppressor gene, which predisposes the individual to common cancers. Although the conditions are generally uncommon, tumour suppressor genes in general are likely to play a fundamental role in the genesis of tumours, which affect a third of all humans in their lifetime. The identification of those causing genetic syndromes is likely to lead to more specific treatment using gene therapy, as well as earlier identification, monitoring and, most hopeful of all, prevention of common cancers.

Familial Adenomatous Polyposis (FAP)

FAP is the model condition by which researchers have hoped to transpose knowledge of a rare genetic disease to a commonly occurring cancer. FAP is an autosomal dominant condition characterized by the development of hundreds to thousands of adenomatous polyps in the colon and rectum, usually by 30 years of age (**Figure 3; see colour**

Table 1 Examples of autosomal dominant syndromes predisposing to cancer and their chromosomal location

Name of disease	Location (chromosomal)	Protein
FAP	5q	APC
NF1	17q	Neurofibromin
NF2	22q	Merlin/ schwannomin
Von Hippel–Lindau	3p	pVHL
MEN1	11q	Menin
MEN2	10q	RET
Gorlin	9q	PTCH
Tuberous sclerosis (TSC1)	11q	Hamartin
(TSC2)	16q	Tuberin
Juvenile polyposis	18q and other(s)	pDPC/SMAD4
Peutz–Jeghers	19p and other(s)	pSTK11/LKB1
Cowden	10q	PTEN
Tylosis	17q	Not found

Table 2 Autosomal recessive and X-linked conditions predisposing to malignancy

Name of condition	Chromosomal location	Protein
Fanconi anaemia	8 loci	4 found
Bloom syndrome	15q	pBLM
Ataxia telangiectasia	11q	pATM
Xeroderma pigmentosa	7 types	2 types
Chediak Higashi	1q	pLYST
Albinism	11q	OCA1, OCA2
Bruton	Xq	BLk
Wiscott Aldrich	Xp	CD43

plate section). If untreated this leads to the almost inevitable development of a colorectal cancer by 60 years of age. The condition may be associated with osteomas and epidermal cysts and this subdivision was designated Gardner syndrome (Gardner, 1951). However, most FAP families show these extraintestinal features to some extent. FAP has, in common with many other conditions, been mapped to a chromosomal region as a result of the finding of a constitutional (present in every cell) chromosomal anomaly in a manifesting case (Herrera et al., 1986). This patient had a small interstitial deletion on the long arm of chromosome 5 and manifested extracolonic features as well as multiple polyps. Following this discovery, Bodmer et al. (1987) localized the gene for FAP to 5q21–q22 by genetic linkage, using families mainly from the well-established St. Marks Polyposis Register in London. Of great interest was that the same region of chromosome 5 was implicated in sporadic colorectal cancer (Solomon et al., 1987). This meant that the gene could be localized more accurately by using tumour material from sporadic

cases as well as from FAP cases. If the tumour is analysed for loss of genetic material using probes mapped to the implicated region of chromosome 5, a deletion map can be drawn. When the normal or 'wild-type' allele is lost from an FAP patient's tumours, the assumption is that a second hit has occurred, removing the only functioning copy of a tumour suppressor gene. The nature of this loss is known as loss of constitutional heterozygosity (LOH).

Once the gene had been localized to a relatively small chromosomal region, several research groups embarked on a project to isolate contiguous sequences of genes spanning the area. Subclones were then used to identify the position of candidate genes, which were expressed in normal colonic mucosa. Two of these genes, *APC* and *MCC* (Kinzler et al., 1991), were thought likely to be involved in tumorigenesis, because of the structure of the proteins for which they encoded. All that remained was to identify mutations in one of these genes, in the germ-line of patients with FAP. This was duly achieved when 10 *APC* germ line mutations were described (Nishisho et al., 1991). These mutations were not only likely to disrupt the protein structure, but were also found only in the *APC* gene. The idea that Gardner syndrome was a separate entity was refuted since the mutations occurred in patients with or without extraintestinal manifestations. However, FAP was one of the first conditions in which a clear correlation between genotype (the genetic change in *APC*) and phenotype (the clinical picture) emerged. Patients with mutations in the early part of the gene (5′: exons 2–5) had a very mild clinical picture with late onset of polyps (Spirio et al., 1993), whereas those with mutations from exon 9 through to codon 1450 of exon 15 had a classical disease course with nearly all patients manifesting the typical congenital retinal pigmentation. However, those with mutations beyond codon 1450 showed typical Gardner syndrome features (osteomas, cysts and desmoid disease) without retinal signs (Davies et al., 1995). There are even families who with extreme mutations in exon 15 show little else other than desmoid disease (Scott et al., 1996).

Currently it is possible to offer predictive genetic tests before symptoms to the majority of at-risk individuals. Although looking for germ-line mutations is laborious and not guaranteed to find the mutation, it is the most reliable. Nonetheless, testing using linkage analysis in families with more than one affected member is still very useful, especially when a germ-line mutation cannot be identified. This, combined with opthalmological screening for congenital hypertrophy of the retinal pigment epithelium (CHRPE), may reduce initial risks of 50% to well below 1% (Burn et al., 1991).

Von Hippel–Lindau

Von Hippel–Lindau (VHL) is another dominantly inherited familial cancer syndrome. The most frequent complications are benign tumours of blood vessels, particularly in the eye (retinal angiomas), and haemangioblastomas of the cerebellum. Other features include renal cell carcinoma, phaeochromocytoma and renal, pancreatic and epididymal cysts. The syndrome is very variable but most individuals present before 40 years of age (Maher *et al*., 1990). The first clue to the location of the gene for VHL was the finding of a reciprocal translocation involving chromosomes 3 and 8 in a family with hereditary renal carcinoma (Cohen *et al*., 1979). Later, Teyssier *et al*. (1986) were able to show deletions of the short arm of chromosome 3 in other renal cell carcinomas. Linkage in families with VHL was confirmed on 3p in 1988 (Seizinger *et al*., 1988). The gene was finally cloned in 1993 (Latif *et al*., 1993) and codes for a relatively small protein.

Type 1 Neurofibromatosis (NF1)

NF1 is more common than NF2, but the disease may be so mild that an affected individual may never present to their doctor. The main manifestations are in the skin, with the appearance of café au lait patches and cutaneous neurofibromas in the first and second decades, respectively. The most famous potential misdiagnosis of NF1 was Joseph Merrick, the 'elephant man,' who in reality probably had Proteus syndrome (Clark, 1994). One potential serious complication of NF1 is optic gliomas, which may occur in up to 15% of cases (Listernick *et al*., 1989). These are usually very low grade and asymptomatic and if they are not specifically sought levels of around 1.5% are found. Other CNS gliomas do occur but their frequency is probably well below 5%. Meningiomas and vestibular schwannomas do not occur in excess frequency in NF1 (McGaughran *et al*., 1999). Phaeochromocytoma and spinal neurofibromas may develop as well as rhabdomyosarcomas, but these are relatively rare. Malignant change in neurofibromas can result in a malignant peripheral nerve sheath tumour (MPNST) in about 10% of NF1 patients in their lifetime (McGaughran *et al*., 1999).

The *NF1* gene was cloned in 1990, although it took over a year fully to characterize the gene from the first discovery of deletions in the germ-line of some familial cases (Viskochil *et al*., 1990). It is a massive gene containing over 300 kilobases of DNA divided into 50 exons (Collins, 1991). The gene transcribes a 327 kDa GAP protein containing 2818 amino acids. The protein, which binds to the oncogenic protein Ras, is found in all tissues. It is expressed at the cellular level in the perinuclear vesicles and microtubules. As p120 GAP is expressed more in the neural crest this may explain why *NF1* specifically affects neural tissue. Although diagnosis is possible by looking for germ-line mutations, this approach has not found any particular hot spots of mutation, although extensive analysis using a number of approaches as for retinoblastoma does detect 95% of mutations (Messiaen *et al*., 2000).

Predictive diagnosis therefore still depends mainly on linkage in existing families.

There is now good evidence that at least two variant conditions of NF1 are caused by mutations in the *NF1* gene. Watson syndrome was shown to be linked to the *NF1* locus (Allanson *et al*., 1991) and NF–Noonan syndrome to be due to mutations in the gene itself (Colley *et al*., 1996).

Type 2 Neurofibromatosis (NF2)

NF2 is an autosomal dominant genetic disease characterized by the development of bilateral vestibular schwannomas (acoustic neuromas) in the second and third decades. Only recently has it been formally separated from the more common NF1 (von Recklinghausen disease), after the National Institutes of Health Consensus Development Conference Statement on Neurofibromatosis (1987). The first probable reported case of NF2 was that of Wishart (1822). Bilateral vestibular schwannoma had been thought to be part of von Recklinghausen neurofibromatosis (NF1) after reports of similarities in cases to those with the peripheral form (Cushing, 1917). Several reports emphasized the paucity of skin findings in families with bilateral vestibular schwannoma (Gardner and Frazier, 1930), and suggested that bilateral vestibular schwannoma represented a separate central form of von Recklinghausen neurofibromatosis. It was not until the separate assignment of NF1 to chromosome 17 (Seizinger *et al*., 1987) and NF2 to chromosome 22 (Rouleau *et al*., 1987) that the diseases were finally shown to be two distinct disorders. NF2, although less common than the type 1 form (incidence 1 in 35 000 compared with 1 in 3000) (Evans *et al*., 1992a), is more likely to present clinically at some time. All cases will develop a CNS tumour by 55 years of age. Although most of these tumours are benign (meningiomas, schwannomas; see **Figure 4**), 6% will develop a malignant glioma or ependymoma (Evans *et al*., 1992b).

The clue to the location of the *NF2* gene was not a constitutional chromosomal anomaly, but rather cytogenetic abnormalities found on chromosome 22 in human meningiomas and later in vestibular schwannomas and other tumours from NF2 patients. This candidate region was then confirmed as the likely location for the *NF2* gene by linkage analysis in a large US family (Rouleau *et al*., 1987). The gene was isolated simultaneously by two groups (Rouleau *et al*., 1993; Trofatter *et al*., 1993), and genotype phenotype correlations have been identified (Evans *et al*., 1998a). Mutations which give rise to a truncated protein are associated with a severe, multitumour, early-onset disease course, whereas those that give a nearly normal protein product (missense mutations) or no product (large deletions) give mild disease. Another feature of NF2 that is likely to be an important factor in other tumour-prone disorders is mosaicism (Evans *et al*., 1998b). If a mutation occurs after conception, say at the

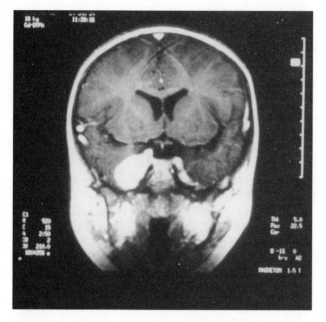

Figure 4 MRI scan of a 26-year-old man with type 2 neurofibromatosis. The scan shows bilateral enhancing tumours in the cerebello-pontine angles and meningiomas around the brain. The risk of developing bilateral tumours by chance is 1 in 2×10^6, yet 95% of individuals with mutations in the *NF2* gene develop bilateral vestibular schwannomas (acoustic neuromas).

eight-cell stage, roughly one eighth of all the cells will have an *NF2* mutation, which means that there are two different cell populations, one of which predisposes to tumours and could be transmitted to any offspring.

Gorlin Syndrome

Gorlin or naevoid basal cell carcinoma syndrome is another autosomal dominant condition which predisposes to malignancy. The condition is characterized by the development of multiple jaw keratocysts in the second decade and basal cell carcinomas in the third decade onwards. Gene mutation carriers also have a recognizable appearance or morphology. They have macrocephaly with bossing of the forehead and the face is usually covered with white milia. The facial features are often coarse and the shoulders slope downwards. Most individuals have a skeletal anomaly such as a bifid rib or wedge-shaped vertebra and ectopic calcification, particularly in the falx, is almost certain by 20 years of age.

Individuals with Gorlin syndrome are also at risk of developing the childhood brain malignancy medulloblastoma, which occurs in 5% of cases (Cowan *et al.*, 1997) and cardiac and ovarian fibromas (Gorlin, 1987; Evans *et al.*, 1993). Malignant transformation has been described in the ovarian fibromas (Strong, 1977), but they usually remain benign, although they can reach a large size and are often calcified (**Figure 5**). The clue to the location

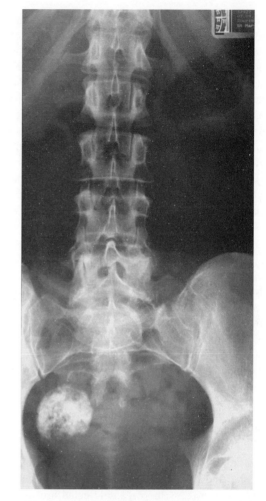

Figure 5 Large calcified ovarian fibroma on abdominal X-ray in a patient with Gorlin syndrome.

of the Gorlin gene again came from tumour deletion studies. Gailani *et al.* (1991) found that 40% of basal cell carcinomas that they studied had deletions of the proximal region on the long arm of chromosome 9. The condition has now been shown to be linked to that region using affected families and there is no locus heterogeneity (Farndon *et al.*, 1992). The gene itself was subsequently identified as a homologue of the drosophila gene *PTCH* (Hahn *et al.*, 1996). As the mean age at onset of medulloblastoma in Gorlin patients is 2 years compared with over 7 years in the general population, and there is loss of the normal copy of the gene in tumours (Cowan *et al.*, 1997), this confirms *PATCHED* as a tumour suppressor in both medulloblastoma and basal cell carcinoma. Basal cell carcinomas occur at great frequency in the periphery of the radiation field 5–10 years after irradiation in Gorlin syndrome (**Figure 6; see colour plate section**).

Tuberous Sclerosis

Tuberous sclerosis is a condition in which hamartomas are a primary feature. These may occur in the brain (the 'tubers' of the name), or in the kidney, heart and elsewhere. Patients have a number of external features, which make early or presymptomatic identification possible. Depigmented patches of skin or 'ash leaf patches' can be seen with a Wood's light and a characteristic facial skin eruption known as adenoma sebaceum is often present. Subungual (under the finger nails) fibromas are another feature peculiar to tuberous sclerosis. Tumours may occur in the heart during foetal life (rhabdomyomas) and the malignancy to which the condition particularly predisposes is the brain tumour glioma. Unusually for a condition which is likely to be caused by one gene, two separate genetic loci have eventually been implicated. In 1987, Fryer et al. (1987) showed linkage to 9q in several families. However, many reports following this had contradictory results. This has now been shown to be due to locus heterogeneity, for although linkage to 9q has been confirmed in some families, the other major locus was actually cloned first in 1993 on chromosome 16 (European Chromosome 16 Tuberous Sclerosis Consortium, 1993). The later cloning of TSC1 was partly due to the fewer individuals affected with the disease at this locus, although the linkage came first as actual families are more numerous (DeVries and Bolton, 2000).

Multiple Endocrine Neoplasias

The multiple endocrine neoplasias are further conditions which predispose to benign tumours and at least one malignancy. In MEN1 the organs affected are the parathyroid glands, pituitary and pancreas. The most serious problem is with islet cell tumours of the pancreas, which secrete gastrin. These cause the Zollinger–Ellison syndrome of which MEN1 makes up a large proportion of cases. The gastrin-secreting tumours may become malignant, seeding to the liver and other organs. However, many cases do not manifest the condition overtly even late in life. The serum calcium level is raised in 90–97% of cases, but laborious testing and repeated screening may be necessary. The availability of genetic tests has, therefore, greatly simplified screening of at-risk individuals. The location of the MEN1 gene was confirmed at 11q13 by linkage analysis in families (Larsson et al., 1988). This and other studies have also shown loss of 11q alleles in the MEN1 tumours. The MEN1 gene was eventually cloned in 1997 (Chandrasekharappa et al., 1997) and the protein product was termed menin. Presymptomatic testing is now available by mutation testing of an affected individual, or by linkage analysis in families with more than one affected individual.

MEN2a or Sipple syndrome is an autosomal dominant disease with high penetrance and variable expression. The association of medullary carcinoma of the thyroid and phaeochromocytoma are the hallmarks of the condition. Parathyroid tumours are less commonly found. MEN2 makes up 25% of all cases of medullary thyroid carcinoma, with nearly all MEN2 cases developing this tumour some time in life. The tumours in MEN2 are often bilateral and are preceded by C cell hyperplasia. Phaeochromocytoma occurs in 50% of individuals and is often multifocal. Screening of at-risk cases involves serum calcitonin estimation and monitoring of blood pressure, and has been greatly enhanced by the development of genetic testing, which removes over 50% of individuals from screening programmes. The test has targeted those in which thyroid cancer can be prevented by early or prophylactic thyroidectomy.

The MEN2a gene was localized to chromosome 10 by linkage analysis using RFLPs (Simpson et al., 1987), and later localized to 10q21.1 by in situ hybridization. Although researchers concentrated on trying to identify a tumour suppressor gene, it was eventually found that MEN2 was due to activating mutations in an oncogene called RET (Mulligan et al., 1993), although MEN2b differs from MEN2a in that the primary feature is the development of mucosal neuromas especially of the tongue. Medullary thyroid cancer is also a major feature and phaeochromocytoma also occurs but, in contrast to MEN1 and MEN2a, there is no parathyroid disease. Both conditions are caused by activating mutations in RET, although most of MEN2b is caused by a single mutation and MEN2a by five different substitutions at cysteine residues.

Other Dominant Syndromes

Tylosis, juvenile polyposis, Peutz–Jeghers syndrome, multiple exostosis and multiple lipomatosis are other dominantly inherited disorders which may predispose to malignancy.

Wilms' Tumour

Wilms' tumour, like retinoblastoma, has also been known for some time to have a hereditary element. However, the genetic basis is far more complex and the familial element much smaller. The first step to identifying a gene came with the discovery of a cytogenetically visible deletion in chromosome 11 in families with autosomal dominant aniridia who appeared to be predisposed to Wilms' tumour (Riccardi et al., 1978). Deletions in this area (11p13) also lead to genital and renal anomalies and mutations within the WT1 gene itself lead to abnormal genital development (Pelletier et al., 1991). At first it was thought that this locus would be similar to retinoblastoma, but WT1 has now been shown to be one of at least three genes involved in Wilms' tumour development. In 1989, Koufos et al. (1989) demonstrated tight linkage to 11p15.5 in a family with

Beckwith–Wiedemann syndrome (a mainly sporadic growth disorder with neonatal hyperinsulinism and features such as exompholos) and Wilms'. Beckwith–Wiedemann syndrome is now known to be due to complex mechanisms involving a number of genes including *CDKN1C* and *IGF2* where there is either loss of maternal copy or gain of paternal copy in an imprinted area (Lam *et al.*, 1999). In addition, Grundy *et al.* (1988) excluded both 11p13 and 11p15 in linkage analysis of a large family with dominant Wilms' tumour. A third and fourth locus has now been confirmed in families manifesting primarily Wilms' tumour alone, but a further locus probably exists.

Autosomal Recessive and X Linked Conditions

A list of these conditions and the chromosomal locations of the predisposing genes can be found in **Table 2**. These are less likely to present to the clinician as they are generally less common and mainly predispose to haematological malignancy.

COMMON CANCER PREDISPOSITION

Recent years have seen an enormous improvement in our understanding of the mechanisms of carcinogenesis. Most cancers require a number of genetic changes in a cell before an invasive tumour results. Few are likely to be caused purely by the loss of two copies of a single tumour suppressor gene as in retinoblastoma and the number of changes probably varies between four and 10. A combination of loss of function of tumour suppressor genes and activation of oncogenes is usually involved. The particular combination and order may alter both the histological and invasive nature of the cancer. There is now evidence that a minority of people who develop common cancers have inherited a faulty gene which puts them at high risk of malignancy, but this is not recognized as a syndrome apart from in the family history. Adenocarcinomas are more likely than carcinomas of squamous epithelium to have a strong hereditary component with 4–10% of all breast, ovarian and colon cancer resulting from an inherited gene defect. The discovery of germ-line (inherited) mutations in the *TP53* gene on the short arm of chromosome 17 in families with a peculiar combination of early and multiple tumours was the first proven example of this. Otherwise, predisposition can be relatively site specific with genes being isolated in recent years for melanoma, prostate cancer, pancreatic cancer and paraganglioma, but this chapter will focus on the three common cancers which have attracted the greatest attention.

Li–Fraumeni Syndrome (LFS)

This cancer predisposition syndrome was first outlined in 1969 by Li and Fraumeni (1969). They reported four families with autosomal dominant predisposition to soft tissue sarcoma, breast cancer and other tumours in children and adults. Many reports have followed, either describing further families or reporting an increased risk of cancers in first degree relatives of cases with soft tissue sarcoma. In 1988, Li *et al.* (1988) analysed 24 kindreds with an aggregation of tumours typical of the syndrome. They showed a predominance of soft tissue sarcoma, osteosarcoma and breast cancer, with an excess of adrenocortical carcinoma, brain tumours and leukaemia. Williams and Strong (1985) applied a segregation analysis to test the hypothesis that the disease was due to an autosomal dominant gene. They not only confirmed this, but also were able to predict that 50% of gene carriers would develop an invasive cancer by 30 years of age and 90% by 70 years. Although the syndrome (also known as SBLA) is rare, its importance lies in the unusual range of cancer predisposition and that it is caused by the first of the major predisposition genes to be identified.

Linkage studies using markers on many chromosomes was not an easy approach owing to the paucity of suitable families, because the condition is so lethal that often no living affected members are available. The genetic fitness of cases is also likely to be reduced owing to development of malignancies in childhood and the faulty gene may therefore die out in families, making fewer available for analysis. Also, until an individual has developed a syndromal cancer, their genetic status is unknown. Penetrance is high but not complete, so one cannot be completely sure of the status of an unaffected individual even in their sixties. The lack of an identifiable phenotype present in many of the conditions described earlier is also a major hurdle. Therefore, Malkin *et al.* (1990) used a candidate gene approach. They argued that the condition was probably due to a mutation in a tumour was an unlikely choice as retinoblastoma had not been observed in any LFS families. They chose the *TP53* gene, which was the second to be recognized, but the first to be cloned. This gene had been implicated in at least half the typical cancers featuring in LFS by analysis of the tumours by mutation and deletion studies. Malkin *et al.* examined the *TP53* gene in normal somatic cells of affected and unaffected members from five families. This was achieved by amplifying the genomic region encoding exons 5–8, which contain most of the conserved domains and are frequently mutated or deleted in tumours. They then sequenced the region using multiple primers. Affected members in all five families showed mutations in this region, with two occurring at codon 248, which is a hot spot for tumour mutations. All were in the conserved region IV in which no polymorphisms had been found in the germ-line before. They were also able to show loss of the 'wild-type' allele in a tumour in one affected family member.

The involvement of *TP53* was then confirmed in a further family by Shrivastava *et al.* (1990). However, the initial impression that the process would be simple does not appear to be the case. A Manchester study (Santibanez-Koref *et al.*, 1991) found that only two out of eight families had *TP53* mutations in exons 5–8, although they did confirm the hotspot at codon 248. Toguchida *et al.* (1991) found eight germ line mutations in 196 osteosarcoma patients but none in 200 controls. In contrast to previous studies, a family history was not present in some of the cases and the mutations were not all in the conserved regions of *TP53*. The absence of family history was not surprising, as one would predict a high new mutation rate in LFS to maintain the frequency of the condition in the population. Subsequent work has shown that with complete gene sequencing it is possible to identify mutations in over 70% of classical families. There is also evidence of genotype phenotype correlations, with much higher penetrance for mutations in the DNA core-binding domain (Birch *et al.*, 1998). Recent evidence has also shown that up to 80% of childhood adrenocortical tumours having germ-line mutations in *TP53* (Varley *et al.*, 1999). This makes this childhood tumour the most hereditary of all malignancies including retinoblastoma. While it is still likely that nearly all LFS families have *TP53* involvement, a mutation in the *hCHK2* gene has now been identified in at least one family (Bell *et al.*, 1999). A typical family with a *TP53* mutation at codon 191 is shown in **Figure 7**. The early age of the breast cancers is particularly noticeable, with one woman having bilateral disease as well as other primary tumours. Clearly, predictive tests in this and other families are now possible. However, until a mutation is found in an affected family member, reassurance of at-risk members is not possible even if the conserved domains are screened.

Breast Cancer

Breast cancer is now known to occur as part of a high penetrance predisposition such as in LFS, and in BRCA1/ 2 families, but may also be caused by mutations in genes such as *ATM* and *PTEN* which confer a risk of <50%. Breast cancer has long been known to have a familial tendency, as discussed earlier, and there is a profusion of supporting literature. Evidence from meticulous epidemiological studies shows that 4–5% of breast cancer is due to a dominant cancer gene with high penetrance and a population frequency in the USA of 0.003 (Claus *et al.*, 1990). Studies in the UK have confirmed this population frequency and gave useful data on which risk estimation can be based. Important factors which point towards a possible familial predisposition are the number of relatives, particularly first degree, who have been affected,

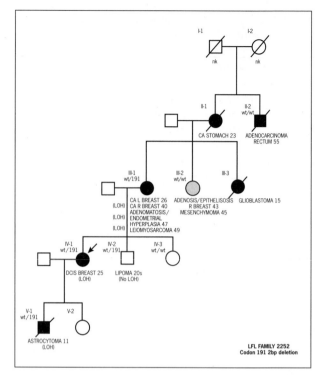

Figure 7   A family tree showing a dominant inheritance pattern of a TP53 codon 191 two base pair deletion in a family with LFS.

the age at which they developed the disease (early onset more significant) and whether bilateral or associated with other tumours.

The search for the gene or genes responsible for dominantly inherited breast cancer was dogged by some of the problems found in LFS. Ascribing status is difficult in unaffected cases even late in life and many of the known affected cases have died. Obtaining samples in some cases may depend on the use of stored paraffin block material, which may be unavailable and relies on having polymerase chain reaction technology and suitable probes, which are of course the norm nowadays. Additionally, as breast cancer is so common, affecting one in 11–12 women in their lifetime in the UK (HMSO, 1998), chance aggregations are likely to occur and non-gene mutation carriers in dominant families may be affected. The other problem, which could only be found by trial and error, was that of locus heterogeneity. Many chromosomal locations had been implicated by cytogenetic and LOH studies on tumour material. Chromosomal regions known to show involvement in more than 20% of tumours by molecular studies are 1p, 1q, 3p, 11p, 13q, 14q, 15q, 17p, 17q and 18q. Many of these regions were already known to contain tumour suppressor genes, e.g. *RB* on 13q, *TP53* on 17p and *DCC* on 18q, and these genes are likely to be involved in a multistage process towards malignancy. In a major breakthrough, Hall *et al.* (1990) were able to show linkage in some breast cancer families to 17q12–21. They looked at over 20 families from whom they had collected samples over many years, including many cases that had subsequently died. Nevertheless, they still had to use a PCR probe to work with paraffin block tumour samples in some cases. When all families were included in the linkage analysis the region on 17q was excluded. However, when the families were stratified in terms of their average age at onset, the first seven families showed a significant linkage to 17q12 (lod score approaching 6). They argued that a large proportion of early-onset breast cancer families (<46 years) were caused by a mutated gene on 17q. Without the work of Hall *et al.*, and subsequently by the Breast Cancer Linkage Consortium, it could have been many years before research was focused on this region. The problem of genetic locus heterogeneity was only overcome by a combination of meticulous collection of samples, innovative ideas and luck. Another possible gene that was implicated at about this time was the oestrogen receptor gene on chromosome 6. However, this has not since been confirmed. Following the discovery of linkage of breast cancer to 17q (Hall *et al.*, 1990), Narod *et al.* (1991) undertook linkage on five families with breast/ovarian aggregation. They found that three of the families were linked to a locus at 17q12–q23 and their additive lod scores reached statistical significance. Subsequent work by the Breast Cancer Linkage Consortium showed that 80% of breast/ovarian families with four or more affected patients were linked the 17q locus (Easton *et al.*, 1993). The following year heralded the identification of the first major breast cancer predisposing gene *BRCA1* (Miki *et al.*, 1994). Surprisingly, *BRCA1* does not appear to be involved as a significant acquired mutation (somatic) in non-hereditary breast cancer. In the same month that the *BRCA1* gene was identified, the location of a second gene dubbed *BRCA2* was announced on chromosome 13. A year later *BRCA2* was cloned and again there was little evidence of involvement in sporadic disease (Wooster *et al.*, 1995). It is now clear that although mutations in *BRCA1* and *BRCA2* account for the majority of high-risk breast cancer families (85%) and nearly all breast/ovarian families, in smaller aggregations they account for <50% of the hereditary element (Ford *et al.*, 1998). While there is no doubt that *BRCA1/2* are highly penetrant genes, initial estimates of the lifetime risk of 85% (Easton *et al.*, 1993) appear slightly high. Population studies do detect *BRCA1* and *BRCA2* mutations in blood samples from apparently sporadic breast cancer patients (Peto *et al.*, 1999). Furthermore, founder mutations in the Jewish and Icelandic populations where *BRCA1/2* mutation frequencies can be as high as 2–2.5%, are associated with lifetime risks of breast cancer of 40–60% (Struewing *et al.*, 1997). Outside populations with significant founder effects the frequencies of *BRCA1/2* mutations combined is probably no higher than 0.2%.

Having identified the most important high penetrance genes, the search is on for lower penetrance genes. Aggregation of breast cancer has been shown to occur in ataxia telangiectasia heterozygotes (Swift *et al.*, 1987, 1991), who are the carriers of the recessive gene which causes a disease which predisposes especially to haematological malignancy in childhood. A mother of an affected child is at 3–5-fold risk of breast cancer, which would fulfil a dominant gene model with 25–40% penetrance and a population frequency of about 0.01. Since the isolation of the *ATM* gene (Savitsky *et al.*, 1995) there have been conflicting studies as to whether this gene is a significant cause of breast cancer. Breast cancer is also thought to occur in 30% of women with Cowden's disease (a condition predisposing to multiple hamartomas), but since the discovery of the underlying gene defects in the *PTEN* gene, no studies have found the gene to be involved in familial aggregations of breast cancer.

Colon Cancer

It has been estimated that about 8% of colorectal cancer is due to the inheritance of a dominant predisposing gene (Solomon, 1990). Only a small proportion of this subset is due to FAP and there are perhaps 10 times as many individuals born with a gene for so-called hereditary nonpolyposis colorectal cancer (HNPCC). This latter inherited form of colorectal cancer has been outlined by Lynch and has in the past often been further subdivided into Lynch syndrome I and II. The type I form was considered to be site specific and to particularly predispose to proximal tumours, which has a major bearing on screening (Lynch *et al.*, 1988). Type II was considered to predispose gene carriers to endometrial, ovarian, pancreatic, upper urinary tract and stomach cancers as well as colorectal and multiple tumours (Lynch *et al.*, 1985). The peak age for these cancers to occur is the fifth decade with proximal colorectal tumours in two-thirds of cases manifesting this complication. The cancers are probably preceded by polyp development, but the mucosa is not lined with hundreds of them as in FAP.

It had been assumed that the gene or genes predisposing to HNPCC were tumour suppressor genes. In 1988, Vogelstein *et al.* (1988) proposed the classic model of progression to cancer in which several genes were involved starting with loss of tumour suppressor genes. Activation of oncogenes at a later stage such as the *ras* genes is also important, but it had not been considered that it was the rate of mutation that was the key factor in HNPCC. The most important tumour suppressor in colorectal cancer, the *APC* gene on chromosome 5 (that causes FAP), had been cloned in 1991 (Nishisho *et al.*, 1991). Clues from tumour studies led to the isolation of several other tumour suppressor genes which are important in colorectal cancer development. The earliest of these was the *TP53* gene, whose position on chromosome 17 was first implicated in 1981. The *DCC* gene on chromosome 18 was shown to be deleted in some colorectal cancers in 1990 and the *MCC* gene on chromosome 5 in 1991. None of these genes was found to be mutated in the germ-line of familial cases of colorectal cancer. The only report of positive linkage had been that of several Lynch type II families to the Kidd blood group on chromosome 18. The major breakthrough came from yeast genetics in which genes involved in repair of DNA suddenly became major candidates for human disease. For some time it had been noticed that tumours in HNPCC and sporadic patients showed instability in the DNA, which was manifested as a different size of microsatellite repeat in the tumour DNA compared with the blood. The discovery that a human version of a yeast DNA mismatch repair gene *MSH2* mapped to recently linked locus on chromosome 2 quickly led to the identification of the first HNPCC gene (Fishel *et al.*, 1993). This then allowed a candidate gene approach, which proved that another mismatch repair gene, *MLH1*, was also an important contributor to HNPCC (Bronner *et al.*, 1994). Since that time, two further genes, *PMS1* and *PMS2*, have been implicated in a tiny proportion of families and more recently *MSH6* has been found to cause HNPCC and also families with endometrial cancer. Although the mismatch repair genes are inactivated in both copies like a tumour suppressor gene, the mechanism to cancer development is different. Although it had been thought that as much as 13% of colorectal cancer could be due to HNPCC, it is now clear that the mismatch repair genes and in particular *MLH1* become inactivated somatically sometimes by methylation. More realistic estimates of HNPCC are therefore that it accounts for 1–2% of colorectal cancer. This means there are significant unidentified genes yet to be discovered.

Ovarian Cancer

Ovarian cancer, like breast and colon cancer, has had many reports of familial aggregation dating back at least to 1950. Increased risk of ovarian malignancy may be inherited as part of several genetic conditions. Gorlin syndrome (Strong, 1977) Peutz–Jeghers syndrome and XY females are all at heightened risk. In addition to this, ovarian cancer is part of HNPCC and breast/ovarian aggregation (now known to be due to *BRCA1* and *BRCA2*). There have been several reports of familial site-specific ovarian cancer (Fraumeni *et al.*, 1975), but many contain cases of breast and other malignancies. The association of breast and ovarian cancer in both family reports and epidemiological studies of breast (Ridolfi *et al.*, 1977) and ovarian cancer (Schildkraut *et al.*, 1988) had suggested the presence of an autosomal dominant predisposing gene.

Tumour studies are less numerous than in either the breast or colon, but loss of constitutional heterozygosity has been found on chromosome regions: 3p, 6q, 11p, 13q, 17p, 17q and Xp. Following the isolation of *BRCA1* and *BRCA2*, it became clear that two of these loci (17q and 13q) were significant for hereditary disease and that apparently site-specific ovarian cancer was mainly caused by *BRCA1* (Steichen-Gersdorf *et al.*, 1994). Whether this predisposition is mainly to ovary or breast may depend on the position of the mutation in each gene (Gayther *et al.*, 1995). It is now thought unlikely that there is a significant other ovarian cancer gene (Ford *et al.*, 1998). Predictive tests are now possible in many families once the underlying mutation has been identified. Current evidence suggests that about 40–60% of women at risk in these families will opt for testing and >50% will opt for prophylactic surgery for the ovaries and or breasts (Meijers-Heijboer *et al.*, 2000).

CONCLUSIONS

The last 10 years has seen an enormous advance in our understanding of cancer and its familial elements. A great deal of this knowledge derives from the study of rare cancer-predisposing syndromes. This research is not esoteric because the cloning of these genes will benefit not only the small proportion of people who suffer from these conditions but also those who suffer from the common cancers occurring in these syndromes. Gene therapy, which could be directed at replacing the function of a deleted tumour suppressor gene, may be available in the early part of the twenty-first century. From the diseases in the first section this could be applied to cancer of the colon, skin, kidney and thyroid as well as virtually all common brain tumours.

The cloning of further tumour suppressor genes for breast, colon and ovarian cancer will have major implications in the treatment of these common cancers. The possibility of preventive treatment in high-risk families is also a real hope.

Currently, predictive genetic tests are available at some specialist genetic centers for FAP, NF1, NF2, von Hippel–Lindau disease, MEN1, MEN2 and tuberous sclerosis, HNPCC, BRCA1 and BRCA2 and can be combined with clinical screening protocols (**Table 3**). These may depend on a suitable family structure (blood samples for linkage are needed on the extended family including two affected cases) as even when the genes are cloned no guarantee can be made of identifying the underlying mutation (see NF1/BRCA1/2/HNPCC). Faster and more sensitive methods of gene mutation identification and sequencing will open the way for more readily available mutation studies in these cloned genes. Even while this chapter is being published further discoveries will be made and much of what is written here will be superseded in 5 years or so. The preceding sections should, however, give the reader a good grasp of the current state of the art and the discoveries that have brought it about.

Table 3   Chromosomal location and implications of various dominant cancer syndromes

Disease	Location	Tumours	Probable earliest tumour (years)	Risk in lifetime (%)	Start of screening (years)
FAP	5q	Adenomas	1st	100	10–16
		Bowel cancer	?4, 7	99	
NF1	17q	Neurofibroma	1st	100	Birth
		Glioma, sarcoma	1st	10	
NF2	22q	Schwannomas	1st	100	Birth
		Meningiomas	1st	60	
		Gliomas		10	
vHL	3p	Haemangioblastoma	1–2	90	5
		Renal carcinoma	20	70	15
MEN1	11q	Parathyroid, insulinoma, gastrinoma	5	95	5
MEN2a	10q	Medullary thyroid cancer, parathyroid, phaeochromocytoma	3	80	3–4
MEN2b	10q	As in MEN2a, except parathyroid	1	100	Birth
Gorlin	9q	Basal cell carcinoma	5	90	Birth
		Medulloblastoma	1	5	
Cowden	10q	Breast	30	30	35
		Thyroid			
LFS	17p	Sarcoma (bone/soft tissue), adrenal, breast cancer, gliomas.	1st	95	1st
BRCA1	17q	Breast, ovary, colon, prostate carcinoma	>16	80–90	30
BRCA2	13q	Breast, ovary, colon, prostate carcinoma	>16	80–90	30
		Male breast		10	
HNPCC	2p,3p 2q,7p	Colorectum, ovary, endometrium, ureter, gastric, pancreas	>16	80	25

REFERENCES

Allanson, J. E., et al. (1991). Watson syndrome: is it a subtype of type 1 neurofibromatosis. *Journal of Medical Genetics*, **28**, 752–756.

Bell, D. W., et al. (1999). Heterozygous germ line hCHK2 mutations in Li–Fraumeni syndrome. *Science*, **286**, 2528–2531.

Birch, J. M., et al. (1998). Cancer phenotype correlates with constitutional TP53 genotype in families with Li–Fraumeni syndrome. *Oncogene*, **17**, 1061–1068.

Bodmer, N. F., et al., (1987). Localisation of the gene for familial adenomatous polyposis on chromosome 5. *Nature*, **328**, 614–616.

Bronner, C. E., et al. (1994). Mutation in the DNA mismatch repair gene homolog hMLH1 is associated with hereditary non-polyposis colorectal cancer. *Nature*, **368**, 258–261.

Burn, J., et al. (1991). The UK Northern Region genetic register for familial adenomatous polyposis coli: use of age of onset, congenital hypertrophy of the retinal pigment epithelium, and DNA markers in risk calculation. *Journal of Medical Genetics*, **28**, 289–296.

Chandrasekharappa, S. C., et al. (1997). Positional cloning of the gene for multiple endocrine neoplasia type 1. *Science*, **276**, 404–407.

Clark, R. D. (1994). Proteus syndrome. In: Huson, S. M. and Hughes, R. A. C. (eds). *The Neurofibromatoses* 402–413 (Chapman and Hall, London).

Claus, E. B., et al. (1990). Age of onset as an indicator of familial risk of breast cancer. *American Journal Epidemiology*, **131**, 961–972.

Cohen, A. J., et al. (1979). Hereditary renal cell carcinoma associated with a chromosomal translocation. *New England Journal of Medicine*, **301**, 592–595.

Colley, A., et al. (1996). Neurofibromatosis/Noonan phenotype: a variable feature of Type 1 neurofibromatosis. *Clinical Genetics*, **49**, 59–64.

Cowan, R., et al. (1997). The gene for the Naevoid Basal Cell Carcinoma (Gorlin) syndrome acts as a tumour suppressor gene in medulloblastoma. *British Journal of Cancer*, **76**, 141–145.

Cushing, H. (1917). *Tumours of the Nervus Acusticus and the Syndrome of the Cerebello-pontile Angle*. (W.B. Saunders, Philadelphia).

Davies, D. R., et al. (1995). Severe Gardner's syndrome in families with mutations restricted to a specific region of the APC gene. *American Journal of Human Genetics*, **57**, 1151–1158.

DeVries, P. J. and Bolton, P. F. (2000). Genotype–phenotype correlations in tuberous sclerosis. *Journal of Medical Genetics*, **37**, E3.

Easton, D., *et al.* (1993). Genetic linkage analysis in familial breast and ovarian cancer: results from 214 families. *American Journal of Human Genetics*, **53**, 305–313.

Eeles, R. A., *et al.* (1996). *Genetic Predisposition to Cancer.* (Chapman and Hall, London).

European Chromosome 16 Tuberous Sclerosis Consortium (1993). Identification and characterisation of the tuberous sclerosis gene on chromosome 16. *Cell*, **75**, 805–808.

Evans, D. G. R., *et al.* (1992a). A genetic study of type 2 neurofibromatosis in the United Kingdom: I prevalence, mutation rate, fitness and confirmation of maternal transmission effect on severity. *Journal of Medical Genetics*, **29**, 841–846.

Evans, D. G. R., *et al.* (1992b). A clinical study of type 2 neurofibromatosis. *Quarterly Journal of Medicine*, **84**, 603–618.

Evans, D. G. R., *et al.* (1993). Complications of the Naevoid Basal Cell Carcinoma Syndrome: results of a population based study. *Journal of Medical Genetics*, **30**, 460–464.

Evans, D. G. R., *et al.* (1998a). Genotype–phenotype correlations in type 2 neurofibromatosis (NF2): Evidence for more severe disease with truncating mutations. *Journal of Medical Genetics*, **35**, 450–455.

Evans, D. G. R., *et al.* (1998b). Somatic mosaicism: a common mechanism for sporadic disease in tumour prone syndromes? Lessons from type 2 neurofibromatosis. *American Journal of Human Genetics*, **63**, 727–736.

Farndon, P., *et al.* (1992). Localisation of the gene for Gorlin (Naevoid basal cell carcinoma) syndrome on chromosome 9. *Lancet*, **i**, 581–582.

Fishel, F. S., *et al.* (1993). A mutator gene homolog MSH2 and its association with hereditary non-polyposis colorectal cancer. *Cell*, **260**, 1027–1038.

Ford, D., *et al.* (1998). Genetic heterogeneity and penetrance analysis of the BRCA1 and BRCA2 genes in breast cancer families. *American Journal of Human Genetics*, **62**, 676–689.

Francke, U. and King, F. (1976). Sporadic bilateral retinoblastoma and 13q⁻ chromosomal deletion. *Medical Pediatrics and Oncology*, **2**, 379–380.

Fraumeni, J. F., *et al.* (1975). Six families prone to ovarian cancer. *Cancer*, **36**, 364–369.

Friend, S. H., *et al.* (1986). A human DNA segment with properties of the gene that predisposes to retinoblastoma and osteosarcoma. *Nature*, **323**, 643–646.

Fryer, A. E., *et al.* (1987). Evidence that the gene for tuberous sclerosis is on chromosome 9. *Lancet*, **i**, 659–661.

Gailani, M., *et al.* (1991). Evidence for a tumour suppressor gene on chromosome 9 in basal cell carcinomas of the skin. *American Journal of Human Genetics*, **49**, Supplement, 454.

Gardner, E. J. (1951). A genetic and clinical study of intestinal polyposis, a predisposing factor for carcinoma of the colon and rectum. *American Journal of Human Genetics*, **3**, 167–176.

Gardner, W. J. and Frazier, C. H. (1930). Bilateral acoustic neurofibromas: a clinical study and field survey of a family of five generations with bilateral deafness in thirty eight members. *Archives of Neurology Psychiatry*, **23**, 266–302.

Gayther, S. A., *et al.* (1995). Germline mutations of the BRCA1 gene in families: evidence for a genotype/phenotype correlation. *Nature Genetics*, **11**, 428–433.

Godbout, R., *et al.* (1983). Somatic inactivation of genes on chromosome 13 is a common event in retinoblastoma. *Nature*, **304**, 451–453.

Gorlin, R. J. (1987). Naevoid basal cell carcinoma syndrome. *Medicine*, **66**, 98–113.

Grundy, P., *et al.* (1988). Familial predisposition to Wilms tumour does not map to the short arm of chromosome 11. *Nature*, **336**, 374–376.

Hahn, H., *et al.* (1996). Mutations of the human homolog of *Drosophila* patched in the naevoid basal cell carcinoma syndrome. *Cell*, **85**, 841–851.

Hall, J. M., *et al.* (1990). Linkage of early onset familial breast cancer to 17q21. *Science*, **250**, 1684–1689.

Herrera, L., *et al.* (1986). Gardner syndrome in a man with an interstitial deletion of 5q. *American Journal of Medical Genetics*, **25**, 473–476.

HMSO (1998). *Cancer Statistics Registration England and Wales 1992.* (London, HM Stationery Office).

Knudson, A. G. (1971). Mutation and cancer: statistical study of retinoblastoma. *Proceedings of the National Academy of Sciences of the USA*, **68**, 820–823.

Koufos, A., *et al.* (1989). Familial Wiedemann–Beckwith syndrome and a second Wilms tumour locus both, map to 11p15.5. *American Journal of Human Genetics*, **44**, 711–719.

Lam, W. W., *et al.* (1999). Analysis of CDKN1C (p57KIP2) mutations in familial and sporadic Beckwith–Wiedemann syndrome (BWS) provides a novel genotype–phenotype correlation. *Journal of Medical Genetics*, **36**, 518–523.

Larsson, C., *et al.* (1988). Multiple endocrine neoplasia type 1 gene maps to chromosome 11 and is lost in insulinoma. *Nature*, **332**, 85–87.

Latif, F., *et al.* (1993). Identification of the von Hippel–Lindau disease tumour suppressor gene. *Science*, **260**, 1317–1320.

Li, F. P. and Fraumeni, J. F., Jr (1969). Soft tissue sarcomas, breast cancer, and other neoplasms: a familial syndrome? *Annals of Internal Medicine*, **71**, 747–752.

Li, F. P., *et al.* (1988). A cancer family syndrome in 24 kindreds. *Cancer Research*, **48**, 5358–5362.

Listernick, R., *et al.* (1989). Optic gliomas in children with neurofibromatosis type 1. *Journal of Pediatrics*, **114**, 788–792.

Liu, Z., *et al.* (1995). Germline mutations in the RB1 gene in patients with hereditary retinoblastoma. *Genes Chromosomes Cancer*, **14**, 277–284.

Lohmann, D. R., *et al.* (1996). Spectrum of RB1 germ-line mutations in patients with hereditary retinoblastoma. *American Journal of Human Genetics*, **58**, 940–949.

Lynch, H. T., *et al.* (1985). Hereditary nonpolyposis colorectal cancer (Lynch syndromes I and II): Clinical description of resource. *Cancer*, **56**, 934–938.

Lynch, H. T., *et al.* (1988). Differential diagnosis of hereditary nonpolyposis colorectal cancer (Lynch syndrome I and

Lynch syndrome II). *Diseases of the Colon and Rectum*, **31**, 372–377.

Maher, E. R., *et al.* (1990). Clinical features and natural history of von Hippel–Lindau disease. *Quarterly Journal of Medicine*, **77**, 1151–1163.

Malkin, D., *et al.* (1990). Germ line p53 mutations in a familial syndrome of breast cancer, sarcomas and other neoplasms. *Science*, **250**, 1233–1238.

McGaughran, J. M., *et al.* (1999). A clinical study of type 1 neurofibromatosis in North West England. *Journal of Medical Genetics*, **36**, 197–203

Meijers-Heijboer, E. J., *et al.* (2000). Presymtomatic DNA testing and prophylactic surgery in families with a BRCA1 or BRCA2 mutation. *Lancet*, **355**, 2015–2020.

Messiaen, L. M., *et al.* (2000). Exhaustive mutation analysis of the NF1 gene allows identification of 95% of mutations and reveals a high frequency of unusual splicing defects. *Human Mutation*, **15**, 541–545.

Miki, Y., *et al.* (1994). A strong candidate for the breast and ovarian cancer susceptibility gene BRCA1. *Science*, **266**, 120–122.

Mulligan, L. M., *et al.* (1993). Germline mutations of the RET proto-oncogene in multiple endocrine neoplasia type 2a. *Nature*, **363**, 458–460.

Narod, S. A., *et al.* (1991). A familial breast–ovarian cancer locus on chromosome 17q12–q23. *Lancet*, **ii**, 82–83.

National Institutes of Health Consensus Development Conference Statement on Neurofibromatosis. (1987). *Archives of Neurology*, **45**, 575–579.

Nishisho, I., *et al.* (1991). Mutations of chromosome 5q21 genes in FAP and colorectal cancer patients. *Science*, **253**, 665–669.

Pelletier, J., *et al.* (1991). WT1 mutations contribute to abnormal genital system development and hereditary Wilms tumour. *Nature*, **353**, 431–434.

Peto, J., *et al.* (1999). Prevalence of BRCA1 and BRCA2 gene mutations in patients with early-onset breast cancer. *Journal of National Cancer Institute*, **91**, 943–949.

Ridolfi, R. L, *et al.* (1977). Medullary carcinoma of the breast. *Cancer*, **40**, 1365–1385.

Riccardi, V. M., *et al.* (1978). Chromosomal imbalance in aniridia–Wilms tumour association: 11p interstitial deletion. *Pediatrics*, **61**, 604–610.

Rouleau, G., *et al.* (1987). Genetic linkage analysis of bilateral acoustic neurofibromatosis to a DNA marker on chromosome 22. *Nature*, **329**, 246–248.

Rouleau, G. A., *et al.* (1993). Alteration in a new gene encoding a putative membrane-organizing protein causes neuro-fibromatosis type 2. *Nature*, **363**, 515–521.

Santibanez-Koref, M. F., *et al.* (1991). P53 Germline mutations in 2 out of 8 families with the Li Fraumeni syndrome. *Lancet*, **ii**, 1490–1491.

Savitsky, K., *et al.* (1995). A single ataxia telangectasia gene with a product similar to PI3-kinase. *Science*, **268**, 1749–1753.

Schildkraut, J. M. and Thompson, W. D. (1988). Relationship of epithelial ovarian cancer to other malignancies within families. *Genetics and Epidemiology*, **5**, 355–367.

Scott, R., *et al.* (1996). Familial infiltrative fibromatosis (Desmoid tumours) caused by a recurrent 3′ APC mutation. *Human Molecular Genetics*, **5**, 1921–1924.

Seizinger, B. R., *et al.* (1987). Genetic linkage of von Recklinghausen neurofibromatosis to the nerve growth factor receptor gene. *Cell*, **49**, 589–594.

Seizinger, B. R., *et al.* (1988). Von Hippel–Lindau disease maps to the region of chromosome 3 associated with renal cell carcinoma. *Nature*, **332**, 268–269.

Shrivastava, S., *et al.* (1990). Germ-line transmission of a mutated p53 gene in a cancer prone family with Li–Fraumeni syndrome. *Nature*, **348**, 747–749.

Simpson, N. E., *et al.* (1987). Assignment of multiple endocrine neoplasia type 2A to chromosome 10 by linkage. *Nature*, **328**, 528–530.

Solomon, E. (1990). Colorectal cancer genes. *Nature*, **343**, 412–414.

Solomon, E., *et al.* (1987). Chromosome 5 allele loss in human colorectal carcinomas. *Nature*, **328**, 616–619.

Spirio, L., *et al.* (1993). Alleles of the APC gene: an attenuated form of familial polyposis. *Cell*, **75**, 951–957.

Steichen-Gersdorf, E., *et al.* (1994). Familial site specific ovarian cancer is linked to BRCA1 on 17q12–21. *American Journal of Human Genetics*, **55**, 870–875

Strong, L. C. (1977). Genetic and environmental interactions. *Cancer*, **40**, 1861–1866.

Struewing, J. P., *et al.* (1997). The risk of cancer associated with specific mutations of BRCA1 and BRCA2 among Ashkenazi Jews. *New England Journal of Medicine*, **336**, 1401–1408.

Swift, M., *et al.* (1987). Breast and other cancers in families with ataxia telangiectasia. *New England Journal of Medicine*, **316**, 1289–1294.

Swift, M., *et al.* (1991). Incidence of cancer in 161 families affected by ataxia telangiectasia. *New England Journal of Medicine*, **325**, 1831–1836.

Teyssier, J. R., *et al.* (1986). Recurrent deletion of the short arm of chromosome 3 in human renal cell carcinomas: shift of the c-raf1 locus. *Journal of the National Cancer Institute*, **77**, 1187–1191.

Toguchida, J., *et al.* (1991). A survey of germ-line and somatic p53 mutations in patients with bone and soft tissue sarcomas. *American Journal of Human Genetics*, **49**, Supplement, 458.

Trofatter, J. A., *et al.* (1993). A novel Moesin-, Ezrin-, Radixin-like gene is a candidate for the neurofibromatosis 2 tumour suppressor. *Cell*, **72**, 1–20.

Varley, J. M., *et al.* (1999). Analysis of a panel of patients with childhood adrenocortical tumours for germline TP53 mutations. *American Journal of Human Genetics*, **65**, 995–1006.

Viskochil, D., *et al.* (1990). Deletions and a translocation interrupt a cloned gene at the neurofibromatosis type 1 locus. *Cell*, **62**, 187–192.

Vogelstein, B., *et al.* (1988). Genetic alterations during colorectal tumour development. *New England Journal of Medicine*, **319**, 525–532.

Williams, W. R. and Strong, L. C. (1985). Genetic epidemiology of soft tissue sarcoma in children. In: Muller H. R. and

Weber, W. (eds), *Familial Cancer, First International Research Conference*. 151–153 (Karger, Basle).

Wishart, J. H. (1822). Case of tumours in the skull, dura mater, and brain. *Edinburgh Medical and Surgical Journal*, **18**, 393–397.

Wooster, R., *et al.* (1994). Localization of a breast cancer susceptibility gene, BRCA2, to chromosome 13q12–13. *Science*, **265**, 2088–2090.

Wooster, R., *et al.* (1995). Identification of the breast cancer susceptibility gene BRCA2. *Nature*, **378**, 789–792.

FURTHER READING

Bishop, D. T. and Thomas, H. J. W. (1990). The genetics of colorectal cancer. *Cancer Surveys*, **9**, 585–604.

Claus, E. B., *et al.* (1994). Autosomal dominant inheritance of early onset breast cancer. *Cancer*, **73**, 643–651.

Devilee, P. J. and Cornelisse, C. J. (1990). Genetics of breast cancer. *Cancer Surveys*, **9**, 605–630.

Eeles, R., *et al.* (eds) (1996). *Genetic Predisposition to Cancer*. (Chapman and Hall, London).

Evans, D. G. R. (1995). Practical implications of the new cancer genetics. In: Peckham, M., *et al.* (eds), *Oxford Textbook of Oncology*. (Oxford University Press, Oxford).

Hodgson, S. and Foulkes W. D. (1998). *Inherited Susceptibility to Cancer*. 3–19. (Cambridge University Press, Cambridge).

Huson, S. M., *et al.* (1989). A genetic study of von Recklinghausen neurofibromatosis in south east Wales. II. Guidelines for genetic counselling. *Journal of Medical Genetics*, **26**, 712–721.

Lemoine N. R., *et al.* (1994). *Cancer: A Molecular Approach*. (Blackwell Scientific, Oxford).

Varley, J., *et al.* (1997). Li–Fraumeni syndrome – A molecular and clinical review. *British Journal of Cancer*, **76**, 1–14.

Chapter 5

Human DNA Tumour Viruses

Beverly E. Griffin and Wilson Caparrós-Wanderley
Imperial College School of Medicine at St. Mary's, London, UK

CONTENTS

INTRODUCTION

Almost all vertebrate species, whether man, monkey or marsupial, have their own cohort of viruses. These are usually species specific, although they may share sequence homologies, genes and gene functions with similar viruses from other species. In practice, this has meant that a detailed study of a virus from one species may have profound impact on predicting the properties of a similar virus in another species, particularly where the viral sequences are available for comparison. However, this is not always the case, as best illustrated for two small, highly related DNA tumour viruses, the primate virus, simian virus 40 (SV40), and the mouse virus, polyomavirus (Py). For SV40, all activities for regulating cell growth, and transformation to a tumorigenic phenotype, are carried out by one viral protein, the large T-antigen (LT). However, with Py, differential splicing of the RNA, made from a single region of the viral genome, gives rise to distinct messages and two proteins – the so-called large and middle T-antigens (LT and MT) – where the function for altering cell growth is carried by one protein, LT, and that for inducing cellular transformation by the other, MT. Thus, cross-species speculations about related viruses need to be made with care. Similarly, the general notions about host range specificity of a virus cannot be deemed absolute, since mutations can occur that result in host alteration. One of the most interesting cases in point, in the DNA virus field, comes from the identification in Africa of a pox virus that appears recently to have crossed the species barrier from monkey to man. The current interest in 'emerging viruses' focuses on the origins of new species and evolutionary and environmental factors that contribute to their birth (Morse, 1993).

This chapter deals with a subset of DNA viruses, those associated with tumour formation, and is restricted to discussing in detail only those viruses where a good case can be made for an association with human cancer. In animal models, such as those employing SV40 and Py, the experimental evidence showing tumour causality in appropriate models is unambiguous. For human disease, the situation is by definition more complicated and causality or association depends on drawing together studies from many fields, including not only virology, but also epidemiology, oncology and molecular biology. Notably, with the four viruses that are discussed in detail, that is, papilloma viruses, two herpesviruses (Epstein–Barr and Kaposi sarcoma-related virus) and hepatitis B virus, all have the ability to persist in infected cells and evade host immune systems. For none of these viruses has a very good *in vitro* lytic system been identified, impeding progress in answering crucial questions about them. Even without this, much progress has been made, mainly owing to the judicious use of molecular methods, and model systems, where identified.

Over the last few years, the International Agency for Research on Cancer (IARC), Lyon, as part of their programme for evaluating carcinogenic risks to humans, has considered four of the human DNA viruses most likely to play a causal, predisposing, or auxiliary role in the development of cancer in humans. These are various members of the papillomavirus (PV) family (related to SV40 and mouse Py, and in former times considered to belong to the same papovavirus family), hepatitis B virus (HBV), and the two members, Epstein–Barr virus (EBV) and Kaposi sarcoma-associated virus (KSHV), of the herpesvirus family. The general conclusion reached by a consortium of individuals contributing to reports on three of these viruses (HPV, HBV and EBV) is that 'there is sufficient evidence' for their carcinogenicity, as it relates to defined forms of cancer (IARC, 1994, 1995, 1997). For KSHV, the most recently identified of these viruses, the conclusion reached in 1998 is that 'KSHV is probably carcinogenic to humans.' The ultimate proof of viral causality of malignancy will be concomitant eradication of the virus and of the disease, and is a target for the future. In the case of HBV, where there are effective antiviral vaccines, this could be realized in the foreseeable future.

PAPILLOMAVIRUSES (PVs)

General Definition and Classification

Papillomaviruses (PVs) are a family of DNA viruses that cause hyperproliferative lesions of the mucosal and cutaneous epithelia (papillomas, warts and condylomas) in a wide variety of higher vertebrates, including humans. Most of these lesions are benign, self-limiting and regress with time, but some of them tend to progress towards malignancy and invasive carcinoma (e.g. carcinoma of the uterine cervix).

All PVs belong to the subfamily Papillomavirus, which constitutes one of the two members of the family Papovaviridae. The other member of this family, the subfamily Polyomavirus, is discussed later in this chapter. PVs and Polyomaviruses were initially grouped together because they share properties of small-sized, nonenveloped virions, icosahedral capsids, superhelical double-stranded DNA genomes, and use the nucleus as site of multiplication. Subsequent research has shown that, despite these similarities, the two genera are not evolutionarily related. They have different genomic organisations, their DNAs do not hybridize and there is no immunological cross-reactivity between them. Furthermore, in contrast to Polyomaviruses, PVs multiply only in differentiating epithelium and cannot be propagated *in vitro* (Howley, 1996).

PVs are highly species specific, hence their classification is based on their host range and DNA relatedness. Each virus is first named after its natural host followed by a number, and sometimes a letter, which indicates, respectively, its type and subtype (e.g. bovine (B)PV-4, Human (H)PV-6b, etc.) (**Table 1**). Classification of different isolates from one species into types and subtypes is based, at present, on their degree of sequence homology. On the basis of the site of infection, HPVs have also been classified into two main groups: cutaneous and mucosal. Each group can, in turn, be subdivided into 'high-' or 'low'-risk types according to the probability of malignant progression associated with the type of lesions they cause. Both this approach and the sequence homology method give rise to equivalent phylogenetic trees (**Figure 1**) (Shah, 1990).

Virion Structure

Nonenveloped icosahedral PVs replicate in the nucleus of squamous epithelial cells. PV particles are about 50 nm in diameter and encapsulate a single copy of the circular 8 kbp double-stranded DNA genome in the form of a chromatin-like complex with cellular histones. They have a density in caesium chloride of 1.34–1.36 g L^{-1} and, owing to the lack

Table 1   PV-associated pathological conditions

Species	Pathology	Virus Type[a]
Deer	Cutaneous fibropapillomas	DPV
Cattle	Alimentary tract carcinoma	**BPV-4**
	Cutaneous fibropapillomas	BPV-2
Cottontail rabbit	Skin carcinomas	**CRPV**
Humans	Skin warts	HPV-1, -2, -3, -7 and -10
	Epidermodysplasia verruciformis	HPV-**5**, -**8**, -17 and -20
	Anogenital warts (condylomas):	
	Exophytic condylomas	HPV-6 and -11
	Flat condylomas	HPV-**16**, -**18**, -**31**, -**33**, -42, -**43**, etc.
	Respiratory tract papillomas	HPV-6 and -11
	Conjunctival papillomatosis	HPV-6 and -11
	Focal epithelial hyperplasia (FEH)	HPV-13 and -32

[a]Virus types predominantly recovered from malignant lesions are indicated in bold.

of lipids, are resistant to ether and other solvents (Pfister and Fuchs, 1994).

The viral capsid is composed of 72 capsomers with a star-shaped morphology and displaying a cylindrical channel along their axis (**Figure 2**). All capsomers are pentamers of the L1 protein, a 55-kDa protein which represents about 80% of the total capsid protein. L1 protein is required for virus attachment to the cell surface receptor and constitutes the basic structural component of the capsid. The remaining 20% of the capsid is composed of a 70-kDa protein known as L2. The exact function(s) of this protein is still unclear, but it may be involved in the efficient self-assembly of the viral capsid and attraction and/or proper positioning of the viral genome during viral assembly (Howley, 1996).

Genomic Organisation

The Papillomavirus genome is divided into an 'early' region (about 4.5 kbp in size), a 'late' region (about 2.5 kbp) and a long regulatory region (LCR) (about 1 kbp). There are two open reading frames (ORFs) in the late region (L1 and L2) and up to eight ORFs (E1 to E8) in the early region. There are no ORFs in the LCR, but this region contains the viral origin of replication and control elements for transcription and replication. In contrast to Polyomaviruses, all ORFs in the Papillomavirus

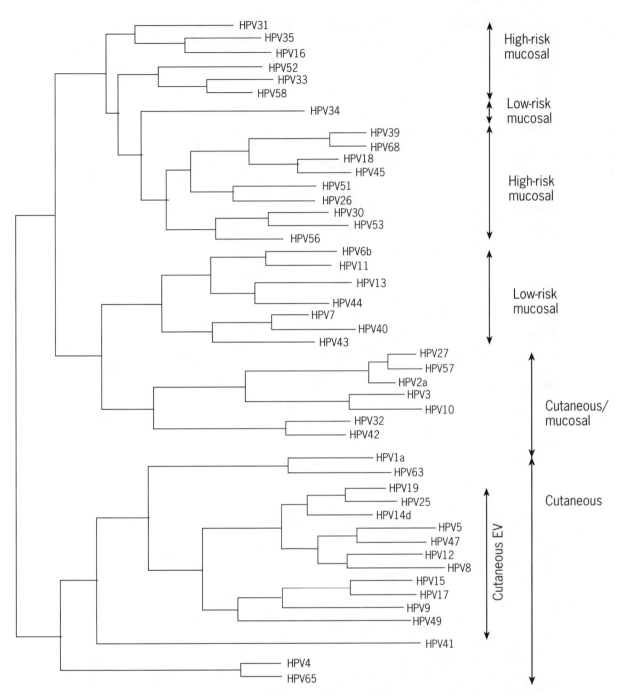

Figure 1   Phylogenetic tree of HPVs, based on DNA sequence homology of a 384-bp fragment of the E6 ORF. The clinical classification of HPV types, according to the site of infection, is indicated on the right. (Adapted from Van Ranst *et al.*, 1992.)

genome are located on one DNA strand (**Figure 3**) (Shah, 1990).

The properties of the proteins encoded by the two late ORFs, L1 and L2, have been described in the previous section.

The **E1** proteins, molecular weights (MW) 68–85 kDa, are essential for viral replication and in this role they are similar to the SV40 large T-antigen. They are

phosphoproteins with DNA-dependent ATPase and ATP-dependent helicase activities. The 5′ portion of the E1 ORF can sometimes be translated as a smaller protein involved in modulation of viral replication (Chow and Broker, 1994).

The **E2** ORF codes for a family of proteins of which only the full-length member, MW 43–48 kDa, can support viral replication. Full-length E2 is also a transcriptional activator whilst truncated forms of E2 (also known as E2C

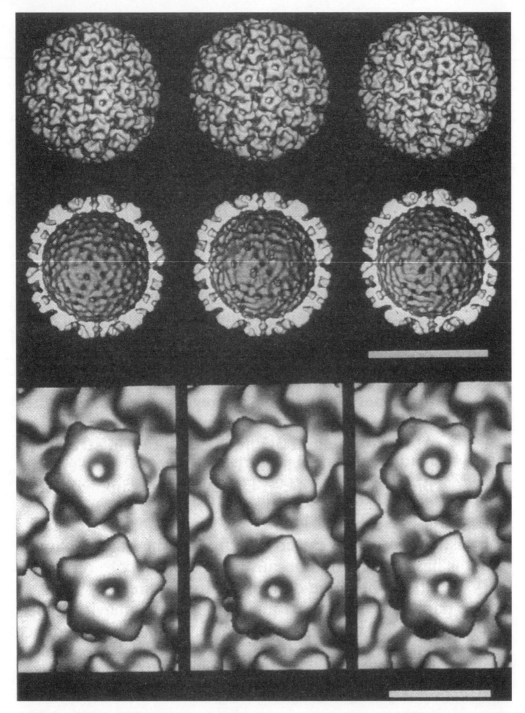

Figure 2   Structure of HPV. Surface-shaded representations of reconstructions of HPV-1 from warts (left columns), L1 capsids (middle columns) and L1L2 capsids (right columns). Outside view of capsids (top row), inside view (middle row) and a close-up view of pentavalent and hexavalent capsomeres (bottom row). Internal density to a radius of 20 nm was computationally removed to show internal features of the capsid. No differences are apparent. Bars = 50 nm (top and middle rows) and 10 nm (bottom row). (From Hagensee *et al.*, 1994, *Journal of Virology*, **68**, 4503–4505.)

and E2M), derived from different promoter usage and alternative mRNA splicing, are transcriptional repressors (Arrand, 1994; Chow and Broker, 1994).

The **E3** ORF is only present in some PVs and its function is not yet known.

The **E4** protein is expressed from a spliced mRNA (E1^E4) as a doublet of MW 17 and 16 kDa. E4 appears to be involved in the disruption of the cytokeratin network during the late phase of the viral life cycle. In HPV1 induced warts, E4 accumulates abundantly (up to 30% of

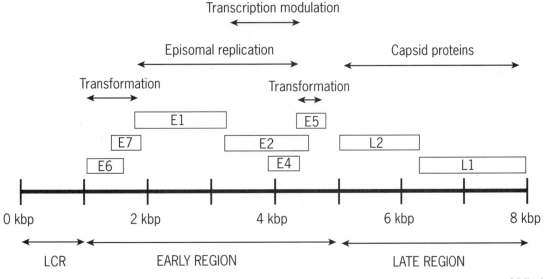

Figure 3 Organisation of a PV consensus genome (in kilobase pairs). The open boxes represent ORFs labelled E1–E6, or L1 and L2, according to their position in the 'Early' or 'Late' region of the genome. Locations of gene functions are listed above the genome. (Adapted from Pfister and Fuchs, 1994.)

the total protein mass) with the capsid proteins, but this does not occur in lesions caused by other PVs (Arrand, 1994).

The **E5** proteins are small (44–90 amino acids) and extremely hydrophobic polypeptides, which are present within intracellular membrane compartments, including the Golgi apparatus. In bovine (B)PVs, E5 is the major transforming protein and appears to stimulate mitogenesis by interfering with growth factor receptor signal transduction pathways (Stöppler *et al.*, 1994).

The **E6** proteins, MW 16–18 kDa, have transforming and transcriptional transactivating activities and are localized in the nuclear matrix and in non-nuclear membrane fractions. E6 and E7 proteins are the major transforming proteins of HPVs. Both proteins appear to have arisen from duplication events involving a Cys-X-X-Cys motif. E6, similarly to adenovirus E1B and SV40 LT, associates with the tumour suppressor p53, resulting in its ubiquitin-dependent degradation. In HPVs, this degradation is mediated only by the E6 proteins of 'high-risk' but not 'low-risk' types, suggesting an important role for this process in the development of malignancy (Stöppler *et al.*, 1994).

The **E7** proteins, MW 14–21 kDa, have transforming and transcriptional transactivating activities and are localized in the cytoplasm and the nucleolus. E7, similarly to the adenovirus E1A and SV40 LT, binds to the retinoblastoma tumour-suppressor gene product Rb-p105. This prevents Rb-p105 from interacting with the E2F transcription factor, thereby allowing initiation of the S-phase of the cell cycle. The E7 proteins of 'high-risk' HPVs are more effective in binding Rb-p105 than that of 'low-risk' types. E7 also has the ability to bind cyclins and cyclin-dependent kinases (cdks) and hence further disrupt the regulation of the cell cycle (Stöppler *et al.*, 1994).

The **E8** ORF is only present in some PVs. In BPV4, the E8 protein is a small hydrophobic polypeptide localized in the cell membrane. E8 contributes to cell transformation by conferring anchorage-independent growth.

There are marked differences in the state and functional activity of PV genomes in benign tumours and in cancers of different species (Shah, 1990; Chow and Broker, 1994; Howley, 1996). In benign lesions the viral genome replicates as multicopy extrachromosomal plasmids. In carcinomas, however, the situation can be completely different. In cattle, the BPV type 4 genome is detected in alimentary tract papillomas but is apparently lost in carcinomas. In cottontail rabbit carcinomas the viral genome is present in the episomal form. In contrast, in some human genital tract cancers the viral genome, generally accompanied by deletions and mutations, is integrated into the cellular DNA. Integration with respect to the cellular DNA is not site-specific, but there is some specificity with respect to the site in the circular viral genome where the break for integration occurs. Viral genomes of HPV 16 and HPV 18 are found to be almost always interrupted in the E1–E2 region, producing a break that disrupts transcription of the E2 ORF, but not transcription of the E6, E7 and part of the E1 ORFs.

Transcription and Replication of the Viral Genome

The subdivision of the viral genome into 'early' and 'late' regions is based on the close association existing between viral replication and squamous epithelial differentiation. Upon entry into the basal stem cells of the epithelium, viral early gene expression is activated at a very low level, leading to the temporary amplification and establishment of the DNA plasmids. Early gene expression in the basal cell layer also stimulates cell growth and, as the epithelial cells move upwards in tissues progressing through their differentiation programme, this pattern of expression is maintained. Finally, in the uppermost layers of the epithelium, viral replication and late gene expression are activated in the now fully differentiated epithelial cells, resulting in the production of infectious viral progeny (Chow and Broker, 1994; Howley, 1996).

Several factors contribute to the transcriptional complexity of PV genomes (Arrand, 1994; Pfister and Fuchs, 1994; Howley, 1996): first, the presence of multiple promoters (for example, the LCR of BPV-1 contains at least seven promoters); second, complex and multiple splice patterns which, associated with the activity of the different promoters and the use of different polyadenylation signals, give rise to an extensive variety of viral mRNAs, many of which are polycistronic; furthermore, some ORFs (e.g. E2 and E6) appear to be represented to different extents in different messages; finally, complex control by proteins and factors produced by the virus (E2, E6 and E7) or the host at both the intracellular (i.e. retinoic acid, NF-IL6, Oct-1, etc.) and extracellular (glucocorticoid hormones, TGF-β1 and -β2, EGF, etc.) levels occurs.

Detection of HPV Infection

Although detection and diagnosis of HPV-associated lesions can normally be achieved by colposcopy, histology and cytology, these methods are unable to identify specific HPV type(s) present in lesions. Serological responses against almost all HPV-derived antigens have been detected in infected individuals. However, the diagnostic utility of these serological responses is questionable because (1) they appear to be, for most antigens, non-type-specific, and (2) they persist for longer than the actual infection. Detection of HPV DNA is, therefore, the only reliable diagnostic tool available to establish current infection by specific HPV types. This approach involves the detection of the viral genome either directly (by Southern blot hybridization) or by polymerase chain reaction (PCR) protocols (Shah and Howley, 1996).

Pathogenesis of Infections

In contrast to some animal PV infections in which fibroblastic proliferation is prominent, the pathological effect of HPV infection is confined to the epithelium. All the layers of the normal epithelium are represented in the lesion, accompanied by certain characteristic histological features. The increased division rate of the basal cell layer leads to an irregularly thickened prickle cell layer, with abnormal mitoses also observed in all suprabasal layers. The granular layer contains foci of cells showing koilocytosis (cytoplasmic vacuolization) and nuclear changes (enlargement, hyperchromasia, degeneration and pyknosis). Koilocytosis is also a feature of the cornified layer of non-nucleated dead cells, which may also display hyperkeratosis (Shah, 1990).

HPV infection can be acquired in a variety of ways such as abrasions of the skin, sexual intercourse and passage through an infected birth canal, and results in a variety of clinical conditions (**Table 1**) (Shah and Howley, 1996). Most of these lesions have benign prognoses, but they may be associated with high levels of morbidity. For example, exophytic anogenital warts, one of the most common sexually transmitted diseases, usually cause itching, burning and pain, and have a significant negative effect on the psychosexual wellbeing of the individual. Other lesions, however, may undergo malignant transformation. In the case of flat anogenital warts, lesions in the uterine cervix may progress towards invasive carcinoma and 50% of the diagnosed population will ultimately die of the disease, accounting for about 15% of cancer-related deaths worldwide. The progression of benign papillomas to invasive cancers has certain characteristics which are shared in different species (Shah, 1990; Shah and Howley, 1996). First, only some of the virus types that infect a species have oncogenic potential. In epidermodysplasia verruciformis (EV), more than 20 different HPV types are recovered from the macular plaques characteristic of this disease. However, only two types, HPV5 and HPV8, predominate in the carcinomas that arise from these lesions. Similarly, over a dozen HPV types infect the human genital tract, but a majority of genital tract carcinomas are associated with only a few viral types, the so-called 'high-risk' types (predominantly HPV 16 and 18). Second, there is a long period between the initial infection and the development of invasive cancers. In humans this period may be between 5 and 40 years. Finally, cofactors are often involved in malignant progression. For example, carcinomas in EV patients arise preferentially in lesions that are exposed to sunlight.

Immunology of Infection

Viral infections are controlled by a combination of non-antigen-specific and antigen-specific immune responses. Most viruses induce these immune responses by causing lytic cell death which, in turn, causes inflammation and stimulates the production of cytokines. PV infection, in contrast, is non-lytic and, consequently little or no local inflammation is induced. This situation probably reflects the reduced ability of PVs to invoke effective immune responses that are capable of eliminating established lesions (Frazer, 1996). Nonetheless, there is evidence of involvement of the immune system in the control of PV infections.

Humoural (antibody) immune responses directed against almost all PV proteins have been detected in infected individuals. However, only antibodies directed against L1 or L2 have been found to be neutralizing and to protect against infection. Antibodies against the E6 and E7 proteins of high risk HPVs, although not effective at the prophylactic level, are commonly associated with carcinoma of the uterine cervix. Antibodies against the E2 and E4 proteins have also been associated with carcinoma of the cervix, but not universally (Frazer, 1996; Shah and Howley, 1996).

The persistence of PV-induced lesions suggests that the development of an effective cellular immune response against PVs following infection is neither immediate nor universal. Nonetheless, several observations suggest that the host's cell-mediated immune response is responsible for limiting the growth and promoting the regression of PV-induced lesions. First, there is a high prevalence of PV-induced lesions and malignant tumours in hosts with suppressed cellular immunity. Second, the regression of anogenital and skin warts in humans is associated with a pronounced local infiltration of mononuclear cells (activated T lymphocytes, macrophages and, to lesser extents, NK cells and B lymphocytes) invading the epidermis and destroying the neoplastic tissue. On this basis, the cellular immune response in spontaneously regressing warts appears to be consistent with a delayed type hypersensitivity (DTH) reaction to foreign antigen. Nonetheless, the presence of specific cytotoxic CD8 + T lymphocytes (CTLs), which are normally involved in the resolution of viral infections, has been notoriously difficult to demonstrate in HPV infections. Indeed, only a handful of studies (i.e. Tarpey et al., 1994; Nakagawa et al., 1997) have shown E6- or E7- specific CTLs in humans. Finally, vaccination with PV antigens has been found to induce a specific T cell proliferative or CTL responses against L1, L2, E2, E6 and E7 in animals and humans (Frazer, 1996; Shah and Howley, 1996).

EPSTEIN–BARR VIRUS (EBV)

History, Definition and Classification

A relevant point to note about EBV (or HHV-4) is that it is almost ubiquitous in the adult human population, with the great majority of individuals carrying antibodies to the virus. Infection of B lymphocytes by EBV is mediated through interaction of a viral envelope glycoprotein with the receptor for the C3d complement component, CD21 (CR2), although, notably, EBV can infect epithelial cells that lack this receptor. The average age of seroconversion to this virus differs markedly in various parts of the world, usually being considerably later in the more socio-economic privileged parts of the world than in crowded, or poorer, populations. Viral antibody prevalence in terms of age is given in **Figure 4**. EBV has a particularly interesting international history. It was first observed by

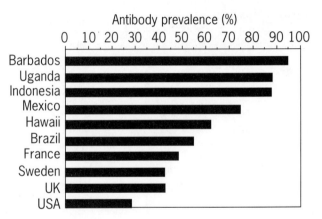

Figure 4 EBV antibody prevalence, age 4-6 years, in different parts of the world. (From IARC, 1997, p. 83.)

Epstein and colleagues in London in the 1960s on electron microscopic examination of a cell line (EB), established with extracts from an African tumour, called Burkitt's lymphoma (BL). From its physical appearance, the virus was defined as a member of the herpesvirus family. BL itself had been identified about 10 years earlier during travels by the Irish-born surgeon, Denis Burkitt in sub-Saharan Africa. Carvings from earlier periods showed this tumour of B lymphocytes to be a disease long prevalent in certain parts of Africa. Later, a genuinely serendipitous finding showed the virus to be the causative agent of infectious mononucleosis. This came about when a laboratory technician in Philadelphia, with no antibodies to EBV, developed mononucleosis and on subsequent testing was found to be EBV-antibody positive. A causal effect for EBV in mononucleosis was thus confirmed (reviewed by Griffin, 1998). An association between EBV and a tumour of epithelial cells, nasopharyngeal carcinoma (NPC), was discovered when sera from these patients were included in a general antibody screening programme in New York, also in the 1960s.

The natural reservoir of EBV, whether in the B lymphocyte or epithelial or other cell population, is still a matter of controversy. EBV is known to exist in circulating lymphocytes in the body (about 1 in $10^5 - 10^6$ in a normal individual). In culture, the virus is capable of extending the lifetime of B lymphocytes for an unlimited time period, a phenomenon called immortalization. EBV is sub-classified as γ-herpesvirus, having a restricted host range with its site of latency residing in lymphocytes, compared for example with α-herpesviruses, such as the simplex viruses, which have broad host ranges, and are latent in sensory ganglia. Herpesvirus classifications are given in **Table 2**. Although many other mammalian herpesviruses, notably those from Old World primates, belong to the γ-herpesvirus subfamily, only one other human herpesvirus identified to date, that of KSHV (HHV-8), belongs to this subclass. A full list of

Table 2   Biological characteristics of herpesvirus subfamilies

Characteristic	Alpha	Beta	Gamma
Genus	Simplexvirus	Cytomegalovirus	Lymphocryptovirus
	Varicella-Zoster virus	Muromegalovirus	Rhadinovirus
Host range	Broad	Restricted	Restricted
Prevalent genomic organisation*	D, E	Variable	B, C
Productive cycle	Short	Long	Long
Spread in culture	Efficient	Moderate	Poor
Site of latency	Sensory ganglia	Lymphoreticular tissues	Lymphocytes
Proliferation of latently infected cells	No	No	Yes

(From IARC, 1997, p. 36.)
*See **Figure 5**.

herpesviruses and their taxonomies is given elsewhere (IARC, 1997).

Unlike the Papillomaviruses, there is no well-defined classification of different strains of EBV. The viral genome is composed of double-stranded DNA, with sizes that range from about 175 to >200 kbp pairs in cells from different sources. In lytically infected (virus producer) cells, the viral DNA is linear and carries small repetitive sequences at each end. In latently infected (non-virus-producing) cells, it is circular, having undergone recombination via its repetitive terminal sequences. With regard to its structure, EBV differs from other human herpesviruses, as illustrated in **Figure 5**, and in organisation more resembles that of its host cell DNA than do the other viruses. Its size variation is not a property that has been used in classification since the viral genome is composed of unique sequences interspersed with repetitive elements, and size is largely dictated by copy numbers of the repeats. The largest of these, called IR1, or *Bam*HI W after the restriction enzyme that cleaves it intact from the DNA (**Figure 6**), is >3000 bp in size. An obvious classification sought, but not found, has been one that would allow for association of specific viral types with different EBV-associated malignancies, two of which are noted above. To date, pathology-specific strains of virus have not been identified. Rather, restricted viral gene expression, in part controlled by the host cell, may play a role in the genesis of a pathological lesion. Genetic polymorphisms, designated 1 and 2, have, however, been identified which differ in sequences of some viral nuclear antigen (EBNA) genes, and to some extent in their biological properties, and their global localization. Unlike the better-defined distinctions of herpes-simplex viruses 1 and 2, which are separately classified, the functional differences between EBV 1 and 2 are not sufficiently distinct to allow for unique classification. Indeed, the polymorphisms may merely reflect 'hotspots' for mutational recombination events in the genome. Such a hypothesis is not totally fanciful. At least one viral isolate, Jijoye (from a primary African BL), on propagation in culture, has given rise to a novel isolate, P3HR-1, with a deletion that maps within one of the key latent EBV genes (that for EBNA-2, see below) affected by the polymorphism in EBV 1 and 2.

Virion Structure

Whereas smaller DNA viruses, such as SV40, Polyoma, Papilloma and Adenoviruses, are nonenveloped, all the herpesviruses have an outer envelope and within this, a capsid that contains the viral DNA. By electron microscopy (EM), in composition and appearance EBV resembles a typical herpesvirus with a toroid-shaped protein core wrapped with genomic DNA, as shown in **Figure 7**. Its nucleocapsid is composed of 162 capsomeres and its outer envelope is made up of glycoprotein (gp) spikes, many of which are composed of a 220/350-kDa protein, the principal target of a virus-neutralizing antibody response. Size variation of this protein reflects the number of glycosylated amino acid residues it contains. To date, gp220/350 is still the prime candidate for producing an EBV vaccine that might prevent, or delay, infection *in vivo*. The high lipid content of the envelope results in relative instability of EB virions at room temperature, and their rapid inactivation by lipid solvents, such as ether and chloroform, or by detergents. This is another difference between the herpesviruses and the small DNA viruses, the latter being generally stable under these conditions. Between the nucleocapsid and the envelope is a region called the tegument, which is frequently distributed asymmetrically, and by EM shows no distinctive features. The composition of the tegument in EBV has been much less carefully studied than in some other herpesviruses, notably herpessimplex viruses.

Genomic Organisation and Key Viral Latent Functions

EBV was the first herpesvirus to have its complete DNA sequenced, as presented simplistically in **Figure 6**, determined (Baer *et al.*, 1984). In its overall structure, with unique sequences interspersed with repetitive elements, the viral genome appears to be a mini-version of its human host, with one notable exception, that is, every repetitive region (IR1–IR4 and TR) includes ORFs, occurs within a gene and also encodes a protein. There is no 'junk' DNA, the role often assigned to repetitive sequences in cellular

Group   Sequence arrangement   Members

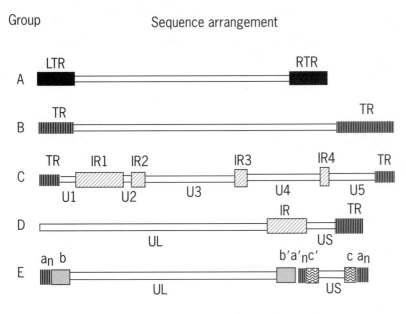

HHV6; HHV7

HV saimiri; HV ateles; mouse HV strais 68 (murine HV-4); KSHV (HHV8)

EBV (HHV4); baboon HV chimpanzee HV

Varicella–zoster virus (HHV3); marmoset HV; bovine HV-1; -5; ovine HV-1

HSV-1 (HHV1); HSV-2 (HHV2); HCMV (HHV5); simiae HV; Marek's disease HV-1 (gallid HV-2); turkey HV-1

Figure 5 Architecture of herpesvirus genomes, showing unique (U) and repetitive (R) regions. Viruses have been grouped in categories (A–E) and their designations are given on the right. According to the nomenclature used by different groups, LTR = left terminal repeat; RTR = right terminal repeat; TR = terminal repeat; IR = internal repeat; UL = long terminal repeat; US = short teminal repeat. Symbols used in group E viruses represent sequence arrangements within repeats. (Adapted from IARC, 1997, p. 35.)

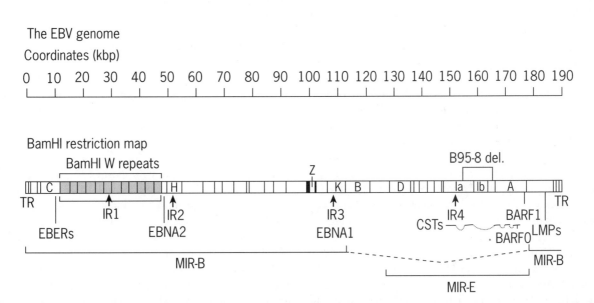

Figure 6 Physical map of the EBV genome, and location of some key gene and repetitive (IR) elements (see **Figure 5**). Coordinates for a 'typical' genome are given and genes allocated to the *Bam*HI restriction enzyme fragment in which they are located (see **Figure 10**). The CSTs encompass several restriction fragments. Its transcript is shown. MIR-B contains the minimum viral sequence required for immortalization of B lymphocytes and MIR-E the minimum for epithelial cells. (From Griffin and Xue, 1998, *Annals of Medicine*, **30**, 249–259.)

DNA, in EBV. Whereas genomes of the smaller tumour viruses, depending upon the stage in the cell cycle in which they are expressed, are classically divided into 'early' and 'late' ORFs, herpesviruses are divided into 'immediate early' (before DNA replication is initiated), 'early' and 'late' genes. An alternative classification divides their genes into 'latent' and 'lytic' functions. The latter, probably simplistic, classification is useful for discussion purposes

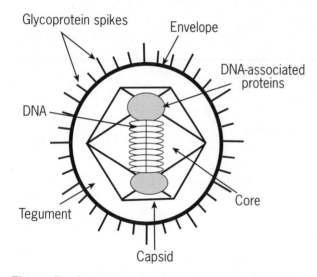

Figure 7 Schematic structure of a herpesvirus. (From IARC, 1997, p. 34.)

Table 3 Nomenclature of latent EBV gene products

Adopted terminology[a]	Alternative nomenclature[a]	
EBNA-1	EBNA-1	EBNA-1
EBNA-2	EBNA-2	EBNA-2
EBNA-3A	EBNA-3	EBNA-3A
EBNA-3B	EBNA-4	EBNA-3B
EBNA-3C	EBNA-6	EBNA-3C
EBNA-LP	EBNA-5	EBNA-4
LMP-1		
LMP-2A	TP-1	
LMP-2B	TP-2	
EBER-1		
EBER-2		

[a]EBNA, EBV nuclear antigen; LMP, latent membrane protein; EBER, EBV-encoded RNA; TP, terminal protein.
(From IARC, 1997, p. 53.)

when dealing with a large and complicated genome. Out of the 100 or so genes encoded by EBV, many of which are still poorly characterized, latent functions, as derived from data mainly drawn from EBV gene expression in B lymphocytes, consist of a small number of species only. These include six discrete EBV nuclear antigens (EBNAs), three discrete membrane antigens (LMPs) and two small RNAs (EBERs), of as yet unknown function. Interestingly, among other viruses studied in detail, only adenovirus encodes similar small RNAs (VA I and II) that structurally resemble EBERS, and although themselves not fully functionally characterized, are thought to modulate translation of viral proteins. For EBV, the EBERs are mainly localized in the nucleus and thus they may play alternative roles. Because of their very high levels of expression, EBERs have proved useful for detecting the presence of EBV in cells although, notably, they are apparently not expressed in all cells. For example, they are not found in a nonmalignant pathology associated with immunosuppression, oral hairy leucoplakia (OHL), where infected cells are frequently undergoing lytic replication. The nomenclatures used for the latent antigens in the EBV field are given in **Table 3**. The rest of the viral genes have been categorically designated as lytic, or lytically related. This distinct dichotomy into latent and lytic gene expression may be reassessed with time, since many EBV-associated tumours have recently been shown to express genes now designated as immediate early (or lytically related). Some of these, which may play initiating roles in the viral lytic cycle, may have other roles in tumours (discussed by Griffin and Xue, 1998). Alternatively, as proposed for KSHV (Ganem, 1998), a small amount of replication and thereby re-infection may be relevant to, and essential for, tumour growth.

These latent functions, on the assumption that most or all may play roles in the alteration of cell growth induced

by EBV, at least for B lymphocytes in culture, are briefly defined as follows (IARC, 1997).

EBNA-1: a DNA-binding protein identified in all EBV-infected cells and responsible for EBV genome replication in latently infected cells. EBNA-1 is not recognized by the host cellular immune system, probably as a consequence of the glycine–alanine-rich repetitive (IR3) sequence within the protein. In transgenic mice, it is tumorigenic. This antigen and its pivotal function in EBV latency has recently been reviewed (Leight and Sugden, 2000)

EBNA-2: a transactivator both of other viral and cellular functions, and a key protein in B cell immortalization in culture. It is not generally expressed in EBV-associated tumours, although this does not rule out an early role in tumour induction. It is expressed in post-transplant lymphoproliferative disorders and in infectious mononucleosis.

EBNA-LP: appears to be important for the stimulation of B cell growth in culture and, like EBNA-2, be a contributing factor in post-transplant lymphoproliferative disorders and infectious mononucleosis. EBNA-2 and EBNA-LP are the first two proteins to be identified following cellular infection with the virus.

EBNA-3A, 3B and 3C: often considered together because they are derived from adjacent regions of the viral genome. EBNA-3A and 3C, but possibly not 3B, are involved in growth stimulation of B cells, but all three may have regulatory roles in the transcriptional control of other key viral functions. EBNA-3C has been compared in its properties to HPV E7 and adenovirus E1A proteins, both associated with cell growth alterations induced by their respective viruses.

LMP-1: often found expressed in EBV-associated tumours. In *in vitro* assays using heterologous promoters like SV40 LT, it is capable of inducing tumorigenic transformation of rodent fibroblasts in culture. It alters cytokeratin expression and inhibits cell differentiation.

This transmembrane antigen may recruit signalling antibodies and is absolutely required for both the initiation and maintenance of B cell growth in culture. In transgenic mice, LMP-1 produces a pathological response in keratinocytes, which has not been fully characterized.

LMP-2A and 2B: map across the terminal junctions of the viral DNA and therefore can only be expressed in latently infected cells, where the genome is circular. They do not appear to be directly involved in the *in vitro* growth stimulation of B cells, but may be important for the maintenance of latency. LMP-2A is a phosphoprotein, stably phosphorylated on tyrosine, and thus may have other unidentified functions.

Two other genes, *BARF1* and *BARF0*: more recently identified, both of which may play key roles, particularly in epithelial cell growth regulation. Their importance to B lymphocyte growth stimulation *in vivo* is less clear. The *BARF1* gene, like LMP-1, is fully competent for inducing tumorigenic cellular transformation of rodent cells, and even B lymphocytes in culture, when expressed under a strong, heterologous promoter. It has some homology with the human intercellular cell adhesion molecule 1 (ICAM-1). In limited studies carried out to date, BARF1 has been found expressed in most EBV-associated nasopharyngeal carcinomas (NPCs) examined. Its activities remain to be fully characterized. The second gene comes from ***Bam*HI I/A transcript**, also called complementary strand transcripts (**CSTs**), or *BARF0* gene. Primary CSTs extend over about 25 kbp of the viral genome (**Figure 6**) and spliced variants of it make up the major transcripts in NPCs. They were first identified in 1989 (Hitt *et al.*, 1989) as a family of processed, multiply spliced polyadenylated RNAs and were subsequenty designated as 'complementary' in recognition of the fact that they were generated from the DNA strand with opposite polarity to that specifying numerous previously known viral genes. Each of the ORFs in the polycistronic CSTs, created by splicing events, overlap genes on the opposite strand, most of which are associated with lytic replication, which has led to the speculation that they may be involved in the maintenance of viral latency. CSTs are expressed also in BLs and other EBV-associated tumours, but at lower levels. They are often designated as latent functions as a consequence of their ubiquitous expression in tumours, but have also been found in lytically infected cells. A protein first described as a product of *BARF0*, the largest and terminal (3' end of the gene, with its termination codon in the polyadenylation signal of the message) of the CST ORFs, was later identified in uninfected cells, casting doubt on its authenticity. BARF1 and CST expression and function(s) in EBV infected cells are key targets for future research.

The locations of some of the genes described on the physical map of EBV are given in **Figure 6**, and their designations and functions, where known, are summarized in **Table 4**. A unique working nomenclature has been established for EBV genes, where B stands for the *Bam*HI restriction DNA fragment containing a particular gene, a letter represents fragment size relative to the other *Bam*HI products (A being the largest and g the smallest in the sequenced B95-8 EBV genome; Baer *et al.*, 1984), R (right) or L (left) denotes its direction (and polarity) on the conventional physical map of the genome, and a number denotes which reading frame is represented within a particular fragment. Thus, *BARF1*, above, is the first rightwardly expressed ORF in the *Bam*HI A fragment. *BARF0* was not predicted by the DNA sequence, so it carries an aberrant designation. The differential expression of these genes in various EBV-associated tumours, or in lymphoblastoid cell lines (LCLs) generated by infecting B lymphocytes with the virus, have now led to subclassifications of viral latency, as simplistically illustrated for EBNAs and LMPs in **Figure 8**, and given in detail in **Table 5**.

The EBV genome also includes two other genes with interesting homologies to human genes: *BCRF1* and *BHRF1,* IL-10 and Bcl-2 homologs, respectively. Their roles in the virus have not been defined.

Cellular Immortalization *In Vitro*

Following a procedure first described for the small DNA tumour viruses, the minimal region of the EBV genome required for growth stimulation of cells in culture has been determined, using transfection protocols and fragments of the viral genome. The results of studies carried out on B lymphocytes (B) and epithelial (E) cells, representing the main tumour cell types associated with EBV tumours, are shown in **Figure 6**. Notably, there is no overlap between the minimal immortalizing regions (MIR-B and MIR-E) in these cells, supporting the argument that cell-type-specific functions may exist within the viral genome. For MIR-E, the data are consistent with findings on the transcription of EBV in NPCs, as determined by analysis of a comprehensive cDNA library made from the tumour (Hitt *et al.*, 1989).

Pathogenesis

EBV is the causal agent for infectious mononucleosis, usually a self-limiting B cell proliferative disease, mainly a problem for economically privileged parts of the world where seroconversion and the development of antibodies to the virus occur late (**Figure 4**). With the hereditary immunodeficiency disorder, X-linked lymphoproliferative disease (XLP), or Duncan syndrome, fortunately rare, infection with EBV is usually fatal. Children that survive are at high risk of developing fatal lymphomas. With the so-called endemic form of Burkitt's lymphoma (BL), an acute problem for sub-Saharan Africa where it is the most prevalent cancer of children, there is a nearly 100% association with EBV. Again, in nasopharyngeal carcinoma (NPC), a head and neck tumour of poorly differentiated epithelial cells found with high frequency among the southern

Table 4   EBV gene products and proposed functions[a]

Open reading frame	Common name	Proposed function
Latent genes		
BKRF1	EBNA-1	Plasmid maintenance
BYRF1	EBNA-2	trans-Activation, transformation
BERF1	EBNA-3A	trans-Activation, transformation
BERF2	EBNA-3B	Unknown
BERF3/4	EBNA-3C	trans-Activation, transformation
BWRF1	EBNA-LP	trans-Activation, transformation
BNLF1	LMP-1	Transformation
BNRF1	LMP-2A/2B	Maintenance of latency
BARF0		Unknown
Immediate early genes		
BZLF1	ZEBRA	trans-Activation, initiation of lytic cycle
BRLF1		trans-Activation, initiation of lytic cycle
BI'LF4		trans-Activation, initiation of lytic cycle
Early genes		
BMRF1		trans-Activation
BARF1		Limited homology to ICAM-1
BALF2		DNA binding
BALF5		DNA polymerase
BORF2		Ribonucleotide reductase subunit
BaRF1		Ribonucleotide reductase subunit
BXLF1		Thymidine kinase
BGLF5		Alkaline exonuclease
BSLF1		Primase
BBLF4		Helicase
BKRF3		Uracil DNA glycosylase
Late genes		
BLLF1	gp350	Major envelope glycoprotein
BXLF2	gp85 (gH)	Virus–host envelope fusion
BKRF2	gp25 (gL)	Virus–host envelope fusion
BZLF2	gp42	Virus–host envelope fusion, binds MHC class II
BALF4	gp110 (gB)	Unknown
BDLF3	gp100–150	Unknown
BILF2	gp55–80	Unknown
BCRF1		Viral interleukin-10
BHRF1		Viral bcl-2 analogue

[a]See **Table 3**. ZEBRA, EBV replication activation; gp, glycoprotein; MHC, major histocompatibility complex; BARFO, major ORF in CSTs, function unknown. (Adapted from IARC, 1997, p. 50.)

Chinese and in some other parts of Asia, the viral association is 100%. These associations (see Introduction), largely based on clinical, epidemiological and serological approaches, have now been known for nearly half a century. What still is not known, however, is the precise contribution of EBV to these diseases, whether causal or merely contributory. If contributory only, in no case has the corresponding co-factor(s) been definitively identified, although there are candidates such as malaria for BL and smoked, salted fish consumption for NPC. What is firmly established, however, is the fact that the geographical, racial and age incidence of individuals that develop these EBV-related malignancies are totally distinct (**Figure 9**).

During the last 20 years, following the cloning and sequencing of the viral genome (Baer et al., 1984), which has allowed for the development of alternative, sensitive assays for identifying EBV and its gene projects, other tumours have been associated to varying degrees with the presence of this virus. These include a variety of tumours of different histopathological types, including subsets of lymphoepitheliomas, Hodgkin disease, stomach and breast cancers and T cell lymphomas. Notably, in none of the cases does the frequency of association approach that seen for endemic BL and NPC. However, the Working Group set up to explore the risk of EBV to humans, (IARC, 1997) concluded that there is sufficient evidence for the carcinogenicity of this virus, in the causation of BL and other non-Hodgkin lymphomas, immunosuppression-related lymphomas, Hodgkin's disease (HD), sinonasal angiocentric T cell lymphoma and NPC, to allow them to conclude that EBV is a human carcinogen. Subsequent to this document, more information on the expression of EBV in breast cancer has been published, and the viral genome has also been identified on two occasions in carcinomas of the liver, previously a preserve of the hepatitis viruses. The future will undoubtedly bring more 'associations' for this ubiquitous virus, and hopefully, if suitable animal models

are identified, notions about its actual role in disease. The sole argument that this virus alone could be sufficient for inducing malignancies under appropriate circumstance comes from the fact that many of the polyclonal lymphomas that develop as a consequence of immunosuppression (natural or induced) have a high frequency of association with EBV.

Immunological Considerations

One of the dominant characteristics about EBV is its adaptation to allow for persistence in its host(s), and gene expression, even in the presence of a functional immune system. EBV co-replicates with host DNA, and EBNA-1, required for latent replication, is tolerated, not eliminated, although there are epitopes for class I and class II HLAs in the viral antigen (Khanna *et al.*, 1999). The dominant feature in this protein that allows for its tolerance appears to be the repetitive (IR3) sequence that it harbours. In some cases of BL, where anti-EBNA-1 may be the sole antibody produced, this would allow for viral persistence. In situations where other antigens are expressed, for example in infectious mononucleosis or other EBV-associated malignancies, memory/activated T-cells appear to be important in limiting cell expansion and in targeting productively infected cells that express lytically related antigens. Immunological data suggest that vaccines designed to control primary EBV infection, a desirable objective in view of its carcinogenic role in humans, may profit by

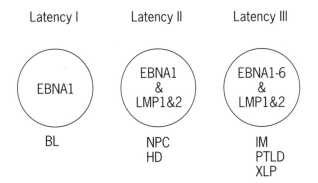

Figure 8 Patterns of latency gene expression in categories designated Latency I–III. BL = Burkitt's lymphoma; NPC = nasopharyngeal carcinoma; HD = Hodgkin's disease; IM = infectious mononucleosis; PTLD = post-transplant lymphoproliferative disease; XLP = X-linked lymphoproliferative disease (from Khanna *et al.*, 1999).

Table 5 Patterns of latent EBV gene expression[a]

Type of latency	Gene product	Co-stimulatory molecules	Examples
IA	EBERs, EBNAI, CSTs		Burkitt's lymphoma
IB	EBERs, EBNA1, CSTs LMP2A		Gastric carcinoma
II	EBERs, EBNA1, CSTs, LMP1, 2A, 2B, BARF1	CD30 CD23 CD40 B7.1 LFA-1, -3 1CAM-1	Hodgkin disease Nasopharyngeal carcinoma T cell lymphoma
III	EBERs, EBNA 1–4, 6 LP, LMP-1, 2A, 2B	CD30 CD23 CD40 CD44 B7.1 LFA-1, -3 1CAM-1	Post-transplant lympho proliferative disorder Infectious mononucleosis
Other	EBERs, EBNA1, 2		Smooth-muscle tumours

[a]See **Tables 3** and **4** and **Figure 8**.
(From Griffin, 2000, *Mutation Research*, **462**, 395–405.)

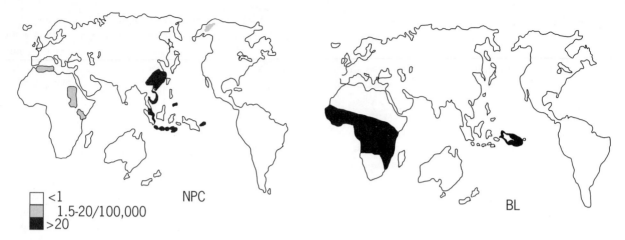

Figure 9   Comparative sites of highest frequencies of nasopharyngeal carcinoma (NPC) and Burkitt's lymphoma (BL), showing their disparate global locations. Black regions are sites of greatest frequencies and grey regions those of intermediate frequencies (for NPCs).

including dominant determinants of antigens associated with the viral life cycle (Khanna *et al.*, 1999). This may be particularly relevant since animal models show that the development of neutralizing antibodies does not always correlate with protection from EBV infection. To this end, many of the dominant epitopes, including those found in latent and some lytically related proteins, have been mapped (**Figure 10**). Some of these might prove of value in the development of cytotoxic T lymphocyte (CTL) epitope-based vaccines, the aim of which would be to reduce morbidity and possibly clear infection. Since evidence suggests that many individuals having EBV-associated tumours retain detectable levels of EBV-specific T cells, needed for surveillance, this may be a reasonable approach. Even for BL, the tumour in which viral gene expression appears most tightly regulated, subpopulations of cells expressing lytically related antigens have been identified in some individuals (Labrecque *et al.*, 1999), making them also candidates for immunotherapeutic approaches. The recognition of the important contribution of EBV to diseases of humans has greatly stimulated efforts over the past few years to control this virus.

KAPOSI SARCOMA-ASSOCIATED HERPESVIRUS (KSHV)

History

In 1872, M. Kaposi, a Hungarian dermatologist, described a pigmented angiosarcoma, now called 'classic' or sporadic Kaposi sarcoma (KS), that mainly affected skin on the lower limbs, and was most prominent in elderly men of Mediterranean and eastern European origin. KS was also an African problem. In the 1960s and 1970s, the frequency and distribution of KS altered, and in many cases could be

related to transplant therapies in other parts of the world. Whereas modest increases in KS were being reported in various countries prior to the onset of the syndromes now covered under the generic name AIDS, its frequency and epidemiology were drastically influenced by the spread of this virus. Over the past decade or so, although the histopathological presentations of all types of KS are identical, this malignancy has been generally subclassified into classic (sporadic), endemic (African), epidemic (AIDS related) and immunosuppression-associated (transplant) types, to reflect its origin. From being a comparatively rare form of cancer, KS is now fairly common in certain parts of the world. Exactly how common, however, is a controversial topic. The epidemiology of this cancer, and particularly the fact that in the early days it was the most common tumour in AIDS patients, with 15–20% of them developing KS, suggested that this disease might have an infectious aetiology (IARC, 1997). Thus, an active search to find such an agent was initiated.

The history of the discovery of KSHV is different from that of EBV, the human virus it most resembles, and owes much to the development of molecular biological methodologies. One of these in particular, called representational difference analysis (RDA), was used by a group in the USA, working with the husband and wife team Moore and Chang (Chang *et al.*, 1994), in their search for a KS infectious agent. RDA consists of generating genomic representative entities from diseased and normal tissues, preferably from the same individual, using PCR amplification. These are stably associated with priming PCR sequences and hybridized to an excess of representative, nonligated amplified sequence, with no attached primers, from normal tissue. Following this procedure, only unique sequences found in the diseased tissues will contain priming sequences on both strands, which allows them to be substrates for subsequent PCR reactions. Repeating such a process enriches the sample for unique sequences.

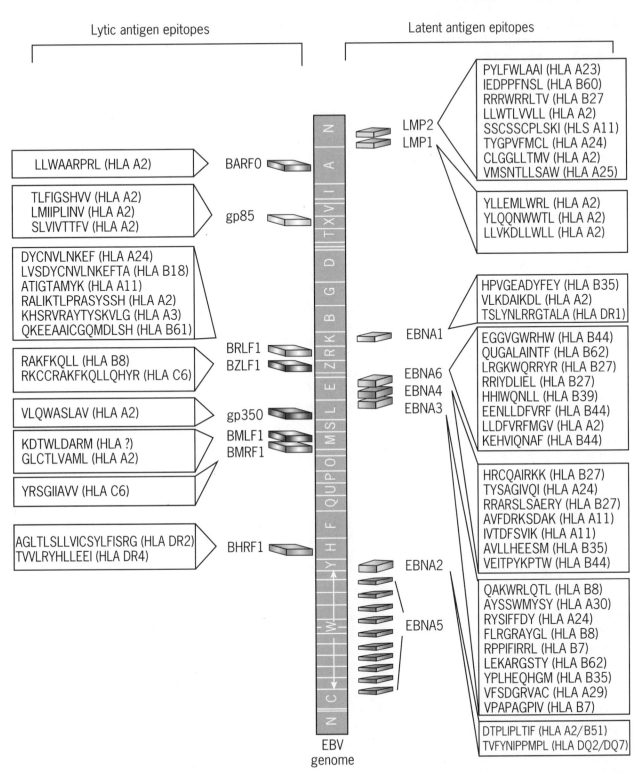

Figure 10 Schematic distribution of HLA class I and class II restricted cytotoxic T lymphocyte epitopes with EBV latent and lytic antigens, at the peptide level. BARF0, the largest ORF in the CST transcripts is given here as a lytic function, although it is also expressed during the latent cycle. (Adapted from Khanna *et al.*, 1999.)

These can then be purified and their sequences determined. By RDA, using tissues from AIDS-associated KS, Chang *et al.* (1994) identified sequences that were homologous with, but distinct from, other members of the γ-herpesvirus family, most notably EBV and the oncogenic primate virus, herpesvirus saimiri. They correctly concluded, as was subsequently shown, that this work was consistent with the presence of a new human herpesvirus in KS lesions. Interestingly, the homologies they identified were with EBV late viral genes (in *BDLF1* and *BcLF1*, see EBV section).

Virion and Genome Structure

KSHV, or HHV8, has morphological features typical of herpesviruses (**Figure 7**), consisting of 100–150 nm particles surrounded by a lipid envelope, with an internal electron-rich central core. Its DNA was assessed by pulsed-field electrophoresis as 160–170 kb, consistent with that of other γ-herpesviruses, but more uniform than that observed with EBV. Both circular and linear forms of KSHV have been identified. Larger genomes reported to exist in some tumour-derived cell lines have been shown to result from DNA duplications, possibly associated with propagation in culture. In the same year, 1996, as the physical studies were reported, the complete sequence of the viral genome was published and an open reading frame map generated. This aptly illustrates the rapidity with which this field was being and has progressed. The sequence study (Russo, 1996) showed that the structure of KSHV was essentially similar to that of herpesvirus saimiri (HVS) (**Figure 5**). For KSHV, the genome has a single 140.5-kb long unique region, containing about 80 ORFs, flanked on either side by variable-length terminal repeats, about 800 bp in size. Within the genome, there were small repeat regions, some but not all of which appeared to be within ORFs, but overall there was little organisational similarity to EBV. In addition to numerous homologies with HVS, the sequence of KSHV also showed homologies with EBV genes, mainly those coding for late viral antigens where similarities that ranged from 44% to greater than 70% were observed. With EBV late genes, *BDLF1* and *BcLF1*, identified in the initial studies of Chang *et al.* (1994), the degree of homology at the DNA level was about 75%. Interestingly, the important viral DNA polymerases of these two viruses have 72% homology, although whether the enzymes themselves can be functionally interchanged is not known.

Although homologies between KSHV and EBV immediate early functions were observed, there were no homologues to EBV latent genes found in the ORFs of KSHV. Different isolates of KSHV appear to have highly conserved genomes. The phylogenetic tree of KSHV, based on aligned amino acid sequences as they relate to other herpesviruses, is shown in **Figure 11**. A close relationship with HVS, from squirrel monkeys (not apparently oncogenic in its natural host but tumorigenic to other nonhuman primates), and with equine herpesvirus 2 (with a more distant relationship with EBV) is seen (IARC, 1997).

Putative Key Tumour Genes

Studies on KSHV genes, to designate them as latent, immediate early, early and late genes, and identify those

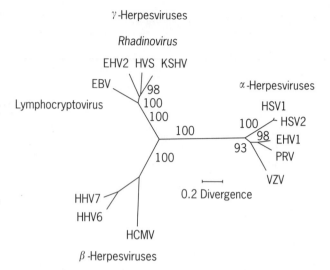

Figure 11 Phylogenetic tree of KSHV (HHV8) in relation to other herpesviruses. The comparison shows KSHV to be most closely related to the γ-herpesviruses, EBV, equine herpesvirus 2 (EHV2) and herpesvirus saimiri (HVS), its nearest relative (see **Figure 5**). (From IARC, 1997, p. 385.)

that may play key roles in the oncogenic activity of this virus, have been initiated. Here, as with other herpesviruses, latent transcripts are defined as constitutively expressed mRNAs which are not susceptible to chemical induction (e.g. with agents such as the promoter-stimulating phorbol ester (TPA) or n-butyrate, which affects chromatin structure) but are susceptible to inhibition by cycloheximide, an inhibitor of protein synthesis. Immediate early genes, on the other hand, are those whose transcripts are inducible, but resistant to the action of cycloheximide. Early gene expression is blocked by cycloheximide, but not by phosphonoacetic acid (PAA), an inhibitor of the virus-encoded DNA polymerase, whereas late lytic cycle gene expression is not blocked by the latter (Sun *et al.*, 1999). The same definitions are used when considering EBV genes. In the case of KSHV, many apparently nonlatent genes have been found expressed in the virally associated tumours (see below), and the same is becoming apparent for EBV. Their roles in these settings are still undefined. Lines derived from primary effusion lymphoma (PEL) cells infected with KSHV have proved useful in identifying some of the genes in KSHV that act as possible tumour-inducing agents. Several of these (ORF 71–73, see below) classified as latent genes since their transcription products are constitutively expressed, are clustered in the viral genome. Notably, a completely different gene designation system from that for EBV has been adopted for KSHV based on gene numbers from the sequence.

LANA (latency associated antigen (ORF 73): a large (226/234-kDa) protein that reacts with sera from AIDS patients, characterized by a typical speckled nuclear pattern. Antibodies to LANA have been postulated to have prognostic value for the likelihood of an individual developing KS. They do not cross-react with EBV-specific antigens.

v-FLIP (ORF 71): so named because of its homology with a cellular anti-apoptotic factor, c-FLIP, which regulates the apoptosis triggered by Fas and other members of this tumour necrosis factor receptor family. In KSHV, these genes are overlapping and probes for v-FLIP also recognize LANA, but not vice versa (Sun *et al.*, 1999). Notably, HVS also expresses a v-FLIP, which appears to be a late function. Interestingly, probes for v-FLIP also recognize a lytic cycle transcript.

ORF K72: tentatively identified as a latent function, with about 30% amino acid homology to the human cellular cyclin, D2, and expressed in persistently infected cells alongside LANA and v-FLIP. In culture, K72 (alternatively, KSHV v-cyclin), phosphorylates the retinoblastoma protein, Rb. K72 is a small ORF (60 amino acids), and may also be transcribed during the lytic cycle thus, like v-FLIP, possibly playing more than one role related to its associated malignancies, in the virus.

In addition to these three apparently latent genes, numerous viral genes associated with later stages of the viral life cycle have also been identified in the sarcomas. One of the immediate early KHVS genes is structurally and functionally related to an EBV-transactivator gene. In functional assays in culture, this viral gene has been found competent to initiate reactivation of a cascade of genes associated with the virus lytic cycle. KSHV also encodes a number of homologues of proinflammatory cytokines, such as IL-6 and macrophage inflammatory protein (MIP), as well as *bcl-2*, a homologue of another anti-apoptotic gene (also found in EBV, in *BHRF1*) and v-GCR, a G protein-coupled receptor. By definition, several of these appear to act as late genes, but to be expressed in tumours.

At this stage in the understanding of KSHV and its role in malignancy, temporal expression of tumour-associated genes thus seems to differ in large part from that of EBV, where the dominant components are latent genes. Whether latent gene expression in tumours may also dominate in the case with KSHV remains to be seen. Data suggesting that KSHV may express proteins related to the membrane-associated oncogenes of EBV, LMP1 and 2A have been obtained (Glenn *et al.*, 1999). For KSHV, on the other hand, it has been proposed that tumour growth may be enhanced by viral chemokines or cytokines expressed by adjacent infected cells that have undergone a switch from latency to a lytic cycle type, giving to such genes an important role in malignancy (Ganem, 1998). Notably, a similar situation exists for some EBV-associated BLs (see above), and may account for the proliferation of this tumour with its remarkable doubling times of 28–60 h.

Many of the studies on gene expression in KSHV are currently being made on PEL cell lines, since growth of cells in culture from KS often results in apparent loss of the viral genome. Whether PEL lines are suitable models for KSHV expression in tumour settings remains to be seen. Like lymphoblastoid cell lines as a model for the role of EBV in BL, they may be imperfect, but nonetheless of value for studying the function of the viral genes.

Pathogenesis

Attempts to detect KSHV in peripheral blood mononuclear cells (PBMCs) from healthy individuals in countries with a low prevalence of KS, even by very sensitive PCR approaches, has not been generally successful. In KS-risk countries, variable associations of the virus with PBMCs have been reported. On the assumption that KSHV may be sexually transmitted, studies on semen specimens have also been carried out, with controversial results. However, sexual behaviour does seem to be a risk factor in transmission of this virus and in the development of KS, the risk running parallel to that of HIV infection. The notion of a KS-associated infectious agent, independent of HIV infection, appears to be real, in that the virus has been identified in all four epidemiological forms of KS, with no significant differences in detection rates (IARC, 1997). In addition to an association with KS, another neoplastic condition, primary effusion lymphoma, a rare, distinct type of non-Hodgkin lymphoma, has also been associated with KSHV infection. The cells in this malignancy are usually large and irregularly shaped, with abundant cytoplasm, and prominent nucleoli and mitotic features, the latter properties also found in BL. Notably, both KSHV and EBV can often be identified in these tumours. In AIDS patients, this is a fulminant lymphoproliferation and the median survival time of the individual is short. Other B and T cell lymphomas, explored for its presence, have not revealed any KSHV. On the other hand, there is evidence for a role for this virus in Castelman disease, at least in AIDS patients. This is a rare, usually polyclonal, non-neoplastic disorder of unknown aetiology, first reported in 1956.

Several scenarios could account for the association of KSHV with these tumours, particularly with KS. First, the virus may be the aetiological agent, and one or more of the functions noted above, or other as yet undiscovered viral gene products, may play a critical role in disease. On the other hand, as often suggested for EBV, the virus may be a contributory factor to the malignancy, e.g. by stimulating cytokines which enhance cell growth. Alternatively, the virus may be a mere passenger with the capacity to infect the cell types now associated with tumours that harbour it. Again, as with EBV, it is difficult to distinguish among these possible scenarios. With both viruses, the fact that viral homologues exist in other primates, which in model studies are shown to produce tumours, can be viewed as supportive evidence for these herpesviruses as acting both risk factors and tumour-inducing agents, under the appropriate conditions.

HEPATITIS B VIRUS (HBV)

History

Jaundice (from *jaune*) is a disease of the liver that has been known for centuries. Its most notable characteristic is an orange–yellow discoloration of the skin and conjunctivae, caused by deposition of elevated levels of bilirubin produced from damaged hepatocytes. Viral hepatitis, a general term for infections of the liver, can be caused by a number of hepatitis viruses, only one of which, HBV, is classified as a DNA virus. HBV is an unusual DNA virus in that it has, as a component of its life cycle, an RNA reverse transcriptase activity, a function normally associated with RNA retroviruses. The mechanism of HBV replication is unique for a DNA virus, in that it involves an RNA intermediate. HBV has a striking tropism for hepatocytes, but also can be detected in PBMCs.

Although viral hepatitis is a major public health problem, the identification of its viral association(s) and of HBV as one of the infectious agents of the disease was long in coming. Prior to its ultimate discovery, epidemiological differences among the diseases had suggested the possible existence of more than one infectious agent. In the early 1960s, Blumberg, looking for inherited polymorphic traits in blood from different parts of the world, identified an antigen, subsequently designated as 'Australia antigen', in sera from an Australian aborigine which reacted specifically with an antibody found in serum from an American haemophilia patient. This antigen proved to be geographically restricted, being relatively rare in American and Western European individuals, but more common in African or Asian populations, and in patients with certain distinct pathologies, including leukaemia, leprosy and Down syndrome. The association of Australia antigen, now known as hepatitis B surface antigen (HBsAg), with viral hepatitis was made several years later. This seminal finding led others to undertake studies aimed at identifying the infectious agent. In 1970, Dane and colleagues first identified, by EM, virus-like particles in the sera of patients with Australia antigen-associated hepatitis (Dane *et al.*, 1970). At this time, it was estimated that of the 3.5 billion people in the world, as many as 175 million might be carriers of HBV. In spite of the millions of viral carriers, the cancer now associated with HBV, hepatocellular carcinoma (HCC), is relatively uncommon, but nonetheless correlates in frequency with those parts of the world with the highest percentages of carriers of the virus, and possibly reflects a progressive disease, initiated by hepatocyte infection and proceeding through the development of chronic hepatitis, to tumour formation.

HBV is the prototype for a family of viruses, now called the Hepadnaviridae, found in woodchucks, ground and tree squirrels and Peking ducks, all sharing distinctive morphologies and genomic characteristics. Studies on these viruses lend support for a causal relationship between HBV and some liver cancers. In particular, the duck hepatitis virus has been associated with the development of hepatoma in its host. The Working Party dealing with the association between HBV and cancer (IARC, 1994) concluded that chronic infection with hepatitis B is carcinogenic to humans. It reached the same conclusion with regard to the RNA virus, hepatitis C (HCV). In making this judgment, several criteria for causality were used, one being that a strong association, as found with the hepatitis viruses, is a better indicator of causality than a weak association.

Virion Structure and the Virus Life Cycle

The HB infectious virion is a 42-nm double-shelled spherical particle (originally called the Dane particle) that consists of an outer envelope composed of HBsAg and an inner core, or nucleocapsid, with its own antigens, hepatitis B core (HBcAg) and e (HBeAg), antigens, together with HBsAg, acting as markers for the presence of intact virions and infectivity. Infectious virions also contain a small (3.2-kb) circular, partially single-stranded DNA, and an endogenous DNA polymerase that can produce a fully double-stranded genome. Electron microsopic (EM) analyses show that in patient's sera, however, the concentrations of incomplete HBsAg structures may exceed those of complete virions. One of these forms is a small (20–25 nm) spherical particle and the other(s) is a tubular or filamentous form varying in size from 20×20–200 nm. Structures of these particles are schematically illustrated in **Figure 12**. Interestingly, similar shaped tubular (or filamentous particles) are also seen in early EM pictures of the small DNA papovaviruses, where they have been postulated to represent precursor forms of the mature, virion spherical particles, although this has not been proved. Interestingly, the major capsid protein, VP1, of papova viruses, expressed on its own *in vitro*, spontaneously reassembles to form viral-like capsid particles, composed of icosohedral (major product) and tubular (minor product) structures.

The site of primary replication of HBV is the liver, although it has been postulated, based on abnormalities observed in patients with acute hepatitis, that haematopoietic stem cells many also support viral replication. HBV infection probably involves viral attachment to specific receptors, although these have not been identified, nor have mechanisms for attachment and penetration been elucidated. Recent data suggest that HBV nucleocapsids do not enter the nucleus. Rather, they are arrested at the membrane and release the partially single-stranded genomic DNA into the nucleus where it is converted to covalently closed-circular (CCC) double-stranded DNA, which in turn serves as the viral transcription template.

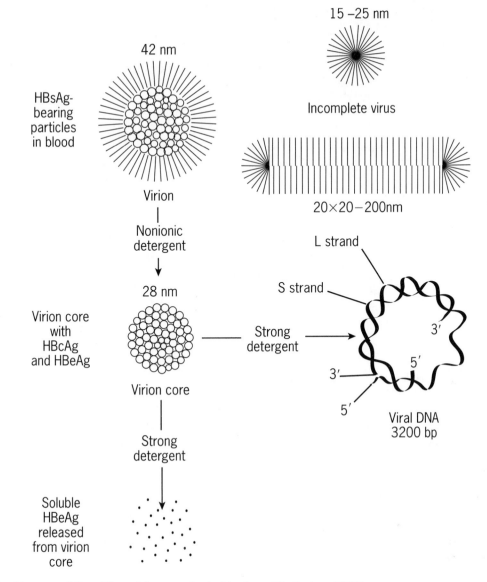

Figure 12   Diagram of the different forms adopted by hepatitis B virus (HBV).

Genome Structure, Replication and Antigens

The viral genome is organized into four transcription units, each with its own independent promoter. They share, however, a common polyadenylation site. Transcription yields four extensively overlapping viral RNAs, with sizes of 3.5, 2.4, 2.1 and 0.7 kb. These are exported into the cytoplasm where viral proteins are translated, and viral particle assembly and genome replication occurs (Chisari, 2000). HBV replication involves reverse transcription of the RNA pregenome (pRNA) to produce minus-strand DNA, the template for plus-strand DNA. Replication results in an encapsidated double-stranded open circular genome that is either recycled back to the the nucleus (to amplify the pool of CCC-DNA) or becomes enveloped by the viral protein and

proceeds to complete the life cycle, as illustrated in **Figure 13**. The transcriptional products themselves are complex.

The 3.5-kb transcript: specifies viral genes reversibly transcribed as a first step in genome replication. The POL protein has numerous activities, acting as reverse transcriptase, DNA polymerase and RNase H, all essential functions for viral replication. The core protein (HBcAg) can form homodimers that self-assemble into capsid particles. In the cytoplasm, these also contain pregenomic viral RNA and POL, and the whole particle acts as the site for viral replication. The precore protein has a sequence that directs it to the endoplasmic reticulum (ER), where it undergoes limited proteolysis to produce the e antigen (HBeAg) which is secreted into the plasma membrane. Its role in the viral life cycle, in spite of its obvious importance, is still poorly understood.

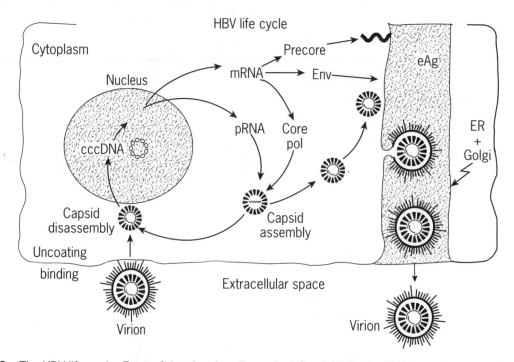

Figure 13   The HBV life cycle. Entry of the virus is still poorly defined. While the RNA containing capsid is maturing into a DNA-containing capsid, it migrates bidirectionally within the cytoplasm. One pathway terminates at the endopasmic reticulum (ER), where it interacts with envelope proteins which trigger an internal budding reaction, resulting in the formation of virions that are transported out of the cell by the default secretory pathway. The second pathway transports the maturing capsid to the nucleus to amplify the pool of covalently closed circular (CCC) DNA. (Adapted from Chisari, 2000.)

The 2.4- and 2.1-kb transcripts: produce the large, middle and small envelope proteins, which share common carboxy termini. The small, but major, transcript encodes the hepatitis B surface antigen (HBsAg). The middle and large transcripts which encode preS-2 and preS-1 antigens, respectively have amino acid extensions. The envelope proteins are cotranslationally inserted into ER membranes, where they aggregate, bud into the lumen and then are secreted by the cell as 22 nm subviral particles (**Figures 12** and **13**) or, if they have enveloped nucleocapsids before budding, become 42 nm infectious virions. The filamentous particles are generated when the large envelope protein is overexpressed. These are not usually secreted, but rather give an histologically distinct appearance (like 'ground glass') to cells, and hypersensitize them to the cytopathic effects of interferon-γ.

The 0.7-kb transcript: encodes the transactivator X protein. In the woodchuck model, the X protein is required to initiate infection. By virtue of its ability to transactivate expression of other genes, X is generally considered to be an important contributor to the pathologies induced by HBV. It was earlier thought to have properties associated with cell transformation and, on overexpression in transgenic mice, it can induce a high baseline incidence of HCC. However, in spite of considerable interest in X, its precise role *in vivo* still seems to

be far from thoroughly characterized and its function as an oncogene has been called into question.

A transcriptional map of HBV, showing antigen locations, is given in **Figure 14**.

Pathogenesis

The natural history, clinical manifestations and geographical variation (as illustrated in **Figure 15**) of HBV infection, are highly variable. Chronic infection with HBV as related to endemicity, geography and mode and time of infection is given in **Table 6** and a brief resumé of the pathological consequences of infection in **Figure 16**. Serological patterns that accompany acute and chronic infections are given in **Figure 17**.

In spite of the wealth of knowledge that has been generated on this virus, the mechanism(s) by which HBV induces cellular transformation remains largely obscure. No viral oncogenes have been identified, and most or all of the viral antigens appear to be primarily involved in one or other aspect of the virus life cycle. In the woodchuck model, the X protein (see above) has been associated with infection. One promising lead on pathogenesis lies in the fact that HBV has a high mutation rate, which, although 100–1000 times lower than that observed with RNA

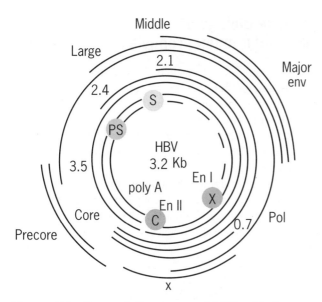

Figure 14 Transcriptional map of HBV, with the partially double-stranded 3.2-kb open circular genome present in virions shown in the centre. The core (C) pre-S (PS), HBs (S) and HBx (X) promoters are given inside round icons. (Adapted from Chisari, 2000.)

viruses, is nonetheless many times greater than normally seen with DNA viruses (IARC, 1994). However, although many HBV gene mutants have been identified and investigated, none to date has been proved beyond reasonable doubt to confer oncogenicity on the gene in question. Alternatively, in hepatocytes, HBV integrates into the host chromosome, giving rise to the possibility of insertional mutagenesis. Viral genome insertions in HCC have not, however, proved specific, nor have they been instrumental in pointing to insertional mutagenesis as explaining a viral role in HCC. The ability of X protein to affect expression of other genes allows for the possibility of either enhancement of expression of cellular genes associated with transformation, or down-regulation of tumour-suppressor genes, but has led to no definitive answers. Although approaches which consist of both direct and indirect influences on aberrant cell growth have been explored, and have generated interesting but frequently conflicting, data, the molecular route(s) by which hepadnaviruses predispose their host to malignancy remains an open question. There will probably be no simple answers, and one or more of the pathways that have been explored to date may play a role in diseases associated with this virus.

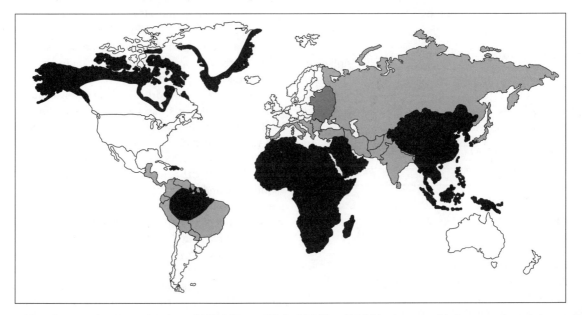

Figure 15 Geographical distribution of HBV. (From IARC, 1994, p. 56.) Black areas: high; grey areas: intermediate; white areas: low. (See **Table 6**.)

Table 6 Chronic infection with HBV: geography, mode and time

Endemicity	Geographical area	Predominant time of infection
High, ≥8%	China, Southeast Asia, Pacific Basin, sub-Saharan Africa, Amazon Basin	Perinatal, childhood
Intermediate, 2–7%	East, central and southern Europe, Middle East, South Asia, Japan	Perinatal, childhood, adulthood
Low, <2%	North America, western Europe, Australia, southern Latin America	Adulthood

(Taken from IARC, 1994, p. 59.)

Hepatitis B virus

- Hepatotropic, noncytopathic, 3.2-kb circular DNA
- Acute, chronic hepatitis, hepatocellular carcinoma (HCC)
- Over 2 billion people infected
- Over 350 million people chronically infected
- 100-fold increased risk (40% lifetime risk) of HCC
- Over 1 million deaths each year

Figure 16   HBV, disease association and frequencies. (Adapted from Chisari, 2000.)

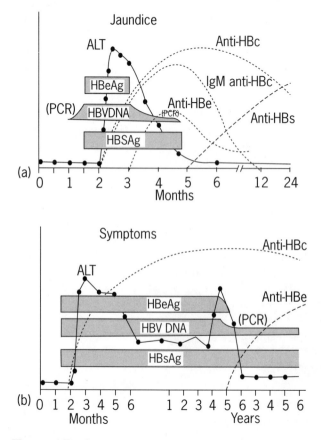

Figure 17   Serological and molecular patterns of HBV expression in (a) acute and (b) chronic HBV infections. Hatched bars show patterns of antigen expression; broken lines indicate periods in which HBV DNA (as noted) is detectable by PCR. Expression of alanine aminotransferase (ALT) used as control. (From IARC, 1994, p. 60.)

A hypothesis, following on from infection through to chronic illness and HCC, as outlined in **Figure 18** (Chisari *et al.*, 2000), draws on all the factors noted above, and others, in predicting a course for disease. Such a complex scenario would emphasize the need for more than viral surveillance for the eradication of HCC.

Immune Biology of HBV and Immunoprophylaxis

The host–cell interactions that allow for the persistence of a virus, and the failure of the immune system to eliminate it in an immunocompetent individual, is a topic of considerable relevance for the DNA tumour virus field. For largely noncytopathic viruses, such as HPV, EBV, KSHV and HBV, they must either overwhelm an effective immune response or adopt mechanisms that allow for avoidance, as suggested by one or more of the hypothesized routes for progression from infection to generation of hepatocellular carcinoma (**Figure 18**). One approach for EBV therapy, as discussed elsewhere, assumes that the immune system may need to, and can, be stimulated specifically to recognize viral genes that might be expressed in its associated tumours, with beneficial effects. As noted, however, realistically such an approach is aimed at reducing morbidity, rather than effecting cure (Khanna *et al.*, 1999). Such an approach may be even more valid for HBV, which can infect virtually all the hepatocytes in the liver, suggesting that the number of infected cells might actually outnumber relevant antigen-specific T-cells by several orders of magnitude in acute hepatitis infections and HCC. Thus, in individual situations where there are not sufficient cytotoxic T cells to contain infection, stimulation of the immune system might prove effective. On the other hand, there are studies to suggest that in some individuals with acute hepatitis, even in the presence of a vigorous T cell response, not all virus may be cleared. This has been explored using sensitive PCR assays where, several decades after complete clinical and serological recovery from this disease, low levels of viral DNA were detected in sera and PBMCs in some cases. Whether this result represents individuals at risk of reinfection and/or developing HCC for other, possibly genetic reasons, remains to be assessed. Notably, in HBV vaccine studies in Taiwan on children of different ethnic origins, unidentified host factors were postulated to explain the hyporesponsiveness seen among some populations (Hsu, 1996).

For HBV, it was earlier demonstrated that serum containing HBsAg retained its immunogenic properties even after heat inactivation. This observation proved the basis for plasma-derived, and later recombinant, s-antigen vaccines against HBV. In the 1980s, large-scale vaccination studies on children were initiated in both Taiwan and China, countries with the highest rates of HBV endemicity in the world, with the reasonable expectations that universal childhood immunization would allow HBV infections to be controlled in these areas within a few generations. In some high-risk areas, vaccination programmes to immunize every newborn child have been initiated and subsequent HCC incidence in these areas is being carefully monitored. As this malignancy, as with

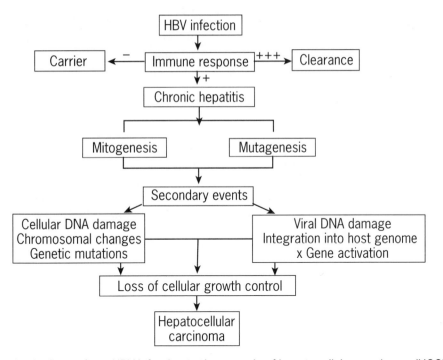

Figure 18   Hypothesis. Route from HBV infection to the genesis of hepatocellular carcinoma (HCC). (Adapted from Chisari, 2000.)

EBV-associated NPC, is mainly confined to adult populations, the data on this topic are not yet available. However, in Taiwan 10 years on, for children who completed a complete course of vaccination (four doses), anti-HBV antigen antibodies were detectable in a high proportion (82%) of them. Interestingly, in China it has now been found that tree shrews (*Tupaia belangeri chinenesis*) can be infected with human HBV and the infection passed to offspring in a high proportion of cases. Thus, a useful model may evolve for studying many of the unanswered questions about the relationship of HBV infection, the development of HCC and the variable responses to vaccination that have been observed.

OTHER DNA VIRUSES

Studies on growth changes in cells in culture or tumours produced by other DNA viruses in model (frequently immunoincompetent) animals, or their isolation from human tumours, have led to their tentative assignment as oncogenic, or potentially oncogenic, viruses. These include the ubiquitous human Polyomavirus, BK, that has been detected in brain tumours of different histological types, and also in KS, osteosarcomas and kidney carcinomas. Another human Polyomavirus, JC, causally associated with a pathological condition, PML (progressive multifocal leucoencephalopathy), has also been explored with regard to tumour formation. Both BK and JC encode large T antigens (LTs) that are related to that of SV40, and *in vitro* their genes stimulate cell growth (Barbanti-Brodano *et al.*, 1998).

However, any significance in malignant growth in humans has not yet been established, although BK remains a candidate human oncogenic virus. The Adenoviruses, of which there are many distinct strains, have genes (*E1A* and *E1B*) that act as oncogenes in culture, interacting with tumour-suppressor genes. They, particularly, Ad12, can induce tumour formation, at least in animal models. Likewise, the human herpesvirus 6 (HHV-6) can transform mouse and human epidermal keratinocytes in culture, generating cell lines that are tumorigenic in athymic mice. Herpes-simplex virus (HSV) sequences have been found in human cervical cancer, but research on this topic was curtailed with the more definitive discovery of papillomaviruses in this malignancy. To date, roles for neither HSV nor HHV-6 in human malignancies have been established. The best evidence for viral causation of human malignancies appears to lie with the four DNA viruses dealt with in detail above, and with some of the RNA viruses, considered elsewhere, although it would be unwise to assume that other, undiscovered, candidate human oncogenic viruses do not exist. Newer, more sensitive methods of analysis make the discovery of novel cancer-related viruses a challenging research field.

REFERENCES

Arrand, J. R. (1994). Molecular genetics of human papillomaviruses. In: Stem, P. L. and Stanley, M. A. (eds), *Human Papillomavirus and Cervical Cancer: Biology and Immunology.* Chap. 2, 28–40. Oxford Medical Publications, Oxford.

Baer, R., *et al*. (1984). DNA sequence and expression of the B95-8 Epstein–Barr virus genome. *Nature*, **310**, 207–211.

Barbanti-Brodano, G., *et al*. (1998). BK and JC human polyoma viruses and simian virus 40: natural history of infection in humans, experimental oncogenicity and association with human tumors. *Advances in Virus Research*, **50**, 69–99.

Chang, Y., *et al*. (1994). Identification of herpesvirus-like DNA sequences in AIDS-associated Kaposi's sarcoma. *Science*, **266**, 1865–1869.

Chisari, F. V. (2000). Viruses, immunity and cancer: lessons from hepatitis B. *American Journal of Pathology*, **156**, 1118–1132.

Chow, L. T. and Broker, T. R. (1994). Papillomavirus DNA replication. *Intervirology*, **37**, 150–158.

Dane, D. S., *et al*. (1970). Virus-like particles in serum of patients with Australia-antigen-associated hepatitis. *Lancet*, **1**, 695–698.

Frazer, I. H. (1996). Immunology of papillomavirus infection. *Current Opinion in Immunology*, **8**, 484–491.

Ganem, D. (1998). Human herpesvirus 8 and its role in the genesis of Kaposi's sarcoma. *Current Clinical Topics in Infectious Diseases*, **18**, 237–251.

Glenn, M., *et al*. (1999). Identification of a spliced gene from Kaposi's sarcoma-associated herpesvirus encoding a protein with similarities to latent membrane proteins 1 and 2A of Epstein–Barr virus. *Journal of Virology*, **73**, 6953–6963.

Griffin, B. E. (1998). Relation of Burkitt's tumor-associated herpes-type virus to infectious mononucleosis. *Reviews in Medical Virology*, **8**, 61–66.

Griffin, B. E. (2000). Epstein–Barr virus (EBV) and human disease: facts, opinions and problems. *Mutation Research*, **462**, 395–405.

Griffin, B. E. and Xue, S.-A. (1998). Epstein–Barr virus infections and their association with human malignancies: some key questions. *Annals of Medicine*, **30**, 249–259.

Hagensee, M. E., *et al*. (1994). Three-dimensional structure of vaccinia virus produced human papillomavirus type 1 capsids. *Journal of Virology*, **68**, 4503–4505.

Hitt, M. M., *et al*. (1989). EBV gene expression in an NPC tumor. *EMBO Journal*, **8**, 2639–2651.

Howley, P. M. (1996). Papillomavirinae and their replication. In: Fields, B. N., *et al*. (eds), *Virology*, 3rd edn. Chap. 65, 2045–2076 (Lippincott-Raven, Philadelphia).

Hsu, L. C. (1996). Ethnic differences in immune responses to hepatitis B vaccine. *American Journal of Epidemiology*, **143**, 718–724.

IARC (1994). *Hepatitis Viruses*, Monograph **59** (IARC, Lyon).

IARC (1995). *Human Papillomaviruses*, Monograph **64** (IARC, Lyon).

IARC (1997). *Epstein–Barr Virus and Kaposi's Sarcoma Herpesvirus/Human Herpesvirus 8*, Monograph **70** (IARC, Lyon).

Khanna, R., *et al*. (1999). Vaccine strategies against Epstein–Barr virus-associated diseases: lessons from studies on cytotoxic T-cell-mediated immune regulation. *Immunological Review*, **170**, 49–64.

Labrecque, L. G., *et al*. (1999). Expression of Epstein–Barr virus lytically related genes in African Burkitt's lymphoma: correlation with patient response to therapy. *International Journal of Cancer*, **81**, 6–11.

Leight, E. R. and Sugden, B. (2000). EBNA-1: a protein pivotal to latent infection by Epstein–Barr virus. *Reviews in Medical Virology*, **10**, 83–100.

Morse, S. S. (1993). *Emerging Viruses* (Oxford University Press, Oxford).

Nakagawa, M., *et al*. (1997). Cytotoxic T lymphocyte responses to E6 and E7 proteins of human papillomavirus type 16: relationship to cervical intraepithelial neoplasia. *Journal of Infectious Diseases*, **175**, 927–931.

Pfister, H. and Fuchs, P. G. (1994). Anatomy, taxonomy and evolution of Papillomaviruses. *Intervirology*, **37**, 143–149.

Russo, J. J. (1996). Nucleotide sequence of the Kaposi's sarcoma-associated herpesvirus (HHV 8). *Proceedings of the National Academy of Sciences of the USA*, **93**, 14862–14867.

Shah, K. V. (1990). Biology of human genital tract papillomaviruses. In: Holmes, K. G., *et al*. (eds), *Sexually Transmitted Diseases*, 2nd edn. Chap. 37, 425–431 (McGraw-Hill, New York).

Shah, K. V. and Howley, P. M. (1996). Papillomaviruses. In: Fields, B. N., *et al*. (eds), *Virology*, 3rd edn. Chap. 66, 2077–2109 (Lippincott-Raven, Philadelphia).

Stöppler, H., *et al*. (1994). Transforming proteins of the papillomaviruses. *Intervirology*, **37**, 168–179.

Sun, R., *et al*. (1999). Kinetics of Kaposi's sarcoma-associated herpesvirus gene expression. *Journal of Virology*, **73**, 2232–2242.

Tarpey, I., *et al*. (1994). Human cytotoxic T lymphocytes stimulated by endogenously processed human papillomavirus type 11 E7 recognize a peptide containing a HLA-A2 (A*0201) motif. *Immunology*, **81**, 222–227.

Van Ranst, M., *et al*. (1992). Phylogenetic classification of human papillomavirus: Correlation with clinical manifestations. *Journal of General Virology*, **68**, 4503–4505.

FURTHER READING

Arrand, J. R. and Harper, D. R. (1998). *Viruses and Human Cancer*. (BIOS Scientific Publishers, Oxford).

Boshoff, C. (1998). Kaposi's sarcoma associated herpesvirus. In: Newton, R., *et al*. (eds), *Cancer Surveys* 33. Infections and Human Cancer.157–190. (Imperial Cancer Research Fund, London).

Evans, A. S. and Kaslow, R. A. (eds) (1997). *Viral Infections of Humans. Epidemiology and Control*, 4th edn. (Plenum Medical Books, New York).

Fields, B. N., *et al*. (eds) (1996). *Fields Virology*, 3rd edn, Vol. 2. (Lippincott-Raven, Philadelpia).

Reitz, M. S., *et al*. (1999). Perspectives on Kaposi's sarcoma: facts, concepts and conjectures. *Journal of the National Cancer Institute*, **91**, 1453–1458.

Rezza, G., *et al.* (1999). Human herpesvirus 8 seropositivity and risk of Kaposi's sarcoma and other acquired immunodeficiency syndrome-related diseases. *Journal of the National Cancer Institute*, **91**, 1468–1474.

Yan, R. Q., *et al.* (1996). Human hepatitis B virus and hepatocellular carcinoma. I. Experimental infection of tree shrews with hepatitis virus. *Journal of Cancer Research and Clinical Oncology*, **122**, 283–288.

Websites

The human papillomavirus database: http://hpv-web.lanl.gov.

Virus databases on-line: http://www.ncbi.nlm.nih.gov/ICTV; http://www.ncbi.nlm.nih.gov/htbin-post/Taxonomy; http://www.virology.net.

Chapter 6

RNA Viruses

Mitsuaki Yoshida
Banyu Tsukuba Research Institute, Tsukuba, Ibaraki, Japan

CONTENTS

GENERAL DESCRIPTION OF RNA TUMOUR VIRUSES

Introduction

It is well established that tumour formation proceeds through multiple steps, each of which consists of mutation and selection of the mutated cells. Various signals for induction of cellular proliferation and fixation of the abnormal phenotypes by genetic mutation promote cellular conversion into a more malignant state. External cellular signals are transduced into the nucleus through multiple pathways and finally induce specific gene expression and cellular responses. Genetic alterations of these signalling pathways, transcriptional machinery or the target genes themselves are the origin of cancers.

Infection by some specific viruses represents one of these genetic alterations and triggers these multiple-step processes for the final induction of specific cancers in both animals and humans. In human cancers, the real causes of the cancers are mostly unknown, and therefore there is no effective way to diagnose healthy individuals who will develop cancers in their near future. This is possible, however, when the cancers result from specific viral infection since the virus carriers are easily identified by their antibodies against specific viruses. Such situations provide an opportunity not only to prevent the cancers, but also to investigate the mechanism of cancers directly in humans.

As human tumour viruses, human T cell leukaemia virus (HTLV) type 1 (HTLV-1), hepatitis C-type virus (HCV), hepatitis B-type virus (HBV), human papillomavirus (HPV) and Epstein–Barr virus (EBV) are well established. Among these, the first two, HTLV-1 and HCV, are the RNA viruses, i.e. they have RNA as their genomes. These two viruses, however, are classified into unrelated groups, HTLV-1 to the retroviridae and HCV to the flabiviridae, which are different in many respects. In this chapter, retroviruses are the main subject.

Viral Replication

The term RNA tumour viruses generally represents retroviruses that contain reverse transcriptase (RT), which transcribes genomic RNA into DNA upon infection. Cores of the viral particles contain two copies of a single-stranded, positive RNA, Gag protein and reverse transcriptase. The core is enveloped with membrane similar to the plasma membrane of host cells, on which the viral Env (envelope) glycoprotein is exposed. The interaction of the Env protein with a receptor on a target cell membrane is required for infection. Interaction of the Env with the receptor induces membrane fusion between the viral particle and cell, allowing the core to be incorporated into the cell, then the genomic RNA is reverse transcribed into complementary DNA (cDNA) by the particle RT (**Figure 1**). The cDNA is then converted to double-stranded DNA and integrated into the host chromosomal DNA forming a 'provirus.' During these processes, a long terminal repeating sequence (LTR) is formed at both ends which contains many elements essential to viral gene

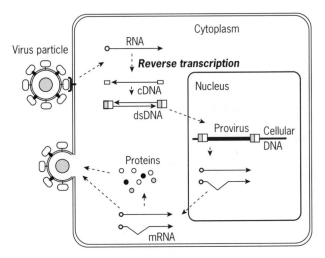

Figure 1   Life cycle of retroviruses.

expression and replication. Details of the mechanism of replication have been reviewed elsewhere (Weiss *et al.*, 1985). Once the proviruses are integrated into germ cells, the retroviruses can be transmitted vertically to successive generations of hosts by transmission of proviral genomes (endogenous viruses), in addition to the standard viral replication and infection (exogenous viruses).

The proviruses are transcribed into RNA by the cellular transcription machinery and a subpopulation of the viral transcripts is spliced into subgenomic mRNA. Both spliced and unspliced viral RNA species are translated into viral proteins; genomic RNA (unspliced RNA) into Gag and Pol proteins and subgenomic RNA into Env protein. The viral proteins and genomic RNA are assembled at specific sites under the plasma membrane into the particles and released by budding. Generally, retroviral replication is not harmful to the host cells except in some cases such as human immunodeficiency virus (HIV). The receptors for a few retroviruses have been identified as membrane proteins, and their expression in many types of cells is consistent with the array of cells at risk of retroviral infection.

Genome Structures and Tumorigenesis

There are two types of retroviral genome; one type carries and the other does not carry host-derived oncogenes (**Figure 2**). Replication-competent retroviruses generally have *gag*, *pol* and *env* genes but do not carry oncogenes. Some of these viruses induce leukaemia or lymphoma after a long latency and are thus called chronic leukaemia viruses. This type of retrovirus induces leukaemia through activation of expression of the adjacent cellular genes by the integrated LTRs. When a provirus is, by chance, integrated in the vicinity of a proto-oncogene and induces abnormal expression of the proto-oncogene it may lead to tumorigenesis. This 'promoter-insertion mechanism of viral carcinogenesis' operates in a variety of tumour systems; *Myc* activation by avian leukaemia virus (ALV) in B cell lymphoma, *erbB* activation by ALV in chicken erythroblastosis and *int1* and *int2* activation by mouse

mammary tumour virus (MMTV) in mouse mammary tumours. Because proviral integration is not site specific, repeated integration through viral replication is usually required before the provirus appears in a tumorigenic site. This explains the long latency after infection for tumorigenesis; however, once it integrates into the right place of the host genome, viral replication is no longer required for tumorigenesis.

Endogenous viruses, which are proviruses vertically transmitted through germ cells, mostly have this type of genome. Many copies of the endogenous viruses are maintained in human cells, as many as thousands in some cases, but they are not very replicative even though they have complete genomes. Various indications of possible participation of endogenous viruses in human cancers have been reported, but, it is still a subject for further study.

The other type of retroviruses carry an oncogene derived from a cellular proto-oncogene (Weiss *et al.*, 1985). Capture of a oncogene in the viral genome, which is derived from host cell DNA, in turn results in a deletion of some portion of the viral genome. Consequently, acute sarcoma/leukaemia viruses are generally replication defective. This type of virus has to be infected together with a chronic leukaemia virus as a 'helper' for their replication. One exception is Rous sarcoma virus, which has the oncogene *src* between *env* and the *3'LTR* and is competent in replication. The viral oncogene of the acute leukaemia viruses is responsible for transformation of infected cells and does not require viral replication or site-specific integration, inducing specific tumours with short latency. In contrast to the broad specificity of retroviral infection *in vitro*, these viruses are able to induce tumours in relatively few tissues *in vivo*. Specificity of retroviral tumorigenesis is restricted by either the class of viral oncogene or the tissue-specific promoter activity of the integrated *LTR*, in addition to the nature of the viral receptors on the host cells.

HUMAN TUMORIGENIC RETROVIRUSES: HTLVs

Human retroviruses include HIV, human endogenous viruses and human foamy viruses. The replication and pathology of HTLV-1 are considered throughout this chapter, but with some exceptions, observations on HTLV-1 are applicable to the other members of the HTLV group (see the following section).

HTLVs and Disease

HTLV-1 is an aetiological factor in adult T cell leukaemia (ATL) (Poeisz *et al.*, 1980; Hinuma *et al.*, 1981; Yoshida *et al.*, 1982). ATL is a unique T cell malignancy with a CD4-positive phenotype. HTLV-1 prevalence and ATL

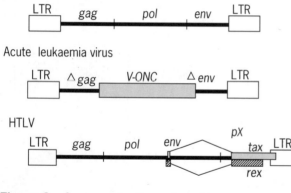

Figure 2 Genome structure of proviruses.

are clustered in southwestern Japan. The sera of ATL patients contain antibodies that react specifically with cell lines established from the ATL patient. The antigens in these cell lines were later proved to be HTLV-1 proteins by molecular characterization of the viral genome. The extensive epidemiological studies on antibodies and ATL clearly established that HTLV-1 is closely associated with ATL. The nationwide and worldwide epidemiology indicated that HTLV-1 infection is also associated with a neurological disease, HAM/TSP (HTLV-1-associated myelopathy/tropical spastic paraparesis).

The genome of HTLV-1 provirus consists of *LTR–gag–pol–env–pX–LTR* (Seiki *et al.*, 1983) and is distinct from the standard retroviral genome, *LTR–gag–pol–env–LTR* (**Figure 2**). The existence of a functional *pX* sequence is unique to this virus, thus HTLV-1 forms an independent retroviral group, HTLV. After characterization of HTLV-1, another virus, HTLV-2, was isolated from a patient with hairy T-cell leukaemia (Chen *et al.*, 1983). The genome is about 60% homologous to HTLV-1, but its pathogenicity is not yet established.

Viruses similar to HTLV-1, simian T cell leukaemia viruses (STLV), were isolated from various species of nonhuman primates, including chimpanzee. The STLVs share a 90–95% identity of genomic sequence with HTLV-1 and some isolates show more homology than those among human isolates. Although STLV is widely distributed in monkeys, no typically leukaemic animals have been observed. A few cases of a leukaemia-like disease have been noted in STLV-infected monkeys in zoos, but an aetiological connection between STLV and the disease remains to be established. Another member of the HTLV group is bovine leukaemia virus (BLV). BLV infects and replicates in B cells of cows and induces B cell lymphoma. BLV also infects lymphocytes of sheep and induces leukaemia after a short latent period.

Epidemiology

Nearly all ATL patients carry antibodies against HTLV-1 proteins. These antibodies are easily detected by indirect immunostaining of cells infected with HTLV-1, by an enzyme-linked immunosorbent assay (ELISA), by a particle-agglutination assay or by Western blotting. Some populations of healthy adults also carry HTLV-1 antibodies and these sero-positive persons are defined as the viral carriers. In fact, HTLV-1 can be detected in such individuals using the polymerase chain reaction (PCR). In considering the epidemiology of HTLV-1, geographic clustering, age-dependent prevalence, genomic variation and geographic origin of HTLV-2 are informative.

Geographic Clustering

HTLV-1 antibodies are recognized in 5–15% of adults clustered in southwestern Japan, the Caribbean islands and South America, Central Africa and Papua New Guinea and the Solomon Islands in Melanesia. The prevalence of sero-positive adults varies significantly from one district to another within these areas of endemicity. For example, in a particular isolated island in Kyushu, Japan, 30–40% of people over 40 years of age might be infected, whereas on a neighbouring island, the prevalence may be far lower. Significantly, ATL and HAM/TSP are also clustered, overlapping HTLV-1 in distribution. ATL patients and healthy carriers found sporadically in nonendemic areas mostly originate from one of the endemic areas.

HTLV-2 is frequently isolated in the United States and other countries from intravenous drug abusers and persons infected with HIV. HTLV-2 is endemic in South America, and also in Pygmy populations in Africa. These regions are likely to be the natural reservoir of HTLV-2 sporadically observed in the other places.

Age-dependent Prevalence

The prevalence of virus carriers increases with age after 20 years increasing sharply around 40–50 years of age and reaching a maximum in people aged between 50 and 60 years. The prevalence is significantly (1.6 times) higher in females than in males, but the incidence of ATL is similar in both sexes. The increase in prevalence among females can be attributed to sexual transmission of HTLV-1 from husbands to wives and also suggests that such infection is not leukaemogenic.

Although global epidemiology identified the age-dependent increase of antibody prevalence, cohort studies over 10 years in Japan revealed that sero-conversion of adults from antibody negative to positive is very rare. These observations are unable to explain the sharp increase of sero-prevalence in the 40–50 years age group. After extensive epidemiological studies of antibody prevalence, it is now accepted that the age-dependent increase is a reflection of the reduction of the infection risk at the early stage of life. Artificial milk became popular around 40 years ago in these areas in Japan, and thus reduced the incidence of breast milk-born infection of HTLV-1 (discussed below).

Genomic Stability

The viral genome is well conserved (over 96%) in Japan and the Caribbean area. Viral isolates from Africa and Papua New Guinea may vary somewhat more, but the variations are very limited. Retroviral genomes are thought to be unstable relative to those of other viruses because reverse transcription has no proofreading mechanism. Such genomic stability stands in sharp contrast to the highly labile genome of HIV. This may be associated with the very low competency of HTLV-1 replication *in vivo*.

Infection of HTLV-1

Infection In Vitro

Viral particles of HTLV-1 show extremely low infectivity *in vitro*, but co-cultivation with virus-producing cells can transmit HTLV-1 to a variety of human cells, including T and B lymphocytes, fibroblasts and epithelial cells, and also cells from monkeys, rats, rabbits and hamsters but, curiously, not mice. In these infected cells, the provirus is integrated into random sites in the chromosomal DNA, and most of the viral genes are successfully expressed. However, in non-T cell lines, the integrated proviruses become latent in expression, otherwise usually inducing the fusion of infected cells forming syncytia that ultimately die.

Only CD4-positive T cells are frequently immortalized upon infection with HTLV-1 (Miyoshi *et al.*, 1981) and the immortalized cells express high levels of IL-2Rα, proliferating in an IL-2-dependent fashion. Animal retroviruses that do not carry an oncogene generally do not immortalize cells *in vitro*, and therefore immortalization by HTLV-1 appears to be unique and suggests that the virus may have a particular function. Accordingly, a contribution of *pX* to this effect has been proposed.

In contrast to *in vitro* infection, the cells of both ATL patients and asymptomatic viral carriers infected *in vivo* are almost exclusively T cells with the CD4 + phenotype. Furthermore, infected cells *in vivo* do not express viral information at significant levels. Reverse transcriptase-mediated PCR (RT-PCR) on mRNA indicates that over 95% of infected cells fail to express viral genes *in vivo* irrespective of whether they are in a transformed or non-transformed state.

Natural Transmission

HTLV-1 can be transmitted *in vivo* through (1) blood transfusion, (2) nursing with breast milk, and (3) sexual relations.

Blood Transfusion

Retrospective studies of blood transfusions showed that 60–70% of recipients of fresh, sero-positive blood were infected with HTLV-1. Transfer of infected cells from donor to recipient is required for viral transmission, and therefore fresh, sero-positive plasma does not support the infection. Blood transfusion-mediated transmission of HTLV-1 seems not to induce ATL (see Sexual Transmission, below), but does induce HAM/TSP. Therefore, rejection of HTLV-1-positive blood can protect recipients against both HTLV-1 infection and development of HAM/TSP. The blood-mediated transmission of HTLV-1 explains a high prevalence of up to 20% of abusers of intravenous drugs by the sharing of unsterilized needles.

Mother to Child

Viral transmission from mother to child was originally suggested by epidemiological evidence: most mothers of sero-positive children were carriers of the virus and about 30% of the children of sero-positive mothers were themselves sero-positive. Neonatal infection was initially suspected, but surveys of lymphocytes in cord blood from a large number of children born to sero-positive mothers have virtually, but not completely, excluded this possibility. Instead, breast milk was found to be a likely source of transmissible virus. Supporting this, milk taken from sero-positive mothers and given to adult marmosets leads to the appearance of antibodies in these monkeys. More direct evidence stems from a practical trial demonstrating that cessation of breast-feeding by sero-positive mothers drastically reduced the sero-conversion rates of their children (see the last section).

Sexual Transmission

Wives with sero-positive husbands are very frequently sero-positive. Conversely, the husbands of sero-positive wives show the same frequency of sero-positivity as do men of the region under study. On these grounds, it seems that the virus can be transmitted from husband to wife but not vice versa. Infected T cells have been found in semen from men infected with HTLV-1 and these cells are considered to transmit the virus from male to female. The higher rate of sero-positivity in female (1.6 times) is explained by this transmission. The sex-specific incidence of ATL does not mirror this difference, suggesting that HTLV-1 infections sexually transmitted to females are not leukaemogenic to ATL.

Viral Gene Expression

Proviral Genome Unique to HTLV-1

The HTLV-1 proviral genome cloned from leukaemic-cell DNA from an ATL patient is 9032 bp long and consisted of *LTR–gag–pol–env–pX–LTR* (Seiki *et al.*, 1983). The presence of a *pX* region on the 3′ side of the *env* gene distinguishes the HTLV-1 genome from those of other retroviruses (**Figure 2**).

In general in retroviruses, the LTRs function as units regulating viral gene expression and replication. Furthermore, the *pX* region of HTLV contains additional, overlapping, regulatory genes (**Figure 3**): *tax*, *rex* and a gene whose function remains unknown, which encode p40tax, p27rex, and p21x. The Tax protein, p40tax, is a potent *trans*-activator of proviral transcription (Sodroski *et al.*, 1984; Fujisawa *et al.*, 1985) and thus is essential to viral gene expression (Yoshida, 1995). The second protein, p27rex, is a *trans*-acting modulator of RNA processing, which allows expression of the unspliced *gag* and *env* mRNAs in the cytoplasm. Expression of these unspliced

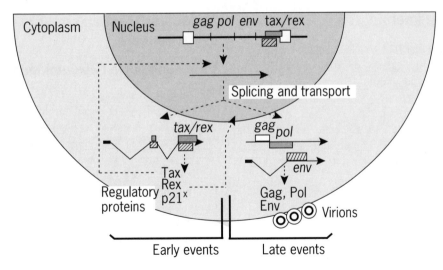

Figure 3 Transcription and viral RNA processing.

mRNAs is essential for expression of the viral structural proteins. Thus, Rex is also essential for HTLV-1 gene expression and replication. These systems are unique among retroviral regulations and have similarities to Tat and Rev systems of HIV, which are also essential for the replication of HIV.

The *pX* sequence is also able to encode various proteins when the sequence is alternatively spliced. The function of some of these products was characterized using expression vectors, but the physiology of these proteins remains to be analysed.

Transcriptional Activation

Retroviral LTR elements contain a TATA box, a transcriptional enhancer and a poly(A) signal, all of which are essential for viral gene expression and replication of RNA tumour viruses. These elements are recognized by cellular transcriptional factors for RNA polymerase II and retroviral gene expression depends upon the cellular machinery of the host. In addition to LTR-mediated regulation, HTLV-1 contains the *tax* gene, which acts in trans to stimulate viral transcription (**Figure 3**). Tax function depends on three direct repeats of the 21-bp sequence transcriptional enhancer, in the LTR. The interaction of Tax with the enhancers has been proposed to be indirect, that is, Tax interacts with a cellular protein that binds to the enhancer DNA to mediate trans-activation.

In addition to the viral genome, Tax activates cellular genes. Since the transcription of the gene for the α-chain of the IL-2 receptor (IL-Rα) was reported to be activated by Tax, many other genes were identified also to be activated but through different mechanisms (see later). These include the gene for GM-colony-stimulating factor (GM-CSF), the proto-oncogenes c-*fos* and c-*jun*, the genes for parathyroid hormone-related protein (PTHrP), MHC class I antigen and many others.

RNA Processing

The primary transcript, the viral genome, of HTLV-1 contains genes for Gag, Pol, Env, Tax, Rex and a few others in this order with some overlapping. Only the first coding frame on an mRNA is translated into protein in eukaryotic cells, and therefore the retrovirus needs to splice the primary transcript into various species of viral mRNA to encode other proteins. This splicing is regulated by Rex, a pX protein of HTLV-1 (**Figure 3**). Viral replication requires three species of mRNA: 8.5-kb genomic (unspliced) RNA as *gag* and *pol* mRNA, a 4.2-kb singly spliced sub-genomic RNA as *env* mRNA and a 2.1-kb doubly spliced mRNA for the expression of Tax and Rex proteins. The viral transcripts early after infection or induction are all spliced into completely spliced *tax/rex* mRNA. Tax and Rex are then expressed, and viral transcription is enormously enhanced and at the same time, unspliced RNA for Gag, Pol and Env are expressed in the cytoplasm. This regulation is essential for viral protein expression, since host-cell mRNAs are generally all spliced into mRNA to be transported to the cytoplasm.

Rex function in turn reduces the level of spliced mRNA that encodes regulatory proteins, including Tax protein, and eventually reduces viral transcription. Thus, Rex enhances the expression of viral structural proteins, but suppresses total viral gene expression. In short, Rex exerts feedback control of the viral gene expression, thus resulting in a transient expression of HTLV-1.

For this regulation, target RNA requires to have a cis-acting element (RxRE) consisting of 205 nucleotides located in the 3' region of the viral RNA. The unique secondary structure of this element allows Rex protein to bind to it. A nuclear export signal in the Rex protein suggests transport of a Rex–RNA complex into the cytoplasm without processing. HIV has a *rev* gene, strikingly similar in function to *rex* of HTLV-1. In the HIV system, Rev protein binds to RvRE in the *env* coding sequence.

Adult T Cell Leukaemia (ATL)

It is now established that HTLV-1 is associated with ATL, HTLV-1-associated myelopathy or tropical spastic paraparesis (HAM/TSP) and uveitis. Other diseases such as chronic lung disease, monoclonal gammopathy, chronic renal failure, strongyloidiasis and nonspecific dermatomycosis are also suggested to associate with the viral infection; however, further systematic studies are required to establish the exact relationships. Here, only ATL is described.

The Leukaemic Cells

ATL cells are T cells with the CD4+ phenotype and, usually, a highly lobulated nucleus. These cells always carry HTLV-1 proviruse(s) and the site of integration is monoclonal in a given ATL patient. In 70–80% of cases of ATL patients examined, one copy of the complete provirus was integrated into each leukaemic cell. Occasionally, one or two copies of defective provirus are integrated into the DNA of a single cell. Even in the defective genomes, preservation of the pX region in defective proviruses suggests its importance in tumorigenesis.

The leukaemic cells express a high level of IL-2Rα on their surfaces. Production of PTHrP, IL-1β or GM-CSF by tumour cells has also been described. In almost all cases, leukaemic cells carry aberrant chromosomes, and there are frequently multiple abnormalities, such as trisomy of chromosome 7 and 14q11, 14q32 and 6/q15 translocations. The abnormality involving 14q32 was found in 25% of ATL patients, but the others appeared less frequently.

Clinical Features

ATL (Uchiyama et al., 1977) is classified into three phases, smouldering, chronic and acute phases, depending on clinical features. In smouldering ATL, patients commonly have from one to several per cent of morphologically abnormal T cells in their peripheral blood, but do not show other signs of severe illness and are therefore thought to be in an early stage of ATL development. In smouldering ATL, the abnormal cells are not aggressively malignant, but are HTLV-1 infected and expanded clonally. The onset of ATL is observed between 20 and 70 years of age, the peak rate of onset being in the 40s and 50s. The male-to-female ratio of ATL is 1.4:1.0. Symptoms of ATL vary from patient to patient, but are frequently complicated by skin lesions, enlargement of lymph nodes, liver and/or spleen and infiltration of leukaemic cells into the lungs and other organs. Patients usually have antibodies to HTLV-1 proteins, show an increased level of serum LDH and suffer from hypercalcaemia. The acute form, or phase, of ATL is aggressive and resistant to treatment; consequently, most patients in this phase die within 6 months of its onset.

Molecular Mechanism of Pathogenesis

Viral Function in Leukaemogenesis

The aetiological role of HTLV-1 in ATL has been demonstrated by sero-epidemiology and molecular biology of HTLV-1 and ATL. The bases of this are as follows: (1) ATL and HTLV-1 geographically overlap (population level); (2) most ATL patients are infected with HTLV-1 (individual level); (3) leukaemic cells from ATL patients are infected with HTLV-1 (cell level); (4) more importantly, the leukaemic cells show monoclonal integration of proviral DNA (molecular level); and (5) HTLV-1 has the capacity to immortalize human T cells in vitro (biochemical level). The evidence in (4) indicates that the leukaemic cells originated from a single HTLV-1-infected cell and, thus, that HTLV-1 plays a causative role in leukaemogenesis. There are estimated to be approximately one million carriers of HTLV-1 in Japan, and about 500 new cases of ATL are reported each year. About 2–5% of all carriers of HTLV-1 are thought to develop ATL during their life span (Tajima, 1990).

The site for provirus integration is monoclonal in ATL cells, but not the same among ATL patients (Seiki et al., 1984). Therefore, the promoter insertion model is unlikely since it requires a common integration adjacent to a proto-oncogene. Consequently, a 'trans-acting function' of HTLV-1 is postulated in leukaemogenesis. Molecular biology studies of HTLV-1 showed that the Tax protein functions as a 'trans-acting factor.' Consistent with these observations, Tax was found to immortalize T cells in an IL-2-dependent fashion, to transform rat embryonic cells in cooperation with c-ras, and to induce mesenchymal tumours in Tax transgenic mice. The central role of Tax in leukaemogenesis is thus proposed.

Trans-activation of Transcription

Activation of Enhancer Binding Protein

Tax trans-activates transcription via specific enhancers such as the 21-bp enhancer in the LTR, the NF-κB binding site in the gene for interleukin-2 receptor α and serum responsive element (SRE) in the c-fos gene. However, Tax is unable to bind directly to the enhancer DNA sequence. Instead, Tax binds to enhancer binding proteins; the first group includes CREB (cyclic AMP-responsive element (CRE) binding protein, CREM (CRE modulator protein), ATF-1 and ATF-2, which bind to the 21-bp enhancer in the HTLV-1 LTR. The second group is the family of NF-κB such as p50, p65, c-Rel and p52, which bind to the NF-κB binding site in IL-2 receptor α gene, and the third group is SRF (serum response factor) which binds to SRE (serum response element) in the c-fos or c-egr gene. These transcription factors are regulated by signal-dependent phosphorylation in normal cells; however, Tax binding permits activation of these factors without specific phosphorylation, thus establishing constitutive activation of these genes.

It is now demonstrated that Tax binding to these transcription factors recruits CBP (CREB binding protein) on to the enhancer–CREB complexes (Kwok *et al.*, 1994), because of Tax's affinity for CBP (**Figure 4**). CBP has a histone-acetylating activity and is normally unable to bind to CREB protein unless it is phosphorylated by protein kinase A. Therefore, the ternary complex of the enhancer–CREB–Tax–CBP without phosphorylation would acetylate histones bound to DNA nearby and thus activate transcription initiation. This simple binding hypothesis, however, may need further careful characterization.

Inactivation of Transcriptional Inhibitors

NF-κB proteins are activated by Tax binding in the nucleus (see the previous section). However, in resting cells, NF-κB proteins are retained in the cytoplasm by forming complexes with IκB. Stimulation of cells induces phosphorylation of IκB protein and its degradation. The released NF-κB then migrates into the nucleus because of its nuclear translocation signal and binds to its specific DNA sequences.

Tax also binds to IκBalpha which results in destabilization of IκB–NF-κB complexes. It is uncertain whether Tax induces phosphorylation of IκB and/or degradation of IκB. Activation of a protein kinase activity by Tax suggests the former mechanism, but the binding of Tax to a component of the proteasome may suggest the latter mechanism. Whatever the mechanism, Tax is able to down-regulate the transcriptional inhibitor, IκB, in the cytoplasm and thus activates NF-κB-dependent transcription. Tax appears to exert its effects via two independent mechanisms targeting an activator, NF-κB, and its inhibitor, IκB.

Trans-repression of Transcription

When the trans-activating function of Tax was extensively investigated, Tax was reported to trans-repress transcription of DNA polymerase beta (Jeang *et al.*, 1990), which is required for repair of damaged DNA. Tax was then demonstrated to trans-repress the transcription of a set of growth-inhibitory genes such as *p18INK4c*, *NF-1*, *lck* and a apoptotic gene *bax*. Furthermore, Tax was also shown to trans-repress p53-dependent transcription, which affects the tumour-suppressor function of p53. These effects, therefore, suggest an abnormally enhanced proliferation of HTLV-1-infected cells. It is of interest to know how a trans-activator, Tax, is able to trans-repress other sets of genes.

The underlying mechanism was in fact shown to be rather simple, that is, inhibition of a transcriptional coactivator family, CBP/P300 (**Figure 4**). An E-box binding protein E47 in *p18INK4c* expression and p53 in p53-dependent transcription are essential to interact with CBP/p300 to achieve efficient expression. In these systems, Tax binds to CBP/p300 and interferes with the interaction between CBP/p300 and enhancer binding proteins, E47 or p53, resulting in trans-repression of specific transcription. This implies that Tax would be able to suppress many other genes since the CBP/p300 protein serves as a coactivator for a huge number of genes. It is therefore suggested that the cascade of Tax activity in transcriptional regulation

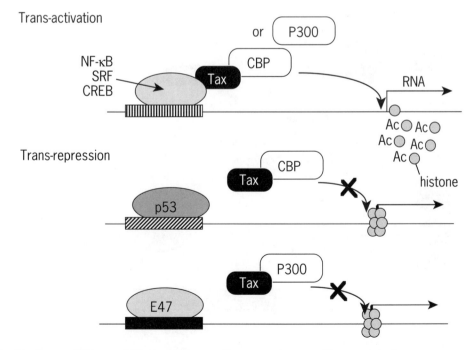

Figure 4 Tax binding to CBP or p300 to activate and repress the specific transcription.

would be unexpectedly wide in its targets and highly variable in its effect, depending on the level of expression.

Inhibition of Tumour-Suppressor Proteins

Independently of transcriptional regulation, the Tax protein was also found to interact with an inhibitor of cyclin-dependent kinase 4 (CDK4), p16INK4a (Suzuki *et al.*, 1996) and a *Drosophila* large disc tumour-suppressor protein, Dlg. Furthermore, the direct binding inhibits the function of tumour-suppressor proteins. These suppressive effects on tumour-suppressor functions strongly suggest that Tax protein contributes to the development of ATL.

Cell Cycle Inhibitor

p16INK4a and p15INK4b are inhibitors of CDK4/6 and their inactivation results in activation of the kinases. Upon activation of CDK4/6, Rb is phosphorylated and is no longer able to bind E2F, thus releasing the active form of E2F, which then binds to target DNA sequences and initiates expression of various genes important for DNA synthesis. Tax binding to and inhibition of both p16INK4a and p15INK4b is able to activate CDK4 and promote cell entry into S phase (**Figure 5**). p16INK4a is frequently deleted in many human tumour cells, particularly in melanoma and haematopoietic tumours, and the deletion has been suspected to play a critical role in tumour induction and progression. Therefore, the functional knockout of the tumour-suppressor protein mimics the effect of gene deletion and may contribute to development of ATL.

With respect to the inactivation of Rb signalling pathway by p16INK4a, it is of interest to point out that DNA tumour viral proteins such as SV40 T-antigen, adenovirus E1A and papillomavirus E6/7 target Rb protein in their transformation (Nevins, 1992). The observation that developmentally unrelated tumour viruses share the common signalling pathway by targeting different molecules suggests that the Rb pathway is critical for the normal regulation of cell proliferation.

hDlg that Associates with APC, Another Tumour-suppressor Protein

Another target of Tax is hDlg, which is a signalling molecule downstream of Wnt/Frizzled and upstream of β-catenin in their signalling pathways. hDlg binds to the C-terminus of the tumour-suppressor protein APC involved in transducing cytostatic signals. Tax binds to the same domain of hDlg *in vitro* and *in vivo* and competes with APC, thus abrogating the growth-retarding signalling. In addition to the competitive displacement of APC from hDlg, Tax further induces hyperphosphorylation of hDlg as demonstrated by its slower migration in gel electrophoresis. It is noteworthy that APC and hDlg are significantly expressed in normal T cells (T. Suzuki and M. Yoshida, unpublished observation), hence these interactions might have roles in T cells, although these are not well understood.

Cell Cycle Check Point Protein, HsMAD1

Cell cycle processes are inspected at checkpoints to determine whether the scheduled processes are verified. Thus, once the checkpoint system is compromised, damaged cells can go through their cell cycle and proliferate, fixing genetic abnormality in the daughter cells. Tax of HTLV-1 can bind to the human homologue (HsMAD1) of yeast mitotic checkpoint protein MAD1 (Jin *et al.*, 1998). HsMAD1 is a component of the mitotic

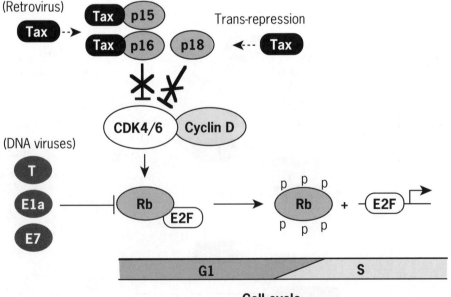

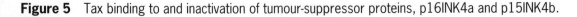

Figure 5   Tax binding to and inactivation of tumour-suppressor proteins, p16INK4a and p15INK4b.

checkpoint system which prevents anaphase and commitment to cellular division until chromosomal alignment is properly completed. Therefore, abrogation of the mitotic checkpoint function of HsMAD1 may be linked to chromosomal abnormalities which are observed at unusually high frequency in ATL cells.

Common Targets with DNA Tumour Viruses

The Tax protein appears to be pleiotropic through interacting with so many cellular regulators: activation and repression of transcription of different sets of genes, inhibition of CDK4 inhibitors and inhibition of tumour-suppressor proteins. Some of the target molecules and target pathways of Tax protein are shared by transforming proteins of DNA tumour viruses, T antigens of SV40, E1A/B of adenoviruses and E6/7 of papillomaviruses. The most striking shared target is the Rb signalling pathway: Tax targets p16INK4a and p15INK4b and the transforming proteins of DNA tumour viruses target Rb, both resulting in activation of E2F family and promotion of cells into the S phase of the cell cycle (**Figure 5**). Other examples shared are the transcriptional target coactivators CBP/p300 and hDlg; CBP/p300 is affected by T antigen and E1A, and hDlg by E6 of high-risk HPV and E4 9ORF1 of adenoviruses.

The genes for p16INK4a and Rb proteins are frequently mutated or deleted in spontaneous human cancer cells and are believed to play critical roles in tumorigenesis. Therefore, functional knockout of these gene products by viral proteins is similarly expected to play crucial roles in specific tumour induction. It is also interesting that developmentally unrelated viruses and spontaneous genetic mutations target the same signalling pathway for malignant transformation. By analogy with these spontaneous mutations or deletions, the virally induced functional inactivation of either p16INK4a or Rb protein would be primarily responsible for the induction of specific tumours in humans.

Possible Mechanism of Pathogenesis

Cooperation of the Pleiotropic Function of Tax Protein

As summarized in the previous section, Tax protein effects are pleiotropic and function at different levels, including transcriptional regulation, cell cycle promotion, tumour-suppressor function and genomic stability. It is reasonable to speculate that the pleiotropic functions of Tax would be mostly cooperative in ATL development (**Figure 6**). This interesting possibility is discussed below.

Cell proliferation. It has been demonstrated that various genes activated by Tax are in fact able to promote cell proliferation *in vitro*; transcriptional activation of lymphokines such as IL-6, GM-CSF, TGF-β and some others, lymphokine receptors such as IL-2Rα and some nuclear oncogenes such as c-*fos*, c-*egr* and c-*jun*, are all growth promoting. These transcriptional trans-activations are mediated independently through NF-κB or SRF and some others through CREB. Furthermore, trans-repression of *p18INK4c*, *lck* and *NF-1* would result in promotion of cell growth, since these genes are mostly growth-retarding. Direct inhibition of tumour-suppressor proteins such as p16INK4a, p15INK4b, cyclin D3 and hDlg all result in abnormal cell proliferation of infected cells. Indeed, most of the genes and proteins targetted directly or indirectly by Tax are likely to cooperate in promotion of cell proliferation upon infection by HTLV-1. This consideration is consistent with the fact that normal cell regulation is protected by redundant mechanisms and also that tumorigenesis proceeds through accumulation of multiple gene abnormalities.

Fixation of genetic abnormality. In addition to the genes discussed in the previous section, Tax also affects

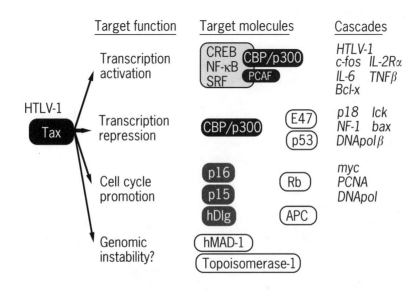

Figure 6 Summary of the pleiotropic function of Tax.

genes which are not directly linked to cell proliferation. These include trans-repression of DNA polymerase-β and Bax, trans-activation of Bcl-X_L and inhibition of topo-isomerase I, PCNA and HsMAD. DNA polymerase-β DNA topoisomerase I and PCNA are involved in repair of damaged DNA and therefore reduction of these activities through any mechanism would result in higher mutation rate fixing genetic abnormality in infected cells. In fact, a mutagenic effect of Tax on host cell chromosomes has been directly demonstrated. In relation to DNA damage and its repair, p53 function is also affected by Tax; p53-dependent transcription is trans-repressed through interfering with p53 binding to CBP (see the previous section). Furthermore, p53 function is impaired by phosphorylation at Ser15. Therefore, Tax is able to abolish the cell cycle checkpoint function of p53, thus leading cells to accumulate DNA mutations. This would also be bypassed through Tax binding to HsMAD, a component of the mitotic checkpoint, suggesting promotion of abnormal cell division.

Escape from apoptosis. It is widely accepted that unbalanced activation of some signalling pathway for cell growth or undesired mutation of critical genes would induce apoptosis and eliminate these abnormal cells. Therefore, tumorigenic mutation or viral function would be counter-acted were apoptosis induction to be effective. Surprisingly, the Tax protein was shown to trans-activate Bcl-X_L and trans-repress Bax, an inhibitor and mediator of apoptosis, respectively, thus preventing apoptosis of these cells. These effects of Tax seem to be critical for finalizing its effects *in vivo*, otherwise potent activities of Tax would be cancelled by elimination of the Tax-expressing cells by apoptosis.

In total, Tax induces abnormal cell growth, genomic instability and fixation of the abnormality through its pleiotropic functions. Tax is therefore concluded to be a tumour initiator and promoter in the development of ATL.

Low Expression of Tax In Vivo

The pleiotropic functions of Tax thus far identified *in vitro* are all consistent with its implication as an aetiological factor for ATL. However, the extremely low expression of Tax *in vivo* offers a different impression from those expected from its properties *in vitro*. Infected T cells in peripheral blood do not produce significant amounts of Tax mRNA and protein, irrespective of whether they are transformed or not. Expression is detected only by sensitive PCR, but not by any other techniques. Semiquantitative PCR indicated that over 95% of infected cells are absolutely negative for expression of the viral message. Such extremely inefficient expression of the viral genes might be beneficial for the virus to escape from host immune responses, but raises a question concerning the role of Tax in tumorigenesis. It should be emphasized that continuous expression of the viral proteins in infected individuals are suggested by the persistent prevalence of the antibodies.

These somewhat mysterious observations may be explained in several ways: first, Tax plays essential roles in the early stages of transformation, but it is no longer required for maintenance of the transformed phenotype. Second, very low levels of Tax may be sufficient for the maintenance of abnormal phenotypes of infected cells. However, this is unlikely because most infected cells are absolutely negative for Tax expression. Third, Tax is transiently expressed in a small population of infected cells at one time and in another cell population at other times. This would be possible in T cells, some of which are stimulated by antigens or other signals, but its activation would be soon terminated unless the stimulation was continuous. Different specificities of stimulation would induce Tax expression in different populations of T cells. However, it is not easy to distinguish these possibilities experimentally.

The other possibility for low expression of HTLV-1 genes is defective proviruses *in vivo* in cells. This is, however, not the case, since the expression of viral genes is rapidly induced when primary cells from infected individuals are cultured. The mechanism for such restriction of viral expression *in vivo* is not well understood. The extremely low expression of Tax in primary tumour cells is in contrast to transforming genes of DNA tumour viruses, which are significantly expressed and responsible for maintenance of the abnormal growth of transformed cells. For example, *E6/E7* genes of human papillomavirus are expressed in the HeLa cell line maintained for a long period in culture and their repression arrests cell growth.

Clonal Expansion of Infected T cells

Another point in question is the clonal burst of infected T cells. Growth stimulation through the pleiotropic functions of Tax would result in a random population of proliferating cells, since it stimulates growth of most T cells infected with HTLV-1. However, leukaemic cells are always monoclonal. Therefore, an additional genetic event is postulated to trigger the clonal selection of infected T cells. However, not much is known about the mechanism of clonal selection for leukaemic cells. It might not be associated with the viral function. The notion that further alteration is necessary is consistent with the long delay in ATL development after HTLV-1 infection.

Prevention of HTLV-1 Infection

Infection by HTLV-1 is easily detected by antibodies against HTLV-1 proteins. Assay kits for ELISA, Western blotting and particle agglutination have been produced for the diagnosis of HTLV-1 infection and are commercially available. Worldwide screening of HTLV-1 prevalence has been carried out using these systems. Transfusion of sero-positive blood results in transmission of HTLV-1 to two-thirds of the recipients. With the introduction of HTLV-1 screening systems in blood banks, sero-positive blood is now rejected in Japan and viral transmission through transfusion has been greatly reduced.

This has also resulted in an effective reduction of trans-fusion-related HAM/TSP. The application of these systems to populations in all endemic areas is now clearly shown to prevent HTLV-1 infection.

The major, natural route of viral transmission is from mother to child through infected T cells in breast milk (Hino *et al.*, 1985). Curiously, mothers with high levels of anti-bodies to Tax protein transmit the virus to their offspring at a higher rate than do those with low titres of Tax antibodies. It is possible that efficient replication of HTLV-1 would stimulate antibody production at high levels but that the antibodies might not significantly inhibit viral replication. Non-breast-feeding has been examined among sero-positive mothers in Nagasaki City, Japan, to prevent the viral transmission into children. By consent, pregnant women are surveyed for HTLV-1 antibodies; those who are sero-posi-tive are encouraged to avoid breast feeding. The trial indi-cated a drastic reduction in the incidence of sero-positive children, from about 30% to just a few per cent. The success of this trial provides direct evidence for viral transmission through milk and suggests the possibility of eliminating ATL in the next few generations.

Epidemiological studies have established that HTLV-1 infects individuals at an early age through breast milk. In fact, within 6–12 months of birth, one-quarter to one-third of children born to sero-positive mothers develop anti-bodies to HTLV-1. A dramatic increase in age-specific rates of sero-positivity is, however, observed only in those over 40 years old. Sexual transmission of HTLV-1 from husband to wife may account for a portion of this increase, but cannot explain the increase in males. One possible speculation to account for this phenomenon is that the age-dependent prevalence is a reflection of the infection in the young period of 0–1 years old. These epidemiological results suggest that prevention of milk and transfusion-mediated transmission might be adequate.

REFERENCES

Chen, I. S., *et al.* (1983). Human T-cell leukemia virus type II transforms normal human lymphocytes. *Proceedings of the National Academy of Sciences of the USA*, **80**, 7006–7009.

Fujisawa, J., *et al.* (1985). Functional activation of the long terminal repeat of human T-cell leukemia virus type I by a trans-acting factor. *Proceedings of the National Academy of Sciences of the USA*, **82**, 2277–2281.

Hino, S., *et al.* (1985). Mother-to-child transmission of human T-cell leukemia virus type-I. *Japanese Journal of Cancer Research*, **76**, 474–480.

Hinuma, Y., *et al.* (1981). Adult T-cell leukemia: antigen in an ATL cell line and detection of antibodies to the antigen in human sera. *Proceedings of the National Academy of Sciences of the USA*, **78**, 6476–6480.

Jeang, K. T., *et al.* (1990). HTLV-I trans-activator protein, tax, is a trans-repressor of the human beta-polymerase gene. *Science*, **247**, 1082–1084.

Jin, D. Y., *et al.* (1998). Human T cell leukemia virus type 1 oncoprotein Tax targets the human mitotic checkpoint protein MAD1. *Cell*, **93**, 81–91.

Kwok, R. P., *et al.* (1994). Nuclear protein CBP is a coactivator for the transcription factor CREB. *Nature*, **370**, 223–226.

Miyoshi, I., *et al.* (1981). Type C virus particles in a cord T-cell line derived by co-cultivating normal human cord leukocytes and human leukaemic T cells. *Nature*, **294**, 770–771.

Nevins, J. R. (1992). E2F: a link between the Rb tumor suppressor protein and viraloncoproteins. *Science*, **258**, 424–429.

Poeisz, B. J., *et al.* (1980). Detection and isolation of the C retro-virus from fresh and cultured lymphocytes of a patient with T cell lymphoma. *Proceedings of the National Academy of Sciences of the USA*, **77**, 7415–7419.

Seiki, M., *et al.* (1983). Human adult T-cell leukemia virus: complete nucleotide sequence of the provirus genome inte-grated in leukemia cell DNA. *Proceedings of the National Academy of Sciences of the USA*, **80**, 3618–3622.

Seiki, M., *et al.* (1984). Nonspecific integration of the HTLV provirus genome into adult T-cell leukaemia cells. *Nature*, **309**, 640–642.

Sodroski, J. G., *et al.* (1984). Trans-acting transcriptional acti-vation of the long terminal repeat of human T lymphotropic viruses in infected cells. *Science*, **225**, 381–385.

Suzuki, T., *et al.* (1996). HTLV-1 Tax protein interacts with cyclin-dependent kinase inhibitor p16INK4A and counteracts its inhibitory activity towards CDK4. *EMBO Journal*, **15**, 1607–1614.

Tajima, K. (1990). The 4th nation-wide study of adult T-cell leukemia/lymphoma (ATL) in Japan: estimates of risk of ATL and its geographical and clinical features. The T- and B-cell Malignancy Study Group. *International Journal of Cancer*, **45**, 237–243.

Uchiyama, T., *et al.* (1977). Adult T-cell leukemia: clinical and hematologic features of 16 cases. *Blood*, **50**, 481–492.

Weiss, R., *et al.* (1985). *RNA Tumor Viruses* (Cold Spring Harbor Laboratory Press, Cold Spring Harbor, NY).

Yoshida, M., *et al.* (1982). Isolation and characterization of retrovirus from cell lines of human adult T-cell leukemia and its implication in the disease. *Proceedings of the National Academy of Sciences of the USA*, **79**, 2031–2035.

Yoshida, M. (1995). HTLV-1 oncoprotein Tax deregulates tran-scription of cellular genes through multiple mechanisms. *Journal of Cancer Research and Clinical Oncology*, **121**, 521–528.

FURTHER READING

Yoshida, M. (2001). Multiple viral strategy of HTLV-1 for dysregulation of cell growth control. *Annual Review of Immunology*, **19**, 475–496.

Chapter 7

Genomic Instability and DNA Repair

Kurt W. Kohn
National Cancer Institute, National Institutes of Health, Bethesda, MD, USA

Vilhelm A. Bohr
National Institute on Aging, National Institutes of Health, Baltimore, MD, USA

C O N T E N T S

INTRODUCTION

Preservation of genome integrity is critical for the functional preservation of dividing cells. Genomic instability and DNA damage set the stage for carcinogenesis, both in the initiation stage and in the evolution toward malignancy. The frequency estimates for various types of DNA damage normally incurred in mammalian cells are summarized in **Table 1**. Multiple mechanisms have evolved to repair DNA damage and preserve genome integrity. Several mechanisms are conserved widely or even universally among organisms and thus play a fundamental role in maintaining the integrity of living species.

Multistage carcinogenesis, the stepwise accumulation of genetic changes favouring malignant behaviour, is brought about jointly by chemical mutagenesis and genomic instability mechanisms. Spontaneous mutations, estimated at perhaps three per cell during a human lifetime, however, are insufficient by themselves to account for cancer incidence (Coleman and Tsongalis, 1999). The probability of accumulating the several (perhaps five or more) genetic changes thought necessary for malignancy is greatly enhanced by the development of genomic instability, which can function as a mutator phenotype. For most malignant tumours, therefore, genomic instability plays an important part in causality (see reviews by Breivik and Gaudernack, 1999).

Genomic instability and/or defective DNA repair are characteristic of several human genetic disorders, including ataxia telangiectasia, Fanconi anaemia, Bloom syndrome, Werner syndrome, xeroderma pigmentosum,

Table 1 Estimated frequencies of DNA lesions normally occurring in mammalian cells

Damage	Events per cell per day
Single-strand breaks	55 000
Depurinations	13 000
Depyrimidinations	650
Guanine-O6 methylation	3100
Cytosine deamination	200
Glucose-6-phosphate adduct	3
Thymine glycol	270
Thymidine glycol	70
Hydroxymethyluracil	620
Guanine-8 oxygenation	180
Interstrand cross-link	8
Double-strand break	9
DNA-protein cross-link	Unknown

Cockayne syndrome and Nijmegen breakage syndrome. Most of these genetic defects predispose affected individuals to the development of malignant tumours (see the chapter *Inherited Predispositions to Cancer*).

GENOMIC INSTABILITY

Genomic instability implies an abnormally high rate of genomic alterations. Not only do tumours contain genome abnormalities, they also have increased genomic heterogeneity among their cells. Two types of genomic instability syndromes have been established in tumours: microsatellite instability and chromosome instability. Malignant tumours almost always have one or the other, but rarely both. Thus malignancy can develop by one route or the other, but does not need both (see review by Coleman and Tsongalis (1999)).

Both types of genomic instability have been observed early in tumour development while the lesions are still small and benign. Genomic abnormalities and variation increase as tumours progress toward malignancy. Genomic variation progresses by a combination of increased rate of variation (genomic instability) and selection of cell clones adapted to the malignant lifestyle (see the chapter *Cell Proliferation in Carcinogenesis*).

Genomic abnormalities can arise by several mechanisms having different regional characteristics in DNA. Local alterations include sequence amplifications, deletions, insertions and point mutations. Chromosomal translocations and rearrangements arise by breakage/rejoining or other recombination events. Mitotic abnormalities give rise to aneuploidy by unequal chromosome segregation and to multiploidy by failure of nuclear division. These processes lead to genomic heterogeneity, which becomes increasingly rampant during the progress of malignancy; the most autonomously replicating genotypes become selected as tumours progress. Thus genomic instability is implicated in both the origin and progression of most malignant tumours.

Microsatellite Instability

Microsatellite instability implies variation in the length of homopolymer regions (particularly poly(A) sequences) or of dinucleotide or trinucleotide repeat regions. Microsatellite instability is caused by a defect in mismatch repair (MMR). For a compilation of microsatellite instability reports for various tumours and a discussion of mechanism of production, see Coleman and Tsongalis (1999).

Microsatellite instability is discussed further in the section on MMR.

Chromosome Instability

Chromosome instability implies not only abnormal variation in gross chromosome number (aneuploidy), but also an increased rate of chromosomal alterations. Aneuploid tumour cells have been estimated to have a 10–100-fold increased rate of chromosome gain or loss and a similar increase in the rate of loss of heterozygosity at specific genomic sites (Lengauer *et al.*, 1998). Sometimes the loss of a chromosome is balanced by the duplication of the remaining allelic chromosome. Loss of heterozygosity of a given genetic region can be detected by DNA electrophoresis and hybridization even when the corresponding chromosome is present in the euploid 2 copies.

For a compilation of frequencies of gain or loss of DNA from each chromosome arm in various tumours (as determined by comparative genomic hybridization), see Rooney *et al.* (1999). Interestingly, some chromosome arms show gains much more often than losses, some show the reverse and many show nearly equal frequencies of gain or loss. For a given tumour type, on the other hand, each chromosome arm may show frequent gain or loss, but rarely both. This may reflect distinctive preferred patterns of selection among different tumour types in the context of chromosome instability.

Although the association of microsatellite instability with defective MMR is well established, the molecular origin of chromosome instability is only beginning to be elucidated. Unlike microsatellite instability, which can be complemented by cell fusion with a chromosome-instability cell type, the converse is not the case: whereas microsatellite instability is a recessive character, chromosome instability is dominant and may be due to a gain-of-function mutation of a single protein (Lengauer *et al.*, 1998). Chromosome instability is not a consequence of increased chromosome number *per se*, because tetraploid cells resulting from the fusion of two cells having microsatellite instability does not yield chromosome instability. Sometimes gross chromosome instability is accompanied by p53 mutation, but the early stages of chromosome instability often appear much earlier than p53 mutation. Moreover, mutation or inactivation of p53 does not by itself affect chromosome stability (Lengauer *et al.*, 1998).

Centrosome Abnormalities

Abnormal centrosome function in cancer cells can cause chromosome instability. Sometimes the centrosomes become overduplicated, causing multifocal spindles and grossly abnormal mitoses. Centrosome dysfunction however is not the only route to aneuploidy. Improper behaviour of the mitotic spindle can be due to a variety of as yet poorly defined defects in mitotic checkpoints, which can cause unequal chromosome segregation between daughter cells.

The molecular basis of centrosome dysfunction is not yet clear. Although abnormal centrosome function is sometimes associated with p53 loss or mutation, this is not a strict association, because normal centrosome function together with aneuploidy has been observed in the presence of mutated p53. Thus, p53 mutation does not by itself cause centrosome dysfunction, but may be implicated in other routes to aneuploidy.

THE NEED FOR DNA REPAIR

Living organisms are constantly exposed to stress from environmental agents and from endogenous metabolic processes. An important factor is exposure to oxidative reagents or oxidative stress, largely arising as a side effect of mitochondrial energy metabolism. The resulting reactive oxygen species (ROS) attack proteins, lipids and DNA. Since proteins and lipids are readily degraded and resynthesized, the most significant consequence of oxidative stress is thought to be DNA modifications, which can become permanent via the formation of mutations and other types of genomic damage.

Many different types of DNA base changes have been observed following oxidative stress, and these lesions are widely considered as instigators of cancer, development, ageing and neurological disorders (for review, see Wiseman and Halliwell, 1996). The endogenous attack on DNA by ROS generates a low steady-state level of DNA adducts that have been detected in the DNA of human cells (Dizdaroglu, 1991). Over 100 oxidative base modifications in DNA have been detected in human cells (Wiseman and Halliwell, 1996). The best known and most widely studied is 8-hydroxyguanosine (8-oxoG). Oxidative DNA damage accumulates in cancerous tissues and is thought to contribute to carcinogenesis. For example, higher levels of oxidative base damage were observed in lung cancer tissue compared with surrounding normal tissue and a ninefold

increase in 8-oxoG, 8-hydroxyadenine and 2,6-diamino-4-hydroxy-5-formamidopyrimidine in DNA in breast cancer tissue compared with normal tissue has been reported (Wiseman and Halliwell, 1996). DNA damage can also occur after direct attack by external or exogenous sources. Radiation from various sources can directly damage bases in DNA. For example, ultraviolet (UV) irradiation from exposure to sunlight creates certain DNA lesions. The main ones are the cyclobutane pyrimidine dimers formed usually between two adjacent thymine bases in DNA and the pyrimidine–6,4–pyrimidine dimer photoproducts. Irradiation from γ-ray sources or X-rays creates many different kinds of lesions in DNA, including base modifications, sites with a loss of base, and breaks in a DNA strand. DNA breaks can be single- or double-stranded. Many food constituents can directly damage DNA. These include carcinogens or chemicals that react directly with DNA or do so after metabolic modification. Some of these agents alkylate DNA bases, some forming bulky adducts. For example, aromatic amines are found in a variety of foods and are known to cause DNA damage and to be highly mutagenic. A number of poisons attack DNA directly. An example is mustard gas or nitrogen mustard which chemically modifies DNA bases and produces cross-links between bases on the same or on opposite DNA strands (Kohn, 1996). Interstrand cross-links cause havoc in the cell by completely blocking the progress of polymerases. DNA repair pathways have evolved to deal with all these lesions in DNA. Some are listed in **Figure 1**, which shows the general pathways of DNA repair, including those that are thought to exist in mitochondria.

Some DNA lesions can be repaired directly back to the original DNA structure, as in the case of the alkyltransferase

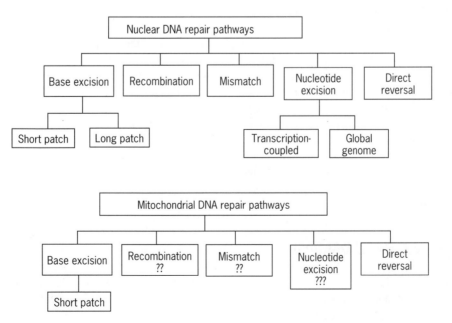

Figure 1   Repair mechanisms for nuclear and mitochondrial DNA in mammalian cells.
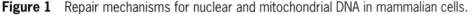

and photolyase reactions. Most lesions, however, require more complex repair mechanisms, such as base excision repair, nucleotide excision repair, mismatch repair and recombinational repair. In general, the more bulky DNA base modifications are removed by nucleotide excision repair, while less bulky ones are repaired by base excision repair pathways. These are not firm distinctions, however, since there is much more overlap between these pathways than previously thought. (See the chapters on *The Formation of DNA Adducts* and *Physical Causes of Cancer*.)

REPAIR BY DNA ALKYLTRANSFERASE

Of all DNA repair mechanisms, the simplest and most perfect is mediated by O^6-alkylguanine-DNA alkyltransferase. It is also the most specialized, applying only to a particular type of chemical damage to DNA bases, namely chemical adducts at the guanine-O6 or cytosine-O4 positions. These types of adducts are produced by chemical carcinogens such as nitrosamines and by chemotherapeutic agents such as nitrosoureas (see the chapter *The Formation of DNA Adducts*). Adducts at the guanine-O6 or cytosine-O4 positions alter the base-pairing preferences and therefore are highly mutagenic. Cells normally contain an alkyltransferase, which efficiently removes alkylations from these positions and restores the original chemistry of the base. Thus the repair is perfect in that the DNA is brought back precisely to its original state.

The alkyltransferase that accomplishes this feat is an unusual enzyme, because it is, in part, its own substrate: it transfers an adduct from a DNA base to a sulfhydryl group at the enzyme's active site. The alkylated sulfhydryl group on the enzyme is so stable that it cannot be removed to regenerate the active enzyme molecule: each enzyme molecule can act only once, whereupon it becomes permanently inactivated. The reaction therefore is stoichiometric rather than catalytic, and fails to meet a classical criterion for an enzyme. Nevertheless, in terms of structure and mechanism, this is clearly an enzyme in that it lowers the energy barrier of a reaction. Its unusual feature is that one of the stable products of the reaction happens to be part of the enzyme protein itself. This same feature, however, makes the repair very fast and efficient. It is one of the few DNA repair processes that can be accomplished in essentially a single step. However, the number of DNA adducts that can be removed is limited by the number of active enzyme molecules present in the cell.

REPAIR OF SINGLE-BASE DAMAGE

Base excision repair (BER) is thought to be the major way in which the cell deals with most types of damage to single bases in DNA, although nucleotide excision repair (NER) (see later) may also play a part. An exceptional case, however, is presented by adducts at the O6 position of guanine; as described above, these adducts can be removed by an alkyltransferase while leaving the normal guanine base in place. The alkyltransferase-mediated repair of guanine-O6 adducts is unusual and remarkable in that it is error free. On the other hand, adducts at the guanine-N7 position, which is the most common alkylation site on DNA, lead to loss of the guanine base. This can occur either through the action of a repair glycosylase or by spontaneous hydrolysis of the glycosidic bond (alkylation at N7 facilitates spontaneous release of guanine from DNA). Either way, the loss of the base leaves the DNA with an unsubstituted deoxyribose unit, known as a base-free site or AP site (AP stands for apurinic/apyrimidinic). A particularly important BER mechanism removes uracil residues that normally arise spontaneously due to the occasional hydrolysis of the 4-amino group of cytosine. This is carried out by a uracil glycosylase.

Hydrolysis of 5-methylcytosines yields a normal base, thymine, which would not be recognized as abnormal by a repair glycosylase. 5-Methylcytosine in mammalian DNA occurs only at 5'-CpG-3' dinucleotides, which consequently are strongly disfavoured in most regions of the genome. Some DNA regions, usually outside of coding sequences, however contain islands rich in CpG sequences which, when methylated, are subject to GC → AT transitions.

REPAIR OF BASE-FREE SITES

Two independent mechanisms exist for repair of base-free (or 'abasic') sites: single-nucleotide gap-filling and long-patch repair. Either process may be preceded by the action of a glycosylase which cleaves the glycosidic bond between the base and sugar moieties of DNA. An AP-endonuclease then cuts the DNA strand containing the base-free site immediately on the 5' side of the lesion, and yields a 5'-sugar-phosphate terminus and a 3'-OH terminus. A repair polymerase (typically Pol β) then extends the 3' end and displaces the base-free sugar residue. In the long-patch mechanism, the displacement of the damaged strand extends to include between 2 and about 10 nucleotide residues. The displaced DNA segment (sometimes referred to as a 'flap') is removed by a flap endonuclease (FEN1). The DNA strand can then be made whole by the action a DNA ligase. Long-patch repair may be carried out via Pol β, which does not require proliferating cell nuclear antigen (PCNA), or via Pol δ which is PCNA dependent (discussed by Prasad *et al.*, 2000). These authors recently found in a reconstituted system of long-patch BER that FEN1 and Polβ can cooperate in the linked processes of strand displacement (a Pol β function) and displaced-strand cleavage (a FEN1 function). The two enzymes mutually stimulated each other in this system.

A PCNA-dependent reconstituted long-patch BER system was found to require replication protein A (RPA) for optimum activity; PCNA and RPA seemed to function coordinately (Dianov *et al.*, 1999).

It is not yet clear how the two base excision repair pathways (involving short- or long-patch repair of the consequent base-free sites) are regulated. It may depend on the type of glycosylase involved or on the type of DNA polymerase. The BER complex situated at the AP site in DNA involves DNA polymerase, FEN1, AP-endonuclease and PCNA, and the organisation of this complex is very important. In addition to the short- and long-patch BER pathways, there appears to be another BER pathway of transcription coupled repair which deals with repair of active genes. As mentioned above, there is much emerging evidence for overlap and interaction between the repair pathways. For example, the xeroderma group G (XPG) protein participates in both BER and NER.

NUCLEOTIDE EXCISION REPAIR (NER)

NER is the most versatile of the DNA repair mechanisms. It repairs a variety of bulky adducts that distort the DNA helix, but only if both chemical damage and helix distortion are present. One of the most important functions of NER is to repair photoproducts due to sunlight UV exposure. One of these products, pyrimidine–6,4–pyrimidine dimers, (representing about 20% of photoproducts), causes large DNA helix distortions and is efficiently repaired by NER. Another photoproduct, cyclobutane–pyrimidine dimers, is more abundant (about 80% of the total), but causes less helix distortion and therefore is less efficiently repaired. The repair of the latter type of lesion may be aided specifically by the XPE protein, but the exact mechanism is not clear. NER also repairs bulky carcinogen adducts, such as DNA adducts of polycyclic aromatic hydrocarbons, and DNA cross-links produced by anti-cancer drugs such as cisplatin. In addition, NER can function (albeit inefficiently) as a backup for base damage that evades BER or the alkyltransferase repair mechanism (see reviews by Balajee and Bohr (2000), Batty and Wood (2000) and de Boer and Hoeijmakers (2000)).

The proteins associated with the seven complementation groups of xeroderma pigmentosum (XP) (XPA to XPG) play parts in the NER mechanism. XP is a highly cancer-prone disease in which the patients suffer from high incidence of skin and internal cancers, due to defective DNA repair. The NER process is depicted in an interaction diagram in **Figure 2**. The diagram shows how the proteins involved in NER assemble at the site of a DNA lesion and cooperate to excise a DNA single-strand segment containing the lesion.

The global form of NER operates throughout the genome. A modified form of NER, known as transcription-coupled repair (TCR), however, operates preferentially at sites of transcription. TCR differs from global NER in the mechanism by which the DNA helix at the lesion site is opened to permit access to the repair machinery. In global NER, the lesion is recognized by the XPC:HR23B heterodimer which then recruits the transcription factor IIH (TFIIH) complex. TFIIH contains two DNA helicases (XPB and XPD) that unwind the DNA locally in opposite directions from the lesion site. At about the same time, XPA comes into play and serves as a nucleus for the assembly of other repair components at the lesion site. XPA may also participate in the recognition of lesions. The DNA unwinding may be assisted by the single-strand binding protein RPA. In addition, RPA can bind several key proteins, including XPA, and thus may assist in assembling the repair complex.

In the case of TCR, a DNA lesion is detected in the course of transcription by RNA polymerase II and its associated proteins. The polymerase stalls at the site of the lesion, which somehow leads to the assembly of the repair complex. Although the details of how this happens are not clear, the polymerase presumably dissociates and is replaced by TFIIH and XPA; it is thought that the Cockayne syndrome group B (CSB) protein plays a part in this process.

TFIIH has at least two modes of action. First, it functions in transcription initiation through the action of its associated helicases, as well as through the action of cyclinH:cdk7 (another component of TFIIH) which phosphorylates the C-terminal tail of RNA polymerase II and thereby allows transcription to start. (Another function of cyclinH:cdk7 is to phosphorylate cyclin-dependent kinases in the course of cell cycle regulation (Kohn, 1999).) Second, the helicases XPB and XPD (which are also part of the TFIIH complex) play an important part in NER and TCR (the helicases bind more tightly in the TFIIH complex than does cyclinH:cdk7, which may not be present in the repair form of TFIIH).

The subsequent steps of NER or TCR, leading to the excision of an oligonucleotide containing the lesion, are summarized in **Figure 2** and its caption. After excision, the resulting gap in the damaged DNA strand must be filled. This is accomplished by DNA polymerse δ or ε, followed by DNA ligase I. The assembly of the polymerase at the $3'$ terminus of the stand gap first requires PCNA, which clamps on to the DNA and RFC, which loads PCNA on to the $3'$ terminus.

When an NER complex has assembled at a DNA lesion, the complex may send a signal indicating the presence of DNA damage. A linchpin in this communication is p53. The ability of p53 to bind RPA could be part of this communication link.

Transcription-coupled NER

As already mentioned, NER has two pathways: (1) transcription-coupled repair (TCR) and (2) global genome repair (GGR). The TCR pathway repairs lesions in the

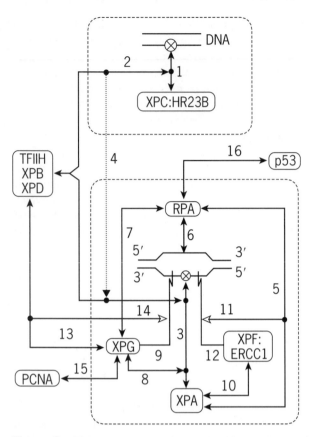

transcribed strand of transcriptionally active genes and is dependent on RNA polymerase II (RNA pol II) (Balajee and Bohr, 2000). The GGR pathway removes lesions from genes regardless of whether they are transcriptionally active or inactive.

Cells of a rare genetic disease, Cockayne syndrome (CS), are defective in TCR, but proficient in GGR of UV-induced DNA damage. Affected individuals suffer from postnatal growth failure resulting in cachectic dwarfism, photosensitivity, skeletal abnormalities, mental retardation, progressive neurological degeneration, retinopathy, cataracts and sensorineural hearing loss. Two complementation groups, CS-A and CS-B, have been identified and the corresponding genes have been cloned. The cellular phenotype of CS includes increased sensitivity to a number of DNA-damaging agents including UV radiation, ionizing radiation and hydrogen peroxide (Friedberg, 1996).

A characteristic feature of CS cells is that they do not recover the ability to synthesize RNA efficiently after UV damage; this phenotype is consistent with a defect in TCR. The *CSA* and *CSB* genes have been cloned and their products characterized. The *CSA* gene product is a 44-kDa protein that belongs to the 'WD repeat' family. Members of this protein family are structural and regulatory proteins,

Figure 2   Molecular interactions in nucleotide excision repair (NER). The symbols used in this and subsequent diagrams are defined in (Kohn, 1999) (or see http://discover.nci.nih.gov/kohnk/interaction_maps.html). The upper dashed box depicts a normal double-stranded DNA helix bearing a lesion which is recognized and bound by a heterodimer consisting of XPC and HR23B. A DNA segment surrounding the lesion is then unwound by the XPB and XPD helicases (components of the TFIIH transcription factor complex). The lower dashed box depicts the region of unwound helix and the excision of a DNA segment containing the lesion. The transition from the closed to the unwound state of the DNA (with its associated proteins) is indicated by the hatched arrow with the solid triangle arrowhead. During this transition, the XPC:HR23B complex is replaced by XPA. XPA serves to assemble several proteins that participate in the excision of the lesion. In the case of transcription-coupled repair (TCR), the DNA helix around the lesion is already unwound due to the transcription process, and therefore repair can begin with XPA (lower box) and does not require XPC or HR23B. The numbered steps are as follows. (1) A lesion in one strand of an intact DNA helix becomes bound by a dimer consisting of the XPC and HR23B proteins. (2) This dimer (XPC:HR23B) binds the TFIIH complex which contains the DNA helicases XPB and XPD (Yokoi et al., 2000). All of these proteins are needed for the initial opening of the DNA helix at the site of the lesion. XPB and XPD function with opposite polarity: ($3' \rightarrow 5'$ and $5' \rightarrow 3'$, respectively) to unwind the DNA for a short distance on both sides of the lesion (no diagram symbol is available for unwinding). (3) XPA is then recruited to the lesion (however, in the case of TCR, the helix is already open owing to the presence of RNA polymerase II, and XPA can bind to the lesion without the aid of XPC:HR23B). (4) The transition arrow (solid triangle arrowhead, shown here hatched) indicates that the DNA helix opens and XPC:HR23B is replaced by XPA, and the TFIIH complex now is bound to XPA instead of to XPC:HR23B. (5) XPA binds the DNA single-strand-binding protein RPA. (6) RPA binds the undamaged strand where the helix has been opened. Thus RPA helps to stabilize the XPA complex at the site of the lesion (the length of the unwound region in NER is similar to the 30 nucleotides required for optimum binding of RPA to DNA single strand). (7) RPA recruits endonuclease XPG. (8) XPG binds XPA while XPA is bound to the lesion (XPG may be required for XPA to replace XPC:HR23B at the site of the lesion; this is not shown in the diagram). (9) XPG incises the lesion-containing strand on the $3'$ side of the lesion (approximately 6–14 nucleotide residues away from the lesion). (10) XPA recruits the XPF:ERCC1 heterodimer to the lesion site. (11) RPA interacts with XPF and directs the endonuclease activity of XPF to the $5'$ side of lesion. (12) XPF incises the lesion-containing strand on the $5'$ side of the lesion (approximately 16–25 nucleotides away from the lesion) (a single-strand segment containing the lesion is thereby released whose modal length is 27 (24–32) nucleotides, independent of the type of lesion. The sites of incision by XPF and XPG may be at or close to the transitions between unwound and helical DNA, since these two enzymes are structure specific endonucleases). (13) TFIIH interacts strongly with XPG. (14) TFIIH may help to position XPG on the $3'$ side of the lesion. (15) XPG recruits PCNA which is required for the subsequent DNA repair synthesis that fills the gap left by the excised strand segment. (16) RPA can bind p53 and thereby perhaps serve to signal the presence of DNA damage. For references, see reviews by Balajee and Bohr (2000); Batty and Wood (2000); and de Boer and Hoeijmakers (2000) and the annotation list for DNA repair in Kohn (1999).

but usually lack enzymatic activity. The *CSB* gene product is a 168-kDa protein that belongs to the SWI/SNF family, which are DNA and RNA helicases with seven conserved sequence motifs. CSB has an acidic amino acid stretch, a glycine-rich region and two putative NLS sequences. CSB is a DNA-stimulated ATPase, but is not able to unwind DNA in a conventional strand displacement assay (Selby and Sancar, 1997).

The precise molecular role of CSB is not clear at present. CSB may facilitate repair of active genes by recruiting DNA repair proteins to actively transcribed regions. *In vitro*, CSB forms a complex with RNA polymerase II, DNA and the RNA transcript in a manner that requires ATP hydrolysis (Tantin *et al.*, 1997). This quaternary complex recruits another molecular complex including the TFIIH core subunits p62 and XPB. TFIIH is a complex factor thought to promote local DNA unwinding during transcription initiation by RNA pol II and promoter escape, as well as in NER (Balajee and Bohr, 2000).

It is also possible that CSB indirectly stimulates TCR by facilitating transcription. Members of the SWI/SNF family are involved in regulating transcription, chromatin remodelling and DNA repair, including such actions as disruption of protein–protein and protein–DNA interactions. The *CSB* gene product could have a similar function. In fact, it is still a matter of debate whether CS is due to a primary defect in transcription or DNA repair (Friedberg, 1996). Some evidence suggests that CSB may indirectly stimulate TCR by facilitating the process of transcription (Balajee *et al.*, 1997; Selby and Sancar, 1997). Thus, CSB may be a transcription elongation factor and a repair-coupling factor acting at the site of RNA pol II-blocking lesions, and the CS phenotype may arise from deficiencies in both transcription and DNA repair. The biological function of CSB in these different pathways may be mediated by distinct functional domains of the protein.

It is well established that the *CSB* phenotype involves a defect in TCR of UV-induced DNA damage, although

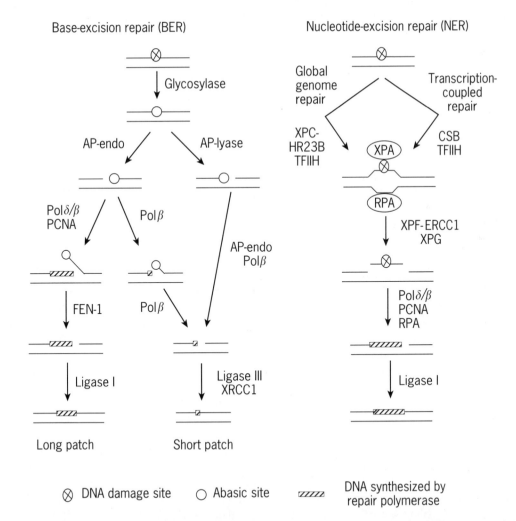

Figure 3 The pathways of base excision repair (BER) and nucleotide excision repair (NER). Some of the proteins involved are shown. The general steps are recognition, incision, replication and ligation. NER has a subpathway called transcription-coupled repair (TCR) and within BER there are two pathways, long-patch and short-patch BER. The individual pathways are described in the text.

CSB may also function in TCR of oxidative damage (Le Page et al., 2000).

The various types of BER and NER are summarized in **Figure 3**.

MITOCHONDRIAL DNA REPAIR IN MAMMALIAN CELLS

Oxidative phosphorylation is an essential metabolic pathway that takes place in the mitochondrion and produces reactive oxygen species (ROS), such as superoxide, hydrogen peroxide, and hydroxyl radicals. Mitochondrial DNA (mtDNA), because of its close proximity to the electron transport chain, is at risk of damage from the ROS produced by oxidative phosphorylation. The most common oxidative DNA lesions in mtDNA are uracil, 8-oxoG and thymine glycol. If unrepaired, uracil can cause GC–AT transition mutations. Thus, it is predicted that insufficient DNA repair capacity in the mitochondrion could lead to mitochondrial dysfunction and degenerative disease including altered energy balance and other pathophysiological states associated with ageing and cancer.

For many years it was thought that mitochondria had no DNA repair capacity, and that this could explain the accumulation of DNA lesions found here with ageing. Recently, however, it has become evident that there is, indeed, efficient DNA repair in these organelles, but that they do not appear to have the same variety of repair pathways that are found in the nuclear DNA. The known or suspected DNA repair mechanisms present in mitochondria are indicated in **Figure 1**. The many question marks at repair pathways indicate lack of concise knowledge; there is renewed interest in the exploration of mitochondrial DNA repair.

There have been reports of recombinational repair and mismatch repair pathways in mitochondria and the general repair pathways in mtDNA were recently reviewed (Croteau et al., 1999). In mtDNA, UV-induced lesions, but not oxidative lesions, are repaired. 8-Oxoguanine is efficiently removed from mtDNA, as it is from actively transcribed genes in the nucleus, and the repair efficiency is similar in all regions of the mitochondrial genome (Croteau et al., 1999).

The mitochondria contain enzymes that participate specifically in BER in the mitochondrion. An early indication of the existence of mitochondrial BER (mtBER) was the isolation of a mammalian mitochondrial endonuclease that recognizes and cleaves AP sites. Later, an in vitro reconstituted repair assay was performed using mitochondrial enzymes from Xenopus laevis and an abasic site-containing DNA substrate (Pinz and Bogenhagen, 1998). A DNA ligase was also purified from mitochondria that may be related to nuclear DNA ligase III. Recently, it was confirmed that the gene encoding human DNA ligase III produces two forms of the ligase, one nuclear and one

mitochondrial (Lakshmipathy and Campbell, 1999). The mitochondrial DNA Pol β possesses a $5'$-deoxyribose phosphate lyase activity via β-elimination, suggesting that Pol β may play a role in mitochondrial BER (Longley et al., 1998). PCNA has also been shown to stimulate Pol β-mediated DNA synthesis, suggesting that PCNA may be an auxiliary factor in mitochondrial mtDNA replication and repair.

DNA MISMATCH REPAIR (MMR)

MMR deals with at least two types of replication errors: (1) single base-pair mismatches and (2) insertion or deletion loops that arise by slippage between the template and replicating strands. Slippage tends to occur in sequence-repeat regions, such as segments of poly(A) or of dinucleotide repeats such as $(AC)_n$, where base pairing near the replication point can easily shift position. Repeated sequences sometimes occur incidentally in coding regions where slippage could cause frame-shift mutations.

A marker for defective repair of insertion/deletion loops is microsatellite instability. Since microsatellites generally occur outside of genes, abnormal length variation of these sequence repeats does not usually cause mutation. Microsatellite instability, however, serves as a sensitive indicator of the harder to detect changes brought about by the same mechanism within genes.

The significance of the MMR mutator phenotype in tumours with microsatellite instability is shown by the finding of frame-shift mutations in numerous tumour-suppressor genes (APC, TGFβ-RII, IGF-IIR, BAX, BRCA1, BRCA2) and some DNA repair genes (hMSH3, hMSH6, BLM) (Buermeyer et al., 1999). These frame shifts usually occur within mononucleotide tracts.

In human cells, MMR is carried out by a choreography of multiprotein complexes made up by hMSH2, hMSH3, hMSH6, hMLH1, hPMS2 and probably hMLH3 (**Figure 4**). Also involved are excision and replication proteins: Pol δ, PCNA, RFC, EXO1 and FEN1, which degrade and replace the error-containing segments of newly synthesized strand. The system must also include a DNA ligase which remains to be identified. How the system distinguishes the newly synthesized strand is unknown, although it may well be through recognition of a strand terminus.

Single base-pair mismatches and insertion/deletion loops are recognized by hMSH2:hMSH6 heterodimers (also known as hMutSα complex) which serve as the starting point for the assembly of a 'repairosome' typically containing hMLH1, hPMS2 and the excision and replication machinery proteins. An alternative route is through hMSH2:hMSH3 heterodimers (hMutSβ) which recruits a repairosome via hMLH1 and hMLH3; this complex can repair insertion/deletion loops, but not single base-pair mismatches. Loss of hMSH2 or hMLH1 thus abrogates the repair of both types of defects. As expected, cells defective

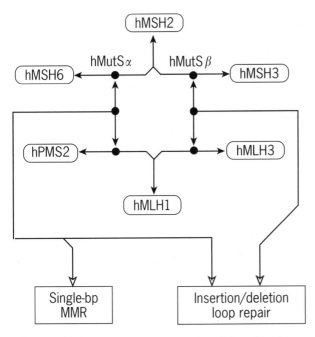

Figure 4 Molecular interactions and functional capabilities of proteins implicated in DNA mismatch repair (MMR). The hMutSα complex, consisting of hMSH2 and hMSH6, combines with hMLH1 and hPMS2 to form the nucleus for a repairosome complex that repairs both insertion/deletion loops and single base-pair mismatches. The hMutSβ complex, consisting of hMSH2 and hMSH3, combines with hMLH1 and hMLH3 and leads to a repairosome complex that can repair insertion/deletion loops, but not single base-pair mismatches.

in *hMSH6* display a mutator phenotype but exhibit little or no microsatellite instability (Jiricny and Nystrom-Lahti, 2000)(because insertion/deletion loops can still be repaired via the hMutSβ path).

It has been proposed that the hMSH2:hMSH6 complex functions akin to a molecular switch, owing to its ADP/ATP-binding ability and ATPase activity (Fishel, 1998). In its ADP-bound state, hMSH2:hMSH6 binds strongly to DNA mismatches. This binding then facilitates the exchange of ADP for ATP (which otherwise occurs only very slowly). In the ATP-bound state, hMSH2:hMSH6 can dissociate from DNA lesions. Its ATPase activity then recycles hMSH2:hMSH6 to the active ADP state. At some point in the cycle, the components of the repairosome are assembled.

MMR, Apoptosis and Chemotherapy Resistance

In addition to its role in DNA repair, the MMR system seems to signal the presence of DNA damage to the apoptosis-initiating system, which may be why MMR-defective tumour cells tend to have increased resistance to DNA-damaging drugs such as cisplatin (see reviews by Li

(1999) and Jiricny and Nystrom-Lahti (2000)). Treatment of a mixture of MMR-proficient and deficient cells with cisplatin resulted in enrichment of the MMR-deficient population (Fink *et al.*, 1998). Moreover, cisplatin resistance in ovarian cancer recently was reported to be linked to suppression of *hMLH1* due to hypermethylation in the gene's promoter region (Strathdee *et al.*, 1999).

MMR-deficient cells also resist killing by alkylating agents that methylate DNA guanine-O6 positions. Such alkylations are mutagenic, because these alkylated guanines base-pair preferentially with T. MMR-deficient cells are alkylation tolerant: they retain the alkylations, but are not killed by them. The cost of survival, however, is mutagenesis. Treatment of *MSH2*-knockout mice with agents that methylate DNA guanine-O6 positions failed to induce apoptosis in the small intestine (a prominent response in wild-type animals) (Toft *et al.*, 1999). This *MSH2*-dependent apoptosis was partially mediated by a p53-dependent pathway.

The apoptosis resistance also carries over to other DNA damaging agents including 6-thioguanine (which becomes incorporated into DNA as a bogus base), cisplatin and topoisomerase blockers. Resistance to these agents is conferred by loss of *MSH2, MSH6, MLH1* or *PMS2* functions (but not by loss of *MSH3* function) in several mammalian systems. In addition to loss of apoptotic response, the resistant cells do not exhibit the usual G2/M cell cycle arrest. The components of the MMR system thus appear to have an essential role in the transmission of DNA damage signals (see reviews by Buermeyer *et al.* (1999) and Li (1999)).

The role of MMR in apoptosis signalling may have relevance for chemotherapy with DNA-damaging agents, because drug resistance may develop by loss of MMR function in a single selection step (Aebi *et al.*, 1996). Loss of MMR may also confer resistance to low doses of ionizing radiation (Fritzell *et al.*, 1997; DeWeese *et al.*, 1998) (see review by Li (1999)).

The route by which signals from the MMR system induce apoptosis remains to be elucidated; it may in part involve phosphorylation of p53 and/or the related p73 family proteins (Duckett *et al.*, 1999; Li, 1999). The function of p73 in the induction of apoptosis in cisplatin-treated cells may be regulated by tyrosine kinase c-Abl (Gong *et al.*, 1999). Since MMR is targeted exclusively to newly synthesized DNA strands (or to strand regions containing nearby strand breaks (Duckett *et al.*, 1999)), base damage in the template strand could not be removed: the MMR system could sense the mismatch caused by the base damage, but would attempt to repair the wrong strand. This futile repair cycle is one model proposed as the initiator of the apoptosis signal. Alternatively, the MMR recognition complex might assemble at damage-induced mismatches near replication forks, block replication and thereby induce apoptosis (Li, 1999).

Thus the MMR system corrects DNA mismatches caused by base damage in newly synthesized DNA strands (or in strands near break sites). However, when presented with damage that it cannot repair, the system sends out an apoptosis-inducing signal. Loss of components of the MMR system allows cells to survive and proliferate while retaining an accumulation of DNA damage. Treatment of MMR-defective tumours with drugs that alkylate DNA at guanine-O6 positions may therefore be ineffective or even detrimental (Li, 1999).

MMR and Colon Cancer

For reasons unknown, MMR defects are associated mainly with cancer of the colon (predominantly right colon), endometrium and ovary. MMR is most closely associated with HNPCC, the most common cancer predisposition syndrome; 70% of HNPCC kindred have germ-line mutations in one of the MMR-associated genes. About 60% of the mutations are in *hMLH1* and about 35% in *hMSH2* (Jiricny and Nystrom-Lahti, 2000; http://www.nfdht.nl). Tumours of HNPCC kindred with mutations in *hMSH2* or *hMLH1* have strong mutator phenotypes and high microsatellite instability (Buermeyer *et al.*, 1999). One copy of the gene is mutated in the germline of HNPCC patients, and both copies are mutated in their tumours (which do not exhibit loss of heterozygosity). Loss of MMR requires inactivation of both copies of one of the critical genes, and occurs with increased probability if one of the copies is already mutated in the germ line. In contrast to other cancers, which usually have rampant aneuploidy and loss of chromosome arms, HNPCC tumours have few allelic losses and often have a diploid karyotype (Rosen, 1997). Although chromosome instability and aneuploidy are early events in the development of most other cancers, the initial tumorigenic event in HNPCC is loss of mismatch repair, which induces more localized genome alterations.

Microsatellite instability is also present in 15% of colon cancer patients who have no family history of colon cancer. As in HNPCC, these sporadic tumours occur predominantly on the right side of the colon. In most of these cases, MMR is inactivated, not by mutations, but by transcriptional silencing of the *hMLH1* gene. The *hMLH1* gene is subject to silencing by hypermethylation of its promoter, which is a primary factor in sporadic gastrointestinal tumours having microsatellite instability. In cell lines derived from such tumours, this methylation can be reversed by treating the cells with 5-azacytidine, which eventually restores hMLH1 expression. In most of the tumours, both copies of *hMLH1* are distinguishably suppressed by hypermethylation, although occasionally one of the alleles is inactivated by mutation. For further details and references, see Buermeyer *et al.* (1999) and Markowitz (2000).

MMR and TGFβ Receptor

TGFβ-RII, a receptor in the TGFβ tumour-suppressor pathway, has a special relationship with MMR-deficient colon and stomach cancers. This relationship is due to two circumstances. First, the coding sequence of the human *TGFβ-RII* gene contains a homopolymer tract of 10 adenines that is subject to frame-shift mutation in MMR-deficient cells. This causes premature transcript termination with loss of most of the cytoplasmic domain of the receptor. Among colon tumours, these *TGFβ-RII* frame shifts are found exclusively and almost universally in those tumours that exhibit microsatellite instability. Second, TGFβ functions in intestinal crypts to cause cell cycle arrest and apoptosis when these cells reach the luminal region of the crypts, which is where TGFβ is concentrated. If signalling through the TGFβ pathway is abrogated, crypt cells can continue to proliferate and can initiate the sequence of changes that eventually leads to malignancy. By contrast, MMR-deficient endometrial cancers have a much lower frequency of *TGFβ-RII* frame-shift mutations than do the MMR-deficient gastrointestinal cancers (reviewed by Markowitz (2000)).

The significance of the TGFβ pathway in colon cancer is confirmed by the occurrence, in 15% of microsatellite-stable colon cancers, of inactivating mutations of the *TGFβ-RII* gene outside the poly(A) tracts. Some microsatellite-stable colon cancers with normal *TGFβ-RII* genes bear mutations in downstream components of the TGFβ pathway, such as Smad2 and Smad4. For a recent review, see Markowitz (2000).

A molecular interaction diagram of the essentials of the TGFβ pathway leading to cell proliferation is shown in **Figure 5** and explained in the caption.

Frame-shift mutation in the poly(A) tract of the *TGFβ-RII* gene is often the initiating lesion in microsatellite instability-high non-familial colon cancers. This was shown by a tight correlation between the adenoma-to-carcinoma transition and poly(A) tract length alteration in retrospective tissue pathology samples (Grady *et al.*, 1998). A more recent study suggested that the initial gene alteration could be in either the *TGFβ-RII* or the *BAX* gene, or in both (Calin *et al.*, 2000). Since BAX is a proapoptotic factor, mutation of this gene may contribute to the apoptosis resistance of some microsatellite instability-high tumours. Nevertheless, TGFβ itself has a proapoptotic effect (pathway unknown) on normal intestinal epithelial cells in culture (references cited by Grady *et al.* (1998)). (See chapter *Signalling by TGF-β*.)

RECOMBINATIONAL REPAIR: REPAIR OF DNA DOUBLE-STRAND BREAKS (DSB) AND CROSS-LINKS

DSB constitute a common type of DNA damage, produced by ionizing radiation, replication blocks and certain DNA-reactive drugs such as bleomycin. The formation and repair of DSB are also part of the immune system's

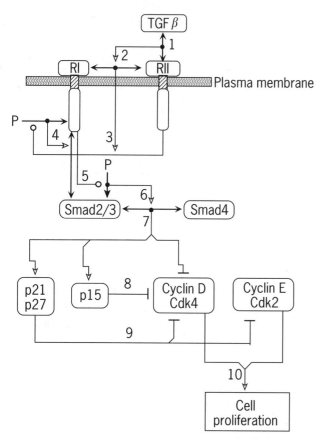

Figure 5 Molecular interaction diagram of the essentials of TGFβ signalling to cell proliferation. (1) TGFβ binds to the type II receptor, TGFβ-RII. (2) This stimulates heterodimer formation between TGFβ-RII and TGFβ-RI. (3) The RII subunit can then phosphorylate the cytoplasmic domain of RI. (4) A phosphorylated site on RI binds Smad2, thereby recruiting this protein to the plasma membrane. (5) This permits the kinase domain of RI to phosphorylate Smad2. (6) Phosphorylated Smad2 binds Smad4. (7) The Smad2:Smad4 heterodimer translocates to the nucleus, where it stimulates the expression of G1/S phase inhibitors p15, p21 and p27, and inhibits the G1/S phase stimulators cyclin D and cdk4 (Massague, 1998; Massague and Wotton, 2000). (8) p15 inhibits Cdk4. (9) p21 and p27 inhibit both Cdk4 and Cdk2 kinase activities. (10) Both cyclin D- and cyclin E-dependent kinases are required for entry of cells into S phase. (For further details, see the chapter *Signalling by TGF-β*.)

V(D)J recombination process. Defects in DSB repair can cause translocations and other DNA rearrangements (Flores-Rozas and Kolodner, 2000). There are two types of recombinational repair of DSB, differing in whether or not the DNA ends to be joined require extensive sequence homology.

Non-homologous End Joining (NHEJ): Repair of DNA Double-strand Breaks

The NHEJ mechanism repairs DNA double-strand breaks without the need for extensive sequence homology between the DNA ends to be joined, although a few complementary base pairs are needed to provide cohesive ends. NHEJ is an error-prone repair process, because it usually creates small deletions. NHEJ is responsible for the rejoining of DSB during V(D)J recombination in the processing of immunoglobulin genes. Defects in NHEJ in mice cause severe combined immune deficiency and radiation sensitivity.

Small deletions are a by-product of NHEJ, because of the need for cohesive DNA ends ('microhomology'), generated by resecting a few nucleotides from one of the DNA strands. The required microhomology may occasionally be as short as a single base pair, although two or three is more efficient. This is in marked contrast to the extensive homology needed by the 'single-strand annealing' repair mechanism, which produces large deletions (see below). NHEJ usually requires resection of only a short region to reach a sequence of microhomology by chance. The exonuclease that resects one of the DNA strands and stops when it detects microhomology is thought to be Mre11, a component of the Mre11: Rad50:Nbs1 module (see the heading The DNA Replication Checkpoint) (Paull and Gellert, 2000).

NHEJ proceeds with the binding of Ku (Ku70–Ku80 dimer) to the ends of the broken DNA (the physical relationship between Ku and Mre11 is unknown). The DNA-bound Ku protein recruits a tight dimer consisting of XRCC4 and Lig4. The DNA ligase activity of Lig4 is thereby activated and efficiently seals the broken strands (**Figure 6**). Ku can also recruit and activate the catalytic subunit of the DNA-dependent protein kinase (DNA-PKcs) to the break site. DNA-PKcs, however, is not as essential as Ku, and its exact role in NHEJ is not clear. DNA-PK may phosphorylate Ku70, or RPA (a single-strand binding heterotrimer that may play a role in the process) or DNA-PK itself (see Nick McElhinny *et al.* (2000) and a review by Karran (2000)).

Homologous Recombination, Another Mechanism of DSB Repair

In mammalian cells, homologous recombination was until recently thought to be much less common than NHEJ. Indeed, transfected DNA usually integrates nonhomologously. However, it now appears that homologous recombination does play a major role in DSB repair (see review by Jasin (2000)).

Repair by homologous recombination is not subject to the loss of nucleotides at the joining site that makes NHEJ error-prone. However, when double-strand breaks occur

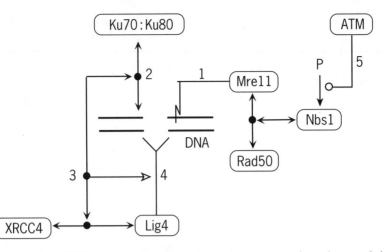

Figure 6   The NHEJ mechanism of DNA double-strand break repair, as currently understood. (1) One DNA strand is resected a short distance by the exonuclease Mre11 (probably functioning as a Mre11:Rad50:Nbs1 trimer) until a point of microhomology is reached, which provides cohesive ends. (2) The double-strand ends bind Ku70:Ku80 dimer. (3) The DNA-bound Ku70:Ku80 recruits Lig4:XRCC4, a tight dimer. (4) Lig4 is thereby activated and brought to the site where it can ligate the strands. Other molecules, such as DNA-PKcs and RPA, may have roles in this process, but their functions remain to be defined. (5) Nbs1 is phosphorylated by ATM in response to DNA damage, as a result of which DNA replication is inhibited (mechanism unknown).

within repetitive sequences (such as Alu-family elements, of which there are about 10^6 copies scattered in the human genome), recombination can occur between Alu elements in different parts of a chromosome or between different chromosomes. This can cause deletion or expansion of regions within a chromosome or translocation between chromosomes. Nevertheless, the preference for recombination between aligned sister chromatids presumably minimizes major chromosome aberrations.

When recombination occurs between homologous chromosomes one of which contains a defective critical gene, the normal copy may be lost. The resulting loss of heterozygosity often can be readily detected. A classical example is the retinoblastoma gene, *Rb*, a recessive tumour suppressor. Heterozygous carriers of a mutant *Rb* gene are susceptible to loss of the functional copy of the gene in an occasional cell, an event that starts the cell on the road to malignancy.

Repair of double-strand breaks or cross-links by homologous recombination requires complementary sequences between the damaged DNA and an undamaged homologue, such as a sister chromatid. First, the 5′-terminating strands of the double-strand break are resected by an exonuclease, so as to leave a 3′-terminated protruding single strand. Repair of DNA cross-links is thought also to begin with processing of the lesion to yield a 3′-terminated protruding strand, but the details of how this is accomplished are unclear.

The protruding 3′-terminus then binds Rad52, a large heptameric doughnut-shaped protein that protects the strand from degradation. Seven Rad52 molecules, assembled as a symmetrical ring, bind specifically to DNA single-strand ends and prevent further exonuclease attack. Although the Rad52 ring has a large central hole, there is no evidence of DNA within the channel. The length of single-strand tail associated with the Rad52 ring is estimated as 36 nucleotides. This terminal region may be exposed and configured to facilitate base pairing with a complementary strand (Parsons *et al.*, 2000).

The single-stranded region behind the Rad52 ring is then covered by a contiguous array of Rad51 molecules to form a nucleoprotein filament, which is capable of strand exchange. Rad51 is a structural and functional homologue, of bacterial RecA that is conserved from yeast to humans. Unlike RecA, however, the eukaryotic Rad51 requires ATP hydrolysis to bind properly on DNA. One Rad51 monomer binds per three nucleotides of DNA single strand. Also, unlike RecA, Rad51 requires a 3′ or 5′ extension of DNA single strand to initiate strand exchange. (see review by Karran (2000) and references cited by Namsaraev and Berg (2000)).

The Rad51 nucleoprotein filament is a loose helix which facilitates invasion of the damaged donor strand into a homologous double-strand region that may be located on another chromatid. The strands of the undamaged recipient DNA become locally separated, while base-paired heteroduplex forms with the donor single strand from the damaged DNA. The pairing between donor and recipient strand ('heteroduplex' region) is extended by a process called 'branch migration' in which the recipient double strand opens, and its original base pairs are replaced by heteroduplex. DNA replication machinery assembles at the 3′-terminus of the donor strand and extends the strand while further displacing the original complementary strand.

Finally, the displaced strand is cleaved by an endonuclease and the donor strand is ligated to the 5′-terminus of the recipient strand.

The second strand of the damaged DNA may be processed by way of a second recombination event. Alternatively, a new complementary strand is synthesized from the template provided by the displaced recipient strand. A distinction between the two mechanisms is that the former involves only leading-strand synthesis, whereas the latter involves both leading- and lagging-strand syntheses.

The rad51–DNA complex may include additional components that provide, as yet undefined functions, conceivably involved in the processing of chromatin structures. Five sequence relatives ('paralogues') of Rad51 have been demonstrated to engage in a pattern of mutual interactions: Rad51B, Rad51C, Rad51D, XRCC2 and XRCC3. As will be described later, these molecules may function together as multiprotein complexes (Schild et al., 2000). Knockout of any of the components conferred a high degree of genomic instability and enhanced sensitivity to the DNA cross-linking agents mitomycin and cisplatin (Schild et al., 2000). Tumours that might have acquired genomic instability by loss of function of one of these paralogues would be predicted to be sensitive to DNA cross-linking and double-strand break-inducing agents.

The Rad51 System for Homologous Recombination Repair

As already mentioned, Rad51 and its relatives (Rad51B, Rad51C, Rad51D, XRCC2 and XRCC3) engage in a pattern of mutual interactions and may function together as multiprotein complexes (Schild et al., 2000). The demonstrated pattern of interactions is summarized in **Figure 7**.

In cells subjected to ionizing radiation or mitomycin, Rad51 aggregates in foci in the nucleus, made visible by immunostaining. The Rad51 foci occur at DNA damage sites in S phase cells, particularly in regions of post-replicative chromatin. This preference conforms with the preferential double-strand break repair when cells are in late S phase or G_2. The foci may represent repair assemblies that function when sister chromatids are available for homologous recombination (Karran, 2000).

The formation of these foci requires Rad51B (Takata et al., 2000), consistent with the ability of Rad51B to enhance interactions between members of the Rad51 complex (**Figure 7**). Another family member, Rad54, is also required (Karran, 2000). Rad54 binds Rad51 (Tan et al. (1999), cited by Karran (2000)) and promotes DNA double-strand break repair carried out by homologous recombination with sister chromatids (Dronkert et al., 2000).

More extended complexes are possible, since Rad51, directly or indirectly, can bind Rad52, Rad54, p53, BRCA1, BRCA2 and c-Abl. Rad52 can bind the single-strand binding protein RPA. Larger assemblies are possible if other protein–protein interactions can exist simultaneously. For example, p53 has been reported to have binding sites (in order from N- to C-terminus) for MDM2, DP1, PARP, c-Abl, RPA, XPB/D, p19ARF, p300/CBP, BRCA1 and 14-3-3. These, and potential chains of further binding interactions, have been summarized in a molecular interaction map (Kohn, 1999) (see also http://discover.nci.nih.gov/

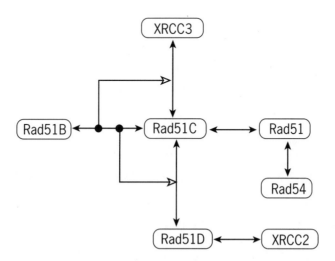

Figure 7   Interaction pattern among Rad51 family members, as reported by Schild et al. (2000) and Tan et al. (1999) (cited by Karran (2000)). The double-arrowed lines indicate demonstrated binary interactions. The interactions seem capable of building up multimolecular assemblies, as suggested by binding experiments using three components and by yeast three-hybrid experiments. The lines with open triangular arrowheads represent the finding that Rad51B enhances the Rad51C interactions with Rad51D or XRCC3. An additional finding (not included in this diagram) was that Rad51B could bind two molecules of Rad51C in the yeast three-hybrid system, suggesting that the complex could in effect become doubled (Schild et al., 2000).

kohnk/interaction_maps.html). Large multimolecular assemblies consisting of different subsets of binding interactions may be formed by remodelling for different functions. The interaction set includes cycles (e.g. Rad51-p53-BRCA1-Rad51 or p53-cAbl-Rad51-BRCA1-p53) which might form a network of molecular chains and perhaps account for the observably large nuclear foci within which DNA repair sites seem to be localized.

Single-strand Annealing

An alternative mechanism of homologous recombination repair, called single-strand annealing, is important when no sister chromatid is available. This mechanism involves resection or realignment of the broken DNA duplex to regions of homology that may be some distance from the break site. Completion of the repair then only requires DNA strand scission of ligation events. Consequently, the segment of DNA intervening between the realigned regions of homology is deleted, which makes this repair mechanism highly error prone.

DNA REPAIR INVOLVING RecQ-FAMILY HELICASES

The RecQ DNA-helicase of *Escherichia coli* is implicated in the suppression of illegitimate recombination and the repair of DNA double-strand breaks. Five human helicases homologous to RecQ are known: BLM, WRN, RecQ4 (also called RecQL4), RecQ5 and RecQ1 (**Figure 8**).

Defects in the first three have been recognized as causes of rare genetic diseases: Bloom syndrome, Werner syndrome and Rothmund–Thomson syndrome, respectively (see the chapter *Inherited Predispositions to Cancer*). All three are associated with genetic instability which appears to be due to loss of a helicase activity. The function of these helicases in mammals is only beginning to be elucidated.

The DNA Helicase Defective in Bloom Syndrome (BLM)

The BLM helicase has been the most extensively studied. It is a large protein (1417 amino acids) which contains the motifs characteristic of DNA and RNA helicases. Bloom syndrome cells exhibit a high frequency of chromosome breaks and exchanges. A characteristic of the BLM defect, not shared by the other helicase defects, however, is an increase in reciprocal exchanges between sister chromatids. The cells have a prolonged S phase, thought to be due to difficulty in dealing with stalled replication forks or abnormal replication fork configurations which may occasionally form in the normal course of events. BLM can unwind relatively short DNA duplexes in an ATP-dependent reaction. It can unwind longer helices when aided by the single-strand binding protein, RPA, to which it binds tightly (via the 70-kDa subunit of the RPA trimer) (Brosh *et al.*, 2000). BLM, however, does not efficiently unwind DNA from a blunt end, suggesting that a single-stranded tail is needed (to which RPA might anchor) in order to initiate unwinding of relatively long duplexes. RPA binding and cooperative function is a characteristic

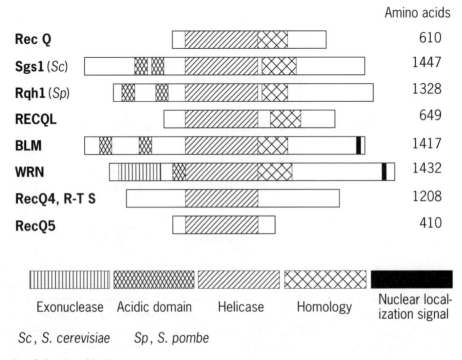

Figure 8　The RecQ family of helicases.

also of the WRN helicase. BLM preferentially unwinds four-stranded DNA helices consisting of Gs stabilized by Hoogsteen pairing; such structures sometimes occur in regulatory regions of genes, and related structures occur in telomeres (Brosh *et al.* (2000) and references cited therein).

BLM recognizes and binds to Holliday junctions (crossover structures between two double helices) and promotes branch migration (movement of the crossover junction along the helices). A possible configuration of a stalled replication fork may form by rewinding of the template strands with displacement of the two newly replicated strands which then pair with each other. The consequent structure is in fact a Holliday junction and could be acted upon by nucleases that normally 'resolve' Holliday junctions. The result would be a double-strand break (Karow *et al.*, 2000) (**Figure 9**). The duplex formed by the pairing of the newly replicated strands could be recognized as a double-strand end by the homologous recombination repair system (e.g. involving Rad52 and Rad51) and lead to homologous recombination between sister chromatids. A role of the Rad52–Rad51–Rad54 repair system is supported by the recent finding that the enhanced sister chromatid exchange in *BLM−/−* cells requires Rad54 (Wang *et al.*, 2000).

BLM is concentrated in part in nuclear foci and, during S phase, also in nucleoli. Nucleoli contain highly repetitive ribosomal DNA sequences which perhaps tend to form homologous crossovers during replication. BLM perhaps helps to prevent or reverse such crossovers, thereby reducing the chance of loss or expansion of ribosomal DNA regions. BLM has been found in a large multi-molecular protein contain BRCA1 and several DNA repair-related proteins (Wang *et al.*, 2000).

The Protein Defective in Werner Syndrome (WRN)

Werner syndrome (WS) is a homozygous recessive disease characterized by early onset of normal ageing including wrinkling of skin, greying of hair, cataracts, diabetes and osteoporosis. Neoplasms, particularly sarcomas, are observed at higher prevalence in WS patients than in normal individuals of the same age. The symptoms of WS begin to appear near puberty, and most patients die before reaching age 50. Because the clinical features of WS are similar to symptoms of ageing in normal individuals of more advanced age, WS is considered to be a segmental progeria. One of the motivations to study WS is its resemblance to ageing; thus, knowledge of the mechanism and molecular basis of WS might give insight into normal ageing and ageing-associated diseases such as cancer.

WS is caused by mutation in a single gene, *WRN*. The protein product of *WRN* is a member of the RecQ family of helicases, which also includes the yeast protein Sgs1 and

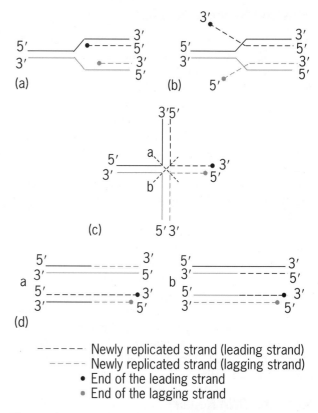

----- Newly replicated strand (leading strand)
----- Newly replicated strand (lagging strand)
• End of the leading strand
• End of the lagging strand

Figure 9 How a helicase defect can lead to a double-strand break involving a parental DNA strand in the vicinity of a stalled replication fork. (a) A normal replication fork. The newly replicated strands are shown by dashed lines with filled circles depicting strand termini. (b) After rewinding of the template helix. This may happen when there is a defect in a helicase that normally operates to unwind the template. The replication fork has backed up, displacing parts of the newly replicated strands. (c) After the displaced segments of newly replicated strands have base-paired with each other. The strands are shown re-configured in order to display the symmetry of a Holliday junction. The Holliday junction can be enzymatically 'resolved' by breakage and rejoining of strands. This can happen in two ways, indicated by the dashed diagonal lines labelled a and b which intersect the strands that are cut and recombined. (d) The final products after the Holliday junction has been resolved in the two possible ways, a and b. In both cases, one of the parental DNA strands becomes joined to newly replicated DNA ending in double-strand termini, equivalent to a double-strand break.

the Bloom syndrome protein (BLM). Biochemical evidence shows that the WRN protein is an NTP-dependent DNA unwinding enzyme (and a DNA-dependent NTPase). It was recently shown that WRN is also a 3′–5′ exonuclease (reviewed in Bohr *et al.*, 2000). Thus, WRN is a helicase, exonuclease and ATPase. WRN is the only member of the RecQ protein family that is a DNA exonuclease.

WRN and Genomic Instability

Despite extensive study of cells from WS patients, the precise molecular deficiencies involved in WS remain to be defined. Genomic instability of WS cells has been well documented and is consistent with a defect in replication, recombination or DNA repair. Some WS cells undergo premature replicative senescence and delayed progression of S phase, and some WS cells are hyper-recombinogenic. The *WRN* homologues *S. cerevisiae Sgs1*, *S. pombe rqh1* and *E. coli recQ* suppress illegitimate recombination. One possibility is that the WRN helicase is an anti-recombinase, but this hypothesis has not been tested directly.

It has been suggested that WS cells are genetically unstable because alternate DNA structures are not properly resolved. One such alternate structure is the DNA triplex, which can form in a DNA sequence-dependent manner. Sequences that can form triple helices are abundant in the human genome. WRN helicase unwinds a 3' tailed triple helix DNA substrate in an NTP-dependent manner. Thus, it is possible that triplex structures persist in WS cells and contribute to the variegated translocation mosaicism observed in WS cells.

WRN and DNA Repair

Some evidence suggests a role for the WRN protein in DNA repair. For example, WS cells are sensitive to the carcinogen 4-nitroquinoline 1-oxide (4-NQO). However, WS cells are not hypersensitive to UV light or several other DNA-damaging agents. WS cells may also be partially defective in transcription. Several observations suggest that WRN may be a general activator of transcription by RNA polymerase II (Balajee *et al.*, 1999).

WRN can proficiently unwind short DNA duplexes (~ 30 bp) in a reaction dependent on nucleoside triphosphate hydrolysis. In the presence of RPA, however, WRN can unwind long DNA duplexes (up to 800 bp). Moreover, WRN can bind directly to RPA (Brosh *et al.*, 1999).

WRN does not preferentially bind DNA damage. It could, however, play an important role as a molecular sensor of DNA damage. It may interact with the DNA minor groove in its action as a helicase, as suggested by studies using the minor groove-binding drugs netropsin and distamycin (Brosh *et al.*, 2000a,b).

The progress of the 3'–5' exonuclease reaction catalysed by WRN is blocked by bulky DNA adducts and oxidative lesions, such as 8-oxoguanine (Cooper *et al.*, 2000; Machwe *et al.*, 2000). Although WRN does not bind preferentially to DNA lesions, it may sense their presence in DNA via protein–protein interactions, perhaps as an early step in damage recognition, and may recruit DNA repair enzymes to the site of a lesion.

WRN can bind to a single-stranded site in a recombination intermediate Holliday structure, where also the RuvA protein binds. This unwinding is ATP dependent,

suggesting that it is due to the helicase activity of WRN. WS cells are not deficient in *in vitro* DNA repair assays for nucleotide excision repair (NER) of various bulky adducts in DNA or in base excision repair (BER) of abasic sites, and they are not generally sensitive to tested DNA-damaging agents, with the exception of 4NQO. Thus, as mentioned above, the influence of WRN on DNA repair may be subtle.

Interaction of WRN with Ku, a Protein Needed for DNA Double-strand Break Repair

WRN interacts physically and functionally with the Ku heterodimer. Ku strongly stimulates the 3'–5' exonuclease activity of WRN but does not affect its helicase or ATPase activities (Cooper *et al.*, 2000). The Ku heterodimer and DNA-PK are key proteins in DSB repair (Featherstone and Jackson, 1999). It has been proposed that a helicase and an exonuclease are required in DSB repair to remove the single-stranded overhangs. Thus, it is tempting to speculate that WRN provides both of these enzymatic functions during DSB repair. However, this model predicts that WS cells would have a defect in DSB repair, and there is no evidence of such a defect at the cellular level at present. Alternatively, the interaction between WRN and Ku may have a role in replication, but the role of Ku in that process is still not clear. Ku-deficient transgenic mice have a distinct senescent phenotype, suggesting that there may be another pathway in which WRN and Ku may cooperate.

Ku, the Ku70 : Ku80 heterodimer, can bind DNA and the catalytic subunit of DNA-PK. In the presence of DNA, Ku activates the kinase activity of DNA-PKcs. Ku, however, may have other functions, independent of DNA-PKcs. Ku can bind at DNA double-strand breaks, or at junctions between DNA single- and double-strand regions. Once bound, Ku can move along the DNA in an ATP-independent manner. There have been some suggestions that Ku might have helicase activity, but recent studies suggest that it does not (Cooper *et al.*, 2000). Since Ku strongly interacts with the WRN helicase it may attract that helicase activity to the site. Multiple Ku units can load on to the same DNA segment (Frit *et al.*, 2000). In addition to DNA-PKcs, Ku may bind other repair-related proteins and perhaps serve as nucleus of a multiprotein repair focus at a point of DNA damage. Ku binds to telomeric ends and may participate in DNA repair or telomerase repair functions here.

What is the Role of WRN in DNA Repair?

In summary, several lines of evidence support the notion that WRN is involved in DNA damage recognition and processing. The WRN exonuclease may function in an early step of DNA repair to recognize DNA lesions. The enzyme recognizes and arrests at some oxidative DNA base lesions. This arrest may then attract DNA repair proteins to the site, including RPA, p53 and PCNA, which have also been implicated in early steps of DNA damage recognition. WRN is likely to be in a protein complex involving various DNA replication proteins (Lebel et al., 1999) and this complex is also likely to contain proteins involved in BER.

DNA REPAIR POLYMERASES

There have been major developments in our understanding of the role of various mammalian DNA polymerases. There are now about 12 characterized DNA polymerases and more are constantly being discovered. In **Table 2** we list some of the properties of these. One of the interesting features under study is that they differ considerably in their fidelity or proofreading of the DNA template. Mutations in these polymerases have been directly associated with human cancer-prone diseases such as xeroderma pigmentosum complementation group V (Woodgate, 1999). This field is evolving very rapidly, and new polymerases are constantly being discovered.

THE Hus1:Rad1:Rad9 SLIDING CLAMP AND Rad17 CLAMP-LOADER MODEL

Hus1, Rad1, Rad9 and Rad 17 are components of a so-called 'Rad checkpoint' DNA damage response system that is conserved from yeast to humans. Although the role of these molecules in mammalian cells is not yet clear, recent evidence suggests a provocative model for their molecular mode of function (Rauen et al. (2000) and references cited therein). Hus1, Rad1 and Rad9 form a heterotrimer complex that resembles PCNA in structure

Table 2   Eukaryotic polymerases and their fidelity in replication of undamaged DNA. (Adapted from Wang, 1999.)

Polymerase	Error frequency (mutations per base pair)
Alpha (α)	10^{-4}
Delta (δ)	10^{-5}
Epsilon (ε)	10^{-6}
Gamma (γ)	10^{-6}
Beta (β)	5×10^{-4}
Zeta (ζ)	10^{-4}
Eta (η)	10^{-2}
Iota (ι)	10^{-1}
Theta (θ)	?
Kappa (κ)	10^{-4}
Lambda (λ)	?
Mu (μ)	10^{-1}

and function. PCNA forms a trimeric clamp that encircles the DNA like a doughnut and binds DNA polymerase, with which it can slide along the DNA, keeping the polymerase from falling off. Like PCNA, the Hus1:Rad1:Rad9 heterotrimer may form a clamp around the DNA. It then perhaps slides along the DNA in search of points of damage, or perhaps it binds and keeps in place a repair polymerase. As in the case of PCNA, a 'clamp loader' is needed to open the trimeric doughnut and reassemble it around the DNA. The clamp loader for PCNA is RFC, a five-subunit protein. Recent evidence suggest that the clamp loader for Hus1:Rad1:Rad9 may be Rad17, which shows sequence homology with all five subunits of PCNA (Rauen et al., 2000).

Hus1:Rad1:Rad9 trimer normally is distributed throughout the nucleus. In response to DNA damage, however, it concentrates in foci and becomes difficult to extract. This may reflect the clamping of the trimer around the DNA. The association of Rad17 with the trimer, however, is transient, as would be expected for a clamp loader.

The biological functions of this system are still poorly understood. The homologous system in yeast seems to control the S and G2 cell cycle checkpoints. In mammals, Hus1 may do more than just monitor DNA damage. Hus1 is expressed in all examined tissues and throughout embryonic development. Hus1-knockout mouse embryos are able to complete gastrulation, but shortly afterwards develop severe abnormalities and die midway in gestation. Some of the embryos survived to the point of having a beating heart. Cells in the Hus1-null embryos proliferated at a normal rate, but died by apoptosis at an abnormally high rate (Weiss et al., 2000). Cells from Hus1-null mouse embryos exhibit increased spontaneous chromosomal abnormalities, suggesting that Hus1 function is needed to maintain chromosome stability (Weiss et al., 2000).

MULTIMOLECULAR ASSEMBLIES AND NUCLEAR FOCI

DNA repair functions may often be organized in large multimolecular structures. Often these structures are assembled in large nuclear foci that can be seen by means of fluorescent antibodies. Components of the repair systems may be localized in foci which function as repair factories where DNA lesions could be brought for processing. Exchangeable components might then be efficiently shared among several repair tasks simultaneously in progress. Nuclear foci sometimes undergo rearrangement or remodelling during the cell cycle or in response to DNA damage or other types of stress. Nuclear foci or molecular repair assemblies have been found involving the Rad51 system already discussed in the section on homologous recombination. Other repair systems that may function as multimolecular assemblies include systems based on Ku (see earlier) and on BRCA1.

A BRCA1-associated Genome Surveillance Complex (BASC)

BRCA1 has several protein-binding domains, and may be associated with large multiprotein complexes in the nucleus, including the DNA repair-related proteins MSH2, MSH6, MLH1, ATM, BLM and the Rad50:Mre11:Nbs complex (Wang *et al.*, 2000a,b). The exact structure and function of these complexes is still not clear, however, because it has been difficult to demonstrate specific direct binding in cells (Jun Qin, personal communication). BRCA1-based multimolecular foci perhaps assemble in alternative arrangements with different components, making it difficult to establish individual interactions *in vivo*. In addition, BRCA-1 directly participates in TCR of oxidative DNA damage.

THE DNA REPLICATION CHECKPOINT

DNA damage during S phase normally causes temporary arrest of DNA replication. Proteins required for this checkpoint include ATM, Mre11, Rad50 and NBS1. Genetic defects occur in ATM (ataxia telangiectasia), NBS1 (Nijmegen breakage syndrome) and Mre11 (ataxia telangiectasia-like disorder) (see the chapter *Inherited Predispositions to Cancer*). In all three syndromes, DNA damage (e.g. by ionizing radiation) fails to arrest replication and leads to extensive chromosome damage (Petrini, 2000). Although the mechanistic details are not yet in, we know a few steps in the process. DNA damage causes phosphorylation of NBS1. This is required for replication arrest. ATM senses the DNA damage and carries out the phosphorylation of NBS1. The activity of JNK (c-Jun N-terminal kinase), which is normally stimulated in response to DNA damage, fails to respond in cells derived from patients having any of the three syndromes (see review by Petrini (2000)). **Figure 6** includes the molecular interactions for which there is evidence.

REFERENCES

Aebi, S., *et al.* (1996). Loss of DNA mismatch repair in acquired resistance to cisplatin. *Cancer Research*, **56**, 3087–3090.

Balajee, A. S. and Bohr, V. A. (2000). Genomic heterogeneity of nucleotide excision repair. *Gene*, **250**, 15–30.

Balajee, A. S., *et al.* (1997). Reduced RNA polymerase II transcription in intact and permeabilized Cockayne syndrome group B cells. *Proceedings of the National Academy of Sciences of the USA*, **94**, 4306–4311.

Balajee, A. S., *et al.* (1999). The Werner syndrome protein is involved in RNA polymerase II transcription. *Molecular Biology of the Cell*, **10**, 2655–2668.

Batty, D. P. and Wood, R. D. (2000). Damage recognition in nucleotide excision repair of DNA. *Gene*, **241**, 193–204.

Bohr, V. A., *et al.* (2000). Werner syndrome protein: biochemical properties and functional interactions. *Journal of Experimental Gerontology*, **35**, 695–702.

Breivik, J. and Gaudernack, G. (1999). Genomic instability, DNA methylation, and natural selection in colorectal carcinogenesis. *Cancer Biology*, **9**, 245–254.

Brosh, R. M. Jr, *et al.* (1999). Functional and physical interaction between WRN helicase and human replication protein A. *Journal of Biological Chemsitry*, **274**, 18341–18350.

Brosh, R. M., Jr, *et al.* (2000a). Potent inhibition of Werner and Bloom helicases by DNA minor groove binding drugs. *Nucleic Acids Research*, **28**, 2420–2430.

Brosh, R. M., Jr, *et al.* (2000b). Replication protein A physically interacts with the Bloom's syndrome protein and stimulates its helicase activity. *Journal of Biological Chemistry*, **275**, 23500–23508.

Buermeyer, A. B., *et al.* (1999). Mammalian DNA mismatch repair. *Annual Review of Genetics*, **33**, 533–564.

Calin, G. A., *et al.* (2000). Genetic progression in microsatellite instability high (MSI-H) colon cancers correletes with clinico-pathological parameters: a study of the TGFβRII, BAX, hMSH3, hMSH6, IGFIIR and BLM Genes. *International Journal of Cancer (Pred. Oncology)*, **89**.

Coleman, W. B. and Tsongalis, G. J. (1999). The role of genomic instability in human carcinogenesis. *Anticancer Research*, **19**, 4645–4664.

Cooper, M. P., *et al.* (2000). Ku complex interacts with and stimulates the Werner protein. *Genes and Development*, **14**, 907–912.

Croteau, D. L., *et al.* (1999). Mitochondrial DNA repair pathways. *Mutation Research*, **434**, 137–148.

de Boer, J. and Hoeijmakers, H. J. (2000). Nucleotide excision repair and human syndromes. *Carcinogenesis*, **21**, 453–460.

DeWeese, T. L., *et al.* (1998). Mouse embryonic stem cells carrying one or two defective Msh2 alleles respond abnormally to oxicative stress inflicted by low-level radiation. *Proceedings of the National Academy of Sciences of the USA*, **95**, 11915–11920.

Dianov, G. L., *et al.* (1999). Replication protein A stimulates proliferating cell nuclear antigen-dependent repair of abasic sites in DNA by human cell extracts. *Biochemistry*, **38**, 11021–11025.

Dizdaroglu, M. (1991). Chemical determination of free radical-induced damage to DNA. *Free Radicals in Biology and Medicine*, **10**, 225–242.

Dronkert, M. L. G., *et al.* (2000). Mouse RAD54 affects DNA double-strand break repair and sister chromatid exchange. *Molecular Cellular Biology*, **20**, 3147–3156.

Drummond, J. T., *et al.* (1996). Cisplatin and adriamycin resistance are associated with MutLα and mismatch repair deficiency in an ovarian tumor cell line. *Journal of Biological Chemistry*, **271**, 19645–19648.

Duckett, D. R., *et al*. (1999). hMutSα- and hMutLα-dependent phosphorylation of p53 in response to DNA methylator damage. *Proceedings of the National Academy of Sciences of the USA*, **96**, 12384–12388.

Featherstone, C. and Jackson, S. P. (1999). Ku, a DNA repair protein with multiple cellular functions? *Mutation Research*, **434**, 3–15.

Fink, D., *et al*. (1998). Enrichment for DNA mismatch repair-deficient cells during treatment with cisplatin. *International Journal of Cancer*, **77**, 741–746.

Fishel, R. (1998). Mismatch repair, molecular switches, and signal transduction. *Genes and Development*, **12**, 2096–2101.

Flores-Rozas, H. and Kolodner, R. D. (2000). Links between replication, recombination and genome instability in eukaryotes. *Trends in Biochemical Science*, **25**, 196–200.

Friedberg, E. C. (1996). Cockayne syndrome – a primary defect in DNA repair, transcription, both or neither? *BioEssays*, **18**, 731–738.

Frit, P., *et al*. (2000). Ku entry into DNA inhibits inward DNA transactions *in vitro*. *Journal of Biological Chemistry*, **275**, 35684–35691.

Fritzell, J. A., *et al*. (1997). Role of DNA mismatch repair in the cytotoxicity of ionizing radiation. *Cancer Research*, **57**, 5143–5147.

Gong, J. G., *et al*. (1999). The tyrosine kinase c-Abl regulates p73 in apoptotic response to cisplatin-induced DNA damage. *Nature*, **399**, 806–809.

Grady, W. M., *et al*. (1998). Mutation of the type II transforming growth factor-beta receptor is coincident with the transformation of human colon adenomas to malignant carcinomas. *Cancer Research*, **58**, 3101–3104.

Jasin, M. (2000). Chromosome breaks and genomic instability. *Cancer Investigations*, **18**, 78–86.

Jiricny, J. and Nystrom-Lahti, M. (2000). Mismatch repair defects in cancer. *Current Opinions in Genetic Development*, **10**, 157–161.

Karow, J. K., *et al*. (2000). The Bloom's syndrome gene product promotes branch migration of Holliday junctions. *Proceedings of the National Academy of Sciences of the USA*, **97**, 6504–6508.

Karran, P. (2000). DNA double strand break repair in mammalian cells. *Current Opinions in Genetic Development*, **10**, 144–150.

Kohn, K. W. (1996). Beyond DNA crosslinking: history and prospects of DNA-targeted cancer treatment – 15th Bruce F. Cain Memorial Award Lecture. *Cancer Research*, **56**, 5533–5546.

Kohn, K. W. (1999). Molecular interaction map of the mammalian cell cycle control and DNA repair systems. *Molecular Biology of the Cell*, **10**, 2703–2734.

Lebel, M., *et al*. (1999). The Werner syndrome gene product co-purifies with the DNA replication complex and interacts with PCNA and topoisomerase I. *Journal of Biological Chemistry*, **274**, 37795–37799.

Lengauer, C., *et al*. (1998). Genetic instabilities in human cancers. *Nature*, **396**, 643–648.

Le Page, F., *et al*. (2000). Transcription coupled repair of 8-oxoguanine in murine cells: the ogg1 protein is required for repair in nontranscribed sequences but not in transcribed sequences. *Proceedings of the National Academy of Sciences of the USA*, **97**, 8397–8402.

Li, G.-M. (1999). The role of mismatch repair in DNA damage-induced apoptosis. *Oncology Research*, **11**, 393–400.

Longley, M. J., *et al*. (1998). Identification of 5′-deoxyribose phosphate lyase activity in human DNA polymerase gamma and its role in mitochondrial base excision repair *in vitro*. *Proceedings of the National Academy of Sciences of the USA*, **95**, 12244–12248.

Machwe, A., *et al*. (2000). Selective blockage of the $3' \rightarrow 5'$ exonuclease activity of WRN protein by certain oxidative modifications and bulky lesions in DNA. *Nucleic Acids Research*, **28**, 2762–2770.

Markowitz, S. (2000). TGFβ receptors and DNA repair genes, coupled targets in a pathway of human colon carcinogenesis. *Biochimica Biophysica Acta*, **1470**, M13–M20.

Massague, J. (1998). TGFb signal transduction. *Annual Review of Biochemistry*, **67**, 753–791.

Massague, J. and Wotton, D. (2000). Transcriptional control by the TGFβ/Smad signaling system. *EMBO Journal*, **19**, 1745–1754.

Namsaraev, E. A. and Berg, P. (2000). Rad51 uses one mechanism to drive DNA strand exchange in both directions. *Journal of Biological Chemistry*, **275**, 3970–3976.

Nick McElhinny, S. A., *et al*. (2000). Ku recruits the XRCC4-Ligase IV complex to DNA ends. *Molecular Cellular Biology*, **20**, 2996–3003.

Parsons, C. A., *et al*. (2000). Precise binding of single-stranded DNA termini by human RAD52 protein. *EMBO Journal*, **19**, 4175–4181.

Paull, T. T. and Gellert, M. (2000). A mechanistic basis for Mre11-directed DNA joining at microhomologies. *Proceedings of the National Academy of Sciences of the USA*, **97**, 6409–6414.

Petrini, J. H. J. (2000). The Mre11 complex and ATM: collaborating to navigate S phase. *Current Opinions in Cell Biology*, **12**, 293–296.

Pinz, K. G. and Bogenhagen, D. F. (1998). Efficient repair of abasic sites in DNA by mitochondrial enzymes. *Molecular Cellular Biology*, **18**, 1257–1265.

Prasad, R., *et al*. (2000). FEN1 stimulation of DNA polymerase β mediates an excision step in mammalian long patch base excision repair. *Journal of Biological Chemistry*, **275**, 4460–4466.

Rauen, M., *et al*. (2000). The human checkpoint protein hRad17 interacts with the PCNA-like proteins hRad1, hHus1, and hRad9. *Journal of Biological Chemistry*, **257**, 29767–29771.

Rooney, P. H., *et al*. (1999). Comparative genomic hybridization and chromosomal instability in solid tumours. *British Journal of Cancer*, **80**, 862–873.

Rosen, N. (1997). Cancers of the gastrointestinal tract. In: Devita, V. T., Jr, *et al*. (eds), In: *Cancer: Principles and Practice of Oncology*. 971–1054 (Lippincott-Raven, Philadelphia).

Schild, D., *et al*. (2000). Evidence for simultaneous protein interactions between human Rad51 parallogs. *Journal of Biological Chemistry*, **275**, 16443–16449.

Selby, C. P. and Sancar, A. (1997). Human transcription-repair coupling factor CSB/ERCC6 is a DNA-stimulated ATPase but is not a helicase and does not disrupt the ternary transcription complex of stalled RNA polymerase II. *Journal of Biological Chemistry*, **272**, 1885–1890.

Strathdee, G., *et al.* (1999). A role for methylation of the hMLH1 promoter in loss of hMLH1 expression and drug resistance in ovarian cancer. *Oncogene*, **18**, 2335–2341.

Takata, M., *et al.* (2000). The Rad51 paralog Rad51B promotes homologous recombinational repair. *Molecular Cellular Biology*, **20**, 6476–6482.

Tantin, D., *et al.* (1997). Recruitment of the putative transcription-repair coupling factor CSB/ERCC6 to RNA polymerase II elongation complexes. *Molecular Cellular Biological*, **17**, 6803–6814.

Toft, N. J., *et al.* (1999). Msh2 status modulates both apoptosis and mutation frequency in the murine small intestine. *Proceedings of the National Academy of Sciences of the USA*, **96**, 3911–3915.

Vogel, H., *et al.* (1999). Deletion of Ku86 causes early onset of senescence in mice. *Proceedings of the National Academy of Sciences of the USA*, **96**, 10770–10775.

Wang, T. S. F. (1999). Cellular DNA polymerases. In: DePamphilis, M. L. (ed.), In: *DNA Replication in Eukaryotic Cells*. 461–493 (Cold Spring Harbor Laboratory Press, Cold Spring Harbor, NY).

Wang, W., *et al.* (2000a). Possible association of BLM in decreasing DNA double strand breaks during DNA replication. *EMBO Journal*, **19**, 3428–3435.

Wang, Y., *et al.* (2000b). BASC, a super complex of BRCA1-associated proteins involved in the recognition and repair of aberrant DNA structures. *Genes and Development*, **14**, 927–939.

Weiss, R. S., *et al.* (2000). Inactivation of mouse *Hus1* results in genomic instability and impaired responses to genotoxic stress. *Genes and Development*, **14**, 1886–1898.

Wiseman, H. and Halliwell, B. (1996). Damage to DNA by reactive oxygen and nitrogen species: role in inflammatory disease and progression to cancer. *Biochemical Journal*, **313**, 17–29.

Woodgate, R. (1999). A plethora of lesion-replicating DNA polymerases. *Genes and Development*, **13**, 2191–2195.

FURTHER READING

Balajee, A. S. and Bohr, V. A. (2000). Genomic heterogeneity of nucleotide excision repair. *Gene*, **250**, 15–30.

Batty, D. P. and Wood, R. D. (2000). Damage recognition in nucleotide excision repair of DNA. *Gene*, **241**, 193–204.

Buermeyer, A. B., *et al.* (1999). Mammalian DNA mismatch repair. *Annual Review of Genetics*, **33**, 533–564.

Flores-Rozas, H. and Kolodner, R. D. (2000). Links between replication, recombination and genome instability in eukaryotes. *Trends in Biochemistry Science*, **25**, 196–200.

Haber, J. E. (2000). Partners and pathways: repairing a double-strand break. *Trends in Genetics*, **16**, 259–264.

Jasin, M. (2000). Chromosome breaks and genomic instability. *Cancer Investigation*, **18**, 78–86.

Jiricny, J. and Nystrom-Lahti, M. (2000). Mismatch repair defects in cancer. *Current Opinions in Genetics Development*, **10**, 157–161.

Lengauer, C., *et al.* (1998). Genetic instabilities in human cancers. *Nature*, **396**, 643–648.

Lindahl, T. and Wood, R. D. (1999). Quality control by DNA repair. *Science*, **286**, 1897–1905.

McCullough, A. K., *et al.* (1999). Initiation of base excision repair: glycosylase mechanisms and structures. *Annual Review of Biochemistry*, **68**, 255–285.

Oshima, J. (2000). The Werner syndrome protein: an update. *BioEssays*, **22**, 894–901.

Pegg, A. E. (2000). Repair of O^6-alkylguanine by alkyltransferases. *Mutation Research*, **462**, 83–100.

Vessey, C. J., *et al.* (2000). Genetic disorders associated with cancer predisposition and genomic instability. *Progress in Nucleic Acids Research*, **63**, 189–221.

Chapter 8

Telomerase

Carmela P. Morales, Woodring E. Wright and Jerry W. Shay
The University of Texas Southwestern Medical Center at Dallas, Dallas, TX, USA

CONTENTS

INTRODUCTION

Intense interest in the enzyme telomerase has occurred in the field of cancer biology over the past 5 years. Recent evidence suggests a role for telomerase during the multi-step process of carcinogenesis. Reactivation or upregulation of telomerase is found in the majority of human cancers and appears to be responsible for the limitless replicative potential of malignant cells, a hallmark of cancer. In normal cells, the 'replicative lifespan' is tightly regulated by an internal divisional clock which limits the number of divisions that a cell can undergo during its lifetime. This divisional clock, known as the telomere, is located at each end of all linear chromosomes. By setting maximum limits on the number of times a cell can divide, telomeres may serve to prevent genetically aberrant cells from accumulating the additional mutations they need to become malignant. For the successful propagation and continued growth of malignant cells, therefore, telomere control on cell growth must be subverted. Current evidence indicates that in almost all human cancers this is achieved by reactivation of the enzyme telomerase.

TELOMERES AND THE 'END-REPLICATION' PROBLEM

Telomeres are long stretches of noncoding DNA located at the ends of all eukaryotic chromosomes (**Figure 1**). In vertebrates, telomeres are comprised of simple, repetitive noncoding DNA sequences. Human telomeres contain the six base pair sequence TTAGGG, repeated many thousands of times.

The length of telomeres varies from chromosome to chromosome. Evidence suggests that as chromosome 'caps,' telomeres have at least three critical functions: to protect chromosome ends from enzymatic degradation and abnormal fusion reactions; to serve as a buffer zone to protect against the 'end-replication' problem; and to serve as a gauge for mitotic age (the divisional clock).

The role of telomeres in maintaining chromosomal integrity was proposed by Barbara McClintock in 1941. Studying telomeres in maize chromosomes, McClintock observed that if not capped by telomeres, the ends of chromosomes had a tendency to fuse. Her observations

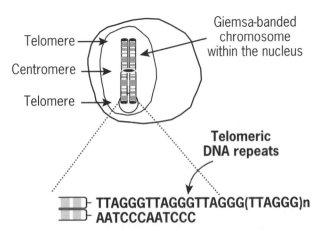

Figure 1 Location of telomeres at the ends of all eukaryotic chromosomes. Telomeres are comprised of the simple DNA sequence TTAGGG, repeated several thousand times (*n*).

were confirmed 50 years later in yeast and mice when it was demonstrated that without telomeric ends, chromosomes undergo aberrant end-to-end fusions, forming multicentric chromosomes with a propensity to break during mitosis, activating DNA damage checkpoints, and in some cases leading to widespread cell death (Zakian, 1989).

The second major function of telomeres relates to the process of semiconservative DNA replication. During each round of cell division, 50–200 base pairs are lost from the ends of linear human chromosomes (Hastie *et al.*, 1990; Lindsey *et al.*, 1991; Allsopp *et al.*, 1992, 1995). This 'end-replication' problem (**Figure 2**) occurs because conventional DNA replication machinery is unable to replicate completely the 3′ ends of chromosomal DNA during the S phase of each cell cycle. The polymerases that copy parental DNA strands prior to cell division synthesize DNA only in the 5′ to 3′ direction and require a short RNA primer to begin. These primers are then degraded and filled in by DNA synthesis extending from the upstream primer. However, at the end of a linear chromosome there is no 'upstream' DNA synthesis to fill in the gap between the final RNA priming event and the end of the chromosome.

This replication strategy predicts that with each round of cell division, there will be progressive shortening of the 3′ end of chromosomal DNA. Telomeric DNA therefore provides a cushion of expendable noncoding sequences to protect against the potentially catastrophic attrition of important chromosomal material.

TELOMERES ARE THE DIVISIONAL CLOCK

The existence of an internal divisional clock was first suggested in 1965 by Leonard Hayflick, who demonstrated that cells maintained in culture have a finite capacity to proliferate. In 1972, Olovnikov suggested that erosion of the chromosome ends could lead to the loss of essential genes and an exit from the cell cycle. Harley *et al.* introduced a modification of the Olovnikov theory, proposing a telomere-based mechanism to account for the process of 'cellular ageing' (Harley *et al.*, 1990). Specifically, it was proposed that after a certain number of divisions, telomeres are no longer sufficient to protect chromosome ends from degradation and aberrant fusion reactions. Through signalling mechanisms that are not entirely understood, a few short telomeres may trigger exit from the cell cycle at G1 and entry into senescence, a postmitotic state characterized not only by a lack of further cell division, but also

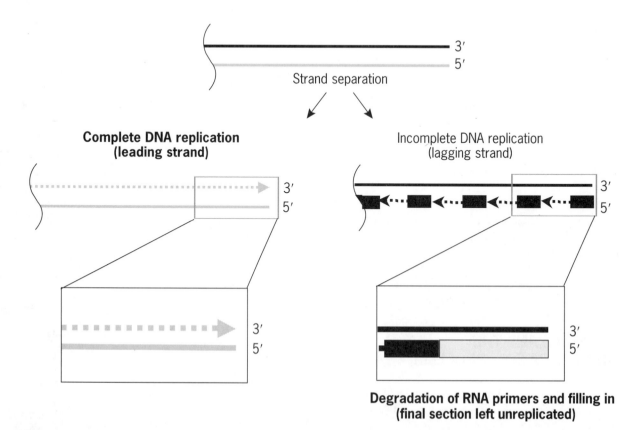

Figure 2   The end replication problem. DNA polymerases require a short RNA primer (black rectangles) to initiate DNA replication in the 3′ to 5′ direction. Since the extreme 3′ end of the chromosome cannot accommodate a primer, this part of the chromosome cannot be replicated, leading to a loss of telomeric DNA with each round of cell division.

by an altered pattern of gene expression and continued metabolic activity for long periods of time. In the case of normal human fibroblasts, a correlation was found between the number of divisions the cells could undergo in culture and initial telomere length, regardless of the age of the fibroblast donor. Additionally, average telomere length in blood and colonic mucosa was shown to decrease with biological age. In adults, sperm telomeres were found to be several kilobase pairs longer than in somatic tissues. Finally, significantly shorter telomere lengths have been demonstrated in some primary cells from patients with the premature ageing syndrome Hutchinson–Gilford progeria compared with normal age-matched controls. These cells also exhibited a reduced proliferative capacity compared with age-matched controls when maintained in culture. Although a large amount of correlative data supported the notion that telomere length determines the proliferative capacity of human cells, a direct test of this hypothesis (**Figure 3**) was lacking. The ability to elongate telomeres experimentally led to the observation that hybrid cells with artificially long telomeres had a longer lifespan than that of cell hybrids in which telomeres had not been elongated (Wright *et al.*, 1996). These observations provided the first direct evidence that telomere length is the counting mechanism that limits the proliferative capacity of human cells.

The ability to alter cellular proliferative capacity by manipulating telomere length provided a mechanistic basis for earlier observations of cellular lifespan *in vitro*. Normal human fibroblasts maintained in culture undergo a finite number of divisions as determined by their initial telomere length, after which they enter a state of growth arrest (senescence), also known as mortality stage 1 (M1).

Cells nearing the end of their lifespan can be forced to proliferate beyond this point by the introduction of certain viruses or oncogenes that abrogate the function of the tumour-suppressor genes *p53* and *pRb*. These observations suggest that p53 and pRb perhaps mediate cell cycle exit at G1 in response to telomere shortening. Bypass of M1 allows additional rounds of cell division until further, critical telomere shortening occurs, resulting in a state of 'crisis,' characterized by widespread cell death. This second stage is known as mortality stage 2 (M2). As a low-frequency ($\sim 10^{-7}$) event in human cells, a subpopulation of cells escapes from crisis, giving rise to cells which now have an unlimited proliferative capacity (immortalized). The characteristic feature of such immortal cells is the ability to maintain their telomeres.

The dual role of telomeric DNA as protector of chromosomal integrity and mitotic clock implicates cellular senescence as a natural and effective initial protection mechanism against the development of cancer. It is generally believed that tumours are initiated by multiple genetic events in cells which result in the inappropriate activation of growth stimulatory signals, an insensitivity to antigrowth signals and a resistance to apoptosis. However, transformation to fully malignant derivatives does not occur in most cases because the majority of these aberrant cells will have exhausted their endowment of allowed divisions.

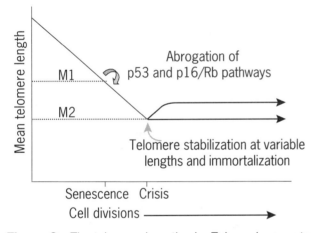

Figure 3 The telomere hypothesis. Telomeric repeats are lost with each round of cell division, leading to a decrease in mean telomere length with accumulated divisions. Upon reaching a certain length, short telomeric DNA sequences trigger entry into the senescence pathway, during which cells remain metabolically active but are no longer able to divide. This stage is also known as mortality stage 1 (M1). Cells can be forced to proliferate beyond this point by abrogating p53 and pRb or their respective pathways. During this period of extended life, cells continue to divide in the face of progressive telomere shortening. After reaching a critically short telomere length, most cells enter a crisis, undergoing widespread cell death (apoptosis). This second stage is also known as mortality stage 2 (M2). Only those rare cells which engage mechanisms that stabilize telomere length are able to continue proliferating for indefinite periods.

TELOMERASE

Early studies demonstrated a significantly shorter telomere length in most cancers compared with noncancerous tissue from the same patient (Hastie *et al.*, 1990). In culture, cancer cells generally have short but stable telomeres, suggesting that human cancers have developed strategies for the maintenance of telomeric DNA at a length above the critical threshold. In 85–95% of human cancers, this telomere stabilization is achieved by reactivation or upregulation of the ribonucleoprotein enzyme telomerase.

Telomerase is an RNA–protein complex which utilizes its RNA as a template for the addition of TTAGGG repeats to the 3′ ends of chromosomes, thereby compensating for losses due to the end-replication problem (**Figure 4**).

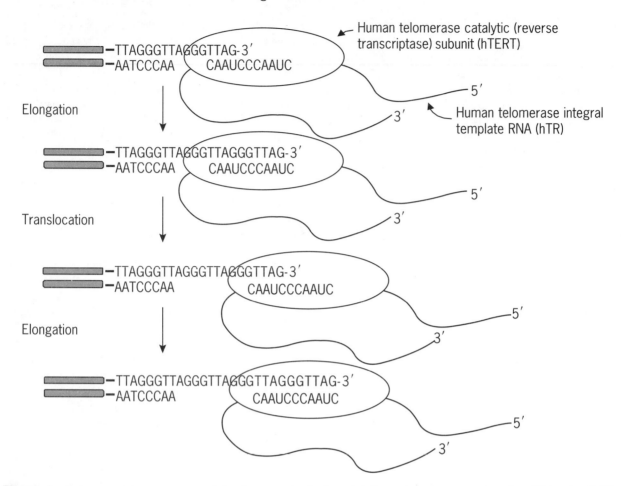

Figure 4   Telomerase is an enzyme minimally comprised of a catalytic protein component and an RNA subunit. The RNA serves as a template for the addition of TTAGGG repeats to the ends of chromosomes, leading to maintenance of telomeric DNA. This enzyme is processive, meaning that a variable number of repeats may be added to a chromosome prior to disengaging the chromosome end.

First discovered in *Tetrahymena* by Elizabeth Blackburn and Carol Greider, telomerase activity has now been detected in extracts from almost all organisms, with the exception of bacteria and viruses, which have circular genomes, and *Drosophila*, which have retrotransposons instead of telomeres. In humans, most adult somatic cells lack telomerase activity. However, telomerase is present at high levels in germ cells, early embryos, activated T and B cells and germinal centres of lymphoid organs. Telomerase activity is also detectable at lower amounts in the basal cells of renewal tissues (skin and intestine). In somatic tissues and cells (including T cells), however, the presence of detectable levels of telomerase activity is not sufficient to prevent long-term telomere attrition. The variable levels of telomerase in normal human tissues are illustrated in **Figure 5**.

In humans, telomerase is composed of two essential components: an integral RNA (hTR), which provides the template for the synthesis of telomere repeats, and a protein subunit (hTERT), which provides catalytic activity.

The cloning of hTERT and hTR made it possible to test directly the hypothesis that telomere shortening regulates the entry into cellular senescence. Using an *in vitro* system, the combination of hTERT and hTR was first shown to reconstitute telomerase activity (Weinrich *et al.*, 1997; Beattie *et al.*, 1998). Second, the introduction of hTERT into telomerase-negative primary cells resulted in telomerase activity. Exogenous hTR was not needed because it is present even in cells that do not normally have telomerase activity. Finally, it was shown that telomere maintenance by exogenous telomerase was sufficient for the immortalization of human mammary epithelial cells, foreskin fibroblasts, retinal pigmented epithelial cells and umbilical vascular endothelial cells. Taken together, these experiments provided direct evidence that short telomere length directs entry into cellular senescence and that telomere maintenance by telomerase is sufficient to bypass this growth arrest under most circumstances. Importantly, the introduction of telomerase prior to either M1 or M2 is sufficient for immortalization, indicating that telomeres

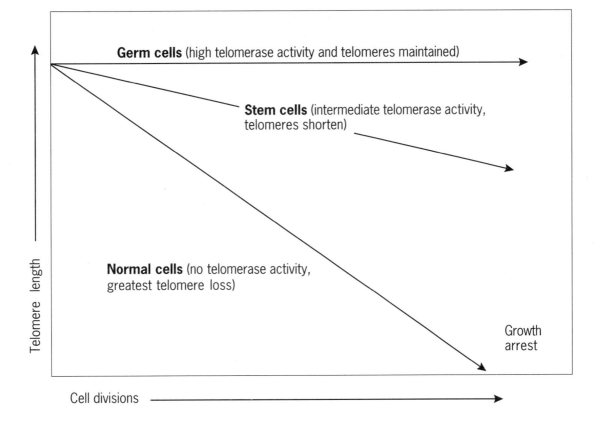

Figure 5   Variable levels of telomerase in normal human tissues. Germ cells of the reproductive system maintain high levels of telomerase activity throughout life and therefore do not sustain telomere shortening. Stem cells of renewal tissues express modest levels of telomerase, leading to a blunted rate of telomere shortening. Somatic cells and tissues lack detectable telomerase activity and sustain the greatest rates of telomere loss.

are associated with both the M1 and M2 stage of growth arrest.

Various factors such as oxidative stress, introduction of an activated Ha-*ras* oncogene and γ-irradiation have been shown to induce a senescent-like state in cells much younger than the Hayflick limit. Several reports have also suggested that in addition to telomerase, inactivation of the Rb/p16^{INK4a} pathway is required for the immortalization of some human epithelial cells. The protein p16^{INK4a} is an inhibitor of cyclin-dependent kinases, and its levels have been shown to increase after only a few passages in culture. During the establishment of human mammary epithelial cells under standard culture conditions, there appears to be a 'self-selection' process, such that only the cells which have lost p16^{INK4a} expression (usually by methylation of the promoter) are able to survive the initial culture period. In these surviving cells, exogenous telomerase expression leads to immortalization. In most cases, no appreciable decrease in telomere length can be demonstrated to account for this 'self-selection' process, termed M0. These observations suggest that the involvement of p16^{INK4a} at M0 is telomere-independent, a finding that stands in direct contrast to the role of p53 in

mediating of growth arrest at the telomere-dependent M1 stage. Recent observations in keratinocytes suggest that the loss of p16^{INK4a} expression is not required if the cells are maintained under optimized culture conditions, such as co-culturing with irradiated fibroblast feeder layers (Ramirez *et al.*, 2001). These findings suggest that artificial cell culture conditions may account for the premature growth arrest (M0) in epithelial cells, and that this response is mediated by induction of p16^{INK4a}.

ASSAYS FOR TELOMERASE

The standard method for measuring telomerase activity is a highly sensitive PCR-based assay termed the TRAP (telomere repeat amplification protocol) assay (**Figure 6**).

In this assay, extracts are first prepared from primary tissue or cultured cells by lysing the cells with a detergent, releasing telomerase into the extract solution. An aliquot of this solution is then added to a reaction mixture containing a short primer and deoxynucleotide triphosphates (dNTPs). If telomerase is present, it will elongate the primer with TTAGGG repeats. The products of this elongation step are

Step 1. Elongation of TS (telomerase substrate) primer by telomerase

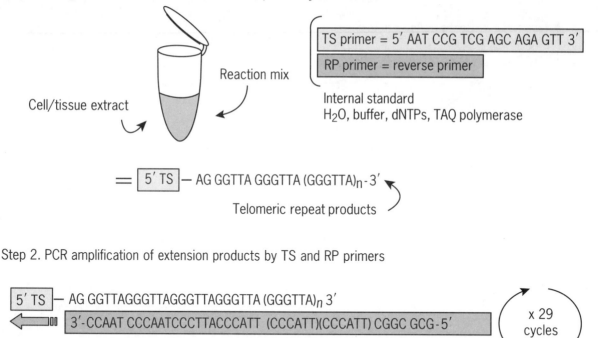

Step 2. PCR amplification of extension products by TS and RP primers

Figure 6 The telomerase activity assay. This sensitive PCR-based assay can be applied to extracts from a variety of cells and tissues. In the first step, extracts are incubated with labelled nucleotides and also a synthetic telomere end (TS primer) at room temperature. If the extract contains telomerase, the enzyme will synthesize the addition of TTAGGG repeats to the TS primer. The second step utilizes PCR to amplify the extended products in the presence of additional primers and polymerases. These amplified products are then separated by electrophoresis to generate the characteristic six-base-pair ladder indicating telomerase activity. ITAS is an internal standard included to control for the possibility of enzyme inhibitors.

heterogeneous in length, representing multiples of the six-base-pair TTAGGG sequence. Using a second primer which is complementary to the telomerase repeat and a DNA polymerase known as TAQ polymerase, each product is amplified using the polymerase chain reaction (PCR). The amplified products are then run on a polyacrylamide gel, creating a six-base-pair ladder. The laddering effect occurs because telomerase is a processive enzyme, adding telomeric repeats in multiples of TTAGGG (**Figure 7**). This amplification protocol increases the sensitivity of the assay such that telomerase activity can be detected in samples containing as few as 0.1% positive cells. An internal standard is also incorporated into the assay, since some tissue extracts contain molecules that inhibit PCR and give false-negative results. In addition, this internal standard permits semiquantitative analysis of relative telomerase activity levels.

Alternative approaches to the measurement of telomerase have recently been developed. Unlike TRAP, which is a functional assay carried out on extracts of cells or tissues, *in situ* techniques are designed to visualize the components of telomerase at a cellular level. *In situ*

hybridization for the RNA component of human telomerase (hTR) can be applied to formalin-fixed, paraffin-embedded tissues as well cultured cells and cell smears. Several studies have demonstrated good concordance between telomerase activity as measured by TRAP and telomerase RNA by *in situ* hybridization. Although normal cells do contain hTR, the levels in normal tissues are sufficiently low that they do not complicate the observation of elevated hTR levels in tumours. Antibodies for the immunhistochemical detection of the telomerase protein component are now becoming commercially available, even though their utility remains to be established. Studies using other antitelomerase antibodies, however, been shown to correlate with telomerase activity by TRAP. These techniques may have some advantages over the PCR-based assay. The excellent morphological preservation of cellular detail provided by *in situ* hybridization or immunohistochemistry may be helpful in localizing telomerase to specific cell types. Furthermore, *in situ* telomerase assays could be readily adapted by clinical laboratories, many of which already utilize such techniques for the detection of other proteins.

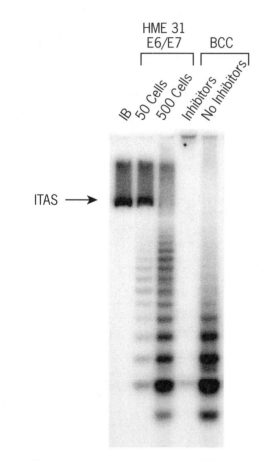

Figure 7 Telomerase activity in two different basal cell carcinomas (BCC). Human mammary epithelial cells expressing the E6 and E7 oncoproteins (HME 31 E6/E7) serve as a positive control for quantitation. The lane containing lysis buffer (LB) serves as a negative control. This representative telomerase assay gel reveals the characteristic 6 base-pair ladder indicative of enzymatic activity, and the internal standard (ITAS) that serves to normalize sample-to-sample variation. Absence of the ITAS signal, as demonstrated in the first BCC sample, indicates the presence of PCR inhibitors. Without this internal control, this sample may be misinterpreted as lacking telomerase activity. Quantitation of telomerase activity is done by determining the ratio of the internal standard to the telomerase ladder.

ASSOCIATION BETWEEN TELOMERASE ACTIVITY AND CANCER

The TRAP assay has made possible the large-scale testing for telomerase activity in a wide variety of human cancers and normal tissues. Using TRAP, telomerase activity has been detected in 85–95% of all human cancers and cancer cell lines, whereas adjacent normal tissue and mortal cells in culture are generally telomerase negative (**Table 1**).

Thousands of individual malignancies representing all of the major organ systems have been tested to date, including those originating from the head and neck, lung, gastrointestinal, pancreatic and biliary tract, liver, breast, male and female reproductive tract, kidney/urinary tract, central nervous system, skin and blood (Shay and Bacchetti, 1997). Preinvasive and preneoplastic lesions, such as colorectal adenomas, high-grade prostatic intraepithelial neoplasia, *in situ* breast carcinoma and those from the head/neck and lung tissue, are positive in 30% to almost 100% of cases. These observations provide strong evidence that most human malignancies are associated with the reactivation or upregulation of telomerase. Given that most normal human cells have the capacity to undergo 60–70 population doublings, it may at first glance seem difficult to invoke telomere shortening as a barrier to cancer formation, because after 60 doublings, a single cell would generate a tumour mass of approximately 10^{15} kg! However, not only do evolving malignancies exhibit high rates of turnover due to chronic, widespread apoptosis and differentiation within the tumour, but also many clonal expansions occur.

A schematic demonstrating the relationship between cell turnover and tumorigenesis is shown in **Figure 8**.

In this scenario, a single healthy cell would be expected to generate a population of 10^6 cells after 20 doublings. As a rare event, one cell in this population acquires a genetic mutation which confers to it a selective growth advantage over the remaining cells. Owing to its newly acquired growth advantage, this cell then generates a clone of similarly altered cells. This process is repeated several times, with each successive generation resulting from an event in a single cell from the previous generation. In some cases, an additional generation is required to convert a minimally functional recessive mutation into a strong phenotype through loss of the remaining wild-type allele (loss of heterozygosity (LOH)). Rarely, a single cell emerges which has acquired sufficient advantageous mutations to result in the development of a malignancy. Using such a scenario, it can be seen that the number of cells in the final tumour grossly underrepresents the number of cells required to produce it. Because so many doublings are required for the development of a cancer, most potentially tumorigenic cells probably senesce owing to critical telomere erosion. Thus, cellular senescence could be viewed as a powerful initial blockade against carcinogenesis.

The timing of telomerase reactivation in human tumours appears to vary considerably from organ to organ. In most cases, the mean telomere length in a variety of tumour types is substantially shorter than those in normal tissues from the same patient. Taken in the context of the telomere hypothesis, these observations suggest that telomerase reactivation or upregulation occurs only after dramatic telomere loss, and serves to stabilize shortened chromosome ends and permit continued cell proliferation. In most colorectal, oesophageal and pancreatic adenocarcinomas, telomerase reactivation appears to be a late event, occurring during the transition from low- to high-grade

Table 1 Telomerase activity in human cancers[a]

Pathology	% Positive	Pathology	% Positive
Head/neck and lung		*Breast*	
Normal oral mucosa	32	Fibrocystic disease/fibroadenoma	0
Head/neck squamous cell carcinoma	86	Carcinoma *in situ*	75
Non-small cell lung carcinoma	78	Carcinoma (ductal and lobular)	88
Small cell lung carcinoma	100	Adjacent tissue	5
Adjacent lung tissue	4	*Reproductive tract*	
Gastrointestinal tract		Normal adult ovary	33
Gastric metaplasia/adenoma[b]	27	Normal myometrium/endometrium	0
Gastric carcinoma	85	Leiomyoma	0
Adjacent gastric tissue	25	Leiomyosarcoma	100
Colorectal adenoma[b]	45	Cervical/vaginal/endometrial cancer	100
Colorectal carcinoma	89	Ovarian carcinoma	91
Adjacent and normal colon tissues[b]	25	Normal adult testis	100
Pancreas and liver		Normal prostate	0
Benign pancreatic lesions (all)	0	BPH without carcinoma[c]	5
Pancreatic carcinoma	95	BPH with carcinoma[c]	11
Adjacent pancreatic tissue	14	High-grade PIN[d]	60
Benign pancreatic brushings	0	Prostate carcinoma	90
Malignant pancreatic brushings	100	*Skin*	
Normal liver tissue	0	Normal epidermis[b]	44
Nonmalignant liver disease (all)[b]	29	Squamous cell carcinoma	83
Hepatocellular carcinoma	86	Basal cell carcinoma	95
Adjacent liver tissue	2	Melanoma	86
Kidney/urinary tract		*Haematological tissues*	
Normal urothelium	0	Myeloma	100
Dysplastic urothelium	43	Lymphoma, low grade	86
Bladder carcinoma (all stages)	92	Lymphoma, high grade	100
Bladder carcinoma (washings)	73	Tonsils, normal	100
Bladder carcinoma (voided urine)	29	Myelodysplastic syndrome	67
Renal cell carcinoma	83	CML, chronic[e]	71
Adjacent renal tissue	0	CML, early accelerated	33
Wilm tumour	100	CML, blast stage	100
Adjacent renal tissue (Wilm)	33	CLL, early[f]	14
Neural tissues		CLL, late	57
Normal retina	0	Acute promyelocytic leukaemia	100
Retinoblastoma	50	Acute lymphocytic leukaemia	80
Glioblastoma multiforme	75	Acute myelogenous leukaemia	73
Oligodendroglioma	100		
Anaplastic astrocytoma	10		
Meningioma, ordinary	17		
Meningioma, atypical	92		
Meningioma, malignant	100		
Ganglioneuroma	0		
Neuroblastoma	94		
Adjacent neural tissue	0		

[a]Adapted from Shay and Bacchetti, 1997. [b]Telomerase activity weak compared with carcinomas. [c]BPH = benign prostatic hypertrophy. [d]PIN = prostatic intraepithelial neoplasia. [e]CML = chronic myelogenous leukaemia. [f]CLL = chronic lymphocytic leukaemia.

dysplasia. Additionally, early-stage neuroblastomas lack or have low levels of telomerase activity, whereas late-stage disease has high levels of telomerase activity. In other malignancies, such as head and neck cancers, lung carcinomas and breast carcinomas, telomerase activity is present in early preneoplastic lesions, albeit at lower levels than frankly malignant tissues. Since most of these data were obtained by studying tissue extracts, it is difficult to determine whether telomerase activity in preneoplastic lesions is due to the infiltration of microscopic quantities of tumour cells or to low-level telomerase activity in pre-neoplastic cells. The development of *in situ* techniques, such as immunohistochemistry with telomerase antibodies or *in situ* hybridization for the telomerase template RNA

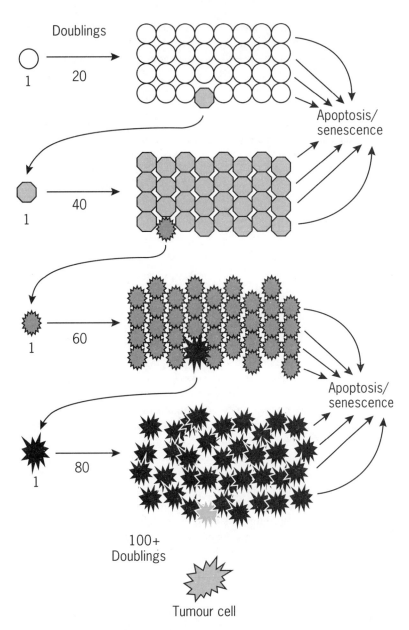

Figure 8 Relationship between cell divisions and tumorigenesis. Within a normal population of cells, a single cell acquires a mutation which endows the cell with a growth advantage. After 20 doublings, a clone of cells emerges, one of which undergoes an additional advantageous mutation. While the other cells senesce or die, this cell survives to generate a clone of similarly mutated cells. The cycle continues until one mutant emerges which has acquired all of the necessary mutations for tumorigenesis. According to this scheme, a fully tumorigenic cell can result in less than 100 doublings.

(hTR), will be important in clarifying these important issues. In the case of cervical cancer, *in situ* hybridization for hTR showed focal increases in hTR expression at the level of *in situ* carcinomas.

Although most human cancers express high levels of telomerase, a substantial portion (10–15%) are telomerase negative. There are several explanations for this observation. First, although the TRAP assay is capable of detecting telomerase activity with only 1–10 tumour cells, because tumours are heterogeneous, some sampled specimens may contain no or insufficient numbers of telomerase-positive tumour cells to be detected by the assay. Second, some cancers may not have reached a point where telomerase activity is required. Such tumours may in fact still be mortal and therefore truly telomerase negative. Third, as mentioned previously, it has been reported that some tissue extracts contain inhibitors of either the elongation or amplification steps of the TRAP assay, leading to false-negative results. Other reasons for false-negative results include technical errors, such as poor sample preservation, sampling error or misloading of the specimen into the reaction mixture. Finally, there is experimental evidence for one or more alternative mechanisms (possibly based on recombination) for lengthening of telomeres (ALT). Some immortalized cell lines show evidence of ALT activity characterized by the absence of telomerase activity but the presence of very long and heterogeneous telomeres. Although the mechanism is not well known, the existence of an ALT pathway has important theoretical implications for telomerase inhibition as a treatment for cancer. To date, however, there is no experimental evidence suggesting that tumour cells with telomerase can be converted to the ALT pathway.

EXPLOITATION OF TELOMERASE IN CANCER DIAGNOSTICS AND PROGNOSTICS

The strong association between telomerase and most human malignancies has prompted a flurry of studies exploring the potential clinical utility of telomerase as a diagnostic cancer marker. In addition to measuring telomerase activity in tissue extracts, the TRAP assay has been successfully applied to a wide variety of samples including bladder washings, sedimented cells in voided urine and colonic effluent, oral rinses, brushes and washes, endoscopic brushings, biliary aspirates, ascitic fluid, blood, fine needle aspirates and frozen sections. Formalin-fixed, paraffin-embedded pathological material can also be tested for the presence of micrometastasis using recently developed in situ hybridization to the telomerase template RNA (hTR) and immunohistochemical detection of the catalytic component (hTERT). In oesophageal carcinomas, a marked increase in hTR occurs during the transition from low- to high-grade dysplasia, suggesting that telomerase is important for the development of advanced lesions in oesophageal carcinogenesis. Although initial data appear promising, these techniques need to be validated by comparison with the standard TRAP assay. However, current evidence demonstrates a good correlation between telomerase activity and in situ levels of hTR.

The utility of telomerase in predicting the outcome of cancer (prognosis) is based on the notion that without telomere maintenance, malignant cells will be unable to sustain long-term proliferation and eventually undergo cell death and tumour regression, contributing to a favourable outcome. The best evidence for such a scenario is in stage 4S neuroblastomas that lack detectable telomerase activity. These cases are associated with large rate of spontaneous tumour regression. This indicates that, at least in some cancers, telomerase is not absolutely required for malignancy but that tumours without telomerase may ultimately regress if they do not engage a mechanism for telomere stabilization. In ordinary meningiomas, a strong correlation was found between telomerase activity and disease relapse. Telomerase activity has also been observed to confer a worse prognosis in other malignancies

such as neuroblastoma, acute myeloid leukaemia, breast cancer and some gastrointestinal cancers.

Another potential role for telomerase is in the detection of residual disease after surgical resection or adjuvant chemo- and/or radiation therapy. Telomerase activity has been detected in cells adjacent to tumours, suggesting the presence of small foci of residual malignant cells. Such information could be used to restage a lesion and identify a subset of patients who would benefit from additional therapy. Although there are reports that inflammatory cells express low levels of telomerase activity, analysis of malignant lymph nodes reveals levels of telomerase at least sixfold higher than their benign counterparts.

TELOMERASE INHIBITION IN CANCER

Several lines of evidence support the notion that inhibition of telomerase may be an effective anti-cancer strategy. As mentioned previously, telomerase is present in most human malignancies. Although the introduction of certain viral oncoproteins or the abrogation of tumour-suppressor genes may confer an extended lifespan, in the absence of a mechanism for telomere maintenance, these cells eventually reach a period of crisis and undergo widespread cell death.

Telomerase is a challenging molecule for drug development because of the long period required to reach sufficient telomere shortening. To be considered telomerase-specific, inhibitors should fulfil several criteria: (1) inhibitors should reduce telomerase activity without initially affecting proliferation; (2) treatment with inhibitors should result in telomere shortening with each round of cell division; (3) treated cells should eventually undergo growth arrest or apoptosis; (4) there should be a correlation between initial telomere length and time to growth arrest or cell death; (5) control of chemically related molecules or inhibitors lacking the ability to inhibit telomerase activity should not have an effect on cell proliferation and telomere length. Numerous conventional chemotherapeutic agents have been reported to inhibit telomerase. These reports are based on observations that treatment with such agents resulted in widespread cell death and loss of telomerase activity. However, the interpretation of the results is suspect since they do not fulfil the criteria expected for telomerase inhibitors.

There are several important theoretical considerations associated with telomerase inhibitor therapy. First, during the initial period of telomere shortening, continued cell proliferation could result in clinically significant tumour growth. Second, discontinuation of therapy for even short periods of time during the treatment period could result in the rapid induction of telomerase and telomere relengthening. Third, selective pressure on tumour cells being treated with telomerase inhibitors could lead to drug resistance due to the emergence of cells with alternative mechanisms of telomere maintenance. Finally, there is a theoretical concern that normal cells with telomerase activity (germ cells and renewal tissues) would also be susceptible to telomerase inhibition. However, these cells generally have a longer than average telomere length and are much more slowly dividing than tumour cells, and thus would be expected to be relatively resistant to the consequences of telomerase inhibition.

The telomerase template RNA (hTR) and the catalytic core of the protein subunit (hTERT) are two obvious choices for drug design since both components are absolutely required for telomerase activity. Agents tested to date include antisense oligonucleotides and synthetic peptide nucleic acids targeted against the template region of telomerase (hTR). Using agents that fulfil these criteria, several groups demonstrated that telomerase inhibition in cultured cancer cells resulted in a marked (70–95%) decrease in telomerase activity, telomere shortening and widespread cell death after periods ranging from 2 to 3 months, depending on the initial telomere length. Discontinuation of the drug resulted in a rapid reactivation of telomerase and regrowth of telomeres to their initial length. In tumour cells that were inhibited until the point of cell death, there was no evidence for the development of resistant cells, suggesting that the alternative mechanism of telomere maintenance may not be readily adopted in these cells.

Overall, these initial observations suggest that sustained telomerase inhibition may be an effective and feasible anticancer strategy. However, given the delayed effect of such agents, the most appropriate setting for telomerase inhibition would appear to be the prevention of relapse due to small numbers of remaining cells or to cells resistant to initial conventional therapy. Other strategies would combine telomerase inhibitors with other agents, such as angiogenesis inhibitors to target tumour cells specifically and effectively. Additional novel and potentially effective approaches against telomerase are beginning to emerge, such as ribozymes directed against the template region of telomerase RNA, which cleave the RNA and render telomerase inactive. Molecules which couple the telomerase promoter to apoptotic genes are also in the early stages of development. Such approaches would be expected to have the dual benefit of optimizing tumour cell specificity while producing a more rapid biological effect. However, the effect of such agents on telomerase-competent stem cells and germ-line cells remains an important consideration.

TELOMERASE FOR THE DEVELOPMENT OF *IN VITRO* MODELS OF CANCER PROGRESSION

The introduction of telomerase into some normal human cells resulted in bypass of M1 and immortalization. After a doubling of their normal lifespan, these immortalized cells maintain a normal diploid karyotype and DNA damage and cell cycle checkpoints remained fully intact, suggesting that normal cells immortalized with telomerase do not develop additional cancer-associated changes. In cells expressing the Simian virus 40 Large T antigen for long periods of time followed by the introduction of an activated *ras* oncogene, the addition of telomerase appears to be sufficient for transformation into full tumorigenicity. Taken together, these results suggest that while telomerase expression *per se* does not result in genomic destabilization, in the context of underlying mutations, telomerase contributes to tumorigenicity by providing aberrant cells with an unlimited proliferative capacity.

The ability of telomerase to immortalize cells without altering the underlying genetic background has also been demonstrated in cells with inherited susceptibility syndromes, such as ataxia–telangiectasia, Bloom syndrome, xeroderma pigmentosum and premature ageing syndromes such as Werner syndrome and Hutchinson–Gilford progeria. Thus, telomerase may be an important tool for establishing premalignant cell lines which can be used for the development of *in vitro* models of cancer progression, for amassing large numbers of cells required for other assays or as standard cellular reagents for microarray analysis. Microarray is a novel technique which utilizes microchip technology to analyze cellular RNA for changes in patterns of genetic expression in mutated cells versus their normal counterparts.

The role of telomerase in cancer progression will undoubtedly represent a major continuing area of investigation in the field of cancer biology. The tight association between telomerase and cancer, the ability to generate immortalized human cell lines for studies of cancer progression and the development of telomerase inhibitors for use as anticancer agents all underscore the fundamental role of telomere maintenance as a major player in the development and continued unlimited growth of cancer cells.

REFERENCES

Allsopp, R. C., *et al.* (1992). Telomere length predicts the replicative capacity of human fibroblasts. *Proceedings of the National Academy of Sciences of the USA*, **85**, 10114–10118.

Allsopp, R. C., *et al.* (1995). Telomere shortening is associated with cell division *in vitro* and *in vivo*. *Experimental Cell Research*, **220**, 194–200.

Beattie, T. L., *et al.* (1998). Reconstitution of human telomerase activity *in vitro*. *Current Biology*, **8**, 177–180.

Harley, C. B., *et al.* (1990). Telomeres shorten during ageing of human fibroblasts. *Nature*, **345**, 458–460.

Hastie, N. D., *et al.* (1990). Telomere reduction in human colorectal carcinoma and with ageing. *Nature*, **346**, 866–868.

Lindsey, J., *et al*. (1991). *In vivo* loss of telomeric repeats with age in humans. *Mutation Research*, **256**, 45–48.

Ramirez, R. D., *et al*. (2001). Putative telomere-independent mechanisms of replicative aging reflect inadequate growth conditions. *Genes and Development*, **15**, 398–403.

Shay, J. W. and Bacchetti, S. (1997). A survey of telomerase activity in human cancer. *European Journal of Cancer*, **33**, 787–791.

Weinrich, S. L., *et al*. (1997). Reconstitution of human telomerase with the template RNA component hTR and the catalytic protein subunit hTRT. *Nature Genetics*, **17**, 498–502.

Wright, W. E., *et al*. (1996). Experimental elongation of telomeres extends the lifespan of immortal × normal cell hybrids. *EMBO Journal*, **15**, 1734–1741.

Zakian, V. A. (1989) The structure and function of telomeres. *Annual Reviews of Genetics*, **23**, 579–604.

FURTHER READING

Cech, T. R. (2000). Life at the end of the chromosome: telomeres and telomerase. *Angewandte Chemie International Edition in English*, **39**, 34–43.

Greider, C. W. (1999). Telomerase activation-one step on the road to cancer? *Trends in Genetics*, **15**, 109–112.

Hanahan, D. and Weinberg, R. A. (2000). The hallmarks of cancer. *Cell*, **100**, 57–70.

Wynford-Thomas, D. (1999). Cellular senescence and cancer. *Journal of Pathology*, **187**, 100–111.

Chapter 9

Apoptosis

John C. Reed

The Burnham Institute, La Jolla, CA, USA

CONTENTS

INTRODUCTION

Cell death is a part of normal physiology for most metazoan species. During development, redundant or unwanted cells are removed through programmed cell death, making important contributions to morphogenesis, organogenesis and other processes (Vaux and Korsmeyer, 1999). Programmed cell death typically occurs through a ritualistic process known as 'apoptosis,' a term adapted from the Greek and which has analogies with the falling away of leaves from trees in the autumn. Among the features of cells undergoing apoptosis are chromatin condensation, nuclear fragmentation, plasma membrane blebbing, cell shrinkage and ultimately shedding of membrane-delimited cell fragments known as apoptotic bodies (Wyllie, 1997).

In adult mammals, programmed cell death plays an essential role in tissue homeostasis, offsetting new cell production with cell death in all self-renewing tissues. Roughly one million cells commit suicide every second in the adult human, thus making room for new cells produced in tissues such as the bone marrow, skin and gut on a daily basis. So massive is the flux of cell birth and death through our bodies that the average person will produce and in parallel eradicate a mass of cells equivalent to his or her entire body weight each year. Consequently, defects in the cell death machinery which prevent the programmed turnover of cells can result in cell accumulation, thereby imparting a selective growth advantage to neoplastic cells without necessarily involving concomitant defects in the cell division cycle (Reed, 1999).

Defects in the pathways responsible for programmed cell death also play important roles in multiple aspects of tumour cell biology, besides cell accumulation. For example, because cancer requires the accumulation within a single clone of multiple genetic lesions, enhanced cell longevity as a result of defective apoptosis may indirectly promote cancer. The genetic instability that characterizes many cancers is also indirectly assisted by defects in apoptosis, since errors in DNA management typically disrupt cell cycle checkpoints, triggering a cell suicide response. Growth factor and hormone independence, hallmarks of many advanced cancers, can also be attributed in part to alternations in the cell death machinery, which permit cancer cells to thrive in the absence of these factors that cells normally require for maintenance of their survival. Metastasis is also assisted by defects in apoptosis, permitting tumour cells to survive in a suspended state (such as during circulation through the blood or lymph), whereas normal epithelial cells undergo apoptosis when detached from extracellular matrix and thus are confined to predefined locations in the body. Immune surveillance mechanisms are also thwarted by defects in apoptosis, since cytolytic T-cells and natural killer (NK) cells depend on components of cell death machinery to kill target cells. Finally, defects in apoptosis pathways contribute to resistance of cancer cells to chemotherapy and radiation, raising the threshold of drug- or radiation-induced damage necessary to trigger a cell suicide response (**Table 1**).

The core cell death machinery consists of families of genes and their encoded proteins, many of which are conserved throughout metazoan evolution (Metzstein *et al.*, 1998). Several protein domains which are entirely or nearly unique to apoptosis pathways are found within apoptosis-suppressing and -inducing proteins, including caspase protease domains, caspase-recruitment domains (CARDs), death domains (DDs), death effector domains (DEDs), caspase-inducible DNA endonuclease (CIDE) domains,

Table 1   Relevance of defective apoptosis to cancer: *pathogenesis, progression, therapy resistance*

Cell accumulation (cell death < cell division)
Longevity (accumulation of genetic lesions)
Genomic instability (tolerate DNA mistakes)
Immune surveillance (resistance to immune attack)
Growth factor/hormone independence (survival without paracrine/endocrine growth factors)
Angiogenesis (resistance to hypoxia; hypoglycaemia)
Metastasis (survival without attachment)
Chemoresistance/radioresistance (increased threshold for cell death)

Table 2   Protein domains associated with apoptosis

Caspase (catalytic) domains
BIR domains (IAPs)
Caspase-recruitment domains (CARDs)
Death domains (DDs)
Death effector domains (DEDs)
Bcl-2 homology (BH) domains
CIDE domains

BIR domains and Bcl-2 homology (BH) domains (**Table 2**) (Reed, 2000). Three-dimensional structures have been obtained for at least one of each of these domains, providing the foundation of a clearer understanding of the molecular mechanisms of apoptosis regulation and, in some cases, ideas for how one might modulate apoptosis proteins with therapeutic intent (Fesik, 2000).

APOPTOSIS IS CAUSED BY PROTEASES

The biochemical events responsible for apoptosis can be linked to the activation in cells of a family of cysteine proteases, known as caspases, which cleave specific target proteins in cells at aspartic acid residues. It is these proteolytic cleavage events which directly or indirectly explain the morphological changes that we recognize as 'apoptosis.' As many as 14 caspase-encoding genes have been identified in humans and mice. Homologous genes are also found in lower organisms within the animal kingdom, such as the nematode *Caenorhabditis elegans* and the fruit fly *Drosophila melanogaster*.

Caspases are initially synthesized as inactive zymogens in cells. How, then, are caspases activated? The answer is by proteolytic cleavage, occurring at conserved aspartyl residues, thus generating the large (~ 20 kDa) and small (~ 10 kDa) subunits that comprise the catalytic component of these enzymes. Structures of several caspases have been solved by X-ray crystallography, revealing a heterotetrameric assembly of two large and two small subunits, with two active sites per molecule. The observations that

caspase zymogen activation involves cleavage at aspartyl residues and that active caspases also cut proteins at aspartyl residues have obvious implications. Namely, pro-caspases can become cleaved and activated either as a result of cleavage by other active caspases or through 'autoproteolytic' mechanisms which will be discussed below. Thus, once some caspase activation has occurred, the process can spread to other caspases through amplification steps in which one active caspase molecule cleaves and activates multiple caspase zymogens, as well as cascades of proteolytic activation of caspases through sequential stepwise mechanisms (Salvesen and Dixit, 1997; Thornberry and Lazebnik, 1998).

At least three mechanisms have been proposed for explaining how the 'first' caspase becomes activated: (1) the induced-proximity model; (2) the 'safety-catch' mechanism; and (3) introduction of an exogenous protease (**Figure 1**). In the induced-proximity model (**Figure 1**), two or more caspase zymogens are clustered together as a result of protein interactions, thus bringing them into close association. Because the zymogen forms of caspases are not entirely without proteolytic activity (some possessing about 1% of the activity of the processed 'active' enzymes), the close proximity allows these weakly active zymogens to trans-process each other, thereby generating the autonomously active proteases. This clustering of caspase zymogens typically is made possible by the presence in certain pro-caspases of an N-terminal prodomain which is located proximal to the portions of the pro-protein that give rise to the p20 (large) and p10 (small) catalytic subunits. These N-terminal prodomains serve as protein-interaction motifs that permit self-association of zymogens or that mediate interactions with adapter proteins which assemble multiprotein zymogen-activation complexes, sometimes referred to as 'apoptosomes' (Salvesen and Dixit, 1999).

Not all caspases possess significant N-terminal prodomains, thus creating a hierarchy of proteolytic cascades in which upstream caspases that possess large prodomains become activated as a result of protein interactions, and these initiator caspases then cleave and activate downstream effector caspases which possess only short N-terminal pro-peptides that are incapable for mediating protein interactions. This hierarchy of caspase proteolytic cascades is also supported by comparisons of the substrate preferences of upstream initiator and downstream target caspases, using combinatorial peptide library screening and other techniques. These studies have revealed the presence of tetrapeptide substrate cleavage sites preferred by upstream caspases within the sequences of the proforms of the downstream caspases, at sites corresponding to the authentic *in vivo* cleavage sites that separate the large and small subunits. The tetrapeptide cleavage sites preferred by the downstream caspases, in turn, are often found in several of the target proteins which are known to become cleaved at aspartyl residues during apoptosis, including

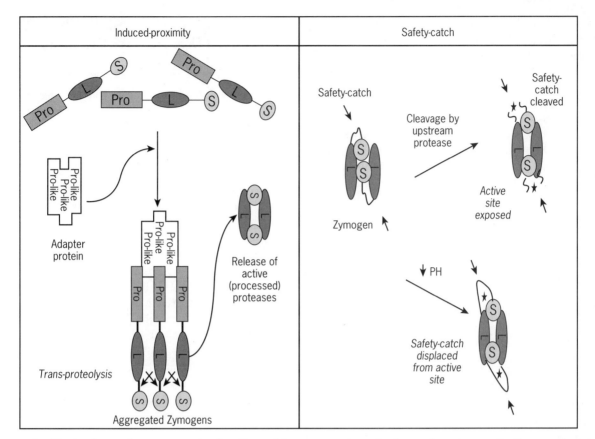

Figure 1 Mechanisms of caspase activation. Two of the proposed mechanisms of caspase activation are depicted, the induced-proximity model and the safety-catch model . In the induced-proximity model, pro-caspase zymogens are present as monomers that are single polypeptide chains with N-terminal prodomains (Pro) followed by the regions corresponding to the large (L) and small (S) catalytic subunits. Bringing these zymogens into close proximity, either by interactions with adapter proteins which typically share sequence and structural similarity with the prodomain regions of pro-caspases (shown) or by overexpression of pro-caspases resulting in self-aggregation (not-shown), allows these proenzymes to trans-process each other. This trans-processing is possible because the zymogens possess weak protease activity. Once proteolytically processed, separating the large and small subunit fragments and (often) removing the N-terminal prodomain, the active protease assembles, consisting of heterotetramer with two L and two S subunits. In the safety-catch mechanism, an autoinhibitory loop in the zymogen is envisioned as occupying or blocking the active site of the enzyme. Typically, cleavage at or near this autoinhibitory loop located between the L and S subunits exposes the active site (indicated by a star), creating the active protease (top). Alternatively, autorepression may be relieved by lowering pH, protonating acidic residues in the autoinhibitory loop and causing the loop to leave the active site of the enzyme (bottom).

the actin-regulatory protein gelsolin, the chromatin-regulatory protein poly-ADP ribosyl polymerase (PARP), the endonuclease inhibitor ICAD and its relatives of the caspase-inducible DNA endonuclease (CIDE)-family proteins, nuclear lamins, certain protein kinases and various other substrate proteins (Thornberry and Lazebnik, 1998; Cryns and Yuan, 1999).

The safety-catch mechanism envisions an auto-repressing loop in the caspase zymogen which occupies the active site of the protease and maintains it in a highly constrained inactive state (**Figure 1**). Activation then is speculated to involve displacement of the auto-repressive loop from the active site, allowing the caspase possibly to auto-process and thereby auto-activate itself. This

mechanism has been proposed for certain downstream effector caspases, such as caspase-3 and -7, which contain three adjacent acidic residues (aspartic or glutamic acid) in the candidate auto-repression loop. Neutralizing the negative charge of these acidic residues by lowering the pH or by site-directed mutagenesis (with conversion to uncharged alanine) lowers the barrier to caspase activation. It remains to be determined whether the proposed safety-catch mechanism can be extended to other caspases.

Finally, an example of caspase activation resulting from introduction of an exogenous protease has come from investigations of mechanisms of target cell killing by cytolytic T cells (Lowin et al., 1995). Here, perforin-mediated channels are used to inject granzyme B, a serine protease with specificity (like caspases) for cleavage of substrates at aspartyl residues. Granzyme B is capable of directly cleaving and activating most caspase-family zymogens. Interestingly, however, intracellular trafficking of granzyme B appears to be under regulation by cellular factors that may limit its interactions with caspases in some scenarios.

Inactivation of caspases can occur through several mechanisms in cancers (**Table 3**). For example, structural alterations in caspase-family genes, such as deletions and loss of function mutations, have been documented in tumour specimens or cancer cell lines, including initiator and effector caspases, suggesting that inactivation or elimination of caspase-family genes represents one mechanism by which malignant cells may escape apoptotic elimination. In addition, some caspase-family genes, including caspase-2 and -9 in mammals, are capable of producing shorter protein isoforms through alternative mRNA splicing that function as trans-dominant inhibitors of their full-length counterparts, possibly by forming heterodimers composed of full-length and truncated procaspases or by competing for binding to upstream activators. Although little work has been performed to date, it is intriguing to speculate that tumours may overexpress the trans-dominant inhibitory isoforms of some caspases as an additional mechanism for subverting apoptosis. Protein phosphoryation is another mechanism capable of directly suppressing caspases in tumours. The only reported example of this so far is human caspase-9, which can become phosphorylated by the kinase Akt (protein kinase-B), thereby suppressing the active caspase-9 enzyme as well as suppressing activation of the pro-caspase-9 zymogen. Interestingly, elevated levels of Akt activity are observed in many tumours as a result of (1) amplification of the Akt-family genes, (2) increased signalling by upstream protein tyrosine kinases and Ras-family oncoproteins, (3) aberrant production of Akt co-activators and (4) inactivation of PTEN—the product of a tumour-suppressor gene which normally suppresses Akt activation by dephosphorylating second messenger polyphosphoinositol lipids (Datta *et al.*, 1999). Theoretically, other post-translational modifications of caspases could also participate in their inactivation in cancers, including *S*-nitrosylation or glutathionylation of the active site cysteine.

Table 3 Mechanisms of caspase inactivation and suppression in cancers

Mechanism	Examples
Mutations in caspase genes	Caspase-3, -5, -8
Expression of dominant-negative caspase isoforms by alternative mRNA splicing	Caspase-2, -9
Phosphorylation	Caspase-9
Nitrosylation	Caspase-3
Overexpression of caspase-inhibiting IAPs	XIAP, cIAP-1, Livin

INHIBITOR OF APOPTOSIS (IAP) FAMILY PROTEINS FUNCTION AS CASPASE INHIBITORS

All protease networks studied to date include inhibitors which control flux through proteolytic cascades and which establish thresholds for protease activation which must be surpassed to trigger biological processes. The inhibitors of apoptosis proteins (IAPs) represent a family of anti-apoptotic proteins conserved throughout metazoan evolution that appear to serve this role. IAPs were first identified in the genomes of baculoviruses, where they suppress apoptosis induced by viral infection of host insect cells. Subsequently, cellular homologues of the baculovirus IAPs were discovered in humans, mice, flies and other animal species (Deveraux and Reed, 1999; Miller, 1999).

Membership in the IAP family requires two things: (1) an ability of the protein to suppress apoptosis, at least when overexpressed in cells, and (2) the presence of at least one copy of a conserved domain known as a BIR domain ('baculovirus IAP repeat'). The BIR domain represents a zinc-binding fold. One to three copies of the BIR domain are found in IAP family proteins, sometimes in association with other domains such as RING fingers, putative nucleotide-binding domains and caspase recruitment domains (CARDs) (described below).

A single BIR domain can be necessary and sufficient for inhibition of certain caspases by human IAP-family proteins. For example, the second of three BIR domains found in the human XIAP protein (where X indicates that the gene maps to the human X-chromosome) directly binds to and potently inhibits ($K_i < 1 \, \text{nmol} \, \text{L}^{-1}$) caspase-3 and -7. Thus, the concept has emerged that BIR domains represent caspase-inhibitory structures that bind active caspases and suppress them within cells. Interestingly, BIR domains do not inhibit all caspases, but rather exhibit clear selectivity. The second BIR domain of XIAP (in combination with adjacent residues), for instance, inhibits the downstream effector proteases, caspase-3 and -7, but does not bind or suppress the upstream initiator proteases, caspase-1, -8, -9 or -10. In contrast, the third BIR domain of XIAP suppresses caspase-9 but not other caspases tested. Although having caspase-inhibitory activity, at least some IAP family proteins may also participate in other processes, particularly signal transduction pathways involved in regulating kinases responsible ultimately for NF-κB induction and JNK activation. Contrasting the roles of IAPs as caspase inhibitors versus signal transduction modulators remains an active area of research.

Altered expression of IAP-family genes has been documented in cancers (LaCasse *et al.*, 1998). For example, the *cIAP-2* gene becomes involved in chromosomal translocations in certain types of lymphomas, resulting in deregulation of this gene. The *cIAP-2* gene also is a target of the transcription factor NF-κB, a member of the

Rel family of oncoproteins which suppresses apoptosis. Moreover, a member of the IAP-family called survivin is inappropriately overexpressed in the majority of human cancers. Survivin is the smallest of the IAPs identified thus far, containing a single BIR domain in humans and mice. This particular IAP-family member is particularly intriguing because it appears to have a dual role in apoptosis suppression and in cell division. The survivin protein is physically associated with the mitotic spindle apparatus during M-phase and beyond into anaphase, evidently playing an essential role in cytokinesis. Homologues of survivin are found in yeast and in *C. elegans*, performing essential functions in cell division but lacking any clear role in cell death control. Thus, it is speculated that survivin's evolutionarily conserved core function is related to cytokinesis, and that an apoptosis checkpoint function for this protein may have evolved later in higher organisms as a way of linking defects in the late stages of cell division to an apoptotic response. Circumstantial evidence implicates survivin in caspase suppression in mammalian cells analogous to other IAPs, but a direct role for this BIR domain containing protein in caspase inhibition remains equivocal. Furthermore, not all BIR-containing proteins are involved in apoptosis regulation, indicating that this zinc-binding fold can serve alternative functions, despite a conserved arrangement of histidine and cysteine residues. Most likely, BIRs are protein-interaction domains that bind and inhibit caspases in some circumstances but not others.

Regardless of the mechanism, overexpression of survivin clearly reduces apoptosis in response to a variety of apoptogenic stimuli whereas antisense-mediated reductions in survivin expression or gene transfer-mediated expression of dominant-negative mutants of survivin sensitize tumour cells in culture to apoptosis induction by anticancer drugs. These findings, coupled with the observation that survivin is rarely expressed in normal adult tissues whereas survivin mRNA and protein levels are markedly increased in most cancers, have elevated the status of survivin as a potential drug-discovery target for cancer therapy (Altieri *et al.*, 1999).

RECEPTOR-MEDIATED MECHANISMS OF CASPASE ACTIVATION

Several mechanisms of caspase activation have been elucidated, including the coupling of ligand binding at cell-surface receptors to caspase activation. Moreover, defects in at least some of these mechanisms have been uncovered in cancers.

The tumour necrosis factor (TNF) family of cytokine receptors includes at least six members that trigger apoptosis and which share a conserved protein-interaction domain in their cytosolic region which is essential for their cytotoxic activity (Ashkenazi and Dixit, 1998; Wallach

et al., 1999). These TNF-family receptors include TNFR1, Fas (CD95), DR3 (weasle; tweak), DR4 (trail receptor-1; Apo2), DR5 (trail receptor-2) and DR6 (**Figure 2**). The conserved cytosolic domain is known as the 'death domain' (DD) and is comprised of a six α-helical bundle which forms trimers and possibly higher-order oligomers in response to ligation of the extracellular domains or simply when these receptors are overexpressed in the absence of their cognate ligands. Hereditary loss-of-function mutations or trans-dominant inhibitory mutations in the DD of Fas (CD95) have been associated with a lymphoproliferative disorder and autoimmunity in the *lpr/lpr* strain of mice and in humans with autoimmune lymphoproliferative syndrome (ALPS). Similarly, somatic mutations in the death domain of Fas have been detected in certain human neoplasms, including myelomas, lymphomas, leukaemias and carcinomas of the lung and bladder.

The DDs of TNF-family death receptors bind adaptor proteins which interact, in turn, with the N-terminal domains of specific initiator caspases (**Figure 2**). The assembly of these multiprotein complexes is thought then to activate the associated pro-caspases by the induced-proximity model described above. Fadd (Mort1) represents one such adaptor protein. This protein contains a DD which binds directly to the DD of Fas, as well as a protein interaction module known as a death effector domain (DED). The DED is similar to the DD in structure, comprised of six α-helices, but constitutes a separate domain family which can be differentiated by sequence homology. Two of the known human caspases contain DEDs in their N-terminal prodomain regions, pro-caspase-8 and -10. These pro-caspases each contain two DEDs upstream of the catalytic segments and are both capable of binding directly to the DED of Fadd. Studies of cells derived from caspase-8 knockout mice have revealed an obligatory role for this initiator caspase in apoptosis induction by Fas and TNFR1. Similarly, gene ablation studies indicate an essential role for Fadd in apoptosis induction by these TNF-family death receptors.

Another example of a caspase-activating adapter protein that associates with TNF-family receptor complexes is Raidd (Cradd). The Raidd protein contains a DD and another protein interaction module known as a CARD domain. The CARD domain of Raidd specifically binds a homologous domain found in the N-terminal prodomain region of pro-caspase-2. Structures of these CARD domains have been solved, revealing again a characteristic fold comprised of six α-helices and suggesting that complementary patches of acidic, basic and hydrophobic residues on the surfaces of these domains account for the selectivity of their interactions with each other but not with other CARD-family proteins. In most cases, interactions of Fadd and Raidd with TNF-family receptors is mediated by an intermediate DD-family protein, Tradd, via associations of their DDs.

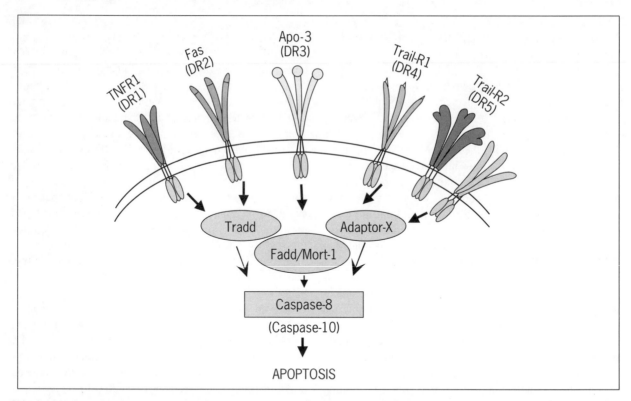

Figure 2   Caspase activation by TNF-family receptors. The currently known human members of the tumour necrosis factor (TNF) receptor family which contain cytosolic death domains (DDs) are depicted. The intracellular DDs of these receptors bind DD-containing adaptor proteins, such as Tradd, Fadd and others yet to be identified. These adaptor proteins then interact with initiator caspases which contain homologous protein interaction domains. The TNF family of receptors provided the first example of a receptor system which transduces signals into cells via proteolysis, thus representing a milestone in cell biology research.

Additional proteins which can participate indirectly in recruitment of pro-caspases to receptors include RIP and RIP-2 (Cardiac) which contain a conserved kinase domain of unknown functional significance in association with either a DD or CARD, respectively. Interestingly, whereas the CARD domain of RIP-2 binds the N-terminal CARD domain of pro-caspase-1, other portions of this protein reportedly interact with TRAF6, an adapter protein that associates with certain TNF-family receptors and Toll-family receptors (**Figure 3**). It should be noted, however, that caspase-1 and its close relatives, human caspase-4 and -5, may be only tangentially involved in apoptosis, and instead are principally involved in proteolytic processing of proinflammatory cytokine precursors, particularly pro-interleukin-1β and pro-IL-18. Caspase-1 knockout mice, for example, are grossly normal and exhibit only very modest defects in apoptosis induction, while manifesting extreme resistance to endotoxin-induced sepsis and displaying profound deficiencies in production of IL-1 and IL-18 *in vivo* (Reed, 1998a).

TNF-family death receptors play important roles in immune system interactions with tumours. One of the principal weapons used by cytolytic T cells for killing tumour targets, for example, is Fas-ligand (FasL). Consequently, defects in Fas-induced apoptosis can contribute to tumour avoidance of immune surveillance mechanisms. Moreover, upon achieving a Fas-resistant state, it has been shown that some tumours can then tolerate expressing FasL on their surfaces, thus using this death ligand as a weapon to kill neighbouring normal cells as well as activated lymphocytes.

Multiple mechanisms of tumour resistance to Fas and other TNF-family death ligands have been elucidated, including prereceptor, receptor and postreceptor defects (**Table 4**) (Tschopp *et al.*, 1998, 1999; Ashkenazi and Dixit, 1999). Prereceptor defects include the production of soluble 'decoy' receptors or fragments of receptors that compete with the transmembrane receptors for ligand binding. For instance, a soluble form of Fas can be produced by alternative mRNA splicing in which the exon encoding the transmembrane anchoring domain is skipped, resulting in production of a secreted version of this receptor. In the case of Trail (Apo2L), three genes have been identified which produce 'decoy' receptors that can compete with the death receptors, DR4 (TrailR1) and DR5 (TrailR1), for binding to Trail, thereby sparing cells from the apoptotic effects of this death ligand. Proteolytic removal of the extracellular domain of TNF-family receptor is also a possibility. Another potential resistance mechanism is found in the SODD (silencer of death domains) protein. SODD (also

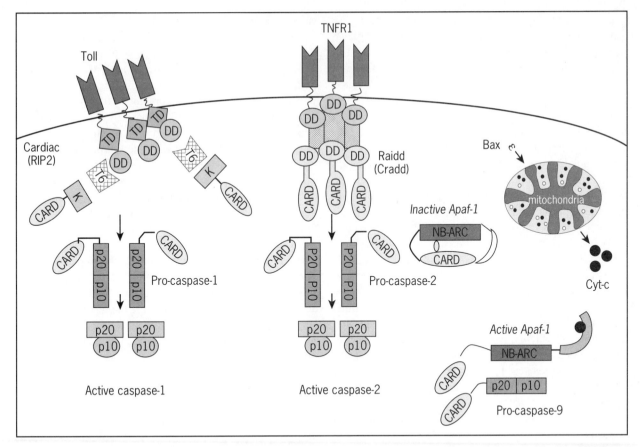

Figure 3 CARD domains and caspase activation. Examples of involvement of CARD-domain proteins in activation of CARD-containing caspases are presented, including examples from the Toll-receptor family (left), tumour necrosis factor receptor-1 (TNFR-1) (middle) and mitochondrial/cytochrome *c* (cyt-c) pathway (right). For each example, the target caspase contains an N-terminal prodomain consisting of a CARD. These CARD prodomains interact with homologous CARDs in various adapter proteins, such as Cardiac (RIP2; Rick) (left) which contains both a CARD and a kinase (K) domain of unknown significance, Raidd (Cradd) (middle) which contains both a CARD domain and a DD, the latter of which binds homologous DD-containing adapter proteins which associate with the TNF-receptor, and Apaf-1 (right), which contains a CARD, followed by a nucleotide-binding oligomerization domain (NB) and then WD repeats which mediates interactions with cyt-c. Release of cyt-c from mitochondria is required for converting Apaf-1 from a latent (inactive) conformation, resulting in activation of Apaf-1 so that it can bind pro-caspase-9 (see **Figure 5** for more details about Apaf-1).

known as BAG4) contains a domain that binds the DDs of TNFR1 and DR3, as well as a conserved Hsp70/Hsc70-binding domain. When overexpressed SODD prevents spontaneous aggregation of DDs, presumably by recruiting Hsp70/Hsc70-family molecular chaperones to these receptors and inducing conformational changes that prevent them from oligomerizing and signalling in the absence of ligand.

Table 4 Mechanisms for interfering with TNF-family death receptors

Mutations in death receptor or ligand genes
Decoy or soluble receptors
SODD (BAG4) suppression of receptor oligomerization
Antiapoptotic DED-family proteins (cFlip; BAR; Bap31)
NF-κB-mediated upregulation of caspase inhibitory proteins

Several postreceptor defects in death receptor signalling have also been uncovered in cancers. For example, FAP-1 is a Fas-binding protein phosphatase that, when overexpressed, can suppress Fas-induced apoptosis through an unidentified mechanism. Some tumours appear to overexpress FAP-1. Moreover, peptidyl antagonists that bind PDZ domains in FAP1 and that block interactions of FAP-1 with Fas have been shown to restore Fas sensitivity to Fas-resistant colon cancer cell lines *in vitro*. Additional antagonists of death receptor signalling include the Flip family of DED-containing proteins. These antiapoptotic proteins contain DEDs that permit them to bind either adapter proteins such as Fadd- or DED-containing pro-caspases such as pro-caspase-8 and -10. Overexpression of cellular Flip (also known as I-Flice, Cash, Casper, Usurpin, Mrit, Rick) or of its viral homologues can prevent assembly of death receptor signalling complexes and interfere with caspase activation. Overexpression of c-Flip has been documented in some tumours, and has been associated in animal models with resistance to immune-mediated suppression of cancer. In addition to cytosolic c-Flip and related proteins, membrane-anchored proteins which contain DEDs capable of binding pro-caspase-8 and/or -10 have been identified. Proteins such as BAR and Bap31 localize to internal membranes, primarily endoplasmic reticulum and/or mitochondria, and can modulate apoptosis signalling by TNF-family death receptors. Finally, activation of the transcription factor NF-κB has been associated with resistance to apoptosis induction by several TNF-family death receptors. NF-κB transcriptionally upregulates the expression of several antiapoptotic proteins, including one or more of the IAP-family proteins, resulting in apoptosis resistance. This observation is directly relevant to mechanisms of TNF-induced apoptosis in that several TNF-family receptors recruit proteins that activate caspases as described above, thus promoting apoptosis, but simultaneously bind other proteins which trigger NF-κB induction, thus preventing apoptosis. The net outcome of engaging TNF-family receptors such as TNFR1, DR3 and DR6 is difficult to predict and can be extremely cell-type and cell-context dependent. Taken together, it is clear that malignant cells have many options for developing mechanisms that thwart apoptosis induction by TNF-family death receptors and ligands.

MITOCHONDRIAL PATHWAYS FOR CASPASE ACTIVATION

In addition to receptor-mediated mechanisms for coupling caspase activation to ligation of specific cell-surface receptors, a pathway has been elucidated which links mitochondrial damage to a mechanism for triggering caspase activation. This mitochondrial pathway for caspase activation is engaged in response to growth factor deprivation, genotoxic injury, hypoxia and many other insults, and is commonly referred to as the 'intrinsic' pathway, in contrast to the receptor-mediated caspase activation mechanisms which are sometimes referred to as the 'extrinsic' pathway (**Figure 4**) (Green and Reed, 1998; Kroemer and Reed, 2000).

What allows mitochondria to trigger caspase activation?—release of cytochrome c from these organelles into the cytosol. Cytochrome c is best known for its role in electron-chain transport, where it transfers electrons from complex III to IV in the respiratory chain. However, following exposure of cells to many apoptotic stimuli, the outer membranes of mitochondria undergo permeability changes that permit cytochrome c and other proteins normally sequestered in the space between the inner and outer membranes of these organelles to leak out and enter the cytosol. Once in the cytosol, cytochrome c binds a

caspase-activating protein, called Apaf-1 (apoptotic protease activating factor-1). Apaf-1 is normally present in the cytosol in an inactive (latent) state in mammals and *Drosophila*. This protein consists of an N-terminal CARD domain, followed by a nucleotide-binding domain, ending with multiple WD repeat domains. The human Apaf-1 protein has been shown to oligomerize, apparently forming octamers, upon binding cytochrome c. This oligomerization is mediated by the nucleotide-binding domain and requires adenine triphosphate (ATP) or deoxy-ATP. Cytochrome c appears to interact with the WD repeat domains and nucleotide-binding domain, promoting a conformational change that results in oligomerization. Once oligomerized, activated oligomerized Apaf-1 molecules bind via their CARD domains to pro-caspase-9, a member of the caspase family which possesses an N-terminal CARD prodomain that has been shown by X-ray crystallography to possess a complementary interaction surface for association with the CARD of Apaf-1 (the interactions in this case are primarily electrostatic, involving associations of a surface patch of acidic residues on the CARD of Apaf-1 with basic residues on the CARD of pro-caspase-9). Activation of pro-caspase-9 then is achieved by the affinity-approximation model. However, rather than releasing processed caspase-9 to cleave and activate additional downstream effector caspases, instead caspase-9 must remain bound to Apaf-1 for maintaining its optimal protease activity. The 'free' processed caspase-9 molecule has only weak protease activity in the absence of Apaf-1, suggesting that the Apaf-1:caspase-9 complex represents the holoenzyme (**Figure 5**). Thus, the next caspase in the cascade, pro-caspase-3, is recruited to the Apaf-1:caspase-9 holoenzyme, where it becomes activated by cleavage at a conserved aspartyl residues separating the large and small subunits of the protease. Processed caspase-3 is then released from the Apaf-1:caspase-9 complex and autocatalytically cleaves and removes its own prodomain, which consists of a short ($\sim$20 amino-acid) segment, thereby generating the mature enzyme. Active caspase-3 then cleaves and activates additional pro-caspases, thus amplifying the proteolytic cascade. This and other downstream caspases also cleave a wide variety of specific substrates that ultimately commit the cell to an apoptotic demise, including CIDE-family proteins which control the activity of an endonuclease which appears to be largely responsible for the fragmentation of the nuclear DNA into oligo-nucleosomal length fragments—a hallmark (although non-obligatory event) of apoptosis.

Mechanisms for regulating the cytochrome c-dependent activation of Apaf-1 may exist, thus providing a means of fine tuning the coupling of mitochondria to caspases (Reed and Paternostro, 1999). For example, the efficiency of cytochrome c-mediated activation of caspases has been shown to be poor under conditions of isotonic salt $\sim$150 mmol L^{-1} (KCl) and neutral pH (7.4). Release of another protein from mitochondria, Smac (second mitochondrial activator

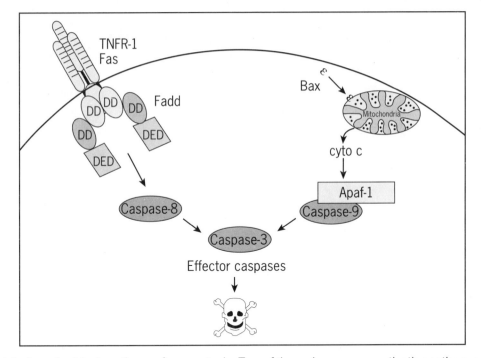

Figure 4   Intrinsic and extrinsic pathways for apoptosis. Two of the major caspase-activation pathways are depicted. The 'extrinsic' pathway is activated by extracellular ligands that bind death receptors such as TNFR-1 and Fas. These death receptors bind, in turn, to adaptor proteins such as Fadd (Mort1) which then bind the initiator pro-caspase, caspase-8. The 'intrinsic' pathway is activated by intracellular signals which induce cyt-c release from mitochondria. Cyt-c binding to the caspase-activator, Apaf-1, results in binding to and activation of pro-caspase-9. Gene ablation studies in mice have shown that pro-caspase-8 and pro-caspase-9 are absolutely required for apoptosis induction by TNF-family death receptors and cyt-c, respectively. Similarly, gene knockout studies in mice indicate that Fadd (Mort1) is critical for caspase activation by most (although perhaps not all) TNF-family death receptors and that Apaf-1 is absolutely required for caspase-activation by cyt-c. Many downstream effector caspases may be cleaved and activated by active caspase-8 and -9, with caspase-3 representing the best documented direct substrate of these upstream initiator caspases.

of caspases), can overcome the dependence on hypotonic salt. Furthermore, some apoptotic stimuli induce mitochondria to extrude protons (H^+), thus acidifying the cytosol and promoting cytochrome-mediated caspase activation. It may be of significance consequently that many growth and survival factors are known to induce cytosol alkalinization as a result of effects on the Na^+/H^+ antiporter, perhaps accounting for some of their antiapoptotic effects. Overproduction of Hsp70 also may interfere with cytochrome *c*-mediated activation of caspases, a finding of possible relevance to cancer given evidence of elevated Hsp70 levels in several kinds of cancer.

Also of relevance to activation of pro-caspase-9, the apical caspase in the mitochondrial pathway, at least two other proteins have been reported to bind pro-caspase-9 and to induce apoptosis through what appears to be cytochrome *c*-independent mechanisms, including an Apaf-1 homologue (CARD4/Nod) and Bcl-10 (hE10; CIPER). Both CARD4 (Nod) and Bcl-10 (hE10; CIPER) possess N-terminal CARD domains that interact with the CARD of pro-caspase-9. Interestingly, chromosomal translocations and somatic point mutations have been described in the

bcl-10 (hE10; CIPER) gene in lymphomas and solid tumours, respectively, which convert it from a pro-apoptotic to an anti-apoptotic protein.

Besides these caspase-9-binding proteins, another way of potentially modulating signalling through caspase-9-dependent pathways involves sequestration of this pro-protease in organellar compartments where it cannot interact with cytosolic proteins such as Apaf-1, CARD4 (Nod) and Bcl-10 (hE10; CIPER). Specifically, pro-caspase-9 has been shown to be stored in the inter-membrane space of mitochondria, along with cytochrome *c*, in some types of terminally differentiated cells. Thus, changes in mitochondrial membrane permeability are required to release pro-caspase-9 into the cytosol where its interacting proteins are located, at least in some cell types. Finally, caspase-9 in humans is a substrate of the kinase Akt, with phosphorylation inhibiting its protease activity through undetermined mechanisms.

Loss of expression of Apaf-1 has been described in melanomas, due to gene hypermethylation. In this regard, in cancers, *in vitro* transformation studies using cells from Apaf-1 and caspase-9 knockout mice suggest that these

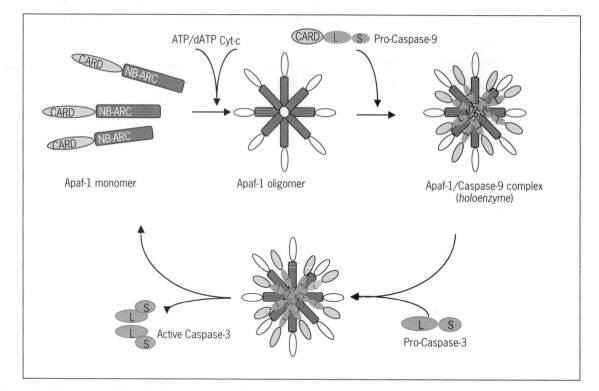

Figure 5   Dynamics of Apaf-1 'Apoptosome.' The sequence of events involved in cyt-c-mediated activation of Apaf-1 and pro-caspase-activation are depicted. Cyt-c plus either ATP or deoxy ATP (dATP) binding to Apaf-1 results in oligomerization mediated by the nucleotide-binding domain (NB-ARC) of this protein. Present estimates suggest that activated Apaf-1 may form an octamer. Oligomerized Apaf-1 binds pro-caspase-9, via a CARD–CARD interaction. Apaf-1-associated pro-caspase-9 molecules are then thought to transprocess each other, cleaving between the large (L) and small (S) subunits. Unlike most other caspases, caspase-9 does not remove its prodomain (CARD) by autoproteolysis. Also, unlike most caspases, after proteolytic processing, caspase-9 must remain associated with its activator Apaf-1 to maintain optimal protease activity. The Apaf-1/caspase-9 complex, therefore, represents the 'holoenzyme' complex. This complex directly recruits pro-caspase-3, which is cleaved by caspase-9, releasing active and processed caspase-3.

pro-apoptotic genes function as tumour suppressors within the p53 pathway. This finding is consistent with other data that suggest that p53 induces apoptosis primarily through a mitochondria-dependent mechanism (intrinsic pathway), although the death receptor (extrinsic pathway) may also be involved in some circumstances, as discussed below.

Bcl-2 FAMILY PROTEINS—REGULATORS OF CYTOCHROME *c* RELEASE AND MORE

A large family of evolutionarily conserved proteins has been identified which regulates the release of cytochrome *c* and other proteins from mitochondria (Adams and Cory, 1998; Reed, 1998b; Gross *et al.*, 1999). The founding member of this family is known as Bcl-2, representing an acronym for B-cell lymphoma-2 and reflecting the original discovery of this gene because of its involvement in chromosomal translocations in B-cell lymphomas. In follicular non-Hodgkin lymphomas, the *Bcl-2* gene on the long arm of chromosome 18 at band q21 frequently

becomes fused with the immunoglobulin (Ig) heavy-chain gene locus on the long-arm of chromosome 14 at band q32, creating t(14;18) (q32; q21) translocations. Because the Ig gene locus is highly active in B cells, the juxtaposed Bcl-2 gene become transcriptionally deregulated, resulting in continuous production of high levels of *Bcl-2* mRNAs and protein. Bcl-2 is an anti-apoptotic protein that uses a C-terminal membrane-anchoring domain to insert into the membranes of mitochondria as well as some other membranes inside cells. Elevated levels of Bcl-2 prevent cytochrome *c* release from mitochondria following exposure of cells to a wide variety of apoptotic agents and conditions, including growth factor deprivation, oxidants, Ca^{2+} overload, chemotherapeutic drugs and X-irradiation. The mechanism by which Bcl-2 family proteins control cytochrome *c* released from mitochondria remains unknown, although several theories have been advanced and are the subject of several reviews devoted entirely to this important topic (Adams and Cory, 1998; Green and Reed, 1998; Reed, 1998b; Gross *et al.*, 1999; Vander Heiden and Thompson, 1999) (**Figure 6**).

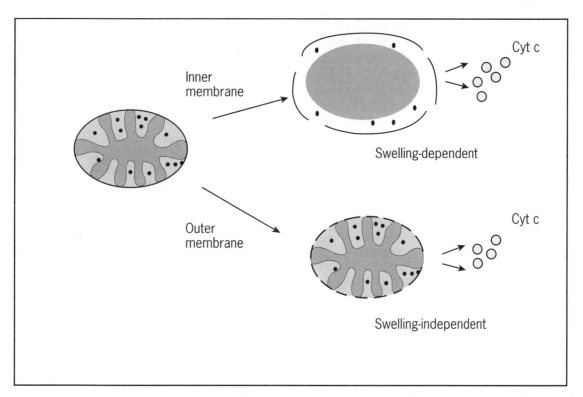

Figure 6   Alternative routes of cytochrome *c* release from mitochondria. Two alternative mechanisms are depicted for inducing release of cyt-c (shown) and other apoptosis-relevant proteins, such as AIF, Smac and intra-mitochondrial caspases (not shown) from the inter-membrane space of mitochondria. The swelling-dependent mechanism (top) involves alterations to the permeability of the inner membrane, causing osmotic disequilibrium and swelling of the matrix space. Because the surface area of the inner membrane, with its folded cristae, is greater than the area of the outer membrane, swelling results in rupture of the outer membrane and release of proteins stored in the inter-membrane space. In the swelling-independent model (bottom), a selective change in outer-membrane permeability occurs, allowing release of cyt-c and other proteins from the inter-membrane space, while inner-membrane integrity and volume homeostasis are preserved.

The Bcl-2 family consists of both anti-apoptotic members, which include in humans Bcl-X_L, Bcl-W, Bfl-1, Bcl-B and Mcl-1, as well as pro-apoptotic members, which include in humans Bax, Bak, Bok, Bad, Bid, Hrk, Bik, Bim, Nip3 and Nix. Homologues of some of these proteins are also found in lower organisms, including *Caenorhabditis elegans* and *Drosophila melanogaster*, where they often play important roles in developmental programmed cell death. Evolutionary conservation of function has been documented by cross-species gene transfer experiments, implying commonality in their mechanisms of action.

Antiapoptotic Bcl-2 family members may possess multiple mechanisms for suppressing cell death. In general, however, these mechanisms can be simplified into two general categories. First, based on determination of their three-dimensional structures or computer modelling predictions of structures, antiapoptotic Bcl-2 family proteins are recognized to be similar to certain types of α-helical ion-channel or pore-forming proteins. Specifically, these Bcl-2 family proteins share structural similarity with the pore-forming domains of certain bacterial toxins which have been implicated in transport of either ions (colicins) or proteins (diphtheria toxin) across membranes. At least *in vitro*, antiapoptotic Bcl-2 family proteins such as Bcl-2 and Bcl-X_L have been documented to form multiconductance ion channels in synthetic membranes, thus providing further experimental evidence in support of a role as channel/pore proteins. Second, antiapoptotic Bcl-2 family proteins also possess at least one hydrophobic pocket on their surface which mediates interactions with other proteins, thus altering the function or intracellular targeting of other proteins which may be relevant in some contexts to cell death. Proteins reported to interact directly or indirectly with antiapoptotic Bcl-2 family members such as Bcl-2 or Bcl-X_L include the caspase activator Apaf-1, the p53-binding protein p53BP2, the Ca^{2+}-dependent phosphatase calcineurin, the protein kinase Raf-1, the Hsp70/Hsc70 molecular chaperone regulators Bag1 and Bag3, the spinal muscular atrophy gene product Smn, the DED-containing proteins BAR and Bap31, and others. It is currently unknown which of these two major functions of antiapoptotic Bcl-2 family proteins is more important for their overall cytoprotective effects in cells. It is clear, however, that Bcl-2 and Bcl-X_L possess cytoprotective functions which are independent of caspase-family cell death proteases and which can be manifested even in yeast, which lack the various Bcl-2/Bcl-X_L-interacting proteins described above. Hence it seems likely that these proteins possess an intrinsic biochemical function. Additional ancillary functions related to interactions with other protein may have been added over evolutionary time to this core-intrinsic function, as a means of integrating multiple pathways with cell life and death decision making (Reed, 1997).

Proapoptotic Bcl-2 family proteins are more structurally diverse than their antiapoptotic counterparts, probably reflecting differences in the mechanisms by which they promote cell death. A subgroup of proapoptotic Bcl-2 family proteins, which in humans includes Bax, Bak, Bok and Bid, appears to possess a similar pore/channel-like protein fold as the antiapoptotic members. Indeed, where tested, these pro-apoptotic Bcl-2 family members have been documented to form multiconductance, sometimes fairly large, channels in synthetic membranes *in vitro*. They also induce cytochrome *c* release from mitochondria when overexpressed in cells as well as when added (where tested) as recombinant proteins to isolated mitochondria *in vitro*. It remains controversial as to the mechanisms that explain why Bax, Bak, Bok and Bid are proapoptotic and induce cytochrome *c* release from mitochondria, whereas the structurally similar antiapoptotic proteins Bcl-2, Bcl-X_L, Bcl-W, Mcl-1, Bcl-B, and Bfl-1 are cytoprotective and block cytochrome *c* release.

By analogy with the bacterial proteins with which they share structural homology, it has been suggested that Bcl-2 family proteins may exist in two dramatically different conformations—one in which two of more α-helices of these proteins are integrated into membranes and another in which they are not integrated into membranes, although they are often tethered to membranes via their C-terminal membrane-anchoring domains. These two conformational states may then dictate whether these proteins are actively forming channels or perhaps interacting with other channel or pore-like proteins in mitochondrial membranes (inserted state) versus whether they assume conformations necessary for interacting with certain other proteins (noninserted state). Thus, the concept of on/off (active/inactive) conformations has emerged as an element in understanding the regulation of Bcl-2 family proteins—which may not correlate necessarily with the levels of expression of these proteins.

Apoptosis (caspase-dependent death) and necrosis (caspase-independent death) share some elements of overlap and the release of cytochrome *c* from mitochondria represents one of these. When cytochrome *c* exits mitochondria, not only can apoptosis be induced through the Apaf-1-dependent mechanisms described above, but also necrosis can ensue owing to failure of mitochondrial electron chain-transport, resulting in inadequate ATP production, increased generation of oxygen free radicals and other disturbances. Several Bcl-2 family proteins have been shown to regulate both apoptosis and necrosis, probably at least in part owing to their direct caspase-independent effects on mitochondrial membrane permeability. Although many mechanisms remain unclear, it can be deduced that these direct effects of Bcl-2, Bax and certain other Bcl-2 family proteins on mitochondria are also independent of CED-4/Apaf-1-family proteins, given that (1) caspases are required neither for induction of cytochrome *c* release by Bax, Bax, and Bok nor for prevention of cytochrome *c* release by Bcl-2 or Bcl-X_L and (2) the only known function of CED-4/Apaf-1 family proteins is regulation of caspases. Interestingly, a variety of data have provided evidence that clonogenic survival often correlates better with caspase-independent cell death than with caspase-dependent apoptosis, suggesting that a cell death commitment point which is regulated by Bcl-2 family proteins exists upstream of caspase activation in the mitochondrial pathway (Green and Reed, 1998).

Members of another subgroup of pro-apoptotic Bcl-2 family proteins, which in humans includes Bad, Bik, Bim and Hrk, lack similarity to pore-forming domains but do possess a short ($\sim$16–20 amino acid) domain found in nearly all Bcl-2 family proteins known as a Bcl-2 homology-3 (BH3) domain. The BH3 domain participates in protein dimerization among Bcl-2 family members, and therefore represents a functionally important region that permits many pro- and antiapoptotic Bcl-2 family proteins to antagonize each other's functions through physical hand-to-hand combat. The BH3 domain consists of a conserved amphipathic α-helix which inserts into the hydrophobic receptor-like pockets found on (or predicted to exist on) the antiapoptotic Bcl-2 family proteins. Bad, Bik, Bim and Hrk all bind selected antiapoptotic Bcl-2 family members via their BH3 domains, thus antagonizing the cytoprotective functions of Bcl-2, Bcl-X_L or similar proteins, but these killer proteins do not interact with themselves, nor do they bind to pro-apoptotic Bcl-2 family members such as Bax, Bak, Bok and Bid. Specificity exists in the preferences for dimerization partners within the network of Bcl-2 family protein interactions, thus creating opportunities for fine-tuning regulation through tissue-specific and temporally dynamic differences in the repertoires of family members expressed.

Several ways of regulating dimerization among Bcl-2 family proteins have been documented. One obvious way is by controlling the levels of various Bcl-2 family members at the transcriptional or post-transcriptional levels, as has been demonstrated for several members of the family. Another mechanism for controlling dimerization involves protein phosphorylation/dephosphorylation. For example, the proapoptotic protein BAD is a substrate for phosphorylation by several protein kinases, including Akt, Pak1, PKA and Raf-1. When phosphorylated on certain sites, BAD is unable to dimerize with Bcl-2 or Bcl-X_L, thus abrogating its proapoptotic function. Elevations in Akt activity in cancers, therefore, suppress apoptosis at least in part through effects on BAD, at least in those cases where BAD is expressed. Conversely, sustained elevations in cytosolic Ca^{2+}, resulting in activation of the protein phosphatase calcineurin, have been shown to result in dephosphorylation and reactivation of BAD. In addition to phosphorylation/dephosphorylation, dimerization among some Bcl-2 family proteins can be regulated by proteolysis. For instance, the proapoptotic protein Bid is normally present in the cytosol in a latent state. Removal of an N-terminal 58 amino acid domain by caspase-mediated cleavage activates the Bid protein, exposing its BH3 domain, thus allowing it to bind other Bcl-2 family proteins including Bcl-2, Bcl-X_L, Bax and Bak. The caspase responsible for Bid cleavage is caspase-8, thus providing a mechanism for cross-talk between the death receptor ('extrinsic') and mitochondrial ('intrinsic') cell death pathways. Yet another mechanism of regulating dimerization among Bcl-2 family proteins can be found in the Bim protein. The longer isoforms of Bim are present in a complex with dynein light chain in association with microtubules, thus sequestering Bim proteins in a location where they cannot interact with other Bcl-2 family members. Release of Bim proteins from microtubule-associated protein complexes allows their translocation to the surfaces of mitochondria and other organelles where antiapoptotic Bcl-2 family dimerization partners reside. Release of Bim from microtubules may be relevant to some of the mechanisms by which microtubulin-interacting anticancer drugs induce apoptosis (Huang and Strasser, 2000).

Many examples of altered expression or structure of Bcl-2 family proteins have been documented in human cancers. In addition to its inappropriate overexpression in lymphomas containing the t(14;18) translocations described above, pathological overexpression of Bcl-2 (without attendant structural changes to the gene) has been estimated to occur in roughly half of all human cancers, including most advanced hormone-refractory prostate cancers, two-thirds of breast cancers and over half of all colon and lung cancers. Examples of upregulation of other antiapoptotic proteins such as Bcl-X_L or downregulation of proapoptotic proteins such as Bax and Bak also exist in human cancers. Moreover, mutations that inactivate the *BAX* gene have been detected. One of the more common mutations involves a homopolymeric stretch of eight guanosine residues, which occurs frequently in cancers that manifest the microsatellite instability phenotype due to errors in DNA mismatch repair enzymes or their regulators. Consistent with their important role in controlling apoptosis sensitivity to chemotherapeutic drugs and X-irradiation, the levels of Bcl-2, Bax or other Bcl-2 family proteins are of prognostic significance for some subgroups of patients with certain types of cancer.

INTERACTIONS OF SIGNAL TRANSDUCTION PATHWAYS WITH APOPTOSIS PATHWAYS

Many upstream inputs exist which link cellular responses to various stimuli with the core components of the apoptosis machinery. An exhaustive review of these connections is beyond the scope of this chapter, but a few deserve special mention.

The transcription factor NF-κB has been implicated in apoptosis suppression in many contexts and appears to be elevated in its activity in many types of cancer (Karin and Ben-Neriah, 2000). NF-κB can consist of various dimerizing pairs of Rel-family members, with the best studied representing a heterodimer of p50 and p65. NF-κB directly upregulates the transcription of several antiapoptotic proteins, including (1) the Bcl-2 family members Bcl-X_L and Bfl-1, (2) the IAP-family member cIAP-2, and possibly cIAP-1 and XIAP under some circumstances, (3) the TRAF-interacting protein A20, which displays antiapoptotic activity in some contexts, and (4) IEX-1L, an anti-apoptotic protein of unknown mechanism. Consequently, NF-κB has emerged as an attractive drug-discovery target for cancer therapy, with most efforts aimed at suppression of the activities of upstream kinases such as the IKKα and IKKβ, which are responsible for phosphorylating IκB-family proteins, the endogenous suppressors of NF-κB—resulting in targeting of these proteins for degradation via a ubiquitin/proteasome-dependent pathway.

As described above, the protein kinase Akt serves as an apoptosis-suppressing link between a variety of growth factor receptors and membrane-associated oncoproteins (Datta *et al.*, 1999). Several apoptosis relevant substrates of Akt have been identified to date, including (1) the proapoptotic Bcl-2 family protein BAD, (2) the apical protease in the mitochondrial pathway caspase-9, (3) Forkhead-family transcription factors that control transcription of the promoters of apoptosis-inducing genes including Fas-L and (4) the NF-κB-inducing kinase IKKα. In each case, the net effect of phosphorylation of these substrates by Akt is increased protection from apoptosis. Multiple mechanisms for achieving abnormally elevated levels of Akt activity have been documented in tumour cells, perhaps the most common of which is mutations in the *PTEN* gene which result in decreased elimination of the second-messenger polyphosphoinositol phospholipids responsible for initiating Akt activation.

The tumour suppressor p53 is a well-known inducer of apoptosis which becomes inactivated in approximately half of all human tumours as a result of gene mutations and deletions, alterations in p53 kinases (ATM, CHK2), changes in the levels of p53 antagonist proteins and their regulators (MDM2, p19-ARF), ectopic expression of viral oncoproteins (HPV E6; SV40 large T antigen) and other mechanisms (Yan *et al.*, 2000). Although p53 has other functions relevant to cell cycle control, DNA repair responses and genetic instability, analysis of transgenic mice (when crossed with oncogene-bearing transgenic mice) suggest that the apoptosis-inducing activity of p53 is probably its most important attribute for suppression of tumorigenesis *in vivo*. How p53 induces apoptosis remains controversial. Three things however seem clear: (1) apoptosis induction by p53 derives from its function as a transcription factor; (2) p53 possesses multiple potential mechanisms for promoting apoptosis; and (3) the specific mechanisms employed are highly tissue-specific and may vary among clonal neoplasms even of the same lineage. Among the documented apoptosis-regulatory genes that make possible contributions to p53-induced apoptosis are the following: (1) the proapoptotic gene *BAX*, whose promoter in humans contains at least four consensus p53-binding sites and which is directly transcriptionally induced by p53; (2) Fas, which is a direct transcriptional target of p53; (3) DR5, another TNF-family member which may be a direct target of p53 trans-activation; and (4) Fas-L, which reportedly can be induced to translocate by p53 from a sequestered Golgi location to the plasma membrane where its receptor (Fas) primarily resides. Given the importance of p53 in inducing apoptosis of cancer cells (as well as certain types of normal cells) following genotoxic injury, this tumour suppressor has received extensive attention as a possible therapeutic target.

Multiple members of the nuclear receptor (NR) family of ligand-responsive transcription factors have been documented as regulators of the transcription of selected apoptosis genes. For example, retinoids which interact with and activate RAR- and/or RXR-family receptors are known to downregulate the expression of the antiapoptotic *BCL-2* and/or *BCL-X$_L$* genes in certain malignancies. Attempts to exploit this attribute of retinoids have been made in the clinic and are likely to continue into the future. Conversely, oestrogen is a positive regulator of *BCL-2* gene expression in mammary epithelial cells and in oestrogen receptor (ER)-positive breast cancers, possibly explaining some of the proapoptotic effects of antioestrogens such as tamoxifen on breast cancer cells *in vivo*. PPAR-γ ligands, which include certain prostaglandins produced by cyclooxygenases and other enzymes, as well as synthetic drugs that engage these receptors, have also been shown to either up- or downregulate transcription of *BCL-2*, depending on cellular context. These and other examples illustrate that many opportunities exist to regulate the output of apoptosis-relevant genes via effects on NR-family transcription factors in cancers.

THERAPEUTIC IMPLICATIONS

Knowledge about the core components of the apoptosis machinery and the various upstream inputs into apoptosis pathways has suggested a wide variety of new strategies for devising new therapies for cancer (Reed, 1999; Nicholson, 2000; Reed and Tomaselli, 2000). The full range of therapeutic modalities can be envisioned, including (1) small-molecule drugs that directly bind to and modulate the activities of specific protein targets; (2) antisense, DNAzyme and ribozyme nucleic acid-based therapeutics; (3) gene therapy using proapoptotic proteins; and (4) biologicals such as recombinant protein ligands or monoclonal antibodies, in the case of cell surface targets. Already proof of concept data have been obtained in animal models for many apoptosis-modulating agents, and some of these have advanced into clinical trials. At the time of this writing, for example, phase III trials are underway exploring the efficacy of antisense oligo-nucleotides directed against *BCL-2* mRNA for patients with a variety of types of refractory tumours. Recombinant Trail (Apo2L) protein is nearing its debut into clinical trials, as an attempt to trigger TNF-family death receptor pathways in tumour cells. Retinoids and PPAR-γ ligands are currently being examined as possible apoptosis sensitizers in leukaemias and solid tumours. Gene therapy trials are underway involving local delivery of p53- or *BAX*-expressing viral vectors, attempting directly to restore p53 or Bax expression in tumour cells. Monoclonal antibodies, recombinant proteins and synthetic peptidyl ligands that induce apoptosis of migrating endothelial cells by interfering with integrin-generated signals for cell survival (probably mediated largely by Akt) are also under investigation in clinical trials, as an approach for inhibiting angiogenesis. Preclinical analysis is also under way of multiple agents, ranging from small molecule organic compounds that restore activity to mutant p53 in malignant cells to synthetic peptides representing BH3 domains of pro-apoptotic Bcl-2 family proteins combined with membrane-penetrating peptides derived from viruses.

Our understanding is also rapidly evolving about the mechanisms by which currently available anticancer agents successfully trigger apoptosis of tumour cells and how resistance develops in all too many instances. A few examples include (1) binding of the triphosphate forms of purine nucleoside analogues to Apaf-1, resulting in improved catalytic efficiency of Apaf-1-mediated activation of caspases relative to endogenous dATP, (2) liberation of the BH3-only proapoptotic Bcl-2 family member Bim from microtubules by agents that disturb normal microtubule polymerization and (3) antioestrogen (tamoxifen)-mediated downregulation of Bcl-2 expression in breast cancers.

Exploiting apoptosis-based therapies for the treatment of cancer must be achieved with an acceptable therapeutic index, resulting in a selective killing of malignant cells. Fortunately, much evidence suggests that the inherent abnormalities found in cancer cells may also render them selectively more vulnerable compared with normal cells when deprived of their roadblocks to apoptosis. For example, several proto-oncogenes which become hyperactive in cancers, such as c-*Myc* and *cyclin-D1 (BCL-1)*, drive rapid tumour cell division but also promote cell death unless apoptosis is concomitantly blocked (Evan and Littlewood, 1998). Genetically unstable cells also suffer errors in cell cycle checkpoint regulation and DNA/chromosome management which can be triggers for apoptosis when cell death pathways are intact. Finally, metastatic cells are potentially vulnerable because they often depend on defects in apoptosis pathways for avoiding cell death as a result of loss of survival signals from unoccupied cell adhesion receptors and from absence of local growth/survival factors. It seems clear, therefore, that apoptosis-based therapies will eventually find their place in the armentarium of weapons that will be used to wage and eventually to win the war on cancer.

ACKNOWLEDGEMENTS

The author acknowledges research funding from the National Cancer Institute, National Institutes of Health, Department of Defense, California Breast Cancer Research Program and CaP-CURE.

REFERENCES

Adams, J. and Cory, S. (1998). The Bcl-2 protein family: arbiters of cell survival. *Science*, **281**, 1322–1326.

Altieri, D. C., *et al.* (1999). Survivin apoptosis: an interloper between cell death and cell proliferation in cancer. *Laboratory Investigations*, **79**, 1327–1333.

Ashkenazi, A. and Dixit, V. (1998). Death receptors: signaling and modulation. *Science*, **281**, 1305–1308.

Ashkenazi, A. and Dixit, V. M. (1999). Apoptosis control by death and decoy receptors. *Current Opinions in Cell Biology*, **11**, 255–260.

Cryns, V. and Yuan, Y. (1999). Proteases to die for. *Genes and Development*, **12**, 1551–1570.

Datta, S., *et al.* (1999). Cellular survival: a play in three Akts. *Genes and Development*, **13**, 2905–2927.

Deveraux, Q. and Reed, J. (1999) IAP family proteins: suppressors of apoptosis. *Genes and Development*, **13**, 239–252.

Evan, G. and Littlewood, T. (1998) A matter of life and cell death. *Science*, **281**, 1317–1322.

Fesik, S. W. (2000) Insights into programmed cell death through structural biology. *Cell*, **103**, 273–282.

Green, D. R. and Reed, J. C. (1998) Mitochondria and apoptosis. *Science*, **281**, 1309–1312.

Gross, A., *et al.* (1999). BCL-2 family members and the mitochondria in apoptosis. *Genes and Development*, **13**, 1899–1911 (1999).

Huang, D. C. and Strasser, A. (2000). Bh3-only proteins—essential initiators of apoptotic cell death. *Cell*, **103**, 839–842.

Karin, M. and Ben-Neriah, Y. (2000). Phosphorylation meets ubiquitination: the control of NF-κB activity. *Annual Reviews of Immunology*, **18**, 621–663.

Kroemer, G. and Reed, J. C. (2000) Mitochondrial control of cell death. *Nature Medicine*, **6**, 513–519.

LaCasse, E. C., *et al.* (1998). The inhibitors of apoptosis (IAPs) and their emerging role in cancer. *Oncogene*, **17**, 3247–3259.

Lowin, B., *et al.* (1995). Perforin and granzymes: crucial effector molecules in cytolytic T lymphocyte and natural killer cell-mediated cytotoxicity. *Current Topics in Microbiology Immunology*, **198**, 1–24.

Metzstein, M., *et al.* (1998). Genetics of programmed cell death in *C. elegans*: past, present and future. *Trends in Genetics*, **14**, 410–416.

Miller, L. (1999). An exegesis of IAPs: salvation and surprises from BIR motifs. *Trends in Cell Biology*, **9**, 323–328.

Nicholson, D. W. (2000). From bench to clinic with apoptosis-based therapeutic agents. *Nature*, **407**, 810–816.

Reed, J. C. (1997). Double identity for proteins of the Bcl-2 family. *Nature*, **387**, 773–776.

Reed, J. (1998a). Caspases and cytokines: roles in inflammation and autoimmunity. *Advances in Immunology*, **73**, 265–287.

Reed, J. (1998b). Bcl-2 family proteins. *Oncogene*, **17**, 3225–3236.

Reed, J. (1999). Dysregulation of apoptosis in cancer. *Journal of Clinical Oncology*, **17**, 2941.

Reed, J. and Paternostro, G. (1999). Post-mitochondrial regulation of apoptosis during heart failure. *Proceedings of the National Academy of Sciences of the USA*, **96**, 7614–6.

Reed, J. C. (2000). Mechanisms of apoptosis. *American Journal of Pathology*, **157**, 1415–1430.

Reed, J. C. and Tomaselli, K. (2000). Drug discovery opportunities from apoptosis research. *Current Opinions in Biotechnology*, **11**, 586–592.

Salvesen, G. S. and Dixit, V. M. (1997). Caspases: intracellular signaling by proteolysis. *Cell*, **91**, 443–446.

Salvesen, G. S. and Dixit, V. M. (1999). Caspase activation: the induced-proximity model. *Proceedings of the National Academy of Sciences of the USA*, **96**, 10964–10967.

Thornberry, N. and Lazebnik, Y. (1998). Caspases: enemies within. *Science*, **281**, 1312–1316.

Tschopp, J., *et al.* (1998). Inhibition of Fas death signals by Flips. *Current Opinions in Immunology*, **10**, 552–558.

Tschopp, J., *et al.* (1999). Apoptosis: silencing the death receptors. *Current Biology*, **9**, R381–R384.

Vander Heiden, M. G. and Thompson, C. B. (1999). Bcl-2 proteins: regulators of apoptosis or of mitochondrial homeostasis? *Nature Cell Biology*, **1**, E209–E216.

Vaux, D. and Korsmeyer, S. (1999). Cell death in development. *Cell*, **96**, 245–254.

Wallach, D., *et al.* (1999). Tumor necrosis factor receptor and Fas signaling mechanisms. *Annual Reviews of Immunology*, **17**, 331–367.

Wyllie, A. H. (1997). Apoptosis: an overview. *British Medical Bulletin*, **53**, 451–465.

Yan, H., *et al.* (2000). Genetic testing—present and future. *Science*, **289**, 1890–1892.

FURTHER READING

Abrams, J. (1999). An emerging blueprint for apoptosis in drosophila. *Trends in Cell Biology*, **9**, 435–440.

Jacobson, M. D., *et al.* (1997). Programmed cell death in animal development. *Cell*, **88**, 347–354.

Metzstein, M., *et al.* (1998). Genetics of programmed cell death in *C. elegans*: past, present and future. *Trends in Genetics*, **14**, 410–416.

Wyllie, A. H., *et al.* (1980). Cell death, the significance of apoptosis. *International Review of Cytology*, **68**, 251–306.

Chapter 10

Signalling by Steroid Receptors

Torsten A. Hopp and Suzanne A. W. Fuqua
Breast Center at Baylor College of Medicine, Houston, TX, USA

CONTENTS

- Introduction
- Structure and Function of Oestrogen Receptors α and β
- The ER is a Ligand-dependent Transcription Factor
- The Importance of Oestrogen Receptor Expression in Cancer Initiation and Progression
- Conclusion

INTRODUCTION

Steroid hormones (androgens, oestrogens glucocorticoids and progestins) play a vital role in the development and maintenance of normal cellular function, as well as regulatory functions within the reproductive organs. These hormones mediate their activities through binding to specific intracellular receptor proteins, called the androgen receptor (AR), oestrogen receptor (ER), glucocorticoid receptor (GR) and progesterone receptor (PR), respectively. The steroid receptors (SRs) are members of a large superfamily of nuclear receptors, which modulate expression of target genes upon binding of their respective hormones (Evans, 1988). One of the important characteristics of this protein family is the highly conserved organisation of functional domains, implying that the underlying mechanism of transcriptional modulation might also be preserved. A highly simplified and schematized model of SR action can be

seen in **Figure 1**: upon binding of the steroid hormone, the SR forms dimers and binds to a specific steroid response element (SRE) in the 5′ flanking region of hormone-responsive genes and stimulates/modulates their transcription.

Recent research studying the molecular mechanism of transcriptional regulation of target genes by SRs has revealed a very complex network of protein–protein interactions in addition to protein–DNA interactions necessary for proper function. Disruption in this intricately regulated circuitry can perturb SR signalling. Specifically, mutations in the AR and ER, and also altered receptor expression, have been found in prostate and breast cancer, and have been associated with cancer progression and hormone resistance. However, our understanding of how these changes can affect the SR signalling pathway is still very limited in many cases. To comprehend the complex network of SR signalling, we will focus here on the ER, which has been extensively studied owing to its importance in the clinical management of breast cancer (Osborne, 1998).

STRUCTURE AND FUNCTION OF OESTROGEN RECEPTORS α AND β

Like many other members of the nuclear receptor family, the ER has more than one form encoded by separate genes. In the case of ER there are two, called *ERα* and *-β*. The human *ERα* gene resides on chromosome 6q25.1 and is transcribed in a single mRNA of 6.5 kb that encodes a protein of 595 amino acids with an approximate molecular mass of 66 kDa (Kumar *et al.*, 1987). Even though the *ERα* gene is transcribed from at least three different promoters in a cell- and tissue-specific manner, only a single open reading frame appears to exist. However, the three promoters transcribe mRNA isoforms which differ in their 5′ untranslated regions, but no biological differences have yet been reported.

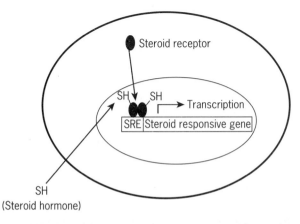

Figure 1 Simplified model of steroid action. Steroids enter a target cell by diffusion through the cell membrane and bind to steroid receptor (filled ovals). The hormone-bound receptor complex stimulates transcription of target genes via interaction with a steroid response element.

The *ERβ* gene is located on chromosome 14q22–24 and encodes a protein of 530 amino acids with a molecular mass of 60 kDa (Mosselman *et al.*, 1996). Unlike *ERα*, several studies indicate that *ERβ* is transcribed as multiple mRNAs and also translated into proteins from at least two reading frames resulting in a second ERβ protein which lacks 53 amino acids of the N-terminus. Overall, ERα and ERβ are highly homologous (49% amino acid identity), but appear to be expressed in different organs and at different developmental stages. Interestingly, ERα is expressed in female organs such as the mammary gland, uterus, ovary, vagina and certain areas of the hypothalamus, whereas ERβ is found in the male in different areas of the hypothalamus when compared with ERα, and in the cerebral cortex. Additionally, *ERβ* mRNA has also been detected in prostate, ovary, uterus, lung, testis and artery.

In Vivo Function of the Oestrogen Receptors

The development of mice lacking the *ERα* (*αERKO*) or *ERβ* (*βERKO*) gene have proved to be valuable tools in evaluating the *in vivo* function of these receptors. The αERKO mice were generated in 1993, and the disruption of ERα expression not only caused infertility in both sexes, but also had profound effects on behaviour (Couse and Korach, 1999). Specifically, pre- and neonatal development of female reproductive organs such as uterus, ovary and mammary gland was almost normal, but maturation of these organs during and after puberty was severely impaired. The αERKO females also failed to display sexual receptivity when treated with the hormonal regime of oestrogen and progesterone that normally induces receptivity in wild-type mice. Surprisingly, adult αERKO males have significantly fewer epididymal sperm than heterozygous or wild-type males, caused by the disruption of spermatogenesis and degeneration of the seminiferous tubules, which becomes apparent 10 weeks after birth. Furthermore, these males develop obesity after sexual maturation, in addition to exhibiting decreased normal male-typical aggressive behaviour, including offensive attacks, and show a reduced number of mount attempts as compared with wild-type animals. Interestingly, both sexes of the αERKO mice also show a 20–25% reduction in bone density, implying that ERα is crucial for proper bone maturation and mineralization. However, the only described case of oestrogen insensitivity in a human male, which was normally masculinized, had incomplete epiphyseal closure with a history of continued growth into adulthood, and also osteoporosis probably induced by increased bone turnover.

More recently, the generation of βERKO mice revealed that ERβ does not affect normal development, and mice lacking ERβ are indistinguishable grossly and histologically as young adults from their littermates (Couse and Korach, 1999). Females are fertile and exhibit normal sexual behaviour, but have fewer and smaller litters owing to reduced ovarian efficiency, and multiple resorbed fetuses. Older males lacking ERβ display signs of prostate and bladder hyperplasia. In contrast to the αERKO animals, the βERKO females exhibit normal breast development and lactate normally, while all components of sexual behaviour in βERKO mice were found to be intact. These observations indicate that unlike ERα, ERβ is essential for normal ovulation efficiency but not for female or male sexual differentiation, fertility or lactation.

Structural and Functional Domains

The ERα and ERβ protein sequences encode all the above-mentioned *in vivo* functions, and can be divided into six functional domains, A–F (**Figure 2**) (Kumar *et al.*, 1987). The N-terminal A/B domain, which contains a hormone-independent transactivation function (AF-1), as well as the C-terminal F domain, demonstrate only weak homology (approximately 17%) between the two ERs. In contrast, the central C domain, which contains the DNA-binding domain (DBD) present in all SRs, possesses 97% homology between ERs α and β, suggesting that they recognize and bind to the same or similar oestrogen response elements (EREs) consisting of inverted repeats of the sequence GGTCA separated by three variable nucleotides (Kumar and Chambon, 1988). This DNA-binding domain consists of two functionally distinct zinc-finger motifs, forming a helix–loop–helix motif typical of many transcription factors. Following the C domain is the D domain, which appears to function as a hinge region between the DBD and the ligand-binding domain (LBD), and demonstrates only moderate homology (30%) between the two ERs. However, recent research demonstrates that this domain contains important binding sites for receptor coactivators/corepressors, as will be discussed later, and might even be involved in post-translational regulation of the ER. Finally, the C-terminal E domain contains the LBD and, even though ERα and ERβ possess only moderate homology (59%) in this domain, both receptors bind with nearly the same affinity to oestradiol and to other natural and synthetic ligands. The E domain also contains a ligand-dependent transactivation function (AF-2) and provides a crucial interface for the interaction with many coactivators, as will be discussed later. Recently, a third AF, AF-2a, was identified in the ER hinge and LBD domains (Norris *et al.*, 1997). AF-2a has been shown to activate transcription in a ligand-independent manner in the absence of both AF-1 and AF-2.

Structure of the Ligand-binding Domain

The LBD can be viewed as a molecular switch that, upon hormone binding, enables the receptor to activate transcription of target genes by direct interaction of the receptor with DNA in the promoter region of these genes

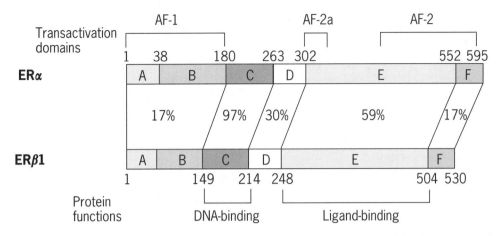

Figure 2 Comparison of ERα and ERβ1 functional domains. The amino acid residues of ERα are shown above domains A–F, and those of ERβ1 are shown below the domains. The degree of homology between them is shown as a percentage. Also shown are the regions for receptor function such as DNA binding, ligand binding and transcriptional activation functions.

and with components of the transcriptional machinery. In addition to the ligand-binding function, the LBD also contains signals necessary for nuclear localization, homo- and heterodimerization, in addition to the above-mentioned AF-2.

Recently, the crystallographic resolution of agonist (oestradiol) and antagonist (raloxifene) bound LBD of ERα revealed a compact structure consisting of 12 α-helices that form the ligand-binding pocket (Brzozowski *et al.*, 1997). This structure appears to be a common motif found also in other SR. The binding of oestradiol into the binding pocket induces important structural changes; in particular, helix 12, that prior to ligand binding extends away from the body of the domain, is repositioned over the ligand-binding pocket and seals this pocket like a 'lid.' This process is thought to trap the ligand in a hydrophobic environment, and also forms a coactivator binding surface on the LBD. Helix 12 is fixed in this active position by contact with both the hormone and amino acid residues in helices 3 and 4 on the surface of the LBD. In contrast, binding of the antioestrogen raloxifene into the binding pocket makes helix 12 extend away from the LBD, a conformation similar to one seen in unliganded receptor.

THE ER IS A LIGAND-DEPENDENT TRANSCRIPTION FACTOR

In the absence of hormone, the ER is thought to exist in a complex with chaperone proteins, like heat shock proteins Hsp90 and Hsp70, which may help to maintain the receptor in an appropriate conformation to respond rapidly to hormonal signals. Upon binding of oestrogen, this oligomeric complex dissociates, allowing the ER to homo- or heterodimerize and to interact with target gene promoters through two possible mechanisms. First, the ER can interact directly with DNA by binding to specific EREs, resulting in a bending of the DNA toward the major groove. This bending is thought to facilitate the interaction of ER with proteins of the transcription complex. Second, ERα is also able to interact indirectly with oestrogen-regulated gene promoters through its association with other transcription factors such as AP-1, NF-κB, C/EBPβ, GATA-1 and SP-1. It is currently thought that gene transcription depends on the formation of a preinitiation complex that consists of basal transcription factors. However, it has recently become clear that ER also recruits a host of ancillary factors, which are called coactivators if they enhance and corepressors if they inhibit receptor transcriptional activity.

The Interaction of ER with Basal Transcription Factors

The initiation of transcription by RNA polymerase II requires the assembly of basal transcription factors such as transcription factor IIA (TFIIA), TFIIB, TFIID, TFIIE and TFIIF. The binding of TFIID is the first and the rate-limiting step in this assembly process. TFIID consists of the TATA-box binding protein (TBP) and more than 10 other TBP- associated factors.

There is ample *in vitro* evidence of direct protein–protein interactions between ERα and basal transcription factors. In particular and consistent with the evidence that TBP recruitment is a rate-limiting step in transcriptional initiation, both the N-terminal AF-1 and the C-terminal AF-2 activation function of ERα have been reported to bind to this basal transcription factor. Another component of TFIID, $TAF_{II}30$, also interacts with the AF-1 of ERα in a ligand-independent manner, and this interaction appears to be required for ERα-mediated transactivation. Following the binding of the TFIID complex to the promoter of target genes, the binding of TFIIB, RNA polymerase II and TFIIF is also required for the assembly of the minimal initiation complex. TFIIB not only contacts DNA sequences both upstream and downstream of the TATA box and other factors of the basal transcription machinery, but also interacts with AF-2 of ERα. However, the significance of all of these interactions is unclear at present since they are not significantly affected by mutations in the ER that are known to disrupt transcriptional activity.

The Interaction of ER with Coactivators

The observation that different classes of SR can interfere with each other's transcriptional activity, termed 'squelching', has indicated that SRs compete for limited amounts of assembly proteins called coactivators or co-repressors, in addition to other factors of the basal transcriptional machinery. Over the last 7 years, a large number of potential coactivators have been identified, they have been extensively reviewed by Klinge (Klinge, 2000). Coactivators are generally defined as proteins that can interact in a ligand-dependent manner with DNA-bound SRs and are able to enhance their transcriptional activity. Furthermore, a coactivator should also be able to interact with components of the basal transcription machinery, but not to enhance basal transcriptional activity on their own, although they often contain an autonomous activation function. As examples, we will focus here on the mechanism of action of the intensively studied SRC family of coactivators and also the Creb binding protein (CBP)/p300 in regulating ER's function.

The SRC Family of Coactivators

Several coactivators have been identified as a family of related proteins, called the SRC family, which includes SRC-1 (also termed ERAP-160 or NcoA-1), SRC-2 (also called GRIP1, NcoA-2, or TIF-2) and SRC-3 (also known as ATCR, RAC3, p/CIP, AIB1 or TRAM-1). These coactivators are all able to stimulate oestradiol-mediated gene transcription and promote the interaction between AF-1 and AF-2 to produce full transcriptional activity. The SRC family shares a common domain structure with an overall sequence similarity of 40% between the three members (**Figure 3**). The highest degree of homology is observed in the N-terminal bHLH (for basic helix–loop–helix) and PAS (for Per/Arnt/Sim homology) domains.

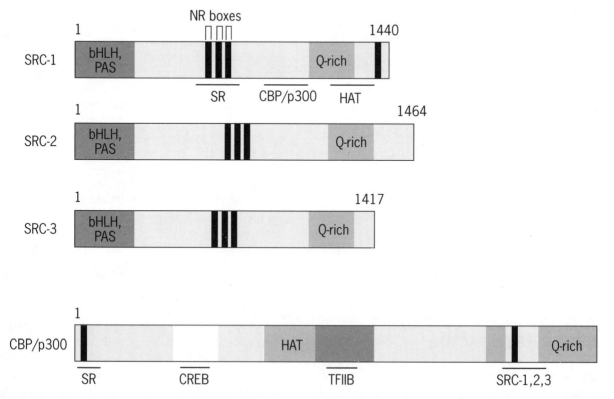

Figure 3   Structural features of the SRC family of coactivators and CBP. Regions to which specific functions of individual coactivators have been assigned are indicated. Below the coactivator representations are also shown the regions of interaction for various nuclear proteins such as steroid receptors (SR), CBP/p300, CREB, TFIIB and SRC1,2,3.

These particular domains mediate homodimeric and heterodimeric interactions between proteins containing these motifs, but their specific function in SRC coactivators remains unknown. It has been speculated that the presence of these motifs might indicate potential cross-talk between the SR pathway and other PAS-containing factors.

Most SR coactivators, including the SRC-family of coactivators, contain one or more copies of a short sequence motif, LXXLL (L stands for leucine and X is any amino acid), that are necessary and sufficient to mediate ligand-dependent direct interaction with the ER. This motif is called the nuclear receptor (NR) box or the receptor-interacting domian (RID). All of the SRC coactivators possess three NR boxes in the central portion of the protein, whereas only SRC-1 has an additional NR box in the extreme C-terminus. Protein structure prediction analyses of these motifs have indicated that they form amphipathic helices with the conserved leucine residues outlining a hydrophobic surface on the face of the helix.

Cocrystallization of the LBD of ERα with NR box peptides, as well as systematic mutagenesis of ERα, have revealed that the helix formed by the NR boxes is able to interact with a hydrophobic groove in the AF-2 domain of ER consisting of ERα residues from helices 3, 4, 5 and 12. This hydrophobic groove is the result of conformational changes induced by hormone binding, as discussed earlier.

The SRC coactivators also contain intrinsic activation domains that retain their activity when tethering the co-activator to DNA. Additonally, SRC-1 and SRC-3 contain an intrinsic histone acetyltransferase (HAT) activity which is thought to modulate chromatin structure by histone acetylation, thus facilitating the access of other transcriptional regulators as well as the assembly of the preinitiation complex. Interestingly, these coactivators together with ER are believed to form a ternary complex with CBP/p300, CREB, and other proteins (**Figure 4**), but the function of this complex remains largely unclear. However, a recent study reporting oestradiol-dependent acetylation of SRC-3

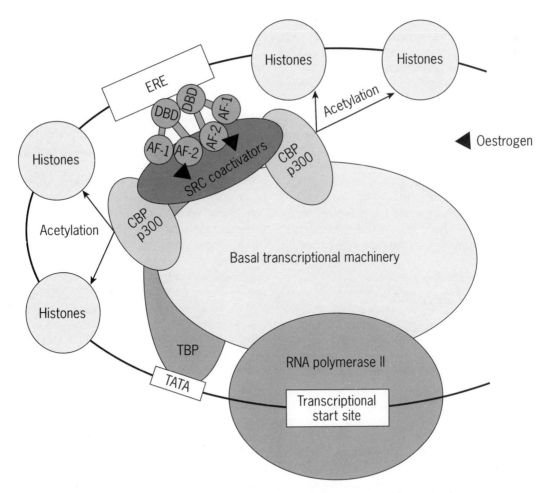

Figure 4 A schematic model of the transcription initiation complex formed at the ERE of an oestrogen-responsive gene. The ER is able to recruit an SRC coactivator upon oestrogen binding, which subsequently results in the recruitment of additional coactivators, such as CBP, and basal transcription factors. However, the precise *in vivo* composition of this complex is still under investigation. Additionally, histone acetylation by CBP/p300 is thought to facilitate the relaxation of chromatin at the target gene promoter, thereby enhancing transcriptional activation.

by CBP/p300 might reveal a new insight into the function of this complex. Surprisingly, acetylation of three lysine residues immediately upstream of the NR box of SRC-3 decreased SRC-3:ERα interactions *in vitro*, and disruption of this interaction appears to be a necessary event for the down-regulation of ER activity. These results indicate that hormone-induced transcription may be dynamically regulated by both histone and SRC-3 acetylation.

The recent development of mice lacking either SRC-1 or SRC-3 provides *in vivo* evidence of a partial functional redundancy between SRC-1 and SRC-2, while the physiological role of SRC-3 in development or disease appears to be different from that associated with SRC-1 expression. In particular, both SRC-1 and SRC-3 knockout mice are viable and fertile. However, in mice lacking SRC-1, oestrogen target organs such as the uterus, prostate, testis and mammary gland display decreased growth and development in response to steroid hormones, as well as increased expression of SRC-2 that is thought to compensate partially for the loss of SRC-1 function. On the other hand, disruption of SRC-3 expression in mice results in dwarfism, delayed puberty, reduced female reproductive function and blunted mammary gland development. This pleiotropic phenotype indicates that SRC-3 plays a critical role in overall growth and sexual maturation.

Interestingly, SRC-1 and SRC-2, but not SRC-3, interact also with ERβ and enhances its hormone-dependent transcriptional activity. In addition, SRC-3 is amplified and overexpressed in many ER-positive breast cancer cell lines, and a large study analysing 1157 clinical breast tumours and 122 ovarian tumours also found amplification of this coactivator gene in a small percentage of breast and ovarian cancers. Expression of SRC-3 seems to correlate with tumour size and with ERα and PR positivity. It has also been reported that SRC-1 and SRC-2 expression is relatively low in breast tumours when compared to normal tissues.

The Cointegrators CBP/p300

The cointegrator CBP and its related functional homologue p300 are thought to be responsible for the integration of numerous environmental stimuli on promoters containing multiple *cis*-acting elements (Goodman and Smolik, 2000). Even though CBP was initially characterized as a coactivator required for efficient activation of cAMP-regulated genes, several studies also implicate this protein as a coactivator for a broad range of transcription factors, including p53, NFκB and the SRs. CBP interacts with ERα in a hormone-dependent manner, and this interaction depends on a crucial NR box in the N-terminal domain of this CBP. Surprisingly, SRC-1 is also able to interact directly with carboxy terminus of CBP and p300, which synergistically enhances ERα-activated gene activity. Despite all the described potential interactions between CBP/p300 and transcription factors, coactivators and the

basal transcription machinery, there is little biochemical evidence for the existence of these complexes *in vivo*. There is only one small study analysing the chromatographic elution of SRC-1-containing complexes from T47D breast cancer cells that indicates the existence of distinct coactivator complexes with different properties and activities.

The central portion of both CBP and p300 encodes a relatively large domain that possesses intrinsic HAT activity. Among the major substrates of acetylation are the core histones, particularly the N-terminal tails of histones H3 and H4 (**Figure 4**). The unmodified forms of these histones are thought to maintain DNA packing into highly organized chromatin structures, thus silencing transcription, while a high degree of histone acetylation correlates with increased promoter activity. More recently, it has been shown that nonhistone proteins such as p53, GATA-1, the AR and SRC-3 (that itself possesses HAT activity) are also substrates for CBP/p300 acetylation. However, the precise function of both histone and nonhistone protein modifications in transcriptional regulation is still largely unclear.

Interaction of ER with Corepressors

Unlike coactivators, only very few corepressors of ER action have been reported to date. These include NCoR (nuclear receptor corepressor; also called RIP13), SMRT (silencing mediator for retinoid and thyroid receptor, also termed TRAC2), REA (repressor of oestrogen receptor activity), SHP (short heterodimer partner) and BRCA-1 (breast cancer susceptibility gene). Repression of ER activity can occur in the absence of hormone or when an antagonist is bound to the receptor.

The corepressors NCoR and SMRT were originally identified by biochemical studies of cellular proteins associated with unliganded thyroid hormone receptor (TR) and retinoid acid receptor (RAR). These corepressors are thought to recruit another complex of proteins, including histone deacetylase (HDAC) activity, to DNA-bound TR and RAR (**Figure 5**). This complex is believed to repress gene expression by maintaining chromatin in a more condensed state which impairs the ready access of critical transcription factors. Upon ligand binding, corepressors are released from TR and RAR, and coactivators and basal transcription factors are then recruited to the receptors. In contrast, unliganded or hormone-bound ERα is unable to interact with either NCoR or SMRT, but the antioestrogen tamoxifen (an oestrogen antagonist which is commonly used in the treatment of ER-positive breast cancer) induces the interaction of ER with these corepressors. Interestingly, the antagonist tamoxifen can be switched into in agonist, much like oestrogen, when ERα's ligand-independent AF-1 is activated by the MAPK pathway (this kind of activation will be discussed later in the section

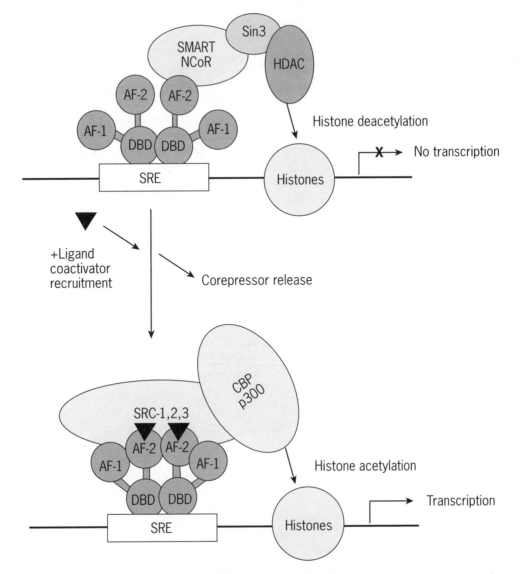

Figure 5   Ligand-dependent switch between an SR associated with either a corepressor or a coactivator complex. The SR is associated with a corepressor (SMRT or NCoR), which in turn recruits a histone deacetylase (HDAC) through its interaction with Sin3. Deacetylation of histones leads to transcriptional repression. Hormone binding disrupts the interaction between SR and repression complex in favour of the association of a coactivation complex. This complex consists in part of a SRC coactivator and CBP/p300, which possess histone acetyltransferase activity that modifies histones resulting in relaxation of chromatin structures and initiation of transcription.

Phosphorylation). This activation results in the release of corepressors from ERα and recruitment of coactivators to this receptor. This phenomenon may well explain why the majority of breast tumours become resistant to tamoxifen.

Regulation of ER Function

The activity of many transcription factors is regulated by post-translational modifications such as phosphorylation, proteasome-mediated degradation and cross-talk with other signal transduction pathways. We will focus upon these three aspects in our discussion of ER function.

Phosphorylation

Stimulation of a number of growth factor receptors and/or protein kinases leads to the phosphorylation of ER resulting in ligand-independent and/or a synergistic increase in transcriptional activation in response to hormone (Kato *et al.*, 2000).

The AF-1 region of ERα contains phosphorylation sites for a number of kinases including MAPK, cyclin A/cdk2 and PI3/AKT. In particular, much work has been focused on phosphorylation of serine residue 118 within the A/B domain of ERα. Phosphorylation of this particular residue by growth factor activated MAPK leads to the enhancement of the N-terminal AF-1 function. MAPK is activated by tyrosine kinase cell membrane receptors, that in turn are stimulated by growth factors such as insulin, IGF-1, EGF and TNF-α. Furthermore, phosphorylation at ER residue 118 also enhances the interaction of this receptor with the p68 RNA helicase, resulting in increased AF-1 but not AF-2 activity.

The phosphorylation of ERβ by MAPK in cells treated with exogenous EGF or via overexpression of activated Ras has been shown to enhance binding between SRC-1 and the ERβ AF-1 domain. This suggests that ligand-independent activation of ERβ also depends on phosphorylation of the N-terminal region, and that this event may be important for the recruitment of coactivators such as SRC-1.

Much less is known about the phosphorylation by the cyclin A/cdk2 or the PI3/Akt kinases and their effects on specific ER function. Specifically, phosphorylation of two serine residues at amino acid 104 and 106 of the ERα by the cyclin A/cdk2 enhances the ERα AF-1 function both in the absence of oestrogen or in the presence of tamoxifen. Furthermore, it was recently shown that PI3 kinase is able to increase both AF-1 and AF-2 activity, whereas Akt, a kinase downstream of PI3 kinase, increases only AF-1 activity. Phosphorylation of the ERα serine residue 167 by Akt also results in protection of breast cancer cells from tamoxifen-induced apoptosis, revealing an important potential mechanism for the onset of resistance to tamoxifen in breast cancer.

Another major ligand-independent phosphorylation site within ERα is the conserved tyrosine 537 residue and the homologous tyrosine 443 residue in ERβ, but the exact consequence of phosphorylation at this site is still controversial and remains under intense investigation. Replacement of this tyrosine residue with other amino acids suggests that phosphorylation at this site is important for hormone binding and transcriptional activation. Specifically, the substitution of tyrosine 537 with alanine, asparagine, or serine results in a mutant ERα that is constitutively active and binds to SRC-1 even in the absence of oestrogen. Another recent study also indicated that phosphorylation of the tyrosine 537 is critically involved in ligand-induced conformational changes of the ERα.

Proteasome-mediated Degradation of the ER

Recently, ubiquitin-dependent, proteasomal degradation of ligand-bound ERα was discovered as an additional mechanism involved in the regulation of hormone receptor-mediated gene transcription. The SRC coactivator family is also a target for degradation via the 26S proteasome. It is well known that the ubiquitin pathway is involved in the degradation of many short-lived proteins (Hershko and Ciechanover, 1998). Through a series of

enzymatic reactions, ubiquitin is covalently linked to proteins targeted for degradation, marking them for recognition by the 26S proteasome, a large multisubunit protease. Abnormalities in ubiquitin-mediated degradation have been shown to cause several pathological conditions, including malignant transformation. In particular, it has recently been shown that ERα is ubiquitinated preferentially in the presence of hormone. It is thought that ERα protein degradation, which occurs through the 26S proteasome complex, is required for continued transcriptional activation by this receptor. ERα degradation could well be an important requisite to dissociate the preinitiation complex resulting in the release of the components necessary for another round of transcription. On the other hand, hormone-induced degradation may also serve as a negative feedback to down-regulate the transcription of oestrogen-responsive genes.

THE IMPORTANCE OF OESTROGEN RECEPTOR EXPRESSION IN CANCER INITIATION AND PROGRESSION

Oestrogen receptor gene expression in breast epithelium is an intricately regulated event, and is thought to play a central role in normal breast development, and also breast cancer evolution. ERα expression is significantly increased in both premalignant and malignant breast lesions, and many of these ERα-positive cells proliferate as compared with normal breast. Furthermore, normal breast epithelium, in addition to breast cancer tissue, contains alternatively spliced ERα and ERβ mRNA variants, but it is still unclear whether changes in the levels of these variants impact upon tumour development or the progression to hormone-independent tumour growth. Single amino acid mutations within the ERα are relatively rare, but may contribute to the progression of breast cancer or metastatic disease. We will next describe the potential role of ERα expression in premalignant disease, as well as the role of specific ER variants and mutations in breast cancer development and progression.

Oestrogen Receptor Expression in Normal Breast and Breast Cancer

In normal nonpregnant, premenopausal human breast, only about 5–10% of the total luminal epithelial cell population expresses ERα, and this expression tends to be highest in the follicular phase of the menstrual cycle. The highest percentage of ERα-expressing cells are found in undifferentiated lobules type 1 (Lob1), with a progressive reduction in the more differentiated Lob2 and Lob3 types. The highest level of cell proliferation is also observed in Lob1, but expression of ERα occurs in cells other than these proliferating cells, indicating that they represent at least two separate cell populations. These data also suggest that oestrogen might stimulate ERα-positive normal cells to produce a growth factor that in turn stimulates neighbouring ERα-negative normal cells to proliferate. In pre-malignant and malignant breast lesions, however, ERα expression is significantly increased in the proliferating cell compartment, suggesting that ERα may be involved in the earliest changes to malignancy. Additionally, approximately two-thirds of breast tumours, at least initially, express abundant levels of ERα, and this expression is associated with lower risk of relapse and prolonged overall survival. Unfortunately, we still understand very little about the precise role of ERα expression in tumour progression.

Owing to its recent discovery, only limited data are available on the expression and function of ERβ in normal breast and its potential role in breast carcinogenesis. Studies of ERβ knockout mice suggest that ERβ plays a limited role in normal breast development and function. However, ERβ expression appears to be important for the growth control of urogenital tract epithelium, and may even afford a protective role against hyperproliferation and carcinogenesis in this particular tissue. This interesting hypothesis might also apply to the mammary gland, and is supported by a recent study reporting that ERβ expression in breast tumours is positively associated with ERα and progesterone receptor expression, as well as negative axillary nodes, DNA diploidy and low S phase fraction, all of which imply that ERβ-positive tumours may have a more favourable prognosis. On the other hand, two studies examining a relatively small number of tumours using RT-PCR determined that coexpression of ERβ and ERα is frequently associated with poor prognostic biomarkers, such as positive axillary nodes and higher tumour grade, and also that ER is significantly elevated in tumours resistant to tamoxifen treatment.

Oestrogen Receptor Variant Forms

Both of the *ER* genes undergo alternative splicing in normal and neoplastic oestrogen-responsive tissues. Alternative splicing results in *ER* mRNA variants with single or multiple exons skipped, and are usually coexpressed along with the wild-type receptor (Hopp and Fuqua, 1998). It is still unclear whether any or all of the *ER* splicing variants are indeed stably translated *in vivo*, and to what extent the formation of heterodimers of these splice variants with ERα and ERβ perturb the ER signalling pathway. *ERα* and *ERβ* variant forms fall into four major groups: (1) transcripts containing precise single or multiple exon deletions, (2) transcripts containing single nucleotide deletions and others in which several hundred nucleotides have been deleted within known exon sequences, (3) truncated transcripts and (4) transcripts containing insertions.

The most frequently observed *ERα* mRNA splice variants are those lacking exon 4, which has been detected in normal and neoplastic tissue, or exon 7, detected in many breast tumours regardless of their receptor expression status. The exon 4-deleted *ERα* variant is missing the nuclear localization signal and part of the hormone-binding domain, thus potentially encoding a protein whose cellular distribution and oestrogen-binding affinity may be different from those of the wild-type ERα. On the other hand, the exon 7-deleted splicing variant potentially translates into a receptor protein missing the C-terminal part of the hormone-binding domain, which includes the hormone-dependent AF-2 function and the F-domain. However, both *ERα* variants, when transfected into mammalian or yeast cells, can block normal ER signalling in certain cell types, but not in others. In addition, expression of the exon 4-deleted *ERα* variant is associated with two biological markers of good clinical outcome (PR positivity and low histological grade), and thus may prove useful as biological marker of good prognosis in clinical samples.

Another dominant-negative inhibitor of ERα signalling is the exon 3-deleted variant, which encodes a variant receptor lacking portions of the DNA-binding domain. This variant is found in both normal tissue and primary breast cancer, and the ratio of the exon 3-deleted variant to wild-type ERα is reduced about 30-fold in breast cancer cell lines as compared with normal tissue. Stable expression of the exon 3-deleted variant in MCF-7 breast cancer cell lines, which contain high levels of endogenous ERα, results in reduction of both invasiveness and anchorage-independent growth.

One of the best studied *ERα* mRNA splice variants is the exon 5-deleted receptor, which is the only variant so far detected at the protein level in breast cancer cell lines and breast tumours. This variant is a truncated 40-kDa protein missing most of the hormone-binding domain, but it retains AF-1 function and demonstrates variable strengths of hormone-independent transcriptional activity depending on the cell type. Expression of this variant was also significantly increased in cancers from patients relapsing after tamoxifen treatment as compared with the respective primary tumour, suggesting that tumours expressing high levels of the exon 5-deleted variant may acquire resistance to tamoxifen. However, it seems likely that other *ERα* splice variants could also be involved in acquired tamoxifen resistance, since multiple *ERα* variants can occur in the same tumour sample and tamoxifen resistance is thought to be multifactorial.

ER Mutations

In contrast to the abundant expression of *ERα* mRNA splice variants in both normal and neoplastic tissue, mutations of the *ERα* gene are seldom found in primary breast cancer. Changes in the *ER* nucleotide sequence fall into at least two groups: (1) polymorphisms, which do not change the amino acid sequence, and (2) missense mutations, which do alter the amino acid sequence (Hopp and Fuqua, 1998).

Polymorphisms have been detected in both primary and metastatic breast cancer, but these silent changes do not appear to correlate with clinical parameters, such as tumour type, size, grade or stage. Like polymorphisms, missense mutations in the $ER\alpha$, which potentially affect normal function, have been found in primary and metastatic breast cancers. However, functional characterization of most of these mutations is still missing.

Recently, a specific somatic mutation in the $ER\alpha$ has been found in many typical hyperplasias, a type of premalignant lesion that carries an increased risk of breast cancer development. The mutation substitutes a lysine with an arginine residue at amino acid 303, at the border between hinge domain and the beginning of hormone-binding domain. This mutant $ER\alpha$ shows much higher sensitivity to oestrogen than wild-type $ER\alpha$, resulting in markedly increased proliferation at subphysiological levels of hormone. Additionally, the mutation enhances the ability of the SRC-2 coactivator to bind at physiological levels of hormone. These data suggest that this mutant receptor may promote or accelerate the development of cancer from premalignant breast lesions.

Another missense mutation, where tyrosine 537 is substituted by asparagine, was isolated from a metastatic lesion from a breast cancer patients. This mutant $ER\alpha$ exhibits a potent, oestradiol-independent transcriptional activity that is only weakly affected by oestrogen, and variably by antioestrogens. As mentioned earlier, phosphorylation of the tyrosine residue at codon 537 is thought to be required for efficient oestrogen binding, and substitution of this amino acid with asparagine may induce conformational changes mimicking hormone binding. Stable expression of this mutant $ER\alpha$ in an $ER\alpha$-negative breast cancer cell line caused increased production of PTHrP, a known stimulator of osteoclastic bone resorption and a major mediator of the osteolytic process. Furthermore, $TGF\beta$, which is abundant in bone marrow, significantly enhanced the transcriptional activity of this mutant receptor, resulting in further stimulation of PTHrP production. These data indicate a central role for the ERTyr537Asn mutant in the pathogenesis of osteolytic bone metastases from breast carcinoma.

The Role of Oestrogen Receptors in Hormone Resistance and Independence

As mentioned earlier, a large number of breast cancers express high levels of $ER\alpha$, and the ER status of patients is highly predictive of response to long-term tamoxifen therapy, an antioestrogen frequently used in the treatment of breast cancer. Unfortunately, most breast cancers eventually acquire tamoxifen resistance, resulting in disease recurrence and the frequent emergence of more aggressive disease. Tamoxifen-resistant tumours often continue to express $ER\alpha$, so that mechanisms for antioestrogen resistance other than the loss of $ER\alpha$ must exist. Interestingly, in some cases antioestrogen resistance is also reversible, e.g. tamoxifen-resistant patients who have been switched to a different type of therapy may later once again respond to tamoxifen.

Potential mechanisms of resistance include alterations in the expression levels of $ER\alpha$ and $ER\beta$ as well as ER splicing variants, ER mutations, interaction with other growth factor signal transduction pathways (such as erbB-2 and AP-1), abnormal expression or function of coactivators and corepressors and metabolic tolerance as a result of altered systemic antioestrogen metabolism.

CONCLUSION

The purpose of this chapter was to review ER signalling and its perturbation in cancer as an example of SR signalling in general. The ER is an important transcriptional activator for genes involved in many essential processes. Cloning and sequencing of the ERs and the resolution of the crystal structures of hormone- and antioestrogen-bound $ER\alpha$, and also the development of mice lacking these receptors, have all increased our understanding of the structure–function relationships of these important transcription factors. However, the fairly recent discovery of receptor coactivators and corepressors has provided another level of complexity to models of oestrogen action. The understanding of the molecular mechanisms of action of the ER is beginning to provide an explanation for the function of clinically useful antiestrogens, and is also suggesting potential new therapeutic targets. Further progress in understanding the fine details of transcriptional activation may also provide new insights into mechanisms of hormone resistance.

ER expression is tightly regulated in normal breast epithelium, but increased $ER\alpha$ and expression of mutant ERs may drive abnormal proliferation in premalignant hyperplasias, providing a fertile environment for genetic alterations which, in turn, are associated with tumorigenesis. Unfortunately, very little is known about the precise role of ER expression during the transition of premalignant disease to cancer and the eventual development of hormone resistance. Continued exploration of the basic molecular mechanisms of ER signalling, as an example of steroid receptor action, will certainly enhance our understanding of underlying causes of some of the most prevalent human cancers, and may also provide new treatment approaches, as well as and new mechanisms to prevent these diseases.

REFERENCES

Brzozowski, A. M., *et al.* (1997). Molecular basis of agonism and antagonism in the oestrogen receptor. *Nature*, **389**, 753–758.

Couse, J. F. and Korach, K. S. (1999). Estrogen receptor null mice: what have we learned and where will they lead us? *Endocrinology Reviews*, **20**, 358–417; Erratum, **20**, 459.

Evans, R. M. (1988). The steroid and thyroid hormone receptor superfamily. *Science*, **240**, 889–895.

Goodman, R. H. and Smolik, S. (2000). CBP/p300 in cell growth, transformation, and development. *Genes and Development*, **14**, 1553–1577.

Hershko, A. and Ciechanover, A. (1998). The ubiquitin system. *Annuual Review of Biochemistry*, **67**, 425–479.

Hopp, T. A. and Fuqua, S. A. (1998). Estrogen receptor variants. *Journal of Mammary Gland Biology and Neoplasia*, **3**, 73–83.

Kato, S., *et al.* (2000). Molecular mechanism of a cross-talk between oestrogen and growth factor signalling pathways. *Genes and Cells*, **5**, 593–601.

Klinge, C. M. (2000). Estrogen receptor interaction with co-activators and co-repressors. *Steroids*, **65**, 227–251.

Kumar, V. and Chambon, P. (1988). The estrogen receptor binds tightly to its responsive element as a ligand-induced homo-dimer. *Cell*, **55**, 145–156.

Kumar, V., *et al.* (1987). Functional domains of the human estrogen receptor. *Cell*, **51**, 941–951.

Mosselman, S., *et al.* (1996). ER beta: identification and characterization of a novel human estrogen receptor. *FEBS Letters*, **392**, 49–53.

Norris, J. D., *et al.* (1997). Identification of a third autonomous activation domain within the human estrogen receptor. *Molecular Endocrinology*, **11**, 747–754.

Osborne, C. K. (1998). Steroid hormone receptors in breast cancer management. *Breast Cancer Research and Treatment*, **51**, 227–238.

FURTHER READING

Elledge, R. M. and Fuqua, S. A. W. (2000). Estrogen and progesterone receptors. In: Harris, J. R., *et al.* (eds), *Diseases of the Breast*. 471–488 (Lippincott Williams & Wilkins, Philadelphia).

Freedman, L. P. (ed.) (1998). *Molecular Biology of Steroid and Nuclear Hormone Receptors* (Birkhauser, Boston).

Chapter 11

Signalling by Cytokines

William L. Farrar, Lihua Wang, Xiaoyi Yang, Weihua Xiao, O. M. Zack Howard
National Cancer Institute, National Institutes of Health, Frederick, MD, USA

Colin Duckett
National Cancer Institute, National Institutes of Health, Bethesda, MD, USA

C O N T E N T S

STRUCTURE AND FUNCTION OF γ_c-DEPENDENT CYTOKINES AND RECEPTORS

Members of the cytokine haematopoietic superfamily often share a common receptor subunit while retaining their own private receptor subunits. One well-documented example is that five cytokines, IL-2, IL-4, IL-7, IL-9 and IL-15, form one group, which is characterized by utilizing the common γ chain (γ_c) as a receptor subunit. The common γ_c subunit was initially cloned as the γ chain of the IL-2R complex. Soon it was discovered that this γ subunit also participates functionally in the receptors for IL-4, IL-7, IL-9 and IL-15 and, therefore, was designated γ_c, where c represents 'common.' This protein is constitutively expressed on essentially all cells of haematopoietic origin. It functions to enhance the binding of cytokines to their receptor, presumably by direct interaction with the ligand and to induce intracellular signals transduction events such as JAK–STAT signal pathway.

γ_c-Dependent Cytokines

γ_c-Dependent cytokines include IL-2, IL-4, IL-7, IL-9 and IL-15. They are peptides or glycoproteins with molecular masses of 14–20 kDa. Crystal structure analysis reveals that IL-2 is an α-helical protein, lacking β-sheet structure, with a four-fork core stabilized by a single intrachain disulfide bond. IL-4 contains six Cys residues that are all involved in intramolecular disulfide bridges. The secondary structure of IL-4 was shown to consist of a four-helix bundle with a unique up–up–down–down helix topology. IL-7, IL-9 and IL-15 contain a similar α-helical structure. Each cytokine is secreted by particular cell types in response to a variety of stimuli and produces a characteristic constellation of effects on the growth, motility, differentiation or function of its target cells. These cytokines exert multiple biological functions (**Table 1**). It is interesting that IL-2, IL-4 and IL-9, all produced by activated T cells, are important immune regulatory cytokines, whereas IL-7 and IL-15, which are primarily produced by nonlymphoid cells, have also been implicated in the regulation of lymphocyte development.

γ_c-Dependent Cytokine Receptors

With the exception of IL-2R and IL-15R, all γ_c-dependent cytokine receptor subunits are members of the cytokine receptor superfamily that contains an evolutionary-related extracellular region that results in a conserved structural fold for binding to helical cytokines. These receptor subunits are type I membrane glycoproteins with a single hydrophobic transmembrane domain. The extracellular domain contains two major regions of homology. The first is a region having four Cys residues located in the N-terminal half of that extracellular domain. The second region of homology is Trp-Ser-X-Trp-Ser(WSXWS), which is referred to as the 'WS motif.' This motif is close to the transmembrane region. The extracellular region also contains two fibronectin type III-like domains found in a series of cell surface molecules with adhesive properties. The functional significance of these domains remains to be clarified.

Table 1   Major properties of human γ_c-dependent cytokines

Cytokine	Mature protein (kDa)	Cellular source	Functional activities
IL-2	15	Activated T_H2 cells Tc cells NK cells T_H0 cells	T cell growth Enhance B cell growth and Ig secretion Augment NK activity Induce LAK Programme T cells for apoptosis Reverse T cell anergy
IL-4	20	Activated T_H2 cells Mast cells Basophils MK1+ CD4+ T cells	T cell growth B cell growth IgG_1 and IgE class switch Enhance expression of MHC class II and CD23
IL-7	17	Bone marrow stroma Thymic stromal cells Intestinal epithelial cells Keratinocytes	T cell growth Proliferation of pre-B cells Viability of TN thymocytes Promotes development of CTL

IL-9	14	Activated T cells	Promotes the growth of mast cells
			Enhances mast cells secretion of
			  IL-6 and expression of
			  granzyme A and B and $FcR\varepsilon$

IL-15	15	Placenta, epithelial cells Skeletal muscle Kidney, lung, fibroblasts Activated monocytes	T cell growth Enhanced NK activity Induce LAK Promote B cell growth and Ig secretion

JAK–STAT SIGNAL PATHWAY

All known γ_c-containing receptors signal through the associated Janus protein tyrosine kinases, JAK1 and JAK3 proteins, although not all γ_c-dependent cytokines activate the same STAT molecules. Phosphorylated tyrosines and flanking amino acid residues in the activated cytokine receptors determine this specificity by providing specific docking sites for the SH2 domains of STATs. Most likely, tyrosine phosphorylation of the receptor proteins is also directly mediated by JAKs. The JAK/STAT signal pathway, therefore, connects activation of the receptor complexes directly to transcription of genes. Upon receptor oligomerization, JAKs are activated, presumably by *trans*-'auto' phosphorylation on tyrosines. Subsequently, JAKs phosphorylate STAT proteins, which form homodimeric or heteromeric complexes via their SH2 domains. These complexes translocate to the nucleus, where they bind to specific targeting sequences and influence gene transcription (Horvath and Darnell, 1997).

Janus Kinases

The Janus kinases (JAKs) are cytoplasmic tyrosine kinases which mediate signalling from a number of cell surface receptors which lack intrinsic tyrosine kinase activity. Four mammalian members of the JAK family are known, JAKs 1–3, and TYK2 (Ihle, 1995). Whereas JAK1, JAK2 and TYK2 are expressed ubiquitously, expression of JAK3 is confined to haematopoietic and lymphoid cells. Characteristic of the structure of JAKs is the presence of two JAK homology (JH) domains, of which the C-terminal (JH1) domain has tyrosine kinase activity. Studies of knockout mice have provided important insights into the function of JAKs *in vivo*. The analysis of JAK3 knockout mice and JAK3-deficient humans has clearly demonstrated the essential, nonredundant role of JAK3 in several cytokine signalling pathways. The similarity with γ_c-deficient mice and humans strongly suggests that the major role of γ_c is the recruitment of JAK3 to each γ_c-receptor. In many cases, other JAKs, such as JAK1, that are found in association with the additional subunits of γ_c-containing cytokine receptors, are not sufficient to initiate signalling. JAK3-deficient mice are viable but exhibit severe defects in the development of lymphoid cells, the residual T cells being functionally deficient. Like JAK3-deficient mice, JAK1 deficiency leads to reduced numbers of T and B lymphocytes. Embryonic fibroblasts from JAK1 knockout mice do not respond to class II cytokine receptor ligands IFNγ and IFNα.

Signal Transducer and Activator of Transcription (STAT)

The STATs (signal transducers and activators of transcription) constitute a family of signal transduction proteins that are activated in the cytoplasm by the binding of extracellular polypeptides to transmembrane receptors and which then regulate the transcription of immediate-response genes. Following their obligatory tyrosine phosphorylation, induced by a cytokine ligand, STATs dimerize, translocate to the nucleus and bind directly to response elements present in the promoters of target genes in order to trigger induction of transcription. Thus far, six mammalian STAT proteins (plus several isoforms) have been identified (Darnell, 1997). Two homologues of STAT5 exist (STAT5A and STAT5B) that are encoded by different genes. Expression of STAT proteins is ubiquitous, except for STAT4, which is expressed in several tissues including spleen, heart, brain, peripheral blood cells and testis. Most STATs are activated by many different ligands. IL-2, IL-7, IL-9 and IL-15 activate STAT3 and STAT5, in contrast to IL-4, which activates STAT6. STAT knockout mice mainly show defects in a single or a few cytokine-dependent processes. Embryonic stem cells deficient for STAT3, or with dominant negative STAT3 proteins, fail to stay in an undifferentiated state in the presence of leucocyte inhibitory factors. STAT5A and STAT5B double knockout mice show loss of function with regard to prolactin and growth hormone receptors, i.e. disturbed ovary and mammary gland development and growth retardation. In addition, these mice lack NK cells, develop splenomegaly and have T cells with an activated phenotype, thus resembling IL-2 receptor β-chain-deficient mice. STAT6 knockout mice lack Th2 function as a consequence of impaired IL-4 and IL-13 signalling.

DISEASES ASSOCIATED WITH PERTURBATIONS IN γ_c RECEPTOR/ JAK/STAT SIGNALLING

Because γ_c-dependent cytokines orchestrate a variety of immune system responses via activating the γ_c receptor/ JAK/STAT signalling pathway, it is not surprising that most circumstances causing an inappropriate inhibition of this signalling pathway have generically immunosuppressive consequences. A number of pathological conditions have been identified with mutations or deregulation in γ_c cytokine receptors or associated signalling molecules.

SCID

Severe combined immunodeficiency (SCID) is a hereditary human disease characterized by functionally inactive T and B cells. The ensuing susceptibility to opportunistic infections is the prevalent cause of premature mortality in young patients suffering from this disease. More than 50% of SCID cases are X-linked. XSCID is commonly associated with mutations, which chromosomally map to Xq13, in the γ-chain of the IL-2, IL-4, IL-7, IL-9 and IL-15 receptors. Strikingly, a form of autosomal SCID exists with clinical symptoms identical with X-SCID, in which the gene encoding JAK3 is affected. A newly identified form of SCID with slightly different clinical features involves mutations in the interleukin 7 receptor chain. γ_c-Deficient mice were shown to have hypoplastic thymuses. Thymic cellularity was reduced by 10–25-fold when compared with normal littermates. CD4 and CD8 staining revealed the presence of all thymocyte subpopulations with a slightly increased proportion of CD4+ 'single positive' cells. In the bone marrow, B cell development was blocked at the pre-B cell stage. Although the cellularity of the spleen was reduced approximately 10-fold, mature T and B cells were detected. Both CD5+ and CD5− B-1 cells were identified in γ_c-deficient mice. The numbers of granulocytes, monocytes/macrophages and erythrocytes were normal or increased.

The phenotype of these γ_c-deficient mice indicated that signalling through γ_c is required for the development of multiple lymphoid lineages but not myeloid and erythroid lineages. When compared with human XSCID, a striking difference in B cell development was observed in mouse models of XSCID. In the mouse, B cell development was substantially inhibited at the pro-B cell stage, whereas in human XSCID, the production of B cells is outwardly normal. IL-7/IL-7R appears to represent the γ_c-dependent cytokine for mouse B cell development. The failure to block B cell development in human XSCID suggests a γ_c-independent pathway for the production of B cells in these patients.

Immunosuppressive Diseases and Suppression of JAK/STAT Signal Transduction

Cytokine receptor signalling substrates, in particular the JAKs and STATs, contribute to tumorigenesis. In *Drosophila*, a dominant mutant Jak kinase causes leukaemia-like abnormalities. In mammals, JAKs and STATs are known to be constitutively activated in haematopoietic cells transformed by diverse oncogenic tyrosine kinases and in a variety of lymphomas and leukaemias. Expression of a constitutively active STAT3 molecule in immortalized fibroblasts causes cellular transformation. Together these data are indicative of a role for constitutive activation of the JAK-STAT pathways in leukaemogenesis.

INTERFERON SIGNALLING PATHWAY

Interferons (IFNs) play a key role in mediating antiviral and antigrowth responses and in modulating the immune response (Seder, 1994; Trinchieri and Scott, 1995; Young and Hardy, 1995). Their signalling pathways provided the first evidence of, and have been used as the model for, the JAK–STAT pathway, which is utilized by many cytokines (Darnell *et al.*, 1994). IFNs can be subdivided into two functional classes, and constitute the largest and most divergent subfamily of cytokines. There are more than 20 members in the type I IFN class (e.g. IFNαs, -β, and -τ) and one member in the type II IFN class, i.e. IFNγ. Type I and II IFNs function via related but distinct signal transduction pathways. In both classes of IFNs, signalling is initiated by the binding of the IFNs to their specific membrane receptors, that are expressed in many different cell types.

Interferon-γ Signalling Pathway

Type II, immune or IFNγ, is secreted by thymus-derived (T) cells under certain conditions of activation and by natural killer (NK) cells. The proximal events of IFNγ signalling require the obligatory participation of five distinct proteins, two IFNγ specific receptors, IFNGR1 and IFNGR2, two Janus kinase family members, JAK1 and JAK2, and one STAT family member, STAT1 (Schindler and Darnell, 1995).

IFNγ receptors contain a minimum of two peptide chains that are expressed in nearly all cell types, displaying a strict species specificity in their ability to bind IFNγ. The 90-kDa IFNGR1 consists of three domains, an extracellular (229aa), an intracellular (223aa) and a transmembrane (21aa). The IFNGR1 contains a constitutive and specific JAK1 binding site in the membrane-proximal region of the intracellular domain and a STAT1 binding and phosphorylation site that is activated upon phosphorylation by JAK1. The 62-kDa IFNGR2 differs from the 90-kDa IFNGR1 in that it contains a JAK2 binding site in its intracellular domain. Both IFNGR1 and IFNGR2 are required to activate functionally the IFNγ signalling pathway. IFNGR1 plays more important roles in mediating ligand binding, ligand trafficking through the cell and signal transduction, whereas IFNGR2 plays only a minor role in ligand binding.

Based on the available data and observations, Stark and colleagues have proposed a model, which has been broadly accepted for the IFNγ signalling pathway (**Figure 1**) (Stark *et al.*, 1998). When a functional IFNγ homodimer binds two IFNGR1s on their extracellular domains, the IFNGR1 and IFNGR2 are brought into close proximity, forming more stable heterodimers together with their preassociated, inactive JAKs, JAK1 and JAK2. The

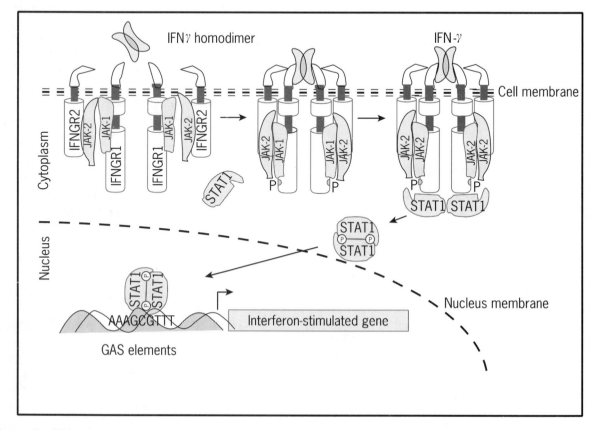

Figure 1   IFNγ signal pathway.

intracellular membrane-proximity domains of IFNGRs are then activated through auto- and transphosphorylation. The activation of the JAKs occurs in sequence, such that JAK2 activates first and is required for JAK1 activation.

Once activated, the JAKs phosphorylate a tyrosine-containing sequence near the C-terminus of IFNGR1, where paired ligand-induced docking sites for STAT1 are formed. Two inactive, monomeric STAT1 proteins then bind to these sites through their SH2 domain and are phosphorylated by the receptor-bound JAK kinases at tyrosine 701, near their C-terminus. After phosphorylation, the STAT1 proteins dissociate from the receptor and form a reciprocal homodimer, which then translocates to the nucleus, inducing the transcription of a set of IFN-stimulated genes (ISGs) via binding to the specific DNA elements residing within the ISGs promoters, and designated as either the interferon stimulated response element (ISRE) or the IFNγ activated site (GAS) (Darnell *et al.*, 1994; Schindler and Darnell, 1995; Stark *et al.*, 1998) (**Figure 1**).

A similar signalling pathway mechanism in which a ligand-induced, tyrosine-phosphorylated docking site on a receptor, and its association with the transcription factor STAT, has been found to mediate responses to other cytokines. As a result, this JAK–STAT signalling pathway mechanism is now the accepted paradigm that illustrates the important mechanism of how cytokine receptors are coupled to their specific STAT signalling systems.

The negative regulation of the IFNγ signalling pathway has also been defined recently by the discovery of a family of proteins known as SOCS/JAB/SSI, which are induced by IFN-γ (and also several other cytokines) and bind to and inhibit activated JAKs (Yasukawa *et al.*, 2000). These discoveries have provided new insights into how JAK–STAT pathways are regulated in response to specific stimuli, and how they function in various tissues and environments.

Interferon-α/β Signalling Pathway

The common pathway for IFNα/β requires seven distinct proteins, which include two IFNα receptors, two JAKs, two STATs and the IRF-family transcription factor p48. The IFNα/β signalling pathways are comparatively illustrated in **Figure 2**, but the fine details of the mechanisms are lacking because information regarding the detailed interactions that play the crucial role for the pathway remain to be elucidated.

The IFNα/β receptors, designated IFNRAs, are composed of a multichain structure on both normal and malignant haematopoietic cells (Novick *et al.*, 1994). All type I interferons, including IFNα, IFNβ, and IFNω, bind to the same receptors (Pestka *et al.*, 1987). It has been clearly established that there are two distinct components comprising the type I IFNRAs, namely the IFNRA1 and

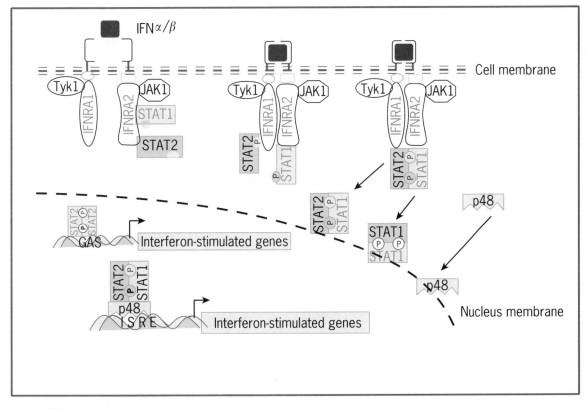

Figure 2 IFNα/β signal pathway.

the IFNRA2. IFNRA1 is a 110-kDa protein. The IFNRA2 subunit occurs in three different forms that are differentially spliced products of the same gene (Colamonici et al., 1994a; Novick et al., 1994), the soluble form of the extracellular domain, IFNRA2a; the alternatively spliced variant with a short cytoplasmic domain, IFNAR2b, which can have dominant negative activity and the only normal, fully functional form, IFNRA2c protein, with a relative molecular mass of 90–100 kDa. Neither IFNAR1 nor IFNAR2 alone binds to IFNα/β with the high affinity of the two-subunit combination (Cohen et al., 1995).

Two members of the Janus family of tyrosine kinases involved in the IFNα/β signalling pathway, Tyk2 and JAK1, are both constitutively associated with the IFNAR1 and IFNAR2c subunits, respectively (Colamonici et al., 1994c, 1995; Domanski et al., 1995, 1997). Upon the binding of IFNα/β to the IFNARs, the tyrosine kinases are activated and IFNAR1 and IFNAR2c are rapidly phosphorylated on tyrosines. Tyk2 also plays a role in stabilizing the IFNAR1 structure because the amount of IFNAR1 is low in Tyk2-null cells. However, the domains required for this role are different from those required to transduce the cytokine induced signal (Velazquez et al., 1995). The activation of tyrosine kinases results in tyrosine phosphorylation of two STAT proteins, STAT1 and STAT2, both preassociated with IFNAR2c in untreated cells (Fu, 1992; Darnell, 1997, 1998). When IFNAR1 is phosphorylated, the SH2 domain of STAT2 binds to it, followed by the phosphorylation of both STATs and subsequent dissociation of the phosphorylated heterodimer from the receptors. In addition to the STAT1–STAT2 heterodimer, much evidence also supports the IFNα/β-mediated induction of STAT1 homodimers (Darnell, 1997; Stark et al., 1998).

The phosphorylated STAT proteins form homo- and heterodimers and then translocate to the nucleus, associating with p48 to regulate gene transcription via binding to specific sequences present in the promoters of interferon-stimulated genes (ISGs) (Darnell, 1997; Ihle, 1996). The association of STAT1–STAT2 heterodimers with p48 to form the mature interferon-stimulated gene factor-3 (ISGF3) complex represents the major transcription factor complex formed in response to IFNα/β, and is required to drive the expression of most ISGs by binding to ISREs. While the STAT1–STAT2 heterodimer and STAT1 homodimer form in response to IFNα/β independently of p48, and can each drive the expression of a minority of ISGs, such as the IRF-1 gene, through GAS elements, the relative amount of STAT protein homo- and heterodimer and its complex formation with p48 depends on the level of p48, which can vary greatly among different cell types (Li et al., 1998). The functionality of p48 in the IFNα/β pathway seems to be that of an adaptor between STAT proteins and the DNA binding sites to redirect gene regulation and achieve the specificity of biological functions of IFNs.

TUMOUR NECROSIS FACTOR: RECEPTORS AND SIGNAL TRANSDUCTION PATHWAYS

The tumour necrosis factor (TNF) receptor superfamily comprises a group of cell surface receptors whose members generally bind ligands that are structurally related to TNF. The TNF ligand is structurally related to lymphotoxin-α (LTα; sometimes referred to as TNF-β), which is secreted from activated T cells, but binds the same receptors as TNF and has similar biological properties. TNF and LTα, however, are the prototype members of a large family of related proteins which includes CD30, CD40, Fas ligand and TRAIL ligand. TNF is a major physiological mediator of inflammation. It initiates the response to Gram-negative bacteria that produce lipopolysaccharide (LPS). TNF has been shown to induce fever, activate the coagulation system, induce hypoglycaemia, depress cardiac contractility, reduce vascular resistance, induce cachexia and activate the acute phase response in the liver.

Ironically, attempts to use TNF in the clinic actually predate its discovery and characterization. Towards the end of the nineteenth century, it was noticed that a small number of cancer patients experienced disease regression after suffering systemic bacterial infections. Subsequently a mixture of killed *Streptococcus pyogenes* and *Serratia marcescens* ('Coley's toxins') were administered to patients with advanced cancer, albeit with very occasional success. This approach became the treatment of choice for over three decades until superseded by advances in radiotherapy, chemotherapy and surgery. With hindsight, the most likely explanation for the results observed with Coley's toxins was the production of TNF, largely by macrophages in response to bacterial lipopolysaccharide present in the cell wall of Gram-negative bacteria such as *Serratia* sp.

TNF and Its Receptors

TNF and LTα are closely related homotrimeric proteins (32% identity). Human TNF is synthesized as a 233 amino acid glycoprotein, containing a long (76 residue) N-terminal leader sequence which anchors it to the cell membrane as a 25-kDa type II membrane protein. A secreted 17-kDa form of TNF is generated through the enzymatic cleavage of membrane-bound TNF by a metalloproteinase termed TNF-α-converting enzyme (TACE). Both soluble and membrane-bound forms of TNF are biologically active, although they have different affinities for the two TNF receptors, and probably as a consequence exhibit different biological properties (see below).

LTα differs from TNF in that it is synthesized as a secreted glycoprotein. Human LTα is synthesized as a 205 amino acid glycoprotein, which in native form exists as a 25-kDa homotrimer. As mentioned above, LTα can bind both TNF receptors with affinities comparable to those of TNF, and has similar biological effects. However, a membrane-bound form of LT has been identified which consists of a heterotrimeric complex containing one LTα subunit noncovalently linked to two molecules of an LTα-related type II membrane protein termed LTβ. The LT$\alpha_1\beta_2$ heterotrimer (also known as mLT) is not cleaved by TACE and is thought to exist exclusively as a membrane-bound complex. mLT does not bind either of the two TNF receptors, but rather exerts its effects on another member of the TNF receptor superfamily, the lymphotoxin β receptor (LTβR). TNF and the two LT subunits are encoded by closely linked single copy genes, which are situated in the class III major histocompatibility locus, within a 25-kb region on the short arm of chromosome 6 in humans, at p21.

The two receptors for TNF (and LTα) are type I transmembrane glycoproteins designated TNFR1 (also termed p60 in humans, p55 in mice) and TNFR2 (also known as p80 in humans, p75 in mice). These receptors are characterized by cysteine-rich repeats of about 40 amino acids in their N-terminal extracellular domains. Each extracellular domain consists of three or four cysteine-rich regions containing four to six cysteines involved in intrachain disulfide bonds. The cytoplasmic domains of these receptors have no obvious similarity to any known kinase and are thought to lack any intrinsic enzymatic activity. Signal transduction is therefore achieved by the recruitment and activation of adaptor proteins which recognize specific sequences in the cytoplasmic domains of these receptors. Recruitment of adaptor molecules activates a number of characteristic signalling pathways that can lead to a remarkably diverse set of cellular responses including differentiation, activation, release of inflammatory mediators and apoptosis. (See also chapter *Apoptosis*.)

Signal Transduction

Death Domains TRADD and FADD

The principal molecule thought to be involved in TNFR1 signal transduction is TNF receptor-associated death domain (TRADD), which is recruited to TNFR1 after activation by TNF. The interaction between TNFR1 and TRADD is mediated by the death domain, a motif found in both adaptor molecules such as TRADD and the cytoplasmic domains of the receptor itself (**Figure 3**). The binding of TRADD to TNFR1 leads to the recruitment and activation of numerous associated signalling molecules. TNF-induced apoptosis is generally thought to be achieved by the interaction of TRADD with FADD (Fas-associated death domain; also known as MORT1), a ~27-kDa protein which oligomerizes with TRADD through the death domains contained in both molecules. Recruitment of FADD is thought to activate a cascade of events which ultimately lead to apoptosis. This is brought about by the

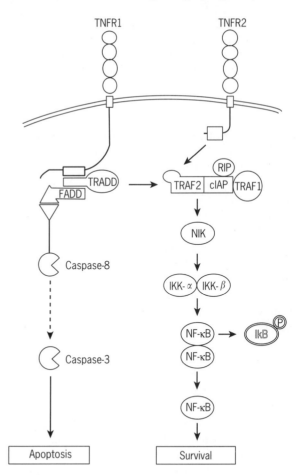

Figure 3   The role of the death domain- and death effector domain-containing molecules in signalling by TNFR1 and TNFR2.

coordinate activation of several members of the caspase family. Caspases are cysteine aspartate proteases which are originally synthesized as zymogens, and are typically converted to their activated form by proteolytic cleavage, often by a distinct caspase upstream in the proteolytic cascade. Caspase-8, which is generally considered to be the apical caspase in the TNF and Fas pathways, is recruited to FADD in the activated complex, and is thought to be activated by self-cleavage induced by an increase in its local concentration. Cleaved caspase-8 can subsequently activate downstream caspases, notably caspase-3, and thereby induce apoptosis.

TRAFs

The cytoplasmic domain of TNFR2 does not contain a death domain. In fact, under many circumstances, TNFR2 signalling can induce proliferation. This is thought to be mediated by the direct interaction of the intracellular signalling intermediate, TRAF2, with the cytoplasmic tail of TNFR2, which leads to the activation of NF-κB. In cells which respond to TNFR2 signals by proliferating, no caspase activation is observed, and presumably no interaction of TRAF2 with TRADD. However, in cells which respond to TNFR2 signalling by undergoing apoptosis, there is mounting evidence that this is effected by a signal crosstalk mechanism with TNFR1, possibly by inducing expression of membrane-bound TNF or by affecting the stability of prosurvival proteins such as TRAF2 (Duckett and Thompson, 1997). As mentioned above, LTα has been shown to bind to both TNFR1 and TNFR2 with comparable affinities and biological outcomes. Membrane LT does not bind to either of these receptors, but binds exclusively to the LTβ receptor. In comparison with TNFR1 and TNFR2, the signal transduction pathways utilized by the LTβ receptor have been less well defined. Signalling by LTβR has been shown to induce apoptosis, although examination of the signalling, cytoplasmic tail has not revealed any obvious homology to the death domain. TRAF3 and TRAF5 have been shown to bind LTβR, but the role of TRAF3 in apoptosis induction is unclear.

TRAF2 is also a central component of the TNFR1 signalling complex, through a direct interaction with TRADD. Although TRAF2 lacks intrinsic enzymatic activity, it has been shown to bind several serine–threonine kinases, including NIK (NF-κB-inducing kinase), RIP (receptor interacting protein) and GCK (germinal centre kinase). Through the recruitment of these kinases, TRAF2 is thought to induce the activation of several transcription factors, particularly NF-κB (nuclear factor-κB), as well as downstream kinases involved in stress responses, notably c-Jun N-terminal kinase (JNK), which are crucial effectors of the TNFR1-mediated proinflammatory reaction. TRADD is also thought to associate with the serine–threonine kinase RIP, and RIP has been shown to interact with another protein, RAIDD (RIP associated Ich-1/CED3 homologous protein with death domain; also known as CRADD), causing the recruitment and activation of caspase-2 and the induction of apoptosis. However, the RAIDD/CRADD pathway is not thought to be the major signalling pathway utilized by TNFR1 to induce apoptosis. Despite the well-defined ability of TNFR1 signalling to induce cell death, the majority of normal cells do not respond to TNF by undergoing apoptosis. It has been proposed that this paradoxical situation can be accounted for by the activation of NF-κB, which has been shown to induce the expression of a number of antiapoptotic proteins. The best described of these are (i) A20, a zinc finger-containing molecule, (ii) A1/BflI, a Bcl-2 homologue, and (iii) c-IAP1/c-IAP2, members of the IAP (inhibitor of apoptosis) family.

Many key signalling intermediates responsible for the induction of NF-κB by the TNF receptors have been identified. NF-κB transcription factors are sequestered in the cytoplasm of cells by a protein called IκB (inhibitor of NF-κB). Phosphorylation of IκB leads to its degradation via ubiquitination by the 26S proteasome. The heterodimeric NF-κB subunits then translocate to the nucleus where they regulate expression of a wide variety of genes involved in inflammatory responses. A complex of two kinases and a regulatory protein are responsible for IκB phosphorylation. The kinases are termed IκB kinases α (IKKα) and β (IKKβ) and are constitutively associated with the regulatory protein IKKγ or NEMO. The serine–threonine kinase NIK, initially identified through its ability to associated with TRAF2, is thought to activate the IKK complex. A naturally occurring mouse mutation termed alymphoplasia (aly) is the result of a point mutation of NIK. Aly/aly−/− mice lack lymph nodes and Peyer patches, and also exhibit disorganized splenic and thymic structures.

Other Pathways

Alternative models have been proposed to account for the diverse range of outcomes following TNFR1 activation. Notably, SODD (silencer of death domains) was identifed in the basis of its ability to bind to the death domain of TNFR1. SODD is found in the TNFR1 receptor complex before receptor activation, but then dissociates from the receptor after ligand binding. It is thought that the SODD preassociation with TNFR1 may prevent spontaneous signalling by death domain-containing receptors. Neutral sphingomyelinase (N-Smase) activation is thought to mediate some of the inflammatory and proliferative responses to TNF through the activation of ERK and phospholipase A2. Other factors have been identifed which bind distinct sites in the cytoplasmic tail of TNFR1, such as FAN (factor associated with N-Smase activation), which is thought to couple the TNFR to activation of neutral sphingomyelinase activity, which in turn results in the production of ceramide and is thereby thought to lead to the activation of MAP kinases.

CHEMOKINE RECEPTOR SIGNAL TRANSDUCTION

Chemoattractant cytokines are typically < 15-kDa proteins which are secreted by many tissue and cell types. Chemokines were recently reviewed (Zlotnik et al., 1999). The classical chemokine-induced biological activity is leucocyte migration, but as the field has matured other chemokine-mediated physiological functions have been identified, including regulation of vascularization in embryogenesis, lymphocyte maturation, cellular activation, regulation of angiogenesis and apoptosis. Although these additional functions have been demonstrated, the components of the distinct signalling cascades are poorly characterized, so this section will focus on chemokine-induced chemotaxis, cell activation and apoptosis.

Seven Transmembrane G-protein-coupled Receptors (GPCRs)

Chemokines bind to and activate seven pass transmembrane G-protein-coupled receptors (GPCRs) that are structurally similar to the rhodopsin (type A) subfamily. The N-terminus of the receptor, which is also the first extracellular domain, is essential for high-affinity ligand binding. The closely packed position of the seven transmembrane domains are maintained by disulfide bonds between the extracellular domains. The disulfide bonding is needed for efficient chemokine-induced signalling but is not necessary for HIV-1 coreceptor activity. The chemokine receptor signal is dependent on a ligand-induced dynamic change in the receptor that results in an increased affinity for Gi and Gq heterotrimeric G-proteins. Fine regulation of the GPCR signal occurs at the membrane where increased phosphatidylcholine in the lipid bilayer enhances GTPase activity of the G-proteins and is essential for the activity of G-protein coupled receptor kinase(s) (GRKs).

Heterotrimeric G-proteins

Chemokine-induced chemotaxis is inhibited by pertussis toxin, indicating that chemokine receptors activate trimeric G proteins in the Gi subfamily. However, activation of phospholipase C (PLC), intracellular calcium (Ca^{2+}) mobilization and cellular exocytosis can be mediated through pertussis toxin-insensitive Gq proteins. The type of cell expressing the GPCR and its activation state regulates which G-protein couples to the receptor, such that chemokine receptors have been reported to couple to several classes of G-proteins.

Heterotrimeric G-proteins are composed of α-, β- and γ-subunits. In the resting G-protein, the α-subunit is bound to GDP. Once activated, GDP is exchanged for GTP and the α-subunit separates from the β–γ-subunits. The α-subunits are apparently necessary for regulation of the GPCR function. Regulators of G-protein signal (RGS) are widely expressed GTPase-activating proteins that contain a 130 amino acid domain that binds $G\alpha$-GTP subunits accelerating the hydrolysis to $G\alpha$-GDP and blocking $G\alpha$ interaction with PLC. Additionally, some $G\alpha$ subunits are substrates for protein kinase C (PKC) resulting in autoregulation of this G-protein-mediated signal. $G\alpha i$ subunits were shown to be nonessential in chemokine-induced chemotaxis. These data indicated that any $G\alpha$ linked to β–γ-subunits, which are essential, could transmit a chemotactic signal. In addition to transmitting the chemotactic signal, β–γ-subunits participate in signal component receptor docking and cell activation.

Heterotrimeric G-proteins interact with several intracellular domains of GPCRs found in the cytoplasmic tail and second and third intracellular loops. The β–γ-subunits were shown to guide GRK2 to its phosphorylation site on a GPCR, suggesting that both the correct membrane lipid composition and G-protein components are needed for GRK regulation of GPCR signal. The G-protein β–γ-subunits directly bind to and activate Raf-1, phosphoinositide 3-kinase gamma (PI3Kγ) and some small GTPases. Raf-1 is a serine/threonine kinase that links the mitogen-activated protein kinase cascade to tyrosine kinase-dependent growth factor receptors. Mutagenesis studies showed that β–γ-subunits bind to Raf-1 with an affinity similar to that between β–γ-subunits and GRKs, suggesting that there maybe a competition between receptor inactivation by GRKs and the mitogenic signal. Stromal-derived factor-1 (SDF-1, also known as CXCL12) is a CXC chemokine that activates the CXCR4 receptor. Recently it was shown that SDF-1-induced chemotaxis and extracellular signal-related kinase (ERK) activation was inhibited by PI3K inhibitor treatment of T lymphocytes. These data show a link between G-protein β–γ-subunits and PI3K and suggest an order of activation.

Mutagenesis of G-protein β-subunits resulted in inappropriate organisation of cellular cytoskeleton (Peracino et al., 1998), and additional studies have shown that small GTPases of the Rho family are essential for chemotaxis and sequestration of β–γ-subunits leads to rearrangement of the actin cytoskeleton, suggesting a link between β-subunits and these small GTPases.

Phospholipase

An approach to demonstrate the role of PLC in the GPCR signal cascade used mice lacking PLC-$\beta2$ and -$\beta3$. Neutrophils from animals lacking both PLC-$\beta2$ and -$\beta3$ did not produce inositol triphosphate (IP$_3$), flux calcium or superoxide in response to chemokines or chemoattractants. Animals lacking only PLC-$\beta2$ clearly showed reduced both IP$_3$ and Ca^{2+} flux in response to interleukin-8 (IL-8 also known as CXCL8) and macrophage inflammatory protein 1 beta (MIP1β, also known as CCL4), but not to the same extent, suggesting that both PLC isoforms participate in signal transduction in neutrophils. In contrast to the calcium flux signal, the chemotaxic response of the neutrophils from animals lacking both PLC-$\beta2$ and -$\beta3$ was not reduced; rather, there was an enhanced chemotactic response to IL-8. The PLC-$\beta2$- and -$\beta3$-deficient animals failed to activate PKC in response to chemoattractants, indicating that the PKC pathway is linked to the $G\alpha$ and not the $G\beta$–γ signal. Additionally, PLC-deficient animals failed to phosphorylate the mitogen-activated protein kinase (MAPK) c-JUN N-terminal kinase (JNK). However, PLC deficiency had no effect on Rac activation, suggesting that cytoskeletal modification is a separate signal in neutrophils.

In addition to activation of PLC, there is strong evidence that phospholipase D (PLD) is also activated by chemokines. The position of PLD in the chemokine signal

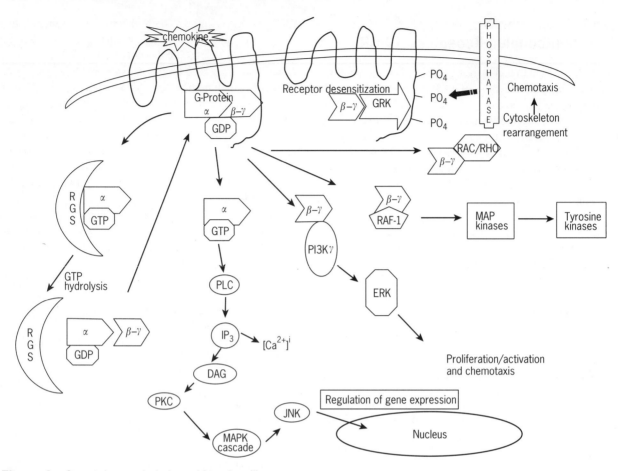

Figure 4   G-protein-coupled chemokine signalling.

cascade is ambiguous because diacylglycerol (DAG) can be interconverted to the lipid hydrolysis product of PLD, phosphatidic acid (PA), suggesting that PLC activity may regulate PLD activity. Additionally, PLD is activated by Ras and Rho family members and PKC. A function for PA in chemokine-induced cell activation has not been identified, but PA is strongly associated with cell vesicle transport, suggesting that PLD may act late in the chemokine-induced cascade by regulating receptor localization to the membrane (**Figure 4**).

Further, PA is in the pathway that leads to respiratory burst (Lennartz, 1999), suggesting that PLD activation by chemokines maybe participate in chemokine-induced NADPH production.

Phosphoinositide 3-Kinase Gamma (PI3Kγ)

PI3Ks have been implicated in many cellular responses, including, proliferation, apoptosis, adhesion and chemotaxis. Recently, a number of groups generated mice deficient in PI3Kγ. All three groups observed a severe reduction ($\leq 85\%$) in chemokine-induced chemotaxis, but there was some activity left, indicating that Gβ–γ may link

to other intracellular components and induce chemotaxis. The least effected was MIP-5-induced chemotaxis (Hirsch *et al.*, 2000). MIP-5 (also known as HCC-2 or CCL-15) has a unique six-cysteine structure. The effect this chemokine has on other intracellular signalling components has not been evaluated, but mutational analysis indicated that the third set of disulfide bonds were not needed to induce chemotaxis. PI3Kγ deficiency had no effect on chemoattractant-induced Rac activation, actin polymerization or calcium flux. PI3Kγ deficiency had a profound inhibitory effect on chemoattractant-induced activation of PKB, ERK1 or ERK2. The activation of ERK1 and ERK2 by PI3Kγ directly links the chemokine GPCR signal to both proliferation and activation signals. Taken together, these data indicate that PI3Kγ is a major component in chemokine-induced chemotaxis and cell activation, but not the only component.

Focal Adhesion Kinases and Tyrosine Phosphatases

Several tyrosine kinases are activated during chemotaxis, but whether the effect is mediated through a GPCR pathway or by an adhesion molecule-activated signal pathway is still unclear. Focal adhesion kinase (FAK) activity is clearly stimulated by RANTES (regulated on activation of normal T cell expression and secreted, also known as CCL5) binding to CC chemokine receptor-5 (CCR5).

SDF-1 and stem cell factor appear to activate related adhesion focal tyrosine kinase (RAFTK), a FAK homology expressed in some leucocytes. The FAK family has been shown to activate or be activated by some MAPK and Rho family members. Thus, although there is no disagreement that focal adhesion kinases are activated in cell migration, their role in chemokine-induced cell migration and activation is unclear.

Studies using tyrosine phosphatase, SHIP-1 and SHP-1-deficient mice showed enhanced chemotaxis and reduced suppression of proliferation in response to chemokines. Activation of CD45, a cell surface glycoprotein with tyrosine phosphatase activity, decreased the cell surface expression of IL-8 receptors and IL-8-induced calcium flux. While it is tempting to theorize a role for these phosphatases in G-protein-mediated chemokine signalling, more research is needed to connect these signals clearly. Recent reviews suggest that the components of adhesion, selectins and integrin receptors, have bidirectional signalling cascades, and that the activation of focal adhesion kinases and tyrosine phosphatases may be an 'outside in' signal.

Apoptosis

Studies of cell death in HIV-1-infected cells showed that CXCR4 is required for this apoptotic signal and the signal is G-protein independent. Pertussis toxin, PI3K inhibitor (wortmannin), ERK pathway inhibitors and MAPK pathway inhibitors had no effect on CXCR4-mediated HIV-1-induced lymphocyte apoptosis. CCR5 does signal through ERK and MAPK when activated by HIV-1. Gp120-independent virus–cell fusion and recombinant gp120 did not induce apoptosis, but, cell surface-expressed gp120 did.

Deletion of the cytoplasmic tail of CXCR4 blocked ligand-induced receptor internalization, but did not block HIV-1-induced apoptosis. Since none of the well-characterized chemokine signal components appear to be necessary for the CXCR4-mediated apoptosis signal, what is? Caspase 3 activity correlates with CXCR4-mediated cell death. These data indicate that HIV-1 induces CXCR4-dependent apoptosis by activating caspase 3.

Musings

The chemokine-induced cellular signal is complex and still poorly characterized. The activation of G-protein subunit-mediated signals is clear, but other non-G-protein-mediated signals still require clarification. Receptor desensitization and resensitization are a great mystery, with few well-characterized components, other than

serine–threonine phosphorylation of the GPCR carboxyl tail. Several groups have shown tyrosine kinase activation in response to chemokines; however, because the cell shape change and activation of these kinases parallel each other, an integrin receptor-mediated signal cannot be ruled out. Further, activation of Janus kinases (JAKs) by chemokines has been demonstrated in human embryonic kidney and lymphocyte cell lines. These studies took place in membrane raft microdomains, so that other components of the rafts may have contributed to the activation. Characterization of chemokine-induced activation of signal transducers and activators of transcription (STATs) has begun. SDF-1, RANTES and MIP1α have been shown to stimulate STAT phosphorylation. However, it remains to determine the mediator, be it binding to a domain on the chemokine receptor or JAK activation. Further structural analysis of chemokine receptors is needed to link conclusive tyrosine kinases and STAT activation to chemokine receptors. After 12 years, our understanding of chemokine-mediated signal transduction is almost ready to enter adolescence, but a long way from a mature field.

REFERENCES

Ahmad, M., et al. (1997). CRADD, a novel human apoptotic adaptor molecule for caspase-2, and FasL/tumor necrosis factor receptor-interacting protein RIP. Cancer Research, 57, 615–619.

Arai, H. and Charo, I. F. (1996). Differential regulation of G-protein-mediated signaling by chemokine receptors. Journal of Biological Chemistry, 271, 21814–21819.

Bach, E. A., et al. (1997). The IFN gamma receptor a paradigm for cytokine receptor signaling. Annual Review of Immunology, 15, 563–591.

Bacon, K. B., et al. (1996). RANTES induces tyrosine kinase activity of stably complexed p125FAK and ZAP-70 in human T cells. Journal of Experimental Medicine, 184, 873–882.

Beutler, B. A. (1999). The role of tumor necrosis factor in health and disease. Journal of Rheumatology, 26, Suppl. 57, 16–21.

Blanco, J., et al. (1999). The implication of the chemokine receptor CXCR4 in HIV-1 envelope protein-induced apoptosis is independent of the G protein-mediated signalling. Aids, 13, 909–917.

Bluyssen, H. A., et al. (1995). Combinatorial association and abundance of components of interferon-stimulated gene factor 3 dictate the selectivity of interferon responses. Proceedings of the National Academy of Sciences of the USA, 92, 5645–5649.

Cohen, B., et al. (1995). Ligand-induced association of the type I interferon receptor components. Molecular and Cellular Biology, 15, 4208–4214.

Colamonici, O. R., et al. (1994a). Interferon alpha (IFN alpha) signaling in cells expressing the variant form of the type I IFN receptor. Journal of Biological Chemistry, 269, 5660–5665.

Colamonici, O. R., et al. (1994b). Ligand-independent anti-oncogenic activity of the alpha subunit of the type I interferon receptor. *Journal of Biological Chemistry*, **269**, 27275–27279.

Colamonici, O. R., et al. (1994c). p135tyk2, an interferon-alpha-activated tyrosine kinase, is physically associated with an interferon-alpha receptor. *Journal of Biological Chemistry*, **269**, 3518–3522.

Colamonici, O. R., et al. (1995). Transmembrane signaling by the alpha subunit of the type I interferon receptor is essential for activation of the JAK kinases and the transcriptional factor ISGF3. *Journal of Biological Chemistry*, **270**, 8188–8193.

Coppolino, M. G. and Dedhar, S. (2000). Bi-directional signal transduction by integrin receptors. *International Journal of Biochemical Cell Biology*, **32**, 171–188.

Darnell, J. E., Jr, et al. (1994). Jak-STAT pathways and transcriptional activation in response to IFNs and other extracellular signaling proteins. *Science*, **264**, 1415–1421.

Darnell, J. E., Jr (1997). STATs and gene regulation. *Science*, **277**, 1630–1635.

Darnell, J. E., Jr (1998). Studies of IFN-induced transcriptional activation uncover the Jak–Stat pathway. *Journal of Interferon and Cytokine Research*, **18**, 549–554.

Domanski, P., et al. (1997). A region of the beta subunit of the interferon alpha receptor different from box 1 interacts with Jak1 and is sufficient to activate the Jak–Stat pathway and induce an antiviral state. *Journal of Biological Chemistry*, **272**, 26388–26393.

Domanski, P., et al. (1995). Homodimerization and intermolecular tyrosine phosphorylation of the Tyk-2 tyrosine kinase. *FEBS Letters*, **374**, 317–322.

Duckett, C. S. and Thompson, C. B. (1997). CD30-dependent degradation of TRAF2 implications for negative regulation of TRAF signaling and the control of cell survival. *Genes and Development*, **11**, 2810–2821.

Fu, X. Y. (1992). A transcription factor with SH2 and SH3 domains is directly activated by an interferon alpha-induced cytoplasmic protein tyrosine kinase(s). *Cell*, **70**, 323–335.

Gonzalez-Amaro, R. and Sanchez-Madrid, F. (1999). Cell adhesion molecules: selectins and integrins. *Critical Reviews in Immunology*, **19**, 389–429.

Gouilleux-Gruart, V., et al. (1997). Activated Stat related transcription factors in acute leukemia. *Leukemia Lymphoma*, **28**, 83–88.

Greenlund, A. C., et al. (1995). Stat recruitment by tyrosine-phosphorylated cytokine receptorsan ordered reversible affinity-driven process. *Immunity*, **2**, 677–687.

Haque, S. J. and Williams, B. R. (1994). Identification and characterization of an interferon (IFN)-stimulated response element-IFN-stimulated gene factor 3-independent signaling pathway for IFN-alpha. *Journal of Biological Chemistry*, **269**, 19523–19529.

Harada, H., et al. (1996). Regulation of IFN-alpha/beta genes-evidence for a dual function of the transcription factor complex ISGF3 in the production and action of IFN-alpha/beta. *Genes and Cells*, **1**, 995–1005.

Hayakawa, F., et al. (1998). Differential constitutive activation between STAT-related proteins and MAP kinase in primary acute myelogenous leukaemia. *British Journal of Haematology*, **101**, 521–528.

Hemmi, S., et al. (1994). A novel member of the interferon receptor family complements functionality of the murine interferon gamma receptor in human cells. *Cell*, **76**, 803–810.

Hirsch, E., et al. (2000). Central role for G protein-coupled phosphoinositide 3-kinase gamma in inflammation. *Science*, **287**, 1049–1053.

Horvath, C. M., et al. (1995). A STAT protein domain that determines DNA sequence recognition suggests a novel DNA-binding domain. *Genes and Development*, **9**, 984–994.

Howard, O. M., et al. (1999). Naturally occurring CCR5 extracellular and transmembrane domain variants affect HIV-1 Co-receptor and ligand binding function. *Journal of Biological Chemistry*, **274**, 16228–16234.

Ihle, J. N. (1996). STATs signal transducers and activators of transcription. *Cell*, **84**, 331–334.

Ihle, J. N. (1995). The Janus protein tyrosine kinase family and its role in cytokine signaling. *Advances in Immunology*, **60**, 1–35.

John, J., et al. (1991). Isolation and characterization of a new mutant human cell line unresponsive to alpha and beta interferons. *Molecular and Cellular Biology*, **11**, 4189–4195.

Kaul, M. and Lipton, S. A. (1999). Chemokines and activated macrophages in HIV gp120-induced neuronal apoptosis. *Proceedings of the National Academy of Sciences of the USA*, **96**, 8212–8216.

Kotenko, S. V., et al. (1995). Interaction between the components of the interferon gamma receptor complex. *Journal of Biological Chemistry*, **270**, 20915–20921.

Lennartz, M. R. (1999). Phospholipases and phagocytosis: the role of phospholipid-derived second messengers in phagocytosis. *International Journal of Biochemical Cell Biology*, **31**, 415–430.

Li, X., et al. (1998). Cooperative binding of Stat1–2 heterodimers and ISGF3 to tandem DNA elements. *Biochimie*, **80**, 703–710.

Li, X., et al. (1996). Formation of STAT1–STAT2 heterodimers and their role in the activation of IRF-1 gene transcription by interferon-alpha. *Journal of Biological Chemistry*, **271**, 5790–5794.

Lim, L., et al. (1996). Regulation of phosphorylation pathways by p21 GTPases. The p21 Ras-related Rho subfamily and its role in phosphorylation signalling pathways. *European Journal of Biochemistry*, **242**, 171–185.

Lopez-Ilasaca, M. (1998). Signaling from G-protein-coupled receptors to mitogen-activated protein (MAP)-kinase cascades. *Biochemical Pharmacology*, **56**, 269–277.

Ma, Q., et al. (1998). Impaired B-lymphopoiesis, myelopoiesis, and derailed cerebellar neuron migration in CXCR4- and SDF-1-deficient mice. *Proceedings of the National Academy of Sciences of the USA*, **95**, 9448–9453.

Matsumoto, M., *et al.* (1999). Activation of the transcription factor ISGF3 by interferon-gamma. *Biological Chemistry*, **380**, 699–703.

Monteclaro, F. S. and Charo, I. F. (1997). The amino-terminal domain of CCR2 is both necessary and sufficient for high affinity binding of monocyte chemoattractant protein 1. Receptor activation by a pseudo-tethered ligand. *Journal of Biological Chemistry*, **272**, 23186–23190.

Moriggl, R., *et al.* (1999). Stat5 is required for IL-2-induced cell cycle progression of peripheral T cells. *Immunity*, **10**, 249–259.

Noguchi, M., *et al.* (1993). Interleukin-2 receptor gamma chain mutation results in X-linked severe combined immunodeficiency in humans. *Cell*, **73**, 147–157.

Nosaka, T., *et al.* (1995). Defective lymphoid development in mice lacking Jak3. *Science*, **270**, 800–802.

Novick, D., *et al.* (1994). The human interferon alpha/beta receptor characterization and molecular cloning. *Cell*, **77**, 391–400.

Pease, J. E., *et al.* (1998). The N-terminal extracellular segments of the chemokine receptors CCR1 and CCR3 are determinants for MIP-1alpha and eotaxin binding, respectively, but a second domain is essential for efficient receptor activation. *Journal of Biological Chemistry*, **273**, 19972–19976.

Pellegrini, S., *et al.* (1989). Use of a selectable marker regulated by alpha interferon to obtain mutations in the signaling pathway. *Molecular and Cellular Biology*, **9**, 4605–4612.

Peracino, B., *et al.* (1998). G protein beta subunit-null mutants are impaired in phagocytosis and chemotaxis due to inappropriate regulation of the actin cytoskeleton. *Journal of Cell Biology*, **141**, 1529–1537.

Pestka, S., *et al.* (1987). Interferons and their actions. *Annual Review of Biochemistry*, **56**, 727–777.

Pfeffer, L. M., *et al.* (1997). The short form of the interferon alpha/beta receptor chain 2 acts as a dominant negative for type I interferon action. *Journal of Biological Chemistry*, **272**, 11002–11005.

Platanias, L. C. and Fish, E. N. (1999). Signaling pathways activated by interferons. *Experimental Hematology*, **27**, 1583–1592.

Platanias, L. C., *et al.* (1992). Expression of the IFN alpha receptor in hairy cell leukaemia. *British Journal of Haematology*, **82**, 541–546.

Porter, A. C., *et al.* (1988). Interferon response element of the human gene 6–16. *EMBO Journal*, **7**, 85–92.

Puck, J. M., *et al.* (1993). The interleukin-2 receptor gamma chain maps to Xq13.1 and is mutated in X-linked severe combined immunodeficiency, SCIDX1. *Human Molecular Genetics*, **2**, 1099–1104.

Ram, P. A. and Waxman, D. J. (1997). Interaction of growth hormone-activated STATs with SH2-containing phosphotyrosine phosphatase SHP-1 and nuclear JAK2 tyrosine kinase. *Journal of Biological Chemistry*, **272**, 17694–17702.

Rane, S. G. and Reddy, E. P. (1994). JAK3: a novel JAK kinase associated with terminal differentiation of hematopoietic cells. *Oncogene*, **9**, 2415–2423.

Ray, M., *et al.* (2000). Inhibition of interferon-gamma signaling by *Leishmania donovani*. *Journal of Infectious Diseases*, **181**, 1121–1128.

Richardson, R. M., *et al.* (1998). Multiple signaling pathways of human interleukin-8 receptor A. Independent regulation by phosphorylation. *Journal of Biological Chemistry*, **273**, 10690–10695.

Russell-Harde, D., *et al.* (1995). Reconstitution of a high affinity binding site for type I interferons. *Journal of Biological Chemistry*, **270**, 26033–26036.

Russell-Harde, D., *et al.* (2000). Role of the intracellular domain of the human type I interferon receptor 2 chain (IFNAR2c) in interferon signaling. Expression of IFNAR2c truncation mutants in U5A cells. *Journal of Biological Chemistry*, **275**, 23981–23985.

Schindler, C. and Darnell, J. E., Jr (1995). Transcriptional responses to polypeptide ligands in the JAK–STAT pathway. *Annual Review of Biochemistry*, **64**, 621–651.

Seder, R. A. (1994). Acquisition of lymphokine-producing phenotype by CD4+ T cells. *Journal of Allergy and Clinical Immunology*, **94**, 1195–1202.

Shuai, K., *et al.* (1996). Constitutive activation of STAT5 by the BCR-ABL oncogene in chronic myelogenous leukemia. *Oncogene*, **13**, 247–254.

Singer, W. D., Brown, H. A. and Sternweis, P. C. (1997). Regulation of eukaryotic phosphatidylinositol-specific phospholipase C and phospholipase D. *Annual Review of Biochemistry*, **66**, 475–509.

Soh, J., *et al.* (1994). Identification and sequence of an accessory factor required for activation of the human interferon gamma receptor. *Cell*, **76**, 793–802.

Stark, G. R., *et al.* (1998). How cells respond to interferons. *Annual Review of Biochemistry*, **67**, 227–264.

Takahashi, M., *et al.* (1997). Mechanotransduction in endothelial cells: temporal signaling events in response to shear stress. *Journal of Vascular Research*, **34**, 212–219.

Takeda, K., *et al.* (1997). Targeted disruption of the mouse Stat3 gene leads to early embryonic lethality. *Proceedings of the National Academy of Sciences of the USA*, **94**, 3801–3804.

Takeda, K., *et al.* (1996). Essential role of Stat6 in IL-4 signalling. *Nature*, **380**, 627–630.

Tau, G. and Rothman, P. (1999). Biologic functions of the IFN-gamma receptors. *Allergy*, **54**, 1233–1251.

Tournamille, C., *et al.* (1997). Close association of the first and fourth extracellular domains of the Duffy antigen/receptor for chemokines by a disulfide bond is required for ligand binding. *Journal of Biological Chemistry*, **272**, 16274–16280.

Trinchieri, G. and Scott, P. (1995). Interleukin-12a proinflammatory cytokine with immunoregulatory functions [editorial]. *Research in Immunology*, **146**, 423–431.

Uze, G., *et al.* (1990). Genetic transfer of a functional human interferon alpha receptor into mouse cells cloning and expression of its cDNA. *Cell*, **60**, 225–234.

Uze, G., *et al.* (1995). Alpha and beta interferons and their receptor and their friends and relations. *Journal of Interferon and Cytokine Research*, **15**, 3–26.

Velazquez, L., *et al.* (1995). Distinct domains of the protein tyrosine kinase tyk2 required for binding of interferon-alpha/beta and for signal transduction. *Journal of Biological Chemistry*, **270**, 3327–3334.

Wong, M. and Fish, E. N. (1998). RANTES and MIP-1alpha activate stats in T cells. *Journal of Biological Chemistry*, **273**, 309–314.

Wu, G., *et al.* (1998). Receptor docking sites for G-protein beta-gamma subunits. Implications for signal regulation. *Journal of Biological Chemistry*, **273**, 7197–7200.

Wu, M. Y., *et al.* (1999). The cytoplasmic domain of the lymphotoxin-beta receptor mediates cell death in HeLa cells. *Journal of Biological Chemistry*, **274**, 11868–11873.

Xia, Z., *et al.* (1998). Expression of signal transducers and activators of transcription proteins in acute myeloid leukemia blasts. *Cancer Research*, **58**, 3173–3180.

Yamamoto, K., *et al.* (1997). cDNA cloning, expression and chromosome mapping of the human STAT4 gene: both STAT4 and STAT1 genes are mapped to 2q32.2q32.3. *Cytogenetics and Cell Genetics*, **77**, 207–210.

Yasukawa, H., *et al.* (2000). Negative regulation of cytokine signaling pathways. *Annual Review of Immunology*, **18**, 143–164.

Young, H. A. and Hardy, K. J. (1995). Role of interferon-gamma in immune cell regulation. *Journal of Leukocyte Biology*, **58**, 373–381.

Zheng, B., *et al.* (1999a). Divergence of RGS proteins: evidence for the existence of six mammalian RGS subfamilies. *Trends in Biochemical Sciences*, **24**, 411–414.

Zheng, J., *et al.* (1999b). Intracellular CXCR4 signaling, neuronal apoptosis and neuropathogenic mechanisms of HIV-1-associated dementia. *Journal of Neuroimmunology*, **98**, 185–200.

Zhou, N., *et al.* (2000). Molecular modeling and site-directed mutagenesis of CCR5 reveal residues critical for chemokine binding and signal transduction. *European Journal of Immunology*, **30**, 164–173.

Zlotnik, A., *et al.* (1999). Recent advances in chemokines and chemokine receptors. *Critical Reviews in Immunology*, **19**, 1–47.

Chapter 12
Signalling by Tyrosine Kinases

Kermit L. Carraway and Coralie A. Carothers Carraway
University of Miami School of Medicine, Miami, FL, USA

CONTENTS

INTRODUCTION

Historical Perspective

Few molecules have been more closely linked to cancer than the protein tyrosine kinases. Tyrosine phosphorylation and the tyrosine kinase enzymes which create phosphotyrosine residues in their substrate proteins were discovered during studies of the oncogenic factors in tumour viruses. The identification of v-Src as the transforming factor of the Rous sarcoma virus and the recognition of its activity as a protein tyrosine kinase conceptualized the oncogene theory of tumorigenesis, creating a model which has dominated much of cancer research over the past two decades. The importance of the work on viral oncogenes in the early research on tyrosine phosphorylation is shown by an accounting of landmark events in this area (**Table 1**) (Hunter, 1998). The discovery of a cellular counterpart (c-Src) of the viral Src (v-Src) tyrosine kinase indicated a much broader role for these enzymes and suggested a major role for c-Src and tyrosine phosphorylation in mediating normal cell behaviours. For example, c-Src has been implicated in such diverse cell functions as platelet aggregation, cell cycle control and cell motility. The diversity of cellular functions of tyrosine kinases was further indicated by early observations that both the epidermal growth factor (EGF) receptor, important in epithelial cell growth, and the insulin receptor, a key component in metabolic regulation, are tyrosine kinases. Another tyrosine kinase receptor, called Sevenless for its role in determining cell fate of a particular cell type, was found to be necessary for normal eye development in the fruit fly (*Drosophila*). These and many other discoveries have demonstrated the critical role that the tyrosine kinases and tyrosine phosphorylation play in normal cell regulation and communication and in developmental biology.

Evolutionarily, tyrosine kinases are primarily, if not exclusively, a product of eukaryotic cells. The emergence of protein tyrosine kinases with the appearance of multicellular

Table 1 Important discoveries in history of tyrosine phosphorylation

1979	Tyrosine phosphorylation of polyoma tumour virus middle T antigen
1980	Protein tyrosine kinase activities of v-Src, c-Src, v-Abl and EGF receptor
1981	Insulin-stimulated protein tyrosine kinase activity of insulin receptor
1982	Sequence similarity of v-Src to cAMP-dependent protein kinase catalytic subunit
	c-Abl gene rearrangement in chronic myelogenous leukaemia
1983	Polyoma middle T association with and activation of c-Src
1984	v-ErbB oncogene derived from EGF receptor
1985	Negative regulation of c-Src by tyrosine phosphorylation
1986	Neu oncogene as EGF receptor family member with activating point mutation
1987	*Drosophila* Sevenless is receptor tyrosine kinase
1988	Acetylcholine receptor regulated by tyrosine phosphorylation
1989	Cell cycle regulatory kinase negatively regulated by Tyr phosphorylation
1990	Src homology-2 domains bind phosphotyrosines
1992	Individual receptor Tyr phosphorylation sites bind distinct SH2-containing proteins
	STAT transcription factors activated by Tyr phosphorylation

(Adapted from Hunter, 1998.)

(metazoan) organisms is indicative of their importance in cell communication and organisation. Sequence information from the Human Genome Project indicates that there are 90 tyrosine kinases encoded in the human genome.

The Kinase Superfamily

Tyrosine kinases are members of a much larger family of protein kinases (Hunter, 1998), which can be categorized by two classifications, one based on specificity for the target amino acid and the other on structure and cellular localization. The major specificity classes are the serine or threonine-specific (Ser/Thr) kinases and the tyrosine-specific (Tyr) kinases which catalyse the phosphorylation of serine and threonine or tyrosine residues, respectively. In addition, a few mixed function kinases, which catalyse both Ser/Thr and Tyr phosphorylation, have been described. The discovery of serine/threonine kinases and their importance in regulating metabolic pathways preceded the discovery of tyrosine kinases by about two decades. The regulation of gluconeogenesis by phosphorylation–dephosphorylation established as a paradigm the reversible regulation of enzymes by the covalent addition and removal of phosphate groups. Further, the discovery of cAMP-dependent kinases was a catalyst for the study of cAMP as a second messenger in the transduction of signals through certain types of receptors. Structural analyses of serine/threonine kinases, particularly the cyclic AMP-stimulated kinase (protein kinase A), have provided models for the catalytic domains and enzymic mechanisms of all of the kinases (Taylor *et al.*, 1995).

Structurally, there are two major classes of kinases, receptor (**Figure 1a**) and nonreceptor (**Figure 1b**), based on elements of their primary sequences which determine their cellular localization. Almost all receptor kinases characterized to date are tyrosine kinases, with the exception of the TGF-β receptor, a Ser/Thr kinase (see chapter on *Signalling by TGF-β*). Receptor kinases are defined by a hydrophobic transmembrane domain, which passes through the plasma membrane, an extracellular ligand-binding domain and a cytoplasmically oriented kinase domain (**Figure 1a**). In contrast, nonreceptor kinases have no transmembrane or extracellular domains, although they may be associated with the cytoplasmic surfaces of cellular membranes by one of two mechanisms. The first is constitutive membrane localization via a lipid modification which anchors the protein to the phospholipid bilayer. The lipid-linked kinases identified to date have been tyrosine kinases, and Src is the prototype of this kinase type, having an N-terminal consensus site for myristoylation (**Figure 2a**). The second membrane localization mechanism involves binding to a nonenzymic membrane receptor to give a binary tyrosine kinase (**Figure 2b**).

Tyrosine phosphorylation is a relatively rare event in normal, unactivated cells, representing <0.1% of total protein phosphate groups (serine, 90%; threonine, 10%). However, tyrosine phosphorylation is transiently increased during normal cell activation and often substantially increased, sometimes constitutively, in tumour cells. The functions of tyrosine kinases are significantly different from those of the serine/threonine kinases. Conceptually, the primary role of tyrosine kinases is to provide a mechanism for transmitting information from a factor outside a cell to the interior of the cell without requiring that the factor cross the cell's exterior membrane barrier. That role is exemplified by the ability of a growth factor or polypeptide hormone in the extracellular milieu, which cannot pass through the membrane, to activate specific gene transcription in the nucleus of a target cell (see **Figure 3a**). This example is only one of the many cell functions mediated by tyrosine kinases (**Table 2**), and these functions must be performed in a variety of cell and organismal contexts. Thus, this versatility of cellular tyrosine kinases requires that they be complex proteins and carry a variety of ancillary domains in addition to their tyrosine kinase domain to be able to interact with various cellular proteins in the performance of these various functions. Src is a prototype for these multiple interactions because it has two domains in addition to that encoding its tyrosine kinase (**Figure 1b**), Src homology 2 (SH2) and Src homology 3 (SH3), as noted below, which are frequently found in associations among signalling components.

Mechanistic

The transfer of a signal from an extracellular factor through the membrane via a tyrosine kinase is usually performed by one of two types of mechanisms, exemplified in **Figures 2b** and **3a**. These two mechanisms use receptor and nonreceptor tyrosine kinases. In the first mechanism (**Figure 3a**) the receptor tyrosine kinase is solely responsible for the transfer of signal across the membrane. In the second mechanism (**Figure 2b**) a nonreceptor tyrosine kinase is coupled to a transmembrane receptor cytoplasmic domain in a binary receptor. In either case it is the activation of the tyrosine kinase accessible to the cytoplasm which is the key step in transferring the signal across the membrane. These mechanisms also define the two types of tyrosine kinases which have evolved (**Figure 1**) and the minimal domains necessary for each type of tyrosine kinase. The receptor tyrosine kinase must have an extracellular ligand-binding domain(s), a transmembrane domain, a kinase domain and sites for docking the cytoplasmic molecules to which the signal is transferred. The cytoplasmic tyrosine kinases must have the kinase domain, a binding domain for attaching to the receptor and sites for docking the cytoplasmic molecules to which the signal is transferred.

The transmission of signal from the kinase at the membrane to the nucleus for activation of transcription can

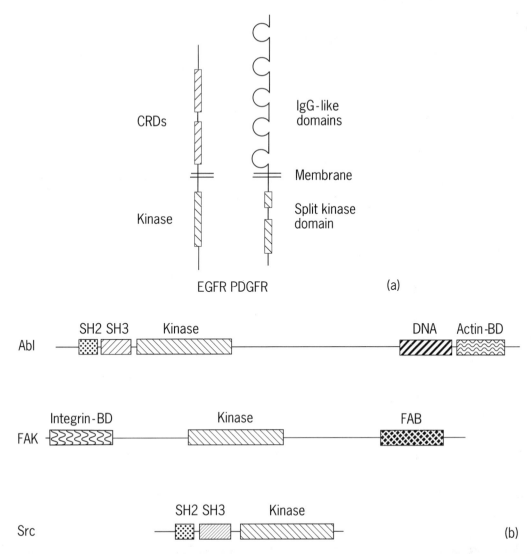

Figure 1   Schematic structures for receptor and nonreceptor protein tyrosine kinases, showing variations in the two classes. (a) Receptor tyrosine kinases ErbB1 (EGF receptor) and PDGF receptor, showing common variations in structure (see also **Table 6**). Ligand-binding sites are contained in the extracellular domains, which are highly variable between different receptor tyrosine kinase families (**Table 6**). CRD, cysteine-rich domain; IgG, immunoglobulin. (b) Nonreceptor (cytoplasmic) tyrosine kinases Abl, FAK and Src. Note the multiple binding domains in the nonreceptor kinases which link them to other functional components in the cell as part of their signalling functions. BD, binding domain; FAB, focal adhesion binding domain. (Adapted from Hunter, 1998.)

also occur by multiple pathways. Two of the most important are illustrated in **Figure 3b**, Ras–MAP kinase and JAK–STAT. The receptor–Ras-MAP kinase pathway consists of four main elements (**Figure 3a** and **b**; **Table 3**): the receptor which receives and transmits the signal through the membrane; an adaptor system (Grb2-SOS) which couples the receptor to a membrane switch (Ras); the Ras switch, which is activated by that coupling mechanism, then activates downstream kinases; and the MAP kinase cascade (Raf–MEK–Erk in **Figure 3**), which ultimately transmits the signal to the nucleus. The central feature of this pathway is the small G protein/GTPase Ras. It is switched on and off in response to its binding of the nucleotide GTP. The binding is controlled by three different types of regulatory proteins: activators which promote the Ras GTPase activity to convert bound GTP to GDP; exchange proteins which replace GDP with GTP; and inhibitors which reduce the GTPase activity. In addition, Ras is not simply an on/off switch. Depending on the cellular context, it can also switch the signal to a different pathway, activating different cell functions. The versatility of this mechanism is illustrated in **Table 4**, which shows some of the multiple downstream components to which Ras can be coupled, again illustrating the multiple cellular functions in which the tyrosine kinases can participate (**Table 2**). Obviously, the complexity of the Ras pathway provides many sites for regulation and for integration of signals by interactions with other pathways.

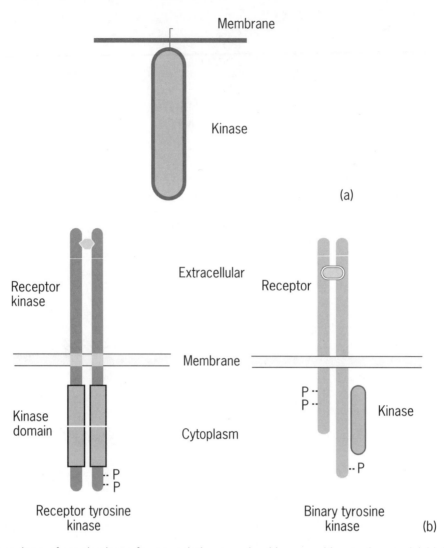

Figure 2   Comparison of mechanisms for associating tyrosine kinases with membrane. (a) Lipid-linked tyrosine kinase; (b) Comparison of structures for transmembrane receptor tyrosine kinases and binary receptor tyrosine kinases. The latter consists of a nonreceptor tyrosine kinase noncovalently linked to a nonenzymic transmembrane receptor.

In the JAK–STAT pathway (**Figure 3b**, also described in the previous chapter, Signalling by Cytokines) the tyrosine kinase JAK phosphorylates a STAT molecule, which translocates to the nucleus. This pathway has the advantage of being much simpler (**Figure 3**), but also has fewer opportunities for regulation.

RECEPTOR TYROSINE KINASES

Mechanism of Signal Transduction

The receptor tyrosine kinase provides a single transmembrane molecule which can transfer information across the membrane from the extracellular milieu to the cytoplasm. This transfer involves two related events: stimulation of

the kinase activity and phosphorylation of tyrosine residues accessible to the cytoplasm of the cell. In the most common model for this process, ligand binding to the extracellular domain results in dimerization of the receptor in the membrane (**Figures 2b**, **3a** and **4**). This mechanism has been demonstrated by high-resolution X-ray crystallographic analysis for the growth hormone receptor activated by its dimeric ligand (Wells, 1996). In some cases the receptors may form larger complexes (e.g. tetramers). Regardless, the receptor association leads to potentiation of the kinase activity, probably through structural (conformational) changes in the kinase domain. The second phase of the information transfer involves the phosphorylation of one or more tyrosine residues of the cytoplasmic domain of the receptor (**Figure 4**). Available evidence suggests that this occurs primarily through cross-phosphorylation (*trans*-phosphorylation). In a receptor

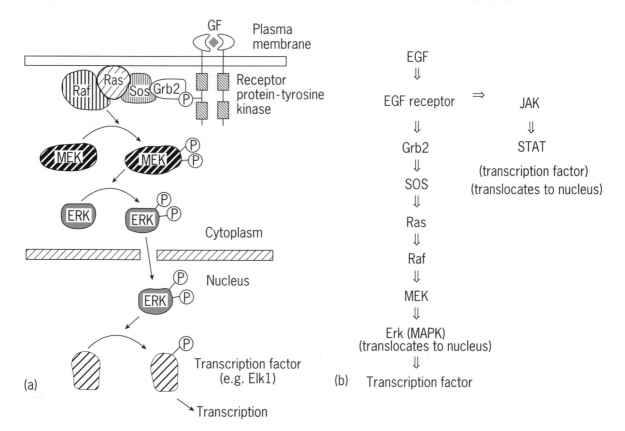

Figure 3 Signal transmission from the extracellular space to the nucleus to activate transcription via the Ras-MAP kinase pathway. (a) Signal translocation; GF, growth factor (b) Comparison of Ras-MAP kinase pathway with JAK–STAT pathway. (Adapted from Hunter, 1998.)

Table 2 Examples of cellular functions regulated by tyrosine kinases

Cell function	Receptor[a]	Downstream effectors[a]
Proliferation	**ErbB**	Ras–Erk (MAPK)
Cell–matrix adhesion	Integrin	**FAK-Src**
Cell–cell adhesion	Cadherin	Catenin-**Src** family
Movement	**PDGFR**	Rac–Rho
Apoptosis control	**IGFR**	PI3K–Akt
Transcription	Cytokine R	**JAK**–STAT
Membrane transport	Channel	**Src** family

[a]Tyrosine kinases are indicated in bold. FAK, focal adhesion kinase; PDGFR, platelet-derived growth factor receptor; IGFR, insulin-like growth factor receptor; PI3K, phosphoinositide 3-kinase; STAT, signal transduction and transcription.

The primary function of the phosphorylated tyrosine residues on the activated receptors is to recruit signalling components from the cytoplasm or cytoplasmic surface of the plasma membrane to initiate signalling pathways (**Figures 3a** and **4**) (Panayotou and Waterfield, 1993). The particular pathway initiated is determined by two complementary factors: the site of the tyrosine on the receptor polypeptide chain and the specificity of the phosphotyrosine-binding domains on the cytoplasmic proteins. The sites of tyrosine phosphorylation on a particular receptor are determined by the ligand–receptor and receptor–receptor interactions, which regulate the accessibility of any particular tyrosine to the kinase catalytic site. Two different types of domains have been found in signalling components which bind to phosphotyrosines to initiate their recruitment to the receptor: SH2 (see **Figures 1b** and **5**) and PTB (**Figure 5**). The SH2 domain is a compact globular unit of about 100 amino acids, which was originally discovered in Src and is found in a large number of signalling components (**Table 5**). Its binding specificity is determined primarily by the phosphotyrosine and 1–5 amino acid residues following it (C-terminal direction) in the receptor amino acid sequence. The PTB domain is also globular and has about 150 amino acids; its specificity is determined by the phosphotyrosine and 1–8 amino acid residues preceding it (N-terminal direction) in the receptor

dimer the kinase on one receptor (half-dimer) would phosphorylate tyrosines on the associated receptor (half-dimer) and vice versa. Thus, the ligand-induced association not only activates the enzyme, but also brings the enzyme and its substrate tyrosine residues into proximity. The significance of the tyrosine phosphorylation is that the phosphotyrosine residues created form sites at which cytoplasmic proteins can bind to initiate intracellular signalling (see **Figure 3a**), thus passing a signal across the membrane without the passage of the activating ligand.

Table 3 Components of pathways regulating transcription

Receptor–Ras–MAPK pathway		Receptor–JAK–STAT pathway	
Component	**Function**	**Component**	**Function**
EGFR	Receptor	EGFR	Receptor
Grb2	Adaptor	JAK	Nonreceptor tyrosine kinase
SOS	GTP exchange protein	STAT	Transcription factor
Ras	G protein switch		
Raf	Ser/Thr kinase		
MEK	Dual-function Tyr/Thr kinase		
Erk (MAPK)	Ser/Thr kinase		
Transcription factor	Transcription factor		

Table 4 Examples of signalling elements and cellular functions coupled to Ras activation

Signalling component	Potential cell function[a]
Rac	Shape, movement
RalGDS	Shape, movement
P120 GAP	Shape, movement
Raf	Transcription, proliferation
PI3K	Proliferation, apoptosis resistance
MEKK	Transcription, stress reaction

[a] Listed functions are illustrative, not inclusive.

sequence. Other types of phosphotyrosine-binding domains have been suggested, but have not been well characterized.

These observations indicate that most components initiating signalling pathways from receptor tyrosine kinases should contain either SH2 or PTB domains. Indeed, identification of proteins with these domains has provided significant insights into signalling. As shown in **Table 5** and **Figure 5**, these proteins include three classes of signalling pathway initiators: enzymes, docking proteins and adaptors. Each of these types of molecules facilitates signalling by a different mechanism. Enzymes actively participate in downstream signalling events. Docking proteins provide additional or surrogate tyrosine phosphorylation sites for further diversification of receptor sites to initiate signalling. Adaptors are involved in assembling complexes of signalling components for initiating and regulating downstream signalling pathways. However, in all three types of mechanisms the key aspect of the pathway is the recruitment and relocalization of the signalling component to the site of the receptor (exemplified by Grb2 in **Figure 3a**) (Panayotou and Waterfield, 1993; Carraway and Carraway, 1995).

Four different rationales can be envisioned for the recruitment of enzymes to initiate signalling pathways. First, recruitment can permit the receptor tyrosine kinase to phosphorylate the recruited molecule, thus changing its activity or binding function. An example of this is phospholipase Cγ, whose recruitment and phosphorylation activates a phospholipid-cleaving enzyme to stimulate a pathway leading to calcium influx into the cytoplasm (**Figure 6**). The calcium plus lipid hydrolysis product diacylglycerol combine to stimulate a potent calcium-dependent serine/threonine protein kinase, protein kinase C, which then has multiple cellular effects. Second, recruitment brings the recruited molecule to the membrane, where it may act upon membrane components as substrates. This mechanism applies to phospholipase Cγ, which cleaves phospholipid molecules found in membranes, and to phosphoinositide 3-kinase, one of the signalling enzymes implicated in oncogenesis, which phosphorylates specific phospholipid molecules in membranes (**Figure 6**). These enzymatic modifications of membrane components may change the organisation of the membranes or produce new signalling molecules, such as the lipid phosphate PIP$_2$, to initiate and perpetuate downstream signalling pathways. It is important to note that the same signalling molecule may initiate different signalling pathways, depending on the cellular context. Both PI3 kinase and phospholipase Cγ can be involved in multiple cellular functions, as previously indicated for Ras (**Table 4**). Third, binding of a molecule to the receptor phosphotyrosine residues may induce its activation by a conformational change (allosteric effect), a mechanism which contributes to the signalling effects of phosphoinositide 3-kinase (**Tables 2** and **4**; **Figure 6**). Fourth, some of the recruited enzymes are protein tyrosine kinases or protein tyrosine phosphatases. Since the receptor tyrosine kinases are often involved in large, multimeric signalling complexes (Carraway and Carraway, 1995), such as focal adhesion sites (see below), this recruitment brings the additional kinases and phosphatases into proximity of their substrates in these complexes and facilitates regulation of the signalling components involved. An important aspect of such complexes is that they are often located at sites influencing cell behaviour, such as sites for membrane-microfilament interactions involved in cell shape and movement (Carraway et al., 1997).

Recruitment of proteins can also amplify signalling potential through the docking protein mechanism. The

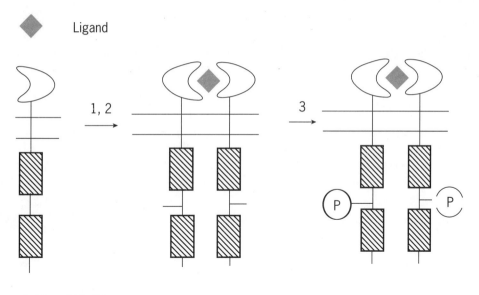

1. Ligand binding

2. Receptor dimerization

3. Cross-phosphorylation

Figure 4   Mechanism for transmission of signal across the membrane by binding of ligand, dimerization of receptor and transphosphorylation of cytoplasmic domain to create sites for recruitment of cytoplasmic signalling components to initiate signalling pathways.

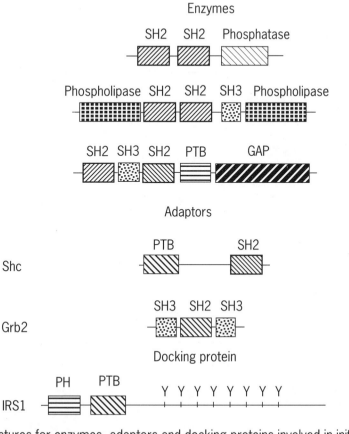

Figure 5   Schematic structures for enzymes, adaptors and docking proteins involved in initiating cellular signalling pathways by binding to tyrosine-phosphorylated receptors or binary receptor complexes. GAP, GTPase activating protein. (Adapted from Hunter, 1998.)

best characterized docking proteins are the insulin receptor substrates (IRSs, **Figure 5**), which regulate a variety of cellular functions, including membrane transport, gene expression, protein synthesis and lipid and carbohydrate metabolism. IRSs contain a PTB domain (**Figure 5**) which allows them to bind the activated insulin receptor. Formation of this insulin–IRS complex increases the number of tyrosines available for phosphorylation and increases the insulin receptor signalling potential. More-over, IRSs act via multiple receptors, including the insulin-like growth factor (IGF) receptor and various cytokine receptors. Phosphorylated tyrosines on IRSs can interact with a variety of SH2-containing components to activate multiple downstream signalling pathways. Among these are the adaptors Grb2, Crk and Nck (**Figure 5**), the phospholipid kinase PI3 kinase, the tyrosine kinase Fyn and the phosphotyrosine phosphatase SHP2 (**Figure 5**).

Adaptor molecules participate in the recruitment and organisation of signalling components from the cytoplasm into membrane complexes. The best studied example is the initiation of the Ras–MAP kinase mitogenic pathway by the adaptor Grb2 (**Figure 3a**). Grb2 contains both SH2 and SH3 domains, allowing it to link a tyrosine-phosphorylated receptor to a cytoplasmic SH3-binding protein containing a proline-rich motif. In the cytoplasm of unactivated cells Grb2 is present as a complex through its SH3 domain with a second protein SOS, a GTP exchange protein which activates Ras. Activation of ErbB1 (EGF receptor) by its ligand EGF creates a phosphotyrosine binding site for the Grb2 SH2 domain on the receptor, recruiting the Grb2–SOS complex from the cytoplasm to the plasma membrane. When associated with the membrane, SOS can bind to and activate the proto-oncogene product Ras. Activated Ras stimulates a series of serine/threonine protein kinases, culminating in the activation of a specific MAP kinase (Erk), which can migrate to the nucleus as a signal for inducing gene transcription (**Figure 3a** and **b**). The key step in initiation is the linkage of the Ras switch protein to the ErbB receptor via the adaptor Grb2. As noted previously, Ras also has the potential to activate other signalling pathways (**Table 4**).

Table 5 Phosphotyrosine-binding proteins which could activate or diversify signalling pathways by binding phosphorylated receptors

Protein	Class/function	Domains
PLC-γ	Phospholipase	SH2 (2), SH3
GAP	GTPase activator	SH2, SH3
Src family	PTK	SH2, SH3
ZAP/SYK	PTK	SH2 (2)
Shp1/2	Tyrosine phosphatase	SH2 (2)
PI3K	Lipid kinase	SH2 (2), SH3
Ship	Lipid phosphatase	SH2
Vav	GTP exhange factor	SH2, SH3
Shc	Adaptor	SH2, PTB
Nck	Adaptor	SH2, SH3 (3)
Grb2, Crk	Adaptor	SH2, SH3 (2)
IRS1/2	Docking protein	PTB
Talin	Focal adhesion protein	SH2
STAT	Transcription factor	SH2, SH3

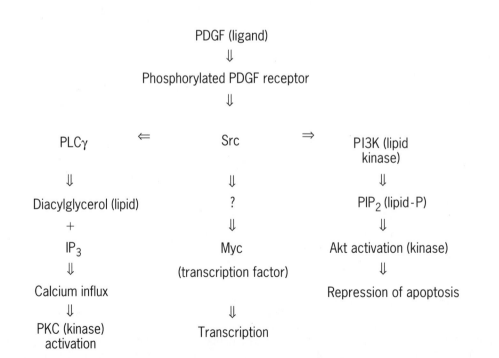

PDGF (ligand)
⇓
Phosphorylated PDGF receptor
⇓

PLCγ ⇐ Src ⇒ PI3K (lipid kinase)

⇓   ⇓   ⇓

Diacylglycerol (lipid)   ?   PIP$_2$ (lipid-P)

+   ⇓   ⇓

IP$_3$ Myc   Akt activation (kinase)

⇓   (transcription factor)   ⇓

Calcium influx   Repression of apoptosis

⇓   ⇓

PKC (kinase) activation   Transcription

Figure 6   Examples of multiple downstream pathways coupled to receptor phosphorylation of PDGF receptor.

Versatility of Receptor Tyrosine Kinase Signalling

One of the hallmarks of the receptor tyrosine kinase mechanism is its versatility, mediating signal transduction via multiple pathways in different organisms, tissues and cells. This versatility allows these enzymes to regulate many of the vast number of cellular processes and interactions required in the development and function of complex multicellular organisms. The bases for the versatility are several-fold, the first being the multiplicity of receptors. There are a minimum of 20 families of mammalian receptor tyrosine kinases, each with different ligand-binding domains and most with multiple members (**Table 6**). Thus, part of the versatility of the receptor tyrosine kinase mechanism arises from the diversity of ligand–receptor interactions available in different tissues of different organisms at different times. Second, many of these individual receptor kinases can bind more than one ligand, as exemplified by the ligand binding patterns of the class I (ErbB) family (**Table 7**), leading to signal diversification. Third, the distribution of receptors in the organism is tissue and cell dependent. Some receptors are widely distributed; others are specifically localized to a small number of sites. Tumours may have aberrant distributions of receptors. Fourth, the distribution of many receptor tyrosine kinases and their ligands is developmentally regulated, being found only during specific stages of the life history of the organism. Fifth, ligands are produced at different sites from the target cells to exert different levels of control, as shown by examples in **Table 8**. Endocrine ligands are produced in different organs and transmitted through the circulation to the site of action. Paracrine ligands are produced by a different cell type or tissue from the target cells, but near the target. The juxtacrine mechanism is a special case of the paracrine ligand in which the ligand and receptor are expressed on the plasma membranes of adjacent cells. Autocrine responses arise from ligands produced by the same cell (cell type) as the receptor-bearing target cell. The intracrine and intramembrane mechanisms are special cases of the autocrine response, in which ligand and receptor are produced in the same cell.

The receptor structure itself contributes to the diversification of signals. Each receptor contains multiple

Table 6   Multiplicity of receptor tyrosine kinases

Receptor family	Extracellular domain[a]	Number in family
ErbB	Cysteine rich	4
PDGF	Ig	5
FLT	Ig	3
Insulin	Cysteine rich, FN III	2
TRK	Ig, leucine rich	3
FGF	Ig, acid box	4
Eph	FN III, CR, Ig	14
Axl	Ig, FN III	3
TIE	Ig, EGF, FN III	2
RET	Cadherin	1
MET	Sema	2
ROR	Ig, CR, kringle	2
MCK10	Factor VIII	2
MuSK	Ig	1
CCK4	Ig	1
ROS	FNIII	1

[a] Ig, immunoglobulin-like; FNIII, fibronectin III-like; CR, cysteine rich.

Table 7   Ligand–receptor couples for the ErbB family

Receptor	Soluble ligands
ErbB1	EGF, TGFα, amphiregulin, HB-EGF, betacellulin, epiregulin
ErbB2	None known
ErbB3	Neuregulins
ErbB4	Neuregulins, HB-EGF, betacellulin, epiregulin

Table 8   Examples of ligand sources and binding mechanisms

Mechanism	Ligand	Receptor	Definition	Example
Endocrine	Insulin	Insulin R	Ligand reaches receptor through circulation	Pancreatic cell insulin; fat cell receptor
Paracrine	Neuregulin	ErbB3	Ligand produced by adjacent cell or tissue	Mesenchymal NRG; epithelial ErbB3
Autocrine	TGF-α	ErbB1	Ligand secreted by same cell bearing receptor	TGF-α secretion by tumour cells with ErbB1
Intracrine	v-sis	PDGF R	Ligand and receptor interact inside cell	v-sis binding to PDGF R in cells
Juxtacrine	Bride of Sevenless (BOSS)	Sevenless	Ligand and receptor in plasma membranes of adjacent cells	BOSS-Sevenless interaction in control of Drosophila eye development
Intramembrane	MUC4	ErbB2	Ligand and receptor in same membrane	MUC4/ErbB2 complexes in tumour cells and epithelia

Table 9 Phosphorylated tyrosine-binding sites for signalling components in PDGF

Sequence position	Binding protein	Class[a]
579	Src, STAT	PTK, TF
581	STAT	TF
716	Grb2	Adaptor
740	PI3K	Lipid kinase
751	Nck, PI3K	Adaptor, LK
771	GAP	GTPase activator
775	STAT	TF
778	Grb7	Adaptor
1009	SHP-2	Tyrosine phosphatase
1021	PLC-γ	Phospholipase

[a] PTK, protein tyrosine kinase; TF, transcription factor; LK, lipid kinase.

tyrosine residues in its cytoplasmic domains which can be phosphorylated to form different binding sites for cytoplasmic signalling proteins. For example, the PDGF receptor contains at least 10 tyrosine residues which have been shown to be phosphorylated in response to ligand activation (**Table 9**). Each different phosphorylated tyrosine potentially represents a different signalling pathway which could be initiated (Claesson-Welsh, 1994), some of which are shown in **Figure 6**, though overlaps and redundancies inevitably reduce that number. By comparing **Table 9** with **Tables 2** and **4**, it is clear that the PDGF receptor has the potential for participating in a large number of cellular functions. Diversity and specificity of signalling are achieved in part by phosphorylation of different combinations of the tyrosine residues in response to different extracellular ligands, an example of a combinatorial mechanism for regulation. A second diversification and specificity mechanism arises from the type of receptor association during receptor activation. Formation of a heterodimer by two different molecules of a receptor family obviously can yield more different phosphorylated tyrosine residues than formation of a homodimer by two identical molecules from the same family. Thus, the number of potential signals is increased. In the case of the ErbB family of receptors (**Table 7**), the four receptors can form 10 different combinations of homodimers and heterodimers in response to different ligands, all of which have been observed and have potentially different signalling capabilities (Riese and Stern, 1998). For this family of receptors, heterodimerization appears to be the preferred mechanism of activation in many physiological contexts (Riese and Stern, 1998).

Regulation of Receptor Tyrosine Kinase Signalling

The complex signalling pathway from the receptor to the nucleus (**Figure 3**, ErbB1 through MAP kinase) involves at least seven different components and provides multiple levels of control of the signal. In any phosphorylation-dependent system, one obvious control mechanism is the removal of the phosphate(s). In a complex chain involving multiple phosphorylations, reversal of any phosphorylation event can potentially break the chain and block the signal. Cells contain a large variety of phosphatases to hydrolyse phosphotyrosine and phosphoserine/threonine residues (Streuli,1996; Cohen, 1997). Contrary to early expectations that phosphatases would provide nonspecific 'off' switches for kinase signalling, both serine/threonine and tyrosine phosphatases exhibit considerable specificity. They even participate directly in the activation of protein tyrosine kinases such as Src family members, as described below. As with the tyrosine kinases, both membrane and nonmembrane forms of tyrosine phosphatases have been observed. Both also contain multiple domains which regulate their associations and locations in cells. Although membrane tyrosine phosphatases contain multiple types of extracellular domains (Streuli, 1996), it is not clear whether they can act as true receptors, since no ligand activation mechanisms for their enzyme activities are known.

Ligand-activated receptor tyrosine kinases can also be regulated by controlling the availability of the ligand to the receptor. Ligands are often synthesized from high molecular weight membrane precursors, which are cleaved proteolytically to release the ligand. Thus, ligand release and availability are determined in part by the activity of the protease(s) involved in the cleavage. One of the factors regulating these proteases is calcium-dependent protein kinase C. Ligand degradation may also contribute to determining ligand availability. Ligand binding to some receptors triggers endocytosis of the ligand–receptor complex into the cell (Sorkin and Waters, 1993), which can lead to three possible fates: (1) the complex may dissociate and the ligand transfer to lysosomes for degradation, while the receptor recycles to the cell surface; (2) the complex may transfer to the lysosome for degradation of both components; (3) both components may recycle to the cell surface. Either mechanism for degrading the ligand reduces its availability. Finally, ligand availability may be determined by interactions with extracellular components, both positively and negatively (Schlessinger et al., 1995). Many ligands contain positively charged amino acid sequences which interact with glycosaminoglycans (GAGs), such as heparin, at the cell surface or in the extracellular matrix. This interaction may affect ligand availability in two ways. In a positive sense cell-surface GAGs or other cell-surface components may recruit ligands to the cell surface and vicinity of the receptors. Cell-surface components, such as GAGs, may also act as coreceptors to form multimeric complexes with ligands and receptors which facilitate the activation of the receptor kinases. In a negative sense GAGs may sequester ligands away from their receptors. By combining the two mechanisms, ligands in a tissue may be held in a GAG 'reservoir' until they are released by an acute event that frees the ligand and consequently initiates receptor activation. Soluble ligand-binding proteins are produced by some tissues and sequester extracellular ligands. For example, a whole family of binding proteins regulate the availability of insulin-like growth factors.

Receptor activation can also be determined by receptor availability, often dictated by receptor turnover, as described above for ligand–receptor complex endocytosis and degradation. These mechanisms appear to be rather receptor specific. For example, ligand binding induces turnover of ErbB1 (EGF receptor) more readily than other ErbB family members. A second aspect of receptor availability is localization. This may occur at either the cellular or subcellular level. At the cellular level only certain cell types or cells in specific locations may contain a given receptor in a tissue. At the subcellular level the receptor location may be restricted to a specific region of the cell surface, e.g. to cell–cell contacts. Localization is particularly important to receptors which act by juxtacrine mechanisms (**Table 8**), since they require appropriate cell–cell contacts for their activation. One example is the Eph family of receptors (**Table 6**), which guide movements of cells and neuronal growth cones in establishing neuronal connections. The mechanism for guidance control involves a repulsive reaction to juxtacrine association of an Eph receptor with its complementary Ephrin ligand on an adjacent cell. This behaviour not only emphasizes the importance of location, but also suggests the possibility of reciprocal signalling, in which both the receptor and ligand initiate pathways and responses to the contact. Once again, this unusual mechanism underlines the diversity which has evolved in receptor tyrosine kinase functions to regulate cellular behaviours in multicellular organisms.

Although ligand-dependent activation is the most common means for stimulation of receptor tyrosine kinase pathways, other mechanisms have been proposed. Overexpression of ErbB2 is sufficient for activation of receptor phosphorylation and cell transformation in some types of cells and has been implicated in neoplasia. One explanation for this effect is that the receptors associate when their concentration reaches a certain level in the membrane, triggering kinase activation and cross-phosphorylation, although the participation of other factors cannot be ruled out. One possible example of indirect activation of ErbB2 through multimerization involves the cell surface molecule CD44, a receptor for the extracellular GAG hyaluronic acid. CD44 has been observed to associate with ErbB2. Hyaluronic acid, an extracellular matrix component, can bind and aggregate CD44 in the cell membrane, thus also aggregating ErbB2 and inducing its activation. Other indirect mechanisms for initiating receptor tyrosine kinase signalling pathways are less easily rationalized. These include stimulation of G protein-coupled receptors, activation by cytokines, cellular stress responses, cell adhesion and membrane depolarization. One possible explanation for these other ligand-independent signalling mechanisms

is that the receptors are not acting as enzymes in these instances, but merely serving as docking proteins such as the IRSs (see above) which are phosphorylated by cytoplasmic tyrosine kinases, such as Src, activated by these other signalling mechanisms. An alternative possibility is that these additional mechanisms trigger proteolytic activities which release ligands from their precursors or sequestration sites to activate receptor tyrosine kinases.

Not surprisingly, ligand mimics have evolved which can modulate receptor signalling. In the fruit fly the secreted protein Argos contains an EGF-like domain and blocks signalling through the ErbB family tyrosine kinase receptor, probably acting as a competitor for the activating ligands. In contrast, mammalian epithelia contain a mucin Muc4 with an EGF-like domain which binds to ErbB2 and potentiates ligand-activated phosphorylation through heterodimer ErbB2/ErbB3. The sequence of each of these mimics differs slightly from the sequences of activating ligands of the receptors. Other receptor-binding proteins associate with the receptor extracellular domains to influence ligand binding and signalling or with the cytoplasmic domain to modulate downstream signalling, although the exact mechanisms have not been well studied. Receptor 'desensitization' is a common phenomenon for many types of receptors, including tyrosine kinases. A frequent mechanism involves phosphorylation of the receptor at specific sites to repress its activity. For example, ErbB1 (EGF receptor) can be desensitized by phosphorylation of serine residues in its cytoplasmic juxtamembrane domain by protein kinase C.

BINARY RECEPTORS

Activation of the JAK/STAT Pathway

Binary receptors consist of a nonmembrane tyrosine kinase subunit noncovalently associated at the cytoplasmic surface of the plasma membrane with a transmembrane receptor (**Figure 2b**). One advantage of the dual subunit system is the ability to 'mix and match' different gene products for the two subunits to create a broader array of different signalling units from the same amount of genetic information, increasing the diversity of signalling potential. Moreover, binary receptors often contain multiple receptor (nonkinase) subunits to provide further specificity and diversity. However, the mechanism of signal transduction across the membrane is remarkably similar to that of the single subunit receptor tyrosine kinases. Binding of ligand to the receptor induces dimerization or multimerization of the receptor with concomitant activation of the kinase. Cross-phosphorylation can then occur on both the receptor and kinase subunits, creating binding sites for cytoplasmic proteins with SH2 or PTB domains. In the case of the binary cytokine receptors (reviewed in detail in the previous chapter, *Signalling by Cytokines*), the associated tyrosine kinases are the Janus kinases (JAKs). The JAKs participate with signal transducing and transcription (STAT) factors in a direct mechanism for regulating transcription (**Figure 3b**). STATs are recruited to phosphorylated receptors via their SH2 domains. Tyrosine phosphorylation of the STATs by receptor-associated JAKs creates SH2 binding sites which can interact reciprocally with the STAT SH2 domains to induce STAT dimerization. The STAT dimers translocate to the nucleus, where they are able to regulate gene transcription (see the previous chapter, *Signalling by TGF-β* for details). The JAK/STAT pathway is thus more direct than the Ras–MAP kinase pathway, which also regulates cell transcriptional activity. Moreover, the JAK/STAT pathway can also be initiated by some receptor tyrosine kinases, such as ErbB1. Conversely, adaptors such as Grb2 are able to bind to some cytokine receptor phosphotyrosines to couple them to Ras and the MAP kinase signalling pathway, and IRS docking proteins can link them to multiple signalling elements. Thus, there appears to be substantial redundancy in signalling pathways. A major concern in signalling research is the molecular mechanisms for coordinating different signalling pathways, whether they derive from the same receptor (pleiotropy) or from different receptors (cross-talk).

Lymphocyte T cell Complex

Even more complex binary receptor tyrosine kinase complexes participate in lymphocyte regulation (Peterson and Koretzky, 1998), as exemplified by the T cell receptor complex. T lymphocytes are the immune cells responsible for defence against invading organisms, such as bacteria and viruses. The T cell has evolved a very sophisticated mechanism for recognizing invader cells, involving recognition of specific proteins unique to the invaders. However, rather than recognizing the intact protein, specialized cells of the immune system degrade the foreign proteins to peptides, which can then be 'presented' for recognition at their cell surfaces. This antigen presentation is performed by a cell-surface protein complex called the major histocompatibility complex (MHC). It is the recognition of the foreign peptide on the MHC molecule by a receptor on the T cell (T cell receptor) that triggers T cell activation. The recognition and activation processes are finely tuned to provide a graded response to the foreign material.

The interaction of the peptide on the MHC of the 'antigen-presenting cell' with the T cell receptor on the T cell is a juxtacrine response (**Table 8**). Moreover, the T cell receptor itself is a highly complex moiety, a multi-component binary receptor. The full receptor contains at least nine polypeptides which can interact with four tyrosine kinases and one or more tyrosine phosphatases. Presumably, this complexity facilitates the regulation of the receptor signalling to provide a graded response instead of a switch (on/off) type of response. The signal development can be best presented as a timed series of events. The T cell receptor initially contains two types of moieties. The peptide recognition moiety is a heterodimer of two transmembrane proteins (α/β or γ/δ, depending on the T cell type) which bind the peptide on the juxtaposed antigen-presenting cell (**Figure 7**). This receptor

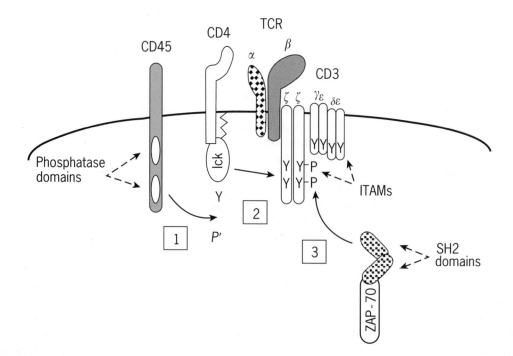

Figure 7 Schematic structure of T cell receptor and some key events in T cell receptor signalling. ITAM, immunoreceptor tyrosine-based activation motif. (From Peterson and Koretsky, 1998, *Clinical and Experimental Rheumatology*, **17**, 107-114.)

heterodimer is associated with two additional transmembrane complexes, a heterodimer and a heterotetramer (CD3). These complexes appear to serve a dual function. First, they act as the tail of a binary receptor to bind specific tyrosine kinases of the Src family for signal initiation. Second, they contain specific sequences called immunoreceptor tyrosine-based activation motifs (ITAMs) which can be phosphorylated to provide binding sites for proteins with SH2 domains, thus serving the function of docking proteins. The kinetic model for T cell activation proceeds when the T cell receptor is engaged by the peptide on the MHC complex of the adjacent cell. This engagement leads to dimerization of the T cell receptor and activation of an associated Src family kinase Fyn. The activated kinase can then phosphorylate the ITAM motifs of the docking proteins to provide recruitment sites for additional molecules. One of the recruited molecules is CD4 (or CD8, depending on the cell type), a binary coreceptor containing a transmembrane component and a second member of the Src family Ick. The CD4 association stabilizes the T cell receptor dimer and provides additional sites for recruitment of SH2-containing components. Among the components recruited to the phosphotyrosine sites created by the Src family members are two additional tyrosine kinases of another family, Zap and Syk.

The result of this complex series of manoeuvers is to recruit a collection of initiators of signalling pathways (**Figure 5** and **Table 5**) to activate the multiple functions of the T cell. The initiators include PLCγ, PI3 kinase, a Ras activator called Vav and the adaptor proteins Shc and Grb2. The activities of the tyrosine kinases are tightly regulated by ancillary molecules. Since Src family kinases can be both positively and negatively regulated by tyrosine phosphorylation (see below), these regulators include the membrane tyrosine phosphatases CD45 and SHP-1 and the nonreceptor tyrosine kinase Csk. CD45 is an activator, while SHP-1 and Csk are both inhibitors of Src family members. The activation mechanisms for Src family members are described in more detail below. Thus, the balance of these activating and inhibiting activities provides mechanisms for generating graded responses. Many of the specifics of the temporal associations and the regulation remain to be discovered, but the T cell receptor provides a clear example of how the binary receptor tyrosine kinase model has evolved to provide a very specific, highly regulated function for higher organisms.

Focal Adhesions

The focal adhesion complex provides another example of the application of the binary receptor principle to a primary cell function. The key tyrosine kinase in this case is the focal adhesion kinase (FAK, see **Figure 1b**). Focal adhesions are sites of cell attachment to the extracellular matrix (see chapter on *the Extracellular Matrix: The Networking Solution*) and of microfilaments to the plasma membrane. Thus, they play a critical role in the determination of cell shape and cell movement (Carraway *et al.*, 1997). Furthermore, cell attachment through focal adhesions has been shown to be necessary for normal progression through the cell cycle for cell proliferation. One of the hallmarks of neoplastic transformation is the ability of the transformed cells to escape this adhesion requirement. Focal adhesions are extremely complex structures, containing dozens of components (Carraway *et al.*, 1997). Precise assembly and disassembly of these structures is necessary for their roles in cell movements and growth regulation. The objective here is to show how the binary model and tyrosine phosphorylation can contribute to the dynamics of these structures.

The receptors involved in the formation of focal adhesions are integrins, a family containing two types of subunits (α and β), which combine to form a large number of different heterodimeric receptors with different specificities for extracellular matrix components. Ligand binding and aggregation of integrin heterodimers induces their oligomerization in the membrane and recruitment of the nonreceptor tyrosine kinase FAK (**Figure 1B**) from the cytoplasm. This event also stimulates tyrosine phosphorylation of FAK, providing SH2 binding sites for the recruitment of Src. Additional phosphorylation of FAK creates sites for binding docking proteins paxillin and Cas. FAK appears to serve as both kinase and docking protein in these complexes, similar to the cytoplasmic domain of a receptor tyrosine kinase. The combined binding sites in these proteins can initiate further recruitment through SH2 domains and other mechanisms of both structural components of the focal adhesion, such as the actin-binding proteins tensin, talin, vinculin and α-actinin, and signalling pathway components. Included among the latter are PLCγ, PI3 kinase, members of the MAP kinase cascade, members of the Src family and the small G proteins Rac and Rho. These small G proteins are relatives of Ras and act as signalling switches for the processes involved in the organisation of microfilaments in cell movements. One of the enzymes recruited is Csk, which can then serve as a regulator of the Src family members. Thus, the tyrosine kinase FAK, acting through a binary receptor mechanism, is able to initiate the assembly of an extremely complex multimeric structure which is critical to multiple cell functions required for cell movements, such as those involved in tumour invasion.

Src Regulation

Since Src family members play such important roles in many cellular processes involving binary receptors, one of the critical questions in understanding these signalling processes is how the Src activity is regulated. This regulation can most easily be considered as an autorepression mechanism (Hubbard *et al.*, 1998) which limits access to the kinase site for catalysis by folding the Src molecule

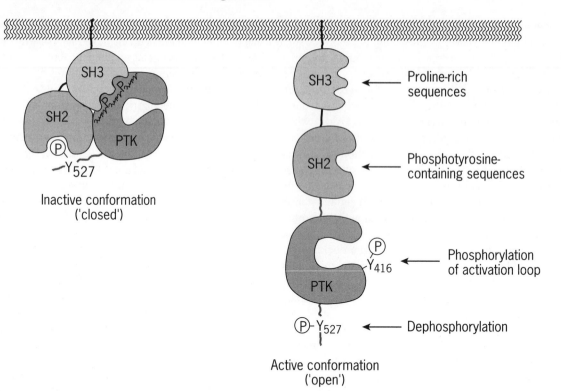

Figure 8 Autorepression/autoactivation model for Src family kinases. (From Hubbard *et al.*, 1998, *Journal of Biological Chemistry*, **273**, 11987-11990.)

into a more compact structure (**Figure 8**). Two interactions are particularly important: (1) the binding of the Src SH3 domain to the peptide linking the SH2 and kinase domains and (2) the binding of the SH2 domain to a phosphorylated tyrosine in the C-terminal tail. Both of these intramolecular interactions must be weak, because they can be displaced by external agents with activation of the enzyme. Thus, Src can be activated by binding appropriate SH3-containing proteins or proteins with SH3-binding motifs. Src can also be activated by protein tyrosine phosphatases, such as CD45 (see **Figure 7**) which cleave the C-terminal phosphotyrosine. Conversely, active Src can be inactivated by phosphorylation of the C-terminal tyrosine by Csk. Activation of Src is also promoted by phosphorylation of a tyrosine near the kinase site to prevent folding of the protein into the compact, inactive form.

NONRECEPTOR TYROSINE KINASE MECHANISMS

Abl

The large number of signalling pathways and cellular functions regulated by the receptor tyrosine kinase and binary receptor mechanisms raises the question whether tyrosine kinases act by any other mode. Unfortunately, it is often difficult to distinguish nonreceptor from receptor mechanisms at the cell level. One highly studied nonreceptor kinase is Abl. Abl is a multidomain molecule whose N-terminal half is similar to the Src family (kinase, SH3 and SH2 domains), but whose C-terminal half has DNA-binding, microfilament-binding and nuclear localization motifs (**Figure 1b**) (Zou and Calame, 1999). Abl is most familiar as the oncogene associated with chronic myelogenous leukaemia. In this cancer Abl is activated as a consequence of a chromosome translocation encoding a fusion protein of Abl and Bcr (breakpoint cluster region). This chimaeric protein appears to be primarily localized to microfilaments in cells. In contrast, normal unactivated Abl is primarily a nuclear protein, although it is able to shuttle between the nucleus and cytoplasmic microfilaments in response to cell adhesion. In the nucleus Abl has been implicated in responses to DNA damage and in cell cycle progression by virtue of its ability to bind p53 and pRb, respectively, both of which are transcription regulators and tumour suppressors. The specific mechanisms for these responses are yet unclear. Abl can also bind RNA polymerase II, the Crk adaptor (**Table 5**) and the protein tyrosine phosphatase SHP1 (**Table 5**). Abl has been implicated in numerous signalling pathways, including those involving PI3K, PKC, Ras, JAK/STAT and Rac. Thus, it has the capacity for participating in multiple cellular functions, arising from both the binding of SH2-containing proteins to its phosphotyrosines and other proteins to other domains or motifs. Other tyrosine kinases which function by nonreceptor mechanisms probably act similarly, although probably not as globally.

Membrane transport and tyrosine kinases

A more direct action of nonreceptor tyrosine kinases is suggested by studies of nonreceptor tyrosine kinase effects on channel activities (Thomas and Brugge, 1997). For example, Src binds K^+ ion channels and induces their phosphorylation, which decreases channel activity. In other cases the relationship between channel function and tyrosine kinase activity is less clear. Aggregation of acetylcholine receptor ion channels can lead to tyrosine phosphorylation of the receptor and association of nonreceptor kinase with the receptor. This and other kinase-channel interaction mechanisms resemble the binary receptor tyrosine kinases, although the consequences for downstream signalling in the specific cases are often unclear. In a number of cases Src family kinases can be activated via ion fluxes into cells through regulated channels. The mechanisms of these activations are varied, involving both receptor and nonreceptor processes. These examples again underline the versatility of the tyrosine kinase functions in many aspects of cell function.

SIGNALLING PATHWAYS AND CELLULAR FUNCTIONS OF TYROSINE KINASES

It should be obvious from the previous sections that tyrosine kinases can initiate multiple signalling pathways. In trying to understand the cellular functions of these kinases, it is useful to describe the downstream effectors and biological effects of these pathways. Such analyses are complicated by the fact that information about some of the pathways is incomplete. Moreover, many of the pathways are branched and have multiple effects. Finally, there are intersections of some pathways which cannot easily be represented by a linear or even a two-dimensional diagram. The major pathways described in this chapter include PLCγ, PI3 kinase and Ras–MAP kinase. However, there are variants of both the PI3 kinases and MAP kinases which involve different cellular functions. For example, at least three different classes of mammalian MAP kinases contribute to cell behaviour by regulating transcription: Erk, p38 and JNK. Each of these responds to different stimuli and results in a different cellular response. Moreover, it is important to remember that these individual pathways are not independent, but form a dynamic network.

The key to understanding the roles of tyrosine kinases is to be able to link these signalling pathways to the cellular functions elaborated by the tyrosine kinases. A preliminary and simplistic effort is shown in **Table 2**. However, all of these complex functions are usually the consequence of multiple pathways. As a result there is not necessarily a linear relationship between any kinase and a function. Moreover, the same pathway may be involved in different, almost contradictory, functions in different cellular contexts. EGF activation of the Ras–Erk pathway in PC12 cells induces proliferation, but NGF stimulation of the same pathway in these cells leads to differentiation. The difference appears to reside in the temporal aspects (kinetics) of the pathway. Another problem in analysing kinase functions is redundancy. This issue is illustrated from 'gene knockout' studies, in which the gene for a particular protein has been eliminated from the mouse genome for analysis of the phenotype of the mutant. For example, the gene for Src can be eliminated from the mouse without severe consequences for the reproduction of the animal. Only when three genes of the Src family are eliminated do the genetic defects become lethal. In contrast, gene deletions are lethal for ErbB2, ErbB3 or ErbB4 and the ErbB ligand heregulin because of a failure of heart development at about embryonic day 10. These studies indicate that the function of a particular kinase in an organism depends on its time and place of expression as well as the consequences of its downstream signalling in the cell and tissue of origin.

TYROSINE KINASES AND CANCER

The functions listed in **Table 2** are important because they include many of the cellular behaviours which are modified in neoplastic transformation of cells (Nicolson, 1976). Thus, the phenotypic changes in tumour cells correspond closely to the functions regulated by tyrosine kinases in cells. However, the relationship of tyrosine kinases and human cancer is not so simple. Formation of diagnosable human tumours appears to require about five genetic changes in a single cell lineage. Contrary to the original oncogene hypothesis, many of these genetic lesions are not in tyrosine kinase-related pathways for cell proliferation. This situation results because tissues have evolved 'tumour suppressors' to act as brakes for cell proliferation and tumour progression. Thus, removal of these suppression mechanisms is as important as enhancement of the progression mechanisms. Surprisingly, reversal of tyrosine phosphorylation by phosphatase action does not appear to be an important tumour-suppressor mechanism. The only tumour-suppressor phosphatase (PTEN) to be identified to date acts more robustly on inositol (lipid) phosphates than on protein phosphates. It may therefore be more important in countering the effects of PI3 kinase than tyrosine kinases.

To understand the role of tyrosine kinases in human cancer, it is instructive to analyse those cancers in which tyrosine kinases have been implicated as contributors (**Table 10**). The list is necessarily limited because providing evidence that a kinase contributes to tumour progression (cause versus effect) is difficult. Furthermore, downstream effectors in tyrosine kinase pathways, such as

Table 10   Tyrosine kinases implicated in neoplasia

Tyrosine kinase	Mechanism of activation	Cancer
ErbB1	Truncation	Glioma
ErbB2	Amplification	Breast
PDGFRβ	Chromosome translocation	Leukaemia
Kit	Mutation	Leukaemia
Met	Mutation, overexpression	Multiple cancers
FGFR	Mutation	Multiple myeloma
Ret	Chromosome translocation	Multiple endocrine
Alk	Chromosome translocation	Lymphoma
Src	Overexpression, activation	Multiple
Yes	Overexpression, activation	Multiple
Abl	Chromosome translocation	CML
JAK2	Chromosome translocation	Leukaemia

R, receptor.

Ras and PI3 kinase, are more proximal to the phenotypic changes in cells and tissues and may thus be more potent oncogenes. However, some tyrosine kinases are very potent oncogenes. A good example is ErbB2, which is an inducer of mammary cancer when its gene is expressed in the mammary gland of mice. Although the reason for this potency is not entirely clear, two observations are likely important. One is that ErbB2 is susceptible to mutations and other events which induce the activation of its tyrosine kinase. The second is that ErbB2 can activate multiple downstream pathways to change the mammary cell phenotype, including both Ras–MAP kinase and PI3 kinase pathways.

The list in **Table 10** suggests that these two factors are important in many instances in which tyrosine kinases contribute to cancer. Particularly noteworthy are activations of tyrosine kinase oncogenes by chromosome translocations. Since tyrosine kinases are frequently autoregulated, displacement of the regulatory regions by truncation (ErbB1) or by chromosome translocation (Abl) can remove the autorepression and activate the kinase. This mechanism is familiar in viral oncogenes. In the instance of v-erbB (ErbB1), the extracellular domain has been truncated, facilitating dimerization and activation of the intracellular kinase. In the case of v-Src, the C-terminal tail is missing. Since this sequence contains the phosphorylated tyrosine which interacts with the SH2 domain (**Figure 8**), phosphorylation of the enzyme at this site is no longer possible as a repression mechanism.

An alternative mechanism for activation of tyrosine kinases in cancer is the autocrine growth loop (Kolibaba and Druker, 1997), in which overexpression or mislocation of a ligand for the receptor kinase aberrantly induces its activation. The cause versus effect relationship of this mechanism in human cancer is also difficult to establish, although it has been well characterized in cell culture studies. Most of the evidence is based on statistical analyses of clinical outcomes. Such studies have implicated TGF-α in oesophageal cancer and insulin-like growth factor in prostate cancer.

OVERVIEW

Tyrosine kinases regulate a large number of cellular functions via an array of signalling pathways. Most, but not all, of these pathways originate at the cell plasma membrane via transmembrane receptor tyrosine kinases or binary receptor–tyrosine kinase couples. Both the tyrosine kinases and their effector pathways are highly regulated and must be integrated both spatially and temporally into the organisation of cellular functions. Mutational activation or overexpression of tyrosine kinases can lead to aberrant cellular behaviours, including neoplastic transformation and tumour progression.

REFERENCES

Carraway, K. L. and Carraway, C. A. C. (1995) Signaling, mitogenesis and the cytoskeleton: where the action is. *BioEssays*, **17**, 171–175.

Carraway, K. L., *et al.* (1997) Signaling and the Cytoskeleton, (Springer, Berlin).

Claesson-Welsh, L. (1994) Platelet-derived growth factor receptor signals. *Journal of Biological Chemistry*, **269**, 32023–32026.

Cohen, P. T. W. (1997) Novel protein serine/threonine phosphatases: variety is the spice of life. *Trends in Biochemical Science*, **22**, 245–251.

Hubbard, S. R., *et al.* (1998) Autoregulatory mechanisms in protein-tyrosine kinases. *Journal of Biological Chemistry*, **273**, 11987–11990.

Hunter, T. (1998) The phosphorylation of proteins on tyrosine: its role in cell growth and disease. *Philosophical Transactions of the Royal Society of London, Series B*, **353**, 583–605.

Kolibaba, K. S. and Druker, B. J. (1997) Protein tyrosine kinases and cancer. *Biochimica Biophysica Acta*, **1333**, F217–F248.

Nicolson, G. L. (1976) Transmembrane control of the receptors on normal and tumor cells. II. Surface changes associated with transformation and malignancy. *Biochimica Biophysica Acta*, **457**, 57–108.

Panayotou, G. and Waterfield, M. D. (1993) The assembly of signalling complexes by receptor tyrosine kinases. *BioEssays*, **15**, 171–177.

Peterson, E. J. and Koretzky, G. A. (1998) Signal transduction in T lymphocytes. *Clinical and Experimental Rheumatology*, **17**, 107–114.

Riese, D. J., II and Stern, D. F. (1998) Specificity within the EGF family/ErbB receptor family signalling network. *BioEssays*, **20**, 41–48.

Schlessinger, J. Lax, I. and Lemmon, M. (1995) Regulation of growth factor activation by proteoglycans: what is the role of the low affinity receptors? *Cell*, **83**, 357–360.

Sorkin, A. and Waters, C. M. (1993) Endocytosis of growth factor receptors. *BioEssays*, **15**, 375–382.

Streuli, M. (1996) Protein tyrosine phosphatases in signalling. *Current Opinions in Cell Biology*, **8**, 182–188.

Taylor, S. S., Radzio-Andzelm, E. and Hunter, T. (1995) How do protein kinases discriminate between serine/threonine and tyrosine? Structural insights from the insulin receptor protein–tyrosine kinase. *FASEB Journal*, **9**, 1255–1266.

Thomas, S. M. and Brugge, J. S. (1997) Cellular functions regulated by Src family kinases. *Annual Reviews of Cellular Development*, **13**, 513–609.

Wells, J. A. (1996) Binding in the growth hormone receptor complex. *Proceedings of the National Academy of Sciences of the USA*, **93**, 1–6.

Zou, X. and Calame, K. (1999) Signaling pathways activated by oncogenic forms of Abl tyrosine kinase. *Journal of Biological Chemistry*, **274**, 18141–18144.

FURTHER READING

Alberts, B., *et al.* (1994). *Molecular Biology of the Cell*, 3rd edn. (Garland Publishing, New York).

Hesketh, R. (1997). *The Oncogene and Tumor Suppressor Gene Factsbook* (Academic Press, San Diego).

Kellie, S. (1994). *Tyrosine Kinases and Neoplastic Transformation* (R. G. Landes, Austin, TX).

Lodish, H., *et al.* (1995). *Molecular Cell Biology*, 3rd edn. (Scientific American Books, New York).

Mendelsohn, J., *et al.* (eds) (1995). *The Molecular Basis of Cancer* (W. B. Saunders, Philadelphia).

Peters, G. and Vousden, K. H. (eds) (1997). *Oncogenes and Tumor Suppressors* (IRL Press, Oxford).

Ruddon, R. W. (1995). *Cancer Biology*, 3rd edn. (Oxford University Press, Oxford).

Websites

http://www.kinase.com/.

http://www.sdsc.edu/kinases/.

http://www.stke.org/.

http://www.mshri.on.ca/pawson/research2.html.

Chapter 13

Signalling by TGF-β

Jing Qing and Rik Derynck
University of California at San Francisco, San Francisco, CA, USA

C O N T E N T S

INTRODUCTION

While normal, differentiating cells closely coordinate their proliferation and differentiation programmes, this balance is deregulated during malignant transformation into tumour cells. Compared with normal cells, transformed cells acquire a higher proliferative index and decreased differentiation, concomitant with a lower degree of dependence on extracellular cues. These changes in cell behaviour and responsiveness often result in part from genetic alterations, whereby defined mutations activate oncogenes or inactivate tumour-suppressor genes. Additionally, changes in the production of stimulatory or inhibitory growth and differentiation factors and/or in the cellular responsiveness to these factors greatly contribute to the behavioural and phenotypic changes in tumour cells. In fact, tumour cells often display autocrine responsiveness to increased endogenous expression of growth factors, and this autocrine stimulation contributes to tumour formation and cancer progression. Similarly, the invasive and metastatic phenotype of the tumour cells also results from mutations, changes in gene expression and/or altered production of cell surface-associated or extracellular mediators, and altered responsiveness to these factors.

Various growth factors and cytokines have been implicated in the progression and behaviour of tumour cells and cancers. Among these, transforming growth factor-β (TGF-β) and its downstream effectors are key determinants of the tumour cell behaviour of carcinomas. The TGF-β production by tumour cells and the responsiveness of tumour cells to autocrine TGF-β and TGF-β in the tumour microenvironment exert both positive and negative effects on cancer development. Accordingly, TGF-β and the TGF-β signalling pathway have been considered as both a tumour suppressor and a promoter of tumour progression and invasion. This chapter introduces the role of TGF-β in tumour development, specifically of carcinomas, and summarizes our knowledge of the TGF-β signalling mechanisms, i.e. the cell surface receptors and downstream effector proteins.

TGF-β EXPRESSION AND ACTIVATION

TGF-β is a secreted polypeptide, which in its receptor-binding, fully active form is a disulfide-bonded and stable dimer. The TGF-β precursor polypeptide comprises an N-terminal signal peptide followed by a large prosegment, which is twice as long as the C-terminal, active TGF-β sequence. Protein purification and cDNA cloning have revealed the existence of three TGF-βs, TGF-β1, -β2 and -β3, each encoded by a different gene and made as a precursor with similar structural organisation. TGF-β1 was the first identified and best characterized TGF-β, and is therefore considered as the prototype of these three TGF-βs, which act through the same receptor system and have similar biological activities in cell culture (Derynck and Choy, 1998). TGF-β1 is also the prototype of the TGF-β superfamily, which comprises about 60–70 structurally related proteins, characterized by seven characteristically spaced cysteines in the C-terminal segment of the precursor polypeptide (Derynck and Feng, 1997; Piek et al., 1999; Massagué et al., 2000). All TGF-β superfamily members are thought to act as dimers that bind to structurally related receptors. TGF-β-related proteins are found in multicellular eukaryotes from *C. elegans* and *Drosophila* to all vertebrates and regulate a variety of developmental and differentiation processes.

TGF-β1 expression is often upregulated in tumour cells and is therefore the focus of most studies on the role of TGF-β in tumorigenesis. With few exceptions, all cells in culture express TGF-β1, but this may be due to the absence of an extracellular matrix substrate. Thus, TGF-β1 expression is repressed when cells are grown on extracellular matrix or once they have deposited their extracellular matrix, a process strongly activated by TGF-β (Derynck and Choy, 1998). TGF-β1 expression in cell culture is therefore not necessarily a reflection of TGF-β expression *in vivo*, but may be a response to injury, consistent with increased TGF-β1 expression at sites of tissue injury. TGF-β itself activates TGF-β1 expression, a positive feedback and amplification response of relevance in tumour development.

Following an intracellular proteolytic cleavage between the prosequence and the active TGF-β sequence, TGF-β is released as a 'latent' complex, which is incapable of binding to the TGF-β receptors and is consequently biologically inactive. This latent complex consists of an active TGF-β dimer in a noncovalent complex with two prosegments, to which one of several 'latent TGF-β binding proteins' is often disulfide linked (Munger *et al.*, 1997). This latent complex represents an important safeguard against 'unneeded' or 'inadvertent' activation and these binding proteins may stabilize and target latent TGF-β to the extracellular matrix, where it is stably sequestered (Munger *et al.*, 1997). The extracellular matrix thus acts as a reservoir, from which TGF-β can readily be made available to cells without the need to induce TGF-β synthesis.

The secretion of TGF-β as a latent complex necessitates the existence of a regulated activation process. While latent TGF-β is efficiently activated by acidic conditions, its physiological activation occurs most likely through proteases, which degrade the TGF-β prosegments and thereby release the highly stable, active TGF-β dimer. Since plasmin activates latent TGF-β and plasminogen is converted into plasmin at sites of cell migration and invasion, we assume that plasmin-mediated activation of TGF-β occurs at sites of angiogenesis and tumour development, thus exposing endothelial and tumour cells to active TGF-β. Matrix metalloproteases may also play a key role in activation of latent TGF-β. For example, the matrix metalloproteases MMP-9 and MMP-2 have the ability to activate latent TGF-β (Yu and Stamenkovic, 2000). Since metalloproteases are frequently expressed by malignant cells, this mechanism may locally activate TGF-β at sites of tumour cell invasion. Other mechanisms of activation may not depend on proteases. For example, the extracellular matrix protein thrombospondin (Ribeiro *et al.*, 1999) and the αvβ6 integrin, which is expressed at the surface of epithelial cells in response to inflammation (Munger *et al.*, 1999), may activate TGF-β through a conformational change in the TGF-β complex. Thus different mechanisms may regulate TGF-β activation in

different physiological contexts, and tumour cells are well equipped to activate TGF-β locally. Finally, high-energy irradiation, which is often used in cancer therapy, also activates TGF-β (Barcellos-Hoff *et al.*, 1994).

CELLULAR RESPONSES TO TGF-β

TGF-β exerts a large variety of cellular responses, which often depend on the cell type and physiological conditions, thus making the responses highly context dependent. Since the role of TGF-β in tumour development is best studied in carcinoma development, we will briefly describe the cellular responses to TGF-β that play a role in the development of carcinomas from normal epithelial cells.

While TGF-β stimulates proliferation of various mesenchymal cell types, including fibroblasts, it is a very potent inhibitor of proliferation of epithelial cells and cells of haematopoietic origin, including various immune cells (Derynck and Choy, 1998; Massagué *et al.*, 2000). The TGF-β signalling process that leads to growth inhibition is considered as a tumour suppressor pathway, which is often inactivated to allow tumour development and cancer progression (de Caestecker *et al.*, 2000; Massagué *et al.*, 2000). Cell cycle progression and proliferation are driven by a complex and interdependent regulation by cyclins, cyclin-dependent kinases (cdks) and cdk inhibitors, which form complexes with each other (Sherr and Roberts, 1999). Accordingly, TGF-β-induced growth arrest, which occurs in the late G_1 phase of the cell cycle, induces a variety of alterations in the levels and activities of cyclins, cdks and cdk inhibitors, although many of these effects could be considered as indirect. Several direct TGF-β effects may play key roles in TGF-β-mediated growth arrest.

The key event that leads to TGF-β-induced growth arrest is the induction of expression of the cdk inhibitors p15$^{\text{Ink4B}}$ and/or p21$^{\text{Cip1}}$, depending on the cell type and context (Massagué *et al.*, 2000) (**Figure 1**). p21$^{\text{Cip1}}$, similarly to the related p27$^{\text{Kip1}}$, interacts with complexes of cdk2 with cyclin E or A and thereby inhibits the cdk2 activity, thus preventing cell cycle progression. p21$^{\text{Cip1}}$ and p27$^{\text{Kip1}}$ also interact with cdk4 and cdk6 and stabilize their interaction with cyclin D, thus playing a role in the activation of these complexes (Sherr and Roberts, 1999). Since the complexes of cdk2 with cyclin E or A act downstream from the complexes of cdk4 or 6 with cyclin D, TGF-β-induced expression of p21$^{\text{Cip1}}$ leads to cell cycle arrest in late G_1. In contrast, p15$^{\text{Ink4B}}$ interacts with and inactivates cdk4 and 6 and prevents their complex formation with cyclin D. In addition, p15$^{\text{Ink4B}}$ binds to the complexes of cdk4 or 6 with cyclin D and thereby not only inactivates the catalytic activity of these cdks, but also displaces p21$^{\text{Cip1}}$ and p27$^{\text{Kip1}}$ from these complexes, thus allowing them to bind to and inactivate the cdk2 complexes with cyclin A and E. Consequently,

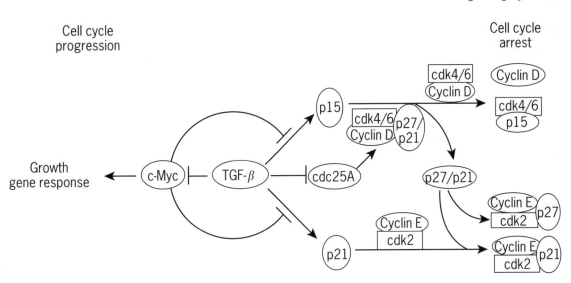

Figure 1 Schematic representation of TGF-β-induced mechanism of growth arrest in late G_1. TGF-β induces the expression of p15Ink4B and p21Cip1 and down-regulates the expression of c-myc and cdc25A. The down-regulation of c-myc expression relieves the inhibition of p15Ink4B and p21Cip1 expression, thus allowing induction of these cdk inhibitors by Smads.

TGF-β-induced expression of p15[Ink4B] inactivates cell cycle progression at two levels, p15[Ink4B]-mediated inactivation of cdk4 and cdk6 and, as a result of p21[Cip1] or p27[Kip1] displacement, inactivation of cdk2 through p21[Cip1] or p27[Kip1] binding (Massagué et al., 2000).

Additional mechanisms may also contribute to TGF-β-mediated growth arrest, again depending on the cell type. For example, TGF-β inhibits cdk4 expression, presumably at the translational level (Ewen et al., 1993). TGF-β also down-regulates the levels of cdc25A (Iavarone and Massagué, 1997), a tyrosine phosphatase, and this decreased activity leads to increased tyrosine phosphorylation of cdk4 and cdk6 and consequent inhibition of their kinase activity. TGF-β also inhibits c-Myc expression in normal epithelial cells, and c-Myc plays a role in growth arrest in response to TGF-β (Massagué et al., 2000; Chen et al., 2001). High levels of c-Myc repress p15[Ink4B] and p21[Cip1] expression, and a decrease in c-Myc levels results in derepression, thus allowing TGF-β-induced transcription of the p15[Ink4B] and p21[Cip1] genes. The TGF-β-mediated decrease in c-Myc levels may also play a role in the down-regulation of cdc25A expression in response to TGF-β, since c-Myc may positively regulate cdc25A expression. Finally, the TGF-β-induced interaction of protein phosphatase 2A with S6 kinase and consequently decreased S6 kinase activity may contribute to TGF-β-mediated growth arrest (Petritsch et al., 2000).

TGF-β regulates the expression of a large variety of genes through activation or repression of transcription. Among the many genes, TGF-β regulates the expression of transcription factors, secreted cytokines and growth factors, extracellular matrix proteins, proteases and integrins

(Derynck and Choy, 1998; Massagué et al., 2000). Which genes are regulated by TGF-β and the extent of this regulation are highly cell type and context dependent. The induction of transcription factors by TGF-β results in a variety of indirect responses, thus enhancing the complexity of the TGF-β response. Similarly, the induction of cytokine and growth factor expression, e.g. interleukin 1 and PDGF, by TGF-β results in indirect, yet physiologically very important, cellular responses. The potent ability of TGF-β to induce the expression of extracellular matrix proteins stands in contrast to other growth factors. TGF-β induces the expression of some, but not all, common extracellular matrix proteins, including collagens and fibronectin. Consequently, TGF-β expression and activation are major determinants of extracellular matrix synthesis and deposition. This activity is often complemented by a TGF-β-induced decrease in protease activity and increased expression of protease inhibitors, which together enhance the increased extracellular matrix deposition. TGF-β also enhances the expression of a variety of integrins, depending on the cell type, often resulting in increased cell adhesion to the extracellular matrix and presumably also increased integrin signalling. Finally, TGF-β is a potent chemoattractant of monocytes, macrophages and fibroblasts (Derynck and Choy, 1998). Consequently, TGF-β activation often results in localized inflammation and chemoattraction of fibroblasts, which, together with the mitogenic effect of TGF-β on fibroblasts and stimulation of extracellular matrix deposition, results in fibrosis (Roberts et al., 1986). These responses may also explain radiation-induced fibrosis, a consequence of TGF-β activation (Barcellos-Hoff et al., 1994).

TGF-β RECEPTORS AND INTERACTING PROTEINS

TGF-β signals through a cell surface receptor complex of two types of transmembrane serine/threonine kinases, named type I and type II receptors (Derynck and Feng, 1997; Massagué, 2000) (**Figure 2**). The type II and type I receptors are structurally related with a high level of sequence conservation in their cytoplasmic kinase domains, besides similarities in their extracellular domains. They autophosphorylate and phosphorylate target proteins on serines and threonines, yet also have tyrosine kinase activity. Both receptor types form cell surface dimers in the absence of TGF-β binding. These type II and type I receptor dimers also have an intrinsic affinity for each other, thus resulting in a heterotetrameric complex, which is stabilized by TGF-β binding. Among the receptors for TGF-β superfamily members, several heteromeric combinations of type II and type I receptors form functional signalling complexes, thus providing a variety of combinatorial type II/type I receptor interactions. In the case of TGF-β, only one type II TGF-β receptor, i.e. TβRII, has been identified. Three different type I receptors have been proposed as type I TGF-β receptors. Most gene expression responses in most cell types are mediated by the TβRI receptor, while the

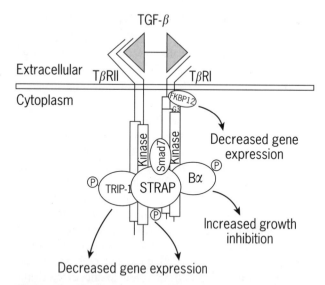

Figure 2   The TGF-β receptor complex with interacting regulatory proteins. The receptor complex consists of two TβRII and two TβRI polypeptides. FKBP12 interacts constitutively with TβRI, while the WD-repeat proteins TRIP-1, STRAP and the Bα subunit of protein phosphatase 2A interact following ligand activation of kinases and are phosphorylated. TRIP-1 interacts with TβRII, while the Bα subunit of protein phosphatase 2A interacts with TβRI. STRAP can interact with either receptor and also interacts and synergizes with Smad7.

potential roles of the ALK-1/TSR-1 and ALK-2/ActRI/Tsk7L type I receptors in TGF-β signalling remain to be better explored. TGF-β receptors are expressed on most, if not all, cell types (Derynck and Feng, 1997).

All three TGF-βs interact with the same TGF-β receptor complex (Derynck and Feng, 1997). TGF-β1 and -β3 interact primarily with the TβRII receptor, yet also contact the type I receptor in the complex. Thus, TβRII binds TGF-β1 and -β3 without a requirement for a type I receptor. In contrast, TGF-β2 does not bind to either TβRII or TβRI alone, but binds efficiently to the heteromeric receptor complex. TGF-β binding to the receptor complexes is enhanced in the presence of the type III receptors β-glycan and endoglin. β-Glycan is an abundant cell surface proteoglycan with a short cytoplasmic domain and no known signalling function. β-Glycan binds all three TGF-βs with high efficiency and may enhance the efficiency of receptor binding of TGF-β, most notably TGF-β2. Endoglin, a structurally related glycoprotein, is primarily expressed by vascular endothelial cells. Endoglin binds TGF-β1 and -β3 with high affinity, but not TGF-β2, and may enhance TGF-β's presentation to the TGF-β signalling receptor complex, similarly to β-glycan (Derynck and Feng, 1997).

Following TGF-β binding to the receptor complex, signalling is initiated through the activities of the cytoplasmic kinase domains of both receptors. The TβRII kinase, when overexpressed, is constitutively active and phosphorylated. Whether this is also the case at endogenous expression levels or whether TGF-β induces TβRII autophosphorylation remains to be clarified. A key event in receptor activation is the phosphorylation, and consequent activation, of the TβRI kinase by the TβRII kinase. TβRII phosphorylates the cytoplasmic domain of TβRI on serine and threonine residues in the 'GS sequence', a sequence which is conserved among the type I receptors and is located immediately upstream from the kinase domain. This phosphorylation then presumably induces a conformational change in the TβRI cytoplasmic domain that activates the kinase and consequently allows TβRI autophosphorylation and phosphorylation of downstream target proteins (Derynck and Feng, 1997; Massagué, 2000).

Several proteins have been shown to interact with the cell surface TGF-β receptor complexes (**Figure 2**). Among these, FKBP12 interacts with the juxtamembrane domain of type I receptors and may regulate its conformation, and dampens the TGF-β receptor activation. FKBP12 interacts constitutively with, yet is not phosphorylated by, the TGF-β receptor (Chen et al., 1997). In contrast, three WD-repeat containing proteins associate with and are phosphorylated by the receptor complex following ligand-induced activation. TRIP-1 interacts with TβRII (Choy and Derynck, 1998), while the Bα subunit of the protein phosphatase 2A interacts with type I receptors (Griswold-Prenner et al., 1998). STRAP, on the other hand, interacts with both TβRII and TβRI and in turn interacts with Smad7 (see below) to decrease TGF-β signalling (Datta and Moses, 2000). Since WD repeats mediate protein–protein interactions, it is likely that these proteins allow interactions of multiprotein complexes with the receptors. These proteins regulate the TGF-β receptor response, but there is currently no solid evidence that they act as effectors of TGF-β responses.

SMAD AND NON-SMAD SIGNALLING

The only characterized signalling effector pathway, initiated by activated TGF-β receptors, is provided by the Smads (Piek *et al.*, 1999; Itoh *et al.*, 2000; Massagué, 2000; Massagué *et al.*, 2000). The Smads, a family of structurally related proteins, are directly activated by the receptors and then translocate into the nucleus to act as ligand-dependent transcriptional regulators of target genes. The Smads are structurally related to each other in two domains, an N- or MH1 domain which corresponds to the N-terminal third of the protein, and a C- or MH2 domain which corresponds to the C-terminal third of these proteins. Based on structural and functional characteristics, the Smads are divided into three subfamilies. Smad1, -5 and -8 and Smad2 and -3 are 'receptor-activated' Smads that are phosphorylated on C-terminal serines by the activated type I receptor. The activated TβRI phosphorylates and thereby activates Smad2 and -3, whereas Smad1, -5 and -8 are activated by BMP receptors. Following their release from the receptors, the activated Smads form a heterotrimeric complex with Smad4, which serves as a common mediator for all receptor-activated Smads. This complex consists of two receptor-activated Smads and one Smad4, raising the possibility of combinatorial interactions among receptor-activated Smads. This Smad complex translocates into the nucleus and cooperates with other transcription factors to activate or repress transcription of defined genes in response to TGF-β (Piek *et al.*, 1999; Itoh *et al.*, 2000; Massagué, 2000; Massagué *et al.*, 2000) (**Figure 3**).

Besides the receptor-activated Smads and Smad4, which act as ligand-induced effectors, two other 'inhibitory' Smads regulate Smad signalling. Smad6 and -7 have much less sequence conservation in their MH1 domain than the other Smads, and interfere with the activation of effector Smads (Piek *et al.*, 1999; Itoh *et al.*, 2000; Massagué, 2000). Smad6 and -7 are able to interact with type I receptors, thus competitively preventing the 'receptor-activated' Smads from being phosphorylated, whereas Smad6 additionally interferes with the heteromeric complex formation of Smad1 with Smad4. Although Smad6 and -7 seem to interact nonspecifically with type I receptors, Smad7 may primarily inhibit TGF-β signalling, whereas Smad6 primarily inhibits BMP signalling.

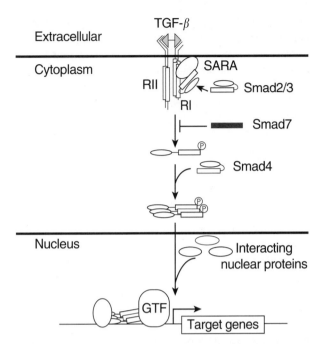

Figure 3 TGF-β-induced signalling through Smads. Following ligand-induced receptor activation, Smad2 and/or -3 interact transiently with the TβRI receptor and this interaction is stabilized by the FYVE-protein SARA. Smad2 and -3 are C-terminally phosphorylated by TβRI and then dissociate from the receptor to form a heterotrimeric complex consisting of two receptor-activated Smads and Smad4. This complex is then translocated into the nucleus where it interacts at the promoter with other transcription factors to regulate gene expression. Smad7 inhibits activation of Smad2 and/or -3 by the receptors.

Accordingly, TGF-β signalling induces Smad7 expression, thus providing a TGF-β induced negative feedback loop, whereas BMP signalling induces Smad6 expression. While the inhibitory functions of Smad6 and -7 can be easily conceptualized as a mechanism of competitive inhibition, the functions of Smad6 and -7 may be more complex (Piek *et al.*, 1999; Itoh *et al.*, 2000). This is suggested by the observations that Smad6 and -7 are primarily localized in the nucleus and that both Smads can cooperate with TGF-β signalling in inhibiting adipocyte differentiation. Smad7 may also act as an effector of TGF-β-induced cell death, whereas Smad6 can function as a corepressor (Piek *et al.*, 1999; Itoh *et al.*, 2000). Further studies are needed to define the functions of Smad6 and -7.

Once inside the nucleus, the Smad complexes function as ligand-dependent transcriptional regulators of target genes (Derynck *et al.*, 1998; Piek *et al.*, 1999; Massagué, 2000; Massagué and Wotton, 2000). TGF-β activates or represses transcription of defined target genes, and many of these responses are direct, i.e. immediate early, responses to TGF-β receptor activation. Smads have mainly been characterized as TGF-β-induced transcription activators, although they may also mediate TGF-β-induced repression of gene expression. Smads activate transcription from a variety of promoters through physical interaction with the transcriptional coactivator CBP/p300, a variety of DNA-binding transcription factors, and defined sequences in the promoter DNA (Derynck et al., 1998; Massagué, 2000; Massagué and Wotton, 2000) (**Figure 4**). Most TGF-β-inducible genes are transcriptionally activated through Smad3, even though TGF-β activates both Smad2 and -3, and some responses, e.g. the induction of $p15^{Ink4B}$ and $p21^{Cip1}$, require the participation and cooperation of both Smad2 and -3 (Feng et al., 2000; Pardali et al., 2000).

The receptor-activated Smads link to the general transcriptional machinery through a direct association with the transcriptional coactivator CBP/p300. This interaction, which is stabilized by Smad4, occurs through the C-terminal sequence of the Smads, and requires receptor-mediated phosphorylation of the C-terminal serines. CBP/p300 thus serves as transcriptional coactivator for Smads, and this interaction is essential for transcriptional activation (Derynck et al., 1998; Massagué, 2000; Massagué and Wotton, 2000). Smads also interact with a variety of DNA binding transcription factors and it is this interaction, together with the DNA binding of Smads, which specifies the promoter binding and transcriptional activation (Derynck et al., 1998; Itoh et al., 2000; Massagué, 2000; Massagué and Wotton, 2000). The versatility of physical interactions with a variety of transcription factors is best illustrated for Smad3. Among others, Smad3 has been shown to interact with bZIP transcription factors (e.g. c-Jun, ATF-2 or CREB), bHLH transcription factors (e.g. TFE3), runt domain transcription factors (AML-1 and -2 and CBFA1/AML3), nuclear receptors (e.g. the vitamin D_3

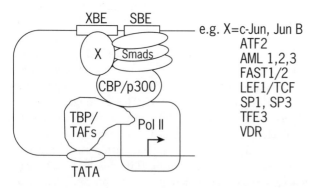

Figure 4 Physical and transcriptional cooperation of TGF-β-activated Smad2 or -3 with other transcription factors at the promoter. The heterotrimeric Smad complex interacts with the CBP/p300 coactivator, which connects to the general transcription machinery. While also interacting with DNA at a Smad binding element (SBE), the Smad complex interacts with one of several possible transcription factors with sequence-specific DNA binding (XBE).

and glucocorticoid receptors) and Sp1, either through the MH1- or MH2-domains of the Smad, depending on the interacting transcription factor. While this interaction is usually direct, stable interaction with the transcription factor may depend on the concomitant interaction of the Smad and the transcription factor with CBP/p300. This physical interaction not only localizes the interacting Smad to a defined promoter sequence, but also allows the Smad to enhance the activity of the interacting transcription factor, presumably as a result of the increased interaction with CBP/p300.

Thus, Smads often serve as coactivators of other transcription factors. This, however, may not always be the case. For example, Smad2 interacts with the DNA binding protein FAST1/2 at an activin-responsive promoter sequence. FAST1/2 does not have transcription activity by itself and therefore serves as a DNA sequence-specific scaffold to allow transcriptional activation by Smad2. Also, the TGF-β-induced transcription of the Smad7 gene is mediated by Smad3, presumably without involvement of other DNA binding, interacting transcription factors. This opportunity may be provided by tandem Smad-binding DNA sequences, which enable permit Smad3 binding to the Smad7 promoter. Finally, while the interacting transcription factor provides high-affinity, sequence-specific binding to the promoter, Smad3 and -4, but not Smad2, are also able to bind DNA. However, Smads have a much lower DNA binding affinity and sequence specificity than most DNA binding transcription factors. Thus, a Smad binding sequence may primarily provide a sequence context conducive to Smad binding in close proximity to the sequence for the high-affinity DNA binding, interacting transcription factor. In this way, the DNA context-dependent binding of a Smad to both the interacting transcription factor and the promoter DNA may explain why TGF-β activates only a select set of the promoters, which show productive DNA binding of the Smad-interacting transcription factor (Derynck et al., 1998; Itoh et al., 2000; Massagué, 2000; Massagué and Wotton, 2000). This cooperation of Smads with other DNA-binding transcription factors also explains why, prior to the characterization of Smads, no consensus TGF-β response element could be defined in TGF-β-responsive genes and why AP-1 and Sp1 binding sequences were shown to be required for TGF-β responsiveness of various promoters.

The TGF-β-dependent recruitment of Smad complexes to the transcription machinery also allows for interactions with additional coactivators or corepressors, which regulate the amplitude of TGF-β-dependent transcriptional activation through Smads (Itoh et al., 2000; Massagué, 2000; Massagué and Wotton, 2000). Besides the interaction of the Smad complex with the CBP/p300 coactivator, Smad4 is able to engage the MSG1 coactivator into the transcription complex to enhance the Smad response. In contrast, recruitment of a corepressor into the complex decreases or inhibits the Smad and TGF-β response.

Several corepressors can interact directly with TGF-β Smads to decrease TGF-β responses. For example, the proto-oncogene product Evi-1 interacts with Smad3 and represses the gene expression and growth-inhibitory responses of TGF-β. Similarly, c-Ski also interacts with receptor-activated Smads and recruits a histone deacetylase to repress Smad-mediated transcription. A similar mechanism may also explain the inhibition by other Smad-interacting corepressors, such as the c-Ski-related SnoN, TGIF, SNIP and SIP1, although, in some cases, their interaction with CBP/p300, or interference with the Smad interaction with CBP/p300, may also play a role (Itoh *et al.*, 2000; Massagué, 2000; Massagué and Wotton, 2000). Enhanced expression of corepressors in tumour cells could selectively block the TGF-β response and its growth-inhibitory effect in tumour cells and thus contribute to cancer progression.

The physical interactions and functional cooperativity of Smads with other transcription factors allows for cross-talk with other signalling pathways (Zhang and Derynck, 1999; Massagué, 2000; ten Dijke *et al.*, 2000) (**Figure 5**). For example, UV radiation, stress and mitogens activate MAP kinase pathways that activate Jun N-terminal kinase, which phosphorylates and activates c-Jun. Activation of

the c-Jun–c-Fos complex by MAP kinase–JNK cascades is therefore likely to regulate TGF-β-induced transcription from promoters with TGF-β-responsive AP-1- and Smad-binding sites. These promoters thus represent targets of convergence for these two types of signalling pathways. TGF-β signalling can also converge with Wnt signalling. This pathway is mediated by β-catenin, which shuttles between the cytoplasm and the nucleus, and serves as coactivator for the nuclear LEF/TCF transcription factors. Smad4 forms a complex with β-catenin and LEF, while Smad3 associates with LEF/TCF, and both Smads can cooperate with these transcription factors at promoters with LEF/TCF and Smad binding sites. Finally, Smad signalling can also converge with STAT signalling. STATs are activated by receptors and translocate into the nucleus to act as DNA binding transcription factors. BMP-activated Smad1 has been shown to form a complex with STAT3, which was activated in response to LIF. This interaction required the presence of the coactivator p300, with which both transcription factors interact. This complex formation is presumably at the basis of the functional cooperativity between Smad and STAT signalling.

The cross-talk of TGF-β/Smad signalling with other pathways can also occur prior to nuclear translocation of

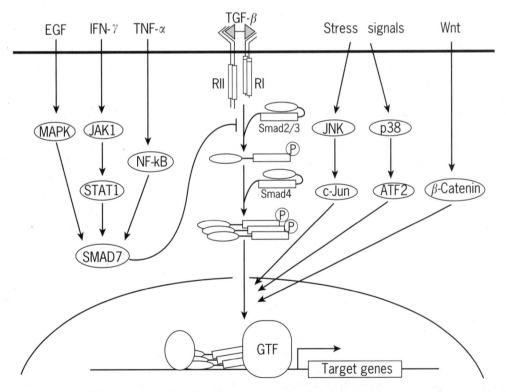

Figure 5   Cross-talk with TGF-β-induced signalling through Smads. A variety of extracellular signals activate JNK and/ or p38 MAP kinase signalling, which leads to phosphorylation of c-Jun or ATF-2, two transcription factors, with which Smads can cooperate at defined promoters. Wnt signalling also cross-talks with Smad signalling, through the ability of activated Smads to associate with β-catenin and/or LEF/TCF at some promoters. Activation of MAP kinase signalling by growth factors, such as EGF, and activation of STAT1 by interferon-γ and of NF-κB by TNF-α all induce Smad7 expression, thus leading to inhibition of TGF-β-induced Smad2/3 activation by Smad7.

Smads (Piek *et al.*, 1999; Zhang *et al.*, 1999; Massagué, 2000; ten Dijke *et al.*, 2000). For example, the linker regions of Smad1, -2 and -3 can be phosphorylated by Erk MAP kinase, which is activated in response to receptor tyrosine kinase and Ras signalling, and this phosphorylation then regulates ligand-induced nuclear translocation (Piek *et al.*, 1999). Some signalling pathways activate expression of an inhibitory Smad, thus leading to decreased Smad activation. While BMPs and TGF-β induce the expression of the inhibitory Smad6 and -7, thus activating autoregulatory negative feedback loops, EGF can also induce Smad6 and -7 expression. This observation suggests that receptor tyrosine kinases regulate Smad signalling through induction of an inhibitory Smad, although other observations suggest Smad activation in response to receptor tyrosine kinase activation. Finally, interferon-γ-induced signalling through STATs and TNF-α-induced activation of NF-κB also activate Smad7 expression, which in turn inhibits TGF-β/Smad signalling. Thus, upregulation of Smad7 may represent a convenient mechanism used by several signalling pathways to inhibit TGF-β responsiveness (Piek *et al.*, 1999; Zhang and Derynck, 1999; Itoh *et al.*, 2000; Massagué, 2000; ten Dijke *et al.*, 2000).

The mechanisms of Smad signalling and regulation, outlined above, now also explain the versatility and context dependence of the TGF-β responses. Indeed, the levels of interacting transcription factors and their activation state, as regulated by other signalling pathways, are important determinants of the TGF-β response. For example, TGF-β-induced transcription resulting from interactions of Smads with AP-1 transcription factors are likely to be regulated by MAP kinase signalling (Piek *et al.*, 1999; Zhang and Derynck, 1999; Itoh *et al.*, 2000; Massagué, 2000; ten Dijke *et al.*, 2000). In contrast, the interaction of the heteromeric Smad2–Smad3–Smad4 complex with Sp1 induces expression of the cdk-inhibitors p15$^{\text{Ink4B}}$ or p21$^{\text{Cip1}}$ in a manner that is unlikely to require MAP kinase signalling (Feng *et al.*, 2000; Pardali *et al.*, 2000). Finally, the presence and identity of corepressors may determine the amplitude of the Smad response and even whether TGF-β receptor activation results in transcriptional activation or repression.

Finally, recent evidence strongly suggests that TGF-β signals through other pathways, distinct from the Smad-mediated regulation of gene expression (Piek *et al.*, 1999; Itoh *et al.*, 2000; Massagué, 2000) (**Figure 6**). TGF-β is able to activate MAP kinase signalling, although the extent and kinetics of activation differ substantially among different cell lines and types. These activation events have been shown to result in activation of Erk MAP kinase, p38 MAP kinase and Jun N-terminal kinase (JNK). p38 MAP kinase and JNK activation occurs through phosphorylation by MKK3, MKK4 and/or MKK6. Activation of p38 MAP kinase and JNK by TGF-β may enhance Smad signalling through Smad phosphorylation

or phosphorylation of c-Jun and ATF-2, transcription factors that cooperate with TGF-β Smads, thus resulting in cross-talk with Smad-mediated transcription. TAK1, a MAP kinase, which is rapidly activated by TGF-β, yet is also involved in other unrelated signalling pathways, may serve as a TGF-β-dependent initiator of these signalling cascades. TGF-β may also activate or stabilize the small GTPases RhoA and RhoB and these may in turn play roles in several TGF-β responses, e.g. a requirement of RhoB for JNK activation (Itoh *et al.*, 2000; Massagué, 2000). Finally, TGF-β also induces an interaction of protein phosphatase 2A with p70/S6 kinase, a kinase known to regulate protein translation and growth control, thus decreasing its activity (Petritsch *et al.*, 2000). While mechanisms of activation by TGF-β and roles of these non-Smad signalling cascades remain to be characterized, these observations strongly suggest that inactivation of Smad pathways may not leave the cell unresponsive to TGF-β.

INACTIVATION OF TGF-β's TUMOUR-SUPPRESSOR FUNCTIONS IN CARCINOMAS

The growth-inhibitory response of epithelial cells to TGF-β strongly suggests that TGF-β signalling may exert tumour suppression. On the other hand, TGF-β1 expression is often upregulated in carcinomas, which then would suggest that tumour cells benefit from TGF-β expression. Accordingly, there is substantial evidence for both tumour promoting and tumour-suppressor roles of TGF-β in carcinoma development. The tumour-suppressor role of TGF-β signalling is best supported by the presence of inactivating mutations in TGF-β receptors and Smads in human carcinomas and by tumour development studies in mouse models.

Somatic mutations in TβRII are common in tumours from patients with hereditary nonpolyposis colorectal cancer (HNPCC), who have germ-line defects in their capacity for DNA mismatch repair (de Caestecker *et al.*, 2000; Massagué *et al.*, 2000) (**Figure 7**). Nucleotide additions to or deletions from the stretch of adenines within the *TβRII* coding sequence give rise to a truncated TβRII, which is incapable of signalling. Consequently, the cells acquire a selective growth advantage, allowing them to progress for tumour development. While TβRII mutations occur frequently in colon cancers, gastric cancers and gliomas with microsatellite instability, they are less common in tumours from the endometrium, pancreas, liver and breast with microsatellite instability. Missense and inactivating mutations in the kinase domain of TβRII have also been reported in colon cancers, which do not display microsatellite instability. Together, inactivating TβRII mutations may be present in 20–25% of all colon cancers.

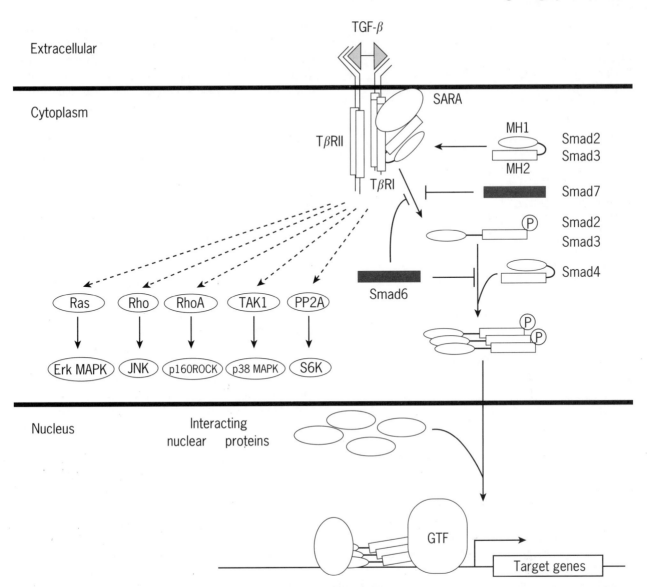

Figure 6 TGF-β-induced signalling through Smads is complemented by several non-Smad signalling mechanisms activated by the TGF-β receptors. Although the exact mechanism of activation remains to be better characterized, TGF-β induces activation of Ras, RhoB and RhoA, as well as TAK1 and the protein phosphatase 2A, thus leading to activation of several MAP kinase pathways, and down-regulation of S6 kinase activity.

Although less common, inactivating TβRI mutations also occur in ovarian cancers, metastatic breast cancers, pancreatic carcinomas and T cell lymphomas. Together, these mutations suggest a function of TβRII and TβRI as tumour suppressors in carcinoma development (de Caestecker *et al.*, 2000; Massagué *et al.*, 2000).

TGF-β receptor expression is often decreased in carcinomas and this down-regulation may allow cells to escape growth inhibition by TGF-β. Several Ets transcription factors regulate the expression of TβRII and reduced expression of these factors correlates with reduced receptor expression in gastric cancers. Transcriptional silencing may also result from hypermethylation of CpG islands in the TβRI or TβRII promoters, or mutations in the TβRII promoter which interfere with transcription factor binding. Decreased TβRII function has been shown to confer resistance against the growth-inhibitory effect of TGF-β, whereas other TGF-β responses, e.g. extracellular matrix protein expression, may not be similarly affected, and increased TβRII expression correlates with sensitivity to the growth inhibitory response of TGF-β. Thus, different signalling threshold requirements may be the basis for the observation that a decrease in TβRII function may primarily affect the growth responsiveness (de Caestecker *et al.*, 2000; Massagué *et al.*, 2000).

Expression of wild-type TβRII in colon or breast carcinoma cell lines, which lack a functional TβRII allele, provided evidence that the TβRII acts as a tumour

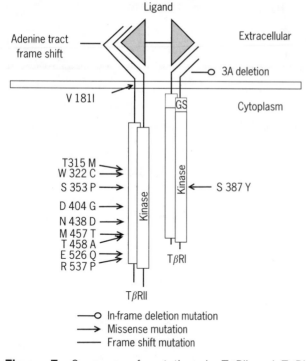

Figure 7 Summary of mutations in TβRII and TβRI found in various cancers.

suppressor (de Caestecker et al., 2000; Massagué et al., 2000). The TβRII-expressing cells were growth inhibited and had suppressed anchorage independence and strongly reduced tumour formation in nude mice, when compared with the parental cells. Transgenic expression of dominant negative forms of TβRII in the skin or mammary gland increased tumour formation, further supporting a tumour suppressor role of TβRII. In addition, mice with an inactivated *TGF-β1* gene also show increased carcinoma development, either spontaneously (Engle et al., 1999) or after carcinogen treatment (Tang et al., 1998). In the latter case, haploinsufficiency of the *TGF-β1* gene increased tumour susceptibility, since the tumours retained one wild-type allele. Consistent with these results, decreased TβRII expression correlated with high tumour grade of human breast cancers. While these observations suggest that loss of TGF-β responsiveness provides a distinct advantage for tumour development, most tumours do not have inactivated TGF-β receptors, and HNPCC patients, who frequently have TβRII mutations in their tumours, have a better prognosis than patients with sporadic colon cancer, who do not have TβRII mutations. Therefore, abrogation of TGF-β signalling, while leading to loss of the growth inhibition by TGF-β and early tumour onset, paradoxically protects against tumour progression, since the tumours do not adopt an invasive phenotype in response to autocrine or paracrine TGF-β (see below). This possibility is supported by mouse studies, in which a functional TβRII was expressed in colon cancer cells that lack TGF-β receptor

expression. Although the transfected cells showed reduced growth rate, they had a strongly increased invasive and metastatic capacity (Oft et al., 1998). Together these findings illustrate the tumour-suppressor role of TGF-β receptors in carcinoma development, and the distinct advantages, provided by TGF-β responsiveness, for cancer progression at later stages.

Mutations in Smads have been found in a variety of carcinomas (**Figure 8**), and, even though generally uncommon, they suggest that some Smads act as tumour suppressors (de Caestecker et al., 2000; Massagué et al., 2000). While no mutations in Smad3 or the inhibitory Smad 6 or -7 have been reported, inactivation of Smad2 or -4 genes occurs by loss of chromosome segments, small deletions, frameshift, nonsense or missense mutations. Smad4 mutations occur primarily in pancreatic carcinomas, in which Smad4 was originally identified as *DPC4* (deleted in pancreatic carcinoma), and colon carcinomas, and less frequently in other carcinomas. While biallelic inactivation of Smad4 is most commonly observed, haploinsufficiency of the Smad4 locus may also contribute to cancer progression, although this interpretation may be confounded by the presence of the Smad2 and DCC loci in close proximity to the Smad4 gene. In contrast to Smad4, Smad2 mutations are rare and occur primarily in colorectal and lung carcinomas. Finally, enhanced Smad7 levels are observed in pancreatic carcinomas and may also decrease Smad responsiveness.

Tumour-associated mutations in Smad4 and Smad2 occur most frequently in the MH2 domain, which mediates heteromeric complex formation and transcriptional activation. C-terminal deletions or mutations often inactivate the Smad, and provide dominant negative interference with wild-type Smad function and TGF-β-induced nuclear translocation. Many mutations also map at the interfaces of Smad heteromerization, suggesting interference with heteromerization. Other mutations decrease the stability, e.g. through increased ubiquitin-mediated degradation of the Smad proteins. Finally, mutations in the MH1 domain of Smad4 interfere with its DNA binding. While most if not all mutations impair Smad functions, some mutations may alter TGF-β signalling to the tumour's advantage. Indeed, the Smad2 mutations *D450E* and *P445H*, found in colorectal carcinomas, enhance the invasive behaviour of the tumour cells, when overexpressed (de Caestecker et al., 2000; Massagué et al., 2000).

While homologous inactivation of the Smad2 or -4 genes results in embryonic lethality and therefore prevents an assessment in tumour progression, several mouse studies suggest a role of Smad4 as tumour suppressors. Mice heterozygous for an inactivated Smad4 gene develop intestinal polyps, which can progress into carcinomas. When combined with an inactivated allele of the adenomatous polyposis coli (*APC*) gene, this double heterozygosity allows the development of highly invasive colon carcinomas with both the *APC* and Smad4 genes

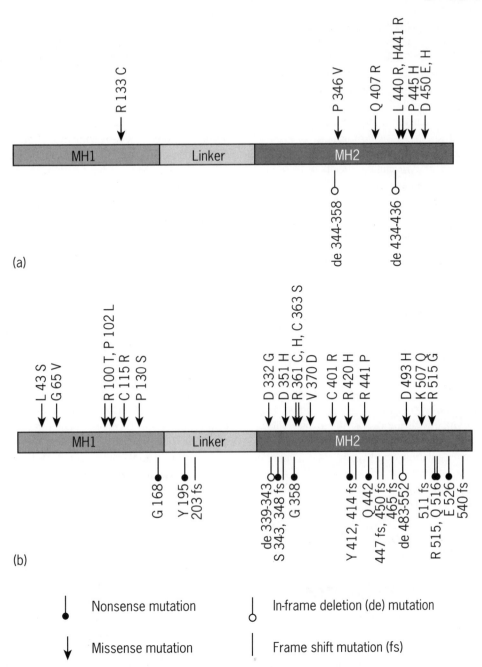

Figure 8   Summary of mutations in (a) Smad2 and (b) Smad4 found in various carcinomas.

inactivated (Takaku *et al.*, 1998). Mice with homozygous inactivation of the Smad3 gene have also been shown to develop colon carcinomas (Zhu *et al.*, 1998), although this phenotype was not seen in two other similar studies. While a role of Smad3 as tumour-suppressor gene is conceivable, no inactivating Smad3 mutations have been observed in human tumours. This could be rationalized by the observation that Smad3 activates most gene expression responses to TGF-β, whereas Smad2 cooperates with Smad3 for TGF-β-induced expression of the p21^{Cip1} or p15^{Ink4B} cdk inhibitors (Feng *et al.*, 2000; Pardali *et al.*, 2000). Smad2 inactivation may therefore inactivate the growth-arrest response, without affecting Smad3 responses, e.g. induction of extracellular matrix proteins, which provide an advantage for tumour development. Importantly, while Smad4 is required for many if not most TGF-β gene expression responses, Smad4-deficient cells may have retained a variety of responses (Sirard *et al.*, 2000). Thus, inactivation of Smad4 or Smad2 function may not abolish, but rather perturb, the complex TGF-β response, and thereby primarily targets the growth inhibitory response to TGF-β. Moreover, different TGF-β responses may have differential sensitivity to Smad signalling. Accordingly, Smad7 overexpression in a colon carcinoma cell line suppressed TGF-β-induced growth arrest, without affecting TGF-β-induced expression of plasminogen activator inhibitor 1, and enhanced anchorage-independent growth and tumorigenicity. Finally, inactivating Smad4 mutations have been found in conjunction with mutations in TβRII or TβRI, strongly suggesting that Smad4 has tumour-suppressing activities which are unrelated to TGF-β signalling.

Oncogene expression or increased proto-oncogene expression may also down-regulate the TGF-β responsiveness and allow for escape of TGF-β's tumour-suppressor effects. For example, *Evi-1*, an oncogene involved in leukaemic transformation of haematopoietic cells, inhibits Smad3 function and thus decreases or abolishes TGF-β responsiveness. The oncogenic effect of *Evi-1* may therefore result in part from interference with TGF-β signalling. Conceptually similarly, c-Ski represses Smad-mediated transcription, thus raising the possibility that its interference with TGF-β responsiveness may contribute to its oncogenic activity. Accordingly, c-Ski expression is often elevated in melanomas and carcinomas, and this has been correlated with decreased TGF-β responsiveness. Finally, c-Myc also inhibits the antiproliferative response to TGF-β. TGF-β downregulates c-Myc expression in epithelial cells, but this repression is lost in various cancer cell lines, concomitant with the loss of the growth inhibitory response to TGF-β (Massagué *et al.*, 2000; Chen *et al.*, 2001). Thus, downregulation of c-Myc by TGF-β may be required for the growth-inhibitory response to TGF-β, and the absence of this downregulation may confer resistance to the tumour-suppressor activity of TGF-β. Clearly, carcinoma cells have developed several strategies to escape the growth-inhibitory response of TGF-β.

CELL-AUTONOMOUS, STIMULATORY EFFECTS OF TGF-β ON TUMOUR DEVELOPMENT

Even though TGF-β signalling exerts tumour-suppressor activity, TGF-β1 expression is often increased in tumour cells and stimulates tumour development and cancer progression. Indeed, autocrine TGF-β signalling can induce morphological changes and invasive behaviour of the tumour cells, while increased TGF-β1 production and activation make the microenvironment more permissive for tumour progression (Akhurst and Balmain, 1999; Dumont and Arteaga, 2000).

Tumour metastasis depends on various factors, including the ability of tumour cells to migrate and invade the stroma and to migrate in and out of the blood vessels. Epithelial to mesenchymal differentiation of tumour cells plays an important role in this invasive phenotype. Fibroblastoid or 'spindle cell' tumours of epithelial origin have been characterized as highly malignant and invasive

(Cui *et al.*, 1996). TGF-β and TGF-β-related proteins have been implicated in epithelial to mesenchymal transdifferentiation both in normal development and in tumour progression. This phenotypic transition is characterized by extensive changes in expression of cell adhesion molecules and a switch from a cytoskeleton of mainly cytokeratin intermediate filaments to one predominantly composed of vimentin. Epithelial to mesenchymal differentiation in culture is thought to correlate with these cell changes that facilitate invasion and metastasis *in vivo*.

TGF-β has been shown to induce epithelial to mesenchymal transition in culture of normal and transformed breast epithelial cells, squamous carcinoma, ovarian adenosarcoma and melanoma cells. The phenotypic changes have been best characterized in NMuMG cells, in which TGF-β induces cell shape changes, down-regulates expression of E-cadherin, ZO-1, vinculin and keratin and induces expression of vimentin and N-cadherin, which has been shown to increase cell motility and scattering (Miettinen *et al.*, 1994; Bhowmick *et al.*, 2001). Although the mechanism of TGF-β-induced epithelial to mesenchymal differentiation is presumably complex, PI-3-kinase signalling and TGF-β-induced Smad and RhoA activation appear to play a role (Bhowmick *et al.*, 2001). In addition, the morphological changes occur rapidly in response to TGF-β, and are reversible. *In vivo*, the effect of TGF-β on the spindle cell phenotype and invasive behaviour of carcinomas has been well documented for skin carcinomas in mice (Cui *et al.*, 1996). Consistent with a tumour-suppressor role, increased expression of activated TGF-β1 reduced the hyperplastic response to the tumour promoter PMA and the number of papillomas after treatment with DMBA. On the other hand, increased TGF-β1 expression enhanced the malignant conversion of skin carcinomas in a carcinogenesis mouse model, and increased the incidence of spindle cell carcinomas (Cui *et al.*, 1996). In another study, expression of a dominant negative TβRII prevented squamous carcinoma cells from undergoing mesenchymal differentiation in response to TGF-β both *in vitro* and *in vivo*. Consequently, the tumours had a differentiated epithelial phenotype and were less malignant and invasive than the parental cells, which developed fibroblastoid spindle cell carcinomas (Portella *et al.*, 1998). A similar role of TGF-β signalling was also apparent in Ras-transformed mammary epithelial cells and a fibroblastoid colon carcinoma cell line (Oft *et al.*, 1998). Expression of a dominant negative TβRII prevented TGF-β-induced epithelial to mesenchymal changes and reverted the colon carcinoma cells to an epithelial phenotype. In addition, blocking TβRII function suppressed invasion *in vitro* and the metastatic phenotype of this colon carcinoma cell line. Finally, restoration of TβRII signalling in HNPCC cells with a mutated TβRII rendered the cells invasive, in contrast to their normally, noninvasive phenotype.

TUMOUR PROGRESSION STIMULATED BY EFFECTS OF TGF-β ON THE TUMOUR ENVIRONMENT

The increased expression and activation of TGF-β1 by tumour cells also makes the microenvironment more conducive to tumour development. Increased TGF-β1 expression by tumour cells, presumably a result of activated Ras/MAP kinase signalling and signal amplification in response to TGF-β1 itself, enhances the TGF-β levels in the tumour microenvironment. The increased protease expression and plasmin generation by tumour cells and the TGF-β1-induced expression of collagenases and other proteases, such as the matrix metalloproteases MMP-2 and MMP-9, result most likely in TGF-β activation and degradation of the extracellular matrix with consequent release of stored TGF-β. Increased TGF-β1 production stimulates synthesis of extracellular matrix proteins and chemoattraction of fibroblasts. All these changes together result in a microenvironment that is conducive for tumour growth and invasion, and for angiogenesis (Akhurst and Balmain, 1999; Dumont and Arteaga, 2000).

Tumour angiogenesis is critical for tumour growth and invasion, since blood vessels are required to deliver nutrients and oxygen to the tumour cells and allow tumour cells to intravasate the blood system, leading to metastatic spread. TGF-β1 acts as a potent inducer of angiogenesis in several assays (Roberts et al., 1986), while mouse models defective in TGF-β signalling illustrate the important role of TGF-β1 in normal vascular development. For example, targetted inactivation of the TGF-β1 or TβRII genes results in embryonic lethality due to defective vasculogenesis and angiogenesis (Dickson et al., 1995; Oshima et al., 1996), while angiogenesis-defective phenotypes are also apparent in mice with null mutations of the genes for Alk-1 (Oh et al., 2000), a TGF-β type I receptor that is expressed in endothelial cells, or endoglin, a TGF-β type III receptor expressed by endothelial cells (Arthur et al., 2000). (See chapter on Angiogenesis.)

Several tumour models illustrate the importance of tumour cell-secreted TGF-β1 in tumour angiogenesis. Increased TGF-β1 secretion by transfected pancreas carcinoma (Stearns et al., 1999) or CHO (Ueki et al., 1992) cells enhanced tumour angiogenesis in immunodeficient mice, whereas local administration of neutralizing antibodies to TGF-β1 strongly reduced tumour angiogenesis (Ueki et al., 1992). TGF-β antibodies also reduced angiogenesis and tumorigenicity of a renal carcinoma cell line in T, NK and B cell-deficient mice. These cells did not have cell-autonomous responses to TGF-β since they lacked TβRII (Ananth et al., 1999). In humans, histological studies of breast tumours correlate high levels of TGF-β1 mRNA with high microvessel density, and each of these factors correlated with poor patient prognosis. Diagnostic studies on other carcinoma types correlate high

tumour burden and circulating plasma levels of TGF-β1, and enhanced tumour angiogenesis and poor patient prognosis. In one study, TGF-β1 levels were also correlated with expression levels of the angiogenic growth factor VEGF (Saito et al., 1999).

The mechanisms whereby TGF-β1 stimulates angiogenesis remain to be further characterized, but presumably combine direct and indirect effects. TGF-β induces expression of VEGF, a potent angiogenic growth factor, which directly stimulates endothelial cell proliferation and migration. TGF-β also induces capillary formation of endothelial cells, cultured on collagen matrix (Choi and Ballermann, 1995). Indirect stimulation of angiogenesis may also occur, since TGF-β is a potent chemoattractant for monocytes, which release angiogenic cytokines, and the TGF-β1-induced changes in the microenvironment stimulate endothelial cell migration and capillary formation. Moreover, the TGF-β-induced expression of MMP-2 and MMP-9, and down-regulation of the protease inhibitor TIMP in both tumour cells and endothelial cells, are expected to enhance the migratory and invasive properties of endothelial cells required for angiogenesis. Thus, both direct effects of TGF-β and effects on the microenvironment stimulate tumour angiogenesis.

Local immunosuppression in response to increased TGF-β1 levels allows tumour cells to escape from immunosurveillance and thus stimulates tumour development and progression (Dumont and Arteaga, 2000). TGF-β1 is the most potent immunosuppressive cytokine known to date, and inhibits proliferation and functional differentiation of T lymphocytes, lymphokine-activated killer cells, natural killer cells, neutrophils, macrophages and B cells (Derynck and Choy, 1998; Letterio and Roberts, 1998; de Visser and Kast, 1999). Several findings illustrate the role of TGF-β-induced, local immunosuppression in tumorigenicity. For example, increased TGF-β1 expression in a tumour cell line prevented cytotoxic T lymphocyte activation and enhanced tumorigenicity, in contrast to parental cells. Such repression can be elaborated by the ability of TGF-β to inhibit the expression and function of interleukin 2 and interleukin 2 receptors (Letterio and Roberts, 1998; de Visser and Kast, 1999). Accordingly, mammary tumour cells, which produce high TGF-β1 levels, inhibited the cytotoxic T lymphocyte response, but this inhibition was overcome by expressing interleukin 2 in these cells. These and other results suggest that TGF-β-mediated suppression of the cytotoxic T cell response promotes tumour development.

TGF-β1 also inhibits other immune functions of relevance to tumour development. Increased TGF-β1 expression by tumour cells decreased natural killer cell activity and promoted tumour formation in nude mice that lack T cells. In addition, anti-TGF-β antibodies suppressed tumour formation and metastasis of a breast carcinoma cell line in nude mice, while enhancing natural killer cell function. This suppression was not seen in beige mice, which lack natural killer cells, thus implicating TGF-β1-induced suppression of natural killer cells in cancer progression (Arteaga *et al.*, 1993). TGF-β-mediated suppression of neutrophil function may also be involved in tumour progression. Indeed, Fas-ligand expressing carcinoma cells underwent neutrophil-mediated rejection, but this rejection did not occur at a site with high TGF-β levels or when TGF-β1 was injected at the tumour site (Chen *et al.*, 1998). Finally, TGF-β down-regulates the expression of the major histocompatibility complex (MHC) class II antigens (Letterio *et al.*, 1996), suggesting that TGF-β1 expression renders the tumour cells less immunogenic. This regulation contributes to the local immunosuppression and to the escape from immune surveillance.

In summary, the mechanisms through which TGF-β signals and exerts its multiple responses are rapidly being characterized. Smads exert multiple gene expression responses, but cross-talk with other signalling pathways and non-Smad TGF-β signalling provide further complexity to the TGF-β response. TGF-β signalling plays an important role in tumour cell behaviour and cancer progression. The growth-inhibitory activity of TGF-β acts as a tumour suppressor in carcinoma development, whose function is often eliminated through mutations in receptors or Smads. In contrast, the increased TGF-β1 expression by tumour cells stimulates tumour development, both in a cell-autonomous manner and through effects on its environment, e.g. stimulation of angiogenesis and localized immunosuppression.

REFERENCES

Akhurst, R. J. and Balmain, A. (1999). Genetic events and the role of TGF-β in epithelial tumour progression. *Journal of Pathology*, **187**, 82–90.

Ananth, S., *et al.* (1999). Transforming growth factor β1 is a target for the von Hippel–Lindau tumour suppressor and a critical growth factor for clear cell renal carcinoma. *Cancer Research*, **59**, 2210–2216.

Arteaga, C. L., *et al.* (1993). Anti-transforming growth factor (TGF)-β antibodies inhibit breast cancer cell tumorigenicity and increase mouse spleen natural killer cell activity. Implications for a possible role of tumor cell/host TGF-β interactions in human breast cancer progression. *Journal of Clinical Investigation*, **92**, 2569–2576.

Arthur, H. M., *et al.* (2000). Endoglin, an ancillary TGFβ receptor, is required for extraembryonic angiogenesis and plays a key role in heart development. *Developmental Biology*, **217**, 42–53.

Barcellos-Hoff, M.-H., *et al.* (1994). Transforming growth factor-β activation in irradiated murine mammary gland. *Journal of Clinical Investigation*, **93**, 892–899.

Bhowmick, N. A., *et al.* (2001). Transforming growth factor-β1 mediates epithelial to mesenchymal transdifferentiation through a RhoA-dependent mechanism. *Molecular Biology of the Cell*, **12**, 27–36.

Chen, Y. G., *et al.* (1997). Mechanism of TGF-β receptor inhibition by FKBP12. *EMBO Journal*, **16**, 3866–3876.

Chen, J. J., *et al.* (1998). Regulation of the proinflammatory effects of Fas ligand (CD95L). *Science*, **282**, 1714–1717.

Chen, C. R., *et al.* (2001). Defective repression of c-myc in breast cancer cells: A loss at the core of the transforming growth factor β growth arrest program. *Proceedings of the National Academy of Sciences of the USA*, **98**, 992–999.

Choi, M. E. and Ballermann, B. J. (1995). Inhibition of capillary morphogenesis and associated apoptosis by dominant negative mutant transforming growth factor-β receptors. *Journal of Biological Chemistry*, **270**, 21144–21150.

Choy, L. and Derynck, R. (1998). The type II transforming factor-β (TGF-β) receptor-associated protein TRIP-1 acts as a modulator of the TGF-β response. *Journal of Biological Chemistry*, **273**, 31455–31462.

Cui, W., *et al.* (1996). TGFβ1 inhibits the formation of benign skin tumors, but enhances progression to invasive spindle carcinomas in transgenic mice. *Cell*, **86**, 531–542.

Datta, P. K. and Moses, H. L. (2000). STRAP and Smad7 synergize in the inhibition of transforming growth factor β signaling. *Molecular and Cell Biology*, **20**, 3157–3167.

de Caestecker, M. P., *et al.* (2000). Role of transforming growth factor-β signaling in cancer. *Journal of the National Cancer Institute*, **92**, 1388–1402.

Derynck, R. and Choy, L. (1998). Transforming growth factor-β and its receptors. In Thompson, A. (ed.), *The Cytokine Handbook*, 3rd edn 593–636 (Academic Press, Boston).

Derynck, R. and Feng, X.-H. (1997) TGF-β receptor signaling. *BBA Reviews in Cancer*, **1333**, F105–F150.

Derynck, R., *et al.* (1998). Smads: transcriptional activators of TGF-β responses. *Cell*, **95**, 737–740.

de Visser, K. E. and Kast, W. M. (1999). Effects of TGF-β on the immune system: implications for cancer immunotherapy. *Leukemia*, **13**, 1188–1199.

Dickson, M. C., *et al.* (1995). Defective haematopoiesis and vasculogenesis in transforming growth factor-β1 knock out. *Development*, **121**, 1845–1854.

Dumont, N. and Arteaga, C. L. (2000). Transforming growth factor-β and breast cancer: tumor promoting effects of transforming growth factor-β. *Breast Cancer Research*, **2**, 125–132.

Engle, S. J., *et al.* (1999). Transforming growth factor β1 suppresses nonmetastatic colon cancer at an early stage of tumorigenesis. *Cancer Research*, **59**, 3379–3386.

Ewen, M. E., *et al.* (1993). TGF β inhibition of Cdk4 synthesis is linked to cell cycle arrest. *Cell*, **74**, 1009–1020.

Feng, X.-H., *et al.* (2000). Smad2, Smad3 and Smad4 cooperate with Sp1 to induce p15Ink4B expression in response to TGF-β. *EMBO Journal*, **19**, 5178–5193.

Griswold-Prenner, I., *et al.* (1998). Physical and functional interactions between type I transforming growth factor-β receptors and Bα, a WD-40 repeat subunit of phosphatase 2A. *Molecular and Cell Biology*, **18**, 6595–6604.

Iavarone, A. and Massagué, J. (1997). Repression of the CDK activator Cdc25A and cell-cycle arrest by cytokine TGF-β in cells lacking the CDK inhibitor p15. *Nature*, **387**, 417–422.

Itoh, S., *et al.* (2000). Signaling of transforming growth factor-β family members through Smad proteins. *European Journal of Biochemistry*, **267**, 6954–6967.

Letterio, J. J. and Roberts, A. B. (1998). Regulation of immune responses by TGF-β. *Annual Review of Biochemistry*, **16**, 137–161.

Letterio, J. J., *et al.* (1996). Autoimmunity associated with TGF-β1-deficiency in mice is dependent on MHC class II antigen expression. *Journal of Clinical Investigation*, **98**, 2109–2119.

Massagué, J. (2000). How cells read TGF-β signals. *Nature Reviews of Molecular and Cellular Biology*, **1**, 169–178.

Massagué, J. and Wotton, D. (2000). Transcriptional control by the TGF-β/Smad signaling system. *EMBO Journal*, **19**, 1745–1754.

Massagué, J., *et al.* (2000). TGF-β signaling in growth control, cancer, and heritable disorders. *Cell*, **103**, 295–309.

Miettinen, P. J., *et al.* (1994). TGF-β induced transdifferentiation of mammary epithelial cells to mesenchymal cells: involvement of type I receptors. *Journal of Cell Biology*, **127**, 2021–2036.

Munger, J. S., *et al.* (1997). Latent transforming growth factor-β: structural features and mechanisms of activation. *Kidney International*, **51**, 1376–1382.

Munger, J. S., *et al.* (1999). The integrin αv β6 binds and activates latent TGF β1: a mechanism for regulating pulmonary inflammation and fibrosis. *Cell*, **96**, 319–328.

Oft, M., *et al.* (1998). TGF-β signaling is necessary for carcinoma cell invasiveness and metastasis. *Current Biology*, **19**, 1243–1252.

Oh, S. P., *et al.* (2000). Activin receptor-like kinase 1 modulates transforming growth factor-β1 signaling in the regulation of angiogenesis. *Proceedings of the National Academy of Sciences of the USA*, **97**, 2626–2631.

Oshima, M., *et al.* (1996). TGF-β receptor type II deficiency results in defects of yolk sac hematopoiesis and vasculogenesis. *Developmental Biology*, **179**, 297–302.

Pardali, K., *et al.* (2000). Role of Smad proteins and transcription factor Sp1 in p21(Waf1/Cip1) regulation by transforming growth factor-β. *Journal of Biological Chemistry*, **275**, 29244–29256.

Petritsch, C., *et al.* (2000). TGF-β inhibits p70 S6 kinase via protein phosphatase 2A to induce G1 arrest. *Genes and Development*, **14**, 3093–3101.

Piek, E., *et al.* (1999). Specificity, diversity, and regulation in TGF-β superfamily signaling. *FASEB Journal*, **13**, 2105–2124.

Portella, G., *et al.* (1998). Transforming growth factor β is essential for spindle cell conversion of mouse skin carcinoma *in vivo*: implications for tumor invasion. *Cell Growth and Differentiation*, **9**, 393–404.

Ribeiro, S. M., *et al.* (1999). The activation sequence of thrombospondin-1 interacts with the latency-associated peptide to regulate activation of latent transforming growth factor-β. *Journal of Biological Chemistry*, **274**, 13586–13593.

Roberts, A. B., *et al.* (1986). Transforming growth factor type β: rapid induction of fibrosis and angiogenesis *in vivo* and stimulation of collagen formation *in vitro*. *Proceedings of the National Academy of Sciences of the USA*, **83**, 4167–4171.

Saito, H., *et al.* (1999). The expression of transforming factor-β1 is significantly correlated with the expression of vascular endothelial growth factor and poor prognosis of patients with advanced gastric carcinoma. *Cancer*, **86**, 1455–1462.

Sherr, C. J. and Roberts, A. B. (1999). CDK inhibitors: positive and negative regulators of G1-phase progression. *Genes and Development*, **13**, 1501–1512.

Sirard, C., *et al.* (2000). Targeted disruption in murine cells reveals variable requirement for Smad4 in transforming growth factor β-related signaling. *Journal of Biological Chemistry*, **275**, 2063–2070.

Stearns, M. E., *et al.* (1999). Role of interleukin 10 and transforming growth factor β1 in the angiogenesis and metastasis of human prostate primary tumor lines from orthotopic implants in severe combined immunodeficiency mice. *Clinical Cancer Research*, **5**, 711–720.

Takaku, K., *et al.* (1998). Intestinal tumorigenesis in compound mutant mice of both Dpc4 (Smad4) and Apc genes. *Cell*, **92**, 645–656.

Tang, B., *et al.* (1998). Transforming growth factor-β1 is a new form of tumor suppressor with true haploid insufficiency. *Nature Medicine*, **4**, 802–807.

ten Dijke, P., *et al.* (2000). Signaling inputs converge on nuclear effectors in TGF-β signaling. *Trends in Biochemical Science*, **25**, 64–70.

Ueki, N., *et al.* (1992). Excessive production of transforming growth-factor β1 can play an important role in the development of tumorigenesis by its action for angiogenesis: validity of neutralizing antibodies to block tumor growth. *Biochimica Biophysica Acta*, **1137**, 189–196.

Yu, Q. and Stamenkovic, I. (2000). Cell surface-localized matrix metalloproteinase-9 proteolytically activates TGF-β and promotes tumor invasion and angiogenesis. *Genes and Development*, **14**, 163–176.

Zhang, Y. and Derynck, R. (1999). Regulation of Smad signaling by protein associations and signaling crosstalk. *Trends in Cell Biology*, **9**, 274–279.

Zhu, Y., *et al.* (1998). Smad3 mutant mice develop metastatic colorectal cancer. *Cell*, **94**, 703–714.

FURTHER READING

Chang, H., *et al.* (1999). Smad5 knockout mice die at mid-gestation due to multiple embryonic and extraembryonic defects. *Development*, **126**, 1631–1642.

Daopin, S., *et al.* (1992). Crystal structure of transforming factor-β2: an unusual fold for the superfamily. *Science*, **257**, 369–373.

Derynck, R., *et al.* (1988). A new type of transforming growth factor-β, TGF-β3. *EMBO Journal*, **7**, 3737–3743.

Hata, A., *et al.* (1998). TGF-β signaling and cancer: structural and functional consequences of mutations in Smads. *Molecular Medicine Today*, **4**, 257–262.

Kim, S. J., *et al.* (2000). Molecular mechanisms of inactivation of TGF-β receptors during carcinogenesis. *Cytokine Growth Factor Review*, **11**, 159–168.

Markowitz, S. D. and Roberts, A. B. (1996). Tumor suppressor activity of the TGF-β pathway in human cancers. *Cytokine Growth Factor Review*, **7**, 93–102.

Massagué, J. (1998) TGF-β signal transduction. *Annual Review of Biochemistry*, **67**, 753–791.

McAdam, A. J., *et al.* (1994). Transfection of transforming growth factor-β producing tumor EMT6 with interleukin-2 elicits tumor rejection and tumor reactive cytotoxic T-lymphocytes. *Journal of Immunotherapy with Emphasis on Tumor Immunology*, **15**, 155–164.

Miyazono, K., *et al.* (2000). TGF-β signaling by Smad proteins. *Advances in Immunology*, **75**, 115–157.

Torre-Amione, G., *et al.* (1990). A highly immunogenic tumor transfected with a murine transforming growth factor type β1cDNA escapes immune surveillance. *Proceedings of the National Academy of Sciences of the USA*, **87**, 1486–1490.

Wotton, D. and Massagué, J. (2001). Smad transcriptional corepressors in TGF β family signaling. *Current Topics in Microbiology and Immunology*, **254**, 145–164.

Chapter 14

Wnt Signal Transduction

Jeffrey R. Miller
University of Minnesota, Minneapolis, MN, USA

CONTENTS

INTRODUCTION

Whether it is a meeting with a colleague, a conversation over coffee with a friend or a telephone call to a loved one, interpersonal communication is an essential part of our daily lives. In our bodies, cells also communicate with one another to coordinate their behaviour and determine their specialized role in the body. Cells utilize elaborate systems of proteins to transmit, receive and respond to signals from neighbouring cells. These systems, or signal transduction pathways, utilize secreted signalling proteins, cell surface and intracellular receptor proteins, protein kinases, transcription factors and other intracellular proteins. Intercellular signals control a variety of processes in the body and ensure, for example, that each cell divides only when its neighbours dictate that it should do so. The importance of such signals becomes apparent when this communication breaks down and cells begin to divide uncontrollably, resulting in cancer. For example, colon cells normally divide at a rate that balances the loss of colon cells due to attrition. Colon cells receive signals that tell them to divide when more cells are needed and are told to stop dividing when the appropriate number of cells is reached. In colon cancer, like many other cancers, defects in this regulatory network cause colon cells to divide continuously leading to tumour formation.

The past 25 years of cancer research have revealed that cancer is a complex disease involving dynamic changes in the genome. This was realized through the discovery that mutations in specific genes, called oncogenes and tumour-suppressor genes, played critical roles in tumour formation. Mutations in these genes result in defects in regulatory pathways that control normal cell proliferation and homeostasis. Dominant gain-of-function mutations produce oncogenes, a gene that is locked in the 'ON' position and leads to hyperactivation of a regulatory pathway. Conversely, recessive mutations inactivate tumour-suppressor genes that normally keep a regulatory

pathway 'OFF'. Coming back to the example of colon cancer, both types of mutations have been uncovered with the end result being the uncontrolled proliferation of colon cells. Thus, understanding the function of oncogenes and tumour-suppressors is vital to gain insights into the molecular causes of cancer and for designing therapeutic agents to treat cancer.

Through modern cloning techniques, a number of oncogenes and tumour suppressors have been identified. Characterization of these genes led to the realization that many oncogenes and tumour suppressors encode components of evolutionarily conserved signal transduction pathways important for controlling embryonic development. The Wnt signal transduction pathway provides one of the most striking examples of this connection. Inappropriate activation of the Wnt signal transduction pathway is implicated in a variety of human cancers, most notably colon cancer. Many cases of colon cancers are associated with either oncogenic mutations in β-catenin, a positive regulator of Wnt signal transduction, or inactivating mutations in APC (the tumour-suppressor protein encoded by the adenomatous polyposis coli gene), a negative regulator of Wnt signalling. In both cases, these mutations lead to the aberrant activation of the Wnt pathway and tumorigenesis. During development, Wnt signalling plays critical roles in controlling a variety of processes including cell fate determination and cell proliferation. For example, Wnt signalling is required for the patterning of the central nervous system and the establishment of the dorsal–ventral axis in frogs. The involvement of Wnt signalling in both embryonic development and cancer has fuelled an extraordinary explosion of interest in understanding the underlying molecular mechanism of Wnt signal transduction. This chapter summarizes the current model for Wnt signal transduction and then discusses how inappropriate activation of Wnt signalling causes cancer. Owing to constraints on space and an effort to present a simplified and coherent picture of Wnt signalling, certain aspects of Wnt signalling will not be covered in this review. For more information, readers should refer to the list of further reading located at the end of this chapter. Additional information on Wnt signalling can also be found on the Wnt gene homepage (http://www.stanford.edu/~rnusse/wntwindow.html) and at the connections map at *Science's* STKE Web site (http://www.stke.org).

THE Wnt SIGNAL TRANSDUCTION PATHWAY

The Wnt signal transduction pathway is one of the major developmentally important signalling pathways with well-characterized roles in a variety of organisms including mice, frogs, fish, flies and worms. Like other intercellular signal transduction pathways, the Wnt pathway utilizes a secreted signalling protein a transmembrane receptor protein and complex intracellular machinery to relay signals from the cell surface to the nucleus. The major components of the Wnt signalling pathway include the Wnt family of secreted proteins, the Frizzled family of trans-membrane receptor proteins and the intracellular proteins Casein Kinase Iε (CKIε), Dishevelled, GBP/Frat, Glycogen Synthase Kinase 3 (GSK3), APC, Axin, β-catenin (Armadillo) and the TCF/LEF family of transcriptional regulators. **Figure 1** presents a schematic representation of each of these proteins showing their important structural and functional domains.

The first insights into the mechanism of Wnt signal transduction came from pioneering studies in the fruit fly, *Drosophila melanogaster*. Researchers used the awesome power of genetics to characterize several fly genes with mutant phenotypes similar to that seen in embryos lacking *wingless*, the fly ortholog of vertebrate *Wnt-1*. These genes were then ordered into a genetic pathway, which has served as a paradigm for understanding Wnt signal transduction in other model systems. In recent years, additional components of the pathway have been identified through a variety of methods, including protein–protein interaction screens. Now, researchers are working to put the pieces of the Wnt signalling puzzle together, a task that is proving to be challenging. However, recent studies examining the complex biochemical relationships between components of the Wnt pathway have provided exciting new insights into the mechanism of Wnt signalling and provides the working model for Wnt signal transduction shown in **Figure 2** and described below.

Wnt signalling is dependent on the presence or absence of the intracellular protein β-catenin. In the absence of Wnt signal, the destruction complex, a multiprotein machine composed of Axin, APC and GSK3, tags β-catenin for destruction by the addition of phosphate groups to serine and threonine residues near the N-terminus of β-catenin.

These phosphoamino acids then act as a binding site for a second complex of proteins, the ubiquitin ligase complex, which covalently adds a small protein called ubiquitin to β-catenin. Proteins tagged with ubiquitin are targetted to the proteasome, the cell's protein incinerator, where they are rapidly destroyed. This process serves to keep the levels of β-catenin in the cell low and the Wnt pathway is OFF. When cells perceive a Wnt signal, a group of proteins including Dishevelled, CKIε and GBP/Frat are activated and together they inactivate the destruction complex. As a result, β-catenin is no longer ubiquitinated and is protected from degradation by the proteasome. These events lead to the accumulation of β-catenin in the cell. As the level of β-catenin rises, it enters the nucleus and interacts with a DNA-binding protein of the TCF/LEF family. Together, β-catenin and TCF/LEF activate expression of specific cassettes of target genes. During development these targets include genes that direct cells to adopt specific cell fates, whereas in human colon cancer cells these targets include genes that control cell growth and proliferation. With this brief introduction in hand, the role that each of these proteins plays in regulating Wnt signalling will now be examined in greater detail.

The Messengers – *Wnt* Genes

W*nt* genes were first identified independently by researchers in two different fields. *Wnt-1* (first called *int-1*) was identified as a preferred integration site for mouse mammary tumour virus (Nusse and Varmus, 1982). Insertion of the mouse mammary tumour virus in regions surrounding the *Wnt-1* gene led to its inappropriate activation and breast cancer. *Wingless (wg)*, the fly counterpart of *Wnt-1*, was identified in the Nobel Prize-winning screen of Nüsslein-Volhard and Weischaus (1980) as a mutation that resulted in segment polarity defects. Cloning of *Wnt-1* and *wg* showed that these genes shared a high degree of sequence identity. This finding brought together researchers in the fields of cancer biology and developmental biology and greatly accelerated our understanding of Wnt signalling. Many additional members of the *Wnt* gene family have since been cloned in many organisms from nematode worms to humans, with each organism possessing multiple related *Wnt* genes. For example, the fruit fly possesses seven and the mouse at least 18 *Wnt* genes. A list of known *Wnt* genes and sequence comparisons can be found on the *Wnt* gene homepage (http://www.stanford.edu/~rnusse/wntwindow.html).

Wnt genes encode secreted glycoproteins typically 350–400 amino acids in length and are characterized by a conserved pattern of 23–24 cysteine residues (**Figure 1**). Wnt proteins appear to act as short-range messengers, acting within several cell diameters of the producing cell. Although Wnt proteins are secreted and can be found associated with the cell surface and extracellular matrix,

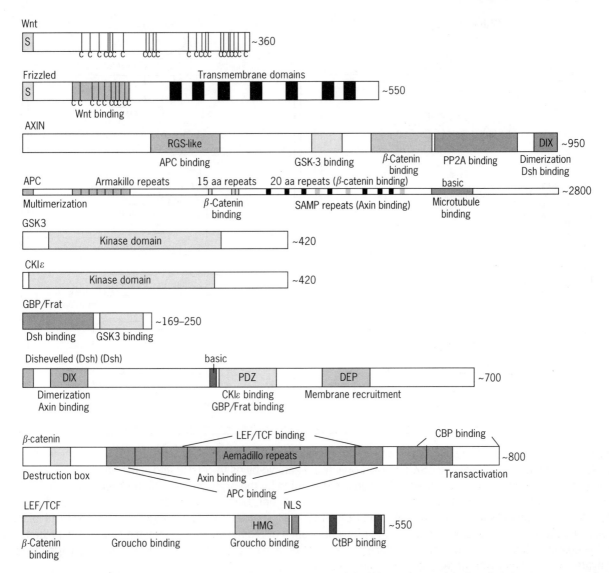

Figure 1   Schematic representation of the major components of the Wnt pathway showing their important structural and functional characteristics. For Wnt and Frizzled: (s) indicates signal sequence and (c) indicates conserved cysteine residues. Axin possesses an RGS domain, found in a family of proteins that regulate signalling via heterotrimeric G-proteins, and a DIX domain, found in both Axin and Dishevelled. Regions implicated in the binding of APC, GSK3, β-catenin, Protein Phosphatase 2A (PP2A) and Dishevelled (Dsh) are shown. APC is very large protein comprised of the following domains: a multimerization domain; seven Armadillo repeats important for localization; a series of β-catenin binding sites (15 amino acid repeats and 20 amino acid repeats), a series of SAMP repeats important for Axin binding; and a basic microtubule binding domain. Both GSK3 and CKIε are serine–threonine protein kinases and the kinase domain is indicated. GBP/Frat is a small protein with an N-terminal Dishevelled binding domain and a C-terminal GSK3 binding domain. Dishevelled possesses the following conserved domains: an N-terminal DIX domain important for dimerization and Axin binding, a centrally located PDZ domain that binds GBP/Frat and CKIε and a C-terminal DEP domain important for membrane recruitment and planar cell polarity signalling. β-Catenin possesses the N-terminal destruction box containing four GSK3 phosphorylation sites and a series of Armadillo repeats. Binding sites for Axin, APC and LEF/TCF have been mapped to the Armadillo repeat region. The N-terminal domain is important for trans-activation. TCF/LEF contains a nuclear localization sequence (NLS) and an HMG box that mediates DNA binding. Binding sites for β-catenin, Groucho, CtBP and CBP/p300 are indicated.

they are notoriously insoluble and troublesome to work with biochemically. The difficulty to acquire soluble forms of Wnt proteins has hindered progress in understanding how cells send and receive Wnt signals. However, several forms of Wnt protein have been recovered from the medium of cultured cells and, using in vitro assays for activity, these soluble forms have been shown to be biologically active. This work will, it is hoped, provide the tools for

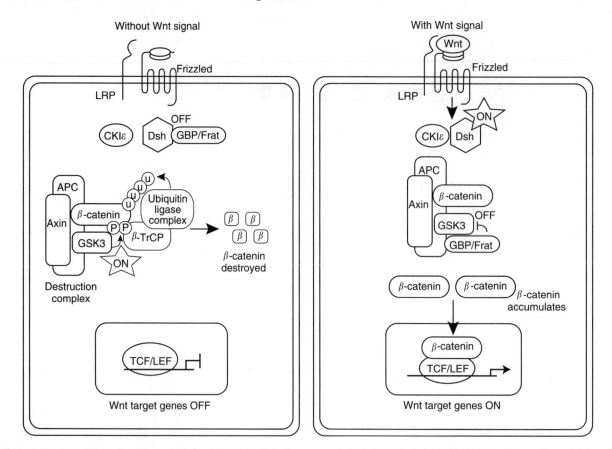

Figure 2   The Wnt signalling pathway. Left: in the absence of Wnt signal, Axin and APC facilitate the addition of phosphate groups to β-catenin by GSK3. Phosphorylated β-catenin binds to β-TrCP and is modified by the addition of a polyubiquitin tag. Proteins tagged with ubiquitin are degraded by the proteasome. The pathway is OFF because β-catenin is rapidly destroyed and its levels in the cell are low. Right: binding of Wnt to cell surface Frizzled and LRP receptors 'activates' Dishevelled (Dsh), CKIε and GBP/Frat by an unknown mechanism. Activation leads to inhibition of the destruction complex and a decrease in the phosphorylation of β-catenin. Thus, β-catenin evades the proteasome and accumulates in the nucleus where it interacts with a DNA-binding protein of the LEF/TCF family. Together, they activate expression of Wnt target genes and the pathway is ON.

understanding how Wnt proteins interact with components of the extracellular matrix and cell surface receptors.

At the Cell Surface – The Reception of Wnt Signals

For many years the identity of Wnt receptors remained elusive, leaving a large gap in our understanding of Wnt signalling. This hole has now been filled with the finding that members of the *Frizzled* gene family can function as Wnt receptors (**Figures 1** and **3**; Bhanot *et al.*, 1996; Yang-Snyder *et al.*, 1996). *Frizzled* genes encode seven-transmembrane proteins with an N-terminal cysteine-rich domain that binds Wnts with high affinity. Like the *Wnt* gene family, members of the *Frizzled* gene family have been identified in a number of organisms from worms to humans with each organism possessing multiple *Frizzled* genes. A list of known *Frizzled* genes and sequence

alignments can be found on the *Wnt* gene homepage (http://www.leland.stanford.edu/~rnusse/wntwindow.html). Work in vertebrate systems has demonstrated that different Wnt proteins preferentially interact with and signal through specific subsets of Frizzled receptors. Given the large number of Wnt and Frizzled genes and, as a consequence, the large number of possible Wnt–Frizzled combinations, deciphering the importance of specific Wnt–Frizzled interactions *in vivo* will be challenging.

Very little is known about how Frizzled proteins function. Structurally, Frizzled receptors resemble other seven-transmembrane receptor proteins that signal through heterotrimeric GTP-binding proteins (G-proteins). Recent evidence suggests that in vertebrates a subset of Frizzled receptors may signal through G-proteins to affect levels of intracellular Ca^{2+}. However, there is no biochemical evidence that Frizzled proteins directly bind G-proteins or that G-proteins are directly involved in promoting the stabilization of β-catenin. Thus, the mechanism of Frizzled

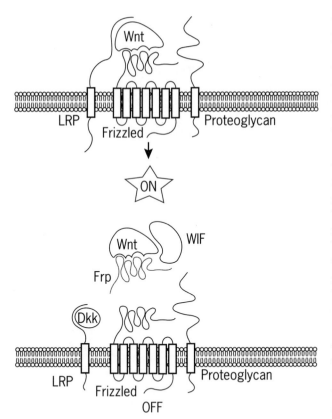

Figure 3   Wnt signalling at the cell surface. Top: Wnt proteins are secreted and bind Frizzled receptors with high affinity at a conserved domain in the N-terminal region. The mechanism by which Frizzled proteins transduce the Wnt signal across the membrane is unclear but may involve signalling through heterotrimeric G-proteins. Wnt proteins also interact with LRP co-receptors. Proteoglycans are also involved in the reception of Wnt signals through an unknown mechanism. Bottom: Wnt signalling is modulated extracellularly by a variety of secreted Wnt inhibitors including members of the secreted Frizzled-related proteins (FRPs), WIF-1 and Dickkopf (Dkk). Binding of these proteins to Wnt is thought to prevent the interaction of Wnt with Frizzled, thereby preventing activation of the pathway.

action and the potential importance of G-proteins in Wnt signalling await further experimentation.

Although compelling evidence exists that Frizzled proteins act as Wnt receptors, it is clear that other cell surface and extracellular molecules also play roles in the reception of Wnt signals (**Figure 3**). For example, members of the LDL-receptor-related family of transmembrane proteins (LRP 5/6) have recently been shown to act as Wnt co-receptors. Proteoglycans, extracellular or cell surface proteins that consist of a protein core and at least one glycosaminoglycan sugar side chain, have been shown to be important regulators of Wnt signalling. In addition, reception of Wnt signals is also modulated extracellularly by a diverse group of secreted Wnt inhibitors. At present, these

Wnt inhibitors include members of the secreted Frizzled-Related Protein family (called FrzB or FRP), Wnt-inhibitory factor-1 (WIF-1), Cerberus and Dickkopf (Dkk). FRPs, WIF-1 and Cerberus can directly bind Wnt proteins and are thought to antagonize Wnt function by preventing their interaction with Frizzled receptors. FRP can also interact with Frizzled, suggesting that FRPs may also antagonize Wnt signalling through the formation of a nonfunctional complex with Frizzled receptors. Dkk functions by binding to LRP and preventing the interaction between LRP, Wnt, and Frizzled. Together, these data demonstrate that the reception of Wnt signals is complex, involving the interplay between Wnt protein, Frizzled and LRP cell surface receptors, proteoglycans and secreted Wnt inhibitors. Understanding the nature and importance of these interactions will require further biochemical analyses of the Wnt reception complex and how this complex transduces the Wnt signal from the outside to the inside of the cell.

From the Membrane to the Nucleus – Transduction of Wnt Signals inside the Cell

Wnt signalling is dependent on the levels of β-catenin in the cell. The pathway is OFF when levels of β-catenin are low and the pathway is ON when levels of β-catenin are high. This begs the question of how the levels of β-catenin are regulated in the cell. The answer to this question requires understanding the function of two competing groups of proteins. On one side, the destruction complex, GSK3, Axin and APC work to destroy β-catenin keeping levels low and the pathway OFF. On the other side, CKIε, Dishevelled and GBP/Frat are activated in response to Wnt and work to antagonize the destruction complex, increasing the levels of β-catenin and turning the pathway ON. The following sections examine the role of each of these groups of proteins in Wnt signalling in more detail.

The Destruction Complex: GSK3, Axin and APC

GSK3, a serine–threonine protein kinase, is the central player in the destruction complex (**Figures 1** and **4**). In the absence of Wnt signal, GSK3 is active and adds phosphate groups to four N-terminal sites of β-catenin (S33, S37, T41 and S45 in human β-catenin). These phosphoamino acids act as a tag on β-catenin, marking it for destruction by the proteasome. The amino acid sequence in β-catenin that is phosphorylated by GSK3 is called the 'destruction box' to denote its involvement in regulating the stability of β-catenin. Mutation of the GSK3 phosphorylation sites within the destruction box significantly diminishes the phosphorylation of β-catenin and results in highly stable forms of β-catenin with increased activity (Yost *et al.*, 1996; Pai *et al.*, 1997). The importance of the destruction box sequence is highlighted by

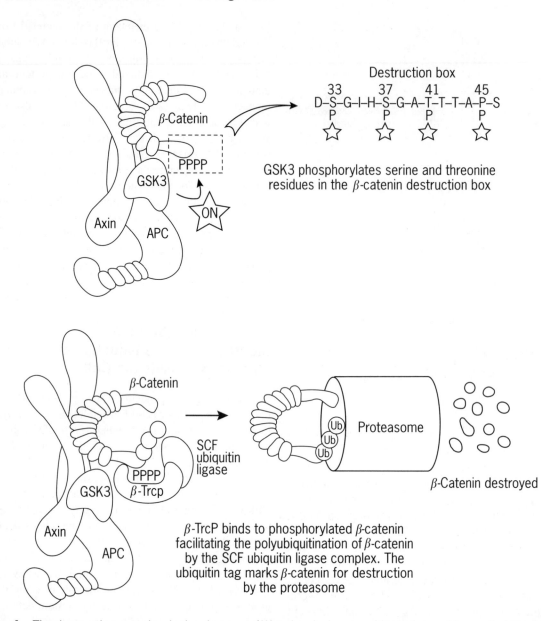

Figure 4   The destruction complex. In the absence of Wnt signal a large multiprotein machine, called the destruction complex, facilitates the rapid destruction of β-catenin. Top: two proteins, Axin and APC, act as scaffold proteins forming the underlying structure of the complex. APC and Axin bind themselves, each other and β-catenin. Additionally, Axin binds GSK3, Dishevelled and PP2A. The binding of GSK3 and β-catenin to Axin is critical for bringing GSK3 in close proximity to β-catenin and stimulating the GSK3-mediated phosphorylation of β-catenin at serine and threonine residues in the destruction box. Bottom: phosphorylated β-catenin is then bound by β-TrCP, which promotes the addition of a polyubiquitin tag to β-catenin. This ubiquitin tag marks β-catenin for rapid destruction by the proteosome, the cell's protein incinerator.

the recent finding that residues within the destruction box are often mutated in human cancers (**Figures 3** and **7**, discussed in detail below).

Axin is a second key component of the destruction complex (**Figures 1** and **4**). Mice lacking functional Axin develop with defects in the patterning of the dorsal–ventral axis, a phenotype similar to that seen following ectopic activation of the Wnt pathway in frogs (Zeng *et al.*, 1997). In addition, over-expression of Axin can inhibit Wnt

signalling and promote the degradation of β-catenin. Axin possesses multiple protein–protein interaction domains and appears to act as scaffold proteins, i.e. it serves as a building block for the construction of multiprotein complexes. Axin binds several components of the Wnt pathway including Dishevelled, APC, GSK3 and β-catenin. The binding of both GSK3 and β-catenin appears to be critical for the function of Axin as this interaction greatly enhances the phosphorylation of β-catenin by GSK3. Thus, Axin appears to promote β-catenin degradation by bringing GSK3 and β-catenin into close proximity, thereby facilitating the phosphorylation of β-catenin by GSK3. Recently, mutations in Axin have been found in hepatocellular carcinomas and colon cancer, underscoring the importance of Axin in regulating the activity of the Wnt signalling pathway (Satoh *et al.*, 2000; Webster *et al.*, 2000).

APC is the third critical component of the destruction complex (**Figures 1** and **4**). APC was originally identified as a tumour-suppressor protein and mutations in APC are found in >80% of all colorectal tumours. The *APC* gene encodes a large, multidomain protein that, like Axin, appears to function as a scaffold protein. APC binds to several components of the Wnt pathway, including Axin, GSK3 and β-catenin. The first clue into the function of APC came from the finding that colorectal adenocarcinoma cell lines harbouring mutations in the *APC* gene possess high levels of β-catenin. Expression of wild-type APC in these cells resulted in a dramatic reduction in β-catenin levels, suggesting that APC is negative regulator of β-catenin stability (Munemitsu *et al.*, 1995). How does APC promote the degradation of β-catenin? Current models predict APC functions in a similar fashion to Axin, stimulating GSK3-mediated phosphorylation of β-catenin. An alternative idea is that APC may function to localize the destruction complex to a specific location in the cell. In support of this hypothesis, mutations in APC that perturb its normal cortical location in the cell also perturb its ability to promote β-catenin degradation (McCartney *et al.*, 1999). These two models are not mutually exclusive and further analysis of APC in a variety of systems should clarify the role APC plays in regulating β-catenin stability.

How does phosphorylation of β-catenin stimulate ubiquitination? The answer to this question came recently with the finding that β-TrCP/Slimb, a component of the SCF ubiquitin ligase complex, plays a critical role in regulating β-catenin degradation (**Figure 4**; Jiang and Struhl, 1998; Kitagawa *et al.*, 1999). β-TrCP/Slimb specifically binds the phosphorylated destruction box of β-catenin, resulting in ubiquitination of β-catenin and subsequent proteolysis by the proteasome. What remains unclear, however, is how β-catenin is delivered to its final destination, the proteosome. Together, these data shed light on how mutations in APC, Axin and β-catenin lead to hyperactivation of the Wnt pathway and cancer. Recessive mutations in the tumour suppressors APC and Axin would lead to the inability of the destruction complex to target β-catenin for degradation in the absence of Wnt signals. Oncogenic mutations in the destruction box of β-catenin would prevent phosphorylation by GSK3 and/or the interaction of β-catenin with β-TrCP/Slimb. In each of these cases, β-catenin would evade proteasomal degradation and accumulate in the cell, leading to inappropriate activation of the pathway. This idea is supported by a number of studies showing that primary human tumour cells harbouring mutations in APC, Axin or β-catenin

display elevated levels of β-catenin. This knowledge provides potential targets for clinical intervention and will be invaluable for the designing and testing new therapeutic agents for the treatment of cancer in humans.

Antagonizing the Destruction Complex: CKIε, Dishevelled and GBP/Frat

How does activation of the Wnt pathway promote the stabilization of β-catenin in the cell? The answer to this question hinges on understanding how Wnt signals, once transduced across the plasma membrane, act to antagonize the destruction complex. Until recently, our knowledge of the molecular events that occur upon Wnt stimulation was limited, but major gaps have been filled with the characterization of the biochemical relationships between intracellular components of the Wnt pathway.

Dishevelled is the most upstream intracellular component of the Wnt pathway and is 'activated' in response to Wnt signals (**Figures 1** and **5**). Dishevelled appears to function as a scaffold protein, acting through its association with other signalling proteins. Dishevelled possesses three highly conserved domains important for its function. The first is an N-terminal DIX domain that shares sequence identity to a C-terminal domain of Axin. The DIX domain has been shown to be important for homodimerization of Dishevelled and the binding of Axin. Second, is a centrally located PDZ domain. PDZ domains are present in a variety of proteins and serve as sites for protein–protein interactions. A number of proteins have been shown to bind Dishevelled through the PDZ domain including CKIε, GBP/Frat and Casein Kinase II. Both the DIX and PDZ domains are required for Dishevelled function in Wnt signalling. Third is the DEP domain found in the C-terminal third of Dishevelled. The DEP domain shares sequence similarity to the *Caenorhabditis elegans* gene *egl-10* and pleckstrin. Although the DEP domain is not required for the ability of Dishevelled to stabilize β-catenin, it is required for the function of Dishevelled in regulating cell polarity in flies and cell movements during gastrulation in vertebrates. It remains unresolved how Dishevelled transduces Wnt signals, but recent studies showing that Dishevelled interacts with Axin suggest that it may play a direct role in antagonizing the destruction complex.

Dishevelled function may also be dependent on its localization within the cell. In *Xenopus*, activation of the Wnt pathway is required for the establishment of dorsal cell fates. Examination of the localization of Dishevelled in early embryos revealed that it associates with small vesicle-like organelles (0.5–1.0 μm in diameter) that are enriched on the dorsal side of the embryo (Miller *et al.*, 1999). This localization appears to be important since treatments that prevent dorsal development also prevent the dorsal enrichment of Dishevelled. Interestingly, time-lapse confocal microscopy analysis of Green Fluorescent Protein tagged Dishevelled (Dishevelled-GFP)

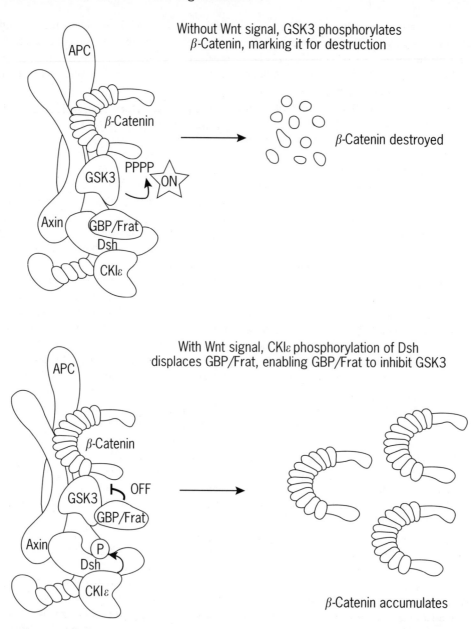

Without Wnt signal, GSK3 phosphorylates
β-Catenin, marking it for destruction

β-Catenin destroyed

With Wnt signal, CKIε phosphorylation of Dsh
displaces GBP/Frat, enabling GBP/Frat to inhibit GSK3

β-Catenin accumulates

Figure 5   A current model of Wnt signalling and stabilization of β-catenin. Top: without Wnt signal, it is thought that Dishevelled might bind Axin and GBP/Frat, sequestering GBP/Frat from GSK3. Bottom: Wnt signal leads to antagonism of the destruction complex. One current model predicts that Dishevelled, through its interaction with Axin, might bring GBP/Frat to the destruction complex. Upon Wnt stimulation, CKIε might phosphorylate Dishevelled, displacing GBP/Frat, allowing it to bind and inhibit GSK3. Through this, or a similar mechanism, Wnt signal may also promote the dissolution of the destruction complex. Inhibition of GSK3 protects β-catenin from degradation and promotes the accumulation of β-catenin in the cell. This model is supported by recent studies but there are other possible mechanisms. Further characterization of the biochemical relationships between components of the destruction complex will help to resolve how Wnt signals stabilize β-catenin.

localization in early embryos demonstrated that Dishevelled-GFP associates with and is transported along the microtubule cytoskeleton towards the prospective dorsal side of the embryo. To view movies of Dishevelled transport in frog embryos, visit the *Journal of Cell Biology* web page at http://www.jcb.org/cgi/content/full/146/2/ 427/DC1. In addition, Dishevelled has also been shown to be associated with the actin cytoskeleton in embryonic kidney cells (Torres and Nelson, 2000). Together these data suggest that Dishevelled localization, perhaps through its association with the cytoskeleton, plays an important role in modulating the activity of the Wnt pathway.

GBP (GSK3 Binding Protein) and its mammalian orthologue Frat function as positive regulators of the Wnt signalling pathway (**Figures 1** and **5**; Yost *et al.*, 1998). GBP/Frat can inhibit GSK3 kinase activity, suggesting that it promotes β-catenin stabilization through direct inhibition of GSK3-mediated phosphorylation of β-catenin. However, it is unclear whether this affect is due to a change in GSK3 activity or through steric blockade of GSK3–substrate interactions.

More recently, CKIε, a serine–threonine protein kinase, was identified as a positive regulator of the Wnt pathway (**Figures 1** and **5**; Peters *et al.*, 1999; Sakanaka *et al.*, 1999). Expression of CKIε stabilizes β-catenin and expression of dominant negative forms of CKIε antagonizes Wnt signalling. Overexpression studies have placed CKIε downstream of Dishevelled and upstream of GSK3. In addition, CKIε can bind to and phosphorylate Dishevelled, suggesting that CKIε could directly affect the activity of Dishevelled.

How do Dishevelled, GBP/Frat and CKIε antagonize the destruction complex? In the absence of Wnt signals, Dishevelled might associate with Axin and bind GBP/Frat, sequestering it from GSK3. Upon Wnt stimulation, CKIε might phosphorylate Dishevelled, causing the displacement of GBP/Frat. Released GBP/Frat would then bind GSK3 that is associated with Axin, thereby inhibiting GSK3 activity. This model is consistent with current data, but so are many others and many questions are unresolved. How do Frizzled receptors transduce Wnt signals? How are Dishevelled, GBP/Frat and CKIε activated in response to Wnt signals? Where in the cell is the destruction complex located and is this location important for signal transduction? These and other questions await further experimental analysis.

In the Nucleus – Regulation of Gene Expression by β-Catenin and TCF/LEF

As we have seen, cells have evolved a very elaborate and complex mechanism for regulating intracellular levels of β-catenin. Wnt signalling frees β-catenin from the destruction complex and it now accumulates in the cell. What happens next? It is now dogma that upon Wnt stimulation β-catenin accumulates and enters the nucleus, where it regulates gene expression. However, when first proposed the idea that the nucleus was the primary location of β-catenin function in Wnt signalling seemed hard to believe. At the time, β-catenin was known as a protein that localized to cell–cell junctions and played a crucial role in regulating cell–cell adhesion. This raised the perplexing question of how a cell adhesion protein could also be a signalling protein in Wnt pathway that affected gene expression in the nucleus. The answer came from studies showing that β-catenin's roles in cell adhesion and signalling were separable and involved the interaction of

β-catenin with distinct sets of protein partners. Several groups also showed that β-catenin, in addition to its membrane localization, also localizes to the nucleus and that Wnt signalling caused an enrichment of β-catenin in the nucleus. Now this idea is so prevalent that nuclear β-catenin localization is used as a diagnostic tool for Wnt pathway activation in development and oncogenic activation of the Wnt pathway in cancer.

In the nucleus, β-catenin binds to a number of different protein partners to regulate gene expression (**Figure 6**). These partners include members of the LEF/TCF family of transcription factors (**Figures 1** and **6**). The LEF/TCF proteins are sequence-specific DNA binding proteins and serve to localize β-catenin to the promoters of Wnt target genes. A number of these target genes have been identified in the past several years and include developmental regulatory genes such as *siamois*, *twin* and *Xnr-3* in *Xenopus* and *ultrabiothorax* in *Drosophila*. Additional targets include regulators of cell growth and proliferation, c-*myc*

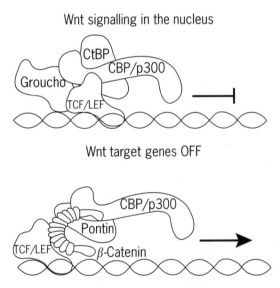

Figure 6 Regulation of gene expression by β-catenin and TCF/LEF. In the absence of Wnt signal, TCF/LEF transcription factors specifically bind to sequences in the promoters of Wnt target genes and act as repressors keeping these genes OFF. This repression is mediated through the interaction of TCF/LEF with a number of transcriptional repressor proteins including members of the Groucho family, CtBP and CBP/p300. Upon Wnt stimulation, β-catenin accumulates in the nucleus and interacts with TCF/LEF. This complex specifically binds to sites in the promoters of Wnt target genes and through interactions with additional transcription factors (e.g. CBP/p300 and Pontin 52) activate transcription. The mechanism by which the β-catenin–TCF/LEF complex activates transcription is unclear, but may involve the displacement of repressors bound to TCF/LEF by β-catenin.

and *cyclin D1*. For a complete list of known targets of the Wnt pathway, see the Wnt gene homepage (http://www.stanford.edu/~rnusse/wntwindow.html).

The mechanism by which β-catenin activates transcription remains unclear. Mutational analyses have identified two regions of β-catenin, one near the N-terminus and the other at the C-terminus, that are important for transcriptional activation. It appears that these sites may serve as protein–protein interaction domains enabling β-catenin to regulate transcription through binding of additional transcriptional regulators (**Figure 6**). Several binding partners have been identified including CBP/p300 (Creb Binding Protein) and Pontin 52. In addition, Lef-1 has been shown to form complexes with several members of the SMAD family of signalling proteins that play a role in Transforming Growth Factor β signalling (see below). Lef-1 and SMADs appear to function cooperatively to stimulate expression of specific developmental target genes such as *twin*.

Another possible mechanism by which β-catenin may activate transcription is by displacing co-repressors from TCF/LEF (**Figure 6**). In the absence of Wnt signals, TCF/LEF proteins can act as transcriptional repressors, preventing transcription of Wnt/β-catenin target genes. TCF/LEF proteins do not appear to act alone but instead require interactions with one of several identified co-repressors. These repressors include members of the Groucho family, CtBP (C-terminal Binding Protein), and CBP/p300. It is thought that the ability of CBP/p300 to act as an activator and a repressor may be due to differences in cellular context. In other words, CBP/p300 can function as either an activator or repressor depending on the situation.

ADDITIONAL REGULATORS OF Wnt SIGNAL TRANSDUCTION

Although the mechanism of Wnt signal transduction described thus far may seem complicated enough, additional players continue to be identified. For example, protein phosphatase 2A appears to play a role in regulating β-catenin stability although it is unclear whether it promotes β-catenin degradation or stabilization. The *Drosophila naked cuticle* gene has recently been shown to be a novel cytoplasmic antagonist that may limit the potency, duration or distribution of Wnt signals. Recent evidence also implicates components of the mitogen-activated protein kinase (MAPK) pathway, transforming growth factor-β-activated kinase (TAK-1) and NEMO-like kinase (NLK) as regulators of Wnt signalling. However, it remains to be determined whether these genes are true components of the Wnt pathway or whether they act in parallel to the canonical Wnt pathway.

In addition to these players, it has become clear that cross-talk between the Wnt pathway and the Transforming Growth Factor β (TGF-β) signalling pathway plays an important role in regulating Wnt/β-catenin signalling both during development and in human disease. For example, the secreted Wnt antagonist Cerberus can also interact with members of the BMP and Nodal families of TGF-β-like signalling molecules, suggesting that Cerberus can function as a multivalent modulator of both Wnt and TGF-β/BMP signalling. In addition, Wnt and TGF-β signalling pathways also cross-talk inside the cell. Several recent papers have shown that TCF/LEF transcription factors interact with members of the SMAD family of TGF-β/BMP signal mediators. Specifically, Lef-1 can form complexes with three different SMAD proteins: SMAD-2 and -3, effectors for TGF-β and Activin signals; and SMAD-4, a ubiquitous effector for all TGF-β/BMP signalling pathways. Through these interactions, SMAD proteins were found to stimulate synergistically transcription of specific Wnt target genes. These data are intriguing since mutations in components of both the Wnt (APC and β-catenin) and TGF-β signalling pathways (TGF-β receptor type II, SMAD-2, -3 and -4) are associated with colorectal cancers. Furthermore, mice double heterozygous for both *APC* and *SMAD-4* display intestinal polyps that develop into more malignant tumours than those in mice heterozygous for *APC* alone (Takaku *et al.*, 1998). Together these data argue that the Wnt and TGF-β pathways cross-talk to regulate cooperatively gene expression and that this synergistic interaction may be important both during development and in cancer.

β-Catenin levels can also be regulated by Wnt-independent mechanisms. For example, expression of integrin-linked kinase in mammalian cells promotes the stabilization and nuclear accumulation of β-catenin (Novak *et al.*, 1998). Presenilin proteins have also been implicated as regulators of β-catenin stability. Mutations in presenilin associated with the rapid onset of Alzheimer disease decrease the stability of β-catenin in neurons. This effect on β-catenin was also correlated with an increase in the susceptibility of neurons to apoptosis resulting from the accumulation of β-amyloid protein. Given the ability of these signalling pathways to modulate β-catenin stability, it seems likely that β-catenin may regulate many cellular processes independent of its role in Wnt signalling.

ONCOGENIC ACTIVATION OF THE Wnt PATHWAY

Tumour formation results from the loss of control over cell proliferation. This occurs through mutations that produce oncogenes with a dominant gain of function or inactivate tumour suppressor genes through recessive loss of function mutations. Both types of mutations lead to defects in regulatory pathways that normally control cell proliferation. Recently, it has become clear that components of the

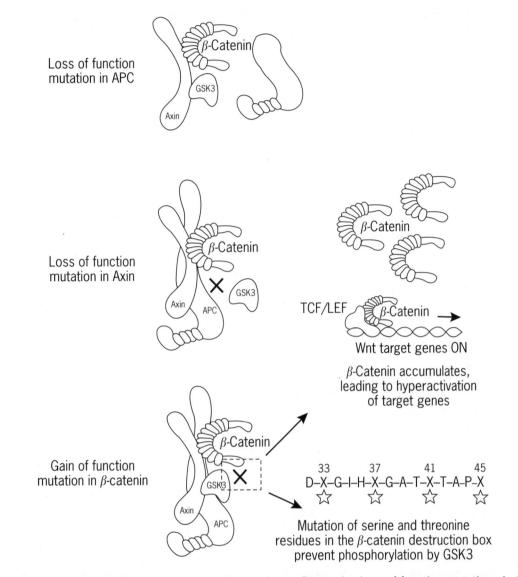

Figure 7 Oncogenic activation of the Wnt signalling pathway. Recessive loss of function mutations in the tumour suppressors APC and Axin disable the destruction complex and lead to the inappropriate accumulation of β-catenin in the cell. Most mutations isolated in *APC* are nonsense mutations that lead to the premature truncation of the protein and loss of critical binding sites for Axin and β-catenin. One mutation found in Axin appears to decrease the binding affinity between Axin and GSK3. Gain of function mutations in β-catenin that allow it to escape regulation by the destruction complex also lead to constitutive activation of the Wnt pathway. The majority of mutations in β-catenin found thus far are missense mutations that alter one of the four potential GSK3 phosphorylation sites in the destruction box. The inappropriate accumulation of β-catenin in the cell then leads to hyperactivation of target genes such as c-*myc* and *cyclin D1*, and uncontrolled cell division.

Wnt signalling pathway are mutated in a variety of human cancers. Thus far, mutations in APC, Axin and β-catenin have been identified in various cancers and these findings have fuelled a great explosion of interest in the relationship between Wnt signalling and cancer. These mutations result in the inability of the cell to regulate appropriately levels of β-catenin (**Figure 7**). Recessive mutations in the tumour suppressor genes *APC* and *Axin* result in defects in the destruction complex allowing β-catenin to escape degradation. Conversely, mutations in β-catenin produce a dominant gain of function protein that evades regulation by the destruction complex. The end result of these mutations is the constitutive activation of Wnt target genes and uncontrolled cell proliferation.

Germline mutations of the *APC* gene lead to familial adenomatous polyposis characterized by the development

Table 1 Current list of human cancers associated with mutations in β-catenin, APC and Axin

β-Catenin	APC	Axin
Colorectal adenoma and carcinoma	Colorectal adenoma and carcinoma	Colorectal
Endometrial carcinoma	Breast cancer	Hepatocellular carcinoma
Hepatoblastoma	Medulloblastoma	
Hepatocellular carcinoma		
Malignant fibrous histiocytoma		
Medulloblastoma		
Ovarian carcinoma		
Pilomatricoma		
Prostate		
Synovial sarcoma		
Uterine		
Wilms' tumours		

of colorectal polyps in the second to third decade of life. In addition, somatic mutations of the *APC* gene are associated with >80% of sporadic colorectal adenomas and carcinomas. More than 95% of germ-line and somatic mutations of the *APC* gene are nonsense mutations that result in the synthesis of a truncated protein that lacks the region of APC important for its function in the destruction complex. Significantly, these truncations in APC remove binding sites for β-catenin and Axin and also putative phosphorylation sites for GSK3 (**Figures 1** and **7**). Colon cancer cells expressing such a truncated form of APC possess very high levels of β-catenin, suggesting that the inability of APC to promote β-catenin degradation is causally linked to tumour formation. In addition to the well-documented link between APC function and colorectal cancer, mutation of *APC* is also implicated in other human cancers including aggressive fibromatosis and breast cancer (**Table 1**). Together these findings highlight the importance of APC in Wnt signalling and oncogenesis.

Recent evidence demonstrates that *Axin*, like *APC*, functions as a tumour-suppressor gene (**Figure 7**, **Table 1**). The *Axin1* gene is mutated in hepatocellular carcinomas and missense mutations in *Axin* have also been isolated in colon cancer cells (Satoh *et al.*, 2000; Webster *et al.*, 2000). One of these mutations was found to diminish the interaction between Axin and GSK3, providing a potential mechanism for oncogenic activation of the Wnt pathway.

The striking connection between Axin- and APC-mediated regulation of β-catenin and oncogenesis suggested that mutations in β-catenin itself might play a role in tumour formation. Consistent with this idea, targeted mutation or deletion of the destruction box sequence results in highly stable forms of β-catenin that are hyperactive (Yost *et al.*, 1996; Pai *et al.*, 1997). Cell lines harbouring activating mutations of β-catenin often display high levels of both cytoplasmic and nuclear β-catenin and constitutive activation of TCF/LEF reporter genes. In addition, expression of an N-terminal truncated form of β-catenin lacking the destruction box in the epidermis of

transgenic mice resulted in the formation of hair follicle-related tumours. These data demonstrate that increasing levels of β-catenin are sufficient to promote tumour formation and implicate the N-terminal destruction box sequence as potential sites for oncogenic activation of β-catenin.

Over the past several years, many studies have shown that mutations in β-catenin exist in a variety of human cancers (**Table 1**). Strikingly, the identified mutations are missense or deletion mutations in the destruction box and most of these alter one of the GSK3 phosphorylation sites (**Figure 7**). In addition to the GSK3 sites, missense mutations at aspartate-32 and glycine-34 have also been reported. These residues, along with serine-37, have been characterized as a ubiquitination target motif based on its similarity with Iκ-B, another protein targeted for degradation by the SCF$^{\beta\text{-TrCP}}$ ubiquitin ligase complex. Together, these data strongly argue that mutations in β-catenin that enable it to evade regulation by the destruction complex play an important role in tumorigenic transformation of many cell types.

What is the consequence of constitutive β-catenin activity? β-Catenin functions as a transcriptional activator in Wnt signalling, suggesting that its role in tumour formation may be through inappropriate activation of genes important for regulating cell division and growth. This idea has gained support with the finding that the c-*myc* and *cyclin D1* genes, both of which are known to promote cell proliferation, are direct targets of β-catenin. c-*myc* is a potent oncogene that regulates cell cycle progression, promoting the G_1/S phase transition. Similarly, *cyclin D1* also plays an important role regulating movement through the cell cycle. Thus, mutations in Axin, APC or β-catenin that result in the stabilization and accumulation of β-catenin may lead to inappropriate expression of target genes, such as c-*myc* and *cyclin D1*. Expression of c-*myc* and *cyclin D1* would then expedite the G_1 to S transition, leading to uncontrolled cell proliferation. Additionally, evidence also suggests that β-catenin may act as a survival factor protecting cells from cell death. Since the transition from G_1 to S phase requires the presence of survival factors, β-catenin may also stimulate this transition directly by preventing apoptosis and permitting cell cycle progression.

CONCLUSION

With the recent completion of the human genome sequence, we have entered a new era in biology and medicine. This achievement has been compared to putting a man on the moon and will undoubtedly revolutionize basic biological and medical sciences. This revolution, however, is only in its infancy. What remains is put the pieces of the puzzle together by characterizing the function of each of the estimated 80 000 human genes. How do these genes instruct cells to divide, to migrate or to die? How do these genes control embryogenesis? How do mutations in specific genes contribute to human disease?

Although many aspects of Wnt signalling remain unclear, we are beginning to put the pieces of the Wnt puzzle together to understand how the genes involved in Wnt signalling communicate signals between cells. In particular, great strides have been made towards understanding the molecular and biochemical mechanics of Wnt signal transduction. These findings underscore the important predictive value of analysing the fundamental mechanisms by which cells signal to one another: by establishing how genes function in specific signalling pathways (e.g. whether they act as repressors or activators), one can make educated guesses how these genes might contribute to human disease. A repressor could be a tumour-suppressor gene and an activator could be an oncogene. Thus, a clear understanding the basics of how cells communicate will lead us to an understanding of how inappropriate activation of signalling pathways leads to cancer. With this information, researchers will hopefully be able to design new therapeutic reagents for treating and preventing cancer.

REFERENCES

Bhanot, P., *et al.* (1996). A new member of the *frizzled* family from *Drosophila* functions as a Wingless receptor. *Nature*, **382**, 225–230.

Jiang, J. and Struhl, G. (1998). Regulation of the Hedgehog and Wingless signalling pathways by the F-box/WD40-repeat protein Slimb. *Nature*, **391**, 493–496.

Kitagawa, M., *et al.* (1999). An F-box protein, FWD1, mediates ubiquitin-dependent proteolysis of beta-catenin. *Embo Journal*, **18**, 2401–2410.

McCartney, B. M., *et al.* (1999). *Drosophila* APC2 is a cytoskeletally-associated protein that regulates *wingless* signaling in the embryonic epidermis. *Journal of Cell Biology*, **146**, 1303–1318.

Miller, J. R., *et al.* (1999). Establishment of the dorsal–ventral axis in *Xenopus* embryos coincides with the dorsal enrichment of dishevelled that is dependent on cortical rotation. *Journal of Cell Biology*, **146**, 427–437.

Munemitsu, S., *et al.* (1995). Regulation of intracellular beta-catenin levels by the adenomatous polyposis coli (APC) tumor-suppressor protein. *Proceedings of the National Academy of Sciences of the USA*, **92**, 3046–3050.

Novak, A., *et al.* (1998). Cell adhesion and the integrin-linked kinase regulate the LEF-1 and beta-catenin signaling pathways. *Proceedings of the National Academy of Sciences of the USA*, **95**, 4374–4379.

Nusse, R. and Varmus, H. E. (1982). Many tumors induced by the mouse mammary tumor virus contain a provirus integrated in the same region of the host genome. *Cell*, **31**, 99–109.

Nüsslein-Volhard, C. and Wieschaus, E. (1980). Mutations affecting segment number and polarity in *Drosophila*. *Nature*, **287**, 795–801.

Pai, L.-M., *et al.* (1997). Negative regulation of Armadillo, a Wingless effector in *Drosophila*. *Development*, **124**, 2255–2266.

Peters, J. M., *et al.* (1999). Casein kinase I transduces Wnt signals. *Nature*, **401**, 345–350.

Sakanaka, C., *et al.* (1999). Casein kinase I-epsilon in the Wnt pathway: regulation of beta-catenin function. *Proceedings of the National Academy of Sciences of the USA*, **96**, 12548–12552.

Satoh, S., *et al.* (2000). *AXIN1* mutations in hepatocellular carcinomas, and growth suppression in cancer cells by virus-mediated transfer of *AXIN1*. *Nature Genetics*, **24**, 245–250.

Takaku, K., *et al.* (1998). Intestinal tumorigenesis in compound mutant mice of both *Dpc4* (*Smad4*) and *Apc* genes. *Cell*, **92**, 645–656.

Torres, M. A. and Nelson, W. J. (2000). Colocalization and redistribution of Dishevelled and Actin during Wnt-induced mesenchymal morphogenesis. *Journal of Cell Biology*, **149**, 1433–1442.

Webster, M. T., *et al.* (2000). Sequence variants of the *axin* gene in breast, colon, and other cancers: an analysis of mutations that interfere with GSK3 binding. *Genes, Chromosomes and Cancer*, **28**, 443–453.

Yang-Snyder, J., *et al.* (1996). A *frizzled* homolog functions in a vertebrate Wnt signaling pathway. *Current Biology*, **6**, 1302–1306.

Yost, C., *et al.* (1996). The axis-inducing activity, stability, and subcellular distribution of beta-catenin is regulated in *Xenopus* embryos by glycogen synthase kinase 3. *Genes and Development*, **10**, 1443–1454.

Yost, C., *et al.* (1998). GBP, an inhibitor of GSK-3, is implicated in *Xenopus* development and oncogenesis. *Cell*, **93**, 1031–1041.

Zeng, L., *et al.* (1997). The mouse Fused locus encodes Axin, an inhibitor of the Wnt signaling pathway that regulates embryonic axis formation. *Cell*, **90**, 181–192.

FURTHER READING

Behrens, J. (2000). Cross-regulation of the Wnt signalling pathway: a role of MAP kinases. *Journal of Cell Science*, **113**, 911–919.

Bienz, M. (1999). APC: the plot thickens. *Current Opinions in Genetics and Development*, **9**, 595–603.

Bienz, M. and Clevers, H. (2000). Linking colorectal cancer to Wnt signalling. *Cell*, **103**, 311–320.

Boutros, M. and Mlodzik, M. (1999). Dishevelled: at the crossroads of divergent intracellular signaling pathways. *Mechanics of Development*, **83**, 27–37.

Cadigan, K. M. and Nusse, R. (1997). Wnt signaling: a common theme in animal development. *Genes and Development*, **11**, 3286–3305.

Czech, C., *et al.* (2000). Presenilins and Alzheimer's disease: biological functions and pathogenic mechanisms. *Progress in Neurobiology*, **60**, 363–384.

Dierick, H. and Bejsovec, A. (1999). Cellular mechanisms of wingless/Wnt signal transduction. *Current Topics in Development in Biology*, **43**, 153–190.

Kikuchi, A. (1999). Roles of Axin in the Wnt signalling pathway. *Cell Signalling*, **11**, 777–788.

Kuhl, M., *et al.* (2000). The Wnt/Ca^{2+} pathway: a new vertebrate wnt signaling pathway takes shape. *Trends in Genetics*, **16**, 279–283.

Miller, J. R., *et al.* (1999). Mechanism and function of signal transduction by the Wnt/beta-catenin and Wnt/Ca^{2+} pathways. *Oncogene*, **18**, 7860–7872.

Peifer, M. and Polakis, P. (2000). Wnt signaling in oncogenesis and embryogenesis – a look outside the nucleus. *Science*, **287**, 1606–1609.

Perrimon, N. and Bernfield, M. (2000). Specificities of heparan sulphate proteoglycans in developmental processes. *Nature*, **404**, 725–728.

Polakis, P. (1999). The oncogenic activation of beta-catenin. *Current Opinions in Genetics and Development*, **9**, 15–21.

Polakis, P. (2000). Wnt signaling and cancer. *Genes and Development*, **14**, 1837–1851.

Roose, J. and Clevers, H. (1999). TCF transcription factors: molecular switches in carcinogenesis. *Biochimica Biophysica Acta*, **1424**, M23–37.

Waltzer, L. and Bienz, M. (1999). The control of beta-catenin and TCF during embryonic development and cancer. *Cancer and Metastasis Reviews*, **18**, 231–246.

Wodarz, A. and Nusse, R. (1998). Mechanisms of Wnt signaling in development. *Annual Reviews in Cell and Development Biology*, **14**, 59–88.

Chapter 15

Extracellular Matrix: The Networking Solution

Nancy Boudreau
University of California San Francisco, San Francisco, CA, USA

Mina J. Bissell
Ernest Orlando Lawrence Berkeley National Laboratory, Berkeley, CA, USA

CONTENTS

INTRODUCTION

One of the fundamental properties of functional differentiated tissues is their unique three-dimensional (3D) organisation which allows individual cells to act in a coordinated manner to carry out complex tissue functions. Although individual cells may be capable of eliciting certain responses to external stimuli such as proliferation, many differentiated functions can be achieved only via the coordinated actions of cells within a tissue. For example, endothelial cells which line the walls of functional blood vessels may individually produce necessary anti-clotting factors but alone cannot function as a conduit for blood. Similarly, although rounded single mammary epithelial cells are capable of expressing the tissue-specific milk protein β-casein, they cannot secrete it and expression is significantly enhanced when cells form multi-cellular complexes (Streuli *et al.*, 1991). Three-dimensional organisation was also found to be essential for the generation of significant populations of functional T cells from CD34 + progenitors. Only by embedding the progenitor cells into a 3D carbon matrix seeded with thymus extract could mature functional T cells be obtained. (Poznansky *et al.*, 2000) Thus 3D organisation is essential not only for developing and establishing functional differentiated phenotypes but also for maintaining tissue specific gene expression and function. Moreover, 3D tissue architecture acts to override the genetic information contained within normal and malignant cells (Weaver *et al.*, 1997).

In order for multi-cellular organisms to acquire and maintain a 3D organisation of their tissues, they have elaborated a complex network of extracellular proteins referred to as the extracellular matrix (ECM). This network of extracellular proteins allows cells to adhere, migrate, proliferate and undergo morphogenesis or alternatively instructs them to undergo programmed cell death (Boudreau and Bissell, 1996).

The significance of the ECM in influencing cellular behaviour was initially overlooked as the ECM was considered merely to provide scaffolding to cells and tissues. However, it has become clear that cellular interactions with the ECM also provide essential information to the cell by initiating intracellular signalling cascades which culminate in changes in gene expression. Furthermore, the ECM also provides structural cues to adherent cells. In turn, these ECM-induced changes in cell morphology and gene expression allow cells to subsequently alter their interactions with the extracellular environment. This 'dynamic reciprocity' is the basis for integrated tissue function and allows cells monitor to constantly their extracellular environment and adjust their responses to maintain differentiated tissue phenotypes. In contrast, tumorigenesis results from the loss of this dynamic interaction between cells and their ECM, and the subsequent aberrant dialogue between cells and their microenvironment prevents cells from achieving or maintaining their functional differentiated state. How cells acquire and maintain their 3D organisation is a fundamental question which largely remains to be understood. In order to understand how the various physical and biochemical properties of ECM components contribute to cellular responses, it is necessary to review the components contributing to ECM-mediated responses in cells.

ECM PROTEINS AND INTEGRIN RECEPTORS

ECM Proteins

The ECM proteins comprise a large family of glycoproteins. These large proteins are often comprised of several distinct subunits. For example, laminin, which is composed of α-, β- and γ-chains, and has a molecular mass of over 10^6 kDa, has up to three variants of each of these chains. The final composition of laminin is tissue specific. For example, laminin 5 is found in basement membranes associated with epithelia and endothelium, while laminin-2 is preferentially found in muscle (for a review, see Ekblom, 1996).

Another major component of the extracellular matrices are the collagens. This family is comprised of over 18 members, which are often expressed in tissue-specific patterns (for a review, see Prockop and Kivirikko, 1995). In addition to laminins and collagens, other major ECM components include fibronectin found in association with cells as well as in the serum, vitronectin also found in serum, and tenascin. These matrix proteins are often found in connective tissue matrices which are rich in collagens and to a lesser extent in association with basement membranes.

Another major class of ECM proteins are the proteoglycans, which, with the exception of hyaluronic acid, consist of membrane-associated globular proteins with specialized sulfated N- and O-linked carbohydrate chains called glycosaminoglycans (GAGs). The most common GAG chains found are the heparan and chondroitin chains which are found in almost all mammalian tissues (for a review, see Bernfield et al., 1999).

The structural and biochemical composition of many ECM proteins has been known for some time. These large proteins are usually multidomain structures capable of interacting with other matrix proteins as well as acting as a potential reservoir for soluble mitogens and morphogens (Woodley et al., 1983; Saskela and Rifkin, 1990; Vu et al., 1998). Indeed, specific matrix proteins rarely exist in isolation but instead are found as members of larger complex matrices comprised of various ratios of individual components. It must be emphasized that the net effect of these complex matrices on cell behaviour is equally complex and not simply the sum of the individual components. One fairly well-characterized type of complex ECM is the basement membrane (BM), which consists primarily of laminin-1 and -5, type IV collagen and other minor components including nidogen, fibronectin and proteoglycans (for a review, see Schwarzbauer, 1999). As the name implies, BMs are found at the basal lateral surface of most epithelial tissues including mammary and intestinal epithelium, hepatocytes, keratinocytes and endothelial cells which line the blood-vessel walls. Although laminin can comprise up to 80% of BM, cells behave very differently when in contact with laminin alone as compared with a complete BM. For example, when endothelial cells are plated on a complete reconstituted BM, they rapidly form an anastomosing network of hollow tube-like structures reminiscent of capillaries (Kubota et al., 1998). In contrast, when plated on laminin alone, they form a continuous 'cobblestone' monolayer of cells (Madri and Williams, 1983). Similarly, mammary epithelial cells will form 3D alveolar structures and express milk proteins when cultured on a complete BM but not when plated on laminin alone (Roskelley et al., 1994). Together these findings emphasize that complex ECMs are necessary to direct complex tissue-type organisation and gene expression. A recent comparative analysis of the Drosophila and C. elegans genomes indicated that these BM proteins have remained highly conserved throughout evolution from C. elegans to vertebrates, emphasizing the essential nature of these proteins in multi-cellular organisms (Hynes and Zhao, 2000).

More often than not, contact with a BM-type ECM leads to growth arrest and differentiation and promotes tissue-specific gene expression. In contrast to BMs, stromal matrices or provisional matrices formed at sites of injury often consist of various ratios of the fibrillar collagens, tenascin, fibronectin as well as other matrix components derived from the circulation, including vitronectin and fibrinogen. These matrices often comprise the bulk of connective tissues surrounding cells other than epithelium such as fibroblasts and chondrocytes. Adhesion to these connective-tissue type matrices often promotes cell migration and proliferation. Interestingly, increased amounts of stromal ECM are often found adjacent to many epithelial tumor cells (Weaver et al., 1996).

In attempting to understand how different ECM components give rise to these markedly different phenotypes, much attention has been focused on different cell-surface receptors for these various ECM components.

Integrins

Cells recognize and respond to different ECM matrices by interacting with cell-surface receptors called integrins. Integrins are a large, specialized family of transmembrane heterodimeric proteins which consist of an α subunit and an often larger β subunit with a cytoplasmic domain. These cytoplasmic domains may directly interact with cytoskeletal proteins and thereby serve to 'integrate' the extracellular and intracellular environments.

The α and β subunits can form up to 19 different combinations which have some selective but also overlapping affinities for various ECM components (see **Tables 1** and **2**). For example, the $\alpha2\beta1$ heterodimer has been shown to bind both collagen I and laminin, whereas the $\alpha6\beta1$ integrin will bind laminin only and not collagen.

Table 1 Integrin heterodimers

Beta subunits	Alpha partners
$\beta1$	$\alpha1, \alpha2, \alpha3, \alpha4, \alpha5, \alpha6, \alpha7, \alpha8, \alpha9, \alpha v$
$\beta4$	$\alpha6$
$\beta3, \beta5, \beta6, \beta8$	αv
$\beta2$	$\alpha L, \alpha M, \alpha X$
$\beta7$	$\alpha4$

Table 2 Integrins for common ECM ligands

ECM ligand	Integrin
Laminin	$\alpha1\beta1, \alpha2\beta1, \alpha3\beta1, \alpha6\beta1, \alpha7\beta1, \alpha6\beta4$
Collagen I	$\alpha1\beta1, \alpha2\beta1, \alpha3\beta1,$
Fibronectin	$\alpha4\beta1, \alpha5\beta1, \alpha v\beta1, \alpha v\beta3, \alpha v\beta6, \alpha v\beta8, \alpha4\beta7$
Tenascin	$\alpha v\beta3, \alpha v\beta6, \alpha v\beta8$
Vitronectin	$\alpha v\beta1, \alpha v\beta3, \alpha v\beta6, \alpha v\beta8$

The ligand recognition sequences of the integrins are determined by the combination of α and β subunits of the heterodimeric molecules, rather than by the α or β chains alone, which may account for some of the substrate overlap. The integrin heterodimers can recognize distinct amino acid sequences present in different ECM ligands. For example, the arginine–glycine–aspartic acid (RGD) recognition domain present in many integrin heterodimers including the $\alpha v\beta3$ and $\alpha5\beta1$ integrins can bind to any ECM component which contains an exposed RGD sequence such as fibronectin and tenascin (Pierschbacher and Ruoslahti, 1984; Joshi et al., 1993). Furthermore, because most ECM proteins contain multiple domains, they may also contain multiple integrin recognition sites. For example, in addition to the RGD domain, tenascin also contains fibronectin-type repeats which can bind other integrins such as $\alpha9\beta1$ in an RGD-independent manner (Yokosaki et al., 1994).

Like the tissue-specific distribution of some ECM components, many of the integrin subunits are often distributed in cell- and tissue-specific patterns. For example, the $\beta2$ integrin is almost exclusively expressed by leukocytes, whereas others such as the $\beta1$ subunit are widely expressed. Although it is tempting to suggest that tissue-specific responses might be determined by the composition of the adjacent ECM as well the particular species of integrin available to interact with it, this relationship is not straightforward. Many integrins exist in inactive conformations, whereby the ligand recognition domains are masked or unavailable to interact with the ECM. Integrin activation can be induced by many different stimuli and provides an additional level of control by which cells can regulate their interaction with the microenvironment (for a review, see Hughes

and Pfaff, 1998). This activation phenomenon, referred to as 'inside-out signalling,' is often induced by binding of the ECM to a particular integrin, which in turn induces signalling cascades to allow other surface integrins to become activated. On the other hand, it has also been shown that activating intracellular signalling pathways can also lead to inactivation of integrins (Hughes et al., 1997). 'Inside-out signalling' is yet another example of the dynamic interplay between cells and their matrices and emphasizes the reciprocal nature of these interactions.

In addition, proteolytic fragments of ECM molecules appear capable of binding many of the same integrins as their full-length counterparts, yet often give rise to dramatically different cellular responses. For example, both the full-length laminin-5 and the $\alpha3$ fragment of laminin-5 which is generated via proteolytic cleavage can bind the $\alpha3\beta1$ integrin. However, in contrast to full-length laminin, the proteolysed fragments increase cellular migration (Gianelli et al., 1997). Thus the net balance of proteolytic activity and structural integrity of the ECM as well as the expression pattern or activation state of integrins all contribute to the coordinated tissue responses to a particular microenvironment.

Signalling by Integrins

Binding of an ECM molecule to its integrin receptor initiates a series of intracellular signalling events which led to changes in cellular behaviour. Signalling via integrins often involves the recruitment of adaptor proteins and activation of a series of cytoplasmic protein kinases. (A detailed description of tyrosine kinase signalling is provided in the chapter on Signalling by Tyrosine Kinases.) The classical integrin-mediated signalling pathways originally described involved the cytoplasmic domains of the β integrin subunit undergoing a conformational change upon ligand binding. This conformational change in turn allows focal adhesion kinase (FAK) to phosphorylate itself. Phosphorylated FAK could then bind to promote the activation of a number of different downstream mediators including members of the Src family of protein kinases, the PI3 kinase pathway, as well as recruitment of adaptor proteins including p130[cas], Crk and the Grb2–Sos complex which recognize phosphorylated intermediates via their SH2 domains. In turn, assembly of these focal adhesion complexes and phosphorylated intermediates leads to the activation of Ras and Raf. Activated Raf then phosphorylates extracellular-related kinase (ERK). Phosphorylated ERK can then translocate to the nucleus and activate cell proliferation via its ability to modulate the activity of transcription factors such as TCF necessary for expression of cell cycle mediators including cyclin D1 and c-fos (**Figure 1**).

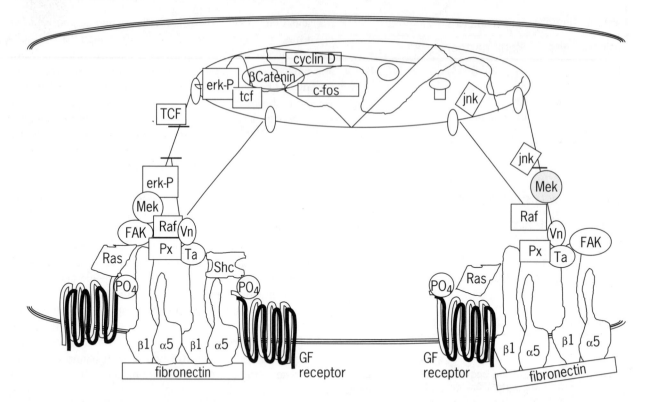

Figure 1 Intracellular signalling pathways which may participate in cell proliferation induced by adhesion to a fibronectin extracellular matrix. Integrins and growth factor receptors are clustered and form focal adhesion complexes which contain vinculin (Vn), paxillin (Px) and talin (Ta), which in turn bind to the cytoskeleton. The growth factor receptors are also phosphorylated (PO_4) and signalling initiated by the focal adhesion complexes allows ERK or JNK to become activated and phosphorylated and translocate to the nucleus where they act as transcription factors to allow expression of genes including *c-fos* or cyclin D1. β-Catenin can also move to the nucleus and form transcriptional complexes with TCF. Note that on this substratum that cells generally become flattened and elongated.

More recently, it has been shown that α integrin subunits could also specifically initiate signalling cascades. Rather than initiating signalling through phosphorylation of FAK, the α chains require the membrane-bound caveolin-1 complex to recruit the Shc adaptor molecule. Shc in turn can interact with the Grb2–Sos complex which then activates Ras and Raf and the MAPK signalling pathways to promote proliferation (Wary *et al.*, 1996, 1998). Recent studies with *Drosophila* have indicated that Shc is required only for a subset of receptor tyrosine kinase activities, further suggesting that recruitment of Shc may impart some specificity to signalling cascades (Luschnig *et al.*, 2000). What is not clear is how different cell types might differentially recruit signalling mediators as many of the α integrin subunits which recruit Shc are ubiquitously expressed.

Another issue which has been raised in studying ECM–integrin-mediated proliferation is the apparent lack of specificity of the signalling intermediates. For example, the signalling mediators employed by integrins to induce cell proliferation are essentially the same factors required for mitogen or cytokine-induced proliferation (Hill and Treisman, 1995). This has led to some debate as to whether integrins were simply permissive for growth factor-induced signalling rather than being capable of independently initiating these signalling cascades. More recent evidence suggests that ECM–integrin binding can independently initiate signalling responses but these signals are relatively transient (Chen *et al.*, 1996). What is clear, however, is that the propagation or amplification of MAPK pathways arising from binding of soluble mitogens to their receptors is absolutely dependent upon cell adhesion to the ECM. For example, in isolated non-adherent fibroblasts, addition of the mitogen PDGF could only promote transient MAPK activation and cell cycle progression to the G1/S boundary. Further progression through the cell cycle including DNA synthesis and expression of cyclin E required that cells be attached to an ECM to sustain a threshold of MAPK activity compatible with cell cycle progression. Moreover, they noted that the shape the cells acquired upon adhesion to fibronectin, rather than adhesion *per se*, was critical for proliferative responses (Zhu and Assoian, 1995; Zhu *et al.*, 1996).

Complex Matrices and Growth Arrest

Although the signalling pathways induced by the interactions of individual ECM ligands with a particular integrin receptor in homogeneous cell populations have been relatively well defined, it is not clear how signalling cascades are impacted by complex multiligand matrices interacting with multiple cell surface integrins. Whether complex interactions like these which normally occur *in vivo* give rise to qualitative, quantitative or spatially modified signalling processes has not been resolved.

Furthermore, many cells, in particular epithelial and endothelial cells, respond to complex BM ECMs by withdrawing from the cell cycle, acquiring a differentiated phenotype and initiating tissue-specific gene expression. Although MAPK activity is significantly attenuated in cells induced to growth arrest on these matrices, it is not yet clear how this is achieved as initial adhesion to these matrices via integrins also activates MAPK, albeit transiently. It may be possible that BM activates phosphatases which are capable of uncoupling the kinase-dependent activity of the MAPK pathway. For example, PTEN is a phosphatase which attenuates integrin-induced phosphorylation of FAK as well as the PI3-kinase pathway (for a review, see Tamura *et al.*, 1999).

Another hypothesis that has been put forward to explain inhibition of cell proliferation by BM binding integrins including $\alpha3\beta1$, $\alpha6\beta1$ and $\alpha2\beta1$ is that they do not efficiently recruit Shc and are not capable of sustaining MAPK activity at a level which would support proliferation (Wary *et al.*, 1996). However, other studies have shown that these same α integrins could not only sustain MAPK but also promote proliferation in both endothelial and epithelial cells (Aplin *et al.*, 1999; Gonzales *et al.*, 1999). Thus other factors which may or may not influence Shc recruitment must be involved in deciding whether cells proliferate or growth arrest using BM integrins.

Interestingly, when cells did proliferate using these same integrins, not only was it independent of Shc but, more importantly, it also appeared that the shape that the cells acquired was a dominant determinant of whether they could sustain MAPK activity and undergo proliferation (Aplin *et al.*, 1999). Indeed, recent evidence suggests that the structure imposed on cells through their interaction with the ECM is responsible for modulating these signalling pathways and ultimately determines whether cells proliferate or undergo growth arrest and differentiate (Roskelley *et al.*, 1994; Chen *et al.*, 1997; Wang *et al.*, 1998). Furthermore, evidence is emerging that ECM-induced changes in cell morphology and architecture may in fact influence the activity of phosphatases such as PTEN (Wu *et al.*, 2000). The role of ECM in modulating the morphology of cells and its influence on mediating intracellular signalling is discussed in the following sections.

INTEGRATION OF CELL MORPHOLOGY AND SIGNALLING BY ECM

Integrin Clustering and Cell Shape

One of the most critical events required for propagation and maintenance of signals generated following binding of integrins by ECM is clustering of the integrin receptors, often at sites known as focal adhesions or focal contacts. Without the appropriate clustering, ligand occupation of the receptor is not sufficient to induce a full biological response (Miyamoto *et al.*, 1996). The clustering is believed to facilitate interactions between the integrin cytoplasmic tails and adaptor proteins to allow focal adhesion complexes to assemble. Not surprisingly, immunoprecipitation of these FA complexes showed that the growth factor (GF) receptors are also found within these integrin-containing complexes. For example, both PDGF-BB and insulin receptors were immunoprecipitated in complexes isolated using antibodies against $\alpha v\beta3$ integrin (Schneller *et al.*, 1997). The colocalization of GF receptors and integrins is believed to facilitate 'crosstalk' between ECM and GF receptors and coordinate or amplify the signals which may be independently generated by the ECM or soluble mitogens.

Clustering of integrins is not only required for integrin-induced migration or proliferation but is also essential for differentiation and tissue-specific gene expression in mammary epithelial cells on BM (Roskelley *et al.*, 1994). This absolute dependence on clustering of integrins for either proliferation or differentiation underscores the importance of having structure imposed upon cytoplasmic signalling mediators.

In addition to structural changes at the level of the focal adhesion, adhesion to different ECMs can induce cells either to spread or to become rounded and polarized. It has become increasingly evident that cell-shape changes are a necessary and integral component of how cell–ECM interactions can generate tissue-specific architectures and gene expression, i.e. in order for ECM to evoke the appropriate response, cells must adopt an appropriate morphology (Roskelley *et al.*, 1994). In general, cell spreading appears to be required for cells to proliferate while cell rounding is a prerequisite for growth arrest. For example, work by Ingber and colleagues has elegantly demonstrated that when endothelial cells are cultured on FN matrices they often adopt a spread morphology and proliferate. However, using micropatterned substrates which forced cells to become rounded while maintaining a similar degree of integrin mediated contact with the matrix, cells were unable to grow in the presence of mitogens (Chen *et al.*, 1997). In contrast, cell rounding, which can be induced by BM-type ECM, is required for other functions such as the expression of the β-casein gene by mammary epithelial cells (Roskelley *et al.*, 1994).

Binding of cells to the ECM not only can ligate and cluster integrins to initiate signalling cascades, but also provides the cells with a morphology to sustain the appropriate response.

What has not been directly established in these studies is how the cell shape impacts on intracellular signalling cascades. It is entirely possible that a cell's shape can determine whether integrins recruit signalling intermediates which interact with the growth-promoting MAPK pathways. For example, perhaps cell rounding, which generally suppresses growth, might preclude recruitment of membrane-associated mediators such as caveolin–Shc complexes and thereby attenuate proliferative signals, whereas cell spreading may support this effect. In order to understand how cellular geometry influences intracellular signalling it is necessary to understand the dynamics of integrin–cytoskeletal interactions which underlie these morphological changes. These are discussed briefly below.

Integrin–Cytoskeletal Connections

The observations that β integrin subunits extend into the cytoplasm has long generated speculation that the integrin cytoplasmic domains directly interact with cytoskeletal elements to bring about the changes in clustering and cell morphology. Functional linkages are supported by an extensive literature which shows that disrupting ECM–integrin interactions with function blocking antibodies leads to significant alterations in cell shape and cytoskeletal organisation. Similarly, directly disrupting the cytoskeleton with a variety of agents will impair integrin-mediated functions (for a review, see Schoenwaelder and Burridge, 1999).

It has now been established that integrins, in particular the $\beta 1$ subunit, can directly interact with either microfilaments (actin) or intermediate filaments of the cell cytoskeleton. This is mediated by binding of proteins including α-actinin, talin, vinculin, filamen and paxillin. Many of these proteins directly interact with integrin cytoplasmic domains as well as actin filaments (for reviews, see Yamada and Geiger, 1997; Critchely, 2000). Furthermore, the ability of integrins to interact with these cytoskeletal proteins also requires that the integrins be clustered in focal adhesions (Calderwood et al., 1999). In addition to clustering, ligand occupancy is also required as the ability of integrins to bind these proteins is masked or suppressed in unoccupied integrins (Miyamoto et al., 1996).

Although integrins may directly interact with many of these cytoskeletal elements, many biological processes such as cell migration require that these interactions be dynamic. One means by which the ECM and integrins can dynamically reorganize the cytoskeleton is through activation of members of the Rac/Rho GTPase family which modulate actin cytoskeleton dynamics and interactions with integrins (for a review, see Bishop and Hall,

2000). For example, activated Rho can induce phosphatidylinositol-4,5-biphosphate (PtdInsP2), which in turn unmasks talin and actin binding sites in vinculin (Gilmore and Burridge, 1996). In addition to mediating dynamic changes in cell shape and motility, integrin-mediated changes in gene expression are also dependent upon Rho activation as induction of collagenase gene expression in fibroblasts by $\alpha 5\beta 1$ integrin ligation could not proceed when Rho was mutated (Kheradmand et al., 1998).

It is believed that these cytoskeletal rearrangements induced by ECM and integrins act to organize or compartmentalize signalling intermediates in such a way as to facilitate or enhance their interactions. Indeed, the attenuation of MAPK activity observed in suspended cells as compared with adherent cells supports this notion (Zhu and Assoian, 1995; Aplin et al., 1999). It has also been suggested that efficient signal transduction also requires that additional factors be recruited to stabilize these interacting protein complexes.

Nonintegrin–Cytoskeletal Linkages and Scaffolding Proteins

Analogous to the adaptor proteins mentioned earlier, scaffolding proteins can act to stabilize the relatively weak interactions between signalling mediators by binding multiple components which interact with each other, as well as with cytoskeleton components. For example, in *Drosophila*, the Ina D scaffold protein involved in photoreceptor signal transduction acts to bind and stabilize up to five partner proteins at a specific subcellular location resulting in the formation of a 'transducisome' (for a review, see Burack and Shaw, 2000). Many of the proteins which carry out these scaffolding functions contain one or more domains capable of facilitating protein–protein interactions. One particularly common domain found in many of these proteins are the PDZ domains (postsynaptic/discs large/Zo-1 domains) (for a review, see Dimitratos et al., 1999). In addition to facilitating interactions between proteins, many of these PDZ domain proteins have been shown to undergo extensive interactions with both the plasma membrane and the cytoskeleton, which probably contributes to their ability to localize these multiprotein complexes or receptors at specific cellular locations (Fanning et al., 1998; Hildebrand and Soriano, 1999).

Although a role for scaffolding proteins in mitogen-induced signalling is well established, there is as yet no direct evidence that integrin signalling pathways employ these proteins. Interestingly, there is evidence that nonintegrin ECM receptors interact with several closely related proteins. Dystroglycan is a component of the dystrophin-associated protein complex found in muscle, neurons and epithelial cells. Dystroglycan not only binds to laminin in the extracellular space but also binds dystrophin, which in turn binds actin in the cytoplasm (Ervasti and Campbell, 1993; Kachinsky *et al.*, 1999). Syndecan, a heparan sulfate proteoglycan, is another nonintegrin ECM receptor capable of binding laminin, while syndecan's cytoplasmic face can bind to CASK. CASK is a specialized type of PDZ protein or MAGUK (membrane associated guanylate kinase), which can also interact with protein 4.1 of the actin cytoskeleton to provide an additional link between the ECM and the cytoskeleton (Cohen *et al.*, 1998). Furthermore, when CASK's interaction with syndecan is disrupted, possibly by proteolytic cleavage, CASK can then shuttle directly to the nucleus and interact with T-brain, a T box transcription factor which induces expression of reelin, another ECM protein which is required for neuronal adhesion, migration and pathfinding (D'Arcangelo *et al.*, 1995; Hseuh *et al.*, 2000). Thus an intact ECM is required to prevent translocation of these factors.

Related members of this PDZ/MAGUK family of proteins have also been implicated in maintenance of cell polarity and cell–cell junctions, a process which is significantly enhanced by adhesion of cells to BM. The relationship between ECM, the establishment of cell junctions and recruitment of these and other proteins in growth arrest and differentiation is discussed in the following section.

Establishment of Polarity and Cell–Cell Junctions

When cells assume their tissue-specific 3D organisation, they also establish extensive cell–cell junctions and exhibit tissue polarity. Not surprisingly, the cytoskeletal and morphological changes induced by cells interacting with the ECM are necessary for the formation of appropriate cell junctions and polarity. Hemidesmosomes, adherens junctions and tight or occludens junctions found in epithelial tissues can be directly influenced by the ECM.

Adherens junction are multiprotein complexes present in most epithelial cells *in vivo*. These complexes are located between adjacent epithelial cells and contain, most notably, E-cadherin in an insoluble complex with α- and β-catenins (for a review, see Fuchs *et al.*, 1997). As mentioned, ECM and integrins play a critical role in assembling and establishing adherens junctions in epithelial tissues, as culturing epithelial cells on BM can promote the formation of polarized 3D spheroids with functional adherens junctions containing E-cadherin and α- and β-catenin (for reviews, see Gumbiner 1996; Weaver *et al.*, 1997). On the other hand, loss of ECM adhesion or disruption of appropriate cell–ECM contacts and 3D morphology interferes with the assembly of junctional complexes. Like most cell–ECM interactions, this relationship between integrins and adherens junctions is dynamic and reciprocal, as establishment of adherens junctions and recruitment of cadherin–catenin

complexes can also feedback to down-regulate expression of the $\beta 1$ integrin associated with growth in keratinocytes (Hodivala and Watt, 1994).

Although the exact mechanisms which link the ECM and adhesion junctions is not clear, both focal adhesions and adherens junctions contain many of the same molecules which interact with the cytoskeleton. For example, vinculin, which localizes to FA via its interactions with talin and β integrins, is also present in adherens junctional complexes. Vasp, a vinculin-binding protein capable of binding G actin and nucleating actin fibril assembly, is not only found in focal adhesions but also recruited to epithelial junctions along with vinculin (Vasioukhin *et al.*, 2000). The use of common cytoskeletal proteins which bind to integrin or cadherin complexes and in turn interact with the actin cytoskeleton suggests an integrated system of cytoskeletal fibres being pulled by potentially competing molecules to generate appropriate cell tension and shape.

What is clear is the requirement for ECM and functional adhesion junctions in maintaining a quiescent differentiated state in epithelial tissues. Interfering with cell-ECM interactions disrupts junctional complex assembly, and β-catenin is no longer retained in insoluble junctional complexes (Weaver *et al.*, 1997; Novak *et al.*, 1998). Free β-catenin can then migrate to the nucleus and form complexes with the transcription factor TCF/LEF, which in turn promotes expression of a number of genes which are incompatible with a quiescent differentiated phenotype including matrilysin, fibronectin and cyclin D1 and the oncogenic c-*myc* gene (He *et al.*, 1998; Crawford *et al.*, 1999; Shtutman *et al.*, 1999).

In addition to β-catenin, many of the MAGUK/PDZ-domain protein family members also figure prominently in the formation and maintenance of junctional complexes in polarized epithelial tissues. Elegant work on *Drosophila* has identified genes critical for epithelial polarization including the PDZ domain protein *scribble*, and a related MAGUK protein called discs large lethal (*dll*). When these genes were mutated, epithelial cells exhibited a loss of polarity and became round and multilayered, further emphasizing that tissue structure is essential to prevent tumorigenesis (Bilder *et al.*, 2000). Although the mammalian homologue of scribble is not yet known, the mammalian homologue of dll, DLG, has been identified as a protein which binds to APC, a junction-associated tumour-suppresser protein which also binds β-catenin to prevent its translocation to the nucleus (Matsumine *et al.*, 1996). Recent evidence has shown that the activity of another tumour suppressor, PTEN, a phosphatase which attenuates integrin-mediated FAK and PI3 kinase activity, could be enhanced by binding to MAGI-2, a MAGUK scaffolding protein related to DLG. Like dll and scribble, MAGI-2 is normally recruited to and anchored in membranes at epithelial tight junctions where it binds PTEN via its PDZ domains (Wu *et al.*,

2000). Although a direct link between the ECM and these particular junction-associated proteins has not been demonstrated, the ability of non-integrin ECM receptors to bind closely related proteins and the critical role of the ECM in organizing the cytoskeleton and cell junction assembly suggest that such interactions are likely.

ECM and integrins have also been directly linked to the formation of hemidesmosomes found on the basolateral surface of epithelial cells which contact the BM. The $\alpha6\beta4$ laminin-binding integrin is a major component of hemi-desmosomes (Sonnenberg et al., 1991). In contrast to other β integrins, $\beta4$ has an unusually long cytoplasmic tail over 1000 amino acids in length. The $\beta4$ tail can directly bind to plectin, a large cytoskeletal protein capable of interacting with both the actin microfilament and intermediate filament cytoskeleton (for a review, see Steinbock and Wiche, 1999). In contrast to other integrins which require activation and clustering to interact with proteins linked to the cytoskeleton, the $\beta4$ integrin cytoplasmic tail appears capable of interacting with hemidesmosome components even in the absence of ligand occupancy (Nievers et al., 2000). A critical role for the $\beta4$ integrin in the formation and function of hemidesmosomes is evident in $\beta4$ integrin-deficient mutants, where blistering of the skin and epidermal detachment were observed due to the lack of hemidesmosome formation (Dowling et al., 1996; Van der Neut et al., 1996) Furthermore, interfering with baso-lateral localization of $\alpha6\beta4$ in breast epithelial cells not only disrupts hemidesmosome formation but also induces these cells to undergo apoptosis (V. M. Weaver and M. J. Bissell, unpublished work).

Together a picture emerges that beyond simple ligation of integrins and induction of signalling cascades, the ECM also directs the changes in cell and tissue architecture via cytoskeletal linkages from both integrin and nonintegrin ECM receptors. The cytoskeletal reorganisation helps to organize hemidesmosomes and adherens junctions and immobilize multidomain scaffolding proteins. This sequestration can either prevent untoward transcriptional activity or enhance the function of growth-suppressing genes such as PTEN or APC.

3D ORGANISATION AND INTEGRATED TISSUE RESPONSES

Mammary Gland

One model which has been invaluable for investigating and understanding how interactions between cells and complex ECMs can direct and maintain the functionally differentiated state of tissues is the adult mammary gland. At the onset of pregnancy, the adult mammary gland undergoes a series of morphological and functional changes which culminate in the establishment of organized acinar structures consisting of polarized epithelial cells which produce and secrete milk proteins. This organogenesis is intimately dependent upon the production and deposition of an intact basement membrane.

Many of the cellular and molecular events which contribute to this functional differentiation have been elucidated through the use of a 3D tissue culture model which mimics the normal postnatal mammary gland morphogenesis which occurs in vivo (Barcellos-Hoff et al., 1989). Either primary or immortalized mammary epithelial cells can be induced to undergo this morphological and functional differentiation by simply plating them on a reconstituted intact BM. The mammary epithelial cells immediately adhere to the BM and within a few days form 3D spheroids which resemble the acinar structure of the gland in vivo both in organisation and in size. Contact with the BM also induces cells to exit the cell cycle, become polarized and form adherens junctions. In contrast, when the same cells are plated on tissue culture plastic without the BM matrix, they adhere primarily to non-BM proteins which are present in the serum including fibronectin and vitronectin using the appropriate integrins. These cells will spread to form monolayers and are not able to form spheroids. These cells also cannot polarize, form proper adherens junctions or exit the cell cycle. Not surprisingly, these cells cannot express the tissue-specific milk protein genes (Barcellos-Hoff et al., 1989; Schmidhauser et al., 1990).

The BM-induced functional differentiation requires the contribution of several different laminin-binding receptors at different stages of this process. Initially the epithelial cells adhere to the BM via laminin-binding $\beta1$ integrins, most likely the $\alpha3$ or $\alpha6$ $\beta1$ heterodimers. Following the initial adhesion, cells begin to round in a manner which is not perturbed when either $\alpha6\beta4$ or other $\beta1$ integrins are blocked. Instead, the E3 fragment of laminin, which probably binds to the nonintegrin ECM receptors dystro-glycan or syndecan, appears necessary for this process (J. Muschler and M. J. Bissell, unpublished work). Furthermore, although the E3-dependent rounding is a prerequisite for the cells to begin expressing milk proteins (Streuli et al., 1995), milk gene expression in rounded cells could also be blocked by antibodies against both the $\alpha6\beta4$ integrin and $\beta1$ integrins but not $\alpha1$, $\alpha5$ or αv integrins (Muschler et al., 1999). This 'division of labour' between both integrin and nonintegrin receptors and the dependence on cell shape emphasize the integrated nature of the response of cells to BM.

In addition to the role for ECM-binding proteins, the organisation of the BM and its presentation to the cells is also critical in eliciting these responses. As mentioned previously, when the BM is cross-linked or fixed so that it is no longer malleable, cells are unable to become rounded and acquire a polarized morphology and cannot express milk proteins despite the cells' ability to adhere strongly to this matrix (Streuli and Bissell, 1990). Furthermore, although the minor BM component nidogen alone is not capable of inducing milk gene expression in these cells, addition of nidogen can enhance the laminin-dependent induction of milk gene expression (Pujuguet *et al.*, 2000). Nidogen normally acts as a bridge between BM laminin and type IV collagen, and thus probably acts to organize the presentation of laminin to the cells (see **Figure 2**).

Furthermore, once these cells have undergone the necessary changes in cell shape, they must also undergo further changes in cell–cell organisation to form 3D alveolar structures, complete with functional adherens junctions and hemidesmosomes. The generation of these 3D structures is particularly critical for maintaining a functional differentiated state, as interfering with this organisation can induce the cells to undergo apoptosis (Boudreau *et al.*, 1996). When this organisation is disrupted, the cells are not able to remain quiescent and begin to progress through the cell cycle, a process which often triggers apoptosis in normally quiescent cell (Evan *et al.*, 1992). Furthermore, the 3D organisation is also essential for meaningful cross-talk between integrins and growth factor receptors (Wang *et al.*, 1998).

Consequences of Disrupted Tissue Organisation

Based on the above, it is clear that 3D tissue-type morphology and the related intracellular organisation imposed by the ECM determine whether cells will differentiate, proliferate or undergo apoptosis. With respect to differentiation, it is clear that in addition to cellular rounding, establishing polarity and forming junctional complexes are equally critical for maintaining this state. It might be predicted

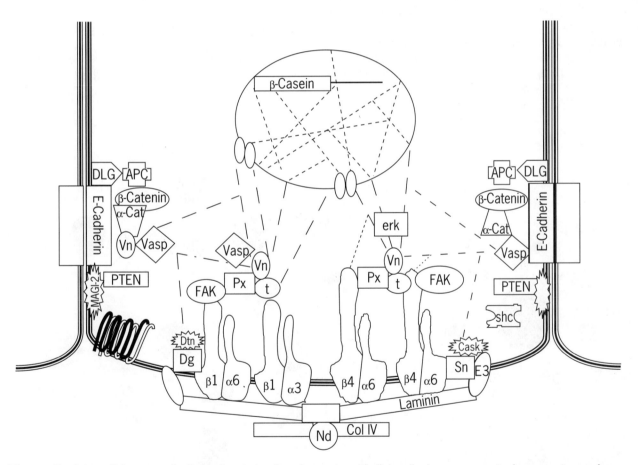

Figure 2 Intracellular organisation of polarized, quiescent epithelial cells in response to basement membrane extracellular matrix. The basement membrane matrix on the basolateral surface of the cells is comprised of several components including laminin, type IV collagen (Col IV) and nidogen (Nd). Laminin binds to $\alpha 6\beta 4$, $\alpha 6\beta 1$ and $\alpha 3\beta 1$ integrins and generates signals which allow transcription of the tissue-specific gene β-casein. Cells also employ non-integrin receptors including dystroglycan (Dg) and syndecan (Sn) to bind to the E3 domain of laminin which help cells to become rounded. Cask and dystrophin (Dtn), which associate with Sn and Dg receptively, can also directly bind the actin cytoskeleton (dashed lines). Additional cytoskeletal links are provided by vinculin (vn) and vasp which associate both with integrin complexes and with adherens junctions which form in the polarizing cells. The adherens junctions contain E-cadherin complexed with β-catenin and α-catenin. Other junction-associated proteins include MAGI-2 and DLG (discs large lethal), which in turn bind the tumour-suppressor proteins PTEN and APC to enhance their activity.

then that interfering with any component of this integrated 3D system not only compromises tissue function but also contributes to the process of deregulated growth control and ultimately tumorigenesis. Perhaps the most informative examples of how critical the ECM and an organized 3D structure are for maintaining differentiated tissue function and preventing tumour development and progression come from studies with tumour cells themselves which lack this organisation.

One system which very clearly demonstrates the strong correlation between loss of tissue organisation and tumour progression is a series of human breast epithelial cells which become increasingly tumorigenic as tissue architecture is progressively lost. The HMT-3522 cell series originated from a purified breast epithelial cell population isolated from a female with fibrocystic breast disease. Although these cells, referred to as S1, can remain relatively stable for over 500 passages, cells could alternatively be induced to undergo tumorigenic progression by selecting cells which would survive in the absence of essential growth factors. These factor-independent cells, designated T4-2, were found ultimately to form tumours when injected into nude mice, while the original S1

population which was maintained at a similar passage number but in defined media containing growth factors were stable and non-tumorigenic (Briand *et al.*, 1987). More importantly, it was observed that whereas S1 cells maintained the ability to form organized, polarized alveolar structures which could undergo growth arrest in response to BM, the tumorigenic derivatives formed progressively disorganized and nonpolarized groups of cells which failed to growth arrest despite the presence of an intact BM. The disorganized T4-2 cells were found to have poorly organized nuclei, adherens junctions, f-actin and aberrant integrin localization and expression (Weaver *et al.*, 1997) (see **Figure 3**). In fact, the extent to which epithelial cells respond to BM and elaborate organized structures is a relatively accurate means of predicting their degree of tumorigenicity with the disorganized cells being more tumorigenic (Petersen *et al.*, 1992).

Aberrations in ECM–Integrins in Cancer

The disruption of normal architecture and morphology in the progressively tumorigenic cells described above could be directly related to the improper expression of high

(a)   (b)

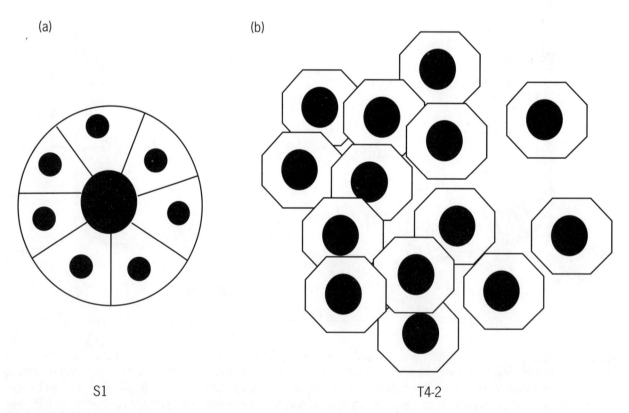

S1   T4-2

Figure 3   Cell morphology and tumorigenicity. (a) Schematic representation of normal, growth-arrested, breast epithelial cells (S1) organized into a acinar structures when cultured in a 3D basement membrane extracellular matrix. Note the basolateral localization of the nucleus in these polarized cells. (b) Tumorigenic derivatives of the normal breast epithelial cells (T4-2) form disorganized clusters when cultured in basement membrane extracellular matrix. The cells do not become polarized or form proper adherens junctions and continue to proliferate. (Adapted from Bissell *et al.*, 1999.)

levels of a number of surface receptors including β1 integrin. In addition, these cells display an aberration in surface expression of α6β4 integrin which would otherwise normally encourage growth arrest. Together these defects might be expected not only to disrupt the formation of hemidesmsomes, but also to impair the establishment of adherens junctions and recruitment of β-catenin (Weaver *et al.*, 1997).

An extensive literature documents a wide range of abnormal cell–ECM interactions in tumour cells. Aberrant integrin expression has been described in a number of breast tumour cells (see review by Zutter *et al.*, 1998). In addition to overexpressing integrins, many tumour cells also lack expression of integrin receptors which might suppress growth, and studies aimed at reintroducing the missing integrins can often result in restoring growth arrest. For example, in tumorigenic intestinal epithelial cells, which lack expression of β4 integrin, transfection of the β4 integrin induced expression of the Cdk inhibitor p21^{WAF1} and led to growth arrest (Clarke *et al.*, 1995). Similarly, introduction of the α2β1 collagen/laminin

receptor missing from a poorly differentiated breast tumour line also induced growth arrest (Zutter *et al.*, 1995).

Although this approach may compensate for a lack of a functional integrin, often integrins are expressed but not properly localized in the tumour cells. In the T4-2 cell series described above, β4 integrin was expressed but not at the cell surface (Weaver *et al.*, 1997) (**Figure 4**). It might be expected that integrins localized to different cellular locations may not be able to access their ligands, particularly if the ECM ligands have a restricted distribution, such as BM laminin. In addition, changing the localization of an integrin often results in the receptor adopting a different conformation, which might also prevent binding even if the ligand is accessible (Bishop *et al.*, 1998).

In addition to deficiencies in ECM receptors, tumour cells often have altered ECMs. For example, many tumour cells are not able properly to synthesize or assemble BMs, which in turn are required for growth arrest (Petersen *et al.*, 1992; Howlett *et al.*, 1994). One of the more common reasons for a loss of organized ECM surrounding tumour cells is the finding that many tumour cells express high

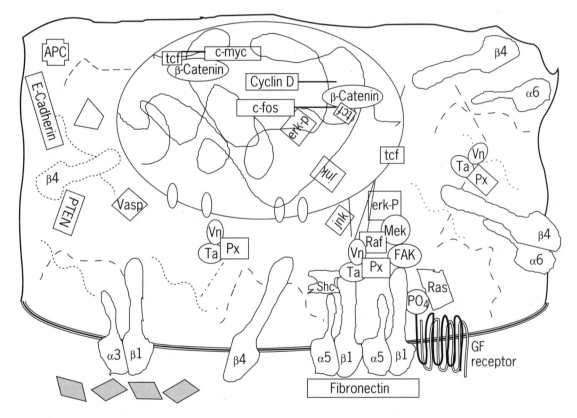

Figure 4 Structural disorganisation of tumour cells. Expression and subcellular localization of integrin subunits including α6 and β4 is disrupted in tumorigenic epithelial cells. In addition the basement membrane may be degraded (grey diamonds) by high levels of matrix-degrading protease activity. Structural connections with the cytoskeleton (dashed lines) are also diminished. Polarity is absent and adherens junctions are not properly formed, allowing free β-catenin to translocate to the nucleus and activate transcription of growth-promoting genes including c-*myc*. Growth-promoting β1 integrin heterodimers (α5β1 is shown here) are present and continue to generate proliferative signals including phosphorylated erk (erk-P), which may translocate to the nucleus and activate additional growth-promoting genes. Growth factor receptors are also active and phosphorylated.

levels of various matrix-degrading proteinases (Barsky *et al.*, 1983; Liotta and Stetler-Stevenson, 1990).

More recent evidence has shown that even in normal cells excessive and sustained proteolytic activity and BM degradation can directly contribute to tumour development and progression. Loss of BM by excessive proteolysis resulted in the transformation of epithelial cells to a mesenchymal phenotype (Lochter *et al.*, 1997). The loss of the syndecan which also binds BM laminin also resulted in normal epithelial cells undergoing a similar transition to an anchorage-independent mesenchymal phenotype (Kato *et al.*, 1995). These results together emphasize how BM not only promotes but also maintains and stabilizes the epithelial cell phenotype. Furthermore, in transgenic mice engineered to overexpress MMP-3 in differentiated mammary epithelial cells, an unusually high incidence of adenocarcinoma was observed in the BM-compromised mammary epithelial cells (Sternlicht *et al.*, 1999). The chronic degradation of the BM in turn was permissive for a number of other genetic alterations which contributed to the tumorigenic phenotype. These findings again emphasize the requirement for BM in maintaining functionally differentiated tissues and for stabilizing the genetic information in the cells.

Apoptosis

It should be emphasized that loss of normal cell–ECM interaction does not immediately result in oncogenic transformation of most cells. The tumours which arise in the MMP-overproducing mice described above require chronic or sustained activity of the protease and loss of basement membrane before overt tumorigenesis is observed. As mentioned earlier, normal mammary epithelial cells initially respond to the loss or degradation of their ECM by undergoing programmed cell death or apoptosis within 48 h (Boudreau *et al.*, 1995). This is viewed as a protective mechanism to help eliminate potentially dangerous cells which have lost the growth suppressive signals normally supplied by the BM.

Although complete loss of adhesive contact with any type of ECM can induce apoptosis in normally adhesive cells (Meredith *et al.*, 1993; Frisch and Francis, 1994), the ability of a cell to respond to more subtle changes in their microenvironment provides a more effective means to eliminate potentially harmful cells. In fact, normal adherent epithelial cells can be induced to undergo apoptosis by simply disrupting their three-dimensional organisation (Boudreau *et al.*, 1996). Even in polarized MDCK epithelial cells, a collagen gel overlay was found to induce apoptosis by simply disorientating cells (Tang *et al.*, 1998). Unfortunately, many tumour cells that have compromised interactions with the ECM fail to recognize alterations in cell morphology and orientation, and are often resistant to apoptosis, even in the complete absence

of adhesion, a phenomenon referred to as anchorage independence. Attempts to restore their sensitivity to apoptotic signals is a major anti-tumorigenic strategy (see the chapter on *Apoptosis*).

It is interesting that not all normal cells immediately respond to loss or degradation of their BM by undergoing apoptosis, nor do they proliferate uncontrollably. In cells which retain a high regenerative potential, such as vascular endothelium and hepatocytes, the loss of BM allows cells to re-enter the cell cycle and divide. Loss of BM will induce endothelial cells to undergo angiogenesis, while hepatocytes can be induced to proliferate and regenerate portions of the liver following a partial hepatectomy (Fausto, 2000). In these cases, however, the amount or degree of cell proliferation which occurs is limited because proliferating endothelial cells or hepatocytes immediately begin to resynthesize and deposit a new BM, which in turn induces the cells to re-establish a 3D tissue organisation and subsequently withdraw from the cell cycle (Kubota *et al.*, 1988; Boudreau *et al.*, 1997). Therefore, cells which do not undergo apoptosis when they re-enter the cell cycle can be directed to growth arrest and differentiate by re-establishing and responding to a functional BM.

Restoring a Cell's Balance of Surface Receptors and Interaction with the BM Can Reverse Tumorigenesis

Although attempting to restore a normal dialogue with the ECM might at first seem somewhat naive to apply to genetically destabilized tumour cells, in fact re-establishing a functional BM and 3D organisation, or restoring a tumour cell's ability to recognize and respond to BM, can in fact induce growth arrest in tumorigenic cells. Transfection of the tumorigenic breast epithelial cell line MDA-435 with the NM-23 tumour suppressor resulted in the ability of the cells to resynthesize and deposit a 3D BM and to form organized, acinar structures leading to growth arrest (Howlett *et al.*, 1994). In the case of the progressively tumorigenic human breast cells mentioned earlier, blocking the excessive $\beta 1$ integrin signalling allowed cells to revert completely to a nontumorigenic phenotype when they were cultured in the presence of a complete basement membrane. This reversion was accompanied by reorganisation into acinar-type structures, establishment of normal adherens junctions containing E-cadherin and associated α- and β-catenins, reorganisation of the actin cytoskeleton and growth arrest. Furthermore, blocking $\beta 1$ integrin also attenuated the high levels of expression and activity of the EGF receptor normally found in these tumorigenic cells. Interestingly, simply blocking $\beta 1$ integrin was not sufficient to downregulate EGF receptor expression or activity if the cells were also prevented from acquiring the corresponding 3D organisation, underscoring the contribution of the basement membrane to this reversion process (Wang *et al.*, 1998). Perhaps the most striking observation made using this system was that when β1 integrin was blocked and cells were allowed to resume their normal interaction with the basement membrane, the resulting 3D structure was sufficient to override a host of genetic alterations that had accumulated as cells progressed toward increasing tumorigenicity (Weaver *et al.*, 1997).

CONCLUSION

Simply stated, cancer is a problem of tissue organisation. Although it has long been recognized that one of the hallmarks in diagnosing tumour cells is their aberrant morphology, both at the tissue, cell and nuclear level, the molecular consequences of this disorganisation are now beginning to be appreciated. By maintaining a proper 3D organisation through dynamic reciprocal interactions with their microenvironment, tissue structure can act in a dominant manner to override a host of genetic aberrations that may otherwise compromise normal tissue function.

A recent large-scale study emphasized an environmental rather than genetic basis of cancer based on findings that the incidence of identical twins developing similar cancers was almost nondetectable, whereas genetically unrelated individuals exposed to similar environments were more likely to do so (Lichtenstein *et al.*, 2000). Although these observations apply to the relationship of an entire organism to its environment, it would appear that the same principles may also apply to tumour development at the cell and molecular level. Thus although cells may harbour genetic alterations from birth or acquire distinct genetic changes over a life span, it is how the cells interact with their immediate extracellular environment which appears to govern cell form, function and fate.

ACKNOWLEDGEMENTS

This work was supported by the Director, Office of Biological and Environmental Research (contract DE-AC03-76SF00098) of the U.S. Department of Energy and by NIH grants CA-57621 and CA-64786 to MJB, and by NIH grant CA-85249 to NB.

REFERENCES

Aplin, A. E., *et al.* (1999). Anchorage-dependent regulation of the Mitogen-activated protein kinase cascade by growth factors is supported by a variety of integrin alpha chains. *Journal of Biological Chemistry*, **274**, 31223–31228.

Barcellos-Hoff, M. H., *et al.* (1989). Functional differentiation and alveolar morphogenesis of primary mammary cultures on reconstituted basement membrane. *Development*, **105**, 223–235.

Barsky, S. H., *et al.* (1983). Loss of basement membrane components by invasive tumors but not by their benign counterparts. *Laboratory Investigation*, **49**, 140–147.

Bernfield, M., *et al.* (1999). Functions of cell surface heparan sulfate proteoglycans. *Annual Review of Biochemistry*, **68**, 729–777.

Bilder, D., *et al.* (2000). Cooperative regulation of cell polarity and growth by drosophila tumor suppressors. *Science*, **289**, 113–116.

Bishop, A. L. and Hall, A. (2000). Rho GTPases and their effector proteins. *Biochemical Journal*, **348**, 241–255.

Bishop, L. A., *et al.* (1998). Lack of intrinsic polarity in the ligand-binding ability of keratinocyte beta1 integrins. *Experimental Dermatology*, **7**, 350–361.

Bissell, M. J., *et al.* (1999). Tissue structure, nuclear organization and gene expression in normal and malignant breast. *Cancer Research (Supplement)*, **59**, 1757–1764.

Boudreau, N. and Bissell, M. J. (1996). Regulation of gene expression by the extracellular matrix. In: Comper, W. E. (ed.), Extracellular Matrix. Volume 2. Molecular Components and Interactions, 246–261 (Harwood Academic Publishers: Amsterdam).

Boudreau, N., *et al.* (1995). Suppression of ICE and apoptosis in mammary epithelial cells. *Science*, **267**, 891–893.

Boudreau, N., *et al.* (1996). Suppression of apoptosis by basement membrane requires three-dimensional tissue organization and withdrawal from the cell cycle. *Proceedings of the National Academy of Sciences of the USA*, **93**, 3509–3513.

Boudreau, N., *et al.* (1997). Hox D3 induces an angiogenic phenotype in endothelial cells. *Journal of Cell Biology*, **139**, 257–264.

Briand, P., *et al.* (1987). A new diploid non-tumorigenic human breast epithelial cell line isolated and propagated in chemically defined medium. *In Vitro Cell Developmental Biology*, **23**, 181–188.

Burack, W. R. and Shaw, A. S. (2000). Signal transduction; hanging on a scaffold. *Current Opinion in Cell Biology*, **12**, 211–216.

Calderwood, D. A., *et al.* (1999). The talin head domain binds to integrin beta subunit cytoplasmic tails and regulates integrin activation. *Journal of Biological Chemistry*, **274**, 28071–28074.

Chen, Q., *et al.* (1996). Integrin-mediated activation of MEK and mitogen-activated protein kinase is independent of Ras. *Journal of Biological Chemistry*, **271**, 18122–18127.

Chen, C. S., *et al.* (1997). Geometric control of cell life and death. *Science*, **276**, 1425–1428.

Clarke, A. S., *et al.* (1995). Activation of the p21 pathway of growth arrest and apoptosis by the β4 integrin cytoplasmic domain. *Journal of Biological Chemistry*, **270**, 22673–22676.

Cohen, A. R., *et al.* (1998). Human CASK/LIN-2 binds syndecan-2 and protein 4.1 and localizes to the basolateral membrane of epithelial cells. *Journal of Cell Biology*, **142**, 129–138.

Crawford, H. C., *et al.* (1999). The metalloproteinase matrilysin is a target of beta-catenin transactivation in intestinal tumors. *Oncogene*, **18**, 2883–2891.

Critchley, D. R. (2000). Focal adhesions – The cytoskeletal connection. *Current Opinion in Cell Biology*, **12**, 133–139.

D'Arcangelo, G., *et al.* (1995). A protein related to extracellular matrix proteins deleted in the mouse mutant reeler. *Nature*, **376**, 719–723.

Dimitratos, S. D., *et al.* (1999). Signaling pathways are focused at specialized regions of the plasma membrane by scafolding proteins of the MAGUK family. *Bioessays*, **21**, 912–921.

Dowling, J., *et al.* (1996). Beta 4 integrin is required for hemidesmosome formation, cell adhesion and cell survival. *Journal of Cell Biology*, **134**, 559–572.

Ekblom, P. (1996). Receptors for laminins during epithelial morphogenesis. *Current Opinion in Cell Biology*, **8**, 700–706.

Ervasti, J. M., and Campbell, K. P. (1993). A role for the dystrophin–glycoprotein complex as a transmembrane linker between laminin and actin. *Journal of Cell Biology*, **122**, 809–823.

Evan, G. I., *et al.* (1992). Induction of apoptosis in fibroblasts by c-myc protein. *Cell*, **69**, 119–128.

Fanning, A. S., *et al.* (1998). The tight junction protein ZO-1 establishes a link between the transmembrane protein occludin and the actin cytoskeleton. *Journal of Biological Chemistry*, **273**, 29745–29753.

Fausto, N. (2000). Liver regeneration. *Journal of Hepatology*, **32**, 19–31.

Frisch, S. M. and Francis, H. (1994). Disruption of epithelial cell–matrix interactions induces apoptosis. *Journal of Cell Biology*, **124**, 619–626.

Fuchs, E., *et al.* (1997). Integrators of epidermal growth and differentiation; distinct functions for β1 and β4 integrins. *Current Opinion in Genetics and Development*, **7**, 672–682.

Gianelli, G., *et al.* (1997). Induction of cell migration by matrix metalloproteinase-2 cleavage of laminin-5. *Science*, **277**, 225–228.

Gilmore, A. P. and Burridge, K. (1996). Regulation of vinculin binding to talin and actin by phosphatidyl-inositol-4,5-bisphosphate. *Nature*, **381**, 531–535.

Gonzales, M., *et al.* (1999). A cell signal pathway involving laminin-5, alpha 3 beta 1 integrin and mitogen activated protein kinase can regulate epithelial cell proliferation. *Molecular Biology of the Cell*, **10**, 259–270.

Gumbiner, B. M. (1996). Cell adhesion: the molecular basis of tissue architecture and morphogenesis. *Cell*, **84**, 345–357.

He, T. C., *et al.* (1998). Identification of c-MYC as a target of the APC pathway. *Science*, **281**, 1509–1512.

Hildebrand, J. D. and Soriano, P. (1999). Shroom, a PDZ domain-containing actin-binding protein, is required for neural tube morphogenesis in mice. *Cell*, **99**, 485–497.

Hill, C. S. and Treisman, R. (1995). Transcriptional regulation by extracellular signals: mechanisms and specificity. *Cell*, **80**, 199–211.

Hodivala, K. J. and Watt, F. M. (1994). Evidence that cadherins play a role in the downregulation of integrin expression that occurs during keratinocyte terminal differentiation. *Journal of Cell Biology*, **124**, 589–600.

Howlett, A. R., *et al.* (1994). A novel function for the nm-23H1 gene; overexpression in human breast carcinoma cells leads to the formation of basement membranes and growth arrest. *Journal of National Cancer Institute*, **86**, 1838–1844.

Hseuh, Y.-P., *et al.* (2000). Nuclear translocation and transcription regulation by the membrane associated guanylate cycles kinase CASK/LIN-2. *Nature*, **404**, 298–302.

Hughes, P. E. and Pfaff, M. (1998). Integrin affinity modulation. *Trends in Cell Biology*, **8**, 359–364.

Hughes, P. E., *et al.* (1997). Suppression of integrin activation; a novel function of a Ras/Raf initiated MAP-kinase pathway. *Cell*, **88**, 521–530.

Hynes, R. O. and Zhao, Q. (2000). The evolution of cell adhesion. *Journal of Cell Biology*, **150**, F89–F86.

Joshi, P., *et al.* (1993). Endothelial cells adhere to the RGD domain and the fibrinogen-like terminal knob of tenascin. *Journal of Cell Science*, **106**, 389–400.

Kachinsky, A. M., *et al.* (1999). A PDZ-containing scaffold related to the dystophin complex at the basolateral membrane of epithelial cells. *Journal of Cell Biology*, **145**, 391–402.

Kato, M., *et al.* (1995). Loss of cell surface syndecan-1 causes epithelia to transform into anchorage-independent mesenchyme-like cells. *Molecular Biology of the Cell*, **6**, 559–576.

Kheradmand, F., *et al.* (1998). Role of Rac1 and oxygen radicals in collagenase-1 expression induced by cell shape change. *Science*, **280**, 898–902.

Kubota, Y., *et al.* (1988). Role of laminin and basement membrane in the morphological differentiation of human endothelial cells into capillary-like structures. *Journal of Cell Biology*, **107**, 1589–1598.

Lichtenstein, P., *et al.* (2000). Environmental and heritable factors in the causation of cancer – Analyses of cohorts of twins from Sweden, Denmark, and Finland. *New England Journal of Medicine*, **343**, 78–85.

Liotta, L. A. and Stetler-Stevenson, W. G. (1990). Metalloproteinases and cancer invasion. *Seminars in Cancer Biology*, **1**, 99–106.

Lochter, A. *et al.* (1997). Matrix metalloproteinase stromelysin-1 triggers a cascade of molecular alterations that leads to stable epithelial-to-mesenchymal conversion and a premalignant phenotype in mammary epithelial cells. *Journal of Cell Biology*, **139**, 1861–1872.

Luschnig, S., *et al.* (2000). The *Drosophila* SHC adaptor protein is required for signalling by a subset of receptor tyrosine kinases. *Molecular Cell*, **5**, 231–241.

Madri, J. A. and Williams, S. K. (1983). Capillary endothelial cell culture: phenotypic modulation by matrix components. *Journal of Cell Biology*, **97**, 153–165.

Matsumine, A., *et al.* (1996). Binding of APC to the human homolog of the *Drosophila* discs large tumor suppressor protein. *Science*, **272**, 1020–1023.

Meredith, J. E., Jr, *et al.* (1993). The extracellular matrix as a cell survival factor. *Molecular Biology of the Cell*, **4**, 953–961.

Miyamoto, S., *et al.* (1996). Integrins can collaborate with growth factors for phosphorylation of receptor tyrosine kinases and MAP kinase activation: roles of integrin aggregation and occu-pancy of receptors. *Journal of Cell Biology*, **135**, 1633–1642.

Muschler, J., *et al.* (1999). Division of labor among the alpha6-beta4 integrin, beta1 integrins, and an E3 laminin receptor to signal morphogenesis and beta-casein expression in mammary epithelial cells. *Molecular Biology of the Cell*, **10**, 2817–2828.

Nievers, M. G., *et al.* (2000). Formation of hemidesmosome-like structures in the absence of ligand binding by the (alpha)6 (beta)4 integrin requires binding of HD1/plectin to the cytoplasmic domain of the (beta)4 integrin subunit. *Journal of Cell Science*, **113**, 963–973.

Novak, A., *et al.* (1998). Cell adhesion and the integrin-linked kinase regulate the LEF-1 and beta-catenin signalling pathways. *Proceedings of the National Academy of Sciences of the USA*, **95**, 4374–4379.

Petersen, O. W., *et al.* (1992). Interaction with the basement membrane serves to rapidly distinguish growth and differentiation pattern of normal and malignant human breast epithelial cells. *Proceedings of the National Academy of Sciences of the USA*, **89**, 9064–9068.

Pierschbacher, M. D. and Ruoslahti, E. (1984). Cell attachment activity of fibronectin can be duplicated by small synthetic fragments of the molecule. *Nature*, **309**, 30–33.

Poznansky, M. C., *et al.* (2000). Efficient generation of human T cells from a tissue-engineered thymic organoid. *Nature Biotechnology*, **18**, 729–734.

Prockop, D. J. and Kivirikko, K. I. (1995). Collagens: molecular biology, diseases, and potentials for therapy. *Annual Review of Biochemistry*, **64**, 403–434.

Pujuguet, P., *et al.* (2000). Nidogen-1 regulates laminin-1-dependent mammary-specific gene expression. *Journal of Cell Science*, **113**, 849–858.

Roskelley, C. D., *et al.* (1994). Extracellular matrix-dependent tissue-specific gene expression in mammary epithelial cells requires both physical and biochemical signal transduction. *Proceedings of the National Academy of Sciences of the USA*, **91**, 12378–12382.

Saksela, O. and Rifkin, D. B. (1990). Release of basic fibroblast growth factor–heparan sulfate complexes from endothelial cells by plasminogen activator-mediated proteolytic activity. *Journal of Cell Biology*, **110**, 767–775.

Schmidhauser, C., *et al.* (1990). Extracellular matrix and hormones transcriptionally regulate bovine 5′ sequences in stably transfected mouse mammary cells. *Proceedings of the National Academy of Sciences of the USA*, **87**, 9118–9122.

Schneller, M., *et al.* (1997). Alphav beta3 integrin associates with activated insulin and PDGF beta receptors and potentiates the biological activity of PDGF. *EMBO Journal*, **16**, 5600–5607.

Schoenwaelder, S. M. and Burridge, K. (1999). Bidirectional signalling between the cytoskeleton and integrins. *Current Opinions in Cell Biology*, **11**, 274–286.

Schwarzbauer, J. (1999). Basement membranes: putting up the barriers. *Current Biology*, **9**, R242–R244.

Shtutman, M., *et al.* (1999). The cyclin D1 gene is a target of the beta-catenin/LEF-1 pathway. *Proceedings of the National Academy of Sciences of the USA*, **96**, 5522–5527.

Sonnenberg, A., *et al.* (1991). Integrin alpha 6 beta 4 complex is located in hemidesmosomes suggesting a major role in epidermal cell-basement membrane adhesion. *Journal of Cell Biology*, **113**, 907–917.

Steinbock, F. A. and Wiche, G. (1999). Plectin; a cytolinker by design. *Biological Chemistry*, **380**, 151–158.

Sternlicht, M. D., *et al.* (1999). The stromal proteinase MMP3/stromelysin-1 promotes mammary carcinogenesis. *Cell*, **98**, 137–146.

Streuli, C. H. and Bissell, M. J. (1990). Expression of extracellular matrix components is regulated by substratum. *Journal of Cell Biology*, **110**, 1405–1415.

Streuli, C. H., *et al.* (1991). Control of mammary epithelial differentiation: basement membrane induces tissue-specific gene expression in the absence of cell–cell interaction and morphological polarity. *Journal of Cell Biology*, **115**, 1383–1395.

Streuli, C. H., *et al.* (1995). Laminin mediates tissue-specific gene expression in mammary epithelia. *Journal of Cell Biology*, **129**, 591–603.

Tamura, M., *et al.* (1999). PTEN gene and integrin signalling in cancer. *Journal of the National Cancer Institute*, **91**, 1820–1828.

Tang, M. J., *et al.* (1998). Collagen gel overlay induces apoptosis of polarized cells in cultures; disoriented cell death. *American Journal of Physiology*, **275**, C921–C931.

Van der Neut, R., *et al.* (1996). Epithelial detachment due to absence of hemidesmosomes in integrin beta 4 null mice. *Nature Genetics*, **13**, 366–369.

Vasioukhin, V., *et al.* (2000). Directed actin polymerization is the driving force for epithelial cell–cell adhesion. *Cell*, **100**, 200–219.

Vu, T. H., *et al.* (1998). MMP-9/gelatinase B is a key regulator of growth plate angiogenesis and apoptosis of hypertrophic chondrocytes. *Cell*, **93**, 411–422.

Wang, F., *et al.* (1998). Reciprocal interactions between beta 1 integrin and epidermal growth factor receptor in three-dimensional basement membrane breast cultures; a different perspective in epithelial biology. *Proceedings of the National Academy of Sciences of the USA*, **95**, 14821–14826.

Wary, K. K., *et al.* (1996). The adaptor protein Shc couples a class of integrins to the control of cell cycle progression. *Cell*, **87**, 733–743.

Wary, K. K., *et al.* (1998). A requirement for caveolin-1 and associated kinase Fyn in integrin signalling and anchorage-dependent cell growth. *Cell*, **94**, 625–634.

Weaver, V. M., *et al.* (1996). The importance of the microenvironment in breast cancer progression: recapitulation of mammary tumorigenesis using a unique human mammary epithelial cell model and a three-dimensional culture assay. *Biochemistry and Cell Biology*, **74**, 833–851.

Weaver, V. M., *et al.* (1997). Reversion of the malignant phenotype of human breast cells in three-dimensional culture and in vivo by integrin blocking antibodies. *Journal of Cell Biology*, **137**, 231–245.

Woodley, D. T., *et al.* (1983). Interactions of basement membrane components. *Biochimica Biophysica Acta*, **761**, 278–283.

Wu, X., *et al.* (2000). Evidence for regulation of the PTEN tumor suppressor by a membrane-localized multi-PDZ domain containing scaffold protein MAGI-2. *Proceedings of the National Academy of Sciences of the USA*, **97**, 4233–4238.

Yamada, K. M. and Geiger, B. (1997). Molecular interactions in cell adhesion complexes. *Current Opinion in Cell Biology*, **9**, 76–85.

Yokosaki, Y., *et al.* (1994). The integrin alpha 9 beta 1 mediates cell attachment to a non-RGD site in the third fibronectin type III repeat of tenascin. *Journal of Biological Chemistry*, **269**, 26691–26696.

Zhu, X. and Assoian, R. K. (1995). Integrin-dependent activation of MAP kinase: a link to shape-dependent cell proliferation. *Molecular Biology of the Cell*, **6**, 273–282.

Zhu, X., *et al.* (1996). Adhesion-dependent cell cycle progression linked to the expression of cyclin D1, activation of cyclinE–cdk2, and phosphorylation of the retinoblastoma protein. *Journal of Cell Biology*, **133**, 391–403.

Zutter, M. M., *et al.* (1995). Re-expression of the alpha 2 beta 1 integrin abrogates the malignant phenotype of breast carcinoma cells. *Proceedings of the National Academy of Sciences of the USA*, **92**, 7411–7415.

Zutter, M. M., *et al.* (1998). Altered integrin expression and the malignant phenotype: the contribution of multiple integrated integrin receptors. *Journal of Mammary Gland Biology and Neoplasia*, **3**, 191–200.

FURTHER READING

Bissell, M. J., *et al.* (1982). Dynamic reciprocity – How does the extracellular matrix direct gene expression? *Journal of Therapeutic Biology*, **99**, 31–68.

Bissell, M. J., *et al.* (1999). Tissue structure, nuclear organization and gene expression in normal and malignant breast. *Cancer Research (Supplement)*, **59**, 1757–1764.

Boudreau, N. J. and Jones, P. L. (1999). Extracellular matrix and integrin signalling: the shape of things to come. *Biochemical Journal*, **339**, 481–488.

Erickson, A. C. and Couchman, J. R. (2000). Still more complexity in mammalian basement membranes. *Journal of Histochemistry and Cytochemistry*, **48**, 1291–1306.

Giancotti, F. and Ruoslahti, E. (1999). Integrin signaling. *Science*, **285**, 28–32.

Werb, Z. (1997). ECM and cell surface proteolysis: regulating cellular ecology. *Cell*, **91**, 439–442.

Chapter 16

Invasion and Metastasis

Lance A. Liotta and Cloud P. Paweletz
National Cancer Institute, National Institutes of Health, Bethesda, MD, USA

CONTENTS

INTRODUCTION

We usually diagnose and treat cancer when it is too late for local therapeutic strategies and most patients already harbour occult or overt metastasis. In fact, 30% of patients are diagnosed with overt metastases, while an additional 30–40% appear metastasis free during initial diagnosis, but harbour occult metastasis instead. Unfortunately for the cancer patient, the existence of metastasis greatly reduces the success of current surgical, chemotherapy and radiotherapy strategies (Astrow, 1994).

During the course of the disease most patients suffer from metastases at multiple sites, not all of which may be occurring at the same time. Furthermore, metastases have the potential to metastasize further: the presence of large identifiable metastases in a given organ is frequently accompanied by a greater number of micrometastases. And lastly, formation of metastatic colonies is a continuous process that commences early in the growth of the tumour and increases with time.

Cancer metastasis is a highly complex process that involves the deregulation of interacting proteins and genes that are responsible for invasion, angiogenesis, circulation of tumour cells in blood vessels, colonization at secondary organ sites, and finally evasion of host defence systems (**Figure 1**). Metastatic dissemination via the lymphatics and the vascular systems is the culmination, and end stage, of a disease process that evolves over 5–20 years. During most of that time period, microscopic lesions are progressing through a series of hyperproliferative and premalignant states through to carcinoma *in situ* presenting a phenomenally long time period for initial screening and treatment of cancer (**Figure 2**). We know that for most types of human solid neoplasia, microinvasive carcinoma emerges from a carcinoma *in situ* precursor lesion (Gallager and Martin, 1969; Zhuang *et al.*, 1995). Preventing the transition from premalignant to invasive/metastatic carcinoma is a major goal for cancer chemoprevention. In order to reach this goal, it will be important to identify molecular targets that are causally associated with the acquisition of cancer invasion.

The malignant tumour is a state that emerges from a host microecology that actually participates in the selection and expansion of the most aggressive neoplastic cells (Aboseif *et al.*, 1999; Hanahan and Weinberg, 2000) (**Figure 3**). Instead of being autonomous, malignant cells communicate extensively with other cells and the extracellular matrix. Sustained proliferation is not unique to cancer cells. In fact, growth pressure alone will not cause a neoplasm to be malignant. Malignant tumour cells migrate across tissue boundaries and have the capacity to survive and grow among 'foreign' cell populations. The true life-threatening behaviour of malignant cancer cells is their propensity to infiltrate and usurp the 'sovereignty' of host tissue societies.

Normal cellular physiology is a tightly regulated process with positive and negative feedback loops that decides whether a cell should differentiate, divide, adapt or commit apoptosis. Genetic changes, such as activation of oncogenes, increased production of growth factors, loss of growth inhibitory cytokines or loss of function of tumour-suppressor genes may result in an imbalance of growth regulation, leading to uncontrolled proliferation. However, unrestrained growth by itself does not cause metastasis, and additional genetic mutations over and above those that cause uncontrolled proliferation are needed. Genetic defects in the cancer cell translate into proteomic derangements in signal transduction pathways. The result of such derangements is a persistent pathological communication state between the tumour cell and the host. Tumour cells that successfully invade and metastasize are selected out because somatic genetic progression has resulted in an altered communication circuit that continues to call up and

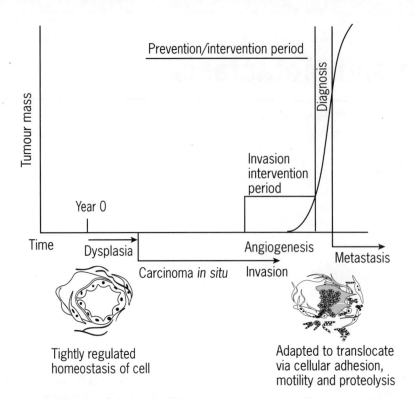

Prevention/intervention period

Diagnosis

Tumour mass

Invasion
intervention
period

Year 0

Time

Dysplasia

Carcinoma *in situ*

Angiogenesis

Invasion

Metastasis

Tightly regulated
homeostasis of cell

Adapted to translocate
via cellular adhesion,
motility and proteolysis

Figure 1   Intervention period for carcinogenesis. Theoretical improvement for intervention strategies as a function of time. Diagnosis of cancer usually is performed late into the disease, when most patients already present with occult metastasis. However, progression of cancer from dysplasia to metastatic dissemination may extend as far back as 10 years, providing a much larger window for intervention strategies before metastasis occurs.

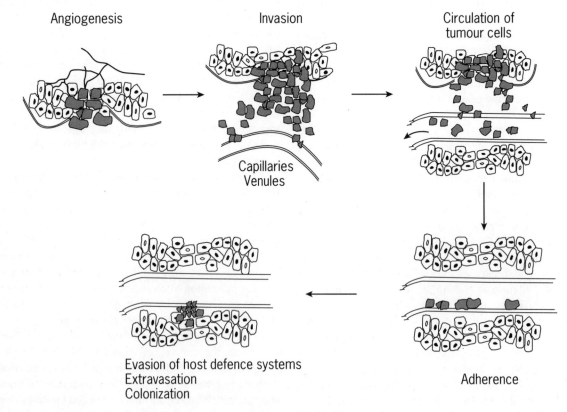

Angiogenesis

Invasion

Circulation of
tumour cells

Capillaries
Venules

Evasion of host defence systems
Extravasation
Colonization

Adherence

Figure 2   Pathogenesis of metastasis. Cancer metastasis is a highly complex process that involves the deregulation of interacting proteins and genes that are responsible for angiogenesis, invasion, circulation of tumour cells in blood vessels, colonization at secondary organ sites and finally evasion of host defence systems.

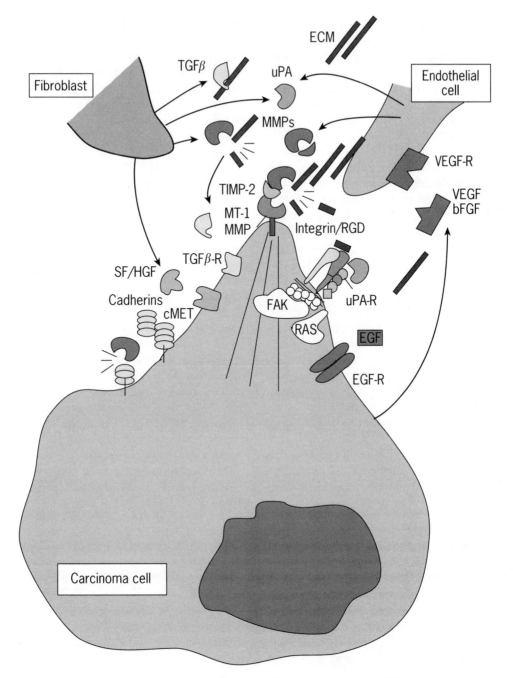

Figure 3   Microecology at the invasion front. Example mediators are shown. Motility and invasion is a bidirectional process. Fibroblasts produce chemoattractants including scatter factor/hepatocyte growth factor (SF/HGF) which stimulates motility of tumour cells by binding to the Met receptor (c-Met). Tumour cells produce angiogenesis factors including vascular endothelial growth factor (VEGF) and basic fibroblast growth factor (bFGF), which bind to receptors on stromal vascular cells causing increased vascular permeability, endothelial proliferation, migration, and invasion. Fibroblasts and endothelial stromal cells elaborate latent enzymes including matrix metalloproteinases (MMPs) and urokinase plasminogen activator (uPA) which dock on the surface of the carcinoma invadopodia and become activated, thereby degrading the ECM, and clearing a pathway. ECM degradation releases bound growth factors such as transforming growth factor beta (TGF-β) and epidermal growth factor (EGF), which bind to cognate receptors (TGFβ-R and EGF-R) on the carcinoma cell. ECM proteolysis also exposes cryptic RGD sites which are recognized by integrins (integrin/RGD). Cross-talk between signal pathways within the carcinoma cells links motility, proliferation and prosurvival.

support invasion and survival. At the biochemical level, the mechanism for initial invasion may parallel, or be similar to, that used by nonmalignant cells that traverse tissue boundaries. Using specialized cell models and new array technology, investigators are uncovering the interplay of specific signal transduction molecules that mediate the malignant state (Clark *et al.*, 2000; Paweletz *et al.*, 2001). Using protein microarray technology, the authors demonstrated that activation of PI3 kinase substrates and suppression of apoptosis are early events in the microenvironment of prostate cancer evolution. This analysis provided direct quantitative evidence that suppression of apoptosis in human PIN and invasive prostate cancer may be associated with phosphorylation of Akt and its substrate GSK3-β. Moreover, the authors verified that downstream components of the apoptotic cascade (cleaved and noncleaved caspase-7, and also cleaved and noncleaved PARP) are shifted toward prosurvival messages at the cancer invasion front. High-grade PIN exhibited a lower level of phospho-ERK compared with normal-appearing epithelium. Invading carcinoma cells contained phospho-ERK levels that were even more reduced compared with PIN. These data are in keeping with known prosurvival pathways, which emanate from Akt through its substrates. Augmentation of the ratio of phosphorylated Akt to total Akt will suppress downstream apoptosis pathways through intermediate substrates such as GSK3β. Reduction in apoptosis will shift the balance of cell birth and death rates favouring the observed accumulation of cells within the epithelial gland. Prosurvival messages are required for migrating cells to resist the proapoptotic signals that take place during the disruption of integrin-mediated adhesion to extracellular matrix molecules. In parallel, transient ERK activation and augmentation of prosurvival pathways may be associated with cellular migration. Activation of Akt, a substrate of PI3K, can therefore promote cell motility and survival as the invading cancer cells leave the gland, invade the stroma and metastasize.

As the tumour cell invader enters foreign soil, it appropriates the local growth signals and ignores its instructions to undergo apoptosis. Tumour cells escaping the primary tumour mass respond to host signals that call up the capacity for motility (Jo *et al.*, 2000), survival (Frisch and Francis, 1994), and proliferation (Brown and Giavazzi, 1995; Kohn and Liotta, 1995). Host cells contribute enzymes and cytokines that aid the tumour cell. For example, tumour cells can penetrate host cellular and extracellular barriers with the help of degradative enzymes produced by the host cells, but locally activated by the tumour (Chambers and Matrisian, 1997; Werb, 1997). The presence of the new malignant cells within the invaded host tissue is associated with a local reorganisation of the stroma, blood vessels, lymphatics and epithelial morphology. We may incorrectly assume that the host response to the tumour is designed to repel an invader. Instead, the host reaction to the tumour cells may be simply an indifferent accommodation process (Wernert, 1997). Regardless, the multifocal disruption and damage associated with the modified microenvironment are ultimately lethal to the host.

Distributions of metastases vary widely with histological type and anatomical location of the primary tumour (**Table 1** and **Table 2**). For some tumour types a frequent

Table 1   Organ preferences of metastasis in some human and animal selected models[a]

Tumour system subline	Lung	Liver	Brain	Ovary	Spleen	Lymph node
Murine B16 melanoma (i.v. or i.c.)						
B16–F1	+	+/–	+/–	+/–	–	+/–
B16–F10	++++	+/–	–	+	+/–	+/–
B16–F15b	+++	–	+++	+	+/–	+/–
Murine RAW117 large cell lymphoma (i.v. or s.c.)						
Raw117-P	+/–	+/–	–	–	+/–	–
Raw117-H10	+/–	++++	–	–	++	–
Murine MTI mammary carcinoma (i.v. or s.c.)						
TC3	+++	+	–	+/–	–	+
Chicken MD lymphoma (i.v.)						
AL-2	–	++++	–	+/–	–	–
AL-3	–	+	–	++++	–	–
Human A375 melanoma (i.v. in nude mice)						
A375-P	+/–	+/–	–	–	–	+/–
A375-SM	++	+/–	–	+/–	–	+
Human PC-3 prostatic carcinoma (i.v. in athymic mice)						
PC-3-125-IN	++++	–	–	–	–	–
PC-3-1-LN	++++	+	–	+	+/–	+++

[a]Metastasis: –, none; +/–, sometimes; +, few; ++, moderate; +++, many; ++++, large numbers and heavy tumour burden; i.v., intravenous; i.c., intracaecum. (Adapted from Nicolson, 1998.)

Table 2 Frequency of metastatic sites

Site	10%	10–30%	30–50%	50–70%	70%
Breast		Kidney, skin, brain	Adrenal	Liver, bone, lung	Lymph nodes
Bladder	Brain, skin	Kidney,bone	Adrenal, lung		
Cervix	Brain, skin	Kidney, bone	Adrenal, lung		
Colorectum	Skin	Brain, kidney, lung	Bone, adrenal, liver	Lymph nodes	
Kidney	Skin, bone	Brain, kidney	Liver	Lung	
Lung	Lung	Kidney, distant nodes	Adrenal, brain	Bone	Liver, local lymph nodes
Melanoma		Kidney	Adrenal, brain, bone, skin	Lung, liver nodes	
Ovary	Brain, skin, kidney	Bone, adrenal	Lung, liver nodes		
Prostate	Brain, skin	Kidney, adrenal, liver, lung	Bone, nodes		

(Adapted from Weiss, 1992, and references therein.)

organ location of distant metastases appears to be the first capillary bed encountered. Lung metastases from sarcoma or colorectal cancer dissemination to the liver can be considered examples of this kind of metastasis. In the gynaecological tumours, distant metastases are seen in two forms: serosal dissemination, such as liver capsule metastases from ovarian cancer, and capillary-associated dissemination, such as lung parenchymal disease. However, not all metastases can be explained by anatomical considerations alone, such as metastasis to the ovary from breast carcinoma or dissemination to the liver from ocular melanomas, and hence must be considered as organ tropism.

The organ preference for metastatic colonization is heavily influenced by communications between the circulating tumour cell and the target host tissue. Various molecular mechanisms attempt to explain preferential organ distribution during metastasis. First, cancers shed equal numbers of tumour cells into the vascular system, and thus tumour cells disseminate equally to all organs, but only grow preferentially in some specific organs. For example, the insulin-like-growth factors are present in liver and lung and have been implicated in growth and motility for breast and lung carcinoma. Second, circulating tumour cells may adhere preferentially to the endothelial luminal surface. Nicolson *et al.* have identified endothelial surface antigens that may mediate preferential adhesion of circulating tumour cells. Lastly, circulating tumour cells may respond to soluble factors diffusing locally out of target organs. Chemokines are growth factor-like molecules which bind to G-protein coupled receptors. Circulating leukocytes and stem cells are known to use chemokine mechanisms to home in on specific organs. They induce leucocytes to adhere tightly to endothelial cells and migrate toward the highest concentration of chemokine. Since this behaviour seemed identical with that required for metastatic tumour cells, Mueller *et al.* hypothesized that tumour cells may co-opt the same chemokines to direct metastatic organ preference. They

conducted a comprehensive survey of known chemokines and found a receptor–ligand pair (CCR4 and CXCL12) which fit the profile expected for breast cancer metastasis homing to bone, lung and liver. *In vitro*, the CXCL12 ligand stimulated breast cancer cells to carry out the basics of invasion: pseudopodial protrusion, directed migration and penetration of extracellular matrix barriers. *In vivo*, using animal models, the authors blocked metastasis to CXCL12-rich lung tissue by treatment with a neutralizing antihuman CXCR4 monoclonal antibody.

ANGIOGENESIS

The transition from normal epithelium to invasive carcinoma is preceded by, or is concomitant with, activation of local host vascular channels and stromal fibroblasts. Stromal cell activation and recruitment by the tumour cell promotes premalignant cell transformation and malignant invasion. For example, during the transition from *in situ* to invasive carcinoma, disorganisation and disruption of the periglandular basement membrane and a local neovascular 'blush' can precede frank malignant conversion (Guidi *et al.*, 1997). Neovascularization offers a portal for dissemination. Locally activated vascular channels at the invasive edge of the tumour are highly permeable and offer a reduced barrier for intravasation (Dvorak *et al.*, 1995). A variety of molecules have been found to mediate angiogenesis *in vitro* and *in vivo*. Among these are basic fibroblast growth factor (bFGF), angiogenin, vascular permeability factor (VPF) and tumour necrosis factor α and β (TNF-α, TNF-β) (Folkman and Klagsbrun, 1987).

Neovascularization is a form of physiological invasion (Fidler and Ellis, 1994; Folkman, 1995). Endothelial cells migrate, elaborate degradative enzymes and traverse extracellular matrix barriers along a chemotropic gradient emanating from the tumour cells. Physiological and malignant invasion employ similar molecular mechanisms.

The difference is that malignant invasion persists. Neovascularization, wound healing and neurite outgrowth during embryogenesis are examples of physiological invasion. In response to trophic signals, vascular cells, wounded epithelial sheets or neurites will migrate, penetrate tissue barriers and establish appropriate new anastomoses (Kohn and Liotta, 1995; Carmeliet and Jain, 2000). However, when the trophic signal is removed or the injury is repaired, physiological invasion ceases. Malignant cells perpetually stimulate host stromal and vascular cells to conduct physiological invasion. Promotion of the local invasive environment creates a permissive field for the malignant cell.

Rapid-growing tumours are capable of shedding up to millions of tumour cells into the vascular circulation by angiogenesis and invasion alone (Liotta *et al.*, 1974). Furthermore, experimental studies show that less than 0.05% of circulating tumour cells are successful in initiation of metastatic colonies, making metastatic dissemination a highly inefficient process (Liotta *et al.*, 1974; Nicolson, 1991). These studies are also clinically validated by the observation that circulating tumour cells are detected in patients who never form a metastasis.

INVASION

Invasion is the active translocation of neoplastic cells across tissue boundaries and through host cellular and extracellular matrix barriers. Invasion is dependent on the coordinated activity of a series of interacting proteins extending from the inside of the cell to the cell surface and the adjacent host cellular and extracellular microenvironment (**Figure 3**). Cellular adhesion, local proteolysis and motility are the triad of necessary functions that mediate invasion. While invasion is not directly caused by growth pressure, nevertheless the genetic and proteomic deregulation that causes invasion can effect neoplastic proliferation indirectly by promoting cancer cell survival.

CELLULAR ADHESION

Normal tissue morphology and organ architecture are tightly regulated by a communication reciprocity between the tissue cells and the extracellular matrix (ECM) and/or basement membrane. Adhesion is more than just anchoring – it is dynamic solid phase signal transduction (Fashena and Thomas, 2000). Receptors sensing changes in the cell-ECM state provide extracellular signals, which trigger corresponding intracellular signal transduction pathways that regulate proliferation, differentiation and migration. Receptors involved in sensing the ECM include growth factor and hormone receptors which recognize ligands solubilized from the ECM and receptors which directly bind to the solid-phase molecules of the ECM. The latter include the integrins, the cell adhesion molecules (CAMs) and cadherins (**Figure 3**).

The integrin family of cell surface extracellular matrix proteins consists of heterodimeric units, designated α (140 kDa) and β (95 kDa). An important aspect of this family is that integrins can exist in a binary 'on' or 'off' state, thereby selectively changing affinity for corresponding ligands (Juliano and Haskill, 1993). Activation of integrins has been shown to be involved in cell migration, cell proliferation and metastatic dissemination. Loss of sustained integrin stimulation (Frisch and Ruoslahti, 1997) has been associated with apoptosis. Integrin interactions with intracellular and extracellular molecules determines function. Such interactions are dictated by the context of the intergrins in the cell function, not the absolute levels of integrins. For example, increased expression of integrin receptors on cell surfaces has been associated with an invasive phenotype of melanoma and squamous carcinoma of the head and neck, whereas loss of integrin expression status has been shown in cancers of breast, prostate and colon (Chammas and Brentani, 1991).

A wide variety of cell–cell adhesion receptors (CAMs) have been studied for their role in cancer invasion. These include, but are not limited to, intercellular adhesion molecules (ICAMs), L-, E- and P-selectins, vascular cell adhesion molecules (VCAMs), neural cell adhesion molecules (NCAMs) and neuroglial cell adhesion molecules (NG-CAMs). Unlike other receptors that bind proteins, selectins bind carbohydrate ligands on endothelial cells. The cadherins comprise a family of transmembrane glycoproteins that mediate Ca^{2+}-dependent cell–cell adhesion (Takeichi, 1991). Special intracellular proteins, the catenins, form zipper-like structures constituting extracellular cell–cell bonds with the cell cytoplasm. These interactions are regulated by tyrosine phosphorylation as well as additional cell to cell communications. Down-regulation of epithelial cadherin transcription, E-cadherin, has been shown to correlate with an aggressive cancer cell phenotype (Frixen *et al.*, 1991; Vlemininckx *et al.*, 1991). For example, transforming Madin–Darbey canine kidney (MDCK) cells by H-*ras* not only diminished E-cadherin expression, but also increased the invasive behaviour of these cells. This effect could be reversed by transfecting E-cadherins back into the transformed cells (Vleminckx *et al.*, 1991). Furthermore, overexpression of E-cadherin in highly invasive tumour types (bladder, breast, lung and pancreas) caused loss of invasiveness. Surface receptors that participate in cell–cell adhesion and interaction can activate signalling pathways responsible for maintaining normal cell and tissue architecture. Deregulation of these receptors in cancer can promote invasion by (a) reducing cell–cell adhesion which prevents shedding of tumour cells and (b) failing to suppress the inappropriate mixing of tumour cell and host cell populations during invasion.

MOTILITY

Translocation of individual cells across tissue boundaries is a necessary component of invasion. Cell motility and migration are not unique to tumour cells. This process is essential for normal immune cell function and for embryological development, organogenesis and gastrulation. Deregulation and persistence of motility may distinguish carcinoma cells from their normal epithelial counterparts (Nabeshima et al., 1997). The direction of tumour cell motility is controlled by a multitude of chemoattractants, including cytokines (hepatocyte growth factor), collagen peptides, formyl peptides and autocrine growth factors (e.g. Autotaxin) (Anzano et al., 1983). These agents may stimulate both the initiation and maintenance of tumour cell motility and the directness of that migration. Chemoattractants can be secreted by host stromal cells or the tumour cells themselves, or be released from the extracellular matrix.

An early event in motility is cytoskeletal remodelling causing extension of a dominant pseudopod toward the direction of movement. This is followed by translocation of the whole cell body (Stossel, 1993; You et al., 1996). The pseudopod of the invading cell has been renamed an 'invadopodia' because it may direct local proteolytic machinery (Bowden et al., 1999) literally to create a tunnel in the extracellular matrix in front of the cell. Protruding invadopodia, in response to chemoattractants, may serve to sense organs for the migrating cell to locate directional clues, to secrete motility-stimulating factors, to promote propulsive traction for locomotion and induce matrix proteolysis. The complexity of tumour cell migration requires that more than one agent is involved in the direction, location, and magnitude of the migratory response. During the course of invasion, the tumour cell must interact with the extracellular matrix components and be exposed to host-derived factors. Tumour cells have receptors for many of these potential attractants. Therefore, the response of tumour cells to autocrine motility stimulation and also endo- or paracrine stimulation by matrix components and host-derived factors is important to tumour motility.

EXTRACELLULAR MATRIX DEGRADATION DURING INVASION

Proteolytic modification of the cell surface and the extracellular matrix is believed to be an essential component of invasion (Liotta et al., 1980), both neoplastic and physiological. The major enzymes that degrade the ECM and cell-associated proteins are (1) the matrix metalloproteinases (MMPs), a family of secreted and membrane anchored proteinases, (2) the adamalysin-related membrane proteinases, (3) the bone morphogenetic protein 1 type metalloproteinases and (4) tissue serine proteinases including tissue plasminogen activator, urokinase, thrombin and plasmin

(Werb, 1997). Major ECM barrier substrates for degradative enzymes include collagens (more than 13 types), proteoglycans, laminin, fibronectin and vitronectin. Each compartment of the ECM contains a different complement of matrix molecules. Collagens I and III are examples of collagens preferentially localized to stroma, while collagens IV and V are predominant in the basement membrane, which forms the border between epithelium and stroma. Proteolysis of the ECM is observed in trophoblast implantation, embryo morphogenesis, wound healing, tissue remodelling and angiogenesis. An imbalance in the ratio of proteinases to protease inhibitor can regulate vascular morphogenesis and invasion (Ura et al., 1989). All classes (serine, aspartyl, cysteinyl and metallo) of matrix-degrading proteinases participate, and coactivate each other, in the tumour–host invasion field (Nakajima et al., 1987; Ostrowski et al., 1988; Reich et al., 1988). Evidence also exists that proteases inside the cell may also be involved during invasion (Koblinski et al., 2000).

A large body of literature exists correlating degradative enzyme activity with cancer invasion and metastasis. The most studied proteases include tissue-type plasminogen activator (tPA), plasmin, cathepsin-D, -B, -L and -G, the urokinase plasminogen activator (uPA), metalloproteinases and the heparanases. Urokinase plasminogen activator, a serine protease, has been shown to correlate with a metastatic phenotype of cells. Antibodies against uPA block human HEP-3 cell invasion and murine B16–F10 melanoma cell metastasis after tail vain injection (Ossowski and Reich 1983; Esheicher et al., 1989). Moreover, overexpression of uPA in H-ras transformed cell lines enhance lung metastases (Axelrod et al., 1989). Inhibition of metalloproteinases has been demonstrated to inhibit cell invasion (DeClerck et al., 1991). MMPs can be divided into three general classes: (1) interstitial collagenases, (2) stromelysins and (3) gelatinases. Interstitial collagenase degrades type I, II, III and VII collagens. Stromelysins degrade type I, III, IV, V and IX collagens, laminin, fibronectin, and gelatin. The third group of the MMP family, the gelatinases (MMP-2 and MMP-9), can degrade collagen type I, II, III, IV, V, VII, IX and X and fibronectin (Emonard and Grimaud, 1990). Association of MMP-2 and MMP-9 with the invasive phenotypes is abundant in the literature. Inhibition of MMP-2 by TIMP-1 reduces cellular invasion in vitro and in vivo. Induction of H-ras oncogene enhances expression of MMP-2 and MMP-9. Invasive colonic, gastric, ovarian and thyroid adenocarcinomas showed positive immunoreactivity for MMP-2, whereas normal colorectal, gastric mucosa and benign ovarian cysts showed reduced or negative staining (Monteagudo et al., 1990; Levy et al., 1991). A delicate balance between TIMPs and MMPs may act as a positive and negative feedback control regulating vascular morphogenesis and invasion (Mignatti et al., 1986). MMPs and TIMPs have direct, and indirect, effects on angiogenesis, which are separate from their proteolytic functions (Chambers et al., 1997; Hoegy et al., 2001). Heparan sulfate proteoglycans (HSPGs), major and ubiquitous components of the ECM, are substrates for heparanases, which cleave heparan sulfate glycosaminoglycan side chains. Augmentation of heparanase activity has been associated with tumour aggressiveness (Nakajima *et al.*, 1988; Vlodavsky *et al.*, 1995). Heparin and similar polysaccharides inhibit metastasis (Parish *et al.*, 1987). Transfection of nonmetastatic murine T-lymphoma Eb cell lines with full-length human heparanase cDNA (Vlodavsky *et al.*, 1999) enhances the metastatic phenotype in animal models. (See the chapters on *Models for Tumour Cell Adhesion and Invasion* and *Tumour Metastasis Models.*)

COORDINATION OF THE MACHINERY OF INVASION AT THE CELL SURFACE

Significant progress has been made in our understanding of the molecular cross-talk between tumour cells and host cells at the invasion front. A cascade of cytokines, motility factors, matrix receptors, enzymes and enzyme inhibitors simultaneously carries out the regulation, steering, proteolysis, traction and locomotion required for invasion (**Figure 3**).

Remodelling of the extracellular matrix, within the immediate pericellular environment of the cell, appears to be a necessary step in local invasion (Liotta *et al.*, 1991; Werb, 1997). The complement of enzyme classes is tightly and exquisitely regulated by a series of activation steps and specific inhibitors. In a striking demonstration of host–tumour interdependence, a majority of the enzymes and inhibitors complexed at the invasion front are contributed by host cells, not by the invading tumour cells (Nakahara *et al.*, 1997; Bowden *et al.*, 1999; Coussens *et al.*, 2000).

The enzyme machinery is confined to the cell surface at the point of invading pseudopodia 'invadopodia' by binding the enzymes to adhesion sites, cell surface receptors and adjacent ECM molecules (Nakahara *et al.*, 1997; Bowden *et al.*, 1999; Hoegy *et al.*, 2001). MT1-MMP, a membrane-anchored ECM-degrading enzyme, contains a transmembrane–cytoplasmic sequence that confines it to microinvasion sites on the tumour cell invadopodia surface (**Figure 3**). In complex with one of the tissue inhibitors of metalloproteinases (TIMP-2) it becomes a receptor and activator of MMP-2 (Nakahara *et al.*, 1997), a soluble MMP produced by stromal fibroblasts and endothelial cells. The serine proteinase uPA is confined to the invading pseudopodia through a cooperation between integrins and the uPA receptor (uPA-R) (Andreasen *et al.*, 1997). uPA-R is an adhesion receptor for vitronectin, and also interacts laterally with integrin β chains. Proteolysis of ECM proteins modifies integrin mediated anchorage, focal adhesions and cytoskeletal architecture and triggers signalling molecules such as focal adhesion kinase (FAK) (Braga, 2000; Fashena and Thomas, 2000). Such heterotypic

complexes direct and confine the enzymatic field at the forward edge of the invading cell, leaving intact the peripheral and distal attachment sites required for traction. As the invading cell moves forward through ECM barriers, the leading edge complex of enzymes, inhibitors and receptors molecules cycle through adhesion, deadhesion and proteolysis. The direction of tumour cell invasion and migration can be influence by chemoattractants and by marking of preferred adhesion pathways. Local attractants include (1) hepatocyte growth factor/scatter factor, which binds to the Met (c-Met) receptor (Wernert, 1997; Jo *et al.*, 2000), (2) proteolysed matrix fragments which are recognized by integrins (Varner and Cheresh, 1996) or (3) cytokines and growth factors, such as EGF and TGF-β released from the degraded matrix (Roberts *et al.*, 1992). Cryptic RGD sites exposed by proteolysis (Davis, 1992; Fukai *et al.*, 1995; Varner *et al.*, 1995; Varner and Cheresh, 1996) may guide the path in front of the invading tumour cells.

The combination of microdissection and protein microarrays has been successfully applied to the microworld of early stage cancer (Clark *et al.*, 2000; Paweletz *et al.*, 2001). Protein lysate microarrays consist of very small mass quantities (picograms) of protein lysates from cell lines, whole lysed tissue or microdissected subpopulations of lysed tissue cells immobilized and arrayed on a solid phase. The array can be probed with antibodies recognizing phosphorylated forms of signal proteins. Detection is highly sensitive, quantitative and precise, so that the state of signal pathways may be profiled. Individual subpopulations of host and tumour tissue cells within a microscopic field of invasion or premalignant transition can be microdissected and individually studied.

In conclusion, the process of cancer invasion is a coordinated effort by tumour cells and host cells within a microinvasion field. Within this field the tumour cells exchange cytokines, enzymes, inhibitors and growth factors which promote invasion by all cells involved. Pericellular remodelling of the ECM is commensurate with invasion. The different events of the metastatic cascade of angiogenesis, adhesion, proteolysis, motility and proliferation may provide useful and novel therapeutic targets. Investigators have identified some of the critical molecules involved in the extracellular cross-talk taking place among and between cells in the invasion field. This synthesis provides strategies for a new therapy concept 'stromal therapy' which targets the tumour–host communication interface. (See the chapter *Targeting the Extracellular Matrix.*)

REFERENCES

Aboseif, S., *et al.* (1999). Mesenchymal reprogramming of adult human epithlelial differentiation. *Differentiation*, **65**, 113–118.

Andreasen, P., *et al.* (1997). The urokinase type plasminogen activator system in cancer metastasis: a review. *International Journal of Cancer*, **71**, 1–22.

Anzano, M. A., *et al.* (1983). Sarcoma growth factor from conditioned medium of virally transformed cells is composed of both type alpha and type beta transforming growth factors. *Proceedings of the National Academy of Sciences of the USA*, **80**, 6264–6268.

Astrow, A. B. (1994). Commentary: rethinking cancer. *Lancet*, **343**, 494–495.

Axelrod, J. H., *et al.* (1989). Expression of human recombinant plasminogen activators enhance invasion and experimental metastasis of Ha-RAS-transformed NIH 3T3 cells. *Molecular Cell Biology*, **9**, 2133–2141.

Bowden, E., *et al.* (1999). An invasion related complex of cortactin, paxillin, and PKC u associates with invadopodia at sites of extracellular matrix degradation. *Oncogene*, **18**, 4440–4449.

Braga, V. (2000). The crossroads between cell–cell adhesion and motility. *Nature Cell Biology*, **2**, E182–E184.

Brown, P. D. and Giavazzi, R. (1995). Matrix metalloproteinase inhibition: a review of anti-tumour activity. *Annals of Oncology*, **6**, 967–974.

Carmeliet, P. and Jain, R. K. (2000). Angiogenesis in cancer and other diseases. *Nature*, **407**, 249–257.

Chambers, A. F. and Matrisian, L. M. (1997). Changing views of the role of matrix metalloproteinases in metastasis. *Journal of the National Cancer Institute*, **89**, 1260–1270.

Chammas, R. and Brentani, R. (1991). Integrins and metastases: an overview. *Tumour Biology*, **12**, 309–320.

Clark, E. A., *et al.* (2000). Genomic analysis of metastases reveals and essential role for RhoC. *Nature Cell Biology*, **406**, 532–535.

Coussens, L. M., *et al.* (2000). MMP-9 supplied by bone marrow-derived cells contributes to skin carcinogenesis. *Cell*, **103**, 481–490.

Davis, G. E. (1992). Affinity of integrins for damaged extracellular matrix: alpha v beta 3 binds to denatured collagen type I through RGD sites. *Biochemical and Biophysical Research Communications*, **182**, 1025–1031.

DeClerck, Y. A., *et al.* (1991). Inhibition of tumor cell invasion of smooth muscle cell layers by recombinant human metalloproteinase inhibitor. *Cancer Research*, **51**, 2151–2157.

Dvorak, H. F., *et al.* (1995). Vascular permeability factor/vascular endothelial growth factor, microvascular hyperpermeability, and angiogenesis. *American Journal of Pathology*, **146**, 1029–1039.

Emonard, H. and Grimaud, J. A. (1990). Matrix metalloproteinases: a review. *Cell Molecular Biology*, **36**, 131–153.

Esheicher, A., *et al.* (1989). Characterization of the cellular binding site for the urokinase type plasminogen activator. *Journal of Biological Chemsitry*, **264**, 1180.

Fashena, S. and Thomas, S. M. (2000). Signaling by adhesion receptors. *Nature Cell Biology*, **2**, E225–E229.

Fidler, I. J. and Ellis, L. M. (1994). The implication of angiogenesis for the biology and therapy of cancer metastasis. *Cell*, **79**, 185–188.

Folkman, J. (1995). Angiogenesis in cancer, vascular, rheumatoid and other disease. *Nature Medicine*, **1**, 27.

Folkman, J. and Klagsbrun, M. (1987). Angiogenic factors. *Science*, **235**, 442–447.

Frisch, S. and Francis, H. (1994). Disruption of epithelial cell–matrix interactions induces apoptosis. *Journal of Cell Biology*, **124**, 619–626.

Frisch, S. M. and Ruoslahti, E. (1997). Integrins and anoikis. *Current Opinions in Cell Biology*, **9**, 701–706.

Frixen, U. H., *et al.* (1991). E-cadherin mediated cell–cell adhesion prevents invasiveness of human carcinoma cells. *Journal of Cell Biology*, **113**, 173–185.

Fukai, F., *et al.* (1995). Release of biologically activities from quiescent fibronectin by conformational change and limited proteolysis by matrix metalloproteinases. *Biochemistry*, **34**, 11453–11459.

Gallager, H. S. and Martin, J. E. (1969). The study of mammary carcinoma by mammography and whole organ sectioning, early observation. *Cancer*, **23**, 855–873.

Guidi, A. J., *et al.* (1997). Vascular permeability factor (vascular endothelial growth factor) expression and angiogenesis in patients with ductal carcinoma in situ of the breast. *Cancer*, **80**, 1945–1953.

Hanahan, D. and Weinberg, R. A. (2000). The hallmarks of cancer. *Cell*, **100**, 57–70.

Hoegy, S., *et al.* (2001). Tissue inhibitor of metalloproteinases-2 (TIMP-2) suppresses TKR-growth factor signaling independent of metalloproteinase inhibition. *Journal of Biological Chemistry*, **276**, 3203–3214.

Jo, M., *et al.* (2000). Cross talk between epidermal growth factor receptor and c-Met signal pathways in transformed cells. *Journal of Biological Chemistry*, **275**, 8806–8811.

Juliano, R. L. and Haskill, S. (1993). Signal transduction from the extracellular matrix. *Journal of Cell Biology*, **120**, 577–585.

Koblinski, J. E., *et al.* (2000). Unraveling the role of proteases in cancer. *Clinica Chimica Acta*, **291**, 113–135.

Kohn, E. C. and Liotta, L. A. (1995). Molecular insights into cancer invasion: strategies for prevention and intervention. *Cancer Research*, **55**, 1856–1862.

Levy, A., *et al.* (1991). Increased expression of the 72 kDa type IV collagenase in human colonic adenocarcinoma. *Cancer Research*, **51**, 439–444.

Liotta, L. A., *et al.* (1974). Quantitative relationships of intravascular tumor cells: tumor vessels and pulmonary metastases following tumor implantation. *Cancer Research*, **34**, 997.

Liotta, L. A., *et al.* (1980). Metastatic potential correlates with enzymatic degradation of basement membranes. *Nature*, **284**, 67–68.

Liotta, L. A., *et al.* (1991). Cancer metastasis and angiogenesis: an imbalance of positive and negative regulation. *Cell*, **64**, 327–336.

Mignatti, P., *et al.* (1986). In vitro angiogenesis on the human amniotic membrane: requirement for basic fibroblast growth factor-induced proteinases. *Journal of Cell Biology*, **108**, 671–682.

Monteagudo, C., *et al.* (1990). Immunohistologic distribution of type IV collagenases in normal, benign, and malignant breast tissue. *American Journal of Pathology*, **136**, 585–592.

Mueller, A., *et al.* (2001). Involvement of chemokine receptors in breast cancer metastasis. *Nature*, **403**, 50–56.

Nabeshima, K., *et al.* (1997). Cohort migration of cancer cells. *Connective Tissue*, **29**, 199.

Nakahara, H., *et al.* (1997). Transmembrane/cytoplasmic domain mediated membrane type 1-matrix metalloproteinase docking to invadopodia is required for cell invasion. *Proceedings of the National Academy of Sciences of the USA*, **94**, 7959–7964.

Nakajima, M., *et al.* (1987). Degradation of basement membrane type IV collagen and lung subendothelial matrix by rat mammary adenocarcinoma cell clones of differing metastatic potentials. *Cancer Research*, **47**, 4869–4876.

Nakajima, M., *et al.* (1988). Heparanase and tumor metastasis. *Journal of Cell Biochemistry*, **36**, 157–167.

Nicolson, G. L. (1991). Gene expression, cellular diversification and tumor progression to the metastatic phenotype. *Bioessays*, **13**, 337–342.

Ossowski, L. and Reich, E. (1983). Antibodies to plasminogen activator inhibit human tumor metastasis. *Cell*, **35**, 611–619.

Ostrowski, L. E., *et al.* (1988). Expression pattern of a gene for a secreted metalloproteinase during late stages of tumor progression. *Molecular Carcinogenesis*, **1**, 13–19.

Parish, C. R., *et al.* (1987). Evidence that sulphated polysaccharides inhibit tumor metastasis by blocking tumor cell-derived heparanase. *International Journal of Cancer*, **40**, 511–518.

Paweletz, C. P., *et al.* (2001). Reverse phase protein microarrays which capture disease progression shown activation of pro-survival pathways at the cancer invasion front. *Oncogene*, **20**, 1981–1989.

Reich, R., *et al.* (1988). Effects of inhibitors of plasminogen activator, serine proteases, and collagenase IV on the invasion of basement membranes by metastatic cells. *Cancer Research*, **48**, 3307–3312.

Roberts, A. B., *et al.* (1992). TGF-beta: regulation of extracellular matrix. *Kidney International*, **41**, 557–559.

Stossel, T. P. (1993). On the crawling of animal cells. *Science*, **260**, 1086–1094.

Takeichi, M. (1991). Cadherin cell adhesion receptors as a morphogenetic regulator. *Science*, **251**, 1451–1455.

Ura, H., *et al.* (1989). Expression of type IV collagenase and procollagen genes and its correlation with tumorigenic, invasive, and metastatic abilities of oncogene transformed human bronchial cells. *Cancer Research*, **49**, 4615–4621.

Varner, J. A. and Cheresh, D. A. (1996). Integrins and cancer. *Current Opinions in Cell Biology*, **8**, 724–730.

Varner, J. A., *et al.* (1995). The integrin α v β3: angiogenesis and apoptosis. *Cell Adhesion Communications*, **3**, 367–374.

Vleminckx, K., *et al.* (1991). Genetic manipulation of E-cadherin by epithelial tumor cells reveals an invasion suppressor role. *Cell*, **66**, 107–119.

Vlodavsky, I., *et al.* (1995). Inhibition of tumor metastasis by heparanase inhibiting species of heparin. *Invasion and Metastasis*, **14**, 290–302.

Vlodavsky, I., *et al.* (1999). Mammalian heparanase: gene cloning, expression and function in tumor progression and metastasis. *Nature Medicine*, **5**, 793–802.

Weiss, L. (1992). Comments on hematogenous metastatic patterns in humans as revealed by autopsy. *Clinical and Experimental Metastasis*, **10**, 191–199.

Werb, Z. (1997). ECM and cell surface proteolysis: regulating cellular ecology. *Cell*, **91**, 439–442.

Wernert, N. (1997). The multiple roles of tumor stroma. *Virchows Archives*, **430**, 433–443.

You, J., *et al.* (1996). Responses of tumor cell pseudopod protrusion to changes in medium osmolality. *Journal of Cell Physiology*, **167**, 156–163.

Zhuang, Z., *et al.* (1995). Identical allelic loss on chromosome 11q13 in microdissected *in situ* and invasive human breast cancer. *Cancer Research*, **55**, 467–471.

FURTHER READING

Carmeliet, P. and Jain, R. K. (2000). Angiogenesis in cancer and other diseases. *Nature*, **407**, 249–257.

Hanahan, D. and Weinberg, R. A. (2000). The hallmarks of cancer. *Cell*, **100**, 57–70.

Kohn, E. C. and Liotta, L. A. (1995). Molecular insights into cancer invasion: strategies for prevention and intervention. *Cancer Research*, **55**, 1856.

Nicolson, G. L. (1998). Organ specificity of tumour metastasis: role of preferential adhesion, invasion and growth of malignant cells at specific secondary sites. *Cancer and Metastasis Reviews*, **7**, 173–188.

Chapter 17

Angiogenesis

Ute Modlich and Roy Bicknell
University of Oxford, John Radcliffe Hospital, Oxford, UK

C O N T E N T S

WHAT IS ANGIOGENESIS?

Like all tissues, tumours depend on a continuous supply of oxygen and nutrients for their survival. The ability to recruit a functional blood supply is therefore central to tumorigenesis. Angiogenesis is the growth of new blood vessels from the pre-exisiting vasculature by budding and sprouting of endothelial cells. This is in contrast to vasculogenesis, which is the *de novo* formation of blood vessels from endothelial precursor cells (called angioblasts) (Rissau, 1997). Vasculogenesis occurs mainly during embryogenesis, in particular the development of tissues of endodermal origin, although some ectodermal and mesodermal derived tissues acquire their vessels through angiogenesis, e.g. the kidney and the brain (Beck and D'Amore, 1997).

In an adult, the vasculature is remarkably quiescent and angiogenesis occurs only very rarely. Diffusion of oxygen in tissues is limited to a distance of about 150 μm. Therefore, tissue growth is restricted to a few cubic millimetres if no new vasculature is formed. Under physiological conditions, angiogenesis is involved in the turnover of tissues in the female reproductive system (endometrium, placenta, follicle maturation and corpus luteum formation in the ovaries) and in wound healing. Angiogenesis is, on the other hand, an essential component of many pathologies such as diabetic retinopathy, rheumatoid arthritis, psoriasis and tumour growth.

'TUMOUR GROWTH IS ANGIOGENESIS DEPENDENT'

Around 30 years ago, it was recognized that the growth of solid tumours is angiogenesis dependent (Folkman, 1971, 1990). Thus, tumours remain in a dormant state of a few millimetres in diameter (prevascular phase) unless they are able to recruit their own vascular bed. This does not mean that the tumour cells are unable to proliferate, but an inadequate supply of oxygen and nutrients results in a high rate of apoptosis (cell death). The tumour exists in a balance of proliferation and regression which precludes tumour expansion (tumour dormancy). Only after a tumour has recruited its own blood supply can it expand in size. This involves the production of angiogenic factors secreted into the tissue by the tumour cells and is known as the 'angiogenic switch' (Hanahan and Folkman, 1996). This induces angiogenesis in the adjacent quiescent vasculature, allowing the growth of new vessels into the tumour.

Why and how new vessels are formed is of great interest in terms of anticancer therapy because inhibition of new vessel formation could restrict tumour growth. The tumour is essentially 'starved'. Such strategies could also include the destruction of tumour vessels which are already formed. Increased understanding of the mechanism of angiogenesis could allow subsequent design of therapeutics which interfere with the process. The aim of this chapter is to describe the sequence of events during angiogenesis and to outline its importance in tumour biology. (See the chapter *Antiangiogenic Therapy*.)

MORPHOLOGY OF BLOOD VESSELS

The entire vasculature is lined by a single layer of specialized cells, the endothelial cells. They form a simple squamous epithelium which rests on a basement membrane and surrounds a lumen in which blood flows (**Figure 1**). The basement membrane contains collagen types I and IV, fibronectin, laminin, entactin and other non-collagen glycoproteins. Endothelial cells, together with their basement membrane, constitute the lamina intima of a blood vessel. The lamina intima is surrounded by pericytes, smooth muscle cells or cardiomyocytes, collectively described as mural cells. Pericytes lie within the basement membrane of the endothelial cells whereas the others surround larger vessels and the endocardium as an additional layer outside the basement membrane (as a part of the lamina media). Pericytes are recruited by endothelial cells during development and play an important role in vessel maturation and stabilization. They appear to suppress the turnover of endothelial cells. During neovascularization pericytes are selectively lost from angiogenic vessels, including the tumour vasculature.

The endothelium in an adult has a surface area of $>1000 \, m^2$. In addition to forming a static physiological barrier, it possesses secretory, synthetic, metabolic and immunological functions. The endothelium is highly heterogeneous; its precise nature varies depending upon the function of the vascular bed in different tissues.

Histologically there are three main taxonomic classes of endothelia. For example, blood vessels of the brain and the retina are especially tight (continuous endothelium), whereas the endothelium of the sinusoidal vessels in the liver, spleen and bone marrow contains intracellular gaps not covered by a basement membrane and so allows cellular trafficking (discontinuous endothelium); the endothelium in endocrine glands, the kidney and small intestine shows intracellular holes (fenestrated endothelium), which allows extensive exchange of substances.

At the molecular level, the endothelium of different tissues varies in its surface phenotype and protein expression. The distinct differences are induced by the extracellular matrix which adapts the endothelium to its functional needs in a tissue. This observation has led to the concept of 'vascular addresses.' It explains the homing of inflammatory cells in specific tissues because they adhere to the vessel wall by attaching to specific endothelial cell surface molecules. The unique vascular addresses of organs are also the reason for tissue-directed metastasis of tumour cells. It has been shown that tumour cells recognize specific adhesion molecules on the endothelium. They adhere there and are subsequently able to extravasate and to invade the tissue. In the tissue stroma they then form micrometastases.

THE TUMOUR VASCULATURE IS DISORGANIZED

The vascular tree of tumour vessels appears 'chaotic' and 'disorganized.' Tumour vessels are also hyperpermeable ('leaky') owing to a discontinuous endothelium and lack of pericytes. Morphologically the vessels appear highly tortuous. The tumour vasculature is formed in two ways: by co-opting pre-existing vessels and by induction of new vessels by angiogenesis. In addition, every tumour induces its own characteristic vascular bed which is different for each tumour type. As a result of persistent growth, the tumour vasculature constantly changes its shape and is dynamic rather than static. In tumours, up to 30% of the vasculature consists of arterio-venous shunts where the blood bypasses the capillaries, precluding exchange of nutrients. Tumour blood vessels lack mural cells as well as appropriate innervation and therefore blood pressure is poorly controlled (only by pre-existing arterioles). The blood flow in the tumour is slow but higher in the tumour periphery than in the centre. Different regions of perfusion can be seen within tumours: necrotic, seminecrotic and well-vascularized regions, in order from the centre of the tumour to the periphery. The blood flow in the periphery of a tumour is higher than that in the surrounding normal tissue (advancing front), whereas in the centre, blood flow can be interrupted transiently resulting in complete stasis; blood flow may then be re-established in the opposite direction.

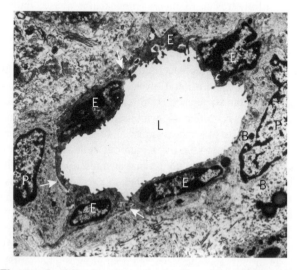

Figure 1   Ultrastructure of a capillary. The vessel lumen (L) is surrounded by five endothelial cells (E). The cells rest on a continuous basement membrame (B). Two pericytes (P) lie within the basement membrane. The endothelial cell contacts (tight junctions) are visible as electron-dense areas of the endothelial cell membranes (arrows).

Extravasation of molecules from the blood occurs through diffusion, convection and partially through transcytosis. Despite the fact that blood flow within tumours is slow, and the vessels are leaky, the delivery of therapeutics into tumours is inefficient. This is due to a high interstitial fluid pressure in the tumour tissue compromising convective movements of therapeutics. In regions of highest pressure in a tumour, the hydrostatic and osmotic pressure in the vessels is opposed by that in the tissue, inhibiting the exchange of substances. This results in hypoxic and hypoglycaemic regions within a tumour. In addition, there are totally anoxic areas. Because the vasculature is dynamic, and perfusion rates in different regions of a tumour change frequently, hypoxic regions can become reoxygenated again. Similarly, normoxic regions can experience sudden oxygen deprivation and become hypoxic. Owing to the poor perfusion of vessels, endothelial cells also can become hypoxic. It has been shown that hypoxia is a potent inducer of many molecules involved in angiogenesis.

These observations highlight the fact that the tumour vasculature is not an extension of 'normal' blood vessels but that it is itself distinct and characteristic. This renders the tumour vasculature an excellent target for antitumour therapy. In addition, targeting the vessels is associated with a number of advantages over current therapies (Augustin, 1998). Targeting its uniqueness should minimize interference with other blood vessels in the body. In addition, endothelial cells are much more accessible than tumour cells to systemically administered therapeutics because of their intimate contact with the blood. Finally, destruction of only a few endothelial cells can have detrimental effects on the tumour. The destruction of a single blood vessel will lead to an amplification of tumour destruction because about 10 layers of tumour cells are dependent on the supply by one blood vessel.

MECHANISMS OF ANGIOGENESIS

A tumour can only continue to expand in size if it induces a blood supply. When a tumour starts to produce angiogenic factors it activates endothelial cells in the vasculature of the surrounding tissue to initiate angiogenesis (**Figure 2**). The angiogenic stimulus induces the endothelial cells of the 'mother' vessels to change from a quiescent to an activated phenotype (Auerbach and Auerbach, 1994). These endothelial cells produce proteolytic enzymes which break down their basement membrane. This is the prerequisite for endothelial cells to migrate into the surrounding tissue towards the angiogenic stimulus. The migrating endothelial cell changes shape to an elongated phenotype (**Figure 3**). They start expressing typical cell surface molecules which allow the cells to migrate along the extracellular matrix. These endothelial cells also start to proliferate and to form new tubes. Finally, these new tubes anastomose into loops

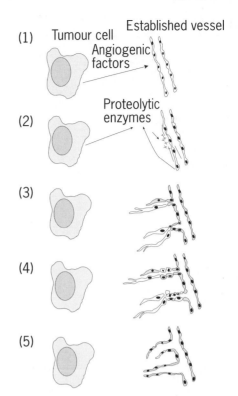

Figure 2 The angiogenic cascade. (1) Angiogenic stimulus; (2) Degradation of the basement membrane and ECM by proteases released from tumour and activated endothelial cells; (3) Migration of EC towards angiogenic stimulus; (4) Endothelial cell proliferation; (5) Tube formation and vessel maturation.

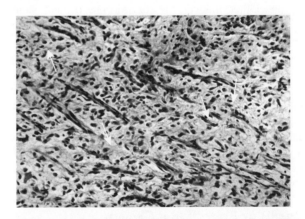

Figure 3 Angiogenic blood vessels in the rat sponge assay (paraffin section, haematoxylin/eosin stained). In this assay inert sponge is implanted subcutaneously. Endothelial cells migrate from the surrounding tissue into the sponge and form new vessels. Some vessels are indicated by arrows.

that allow blood flow. The recruitment of pericytes and smooth muscle cells completes angiogenesis through blood vessel maturation. The endothelial cells in the new vessels then revert to a quiescent phenotype.

Table 1 Angiogenic factors

Growth factors
Vascular endothelial growth factor (VEGF)
Placenta growth factor (PlGF)
Basic fibroblast growth factor (bFGF or FGF-2)
Acidic fibroblast growth factor (aFGF or FGF-1)
Transforming growth factor-α (TGF-α)
Transforming growth factor-β TGF-β
Platelet-derived growth factor (PDGF)
Hepatocyte growth factor (HGF)
Granulocyte colony-stimulating factor (G-CSF)

Cytokines
Tumour necrosis factor-α (TNF-α)
Interleukin 1 (IL-1)

Chemokines
Interleukin 8 (IL-8)

Enzymes
Platelet-derived endothelial cell growth factor (PD-ECGF)
Angiogenin

Prostaglandins
PGE$_1$
PGE$_2$

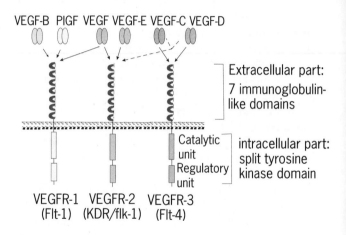

Figure 4 VEGF receptors and their ligands.

ANGIOGENIC FACTORS

In the last 20 years, many factors that have angiogenic activity have been identified. The first to be identified were the fibroblast growth factors (aFGF or FGF-1 and bFGF or FGF-2), which are now known to be pleiotrophic growth factors. Others include the transforming growth factors (TGF-α and TGF-β), platelet-derived growth factor (PDGF), hepatocyte growth factor (HGF), granulocyte colony-stimulating factor (G-CSF), tumour necrosis factor-alpha (TNF-α), platelet-derived endothelial cell growth factor (PD-ECGF, thymidine phosphorylase), interleukin-8 and prostaglandins (PGE$_1$, PGE$_2$) (**Table 1**). All of these have been studied extensively and have been shown to be angiogenic (Folkman and Shing, 1992), but none of these are endothelial cell specific. The only growth factor known to be specific for endothelial cells is vascular endothelial growth factor (VEGF).

Vascular Endothelial Growth Factor (VEGF)

VEGF was the first member to be identified of a growing family of vascular endothelial growth factors and is now referred to as VEGF-A. Other members include VEGF-B to E and placenta growth factor (PlGF-1 and 2). VEGFs are homodimeric proteins and mediate their activity through tyrosine–kinase receptors (VEGF-receptors, VEGFR1-3) which are almost exclusively expressed on endothelial cells. VEGFR-1 (flt-1, fms-like kinase-1) binds VEGF-A, VEGF-B and PlGF with strong affinity whereas VEGFR-2

(flk-1, foetal liver kinase-1 or the human homologue KDR, kinase-insert domain receptor) binds VEGF-A, VEGF-C and VEGF-D with lower affinity. VEGFR-3 (flt-4) is only expressed on lymphatic endothelium and is the ligand for VEGF-C which induces lymphangiogenesis. VEGF-D has been discovered to be an additional ligand for the VEGFR-3. VEGF-E seems to signal mainly through VEGFR-2 (**Figure 4**).

Of all the VEGFs, VEGF-A has been studied most intensively (for a review, see Neufeld *et al.*, 1999). It exists in at least five different splice variants (VEGF$_{121,145,165,189,206}$) encoding isoforms of differing length derived from a single gene. With the exception of VEGF$_{121}$, which is secreted, all VEGFs are heparin binding. Therefore, they accumulate in the extracellular matrix and can be released from there by proteolytic enzymes. There is, in addition, a sixth 110 amino acid isoform of VEGF arising from proteolytic cleavage of VEGF$_{189}$, when bound to the cell surface. Heparan sulfate proteo glycans are known to modulate growth factor signalling of many heparin-binding growth factors from their respective receptors, and the same might apply to VEGF signalling.

VEGF is an endothelial cell mitogen and chemoat-tractant, it promotes cell migration, inhibits apoptosis and modulates the permeability of the endothelial cell layer (it was first identified as vascular permeability factor (VPF) in 1983). Hence it has major roles as a key regulator in angiogenesis and vasculogenesis. Mice deficient in one allele of VEGF (VEGF +/− mice) show early embryonic death (embryonic day 11–12) due to cardiovascular defects in most sites of early blood vessel formation (embryo and yolk sac). This suggests that a minimal dosage requirement for the growth factor exists because a single allele could not rescue the phenotype. Microinjection of VEGF into quail embryos during development induces uncontrolled and unlimited vascularization at sites that are normally avascular. Together these observations show that the level of VEGF expression is tightly regulated and that small variations can have fatal effects.

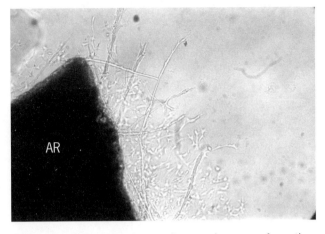

Figure 5 Rat aortic ring angiogenesis assay. A section of a rat aorta is placed in a fibrin gel in cell culture. Endothelial cells from the inner lining of the aortic ring (AR) sprout into the fibrin gel. Some of the newly formed tubes are seen to anastomose.

VEGFR-2-deficient mice (*flk-1* $-/-$ mice) die *in utero* between embryonic days 8.5 and 9.5. Endothelial cells in these animals fail to differentiate from their angioblastic precursors and the animals die as a result of a total lack of vascular structures. VEGFR-2 is the earliest marker for differentiation towards endothelial cells in development. Similarly, VEGFR-1-deficient mice (*flt-1* $-/-$) show abnormal and disorganized vascular structures and die between embryonic days 9.5 and 10.5. These two gene-targeted mice, despite both developing vascular defects and being embryonic lethal, show very different phenotypes. Furthermore the VEGF receptors do not show redundancy in their function.

VEGF has been established as an angiogenic factor *in vitro* in two- and three-dimensional cell culture systems (**Figure 5**). VEGF also proved its angiogenic properties in the rabbit cornea assay and the chick chorioallantoic assay. Tumour cells overexpressing VEGF form faster-growing tumours and contain significantly more blood vessels than tumours formed from untransfected control cells. VEGF also synergizes with bFGF and the angiogenic effects of each growth factor are potentiated.

VEGF expression is regulated by hypoxia and hypoglycaemia, and especially high levels are present within hypoxic regions in tumours. Oxygen tension in tumours is about 50 times lower than in normal tissues and hypoxia could be a major factor driving tumour angiogenesis. The cellular response to hypoxia is mediated by the hypoxia-inducible factor Hif-1. Hif is a dimer comprised of two subunits by Hif-1α and Hif-1β. This dimeric complex recognizes a specific DNA sequence, known as the hypoxia-response element (HRE), which is found within the promoters of hypoxia regulated genes such as the VEGF promoter. The promoter of VEGFR-1 also contains hypoxia response elements whereas the promoter of VEGFR-2 does not. Hence

the expression of VEGFR-1 is enhanced by hypoxia directly but not the VEGFR-2. The expression of VEGFR-2 can be induced by binding of VEGF to VEGFR-2 and as a result the VEGFR-2 is indirectly upregulated by hypoxia.

Macrophages in Tumour Angiogenesis

Unlike physiological angiogenesis, tumour growth is usually accompanied by an inflammatory response. Widespread infiltration of inflammatory cells during angiogenesis is a feature of wound healing. Thus, tumours have been described as 'wounds which do not heal.' Tumours recruit inflammatory cells, especially macrophages (tumour-associated macrophages (TAMs)). In some tumours macrophages can represent up to 50% of the cell population and are often the major source of angiogenic molecules in a tumour (see **Figure 6**). Tumour cells express the very potent monotactic chemokine MCP-1 (monocyte chemotactic protein-1) which attracts macrophages into the tumour. TAMs have two important functions within the tumour. First, they confer antitumour effects by their immunological functions and have been implicated as part of the host immune defence mechanism against tumours. Second, those same cells can promote angiogenesis through secretion of cytokines, such as interleukin 1 and TNF-α, chemokines and growth factors (VEGF, bFGF, EGF, PD-ECGF and HGF).

Chemokines act as chemoattractants for haematopoietic cells and confer similar effects on endothelial cells (Moore *et al.*, 1998). Chemokines are grouped into two main subfamilies, the CC-chemokines and the CXC-chemokines, based on their structure. In CXC-chemokines the two cysteines near the N-termini are separated by a single amino acid whereas in CC-chemokines these cysteines are adjacent. Endothelial cells express all known receptors for CXC-chemokines (CXCR-1 to CXCR-4 and DARC) but none of the receptors for CC-chemokine (there are to date eight identified receptors). This corresponds well with the observation that CC-chemokines have no direct effects on endothelial cells (members of the CC-chemokine subfamily are MCP-1 and RANTES). The subfamily of CXC-chemokines includes interleukin 8 (IL-8), platelet factor-4, growth-related antigen (GRO-β) and interferon-γ-inducible protein (IP-10). In addition, Il-8 was shown to induce endothelial cell proliferation and to induce angiogenesis *in vivo*. This effect can be potentiated by IL-1 and TNF-α. Interestingly, a number of chemokines from this sub-family have an antiangiogenic function (platelet factor-4, GRO-β, IP-10). These CXC-chemokines have in common that they lack the ELR-motif (glutamine–leucine–arginine) between the first cysteines. The pro- or anti-angiogenic properties of a chemokine might be dependent on this motif.

Macrophages secrete TNF-α, a multifunctional cytokine which has both angiogenic and antiangiogenic properties. These conflicting reports are a result of different actions of TNF-α at high and low doses. Whereas high doses of TNF-α

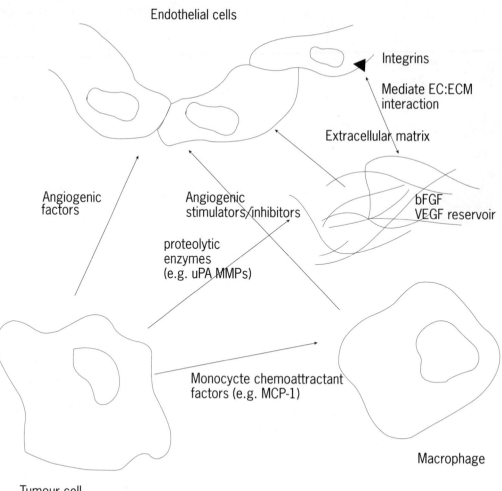

Figure 6 Interaction between tumour cells, endothelial cells and macrophages. Tumour cells produce angiogenic factors, which induce endothelial cells to initiate angiogenesis. Tumour cells also secrete chemoattractants, that recruit macrophages, and proteolytic enzymes, which can release growth factors from the extracellular matrix. Endothelial cells interact with the extracellular matrix by adhesion molecules (e.g. integrins), which mediate endothelial cell migration.

are directly cytotoxic to tumours, it is angiogenic at low doses. Because of its direct cytotoxic effects, TNF-α was studied following systemic administration *in vivo*. Unfortunately, the side effects were severe and may be related to the fact that TNF-α is the major mediator of septic shock. At high doses, TNF-α exerts its antitumour effects mainly through its cytotoxicity on endothelial cells and inhibition of angiogenesis rather than through actions on tumour cells. These findings are consistent with the fact that tumour cells are often insensitive to TNF-α alpha-mediated cytotoxicity.

At low doses, TNF-α induces endothelial cell migration and tube formation *in vitro*, but it also inhibits endothelial cell proliferation. It is chemotactic for leukocytes and induces IL-1 and GM-CSF expression. It also induces the expression of E-selectin, ICAM-1 and VCAM-1 on endothelial cells and can mediate leukocyte recruitment into the tissue stroma.

Fibroblast Growth Factors

aFGF and bFGF are endothelial cell mitogens and stimulate endothelial cell migration. They induce the production of proteases by endothelial cells and stimulate tube formation in three-dimensional cell culture systems. They are angiogenic in all *in vivo* assays and are today often used as a positive control in angiogenesis assays. Because of their heparin-binding abilities, FGFs are bound to the extracellular matrix and are released by proteases involved in the angiogenic cascade. Endothelial cells are not only reactive to FGFs through two FGF receptors but they also produce bFGF themselves. In this way, endothelial cells respond to FGF in both paracrine and autocrine manner. The FGFs interact with almost all molecules involved in angiogenesis. A complete discussion of this growth factor is beyond the scope of this chapter (for a detailed review, see Christofori, 1997).

THE BREAKDOWN OF THE BASEMENT MEMBRANE

Angiogenesis is an invasive process involving migration of endothelial cells into the surrounding tissue. In the first instance, this requires the degradation of the basement membrane of the pre-existing vasculature, to enable endothelial cells to leave the organized structure of the vessel wall. Several proteolytic enzymes are involved in the degradation of the extracellular matrix (ECM). They include the plasminogen activator system and the matrix metalloproteinases (MMPs).

The Plasminogen Activator System

The plasminogen activator (PA) system includes the uro-kinase plasminogen activator (uPA) and the tissue-type plasminogen activator (tPA), both of which convert plasminogen into plasmin. The major physiological function of plasmin is to degrade fibrin; however, it also degrades components of the ECM such as laminin and collagen. In addition, it also activates metalloproteinases and elastase. Whereas tPA functions during fibrinolysis, uPA functions mainly in angiogenesis. uPA is secreted as a proenzyme and binds to its receptor on the cell surface, where it becomes activated. By binding to the uPA receptor it also activates downstream signals, resulting in induction of cell migration and invasion. In fact, the presence of the uPA receptor seems to be critical for cell migration because very little migration could be observed in uPA receptor negative cells. Endothelial cells express uPA as well as an uPA inhibitor (PAI). PAI binds to the active uPA and stimulates its internalization into cells following binding to the uPA receptor, resulting in its breakdown. The expression of uPA and its receptor can be induced by FGF-2. This effect is mediated via the FGF receptors. Hence it seems likely that the FGF-2-induced migration in endothelial cells is mediated by uPA. Because of its heparin-binding ability, FGF accumulates in the ECM and is released by proteases including plasmin. Therefore, uPA and FGF increase their function in an autocrine manner because uPA is expected to release FGF-2 and at the same time FGF-2 induces migration through uPA.

The Matrix Metalloproteinases

The MMPs are a family of extracellular endopeptidases which are secreted by a variety of cells including epithelial cells, fibroblasts and inflammatory cells. Endothelial cells express MMP-1, MMP-2, MMP-9 and the membrane-associated MT-1-MMP (for a review, see Stetler-Stevenson, 1999). These endopeptidases are secreted as inactive proenzymes and need to be activated by cleavage of a pro-teolytic fragment. The substrates of the different endopeptidases include all known components of the ECM but the specific substrate of each enzyme has not yet been identified. Four different endogenous inhibitors of MMPs have been identified; they are the tissue inhibitors of metalloproteinases TIMP-1 to -4. Endothelial cells studied in a two-dimensional culture produce only very low levels of MMPs, whereas expression can be induced in endothelial cells by growing them in three-dimensional collagen gel systems. In addition, changes in cell shape also alter MMP expression (especially mechanical stress) and it has been suggested that integrins, as the mediators of cell–matrix interactions, are involved in the regulation of MMP expression. This has been shown for the $\alpha2\beta1$ and the $\alpha v\beta3$ integrins. The $\alpha v\beta3$ integrin interacts with MMP-2 through the C-terminal hemopexin-like (PEX) domain of MMP-2. This is interesting because the PEX domain does not contain the integrin binding RGD motif. The PEX domain is also the binding site for TIMP-2. TIMP-2 binding of MMP-2 is necessary for the MT-1-MMP-mediated activation of MMP-2 from the proenzyme. So PEX can inhibit angiogenesis by direct competition to MMP-2 in two different ways. First, PEX inhibits activation of MMP-2 by binding to TIMP-2. Second, PEX binds to the integrin on the cell surface, which would be a prerequisite for MMP-2 activation. Natural breakdown products of MMP-2 are generated and PEX accumulates in tissues where neovascularization occurred. These findings suggest that endogenous PEX acts as a natural inhibitor of MMP-2 function and as a result is an endogenous inhibitor of angiogenesis.

Angiogenesis Inhibitors Encrypted within Larger Proteins

Similarly to PEX, several other endogenous angiogenesis inhibitors have been characterized which are all fragments of larger molecules. These inhibitors are formed by proteolytic breakdown of their parent molecules. The first of these inhibitors was identified as early as 1985 and is a 29-kDa fragment of fibronectin. It has been shown to inhibit endothelial cell proliferation. Fibronectin itself is an abundant molecule which has no such inhibitory function.

More recently discovered endogenous angiogenesis inhibitors are angiostatin and endostatin (for reviews, see Kim Lee Sim, 1998; Oehler and Bicknell, 2000). Angiostatin is a 36-kDa fragment of plasminogen which is cleaved by macrophage-derived MMPs or proteases derived from tumours (e.g. prostate carcinomas). Endostatin is a 20-kDa fragment of collagen XVIII. Systemic administration of both angiostatin and endostatin induces tumour regression by destruction of the tumour vasculature. They also inhibit the formation of new blood vessels in a tumour. They therefore maintain a tumour in a state of dormancy. Both molecules have been identified in the urine or serum of tumour-bearing mice. In these animals a primary tumour existed but metastases did not occur. Based on these findings, and on the clinical observation that primary tumours suppress the growth of metastasis, it was concluded that inhibitory factors are produced by the primary tumour. The inhibition of metastatic spread was a direct result of angiogenesis inhibition, and angiostatin and endostatin act specifically on endothelial cells. In addition, both molecules are endogenous factors which are generated by proteolytic cleavage of larger molecules. These 'mother' molecules have no inhibitory function but have angiogenesis promoting effects.

N-Terminal fragments of the human prolactin/growth hormone family are antiangiogenic whereas the hormones themselves are angiogenic. They have also been shown to stimulate the expression of PAI. During the maturation of type I collagen, a ~90-kDa N-terminal fragment is cleaved which is homologous to a domain of the antiangiogenic matrix molecule thrombospondin. The fragment has antiangiogenic effects both *in vitro* and *in vivo*. Restin is a 22-kDa fragment of collagen XV that has been found by homology search with endostatin. It inhibits endothelial cell migration *in vitro* but does not effect proliferation. Vasostatin inhibits bFGF-induced angiogenesis *in vitro* and *in vivo*. It is a 180-kDa fragment of calreticullin. Calreticullin has been shown to exert similar effects.

It seems that endogenous antiangiogenic factors are released under physiological conditions. It might be true that the vasculature is kept in a quiescent state by a balance between angiogenesis-promoting factors and

Table 2 Naturally occurring angiogenesis inhibitors

Enzyme inhibitors
Tissue metalloproteinase inhibitors (TIMP1-4)
Plasminogen activator inhibitor (uPAI)

Angiogenesis inhibitors encrypted in larger proteins
29-kDa fragment of fibronectin
16-kDa fragment of prolactin
Angiostatin: 36-kDa fragment of plasminogen
Endostatin: 20-kDa fragment of collagen type XVIII
90-kDa N-terminal fragment of collagen type I,
    homologue to a thrombospondin domain
Cleaved conformation of antithrombin
PEX: hemopexin-like domain of MMP-2
Vasostatin: N-terminal domain of calreticulin
Restin: 22-kDa fragment of collagen XV

Cytokines
Tumour necrosis factor-alpha (TNF-α)
Interferon

Chemokines
Platelet factor-4
Growth-related antigen (GRO-β)
Interferon-γ-inducible protein (IP-10)

angiogenesis inhibitors and that a deregulation of this balance induces angiogenesis (endogenous angiogenesis inhibitors; see **Table 2**).

MIGRATION

During the formation of new vascular sprouts, endothelial cells migrate into the surrounding tissue following chemoattractant stimuli. Migrating endothelial cells adapt their shape and become elongated with multiple pseudopodia. They cover a larger surface and are therefore in more intimate contact with components of the ECM. Consistent with this, they upregulate the expression of receptors which mediate cell–ECM contacts. Integrins are the major ECM receptors. They are transmembrane heterodimeric cell adhesion molecules which are composed of an α and a β subunit. There are at present 20 members of this family derived from 15 α and eight β chains. Integrins mediate adhesion to all known components of the ECM while one of them can often recognize more than one ECM molecule. Integrins also bind to cell surface molecules of the immunoglobulin superfamily (ICAM-1, ICAM-2 and VCAM-1) and in this situation are involved in cell–cell adhesion processes.

Some integrins recognize ECM molecules through the so-called RGD motif (Arg-Gly-Asp), which is present in fibronectin, vitronectin, proteolysed collagen, fibrinogen, von Willebrand factor, osteopontin and thrombospondin. The $\alpha_5\beta_1$, $\alpha_{IIb}\beta_3$ and most $\alpha_v\beta$ integrins bind the RGD motif. Some integrins, such as $\alpha_2\beta_1$, bind to an Asp-Gly-Gly-Ala sequence in type I collagen. Both $\alpha_2\beta_1$ and $\alpha_1\beta_1$ integrins are upregulated on migrating endothelial cells following treatment with VEGF and the migration of endothelial cells on a collagen matrix can be inhibited by antibodies against the α chains of these two integrins. An *in vivo* model of angiogenesis was inhibited by combinations of the same antibodies without effects on non-angiogenic vessels.

The most extensively studied integrin involved in angiogenesis is the $\alpha_v\beta_3$ integrin (Eliceiri and Cheresh, 1999). It is upregulated on tumour blood vessels, during wound healing and retinal neovascularization. Angiogenesis is inhibited by a specific monoclonal antibody (LM609) which blocks binding of this integrin and thus disrupts endothelial cell–ECM adhesion. In the chick chorioallantoic membrane assay and in the rabbit cornea eye pocket assay LM609 blocked bFGF-induced angiogenesis whilst VEGF-induced angiogenesis was inhibited by antibodies against the $\alpha_v\beta_5$ integrin. A humanized form of the antibody LM609 (Vitaxin) is in clinical trials.

The RGD peptide itself is able to induce blood vessel regression *in vitro* and *in vivo* through competition with matrix proteins for their integrin binding site. Adhesion is required for endothelial cell survival and these cells undergo apoptosis when adhesion is disrupted. Endothelial cells of quiescent vessels are less sensitive to antiadhesive treatment than angiogenic and migrating cells. Experiments with endothelial cells grown on RGD-coated beads showed that binding to the ligand (in this case the RGD peptide on the bead) is not sufficient to prevent endothelial cells from undergoing apoptosis. It was suggested that spreading of endothelial cells is necessary for survival. It has also been postulated that the mechanical force generated by cell–ECM interactions mediates gene expression by changes in the cytoskeleton and nuclear morphology.

Integrins interact with the cytoskeleton through their cytoplasmic domains. This interaction is initiated by binding of integrins to the ECM. The mechanical properties of the ECM modulate the strength of this interaction. In fibroblasts the binding of integrins to the cytoskeleton enables the cells to pull themselves forward over a stationary substrate by retrograde movement of the cytoskeleton. This mechanism allows them to migrate. Similarly, integrins are involved in endothelial cell migration.

Integrins also act as signalling receptors. Binding to ECM has been shown to result in elevated intracellular calcium levels, elevated pH, activation of the inositol and DAG pathways and tyrosine phosphorylation. Furthermore, ligand binding to $\alpha_v\beta_3$ is essential for the sustained activation of MAP kinases by angiogenic factors. Tyrosine phosphorylation of VEGFR-2 by VEGF was enhanced by growing endothelial cells on vitronectin, a ligand for $\alpha_v\beta_3$. This was inhibited by antibodies directed against the β_3 integrin subunit. As mentioned earlier, $\alpha_v\beta_3$ integrin binds to MMP-2 and is involved in proteolysis.

PROLIFERATION

Another important step in angiogenesis is the proliferation of endothelial cells. This would provide new vasculature with additional endothelial cells to cover the inner surface of the new vessels. Indeed, many angiogenic factors have mitogenic activity, e.g. bFGF and VEGF.

The turnover rate of endothelial cells in the adult human body is extremely low. Incorporation experiments with radioactively labelled thymidine (H^3TdR) in rabbits *in vivo* estimated a proliferative index for endothelial cells in retinal vessels of about 0.01% (1 h after injection). Following two days of treatment with H^3TdR, about 0.2% of the endothelial cells showed incorporation of thymidine and a turnover time of ~1000 days was calculated. Interestingly, pericytes were discovered to have an even lower proliferation index (0.06%). In contrast, rapidly renewing tissues were shown to have much higher labelling indices, such as the epithelium of the cornea (3%) and the epithelium of the duodenum (14%). In a separate study, endothelial cell proliferation indices of different tissues were compared. Endothelium of the brain and muscle was especially quiescent (0.8% and 0.5% of cells incorporated

H^3TdR after 3 days), whereas higher indices were measured in the liver endothelium (4.4% after 3 days).

In contrast to endothelial cells within normal tissues, endothelial cell proliferation indices in tumours is several orders of magnitude higher. Labelling indices in experimental tumours in animals have been reported as up to 32% (anaplastic sarcoma of Wistar rats). Others have estimated proliferation indices between 4.5 and 20%. There was, however, no correlation between the tumour growth rate and the endothelial cell proliferation index. Some studies have reported higher proliferation indices for tumour cells than for endothelial cells (35–11.4%), whereas others have shown the opposite. In general, however, the endothelial cell proliferation is higher in the tumour periphery than in the centre. Artefactual results caused by inadequate perfusion of the tumour centre can be excluded because tumour cells were efficiently labelled.

Endothelial cell proliferation indices in animal tumour models differ significantly from those obtained from human tumours. Endothelial cell proliferation is considerably slower in human tumours than in experimental tumours in animals (2.2–2.8% in breast carcinomas, 5% in gliomas, 0.1–0.6% in prostatic carcinomas). However, these endothelial cell proliferation indices are still significantly higher than in benign human tissues (benign breast tissue, 0.06%; benign hyperplasia in the prostate, 0.023%). These observations argue for active proliferation of endothelial cells during tumour-induced angiogenesis.

The discrepancy between human and experimental tumours becomes obvious if one looks at the rate of growth of experimental tumours. Within 1 week these tumours grow to about 20% of the body weight of the animals, a rate unthinkable in human tumours. Nonetheless, the proliferation indices for endothelial cells in human tumours are 30 times higher than the proliferation indices for normal tissues.

VESSEL FORMATION AND MATURATION

In the final stage of angiogenesis, vessel assembly and maturation result in a vessel that is a stable conduit for blood flow. This is achieved by two processes, namely anastomosis of the developing sprouts and recruitment of pericytes.

Subsequent to the degradation of the basement membrane and outgrowth of vessel sprouts, the sprouts develop into hollow tubes and two sprouts may then join to form a tube through which blood flows. Once formed, the endothelial tubes recruit a layer of pericytes to surround and stabilize the vessel. Pericytes are recruited as local mesenchymal cells, and induced to differentiate into pericytes by the endothelial cells. These cells are large with a prominent nucleus and multiple long processes that embrace the vessel. They also secrete factors, such as

TGF-β, which stabilize the endothelial cells and prevent their proliferation. Furthermore, pericyte density is negatively correlated with the turnover time of the endothelial cells in various tissues, consistent with the stabilizing actions of these cells.

In addition to the pericyte-derived vessel-stabilizing factors, angiopoietin-1 (Ang-1) is a local tissue-derived vessel-stabilizing factor that acts on the receptor Tie-2. Tie-2 is a receptor–tyrosine kinase and is mainly expressed on endothelial cells. The closely related ligand angiopoietin-2 (Ang-2) acts as an antagonist to Ang-1 on this receptor. The related receptor–tyrosine kinase Tie-1 is mainly expressed on endothelium during embryogenesis but downregulated in adulthood. Its ligands have so far not been identified. Targeted disruption of the *Tie-2* gene in mice results in embryonic death between days 9.5 and 10.5 and these animals show heart defects and disorganized vessels on sites where vessels form by vasculogenesis. The endothelial cells appear rounded and have only weak connections with their mural cells. A similar but milder phenotype was developed in *Ang-1* −/− mice which die on embryonic day 12.5. In addition mice overexpressing Ang-2 show very similar phenotypes to *Tie-2* and *Ang-1* −/− mice. These observations show that the angiopoietins and Tie-2 are factors controlling the 'tightness' of vessels and that indeed the angiopoietins have antagonistic effects. *Tie-1* −/− mice die between embryonic day 13.5 and birth as result of the loss of vascular integrity. These animals show 'electron light' endothelial cells because of numerous intra- and intercellular holes which allows blood and plasma extravasation.

During development Ang-1 and Ang-2 are expressed throughout the vasculature, both by the developing endothelium and by its supporting cells, with Ang-2 antagonizing the vessel-stabilizing and maturation function of Tie-2, allowing vasculogenesis and angiogenesis. Ang-1 continues to be expressed into adulthood, but Ang-2 in only expressed in areas that undergo vascular remodelling, such as the female reproductive system. Indeed, expression of Ang-2 appears to be permissive of angiogenesis, suggesting a requirement for 'dematuration' to initiate vessel sprouting (Lauren *et al.*, 1998). Vessels which are destabilized by Ang-2 can respond to VEGF and initiate angiogenesis. Without an angiogenic stimulus blood vessels influenced by Ang-2 will regress (Holash *et al.*, 1999). Only vessels where no pericytes support the endothelial cells can undergo regression whereas the contact of endothelial cells with pericytes prevents regression.

THE PROGNOSTIC SIGNIFICANCE OF TUMOUR ANGIOGENESIS

This chapter has presented evidence that tumour growth is angiogenesis dependent and in the chapter on *Antiangiogenic Therapy* it is shown that inhibition of tumour angiogenesis is currently one of the most exciting avenues of anti-cancer therapy. To conclude this chapter, we will review the prognostic significance of tumour angiogenesis. This encompasses primarily three areas of interest: (1) analysis of the primary tumour microvessel density, (2) expression of angiogenic factors within tumours and (3) analysis of systemic markers of active angiogenesis.

Intratumoural Microvessel Density

In 1991 it was shown that the presence of vascular hotspots, that is, areas of high vascular density, within primary human breast tumours correlated with poor patient survival. This was the first such study linking tumour vascularization, or the end result of angiogenesis, with prognosis. Subsequently, many similar studies have appeared showing a correlation between the presence of vascular hotspots and prognosis in a wide range of different tumour types. Making use of this information in the clinic has, however, proved difficult. To date no simple, quick and reliable way to quantitate the vascular density has appeared. All methods require examination of slides by an experienced pathologist, which is time consuming, expensive and potentially subjective. Nevertheless, proof of the correlation between angiogenesis and prognosis encourages the search for less subjectively quantitated molecular markers of tumour angiogenesis that could substitute for the assessment of vascular density. Such markers will no doubt be found in time.

Systemic Markers of Active Angiogenesis

Angiogenesis is an active process occurring within the tumour, but (excluding women in the menstrual cycle) in the healthy individual not elsewhere in the body, thus metabolic changes arising as a result of the angiogenesis could in principle provide a diagnostic test of tumorigenesis. Potential markers include plasma levels of angiogenic factors and markers of activated endothelium. Amongst angiogenic factors, VEGF has received the most attention as a potential prognostic marker. Thus, studies have suggested that serum VEGF could be a predictor of relapse-free survival in primary human breast cancer. Recently, high urinary VEGF has been shown to correlate with recurrence in bladder cancer, providing an easily accessible marker with which to monitor the disease. Thymidine phosphorylase (platelet-derived endothelial cell growth factor) was shown to be elevated in cancer patients some 15 years before it was recognized to have angiogenic activity and to be elevated in virtually all primary tumours. No doubt more studies will follow.

Other markers of vascular activity are the endothelial leukocyte adhesion molecules VCAM and E-selectin. VCAM and E-selectin mediate leukocyte exit from the blood through the endothelium. Both molecules are upregulated on endothelium in inflammatory sites. This is also widespread in tumour endothelium where tumours are frequently awash with inflammatory cytokines. Several studies are now examining whether the presence of VCAM or E-selectin in the plasma are useful markers of tumour angiogenesis.

REFERENCES

Auerbach, W. and Auerbach, R. (1994). Angiogenesis inhibition: a review. *Pharmacology and Therapeutics*, **63**, 265–311.

Augustin, H. G. (1998). Antiangiogenic tumour therapy: will it work? *Trends in Pharmacological Science*, **19**, 216–222.

Beck, L. and D'Amore, P. A. (1997). Vascular development: cellular and molecular regulation. *FASEB Journal*, **11**, 365–373.

Christofori, G. (1997). The role of fibroblast growth factors in tumor progression and angiogenesis. In: Bicknell, R., *et al.* (eds), *Tumour Angiogenesis*, 201–237 (Oxford, Oxford University Press).

Eliceiri, B. P. and Cheresh, D. A. (1999). The role of the αv integrins during angiogenesis: insight into potential mechanisms of action and clinical development. *Journal of Clinical Investigation*, **103**, 1227–1230.

Folkman, J. (1971). Tumor angiogenesis: therapeutic implications. *New England Journal of Medicine*, **285**, 1182–1186.

Folkman, J. (1990). What is the evidence that tumor growth is angiogenesis dependent? *Journal of the National Cancer Institute*, **82**, 4–6.

Folkman, J. and Shing, Y. (1992). Angiogenesis. *Journal of Biological Chemistry*, **267**, 10931–10934.

Hanahan, D. and Folkman, J. (1996). Patterns and emerging mechanisms of the angiogenic switch during tumorigenesis. *Cell*, **86**, 353–364.

Holash, J., *et al.* (1999). New model of tumor angiogenesis: dynamic balance between vessel regression and growth mediated by angiopoietins and VEGF. *Oncogene*, **18**, 5356–5362.

Kim Lee Sim, B. (1998). Angiostatin and endostatin: endothelial cell-specific endogenous inhibitors of angiogenesis and tumour growth. *Angiogenesis*, **2**, 37–48.

Lauren, J., *et al.* (1998). Is angiopoietin-2 necessary for the initiation of tumor angiogenesis? *American Journal of Pathology*, **153**, 1333–1339.

Moore, B. B., *et al.* (1998). CXC chemokines mechanism of action in regulating tumor angiogenesis. *Angiogenesis*, **2**, 123–134.

Neufeld, G., *et al.* (1999). Vascular endothelial growth factor (VEGF) and its receptors. *FASEB Journal*, **13**, 9–22.

Oehler, M. K. and Bicknell, R. (2000). The promise of anti-angiogenic cancer therapy. *British Journal of Cancer*, **82**, 749–752.

Rissau, W. (1997). Mechanisms of angiogenesis. *Nature*, **386**, 671–674.

Stetler-Stevenson, W. G. (1999). Matrix metalloproteinases in angiogenesis: a moving target for therapeutic intervention. *Journal of Clinical Investigation*, **103**, 1237–1241.

FURTHER READING

Bicknell, R., *et al.* (eds) (1997). *Tumour Angiogenesis*. (Oxford, Oxford University Press).

Chapter 18

Cell Proliferation in Carcinogenesis

Nicholas A. Wright
Imperial Cancer Research Fund and University of London, London, UK

CONTENTS

INTRODUCTION

Investigators in the field of cancer research have always regarded cell proliferation, *a fortiori*, as of paramount importance. The reasons for this are not difficult to identify. It is generally accepted that tumours arise as a result of a series of mutations occurring in a cell, often said to be a stem cell. In the colorectal epithelium, for example, several of the mutations required for malignant transformation have been identified; such a series of mutations accumulate in a single cell and its progeny, and this single cell, having acquired properties which endow it with characteristics ensuring its growth and survival, undergoes a series of divisions which eventually result in the development of a neoplasm. A similar series of molecular events is envisioned for the development of other tumours such as the lung, gastric carcinoma and skin. These mutations are thought to confer upon the transformed cell an advantage which enables it to survive – as a mutated clone – and replace the normal cells in the tissue, eventually establishing itself as a neoplasm.

Thus neoplasms are clonally derived, that is, the single cell transformed is the ancestor of all cells which compose the neoplasm. Once established, a mechanism must ensure the growth and propagation of the mutated clone within the epithelium. It is often said that the mechanism lies in an inherent ability of the mutated clone to outgrow its normal counterparts – the 'carcinogenic advantage' is thus a proliferative advantage.

A second reason for the putative importance of cell proliferation in this context is the spread of the mutated clone as it evolves and establishes itself within the host tissue. Third, when a mutant clone has indeed established itself, we observe the phenomenon of tumour growth as the lesion becomes macroscopically evident. During this phase, cell proliferation, in the context of cell birth and cell loss, defines the rate of growth of the tumour.

Finally, when such a lesion is treated, there have been attempts to predict the outcome by the components of cell proliferation.

We shall examine these proposals in turn. Central to our initial proposal is the concept that tumours are indeed clonally derived.

HOW DO TUMOURS BEGIN IN HUMANS?

We often say that tumours arise from a single cell, and therefore form clonal populations. 'If a proliferation is clonal it is a neoplasm' is a statement often heard. Tumour clonality is an important concept in our attempts to understand malignant transformation, and it is worthwhile reminding ourselves of the experimental basis of this proposal. Why do we believe that epithelial tumours, such as the early adenoma in the colonic mucosa, are clonal proliferations? The main methods which have been used for the analysis of clonality in human tumours have been based on X-chromosome inactivation analysis and the detection of somatic mutations. Viral integration, e.g. by Southern blotting in Epstein–Barr virus (EBV)-associated tumours or in hepatitis B- or C-associated liver tumours, are also useful; there is excellent agreement between X-inactivation and EBV integration in nasophayrngeal carcinoma, for example.

In early X-chromosome inactivation studies, the haplotypes of glucose-6-phosphate dehydrogenase (G6PD) were used (Beutler *et al*., 1967; Fialkow, 1976), replaced more recently by methods based on restriction length polymorphisms of X chromosome-linked genes such as glycerophosphate kinase (PGK), the androgen receptor gene (HUMARA), hypoxanthine phosphoribosyltransferase (HPRT), the M27β probe for *DXS285* and p55 and glucose-6-phosphate dehydrogenase. Early on in embryogenesis, genes on one of the two X chromosomes are randomly inactivated by methylation of cytosine residues within promoter regions; once methylated, such CpG islands are functionally and heritably inactive and it is usually believed that this inactivation is stable, even during malignant change. Thus in approximately half of the cells of the embryo the paternal X chromosome is active, and in the rest it is the X chromosome from the mother. The pattern of fragments produced by DNA digestion with a methylation-sensitive enzyme such as SnaB1 and a further endonuclease corresponding to a restriction fragment length polymorphism, in PGK–BstCX1, for example, can be used to investigate the clonality of any tissue specimen. Informative cases in woman using these markers are reported to vary from 45% with PGK and HUMARA to over 90% with M27β/DXS255.

But can we be certain that the results from such studies will be reliable? Well, the methylation pattern of DNA can be abnormal in malignancy, with both increases and reductions in methylation, and the possibility exists that X-chromosome inactivation may not be valid as an indicator of clonality because of such abnormalities in DNA methylation (Jones, 1996). Moreover, it is possible that X inactivation might be nonrandom, being either constitutive or cell-type specific. Studies in normal haematopoietic and lymphoid tissues have shown skewed X inactivation, possibly favouring the paternal or the maternal X chromosome, which could indicate a nonrandom X-chromosome inactivation pattern. Although there are claims that extremely unbalanced inactivation of the X chromosome is an uncommon phenomenon, skewed inactivation is seen in 23% of women with HPRT and PGK and 22–33% with M27β, in peripheral blood and in bone marrow and skin, indicating tissue specificity, and perhaps related to the number of stem cells in the tissue at the time of X chromosome inactivation. If this number is small, it will result in skewing, with increased probability as the stem cell pool size diminishes (Fialkow, 1973). Moreover, in some embryonic tumours such as retinoblastoma and Wilms' tumour, with LOH on 13q and 11p, respectively, show preferential loss of maternal and paternal alleles. This is also seen in sporadic osteosarcoma. Hence X inactivation analysis is not without its problems, and conclusions drawn from it must be viewed critically.

In mutation analysis, finding the same mutation in key genes, such as k-*ras* or *p53* in multiple tissue sample from the same tumour, or from unconnected tumours, has also been said to indicate a clonal origin, but we should note the possibility that the same mutation is induced in separate precursor cells by a single carcinogen, e.g. aflatoxin causes specific *p53* mutations in hepatocellular carcinomas.

The demonstration of heterogeneity of microsatellite instabilities, e.g. in multiple gastric carcinomas, has also been proposed as a marker for polyclonality – origin from more than one cell – but if genome alterations continue to occur at microsatellite loci with evolution of the tumour, with resulting genetic diversity within the same clone, then microsatellite instability will not be an appropriate molecular marker of clonality. The presence of cytogenetically unrelated abnormal clones demonstrated by karyotypic analysis has also been used as evidence of polyclonality, but the existence of such clones might, however, be due to chromosomal rearrangement in non-neoplastic epithelial or stromal cells: cytogenetically abnormal clones are present in apparently non-neoplastic breast lesions such as fibrocystic disease (from which breast carcinoma probably arises). Mutated clones have been reported even in histologically normal breast epithelium, with several at potential tumour-suppressor gene sites, indicating that genetic abnormalities accumulate before pathological changes can be detected.

We should note that these observations involve the biochemical or molecular examination of homogenized tissues, and in human tissues there have been few opportunities to observe directly the clonal development of very early tumours, and this introduces other problems. In development, a clone is a family of cells which derive from a common progenitor, and these remain more or less contiguous throughout the growth of the embryo. A patch, on the other hand, is defined as a group of cells which share the same genotype, contiguous at the moment of consideration, which, for the current argument, share the same X-chromosome inactivation pattern. Clone size and patch size are not strictly equivalent, since multiple clones of the same genotype could contribute to a single patch; similarly, a single clone could be anatomically separated into different patches.

Figure 1 illustrates this concept as it applies to the clonal origin of tumours. A tumour arising from the centre of a patch will be of clonal origin when assessed by the pattern of X inactivation. The only chance of detecting a polyclonal proliferation would be when such a lesion arises from the margin of a patch boundary (Schmidt and Mead, 1990). This is seen in normal mouse epidermis at patch boundaries, where hair follicles appear polyclonal, but of course are clonal within patches. As X inactivation occurs at about the time of implantation, the pool of stem cells is small, $\sim$15 cells for the skin. Skewing towards one parental allele is therefore very possible, and indeed this is seen in human skin specimens, indicating a large patch size. Polyclonal tumours would be commonest at patch boundaries, the incidence being dependent on the size of the patch, and the incidence of such tumours could be small. And if such rare polyclonal lesions are found, because of a large patch size, it is usually explained away by the lesion consisting of more than one tumour, of clonal origin, that have mixed or collided (Farber, 1990, 1997). However, the rarity of such lesions would indeed be expected if as seems likely, X-linked patches are fairly large.

This is well illustrated by an example: for many years, based in X-chromosome inactivation analysis, it has been believed that atheromatous plaques, occurring in the walls of large- and medium-sized arteries, are monoclonal, and

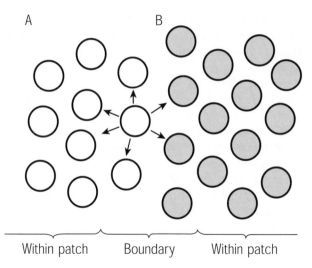

Within patch   Boundary   Within patch

Figure 1   Demonstrating the importance of patch size in the clonal histogenesis of tumours. Different patches are shown, for example, illustrating a different pattern of X-inactivation. In the patches are tissues units, e.g. colonic crypts. A tumour arising within a patch will show a single pattern of X-inactivation of the other marker, and the only chance of detecting a polyclonal tumour is if such a lesion arose from the border of the patch, i.e. between A and B. (From Schmidt and Mead, 1990, *Bioessays*, **12**, 37–40.)

such plaques have even been regarded as some sort of benign neoplasm (Benditt and Benditt, 1973). This clonal proliferation is supported by X-inactivation studies, and was proposed to be due to a somatic mutation, induced perhaps by genotoxic chemicals, or an infection, giving a hit in a single cell, which then develops into an atheromatous plaque (Murry *et al.*, 1997). However, by mapping X-chromosome inactivation patterns in human aortic smooth muscle, using the HUMARA method, the patch size in aortic media and intima was found often to exceed 4 mm, indeed a large area in terms of numbers of cells (Chung *et al.*, 1998). Because of this large patch size, X-chromosome inactivation analysis cannot distinguish between a monoclonal and a polyclonal origin for atheromatous plaques. This underlines the importance of knowledge of the patch size in such studies.

The study of multiple lesions in the same patient does provide a way of avoiding the problem of patch size, especially if more than one clonal marker is used. Thus the probability that all the tumours examined would have the same X-chromosome inactivation pattern is 0.5^{n-1}, where n equals the tumour number. For example, if allele loss on 9q, an independent event, was also present, then the probability that the same pattern in each tumour is due to chance is $(0.5^{n-1})(0.5^{n-1})$, and so on for each independent marker used.

Similarly, when methods based on the analysis of homogenized tissues give results suggesting polyclonality, this is usually attributed to contamination with underlying stromal cells of different clonal derivation and some results are attributed to normal tissue contamination even when the incidence of polyclonal tumours amounts to 40% of the total. However, it is clear that even the fibroblasts or myofibroblasts very closely applied to the epithelium in the colonic crypt are of different clonal derivation, and there may be invading inflammatory cells, which, if numerous enough, can give rise to disparate results in clonality analyses involving PCR techniques. Normal tissue can be trapped and enclosed by surrounding neoplastic tissue, and again give discordant results. Finally, the problem of poor sampling may give a false impression of monoclonality in a polyclonal tumour.

It is also important to know when, during the life history of the development of the tumour, it is examined. Mature lesions are inappropriate, since tumours of polyclonal origin may become clonal because of clonal evolution (Nowell, 1976, 1986). All clones, except one, are eliminated or reduced to the point of being undetectable, seen in chemically induced mouse fibrosarcomas, initially polyclonal, which evolve to a clonally derived population in time, because of the later selection of a dominant clone (Woodruff *et al.*, 1982). This is also seen in colorectal adenomas, where heterogeneity of k-*ras* mutations is observed, which is lost after the lesion has evolved to become an invasive carcinoma (Ajiki *et al.*, 1994). As noted above, genetic heterogeneity in a tumour does not necessarily indicate a polyclonal origin, since genetic instability is a major feature of malignant tissues and many new clones may arise during tumour development.

Having critically reviewed the available methods, let us see what they say about how tumours arise in humans.

Non-neoplastic and Preneoplastic Lesions

Many tumours arise from preneoplastic lesions, not themselves neoplastic, which were previously regarded as hyperplasias, which involve changes in many cells and therefore by definition polyclonal. However, such lesions are often clonal proliferations themselves. Extremely relevant is the growing recognition that mutations in important genes such as *p53* are found in tissues such as squamous epithelium preceding any dysplastic change, such as sun-exposed normal epidermis. Clones of keratinocytes with immunoreactive p53 and p53 mutations (exons 5–8) are seen in sun-exposed but otherwise normal skin. This has also been reported in morphologically normal mucosa from individuals with upper aerodigestive tract tumours. Moreover, microsatellite instability has been found in normal mucosa from patients with ulcerative colitis, reflecting the increased risk of malignancy in these patients, since microallelotyping shows no allelic loss in transitional mucosa adjacent to colorectal neoplasms.

However, such losses have been reported in normal breast tissue.

In the gastric mucosa of a single patient, three separate hyperplastic polyps of the fundus have been found which harbour foci of dysplasia showed the same k-*ras* codon 12-point mutation, present in both hyperplastic and dysplastic areas. An explanation is that the progeny of a single transformed cell spreads through the mucosa: either surface spreading and surface implantation has occurred or a single cell could populate a gastric gland, which then spreads through the mucosa by gland fission.

In the female ovary, malignant tumours, endometrioid carcinomas, are thought to arise from foci of endometriosis and the majority of such endometriotic foci are clonal (Jimbo *et al.*, 1997). Endometriosis arises either from implantation of shed endometrial cells, or from metaplasia of the pelvic peritoneum: if patch size considerations can be excluded, this means from a single endometrial or mesothelial cell. Endometriotic foci can show aneuploidy and loss of heterozygosity at candidate tumour-suppressor loci in 9p, 11q and 22q. The derivative tumours, the endometrioid carcinomas, are clonally derived, arising from a monoclonal proliferation that itself can show genetic defects.

The preneoplastic lesions from which breast cancers develop – proliferative breast disease and similar lesions – show cytogenetic abnormalities indicating the presence of multiple clones. X-chromosome inactivation studies and detection of microsatellite alterations both show that atypical duct hyperplasia and intraduct papillomas appear clonal proliferations and consequently cytogenetic alterations have already occurred at this stage (Lakhani *et al.*, 1995).

Naevocellular naevi, either congenital or acquired, are, in some cases, the precursor lesions of malignant melanomas, are apparently polyclonal lesions on X-chromosome inactivation analysis (HUMARA and PGK combined), but malignant melanomas are clonal. So such naevi are presumably hamartomas – an abnormal proliferation of cells in an organ or tissue where these cell types would normally be found. However, hamartomas in tuberous sclerosis, where multiple cell types are seen, show clonal 9q34 or 16p13.3 LOH and clonal X-inactivation patterns, while pulmonary chondroid hamartomas also contain clonal cytogenetic abnormalities in the chondroid component.

In the human liver opinion is divided concerning the clonality of lesions often regarded as preneoplastic: some maintain that while lesions such as benign adenomatous hyperplasia and focal nodular hyperplasia are polyclonal, but hepatic adenomas and even small (<25 mm) hepatocellular carcinomas are clonal. Others, examining the integration patterns of hepatitis B virus, claim that atypical adenomatous hyperplasisa and focal nodular hyperplasias are clonal. Hepatocellular carcinoma is frequently multifocal and whether these arise from a single clone or

independently is controversial, but most authors agree that an independent origin is more likely. Thus, after liver damage, clonal selection occurs during regeneration, leading to the genesis of persistent benign focal proliferations, which may be themselves clonal. This is followed by the development of clonal hepatocellular cancer from one or more such nodules. There is also substantial evidence from hepatitis B and C virus integration that between 0.5 and 43% of regenerative nodules in the resulting cirrhosis are monoclonal (Aihara *et al.*, 1994), whereas in other types of cirrhosis, some 54% of regenerative liver nodules are clonal, but that the associated hepatocellular carcinomas are clonal by X-inactivation analysis, and differ from the nodules by 18q loss. This suggests that regenerative liver nodules showing a polyclonal pattern evolve into a clonal population, developing into hepatocellular carcinomas, which are also clonal.

Preinvasive Lesions

The field cancerization hypothesis states that multiple cells form independent tumours, since carcinogenic exposure affects multiple cells in the field (Slaughter *et al.*, 1953), and predicts that second primary or synchronous tumours arise from independent genetic events. Thus 11% of individuals with oral cancer had multiple upper aerodigestive tract tumours, and multiple invasive foci are associated with overlying areas of *in situ* squamous carcinoma in these lesions. There is now genetic evidence for such an independent origin: in the upper aerodigestive tract, multiple synchronous squamous tumours appear independent and multicentric in origin. However, the concept of clonal origin and expansion is problematic in organs where several metachronous tumours appear; such a synchronous or second primary tumour may indicate recurrence or indeed lateral spread from a single tumour. Thus, although the field cancerization hypothesis would predict a multicentric, polyclonal origin, with the demonstration of a clonal origin for these tumours, lateral migration from the original clone would be a distinct possibility.

There is conflicting evidence for the nature of field cancerization from the study of tumours of the upper aerodigestive tract and adjacent mucosa. In laryngeal and pharyngeal tumours, multiple samples taken at tumour-distant sites show different and independent mutations in the *p53* gene, favouring a discontinuous, multifocal and polyclonal process, rather than migration of premalignant basal keratinocytes giving a clonal development of multiple primary, secondary or recurrent tumours.

In the stomach, discordant mutation patterns of *APC*, *MCC* and *p53* are found in many cases of multiple gastric carcinomas, again in accord with a multicentric origin, and this is also seen in multiple colorectal tumours, parathyroid adenomas and in separate (Emmert-Buch *et al.*, 1995) intraepithelial neoplastic lesions, which show different clonal patterns of allele loss at 8p12-21, suggesting an independent origin. However, multiple synchronous carcinomas in the bladder and other pelvic organs apparently show a common clonal origin – X-chromosome inactivation and allele loss at 9q and 17p are identical, as are c-erB2 and *p53* mutations in multiple synchronous urothelial tumours (Lunec *et al.*, 1992). Multiple serous adenocarcinomas in the ovaries, peritoneum and endometrium show the same p53 mutation and clonal cytogenetic abnormalities, findings confirmed by X-chromosome inactivation. Multiple sites of occurrence of sporadic ovarian cancer on the ovarian surface and pelvic peritoneum are clonal, as assessed by LOH, p53 mutations and X-chromosome inactivation analysis in the same patient (Jacobs *et al.*, 1992).

In multifocal breast carcinomas, an increasingly common finding, karyotypically identical clones are detectable, indicating intramammary spread from a single carcinoma either by focal lymphatic spread or by intraductal spread. Moreover, in phyllodes tumours, widely separated deposits show the same monoclonal stromal component.

If lesions some distance away from each other are clonal, how can this be explained? Of course, there is always the possibility, always very difficult to exclude, that the disease process which causes the tumour to develop has a characteristic genetic fingerprint, therefore seen in all examples of the tumour. The other possibility is that of a common mutated progenitor cell, and the expansion of this mutant clone in some way, at an early stage in tumour development. Examination of *p53* mutations in the nonmalignant but dysplastic tracheobronchial mucosa of individuals who smoke shows the same G:C to T:A transversion in codon 245 at multiple sites in both lungs (Franklin *et al.*, 1998). Thus the expression and dispersion of a single mutant progenitor bronchial epithelial cell clone throughout the airways is possible, aided possibly by a proliferative advantage. p53 mutations are early events in upper aerodigestive tract carcinogenesis, prior to the development of invasive lesions, being found in premalignant lesions of the head and neck, lung and oesophagus. p53 mutations apparently do not show an increased incidence with cancer progression, but do show clonal fidelity in a variety of tumours. An early event, prior to p53 mutation, might establish a mutated clone, which migrates laterally, possibly aided by a mutation in a cell cycle control gene, or a cell adhesion gene. In multiple bladder cancer, all tumours lose the same 9q allele as an early event (Chung *et al.*, 1995, 1996), possibly encoding for a growth control or adhesion molecule, and cells repopulate the urothelium by lateral migration or mucosal seeding. In most discontinuous foci of CIN3 in the cervix, individual lesions show the same X-chromosome inactivation pattern, suggesting intraepithelial spread. In the skin, it is not uncommon to see migration of morphologically abnormal cells laterally from a lesion such as Bowen's disease.

The multiple deposits of Kaposi sarcoma, a widely disseminated malignancy, appear clonal in any one patient, indicating a clonal origin and wide intravascular dissemination, or an initial vascular hyperplasia, with later clonal evolution. Diffusely infiltrating gliomas are clonal, and multiple discrete meningiomas share clonal neurofibromatosis 2 (*NF2*) mutations, while most individual meningiomas appear clonally derived.

Sporadic, multinodular goitres contain nodules which are regarded as being hyperplastic and therefore polyclonal, but there is substantial X-chromosome inactivation evidence that many of these nodules are clonal populations. The presence of a TSH receptor mutation may be pivotal; most cases showed monoclonality on HUMARA analysis, raising the possibility that during thyroid hyperplasia a cell with a mutation at this locus leads to the initiation of autonomous clonal growth. Multiple nodules in the same patient are mostly clonal, with activation of the same allele, indicating intraglandular spread by follicular budding, although clonal nodules with different X-chromosome inactivation patterns can be seen in the same gland. This could mean a different pathogenetic mechanism for clonal and polyclonal nodules, or indeed evolution of clonal from polyclonal nodules, as we have seen above in the liver. Most follicular, papillary and anaplastic carcinomas are clonal. Parathyroid adenomas are monoclonal, as indicated by X-chromosome inactivation and the identification of clonal abnormalities of the parathyroid hormone gene. In MEN1, where all four parathyroids are enlarged and appear hyperplastic, allelic loss on 11q indicates that proliferation is clonal, although when LOH on 11q is combined with X-chromosome inactivation studies, the parathyroid lesions in MEN1 were shown to be polyclonal, suggesting that multiple neoplastic clones grow, coalesce and replace the parathyroid gland. Sporadic parathyroid hyperplasias, which are either a primary phenomenon or secondary to such conditions as chronic renal failure, were previously regarded as polyclonal proliferations, but X inactivation and allelic loss of 11q shows that 38% of primary parathyroid hyperplasias and 64% of hyperplasias secondary to renal failure harbour clonal proliferations. Again we can interpret this as clonal neoplastic evolution from a pre-existing polyclonal hyperplasia. Diffuse parathyroid hyperplasias in uraemia are polyclonal, but the individual nodules in nodular hyperplasia are clonal, indeed showing different clonal patterns of X inactivation in the same gland, once more favouring the hypothesis that monoclonal proliferations evolve from hyperplasias. These findings favour the view that hyperplasia begins in endocrine glands as a polyclonal process, but then becomes a clonal hyperplasia, and the borderline between this phase and that of a benign clonal neoplasm is difficult to delineate.

Invasive carcinomas of the cervix, which are clonal in origin, arise in areas of cervical intraepithelial neoplasia (CIN). Severe dysplasia or CIN3 is also a clonal proliferation, although lesser degrees of dysplasia (CIN2) appear more commonly polyclonal in X-inactivation studies. In this respect, some vulvar hyperplasia, considered to be preneoplastic lesions in this tissue, appear clonal: the derivative VIN and invasive carcinomas are also clonal proliferations. In nasopharyngeal carcinoma (NPC), combined X-inactivation studies (PGK), X-linked RPLPs, and EBV integration show that carcinomas are mainly clonal, but hyperplastic epithelia, and early atypical hyperplastic epithelia, are polyclonal, and clonality emerges only at the moderate/severe dysplastic stage.

A relationship between intestinal metaplasia and carcinoma of the stomach and lower oesophagus has long been suspected: the non-dysplastic metaplasia adjacent to carcinomas is clonal on X-inactivation analysis (HUMARA), and also shows LOH for *APC*, changes also seen in the dysplastic and neoplastic tissues of Barrett oesophagus. Although it is not yet clear if the *APC* change is clonal, microsatellite analysis shows allelic imbalance not only on 5q but at multiple other sites, in both premalignant and malignant Barrett epithelium, supporting the concept of clonal expansion from metaplasia through dysplasia to carcinoma (Zhuang *et al.*, 1996).

In most, but not all, of the above discussion the commonality has been the need to homogenize the tissue, albeit, in some cases, after microdissection. Evidence from studies where direct observation is possible gives disparate results. In a patient with familial adenomatous polyposis, who was also a sex chromosome chimaera (XO/XY), the colon contained hundreds of adenomas, ranging in size from monocryptal adenomas to microadenomas 2.5 mm in diameter; no larger adenomatous polyps were seen (Novelli *et al.*, 1996). If an adenoma was of clonal origin, all dysplastic crypts within it would be expected to be entirely XO or entirely XY. Localization of the Y chromosome in tissue sections showed that monocryptal adenomas were entirely XO or XY, with no mixed pattern. However, many adenomas (76%) were polyclonal. Isoenzyme studies of G6PD in black females have shown that colonic adenomas from patients with Gardner's syndrome were polyclonal (Hsu *et al.*, 1983), while studies using X-linked RFLPs show that both spontaneous and familial adenomas are clonal (Fearon *et al.*, 1987). The minimum size of the adenomas in this might explain the discrepancy, through monoclonal conversion as size increases. Polyclonal derivation of adenomas has also been found in chimaeric mice – made between a *Min* mouse (which has an *APC* mutation) and a *Min*/ROSA mouse (Merrit *et al.*, 1997), and in *Apc*+/^{min}/ +/− (De Wind *et al.*, 1998) mouse chimaeras. Possible mechanisms of polyclonality in these lesions include 'field' effects causing adenomas to cluster (nonrandom collision), a passive process involving fusion of two or more *APC*-negative clones early in tumour development, but the high frequency of mixed adenomas found in both these studies is inconsistent with a random appearance of *APC*-negative clones in the mucosa, and suggests that some regions of the intestine have an increased potential for initiation. Multiple clones may be required for early adenoma growth, or perhaps early adenomas may induce adenomatous growth in surrounding crypts, especially in FAP since all cells already have a single *APC* mutation and perhaps some derangement of APC function. These latter scenarios imply active cooperation between clones. Indeed, conversion of normal crypts to adenomatous crypts apparently occurs at the margins of FAP adenomas.

What can we conclude? In many tissues the bulk of the evidence indicates that preneoplastic changes occur which are hyperplastic, but polyclonal, indicating increased rates of cell production among many cells. After some time, a genetic event occurs in which a clone of cells appears, which expands and establishes itself. This clone has a 'carcinogenic advantage,' which allows such expansion. Further growth of the clone is associated with genetic evolution and the appearance of mutations, which lead to the development of an early clonal neoplasm. Further clonal evolution develops the invasive phenotype. However, we must concede that further studies, with methods which allow the direct examination of clonality, might provide different conclusions, and we cannot disregard the concept that the earliest lesions are polyclonal, needing the cooperation of several clones, and that monoclonality is itself the result of further clonal evolution.

HOW DO CLONES ESTABLISH THEMSELVES?

The simplest way in which we can conceive of a single mutated cell establishing itself among a population of normal cells is if the mutation selects for an advantage that involves factors which modulate cell proliferation – the ability to divide faster – or the ability to survive longer. While conceptually these are significant advantages to being able to survive longer, or indefinitely, in the genesis of a neoplasm, it is, in practice, very difficult to demonstrate. While some early neoplastic lesions do show abnormal expression of genes involved in apoptosis, this is a far cry from demonstrating a aggregation of cells brought about by reduced cell death. Moreover, simple modelling approaches have suggested that mechanisms involving apoptosis are unlikely to be involved at this stage.

Is there any evidence that very early neoplastic lesions show an increased cell production rate? Using the colon as a paradigm, the earliest lesions detectable, the so-called 'aberrant crypt foci,' show increased labelling indices with a number of markers of cell proliferation, whereas in established adenomas, the rate of cell production also increases as assessed by these markers. The importance of even a minor increase in cell proliferation can be assessed by examination of how a mutated stem cell – of which there are several in each intestinal crypt – competes with its colleagues for ascendancy, and in some cases succeeds, populating the crypt with its progeny. Intestinal crypts, in both animals and humans, are clonal populations, ultimately derived from a single cell. The evidence from this comes from the analysis of chimaeric mice and mice heterozygous for a defective G6PD gene carried on the X chromosome and randomly expressed after Lyonization. In these chimaeras, crypts are always composed wholly of cells from one component mouse strain (Ponder *et al.*, 1985), and with similar findings in the G6PD heterozygote crypts are indeed clonal populations and the stem cell repertoire includes all intestinal crypt and gastric gland lineages. **Figure 2 (see colour plate section)** shows the results of an experiment in which mice showing uniform staining for G6PD are given a single dose of mutagen: in the weeks that follow, crypts appear which are composed of cells with a different, mutated phenotype. There is an induction of a rapid, but transient, increase in crypts which show a partial, or segmented, mutated phenotype (**Figure 2a**) (Park *et al.*, 1995). Later, there is an increase in crypts showing a wholly mutated phenotype. The emergence of the partially mutated crypts, and their replacement by wholly mutated crypts, can be explained by a mutation at the G6PD locus in a single stem cell from which all lineages are derived. The partially mutated crypts are crypts in the process of being colonized by progeny from the mutated stem cell, and this crypt will ultimately develop into a wholly mutated crypt.

Approximately 9% of the Caucasian population secrete sialic acid lacking in *O*-acetyl substituents, readily recognized by histochemical staining. This is explained by genetic variability in the expression of the enzyme *O*-acetyl transferase (OAT) and this 9% of the population is homozygous for inactive *OAT* genes, *OAT−/OAT−*. Some 42% of the population are heterozygous, *OAT−/OAT+*, and loss of this gene converts the genotype to *OAT−/−OAT−*. This is indeed seen in about 42% of the population, and again is explained by a mutation or loss of the gene by nondisjunction in a single crypt stem cell and the colonization of this crypt by the clonal progeny of the mutated stem cell.

If we again imagine that a stem cell carries a mutation, not in its *G6PD* or its *OAT* gene, but in a cell cycle gene, increasing its cell production rate, then the monoclonal conversion process will not be stochastic, with equal competition between stem cells, but the mutant stem cell would have an advantage, and would succeed in colonizing the crypt. **Figure 2c** shows a further method in which mutated clones can be propagated – the mutated clone has expanded by crypt fission, where crypts divide to make two daughter crypts, and thus spread through the mucosa. If a gene controlling crypt fission became mutated, then of course the crypt would spread further through the mucosa.

Indeed, in conditions such as ulcerative colitis, large areas of the mucosa become occupied by the same aneuploid stem line, conceptually, at any rate, the result of increased crypt fission.

In squamous epithelium we have seen above that tiny p53-positive clones, containing mutated p53, occur early in the carcinogenic process. These clones may owe their existence to prolonged survival, given the presence of a mutated *p53* gene. However, there is substantial evidence that rates of cell production, in preneoplastic lesions such as actinic keratosis, are elevated. In fact, it is possible to predict the shape of preinvasive skin lesions such as actinic keratosis, Bowen disease and lentigo maligna, by assuming different values for the carcinogenic advantage, in terms of increased cell production. Similar observations of elevated rates of cell production have been recorded in other situations where there is a defined morphological sequence of carcinogenesis – in the liver, bladder, oesophagus and lung, for example.

We have seen above that, in many tissues, clonal evolution occurs on a background of hyperplasia, implicitly involving increased cell production. It is further evident that the establishment of the mutated clone is, in many tissues, associated with an increase in cell production rate. It is easy to conceive now such increases in cell proliferation, in cells such as stem cells, can lead to the establishment and development of a mutated clone (**Figure 2**). However attractive the concept seems, we cannot say definitively whether such increased cell proliferation of stem cells is involved. For example, in **Figure 2**, increased longevity, or changes in the adhesion molecule status of the progeny, could give much the same result. An ability to study cell proliferation, and then expression of cell cycle-related genes, in stem cells during carcinogenesis, would be a very useful, if experimentally difficult, prospect.

HOW DO ESTABLISHED TUMOURS GROW?

The basic concepts of cell proliferation in tumour growth have been extensively and well reviewed.

Tumour Growth Curves

There has been extensive analysis of tumour growth curves – obtained by plotting the volume or weight of the tumour against time – in the past, in the (forlorn) expectation that basic truths about the nature of tumour growth might be discovered. Although this has not been the case, some interesting facts have emerged. Many tumours, usually transplantable, growing in experimental animals, initially grow in an exponential manner, that is, after an initial lag phase, there is logarithmic growth (**Figure 3**). However, as growth proceeds, and the

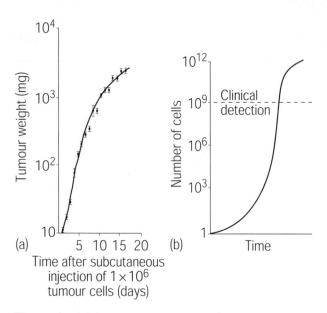

Figure 3   (a) A typical growth curve for a rapidly growing mouse tumour, with the curve fitted by eye; (b) idealized growth curve for a human tumour, showing the initial lag phase, a period of exponential growth and a retardation in the rate of increase of tumour cell number at large size. Note the long latent period before clinical detection.

tumour increases in volume, growth progressively slows. This is the so-called Gompertzian growth curve, where growth retardation is itself exponential. Although such tumours rarely obey such a growth curve in its entirety, it is usually a good approximation. Note that, at the asymptote, growth is barely discernible. Most experimental tumours in rodents grow very rapidly, particularly the transplantable ones, since they have been selected for a rapid growth rate.

In humans, tumours grow much more slowly; most of the doubling in cell number has occurred before the tumour becomes clinically evident. In circumstances where it has been possible to measure the rates of tumour growth, e.g. by serial observation of pulmonary primary or metastatic lesions, a number of tumours do indeed appear to grow exponentially. However, in other cases, growth is extremely variable, with periods of quiescence followed by rapid growth. Some human tumours grow extremely slowly, e.g. colorectal carcinoma has a reported doubling time (the time taken for the tumour to double in size) of over 600 days. Others, such as childhood or embryonal tumours, show doubling times of 10–20 days. There is some evidence that tumour growth rates vary with age; for example, breast carcinomas in women below the age of 50 years show a median doubling time of 80 days, whereas women over the age of 50 years show a doubling time of 140 days.

Kinetic Parameters During Tumour Growth

Why does tumour growth slow down? Well, the net rate of growth is defined by the relationship between the rate of cell production – the birth rate – and the rate of cell death or other modes of loss, the cell loss rate. In the earlier phases of growth, as seen in the early exponential part of the curve in **Figure 3**, most cells are growing exponentially; thus every cell which divides contributes two cells to the population, with effectively no cell loss. What defines the rate at which the exponential portion of the curve ascends?: two parameters – the cell cycle time (the interval between two divisions of the same cell) and the growth fraction, or proliferating population (the proportion of cells in the tumour which are dividing). There is no evidence in solid experimental tumours, at any rate, that the cell cycle time changes at all during tumour growth, but as growth advances, there are substantial studies showing that the growth fraction declines with time. In experiments where the growth fraction has been measured in different parts of the tumour, it is the areas furthest from the blood supply that show the largest reductions in growth fraction – the centre of the tumour in most lesions, or when the tumour is 'corded,' or shows cords of surviving tumour cells surrounding blood vessels – in the distal portions of the cord.

While the decline in the growth fraction is certainly responsible for a proportion of the decline in the rate of tumour growth, by far the largest factor is the considerable increase in the cell loss rate. This is due, of course, to the tumour outgrowing its blood supply and to large numbers of cells in the lesion dying. In fact, at the asymptote in the curve, where the curve levels off, the rate of cell loss almost equals the rate of cell birth, with little resulting in the way of net growth. It is sometimes useful to define a cell loss factor, ϕ, which is the ratio of the cell loss rate to the birth rate. At the asymptote in **Figure 3**, this will be close to 1.

Where data are available, experience culled from animal tumours is also applicable to humans. However, measurements are usually confined to the later phases of tumour growth, since most lesions present, biologically speaking, very late. Thus many carcinomas appear to be low-growth fraction, high-cell loss lesions. In clinically detected colorectal carcinomas, for example, the cell cycle time is 48 h, the growth fraction is 14% and the cell loss factor 98%, i.e. for every 100 cells which are born, two survive. At least this gives us some insight into why such tumours are difficult to treat with modalities such as radiation and cytotoxic chemotherapy. Of the surviving cells in the tumour, some 86% are not in the cell cycle, mainly because they are hypoxic. Such cells would be resistant to irradiation, and even many fractions might not recruit many cells into cycle. Similarly, 5-fluorouracil, commonly used in these lesions, is, in the main, an S-phase poison. With so few cells in cycle, a brisk response would not be expected, unless the growth fraction is increased by debulking and redistribution.

CELL PROLIFERATION IN PROGNOSIS AND CANCER THERAPY

There has been a great deal of effort and energy expended in attempts to relate measurements of cell proliferation to both prognosis and the prediction of tumour response, and to define subgroups requiring additional or adjuvant therapy. It is probably true to say that such attempts have failed.

It is now some 80 years since measurements of mitotic activity were first routinely made in human tumours, and some 40 years since tritiated thymidine, the first real S-phase-specific marker, became available. Since then, measurements using techniques such as flow cytometry, bromodeoxyuridine labelling and the several antibodies against the Ki67 antigen, have followed. to say nothing of numerous attempts to clone human tumour cells *in vitro* and predict their levels of chemosensitivity against a panel of agents, a method recently resurrected. There have also been attempts to plan chemotherapeutic regimens on the basis of measurements of cell proliferation, e.g. the so-called 'synchronization therapy' for head and neck cancers and acute leukaemias, where doses of cytotoxics are given when the tumour cells are 'synchronized' in a cell cycle phase most sensitive to the agent in question.

It is perhaps salient to ask which of these measurements are generally and routinely used in cancer treatment outside of research protocols. Precious few, is the sobering answer. In tumour diagnosis, pathologists routinely do a formal mitotic count (rather than merely observe the presence of mitoses) in smooth muscle cell tumours of the uterus, some central nervous system tumours and stromal tumours of the gastrointestinal tract. In the grading of tumours, and therefore in the prediction of prognosis, mitotic counts are routinely carried out in a number of circumstances, as in the assessment of grade of invasive ductal carcinoma of the breast as a component of the Nottingham Prognostic Index or sometimes in ovarian carcinomas, either as a raw count as a component of a morphometric index. And have more sophisticated measurements reached routine status? Some advocate the use of Ki67 in the differential diagnosis of difficult melanocytic lesions, but there has been little use of such methods elsewhere. Perhaps the advent of new markers, such as antibodies against the minichromosome maintenance proteins, said to be more sensitive than Ki67, may make a difference.

CONCLUSIONS

In human cancer, it is clear that cell proliferation is involved in the origin and evolution of mutated clones, although the details at present elude us. Cell proliferation studies give us insight into how tumours grow, and in some instances why treatment is so difficult. Measurements of cell proliferation are at present of little routine value in diagnosis and prognosis. It is clear that a great deal of work needs to be done if we are to understand fully the role of cell proliferation in tumour development.

REFERENCES

Aihara, T., *et al.* (1994). Clonal analysis of regenerative nodules in hepatitis C virus-induced liver cirrhosis. *Gastroenterology*, **107**, 1805–1811.

Ajiki, T., *et al.* (1994). K-*ras* gene mutation related to histological atypias in human colorectal adenomas. *Biotechnical Histochemistry*, **70**, 90–94.

Benditt, E. P. and Benditt, J. M. (1973). Evidence for a monoclonal origin of human atherosclerotic plaques. *Proceedings of the National Academy of Sciences of the USA*, **70**, 1753–1756.

Beutler, E., *et al.* (1967). Value of genetic variants of glucose-6-phosphate dehydrogenase in tracing the origin of malignant tumours. *New England Journal of Medicine*, **276**, 389–391.

Chung, G. T. Y., *et al.* (1995). Sequential molecular changes in lung cancer development. *Oncogene*, **11**, 2591–2598.

Chung, G. T. Y., *et al.* (1996). Clonal evolution of lung tumours. *Cancer Research*, **56**, 1609–1614.

Chung, I.-M., *et al.* (1998). Clonal architecture of normal and atherosclerotic aorta. Implications for atherogenesis and vascular development. *American Journal of Pathology*, **152**, 913–923.

De Wind, N., *et al.* (1998). Mouse models for hereditary non-polyposis colorectal cancer. *Cancer Research*, **58**, 248–255.

Emmert-Buch, M. R., *et al.* (1995). Allelic loss on chromosome 8p12–21 in microdissected prostatic intraepithelial neoplasia. *Cancer Research*, **55**, 2959–2962.

Farber, E. (1990). Clonal adaptation during carcinogenesis. *Biochemical Pharmacology*, **39**, 1837–1846.

Farber, E. (1997). Monoclonal and polyclonal development of digestive tract tumors in chimeric mice. *Japanese Journal of Cancer Research*, **88**, 663.

Fearon, E. R., *et al.* (1987). Clonal analysis of human colorectal tumours. *Science*, **238**, 193–197.

Fialkow, P. (1973). Primordial cell pool size and lineage relationships of five human cell types. *Annals of Human Genetics*, **37**, 39–48.

Fialkow, P. J. (1976). Clonal origin of human tumours. *Biochimica Biophysica Acta*, **458**, 283–321.

Franklin, W. A., *et al.* (1997). Widely dispersed p53 mutation in respiratory epithelium. *Journal of Clinical Investigation*, **100**, 2133–2137.

Hsu, S. H., *et al.* (1983). Multiclonal origin of polyps in Gardner syndrome. *Science*, **251**, 951–953.

Jacobs, I. J., *et al.* (1992). Clonal origin of epithelial ovarian carcinoma; analysis by loss of heterozygosity, p53 mutation, and X-chromosome inactivation. *Journal of the National Cancer Institute*, **84**, 1793–1798.

Jimbo, H., *et al.* (1997). Evidence for monoclonal expansion of epithelial cells in ovarian endometrial cysts. *American Journal of Pathology*, **150**, 1173–1178.

Jones, P. A. (1996). DNA methylation errors and cancer. *Cancer Research*, **56**, 2463–2467.

Lakhani, S. R., *et al.* (1995). Atypical ductal hyperplasia of the breast: clonal proliferation with loss of heterozygosity on chromosomes 16q and 17p. *Journal of Clinical Pathology*, **48**, 611–615.

Lunec, J., Challen, C., Wright, C., Mellon, K. and Neal, D. (1992). *c-erB2* amplification and identical p53 mutations in comcomitant transitional carcinomas of renal pelvis and urinary bladder. *Lancet*, **339**, 439–440.

Merrit, A. J., *et al.* (1997). Polyclonal structure of intestinal adenomas in ApcMin/+ mice with concomitant loss of Apc+ from all tumor lineages. *Proceedings of the National Academy of Sciences of the USA*, **94**, 13927–13931.

Murry, C. E., *et al.* (1997). Monoclonality of smooth muscle cells in human atherosclerosis. *American Journal of Pathology*, **151**, 697–706.

Novelli, M. R., *et al.* (1996). Polyclonal origin of colonic adenomas in an XO/XY patient with FAP. *Science*, **272**, 1187–1190.

Nowell, P. C. (1976). The clonal evolution of tumour cell populations. *Science*, **194**, 23–28.

Nowell, P. C. (1986). Mechanisms of tumor progression. *Cancer Research*, **46**, 2203–2207.

Park, H.-S., *et al.* (1995). Crypt fission in the small intestine and colon: a mechansim for the emergence of glucose-6-phosphate locus-mutated crypts after mutagen treatment. *American Journal of Pathology*, **147**, 1416–1427.

Ponder, B. A. J., *et al.* (1985). Derivation of mouse intestinal crypts from single progenitor cells. *Nature*, **313**, 689–691.

Schmidt, G. H. and Mead, R. (1990). On the clonal origin of tumours – lessons from studies of intestinal epithelium. *Bioessays*, **12**, 37–40.

Slaughter, D. P., *et al.* (1953). 'Field cancerisation' in oral stratified squamous epithelium. *Cancer*, **6**, 963–968.

Woodruff, M. F. A., *et al.* (1982). Clonal interaction in tumours. *Nature*, **299**, 822–824.

Zhuang, Z., *et al.* (1996). Barrett's esophagus: metaplastic cells with loss of hetrozygosity at the *APC* gene locus are clonal precursors to invasive adenocarcinoma. *Cancer Research*, **56**, 1961–1964.

FURTHER READING

Garcia, S., *et al.* (1999). Field cancerization, stem cells and clonality: the spread of mutated clones in epithelial sheets. *Journal of Pathology*, **187**, 61–81.

Garcia, S., *et al.* (2001). The clonal origin and clonal evolution of human epithelial tumours. *International Journal of Experimental Pathology*, **81**, 117–143.

Hall, P. A., *et al.* (eds) (1992). *Clinical Aspects of Cell Proliferation* (Springer, Heidelberg).

Kinzler, K. W. and Vogelstein, B. (1997). Gatekeepers and caretakers. *Nature*, **386**, 761–763.

Pretlow, T. P., *et al.* (1994). Aberrant crypt foci and colon tumours in F344 rats have similar increases in proliferative activity. *International Journal of Cancer*, **56**, 599–602.

Quinn, C. and Wright, N. A. (1990). The clinical assessment of proliferation and growth in human tumours; evaluation of methods and applications as diagnostic variables. *Journal of Pathology*, **160**, 93–102.

Shibata, D. (1998). The dynamics of early intestinal tumour proliferation: to be or not to be. In Precancer: Biology, Importance and Possible Prevention. *Cancer Surveys*, **32**, 181–200.

Steele, G. G. (1977). *Growth Kinetics of Tumours* (Clarendon Press, Oxford).

Wright, N. A. and Alison, M. R. (1984). *The Biology of Epithelial Cell Populations*, Vols 1 and 2 (Oxford University Press, Oxford).

Wright, N. A. (2001). Stem cell repertoire in the intestine: the origins of self-renewal, cell lineage and cancer. *International Journal of Experimental Pathology*, **81**, 89–116.

Part B
The Causation and
Prevention of Cancer

Chapter 19

Identifying Cancer Causes Through Epidemiology

Hans-Olov Adami
Karolinska Institutet, Stockholm, Sweden

Pagona Lagiou
University of Athens Medical School, Goudi, Athens, Greece

Dimitrios Trichopoulos
Harvard School of Public Health, Boston, MA, USA

C O N T E N T S

INTRODUCTION

Cancer control is an important objective of contemporary medicine. It may be achieved through primary prevention (e.g., reduction of exposure to carcinogenic agents or increase in resistance towards them by immunization or other procedures), down-staging (earlier recognition of clinical symptoms or signs), screening for preclinical diagnosis of asymptomatic cancer or preneoplastic conditions, curative and palliative treatment and rehabilitation schemes. Although these approaches are complementary, there are strong theoretical arguments and overwhelming empirical evidence suggesting that primary prevention represents the most promising strategy for effective cancer control. Implementation of primary prevention requires identification of carcinogenic agents and of the conditions that favour the exposure of susceptible individuals to these agents. An agent is considered to be carcinogenic when a change in the frequency or intensity of exposure to this agent is accompanied by a predictable change in the frequency of occurrence of cancer of particular type(s) at a later time.

The issue of causal inference has generated intense debates among both philosophers and scientists (Rothman, 1988). In a simplified scheme that reflects, to a considerable extent, the ideas of Sir Karl Popper (Buck, 1975), causal inference follows a pattern of interconnected cycles. Each cycle includes an examination of the existing data in the light of the prevailing views and questions, formulation of an aetiological hypothesis that adequately addresses these questions and evaluation of the compatibility of the hypothesis with new sets of data specifically generated or assembled for this purpose. Compatibility cannot be equated to proof, but a hypothesis gains credibility when it repeatedly resists refute.

In 1969, the World Health Organisation (WHO), through its International Agency for Research on Cancer (IARC), initiated a programme to evaluate carcinogenic risks to humans and to produce monographs on individual agents, groups or mixtures (IARC, 1987). For the evaluation, evidence for carcinogenicity in humans and experimental animals, and also other relevant data in experimental systems and humans, are taken into account. However, in the final overall evaluation, an agent is judged to be 'conclusively' carcinogenic in humans when there is sufficient evidence of carcinogenicity in humans derived from relevant and valid epidemiological studies. Evidence for carcinogenicity in experimental animals and *in vitro* experimental systems is given less weight, because of well-known problems related to species specificity. Series of clinical case reports are also considered, since they can be thought of as incomplete epidemiological processes, with 'control' information based implicitly on background clinical experience and information.

THE 'NATURAL HISTORY' OF THE EPIDEMIOLOGICAL IDENTIFICATION OF A CANCER CAUSE

The formulation of aetiological hypotheses is usually based on the examination of existing data. These data may represent the results of studies in experimental animals, e.g. the occurrence of papillary carcinoma in the bladder of mice after exposure to tobacco tar encouraged investigators to examine whether an association between tobacco smoking and bladder cancer also existed in humans. In other instances, the data may refer to 'unusual' or 'interesting' cases reported in the clinical literature, e.g. the hypothesis linking inorganic trivalent arsenic compounds to skin cancer (IARC, 1980a) and phenacetin-containing analgesics to renal pelvic carcinoma (IARC, 1980b) have been based, to a large extent, on clinical observations and pathophysiological considerations. There have also been situations where hypotheses were developed and subsequently tested on the basis of biological and theoretical arguments. For example, it was hypothesized that passive smoking may cause lung cancer, because sidestream smoke is not qualitatively different from mainstream smoke, and there is no threshold in the dose-dependent relation between active smoking and risk of lung cancer (Trichopoulos, 1994).

In most instances, however, aetiological hypotheses are developed on the basis of statistical associations between the cancer under consideration on the one hand, and various personal characteristics of the affected individuals, in addition to the time and place occurrence pattern of their disease, on the other. By revealing who, when and where are affected by a particular cancer, one has already gone a long way towards discovering why the particular cancer has occurred. Such observations, collectively considered under the term 'descriptive epidemiology,' represent either the products of routinely recorded information or the byproducts of analytical epidemiological studies designed to address other specific aetiological hypotheses.

An aetiological relation presupposes the existence of a statistical association, but for diseases such as cancer, which are defined according to criteria at the histological, cytological or subcellular level, a cause does not have to be, and usually is not, either necessary or sufficient. For example, not all hepatitis B virus carriers develop hepatocellular carcinoma, and this cancer can develop without the presence of, or even exposure to, the hepatitis B virus (Stuver, 1998). Furthermore, the existence of a statistical association between a particular agent and a particular form of cancer does not necessarily imply the existence of an underlying causal relation. It is possible, in fact common, that the association reflects coexistence of the particular agent with another agent (the confounding factor) which represents the real cause of the particular cancer. Thus, lung cancer patients may report excessive use of alcoholic beverages, simply because in several cultures tobacco smoking and alcohol drinking tend to be positively correlated (**Figure 1**). Even in the absence of confounding, a statistical association is not an infallible indication of a causal relation. Non-smoking lung cancer patients, for example, may report higher alcohol intakes compared with healthy individuals, because they provide more truthful and accurate histories of habits for which there is real or perceived social disapproval (information bias).

Analytical epidemiological studies are designed to explore whether an association between a particular agent or characteristic and a particular cancer actually exists, and what is its real strength after eliminating, as far as possible, all recognizable effects of confounding and bias. The most commonly used measures of strength of the association between a particular agent or characteristic and a particular cancer is the relative risk; this generic term covers the rate ratio, the risk ratio and the odds ratio. The relative risk indicates how many times higher (or lower) is the frequency of occurrence of the particular cancer among individuals exposed to the agent (or possessing the characteristic), compared with individuals not exposed to the agent (or not possessing the characteristic).

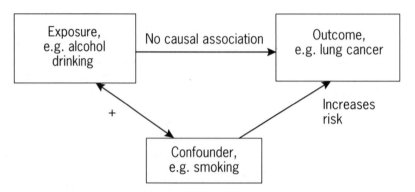

Figure 1   Confounding of the association between consumption of alcoholic beverages and lung cancer by tobacco smoking.

Analytical epidemiological studies have been traditionally designated as cohort or case control. In cohort studies, exposed and nonexposed individuals are followed over time and the frequency of occurrence of the cancer under investigation in the two (or more, if several exposure levels can be ascertained) groups is calculated, allowing the direct estimation of the incidence rate ratio, which is a variant of the relative risk (**Figure 2**). In case-control

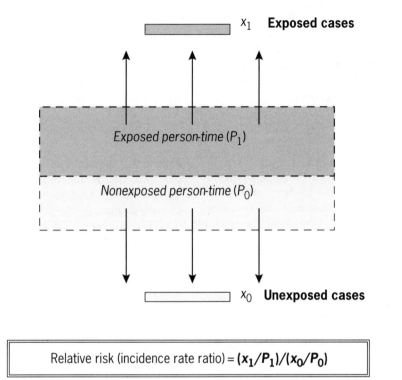

x_1 **Exposed cases**

Exposed person-time (P_1)

Nonexposed person-time (P_0)

x_0 **Unexposed cases**

Relative risk (incidence rate ratio) = $(x_1/P_1)/(x_0/P_0)$

Figure 2   A cohort study. (Adapted from Walker, 1991.)

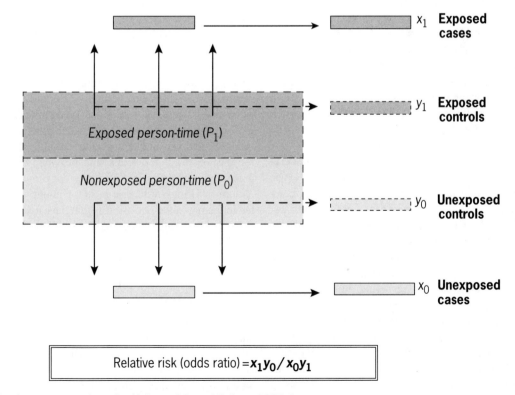

x_1 **Exposed cases**

Exposed person-time (P_1)

y_1 **Exposed controls**

Nonexposed person-time (P_0)

y_0 **Unexposed controls**

x_0 **Unexposed cases**

Relative risk (odds ratio) = $x_1 y_0 / x_0 y_1$

Figure 3   A case-control study. (Adapted from Walker, 1991.)

studies, patients with a recent diagnosis of the cancer under investigation are compared with individuals free of this cancer. These individuals (controls) should be representative of the population which gave rise to the cases with respect to the antecedent frequency of exposure to the agent under study. It can be shown that this design permits the calculation of the odds ratio, which is another variant of the relative risk. The actual frequency of occurrence of the cancer under consideration among exposed and non-exposed individuals usually cannot, however, be calculated in a case-control study (**Figure 3**).

In both cohort and case-control studies, measurable confounding factors and identifiable biases can be controlled for in the analysis, either by stratification or by multivariate modelling (Breslow and Day, 1980, 1987). Contemporary authors have indicated that a sharp distinction between cohort and case-control studies is artificial and unjustifiable (Miettinen, 1985; Rothman and Greenland, 1998). However, most epidemiological studies are still reported under these headings and their distinction may be useful for readers who are not methodologically orientated.

DESCRIPTIVE CANCER EPIDEMIOLOGY

Descriptive cancer epidemiology examines the distribution of individual cancer types by a number of characteristics. These characteristics may refer to individuals themselves (personal characteristics, including age, gender, occupation, education, marital status, etc.), to the place of disease initiation or occurrence (place characteristics, including the country and region of residence, the urban or rural nature of the area, the altitude, the latitude, etc.) or the time pattern of occurrence (time characteristcs, including long-term trends, time elapsing between exposure to a certain agent and the appearance of a particular cancer, etc.). Certain characteristics are inherently multidimensional, e.g. migration refers to individuals, in addition to the country of origin and the time of migration.

In most instances, descriptive epidemiological associations can only generate aetiological hypotheses, because observed associations are frequently confounded by many factors and are also subject to a number of potential biases. For example, the high incidence of stomach cancer in Japan (**Figure 4**) can be attributed to a number of intercorrelated genetic, nutritional and socio-cultural characteristics of the Japanese people. However, on rare occasions, descriptive epidemiological data can be revealing by themselves, particularly when an otherwise rare tumour occurs frequently among persons with a certain defining characteristic, usually their occupation or medical treatment for an earlier condition. For example, the high incidence of cancer of the nasal cavity among workers in nickel refineries strongly suggests that the agents or the processes involved in nickel refining are carcinogenic.

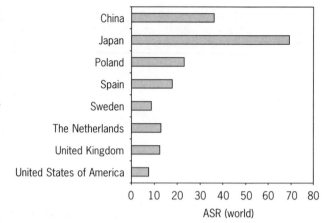

Figure 4   Age-standardized incidence rates of stomach cancer among males. (Based on data from Ferlay et al., GLOBOCAN 2000: Cancer Incidence, Mortality and Prevalence Worldwide, Version 1.0. IARC CancerBase No. 5. IARC Press, Lyon, 2001.)

Personal Characteristics

Among the many personal characteristics, those most frequently explored in descriptive epidemiology are age, gender, religion, marital status, occupation and socio-economic class. These characteristics are rarely themselves aetiologically relevant, but they are commonly correlated with exposure to carcinogenic factors, and for this reason they are frequently considered risk indicators or risk factors. Furthermore, several of these characteristics are readily available because they are routinely recorded for administrative reasons.

Because the incidence of most cancers increases rapidly with age, exceptions to this pattern may have aetiological significance. Acute leukaemia, for example, shows both an early and a late peak, which led investigators to consider intrauterine carcinogenesis. The subsequent discovery that intrauterine exposure to ionizing radiation may increase the risk of childhood leukaemia provided empirical support to this hypothesis. Similarly, the bimodal incidence pattern of Hodgkin disease in many countries (**Figure 5**) led to the prevailing hypothesis that the early peak is due to an infectious agent. Finally, the slowing of the rate of increase of the incidence of breast cancer after menopause has underlined the importance of ovarian oestrogens in the aetiology of this disease.

Many cancers are more common among men than among women. This has been attributed, in many instances, to the higher past exposure of men to tobacco smoking and alcohol drinking. However, some intriguing gender differences remain unexplained. The incidence of hepatitis B-positive hepatocellular carcinoma is three times higher among men, even though the prevalence of chronic hepatitis B virus infection is only two times higher among them.

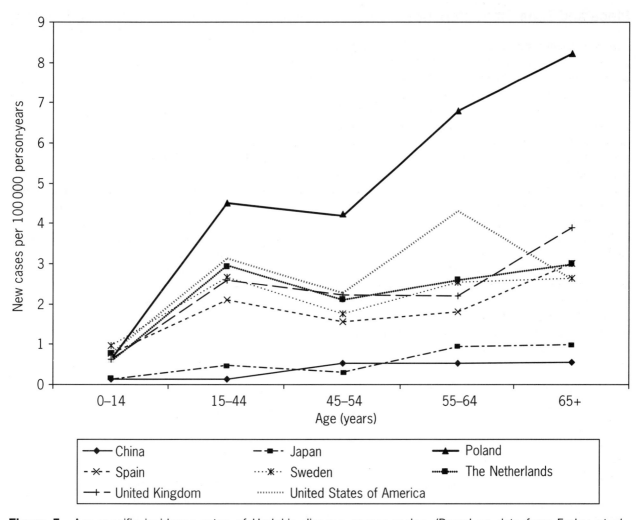

Figure 5   Age-specific incidence rates of Hodgkin disease among males. (Based on data from Ferlay *et al.*, GLOBOCAN 2000: Cancer Incidence, Mortality and Prevalence Worldwide, Version 1.0. IARC Cancer Base No. 5. IARC Press, Lyon, 2001.)

In contrast, the incidence of gallbladder cancer (and also cholelithiasis) is considerably more common among women.

Religion, ethnic origin and race are frequently inter-related. The realization that environmental factors, including lifestyles, are more important than hereditary factors in explaining cancer variation among population groups (Lichtenstein *et al.*, 2000) has suggested that those groupings should be viewed in the socio-cultural, rather than genetic, context. Several hypotheses concerning cancer causation have been generated by the unusual lifestyles and cancer occurrence patterns among Mormons and Seventh Day Adventists in the United States. Also, the low incidence of cervical cancer among nuns has led to the hypothesis that sexual activity is an important determinant of this cancer.

Marital status has been an important parameter for the formulation of aetiological hypotheses concerning cancer

occurrence in the female reproductive organs. Marital status associations, most likely reflecting underlying causal links of nulliparity with breast cancer, sexual activity with cervical cancer and low parity with ovarian cancer, are stronger in socio-cultural settings in which marital status is strongly correlated with sexual activity and reproduction.

Several forms of cancer, notably cancers of the stomach and uterine cervix, are more frequent in the lower socio-economic classes, and these observations have led to the development of aetiological hypotheses implicating, respectively, particular dietary patterns (salty foods, inadequate intake of vegetables and fruits), or inadequate hygienic conditions and infrequent utilization of barrier contraceptive methods. Furthermore, occupational mortality statistics have been extremely valuable in pointing out occupations that increase the risk of particular types of cancer.

Place and Time Characteristics

Cancer mortality statistics by site, age and gender are published, on an annual basis, by the WHO for most countries of the world. Furthermore, the IARC publishes, every 5 years, Cancer Incidence in the Five Continents, containing data – by site, age and gender – generated by a worldwide network of cancer registries (Parkin *et al.*, 1992). Correlations between the incidence of, or mortality from, particular cancers in various countries on the one hand, and per capita consumption in these countries of various food groups or nutrients on the other, generated hypotheses about the nutritional aetiology of several cancers (Armstrong and Doll, 1975).

National cancer rates have also been used extensively in studies of migrant populations, to distinguish the relative importance of heredity and environment (including lifestyle) in the generation of the large international variability of cancer occurrence at most sites. In migrant populations, e.g. Japanese migrating to the United States, the incidence of large bowel cancer approaches that of the host country within a few decades, whereas for stomach cancer a

whole lifetime is needed (Haenszel and Kurihara, 1968) and for breast cancer several generations may be required for incidence assimilation (Ziegler *et al.*, 1993). Lastly, large-scale geographic patterns have been used to generate hypotheses linking malaria endemicity with the occurrence of Burkitt lymphoma (Burkitt, 1970) and sunlight exposure with the incidence of skin cancer (Scotto *et al.*, 1982).

Long-term temporal trends of lung and stomach cancer in developed countries (**Figure 6**) have led to hypotheses implicating tobacco smoking and food preservation modalities in their aetiology. Specifically, the rapid rise of lung cancer mortality among men during the first half of the twentieth century, and the much slower rise of the corresponding mortality among women, indicated that a novel strong carcinogen became widespread among men but much less so among women. Few agents, besides tobacco, would meet these criteria, and many analytical epidemiological studies have demonstrated that smoking was indeed the responsible factor. Whilst no comparable clear explanation exists for the remarkable decline in stomach cancer mortality, many investigators speculate that the large-scale

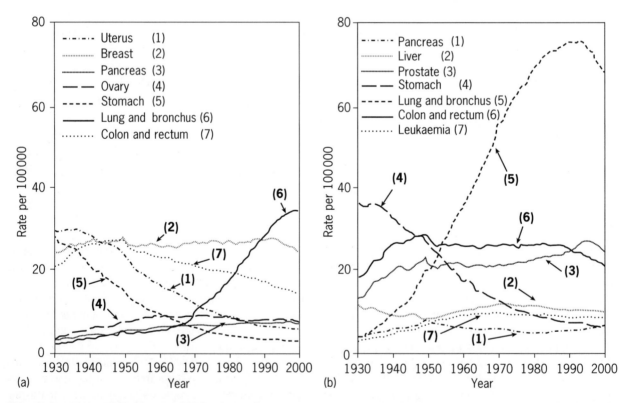

Figure 6   Age-adjusted (to the 1970 US standard population) cancer death rates by site among (a) Females and (b) males in the USA from 1930 to 1996, expressed per 100 000 person-years. (a) Uterus cancer death rates are for uterine cervix and uterine corpus combined. Note: Owing to changes in ICD coding, numerator information has changed over time. Rates for cancers of the uterus, ovary, lung and bronchus, and colon and rectum are affected by these coding changes. (b) Note: Owing to changes in ICD coding, numerator information has changed over time. Rates for cancers of the liver, lung and bronchus, and colon and rectum are affected by these coding changes. (From Greenlee et al., 2000, *Cancer Journal for Clinicians*, **50**, 7–33.)

introduction of refrigeration for food preservation may have been responsible.

Clustering in both time and place, a characteristic of diseases caused by infectious agents, has been investigated using an ingenious procedure developed by Knox (1963) for cases of acute childhood leukaemia. Notwithstanding inconclusive results, the hypothesis postulating involvement of infectious agent(s) is still widely entertained.

FORMULATION OF AETIOLOGICAL HYPOTHESES

The reasoning leading to the generation of aetiological hypotheses follows, explicitly or implicitly, a set of rules which focus on difference, agreement, concomitant variation and analogy (MacMahon and Trichopoulos, 1996).

According to the rule of difference, when both a particular set of factors and the incidence of a particular cancer differ between two populations, one or more of these factors will likely contribute to the occurrence of the disease. When the difference in incidence is large, in relative terms, and only one or two factors form the differentiating set, then the hypothesis is more likely to be correct, and vice versa. Thus, the relatively high incidence of Kaposi sarcoma among homosexual men in the United States in the early 1980s indicated that sexual preference was involved in the occurrence of the disease, since few other, if any, characteristics distinguish homosexual from heterosexual men. Also, the lower incidence of cervical cancer among nuns points to sexual activity as an important causal factor, since nuns differ from other women with respect to only a few characteristics and practices. By contrast, the usually higher incidence of lung cancer in large cities cannot be attributed confidently to air pollution, since city dwellers differ from rural inhabitants with respect to a number of exposures, including those related to occupation, diet, smoking, environmental tobacco smoke and radon.

The rule of agreement focuses on common factors identifiable in different settings characterized by a high incidence of particular cancers. Thus, exposure to ionizing radiation was the common factor characterizing patients with ankylosing spondylitis therapeutically irradiated and children diagnostically X-rayed *in utero*, when both groups were found to have increased incidence of leukaemia. Also, multiplicity of sexual partners is the likely common factor characterizing women with squamous carcinoma of the uterine cervix and male homosexuals with anal cancer.

Concomitant variation represents a quantitative expression of the first two rules, particularly the first. The concomitant variation of per capita fat consumption and the incidence of, or mortality from, colorectal cancer, in international correlations (Armstrong and Doll, 1975) was important for the hypothesis linking fat consumption to colorectal cancer – a hypothesis supported by the results of many, although not all, analytical epidemiological studies. Correlations based on countries, regions or other population groups (as distinct from correlations based on individuals) are termed population, group or ecological correlations. From the epidemiological point of view, they may be considered half-way between descriptive and analytical studies, and their aetiological importance is, as a rule, limited.

Inference by analogy represents the fourth and arguably the softest rule. The paradigm of poliomyelitis, in which early infection is harmless, whereas late infection causes the paralytic form of the disease, has been invoked by several authors in attempts to explore the aetiology of childhood leukaemia.

The credibility of an aetiological hypothesis developed on the basis of descriptive epidemiological data increases substantially if the suspected agent causes cancer in experimental animals, preferably in more than one species and in the same organ as in humans. In the absence of a satisfactory experimental model, demonstration of *in vitro* mutagenicity provides supportive evidence, as does the identification of a likely pathogenetic mechanism. Nevertheless, the ultimate criterion of the validity of an aetiological hypothesis – whether derived from descriptive epidemiological findings or formulated on the basis of experimental data, clinical information or theoretical considerations, or any combination of the above – is in most cases epidemiological. Specifically, an aetiological hypothesis is refuted when it generates predictions that appear incompatible with the collective evidence of analytical epidemiological studies. In contrast, it remains provisionally valid when it generates predictions compatible with the accumulated empirical evidence from human studies.

EPIDEMIOLOGICAL STUDIES EVALUATING CANCER CAUSATION

In theory, the best empirical evidence regarding causation should come from randomized trials in humans. Studies in humans do not face the pitfalls inherent in the reasoning by analogy from animal to human data, whereas randomization allows control for distorting influences by both known and unsuspected confounding factors; in addition, double-blind designs minimize the potential for several types of bias. Indeed, therapeutic clinical trials are also aetiological studies exploring the causation of a better clinical outcome by a certain process, the study treatment. However, experimental studies of cancer causation cannot be undertaken in humans for ethical reasons, except when there is evidence that a particular factor may actually protect from cancer (in which instance the absence of the factor can be thought of as the carcinogenic agent). Even under these conditions, experimental studies in humans are still impractical. Among cancer patients, the outcome under investigation (death, metastasis or recurrence) is a relatively frequent effect, and the corresponding study size can be manageable. Among healthy individuals, the frequency of occurrence of any particular cancer is low and the corresponding study size must be very large, making the follow-up and compliance problems exceedingly difficult. Nevertheless, a few such studies have been undertaken, either by investing large resources (e.g. the IARC study targetting the prevention of hepatocellular carcinoma in the Gambia through active immunization against hepatitis B virus) or by reducing the required sample size by focusing on preneoplastic conditions that identify high risk individuals.

Epidemiological studies specifically designed to address a particular aetiological hypothesis are usually called analytical. The objective of analytical studies is to document causation between exposures and a certain disease. In analytical investigations, measurements and categorical assignments apply to individuals, whereas this is not necessary in descriptive epidemiological studies. Thus, in order to examine in an analytical study whether chronic carriers of hepatitis B virus (HBV) are more likely to develop liver cancer than noncarriers, it is necessary to classify the individuals under study according to their HBV carrier state and the development or not of liver cancer during a specified time period (Hennekens and Buring, 1987; MacMahon and Trichopoulos, 1996; Rothman and Greenland, 1998).

Ecological studies in epidemiology, as opposed to individual-based studies, occupy an intermediate position between descriptive and analytical investigations, in that they share many characteristics with descriptive studies, but may also serve aetiological objectives. In ecological studies, the exposure and the disease under investigation are ascertained not for individuals but for groups or even whole populations (Morgenstern, 1982). Thus the prevalence of HBV in several populations could be correlated with the incidence of liver cancer in these populations, even though no information could be obtained as to whether any particular individual in these populations was or was not an HBV carrier and has or has not developed liver cancer.

When an exposure is fairly common (e.g. smoking, sunlight, poverty, even prevalence of HBV carriers), ecological studies should be able to reveal the effects of these exposures. Thus, following the increase in tobacco consumption, the incidence of lung cancer increased sharply over time; skin melanoma is more common in geographic latitudes with more sunshine exposure; stomach cancer is generally more common in low-income social strata; and the incidence of primary liver cancer is higher in populations with higher prevalence of HBV (Tomatis, 1990). As a corollary, the inability of ecological studies to demonstrate an association between a widespread exposure that has rapidly increased over time (e.g. extremely low-frequency

magnetic fields) and the incidence of a disease allegedly caused by these fields (e.g. childhood leukaemia) challenges the causal nature of the positive association reported from some analytical investigations.

In analytical epidemiological studies, there are several ways through which an association, or lack thereof, is assessed, but the most common measure is the relative risk. A value equal to 1 implies that the exposure under study does not affect the incidence of the disease under consideration. In contrast, values <1 and >1 indicate, respectively, an inverse or a positive association (MacMahon and Trichopoulos, 1996; Rothman and Greenland, 1998). When the relative risk is >2 and the associated unbiased, unconfounded, precise and causal, an exposed-case patient is more likely than not to have developed the disease because of the exposure. When the relative risk is >1 but <2 the exposed patient is more likely than not to have developed the disease for reasons other than the exposure. This is because a relative risk of, say, 1.5 has a baseline component equal to 1 that characterizes the unexposed, and a component equal to 0.5 that applies only to the exposed (MacMahon and Trichopoulos, 1996). For instance, if the risk of a nonsmoking 55-year-old man developing lung cancer in the next 10 years is 1%, and that of a same age and gender smoker is 5% (relative risk 5), only 4% in the smoker's risk (i.e. 4/5 of the total 5%) can be attributed to his smoking.

Cohort Studies

In cohort studies (**Figure 2**), individuals are classified according to their exposure and are followed over time for ascertainment of the frequency of disease occurrence in the various exposure-defined categories. In each category the frequency of occurrence is calculated either as risk (proportion of those who developed the disease under study among all individuals in this category) or as incidence rate (number of those who developed the disease divided by the sum of the time each of the individuals in this category has been under observation). Defining characteristics of cohort studies are that they are exposure based and are patently or conceptually longitudinal.

In cohort studies, the groups to be studied are selected on the basis of exposure. In some studies the groups are chosen on the basis of a particular exposure (special exposure cohorts), whereas in others, groups offering special resources for follow-up are initially chosen and the individuals are subsequently allocated according to exposure status (general population cohorts). The first approach may be necessary when rare exposures need to be studied, while the second approach is appropriate when the exposure under consideration is fairly common in general populations (e.g. smoking or major dietary components).

The cohort study groups are observed over a period of time to determine the frequency of occurrence of disease among them. The distinction between retrospective and prospective cohort studies depends on whether or not the cases of disease have occurred in the cohort at the time the study began. In a retrospective cohort study, all the relevant exposures and health outcomes have already occurred when the study is initiated. In a prospective cohort study, the relevant causes may or may not have occurred at the time the study began, but the cases of disease have not yet occurred and, following selection of the study cohort, the investigator must wait for the disease to appear among cohort members.

From a methodological point of view, there are two types of cohort studies: closed or fixed cohorts and open or dynamic cohorts. Closed cohorts are frequent in occupational epidemiology and study of outbreaks, whereas open cohorts dominate cancer epidemiology and are the basis for most case-control studies. The key distinction between open and closed cohorts is how membership in the cohort is determined. In a closed cohort, membership is determined by a membership-defining event which occurs at a point in time. Studies based on follow-up of closed cohorts may be analysed using either cumulative incidence (risk) measures or by counting person-time and calculating incidence rate measures. Analyses based on cumulative incidence measures are useful only under certain conditions (that is, no loss to follow-up; no competing risks; exposure status unchanged throughout follow-up; study subjects followed for the same period of time). Whether or not these assumptions are met, it is always valid to conduct analyses based on person-time, using incidence rate measures in the setting of a closed cohort.

Open cohorts are composed of individuals who contribute person-time to the cohort, while meeting criteria for a membership-defining state. Once individuals can no longer be characterized by this state, they cease to contribute person-time to the corresponding cohort. In studies based on open cohorts it is not possible to measure cumulative incidence (risk) directly. Instead, analyses are based on person-time using incidence rate measures. Thus, if among 5000 non-smoking men followed for an average period of 10 years ($P_0 = 50\,000$ person-years) $x_0 = 25$ were diagnosed with lung cancer, whereas among $10\,000$ smoking men followed for an average period of 8 years ($P_1 = 80\,000$ person-years) $x_1 = 600$ were diagnosed with lung cancer, the incidence rate among nonexposed would be 50 per 10^5 person-years, that among exposed 750 per 10^5 person-years and the incidence rate ratio would be $(600/80\,000)/(50/50\,000) = 15$.

Case-control Studies

In case-control studies (**Figure 3**), patients recently diagnosed with the disease under consideration form the case series, and their exposure to the factor under investigation is ascertained through questionnaires, interviews, examination of records, undertaking of laboratory tests in biological samples and other means. The pattern of exposure to the study factor in the population that generated the case series is then evaluated through a properly selected control series. If only two categories of exposure are relevant (exposed and unexposed), the relative risk can be estimated by multiplying exposed cases with unexposed controls and dividing this product by the product of unexposed cases and exposed controls (the so-called odds ratio, that adequately estimates rate ratio and risk ratio). Thus, if among 200 male patients diagnosed with lung cancer (cases), $x_1 = 150$ were smokers and $x_0 = 50$ non-smokers, whereas among 300 men of similar age as the cases but without lung cancer (controls), $y_1 = 50$ were smokers and $y_0 = 250$ were nonsmokers, the odds ratio $x_1 y_0 / x_0 y_1$, which is a good approximation to the relative risk, is $(150 \times 250)/(50 \times 50) = 15$.

Two features of case-control studies make them susceptible to bias: the ascertainment of exposure after the occurrence of disease (information bias), and suboptimal processes for control selection (selection bias) (Hennekens and Buring, 1987; MacMahon and Trichopoulos, 1996; Rothman and Greenland, 1998).

Some case-control designs, in particular the population-based ones, are methodologically superior to other case-control variants. A case-control study is called population-based when controls are chosen from the clearly defined population from which all cases have arisen – in other words, had one of the controls developed the disease under study it would have definitely been included among the cases. Cohort studies, however, generally produce more credible results than those emerging from case-control investigations, because, if properly designed and implemented, they are, as a rule, free from information and selection bias.

Frequently, case-control studies are matched, in the sense that controls are chosen so as to match particular cases with respect to gender, age, race or any other factor that is probably related to the disease under study but not intended to be analysed in the particular study. Matching is not strictly necessary, nor does it confirm the validity of results, but it improves statistical efficiency, i.e. statistical power, or the ability to substantiate a true association (Rothman and Greenland, 1998). If matching has been used in the enrollment of cases and controls, the statistical analysis should accommodate the matching process, through either a matched analysis (e.g. conditional modelling) or unmatched analysis with explicit control of the matching factors (proper application of unconditional modelling).

The advantages and disadvantages of cohort and case-control studies in exploring the causes of cancer in humans are described in several textbooks on epidemiology. Briefly, cohort (or prospective or follow-up) studies trace in a more natural way the time sequence of causal phenomena. However, the case-control approach is, in essence, an extension of a practice familiar to physicians, that of case history taking. Confounding is just as common in cohort as in case-control studies, but information bias concerning exposure to suspected agent(s) is more common in case-control investigations, since the existence of a serious disease, such as cancer, can affect recollection and reporting, as well as several directly ascertainable biochemical and immunological variables. By contrast, case-control studies are usually more powerful, in the statistical sense, since the frequency of exposure to many suspected agents is more common than the frequency of occurrence of most cancers during a not-too-long period of follow-up.

CHANCE, CONFOUNDING AND BIAS

Three issues need to be resolved before an epidemiological association could be considered true and therefore deserve interpretation in causal terms: chance, confounding and bias.

Probabilistic processes always have a built-in uncertainty, but we can reduce the chance-related uncertainty by using progressively larger numbers in a study, and we can assess its possible influence by utilizing statistical procedures that generate what has become known as the P value. This value indicates how likely one would have been to observe an association as extreme as, or more extreme than, that found between a particular exposure and a certain disease, if there were in fact no association. The true meaning of the P value, however, is poorly understood and the concept itself is widely misused.

P values are traditionally expressed as numerical fractions of unity. For example, a P value of 0.1 for a particular positive association indicates that there is a 10% chance that such an association or more extreme (or a symmetrically opposite one, i.e. an inverse association) would appear by chance, even if there were in reality no association at all. In essence, the P value is interpretable as such when only one comparison or one test is performed. When multiple comparisons or multiple tests are carried out, the set of the respective P values lose their collective interpretability. Procedures for adjusting P values according to the number of comparisons undertaken or tests performed have been proposed, but they are not universally accepted (Rothman, 1990) and are rarely utilized. However, other things being equal, the real significance of a certain P value is weaker when the number of tests performed is larger. P values can be more confidently interpreted as suggestive of real phenomena or genuine associations when there is independent evidence in support of the process that generated the P value.

A P value of 0.05 or smaller is traditionally treated in medical research as evidence that an observed association may not have arisen by chance. However, small P values, including values considerably smaller than 0.05, do not guarantee that an association (or difference) is genuine, let alone causal. Even when the P value is very small and

was generated from a randomized trial, it could still be dismissed when the relevant result makes no sense (Miettinen, 1985). As a corollary, our daily lives are full of highly unlikely events and coincidences and, at the extremes, thousands of people have become wealthy from lotteries and many more have died in strange accidents, even though the probabilities of the respective events are extremely small. The lesson is simple: highly unlikely events that would have been associated with extremely small P values do happen by chance. In addition to small P values, science requires judgement relying on sound substantive knowledge in order to discard chance.

The P value itself does not convey information about the strength of the respective association: a weak association may be statistically highly significant (very small P) when the study is large, and a strong association may be statistically nonsignificant (large P) when the study is small (Rothman and Geenland, 1998). In order to integrate information about the strength of an association (as reflected in the relative risk effect measure) and its statistical significance, the concept of confidence interval has been developed. The confidence interval describes the range of values that the true relative risk is likely to take with, for example, 95% confidence (95% confidence interval) on the basis of the data through which the association was evaluated. The confidence interval is intimately linked to the P value, so that for a statistically significant ($P < 0.05$) association, the 95% confidence interval of the measure of this association (e.g. the relative risk) does not include ('rejects') 95 times out of 100 the value of this measure which would have indicated no association (the no association value, also called the 'null value,' is 1 for relative risk).

Random variation *per se* in epidemiological studies is not an insurmountable problem. Larger studies and eventually combined analyses, through systematic statistical evaluations of results of several independent investigations, can effectively address genuine chance-related concerns. Such combined analyses have been termed meta-analyses and pooled analyses. There is no real distinction between the two terms, although meta-analysis has been more frequently used when published data are combined, whereas in pooled analysis primary data from different studies may be made available to the investigator who undertakes the task to combine them. Meta-analyses and pooled analyses have been widely and effectively used for randomized clinical trials and intervention studies, in which confounding and bias are of limited concern (Sacks *et al.*, 1987). For observational epidemiological studies, however, the role of meta-analysis is not universally accepted (Shapiro, 1994; Feinstein, 1995), because no statistical summarization can effectively address problems generated by residual confounding, unidentified bias and the different ways investigators choose to present their results.

Confounding is the phenomenon generated when another factor that causes the disease under study, or is otherwise strongly related with it, is also independently related to the exposure under investigation (**Figure 1**). Thus, if one wishes to examine whether hepatitis C virus (HCV) causes liver cancer, hepatitis B virus (HBV) would be a likely confounder because HBV causes liver cancer and carriers of HBV are more likely to also be carriers of HCV (because these two viruses are largely transmitted by the same route). Hence, if the confounding influence of hepatitis B is not accounted for in the design (by limiting the study to hepatitits B-negative subjects) or in analyses of the data, then the strength of the association between hepatitis C and liver cancer would be overestimated.

A more trivial example is the strong association between carrying matches (or a lighter) on the one hand and developing lung cancer on the other. Neither matches nor lighters cause lung cancer and their association to the disease is due entirely to confounding by cigarette smoking. The confounding factor, cigarette smoking, is the true cause of lung cancer and the dependence of cigarette lighting on matches or lighters generates the confounded entirely spurious association of the latter two factors with the disease.

There are several ways to deal with confounding, some simple, some more complicated. They all assume that two conditions are satisfied: (1) that all the confounders have been identified or at least suspected and (2) that the identified or suspected confounders can be adequately measured (Greenland, 1980). When the study is fairly large, it is always possible to evaluate in the analysis all suspected confounders, but the ability to conceptualize and measure all of them accurately frequently goes beyond the control of the investigator. The result is what has been termed residual confounding (Greenland, 1980; MacMahon and Trichopoulos, 1996; Rothman and Greenland, 1998).

Compounding the problems of epidemiological studies is that the data are never of optimal quality. Data collection relies on the memory of and accurate reporting by study participants, laboratory procedures or existing records. None of these sources is perfect, and frequently the errors are unequal between the compared groups and generate biased results. A reasonable concern is that cases, or their relatives, are inclined to link the disease under study to particular exposures for conscious or subconscious reasons. Cases may also try harder than controls or their relatives do to recall or identify past exposures (information bias).

A well thought-out protocol, standardized procedures and built-in quality control measures can reduce bias and allow quantification of its potential impact. However, complete assurance that bias has been eliminated can never be achieved. In addition, the reliance of case-control studies on a control series that simultaneously has to meet criteria of compliance, comparability to the case series, statistical efficiency and general practicality makes them susceptible to selection bias of unpredictable direction and magnitude (Wacholder *et al.*, 1992a–c). Hospital controls, neighbourhood controls and controls enrolled through searches of telephone lists have their own problems, and these have been extensively discussed (MacMahon and Trichopoulos, 1996).

When results of an observational epidemiological study designed to address a specific hypothesis are striking, the study is large and there is no evidence of overt confounding or major biases, it is legitimate to attempt aetiological inferences. The rationale is that powerful confounding presupposes strong risk factors that are unlikely to be missed, and that major biases can be traced to gross and easily identifiable protocol violations. Interpretation becomes particularly problematic when a weak association turns out to be statistically significant perhaps in a large but imperfect data set. Although that association could reflect a weak but genuine causal association, it might more likely be the result of residual confounding, subtle unidentifiable bias or chance following a multiple testing process.

Repeated demonstration of an association of similar direction and magnitude in several studies, undertaken by different investigators in different population groups, increases confidence in a genuine causal basis but cannot conclusively establish this. Nor do meta-analyses prove causality; these techniques essentially address the issue of chance and provide no guarantee that a particular bias, unrecognized confounding or selective reporting have not operated in the constituent studies. It is at this stage that biology confronts epidemiology and the ability to reconcile the two perspectives should be the guiding principle in interpreting epidemiological results.

INFERENCE OF CANCER CAUSATION IN EPIDEMIOLOGY

Criteria for inferring causation from epidemiological investigations have been proposed, over the years, by several authors (MacMahon *et al.*, 1960; US Department of Health, Education and Welfare, 1964; Hill, 1965; IARC, 1987; Evans, 1993). The philosophy of causation in epidemiology and medicine has also been examined in various essays (Rothman, 1988). In spite of differences in emphasis, a similar set of principles have been invoked by most authors. Sir Austin Bradford Hill (Hill, 1965) advocated the nine widely used criteria listed in **Table 1** to distinguish causal from noncausal associations. These criteria, although sensible and useful, do not separately address the inherently different issues that are posed by the results of a single study, the results of several studies and the likelihood of causation in a certain individual (Cole, 1997). In reality, the perceived likelihood of an association between a particular exposure and a certain disease being causal moves forward or backward in a continuous

Table 1 The Hill criteria for inferring causation (Hill, 1965)

Strength	A strong association is more likely to be causal. The measure of strength of an association is relative risk and not statistical significance
Consistency	An association is more likely to be causal when it is observed repeatedly and in different populations
Specificity	When an exposure is associated with a specific outcome only (e.g. a cancer site or even better a particular histological type of this cancer), then it is more likely to be causal. There are exceptions, however (e.g. smoking causing bronchitis, lung cancer, pancreatic cancer)
Temporality	A cause should not only precede the outcome (disease), but also be compatible with its latency period (in noninfectious diseases) or its incubation period (infectious disease)
Biological gradient	This criterion refers to the presence of a dose–response relationship. If the frequency of the outcome increases when an exposure is more intense or lasts longer, then it is more likely that the association is causal
Plausibility	An association is more likely to be causal when it is biologically plausible
Coherence	This criterion implies that a cause and effect interpretation of an association should not conflict with what is known of the natural history and biology of the disease
Experimental evidence	If experimental evidence exists, then the association is more likely to be causal. Such evidence, however, is seldom available in human populations
Analogy	The existence of an analogy (e.g. if a drug causes birth defects, then another drug could also have the same effect) could enhance the credibility that an association is causal

spectrum as research results accumulate. The evidence for causality is declared as sufficient when a particular threshold has been reached (MacMahon and Trichopoulos, 1996; Cole, 1997).

Criteria for causality can be invoked, explicitly or implicitly, in evaluating the results of a single epidemiological study, although, in this instance, a firm conclusion is all but impossible (single study level, or level I, according to the classification introduced by Cole and used here (Cole, 1997)). Criteria for causality are more frequently used for the assessment of evidence accumulated from several epidemiological studies and other biomedical investigations. At this stage, the intellectual process is inductive, moving away from the specifics towards generalization (several studies level, or level II).

Regulatory agencies and policy makers may recommend standards, set limits or authorize action even when the scientific evidence is weak, particularly at levels surrounding the proposed standards or limits. These procedures serve public health objectives by introducing a wide safety margin, but should never be confused with the establishment of causation based on scientific considerations alone. Finally, when causation has been established at level II, then, and only then, can the cause of the disease in a particular individual be considered (specific person level, or level III). At this level, the intellectual process is deductive and deterministic, moving from the general concept of disease causation to the examination of what has caused disease in a particular individual.

Whereas causality can be conclusively established between a particular exposure as an entity and a particular disease as an entity, it is not possible to conclusively establish such a link between an individual exposure and a particular disease of a certain individual, e.g. smoking and development of lung cancer. It is possible, however, to infer deductively that the specific individual's illness more likely than not was caused by the specified exposure. For this conclusion all the following criteria must be met (Cole, 1997):

- The exposure under consideration, as an entity, must be an established cause of the disease under consideration, as an entity (level II).
- The relevant exposure of the particular individual must have properties comparable (in terms of intensity, duration, associated latency, etc.) to those of the exposure that, as an entity, has been shown to cause the disease under consideration, again as an entity.
- The disease of the specified person must be identical with or within the symptomatological spectrum of the disease which, as an entity, has been aetiologically linked to the exposure.
- The patient must not have been exposed to another established or likely cause of this disease. If the patient has been exposed to both the factor under consideration (e.g. smoking) and to another causal factor (e.g. asbestos), individual attribution becomes a function of several relative risks, all versus the completely unexposed: relative risk of those who only had the exposure under consideration, relative risk of those who had only been exposed to the other causal factor(s) and relative risk of those who have had a combination of these exposures.
- The scientifically defensible, properly adjusted, relative risk of the disease among individuals who have had the exposure under consideration at the given magnitude should be >2. Only then (as previously discussed) is the diseased individual more likely than not to have developed the disease because of the specified exposure (US Department of Health, Education and Welfare, 1964; MacMahon and Trichopoulos, 1996). If, for

example, the relative risk is 2.5, the component 1 of the background risk is less than the component 1.5 of the excess risk and the individual is more likely than not to have developed the disease because of the exposure.

CONCLUSION

Modern epidemiology has become a rich and powerful toolbox for the study of biological phenomena in humans. Because manipulation of exposures, many of which may be harmful, is usually neither feasible nor ethical, epidemiologists have to base their inferences on experiments that human subjects undertake intentionally, naturally or even unconsciously. The study of risk of lung cancer among smokers compared with nonsmokers is one classical example of a 'natural' experiment. Because human life is characterized by a myriad of complex, often interrelated behaviours and exposures − ranging from genetic traits and features of the intrauterine environment to growth rate, physical activity, sexual practices, use of tobacco, alcohol and pharmaceutical compounds, dietary intake, exposure to infections, environmental pollutants and occupational hazards, etc. − epidemiologic investigation is difficult and challenging. Given this complexity, it is not surprising that from time to time epidemiological studies generate results that appear confusing, biologically absurd or even contradictory. However, it is reassuring that a wealth of new knowledge has been generated by epidemiological studies over the last few decades, and that this knowledge now lays the scientific ground for primary prevention of many major cancers and other chronic diseases among humans globally.

Given the multitude of problems with which epidemiological studies have to deal, the variability of the conditions under which they are undertaken and the abundance of potential sources of confounding and bias, it is remarkable that their results are as consistent as they are. However, it should be stressed that, in epidemiology, more than in any other field of biomedical research, it is the collective evidence that matters, rather than the results of a particular study, however large and well done the latter may be. Only the quality-adjusted collective evidence can address the issues of hidden bias and confounding that may find their ways into any particular study, and only the collective evidence can provide an approximation to generalizability.

REFERENCES

Armstrong, B. and Doll, R. (1975). Environmental factors and cancer incidence and mortality in different countries, with special reference to dietary practices. *International Journal of Cancer*, **15**, 617−631.

Breslow, N. E. and Day, N. E. (1980). *Statistical Methods in Cancer Research. Vol. I. The Analysis of Case-control Studies.* IARC Scientific Publication No. **32**, 5−338 (International Agency for Research on Cancer, Lyon).

Breslow, N. E. and Day, N. E. (1987). *Statistical Methods in Cancer Research. Vol. II. The Design and Analysis of Cohort Studies.* IARC Scientific Publication No. **82**, 1−406 (International Agency for Research on Cancer, Lyon).

Buck, C. (1975). Popper's philosophy for epidemiologists. *International Journal of Epidemiology*, **4**, 159−168.

Burkitt, D. P. (1970). Geographical distribution. In: Burkitt, E. P. and Wright, D. H. (eds), *Burkitt's Lymphoma*. 186−197 (Livingstone, Edinburgh).

Cole, P. (1997). Causality in epidemiology, health policy and law. *Environmental Law Reporter*, **27**, 10279−10285.

Evans, A. (1993). *Causation and Disease: A Chronological Journey* (Plenum, New York).

Feinstein, A. R. (1995). Meta-analysis: statistical alchemy for the 21st century. *Journal of Clinical Epidemiology*, **48**, 71−79.

Greenland, S. (1980). The effect of misclassification in the presence of covariates. *American Journal of Epidemiology*, **112**, 564−569.

Haenszel, W. and Kurihara, M. (1968). Studies of Japanese migrants. I. Mortality from cancer and other diseases among Japanese in the United States. *Journal of the National Cancer Institute*, **40**, 43−68.

Hennekens, C. H. and Buring, J. E. (1987). *Epidemiology in Medicine* (Little, Brown, Boston).

Hill, A. B. (1965). The environment and disease: association or causation? *Proceedings of the Royal Society of Medicine*, **58**, 295−300.

IARC (1980a). *IARC Monographs on the Evaluation of the Carcinogenic Risk of Chemicals to Humans. Vol. 23. Some Metals and Metallic Compounds.* 39−142 (International Agency for Research on Cancer, Lyon).

IARC (1980b) *IARC Monographs on the Evaluation of the Carcinogenic Risk of Chemicals to Humans.* Vol. 24, Some Pharmaceutical Drugs. 135−62. (International Agency for Research on Cancer, Lyon).

IARC (1987). *IARC Monographs on Carcinogenic Risks to Humans. Overall Evaluations of Carcinogenicity: an Updating of IARC Monographs Volumes 1 to 42*, Supplement 7. 440 (International Agency for Research on Cancer, Lyon).

Knox, G. (1963). Detection of low intensity epidemicity. Application to cleft lip and palate. *British Journal of Preventive and Social Medicine*, **17**, 121−127.

Lichtenstein, P., *et al.* (2000). Environmental and heritable factors in the causation of cancer − analyses of cohorts of twins from Sweden, Denmark, and Finland. *New England Journal of Medicine*, **343**, 78−85.

MacMahon, B. and Trichopoulos, D. (1996). *Epidemiology: Principles and Methods* (Little, Brown, Boston).

MacMahon, B. *et al.* (1960). *Epidemiologic Methods* (Little, Brown, Boston).

Miettinen, O. S. (1985). *Theoretical Epidemiology: Principles of Occurrence Research in Medicine.* (Wiley, New York).

Morgenstern, H. (1982). Uses of ecologic analysis in epidemiologic research. *American Journal of Public Health*, **72**, 1336–1344.

Parkin, D. M., *et al.* (eds) (1992). *Cancer Incidence in Five Continents*, Vol. VI. IARC Scientific Publication No. 120 (International Agency for Research on Cancer, Lyon).

Rothman, K. J. (ed.) (1988). *Causal Inference* (Epidemiology Resources, Chestnut Hill, MA).

Rothman, K. J. (1990). No adjustments are needed for multiple comparisons. *Epidemiology*, **1**, 43–56.

Rothman, K. J. and Greenland, S. (1998). *Modern Epidemiology*, 2nd edn (Lippincott-Raven, Philadelphia, PA).

Sacks, H. S., *et al.* (1987). Meta-analysis of randomized controlled trials. *New England Journal of Medicine*, **316**, 450–455.

Scotto, J., *et al.* (1982). Solar radiation. In: Schottenfeld, D. and Fraumeni, J. F. (eds), *Cancer Epidemiology and Prevention*. 254–276 (W. B. Saunders, Philadelphia, PA).

Shapiro, S. (1994). Meta-analysis/Shmeta-analysis. *American Journal of Epidemiology*, **140**, 771–778.

Stuver, S. O. (1998). Towards global control of liver cancer? *Seminars in Cancer Biology*, **8**, 299–306.

Tomatis, L. (ed.) (1990). *Cancer: Causes, Occurrence and Control*. IARC Scientific Publication No. 100 (International Agency for Research on Cancer, Lyon).

Trichopoulos, D. (1994). Risk of lung cancer from passive smoking. *Principles and Practice of Oncology: PPO Updates*, **8**, 1–8.

US Department of Health, Education and Welfare (1964). *Smoking and Health. Report of the Advisory Committee to the Surgeon General of the Public Health Service*. Publication 1103 (US Government Printing Office, Washington, DC).

Wacholder, S., *et al.* (1992a). Selection of controls in case-control studies: I. Principles. *American Journal of Epidemiology*, **135**, 1019–1028.

Wacholder, S., *et al.* (1992b). Selection of controls in case-control studies: II. Types of controls. *American Journal of Epidemiology*, **135**, 1029–1041.

Wacholder, S., *et al.* (1992c). Selection of controls in case-control studies: III. Design options. *American Journal of Epidemiology*, **135**, 1042–1050.

Ziegler, R. G., *et al.* (1993). Migration patterns and breast cancer risk in Asian-American women. *Journal of the National Cancer Institute*, **85**, 1819–1827.

FURTHER READING

Authors' Work

Adami, H.-O. and Trichopoulos, D. (eds) (1998). Progress and enigmas in cancer epidemiology. *Seminars in Cancer Biology*, **8**, 215–314.

Adami, H.-O. and Trichopoulos, D. (1999). Epidemiology, medicine and public health. *International Journal of Epidemiology*, **28**, s1005–s1008.

MacMahon, B. and Trichopoulos, D. (1996). *Epidemiology: Principles and Methods*, 2nd edn (Little, Brown, Boston).

Saracci, R. and Trichopoulos, D. (1996). Aetiological leads. In: Peckham, M., *et al.* (eds), *Oxford Textbook of Oncology*. 167–174 (Oxford University Press, Oxford).

Trichopoulos, D. and Adami, H.-O. (2001). Concepts in cancer epidemiology and etiology. In: Adami, H.-O., *et al.* (eds), *Cancer Epidemiology* (Oxford University Press, Oxford).

Trichopoulos, D., *et al.* (1997). Epidemiology of cancer. In: DeVita, V. T., Jr, *et al.* (eds), *Cancer: Principles and Practice of Oncology*, 5th edn. 231–257 (Lippincott-Raven, Philadelphia, PA).

Other Publications

Breslow, N. E. and Day, N. E. (1980). *Statistical Methods in Cancer Research. Vol. I. The Analysis of Case-control Studies*. IARC Scientific Publication No. 32, 5–338 (International Agency for Research on Cancer, Lyon).

Breslow, N. E. and Day, N. E. (1987). *Statistical Methods in Cancer Research. Vol. II. The Design and Analysis of Cohort Studies*. IARC Scientific Publication No. 82, 1–406 (International Agency for Research on Cancer, Lyon).

Hennekens, C. H. and Buring, J. E. (1987). *Epidemiology in Medicine* (Little, Brown, Boston).

Rothman, K. J. and Greenland, S. (1998). *Modern Epidemiology*, 2nd edn (Lippincott-Raven, Philadelphia, PA).

Schottenfeld, D. and Fraumeni, J. F. (eds) (1996). *Cancer Epidemiology and Prevention*, 2nd edn (Oxford University Press, New York).

dos Santos Silva, I. (1999). *Cancer Epidemiology: Principles and Methods* (International Agency for Research on Cancer, Lyon).

Szklo, M. and Javier Nieto, F. (1999). *Epidemiology: Beyond the Basics* (Aspen, Gaithersburg, MD).

Tomatis, L. (ed.) (1990). *Cancer: Causes, Occurrence and Control*. IARC Scientific Publication No. 100 (International Agency for Research on Cancer, Lyon).

Walker, A. M. (1991). *Observation and Inference: An Introduction to the Methods of Epidemiology* (Epidemiology Resources, Boston).

Chapter 20

Mechanisms of Chemical Carcinogenesis

Nigel J. Gooderham and Paul L. Carmichael
Imperial College School of Medicine, London, UK

CONTENTS

INTRODUCTION

The concept that chemicals can cause cancer (chemical carcinogenesis) has been accepted for some time. As long ago as 1775, the English physician Sir Percival Pott noted the incidence of scrotal cancer in chimney sweeps and perceptively suggested that the disease was related to their occupation. He further suggested that it was soot that was the cause of their disease. Since this observation, the number of chemicals strongly associated with the development of cancer has substantially increased. Other notable historical examples include the development of skin tumours associated with oils and bladder cancers due to exposure to dyes and pigments. A more detailed account of the history of chemicals and cancer can be found in Lawley (1994).

The list of chemicals that can induce cancer is extensive; they can show high specificity for the organ in which the tumour is induced and in the molecular mechanisms through which they operate. Early observations of chemical carcinogenicity were often made using crude mixtures such as coal tars and subsequent studies have shown that these mixtures comprise a complex range of chemical entities. Chemical carcinogens include organics and inorganics, fibres and particulates, and biologically active materials such as hormones. The organic chemicals probably comprise the largest group.

CHEMICALS CAN CAUSE CANCER

Many chemicals are direct-acting carcinogens yet many more require metabolic activation in order to exert their carcinogenicity. In most cases it is chemical reactivity that dictates this carcinogenicity and therefore factors and environments, which influence this reactivity, are important in the nature and site of the carcinogenic action.

Organic Chemical Carcinogens

The diversity of organic chemicals that have been shown to cause cancer is considerable. Notable examples are shown in **Figure 1**. They range from low molecular mass simple halogenated hydrocarbons to very complex multiheterocyclic molecules. All possess, or have the potential to possess, key functionalities that are intimately involved in their carcinogenic action. Some of the first chemicals found to be carcinogens were the polycyclic aromatic hydrocarbons (PAHs). These chemicals are major components of coal tars and soots and application to the skin of rodents showed them to be powerful carcinogens. Many of these PAHs have been identified (**Figure 2**) and include benzo[*a*]pyrene, dibenz[*a,c*]anthracene, 3-methylcholanthrene, 7,12-dimethylbenz[*a*]anthracene and chrysene. All are multi-ring aromatic chemicals composed of carbon and hydrogen. Substituted PAHs in which a nitro or amino or azo function is incorporated into the structure are also carcinogenic; examples include 4-dimethylaminoazobenzene, 2-naphthylamine, benzidine and 1-nitropyrene (**Figures 1** and **2**). However, aromaticity is not an obligatory feature for chemicals that cause cancer and a group of lower molecular mass chemicals, the nitrosoamines and nitrosoamides, are equally potent carcinogens.

Other examples of cancer-causing organic chemicals include aflatoxins, which are generated by the mould *Aspergillus flavus*. Indeed, aflatoxin B_1 is one of the most potent hepatocarcinogens known, capable of inducing tumours in rodents, fish, birds and primates, including

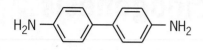

Benzidine

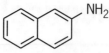

2-Naphthylamine

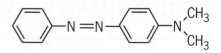

4-Dimethylaminoazobenzene

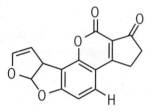

2-Acetylaminofluorene

Ethyl carbamate

Dimethylnitrosamine

Ethionine

Vinyl chloride

Methylnitrosourea

Aflatoxin B$_1$

Nitrogen mustard

β-Propiolactone

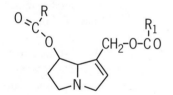

Pyrrolizidine alkaloids

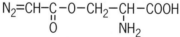

Azaserine

Dimethylhydrazine

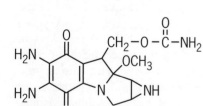

Mitomycin C

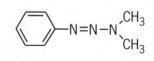

3,3-Dimethyl-1-phenyltriazine

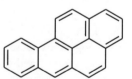

Benzo[a]pyrene

Figure 1 Examples of chemicals that can cause cancer.

humans. The mould is a contaminant of many food crops (e.g. grains and peanuts), especially when stored under warm, humid conditions, and is a significant hazard in many parts of the world, especially Africa and Asia (Wogan *et al.*, 1992). However, the aflatoxins are not the only naturally produced organic carcinogens that present a hazard to humans; other notorious examples include hydrazine derivatives in certain mushrooms, cycasin from

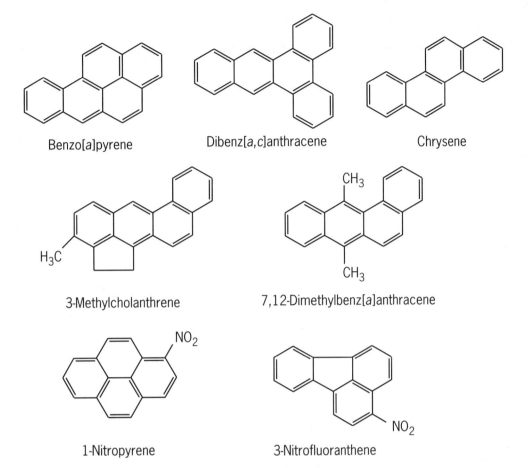

Figure 2   Examples of carcinogenic polycyclic aromatic hydrocarbons.

cycad nuts, pyrrolizidine alkaloids and ptaquiloside in various plants (see the chapter *Dietary Genotoxins and Cancer*).

Although most of the aforementioned chemicals require metabolic activation in order to exert their carcinogenicity, there are many examples of chemical carcinogens whose structure incorporates inherently reactive functional groups. Such chemicals are direct-acting carcinogens (see **Figure 3**). In each case, the reactivity of the key functional group enables the chemical to damage directly DNA, proteins and other cellular macromolecules.

Inorganic Chemical Carcinogens

Although the carcinogenic potential of many elements has not been adequately evaluated, several are known to be carcinogenic in laboratory animals and good epidemiological data support their potential as human carcinogens. Notable examples include compounds of cadmium, chromium and nickel that have all been shown to cause cancer in animals and are established human carcinogens with documented industrial exposure. In contrast, in the case of arsenic, there is significant evidence for it being a human carcinogen despite negative animal data. Other elements that are clearly carcinogenic in animals and therefore are

suspect human carcinogens include beryllium, cobalt, iron, lead, titanium and zinc (Sky-Peck, 1986).

Inert Chemical Carcinogens

Some chemicals are carcinogenic even in the absence of chemical reactivity; their physical presence in tissues can be enough to form a tumour. Implantation of certain plastics and fibres into animals can induce sarcomas, usually at the site of implantation. It is the physical size and nature of the material that appear to be important for the development of cancer and not the chemical composition (Brand *et al.*, 1975). Although rodents are susceptible to these agents, other species are resistant, e.g. the guinea pig, and interestingly, implantation of plastic and other inert materials into humans, in the form of prostheses, rarely generates a sarcoma. Of more importance to humans are the fibres that are known to cause cancer; asbestos is notorious in this respect and human exposure results in mesothelioma and bronchiogenic carcinoma. The development of asbestos-induced neoplastic disease is related to the crystal structure and dimensions of the fibres rather than the chemical composition of the material (Lippmann, 1993). Fibres that are about 5 μm in length with a diameter of <0.5 μm induce mesothelioma, whereas

$$ClCH_2-O-CH_2Cl$$

Bis(chloromethyl) ether

$$H_2N-NH_2$$

Hydrazine

$$BrCH_2-CH_2Br$$

Ethylene dibromide

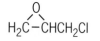

Dimethyl sulfate

Methyl methanesulfonate

$$\overset{\overset{\displaystyle NO}{\displaystyle |}}{H_3C-N-CONH_2}$$

N-Methylnitrosourea

$$\overset{\overset{\displaystyle NO}{\displaystyle |}\ \overset{\displaystyle NH}{\displaystyle ||}}{H_3C-N-CNHNO_2}$$

N-Methyl-N'-nitro-N-nitrosoguanidine

$$\overset{\overset{\displaystyle O}{\diagup\!\diagdown}}{H_2C-CHCH_2Cl}$$

Epichlorohydrin

$$\overset{\overset{\displaystyle O}{\diagup\!\diagdown}}{H_2C-CH_2}$$

Ethylene oxide

$$\overset{\overset{\displaystyle H}{\overset{\displaystyle N}{\diagup\!\diagdown}}}{H_2C-CH_2}$$

Ethylenimine

$$CH_3-N\overset{\diagup CH_2CH_2Cl}{\diagdown CH_2CH_2Cl}$$

Nitrogen mustard

$$S\overset{\diagup CH_2CH_2Cl}{\diagdown CH_2CH_2Cl}$$

Sulfur mustard

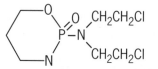

Cyclophosphamide

Benzyl chloride

$$\overset{H_2C-CH_2}{\underset{O-C\diagdown\!_O}{|\qquad|}}$$

β-Propionolactone

Figure 3 Examples of direct-acting chemical carcinogens.

fibres that are $\geq 10\,\mu m$ in length induce carcinoma. Since not all asbestos fibres conform to these dimensions, different types and sources of asbestos vary in their carcinogenic potency.

Hormonal Chemical Carcinogens

The first link between hormones and carcinogenesis can probably be ascribed to the Italian physician Ramazzini, who in the eighteenth century observed an increased incidence of breast cancer among nuns. It is now well established that never having children is associated with an increased breast cancer risk and, over a century after Ramazzini's observations, George Thomas Beatson (1896) pointed out that a relationship existed between breast cancer and the ovary, the major site for the production of oestrogen. Indeed, the case for endogenous oestrogens in cancer promotion is well established but increasingly concern has arisen regarding external phyto- and xeno-oestrogens in our environment and the role they may play in carcinogenesis. Furthermore, the administration of chemicals that alter the synthesis or secretion of hormones can lead to neoplastic disease. For example, chemical modulation of thyroid and pituitary growth hormone can lead to neoplasms and changes in human growth hormone, transforming or insulin-like growth factors and testosterone (**Figure 4**) are all associated with carcinogenicity under circumstances where their normal function is interfered with. In each case there is an interruption to the normal hormonal relationship experienced by the target organ. An increasing number of synthetic compounds that possess steroid hormone and antisteroid hormone activity

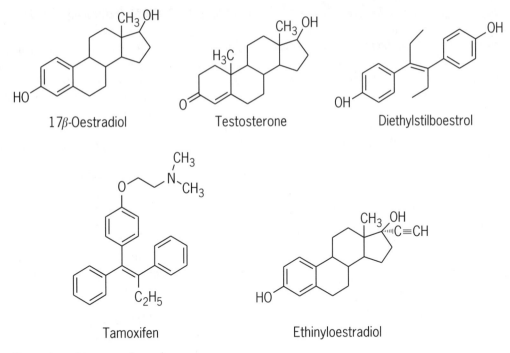

Figure 4   Examples of hormonal carcinogens.

METABOLISM OF CHEMICAL CARCINOGENS

have been found to be chemical carcinogens (**Figure 4**). One of particular interest has been the highly effective anti-breast cancer agent tamoxifen, which also possesses carcinogenic activity in the uterus in a small proportion of women using the drug (Carmichael, 1998).

METABOLISM OF CHEMICAL CARCINOGENS

Many chemicals require metabolic activation in order to exert their carcinogenic potential. The pioneering studies of Elizabeth and James Miller showed that metabolic activation of azo dyes led to their covalent binding to cellular macromolecules. They went on to show with the model carcinogen 2-acetylaminofluorene that hydroxylation of the amide nitrogen generated a metabolite that was more carcinogenic than the parent molecule. Subsequently it was found that these primary products of metabolism, although activated, could be further metabolized to even more reactive derivatives (Miller, J. A., 1970 and Miller, E. C., 1978). It was the Millers who understood that these products were potent electrophiles and comprehensively described their rapid covalent interactions with cellular macromolecules (Miller and Miller, 1981). This led to their proposal that chemical carcinogens that require such metabolic conversion in order to exert their carcinogenic effect should be called procarcinogens and that their highly reactive electrophilic metabolites were ultimate carcinogens. This further led to the concept of

proximal carcinogens (e.g. *N*-hydroxy-2-acetylaminofluorene), which were intermediates between the parental procarcinogen and the ultimate carcinogenic metabolite. Although this concept has now been with us for more than two decades, the structure of many ultimate carcinogens is still not thoroughly understood and in many cases may comprise a number of different metabolites of the same parent compound.

There are a number of these metabolic pathways that together are part of a more extensive defence system, the overall role of which is ideally to process and detoxify noxious chemicals. Enzyme-catalysed and diverse in nature, these reactions have been defined and split into what are called phase I and phase II metabolism (Williams, 1971). Phase I can be separated into oxidation, reduction and hydrolytic reactions and phase II comprises a series of conjugation reactions in which a polar endogenous group is added to the xenobiotic chemical. The overall effect of this biochemistry is to convert xenobiotics, which are often lipophilic molecules, into more polar water-soluble and therefore more readily excreted products. Generally, phase I reactions unmask or introduce a functional group into the molecule and phase II metabolism conjugates the derivative with a polar water-soluble endogenous molecule, that is often acidic in nature. However, it is these same pathways of detoxification metabolism that can inadvertently bioactivate chemical carcinogens. For a more detailed description of phase I and phase II metabolism reactions and associated enzymology, the reader is directed to Jakoby *et al*. (1982), Parkinson (1996) and Gonzalez (1989).

The majority of procarcinogens are activated by mechanisms involving two-electron-mediated metabolic reactions primarily catalysed by the mixed function oxidase enzyme systems, often involving cytochrome P-450 enzymes. However, a number of one-electron reactions are known to be capable of activating xenobiotics in co-oxidation processes. For example, PAHs have been found to be bioactivated during the synthesis of prostaglandins from arachidonic acid. A key enzyme in this process is prostaglandin H synthetase, which catalyses the oxygenation of arachidonic acid to the endoperoxide prostaglandin G_2 and also has peroxidase activity, whereby it reduces the hydroperoxide prostaglandin G_2 to the alcohol prostaglandin H_2. In these reactions the peroxidase activity of the enzyme yields a free radical product that can donate electrons to xenobiotics (Eling et al., 1990). Other enzyme systems which can participate in these one-electron activation reactions include constitutive peroxidases such as myeloperoxidase and lactoperoxidase, both of which are capable of activating xenobiotics. Although these co-oxidation pathways are not as quantitatively important as the mixed-function oxidase activities, their presence in tissues that lack mixed function oxidase activity can be an important contributor to xenobiotic activation.

CHEMICALS CAN DAMAGE DNA

As discussed above, the metabolism of chemical agents to reactive species is a common feature of carcinogenicity. Once bioactivated (often via proximal carcinogens or intermediate chemicals formed on the way to the creation of the ultimate carcinogen), for most classical chemical carcinogens, some form of DNA damage is the norm. Because of this DNA-damaging activity, such agents are known as genetic or genotoxic carcinogens. However, this is not the case for all chemical carcinogens and some agents bring about carcinogenicity through no direct alteration or damage to the DNA. These agents can be classified as a separate group known as epigenetic carcinogens and their effects are commonly mediated through other changes involving growth factor expression or complex effects on signal transduction mechanisms (see the chapter *Non-genotoxic Causes of Cancer*). Some of the common ways in which chemical agents may be genotoxic are summarized in **Figure 5**.

The nature of carcinogen damage to DNA is dependent upon the chemical agent and its metabolism, but can often include simple changes to the DNA such as the hydroxylation of the bases. Products of such damage

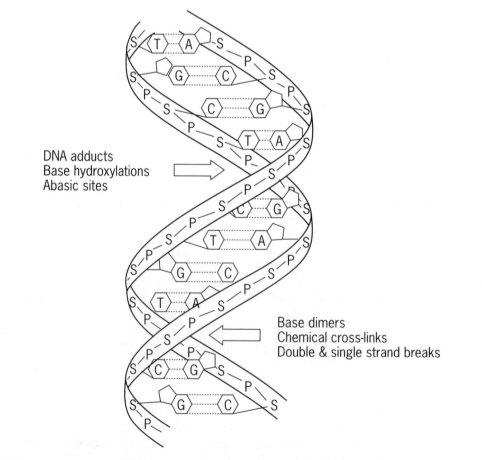

DNA adducts
Base hydroxylations
Abasic sites

Base dimers
Chemical cross-links
Double & single strand breaks

Figure 5   Carcinogen damage to DNA.

include 8-hydroxydeoxyguanosine (formed by the hydroxylation of guanine bases), which is considered to be a mutagenic lesion in DNA, and believed to be formed by attack of the DNA by highly reactive free radicals. Free radicals are a common product of a number of chemical carcinogens, which either carry an unpaired (and so-called radical) electron on the molecule, or are formed from oxygen (oxygen free radicals) via metabolism. Hydroxylations and other more extensive radical damage may result in the loss of bases and the creation of abasic sites, either apurinic or apyrimidinic. Free radical attack of DNA is also responsible for the formation of genotoxic strand breaks in the DNA. These can be formed at either one strand or may span both sides of the sugar–phosphate backbone resulting in a double-strand break.

One of the most important ways, however, in which genotoxic carcinogens may bring about DNA damage is through a chemical binding directly to the DNA. For some small molecules this binding may be considered an alkylation, although some longer chain molecules are capable of forming cross-links across the bases. For many chemical carcinogens the product of their bioactivation (via the creation of an electron- and DNA-seeking electrophile) is the formation of what are known as 'DNA adducts.' These covalent modifications of the DNA, normally at the bases, are generally considered to be one of the primary initiating events (see below) in chemical carcinogenesis and they are formed by many of the agents mentioned above, including PAHs, aflatoxins and aromatic amines. With chronic exposure to such genotoxic agents, DNA adducts may reach steady-state levels in target tissues. During cell replication the DNA adducts can result directly in mutations in genes that control cell growth and thus lead to neoplasia. The levels of these DNA adducts appear to be dose related and are generally predictive of tumour incidence across species. Thus, the accurate estimation and identification of human carcinogen-induced DNA adducts is one of the most important predictive tools or biomarker for the assessment of human cancer risk (discussed in the chapter The Formation of DNA Adducts).

The position and nature of carcinogen-induced DNA adducts dictate the type of mutation that can result (Dogliotti, 1996). For example, small alkylating agents will adduct to guanine at the N7 position owing to the highly nucleophilic nature of the site. In contrast, other more bulky aromatic amine agents will attack the purine ring preferentially, such as the C8 position of guanine and others such as diol epoxides of PAHs bind to the N2 and N6 positions. The adduct products of these reactions are converted to mutations when the cell attempts to repair the damage or replicate itself. These include point mutations, frameshifts involving loss or gain of either a single or multiple bases, chromosomal aberrations, anueploidy or polyploidy. Once introduced, the mutation becomes fixed within the DNA sequence and therefore heritable. The type of mutation that a chemical induces is dependent upon the way in which the chemical interacts with the DNA. The site of chemical attack is important but so is the influence of the bulk of the chemical and the way in which it can influence the structure of the DNA. For example, the amide 2-acetylaminofluorene differs from the amine 2-aminofluorene only by the presence of a carbonyl group. Both chemicals are metabolically activated via their N-hydroxy derivatives, yet the bulk of the amide–DNA adduct intercalates within the DNA, distorting the helix whereas the bulk of the amine–DNA adduct remains on the helix exterior. The consequence of these different arrangements is that the amide adduct results in frameshift mutations whereas the amine causes transversions.

The Fate of Carcinogen DNA Damage

Regardless of the specific nature of the carcinogen damage to DNA, it is important to note that aberrations at the primary sequence may not necessarily result in cancer. Indeed, there are at least three possible fates for such carcinogen damage. These are summarized in **Figure 6**.

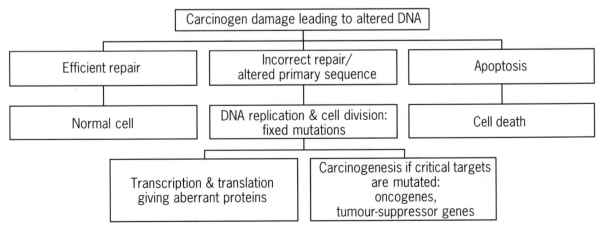

Figure 6   Possible fates for carcinogen-damaged DNA.

In some circumstances, the damage to the genetic machinery by a potential chemical carcinogen may be so extensive or be recognized as so crucial that cells initiate the process of apoptosis or programmed cell death. This behaviour and the involvement of such important proteins as p53 are discussed in detail elsewhere in this book, but through this activity, affected cells may effectively commit suicide and thus prevent the formation of potentially cancerous clones. However, if the carcinogen-altered DNA remains unchanged or if repair of the DNA is incorrect, then following DNA replication and cell division, daughter cells may contain fixed mutations. Transcription and translation of mutated genes in daughter cells will give rise to incorrect or inappropriate proteins being produced but carcinogenesis will not occur unless critical gene targets in the DNA are mutated (see later).

It follows, therefore, that repair of DNA-carcinogen damage in cells should ideally be fast, efficient and highly accurate. Indeed, mammalian cells invest a great deal of effort in order to achieve this and there are many genes and enzymes involved in maintaining the fidelity of the DNA sequence. These include enzymes that can bring about the reversal of DNA damage or repair the DNA through either base excision or nucleotide excision.

The Repair of Chemical-damaged DNA

Clearly the most straightforward way for a cell to repair a gene lesion is to remove it directly and thus regenerate the normal base at its correct position. One example of such direct removal involves the photodamage to DNA caused by ultraviolet (UV) radiation. UV radiation creates a number of photoproducts in DNA including the formation of mutagenic pyrimidine dimers between neighbouring thymine bases. Of these, the cyclobutane–pyrimidine photodimer can be repaired by a photoreactivating enzyme, although a 6–4-photoproduct cannot be repaired. The enzyme operates by binding to the photodimer and splits it back to the original bases, although the enzyme requires light energy and hence cannot work in the dark. Another enzyme involved in the direct removal of DNA damage is alkyltransferase, which can remove certain alkyl groups from altered guanine bases, although if the levels of alkylation are high enough then the enzyme activity can become saturated.

There are several pathways for excision of altered bases, often with the concomitant removal of neighbouring bases. Some systems recognize any lesion that causes a significant distortion of the DNA double helix and creates endonucleolytic cuts, several bases away and on either side of the lesion. The simple loss of a purine or pyrimidine may also initiate endonuclease cutting. The single-stranded DNA containing the damaged or missing base can then be removed and the short gap is filled in by DNA polymerases. Through this form of excision repair, bulky DNA adducts formed from the binding of PAHs and aflatoxins can be removed, as can certain UV-damaged bases. For some forms of damage (e.g. alkylation), DNA glycosylases remove just the altered base, leaving an apurinic or apyrimidinic (AP) site. The AP site is subsequently excised by endonucleases as above. Some repair pathways are capable of recognizing errors even after DNA replication has taken place. One of these systems, termed the mismatch repair system, can detect mismatches that occur during DNA replication (Friedberg, 1985). (See also chapter on *Genomic Instability and DNA Repair*.)

CHEMICALS CAN INDUCE MUTATIONS

The interaction of a chemical with DNA is not, in itself, a mutagenic event. The interaction of a xenobiotic with DNA can lead to mutagenesis due to attempts by the cell to repair the damaged DNA or during replication of the damaged DNA. Either way, a mistake may be made in which an inappropriate base is inserted or is lost (or a series of bases are inserted or are lost) from the region of DNA, with the consequence that a mutation is acquired, which is heritable. If the mutation occurs in a crucial piece of DNA, i.e. within a structural sequence that codes for an important gene controlling cell growth or a sequence that regulates the expression of such a gene, then the consequences may be disastrous. However, despite the human genome (some three billion bases) coding for approximately 28 000 genes, the majority of the DNA in a cell does not code for crucial information and mutations are usually not significant. However, the threat to the cell by DNA-damaging influences is substantial and it is not surprising that numerous proteins are involved in the detection and repair of damaged DNA.

Since mutation is evidence that a chemical is capable of inducing heritable genetic change, and since tumours often contain characteristic mutational patterns or mutational spectra in critical genes, the notion arises that the carcinogenic process is heavily dependent upon the acquisition of mutation in key genes (Harris, 1991). Furthermore, the observation that acquisition of specific types of mutation in such key genes is consistently associated with the formation of tumours, strengthens the argument that these changes are a driver of tumorigenesis. Although it is often difficult to detect and evaluate cancer-causing mutations in primary target cells and tissues, it is relatively straightforward to detect and identify mutations in surrogate reporter genes, and from information such as mutation frequency, nature and sequence context, the potential for a particular chemical to participate in the cancer process can be evaluated. This realization has driven the development of assays designed to evaluate mutagenic potential (and therefore carcinogenic potential). Currently systems are available to assess not only crude mutagenic activity, but also the likelihood of specific transitions, transversions (point mutations) or deletions or insertions (frameshift mutations) or clastogenicity or aneuploidy. Since each of these types of DNA damage are detectable in tumours, the ability of a xenobiotic to induce such damage and therefore the relevance of the chemical to the neoplastic process can be assessed. For a more detailed description, see the chapter *Short-Term Testing for Genotoxicity*.

In vivo chemical-induced mutation is often subtle and insidious and it is usually difficult to ascribe particular mutations with exposure to a specific chemical, because evidence of the chemical is removed (loss of the DNA-chemical adduct) by introduction of the mutation. However, different classes of reactive chemicals appear to have a preference for individual DNA bases. For example, activated aromatic amines and PAHs appear to target guanine bases preferentially, probably owing to the fact that guanine is the most basic of the four nucleic acid bases. Some activated xenobiotics tend to induce transversions whereas others cause transitions or deletions. This has led to the concept of mutational fingerprints in which a specific activated xenobiotic is thought to induce a particular type of mutagenic response with a frequency which is greater than that expected by chance alone (Thilly, 1990; Aguilar et al., 1993; Yadollahi-Farsani et al., 1996). The concept of mutational fingerprints raises the prospect of identifying chemical causality in the occurrence of a particular type of mutational event, despite the fact that direct evidence for involvement (presence of the chemical) is not available.

The cooked food-borne carcinogen 2-amino-1-methyl-6-phenylimidazo[4,5-*b*]pyridine (PhIP) offers an example of a chemical whose mutagenic effects are characteristic and predictable (see **Table 1**). Numerous *in vitro* studies have shown this chemical to be an effective bacterial and mammalian cell mutagen (Gooderham et al., 1997). DNA sequence analysis of PhIP-induced mutation indicates that activation of this promutagen to damaging electrophilic species results in predominantly guanine-based mutation events. Several studies have shown the spectrum of these mutations to comprise mainly G to T transversions, with a few guanine transitions, and a significant percentage of frameshift mutations involving loss of G–C base pairs but not A–T base pairs (**Table 1**). Interestingly, PhIP-induced mutation appears to involve little or no mutation at A–T base pairs. It has also been commonly observed that PhIP-induced guanine mutation occurs primarily on the non-transcribed DNA strand, implying that damage induced on the transcribed strand is preferentially and successfully repaired. Additionally, detailed examination of the sequence context of PhIP induced mutation, shows that there appears to be a preferred motif (5′ GGGA 3′) within which the mutations are detected. It has been suggested that collectively, these observations describe a PhIP 'mutation fingerprint' and that the appearance of such a combination of mutational changes could be evidence for involvement of the chemical in their causation (Gooderham et al., 1996). In the case of PhIP, the nature and preferences of its DNA reactive species (PhIP nitrenium ion) tend to support the type of mutagenic outcome associated with the chemical. PhIP activated by cytochrome P-450-1 family enzymes is oxidised to the *N*-hydroxy derivative. Subsequent esterification of the *N*-hydroxy metabolite generates the acetoxy or sulfoxy derivatives, which spontaneously decompose, forming the highly reactive nitrenium ion (see **Figure 7**). The nitrenium ion shows preference for attacking guanine bases leading to the deoxyguanine-C8-PhIP (dG-C8-PhIP) and dG-N2-PhIP products. The inherent basicity of the purine molecule is a likely driver of the reaction and therefore it is no surprise that monotonous runs of guanine present as highly susceptible targets.

As discussed, the mechanisms whereby mutations arise and their chemical nature can vary considerably. In some instances, adducted DNA can base pair with its correct complementary base, apparently unaffected by the adduct whereas in other cases base pairing becomes degenerate and inappropriate bases are used during repair or replication. If the adduct is not correctly repaired, then replication can result in a mutation being fixed. In other instances, the presence of the adduct physically blocks DNA synthesis, effectively terminating the process at that point. Since such blocks would be lethal, the cell uses bypass mechanisms to overcome the block and adenine is frequently used to pair with the damaged (adducted) base. If adenine is not the original complementary base, then a mutation has been introduced into the sequence.

The ability of chemicals to induce mutation is an important aspect of their involvement in carcinogenesis. This is particularly true for the initiation process but it also

Table 1 PhIP induces a mutation fingerprint *in vitro* and *in vivo*

Mutation type	Percentage of mutations					
	hprt[a]	hprt[b]	dhfr[c]	lacZ[d]	lacI[e]	lacI[f]
Base substitutions	83	89	80	66	71	71
At GC pairs						
GC→TA	63	56	65	33	49	43
GC→AT	15	27	5	25	10	10
GC→CG	5	6	5	5	9	15
At AT pairs	0	0	5	3	3	3
Single bp frameshifts	13	9	5	22	26	22
(GC bp)	13	9	5	20	26	21
(AT bp)	0	0	0	2	0	1
Other mutations	4	2	15	12	3	8

[a] hprt gene in V79 Chinese hamster fibroblast cells (Yadollahi-Farsani et al., 1996)
[b] hprt gene in TK6 human lymphoblastoid cells (Morganthaler and Holzhauser, 1995).
[c] dhfr gene in CHO Chinese hamster ovary cells (Carothers et al., 1994).
[d] lacI gene in Muta™mouse mice large intestine (Lynch et al., 1998).
[e] lacZ gene in Big Blue mice large intestine (Okonogi et al., 1997).
[f] lacZ gene in Big Blue rat mammary gland (Okochi et al., 1999).

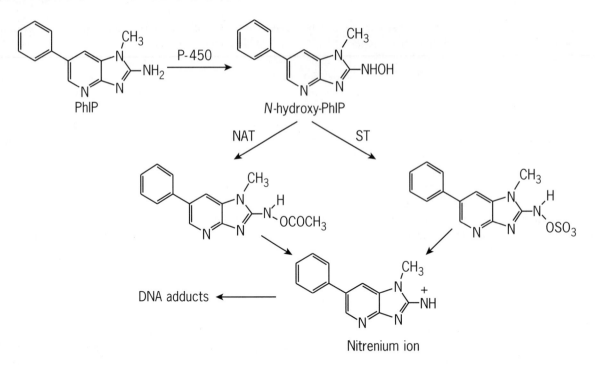

Figure 7   The metabolic activation of 2-amino-1-methyl-6-phenylimidazo[4,5-*b*]pyridine (PhIP). P-450, cytochrome P-450; NAT, *N*-acetyltransferase; ST, sulfur transferase.

contributes to promotion and progression stages during which cells continue to accumulate genetic damage at key gene sites (see later).

EXAMPLES OF CHEMICAL CARCINOGENS AND THEIR METABOLISM

2-Acetylaminofluorene

2-Acetylaminofluorene (2-AAF) is a potent mutagen and carcinogen, which induces tumours in a number of species in the liver, bladder and kidney. As previously mentioned, metabolism of this compound is the key to its carcinogenicity. 2-AAF is a substrate for cytochrome P-450 enzyme, of which there is a superfamily in mammals (Gonzalez, 1989; Porter and Coon, 1991). The product of this metabolism (**Figure 8**) is *N*-hydroxy-2-acetylaminofluorene (*N*-OH-2-AAF), which is a more potent carcinogen that the parent molecule. The formation of *N*-hydroxy metabolites has been found for many aromatic amine, amide, nitro and nitroso compounds, many of which exert toxicity through this type of derivative. For nitro and nitroso compounds, the *N*-hydroxy metabolite is formed by reduction rather than oxidation.

In the case of 2-AAF, the *N*-hydroxy metabolite is not the ultimate carcinogen but a proximal carcinogen, and this compound undergoes several enzymic and non-enzymic rearrangements. The compound can be *O*-acetylated by cytosolic *N*-acetyltransferase enzyme to yield the *N*-acetyl-*N*-acetoxy derivative, which can spontaneously rearrange to form the arylamidonium ion and a carbonium ion and interact directly with DNA to produce DNA adducts. In addition to esterification by acetylation, the *N*-OH-2-AAF can be *O*-sulfated by cytosolic sulfur transferase enzyme giving rise to the *N*-acetyl-*N*-sulfoxy product. This is again unstable and spontaneously generates the arylamidonium ion and carbonium ion, which can adduct to DNA. In addition, the cytosolic *N*,*O*-aryl-hydroxamic acid acyltransferase enzyme catalyses the transfer of the acetyl group from the N atom of the *N*-OH-2-AAF to the O atom of the *N*-OH group to produce *N*-acetoxy-2-aminofluorene (*N*-OH-2-AF). This reactive metabolite spontaneously decomposes to form a nitrenium ion, which will also react with DNA. However, the product of this latter reaction is the deacetylated aminofluorene adduct (see **Figure 8**). The interconversion of amide and amine metabolites of 2-AAF can further occur via the microsomal enzyme deacetylase, producing the *N*-hydroxy metabolite of the amine derivative. Subsequent esterification of the aryl hydroxylamine by sulfur transferase yields the reactive sulfate ester, which also spontaneously decomposes to form the reactive nitrenium ion. The reactive nitrenium, carbonium and arylamidonium ion metabolites of 2-AAF react with the nucleophilic groups in DNA, proteins and endogenous thiols such as glutathione (Miller and Miller, 1981). These interactions can be demonstrated *in vitro* and *in vivo*. Other metabolites such as the *N*,*O*-glucuronide, although not directly activated products, can be important in the carcinogenic process due to the fact that they are capable of degradation to proximal

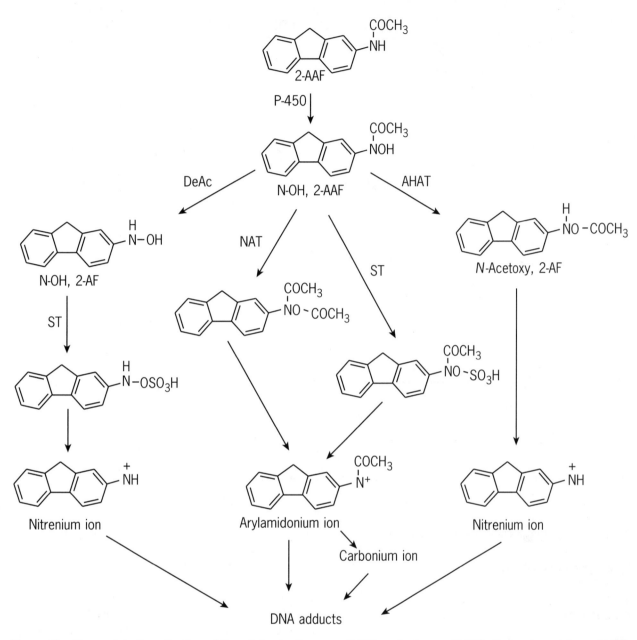

Figure 8   The metabolic activation of 2-acetylaminofluorene. P-450, cytochrome P-450; DeAc, deacetylase; AHAT, *N,O*-arylhydroxamic acid acyltransferase; NAT, *N*-acetyltransferase; ST, sulfur transferase.

N-hydroxy metabolites. Thus, the *N,O*-glucuronide of *N*-OH-2-AAF is less reactive than the acetoxy and sulfate esters, yet it may be involved in the formation of bladder tumours. The mechanism for this is thought to involve degradation of the glucuronide in the bladder due to the acidic pH of urine giving rise to the *N*-hydroxy proximal carcinogen, which is then a substrate for esterification.

N-Hydroxylation of 2-AAF is not the only route of metabolism. Ring hydroxylation, catalysed by cytochrome P-450 enzymes, can also occur which generates metabolites that are not carcinogenic *per se*. These ring-hydroxylated products can be further metabolized to glucuronidated products that are readily excreted.

Benzidine

As can be seen from the example of 2-AAF, the reactivity and carcinogenicity of aromatic amides can involve their conversion to aromatic amines. Another example of this class of chemical carcinogen is benzidine. Benzidine (**Figure 9**) is a carcinogenic bifunctional aromatic amine. It can undergo several routes of metabolism, but with regard to its carcinogenicity, *N*-hydroxylation and *N*-esterification are important. The amine function at both ends of the molecule is subjected to *N*-acetylation to the corresponding amide and they can also be *N*-hydroxyl-ated by cytochrome P-450 enzymes. The resulting aryl

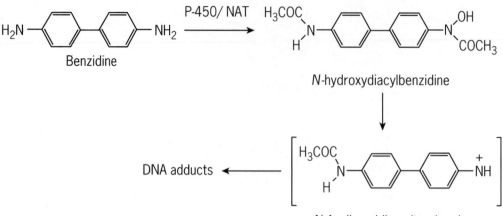

Figure 9   The metabolic activation of benzidine. P-450, cytochrome P-450; NAT, *N-acetyltransferase.*

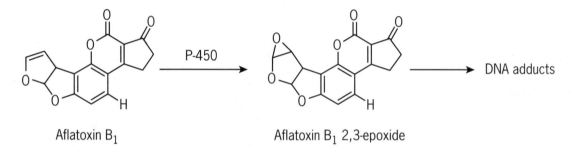

Figure 10   The metabolic activation of aflatoxin B_1. P-450, cytochrome P-450.

hydroxamic acid is unstable and rearranges to form electrophilic nitrenium ion derivatives which will rapidly interact with cellular nucleophiles such as DNA, forming DNA adducts (Searle, 1984).

Aflatoxin B_1

Aflatoxin B_1 is one of a family of mycotoxin contaminants of food crops such as grain and groundnuts. Produced by *Aspergillus flavus*, especially in hot and humid conditions, there are four main types of aflatoxin, B_1, B_2, G_1 and G_2. Aflatoxin B_1 is not only the most toxic, but is also the most carcinogenic. Contamination of food with aflatoxins is a significant problem in parts of Africa and Asia where conditions are particularly favourable for the growth of the *Aspergillus* organism. Indeed, epidemiological studies show that in areas of the world where contamination of food supplies with aflatoxins is high, there is an associated incidence of human hepatocellular carcinoma. Although contamination of grain crops with aflatoxins is not restricted to these parts of the world, in the developed countries food surveillance programmes backed up by tight legislative control regulating maximum permissible levels of aflatoxins in food

crops control human exposure to these potent chemical carcinogens.

The basis of the carcinogenicity of aflatoxin B_1 centres on the carbon–carbon double bond (**Figure 10**) in the terminal furan ring of the molecule (Wogan *et al.*, 1971). The chemical is a substrate for cytochrome P-450 enzymes that oxidize the carbon–carbon double bond. The epoxide product is an electrophile that rapidly reacts with cellular nucleophiles such as DNA and the resulting DNA–aflatoxin B_1 adduct is powerfully promutagenic. This and the fact that it is highly hepatotoxic makes aflatoxin B_1 one of the most powerful carcinogens known.

Benzo[a]pyrene

The PAHs are a large group of environmentally important chemical carcinogens. Benzo[*a*]pyrene is a prominent example of these compounds, being ubiquitous in our environment since it is present in the smoke and fumes from many diverse sources, including cigarettes, exhaust fumes and the burning of many different organic materials including wood and fossil fuels. It is one of the most extensively studied PAHs. It is a substrate for the mixed-function oxidases, being extensively converted to a variety

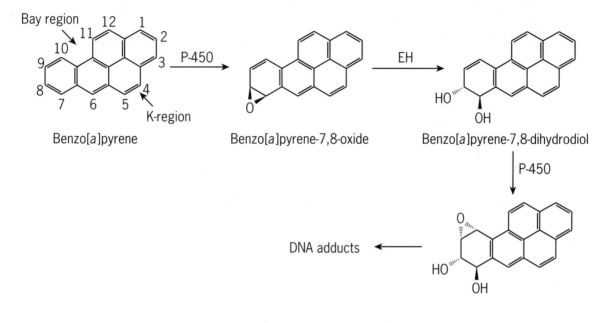

Figure 11   The metabolic activation of benzo[a]pyrene. P-450, cytochrome P-450; EH, epoxide hydrolase.

of different oxidized metabolites including epoxides, phenols, diols, dihydrodiols and their conjugated products, particularly with glutathione, glucuronic acid and sulfate. The genetic toxicity of the PAHs is based around the formation of their epoxides (Sims *et al.*, 1974). For example, with benzo[a]pyrene, cytochrome P-450-1 family enzymes can generate a series of epoxides around the different rings of the molecule, some of which are known to be more carcinogenic than others. Electronically, the most reactive portion of the benzo[a]pyrene molecule is the so-called 'K region' (see **Figure 11**), yet it is epoxides of the 'bay region,' which are thought to be the most tumorigenic. The formation of the ultimate carcinogen of benzo[a]pyrene involves cytochrome P-450-mediated epoxidation at the 7,8-position of the molecule. This epoxide is hydrolysed by the enzyme epoxide hydrolase to form the 7,8-dihydrodiol. The dihydrodiol subsequently undergoes cytochrome P-450-mediated oxidation, forming the 7,8-dihydrodiol-9,10-epoxide, which is thought to be the ultimate carcinogen. However, diastereoisomers of these metabolites are formed metabolically and the (+)-benzo[a]pyrene, (7R,8S)-dihydrodiol-(9S,10R)-epoxide formed by cytochrome P-450 1A1 and epoxide hydrolase generates a species that is more mutagenic than other isomers. Interestingly, although the K region 4,5-epoxide is highly mutagenic, the bay region 7,8-dihydrodiol-9,10-epoxide is carcinogenic whereas the 4,5-epoxide and the 9,10-epoxide are not, indicating the requirement for the specific dihydrodiol formation. Other metabolites of benzo[a]pyrene are known to be cytotoxic and mutagenic, e.g. the 3,6-quinone derivative, but have poorer carcinogenic potential (Conney, 1982).

Dimethylnitrosamine

The nitrosamines are another extensively studied family of chemical carcinogens. Dimethylnitrosamine, representative of this family, is hepatotoxic, mutagenic and carcinogenic, causing kidney tumours with acute exposure and liver tumours after chronic exposure (Magee *et al.*, 1976). Additionally, tumours of the stomach, oesophagus and central nervous system are found. Again, cytochrome P450 enzymes are central to the metabolic activation of dimethylnitrosamine, involving N-demethylation to N-methylnitrosamine. This metabolite rearranges to form methyldiazohydroxide, then methyldiazonium ion and ultimately methyl carbonium ion. It is the methyl carbonium ion that is the DNA-damaging species since it is a highly reactive alkylating agent (see **Figure 12**). The degree of DNA methylation that occurs after exposure to dimethylnitrosamine correlates with susceptibility to tumour formation. The DNA sites that appear to be most sensitive to alkylation are the N^7 position of guanine and to a lesser extent the O^6 position of guanine, but it is the latter site that appears to correlate best with mutagenicity and carcinogenicity. Alkylation at guanine O^6 leads to guanine–thymidine mispairing, causing a GC to AT transition. Paradoxically, acute doses of dimethylnitrosamine cause greater DNA methylation in the liver than the kidney, yet tumours are preferentially found in the kidney. Clearly, although the liver has more metabolic activation capacity, it also has better protective mechanisms. This balance between activation and protective mechanisms is also likely to be a significant factor in the susceptibility

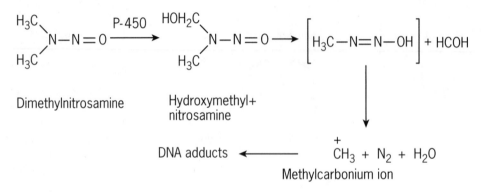

Figure 12   The metabolic activation of dimethylnitrosamine. P-450, cytochrome P-450.

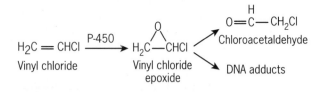

Figure 13   The metabolic activation of vinyl chloride. P-450, cytochrome P-450.

nucleic acids and protein. The available evidence suggests that the epoxide is the predominant species binding to DNA where it reacts with deoxyguanosine at the N^7 position and with RNA to give $1,N^6$-ethenoadenosine and $3,N^4$-ethenocytidine, whereas the chloroacetaldehyde probably binds to protein.

of other organs and tissues to dimethylnitrosamine-induced carcinogenesis.

Vinyl chloride

Vinyl chloride is a simple halogenated allyl compound that is extensively used in the plastics industry, being the starting point for a number of polymer syntheses, particularly the manufacture of poly(vinyl chloride). A gas at room temperature and therefore usually stored as a liquified gas under pressure, the use of the material in an industrial setting is substantial and numerous workers have suffered well-documented accidental occupational exposure, for example being overcome by vinyl chloride solvent narcosis during the cleaning of reaction vessels. Acute exposure to the material is associated with an unusual form of liver tumour, known as haemangiosarcoma, a tumour of reticuloendothelial cells, and not hepatocytes, giving rise to tumours of the hepatic vasculature. This very rare type of liver cancer has only been observed in workers who have been exposed to vinyl chloride.

For tumorigenicity, vinyl chloride requires metabolic activation by cytochrome P-450 enzymes (Bolt, 1988). Oxidation to the epoxide intermediate (**Figure 13**) is the first step resulting in the subsequent formation of chloroacetaldehyde. Although a number of other metabolites are known to be generated, the tumorigenicity of the compound is likely to be dependent upon the epoxide and chloroacetaldehyde metabolites, both of which react with cellular nucleophiles. Subsequently glutathione is depleted and the excess reactive metabolites can then react with

THE BIOLOGY OF CHEMICAL CARCINOGENESIS

The involvement of chemicals in damaging DNA is only one part of their potential role in carcinogenesis. In progressing to the neoplastic state, cells must undergo fundamental changes in their biology and many of these changes can be driven by chemical intervention of essential cellular activity. Current perception of the neoplastic process has been shaped by fundamental studies performed in the 1940s using PAHs with the mouse skin carcinogenesis model (Berenblum and Shubik, 1947). From such studies emerged the concept of the multistep nature of carcinogenesis and the defining of these steps as initiation, promotion and subsequently progression (see **Table 2**).

Initiation

A key feature of the initiation process (**Table 2**) is the requirement for cell replication (Pitot and Dragan, 1996). Once a chemical has damaged DNA by forming an adduct, or inducing a strand break, etc., and provided that the cell recognizes the damage, repair processes will intervene. Should the damage be misrepaired, or not recognized by the cell, then the outcome can be (1) aberrant transcription of the affected DNA if it is a structural gene lesion and on the transcribed strand, (2) altered expression if the damage is located within a regulatory sequence or (3) no effect if the damage is within noncoding or nonregulatory DNA. If the damage is at a critical gene site or extensive, then the cell may opt to apoptose. However, since the cell has two copies of each autosomal gene loci, compensation for the

Table 2   The stages of initiation, promotion and progression

Initiation	Promotion	Progression
Irreversible	Reversible	Irreversible
Cell not morphologically recognizable		Morphologically discernable
Single exposure to chemical is sufficient	Requires multiple exposure to chemical	Driven by multiple and varied exposure
Can occur spontaneously	Endogenous and exogenous chemicals can promote	Cells show altered sensitivity to endogenous chemicals
'Fixed' by cell division	Expanded through cell division	Driven by cell division and migration
No obvious dose–response threshold	Measurable dose–response threshold and maximum effect	Effect of individual chemicals difficult to discern
Involves simple mutation (transitions, transversions, frameshifts)	Does not necessarily involve mutation	Frequently involves complex mutation
Can involve single genes	Often involves multiple genes	Usually involves chromosomal alterations (clastogenicity, aneuploidy, polyploidy)
Proto-oncogenes and tumour-suppressor genes can be mutated	Altered levels of gene expression rather than mutation	Substantial alteration in gene expression due to multiple mutational events
Simple genotypic changes with corresponding phenotype change	Epigenetic phenotype changes	Complex phenotypic change
Limited growth advantage over surrounding cells	Chemical mediated selective growth advantage	Significant growth advantage due to genetic change and environment

(Adapted from Pitot and Dragan, 1996.)

damaged gene is often possible. The only cell directly affected is the recipient of the damage, the initiated cell. However, if division occurs, a daughter cell will inherit the mutation, which becomes fixed irrespective of whether it was misrepaired or remained as an unrepaired adduct in the parent cell, and will be inherited in all future generations of this lineage. If the cell type is generally quiescent, then the effect of the DNA lesion is unlikely to become apparent unless the cell experiences a proliferative stimulus (e.g. by promotion). However, if the cell is normally proliferative (e.g. a stem cell), then there is a much greater chance of neoplastic development, even in the absence of concerted promotion.

Promotion

Once the initiated cell has been encouraged to replicate, the initiated genetic damage is irreversibly fixed. Yet the phenotypic characteristics of the initiated cell remain insidious because it is surrounded by (and perhaps compensated by) normal cells. When the initiated cell is subjected to promotional influences, the effect is to encourage clonal expansion of the initiated cell. A key feature of the promotion response is its reversibility, i.e. if the promoting agent is removed, the initiated cell population is no longer encouraged to proliferate (Boutwell, 1964). The promotional stimulus is usually not a direct interaction of the promoting agent on DNA but acts to encourage growth and proliferation of the cell by exaggerating favourable environmental conditions, especially for initiated cells (see **Table 2**). This can be achieved by chemical interference with normal cellular signal transduction mechanisms with the consequence of enhanced transcription and translation.

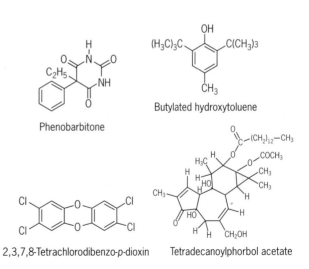

Phenobarbitone

Butylated hydroxytoluene

2,3,7,8-Tetrachlorodibenzo-*p*-dioxin   Tetradecanoylphorbol acetate

Figure 14   Examples of chemical promoters.

A number of well-characterized promoting agents, both natural and xenobiotic, are shown in **Figure 14**. A good example is tetradecanoylphorbol acetate (TPA), a naturally occurring component of croton oil. This chemical interacts with the key protein, protein kinase c, causing enhanced signalling via inositol triphosphate and diacylglycerol pathways, resulting in increased transcription and strong stimulation of growth. 2,3,7,8-Tetrachlorodibenzo-*p*-dioxin (TCDD) is another example of a xenobiotic with exceptional promoting activity, being particularly effective in the liver, lung and skin. There are also a number of very powerful naturally occurring promoting agents including androgens and oestrogens (Taper, 1978). In all cases removal of the agent can rapidly lead to regression of the preneoplastic lesion.

Another important characteristic of promoting agents is the existence of concentration thresholds. Thus a minimum dose of agent is required before effective promotion can be detected, after which there is a dose–response relationship before a maximum response is reached. This latter effect is probably due to saturation of physiological targets, usually endogenous receptors. Other physiological factors can alter the impact of promoting chemicals, e.g. diet and hormonal status will influence the promotion of numerous preneoplastic lesions including those in the mammary and hepatic tissues.

Progression

As the initiated cell population is expanded during promotion, individual cells acquire further genetic damage, which can be either agent-mediated or spontaneous, thereby introducing genetic heterogeneity into the promoted population. Acquisition of these changes is irreversible and progressive (**Table 2**). Ultimately, some promoted cells will acquire karyotype instability, which can bestow growth advantage over surrounding cells. In some cases this will remove environmental constraints over such cells, allowing them to escape proximal cellular and humoural influences. In many cases, such cells will have acquired clastogenic changes that bestow significant phenotypic change (Foulds, 1965; Welch and Tomasovic, 1985).

CRITICAL GENE TARGETS

The reaction between an activated carcinogen and DNA is concentration dependent. Since DNA comprises only four bases then, in theory, chemicals should damage DNA at any site within the genome. In practice there appears to be preferred sites at which attack occurs. The factors which govern the chance of attack at such sites would be expected to include accessibility, the presence of modifying influences (extent of methylation or association with nuclear proteins), etc. Furthermore, factors such as (1) DNA repair, (2) the presence of transcriptionally active or silent genes, (3) the role of the gene in normal cell function, (4) whether the chemical attacks a structural domain of the gene or (5) a regulatory domain and (6) whether the DNA target has any function whatsoever, will affect outcome. Although DNA is chemically the same throughout the genome, some sections (containing critical genes) are clearly more important to the correct functioning of the cell than are others. The number of currently recognized critical gene targets is only a fraction of the estimated 28 000–30 000 genes of the human genome, but is growing. These critical genes are involved in controlling the growth and differentiation of cells, damage or mutation of which is highly correlated with the neoplastic process; such genes are described as oncogenes or tumour-suppressor genes.

Oncogenes

Under normal circumstances oncogenes exist as proto-oncogenes (Garrett, 1986); they code for proteins that are involved in important pathways within the cell such as growth, signal transduction, cell cycle and nuclear transcription. Chemical-induced damage to key sites within the proto-oncogene can convert the sequence to one that codes for an aberrant protein. The product of this genetic change (conversion to an oncogenic variant of the gene) is a protein that has an altered sequence due to loss, gain or replacement of amino acids, and no longer responds to appropriate controlling stimuli. The activation of proto-oncogenes to oncogenes can be achieved by several well-recognized processes (Pitot, 1986). These may include (1) mutation of the structural gene, (2) mutation of regulatory sequences, (3) amplification of the structural gene, (4) translocation of the gene to a site of inappropriate gene regulation (e.g. within the control of a powerful promoter sequence) after clastogenic events or (5) epigenetic alteration of either structural or regulatory sequences leading to altered regulation of gene expression (e.g. altered gene methylation). Each of these mechanisms generates a functionally dominant gene and can be induced by chemical interaction at key sites within DNA. Examples of specific oncogenes are described in **Table 3** and can be grouped into functional biochemical classes, which code for key regulatory activities involved in correct functioning of the cell. These genes tend to be involved in pathways that mediate cell growth, differentiation and signalling. The ability of mutagenic chemicals to activate oncogenes is well established. A good example is the codon 12 K-*ras* mutations found in aberrant crypt foci in the colon of rats treated with azoxymethane (Shivapurkar *et al.*, 1994).

Tumour-suppressor Genes

Tumour-suppressor genes normally act to suppress the neoplastic phenotype. As with oncogenic activation, chemical damage to a tumour-suppressor gene can give rise to a protein with altered activity, in this case making it unable to operate as a suppressor of the cancer process (Knudson, 1993). Since these genes tend to be functionally recessive, full loss of phenotypic expression often requires mutation or loss of both alleles and chemicals tend to destroy or alter the normal cellular activity of the tumour-suppressor gene. Many of these genes have a nuclear location/ function and are directly involved in maintaining genome integrity. Examples of tumour-suppressor genes are given in **Table 3**. Chemical-mediated damage of the *p53* gene is a frequently encountered event in chemical-induced neoplastic disease. For example, aflatoxin B$_1$ exposure is associated with a high incidence of hepatocellular carcinoma in parts of Africa. Examination of the *p53* gene in these tumours reveals characteristic mutations at specific

Table 3   Examples of critical genes involved in carcinogenesis

Gene	Function	Localization
Oncogenes		
SIS, FGF, INT2, WNT1	Growth factors	Extracellular
MET, NEU, EPH, EGRF, FMS, KIT, HER2, RET, ROS,	Receptor/protein tyrosine kinases	Extracellular/cell membrane
SRC, ABL1, FPS, FGR, FYN, HCK, LCK, YES	Nonreceptor tyrosine kinases	Cell membrane/cytoplasmic
MAS	Receptors lacking protein kinase activity	Cell membrane/cytoplasmic
RAS, GIP2, GSP	Membrane-associated G proteins	Cell membrane/cytoplasmic
BCR, DBL, ECT2	RHO/RAC-binding proteins	Cytoplasmic
RAF, PIM1, BCR, EST, MOS,	Cytoplasmic protein serine kinases	Cytoplasmic
STY	Protein serine, threonine and tyrosine kinase	Nuclear
BCL1, CRK, ODC, NCK	Cytoplasmic regulators	Cytoplasmic
MYC, FOS, JUN, BCL3, CBL ERBA, ETS, HOX, MYB, MYCL, REL, TAL1, SKI	Nuclear transcription factors	Nuclear
BCL-2	Mitochondrial membrane factor	Mitochondrial/cytoplasmic
Tumour-suppressor genes		
NF1	GTPase activation	Cell membrane/cytoplasmic
RB-1	Cell cycle-regulated nuclear transcription repressor	Nuclear
P53	Cell cycle-regulated nuclear transcription repressor	Nuclear
WT1	Zinc finger transcription factor	Nuclear
HMLH1	Mismatch DNA repair	Nuclear
BRCA1	DNA repair enzyme	Nuclear
APC	Regulates cytoskeletal networks	Cytoplasmic
DCC	Cell adhesion molecule	Plasma membrane
VHL	Signal transduction or cell–cell contact	Plasma membrane
NME	Cell receptor	Plasma membrane
CMAR/CAR	Cell attachment	Plasma membrane
WNT	Growth factor	Extracellular matrix
YES1	Tyrosine kinase	Plasma membrane

(Adapted from Hesketh, 1994.)

hot spots (e.g. codons 248/249). These tumours and p53 mutations can be reproduced *in vivo* in animals and *in vitro* in cells exposed to pure aflatoxin B_1 (Aguilar *et al.*, 1993).

CONCLUSION

Cancer is often perceived as largely due to inherited defective genes, a view fuelled by recent discoveries in this area. However, the biggest cause of human cancer is the influence of chemical carcinogens. Indeed, the biggest contributors to the burden of human cancer (estimated to be about 90% of all cancers) are carcinogens contained within tobacco smoke, diet and the environment (Doll and Peto, 1981).

Carcinogenesis is a multistep process and many of these steps can be influenced by chemicals. Clearly a chemical with carcinogenic or mutagenic properties should be used with caution, especially in cases where it would come into contact with humans. Yet there will be some instances where the benefit of using the chemical will outweigh its immediate risk, e.g. as a chemotherapeutic agent. Under such circumstances its use must be carefully regulated and monitored.

As discussed, many chemicals are carcinogenic through metabolic bioactivation and genotoxic activity at the level of the genome. However, this primary activity is only one factor in a sequence of complex events. Of thousands of chemicals tested, a few hundred have been identified as carcinogenic in rodents and around 50 are human carcinogens. With the development of new pharmaceuticals and industrial chemicals, carcinogenicity testing has become an essential activity and has led to a clearer understanding of the mechanistic basis of the carcinogenicity process.

The value of understanding the mechanisms whereby a chemical causes cancer cannot be underestimated. It provides a rational basis for risk assessment allows predictions of possible outcomes and informs the development of alternatives or strategies, which reduce risk. In the case of therapeutically useful agents, it indicates how improved pharmaceuticals can be conceived and employed. It is also increasingly evident that each chemical with carcinogenic properties is unique and that grouping chemical carcinogens on the basis of their structural attributes is not always appropriate and thus prediction of genetic toxicity should always be confirmed by experimental data. In this respect, the development of new technologies such as transgenic animals that have altered expression of proto-oncogenes and tumour-suppressor genes greatly add to the battery of systems available for helping us understand cancer. Such models will continue to provide substantial information on the mechanisms through which chemicals and biological processes interact to drive the neoplastic process.

REFERENCES

Aguilar, F., et al. (1993). Aflatoxin B1 induces the transversion of G→T in codon 249 of the p53 tumour suppressor gene in human hepatocytes. Proceedings of the National Academy of Sciences of the USA, 90, 8586–8590.

Beatson, G. T. (1896). On the treatment of inoperable cases of carcinoma of the mamma: suggestions for a new method of treatment with illustrative cases. Lancet, 2, 104–107.

Berenblum, I. and Shubik, P. (1947). A new quantitative approach to the study of the stages of chemical carcinogenesis in the mouse's skin. British Journal of Cancer, 1, 383–391.

Bolt, H. M. (1988) Roles of etheno–DNA adducts in tumor-igenicity of olefins. CRC Critical Reviews in Toxicology, 18, 299–309.

Boutwell, R. K. (1964). Some biological aspects of skin carcinogenesis. Progress in Experimental Tumor Research, 4, 207–250.

Brand, K. G., et al. (1975). Etiological factors, stages, and the role of the foreign body in foreign body tumourigenesis. A review. Cancer Research, 35, 279–286.

Carmichael, P. L. (1998). Mechanisms of action of antiestrogens: relevance to clinical benefits and risks. Cancer Investigation, 16, 604–611.

Carothers, A. M., et al. (1994). Mutation and repair induced by the carcinogen 2-(hydroxylamino)-1-methyl-6-phenylimi-dazo[4,5-b]pyridine (N-OH-PhIP) in the dihydrofolate reductase gene of Chinese hamster ovary cells and con-formational modelling of the dG-C8-PhIP adduct in DNA. Chemical Research in Toxicology, 7, 209–218.

Conney, A. H. (1982). Induction of microsomal enzymes by foreign chemicals and carcinogenesis by polycyclic aromatic hydrocarbons: GHA Clowes Memorial Lecture. Cancer Research, 42, 4875–4917.

Dogliotti, E. (1996). Mutational spectra: from model systems to cancer-related genes. Carcinogenesis, 17, 2113–2118.

Doll, R. and Peto, R. (1981). The Causes of Cancer (Oxford University Press, Oxford).

Eling, T. E., et al. (1990). Prostaglandin H synthatase and xeno-biotic oxidation. Annual Review of Pharmacology and Toxicology, 30, 1–45.

Foulds, L. (1965). Multiple etiologic factors in neoplastic devel-opment. Cancer Research, 25, 1339–1347.

Friedberg, E. C. (1985). DNA Repair (Freeman, New York).

Garrett, C. T. (1986). Oncogenes. Clinica Chemica Acta, 156, 1–40.

Gonzalez, F. J. (1989). The molecular biology of cytochrome P450s. Pharmacological Reviews, 40, 243–288.

Gooderham, N. J., et al. (1996). Heterocyclic amines: evaluation of their role in diet associated human cancer. British Journal of Clinical Pharmacology, 42, 91–98.

Gooderham, N. J., et al. (1997). Assessing human risk to het-erocyclic amines. Mutation Research, 376, 53–60.

Harris, C. C. (1991). Chemical and physical carcinogenesis: advances and perspectives for the 1990s. Cancer Research, 51, 5023s–5044s.

Hesketh, R. (1994). The Oncogene Handbook (Academic Press, London).

Jakoby, W. B., et al. (1982). Metabolic Basis of Detoxification: Metabolism of Functional Groups. 1–375 (Academic Press, New York).

Knudson, A. G. (1993). Antioncogenes and human cancer. Pro-ceedings of the National Academy of Sciences of the USA, 90, 10914–10921.

Lawley, P. D. (1994). Historical origins of current concepts of carcinogenesis. Advances in Cancer Research, 65, 17–111.

Lipmann, M. (1993). Biophysical fibres affecting fibre toxicity. In: Wahrheit, D. B. (ed.), Fibre Toxicology. 259–303 (Academic Press, San Diego).

Lynch, A. M., et al. (1998). Genetic analysis of PhIP intestinal mutations in Muta™ Mouse. Mutagenesis, 13, 601–605.

Magee, P. N., et al. (1976). N-Nitroso compounds and related carcinogens. In: Searle, C. E. (ed.), Chemical Carcinogens. 491–625 (American Chemical Society, Washington, DC).

Miller, E. C. (1978). Some current perspectives on chemical carcinogenesis in humans and experimental animals: Pre-sential Address. Cancer Research, 38, 1479–1496.

Miller, E. C. and Miller, J. A. (1981). Searches for ultimate chemical carcinogens and their reactions with cellular macromolecules. Cancer, 47, 2327–2345.

Miller, J. A. (1970). Carcinogenesis by chemicals: an overview – GHA Clowes Memorial Lecture. Cancer Research, 30, 559–576.

Morgenthaler, P. M. and Holzhauser, D. (1995). Analysis of mutations induced by 2-amino-1-methyl-6-phenylimi-dazo[4,5-b]pyridine (PhIP) in human lymphoblastoid cells. Carcinogenesis, 16, 713–718.

Okochi, E., et al. (1999). Preferential induction of guanine deletion at 5'-GGGA-3' in the rat mammary glands by 2-amino-1-methyl-6-phenylimidazo[4,5-b]pyridine (PhIP). Carcinogenesis, 20, 1933–1938.

Okonogi, H., et al. (1997). Agreement of mutational character-istics of heterocyclic amines in lacI of Big Blue mouse with those in tumour related genes in rodents. *Carcinogenesis*, **18**, 745–748.

Parkinson, A. (1996). Biotransformation of xenobiotics. In: Klaassen, C. D., *et al.* (eds), *Casarett and Doull's Toxicology: the Basic Science of Poisons*. 113–186 (McGraw-Hill, New York).

Pitot, H. C. (1986). Oncogenes and human neoplasia. *Clinical Laboratory Medicine*, **6**, 167–179.

Pitot, H. C. and Dragan, Y. P. (1996). Chemical carcinogenesis. In: Klaassenm, C. D., *et al.* (eds), *Casarett and Doull's Toxicology: the Basic Science of Poisons*. 201–267 (McGraw-Hill, New York).

Porter, T. D. and Coon, M. J. (1991). Multiplicity of isoforms, substrates and catalytic and regulatory mechanisms. *Journal of Biological Chemistry*, **266**, 13469–13472.

Searle, C. E. (1984). *Chemical Carcinogens*, 2nd edn (American Chemical Society, Washington, DC).

Shivapurkar, N., *et al.* (1994). Sequence analysis of k-ras mutations in aberrant crypt foci and colonic tumours induced by azoyxmethane in Fisher-344 rats on high-risk diet. *Carcinogenesis*, **15**, 775–778.

Sims, P., *et al.* (1974). Metabolic activation of benzo[*a*]pyrene proceeds by a diol epoxide. *Nature*, **252**, 326–328.

Sky-Peck, H. H. (1986). Trace metals and neoplasia. *Clinical Physiology and Biochemistry*, **4**, 99–111.

Taper, H. S. (1978). The effect of estradiol-17-phenylpropionate and estradiol benzoate on *N*-nitrosomorpholine-induced liver carcinogenesis in ovariectomised female rats. *Cancer*, **42**, 462–467.

Thilly, W. G. (1990). Mutational spectrometry in animal toxicity testing. *Annual Review of Pharmacology and Toxicology*, **30**, 369–385.

Welch, D. R. and Tomasovic, S. P. (1985). Implications of tumour progression on clinical oncology. *Clinical and Experimental Metastasis*, **3**, 151–188.

Williams, R. T. (1971). *Detoxification Mechanisms*, 2nd edn (Wiley, New York).

Wogan, G. N. (1992). Aflatoxins as risk factors for hepatocellular carcinoma in humans. *Cancer Research*, **52**, 2114s–2118s.

Wogan, G. N., *et al.* (1971). Structure–activity relationships in toxicity and carcinogenicity of aflatoxins and analogues. *Cancer Research*, **31**, 1936–1942.

Yadollahi-Farsani, M., *et al.* (1996). Mutational spectra of the dietary carcinogen 2-amino-1-methyl-6-phenylimidazo [4,5-*b*]pyridine (PhIP) at the Chinese hamster *hprt* locus. *Carcinogenesis*, **17**, 617–624.

FURTHER READING

Balmain, A. and Brown, K. (1988). Oncogene activation in chemical carcinogenesis. *Advances in Cancer Research*, **51**, 147–182.

Dipple, A., *et al.* (1985). Metabolism of chemical carcinogens. *Pharmacology and Therapeutics*, **27**, 265–296.

Guengerich, F. P. (1992). Metabolic activation of carcinogens. *Pharmacology and Therapeutics*, **54**, 17–61.

Hodgson, E. and Levi, P. E. (1994). *Biochemical Toxicology*, 2nd edn (Appleton and Lange, Norwalk, CT).

Levine, A. J. (1993). Tumour suppressor genes. *Annual Review of Biochemistry*, **62**, 623–651.

Timbrell, J. (2001). *Principles of Biochemical Toxicology*, 3rd edn (Taylor and Francis, London).

Vainio, H. (1992). *Mechanisms of Carcinogenesis in Risk Identification. IARC Publications*, No. 116 (International Agency for Research on Cancer, Lyon).

Chapter 21

The Formation of DNA Adducts

David H. Phillips
Institute of Cancer Research, Sutton, UK

CONTENTS

DNA DAMAGE BY CARCINOGENS

A property common to many chemical carcinogens is that they, or one or more of their metabolites, are DNA reactive. Cellular responses to DNA damage in mammalian cells include DNA repair, cytotoxicity, apoptosis, mutagenesis and transformation to malignancy. These processes are either fundamental to maintaining the integrity of the cell or they set the cell on a path to mortality or malignancy. Thus the study of reactions between carcinogens and DNA, and the biological consequences of these reactions, is central to understanding the early stages of the carcinogenic process.

The identification of DNA as the genetic material and the solving of its structure occurred about 50 years ago, but it was not immediately appreciated that carcinogens exert their biological effects by damaging it. Although the discovery that carcinogens could form covalent bonds with cellular macromolecules dates from about the same time, for some years afterwards the prevailing hypothesis was that the deletion of key proteins was critical to the carcinogenic process. However, the demonstration in the 1960s that the potency of a series of carcinogens correlated with their ability to bind to DNA *in vivo*, and not with the extent of binding to protein or RNA (Brookes and Lawley, 1964), led to the acceptance of DNA as the critical target in carcinogenesis. Subsequently, the discovery of several classes of genes that control cellular function and maintain cellular integrity and which are commonly mutated in tumours (oncogenes, tumour-suppressor genes and mismatch repair genes) has made it evident that if certain critical genes are modified by carcinogens, the mutations that may ensue from erroneous replication of the damaged gene template will contribute to the transformation of a normal cell into a malignant one. Finally, the types of genetic alterations commonly found in tumour cells – point mutations, deletions, translocations, gene amplifications – can also be induced in cells by treatment with DNA adduct-forming chemicals. Given the long latency of most types of human and experimental cancer, it is not possible to observe directly the biological consequences of DNA adduct formation *in vivo*. Nevertheless, the very strong correlation between this early biochemical event and the subsequent biological manifestation of malignancy in many different studies places the cause-and-effect association beyond reasonable doubt.

Carcinogen-induced DNA damage can take several forms. It can result in breaks in the sugar–phosphate backbone of the molecule, either in one of the two strands of the double helix, or in both. Covalent binding of the carcinogen results in the formation of a chemically altered base (or, occasionally, phosphate group) in DNA that is termed an adduct. As DNA adducts are usually studied by fragmenting the DNA either chemically or enzymatically, the term nucleotide adduct describes a fragment consisting of carcinogen–base–deoxyribose–phosphate, nucleoside adduct consists of carcinogen–base–deoxyribose and a base adduct is the carcinogen-modified base only. Some carcinogens are bifunctional and can give rise to both monoadducts and cross-links in DNA, the latter being either intra- or interstrand cross-links. Many cancer chemotherapeutic agents have this property, and it is widely held that interstrand cross-links are cytotoxic (accounting for the therapeutic properties of the drugs), whereas the monoadducts and intrastrand cross-links are potentially mutagenic and carcinogenic (Lawley and Phillips, 1996).

Most chemical carcinogens are not biologically active as such, but undergo metabolic activation in mammalian cells to reactive intermediates that react with DNA (see also the chapter *Mechanisms of Chemical Carcinogenesis*). Why do mammalian cells do this? The answer is that it is an aberration of the general mechanisms that cells employ to rid themselves of toxins, generally by making them water soluble. Metabolism of xenobiotic (foreign) compounds is carried out in mammalian cells by broad spectrum oxidative enzymes (Phase I metabolism) that introduce polar groups (e.g. hydroxyl groups) into molecules and render the molecules suitable substrates for conjugation (Phase II metabolism) with one of a variety of hydrophilic groups. The resulting conjugate is substantially more water soluble than the parent compound and thus more readily excreted from the organism. Phase I metabolites are often formed through transient generation of reactive compounds such as epoxides, but are rapidly converted to hydroxyl groups by further enzymatic conversion or by nonenzymatic reaction with water. However, if they are slow to convert, their presence in the cell may lead to their reaction with DNA. Similarly, most Phase II metabolites are water soluble and chemically stable, ideal properties for their efficient elimination from the cell and subsequent excretion from the organism; however, some carcinogens are converted to conjugates that are reactive, and the loss of the conjugated function generates a highly reactive carbocation that reacts with DNA.

There have been two approaches to determining the pathways of activation of carcinogens. In the first,

metabolites of the carcinogen are isolated and identified, and their abilities to induce tumours and other genotoxicity endpoints are investigated. In the second approach, DNA adducts are detected and identified, and the pathways by which they are formed are deduced by determining the metabolites that can also give rise to them, and the cofactors necessary for their formation.

An example of a carcinogen that is metabolically activated to a reactive Phase I metabolite is benzo[*a*]-pyrene (BaP), a polycyclic aromatic hydrocarbon (PAH) that is widespread in the environment through its formation during the incomplete combustion of organic material (wood, coal, petrol, tobacco, etc.). Although it is converted to many different metabolites, one cytochrome P450(CYP)-dependent pathway results in metabolic activation (**Figure 1**). The initial epoxide formed is rapidly metabolized further by epoxide hydrolase to a dihydrodiol (called the proximate carcinogen), but this metabolite then undergoes further metabolism to a dihydrodiol epoxide, BPDE (the ultimate carcinogen). This time, the molecule is not a good substrate for epoxide hydrolase and although it is chemically unstable (i.e. it is reactive), it is sufficiently long-lived in mammalian cells to be able to migrate to the nucleus and react with DNA, via formation of a carbocation, to form chemically stable DNA adducts (Phillips, 1983).

An example of a carcinogen activated by Phase II metabolism is tamoxifen (**Figure 2**). In the liver of rats, where it causes hepatocellular carcinoma, it is converted first to α-hydroxytamoxifen (the proximate carcinogen) by a CYP-dependent Phase I step. This metabolite then undergoes Phase II metabolism by sulfotransferase to a sulfate ester conjugate. This compound dissociates to form

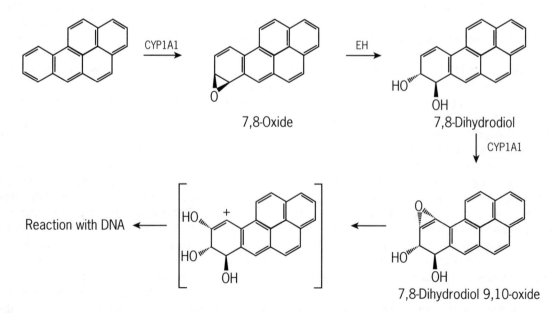

Figure 1   Major pathway of metabolic activation of benzo[a]pyrene. CYP1A1, cytochrome P450 1A1; EH, epoxide hydrolase.

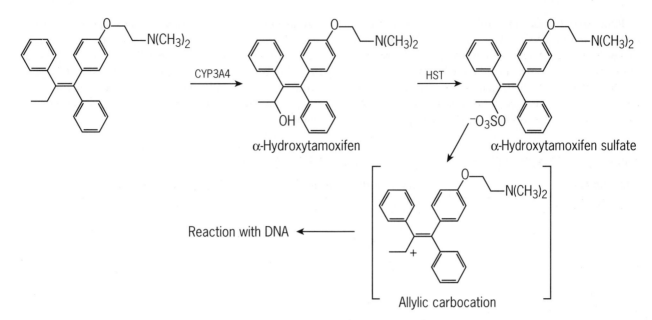

Figure 2 Major pathway of metabolic activation of tamoxifen. CYP3A4, cytochrome P450 3A4; HST, hydroxy-steroid sulfotransferase (SULT2A family).

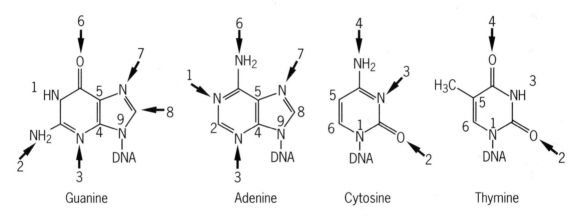

Figure 3 DNA bases and sites at which they are bonded to carcinogens.

a reactive carbocation that reacts with DNA to form DNA adducts (Davis *et al.*, 1998).

This chapter describes the formation of DNA adducts by carcinogenic chemicals, with particular emphasis on their detection in human tissues, and the role of such studies in investigating the aetiology of cancer, in monitoring human exposure to environmental carcinogens and in determining cancer risk.

ADDUCTS FORMED BY CHEMICAL CARCINOGENS

Most of the covalent binding of carcinogens to DNA involves the modification of the purine and pyrimidine bases, although some agents also react with the phosphodiester linkages. Guanine is the most commonly and extensively modified base, with interactions occurring at N^2, N-3, O^6, N-7 and C-8 (**Figure 3**). Adducts with adenine are formed at the N-1, N-3, N^6 and N-7 atoms. Pyrimidine adducts are formed at the O^2, N-3, N^4 and C-5 of cytosine and at the O^2 and O^4 of thymine.

Alkylating agents that react by a predominantly S_N2 mechanism show a greater affinity for the ring nitrogens in DNA bases, these being the most nucleophilic sites in DNA (Osborne, 1984). As the S_N1 character of the reaction increases (i.e. via generation of an electrophilic carbocation that is the reactive species), so the proportion of the reaction that occurs at exocyclic groups increases (Lawley, 1984). Thus the ratio of O^6/N-7 alkylation of guanine in DNA is 0.7 for *N*-ethylnitrosourea (ENU), 0.1 for *N*-methylnitrosourea (MNU) and 0.004 for methyl methanesulfonate (MMS) (Lawley, 1984).

Representative examples of active metabolites of carcinogens and of their reaction sites with DNA are shown in **Table 1**. More comprehensive reviews of carcinogen–DNA interactions can be found elsewhere (Osborne, 1984; Cooper and Grover, 1990; Hemminki *et al.*, 1994). PAHs, activated by diol epoxide formation, mainly form stable DNA adducts at the exocyclic amino groups of guanine and adenine. The more distorted from planarity the ultimate carcinogen, the greater is the proportional reactivity with adenine relative to guanine (Dipple, 1994). Tamoxifen also reacts at these sites. Nitroaromatic polycyclic hydrocarbons, activated at the nitro group, react with the C-8 position of guanine. Aromatic amines and heterocyclic amines also modify predominantly the C-8 position of

Table 1   Some representative carcinogens, their active metabolites and sites of modification of DNA

Carcinogen	Major active metabolite	Site of modification of DNA
Benzo[a]pyrene (BP)	BP 7,8-diol 9,10-epoxide	N^2-Guanine, N^6-adenine
Benzo[c]phenanthrene (BcPh)	BcPh 4,3-diol 2,1-epoxide	N^6-Adenine, N^2-guanine
Aflatoxin B_1 (AfB$_1$)	AfB$_1$ 8,9-epoxide	N7-Guanine
Tamoxifen	α-Hydroxytamoxifen sulfate	N^2-Guanine, N^6-adenine
2-Acetylaminofluorene (AAF)	N-Acetoxy-AAF	C8-Guanine, N^2-guanine
Vinyl chloride	Chloroethylene oxide	3,N^4-Cytosine, 1,N^6-adenine, 3,N^2-guanine
2-Amino-1-methyl-6-phenylimidazo-[4,5-b]pyridine (PhIP)	N-Acetoxy-PhIP	C8-Guanine
1-Nitropyrene (1-NP)	N-Hydroxy-1-aminopyrene	C8-Guanine

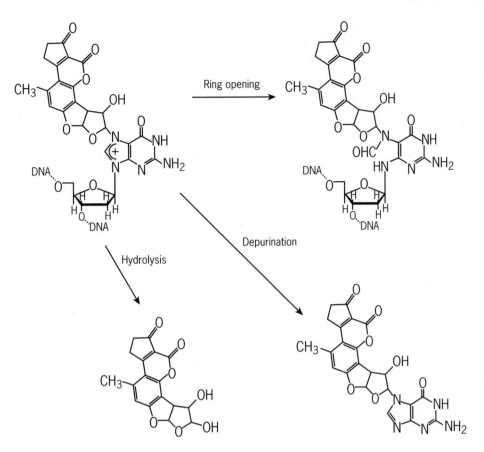

Figure 4 Conversion of the unstable aflatoxin-*N7*-guanine adduct in DNA to stable products.

guanine. Aflatoxin B₁, a mycotoxin, is metabolized to an epoxide that reacts at the N-7 position of guanine. This adduct structure is electronically charged and unstable. It can undergo one of three processes spontaneously: (1) hydrolysis to yield aflatoxin dihydrodiol and unmodified DNA; (2) depurination to yield an aflatoxin-base adduct, leaving an apurinic site in DNA; or (3) imidazole ring-opening to yield a stable adduct (**Figure 4**). Some compounds form cyclic adducts, in which two positions on the same base are modified by the same molecule. An example is vinyl chloride (and other vinyl halides), which forms etheno adducts with cytosine, adenine and guanine (**Figure 5**).

The large variety of DNA sites attacked by carcinogens leads to the question of whether some modifications are

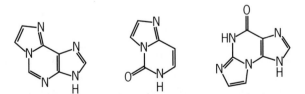

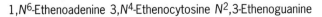

1,*N*⁶-Ethenoadenine 3,*N*⁴-Ethenocytosine *N*²,3-Ethenoguanine

Figure 5 Structures of etheno adducts formed by vinyl halides and by products of lipid peroxidation.

more biologically important than others. This is still a matter of debate, with some suggestions that adenine adducts formed by PAHs are more consequential than guanine adducts, even though benzo[*a*]pyrene forms very few of the former. Others have proposed that unstable, depurinating adducts are more important than stable adducts in causing mutations from which tumour initiation proceeds, although this theory has been challenged. Substitution at N-7 of guanine by simple alkylating agents appears to be ineffectual in causing mutations, whereas adducts at the O^6 position are highly promutagenic . On the other hand, aflatoxin B₁ appears to modify only N-7 in guanine, and is among the most potent carcinogens known (Osborne, 1984). Methylation of DNA at the O^6 position, a base-pairing position, will cause guanine to mispair with thymine, thereby causing a G → A transition after a round of replication (Lawley, 1984). The 7-position of guanine, however, is non-pairing; methylation produces little or no alteration to the tertiary structure of DNA, but substitution with a bulky molecule like aflatoxin B₁ would cause considerable distortion (and also leads to ring opening of the purine), which could in itself lead to replication errors by DNA polymerases.

There is also some evidence that DNA modification by carcinogens does not occur at random, but is influenced to some extent by DNA sequence (Osborne, 1984).

Additionally, the potential for an adduct to give rise to a mutation may be dependent, to some extent, on its sequence context, giving rise to the concept of hotspots for DNA damage and mutation in some genes. Some of these possibilities are discussed later in this chapter.

METHODS OF DNA ADDUCT DETECTION

The last 25 years have seen the development of a number of sensitive methods for the detection and characterization of DNA adducts in mammalian cells and tissues (Phillips, 1990; Strickland et al., 1993; Phillips et al., 2000; Poirier et al., 2000), the most important of which are reviewed briefly here.

Radiolabelled Compounds

Because only a very small proportion of an applied dose of a carcinogen becomes bound to DNA in the exposed cells or tissue, very sensitive methods of detection are required to study DNA adduct formation in vivo. Most of the early work on adducts was done using radiolabelled carcinogens and, although other methods now provide comparable or greater sensitivity, the method still has its uses. With compounds labelled either with ^{3}H or ^{14}C, at a position of the molecule where the isotope will not be lost as a result of metabolism, detection of radioactivity in DNA isolated from the exposed animal or cultured cells is the starting point for the characterization of the DNA binding. Sensitivities of detection of one adduct in 10^8 nucleotides are achievable with ^{3}H labelling, although ^{14}C labelling is less sensitive because of the much longer half-life of ^{14}C than ^{3}H (Phillips et al., 2000).

Limitations to the use of the method are the high costs of synthesizing radiolabelled compounds and the difficulty in doing chronic, multidose, exposure studies due to the hazards of the use of radioactive materials in these circumstances. Furthermore, it is seldom possible to use radioactive test compounds in studies involving human subjects. However, the recent adaptation of accelerator mass spectrometry (AMS) enables isotope ratios to be measured with great sensitivity in biological samples. With this method, the binding of a radiolabelled carcinogen to DNA is detected not by means of its decay (thereby linking the sensitivity to the half-life of the isotope) but by measuring the abundance of the radioisotope relative to that of the natural isotope. For ^{14}C it is possible to detect one part in 10^{15} parts total carbon, and in practice limits of adduct detection of greater than one in 10^{11} nucleotides have been achieved (Phillips et al., 2000). Because of this high sensitivity, it has been possible to obtain ethical approval to give minute amounts of a radioactive carcinogen, e.g. the mutagen formed in cooked food, 2-amino-1-methyl-6-phenylimidazo[4,5-b]pyridine (PhIP), to human subjects prior to surgery and to detect DNA adducts in the excised tissue. AMS does not give structural information on DNA adducts, and characterization requires chromatographic comparison with synthesized standards. Nevertheless, its ultra-sensitivity provides a means of establishing whether carcinogens thought to be nongenotoxic in their mechanism of action, such as 2,3,7,8-tetrachlorodibenzo-p-dioxin (TCDD), are truly devoid of DNA binding activity.

^{32}P Postlabelling

The ^{32}P postlabelling method of analysis comprises a procedure for introducing a radiolabel into a DNA adduct after it has formed, by enzymatic phosphorylation of the deoxyribose group of the nucleotide adduct (Phillips, 1997). Chromatographic separation of the labelled adducts followed by detection and quantitation by measuring ^{32}P decay provides a highly sensitive assay, requiring only small (1–10 µg) quantities of DNA. Adducts from different classes of carcinogens with diverse structures can be detected by this method, including PAHs, aromatic amines, heterocyclic amines, unsaturated aldehydes, simple alkylating agents, reactive oxygen species and UV radiation (Beach and Gupta, 1992). It is also able to detect adducts formed from complex mixtures of chemicals, such as tobacco smoke and fossil fuel products. It is sensitive enough to detect adduct levels as low as one per mammalian cell. A limitation of the method is that it does not provide structural information; identification of adducts is reliant on co-chromatography with characterized synthetic standards. Adduct levels may be underestimated if the DNA is not completely digested or if the nucleotide adduct is not efficiently ^{32}P labelled by polynucleotide kinase (Phillips et al., 2000).

Immunoassays

Antisera elicited against carcinogen–DNA adducts can be used in immunoassays to detect adducts in human or animal tissues. Antibodies have been raised against a variety of carcinogen-modified DNAs, including those containing adducts of PAHs, aromatic amines, methylating agents, tamoxifen, UV radiation and oxidative damage. Immunoassays are highly sensitive but generally require more DNA for analysis than ^{32}P postlabelling. The assay is relatively inexpensive to perform and can be automated. Various sensitive methods (radioactive, colorimetric, fluorescent and chemiluminescent) have been developed for detecting bound antiserum. When combined with histochemistry it can be used to localize adducts within biological samples. Antibodies raised against a particular adduct can show cross-reactivity with adducts formed by other carcinogens of the same class, which can obscure both the nature of the adducts detected and the levels at which they are present. Nevertheless, this cross-reactivity does at least afford the opportunity to use immunoaffinity chromatography as a means of extracting adducts of a specific class, such as PAHs, for further analysis by other methods.

Mass spectrometry and other physicochemical methods

Mass spectrometry is the most chemically selective method for DNA adduct detection and it can provide unequivocal identification of the nature of an adduct. This selectivity comes at a price, that of sensitivity, which has limited its application to human DNA adduct studies. However, it is a method in which technological advances are being made rapidly, and it can be predicted with confidence that in the near future it will provide much valuable data on the nature of DNA modifications in human tissues, as well as in experimental studies (Phillips *et al.*, 2000; Poirier *et al.*, 2000). Most studies to date have used mass spectrometry combined either with gas chromatography (GC-MS) or liquid chromatography (LC-MS). Earlier methods required volatility to be a property of a molecule for its characterization by mass spectrometry, necessitating derivatization of polar species such as adducts, but softer ionization conditions (e.g. fast atom bombardment (FAB)) have overcome this limitation to some extent (Weston, 1993; Phillips and Farmer, 1995). With the advent of newer methods, such as electrospray ionization (ESI) and matrix-assisted laser desorption/ionization (MALDI), it will also become possible to investigate the presence of adducts in intact (high molecular mass) biomolecules including DNA and protein.

A number of carcinogens form adducts that are highly fluorescent, enabling their detection by fluorescence spectroscopy. These include adducts formed by PAHs and aflatoxins, cyclic (etheno) adducts and some methylated adducts. They can be analysed in intact DNA, DNA digests or as hydrolysis products. Low-temperature fluorescence spectroscopy (e.g. fluorescence line narrowing spectroscopy (FLNS) (Jankowiak and Small, 1991)) reveals considerable spectral fine structure that is lost at ambient temperature and that can be diagnostic for certain carcinogens, also revealing information about the conformation of the adducts.

Some adducts, notably the oxidative DNA lesion 8-hydroxy-2′-deoxyguanosine, are readily detected by high-performance liquid chromatography (HPLC) combined with electrochemical detection (ECD) (Halliwell and Dizdaroglu, 1992). The method has also been used to detect N7-methylguanine in combination with immuno-affinity purification.

Another specific method that can be used to detect adducts by means of their elemental content is atomic absorption spectrometry. An example of its use is the detection of platinum bound to DNA as a result of the treatment of cancer patients with platinum drugs (Weston, 1993). The method gives only the level of the element present, and no structural information.

EVIDENCE FOR THE BIOLOGICAL SIGNIFICANCE OF DNA ADDUCTS

While it is widely assumed that the formation of DNA adducts is an early and obligatory event in the process by which many carcinogens initiate tumours, it is by no means a sufficient event, and the long delay between carcinogen treatment and tumour appearance precludes a direct cause-and-effect demonstration. Nevertheless, it is the case that inhibition of DNA adduct formation will decrease the incidence of tumours formed subsequently, and increasing the adduct levels generally leads to a higher tumour yield.

That chemical modification of DNA can result in the same alterations as observed in mutated genes in tumours was observed with the H-*ras*-1 proto-oncogene transfected into NIH3T3 cells. Prior modification of the plasmid containing the gene resulted in mutations occurring in the DNA after transfection and replication of the host cells, manifested as the appearance of transformed foci. Mutations that activate *ras* genes occur in a few codons in the gene, so correlations between the sites of mutations in such experiments are less informative than in genes where there are many possible sites of DNA damage and mutation which can lead to altered function of the gene product. Such a gene is *p53*, where correlations can be usefully sought between the mutation spectra observed in different human tumours and clues sought to the nature of the initiating agent (Hainaut *et al.*, 1998). This has led to strong evidence for the involvement of aflatoxin B_1 in the initiation of liver cancer in regions of high incidence in China. With respect to lung cancer, codons 157, 248 and 273 of the *p53* gene are frequently mutated in these tumours. $G \rightarrow T$ transversions are much more common in lung cancer of smokers than that of non-smokers, and these types of mutation are characteristic of bulky carcinogens, such as the PAHs which are present in tobacco smoke. When the sites of DNA adduct formation by benzo[*a*]pyrene diol epoxide, the reactive metabolite of benzo[*a*]pyrene, in the *p53* gene in HeLa cells and bronchial epithelial cells were determined, it was found that codons 157, 248 and 273 were preferentially modified (Denissenko *et al.*, 1996).

Ultraviolet (UV) radiation causes DNA damage chiefly by dimerization of adjacent pyridines in the same DNA strand. The biological importance of these lesions is illustrated by the fact that sufferers of xeroderma pigmentosum (XP), who have a deficiency in nucleotide excision repair mechanisms that remove pyrimidine dimers from DNA, are prone to sunlight-induced skin cancer. Moreover, mutations in the *p53* gene found commonly in such tumours, but rarely in tumours of internal organs, are tandem mutations occurring at pyrimidine pairs ($CC \rightarrow TT$ transitions), highly suggestive that they arose from UV-induced pyrimidine dimers (Dumaz *et al.*, 1993).

Thus, there are examples of genetic changes in tumours that closely match the genetic changes that can be induced experimentally in cellular DNA by specific genotoxic agents. These tumour-specific mutations in *p53* and the demonstration that chemically modified DNA transforms cells show that the mutations observed in human tumours could have arisen from the formation of carcinogen–DNA adducts *in vivo*. Clonal expansion of the mutated cells and the acquisition of further genetic alterations eventually leads to malignancy (Fearon and Vogelstein, 1990).

Another piece of evidence that strongly links DNA adduct formation to tumour initiation is the demonstration that XPA knockout mice, which are deficient in nucleotide excision repair, are highly sensitive to tumour induction by carcinogens that form stable adducts that would be removed from DNA in normal mice by this repair mechanism (van Steeg *et al.*, 1998).

DNA ADDUCT DOSIMETRY

From a number of animal studies, it has been demonstrated that at chronic low doses, there is a linear relationship between the amount of carcinogen administered and the level of DNA adducts that results (Poirier and Beland, 1992). Adducts can be lost from DNA by depurination and by DNA repair, and can be diluted by DNA replication and cell division, so if the exposure is chronic, a steady-state level will be attained; typically this takes about 1 month of dosing. Where exposure is acute or of limited duration, it is clear from animal studies that a small proportion of the adducts persist in tissues for long periods, even in the presence of cell proliferation (e.g. in skin). Thus, the detection of DNA adducts can provide evidence of prior exposure to carcinogens even if the exposure was limited to a single dose.

It is also evident that DNA adducts may be formed in some tissues in the absence of tumour formation, indicating that adduct formation alone may not be sufficient for carcinogenesis (Poirier *et al.*, 2000). Other tissue-specific events, such as cell proliferation, are required. Nevertheless, tumours do not form in the absence of adducts, and interventions that reduce adduct formation (e.g. co-administration of enzyme inhibitors or inducers) result in inhibition of carcinogenesis.

An analysis of adduct levels and tumour rates in experimental animals for 27 different chemicals has shown that the adduct levels required to produce a 50% incidence in liver tumours in rats or mice varies between 53 and 5543 adducts per 10^8 nucleotides (Otteneder and Lutz, 1999). This is a narrow range considering the diversity of the chemicals and their interactions with DNA. The analysis also shows that low levels of adducts are detectable in animal bioassays in which tumours were not observed. Thus it is accepted that there are uncertainties concerning the biological significance of low levels of DNA adduct formation, but there are not, as yet, sufficient data with which to define a threshold below which adduct levels can be deemed biologically irrelevant (Phillips *et al.*, 2000).

ADDUCTS DETECTED IN HUMAN TISSUES

Studies of humans occupationally exposed to carcinogens have demonstrated the formation of DNA adducts in human tissues (see also the chapter *Occupational Causes of Cancer*). Many of these studies have involved exposure to PAHs with adduct formation being monitored in white blood cells or peripheral lymphocytes; for example, adduct levels are elevated in iron foundry workers, coke oven workers, aluminium plant workers, bus drivers exposed to diesel exhausts and roofers (Phillips, 1996). The same is true of residents of polluted regions of Poland, the Czech Republic and China (Perera, 2000). In some studies, dietary exposure to PAHs appears to be a stronger determinant of adducts in blood cells than does occupational exposure, so it is important that such factors be taken into consideration in interpreting the results of human biomonitoring studies.

Although DNA adducts of some sort have been detected in many studies of human tissues, there are still only a few studies in which the nature of the adduct has been unequivocally identified, and fewer still in which the origin of the DNA binding species can be defined. These limitations derive from the fact that many studies, particularly those employing ^{32}P postlabelling analysis, rely on the co-chromatography of the human adducts with synthetic standard adducts, rather than providing structural identification as such; although this can give reasonably reliable indications of the nature of the adducts formed *in vivo*, it cannot be considered sufficient evidence of identification. Thus those examples listed in **Table 2** all come from studies in which unambiguous physicochemical data (e.g. mass spectra or fluorescent spectra) on the properties of the adducts were obtained. In some cases, the nature of the DNA damaging agents can be deduced from the adduct, but in others, there is uncertainty or ambiguity because there is more than one potential source of the adduct.

As a general rule, several types of adduct have been detected in human DNA, at various levels. Thus 8-hydroxyguanine, originating from oxidative and free radical processes (see section on *Endogenous DNA Adducts*), is typically at levels of one in 10^4–10^5 nucleotides; etheno adducts, from lipid peroxidation or vinyl halides, are formed at between one in 10^7 and one in 10^8 nucleotides; O^6-methylguanine (formed by alkylating agents) is typically at one in 10^6–10^7 nucleotides; and bulky adducts (arising from smoking, pollution and diet) are often found at one in 10^7–10^8 nucleotides. With the exception of smoking-related adducts (see section on *Tobacco Exposure*) these can be regarded as approximate 'background' levels of DNA damage in human tissues due to environmental and/or endogenous DNA-damaging agents. Thus,

Table 2   Identified DNA adducts in human tissues

Adduct	Tissues
2-Amino-1-methyl-6-phenylimidazo[4,5-b]pyridine (PhIP, a food mutagen/heterocyclic amine) adducts	Colon
4-Aminobiphenyl (ABP, an aromatic amine) adducts	Bladder
4-(N-methyl-N-nitrosamino)-1-(3-pyridyl)-1-butanone (NNK, a tobacco-specific nitrosamine) adducts	Lung
Benzo[a]pyrene (BaP, a polycyclic aromatic hydrocarbon) adducts	Placenta, lung, leukocytes
Aflatoxin B_1 (AfB$_1$, a mycotoxin) adducts	Urine
Malondialdehyde-guanine	Liver, leukocytes
Thymine glycol	Placenta
5-Hydroxyethyluracil	Leukocytes
N7-(2-Hydroxyethyl)guanine	Liver
N^2,3-Ethenoguanine	Liver
8-Hydroxyguanine	Many tissues

when measuring adducts in a group of individuals suspected of being highly exposed to carcinogens and/or at elevated risk of cancer, it is important that such measurements be compared with the levels in a suitably selected control group of individuals.

DNA adducts have been detected in cancer patients undergoing chemotherapy (with, for example, platinum-based drugs, cyclophosphamide, melphalan, mitomycin C and the methylating agents dacarbazine and procarbazine) and studies have revealed considerable inter-individual variation in adduct levels among patients receiving similar dosage (Lawley and Phillips, 1996). It remains to be established whether such measurements may provide indications of therapeutic response.

ADDUCTS IN URINE

Because some adducts are chemically unstable and cause depurination of DNA, the excreted products, modified bases, can be detected in the urine (Shuker and Farmer, 1992). Examples of this include aflatoxin–guanine adducts where food contamination by this mycotoxin is endemic (e.g. in areas of Africa and China). Ethylated bases in urine can also serve as markers of exposure to ethylating agents. The method is of less use as a biomarker of exposure to methylating agents because there are instances in which methylated bases (e.g. 3-methyl-guanine) are ingested in the diet. Another caution is that carcinogen–purine adducts in urine may derive from both DNA and RNA. Urine contains significant numbers of exfoliated bladder epithelial cells, whose DNA can be isolated and analysed for the presence of adducts. An example is the case of a worker acutely exposed to MOCA (4,4′-methylenebis(2-chloroaniline)), whose urine samples yielded significant levels of adducts in the exfoliated urothelial cells for some weeks following the exposure.

TOBACCO EXPOSURE

The relationship between DNA adduct formation and tobacco smoke has been a fruitful area of research in which to explore the validity of the biomarker for a number of reasons (see also the chapter *Tobacco Use and Cancer*). First, a large proportion of the human population is regularly and habitually exposed to tobacco smoke because smoking is an addiction. Second, tobacco smoke contains at least 50 compounds that are known to be carcinogenic, including representatives of several distinct classes of compounds (PAHs, aromatic amines, N-nitrosoamines, azaarenes, aldehydes, other organic compounds and inorganic compounds). Most of these compounds are genotoxic carcinogens that form DNA adducts. Third, epidemiological studies have provided clear evidence that tobacco smoking causes not just lung cancer but also cancers in many other organs.

Many studies have compared DNA from smokers, ex-smokers and nonsmokers and have found that the levels of adducts in smokers are elevated in many target tissues: lung, bronchus, larynx, bladder, cervix and oral mucosa (Phillips, 1996). In some of these studies a linear correlation between estimated tobacco smoke exposure and adduct levels has been observed. In tissues of the respiratory tract adduct levels in ex-smokers tend to be intermediate between smokers and nonsmokers, indicating that adducts are removed through DNA repair and/or cell turnover. The half-life of adduct persistence appears to be between 1 and 2 years. This value is longer than would be predicted from adduct persistence studies in animals. A possible explanation is that the lungs of an ex-smoker continue to accumulate adducts after cessation of smoking owing to the continued presence in the lung of smoke and tar deposits.

For some of these studies specific adducts have been detected, but in others a more general measure of DNA damage has been made, namely aromatic/hydrophobic adducts detected by ^{32}P postlabelling, or PAH–DNA adducts detected by immunoassay. Recent studies have found that when adduct levels are adjusted to take account of the level of tobacco smoke exposure, lung DNA from women smokers is more highly adducted that that of male smokers. This finding is interesting in view of the epidemiological evidence that women are at a 1.5–2-fold greater risk of lung cancer from smoking. It would appear that the adduct analysis provides biochemical, mechanistic evidence to support the morbidity data. The reason for the higher level of adduction in women could be related to levels of expression of metabolizing enzymes (e.g. CYP enzymes) that activate tobacco smoke carcinogens to DNA binding species (Mollerup et al., 1999).

Some, but not all, studies have shown elevated levels of lung adducts in cancer cases compared with controls. The relationship between adduct levels in target tissues (e.g. lung) and other tissues (e.g. blood) has been investigated to see whether the latter can serve as a more readily accessible surrogate source of DNA than the former. Results for smoking-related adducts have been inconsistent (Perera, 2000; Poirier et al., 2000), perhaps because other sources of exposure to some classes of carcinogens, such as the PAHs, which are also ingested as dietary contaminants, may contribute to the overall level of adducts in the blood but not to the same extent in the lung.

It should be emphasized that by measuring adducts in smokers at the time of cancer diagnosis, investigators are not looking at the biochemical events causal in the initiation of those tumours, as these would have occurred decades earlier. However, because smoking is addictive and habitual for most tobacco users, DNA adducts in tumour-adjacent tissue at the time of tumour manifestation can still serve as a useful biomarker that gives an indication of an individual's probable steady-state level of DNA damage maintained over a long period of time.

ENDOGENOUS DNA ADDUCTS

Thus far, the emphasis has been on exogenous, environmental sources of carcinogens, but there is a large body of evidence that shows that DNA is also subject to modification by a number of endogenous processes arising from normal metabolism, oxidative stress and chronic inflammation (Marnett and Burcham, 1993; Marnett, 2000). **Table 3** shows a list of endogenous DNA adducts that have been detected in human tissues.

The most abundant oxidized base is 7,8-dihydro-8-oxo-2'-deoxyguanosine (8-oxo-dGuo), but at least 30 other base modifications have been characterized in oxidized DNA. Some of these, including 8-oxo-dGuo, can be formed as a result of free radical attack on DNA (for example, by the hydroxyl radical) whereas others appear to a consequence of normal aerobic metabolism. Being the most abundant oxidative lesion, 8-oxo-dGuo is often used as a biomarker for oxidative DNA damage in humans.

Etheno adducts (see **Figure 5**) can be generated in DNA as a result of lipid peroxidation (Marnett and Burcham, 1993; Marnett, 2000), making them adducts of endogenous origin. Etheno bases are removed from DNA by a repair mechanism involving glycosylases, but the rate of removal appears to be slow. These lesions are efficient

Table 3 Endogenous DNA adducts detected in human tissues. (Adapted from Marnett and Burcham, 1993.)

Adduct	Tissue	Adduct levels (per 10^7 bases)	Method
7,8-Dihydro-8-oxo-2'-deoxyguanosine (8-oxo-dGuo)	Leukocytes	12 ± 7	HPLC-ECD
5-Hydroxy-2'-deoxycytidine (5-OH-dCyd)	Leukocytes	10 ± 5	HPLC-ECD
5-Hydroxy-2'-deoxyuridine (5-OH-dUrd)	Leukocytes	7 ± 6	HPLC-ECD
5,6-Dihydroxy-5,6-dihydro-2'-deoxyuridine (dUrdg)	Leukocytes	20 ± 15	HPLC-ECD
7,8-Dihydro-8-oxo-2'-deoxyadenosine (8-oxo-dAdo)	Leukocytes	230	GC-MS
5-(Hydroxymethyl)-2'-deoxyuridine (5-HmdUrd)	White blood cells	2300 ± 480	GC-MS
8-Hydroxy-6-methyl-1,N^2-propano-2'-deoxyguanosine (8-OH-6-Me-PdGuo)	Liver	6	^{32}P postlabelling
8-Hydroxy-1,N^2-propano-2'-deoxyguanosine (8-OH-PdGuo)	Liver	10	^{32}P postlabelling
1,N^6-Etheno-2'-deoxyadenosine (εdAdo)	Liver	0.7 ± 0.4	^{32}P postlabelling
3,N^4-Etheno-2'-deoxycytidine (εdCyd)	Liver	2.8 ± 0.9	^{32}P postlabelling
3-β-D-2'-Deoxyribofuranosylpyrimido [1,2-a]purin-10(3H)-one (M_1dGuo)	Liver, white blood cells, pancreas, breast	0.1–12	^{32}P postlabelling, MS, immunoassay

premutagenic lesions and, although they can also be formed by exogenous agents such as vinyl halides, they appear to have some credentials for consideration as endogenous origins of mutagenic and carcinogenic processes. Another promutagenic exocyclic base adduct that has been detected in human DNA is M_1dGuo (3-β-D-2'-deoxyribofuranosylpyrimido[1,2-a]purin-10(3H)-one), a product of the reaction of malondialdehyde (itself a product of lipid peroxidation and prostaglandin biosynthesis) with DNA (Marnett, 1999).

The use of ^{32}P postlabelling analysis has revealed the existence of a large variety of moderately polar lesions in DNA, termed I-compounds. The patterns observed are tissue- and species-specific and show, in experimental animals, significant increases with age. The levels of many of them are also dependent on the diets used to feed the animals. Paradoxically, their levels are actually lower in circumstances which result in tumour formation, such as feeding rats a choline-deficient diet or the administration of enzyme inducers, and they are lower in rat liver tumours than in normal liver. Furthermore, some I-compounds are subject to circadian rhythms.

There are many uncertainties about the role of endogenous DNA adducts in carcinogenesis. Some chemical carcinogens have been shown to cause oxidative damage to DNA as well as forming DNA adducts directly themselves. Other so-called nongenotoxic carcinogens, which do not directly damage DNA, are suspected of increasing levels of oxidative lesions in DNA, but it remains unclear whether this is a mechanism by which they induce tumour formation.

Several of the endogenous DNA adducts are found in human DNA at levels significantly higher than the levels of adducts from exogenous (environmental) carcinogens. Relatively little is known about the relationship between endogenous adduct levels and development of cancer. It might be expected that their levels would be increased in circumstances that ultimately lead to cancer. However, aside from evidence that oxidative DNA damage appears, in some instances, to be higher in tumour tissue than in normal adjacent tissue (e.g. in breast), other evidence for I-compounds suggests that their levels decrease with increasing cancer susceptibility. Until the nature of these compounds is more clearly understood, what their cellular function is remains a matter of speculation.

RISK ASSESSMENT

Elevated levels of adducts in human tissue are clearly biomarkers of exposure. Case-control studies, because they are retrospective, cannot establish causality (Perera, 2000). In order to determine the potential of DNA adducts as biomarkers of risk, it is necessary to examine their presence in subjects prior to the onset of disease, and then investigate at a later date whether those individuals in a cohort with higher adduct levels are the ones that subsequently develop tumours. To date only a few studies have done this. One study monitored aflatoxin B_1 exposure in Chinese men in Shanghai (Qian et al., 1994); 18 244 volunteers each gave a single urine sample, which was stored for future analysis. Fifty-five men subsequently developed liver cancer and their urine samples were analysed along with matched control samples. Levels of aflatoxin adducts in the samples were significantly higher in the cases than in the controls, indicating that this parameter was indeed a biomarker of risk. Interestingly, the more classical methods of measuring exposure, based on estimating dietary consumption from food analysis and questionnaires, failed to identify the cases as being more exposed to aflatoxin B_1 than the controls. Thus the use of a DNA adduct biomarker in this instance revealed a link between exposure and risk of cancer that more classical epidemiological methods of exposure assessment failed to demonstrate.

In another such nested case-control study, the predictive value of DNA adducts in white blood cells for lung cancer risk was determined amongst male smokers. Those smokers who subsequently developed lung cancer had significantly higher levels of aromatic DNA adducts, determined by ^{32}P postlabelling, than those who did not (Tang et al., 2000).

The limitations to the wider use of these methods for risk assessment are those which are generally encountered in prospective studies, namely that large numbers of subjects need to be recruited to the study and that it can take many years for the cases to appear and for the analyses on cases and matched controls to be conducted. In addition, the preservation and long-term storage of the biological samples of every individual recruited must be accomplished, adding considerably to the costs of the study.

In the field of genetic toxicology testing and regulatory affairs, the assessment of the potential carcinogenic and mutagenic properties of new compounds is of paramount importance. A number of in vivo and in vitro tests have been developed with different genetic endpoints, including bacterial mutagenicity, mammalian cell mutagenicity, micronucleus formation and aneuploidy (Phillips and Venitt, 1995), but no single test is reliably predictive (see also the chapter Short Term Testing for Genotoxicity). Many compounds are positive in some tests but negative in others, leaving uncertainties about the true characteristics of the compound. In these circumstances, investigating the compound for DNA adduct formation in suitable experimental systems may help to clarify the issue (Phillips et al., 2000). A good example of such a compound, already mentioned, is tamoxifen, which is a potent liver carcinogen in rats but negative in most regulatory short-term tests for genotoxicity. Despite this, it gives rise to DNA adducts in the target tissue and is considered to be carcinogenic to rats by a genotoxic mechanism.

GENE–ENVIRONMENT INTERACTIONS

From early studies in which short-term explant cultures of human tissue or primary cultures of human cells were treated with carcinogens, it was evident that there was a wide range of DNA adduct formation with samples from different individuals. This variability is also observed in studies of DNA adducts formed *in vivo* in individuals apparently exposed to similar levels of carcinogens and points to the influence of genetic differences in carcinogen metabolism and/or DNA repair.

Detailed discussion of the potential role of polymorphisms in carcinogen-metabolizing enzymes in determining cancer susceptibility is beyond the scope of this chapter, but what can be commented on here are those studies where correlations have been sought between DNA adduct levels and genotype.

Polymorphisms in the *CYP1A1* gene have been extensively studied, although there is still disagreement as to whether these have functional consequences for the activity or inducibility of the enzyme. Two of these are the Msp1 polymorphism (loss/gain of a restriction site) and an exon 7 polymorphism that results in the coding for valine in place of isoleucine (Perera and Weinstein, 2000). One study has found that US smokers with the exon 7 variant allele had higher levels of DNA adducts in their white blood cells than smokers with the normal allele (Perera and Weinstein, 2000). Newborn babies with the *CYP1A1* Msp1 restriction site had higher levels of adducts in placenta and cord blood than those without it (Whyatt *et al.*, 2000). Polymorphisms in other *CYP* genes may also be important but have been less well studied.

A number of polymorphisms in Phase II metabolizing enzymes are also of interest. The *null* genotype of *GSTM1* (in which glutathione *S*-transferase μ1 is absent) is associated with a greater risk of lung cancer, although, curiously, the gene does not appear to be expressed in the lung. Individuals with the *GSTM1 null* genotype have higher levels of lung DNA adducts (Perera and Weinstein, 2000). Polymorphisms in other members of the GST family, such as *GSTP1* and *GSTT1*, are also suspected of influencing carcinogen–DNA adduct levels in the lung. Combinations of polymorphisms in Phase I and II enzymes may additionally refine susceptibility to DNA adduct formation and cancer risk from carcinogen (e.g. tobacco smoke) exposure.

In studies of breast cancer risk, there is evidence that possession of the *GSTM1 null* genotype results in higher levels of PAH–DNA adducts in breast tumour tissue (Perera and Weinstein, 2000), and in another study possession of 'slow' alleles of *N*-acetyltransferase 2 (*NAT2*), which detoxifies carcinogenic aromatic amines, resulted in higher levels of aromatic/hydrophobic adducts (Pfau *et al.*, 1998).

Currently there is much interest in how combinations of polymorphisms in different Phase I and Phase II metabolizing enzymes may, together, confer greater risk on certain individuals than others of DNA adduct formation and, ultimately, cancer risk. As yet, however, no correlations have been found that can account for the very wide range of interindividual variability in carcinogen–DNA adduct formation among human subjects.

CONCLUSION

The formation of DNA adducts by many carcinogens is causally associated with their mechanism of tumour initiation. Mutations in key genes as a consequence of adduct formation are found in many tumours and the altered proteins that they encode have functions that accord with the phenotypic differences between normal and malignant cells. While the formation of adducts is a necessary, but not sufficient, event for malignant transformation, enhancement of adduct formation will increase tumour formation, and inhibition of adduct formation will restrict it (see also the chapter *Mechanisms of Chemical Carcinogenesis*).

The detection and characterization of DNA adducts in mammalian tissues are research fields that are still undergoing rapid development, and in recent years it has become possible to detect adducts with high levels of sensitivity and/or selectivity. Among the many uses for DNA adduct determination, those currently of greatest interest include monitoring human exposure to environmental carcinogens, investigating the mechanism of activation and tumour initiation of carcinogens, monitoring DNA repair and investigating endogenous DNA damage and oxidative processes. DNA adduct detection has an important role to play in the burgeoning field of molecular epidemiology. It is also a supplementary procedure for assessing new compounds for genotoxic activity and can, potentially, provide valuable data for assessing patient response to cytotoxic chemotherapy.

REFERENCES

Beach, A. C. and Gupta, R. C. (1992). Human biomonitoring and the ^{32}P-postlabelling assay. *Carcinogenesis*, **13**, 1053–1074.

Brookes, P. and Lawley, P. D. (1964). Evidence for the binding of polynuclear aromatic hydrocarbons to the nucleic acids of mouse skin: relation between carcinogenic power of hydrocarbons and their binding to DNA. *Nature*, **202**, 781–784.

Cooper, C. S. and Grover, P. L. (eds) (1990). *Chemical Carcinogenesis and Mutagenesis*. Vols I and II. *Handbook of Experimental Pharmacology*, Vol. 94. (Springer, Berlin).

Davis, W., *et al.* (1998). The metabolic activation of tamoxifen and α-hydroxytamoxifen to DNA binding species in rat hepatocytes proceeds via sulphation. *Carcinogenesis*, **19**, 861–866.

Denissenko, M. F., et al. (1996). Preferential formation of benzo[a]pyrene adducts at lung cancer mutational hotspots in P53. Science, 274, 430–432.

Dipple, A. (1994). Reactions of polycyclic aromatic hydrocarbons with DNA. In: Hemminki, K., Dipple, A., et al. (eds), DNA Adducts: Identification and Biological Significance. 107–129 (IARC, Lyon).

Dumaz, N., et al. (1993). Specific UV-induced mutation spectrum in the p53 gene of skin tumors from DNA-repair-deficient xeroderma pigmentosum patients. Proceedings of the National Academy of Sciences of the USA, 90, 10529–10533.

Fearon, E. R. and Vogelstein, B. (1990). A genetic model for colorectal tumorigenesis. Cell, 61, 759–767.

Hainaut, P., et al. (1998). IARC Database of p53 gene mutations in human tumors and cell lines: updated compilation, revised formats and new visualisation tools. Nucleic Acids Research, 26, 205–213.

Halliwell, B. and Dizdaroglu, M. (1992). The measurement of oxidative damage to DNA by HPLC and GC/MS techniques. Free Radical Research Communications, 16, 75–87.

Hemminki, K., Dipple, A., Shuker, D. E. G., Kadlubar, F. F., Segerback, D. and Bartsch, H. (eds) (1994). DNA Adducts: Identification and Biological Significance. (IARC, Lyon).

Jankowiak, R. and Small, G. J. (1991). Fluorescence line narrowing: a high-resolution window on DNA and protein damage from chemical carcinogens. Chemical Research in Toxicology, 4, 256–269.

Lawley, P. D. (1984). Carcinogenesis by alkylating agents. In: Searle, C. E. (ed.), Chemical Carcinogens, 2nd edn. Vol. 1, 325–484 (American Chemical Society, Washington, DC).

Lawley, P. D. and Phillips, D. H. (1996). DNA adducts from chemotherapeutic agents. Mutation Research, 355, 13–40.

Marnett, L. J. (1999). Lipid peroxidation–DNA damage by malondialdehyde. Mutation Research, 424, 83–95.

Marnett, L. J. (2000). Oxyradicals and DNA damage. Carcinogenesis, 21, 361–370.

Marnett, L. J. and Burcham, P. C. (1993). Endogenous DNA adducts: potential and paradox. Chemical Research Toxicology, 6, 771–785.

Mollerup, S., et al. (1999). Sex differences in lung CYP1A1 expression and DNA adduct levels among lung cancer patients. Cancer Research, 59, 3317–3320.

Osborne, M. R. (1984). DNA interactions of reactive intermediates derived from carcinogens. In: Searle, C. E. (ed.), Chemical Carcinogens, 2nd edn. Vol. 1, 485–524 (American Chemical Society, Washington, DC).

Otteneder, M. and Lutz, W. K. (1999). Correlation of DNA adduct levels with tumor incidence: carcinogenic potency of DNA adducts. Mutation Research, 424, 237–247.

Perera, F. P. (2000). Molecular epidemiology: on the path to prevention? Journal of the National Cancer Institute, 92, 602–612.

Perera, F. P. and Weinstein, I. B. (2000). Molecular epidemiology: recent advances and future directions. Carcinogenesis, 21, 517–524.

Pfau, W., et al. (1998). DNA adducts in human breast tissue: association with N-acetyltransferase-2 (NAT2) and NAT1 genotypes. Cancer Epidemiology, Biomarkers and Prevention, 7, 1019–1025.

Phillips, D. H. (1983). Fifty years of benzo(a)pyrene. Nature, 303, 468–472.

Phillips, D. H. (1990). Modern methods of DNA adduct determination. In: Cooper, C. S. and Grover, P. L. (eds), Chemical Carcinogenesis and Mutagenesis, Vol. 1. Handbook of Experimental Pharmacology, Vol. 94. 503–546 (Springer, Berlin).

Phillips, D. H. (1996). DNA adducts in human tissues: biomarkers of exposure to carcinogens in tobacco smoke. Environmental Health Perspectives, 104, Supplement 3, 453–458.

Phillips, D. H. (1997). Detection of DNA modifications by the ^{32}P-postlabelling assay. Mutation Research, 378, 1–12.

Phillips, D. H. and Farmer, P. B. (1995). Protein and DNA adducts as biomarkers of exposure to environmental mutagens. In: Phillips, D. H. and Venitt, S. (eds), Environmental Mutagenesis. 367–395 (Bios, Oxford).

Phillips, D. H., et al. (2000). Methods of DNA adduct determination and their application to testing compounds for genotoxicity. Environmental Molecular Mutagenesis, 35, 222–233.

Phillips, D. H. and Venitt, S. (eds) (1995). Environmental Mutagenesis. (Bios, Oxford).

Poirier, M. C. and Beland, F. A. (1992). DNA adduct measurements and tumor incidence during chronic carcinogen exposure in animal models: implications for DNA adduct-based human cancer risk assessment. Chemical Research in Toxicology, 5, 749–755.

Poirier, M. C., et al. (2000). Carcinogen macromolecular adducts and their measurement. Carcinogenesis, 21, 353–359.

Qian, G. S., et al. (1994). A follow-up study of urinary markers of aflatoxin exposure and liver cancer risk in Shanghai, People's Republic of China. Cancer Epidemiology, Biomarkers and Prevention, 3, 3–10.

Shuker, D. E. G. and Farmer, P. B. (1992). Relevance of urinary DNA adducts as markers of carcinogen exposure. Chemical Research in Toxicology, 5, 450–460.

Strickland, P. T., et al. (1993). Methodologies for measuring carcinogen adducts in humans. Cancer Epidemiology, Biomarkers and Prevention, 2, 607–619.

Tang, D., et al. (2000). Aromatic DNA adducts as a predictor of lung cancer risk in a case-control study. Proceedings of the American Association for Cancer Research, 41, 221.

van Steeg, H., et al. (1998). Use of DNA repair-deficient XPA transgenic mice in short-term carcinogenicity testing. Toxicology and Pathology, 26, 742–749.

Weston, A. (1993). Physical methods for the detection of carcinogen–DNA adducts in humans. Mutation Research, 288, 19–29.

Whyatt, R. M., et al. (2000). Association between polycyclic aromatic hydrocarbon–DNA adduct levels in maternal and newborn white blood cells and glutathione S-transferase P1 and CYP1A1 polymorphisms. Cancer Epidemiology, Biomarkers and Prevention, 9, 207–212.

FURTHER READING

Cooper, C. S. and Grover, P. L. (eds) (1990). *Chemical Carcinogenesis and Mutagenesis*, Vols I and II. *Handbook of Experimental Pharmacology*, Vol. 94 (Springer, Berlin).

Groopman, J. D. and Skipper, P. L. (1991). *Molecular Dosimetry and Human Cancer: Analytical, Epidemiological and Social Considerations.* (CRC Press, Boca Raton, FL).

Hemminki, K., *et al.* (eds) (1994). *DNA Adducts: Identification and Biological Significance.* (IARC, Lyon).

Phillips, D. H. and Venitt, S. (eds) (1995). *Environmental Mutagenesis.* (Bios, Oxford).

Schulte, P. A. and Perera, F. P. (1993). *Molecular Epidemiology: Principles and Practice.* (Academic Press, San Diego).

Chapter 22

Physical Causes of Cancer

Jeffrey L. Schwartz
University of Washington, Seattle, WA, USA

C O N T E N T S

INTRODUCTION

Unlike most chemical and viral carcinogens, physical carcinogens act by imparting energy into the biological material. If the energy imparted produces changes in the bonds holding molecules together, this will yield chemical changes and possibly biological effects. Radiation is the primary physical agent to which we are exposed in our environment. Radiation is a ubiquitous component of our environment. We are exposed to ultraviolet (UV) radiation from the sun, γ-rays from cosmic radiation and the decay of isotopes in building materials, air, water and food, and α-particles from radon and radon daughters that seep into our basements. We are exposed to X-rays and ultrasound from medical procedures, and both microwaves and radiofrequency (RF) radiation from various consumer products, including cellular telephones. Power generation leads to a host of different types of radiation exposure including electric and magnetic fields (EMFs). There is no way to avoid completely exposure to these potentially harmful levels of radiation. Understanding the risks associated with exposure can aid in developing appropriate protection standards and approaches to reducing risks.

Definitions

The amount of energy deposited in biological tissue, and therefore the types of changes seen in cells, depend on the nature of the radiation (**Table 1**). Ionizing radiation refers to those types of radiation that produce the ejection of an orbital electron from an atom or molecule and result in the formation of an ion pair. The ionization potential of most molecules in biological materials is 10–15 electronvolts (eV), so in order to be ionizing, the radiation must be able to impart at least that much energy. Ionizing radiation can be either electromagnetic (X-rays and γ-rays) or particulate (neutrons and α-particles). Energy loss varies with the energy of the incoming photon or particle, the charge of the particle and the character (atomic number, electron density) of the absorbing medium. The density of energy deposition along a track length has a profound influence on the subsequent biological effect. The spatial rate of energy loss along a track length is described by the term 'linear energy transfer' (LET). LET is defined as the energy lost (in kiloelectronvolts) per unit track length (in micrometres). X-rays and γ-rays are considered sparsely ionizing, low-LET radiation with ionization or ionization clusters being spaced relatively far apart. The LET for ^{60}Co γ-rays is $0.25 \, \text{keV} \, \mu\text{m}^{-1}$, and that for 250-kV X-rays is about $3.0 \, \text{keV} \, \mu\text{m}^{-1}$. Energetic particles tend to be more densely ionizing and have a higher LET than X-rays and γ-rays, although this is very dependent on the energy of the particle. The LET for a radon-derived α-particle is between 80 and $100 \, \text{keV} \, \mu\text{m}^{-1}$. For energetic particles, the LET varies over the track length as the particle interacts and the energy spectrum changes. For high-energy particles, the density of ionization at the beginning of the track is fairly sparse and the LET is correspondingly low. As the particle loses energy, the density of ionization and the LET increases. At the end of the track, one may see a peak of ionization density (Bragg peak).

Table 1 Examples of ionizing and non-ionizing radiation

Ionizing radiation (> 10–15 eV)	Nonionizing radiation (<10 eV)
X-rays	UV
Gamma-rays	Microwaves
Alpha-particles	RF radiation
Neutrons	Ultrasound
	EMF

The major mode of energy loss for radiation having energy of 1–10 eV (nonionizing radiation) is excitation. Excitation refers to elevation of an electron to a higher ('excited') state. This state is transient, and when the electron returns to a ground state, the energy released can be in the form of visible light (fluorescence, phosphorescence) or chemical change (e.g. pyrimidine dimer formation). UV radiation is the major nonionizing radiation hazard in our environment. For UV radiation, both the wavelength and the fluence determine biological effects. UV radiation is subdivided into three wavelength bands, UVA (313–400 nm), UVB (290–315 nm) and UVC (220–290 nm). UVC is the most potent band for biological effects because DNA absorbs most strongly at the 254-nm wavelength. However, most UVC radiation is quickly absorbed in air. Thus UVB, which is also DNA damaging and potentially carcinogenic, is considered the greater environmental hazard.

For electromagnetic radiation that produces <1 eV, such as microwave and RF radiation, the energy deposited results primarily in molecular vibration and heat. These types of radiation are usually expressed by their frequency. Microwave radiation ranges from 300 MHz to 300 GHz, RF radiation from 300 Hz to 300 MHz and extremely low-frequency (ELF) radiation from 30 to 300 Hz.

Ultrasound consists of high-frequency acoustic waves too fast for us to hear. Human hearing cannot go beyond about 18 000 vibrations per second, or 18 kHz. The effects of ultrasound are usually classified into thermal, direct and cavitation effects. For nonthermal effects of ultrasound, cavitation is considered to be the most important. Under the right conditions, irradiation of a liquid with ultrasound leads to the formation and collapse of gas- and vapour-filled bubbles or cavities in the solution. The collapse of these bubbles can be violent enough to lead to chemical effects.

X- and γ-rays, UV radiation, microwaves and RF radiation are all forms of electromagnetic radiation. EMFs are not electromagnetic radiation, but mixtures of electric and magnetic fields. These fields emanate from electric power lines and all devices that use electricity. Electricity is usually delivered as alternating current. The resulting EMFs are of extremely low frequency and low energy. At the atomic level, weak electric and magnetic fields are too small to produce chemical changes by themselves. However, EMFs might act to modify biological processes by causing small changes in the frequency of events that trigger different signal transduction pathways. In this regard, all aspects of a field, including its frequency, amplitude and pattern, may be important.

Units of Dose and Activity

Radiation exposure is usually expressed either as energy incident on a surface or energy absorbed per gram of tissue. For ionizing radiation (**Table 2**), the gray (Gy) is the Système Internationale (SI) unit of dose that is most

Table 2   Ionizing radiation units

Type of unit	Unit	Definition
Dose	Gray (Gy)	$1 \, J \, kg^{-1}$
	Rad	1 rad = 0.01 Gy
Dose-equivalent	Sievert (Sv)	Dose × quality factor
	Rem	1 rem = 0.01 Sv
Activity	Bequerel (Bq)	1 dps[a]
	Curie (Ci)	$1 \, Ci = 3.7 \times 10^4 \, MBq$

[a] Disintegration per second.

often used. It is equal to $1 \, J \, kg^{-1}$. An older term still in use is the rad, which is equal to 0.01 Gy. For ionizing radiation, the unit of absorbed dose does not take into account the differences in efficiency with which one type of radiation might act. Therefore, to describe exposures to different types of radiation, a dose equivalent is used. The dose equivalent is calculated by multiplying the absorbed dose by a quality factor that takes into account the biological effectiveness of the radiation. The quality factor for ^{60}Co γ-rays is 1. For some energies of α-particles, the quality factor can be as high as 100. The original term used to compare radiation of different qualities was the rem (roentgen equivalent in man), which was equal to the dose in rad times a quality factor. The present SI term is the sievert (Sv), which is equal to the dose in gray times a quality factor.

Radioactive isotopes decay, producing ionizing radiation at a rate specific for the type and concentration of the isotope. The intensity of the source (activity) is determined by the rate of nuclear transformations per unit time. The SI term used to describe activity is the becquerel (Bq), which is equal to one disintegration per second. The older term sometimes used is the curie (Ci), which was originally defined as the activity associated with 1 g of ^{222}Ra and later was defined as 3.7×10^{10} disintegrations per second; 1 Ci is equal to 3.7×10^4 MBq. Activity is a rate measure. It is not equivalent to dose and, without knowledge of the nature of the decay produced, it is not possible to assign dose or biological effect solely on the basis of activity measures.

Exposure to UV radiation is expressed in joules per square centimetre ($J \, cm^{-2}$). Dose for UV radiation, is in joules. The UV index is another term used to describe UV dose rate. The UV index is a forecast of the amount of skin damaging UV radiation expected to reach the Earth's surface at the time when the sun is highest in the sky. The UV index ranges from 0 at night time to 15–16 in the tropics at high elevations under clear skies. The higher the UV index, the greater is the dose rate of skin-damaging UV radiation.

Incident microwave or RF energy is expressed as energy flux or power density in watts per square centimetre ($W \, cm^{-2}$). The specific absorption rate (in watts per kilogram) is the measure of energy absorbed. Ultrasound exposure is similarly expressed in watts per square centimetre and also by their frequency in hertz. EMFs are described by frequency, amplitude and pattern. Magnetic field strength, a key component of EMF, is expressed in tesla or gauss ($1\,T = 10^4\,G$).

Sources of Exposure

Ionizing radiation exposure varies widely for different populations. In part, exposure levels depend on altitude and latitude. The atmosphere attenuates dose from extraterrestrial sources of radiation; thus higher elevations receive greater doses of γ-rays from cosmic radiation. In the USA, the highest background exposures in a heavily populated area occur in Denver, which experiences about 0.25 mSv per year more than the US average. Higher exposure levels also accompany high-altitude flight. For flights at around 40 000 feet, the average exposure is between 0.005 and $0.01\,\mathrm{mSv\,h^{-1}}$.

The Earth's magnetic field acts to deflect the protons from cosmic radiation towards the poles. Thus the polar regions tend to receive greater doses of ionizing radiation. There are also areas in the world where the natural background is higher than the average. These areas include the monozite regions of India and Brazil. Background radiation levels in these areas may exceed 10 times the world average.

The average yearly dose of ionizing radiation in the USA is 3.6 mSv (360 mrem). To put this number in perspective, for a typical dental X-ray, the equivalent dose is 0.01–0.02 mSv and a chest X-ray is about 0.1 mSv. Cosmic rays and γ-rays from naturally occurring isotopes account for about 1 mSv per year (**Table 3**). Radon accounts for about 2 mSv per year. That is not to imply that we are exposed to large levels of radon. Instead, the α-radiation associated with radon decay has a high quality factor of around 20, hence

Table 3   Sources of ionizing radiation exposure (in the USA)

Source	Amount (mSv per year)
Natural	3.0
Radon	2.0
Cosmic	0.3
Terrestrial	0.3
Internal	0.4
Artificial	0.6
Medical	0.5
Consumer	0.1
Other	
Work, nuclear power generation, fallout	<0.01
Total	3.6

the dose equivalent is high. As for anthropogenic radiation exposure, medical exposures account for about 0.5 mSv per year, while exposures from consumer products make up about 0.1 mSv per year. There are also exposures associated with a variety of other activities, including the use of coal-fired power plants, tobacco products and, as mentioned above, travel at high altitudes.

There are substantial daily and seasonal variations in UV exposure levels. The atmosphere also acts to attenuate dose of UV radiation from the Sun. Most UV radiation is absorbed by the ozone layer or reflected back into space. Atmospheric ozone, which is principally located in the stratosphere, is a strong absorber of UVB radiation. Ozone is formed when molecular oxygen is split by UV radiation. The singlet oxygen atom that results can combine with other molecules of molecular oxygen to form ozone. Ozone production is normally balanced by its destruction through similar photochemical events. In addition, ozone is depleted by the chlorine contained in chlorofluorocarbons (CFCs), a family of commonly used industrial compounds. In part due to these CFCs, the amount of ozone screening the Earth has decreased by an average of 3% per year over the last decade, and a polar ozone hole over the South Polar region has developed. The reduction in ozone has resulted in a corresponding increase in UV levels.

There are a myriad of consumer products that generate radiation. Microwave ovens and cellular telephones provide a common source of microwave and RF radiation. There are a number of medical and consumer devices that use ultrasound. All electrical devices also generate EMFs. Transmission power lines generate both strong electric fields and strong magnetic fields. Distribution lines generate weak electric fields but can generate strong magnetic fields. Exposure levels to EMFs around the home are in the range 0.1–2.5 mG. For homes near power lines, these levels may be as high as 5–10 mG. Immediately under the power line, magnetic field levels of 60–100 mG may be found. The Earth's magnetic field has a strength of about 500 mG, although, unlike EMFs, it is not changing directions 50–60 times per second and is therefore not comparable to electrically generated EMFs. EMFs also show intermittent spikes in frequency (transients) and harmonics, which are multiples of the standard frequency.

GENOTOXICITY

Cancer is a genetic disease and therefore, at some point, carcinogen exposure must result in genetic alterations (see also the chapter *Mechanisms of Chemical Carcinogenesis*). These can be produced directly through an interaction of the radiation with DNA, indirectly, through some intermediate molecule that in turn damages DNA, or radiation may produce epigenetic alterations in cell growth or metabolism that ultimately lead to the transformed phenotype.

Ionizing Radiation

Ionizing radiation induces a variety of different types of DNA alterations, including nucleotide-base alterations and breaks in the sugar–phosphate backbone (Schwartz, 1995). Normally, cells handle these base alterations and single-strand breaks very well using base excision repair processes. Base excision repair is an error-free process that removes damaged bases and then takes advantage of an intact complementary strand to fill in missing information. Defects in excision repair can lead to mutagen sensitivity and cancer susceptibility (see also the section *The Molecular Basis of Cell and Tissue Organisation*).

For X-rays, about one in 10–20 breaks span both strands of the DNA molecule. This ratio of double-to single-strand breaks increases with increasing LET. DNA double-strand breaks can form directly as a result of radiation exposure, or can develop during excision repair due to the formation of overlapping gaps. DNA double-strand breaks are repaired by homologous and nonhomologous recombination processes. These are inherently error-prone and can lead to large deletions and rearrangements. DNA double-strand breaks have been shown to be the primary lethal and mutagenic lesion induced by ionizing radiation. (See also the chapter *Genomic Instability and DNA Repair*.)

Most of the genetic alterations seen in irradiated cells are large deletions and rearrangements. This is mostly a reflection of the nonhomologous repair of DNA double-strand breaks. Because radiation involves the loss of so much genetic material, it is a relatively weak mutagen. Most of the genetic changes lead to cytotoxicity. The nature of the alterations induced by radiation is very dependent on gene locus. Some loci can tolerate the loss of large amounts of genetic material. These loci would tend to be more sensitive to mutation induction and would show primarily large deletion. Other loci, because of their proximity to essential genes, are less tolerant of large deletion formation. These loci will be less sensitive to mutation induction and show far smaller types of genetic changes.

The dose response for mutation induction by X-rays and γ-rays has a quadratic portion to it, suggesting that most mutations develop from the interaction of two breaks (**Figure 1**). Fractionating the dose or reducing the dose rate will in general lead to a reduction in the effectiveness of the radiation by allowing time for repair of these sublethal lesions. As LET increases, both the frequency and the shape of the dose response change. High-LET radiation such as α-radiation is more effective at inducing mutations and their dose response is linear, suggesting that a single α-track can produce enough damage for lesion interaction. Fractionation of high-LET radiation usually has little effect on radiation-induced genotoxicity. The lack of sparing at low dose rates is presumed to be due to the inability of cells to repair damage induced by high-LET radiation.

Recent studies have demonstrated that ionizing radiation can induce genetic instability in exposed cells.

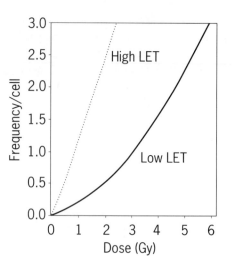

Figure 1 Examples of low- versus high-LET dose responses.

Delayed appearance of elevated frequencies of gene and chromosome mutations has been reported for cells exposed both *in vitro* and *in vivo*. The target for the effect is unknown. Instability is a frequent byproduct of radiation exposure. Rates as high 3% Gy^{-1} have been reported. (See also the chapter *Genomic Instability and DNA Repair*.)

Exposure to ionizing radiation can also induce alterations in gene expression as part of a generalized stress response. This stress response can affect DNA repair, cell toxicity and cell growth. As such, they may lead to more permanent genetic effects. While DNA damage can initiate these stress responses, other targets of radiation have also been identified. Alterations in redox levels or energy levels or specific molecular alterations in key protein molecules may trigger these responses. For example, direct activation of TGF-β by ionizing radiation can influence cell growth and apoptosis.

UV Radiation

The excitations induced by UV exposure will also produce DNA base changes and breaks in the sugar–phosphate backbone. The most important alterations appear to be cyclobutanepyrimidine dimers and pyrimidine-(6,4)-pyrimidone photoproducts. Replication of DNA containing these lesions leads to C to T transitions at dipyrimidine sites. Nucleotide excision repair processes normally repair these base alterations efficiently and without error. Like ionizing radiation, UV radiation can also induce alterations in gene expression as part of a generalized stress response. (See also the chapter *Genomic Instability and DNA Repair*.)

RF and Microwave Radiation

RF and microwave radiation do not produce enough energy to induce chemical change. They can lead to heat, however, and excessive heat may lead to more permanent genotoxic changes (Moulder *et al.*, 1999). Heat can also lead to the induction of a stress response, the spectrum of which overlaps with that seen with ionizing and UV radiation. It remains to be shown whether subthermal levels of microwave or RF exposure such as most of us experience can lead to permanent genetic effects. Most studies report no evidence that prolonged exposures to subthermal levels of microwave or RF radiation lead to genetic or epigenetic changes. The few positive studies suggest that the effects, if any, are small.

Ultrasound

Cavitation is considered to be the primary nonthermal effect of ultrasound that might lead to biological effects (Miller, 1987). Cavitation can lead to cell membrane damage by mechanical forces produced by cavitation. Ultimately, this can cause cell lysis. Cavitation can also lead to the formation of free radicals that can further damage cells. Alterations in cell morphology, membrane transport and cell growth following ultrasound exposure have all been reported, but the effects are small and transient. Ultrasound-induced free radicals have the potential to damage DNA. However, most reports on DNA damage or mutation following ultrasound exposure are negative. The few positive studies that demonstrate DNA strand breakage and gene mutations are for very high intensity exposures. Almost all of these studies are *in vitro* studies. It is less clear whether similar effects will be seen *in vivo*.

EMF

In vitro studies with EMF exposure have focused on endpoints commonly associated with cancer, including cell proliferation, signal transduction alterations and differentiation inhibition as well as on more traditional DNA damage endpoints (Moulder *et al.*, 1999). Effects on gene expression, cell growth and signal transduction were reported for magnetic flux densities $> 100\,\mu T$ or internal electric field strengths $> 1\,mV\,m^{-1}$, but no consistent alterations have been reported for lower intensities. There are no reported direct effects on DNA. Disruption of normal circadian rhythm of melatonin was one postulated mechanism of EMF action. Studies on EMF effects suggest some effect on melatonin, but the significance of this observation for carcinogenesis is not obvious.

CARCINOGENESIS

It has clearly been established that ionizing and UV radiation are both carcinogens. In contrast, the epidemiological evidence for an association between cancer and microwave and RF radiation, ultrasound or EMF exposure is weak and inconsistent.

Ionizing Radiation

Information on cancer induction by human populations comes from epidemiological studies of exposed human populations (National Research Council, 1990, 1999; Schwartz, 1995). For ionizing radiation, the largest single group of exposed individuals are those Japanese exposed to the atomic bombs at Hiroshima and Nagasaki. About 280 000 individuals survived the immediate effects and about 80 000 have been followed for long-term effects. Other exposed populations include early radiation workers such as radium dial painters, uranium miners and populations exposed for therapeutic reasons. These and other smaller groups of exposed individuals serve as the human database for estimating risk for developing cancer following ionizing radiation exposure. (See also the chapter *Identifying Cancer Causes through Epidemiology*.)

At the molecular, cell and tissue levels, cancers induced by ionizing radiation are so far indistinguishable from those that occur spontaneously. Unlike with many chemical mutagens and UV radiation, there are no specific mutations associated with radiation exposure that are also seen in radiation-induced tumours. Recent studies suggest that the initiating event in radiation carcinogenesis may be the induction of genetic instability. (See also the chapter *Molecular Epidemiology of Cancer*.)

The types of tumours seen following radiation exposure are usually the same as seen spontaneously. The effect of radiation on cancer induction is usually inferred from the increase in frequency over background. Radiation-induced tumours appear in almost all tissues of the body, but sensitivity varies greatly for specific tissues and organs (**Table 4**). In general, the thyroid, female breast and certain blood forming organs are considered the most sensitive to induction by ionizing radiation in humans, while kidney, bone, skin, brain and salivary gland are considered the least sensitive. The lymphatic system, lung, colon, liver, and pancreas are among those tissues with moderate sensitivity. The differential sensitivity probably reflects a complex number of factors; it is not simply a reflection of spontaneous frequencies.

The types of cancers observed are also related to the nature of exposure. Many different types of cancer have been seen in the atomic bomb-exposed individuals who in general experienced total body irradiation. Early radiation workers exposed occupationally showed increases in skin

Table 4   Relative ionizing radiation sensitivity of tissues

Sensitive	Moderate	Resistant
Thyroid	Lung	Kidney
Breast	Colon	Bone
Blood-forming tissues	Liver	Skin
	Pancreas	Salivary gland
	Lymphatic system	Brain

cancer and leukaemias, reflecting the nature of their exposure. Many worked with radium, a bone-seeking isotope. Others studied relatively low-energy X-rays where skin would be the primary tissue exposed. Radium dial painters were a group (mostly women) who painted watch dials with a radioactive solution. In the course of their work, they ingested radium. The radium deposited in bone, resulting primarily in higher incidences of bone cancers. Uranium mineworkers inhaled radon gas. The α-radiation exposure resulting from that inhaled radon led to a higher incidence of lung cancer. Thorotrast was a contrast agent used in the late 1920s and early 1930s. It is a colloidal preparation of thorium-232 dioxide that tends to concentrate in the liver. Thorium is an α-emitter. Excess liver cancers and leukaemias were seen in these patients. During the late 1930s, patients in the UK with ankylosing spondylitis were treated with radiation to reduce bone pain. An excess of leukaemias has been reported in these individuals. In the past, radiation has been used to reduce thymus size in children and also for the treatment of tinea capitus. The critical organ exposed was the thyroid. These exposed children later showed excesses in the incidence of thyroid cancers.

The latent period for cancer induction following radiation varies with tumour type, radiation type, dose and dose rate. Leukaemias have the shortest latent periods (mean, 5–10 years), which no doubt accounts for their being seen with most radiation exposures. Solid tumours show latencies of between 20 and 30 years.

In general, the dose response for the induction of tumours by radiation follows a sigmoidal response. At low doses, there is little induction. A steep increase and then saturation or even decrease in tumour frequency at high doses follow. The dose response will vary depending on tissue type, dose rate and tumour latency time. As mentioned above, most of the available data on human carcinogenesis come from individuals exposed to relatively high doses of radiation. No human data exist for proven carcinogenic effects of radiation below 0.1 Sv. The dose response at low levels of exposure remains unknown. One predicts response in this region by extrapolation. Animal studies have suggested that the shape of this crucial portion of the curve may vary greatly from tissue to tissue and animal to animal. At present, linear extrapolation of high-dose effects is used to estimate risk for low doses of radiation. This is considered the most conservative approach. However, there is growing evidence for non-linearity at low doses (Pollycove, 1998). Some investigators have suggested that cells can adapt to low dose exposure and thus linear extrapolation overestimates risk at low doses.

As the LET of the radiation increases, the carcinogenic effects seen also increase in severity up to about 100 keV μm^{-1} (**Figure 2**). As LET increases beyond this point, the effect on carcinogenesis usually declines. This reflects 'overkill,' where individual ionization events are not less effective, but the increasing amounts of the energy released per ionization event are wasted.

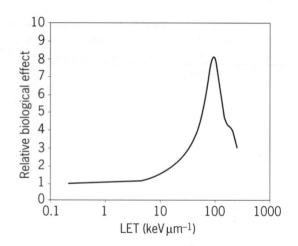

Figure 2   Variation of biological effect with LET. RBE is defined as the ratio of doses (standard: experimental) that yield the same biological effect.

As with other biological effects, protracting the dose over long periods of time reduces cancer incidence, and the effectiveness of fractionated or low-dose-rate irradiation in causing tumours is different for low- and high-LET radiation. Most studies on fractionated low-LET radiation have resulted in a reduction of tumour incidence for a given total dose. Presumably, fractionation of the dose allows for time to repair sublethal and subcarcinogenic damage. In contrast, fractionation of high-LET radiation or low-dose exposure usually has little effect on radiation-induced tumour formation. For some types of radiation, such as fission-spectrum neutrons, reducing the dose rate actually leads to increased transformation and more tumours. This is known as the inverse dose-rate effect. The largest inverse dose-rate effects are seen for fission-spectrum neutrons, with monoenergetic neutrons yielding reduced enhancements, and charged particles having LETs > 120 keV μm^{-1} producing little or no enhancement. The inverse dose-rate effect is most prominent at low doses (< 20 cGy) and low dose rates (< 0.5 cGy min^{-1}).

Sensitivity to tumour induction varies for different species and strains of animals, is different for males and females and also shows interindividual variability (Schwartz, 1995). This variability suggests that the initial damage, which is presumed to be the same for a given dose and type of radiation, is subject to a number of host factors that modify response. Presumably these include repair capability, presence of endogenous viruses, cell proliferation status, endocrine levels, immune competence, age of irradiation and factors associated with genetic susceptibility. There are a number of genetic syndromes that show radiation sensitivity and cancer susceptibility (Murnane and Kapp, 1993).

Radiation risk is defined as the increase in the number of cancer deaths over that expected for an unirradiated population. It is expressed in units per person exposed per gray of radiation. Estimates based on linear extrapolation of the atomic-bomb data and on other more limited data from pooled results of various partial body exposures give total cancer mortality risks for a general population exposed to whole body radiation of $(1-4) \times 10^{-2}$ per person-Gy.

UV Radiation

There is extensive epidemiological evidence supporting the direct role that sunlight plays in human skin cancer (van der Leun, 1984; de Gruijl, 1999; Green et al., 1999). (See also the section Systemic Oncology.) Patients who develop skin cancer generally have decreased melanin pigmentation. Melanin normally acts to protect skin from UV radiation by absorbing it. People with light complexions and who sunburn easily have a higher incidence of tumours. Basal cell carcinomas, the most common skin cancers in Caucasians, are found primarily on sun-exposed areas such as the head and neck where a dose–response relationship exists. There is even stronger evidence for the role of sunlight in causing squamous cell carcinomas of the skin. Although both types of tumours are more prevalent in geographical areas of high sun light exposure, there is a much greater increase in squamous cell carcinomas with decreasing latitude and increasing sunlight exposure. A reasonable correlation also exists between sunlight exposure and melanoma, but the relationship is not as clear as with basal and squamous cell carcinomas. Unlike basal and squamous cell carcinomas, melanomas occur most frequently on the upper back in males and lower extremities in females. Melanoma incidence does not follow a pattern of increased risk with cumulative UV exposure, whereas the incidences of basal and squamous cell carcinomas do increase with cumulative exposure. The risk of skin cancer is highly dependent on UV wavelength. (See also the chapter Identifying Cancer Causes through Epidemiology.)

Microwave and RF Radiation

Studies on microwave and RF radiation and cancer have included analyses of a wide variety of different populations, including radar laboratory workers, foreign service workers, military personnel and electrical workers (National Research Council, 1997; Moulder et al., 1999; National Institute of Environmental Health Sciences, 1999). In addition, there have been a number of animal studies that have looked at the effects of exposure. For many of the epidemiological studies, there is no precise information on dose. Often occupation is used to define exposure groups. In general these studies either find no effect of nonthermal levels of microwave or RF radiation on tumour induction, or show weak and inconsistent results. There is no evidence for any single type of tumour being induced by exposure, and no strong evidence for any dose–response relationship.

There have also been a number of long-term exposure studies with mice and rats. Too many of the animal studies

suffer from poorly controlled exposures where heat stress is a component of exposure. Still, taken together, these studies do not support an effect of nonthermal levels of RF exposure on cancer induction. There is also mixed evidence for a tumour-promoting effect of RF exposure. Some groups have reported that RF exposure shortens tumour latency time and increases tumour frequency in carcinogen-exposed mice and in lymphoma-prone transgenic mice. Others see no effect on the promotion of spontaneous or chemically induced tumours. Hence it is not possible to conclude that nonthermal exposures to microwave or RF radiation have any effect on cancer induction or progression. (See also the chapter Non-Genotoxic Causes of Cancer.)

Ultrasound

There is no reported evidence for cancer induction by ultrasonic exposure. There are some suggestions that ultrasound might encourage neoplastic growth and promote metastases, but no strong evidence for either effect (Miller, 1987). (See also the chapter Non-Genotoxic Causes of Cancer.)

EMFs

The evidence for carcinogenic effects of EMFs is weak. The strongest evidence comes from epidemiological studies that observe associations between EMF exposure and leukaemia. The initial study by Wertheimer and Leeper (1979) suggested a causal association between risk of childhood leukaemia and exposure to magnetic fields. Wire code classifications were used to estimate exposure. Subsequent studies on this association have come to mixed conclusions. In general there appears to be at most a small increased risk of childhood leukaemia associated with EMF exposure (National Research Council, 1997; Moulder et al., 1999; National Institute of Environmental Health Sciences, 1999). There were also initial suggestions of an association between EMF exposure and brain cancers and lymphomas in children, but subsequent studies have not borne out this risk. Epidemiological reports of adult cancer induction by EMF were based primarily on occupational exposures. As with childhood leukaemia, there were mixed results for an association between EMF exposure and chronic lymphocytic leukaemia, suggesting at most a weak risk. The evidence for increased risk based on residential studies of adults is even weaker. (See also the chapter Non-Genotoxic Causes of Cancer.)

There have been numerous animal carcinogenicity studies of EMFs. The animal studies are all negative. There are no data to support any association between leukaemia and EMF exposure. Similarly, no evidence for any significantly increased frequency of tumours or changes in tumour latency or size was observed. The lack of any experimental data to back up the epidemiological data suggests that there might be other factors that explain the increased risk of cancer. However, none has yet been identified.

RISK MODELS AND PROTECTION STANDARDS

There are a number of ways to model risk. Absolute risk refers to the number of cancers induced over spontaneous levels. Relative risk is a multiplicative increase over spontaneous. As cancer latency periods are generally long, time-dependent relative risk models are also used. With ionizing radiation, there are a number of other dependent variables that are considered in developing risk models. These include dose and $(dose)^2$, age at exposure, time since exposure and gender.

Risk estimate development for ionizing radiation is handled by the BEIR (Biological Effects of Ionizing Radiation) Committee in the USA and by UNSCEAR (United Nations Scientific Committee on the Effects of Atomic Radiation) for the United Nations. The NCRP (National Council for Radiation Protection) in the USA and the ICRP (International Commission of Radiation Protection) for the United Nations use BEIR/UNSCEAR information to develop appropriate radiation protection standards. Total cancer mortality risks for a general population exposed to whole-body radiation is currently based on linear extrapolation of the atomic-bomb data and on other more limited data from pooled results of various partial body exposures. Risks are 5×10^{-2} per person-Sv for low dose and low dose rates and 10×10^{-2} per person-Sv for high dose and high dose rates. The values for the working (adult) population are about 80% of those for the general (adult and child) population. Exposures to the general public are limited to 1 mSv per year while occupational standards are 50 mSv per year. Embryo exposure is limited to 0.5 mSv per month.

There are no corresponding limits for UV or ultrasound exposures, although protective measures are usually required for working with UV- or ultrasonic-producing equipment. For microwave radiation, the recommended exposure limit is $10 \, \text{mW cm}^{-2}$. It is based on thermal effects of microwaves. RF limits are one-tenth of the microwave standard. The International Commission on Non-Ionizing Radiation Protection has set up guidelines for EMF exposure. Magnetic field exposures are limited to 1 G for the general public (10 G for short-term exposure) and 5 G (50 G for short-term exposure) for the occupationally exposed.

SUMMARY AND CONCLUSIONS

As mentioned at the beginning of this chapter, radiation is a ubiquitous component of our environment. There is no way to avoid exposure to radiation. Furthermore, as our technology advances, our exposure to various forms of radiation increases in both amount and complexity.

It has clearly been established that ionizing and UV radiation are both carcinogens. They represent the primary physical carcinogens in our environment and most efforts at reducing cancer risks are appropriately focused on these agents. There remain questions as to mechanisms of carcinogenesis for ionizing radiation, and in particular the effects of low-level exposures. Most ongoing studies in this area are attempting to address these questions. The answers may have a profound effect on radiation protection standards.

In contrast to ionizing and UV radiation, the evidence for an association between cancer and microwave and RF radiation, ultrasound or EMF exposure is weak and inconsistent. The levels of exposure to these types of radiation are increasing, as are the numbers of individuals exposed. There is also some uncertainty as to potential interactions between different types of radiation. Hence there are likely to be continuing investigations into the effects of these different types of radiation exposures.

ACKNOWLEDGEMENTS

This work was supported by the National Cancer Institute (NCI) and the National Aeronautics and Space Administration (NASA) through NIH grant CA-73931 and by a grant from the Department of Energy (DE-FC03-00ER62908).

REFERENCES

de Gruijl, F. R. (1999). Skin cancer and solar UV radiation. *European Journal of Cancer*, **35**, 2003–2009.

Green, A., *et al.* (1999). Sun exposure, skin cancers and related skin conditions. *Journal of Epidemiology*, **9**, S7–S13.

Miller, D. L. (1987). A review of the ultrasonic bioeffects of microsonation, gas-body activation, and related cavitation-like phenomena. *Ultrasound in Medicine and Biology*, **13**, 443–470.

Moulder, J. E., *et al.* (1999). Cell phones and cancer: what is the evidence for a connection? *Radiation Research*, **151**, 513–531.

Murnane, J. P. and Kapp, L. N. (1993). A critical look at the association of human genetic syndromes with sensitivity to ionizing radiation. *Seminars in Cancer and Biology*, **4**, 93–104.

National Institute of Environmental Health Sciences (1999). *Health Effects from Exposure to Power-line Frequency Electric and Magnetic Fields*. NIH Publication No. 99-4493. (NIEHS, Washington, DC).

National Research Council (1990). Committee on the Biological Effects of Ionizing Radiation (BEIR V). *Possible Health*

Effects of Exposure to Low Levels of Ionizing Radiation: BEIR V. (National Academy Press, Washington, DC).

National Research Council (1997). Committee on the Possible Effects of Electromagnetic Fields on Biologic Systems. *Effects of Exposure to Residential Electric and Magnetic Fields.* (National Academy Press, Washington, DC).

National Research Council (1999). Committee on Health Risks of Exposure to Radon (BEIR VI). *Health Effects of Exposure to Radon: BEIR VI.* (National Academy Press, Washington, DC).

Pollycove, M. (1998). Nonlinearity of radiation health effects. *Environmental Health Perspectives*, **106**, Supplement 1, 363–368.

Schwartz, J. L. (1995). Radiation carcinogenesis and the development of radiation injury. In: Arcos, J. C. and Arcos, M. F. (eds). *Chemical Carcinogenesis: Modulation and Combination Effects*. 473–508 (Bikrkhäuser, Springer International, Boston).

van der Leun, J. C. (1984). UV-carcinogenesis. *Photochemistry Photobiology*, **39**, 861–868.

Wertheimer, N. and Leeper, E. (1979). Electrical wiring configurations and childhood cancer. *American Journal of Epidemiology*, **109**, 273–284.

FURTHER READING

Hall, E. J. (2000). *Radiobiology for the Radiobiologist*, 5th edn. (Lippinicott, Williams & Wilkins, Philadelphia).

Websites

www.epa.gov
www.lowdose.org
www.osha.gov

Chapter 23

Non-genotoxic Causes of Cancer

Susan K. Murphy and Randy L. Jirtle
Duke University Medical Center, Durham, NC, USA

C O N T E N T S

INTRODUCTION

Genotoxic agents are characterized by their ability to induce DNA changes that alter the coding information within the primary nucleotide sequence either directly or through a reactive metabolite. These nucleotide mutations are widely accepted as the molecular events responsible for inactivating both alleles of a tumour-suppressor gene according to the Knudson 'two-hit model' of carcinogenesis (Knudson, 1971). However, agents that induce epigenetic alterations to the genome, or DNA structural changes in the absence of nucleotide sequence alterations, have increasingly been demonstrated to also play a fundamental role in cancer formation. These non-genotoxic agents induce heritable changes in the DNA that can disrupt gene regulatory regions. Epigenetic changes are potentially even more potent than genetic mutations in causing cancer since the resulting chromatin structural alterations can exert regional influences, thereby disrupting the normal transcriptional activity of multiple genes. This chapter will focus on the mechanisms of chromatin structure modulation and the potential role of epigenetics in the formation and treatment of cancer.

EPIGENETIC CHARACTERISTICS OF DNA

The double helical structure of DNA is remarkable in its simplicity, yet correct gene function requires not only that the base sequence is faithfully transcribed, but also that expression is both spatially and temporally regulated in a tightly controlled manner. The process of development in multicellular organisms depends on the differential repression or activation of particular genes in a cell type-specific

manner, and this programming information must be maintained throughout the life of the individual. This is referred to as 'cellular memory,' and is controlled by epigenetic mechanisms (Riggs and Porter, 1996). Epigenetic regulation is therefore fundamentally important to the control of gene expression. Two major classes of epigenetic modification are instrumental in determining this complex level of gene regulation: histone acetylation and cytosine methylation.

Chromatin Structure

The human genome consists of approximately three billion base pairs of DNA divided amongst 22 pairs of autosomes and two sex chromosomes. If left in its native form, the genome would be several metres in length. The problem of packaging and organizing the DNA within the nucleus is overcome by the coordinated compaction of the genome by specialized DNA-binding proteins, including the histone proteins. 'Chromatin' refers to the combination of DNA together with these proteins and is organized into two major types of subchromosomal domains. Heterochromatin is tightly compacted and less transcriptionally active while euchromatin is less compacted and more likely to be transcribed. The chromatin structure also varies with the phases of the cell cycle. It is relaxed and transcriptionally active during interphase whereas it is condensed and inactive during mitosis. (See chapter on *Regulation of the Cell Cycle*.)

Histones are a family of proteins that provide the scaffolding for chromatin assembly and, consistent with this function, are among the most highly conserved proteins throughout evolution. The histones share the same basic structure consisting of a globular head and a positively charged, nonglobular tail. Histones H2A, H2B, H3 and H4

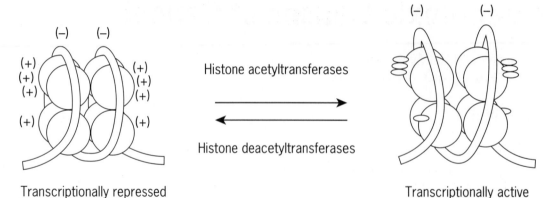

(−)   (−)   (−)   (−)

(+)   (+)
(+)   (+)
(+)   (+)

(+)   (+)

Histone acetyltransferases

Histone deacetyltransferases

Transcriptionally repressed   Transcriptionally active

Figure 1   Histone acetylation and gene transcription. The nucleosomal core consists of eight histone proteins: two copies each of histones H2A, H2B, H3 and H4 (spheres). Approximately 150 base pairs of DNA are wrapped around each histone octamer. In transcriptionally inactive chromatin, the histones lack acetyl groups and are tightly compacted with the DNA. In transcriptionally active chromatin, histones H3 and H4 are acetylated (ovals) on their N-terminal tails. This post-translational modification neutralizes the inherent positive charge of the histone tails that in turn is thought to decrease the affinity of the histones for the negatively- charged DNA phosphate backbone. This contributes to an open chromatin structure in which the DNA is more loosely wrapped around the histones, and is receptive to interaction with transcription factors.

together form a heterooctamer core around which approximately 150 base pairs of DNA are wrapped to form discrete units called nucleosomes (**Figure 1**). Internucleosomal segments are bound by histone H1 and link each nucleosome to the next. The nucleosomes are further bundled into higher order structures to form compacted and organized chromatin. Histone–DNA interactions are modulated in part by reversible acetylation of the ε-amino groups of the histones lysine side chains. The lysine residues carry positive charges thought to contribute to the histone's affinity for negatively charged DNA. Acetylation of these lysine side chains neutralizes the positive charge thereby decreasing the ability of histones to interact with DNA, resulting in a more open chromatin configuration and increased transcription (**Figure 1**). Acetylation of histones by histone acetyltransferase (HAT) is reversed by the action of histone deacetylase (HDAC). The latter enzyme reduces transcriptional activity by promoting chromatin condensation and inhibiting access of the transcription machinery to the DNA. Histone modifications at distinct lysine residues may also allow for the recruitment of proteins capable of regulating transcription in a gene-specific manner.

CpG Methylation

Genome structure is also influenced by cytosine methylation, the only known biological base modification of DNA. Indeed, methylated cytosine has been referred to as the 'fifth base' because of its ability to convey heritable information. The extent of cytosine methylation plays a major role in the organisation of the genomic DNA. Densely methylated DNA is located in condensed

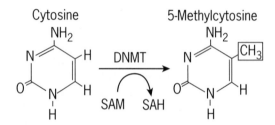

Cytosine   5-Methylcytosine

Figure 2   Methylation of cytosine. Cytosine methylation is performed by DNMT (DNA methyltransferase), and occurs predominantly at CpG dinucleotide pairs, although cytosines in the context CpNpG are sometimes also methylated. The DNMT enzyme transfers a methyl group from S-adenosylmethionine (SAM) to the 5-carbon position of cytosine (boxed CH_3), forming 5-methylcytosine and leaving S-adenosylhomocysteine (SAH).

heterochromatin while sparsely methylated DNA is located in the more relaxed euchromatin. Methylation is the best studied epigenetic modification that occurs in cancer, and will be the main focus of the remainder of this chapter.

The genomic methylation patterns in gametic DNA are erased by a genome-wide demethylation shortly after fertilization. This is followed by *de novo* re-establishment of the methylation patterns after implantation. The mechanisms involved and the proteins guiding the erasure and resetting of the methylation patterns in the genome during embryogenesis are not yet fully understood. Several known DNA methyltransferases (DNMTs) in mammals, including DNMT1, DNMT3a and DNMT3b, catalyse the transfer of a methyl group from S-adenosylmethionine (SAM) to the 5-carbon position of cytosine (**Figure 2**).

This reaction occurs most commonly when cytosine is in a CpG dinucleotide sequence. All three enzymes are capable of performing both *de novo* and maintenance methylation (see below), but DNMT3a and DNMT3b appear to act by transferring methyl groups to previously unmodified CpG sequences, a process that occurs predominantly during embryogenesis.

In contrast, DNMT1 is thought to be the major maintenance DNA methyltransferase enzyme. The palindromic nature of the CpG target of DNMT1 is a key feature in the heritability of the DNA methylation profile during cell replication (**Figure 3**). During DNA synthesis, the nascent daughter strand is methylated by the methyltransferase enzyme positioned at the replication fork. DNMT1 preferentially recognizes the hemimethylated state of the two strands, and copies the methylation pattern of the parent strand on to the daughter strand. Thus, somatic cell methylation profiles represent epigenetic information that is faithfully replicated from one generation to the next.

The incidence of CpG dinucleotides in the genome is about 5–10-fold less than the approximate 6% frequency expected from the random distribution of the 16 possible dinucleotide combinations. The mammalian genome is thought to have progressively lost many of the methylated cytosines within CpG dinucleotide pairs during the course of evolution. This most likely occurred by endogenous deamination of methylated cytosines to form thymine (**Figure 4**). Although 60–80% of the CpGs within the mammalian genome are methylated, cytosines that reside in CpG islands, ranging from 200 to 4000 bases in length, are protected from methylation. They are therefore resistant to mutation by methyl group-driven deamination. These CpG islands are located near the promoter regions of approximately 50–60% of the genes within the genome, including all housekeeping genes. It is not unusual to find CpG islands also located within the 5′ coding region of genes or even in downstream introns.

The biological function of CpG methylation is not clearly understood. Methylation of genomic DNA is a modification employed by numerous species, including bacteria, plants and mammals; however, methylation is not detectable in yeast, *Drosophila* or *Caenorhabditis elegans*. Methylation serves as a host defence mechanism in prokaryotes to protect against the introduction of foreign DNA. DNA methylation in eukaryotes is proposed to similarly serve in host defence by protecting cells from transcription and transposition of endogenous retroviral sequences, and/or to reduce transcriptional 'noise' from very large genomes (Baylin *et al.*, 1998; Robertson and Wolffe, 2000). The CpG islands associated with many of the genes located on the inactive X chromosome in females are also extensively methylated whereas the same alleles on the active X chromosome are unmethylated. Furthermore, the silenced allele of imprinted genes usually exhibits parent of origin-dependent dense methylation of at least one associated CpG island.

Hypermethylation of promoter region CpG dinucleotides is strongly correlated with the transcriptional silencing of genes. The causal relationship between cytosine methylation and gene silencing in mammals is supported by studies both *in vitro* and *in vivo*. Transfection experiments using reporter constructs with a methylated promoter

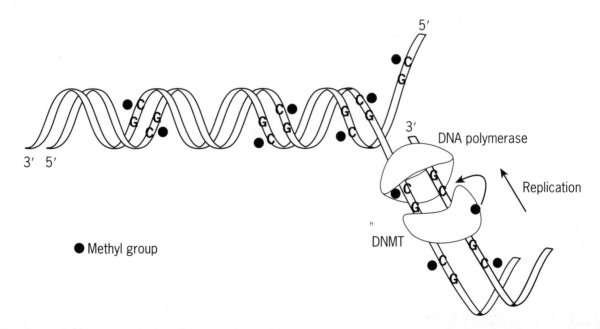

Figure 3 Replication and methylation of hemimethylated DNA. During DNA replication, the newly synthesized daughter strand is methylated by DNMT (DNA methyltransferase) within 1 min of synthesis. DNMT1 recognizes the hemimethylated state of the parent/daughter strand duplex and copies the methylation pattern of the parent strand CpG dinucleotide on to the daughter strand.

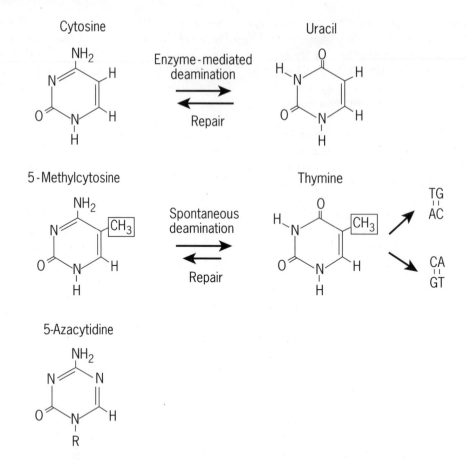

Figure 4   Structures of cytosine, uracil, 5-methylcytosine, thymine and 5-azacytidine (5-azaC). Cytosine is subject to DNMT mediated deamination to form uracil. DNA containing uracil is repaired by uracil DNA glycosylase. Spontaneous deamination of 5-methylcytosine produces thymine and repair of the resultant T–G mismatch is inefficient. Subsequent replication results in the production of either a TpG or CpA dinucleotide pair, depending on the strand affected by the original deamination event. When incorporated into either DNA or RNA, 5-azaC forms a covalent bond to DNMT (DNA methyltransferase) that results in sequestration of the enzyme followed by a progressive depletion of DNA methylation.

region show reduced transcription relative to that for constructs with unmethylated promoters. The DNMT inhibitor 5-azacytidine (5-azaC) (**Figure 4**) causes transcriptional reactivation of endogenous genes with hypermethylated promoters. Furthermore, homozygous disruption of *Dnmt1* in mice results in a three fold reduction in genomic 5-methylcytosine content, embryonic death (Li *et al.*, 1992), and biallelic expression of imprinted genes (Li *et al.*, 1993). These results emphasize the importance of cytosine methylation in gene regulation and embryogenesis. The deviations from normal methylation patterns frequently observed in cancer cells further suggest that epigenetic perturbations are mechanistically involved in oncogenesis.

MOLECULAR MODULATORS OF EPIGENETIC SIGNALS

Several protein complexes play fundamental roles in transcriptional control by recognizing and binding to methylated DNA. They can block the formation of transcription initiation complexes at methylated promoters by steric hindrance. The methyl CpG proteins (MeCP1 and MeCP2) are also capable of directing transcriptional repression through coordinated chromatin alterations. MeCP1 is a ubiquitously expressed protein that binds densely methylated DNA in a sequence-independent manner. It forms a complex with the methyl binding domain protein (MBD2), which further associates with HDACs. The HDACs are thought to contribute to the MeCP1-mediated transcriptional repression by causing chromatin condensation (Hendrich and Bird, 2000).

MeCP2 recruits several other proteins including a repressor of transcription, Sin3A, and an HDAC complex that induces chromatin condensation by deacetylating histone proteins (**Figure 5**) (Jones *et al.*, 1998; Nan *et al.*, 1998). Unlike MeCP1, MeCP2 can bind to DNA via a single methylated CpG dinucleotide; however, the efficiency of repression coordinated by the MeCP2 complex is dependent on the density of methylated CpGs (Magdinier *et al.*, 2000). Dense promoter methylation may in itself

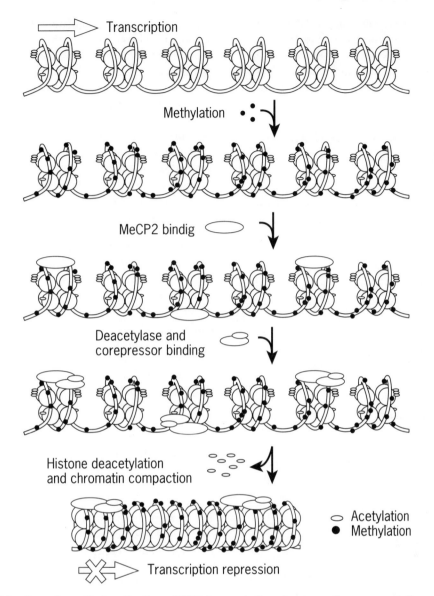

Figure 5   Model for the epigenetic inactivation of DNA transcription. A schematic representation of transcriptionally active open chromatin with acetylated histones is shown at the top. Cytosine methylation of the normally unmethylated promoter region is followed by recognition and binding by MeCP2 (methyl CpG protein). MeCP2 recruits HDAC (histone deacetylase) and other corepressor proteins that function to locally deacetylate histones followed by condensation of the chromatin; the result is promoter silencing. (Adapted from Jones and Laird, 1999.)

further inhibit the access of HAT activity to the hypo-acetylated histones, preventing conversion to a more active chromatin configuration.

Recent studies supporting a link between DNA methylation and chromatin structure formation have shown that DNMT1 also interacts with HDAC2 to repress transcription (Fuks *et al.*, 2000; Robertson and Wolffe, 2000; Robertson *et al.*, 2000; Rountree *et al.*, 2000). During DNA replication, unincorporated histones arrive at the replication fork in an acetylated state. DNMT1 and HDAC2 are both positioned at the replication foci when heterochromatin is replicated during late S phase. This association with HDAC2 could provide a mechanism

whereby histones are deacetylated during assembly to facilitate the faithful structural reproduction of condensed chromatin from one cell to the next during cell division (Rountree *et al.*, 2000).

Cytosine methylation and histone acetylation are proposed to act synergistically in the progressive silencing of genes. One model that accounts for tumour-suppressor gene silencing by epigenetic mechanisms invokes abnormal hypermethylation of the promoter CpG island followed by recruitment of methyl-DNA-binding proteins, including complexes such as MeCP2 that direct HDACs to the area of hypermethylation. Histone deacetylation, probably accompanied by other chromatin remodeling events, can then cause local chromatin condensation and subsequent transcriptional repression (**Figure 5**) (Jones and Laird, 1999; Rice and Futscher, 2000). Thus, epigenetic events are poised to function mechanistically in carcinogenesis by silencing tumour-suppressor genes.

EPIGENETIC CHARACTERISTICS OF TUMOUR CELLS

There is widespread documentation of significant changes in the epigenome of cancer cells. These changes include an overall level of genomic hypomethylation coupled with gene-specific hypermethylation. Hypomethylation events are more generalized, and could lead to the activation of endogenous retroviral elements and any associated proto-oncogenes. However, gene-specific hypomethylation is unlikely to play a major role in oncogenesis since promoter CpG islands are normally unmethylated, with the notable exceptions of imprinted alleles and genes on the inactive X chromosome. In contrast, promoter-specific hypermethylation can lead to the silencing of tumour-suppressor genes.

Inherent Mutability of Methylated Cytosine

The methylation of CpG dinucleotides creates mutagenic susceptibility targets that can subsequently undergo endogenous deamination to form TpG (CpA on the opposite strand) dinucleotide pairs (**Figure 4**). In contrast to cytosine deamination that results in DNA containing uracil, 5-methylcytosine deamination creates a C to T base substitution that is not as readily recognized by DNA repair proteins as being misplaced in the DNA strand. This contributes to inefficient repair of these lesions, and subsequent accumulation of this type of mutation in the genome. Deamination of 5-methylcytosine in *p53* and *HPRT* is a frequent mutational event associated with human cancers (Pfeifer *et al.*, 2000). Although the spectrum of mutations within *p53* varies between different forms of cancer, 50% of all point mutations in colon cancer arise from transition mutations of normally methylated CpG dinucleotides. In contrast, only 10% of liver and lung cancers contain these same mutations. In addition to the potential direct mutational inactivation of a gene by a CpG to TpG transition, these mutated sequences could hinder the interaction between DNA and specific proteins involved in transcriptional regulation.

Alterations in CpG Island Methylation

The genome regions subject to hypermethylation in cancer cells are the CpG islands associated with gene promoters. A study undertaken to identify all differentially methylated CpG islands in cancer estimated that of the 45 000 CpG islands in the human genome, 600 exhibit methylation patterns in tumors different from those in normal tissues (Costello *et al.*, 2000). These methylation changes appear to occur early in the neoplastic process, and some are even cancer-type specific, suggesting that CpG island hypermethylation is mechanistically involved in carcinogenesis rather than being a consequence of neoplastic transformation. An increase in DNA methylation also occurs with ageing. Consequently, the increased cancer predisposition observed with ageing may be partially attributable to the age-dependent increases in genome methylation (see below).

A tumour-suppressor gene inactivated by CpG island hypermethylation would have a number of important characteristics. These include (1) dense methylation of the normally unmethylated CpG island present in the promoter region, (2) an absence of coding region mutations in the tumour, (3) a deficiency of gene-specific transcripts in the tumour, (4) gene reactivation in the tumour with DNMT inhibitors (e.g. 5-azaC) and (5) loss of gene function from hypermethylation comparable to that seen for inactivating mutations (Baylin *et al.*, 1998). It is important to note that alterations in CpG methylation are mitotically heritable (**Figure 3**), and can potentially result in the clonal expansion of neoplastic cells if the epigenetic changes provide a selective growth advantage.

Hypermethylation of Genes in Cancer

The normally unmethylated promoter for many genes is increasingly methylated during neoplastic progression. **Table 1** lists genes whose promoter regions are hypermethylated in cancer, and a number of them are described in further detail below.

p16 located at human chromosome 9p21 is the best documented example of tumour suppressor gene inactivation by promoter CpG island hypermethylation. *p16* is involved in the process of cell cycle regulation. *p16* encodes for a cyclin-dependent kinase inhibitor that blocks cell cycle progression by inhibiting the action of cyclin D. Cyclin D binds to cyclin-dependent kinases and forms a complex that phosphorylates the Rb protein, allowing progression through the cell cycle. Thus, *p16* inactivation would enable cells to proceed inappropriately through cell cycle check points.

p16 was initially identified as a tumour suppressor in melanoma; however, its function as a tumour suppressor was questioned early on because many tumours with LOH at this gene locus lacked mutations in the remaining allele. This apparent discrepancy was ultimately explained by the finding that the promoter of the nonmutated allele was often hypermethylated. Promoter region hypermethylation is also frequently the only detectable alteration, suggesting that the two 'hits' required to inactivate a tumour suppressor can both be epigenetic in origin. *p16* promoter methylation also appears to be an early event in carcinogenesis since it is

Table 1 Genes subject to hypermethylation cancer

Gene	Locus	Function	Tumour type(s)
Tumour-suppressor genes			
APC	5q21	Regulation of β-catenin; cell adhesion	Colorectal, gastrointestinal
BRCA1	17q21	DNA damage repair	Breast, ovarian
CDH1 (E-cadherin)	16q22.1	Homotypic epithelial cell–cell adhesion	Bladder, breast, colon, liver
LKB1	19p13.3	Serine, threonine kinase	Hamartomatous colon, papillary breast
MLH1	3p21.3	DNA mismatch repair	MSI positive colorectal and endometrial
p15 (CDKN2B)	9p21	Cyclin-dependent kinase inhibitor	Acute leukaemias, Burkitt lymphoma, multiple myelomas
p16 (CDKN2A)	9p21	Cyclin-dependent kinase inhibitor	Lung, gliomas, breast, colon, bladder, nasopharyngeal, melanomas, prostate, thymomas, multiple myelomas, lymphomas
PTEN	10q23.3	Regulation of cell growth and apoptosis	Prostate
RB	13q14.2	Sequesters E2F transcription factor	Retinoblastoma
VHL	3p25	Inhibits angiogenesis, regulates transcription	Renal cell carcinoma
Candidate tumour-suppressor and other genes			
14-3-3-σ (stratifin)	1p	Cell cycle control	Breast
CALCA (calcitonin)	11p15.2-p15.1	Reduces serum calcium	Various carcinomas, leukaemia
CD44	11p13	Metastasis suppressor	Prostate
DAP-kinase 1	9q34.1	γ-IFN-induced promoter of apoptosis	Burkitt lymphoma, other B cell malignancies
EDNRB	13q22	Endothelin receptor	Prostate
ER	6q25.1	Oestrogen-induced transcriptional activation	Breast, colon, lung, leukaemia
FHIT	3p14.2	Dinucleoside oligophosphate hydrolase	Oesophageal
GST-π	11q13	Cellular detoxification	Prostate
H-cadherin	16q24.2-q24.3	Cell adhesion	Lung
HIC1	17p13.3	Zinc finger protien	Brain, breast, colon, renal
IGF2	11p15.5	Growth factor, paternally expressed	Rhabdomyosarcoma, Wilms tumour
MDG1	1p33-p32	Fatty acid-binding protein	Breast
MYO-D1	11p15.4	Myogenesis	Bladder, lung
O^6-MGMT	10q26	DNA repair	Brain, colon, lung, lymphomas
p73	1p36	Apoptotic response	Neuroblastoma, T and B cell malignancies
RASSFIA	3p21.3	Ras effector homolog	Lung
RAR-β2	3p24	Retinoic acid receptor/ transcription factor	Breast, colon, pancreas
TIMP-3	22q12.3	Inhibitor of matrix metalloproteinases	Brain, renal

already present in the preinvasive stages of cancer. In colon cancer, where *p16* is frequently hypermethylated, there is also a paucity of mutations in the *Rb* tumour-suppressor gene, indicating that *p16* inactivation alone is sufficient to circumvent the cell cycle G_1 block (Baylin *et al.*, 1998). *p16* hypermethylation has now been implicated in many forms of cancer, including those that originate in the breast, bladder, brain, colon, oesophagus, head and neck, and lung (Liggett and Sidransky, 1998).

p15 and *p16* are positioned 15 kb apart at chromosome location 9p21, and both encode for cyclin-dependent kinase inhibitors. Whereas *p16* inactivation is found principally in solid tumours, loss of *p15* function occurs mainly in haematopoietic cell cancer. The constitutive expression of *p16* differs markedly from that of *p15*, which is more limited and regulated by transforming growth factor-β (Baylin *et al.*, 1998). Hypermethylation in this chromosomal region can affect both *p15* and *p16* promoter

CpG islands simultaneously or it can be specific to either gene promoter. For example, in Burkitt's lymphomas both *p15* and *p16* are hypermethylated, whereas only *p15* is commonly hypermethylated in adult acute myelogenous leukaemia (AML), paediatric AML, adult acute lymphocytic leukaemia (ALL) and paediatric B cell ALL (Baylin *et al.*, 1998). *p15* promoter hypermethylation is also present in the myelodysplastic state preceding leukaemia, indicating that DNA methylation of the *p15* promoter is an early carcinogenic event.

hMLH1 on chromosome 3p21.3 encodes for a protein essential for DNA mismatch repair. (See chapter on *Genetic Instability and DNA Repair.*) Disruption of *hMLH1* expression is frequently found in patients with hereditary nonpolyposis carcinoma, and also to a lesser extent in sporadic colon cancers (Tycko, 2000). The inactivation of *hMLH1* results in microsatellite instability (MIN + phenotype) which is characterized by errors in replication at one to four base pair repetitive microsatellite DNA sequences. *hMLH1* hypermethylation and the concomitant loss of gene expression is estimated to be present in approximately 70% of sporadic MIN+ colorectal carcinomas whereas it is infrequent in MIN− tumours (Herman *et al.*, 1998). *DNMT* inhibitors can restore DNA mismatch repair activity by causing the demethylation of the hypermethylated *hMLH1* promoter (Herman *et al.*, 1998).

E-CADHERIN is located at chromosomal position 16q22.1. E-CADHERIN is involved in the calcium-dependent regulation of cell growth and differentiation by virtue of its ability to mediate homotypic cell-to-cell adhesion. Disruptions in these cellular adhesions are prominent in cancer cells with reduced *E-CADHERIN* expression, providing support for its normal role in preventing tumour invasion and metastasis. LOH at this chromosome location occurs often in breast cancer, and inactivating mutations in *E-CADHERIN* are also found in a variety of other solid tumours. Furthermore, decreased expression of *E-CADHERIN* in both breast and prostate cancers correlates with hypermethylation of the CpG island that encompasses the transcription start site (Baylin *et al.*, 1998).

ER (Oestrogen receptor) at chromosome location 6q25 is expressed in a wide variety of tissues, and it encodes for a transcription factor that is activated only upon ligand binding. The presence of ER protein in breast cancer is prognostic for increased survival and lower risk of relapse. (See chapter on *Signalling by Steroid Receptors.*) Hypermethylation of the *ER* promoter has been found in a variety of tumour types including breast, colon and lung cancer as well as leukaemia (Baylin *et al.*, 1998). An increase in *ER* promoter methylation in the normal colon also occurs with ageing, and this epigenetic change may predispose humans to colon cancer (Baylin *et al.*, 1998; Issa, 2000).

GELSOLIN encodes for a calcium-dependent actin filament severing and nucleating protein whose expression directly correlates with the induction of cellular differentiation (Hoshikawa *et al.*, 1994). *GELSOLIN* expression is always decreased during malignant transformation (Hoshikawa *et al.*, 1994). Epigenetic silencing of *GELSOLIN* is a common feature of most human breast malignancies, a condition that is reversed in cultured cells by treatment with either HDAC inhibitors such as trichostatin A or DNMT inhibitors such as 5-azaC (Tycko, 2000). The ability to reverse silencing of *GELSOLIN* by either one of these agents alone is unusual since many other genes silenced by hypermethylation require treatment first with a DNMT inhibitor followed by a HDAC inhibitor to achieve substantial gene reactivation (Cameron *et al.*, 1999).

O⁶-MGMT on chromosome 10q26 encodes for the enzyme methylguanine–DNA methyltransferase. This ubiquitous protein is responsible for repairing mutagenic and carcinogenic O^6-alkylguanine adducts. The CpG island associated with the promoter of *O⁶-MGMT* is hypermethylated and transcriptionally silenced in multiple solid tumour types, including those originating in the brain, colon and lung (Herman and Baylin, 2000). *O⁶-MGMT* loss of function in colon cancer also plays a major role in determining the type and extent of mutations found in the oncogene K-*RAS*. G to A transition mutations result from unrepaired O^6-alkylguanine adducts, and they are the major type of K-*RAS* mutations present in human colon cancer. The finding that 70% of these K-*RAS* mutations are associated with a hypermethylated *O⁶-MGMT* promoter suggests that epigenetic inactivation of this gene is involved in the formation of this disease (Herman and Baylin, 2000)

p73 is located at chromosome position 1p36, and encodes for a protein proposed to act as a neuroblastoma tumour suppressor. *p73* maps to an area of 1p36 commonly found to have LOH in neuroblastomas; however, the remaining allele in these tumours frequently lacks mutations. Wild-type p73 is reported to interact with c-Abl in promoting apoptosis, while a truncated p73 functions as an anti-apoptotic protein during neural development in mice. Several studies have concluded that the maternal allele of *p73* is functionally inactivated by the epigenetic process of genomic imprinting (see below). Although it is presently unclear if imprinting at the *p73* locus is mechanistically involved in carcinogenesis, *p73* promoter hypermethylation has clearly been documented in both T cell acute lymphoblastic leukaemias and Burkitt lymphomas (Herman and Baylin, 2000).

14-3-3-σ (*STRATIFIN*) on chromosome 1p is a member of the 14-3-3 family of proteins that mediate signal transduction by binding to other proteins containing phosphoserine motifs. *14-3-3-σ* transcription is induced by DNA damage through a p53 response element in the promoter. It is involved in the maintenance of cell cycle arrest at G₂, and it prevents entry into mitosis by sequestering the cdc2–cyclinB1 mitotic initiation complex in the cytoplasm. The promoter CpG island of *14-3-3-σ* is frequently hypermethylated with transcriptional silencing in 91% of breast cancers while point mutations in the coding region and LOH occur infrequently (Ferguson *et al.*, 2000). This transcriptional silencing is relieved by treatment of 14-3-3-σ-deficient breast cancer cell lines with 5-azaC.

BRCA1 (breast cancer type 1) is located on human chromosome 17q21. It encodes for an $\sim$220-kDa nuclear phosphoprotein component of the RNA polymerase II holoenzyme complex. *BRCA1* is implicated in diverse cellular functions, including cell cycle control, chromatin structure-imposed transcriptional regulation and DNA damage response. Approximately 50% of familial forms of breast and ovarian cancer harbour germ-line mutations in *BRCA1*. Whereas 40–80% of sporadic breast carcinomas and 30–60% of sporadic ovarian carcinomas show LOH at this chromosomal location and have decreased levels of *BRCA1* mRNA, somatic mutations in *BRCA1* are very rare (Bianco *et al.*, 2000; Esteller *et al.*, 2000a).

The promoter of *BRCA1* is contained within a 2.7-kb CpG island. The 5' end of this large CpG island is unusual in that it is normally methylated in somatic cells but not in the gametes. A repeat element located within this CpG island may be responsible for facilitating methylation of this region. *BRCA1* expression in normal breast, cervical and kidney cells is enhanced up to fivefold by treatment with DNMT inhibitors, suggesting that methylation of the 5' portion of the CpG island in normal tissues may function in regulating *BRCA1* expression (Magdinier *et al.*, 2000). Interestingly, *BRCA1* promoter methylation is significantly increased in medullary and mucinous subtypes of breast carcinomas relative to ductal subtypes; *BRCA1* methylation is also observed in conjunction with LOH in ovarian cancer (Esteller *et al.*, 2000a). Evidence also suggests that *BRCA1* hypermethylation is specific to breast and ovarian cancer since the *BRCA1* promoter is not abnormally methylated in primary colorectal and liver carcinomas or in leukaemias (Bianco *et al.*, 2000; Esteller *et al.*, 2000a).

APC (adenomatous polyposis coli) tumour-suppressor gene is located at chromosome 5q21. It encodes for a large protein that normally associates with and negatively regulates signalling of the cell adhesion protein, β-catenin. Familial adenomatous polyposis (FAP) is an inherited disorder arising from germ-line mutations in *APC*. (See chapter on *Inherited Predispositions to Cancer*.) The majority of these mutations produce truncated proteins that are incapable of mediating β-catenin degradation, thereby resulting in the activation of genes involved in cell growth (Esteller *et al.*, 2000b). *APC* is genetically inactivated early in the genesis of both familial and sporadic forms of colorectal carcinoma. The identification of FAP cases where either one or both alleles of *APC* lacked genetic lesions suggested an alternative form of *APC* repression. Methylation analyses confirmed that the *APC* promoter is commonly hypermethylated in colorectal adenomas and other cancers associated with the gastrointestinal tract, but not in brain, head and neck, lung and ovarian cancer (Esteller *et al.* 2000b).

HIC1 (hypermethylated in cancer) on chromosome 17p13.3 encodes for a zinc finger protein transcription factor that is a candidate tumour suppressor activated by p53 (Baylin *et al.*, 1998). The normally unmethylated *HIC1* contains a CpG island that spans the entire gene, and hypermethylation of this CpG island has been documented in many solid tumours including those of the breast, colon, kidney and lung as well as in leukaemia. *HIC1* hypermethylation occurs in both acute lymphoblastic leukaemias (53%) and acute myeloid leukaemias (10%) (Issa *et al.*, 1997). Furthermore, *HIC1* promoter hypermethylation is more prominent during blast crisis in chronic myelogenous leukaemia and the progression stage of acute lymphocytic leukaemia. This suggests that *HIC1* methylation is a later event in the genesis of leukaemia.

RAR-β2 (retinoic acid receptor beta) is located on chromosome 3p24. It is one of three known retinoic acid receptors that together belong to the nuclear receptor superfamily. *RAR-β* encodes for a putative tumour-suppressor protein that functions as a transcription factor when bound to retinoic acid (RA). RAR transcription factors bound to RA heterodimerize with retinoid X receptors, and then bind to retinoic acid responsive elements (RAREs) within the regulatory regions of RA-inducible genes. Transfection of *RAR-β* cDNAs into non-expressing tumour cells results in growth suppression, whereas transgenic mice expressing *RAR-β* antisense RNAs demonstrate enhanced tumorigenesis. These results demonstrate that *RAR-β* normally has an antiproliferative function. RAR-β levels are decreased in a number of cancers, including those that develop in the breast, cervix, head and neck, lung and ovary. Analysis of primary breast tumours indicates that approximately one-third have hypermethylation at the *RAR-β2* promoter (Sirchia *et al.*, 2000). Loss of both RAR-β and ER function in breast cancers is correlated with resistance to RA treatment. The *RAR-β2* promoter is abnormally hypermethylated in several forms of cancer including breast cancer, colon carcinoma and pancreatic carcinoma, but its methylation status appears to not be related to the presence of functional ER protein (Sirchia *et al.*, 2000).

IMPRINTED GENES AS CANCER SUSCEPTIBILITY LOCI

Genomically imprinted genes provide strong evidence that transcriptional silencing results from DNA methylation. This subset of genes is normally monoallelically expressed in a parent of origin-dependent manner. Imprinted gene expression in somatic cells depends upon the sex of the parent from which the allele originated, but not the sex of the individual. Every imprinted gene thus far examined has been associated with at least one differentially methylated CpG island. The epigenetic changes that confer the heritable imprint mark have not yet been unambiguously defined, but cytosine methylation is the strongest candidate. Histone acetylation has also been proposed to be mechanistically involved in imprinted gene regulation since parental-specific differences in acetylation are associated with imprinted genes (Hu *et al.*, 1998). Approximately 40 imprinted genes have been identified in humans to date, and estimates predict the presence of 100–200 imprinted genes in the entire genome (Barlow, 1995). The normal silencing of the imprinted allele is equivalent to a first 'hit' in the 'two-hit hypothesis' for carcinogenesis (**Figure 6**) (Knudson, 1971). A single genetic or epigenetic alteration in the expressed allele could therefore completely abrogate function of an imprinted gene. Since most imprinted genes are involved in cell growth and all are functionally haploid, they represent unique susceptibility loci for cancer development.

Human *IGF2* and *H19* are located in a chromosomal region (11p15.5) harbouring a cluster of imprinted genes. *IGF2* encodes for a potent mitogenic factor involved in cell growth and embryonic development whereas *H19* transcripts are non-coding. The reciprocally imprinted *IGF2* and *H19* genes are expressed from the paternally and maternally inherited alleles, respectively. The epigenetic regulation of this locus has been intensively studied in normal and malignant tissues. IGF2 overexpression occurs commonly in cancer (for a review, see Reik *et al.*, 2000), and loss of imprinting is one mechanism responsible for the dysregulation of this influential growth factor (Rainier *et al.*, 1993).

Human *IGF2* has four promoters that function in a tissue-specific manner (Vu and Hoffman, 1994). Promoters 2 to 4 are contained within a CpG island, and transcripts derived from these promoters are monoallelically expressed. In contrast, the P1 promoter 20 kb upstream of P2 is not associated with this CpG island, and drives biallelic expression of IGF2 in the liver (Vu and Hoffman, 1994; Baylin *et al.*, 1998). During the ageing process, the P2 to P4 promoters of the normally unmethylated paternal allele are subject to incremental increases in methylation, and methylation of these promoters is also enhanced in cancer. Hypermethylation of this region in tumour cells results in decreased expression originating from the P3 promoter with the switching of IGF2 transcription regulation to the non-imprinted P1 promoter (Vu and Hoffman, 1994). The ability of *IGF2* to undergo such promoter switching can be regarded as an epigenetic mechanism by which tumour cells can gain a selective growth advantage. Interestingly, the mouse *Igf2* does not have the equivalent of the human P1 promoter, and

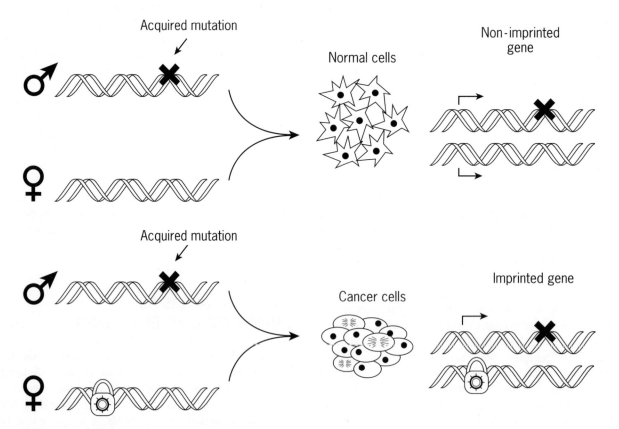

Figure 6   Imprinted genes as susceptibility loci in cancer. For most nonimprinted genes, an acquired mutation (X) does not contribute directly to carcinogenesis because of the presence of a second transcriptionally active wild-type allele. In contrast, acquisition of a genetic or epigenetic mutation on the active allele of an imprinted tumour-suppressor gene (paternal in this example) can directly result in cancer by inactivation of the single functional copy of the gene.

therefore biallelic expression cannot occur via this mechanism in mice. This fundamental difference between species in regulating *IGF2* expression is important to consider when extrapolating carcinogenic risk estimates from mice to humans. (See chapter on *Advantages and Limitations of Models for Cancer and Malignant Cell Progression*.)

The epigenetic control of *IGF2* imprinting has recently been further refined with the demonstration that imprinted expression of both *IGF2* and the adjacent, reciprocally imprinted *H19* depends on the presence of differentially methylated CTCF (vertebrate enhancer blocking protein) DNA-binding sites between these two genes (**Figure 7**) (Bell and Felsenfeld, 2000; Hark *et al.*, 2000; Kanduri *et al.*, 2000). The mechanism of CTCF-mediated transcriptional repression also involves CTCF interaction with HDACs (Lutz *et al.*, 2000). In the case of *IGF2*, methylation of the paternal allele at the CTCF recognition sites prevents CTCF binding. In contrast, CTCF proteins bind to the unmethylated maternal allele, creating a physical boundary. This prevents the enhancer elements located downstream of *H19*

from interacting with the *IGF2* promoter. Consequently, *IGF2* and *H19* are reciprocally imprinted, and transcribed from the paternal and maternal alleles, respectively. Deletion of this CTCF binding region on the maternal allele results in biallelic expression of *IGF2* (Thorvaldson *et al.*, 1998; Srivastava *et al.*, 2000). In colorectal cancers with loss of imprinting for *IGF2*, abnormal methylation of the maternal CTCF binding sites has been observed (Nakagawa *et al.*, 2001). Together with the demonstration that methylation of CpGs within the CTCF binding site block CTCF binding (Kanduri *et al.*, 2000), these results suggest a mechanistic link between the CTCF epigenetic control elements, loss of *IGF2* imprinting, and carcinogenesis.

We have recently provided evidence that another pair of human imprinted genes utilizes a similar mechanism to control their reciprocal imprinting pattern. The *DLK1/GTL2* domain at chromosome 14q32 encodes for the paternally expressed *DLK1* and the maternally expressed *GTL2* genes. *DLK1* is involved in several cellular differentiation processes including adipogenesis, haematopoiesis and

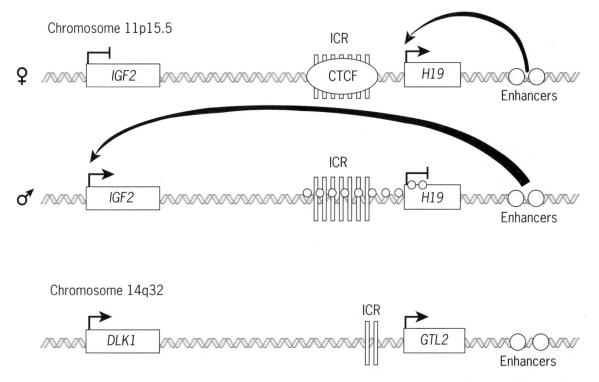

Figure 7 Cancer predisposition and methylation-dependent chromatin boundary elements. The reciprocally imprinted *IGF2* and *H19* genes at 11p15.5 are separated by approximately 100 kb of DNA that contains a differentially methylated ICR (imprint control region). The ICR contains seven methylation-sensitive CTCF (vertebrate enhancer blocking protein) binding sites (vertical bars). CTCF proteins are blocked from binding the methylated (small circles) paternal allele but the unmethylated maternal allele binds CTCF resulting in the formation of a chromatin boundary element. This boundary is thought to divert the enhancer elements, located downstream of *H19*, away from the maternal *IGF2* promoter and toward the available *H19* promoter, resulting in maternal *H19* expression. In contrast, the paternal *IGF2* is expressed because its promoter is subject to enhancer influence since methylation of the paternal ICR prevents CTCF binding and boundary formation. A second set of reciprocally imprinted genes was identified at 14q32 (Wylie *et al.*, 2000). *DLK1* and *GTL2* share spatial, structural, and expression characteristics with the *IGF2/H19* locus and there are two differentially methylated consensus CTCF binding sites between these two genes.

neuroendocrine differentiation, and may play an important role in neuroendocrine tumorigenesis (Laborda, 2000). Like *IGF2* and *H19*, *DLK1* and *GTL2* are also separated by differentially methylated consensus CTCF binding sites. Furthermore, enhancer element sequences are located downstream from *GTL2* that are identical with those found downstream of *H19* (**Figure 7**) (Wylie *et al.*, 2000). These findings suggest that this mechanism of epigenetic regulation may be commonly employed to coordinate the expression of juxtapositioned reciprocally imprinted genes. Thus, specific mutation of these CTCF binding sites and/or the CTCF binding proteins could potentially alter the expression of a number of imprinted genes in the genome.

NON-GENOTOXIC MEDIATORS OF CARCINOGENESIS

Non-genotoxic carcinogens induce cancer by causing epigenetic changes in the genome rather than by directly mutating the DNA base composition. Furthermore, both endogenous and exogenous factors can cause these epigenetic changes. Oxidation of guanine by endogenous chemicals often results in the formation of 8-hydroxyguanine that can contribute directly to genetic alteration because it is a potentially miscoding base, and also impair normal epigenetic DNA modification by impeding the methylation of adjacent cytosines. This is also true for photodimers, abasic sites, base alkylations and other oxidative DNA lesions that not only directly damage DNA, but also lead to heritable alterations in normal genomic methylation patterns (Wachsman, 1997; MacPhee, 1998). Additionally, a number of exogenous chemical agents are now known that induce both genome wide and gene specific chromatin structure changes by altering DNA methylation directly or by modifying DNMT activity (**Table 2**) (Baylin *et al.*, 1998). Below is a brief description of specific compounds and factors that cause cancer through non-genotoxic mechanisms.

Nickel

Studies with carcinogenic nickel have led to development of a model for the potential epigenetic mechanisms by which non-genotoxic carcinogens inactivate tumor suppressor genes (Costa, 1995). Water-insoluble Ni^{2+} is a non-genotoxic carcinogen that localizes to the nucleus following its cell entry by phagocytosis. There it is thought to act through its affinity for heterochromatic regions of the genome. Chromosomal damage in these regions presumably results from oxidation that occurs when Ni^{2+} binds to chromatin proteins. These genotoxic events are normally not detrimental since the affected heterochromatin is usually genetically inactive; however, nickel also appears to cause harmful epigenetic modifications.

Table 2   Agents that influence DNA methylation

Induce hypomethylation	Induce hypermethylation
1,3-Bis(2-chloroethyl)-1-nitroso-urea	3′-Azidodideoxythymidine (AZT)
4-Nitroquinoline 1-oxide	3-Deazaadenosine
4-Nitrosodiethylamine	5-Fluorouracil
4-Nitroso-*N*-ethylurea	5-Fluorodeoxyuridine
5-Azadeoxycytidine	Aphidicolin
5-Fluorodeoxycytidine	Butyrate
6-Thioguanine	Cisplatinum
7,12-Dimethylbenz[*a*]-anthracene	Colchicine
Aflatoxin B_1	Etoposide
Benzo[*a*]pyrene	Doxorubicin
Butyrate	Nalidixic acid
Butyryl-cAMP	Propionate
Bromobenzene	Trapoxin
Cyclophosphamide	Trichostatin
Ethionine	Vinblastine
Hydralazine	Vincristine
Lead nitrate	
MNNG, other alkylating agents	
N-Methyl-*N*-nitrosourea	
Novobiocin	
Oestradiol	
Procainamide	
Pseudoisocytidine	
Retinoic acid	
Teniposide	
Toposide	
Topoisomerase II inhibitors	

(Adapted from Holliday, 1991 and Wachsman, 1997.)

This is postulated to result from nickel binding to oxygen atoms in the DNA phosphate backbone within heterochromatin and inducing a localized increase in DNA methylation. If this nickel-induced DNA methylation spreads outward to encompass adjacent euchromatic regions, tumour-suppressor genes within the proximity of the epimutated heterochromatin can be aberrantly silenced (Costa, 1995).

Peroxisome Proliferators

Peroxisomes are cytoplasmic organelles that are present in all eukaryotic cells except red blood cells. They are bounded by a single membrane and function in the metabolism of many substrates including long-chain fatty acids, sterols, dicarboxylic acids, prostaglandins, xenobiotics and oxygen free radicals. They are also involved in the synthesis of cholesterol, ether lipids, carbohydrates and bile acids (Masters and Crane, 1998). While peroxisomes are present in cells throughout the body, their density is cell-type dependent, with the largest number present in mammalian liver and kidney (Masters and Crane, 1998).

Peroxisomes are induced by a group of compounds collectively called peroxisome proliferators. These agents markedly increase peroxisome number, and they can also stimulate replicative DNA synthesis while suppressing apoptosis (Masters and Crane, 1998). Although this class of agents induces peroxisome proliferation in mice and rats through its interaction with the peroxisome proliferator activated receptor alpha (Peters et al., 1997), guinea pigs do not exhibit this effect, and neither do dogs, marmosets or humans. There is strong evidence that peroxisome proliferators are hepatocellular carcinogens in rodents; however, there is a substantial species-specific difference in the carcinogenic response to these agents (Roberts, 1999). They are considered to be non-genotoxic carcinogens since they act independently of covalent DNA binding and without evidence of genetic mutation. The mechanism by which peroxisome proliferators cause cancer is still under active investigation, but it is thought to involve increased oxidative stress caused by prolonged agent exposure (Masters and Crane, 1998). Importantly, accumulated data indicate that peroxisome proliferators do not constitute a serious carcinogenic risk to humans and other primates.

Diet

S-Adenosylmethionine (SAM) is the methyl donor for various methylation reactions in mammalian cells, including DNA methylation (**Figure 2**). A dietary deficiency in SAM precursors or cofactors involved in SAM biosynthesis (such as folate) leads to genomic hypomethylation, and diets deficient in these components have been widely used to induce liver tumours in rodents (Laird, 2000). In humans, dietary deficiency of methyl donors correlates with an increased risk for liver and colon tumours (Giovannucci et al., 1993). This hypomethylation is thought to be caused by either a deficiency in methyl group donors or by DNMT-enhanced cytosine deamination, but the mechanism has not yet been established (Laird and Jaenisch, 1996; Zingg and Jones, 1997). With the increasing awareness of the importance of DNA methylation in cancer formation, there is an expanding commercial interest in human dietary supplements fortified with methylation precursors such as SAM and folate. Studies to determine the specific contribution of diet to changes in DNA methylation patterns are certainly called for, and will help clarify the need for dietary intervention as a preventative or therapeutic measure against cancer.

Ageing

DNA hypomethylation was originally suspected to be responsible for the gene expression changes often observed with the ageing process. Interestingly, age-related decreases in DNA methylation occur primarily in the coding and intronic regions of genes, and they correlate

poorly with observed reductions in gene expression (Issa, 2000). This disparity was clarified by studies showing that reduced gene expression that occurs with age results from a progressive increase in gene specific promoter methylation rather than generalized genomic hypomethylation.

These age-related increases in promoter CpG island methylation occur in a number of genes involved in cancer, including IGF2, Versican, PAX6, and N33 in colon cancer and HIC1 in prostate cancer (Issa, 2000). It is likely that many other genes will also fall into this category, because several studies designed to isolate differentially methylated CpG islands in cancer have identified a number of CpG islands that exhibit increased methylation with both ageing and neoplastic transformation (Issa, 2000). Not all age-dependent hypermethylation events result in cancer. The ER gene is hypermethylated in nearly all primary colon cancers, yet the normal colon of patients both with and without colon cancer has about the same yearly increase in ER promoter CpG island methylation (Issa, 2000). Since age-related hypermethylation varies among individuals of the same age, it is likely that genetic predisposition to epimutations, as well as exposure to environmental factors are involved in cancer formation. Thus, there is now compelling evidence of a mechanistic link between the ageing process and tumorigenesis in that age-related promoter hypermethylation frequently occurs in genes known to be involved in cancer formation (Issa, 2000).

DIAGNOSTIC AND THERAPEUTIC POTENTIAL OF EPIGENETIC ABNORMALITIES

Cancer Diagnosis

Sequencing data obtained from the human genome project are currently undergoing analysis to construct a human epigenetic map based on CpG content. This knowledge coupled with cross-species comparisons of the epigenome will be invaluable in deciphering the epigenetic elements involved in gene regulation (e.g., Hardison, 2000; Killian et al., 2000; Vu and Hoffman, 2000; Wylie et al., 2000). Epigenetic alterations in genes are early oncogenic events in some cancers, and detection of these early abnormalities may aid in protecting people from cancer through dietary alterations or pharmacological intervention (Laird, 1997). With increasing awareness of the importance of epigenetics in cancer formation, and the advent of laboratory techniques such as bisulfite DNA sequencing, methylation-sensitive PCR (**Figure 8**) and gene expression profiling by DNA microarrays, it is likely that methylation profiles will ultimately be used to predict an individual's predisposition to cancer, assist in cancer diagnosis and determine optimal therapeutic approaches (Esteller et al., 2001).

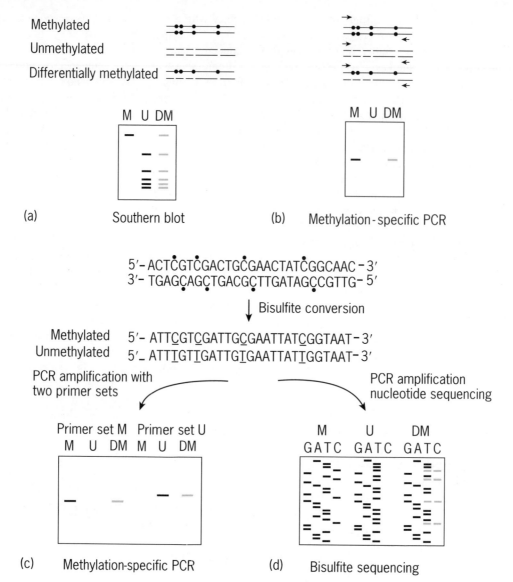

Figure 8 Methods used to analyse CpG methylation. Cytosine methylation is indicated by the circles. (a) Southern blotting depends on methylation-sensitive restriction enzymes to discriminate between methylated and unmethylated alleles. DNA is digested and fractionated on an agarose gel followed by blotting with a probe specific to the region of interest. Methylated recognition sites are resistant to digestion and will yield larger DNA fragments on the blot than unmethylated DNA. (b) Methylation-specific PCR requires digestion with methylation sensitive restriction enzymes, followed by PCR amplification. Methylated (uncut) DNA will yield an amplification product whereas unmethylated DNA will not be amplified. Bisulfite conversion of unmethylated cytosines precedes analysis by either a modification of methylation-specific PCR (c) or bisulfite sequencing (d). Sodium bisulfite treatment of DNA leads to the conversion of unmethylated cytosines to uracils while methylated cytosines are protected from conversion. Subsequent PCR using two independent primer sets designed to bisulfite protected and bisulfite converted sequence amplify methylated (M) and unmethylated (U) alleles, respectively. Bisulfite sequencing is the most direct means of analysing the methylation status of individual cytosines. Fully methylated cytosines are evident in the C lane of a sequencing gel using this method, while unmethylated cytosines are converted to thymines in the PCR amplification step prior to sequencing. Alleles having differential cytosine methylation (DM) are evident by the presence of bands in both the C and T lanes.

Cancer Treatment

A promising feature of alterations in DNA methylation patterns and chromatin structure in cancer cells is their potential for reversibility, because these modifications occur without changing the primary nucleotide sequence. The two major pharmacological targets associated with these epigenetic changes are DNMT and HDAC. The DNMT inhibitor 5-azaC is structurally similar to cytosine (**Figure 4**), but when incorporated into DNA it forms a stable covalent bond with DNMT that inhibits further methylation by the sequestered enzyme. Consequently, overall genomic hypomethylation develops with subsequent rounds of DNA replication.

5-AzaC is efficacious in treating patients with acute leukaemia. It has also undergone clinical testing for the treatment of solid tumours; however, 5-azaC produces a high level of normal tissue toxicity and mutagenicity. These untoward side effects are not due to the resulting hypomethylation, but are attributed to the presence of the incorporated DNMT–5-azaC complexes in the genomic DNA (Laird, 1997). More specific strategies to inhibit the action of DNMT are being developed, including the use of antisense molecules. In this approach, antisense DNAs complementary to the DNMT mRNA inhibit methyltransferase activity by preventing DNMT translation. HDAC inhibitors, such as trichostatin A and sodium butyrate, have been shown to increase the level of histone acetylation in cultured cells, and to cause growth arrest, differentiation and apoptosis. Consequently, they are currently being tested in clinical trials as therapeutic agents for cancer.

Refinement in our understanding of the specific contributions of methylation and histone deacetylation to tumour-suppressor gene silencing in each type of cancer may make custom-designed treatments for gene reactivation possible. For example, *GELSOLIN* silencing can be reversed by treatment with HDAC inhibitors alone, while other tumour-suppressor genes achieve higher levels of reactivation when DNMT and HDAC inhibitors are used together. *RAR-β2* provides another example of the specificity of epigenetic reactivation. Loss of *RAR-β* expression by promoter hypermethylation can result in tumour resistance to treatment with all-*trans*-retinoic acid. Thus, demethylating agents in combination with all-*trans*-retinoic acid have been proposed for the treatment of cancers lacking *RAR-β* expression because of promoter hypermethylation (Côté and Momparler, 1997). Combining trichostatin A with all-*trans*-retinoic acid not only reactivated *RAR-β* in breast cancer cells, but also significantly reduced cell proliferation (Sirchia *et al.*, 2000).

Another novel therapeutic approach proposes to use genetically engineered proteins to reactivate genes with epigenetically silenced promoters. In this approach, a chimeric fusion protein containing DNA-binding zinc finger motifs joined to protein domains having, or capable of recruiting HAT activity for example, might be used to target and alleviate localized areas of chromatin condensation in the promoter regions of silenced tumour suppressor genes. The specificity of the target sequence binding originates from the customized site-specific DNA contacts of the zinc finger domain. Once bound to the target sequence, the chromatin modifier activity would act locally to alleviate chromatin condensation and promote gene reactivation. These proteins could be tailored to virtually any sequence, and would be tethered to the particular protein domains required for the activation of the affected gene promoter (e.g. Liu *et al.*, 2001). Combinations of these chimeric proteins might also expedite a positive clinical outcome by targeting multiple silenced genes simultaneously. Epigenetic cancer therapy also has major potential advantages over conventional therapeutic approaches. First, intact copies of tumour-suppressor genes do not need to be transfected into cells because they are already present in the cancer cell genome; they only need to be reactivated. Second, if gene-specific approaches are used to reactivate epigenetically silenced tumour-suppressor genes there should be little normal tissue toxicity, enabling them to be safely combined with more conventional therapies.

CONCLUSION

Recent years have seen a shift in thinking regarding the molecular basis for gene inactivation in cancer toward accommodating both genetic and epigenetic mechanisms. There has been a dramatic increase in the number of literature reports documenting hypermethylation of specific genes in numerous types of cancer, and it is clear that abnormal promoter hypermethylation is a prominent aetiological event. The specific mechanisms leading to epigenetic inactivation of genes in cancer must be further defined in addition to the roles of repressor complex components that coordinate silencing of these specific genes. With this knowledge, it may be possible to implement strategies in susceptible individuals to prevent deleterious epigenetic alterations that would otherwise lead to cancer. There is also the exciting possibility of developing novel therapeutic approaches for specifically alleviating abnormal promoter hypermethylation in tumours. The sequences involved in establishing the epigenetic profile of chromatin are clearly of fundamental importance to oncogenesis. Cross-species sequence comparisons in the future will greatly facilitate our ability to move from a single-gene to a genome-wide approach to identify conserved regulatory elements and determine their role in the epigenetic control of gene expression.

ACKNOWLEDGEMENTS

Research in the Jirtle laboratory was supported by NIH grants CA25951 and ES08823, DOD grant DAMD17-98-1-8305, Sumitomo Chemical Company, Ltd, and AstraZeneca Pharmaceuticals, Ltd.

REFERENCES

Barlow, D. P. (1995). Gametic imprinting in mammals. *Science*, **270**, 1610–1613.

Baylin, S. B., *et al.* (1998). Alterations in DNA methylation: a fundamental aspect of neoplasia. *Cancer Research*, **72**, 141–196.

Bell, A. C. and Felsenfeld, G. (2000). Methylation of a CTCF-dependent boundary controls imprinted expression of the *Igf2* gene. *Nature*, **405**, 482–485.

Bianco, T., *et al.* (2000). Tumour-specific distribution of *BRCA1* promoter region methylation supports a pathogenic role in breast and ovarian cancer. *Carcinogenesis*, **21**, 147–151.

Cameron, E. E., *et al.* (1999). Synergy of demethylation and histone deacetylase inhibition in the reexpression of genes silenced in cancer. *Nature Genetics*, **21**, 103–107.

Costa, M. (1995). Model for the epigenetic mechanism of action of nongenotoxic carcinogens. *American Journal of Clinical Nutrition*, **61(suppl.)**, 666S–669S.

Costello, J. F., *et al.* (2000). Aberrant CpG-island methylation has non-random and tumour-type-specific patterns. *Nature Genetics*, **25**, 132–138.

Côté, S. and Momparler, R. L. (1997). Activation of the retinoic acid receptor gene by 5-aza-2'-deoxycytidine in human DLD-1 colon carcinoma cells. *Anticancer Drugs*, **8**, 56–61.

Esteller, M., *et al.* (2000a). Promoter region hypermethylation and *BRCA1* inactivation in sporadic breast and ovarian tumors. *Journal of the National Cancer Institute*, **92**, 564–569.

Esteller, M., *et al.* (2000b). Analysis of *Adenomatous Polyposis coli* promoter hypermethylation in human cancer. *Cancer Research*, **60**, 4366–4371.

Esteller, M., *et al.* (2001). A gene hypermethylation profile of human cancer. *Cancer Research*, **61**, 3225–3229.

Ferguson, A. T., *et al.* (2000). High frequency of hypermethylation at the 14-3-3 locus leads to gene silencing in breast cancer. *Proceedings of the National Academy of Sciences of the USA*, **97**, 6049–6054.

Fuks, F., *et al.* (2000). DNA methyltransferase Dnmt1 associates with histone deacetylase activity. *Nature Genetics*, **24**, 88–91.

Giovannucci, E., *et al.* (1993). Folate, methionine, and alcohol intake and risk of colorectal adenoma. *Journal of National Cancer Institute*, **85**, 875–884.

Hardison, R. C. (2000). Conserved noncoding sequences are reliable guides to regulatory motifs. *Trends in Genetics*, **16**, 369–372.

Hark, A. T., *et al.* (2000). CTCF mediates methylation-sensitive enhancer-blocking activity at the *H19/Igf2* locus. *Nature*, **405**, 486–489.

Hendrich, B. and Bird, A. (2000). Mammalian methyltransferases and methyl-CpG-binding domains: proteins involved in DNA methylation. *Current Topics in Microbiology and Immunology*, **249**, 35–54.

Herman, J. G. and Baylin, S. B. (2000). Promoter-region hypermethylation and gene silencing in human cancer. *Current Topics in Microbiology and Immunology*, **249**, 35–54.

Herman, J. G., *et al.* (1998). Incidence and functional consequences of *hMLH1* promoter hypermethylation in colorectal carcinoma. *Proceedings of the National Academy of Sciences of the USA*, **95**, 6870–6875.

Holliday, R. (1991). Mutations and epimutations in mammalian cells. *Mutation Research*, **250**, 351–363.

Hoshikawa, Y., *et al.* (1994). Trichostatin A induces morphological changes and gelsolin expression by inhibiting histone deacetylase in human carcinoma cell lines. *Experimental Cell Research*, **214**, 189–197.

Hu, J. F., *et al.* (1998). The role of histone acetylation in the allelic expression of the imprinted human insulin-like growth factor II gene. *Biochemical Biophysical Research Communications*, **251**, 403–408.

Issa, J. P. (2000). CpG-island methylation in aging and cancer. *Current Topics in Microbiology and Immunology*, **249**, 101–118.

Issa, J. P., *et al.* (1997). *HIC1* hypermethylation is a late event in hematopoietic neoplasms. *Cancer Research*, **57**, 1678–1681.

Jones, P. A. and Laird, P. W. (1999). Cancer epigenetics comes of age. *Nature Genetics*, **21**, 163–167.

Jones, P. L., *et al.* (1998). Methylated DNA and MeCP2 recruit histone deacetylase to repress transcription. *Nature Genetics*, **19**, 187–191.

Kanduri, C., *et al.* (2000). Functional association of CTCF with the insulator upstream of the *H19* gene is parent of origin-specific and methylation sensitive. *Current Biology*, **10**, 853–856.

Killian, J. K., *et al.* (2000). *M6P/IGF2R* imprinting evolution in mammals. *Molecular Cell*, **5**, 707–716.

Knudson, A. G., Jr. (1971). Mutation and cancer: statistical study of retinoblastoma. *Proceedings of the National Academy of Sciences of the USA*, **68**, 820–823.

Laborda, J. (2000). The role of the epidermal growth factor-like protein dlk in cell differentiation. *Histology and Histopathology*, **15**, 119–129.

Laird, P. W. (1997). Oncogenic mechanisms mediated by DNA methylation. *Molecular Medicine Today*, **3**, 223–229.

Laird, P. W. (2000). Mouse models in DNA-methylation research. *Current Topics in Microbiology and Immunology*, **249**, 119–134.

Laird, P. W. and Jaenisch, R. (1996). The role of DNA methylation in cancer genetics and epigenetics. *Annual Review of Genetics*, **30**, 441–464.

Li, E., *et al.* (1992). Targeted mutation of the DNA methyltransferase gene results in embryonic lethality. *Cell*, **69**, 915–926.

Li, E., *et al.* (1993). Role for DNA methylation in genomic imprinting. *Nature*, **366**, 362–365.

Liggett, W. H. and Sidransky, D. (1998). Role of the *p16* tumor suppressor gene in cancer. *Journal of Clinical Oncology*, **16**, 1197–1206.

Liu, P., *et al.* (2001). Regulation of an endogenous locus using a panel of designed zinc finger proteins targeted to accessible chromatin regions. *Journal of Biological Chemistry*, **276**, 11323–11334.

Lutz, M., *et al.* (2000). Transcriptional repression by the insulator protein CTCF involves histone deacetylases. *Nucleic Acids Research*, **28**, 1707–1713.

MacPhee, D. G. (1998). Epigenetics and epimutagens: some new perspectives on cancer, germ line effects, and endocrine disrupters. *Mutation Research*, **400**, 369–379.

Magdinier, F., *et al.* (2000). Regional methylation of the 5′ end CpG island of *BRCA1* is associated with reduced gene expression in human somatic cells. *FASEB Journal*, **14**, 1585–1594.

Masters, C. and Crane, D. (1998). On the role of the peroxisome in cell differentiation and carcinogenesis. *Molecular and Cellular Biochemistry*, **187**, 85–97.

Nakagawa, H., *et al.* (2001). Loss of imprinting of the insulin-like growth factor II gene occurs by biallelic methylation in a core region of *H19*-associated CTCF-binding sites in colorectal cancer. *Proceedings of the National Academy of Sciences of the USA*, **98**, 591–596.

Nan, X., *et al.* (1998). Transcriptional repression by the methyl-CpG-binding protein MeCP2 involves a histone deacetylase complex. *Nature*, **393**, 386–389.

Peters, J. M., *et al.* (1997). Role of PPAR alpha in the mechanism of action of the nongenotoxic carcinogen and peroxisome proliferator, Wy-14,643. *Carcinogenesis*, **18**, 2029–2033.

Pfeifer, G. P., *et al.* (2000). Mutation hotspots and DNA methylation. *Current Topics in Microbiology and Immunology*, **249**, 1–20.

Rainier, S., *et al.* (1993). Relaxation of imprinted genes in human cancer. *Nature*, **362**, 747–749.

Reik, W., *et al.* (2000). Igf2 imprinting in development and disease. *International Journal of Developmental Biology*, **44**, 145–150.

Rice, J. C. and Futscher, B. W. (2000). Transcriptional repression of *BRCA1* by aberrant cytosine methylation, histone hypoacetylation and chromatin condensation of the *BRCA1* promoter. *Nucleic Acids Research*, **28**, 3233–3239.

Riggs, A. D. and Porter, T. N. (1996). Overview of epigenetic mechanisms. In: Russo, V.E.A., *et al.* (eds), *Epigenetic Mechanisms of Gene Regulation*. 29–45 (Cold Spring Harbor Laboratory Press, Cold Spring Harbor, NY).

Roberts, R. (1999). Peroxisome proliferators: mechanism of adverse effects in rodents and molecular basis for species differences. *Archives of Toxicology*, **73**, 413–418.

Robertson, K. D. and Wolffe, A. P. (2000). DNA methylation in health and disease. *Nature Reviews in Genetics*, **1**, 11–19.

Robertson, K. D., *et al.* (2000). DNMT1 forms a complex with Rb, E2F1 and HDAC1 and represses transcription from E2F-responsive promoters. *Nature Genetics*, **25**, 338–342.

Rountree, M. R., *et al.* (2000). DNMT1 binds HDAC2 and a new co-repressor, DMAP1, to form a complex at replication foci. *Nature Genetics*, **25**, 269–277.

Sirchia, S. M., *et al.* (2000). Evidence of epigenetic changes affecting the chromatin state of the retinoic acid receptor β2 promoter in breast cancer cells. *Oncogene*, **19**, 1556–1563.

Srivastava, M., *et al.* (2000). H19 and Igf2 monoallelic expression is regulated in two distinct ways by a shared *cis* acting regulatory region upstream of H19. *Genes and Development*, **14**, 1186–1195.

Thorvaldsen, J. L., *et al.* (1998). Deletion of the H19 differentially methylated domain results in loss of imprinted expression of H19 and Igf2. *Genes and Development*, **12**, 3693–3702.

Tycko, B. (2000). Epigenetic gene silencing in cancer. *Journal Clinical Investigation*, **105**, 401–407.

Vu, T. H. and Hoffman, A. R. (1994). Promoter-specific imprinting of the human *insulin-like growth factor-II* gene. *Nature*, **371**, 714–717.

Vu, T. H. and Hoffman, A. R. (2000). Comparative genomics sheds light on mechanisms of genomic imprinting. *Genome Research*, **10**, 1660–1663.

Wachsman, J. T. (1997). DNA methylation and the association between genetic and epigenetic changes: relation to carcinogenesis. *Mutation Research*, **375**, 1–8.

Wylie, A. A., *et al.* (2000). Regulatory motifs of the novel imprinted domain, *DLK1/GTL2*, mimic those of *IGF2/H19*. *Genome Research*, **10**, 1711–1718.

Zingg, J. and Jones, P. A., (1997). Genetic and epigenetic aspects of DNA methylation on genome expression, evolution, mutation, and carcinogenesis. *Carcinogenesis*, **18**, 869–882.

FURTHER READING

Baylin, S. B., *et al.* (2001). Aberrant patterns of DNA methylation, chromatin formation and gene expression in cancer. *Human Molecular Genetics*, **10**, 687–692.

Cheung, P., *et al.* (2000). Signaling to chromatin through histone modifications. *Cell*, **103**, 263–271.

Murphy, S. K. and Jirtle, R. L. (2000). Imprinted genes as potential genetic and epigenetic toxicological targets. *Environmental Health Perspectives*, **108(Suppl. 1)**, 5–11.

Reik, W. and Walter, J. (2001). Genomic imprinting: parental influence on the genome. *Nature Reviews Genetics*, **2**, 21–32.

Wade, P. A. (2001). Transcriptional control at regulatory checkpoints by histone deacetylases: molecular connections between cancer and chromatin. *Human Molecular Genetics*, **10**, 693–698.

Websites

http://www.geneimprint.com (Genomic Imprinting website).

http://www3.mdanderson.org/leukemia/methylation (MD Anderson resource on CpG island methylation in ageing and cancer).

http://dnamethsoc.server101.com/ (DNA Methylation Society homepage).

http://www.cancer.med.umich.edu/learn/1learn.htm (University of Michigan Comprehensive Cancer Center homepage).

http://condor.bcm.tmc.edu/ermb/tgdb (The Tumor Gene Database).

http://nhgri.nih.gov/histones/ (The Histone Sequence Database).

Chapter 24

Infectious Agents and Cancer

Robert Newton
ICRF Radcliffe Infirmary, Oxford, UK

CONTENTS

INTRODUCTION

Infections play an important role in cancer. With the exception of canine venereal transmissible sarcoma, cancer is not itself contagious, but the underlying cause can be. Not only is the process whereby infection leads to cancer important for gaining insights into oncogenesis, but also control or elimination of infection holds promise for cancer prevention.

Historical Perspective

Transmissible agents have a venerable part in the history of cancer research. In 1911, Peyton Rous, often considered to be the father of tumour virology, was the first to demonstrate the acellular transmission of a sarcoma between chickens (the term 'virus' had not yet been coined). The research community was not receptive to the notion that a chronic disease may have an infectious cause and it was to be 55 years before Rous received the Nobel Prize for his seminal discovery. In the 1930s, Shope discovered oncogenic pox viruses and papillomaviruses in rabbits. In 1936, Bittner demonstrated that predisposition to breast cancer in C3H mice was transmitted in breast milk. In 1951, Gross discovered the first murine leukaemia virus and, in 1960, Hilleman identified SV40 virus as a contaminant of polio vaccine grown in monkey kidney cultures. However, the concept that infections might cause chronic diseases, such as cancer, can be traced back even further. For example, in the nineteenth century, the simple epidemiological observation that cancer of the uterine cervix was relatively common in prostitutes, but unknown in celibate nuns, led to the suggestion that the cause might be linked to sexual behaviour and perhaps even be sexually transmitted. In 1905, several years before Rous published his work on chicken sarcomas, Goebel drew attention to 'the occurrence of bladder tumours due to bilharziasis' (shistosomiasis).

In 1964, the first human tumour virus (the Epstein–Barr virus (EBV)) was discovered using electron microscopy, in Burkitt lymphoma cells, by Epstein, Achong and Barr. Later, EBV was also detected in undifferentiated naso-pharyngeal carcinoma and subsequently in several other tumours. By the 1970s, cancer viruses were in fashion. President Nixon 'declared war' on cancer (National Cancer Act, 1971) and funding was increased for the National Cancer Institute's 'special virus cancer programme.' Although the 1970s saw many important developments, including the discovery of oncogenes and tumour-suppressor genes (*TP53*), no new cancer viruses were identified and interest began to wane. This was to change in the early 1980s, with several major discoveries. In 1980, Poiesz, Gallo and colleagues discovered the human T cell leukaemia virus, which is associated with endemic leu-kaemia/lymphoma, particularly in Southern Japan and the Caribbean. In 1981, the large-scale prospective epidemio-logical studies of Beasley *et al.*, in Tiawan, confirmed the long-suspected causal association between the hepatitis B virus and liver cancer. In 1983, zur Hausen and colleagues isolated HPV 16 from a human cervical cancer specimen, Marshall and Warren identified *Helicobacter pylori* (later associated with gastric cancer), and the HIV (dis-covered by Barré-Sinoussi) emerged as an important cause of several cancers. Hepatitis C virus, a cause of liver cancer, was discovered in 1989 and, in 1994, Chang and Moore identified the Kaposi sarcoma-associated herpes-virus (HHV-8).

The Global Burden of Cancers Caused by Infections

It is estimated that approximately 15% of cancers (between about 1.2 and 1.5 million cases per year, worldwide) are attributable to viral (11%), bacterial (4%) and helminth (0.1%) infections (**Table 1**). Collectively, infectious agents are the most important known cause of cancer after tobacco.

Table 1   Cancers attributable to infections (these are conservative estimates, adapted from Parkin *et al.*, 1999)

Infection	Cancer(s)	No. of cases worldwide
Human papillomaviruses	Cervical cancer	360 000
	Other female genital cancers	
Hepatitis B virus	Liver cancer	230 000
Epstein–Barr virus	Burkitt lymphoma	100 000
	Hodgkin disease	
	Nasopharyngeal cancer	
Epstein–Barr virus/HIV	Non-Hodgkin lymphoma	9 000
Human herpesvirus-8/HIV	Kaposi sarcoma	45 000
Human T cell leukaemia virus	Leukaemia	3 000
Hepatitis C virus	Liver cancer	110 000
Helicobacter pylori	Gastric carcinoma	350 000
	Gastric lymphoma	
Schistosomes	Bladder cancer	10 000
Liver flukes	Cholangiocarcinoma	1 000

A better understanding of the role of infectious agents in the aetiology of cancer is a public health imperative, because such cancers are theoretically preventable by vaccination or early treatment of infection. Furthermore, cancer-causing infections often cause substantial morbidity and mortality from non-malignant conditions. Therefore, an additional benefit of any scheme to reduce the burden of cancers caused by infections would also involve a reduction in the incidence of other diseases.

The majority of infection attributable cancers (perhaps 1 million cases per year) occur in the developing world, reflecting the higher prevalence of the major causative agents, particularly hepatitis B, human papillomaviruses (HPV), *H. pylori* and human immunodeficiency virus (HIV). It is conservatively estimated that if these infectious diseases were controlled, up to one in four cancers in developing countries and one in 10 cancers in developed countries might be prevented. This chapter briefly reviews the association between certain infections and cancer, outlines the mechanism by which disease might be caused (if known) and presents comments on the potential for prevention of such tumours.

VIRUSES

Human Papillomaviruses (HPV)

The papillomaviruses are double-stranded DNA viruses. About 100 subtypes have been distinguished to date, many of which can infect humans, and at least as many again await formal characterization. Several specific subtypes have been associated with cancer in humans. Indeed, more cancers are attributable to HPV infection than to any other transmissible agent (**Table 1**). Most of these are cervix cancers, but other anogenital tumours and cancers at distant sites may also be caused by HPV.

After cancer of the breast, cervix cancer is the most common female malignancy worldwide. The risk of disease is increased among women reporting multiple sexual partners, early age of first sexual intercourse and among those whose male partners have multiple partners, all features that implicate a sexually transmitted aetiological agent. Of the known HPV types, about 30 can infect the female genital tract. Some of these are associated with benign lesions, such as warts (e.g. HPV 6 and 11) while others, so-called 'high-risk' types, are associated with invasive cancer and advanced precancerous lesions (e.g. HPV 16, 18, 31, 33, 45, 51, 52, 58, 59).

HPV infection is one of the most common sexually transmitted infections of women and probably also of men. Viral DNA is detectable in a large proportion of women shortly after becoming sexually active and the main determinant of infection is the number of sexual partners. The prevalence of infection varies between populations, but is of the order of 20–30% in women aged 20–24 years, declining to 5–10% in women over the age of 40 years. Follow-up of young, sexually active cohorts of women suggest that the incidence of HPV infection is about 15% per year, with more than 50% of women becoming infected at some stage in their lives. Most infections are cleared spontaneously, but a small proportion become persistent and it is these that carry the risk of neoplastic change. Much less is known about HPV infection in men and their reservoir of infection has not been clearly identified, although the glans penis and internal meatus are the most likely locations.

HPV infection of the genital tract can be latent, or associated with cellular alterations known as cervical intra-epithelial neoplasia (CIN) (sometimes called squamous intraepithelial lesions (SIL)), graded according to severity from 1 to 3, depending on the degree of nuclear and cytoplasmic change. All grades are considered to be manifestations of HPV infection; grade 1 lesions are generally benign and often resolve, whereas high-grade lesions are more likely to persist and progress. The time taken to progress from one grade to another and then to invasive disease is unknown, but has been estimated to be several years, possibly more than a decade. The features associated with HPV-mediated progression of CIN are not clear, but persistent infection is more likely in older women infected with 'high-risk' HPV subtypes. The quality of the immune response to infection is likely to be important and some HLA associations have been reported. Other possible factors include high parity, concomitant venereal infections and tobacco use (see IARC (1995) and Herrero and Muñoz (1999) for a more thorough review).

The evidence for a causal role of HPV infection in the aetiology of CIN and invasive cancer of the cervix is overwhelming. Virtually all squamous cell cancers and more than 90% of adenocarcinomas of the cervix contain HPV-DNA. A recent study by Walboomers et al. (1999) identified HPV-DNA in 99.7% of almost 1000 invasive cancers in a worldwide study. HPV 16 accounts for about 55% of tumours and is particularly dominant in Western countries. HPV 18 and 45 are relatively more important in tropical areas and account for about 15 and 10% of cervix cancers, respectively. Data from case-control and cohort studies consistently suggest that the risk of invasive cervix cancer or CIN is very high in association with HPV infection (relative risks of greater than 50 in HPV infected women compared with uninfected women). Furthermore, the risk increases with increasing viral load, as measured by the amount of HPV-DNA.

Molecular analyses support the epidemiological evidence. The high-risk HPV subtypes exhibit transforming potential and can immortalize cells, processes fundamental to the development of malignancy. The HPV genome contains two oncogenes, E6 and E7, and despite the frequent loss of much of the viral genome in cervical cancer cells, these regions are consistently maintained and expressed. The protein products of the E6 and E7 oncogenes affect the normal function of cellular proteins, essential for regulating cell growth. TP53 and Rb are important tumour-suppressor proteins and loss of their function is a common theme in most human cancers, regardless of origin. E6 interferes with p53 and E7 with the Rb protein and this is likely to be central to the oncogenic activity of certain HPVs (Phillips and Vousden, 1999).

There is some evidence that high-risk HPV types also play a role in the aetiology of cancers at other anogenital sites (IARC, 1995). These include cancers of the anus, penis, vagina and certain histological subtypes of vulval cancer. However, these tumours are sufficiently rare (particularly in comparison with cancer of the cervix), as to have only a limited impact on public health. A proportion of tumours of the head and neck (including conjunctiva), oesophagus, lung, bladder and prostate may also be associated with HPV infection, although the evidence remains scant. Of more public health importance is the suggestion that HPV subtypes 5 and 8 may cause a proportion of squamous cell carcinomas of the skin. Epidermodysplasia verruciformis is a rare hereditary disease characterized by impaired cell mediated immunity. Patients with this condition suffer from multiple skin warts, which often progress to squamous carcinoma. HPV 5 and 8 have been consistently identified in these tumours (McGregor and Proby, 1996); similar subtypes have been found in warts and malignant skin lesions of renal transplant and other immunosuppressed patients. The role of HPV 5 and 8 in the aetiology of squamous cell skin cancers occurring in the general population is uncertain.

Prevention of HPV-associated cancers, particularly cervix cancer, is a public health priority. In the long-term, vaccination holds the most promise for the eradication of such tumours, but of more immediate value is screening. Cervical cancer screening programmes rely on the detection of treatable precancerous lesions by exfoliative cervical cytology, and are known to be effective at reducing the incidence of and mortality from invasive disease. Several studies suggest that detection of high-risk HPV types is more sensitive for detecting CIN than conventional cytology, although the rates of false positives are also higher (Cuzick, 1999). The inclusion of HPV detection as part of the normal cytological screening programme may, therefore, lead to better disease detection, increased intervals between screens and early cessation of screening in women without HPV infection (IARC, 1992). Large trials are needed to determine the value for prevention and cost effectiveness of such an approach.

Prophylactic HPV vaccines are based on the induction of neutralizing antibodies able to prevent infection and associated lesions. Their development has been slowed by the inability to propagate HPV in tissue culture and the consequent lack of a source of antigens, in particular, the structural proteins L1 and L2. These problems have largely been solved with the generation of virus-like particles (VLPs), obtained by expression of the major capsid proteins, which because they are indistinguishable from authentic virions except that they lack a viral genome, can induce neutralizing antibodies. Such vaccines have proven efficacy in protecting against infection in many animal models. Several VLP-based vaccines have been produced to protect against human HPV types (6, 11, 16, 18, 31 and 33) and are being tested in phase I and II trials (Coursaget and Muñoz, 1999). It will be many years before large-scale phase III clinical trials yield results, but such vaccines hold great promise for the ultimate prevention of HPV-associated cancers.

Hepatitis B Virus

The role of chronic infection with hepatitis B virus (HBV) in the aetiology of primary liver cancer, specifically hepatocellular carcinoma, is well established (IARC, 1994a). Hepatitis B is one of the most common infectious

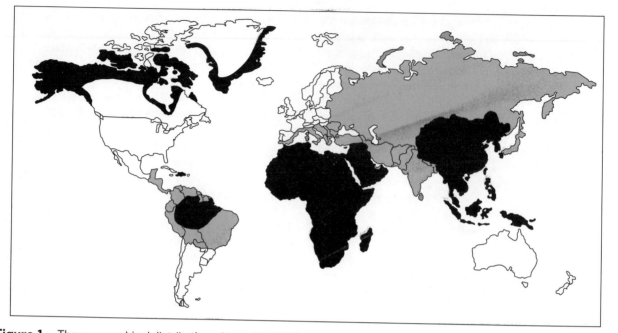

Figure 1   The geographical distribution of hepatitis B infection. Black, ≥8%, high; grey, 2–7.9%, intermediate; white, <2%, low (from WHO).

diseases worldwide, with between 300 and 350 million chronic carriers – up to 10% of the population in high prevalence areas – two-thirds of whom will develop chronic hepatitis. Of those, 20–25% will eventually die from primary liver cancer or cirrhosis. As a result, primary liver cancer is one of the most common cancers, particularly in parts of sub-Saharan Africa, China and South-east Asia, where the virus is prevalent (**Figure 1**). The hepatitis B virus is responsible for causing up to a quarter of a million cancers per year (**Table 1**), about 50–55% of the total number of liver cancers, and is the second most important oncogenic virus (Parkin *et al.*, 1999).

Hepatitis B virus belongs to a group of hepatotropic double-stranded DNA viruses (with a single-stranded region of variable length), called hepadnaviruses and is characterized by the fact that it replicates through an RNA intermediate, via reverse transcription. The genome contains four genes, S, C, pol (the largest gene, coding for reverse transcriptase) and X. The virion, or 'Dane particle,' has an outer protein coat encoded by the S gene (hepatitis B surface antigen (HBsAg), the so-called 'Australia antigen,' discovered by Blumberg in 1963, in the serum of an aboriginal man), and an inner protein core (hepatitis B c antigen (HbcAg)) coded by the C gene. The terminal region of the C gene encodes the hepatitis B e antigen (HbeAg) and the X gene encodes a protein that up-regulates transcription from all the viral and some cellular promoters.

Transmission of HBV occurs from a person with acute infection or carrier status (i.e. HBsAg positive on at least two occasions, 6 months apart) who has circulating virus. Individuals who are HBeAg positive are particularly infectious since the presence of this antigen correlates with high serum levels of HBV-DNA. The mode of transmission is not completely clear but varies with age, occurring primarily at three stages in life. First, transmission can occur from a mother to her child. Neonates born to HBeAg-positive mothers have about a 90% chance of becoming infected, whereas children of HBeAg-negative mothers have a 30% probability of infection. This is a particularly important means of transmission in China, but is probably less important in Africa where, for reasons that are not known, fewer infected mothers are HBeAg positive. Transmission in childhood is probably the most important age for infection globally and is associated with residence with infected siblings; the exact means of virus spread within households is unknown. In adult life, the major routes of transmission are by needles and sexual intercourse. Since the introduction of screening for HBV in blood products, the predominant mode of needle transmission is by the sharing of needles amongst intravenous drug users. Sexual transmission has been most clearly documented in countries of Europe and North America, where the prevalence of HBV is low, but may also have a limited role in endemic countries (IARC, 1994a).

The principle risk factor for HBV-induced liver cancer (and cirrhosis) is persistence of replicative infection (as it is with human papillomavirus infection and cancer of the cervix) and a key determinant of persistence is the age of infection. About 90% of children infected in the perinatal period become chronic carriers; up to 5 years old, around 20–30% of those infected become chronic carriers and above this age, the proportion is probably less than 5%. Presumably, the relationship between persistence of infection and age is due to changes in the ability of the immune system to contain the virus, but the determinants of this are unclear (Wild and Hall, 1999). At all ages, males are more likely than females to become chronic carriers. Other factors are known to contribute to the risk of liver cancer in those chronically infected with HBV, including coinfection with the hepatitis C virus. Similarly, exposure to aflatoxins, common in parts of Africa and Asia, leads to a roughly 10-fold increase in the risk of malignancy above the excess associated with HBV infection.

The mechanisms whereby HBV may induce primary liver cancer are not fully understood. In most instances, the tumour is preceded by several decades of chronic hepatitis or cirrhosis and the associated rapid cell turnover may render host DNA more susceptible to malignant change. Mutagenesis may be induced by the associated inflammatory response or exogenous carcinogens, or may result from genetic instability following integration of the viral genome. Another possible mechanism involves the activation of cellular genes by the hepatitis B virus X gene product: it encodes a protein that may interact with the TP53 and deregulate the cell cycle.

Prospects for prevention of HBV-induced liver cancer are good. Screening of blood and organ donors has reduced the spread of infection among adults in developed countries. Similarly, screening for infection among high-risk pregnant women, such as those from endemic countries, is of value. There is ample evidence that the use of hepatitis B immunoglobulin within hours of birth, followed by hepatitis B vaccine on multiple occasions, is effective in reducing the infection rate in infants born to infected mothers by more than 80% and the carrier rate by more than 90% (reviewed by Cuzick et al., 1999). The best hope for prevention, however, lies with mass vaccination against HBV, particularly in populations where infection is most prevalent. Furthermore, there is also some interest in the development of therapeutic vaccines; these might eventually be used to treat liver cancer patients, by inducing an effective immune response to virus-infected cells.

The safety and effectiveness of prophylactic HBV vaccines have been clearly demonstrated in numerous studies, since they became widely available in 1982. Early vaccines were based on purified HbsAg from patients with HBV-induced liver cancer, but these were superseded in 1987 by vaccines produced using recombinant technology. Such vaccines are highly immunogenic and induce protective antibodies in 90–100% of healthy recipients (reviewed by Coursaget and Muñoz, 1999). Some studies have demonstrated protection from infection for up to 12 years. In a study in the Gambia with 10 years of follow-up, hepatitis B vaccine prevented 83% of infections and 94% of chronic carriage (Gambia Hepatitis Study Group, 1987). Although it will be many years before an effect on the incidence of liver cancer is noted in clinical trials, the introduction of mass vaccination in Taiwan has been associated with a sharp decline in the incidence of liver

cancer in children (Chang et al., 1997). Currently, 80 countries, mostly in high-risk endemic areas, have routine hepatitis B vaccination programmes. Despite this, it is estimated that only a third of infants who might benefit from vaccine worldwide actually receive it. (See also chapter on *Human DNA Tumour Viruses*.)

Epstein–Barr Virus (EBV)

The Epstein–Barr virus is a ubiquitous human herpesvirus of the family Gammaherpesviridae that infects more than 90% of the world's population. The virion consists of a core wrapped with DNA and is contained within a capsid, which is surrounded by a membranous envelope with glycoprotein spikes. The genome is a relatively large 172-kb double-stranded DNA molecule encoding about 100 genes. There are two major subtypes of EBV which differ with respect to some of the genes coding for nuclear proteins in latently infected cells, but there is no evidence that one subtype is more strongly associated with disease than the other.

The EBV is transmitted orally, either by exchange of virus particles or infected cells in buccal fluid and, like other herpesviruses, it establishes a latent infection, with life-long persistence in the infected host. Asymptomatic primary infection usually occurs in childhood, although in more developed countries infection may be delayed. If primary infection occurs in adolescence, about 50% of cases may develop the clinical syndrome of infectious mononucleosis and most of what is known of the events occurring at primary infection are extrapolations from the study of such individuals.

It is not known whether the initial target cell for orally transmitted virus is a B lymphocyte, made accessible by damage to the oral mucosa, or an epithelial cell of the mucosa itself. However, following primary infection, foci of productive (lytic) infection are established in the oropharyngeal mucosa and a large pool of latently infected B cells can be found both in the blood and in lymphoid tissues. The overgrowth of virally transformed B cells is controlled by specific cytotoxic T cell responses, the absence of which (in allograft recipients and others with impaired T cell function) can result in EBV-driven lympho-proliferation and even lymphoma.

A recent review of the role of the EBV in the aetiology of cancer concluded that there is sufficient evidence for the carcinogenicity of EBV in the causation of several types of lymphoma (including Burkitt lymphoma, Hodgkin disease and immunosuppression-related lymphomas) and undifferentiated nasopharyngeal carcinoma (IARC, 1997). Other cancer types have also been linked to infection with EBV, although the evidence for causality is less clear. In total, it is estimated that the EBV may be responsible for up to about 100 000 cancers per year worldwide (**Table 1**; Parkin et al., 1999).

Burkitt lymphoma occurs throughout the world with varying frequency, but everywhere it represents a significant proportion of malignant lymphomas in children. There are two broad types of Burkitt lymphoma, which although histologically indistinguishable, differ in several other important ways. The 'endemic' form of the disease was first described in 1958 in parts of sub-Saharan Africa, South-east Asia and Papua New Guinea. It is particularly frequent where malarial infection is heavy and widespread. In these areas it is the most common childhood malignancy, with a peak incidence between 5 and 8 years old. It often presents with facial lesions and is associated with infection with EBV. Viral DNA is almost invariably identified in tumour tissue in monoclonal form, indicating that the original malignant clone must have arisen from a single virus infected cell. Furthermore, high antibody titres to EBV infection in young children are predictive of the subsequent development of the tumour (de-Thé et al., 1978). This is in contrast to the sporadic form of Burkitt lymphoma seen throughout the rest of the world, which usually presents with abdominal lesions, occurs at older ages (particularly in teenagers) and is only associated with EBV infection in about a third of cases. In Western populations, sporadic Burkitt lymphoma is about 1000 times more common in HIV-infected individuals than in those uninfected with HIV and about half of these tumours are also associated with EBV infection. Both the endemic and sporadic Burkitt lymphoma involve c-*MYC* gene translocations, but the breakpoints in each type are different: in the endemic disease, the breakpoints tend to be far upstream of the oncogene, whereas in the sporadic form, the breakpoints tend to be adjacent to or within the oncogene. It is therefore possible that the endemic and sporadic forms of Burkitt lymphoma have different aetiologies, with only a proportion (mostly the endemic cases) being caused by EBV infection.

Nasopharyngeal carcinoma of undifferentiated or poorly differentiated type is an epithelial EBV-associated tumour, which, like Burkitt lymphoma, is characterized by marked geographic and population differences in incidence. It is common in southern China and South-east Asia, where it may represent up to 20% of all cancer cases. It also occurs relatively frequently in Eskimo populations and in Mediterranean Africa. Despite this geographical restriction, more cases of nasopharyngeal cancer are attributed to infection with the EBV, than any other cancer (Parkin et al., 1999).

The identification of an association between nasopharyngeal cancer and EBV occurred by chance, when patients with the tumour were chosen as controls in a case-control study of Burkitt lymphoma and were found to have high antibody titres to the virus. Specifically, elevated immunoglobulin A (IgA) antibodies to the EBV viral capsid antigens (VCA) predate the development of nasopharyngeal cancer by several years and are also correlated with tumour burden and recurrence. Measurement of IgA levels has formed the basis of a screening programme in southern China, where about 5% of individuals aged 30 years or more are positive for IgA/VCA and 5–12% of these have

nasopharyngeal cancer (IARC, 1997). In addition, clonal EBV-DNA is consistently detected in tumour tissue (but not in normal nasopharyngeal epithelium), suggesting that the tumour develops from a single EBV-infected cell.

Because the EBV is ubiquitous, the geographical variation in the incidence of nasopharyngeal cancer may be explained by the combined influences of genetic predisposition in particular racial groups and of local environmental or dietary factors, although the exact nature of these effects is not clear. Salted and preserved food in the diet and a lack of fresh fruits and vegetables are currently the most clearly established cofactors. Another possibility is that particular strains of EBV, which carry a higher risk for nasopharyngeal carcinoma, are common where the disease occurs, although evidence for this remains scant.

Hodgkin's disease is a malignant lymphoma characterized by the loss of lymph node architecture, with the majority of infiltrating cells being benign. Indeed, the malignant cells – the Reed–Sternberg cells – constitute only about 2% of tumour mass. The disease occurs worldwide and in Western populations it has a distinctive age distribution with two peaks of incidence, at ages 25–30 and over 45 years. Sero-epidemiological studies indicate that high antibody titres to EBV precede the development of Hodgkin's disease and a history of infectious mononucleosis is a strong risk factor. Furthermore, about half of cases have evidence of clonal EBV-DNA in tumour tissue. Parkin et al. (1999) estimated that about half of the 60 000 new cases annually are related to infection with the EBV.

Some other lymphomas may be related to EBV, but the overall number of cases is likely to be relatively small. Non-Hodgkin lymphomas associated with HIV, or immunosuppressive therapy, are characterized by a number of features, including an aggressive clinical course. High-grade disease is common and extra-nodal sites are often involved, with lesions in the central nervous system being virtually unknown, except in the immunosuppressed. The most common subtype of non-Hodgkin lymphoma both in those with HIV infection and in immunosuppressed transplant recipients, is B cell immunoblastic lymphoma. Post-transplant immunoblastic lymphomas are nearly always associated with EBV and probably represent the end result of an EBV-driven lymphoproliferation in the absence of effective T cell immunity. EBV sequences are detectable in about 50% of HIV-associated immunoblastic lymphomas (although 100% of primary cerebral lymphomas), suggesting that other factors may also be important (Newton et al., 1999a). Several nonspecific host factors have been suggested to play a role in lymphomagenesis in immunosuppressed individuals, such as disrupted immunosurveillance, chronic antigenic stimulation and cytokine dysregulation, all of which might be responsible for expanding the B cell population from which a lymphoma subsequently develops.

Infection with the EBV has also been associated with a number of very rare T cell lymphoma subtypes and with lymphoepithelial carcinomas of the stomach, lung and salivary gland. In addition, smooth muscle tumours (leiomyosarcomas) in immunosuppressed individuals uniformly contain EBV. The number of such cancers, however, is small.

The development of vaccines to control the diseases associated with EBV infection are at an early stage of development, but may be used in a number of ways. First, prophylactic vaccines may modify or prevent primary infection. Normally, infection occurs during the first few years of life, but such vaccines would be particularly useful for the prevention of infectious mononucleosis, which results in 50% of individuals in whom infection is delayed until adolescence. Second, postinfection vaccination may be used to modify the existing immune status of an infected individual and could have some value in preventing the development of nasopharyngeal carcinoma in those who have high IgA antibodies against EBV. Finally, therapeutic vaccination might be selectively targeted against viral antigens expressed in tumour cells. However, for the time being, the effect of any form of vaccination against the EBV remains speculative.

Human Herpesvirus-8 (HHV-8/KSHV)

Before the HIV epidemic, Kaposi sarcoma showed a greater geographical variation in incidence than almost any other cancer. It was as common in parts of sub-Saharan Africa, such as Uganda and eastern Zaire, as colon cancer is in Europe and the USA, representing up to 9% of all cancers in men. Kaposi sarcoma was also endemic, although much rarer, in countries around the Mediterranean, particularly Italy, Greece and the Middle East, but was almost nonexistent elsewhere in the world, except in immigrants from those endemic countries. In all of these areas, Kaposi sarcoma was more common in men than in women (Newton et al., 1999a).

It was the appearance of aggressive forms of Kaposi sarcoma in the USA in the early 1980s that heralded the onset of the HIV epidemic in Western countries. Although the incidence of Kaposi sarcoma has increased in populations at high risk of HIV in northern Europe and the USA, it existed at such a low level before the onset of the epidemic that it remains a relatively rare tumour. However, parts of Africa with a high prevalence of HIV and where Kaposi sarcoma was relatively common even before the era of acquired immunodeficiency syndrome (AIDS), have seen an explosion in the incidence of the disease. In the last 10–15 years the incidence of Kaposi sarcoma has increased about 20-fold in Uganda and Zimbabwe, such that it is now the most common cancer in men and the second most common in women (IARC, 1997).

In 1994, Chang, Moore and colleagues identified sequences of a new herpesvirus in a biopsy specimen of Kaposi sarcoma from an HIV-infected homosexual man, using representational difference analysis. The virus – human herpesvirus-8 (HHV-8) or Kaposi sarcoma-associated herpesvirus (KSHV) – has been consistently associated with Kaposi sarcoma and is now considered to be the principal cause of the disease. Genomic sequences of HHV-8 are present in tumour cells of Kaposi sarcoma lesions (specifically in the spindle cells, which constitute the bulk of the tumour) in virtually all subjects, but are not found in other tissues (with the exception of blood). The presence of HHV-8, detected by polymerase chain reaction (PCR) or serology, in peripheral blood, predicts the subsequent development of Kaposi sarcoma, particularly in individuals with high anti-HHV-8 antibody titres.

HHV-8 is not a ubiquitous virus, but is most prevalent in groups or populations at highest risk of developing Kaposi sarcoma, such as HIV-infected homosexual men in the USA and in African populations where the tumour has long been endemic (Boshoff, 1999). The proportion of adults in the general population with antibodies against HHV-8 ranges from fewer than 5% in northern America and northern Europe to around 10% in southern Europe and more than 30% in black Africans. In the United States and Europe, more than 30% of HIV-infected homosexual men have been found to have antibodies against HHV-8.

The modes of transmission of HHV-8 are yet to be fully elucidated. In the USA, sex between men may be an important route of transmission since this is the main behavioural risk factor for Kaposi sarcoma and indeed there is now some evidence that this is so. In some African countries, where HHV-8 is relatively common, the seroprevalence does not vary by sex and has been found to increase with age, from birth, through childhood and into adult life. This suggests that some transmission from a mother to her child and from child to child is also likely.

HHV-8 is a gamma-herpesvirus, closely related to the EBV, and infects CD19+ B cells as well as the endothelial derived spindle cells of a Kaposi sarcoma lesion. In addition to its role in Kaposi sarcoma, the virus also causes a rare type of lymphoma (primary effusion lymphoma) and a lymphoproliferative B cell disorder (a subtype of Castleman disease). The mechanism by which HHV-8 causes disease is controversial, although the genome encodes several putatively transforming genes in addition to genes encoding a number of regulatory cytokines and angio-proliferative factors that may facilitate tumour growth. HHV-8 infection alone, however, may not be enough to induce disease. Cofactors such as immunosuppression, as a result of advancing age, HIV/AIDS or therapy following tissue transplantation are presumably required.

Human T Cell Leukaemia Virus Type 1 (HTLV-1)

HTLV-1 is the main causal agent of adult T cell leukaemia/lymphoma, a disease characterized by malignant proliferation of CD4-positive T lymphocytes. Clinical features include hypercalcaemia, lymphadenopathy, skin lesions due to leukaemic cell infiltration, involvement of the spleen and liver and immunodeficiency. The prognosis of patients with acute adult T cell leukaemia/lymphoma is poor, and few survive more than a few months following diagnosis. HTLV-1 also causes slowly progressive myelopathy (tropical spastic paraparesis) and uveitis.

HTLV-1 is an enveloped retrovirus, of the family Oncornavirinae, containing two covalently bound genomic RNA strands, which are combined with several viral enzymes, including reverse transcriptase. The prevalence of infection with HTLV-1 varies widely worldwide, with high levels in diverse geographic areas. Antibodies to HTLV-1 are found in 5–15% of indigenous adult populations in southern Japan, the Caribbean, South America, central Africa, Papua New Guinea and the Solomon Islands. Within endemic areas, clusters of especially high prevalence can occur. Carriers can be found elsewhere in the world, but are mostly individuals who moved from endemic areas. It is estimated that there are between 15 and 20 million infected individuals in the world (IARC, 1996).

Three modes of transmission of HTLV-1 have been identified: mother-to-child transmission, mainly due to breast-feeding beyond 6 months, sexual transmission, predominantly from men to women, and transmission by transfusion of cellular blood products and through intravenous drug use. Control and prevention of infection depends on reducing transmission by these three major routes. Perinatal transmission has been greatly reduced in Japan by avoidance of prolonged breast feeding and several countries have introduced universal screening of blood donors. Passive and active immunization is effective in animal models but no preventive vaccine is yet available for humans.

Adult T cell leukaemia/lymphoma (ATLL) occurs almost exclusively in areas where HTLV-1 is endemic, such as Japan, the Caribbean and West Africa, and cases described elsewhere have generally been in immigrants from those endemic regions, or their offspring. Early studies showed that infection with HTLV-1 is so closely associated with adult T cell leukaemia that it is now part of the diagnostic criteria used for defining the disease. All antibody-positive cases of adult T cell leukaemia have monoclonally integrated HTLV provirus in the malignant cells, suggesting that the tumour is an outgrowth of an individual T cell clone. The virus is able to immortalize human T lymphocytes, a property that has been related to a specific viral gene *tax*, which has been identified as a transforming factor. ATLL develops in about 2–5% of HTLV-1-infected individuals and is especially frequent among those infected early in life. No other environmental cofactors for disease have so far been identified. (See chapter on *RNA Viruses*.)

Hepatitis C Virus (HCV)

The identification of HCV in 1989 by Choo and colleagues arose from an investigation of the causes of post-transfusion non-A, non-B hepatitis. It is a single-stranded RNA virus assigned to a separate genus within the family Flaviviruses (which includes yellow fever virus and dengue virus) and is completely unrelated to the HBV. To date, six major subtypes of HCV have been identified, which have different geographical distributions. Acute infection often causes only mild illness, but it is becoming increasingly clear that HCV is responsible for substantial morbidity and mortality, particularly from chronic liver disease and hepatocellular cancer (IARC, 1994a). It may also play a role in the aetiology of other malignancies, such as non-Hodgkin lymphoma and cancers of the oral cavity (Tanaka and Tsukuma, 1999).

The prevalence of infection with HCV varies around the world and is estimated to be about 1–1.5% in Europe and the USA, about 3% in Japan and Oceania (excluding Australia and New Zealand) and up to 3.6% in Africa (Parkin *et al.*, 1999). In most countries, the prevalence of infection is the same in men as it is in women and increases steadily with age. Transmission is primarily by the parenteral route and, before the introduction of screening for hepatitis C, blood transfusions were a major source of infection. Intravenous drug users comprise a substantial proportion of identified cases in western populations and health-care workers, renal dialysis patients and those with clotting disorders are also at an increased risk. Both sexual and perinatal transmission occur and household contact with an infected family member may also account for a proportion of cases. However, almost half of all hepatitis C-infected individuals have no identifiable risk factors.

In contrast to hepatitis B, as many as 85% of hepatitis C virus infections become persistent and at least two-thirds of those individuals go on to develop chronic liver disease, including hepatocellular carcinoma. The risk of liver cancer in chronically infected individuals is around 20-fold higher than in the general population (more in people coinfected with HBV) and it has been estimated that HCV causes around 110 000 cancers per year (Parkin *et al.*, 1999; **Table 1**). This represents about 25% of all liver cancers, with particularly high proportions in Africa (41%), Japan (36%) and Oceania (33%). Although a similar proportion of men and women become chronic carriers of HCV, the development of cancer is more frequent in men. Alcohol and tobacco have been implicated as cofactors and may account for this discrepancy.

The mechanism by which HCV causes cancer is not clear. The virus can replicate in hepatocellular carcinoma cells, but there is no evidence that DNA sequences are integrated into the host genome. Nearly all cases of liver cancer associated with hepatitis C occur in the presence of cirrhosis or severe chronic hepatitis. Indeed, progression from chronic active hepatitis to cirrhosis to hepatocellular carcinoma has been documented in prospective studies (Tanaka and Tsukuma, 1999). In the absence of genomic integration, it is possible that the emergence of a malignant clone reflects a multifactorial process of inflammation, necrosis and cellular regeneration. Whether HCV contributes more directly to carcinogenesis is not known.

There are currently no practical strategies for the prevention of HCV infections, with the exception of blood-screening programmes (which have greatly reduced post-transfusion hepatitis). Although evidence remains scant, safe sexual practices and distribution of clean needles to intravenous drug users might reduce a small proportion of cases and perinatal transmission might be reduced with carefully managed deliveries and limitation of breast feeding. The efficacy of postexposure prophylaxis with immunoglobulin has yet to be confirmed. Efforts to develop a vaccine have been hampered by the inability to produce large amounts of immunogen *in vitro*, the fact that correlates of immunity are ill-defined and by the lack of an animal model. Although offering the greatest hope of prevention, vaccination against hepatitis C remains only a theoretical possibility.

Human Immunodeficiency Virus (HIV)

There is little evidence that HIV has a direct oncogenic effect in relation to the development of a specific cancer. Instead, it appears to facilitate the development, via its effects on the immune system, of a number of cancers, all of which are known (or thought) to be caused by other infectious agents. The abbreviation HIV is used throughout this chapter and refers specifically to HIV-1; reports on the association of cancers with HIV-2 are infrequent.

The human immunodeficiency virus was discovered in 1983 (Barré-Sinoussi *et al.*, 1983) and firmly associated with AIDS in 1984 (Gallo *et al.*, 1984). It is a human retrovirus, belonging to the lentivirus sub-family and is distinguished by its single-stranded RNA genome, which replicates via a DNA intermediate through the action of the enzyme 'reverse transcriptase' and integrates into the host chromosomal DNA. Although the first cases of HIV disease were reported as recently as 1981, the epidemic continues to escalate and the World Health Organisation (WHO) estimates that over 38 million young adults have been infected, the majority in sub-Saharan Africa. The three primary routes of transmission – sexual intercourse, blood contact and from mother to infant – were proposed on the basis of the epidemiology of AIDS, even before the identification of HIV. Of those, heterosexual transmission accounts for over 80% of new infections worldwide, while the importance of contact with infected blood products is declining since the introduction of routine screening procedures in blood banks.

The immunosuppression resulting from infection with HIV is causally associated with Kaposi sarcoma and non-Hodgkin lymphoma and, in the light of data emerging from sub-Saharan Africa, with squamous cell carcinoma of the conjunctiva. Recent evidence for two other cancers, Hodgkin disease and leiomyosarcoma in children, also suggests a definite increase in risk associated with HIV infection. The scale of the excess risk of these cancers in HIV-infected compared with uninfected individuals tends to be very large, 10-fold or more. However, people with HIV infection do not experience large excess risks of most cancers, including cancer of the uterine cervix and hepatocellular carcinoma, neither of which appear to be increased markedly in people with AIDS (IARC, 1996; Newton *et al.*, 1999a).

The cancers identified as being HIV-associated have been linked (with varying degrees of certainty) to other infectious agents. Kaposi sarcoma is caused by the newly discovered human herpesvirus 8. Certain types of non-Hodgkin lymphoma have been linked to infection with the EBV and HHV-8, and conjunctival carcinoma has been linked to human papillomavirus (HPV) infection in some studies, but not others (IARC, 1995; Newton, 1999a). Thus, infection with the HIV appears to facilitate the development of certain cancers with an infectious aetiology. It is not clear why other cancers which are caused by infections, such as hepatocellular carcinoma, are not also AIDS associated.

Many of the increases in cancer risk found in people with HIV disease are similar to the findings in immuno-deficient children and in transplant recipients, suggesting that it is the impairment of immune function that is the major factor leading to the appearance of these tumours (Beral and Newton, 1998). In addition, the risk of Kaposi sarcoma and non-Hodgkin lymphoma increases with increasing severity of immunosuppression, suggesting that this is the principle mechanism favouring their development. Also, both tumour types have been shown to regress following treatment with highly active antiretroviral therapy, which leads to improvements in immune function (IARC, 1996).

It has been estimated that, in 1990, there were about 52 000 additional cases of cancer that were a consequence of infection with the HIV (**Table 1**, Parkin *et al.*, 1999). This conservative estimate is based on the known impact of infection with the virus on just two cancers with which it has been most clearly linked: Kaposi sarcoma and non-Hodgkin lymphoma. In populations with a high prevalence of HIV infection, the impact of the epidemic is clearly reflected in cancer registry statistics, although if Kaposi sarcoma and non-Hodgkin lymphoma are excluded, there is little evidence of an increase in the incidence of all other cancers combined. In Uganda and Zimbabwe, for example, the incidence of Kaposi sarcoma has increased between 10- and 20-fold in the era of AIDS, such that it is now the most common cancer in males in both countries and amongst the most common in females. There is evidence of a reduction in risk of both Kaposi sarcoma and non-Hodgkin lymphoma in those on antiretroviral therapy. However, in the developing world, where such treatment is prohibitively expensive and therefore not widely available, the incidence of HIV-associated cancers is likely to increase with the spread of the HIV epidemic.

In the absence of an effective vaccine, behavioural change is still the most important method of controlling the spread of HIV. Transmission of the virus in blood and blood products has been largely halted in developed countries, with the introduction of screening and education in combination with needle exchange programmes, which have been shown to be effective in reducing the spread of HIV among intravenous drug users. The bulk of transmission of HIV is sexual, however, and preventive activities include reducing the number of sexual partners, modifying the types of sexual contact and the use of condoms. Several behavioural interventions in high-risk populations have been tried, with variable results, but continued education remains a high priority.

BACTERIA

Helicobacter pylori

Helicobacter pylori is a spiral, flagellated, Gram-negative bacteria that colonizes the human gastrointestinal tract and lives beneath the mucus overlaying gastric epithelium. It causes gastritis in all infected people and although many cases remain asymptomatic, some result in gastric or duodenal ulceration. In a very small proportion of infected individuals, *H. pylori* may be involved in the aetiology of gastric adenocarcinomas and the much rarer primary gastric non-Hodgkin lymphoma — about a third of all gastric cancer cases have been attributed to *H. pylori* infection (IARC, 1994b; Danesh, 1999; Parkin *et al.*, 1999).

It is estimated that about 50% of the world's population are chronically infected with *H. pylori*. The prevalence of infection is highest in developing countries and increases rapidly during the first two decades of life, such that 80–90% of the population may be infected by early adulthood. In most developed countries, the prevalence of infection is substantially lower at all ages, particularly in childhood. Everywhere, the prevalence of *H. pylori* is strongly correlated with markers of poverty and, indeed, has been decreasing in developing countries for decades, presumably because of improvements in living conditions. Transmission occurs from person to person, probably from mouth to mouth, faecal–orally or both.

In 1990, there were about 750 000 deaths attributable to gastric cancer, making it the fourteenth leading cause of death in the world and the second leading cause of cancer death (Murray and Lopez, 1997). Despite rapidly declining incidence rates in developed countries, gastric cancer is set to remain a major cause of death for many years, a result of population ageing, population growth in developing countries and a poor prognosis. Data from prospective sero-epidemiological studies suggest that infection with *H. pylori* results in a 2–4-fold increase in the risk of gastric cancer. With average seroprevalence rates of about 80% in developing countries and 50% in the developed world, it is estimated that about 340 000 new cases of gastric cancer each year are attributable to *H. pylori* infection — about 40% of the world total of gastric cancers (Parkin *et al.*, 1999; **Table 1**). Similarly, about 4000 cases per year of gastric non-Hodgkin lymphoma (which represent about 3% of all gastric cancers) have been attributed to *H. pylori* infection.

The mechanisms by which *H. pylori* might increase the risk of gastric cancer are unclear. The bacteria cause lifelong inflammation, possibly leading to the production of mutagenic compounds, as well as loss of gastric acidity and epithelial cell proliferation. Any or all of the above might contribute to carcinogenesis. There is evidence that the development of cancer is preceded by progressive changes to the stomach mucosa, from inflammation, to atrophy and cellular proliferation, a process that is thought to be related to infection with *H. pylori*. This may be particularly true of the proinflammatory strains of *H. pylori* — those that possess the cytotoxin-associated gene A — because they markedly affect gastric cytokine levels and promote cell turnover, without a corresponding increase in apoptosis. Therefore, *cagA* strains of *H. pylori* might be expected to show a stronger association with gastric cancer, but the evidence for this remains scant.

Drug therapy consisting of two antibiotics in combination with either a bismuth preparation or an acid inhibitor for 14 days is effective in eradicating *H. pylori* in about 80% of cases. Given the high incidence of stomach cancer, the availability of screening tests and eradication regimens, but the relatively low progression rates to cancer in people with *H. pylori* infection, very large randomized trials are needed to establish the value of eradication for the prevention of gastric cancer. In order to achieve statistically reliable results, up to 100 000 people aged 60 years may have to be randomized to eradication therapy or placebo and followed for at least two decades (Danesh, 1999). However, the large-scale use of antimicrobial treatment is problematic — eradication has proved to be difficult in some developing countries and reinfection is common. Furthermore, extensive use of antibiotics may lead to the development of resistant strains (Coursaget and Muñoz, 1999).

In the future, immunization may be a better strategy for the prevention of *H. pylori*-associated diseases, particularly in developing countries. It has been demonstrated in mouse models that *H. pylori* vaccines not only can protect against infection, but may also induce regression of associated lesions. However, in models more relevant to humans, such as monkeys, the results have been disappointing. In phase I trials of a recombinant vaccine in humans, no adverse events were observed, but neither were there any changes in gastric bacterial density. Further work is required to identify appropriate target antigens and delivery systems and to understand the mechanism of protective immunity.

HELMINTHS

Schistosomes

Schistosomiasis (or 'bilharzia') is the generic term given to disease caused by the parasitic blood flukes of the genus *Schistosoma*, class Trematoda of the phylum Platyhelminthes (or flatworms). The genus contains 19 species of which three (*S. mansoni, S. haematobium* and *S. japonicum*) are of major importance to humans. Most infections are subclinical, but in those who develop severe disease the clinical features vary, depending on the species of schistosome. Cancer is an important but relatively rare outcome of infection; the bulk of morbidity and mortality is caused by nonmalignant conditions, such as renal or hepatic failure.

Infection occurs via exposure to water containing the larvae (cercariae). The worms mature in the veins that drain the bladder (*S. haematobium*) or intestine (other species). The adults can survive in the body for several years producing eggs, some of which leave the body in urine or faeces and hatch in water, freeing the miracidium larva. This stage infects certain types of fresh water snail, within which the parasites multiply asexually to produce free-swimming cercariae. These infect humans via skin penetration. Retained eggs elicit hypersensitivity reactions and cause disease of the urogenital system (*S. haematobium*) or of the liver and intestines (other species).

It is estimated that 200 million people in 74 countries are infected with schistosomes and over 600 million are at risk of infection. The geographical distribution of schistosomiasis corresponds to the distribution of susceptible snail hosts, which are present in many tropical and subtropical regions. *S. mansoni* is the most widespread species and is found in 54 countries in Africa, the eastern Mediterranean, South America and the Caribbean. *S. haematobium* has a similar distribution to *S. mansoni* in Africa and the eastern Mediterranean, where coinfection is relatively common, but does not occur in the Americas. *S. japonicum* is endemic in China, the Philippines and Indonesia (WHO, 1993; **Figure 2**). Within endemic areas, however, transmission tends to be highly focal (depending as it does on exposure to contaminated fresh water) and the prevalence and intensity of infection may vary between different communities, or even between households.

Contact with contaminated freshwater is the most important risk factor for infection with schistosomes. The level of contamination can depend on the size and distribution of the intermediate snail population, human population density and behaviour in relation to bodies of fresh water and, climatic and hydrological features (WHO, 1993). Infection is acquired cumulatively over a period of years and the severity is strongly related to the worm burden, or intensity of infection. The age distribution of all schistosome infections is similar, with a characteristic peak in both prevalence and intensity (as measured by active egg excretion) in the second decade of life and a gradual decline thereafter, probably resulting from changes in behaviour in relation to water exposure (WHO, 1993; IARC, 1994b).

Once inside a human host, worm pairs of the species *S. haematobium* reside primarily in the small venules that drain the bladder and ureters and are associated with disease of the urinary system. A causal association between infection with *S. haematobium* and bladder cancer was first postulated near the beginning of the twentieth century and has since been supported by clinical and experimental observations. Bladder cancers associated with schistosomiasis are primarily of the squamous cell type, rather than the transitional cell carcinomas that predominate in nonendemic parts of the world.

The link between infection with *S. haematobium* and bladder cancer is established first from the observation of elevated incidence rates in places where infection is endemic. Furthermore, the sex ratio of squamous cell carcinoma of the bladder in different countries correlates with the relative involvement of men and women in agricultural work (a risk factor for infection). Numerous case series and case-control studies confirm that *S. haematobium* is an important cause of bladder cancer in endemic countries. Infection may play a role in the aetiology of other cancers, in particular cancer of the uterine cervix, although this has yet to be established.

Worm pairs of the species *S. japonicum* reside in the venules that drain the gastrointestinal tract or in the liver, and chronic infection is associated with diseases of these organs. Data from ecological studies, case series and case-control and cohort studies indicate that in endemic areas, *S. japonicum* is probably an important cause of primary liver cancer and colorectal cancer (Chen *et al.*, 1990; IARC, 1994b; Newton *et al.*, 1999b). There are case reports of *S. japonicum* occurring in conjunction with a range of other cancers, but whether it plays an aetiological role is not clear.

The precise mechanism(s) by which schistosomiasis induces cancer is not known, although several possible explanations have been proposed (IARC, 1994b). These can be broadly categorized as involving (1) exogenous or endogenous agents which either induce DNA damage or have a tumour-promoting activity, (2) altered host metabolism, (3) pathological changes leading to increased cell proliferation and (4) altered immune responses. In relation to *S. haematobium* and bladder cancer, the first suggestions involved the effects of chronic inflammation and urinary retention. More generally, alteration of liver function by hepatic schistosomiasis leads to the production and excretion of potentially carcinogenic tryptophan metabolites, although the importance of these *in vivo* is not clear. In addition, chronic bacterial infection of the bladder can complicate schistosomal infestation, leading to the production of carcinogenic nitrosamines from precursors in urine.

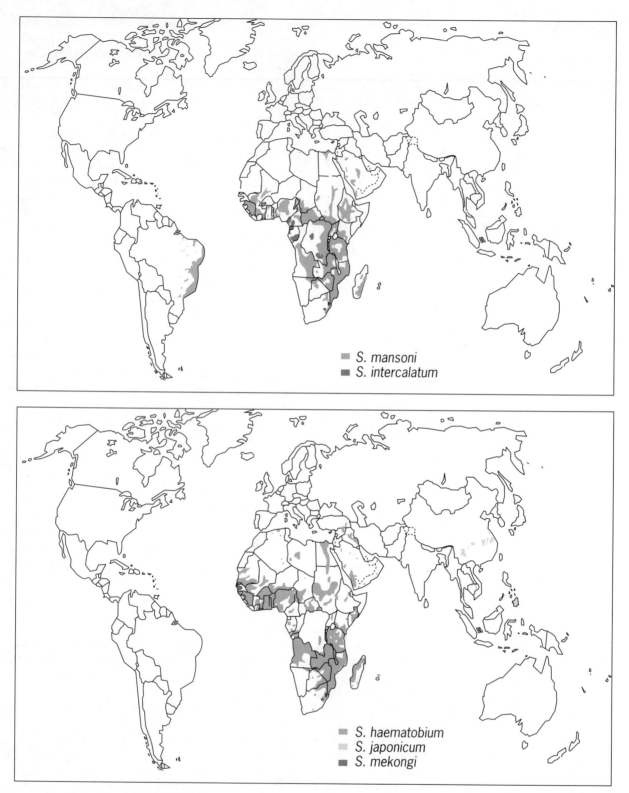

Figure 2 The geographical distribution of schistosomiasis (from WHO).

Safe, effective chemotherapy against all the schistosomes that infect humans has been available for more than two decades (WHO, 1993). The most versatile drug currently available is praziquantel, which is effective in a single oral dose, although it is relatively expensive if used extensively (approximately US $0.35 per treatment). However, treatment can result in resolution of infection, prevention or arrest of disease in heavily infected people and reversal of some manifestations of infection, such as haematuria.

Avoidance of contaminated water would prevent infection with schistosomes and is a relatively simple thing for occasional visitors to endemic areas to achieve. Control and prevention of infection in the community, however, where residents do not always have the luxury of avoiding contact with contaminated water, are complex. Many countries have initiated control programs involving a many pronged approach, including (1) the use of chemotherapy to remove adult worms, (2) elimination of the snail inter-mediate hosts by habitat modification or chemical attack, (3) changing human behaviour through health education and (4) providing safe water supplies and sanitation.

Use of these integrated control measures over many decades has led to the recent eradication of schistosomiasis in Japan, Tunisia and Monserrat (WHO, 1993). In China, 40 years of unremitting control measures have reduced the prevalence of infection by about 90%. Elsewhere in the World, including Brazil, Egypt, Iran, the Philippines and Venezuela, significant reductions in disease prevalence have been achieved. Even in places where the prevalence of infection has remained high, serious manifestations of disease are becoming less common with the use of effect-ive chemotherapy, although declines in cancer incidence are not yet apparent (WHO, 1993). Despite this, the number of cases of schistosomiasis worldwide was esti-mated to be the same in 1993 as it was in 1984 (WHO, 1993). In endemic areas, populations (and hence the number of susceptible hosts) continue to grow. In addition, developments in water resource management, land use and irrigation have led to a spread of schistosomiasis to new areas. There is currently no vaccine available, although intensive efforts are being made to develop one, and so the use of complex, integrated control measures remains paramount.

Liver Flukes

Three species of food-borne liver flukes, *Opisthorchis viverrini*, *O. felineus* and *Clonorchis sinensis*, of the class Trematoda, are pathologically important to humans. They establish chronic infection within the intrahepatic bile ducts and occasionally in the pancreas and gall-bladder and have been associated with diseases of these organs. Infection is acquired by eating raw or undercooked fresh-water fish, which contain the infective stage (meta-cercaria). The flukes migrate to the biliary tree via the ampulla of Vater and mature in the intrahepatic bile ducts, producing eggs, which are excreted in faeces. If the eggs reach fresh water and are consumed by an appropriate species of snail, they hatch, undergo asexual reproduction to produce free-living larvae, which can infect freshwater fish and become encysted metacercariae (IARC, 1994b; Vatanasapt *et al.*, 1999).

O. viverrini is common in north-east Thailand and Laos, where it is estimated that up to 9 million people are infected (about one-third of the population). About 1.5 million people are infected with *O. felineus*, mainly in central Russia, and 7 million are infected with *C. sinensis*, in Korea, China, Macao and Vietnam (**Figure 3**). The distribution of human infection depends not just on that of the flukes, but also on the habit of eating raw freshwater fish. Infection usually occurs in the first decade of life and men are often more affected than women.

Cholangiocarcinoma has long been recognized as a serious complication of liver fluke infection. This tumour is very rare throughout most of the world, but in endemic areas the number of cases of cholangiocarcinoma is usually higher than that of hepatocellular carcinoma. Evidence from ecological studies relating the prevalence of anti-bodies to liver fluke infection (or of eggs in faeces) to the incidence of cholangiocarcinoma suggest a causal link. Case-control studies indicate that infected individuals have about a fivefold increase in the risk of cancer compared with the uninfected, a finding that is supported by data from animal studies.

The pathological changes associated with acute liver fluke infection include oedema, desquamation and acute inflammation in the bile ducts. Chronic infection is char-acterized by goblet cell metaplasia, adenomatous hyper-plasia and thickening of the walls. It is thought that cholangiocarcinoma arises from this pre-existing damage, as part of a progressive process. The mechanisms by which this might occur are poorly understood.

The antihelminthic drug praziquantel is currently the drug of choice for the treatment of liver fluke infection, both for the individual patient and for community-based treatment programmes. The best way to reduce the inci-dence of cholangiocarcinoma is to control liver flukes. Eradication programmes need continuous and intensive health education, together with drug treatment for existing infections. Mass treatment without health education is unlikely to be effective. Health education should focus on the need to cook fish and fish products properly. As yet, eradication programmes have had little effect on the incidence of cholangiocarcinoma and a vaccine is not available.

THE FUTURE

Given that the discovery of an infectious cause of cancer (or any other chronic disease) has such important impli-cations for prevention, how does one identify and confirm a causal association? First, this requires an insight into which diseases may be linked to infection. Certain epi-demiological features of a cancer may offer clues as to an infectious aetiology. These include a high incidence of disease in people who are prone to infections (such as the immunosuppressed), large variations in incidence by geographical region or other patterns of clustering, apparent improvements with antimicrobial treatments and a strong correlation with markers of poverty. So what

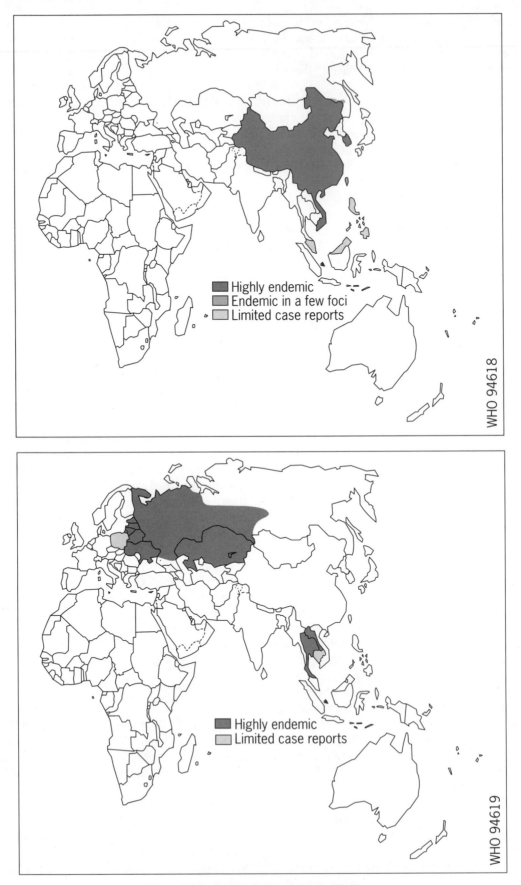

Figure 3 The geographical distribution of liver fluke infections (from WHO).

cancers might next be linked to infections? It is dangerous to prophesy, but there is considerable speculation about leukaemias and lymphomas, squamous cell skin cancers and even breast cancer. Second, the relevant infection must be identified and isolated from tumour tissue or diseased individuals. Finally, causality must be established. The relative risk of a specific cancer in an infected individual is usually very high, but it is harder to identify large excess risks in infected individuals when the cancer is a rare outcome of a common, or even ubiquitous, infection. In such instances, establishing causality may depend in part, for example, on identifying abnormal immunological responses to infection in diseased individuals, compared with those who are without disease (e.g. differences in antibody titre to infection).

As for prevention of cancers caused by infections, it is clear that vaccination programmes, although ultimately cost effective, require a long-term commitment, involving substantial investment of time, money and effort. In the meantime, an understanding of the biology and epidemiology of the relevant infections is essential to reduce the associated cancer burden in other ways. In certain circumstances, many infections can be avoided by behaviour modification or screening of blood products, for example. In addition, the risk of transmission of an infection from a pregnant mother to her child may be reduced with changes in breast-feeding behaviour or the use of anti-viral therapies. Perhaps one of the most exciting possibilities involves the introduction of HPV testing within the framework of the cervical screening programme, as a means of identifying women at high risk of disease, for intensive follow-up.

All of the above makes a strong case for a coordinated effort by clinicians, molecular biologists and epidemiologists to search for new − as well as known − infections in human tissues and to study their possible associations with disease. Research into a problem, however, is not the whole story. Understanding the causes of cancer is often difficult − prevention requires something more: a commitment to invest in public health.

REFERENCES

Barré-Sinoussi, F., *et al.* (1983). Isolation of a T-lymphotropic retrovirus from a patient at risk for aquired immunodeficiency syndrome (AIDS). *Science*, **220**, 868–871.

Beral, V. and Newton, R. (1998). Overview of the epidemiology of immunodeficiency-associated cancers. *Monographs of the National Cancer Institute*, **23**, 1–6.

Boshoff, C. (1999). Kaposi's sarcoma associated herpesvirus. In: Newton, R., *et al.* (eds), *Cancer Surveys, Vol. 33, Infections and Human Cancer* (Cold Spring Harbor Laboratory Press, Cold Spring Harbor, NY), pp. 157–190.

Chang, M. H., *et al.* (1997). Universal hepatitis B vaccination in Taiwan and the incidence of hepatocellular carcinoma in children. *New England Journal of Medicine*, **336**, 1855–1859.

Chen, J., *et al.* (1990). *Diet, Life-style and Mortality in China: A Study of the Characteristics of 65 Chinese Counties* (Oxford University Press, Oxford, Cornell University Press, Ithaca, NY and People's Medical Publishing House, Beijing).

Coursaget, P. and Muñoz, N. (1999). Vaccination against infectious agents associated with human cancer. In: Newton, R., *et al.* (eds), *Cancer Surveys, Vol. 33, Infections and Human Cancer* (Cold Spring Harbor Laboratory Press, Cold Spring Harbor, NY), pp. 355–382.

Cuzick, J. (1999). Screening. In: Newton, R., *et al.* (eds), *Cancer Surveys, Vol. 33, Infections and Human Cancer* (Cold Spring Harbor Laboratory Press, Cold Spring Harbor, NY), pp. 345–354.

Danesh, J. (1999). Is *Helicobacter pylori* infection a cause of gastric neoplasia? In: Newton, R., *et al.* (eds), *Cancer Surveys, Vol. 33, Infections and Human Cancer* (Cold Spring Harbor Laboratory Press, Cold Spring Harbor, NY), pp. 263–272.

de Thé, G., *et al.* (1978). Epidemiological evidence for a causal relationship between the Epstein–Barr virus and Burkitt's lymphoma from a Ugandan prospective study. *Nature*, **274**, 756–761.

Gallo, R. C., *et al.* (1984). Frequent detection and isolation of cytopathic retrovirus (HTLV-III) from patients with AIDS and at risk for AIDS. *Science*, **224**, 500–503.

Gambia Hepatitis Study Group (1987). The Gambia Hepatitis Intervention Study. *Cancer Research*, **47**, 5782–5787.

Herrero, R. and Muñoz, N. (1999). Human papillomavirus and cancer. In: Newton, R., *et al.* (eds), *Cancer Surveys, Vol. 33, Infections and Human Cancer* (Cold Spring Harbor Laboratory Press, Cold Spring Harbor, NY), pp. 75–98.

IARC (1992). *The Epidemiology of Cervical Cancer and Human Papillomavirus*. IARC Scientific Publications, Vol. 119 (International Agency for Research on Cancer, Lyon).

IARC (1994a). *IARC Monographs on the Evaluation of Carcinogenic Risks to Humans, Vol. 59, Hepatitis Viruses* (International Agency for Research on Cancer, Lyon).

IARC (1994b). *IARC Monographs on the Evaluation of Carcinogenic Risks to Humans, Vol. 61, Schistosomes, Liver Flukes and Helicobacter pylori* (International Agency for Research on Cancer, Lyon).

IARC (1995). *IARC Monographs on the Evaluation of Carcinogenic Risks to Humans, Vol. 64, Human Papillomaviruses* (International Agency for Research on Cancer, Lyon).

IARC (1996). *IARC Monographs on the Evaluation of Carcinogenic Risks to Humans, Vol. 67, Human Immunodeficiency Viruses and Human T-cell Lymphotropic Viruses* (International Agency for Research on Cancer, Lyon).

IARC (1997). *IARC Monographs on the Evaluation of Carcinogenic Risks to Humans, Vol. 67, Epstein–Barr Virus and Kaposi's Sarcoma Herpesvirus/Human Herpesvirus 8* (International Agency for Research on Cancer, Lyon).

McGregor, J. M. and Proby, C. M. (1996). The role of papillomaviruses in human non-melanoma skin cancer. In: Leigh, I. M., *et al.* (eds), *Cancer Surveys, Vol. 26, Skin Cancer* (Cold Spring Harbor Laboratory Press, Cold Spring Harbor, NY), pp. 219–236.

Murray, C. J. L. and Lopez, A. D. (1997). Mortality by cause for eight regions of the world: global burden of disease study. *Lancet*, **349**, 1269–1276.

Newton, R., *et al.* (1999a). Human immunodeficiency virus infection and cancer. In: Newton, R., *et al.* (eds), *Cancer Surveys, Vol. 33, Infections and Human Cancer* (Cold Spring Harbor Laboratory Press, Cold Spring Harbor, NY), pp. 237–262.

Newton, R., *et al.* (1999b). Schistosomes and human cancer. In: Newton, R., *et al.* (eds), *Cancer Surveys, Vol. 33, Infections and Human Cancer* (Cold Spring Harbor Laboratory Press, Cold Spring Harbor, NY), pp. 291–312.

Parkin, D. M., *et al.* (1999). The global health burden of infection associated cancers. In: Newton, R., *et al.* (eds), *Cancer Surveys, Volume 33, Infections and Human Cancer* (Cold Spring Harbor Laboratory Press, Cold Spring Harbor, NY), pp. 5–34.

Phillips, A. C. and Vousden, K. H. (1999). Human papillomavirus and cancer: the viral transforming genes. In: Newton, R., *et al.* (eds), *Cancer Surveys, Vol. 33, Infections and Human Cancer* (Cold Spring Harbor Laboratory Press, Cold Spring Harbor, NY), pp. 55–74.

Tanaka, H. and Tsukuma, H. (1999). Hepatitis C virus. In: Newton, R., *et al.* (eds), Cancer Surveys, Vol. 33, Infections and Human Cancer (Cold Spring Harbor Laboratory Press, Cold Spring Harbor, NY), pp. 55–74.

Vatanasapt, V., *et al.* (1999). Liver flukes and liver cancer. In: Newton, R., *et al.* (eds), *Cancer Surveys, Vol. 33, Infections and Human Cancer* (Cold Spring Harbor Laboratory Press, Cold Spring Harbor, NY), pp. 313–344.

Walbloomers, J. M., *et al.* (1999). Human papillomavirus is a necessary cause of invasive cervical cancer worldwide. *Journal of Pathology*, **189**, 12–19.

WHO (1993). *The Control of Schistosomiasis*. Second Report of the WHO Expert Committee. WHO Technical Report Series, No. 830 (World Health Organization, Geneva).

Wild, C. P. and Hall, A. J. (1999). Hepatitis B virus and liver cancer: unanswered questions. In: Newton, R., *et al.* (eds), *Cancer Surveys, Vol. 33, Infections and Human Cancer* (Cold Spring Harbor Laboratory Press, Cold Spring Harbor, NY), pp. 35–54.

FURTHER READING

Newton, R., *et al.* (eds) (1999). *Cancer Surveys, Vol. 33, Infections and Human Cancer* (Cold Spring Harbor Laboratory Press, Cold Spring Harbor, NY).

Parsonnet, J. (ed.) (1999). *Microbes and Malignancy: Infection as a Cause of Human Cancer* (Oxford University Press, Oxford).

Chapter 25

Short-term Testing for Genotoxicity

David Gatehouse

GlaxoWellcome Research and Development Limited, Ware, UK (Present address: Concave Laboratories Ltd, Harrogate, UK)

CONTENTS

INTRODUCTION

It has been known for several hundred years that exposure to particular chemicals or complex mixtures can lead to cancer in later life. There has been accumulating evidence that many cancers can arise from damage to DNA and the resulting mutations. This has been discussed in detail in the preceding chapters. As a consequence of this, it has become necessary to determine whether widely used chemicals or potentially useful new chemicals possess the ability to damage DNA. Data concerning the genotoxicity of a new chemical have become part of the basic toxicological information package. They are needed for decision making and to reduce risks that might otherwise be unforeseen.

The field of genetic toxicology began in the 1960s when several seminal conferences were held focusing on chemical mutagens and in particular their effects on germ cells and the risk to future generations. Although germ cell risk was the initial concern, this was broadened in the 1970s when evidence relating genotoxicity and carcinogenicity began to accumulate. This was further supported by the use of *in vitro* metabolic activation systems capable of producing electrophilic metabolites, and the fact that early analysis of rodent carcinogens and noncarcinogens suggested that almost all carcinogens were also genotoxic. This view has now been modified, since it is clear that nongenotoxic carcinogens also exist, as discussed in an earlier chapter (see the chapter *Non-Genotoxic Causes of Cancer*). From this time onwards, various national expert committees were formed to advise governments on the type of approach that should be taken to screen new chemicals for carcinogenic risk (and any potential heritable effects). Consequently, numerous guidelines have been prepared over the past 20 years describing the tests which should be used to investigate the genotoxicity of chemicals. It is not the intention of this chapter to give an exhaustive list of these guidelines, except to mention that a harmonized approach to the genotoxicity testing of drugs has recently been introduced as a result of the International Conference on Harmonisation (ICH) programme. In this process, areas of disharmony were identified and differences in regulation with respect to genotoxicity were discussed, resulting in the creation of two guidelines (referenced at the end of this chapter). At the same time as the ICH process was occurring, the Organisation for Economic Cooperation and Development (OECD) also updated a number of its genotoxicity guidelines. Both processes influenced each other resulting in similar recommendations. A summary of the testing strategy recommended by the ICH is given in **Figure 1**.

In this chapter, the individual test systems that are required for genotoxicity screening will be described together with a discussion on how the results obtained should be interpreted. As well as the primary test systems, there will also be a description of the supplementary assays that may be required when investigating positive effects. It is not intended to give detailed guidance on the performance of these tests. For this information, the reader is directed to the Further Reading list at the end of the chapter. The chapter concludes with a brief overview of some of the new developments in the field.

---

1. A test for gene mutation in bacteria
2. An *in vitro* test with cytogenetic evaluation of chromosomal damage with mammalian cells or an *in vitro* mouse lymphoma tk assay
3. An *in vivo* test for chromosomal damage using rodent haematopoietic cells

---

Figure 1   Recommended ICH genotoxicity test battery.

PRIMARY TEST SYSTEMS

In Vitro Metabolic Activation

Before describing the individual *in vitro* test systems, it is necessary to mention briefly a factor of critical importance in genotoxicity screening, namely the need to include some form of *in vitro* metabolizing system. This is because most of the indicator cells (bacteria and mammalian cells) possess a very limited capacity for endogenous metabolism of xenobiotics. Many carcinogens and mutagens are unable to interact with DNA unless they have undergone some degree of metabolism (see also the chapter *Mechanisms of Chemical Carcinogenesis*). To improve the ability of the test systems to detect as many authentic *in vivo* mutagens and carcinogens as possible, extracts of mammalian liver (usually rat) are incorporated. The liver is a rich source of mixed-function oxygenases capable of converting carcinogens to reactive electrophiles. Crude homogenate such as the 9000 *g* supernatant (S9 fraction) is used, which is composed of free endoplasmic reticulum, microsomes, soluble enzymes and some cofactors. The oxygenases require the reduced form of nicotinamide adenine dinucleotide phosphate (NADPH), which is normally generated *in situ* by the action of glucose-6-phosphate dehydrogenase on glucose-6-phosphate and reducing NADP, both of which are normally supplied as cofactors. Normal uninduced S9 preparations are of limited value for screening as they are deficient in particular enzyme activities. In addition, species and tissue differences are most divergent in such preparations. These problems are reduced when enzyme inducers are used, and most commonly preparations are made from rat livers after enzyme induction with Aroclor 1254, which is a mixture of polychlorinated biphenyls. Concern about the toxicity, carcinogenicity and persistence of this material in the environment has led to the introduction of alternatives, such as a combination of phenobarbitone and β-naphthoflavone. This combination induces a similar range of mono-oxygenases and has been recommended as a safer alternative to Aroclor (Elliott *et al.*, 1992).

It should be noted that this system is only a first approximation to the complex metabolic processes that occur *in vivo*, and in particular there is little account taken of the phase II detoxification reactions. Such factors should be considered when interpreting positive *in vitro* results which are only seen in the presence of S9 mix.

In Vitro Tests for Gene Mutation in Bacteria

The most widely used assays for detecting chemically induced gene mutations are those employing bacteria. These assays feature in all test batteries for genotoxicity as it is relatively straight forward to use them as a sensitive indirect indicator of DNA damage. Bacteria can be grown in large numbers overnight, permitting the detection of rare mutational events. The extensive knowledge of bacterial genetics that was obtained during the twentieth century allowed the construction of special strains of bacteria with exquisite sensitivity to a variety of genotoxins. An offshoot of the studies on genes concerned with amino acid biosynthesis led to the development of *Escherichia coli* and *Salmonella typhimurium* strains with relatively well defined mutations in known genes. The most commonly used bacteria are the *S. typhimurium* strains which contain defined mutations in the histidine operon. These were developed by Bruce Ames, and form the basis of the 'reverse' mutation assays (Ames *et al.*, 1971). In these assays, bacteria which are already mutant at the histidine locus are treated with a range of concentrations of test chemical to determine whether the compound can induce a second mutation that directly reverses or suppresses the original mutations. Thus, for the *S. typhimurium* strains which are histidine auxotrophs, the original mutation resulted in the loss of ability to grow in the absence of histidine. The second mutation (induced by the chemical) restores prototrophy, i.e. the affected cell is now able to grow in the absence of histidine, if provided with inorganic salts and a carbon source. This simple concept underlines the great strength of these assays for it provides enormous selective power which can identify a small number of the chosen mutants from a population of millions of unmutated cells and cells mutated in other genes. Each of the *S. typhimurium* strains contains one of a number of possible mutations in the histidine operon, and each can be reverted by either base-change or frameshift mutations. The genotype of the most commonly used strains is shown in **Table 1**, together with the types of reversion events that each strain detects.

In order to make the bacteria more sensitive to mutation by chemical agents, several additional traits have been introduced. Ames and colleagues realized that many carcinogens (or their metabolites) are large molecules that are often unable to cross the protective cell wall of the bacteria. Wild-type cells produce a lipopolysaccharide that acts as a barrier to bulky hydrophobic molecules. Consequently, an *rfa* mutation was introduced into the *Salmonella* strains, which resulted in defective lipopolysaccharide and increased permeability.

Bacteria possess several major DNA repair pathways that appear to be error-free. The test strains were constructed, therefore, with a deletion removing the *uvrB* gene. This codes for the first enzyme in the error-free excision repair pathway, and so gene deletion renders the strains excision repair deficient, thus increasing their sensitivity to many genotoxins by several orders of magnitude. Lastly, some of the bacterial strains do not appear to possess classical error-prone repair as found in other members of the Enterobacteria such as *E. coli*. This results from a deficiency in *umuD* activity. This deficiency is overcome by insertion of a plasmid containing *umuDC* genes. Plasmid

Table 1 Genotype of commonly used strains of *S. typhimurium* LT2 and reversion events detected by these strains

Strain	Histidine mutation	Full genotype[a]	Reversion events
TA1535	hisG46	rfa Dgal chlD bio *uvr*B	Subset of base pair substitution events, extragenic suppressors
TA100	hisG46	rfa Dgal chlD bio *uvr*B (pKM101)	
TA1538	hisD3052	rfa Dgal chlD bio *uvr*B	Frameshifts
TA98	hisD3052	rfa Dgal chlD bio *uvr*B (pKM101)	Frameshifts
TA1537	hisC3076	rfa Dgal chlD bio *uvr*B	Frameshifts
TA97	hisD6610	his O $_{1242}$rfa Dgal chlD bio *uvr*B (pKM101)	Frameshifts
TA102	hisG428	his D (G) $_{8476}$rfa galE (pAQ1) (pKM101)	All possible transitions and transversions small deletions and extragenic suppressors

[a]rfa = Deep rough; galE = UDP galactose 4-epimerase; ChlD = nitrate reductase (resistance to chlorate); bio = biotin; *uvr*B = UV endonuclease component B; D = deletion of genes following this symbol; pAQ1 = a plasmid containing the his G_{428} gene; pKM101 = a plasmid carrying the *uvr*A and B genes that enhance error-prone repair.

pKm101 is the most useful (Mortelmans and Dousman, 1986) conferring on the bacteria sensitivity to mutation without a concomitant increase in sensitivity to the lethal effects of test compounds. Further sensitivity is gained by the fact that the initial mutation responsible for the histidine growth requirement is situated at a site within the gene that is particularly sensitive to reversion by specific classes of genotoxin (i.e. hotspots). The incorporation of strain TA102 into the test battery has been proposed, as the target mutation has an AT base pair at the critical site. This allows the detection of genotoxins not detected by the usual battery of *S. typhimurium* strains that possess mutations exclusively at GC base pairs. As an alternative many guidelines recommend the use of the *E. coli* WP2 trpE strains which contain a terminating ochre mutation in the *trpE* gene. The ochre mutation involves an AT base pair, and so reverse mutation can take place at the original site of mutation or in the relevant tRNA loci. A combination of *E. coli* WP2 *trpE* (pKm101) and *E. coli* WP2 *trpE uvrA* (pKm101) can be used as alternatives to *S. typhimurium* TA102 for the detection of point mutations at AT sites.

Consequently in the recently published ICH Guidelines (ICH, 1998), the following base set of bacterial test strains were recommended:

S. typhimurium: TA98, TA100, TA1535
S. typhimurium: TA1537, or TA97, or TA97a
S. typhimurium: TA102, or *E. coli* WP2 *uvrA* or *E. coli* WP2 *uvrA* (pKm101)

The use of the repair-proficient *E. coli* strain WP2 (pKm101) allows the detection of cross-linking agents that require an intact excision repair pathway to generate mutations and this strain may also be selected.

It is not the intention of this chapter to give detailed instruction on the performance of these assays. For this information, the reader is directed to other detailed references (Gatehouse *et al.*, 1994; Tweats and Gatehouse, 1999). In general, the most widely used protocol is the

'plate incorporation assay.' In this method, the bacterial strain, test material and an *in vitro* metabolic activation system (S9 mix) are added to a small volume of molten agar containing a trace of histidine and biotin. The mixture is poured across the surface of a basal agar plate and allowed to set prior to incubation at 37 °C for 48–72 h. The trace of histidine allows the growth of the auxotrophic bacteria in the presence of the test compound and/or any *in vitro* metabolites. The period of several cell divisions is essential to allow fixation of any premutagenic lesions that have been induced in the bacterial DNA. Exhaustion of the histidine halts growth of the auxotrophic cells. Only those cells that have been reverted to histidine independence will continue to grow and form discrete visible colonies. The growth of nonreverted cells forms a visible background lawn, the thinning of which can be used as a non-quantitative indication of drug related toxicity. Revertant colonies can be counted manually or by use of an Image analyser. Untreated (vehicle) and suitable positive controls are included. The test concentration range is determined by performance of a preliminary toxicity test, whilst for nontoxic compounds a maximum concentration of 5 mg per plate is recommended. Some genotoxins are poorly detected using the plate incorporation procedure, particularly those that are metabolized to short-lived reactive electrophiles (e.g. aliphatic nitrosamines). In these cases, a preincubation procedure should be used in which bacteria, test compound and S9 mix are incubated together in a small volume at 37 °C for 30–60 min prior to agar addition. This maximizes exposure to the reactive species and limits nonspecific binding to agar.

Several statistical approaches have been applied to the results of these assays. In general, positive results should be statistically significant, dose related and reproducible. Bacterial mutation tests have been subjected to several large-scale trials over the years (e.g. Tennant *et al.*, 1987). These studies were primarily concerned with assessing the correlation between results obtained in the assays and the carcinogenic activity of chemicals. Most of the studies suggest that there is a good qualitative relationship between genotoxicity in the *Salmonella* assay and carcinogenicity for many, although not all, chemical classes. This figure varies between a sensitivity of 60 and 90% dependent upon chemical class. The bacterial assays seem to be particularly efficient in detecting trans-species, multiorgan animal carcinogens (Ashby and Tennant, 1988).

In Vitro Tests for Gene Mutation in Mammalian Cells

Although the prokaryotic systems described above are extremely versatile, rapid and mostly accurate in detecting genotoxins, the intrinsic differences between prokaryotic and eukaryotic cells in terms of genome structure and organization necessitate the use of mammalian test systems within any screening battery designed to detect the widest spectrum of genotoxins. A variety of *in vivo* mutation systems have been described in the literature but only a few have been defined adequately for quantitative studies (Cole *et al.*, 1990). Unlike the bacterial reverse mutation systems, these tests are based upon the detection of forward mutations. A defined large number of cells are treated with the test agent and then, after a set interval (termed the expression period), the cells are exposed to a selective toxic agent, so only those cells that have mutated can survive. Usually mutation is measured in genes located on the X chromosome in male cells (XY) where only one copy of the target gene is present, or in cells (called heterozygotes) where two copies of the gene are present but only one copy is active, as the other has been inactivated through mutation or deletion. The most common systems make use of genes which are not essential for cell survival but allow the cell to salvage nucleic acid breakdown products (nucleotides) from the culture medium for reuse in metabolism. Toxic nucleotides placed in the culture medium will be transported into normal (nonmutated) cells that consequently die. However, loss of the salvage enzyme through genotoxic damage (mutation, chromosome deletions or rearrangements) of the corresponding gene will render the cell resistant to the toxic nucleotide and so it will survive. The surviving mutant cells can be detected by colony formation in tissue culture plates. The two most popular genes for measuring mutation *in vitro* are those coding for hypoxanthine guanine phosphoribosyl transferase (*Hgprt*) and thymidine kinase (*tk*). The former is located on the X chromosome in both human and Chinese hamster cells and loss of activity in this gene can be measured by resistance to the antimetabolite 6-thioguanine. The TK gene is located on chromosome 11 in mouse cells and on chromosome 17 in humans. Loss of activity in this gene can be measured by resistance to the toxic chemical trifluorothymidine (Clive *et al.*, 1987). Three cell lines have been used most extensively for routine *in vitro* mutation assays. Two are Chinese hamster cell lines (V79 and CHO) and one is a heterozygous mouse line, mouse lymphoma

(L5178Y). The Chinese hamster cells have been used extensively over the past 15–20 years, but more recently there has been a significant move towards the use of the heterozygous mouse lymphoma L5178Y cell line because of the variety of genetic events detected in this system. In fact, recently published ICH guidelines recommend this system as the method of choice when evaluating the potential genotoxicity of new drugs.

The theoretical basis for the mouse lymphoma assay is shown in **Figure 2**. Two main protocols have been devised for performing the assay, plating the cells in soft agar or a fluctuation test approach. Mitchell *et al.* (1997) published a full evaluation of this assay. In these tests, ideally the highest test concentration should produce at least 80% toxicity (i.e. no more than 20% survival).

At least two types of colony are obtained when mutations at the *tk* locus are selected, large colonies which grow at the normal rate and slow-growing small colonies. Initial molecular analysis of these colonies indicated that a high percentage of small colony mutants have a wide variety of visible chromosome 11b aberrations, whereas large colonies do not. However, recent chromosome painting analysis of colonies indicates that this initial generalized premise on colony size may be oversimplistic. What is clear is that a wide range of mutations and genetic events can be detected by the L5178Y system, including both point mutations and chromosomal damage.

Recently, the *p53* status of a number of L5178Y cell lines has been investigated, and it has been found that the cells contain two mutant *p53* alleles resulting in a

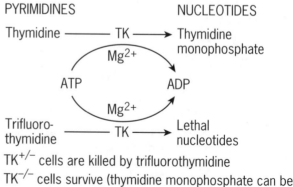

The gene coding for thymidine kinase (TK) is on mouse chromosomes number 11

The mouse lymphoma L5178Y line is TK$^{+/-}$, i.e. one gene copy is already inactivated by mutation

∴ Each cell contains only one functional gene

∴ One mutational event can render the cell TK$^{-/-}$

PYRIMIDINES   NUCLEOTIDES

Thymidine ———— TK ——→ Thymidine monophosphate

Mg^{2+}

ATP   ADP

Mg^{2+}

Trifluoro-thymidine ———— TK ——→ Lethal nucleotides

TK$^{+/-}$ cells are killed by trifluorothymidine
TK$^{-/-}$ cells survive (thymidine monophosphate can be synthesized *de novo* via thymidylate synthetase, etc.)

Figure 2   The theoretical basis of the L5178Y TK$^{+/-}$ mouse lymphoma assay.

dysfunctional p53 protein (Storer *et al.*, 1997). As this tumour-suppressor protein is so important in regulating cellular responses to DNA damage, this may account for the sensitivity of these cells to genotoxins. It has been suggested that the *p53* status of the cells makes them even more appropriate for use in screens for genotoxic carcinogens, as the development of cancer is often associated with mutant p53 protein. A system that contains a component evaluating a chemicals' ability to induce additional mutations in *p53*-deficient cells may provide a more appropriate model for the human situation.

In Vitro Tests for Chromosome Damage in Mammalian Cells

An alternative method to measuring mutation induction within mammalian genes involves the examination of mammalian chromosomes microscopically for the presence of visible damage.

In simplest terms these tests generally involve exposure of cultured cells to the test material in the presence and absence of a metabolic activation system. The cells are then harvested at one or more time intervals after treatment. Before fixation the cells are exposed to a mitotic poison to arrest them in metaphase and then to hypotonic solution to swell them. They are fixed, metaphase spreads are prepared and after staining (usually with Giemsa) they are analysed microscopically. Gross damage to the chromosomes such as terminal deletions, breaks and exchanges are recorded. Much of this damage is lethal to the cell during the cell cycle following induction of the damage. However, such changes are used as indicators of the presence of nonlethal more subtle changes (e.g. reciprocal translocations and small deletions) which are difficult to observe microscopically, but which may have important consequences in both somatic and germ cells.

Established cells (e.g. Chinese hamster fibroblasts) or primary cells (e.g. human peripheral lymphocytes) can be used. Both have advantages and disadvantages. The Chinese hamster cells contain a small number of chromosomes facilitating rapid analysis, but can contain karyotype abnormalities. The human lymphocytes, on the other hand, are karyotypically stable, but donor variation in responsiveness to some mutagens may be an issue.

A detailed discussion of the test procedures employed was given by Scott *et al.* (1990). Detectable levels of chromosome aberrations are often found only at doses which induce some evidence of cytotoxicity, and consequently the recommended protocols require that the maximum test concentration should induce > 50% reduction in cell number or culture confluency for cell lines, or an inhibition of mitotic index by > 50% for lymphocytes. However, there are growing concerns as to the relevance of genotoxic effects which are found only at highly cytotoxic concentrations.

In Vivo Tests for Chromosome Damage in Rodents

Although there are a number of methods available for measuring chromosome damage *in vivo*, by far the most popular and extensively validated technique is the micronucleus test. In this assay damage is induced in the immature erythroblast population in the bone marrow. Chromosome breakage is detected in the form of centric and acentric fragments which form micronuclei observable microscopically within these cells after the main nucleus has been expelled. This test is also sensitive to numerical changes, thus allowing the detection of chemicals that cause whole chromosome loss (aneuploidy) in the absence of clastogenic activity. The basis for the assay is given in **Figure 3**. When the immature erythroblast matures into a polychromatic erythrocyte, the micronucleus, the formation of which results from either chromosome loss during cell division or from chromosome breakage, is not extruded with the nucleus. Young polychromatic erythrocytes (usually 2000) are examined in the bone marrow of rodents that have been previously exposed to the test material by an appropriate route. Analysis is carried out at two time points (usually 24 and 48 h) after a single exposure. As an alternative, multiple dosing can be used, usually three or more daily doses, in which case the bone marrow is analysed 24 h after the last dose. In addition to micronucleus incidence, the ratio of polychromatic to normochromatic erythrocytes is also assessed as an indication of any compound-related cytotoxic or cytostatic effect within the marrow. Male animals are sufficient for use in the test, unless there are obvious differences in toxicity or metabolism between male and female rodents. In these studies the test substance is evaluated at the maximum tolerated dose (i.e. one which produces some signs of toxicity such as hypoactivity, ataxia, ptosis, etc.). The highest dose to use when toxicity is not evident ranges from 2 to $5\,g\,kg^{-1}$ according to different regulatory guidelines. A more detailed discussion of the study design and test procedure was given by Hayashi *et al.* (2000).

Micronuclei can also be detected in reticulocytes circulating within peripheral blood, and in future it is likely that such studies, using either bone marrow or blood as the target tissue, will be incorporated into standard rodent toxicology studies, rather than be performed as stand-alone experiments. Also, it is possible that the use of flow cytometric techniques will replace microscopic analysis as a means of generating results more quickly and accurately (Dertinger *et al.*, 1997).

In Vivo Test for Unscheduled DNA Synthesis in Rat Liver

It is recognized that there is a need for an assay that can complement the micronucleus assay, by using tissue other

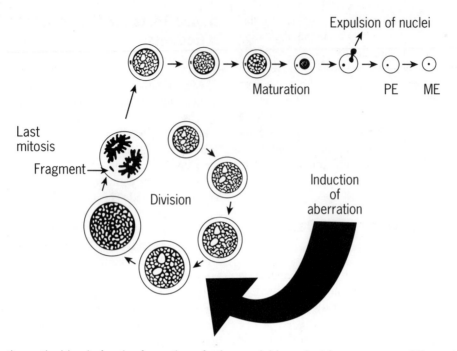

Figure 3 The theoretical basis for the formation of micronuclei in rodent bone marrow. PE = polychromatic erythrocyte; ME = mature erythrocyte.

than the bone marrow. This is because in some instances genotoxins will fail to be detected in the bone marrow owing either to poor drug distribution or other organospecific effects. It is important to note that such an assay is only likely to be needed if there is clear, unequivocal evidence of genotoxic effects in one or more of the *in vitro* tests and the *in vivo* micronucleus test is negative. At the present time the preferred approach is to investigate unscheduled DNA synthesis (UDS) in rat liver *in vivo*. The liver, as the major organ of xenobiotic metabolism, is an appropriate target and this assay fulfils a useful complementary role when used in conjunction with the micronucleus test, allowing the detection of a wider spectrum of genotoxins (**Table 2**). However, new test systems that allow the investigation of genotoxic effects in other tissues are now becoming increasingly available and will be discussed in the next section.

UDS assays quantify the resultant excision repair of DNA following a permanent change such as covalent binding of an activated mutagen or a reactive chemical species generated intracellularly. Cells undergoing such repair synthesize DNA at stages of the cell cycle other than S-phase, where normal replicative (scheduled) DNA synthesis takes place, hence the term 'unscheduled DNA synthesis.' This technique is potentially highly sensitive because the whole genome is theoretically a target for chemical reaction.

A detailed description of the methodology was given by Madle *et al.* (1994). Briefly, rodents, usually rats, are treated with the suspect chemical by an appropriate route. For nontoxic compounds an upper limit of $2\,g\,kg^{-1}$ is

Table 2 *In vivo* genotoxicity results for 12 *in vitro* genotoxins and *in vivo* carcinogens

Chemical	Mouse micronucleus test	Rat liver UDS
Dimethylnitrosamine	−	+
Diethylnitrosamine	−	+
2,4-Dinitrotoluene	−	+
3′-Methyldimethylam- inoazobenzene (DAB)	−	+
6BT (DAB analogue)	−	+
Dimethylhydrazine	−	+
Cyclophosphamide	+	−
Benzo[a]pyrene	+	−
Hexamethylphosphoramide	+	−
2-Acetylaminofluorene	+	+
Benzidine	+	+
N-Methyl- N-nitronitrosoguanidine	−	−

recommended, whereas for compounds eliciting toxicity a dose approaching the maximum tolerated dose should be used. A single-dose regimen is the most common procedure, and two sampling times are employed (12–16 and 2–4 h after treatment). At these times, viable hepatocyte populations are prepared by perfusing the livers with collagenase. Quantification of UDS is achieved by determining the uptake of the radiolabelled nucleotide [^{3}H]thymidine during DNA repair. A microautoradiographic procedure is the most favoured method in which slide preparations are made, on which the cells are fixed, developed autoradiographically and then stained prior to analysis with the aid of an image analyser. Cells undergoing repair are identified by increases in the number of silver grains overlying the nuclei. S-phase cells exhibit extremely high numbers of nuclear silver grains and are excluded from analysis. Hepatocytes from untreated control animals are included, and the net nuclear grain counts are compared. For a positive response there should be a net nuclear grain count for at least one dose and sampling time which exceeds a laboratory-specific threshold justified on the basis of historical control data.

SUPPLEMENTARY TEST SYSTEMS

The assays outlined in the previous section form the basis of most test batteries within a range of regulatory guidelines concerned with the testing of drugs, chemicals, food additives, etc., for genotoxicity. However, the current testing strategies are still deficient in a number of respects. Regulatory guidelines for genotoxicity screening are a compromise. Although there are accepted tests for measuring chromosome damage in vitro and in vivo, at present there is no validated test in widespread use to detect point mutation in vivo. Studies have shown that many carcinogens induce tumours in specific tissues, hence there is also a need for an in vivo genotoxicity test that could be applied to any tissue. In addition, the need for a specific assay to detect genome mutation (i.e. chromosome loss/gain) is currently under debate within some regulatory authorities. All of these areas are the subject of active research and at the present time new assay procedures are becoming available to meet these needs.

Transgenic Models

With the advent of the new DNA technologies, several promising transgenic mouse models are now being validated for use as in vivo genotoxicity screens. If suitable, these assays would enable somatic mutation to be measured within most tissues of the exposed animal, and more importantly enable mutation induction and specificity to be measured in the actual target tissue for carcinogenesis. At present the two best validated mouse transgenic models are based on the insertion of the bacterial genes LacI or LacZ into the mouse genome. In the first, called the 'Muta-Mouse,' an E. coli lacZ (β-galactosidase) gene was cloned into a lambda-bacteriophage vector, and then micro-injected into the pronucleus of (BALB/c × DBA/2) CD2 F1 eggs. In the second, called the 'Big Blue,' a lacI (lac repressor) gene cloned into a lambda shuttle vector was integrated into the genome of an inbred C57B/6 mouse. In both cases the transgenic mouse is treated with the test compound by the likely route of exposure, and genomic DNA is isolated from the desired tissues. The lambda vector is rescued from the genomic DNA by mixing with an in vitro 'Lambda-packaging' extract that excises the target lambda sector and packages the DNA into a lambda

phage head. These phages are then used to infect host E. coli strain. For the lacZ system a lacZ⁻ E. coli C indicator strain is used. For the lacI system the E. coli SCS-8 indicator strain is used which has a deleted lac region and contains a LacZ⁻ gene on a phi 80 insert.

For the lacZ system the bacteria and the lambda phage containing the rescued DNA are incubated in soft agar with a chromogenic agent (X-gal). After 16 h of incubation the lysis plaques produced by the phage are scored. If a phage contains a normal LacZ gene, the X-gal is metabolized to a blue product. If a mutated LacZ gene is carried by the phage, the X-gal remains intact and no colour is produced. Thus scoring consists of counting clear plaques against a background of nonmutated blue plaques. For the lacI system a similar plating routine is carried out. In this case mutants are detected as blue mutant plaques against a background of nonmutant colourless plaques. These can arise due to mutations that inactivate the lac repressor protein or lacI promoter or mutations within the lac repressor binding domain which block repressor binding to the lacZ operator. The density of plaques is limited to 1500 pfu per plate to ensure accuracy in detection of plaques with a mutant phenotype.

However, for both systems the detection of mutants by the colour selection method is laborious and expensive. For this reason, the 'MutaMouse' model has been adapted to a positive selection method using galE⁻ mutants of E. coli. This permits high plating densities and minimizes the need for multiple platings. In this system the phage containing the rescued vectors are used to infect E. coli lac⁻galE⁻ cells, which are then plated in the presence and absence of phenylgalactosidase (P-gal). In the presence of P-gal only lacZ⁻ bacteria will grow and produce plaques. Those containing lacZ⁺ (i.e. nonmutated gene) produce the enzyme β-galactosidase which converts P-gal to galactose. This is further converted to a toxic intermediate UDP-galactose which accumulates in the galE⁻ E. coli and kills the cells. **Figure 4** gives a summary of the procedure for the 'MutaMouse' system.

The optimal protocol for this type of assay has yet to be finalized. The role of cell proliferation and its effects on mutation fixation (expression), the need for single or multiple doses and the effects of age and DNA packaging efficiency on assay sensitivity remain to be optimized. However, there has been considerable progress in the validation of these techniques in recent years and they are now being used as in vivo screens to detect point mutation induction in a variety of tissues. The strategy for using these assays has been discussed by Gorelick (1995).

The systems described here are only the first generation of tests arising from the application of transgenic technology, and many of the basic parameters of assay conduct and data interpretation are still underdeveloped. It remains to be shown that mutational analysis of these transgenics is a true reflection of mutation of resident endogenous genes. The lacI/lacZ models are unsuited for the detection of

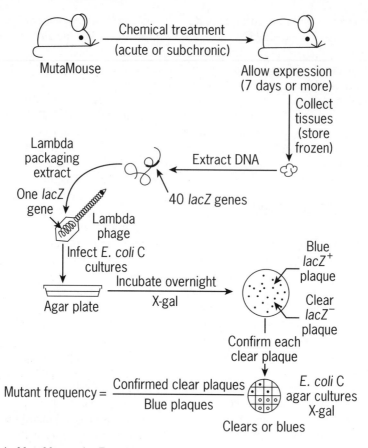

Figure 4   The transgenic MutaMouse *lacZ* system.

deletion mutations induced by clastogens, probably owing to the difficulty in packaging lambda phage vectors <42 or >52 kb. A new method using plasmid based transgenic animals may overcome these restrictions since recovery of plasmids is not so size dependent. It is believed that this system is potentially 10–20 times more efficient at rescuing *lac* genes (Dolle *et al.*, 1996). (See also chapter on *Transgenic Technology in the Study of Oncogenes and Tumour Suppressor Genes*.)

Comet Assay

The use of transgenic mouse assays is one of several promising approaches that could provide an *in vivo* assay capable of detecting genotoxic damage in any tissue. Another possible method utilizes microgel electrophoresis and is called the single-cell gel electrophoresis assay or 'comet' assay. This is a rapid and simple system for measuring alkali labile sites and overt strand breaks in the DNA of mammalian cells (Fairbairn *et al.*, 1995). Damaged (fragmented) DNA penetrates further than undamaged DNA into the agar following electrophoresis. The basis for this assay is represented in **Figure 5**. The technique can be applied to virtually any cell population or tissue type from which a single-cell suspension can be prepared. After treatment, the cells are suspended in agar and exposed to strong alkali,

which denatures the proteins and permits DNA unfolding. Electrophoresis is then performed during which time the supercoiled DNA relaxes and fragmented DNA is pulled towards the anode. After electrophoresis, the slides are neutralized and stained with a DNA-specific stain such as propidium iodide, when the cell ghosts with damaged DNA are visible as comets of various sizes (hence the name), whereas those with undamaged DNA are visible as round images. The most common method of measurement is the tail moment, which takes into account the degree of DNA migration (comet length), and the DNA content within the comet. The technique has been adapted so that primary somatic cells of a variety of tissues can be studied, including cells from the GI tract, nasal mucosa and lung. The method requires only extremely small numbers of cells (from 1000 to 10 000) and results can be generated very quickly within a couple of days. It still requires further validation as the *in vivo* protocols are poorly defined, but the method holds great promise as an important tool for detecting DNA damage in virtually any mammalian cell population.

Tests for Aneuploidy (*In Vitro* Micronucleus Test)

Aneuploidy is considered to be a condition in which the chromosome number of a cell or individual deviates from

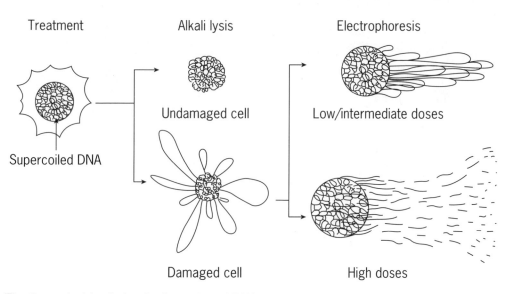

Figure 5   The theoretical basis for the formation of DNA comets.

a multiple of the haploid set. The maintenance of karyotype during cell division depends upon the fidelity of chromosome replication and the accurate segregation of chromosomes to daughter cells. In turn, these events depend upon different cell organelles functioning correctly and a number of metabolic activities related specifically to cell division (e.g. synthesis of nuclear spindle, proteins, etc.). Aneuploidy can occur through errors of many types, hence there are numerous cellular targets that can lead to chromosome gain or loss. Briefly, the mechanisms by which aneuploidy can occur fall into several categories, including damage to the mitotic spindle and associated elements, damage to chromosomal substructures, chromosome rearrangements, alterations to cellular physiology and mechanical disruption. The importance of aneuploidy to adverse human health is well accepted and the effects of aneuploidy include birth defects, spontaneous abortions and infertility. Tumour cells frequently have alterations in chromosome number and several specific aneuploidies have been associated with tumour development, although whether this is the cause or the effect of tumorigenesis is not clear.

When chromosomes fail to segregate correctly, this process of nondisjunction can lead to the production of both monosomic and trisomic progeny cells. If chromosomes are lost from the dividing nucleus they produce monosomic progeny without the reciprocal trisomic cell and the expelled chromosomes become membrane bound and are detected as micronuclei outside the main progeny nuclei. Consequently, chromosome loss can be measured by monitoring micronucleus formation and the *in vitro* micronucleus assay using mammalian cells provides such a technique (Fenech and Morley, 1985). This methodology has also been proposed as a simpler method for detecting chromosome breakage as micronuclei may also arise from acentric chromosome fragments (lacking a centromere) which are unable to migrate with the rest of the chromosomes during the anaphase of cell division. Because micronuclei in interphase cells can be assessed much more objectively than chromosomal aberrations in metaphase cells, there is not such rigorous a requirement for training personnel and slides can be scored more quickly. This makes it practical to score thousands instead of hundreds of cells per treatment and thus imparts greater statistical power to the assay. Micronuclei formed by aneuploidy induction can be distinguished from those produced by clastogenic activity by the presence of centromeric DNA or kinetochore proteins in the micronuclei. Fluorescent *in situ* hybridization (FISH) with pancentromeric DNA probes can be used to detect the former, whereas specific antibodies can be used to detect the presence of kinetochores.

The *in vitro* micronucleus assay may employ cultures of established cell lines, cell strains or primary cultures, including human and Chinese hamster fibroblasts, mouse lymphoma cells and human lymphocytes. To analyse the induction of micronuclei it is essential that nuclear division has occurred in both treated and untreated cultures. It is therefore important to provide evidence that cell proliferation has occurred after test chemical exposure. Analysis of the induction of micronuclei in human lymphocytes has indicated that the most convenient stage to score micronuclei in this cell system is the binucleate interphase stage. Such cells have completed one mitotic division after chemical treatment and are thus capable of expressing micronuclei. Treatment of the cells with the inhibitor of actin polymerization cytochalasin B inhibits microfilament assembly and cytokinesis, thus preventing the separation of daughter cells after mitosis and trapping them at the binucleate stage. A schematic for this method is shown in **Figure 6**.

The principle of the method is to expose cell cultures to the test substance in both the presence and absence of an

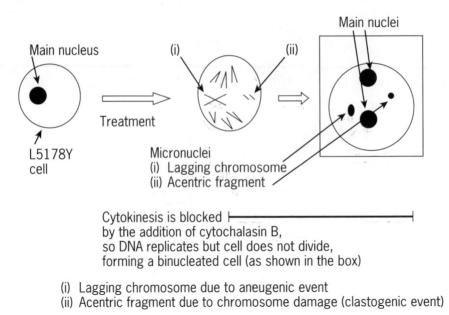

Cytokinesis is blocked |————————————————|
by the addition of cytochalasin B,
so DNA replicates but cell does not divide,
forming a binucleated cell (as shown in the box)

(i) Lagging chromosome due to aneugenic event
(ii) Acentric fragment due to chromosome damage (clastogenic event)

Figure 6   The basis for the *in vitro* micronucleus assay using cytochalasin B.

in vitro metabolizing system. After exposure, the cultures are grown for a period sufficient to allow chromosome damage or chromosome loss to lead to the formation of micronuclei in interphase cells. Harvested and stained interphase cells are then analysed microscopically for the presence of micronuclei. Micronuclei should only be scored in those cells which have completed nuclear division following exposure to the test chemical, normally for a period equivalent to approximately 1.5 normal cell cycles. Slides can be stained using various methods but fluorescent DNA-specific dyes are preferred as they will facilitate the detection of even very small micronuclei. At least 1000 cells per duplicate culture should be scored to assess the frequency of cells with one, two or more micronuclei. If the cytokinesis-block technique is used, micronucleus analysis is restricted to binucleate cells, and at least 1000 lymphocytes per duplicate culture should additionally be classified as mononucleates, binucleates or multinucleates to estimate the cytokinesis-block pro-liferation index, which is a measure of cell cycle delay.

At present, regulatory guidelines mainly focus on gene mutations and structural chromosome damage and do not address the induction of numerical abnormalities. How-ever, this is currently under review, and it is recommended that such studies should be carried out, using a method such as the *in vitro* micronucleus assay, in the following situations: in the standard *in vitro* cytogenetics assay when there is evidence of an increased mitotic index, an increase in polyploidy or some evidence of increases in chromo-some number on the slides (loss is not a useful measure-ment as this is a natural phenomenon due to slide artefacts), if there is a structural relationship with a known aneugen or if the mechanism of action involves mod-ification of cell division.

It will continue to be of considerable importance to establish a specific role for chromosome loss in tumour development. The analysis of aneuploidy in interphase cells of solid tumours using FISH will be greatly advan-tageous in this respect. For cancer risk assessment pur-poses, results from aneuploidy assays can be considered particularly useful when the mode of action of a chemical is known to result in chromosome loss or nondisjunction.

INTERPRETATION OF RESULTS

Comparative trials have shown that false-positive and false-negative results in relation to cancer predictivity can be generated by each genotoxicity test. Experimental conditions such as the limited capacity of the *in vitro* metabolic activation system can lead to false-negative results in *in vitro* tests, whilst culture conditions such as changes in pH and high osmolality are known to cause false-positive results in *in vitro* mammalian assays. Guidelines for testing new chemical entities require a battery of tests measuring effects on a variety of genetic endpoints designed to detect the widest spectrum of gen-otoxins. This reduces the risk of false-negative results, whilst a positive result in any one *in vitro* assay does not necessarily mean that the chemical poses a genotoxic/ carcinogenic hazard to humans. Further investigation in relevant *in vivo* assays is required to put the results into perspective. The *in vivo* tests have advantages in terms of relevant metabolism, etc., and also allow the influence of detoxification mechanisms to be assessed. The final assessment of the genotoxic potential of a chemical should take into account the totality of the findings and chemical class information when available. A risk–benefit approach

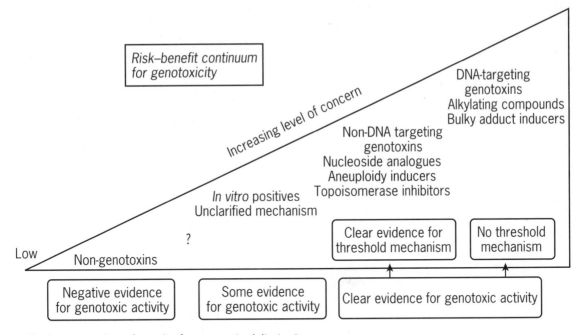

Figure 7   Interpretation of results from genotoxicity tests.

can be applied, such as that illustrated in **Figure 7**, which shows increasing levels of concern as the amount of positive data accumulates.

Unequivocally genotoxic chemicals are presumed to be trans-species carcinogens. Such chemicals should show 'clear evidence of genotoxicity,' for example, those which are positive in *in vivo* tests with supporting evidence from *in vitro* tests would be placed in this category. At the other end of the continuum are the nongenotoxic chemicals for which there is negative evidence from genotoxicity tests. In this case the chemicals should be negative in the standard battery of tests (**Figure 1**) with appropriate consideration of structural alerts, metabolism and exposure. It should be accepted that there is a low level of concern for these nongenotoxins, although it should be remembered that some chemicals could be carcinogenic by nongenotoxic mechanisms of action (see also the chapter *Non-genotoxic Causes of Cancer*). A number of chemicals have to be classified somewhere between these two extremes, that is, they show 'some evidence for genotoxic activity.' Certainly chemicals exist which show significant genotoxicity in *in vitro* tests without supporting evidence from *in vivo* tests. It is also known that due to the inherent limitations of currently employed *in vivo* genotoxicity tests, some of these chemicals may be carcinogenic through genotoxic mechanisms.

In the past, the existence of acceptable thresholds for exposure has not been considered in the field of genetic toxicology and in this respect risk–benefit consideration differed from other fields of toxicology. Chemicals representing a high level of concern and for which thresholds

would not exist are probably those which target DNA directly, e.g. alkylating agents and bulky adduct inducers, although for some the risk might be low due to effective DNA repair. However, in recent years there has been a growing awareness of the existence of thresholds for those chemicals that act through non-DNA targets. Examples of such chemicals include nucleoside analogues, topoisomerase inhibitors and aneugens. In the last case, this can be illustrated by an example. For accurate segregation of chromosomes at mitosis, the spindle apparatus plays a significant role. A component of this is the attachment of multiple microtubules to the kinetochore and a smaller number to the chromosome arms. The number of microtubules that are attached varies among chromosomes, and so it is reasonable to assume that the average is above the minimum necessary. The effect of a chemical on microtubule formation or attachment to the chromosome might be to reduce the number attached but produce no effect until the number falls below the minimum necessary for segregation. This mechanism would be predicted to have a threshold type of dose response. Similar arguments can be made for perturbations of other components of a mitotic apparatus.

A more contentious area to which threshold arguments have been applied is the association between a number of cytotoxicity parameters and *in vitro* chromosomal damage. It is possible that a number of false-positive results arise *in vitro* from the evaluation of chemicals at concentrations that are overtly cytotoxic. However, the existence of cytotoxic clastogens and cytotoxic nonclastogens in the same chemical class indicates that this is an oversimplistic view. Consequently, this area requires further research before an association between severe cytotoxicity and clastogenesis *in vitro* can be considered sufficient to suggest some type of threshold, and allow the conclusion that such results are less relevant to the *in vivo* situation.

FUTURE DEVELOPMENTS

Genetic toxicology is still an evolving science and there are a number of new techniques under development that could impact on the way in which screening is performed in the future. In conclusion to this chapter, a few examples will be briefly described.

High-throughput Screening

Chemical synthesis techniques are creating millions of new compounds and to cope with the vast numbers of tests required an approach termed high-throughput screening is being developed. A new branch of chemistry, called combinatorial chemistry, has emerged which allows chemists to take a number of relatively simple molecules and to combine them in every single possible permutation and in turn combine the products of these combinations. The result is a huge number new compounds which must be screened quickly and cheaply. However, as only tiny quantities are available, screening needs to be miniaturized. The essential elements of ultrahigh-throughput screening are easily measurable tests to determine whether the compound interacts with the target coupled with a high degree of automation and miniaturization. This presents a new challenge for genotoxicity screen development, and there are currently a number of new bacterial assays which allow such screening to take place using microwell technology (plates containing from 96 up to 1536 wells). One possible technique involves the measurement of SOS repair in bacteria. Many carcinogens and mutagens generate DNA lesions which block replication, often because of their bulky character, and result in the induction of the SOS response. This response in turn increases mutagenesis and survival by allowing replicative bypass of the DNA lesions. As the induction of the SOS response strongly correlates with DNA damage, spectrophotometric assays based on the expression of a β-galactosidase reporter gene transcribed from an SOS promoter have been developed. The SOS chromotest and the umu test are such examples. The attraction of these assays is that they have a simple spectrophotometric endpoint that is amenable to rapid automated scoring. An improvement to these assays has been the replacement of the chromogenic reporter system by expression of luciferase, an enzyme which catalyses ATP-dependent light emission from the substrate luciferin (Rettberg *et al.*, 1999). It can be seen that although the standard *S. typhimurium* and *E. coli* strains are still essential for routine genotoxicity screening, the introduction of newly engineered varieties and assay miniaturization will provide much more rapid assays in the future.

Expert Computer Systems for Predicting Genotoxicity

An alternative way of screening large numbers of chemicals for genotoxicity is to develop software programs which can predict the likely outcome of the *in vitro* and *in vivo* tests, so-called '*in silico*' screens. There are now several commercially available systems that allow genotoxicity (and carcinogenicity) predictions to be made (**Table 3**).

The reliability of any expert system for predicting genotoxicity is crucially dependent on the quality of the database and the rulebase. The database and rulebase associated with an expert system enable the user to rationalize individual model predictions. Individual rules within the rulebase are generally of two main types. Some rules are based on mathematical induction, that is, by the extraction of correlations from a particular data set, whereas other rules are based on existing knowledge and expert judgement. Rules of the former type, 'induced rules,' offer the advantage of extending existing knowledge

Table 3 Commercially available expert systems for predicting genotoxicity and carcinogenicity

System	Acronym	Source	Type
Deductive Estimation of Risk from Existing Knowledge	DEREK	LHASA UK (Leeds University, UK)	Knowledge-based
Computer-assisted Structure Evaluation	CASE	Multicase Inc. (Cleveland, OH, USA)	Correlative
Toxicity Prediction by Computer-assisted Technology	TOPKAT	Health Design Inc. (Rochester, NY, USA)	Correlative
Hazard Expert	–	CompuDrug Chemistry Ltd (Budapest, Hungary)	Correlative
Oncologic	–	LogiChem Inc. (Boyertown, PA, USA)	Knowledge-based

without being biased toward particular mechanisms of toxic action. Their disadvantage, however, is that they may be nothing more than empirical relationships devoid of biological meaning. In contrast, rules of the latter type, 'expert rules' or 'knowledge-based rules,' are likely to have a strong mechanistic basis, but they are expressions of existing knowledge rather than of new knowledge. Typically, induced rules are (quantitative) structure–activity relationships, whereas expert rules are often based on reactive chemistry. A system based on induced rules is called a 'correlative system' whereas a system based on expert rules is referred to as a 'knowledge-based system.'

Many structural factors affect the mutagenicity and carcinogenicity of chemicals, including: (1) the intrinsic reactivity (electrophilicity); (2) the electron density in and near reactive centres; (3) substituent effects, e.g. steric hindrance; (4) susceptibility to metabolic activation and detoxification; (5) the stability of reactive forms of chemicals; (6) the ability of chemicals and their metabolites to traverse biological membranes; (7) the size and shape of molecules which control access to target sites on DNA; (8) the type and conformation of adducts formed between the chemical and DNA; and (9) the susceptibility of the adduct to DNA repair. Ideally, expert systems should take all of these factors into account when assessing the activities of mutagens and carcinogens.

At the present time, the available systems are still undergoing development and validation. Each system has particular strengths and weaknesses, and it seem unlikely that any one system will come to be regarded as the best and only choice for chemical risk assessment. The ideal situation might be an integrated approach that exploits the strengths of all of the available systems. In view of the possible presence of unknown contaminants with potent genotoxicities in a sample, expert systems can be used for screening purposes but not for providing a complete assurance of safety. They may be especially useful during the development of pharmaceuticals as a means of providing a high throughput screen which is potentially useful for early compound prioritization.

Metabolically Competent Cell Lines

One of the weakest elements within current *in vitro* genotoxicity screens is in the provision of an exogenous metabolizing system for the activation of pro-mutagens to DNA-reactive metabolites. First, such systems (usually rat liver S9 fraction with appropriate cofactors, see earlier) can be poor models for the likely human metabolism of a novel chemical. Second, they have the disadvantage that reactive metabolites formed exogenously may be unable to penetrate the cell membrane, or have short half-lives. The generation and detection of a genotoxic metabolite within the same cell therefore has obvious advantages. These problems may be alleviated by the introduction of human cDNAs expressing the appropriate metabolizing enzymes

into cell lines that also possess those features required for the detection of genotoxic effects. A number of these so-called 'metabolically competent' cell lines have been developed, such as those derived from hepatocytes (e.g. HepG2 cells) or human B-lymphoblastoid cells (e.g. MCL5 cells). In the latter case, a panel of human cell lines have been developed expressing either individual or multiple human cytochrome P450s (Crespi *et al.*, 1991). Although the use of these cell lines for genotoxicity screening has yet to be fully exploited, they do seem to provide an elegant system to overcome some of the failings inherent within current *in vitro* assays. Furthermore, the use of human cytochromes might reveal the formation of unique genotoxic human metabolites that could remain undetected with standard assays.

REFERENCES

Ames B. N. (1971). The detection of chemical mutagens with enteric bacteria. In: Hollander, A. (ed.), *Chemical Mutagens, Principles and Methods for Their Detection*, Vol. 1. 267–282 (Plenum Press, New York).

Ashby, J. and Tennant, R. W. (1988). Chemical structure, *Salmonella* mutagenicity and extent of carcinogenicity as indices of genotoxic carcinogens among 222 chemicals tested in rodents by the US NCI/NTP. *Mutation Research*, **204**, 17–115.

Clive, D., *et al.* (1987). Guide for performing the mouse lymphoma assay for mammalian cell mutagenicity. *Mutation Research* **189**, 145–156.

Cole, J., *et al.* (1990). Gene mutation assays in cultured mammalian cells. In: Kirkland, D. J. (ed.), *UKEMS Subcommittee on Guidelines for Mutagenicity Testing Report Part 1 Revised* 87–114 (Cambridge University Press, Cambridge).

Crespi, C., *et al.* (1991). A metabolically competent human cell line expressing five cDNAs encoding procarcinogen activation enyzmes: application to mutagenicity testing. *Chemical Research and Toxicology*, **4**, 566–572.

Dertinger, S. D., *et al.* (1997). Flow cytometric analysis of micronucleated reticulocytes in mouse bone marrow. *Mutation Research*, **390**, 257–262.

Dolle, M. E. T., *et al.* (1996). Evaluation of a plasmid-based transgenic mouse model for detecting *in vivo* mutations. *Mutagenesis*, **11**, 111–118.

Eliott, B., *et al.* (1992). Report of UKEMS Working Party: Alternatives to Aroclor1254 induced S9 in *in vitro* genotoxicity assays. *Mutagenesis*, **7**, 175–177.

Fairbairn, D. W., *et al.* (1995). The comet assay: a comprehensive review. *Mutation Research*, **339**, 37–59.

Fenech, M. and Morley, A. (1985). Measurement of micronuclei in lymphocytes. *Mutation Research*, **147**, 29–36.

Gatehouse, D., *et al.* (1994). Report from the Working Group on Bacterial Mutation Assays. *Mutation Research*, **312**, 217–233.

Gorelick, N. (1995). Overview of mutation assays in transgenic mice for routine testing. *Environmental and Molecular Mutagenesis*, **25**, 218–230.

Hayashi, M., *et al.* (2000). *In vivo* rodent erythrocyte micronucleus assay: II. The method for continuous repeat treatment and review of some aspects on the applications of the micronucleus assay. *Environmental and Molecular Mutagenesis*, **35**, 234–252.

ICH (1998). D'Arcy, P. F. and Harron, D. W. G. (eds), *Proceedings of the Fourth International Conference on Harmonisation, Brussels, 1997*. (Queens University of Belfast, Belfast).

Madle, S., *et al.* (1994). Recommendations for the performance of UDS tests *in vitro* and *in vivo*. *Mutation Research*, **312**, 263–285.

Mitchell, A. D., *et al.* (1997). The L5178Y tk+/− mouse lymphoma specific gene and chromosomal mutation assay. A Phase III Report of the US EPA GeneTox Programme. *Mutation Research*, **394**, 177–303.

Mortelmans, K. E. and Dousman, L. (1986). Mutagenesis and plasmids. In: de Serres, F. J. (ed.), *Chemical Mutagens, Principles and Methods for their Detection*, Vol. 10. 469–508 (Plenum Press, New York).

Rettberg, P., *et al.* (1999). Microscale application of the SOS-LUX Test as a biosensor for genotoxic agents. *Analytica Chimica Acta*, **387**, 289–296.

Scott, D., *et al.* (1990). Metaphase chromosome aberration assays *in vitro*. In: Kirkland, D. J. (ed.), *UKEMS Subcommittee on Guidelines for Mutagenicity Testing. Report Part 1. Revised Basic Mutagenicity Tests. UKEMS Recommended Procedures*. 3–86 (Cambridge University Press, Cambridge).

Storer, R., *et al.* (1997). The mouse lymphoma L5178Y tk+/− cell line is heterozygous for a codon 170 mutation in the p53 tumour suppressor gene. *Mutation Research*, **373**, 157–165.

Tennant, R. W., *et al.* (1987). Prediction of chemical carcinogenicity in rodents from *in vitro* genetic toxicity assays. *Science*, **236**, 933–941.

Tweats, D. and Gatehouse, D. (1999). Mutagenicity. In: Ballantyne, B., *et al.* (eds), *General and Applied Toxicology*, 1017–1078 Vol. 2 (Macmillan Reference, London).

FURTHER READING

Ballantyne, B., *et al.* (eds) (1999). *General and Applied Toxicology*, 2nd edn, Vol. 2. Part 5: *Genetic Toxicology, Carcinogenicity and Reproductive Toxicology*. (Macmillan, London).

Cartwright, A. C. and Matthews, B. R. (eds) (1997). *International Pharmaceutical Product Registration, Aspects of Quality, Safety and Efficacy*. Ch. 14, Mutagenicity (Ellis Horwood, Chichester).

EU (1998). *Testing of Medicinal Products for their Mutagenic Potential. The Rules Governing Medicinal Products in the European Union*, Vol. 3B, 45–50 (European Union, Brussels).

ICH S2A (1996). *Guidance on Specific Aspects of Regulatory Genotoxicity Tests for Pharmaceuticals*. http://www.ifpma.org/ich1.html.

ICH S2B (1997). A Standard Battery for Genotoxicity Testing of Pharmaceuticals. http://www.ifpma.org/ich1.html.

Kirkland, D. (ed.) (1990). Basic Mutagenicity Tests: *UKEMS Recommended Procedures*. (Cambridge University Press, Cambridge).

Kirkland, D. J. and Fox, M. (eds) (1993). Supplementary Mutagenicity Tests: *UKEMS Recommended Procedures*. (Cambridge University Press, Cambridge).

Muller, L. (1998). The significance of positive results in genotoxicity testing. In: D'Arcy, P. F. and Harron, D. W. G. (eds), *Proceedings of the Fourth International Conference on Harmonisation* 253–259 (Greystone Books, Antrim).

Muller, L., *et al.* (1999). ICH – Harmonised guidance on genotoxicity testing of pharmaceuticals: evolution reasoning and impact. *Mutation Research*, **436**, 195–225.

OCED (1998). *Ninth Addendum to the OECD Guidelines for the Testing of Chemicals*. (OECD, Paris).

Sofuni, T. (1998). The role of the mouse lymphoma assay in genotoxicity testing. In: D'Arcy, P. F. and Harron, D. W. G. (eds), *Proceedings of the Fourth International Conference on Harmonisation*. 241–245 (Greystone Books, Antrim).

Chapter 26

Cancer Bioassays for Pharmaceuticals: a Regulatory Perspective

Joseph F. Contrera and Joseph J. DeGeorge

US Food and Drug Administration, Center for Drug Evaluation and Research (CDER), Rockville, MD, USA

CONTENTS

INTRODUCTION

In the development of human pharmaceuticals, the lifetime 2-year mouse and rat carcinogenicity studies are the most costly toxicology studies in both time and resources. The outcome of these studies can also seriously impact the marketability of a product. The rodent carcinogenicity bioassay is a pivotal component regulatory policy and, until recently, the design of the studies had changed little over the last 20 years. The acceptability of the current 2-year rodent carcinogenicity bioassay was based upon the reasonable expectation of a relationship between a biological outcome in animals (neoplasia) and the desired regulatory endpoint (the assessment of potential human carcinogenic risk). The carcinogenicity bioassay was never formally validated, but evolved over years. The study gained acceptance by the scientific community after the accumulation of sufficient experience and the ability to identify compounds known or reasonably expected to be human carcinogens. Study protocols evolved with use, influenced greatly by practical considerations of statistical power, assay sensitivity and economic considerations. A similar process is now under way for the development and regulatory application of *in vivo* alternatives to the lifetime rodent carcinogenicity study such as transgenic models. Information derived from *in vivo* transgenic carcinogenicity models can contribute additional insights (Goldsworthy *et al.*, 1994; Harris, 1995) into the mechanism of carcinogenesis and potential human risk that may be of greater value and potential relevance to humans than information from a conventional 2-year rodent study. New cancer bioassays and new approaches to carcinogenicity assessment that accompany them will significantly improve our ability to evaluate the potential carcinogenic risk of pharmaceuticals. (See section on *Treatment of Human Cancer*.)

BACKGROUND

Study Design and Analysis

The design of rodent carcinogenicity studies for pharmaceuticals is essentially the same as the design employed for industrial and environmental chemicals and US National Toxicology Program (NTP) rodent carcinogenicity studies. Male and female rats and mice are divided randomly into one or two control and three treatment groups of 50–70 animals per group per species. Historically, the highest dose in the studies analysed generally approximates the maximum tolerated dose (MTD) in the test species, and is administered daily usually in the feed or by oral gavage for 2 years. The rodent strains most often used in NTP studies is the inbred Fisher 344 rat and the hybrid B6C3F1 (C3H × C57B16) mouse. In pharmaceutical studies submitted to the Food and Drug Administration (FDA), the predominant rodent strains are the Sprague–Dawley-derived CD rat and the CD-1 Swiss–Webster-derived mouse. Despite our long experience with these assays, the significance of tumours from lifetime exposure at the maximum tolerated dose, dose–response extrapolation and the relevance of rodent tumours to humans continue to be highly controversial issues.

In studies reviewed by the FDA Center for Drug Evaluation and Research (CDER), tumour findings are usually classified as positive if either benign and/or malignant findings are statistically significant in pairwise comparison with concurrent controls by Fisher's exact or equivalent analysis, or by trend analysis. An adjustment for rare and common events that was recommended by Haseman (1983) is also applied to tumour findings. Tumours are considered significant in pairwise comparisons if they attained a level of $p \leq 0.01$ for common tumours and $p \leq 0.05$ for rare tumours ($\leq 1\%$ background incidences rate). The incidences of benign and malignant tumours (adenomas and carcinomas) are combined where appropriate and evaluated statistically (McConnell *et al.*, 1986). Until recently, the results of such studies were generally viewed as either positive or negative since there was little supporting mechanistic, pharmacokinetic or comparative metabolism information to support decisions on the relevancy of the findings for humans. Discussions regarding study results primarily focused on whether an adequate dose was achieved without exceeding the MTD, and whether statistically significant increases in tumours were of biological significance. If biological significance was concluded, the predicted risk to humans was then considered in relation to the potential benefit of the drug in considering product market availability.

It has now become clear within the scientific and regulatory communities that there are important distinctions between pharmaceuticals and nonpharmaceuticals that influence study design and the evaluation of study results. Five of the more critical, interrelated distinctions of pharmaceuticals are as follows:

1. they are designed to have biological activity;
2. they are extensively evaluated in test species and in humans for their pharmacodynamic properties, including toxic effects;
3. they are tested under conditions where systemic exposure to drug and metabolites can be qualitatively and quantitatively compared between species;
4. they are used in humans in well controlled settings where benefits are provided to the user; and
5. they are developed only in limited circumstances when frank genotoxicity is observed.

Advances in analytical technology have greatly expanded the quantity and quality of supporting mechanistic, pharmacokinetic and comparative metabolism information in recent years. In conjunction with a large pharmaceutical database of carcinogenicity test results (Contrera *et al.*, 1995, 1997), these advances have supported a redefinition of dose selection criteria, carcinogenicity test methods and study evaluation procedures by the International Conference on Harmonization (ICH) of Technical Requirements for the Registration of Pharmaceuticals for Human Use. ICH guidances defining multiple acceptable endpoints for dose selection, acceptable test methods and an integrative 'weight of evidence' approach to evaluating the relevance of study results are now internationally adopted for human pharmaceuticals and available on the FDA CDER website (http://www.fda.gov/cder/guidance).

Study Reproducibility

With over 40 different organ and tissue sites examined in an average 2-year rodent carcinogenicity study, there is a high probability that statistically significant treatment-related

tumour findings will arise by chance. It has been estimated that there is a 50% chance of identifying at least one false-positive tumour type in a treated group by chance alone when evaluating a mouse or rat carcinogenicity study (Haseman *et al.*, 1986). This is particularly true for common spontaneous tumours observed in older animals. In assessing the results of rodent carcinogenicity studies, the magnitude of the treatment-related carcinogenic response is an important factor when evaluating possible false-positive findings. The greater the treatment-related tumour incidence rate compared with concurrent controls, the more likely it is that the finding may be real (Haseman and Clark, 1991). Likewise, supporting evidence such as concordant findings across species and/or gender, tumour-related toxicity or pharmacodynamic target organ responses also help to substantiate tumour findings and rule out statistical false positives.

The significant potential for false-positive findings in 2-year rodent carcinogenicity studies also raises the question of study reproducibility. Unfortunately, there are only limited data addressing the repeatability or reproducibility of the results of carcinogenicity studies. Two-year rodent carcinogenicity studies are rarely repeated because of their considerable cost in time and resources. When they are repeated, it is generally due to failure of the original study or protocol deficiencies and therefore the results of repeated studies are rarely comparable owing to protocol and other differences between studies (e.g. dose, strain differences). A retrospective analysis of 18 NTP rodent carcinogenicity studies of colour additives in which two identical concurrent control groups were used demonstrated that significant variability can occur in the tumour incidence between two apparently identical control groups (Haseman *et al.*, 1986). The difference in tumour incidence between identical controls in these studies was often sufficiently large enough to alter the statistical significance of treatment-related tumours. These results suggest that variability inherent in 2-year rodent carcinogenicity studies may place a limit on the sensitivity value of these studies for single-gender, single-species tumour findings. An increasing number of carcinogenicity studies for pharmaceuticals now incorporate two identical but separately housed and analysed control groups (C1 and C2) to assess the variation in the spontaneous control tumour rate and reduce false-positive findings. In analysing dual control studies it is important to compare the tumour incidence of treated groups with each control group separately (C1 vs treated; C2 vs treated), in addition to a comparison against combined controls (C1 + C2 vs treated). Tumours are considered biologically significant when statistical significance is achieved compared with each of the control groups. Tumour findings are generally considered to lack biological significance when a treated group fails to achieve statistical significance compared with either control group. In cases where only one comparison shows significance, consideration of the tumour incidence rates from contemporary historical controls may play a role in assessing the results of the study.

Test Species, Strains and Genetic Drift

Genetically inbred rodent strains are employed in the 2-year rodent carcinogenicity bioassay to minimize variability in tumour responses due to genetic differences. The use of rodents and the rodent strains currently used in carcinogenicity studies were not selected on the basis of their suitability as human surrogates but for pragmatic reasons such as reasonable sensitivity to carcinogens, an acceptable spontaneous tumour rate and reasonable lifespan and animal size. The large accumulated historical record and experience with currently used rodent strains is a major reason for their continued use, although this has also retarded the development of improved rodent strains. Although inbred strains are employed to reduce genetic diversity and variability in carcinogenicity studies, genetic drift is still a concern. For many rodent strains this has resulted in progressively larger, more obese animals with higher spontaneous tumour rates and reduced lifespan. This genetic drift has compromised assay sensitivity and the usefulness of some rodent strains in carcinogenicity testing and has diminished the value of the historical tumour record for these strains (Rao et al., 1990; Keenan et al., 1992, 1995). The relative sensitivity of most rodent strains commonly used in 2-year carcinogenicity studies has not been fully evaluated employing identical study protocols and a reference set of known human carcinogens. Positive controls of known carcinogens could address this, but they are rarely used in the standard 2-year rodent carcinogenicity study protocols (although they are usually used in the design of transgenic animal carcinogenicity studies). Evidence suggests that there are similarities and significant variations among different rodent strains in their sensitivity to various carcinogens and differences in the nature and incidence of spontaneous tumours (Drew et al., 1983; Haseman, 1983; Dragani et al., 1995). Many of these differences may be due to species and strain-related (genetic) differences in metabolism and pharmacokinetics. A wide variability in spontaneous tumour incidence can also occur within a rodent strain (Ward and Vlahakis, 1978; Barrett and Wiseman, 1992). In addition, it is now apparent that ad libitum feeding and body weight in rodent carcinogenicity studies have been an uncontrolled variable that significantly influenced the sensitivity of the bioassay to carcinogens (Tarone et al., 1981; Keenan et al., 1992; 1995). The tumorigenic response to a potent carcinogen such as aflatoxin was demonstrated to be significantly altered by varying the caloric intake and body weight of rodents (Everett, 1984).

Tumour Site Concordance

Tumour site concordance of rats and mice is relatively poor. In the FDA, NTP and CPD databases only 20–30% of all compounds with positive findings produced tumour findings in at least one common site in the rat and mouse (Gold et al., 1989; Huff and Haseman 1991; Contrera et al., 1997). The lack of site specificity has been cited as part of the rationale for a reduced 2-year study protocol employing only male rats and female mice (Haseman and Lockhart, 1993; Lai et al., 1994). Since tumour site cannot be reliably predicted between rodent species, extrapolation of rodent tumour sites to humans has also been questioned (Freedman et al., 1996). There appears to be better transspecies tumour site concordance for a select subset of International Agency for Research on Cancer (IARC) 1, 2A and 2B classified pharmaceuticals (Marselos and Vainio, 1991). This apparent concordance may be related to the genotoxic nature of a majority of the nonhormonal compounds in this group (Shelby and Zeiger, 1990).

SYNOPSIS OF CARCINOGENICITY GUIDANCES

The International Conference on the Harmonization of Technical Requirements for Registration of Pharmaceuticals for Human use (ICH)

ICH Guidance S1A: The Need for Long-term Rodent Carcinogenicity Studies of Pharmaceuticals

1. Carcinogenicity studies are performed for any pharmaceutical expected to be used clinically for 6 months on a daily basis or those that will be used repeatedly in an intermittent manner to treat a chronic or recurrent condition.
2. Carcinogenicity studies are performed when there is cause for concern. This can include evidence of genotoxicity, a similarity to known carcinogens (e.g. SAR), the presence of preneoplastic findings in toxicity studies or long-term tissue retention of drug or drug-related products associated with pathophysiological responses.

For human pharmaceuticals, clinical considerations primarily determine the need for carcinogenicity studies and influence the assessment of benefit–risk. Clinical considerations include the expected duration of treatment, the severity of the disease or disorder, the nature of the patient population (e.g. children; the elderly) and the availability of other therapies and their toxicity profile.

ICH Guidance S1B: Testing for the Carcinogenic Potential of Pharmaceuticals

1. Carcinogenicity testing is generally done in two rodent species.

2. Use of an appropriate *in vivo* alternative to a second 2-year rodent carcinogenicity study is an option; however, the scientific justification for the use of any alternatives with a specific pharmaceutical is considered for acceptance of the assay.

The Basis for Carcinogenicity Studies in Two Rodent Species

The rodent carcinogenicity databases of the USA, the European Union and Japan were evaluated by the ICH safety expert working group. This analysis supported a more flexible approach to the then existing requirement for 2-year carcinogenicity studies in two rodent species. In the FDA database there is a significant (74%) concordance in the results of rat and mouse carcinogenicity studies and this is in accord with the results from the databases of the other ICH regions and the rodent carcinogenicity database of National Toxicology Program (NTP). Approximately 78% of all positive compounds identified in rat or mouse carcinogenicity studies would be identified in a rat study alone. Mouse-only carcinogenicity studies would be relatively less effective in this regard, identifying only 64% of all compounds with positive tumour findings identified in rat or mouse carcinogenicity studies (Contrera *et al.*, 1997).

In considering the contribution of the second rodent species carcinogenicity study, there was recognition that the identification of compounds with trans-species tumorigenic effects is an important component of the weight of evidence for the assessment of human carcinogenic potential. Compounds that produce trans-species tumours are considered to pose a relatively higher risk to humans than single species-positive compounds (Tennant, 1993; Gray *et al.*, 1995). It is postulated that the capacity of a drug to induce neoplasia across species suggests that the mechanism(s) involved in the induction of the neoplasia are conserved and, therefore, may have more significance to humans. Thus, compounds that produce rodent trans-species tumours are generally considered more potentially hazardous than compounds with single-species, single-site tumour findings. A major regulatory concern in relying on the results of a single carcinogenicity study in a rodent species is that, although all trans-species carcinogens would be detected employing a single species study, it would not be possible to identify trans-species carcinogens. In the FDA database, 52 of 125 drugs (42%) with tumour findings are trans-species positive (Contrera *et al.*, 1997). Within this group there is a relatively high proportion of unmarketed drugs, older drugs and drugs that are marketed with restricted clinical indications related to carcinogenicity findings. Trans-species rodent tumour findings have also contributed significantly to regulatory decisions that prevented the marketing of a drug or resulted in the removal of a drug from the market. For example, trans-species rodent tumour findings contributed to the withdrawal of iodinated glycerol from the US market.

There are circumstances where tumour findings in a single rodent species can influence the weight of evidence when assessing potential cancer risk. Benzene is classified a human carcinogen by the IARC, on the basis of some human evidence and carcinogenic findings only in the mouse. Methapyrilene, an antihistamine, was removed from the market in the USA primarily owing to hepatocarcinogenicity with short latency in rats (Lijinsky *et al.*, 1980). The IARC classified the tranquillizer oxazepam as a possible (2B) human carcinogen mainly as a result of the strength of mouse liver findings (IARC, 1996). Thus, the elimination of carcinogenicity testing in a second rodent species, likely the mouse, would significantly reduce the evidence available on which to base regulatory decisions regarding potential human risk. In the absence of a second species study, regulatory decisions would by necessity be based primarily upon the results of a single conventional carcinogenicity study, usually conducted in the rat. In this situation, more reliance may be placed on positive tumour findings in rats and these findings would effectively be regarded as equivalent to positive findings in two rodent species. As importantly, the ICH concluded that elimination of the second test species would not contribute to improving the assessment of potential human carcinogenic risk and would not advance the state of regulatory science.

The Optional Use of an Alternative to the Second 2-Year Rodent Carcinogenicity Study

The ICH evaluation of rodent carcinogenicity studies supported greater flexibility in the requirement for 2-year carcinogenicity studies in two rodent species. It was also acknowledged that compounds that produce tumours in two species may pose a higher risk to humans than those that produce tumours in only one species. Although it was concluded that studies in two species were usually necessary, the additional information from a second species does not need to be derived from a standard 2-year rodent carcinogenicity study. Some short-term *in vivo* transgenic mouse carcinogenicity models were considered sufficiently characterized to be used as alternatives to a conventional 2-year mouse study (Contrera *et al.*, 1997). Advances in molecular biology have identified a growing number of genes such as proto-oncogenes and tumour-suppressor genes that are highly conserved across species and are associated with a wide variety of human and animal cancers. *In vivo* transgenic rodent models incorporating such mechanisms have application in identifying mechanisms involved in tumour formation and as selective tests for carcinogens. The generation of transgenic rodent models can be considered as a further extension of genetic manipulation by selective breeding that has long been employed in science and agriculture.

The ICH guidance contains provisions for the use of an *in vivo* transgenic or other suitable alternative to a second rodent study. One option is a single 2-year rodent carcinogenicity study in the most appropriate species (usually the rat), and an additional short-term *in vivo* carcinogenicity study such as a transgenic mouse model in place of a 2-year mouse study. Transgenic models have been developed that contain regulated transgenes, unexpressed reporter genes or knocked out alleles of tumour-suppressor genes. (See section on *In Vitro and Animal Models for Human Cancer*.) Promising *in vivo* transgenic rodent models include the *TG.AC* v-Ha-*ras* oncogene-based mouse model (Tennant *et al.*, 1996; Spalding *et al.*, 1999), the human c-Ha-*ras* transgenic mouse model (Yamamoto *et al.*, 1996), the *p53*-deficient mouse (Tennant *et al.*, 1995, 1996) and the *XPA*-deficient mouse model (De Vries *et al.*, 1997). Although transgenic models incorporating these relatively specific genetic mechanisms may not be responsive to all compounds that tested positive in the 2-year mouse or rat study, transgenic models can and have been developed that incorporate carcinogenic response elements that are known to be present and functioning similarly in humans. Positive findings in such transgenic models can offer valuable insights into the potential relevance and applicability of tumour findings to humans that are not readily available from standard 2-year rodent studies. In addition to providing carcinogenicity information from a second species, transgenic studies have contributed mechanistic information to the weight of evidence assessment of the potential carcinogenic risk of pharmaceuticals. The nature of the carcinogenic mechanisms underlying a tumour finding in a 2-year rodent study and the potential implications to humans can be addressed by an appropriate transgenic study. A tumour finding in a 2-year rodent study for a compound that was found to be clastogenic in a nonstandard genotoxicity study may have greater regulatory significance if it is demonstrated that the compound also produces tumours in *p53*-deficient mice (Dunnick *et al.*, 1997). Since the *p53*-deficient mouse model is considered to be sensitive mainly to genotoxic carcinogens, the finding in the *p53* model suggests that the carcinogenic effect of the compound is derived from the genotoxicity observed. The specific molecular basis of the carcinogenic effect may also be further evaluated and provide further insights regarding the relevance of the finding to humans.

The choice of an appropriate species for a 2-year study should be supported by pharmacokinetic and metabolism information in the appropriate rodent strain and in humans. The use of one 2-year rodent study supplemented by a short-term *in vivo* carcinogenicity study in a second rodent species would be sufficient to identify most compounds that produce tumour findings in two rodent species. Together with comparative systemic exposure information in rodents and humans, the additional mechanistic information improves and strengthens the assessment of the potential carcinogenic risk of a compound to humans.

The treatment duration for transgenic mouse studies is generally 6–9 months with 15–20 male and female animals per group and three dose groups. The relatively small number of animals required for transgenic studies compared with 50 or more in 2-year studies is due largely to the low spontaneous background incidence of tumours and mortality in 6-month studies. A major difference in the design of transgenic studies compared with 2-year studies is the use of a positive control treated with a known carcinogen. The use of a positive control is considered essential for evaluating assay sensitivity. Dose selection studies for transgenic animals have been performed in either the transgenic animals themselves or the appropriate related wild-type strain. For example, in the case of the *p53*-deficient heterozygous mouse, the C57BL/6 wild-type mouse has been employed for dose-ranging studies. For compounds tested in both 2-year mouse carcinogenicity studies and transgenic models where the route of administration allows for a direct comparison, other than an earlier onset of tumours, transgenic models do not appear to be more sensitive than wild-type animals (i.e. doses showing positive responses are similar in both tests). (See also chapter *Transgenic Technology in the Study of Oncogenes and Tumour-Suppressor Genes*.)

The Issue of Assay Validation

For regulatory applications it is important to use bioassays which have been sufficiently characterized. In a discussion of the application of transgenic rodents in carcinogenicity testing it is necessary to consider objectively the relative strengths and deficiencies of transgenic models in the context of the strengths and deficiencies of the standard 2-year rodent carcinogenicity study. Study protocols for the 2-year bioassays have evolved over time until a relatively standard protocol developed, influenced by practical considerations of statistical power, assay sensitivity and economic/resource considerations. The current study gained acceptance by the scientific and regulatory community after an accumulation of a sufficient body of experience and the demonstrated ability to identify compounds reasonably expected to be carcinogens based on human and other data. Regulatory agencies began to apply the results of rodent carcinogenicity studies on the basis of relatively limited experience with these assays. No effort has been undertaken to evaluate or validate the existing design systematically. In contrast, there is an effort under way to evaluate systematically the application of transgenic models for carcinogenicity assessment, both at the NIEHS and as a collaborative effort by academia, government and industry coordinated by International Institute for Life Sciences (ILSI) Alternatives to Carcinogenicity Testing Committee. To date, the results of this effort to characterize systematically alternative methods are encouraging. Concern has been raised, however, about the application of transgenic models for quantitative risk assessment. The data available suggest that it is feasible, provided that there is adequate consideration of the response characteristics of the model being used. At present these assays may more readily be employed as qualitative assessments, and quantitative assessments could be generated only in conjunction with standard assay data. It is also worth noting that the 2-year rodent carcinogenicity study was originally intended to be a qualitative screen for potential carcinogens and may itself be poorly suited for accurate quantitative risk assessment (Huff, 1993).

ICH Guidance S1C: Dose Selection for Carcinogenicity Studies of Pharmaceuticals

Several methods of dose selection are now in use:

1. maximum tolerated dose;
2. a pharmacokinetic endpoint (25-fold rat/human AUC ratio);
3. a dose-limiting pharmacodynamic endpoint;
4. saturation of absorption;
5. maximum feasible dose;
6. limit dose.

Maximum Tolerated Dose (MTD)

The MTD has been defined by the ICH for pharmaceuticals as 'the top dose or maximum tolerated dose is that which is predicted to produce a minimum toxic effect over the course of a carcinogenicity study.' Such an effect may be predicted from a 90-day dose range-finding study in which sufficient toxicity is observed. Toxicological factors to consider are alterations in physiological function which would be predicted to alter the animal's normal lifespan or interfere with interpretation of the study. These factors include not more than a 10% decrease in body weight gain relative to controls, target organ toxicity and significant alterations in clinical pathological parameters. This definition is considered in the ICH guidance to be equivalent to definitions of the MTD used earlier by the EU, Japan, the US FDA and the US National Toxicology Program.

A Pharmacokinetic Endpoint for Dose Selection

It has been claimed that the high doses required to achieve the MTD are likely to produce tissue damage and associated increased cellular proliferation which may increase the probability of positive tumour findings in carcinogenicity studies. It has also been stated that tumours generated at doses well above the clinical range may be of little of no relevance to human risk (McConnell, 1989; Ames and Gold, 1990; Perera, 1990; Carr and Kolbe, 1991; Cogliano et al., 1991; Rall, 1991). This issue is especially relevant to nongenotoxic drugs with low rodent toxicity which may require the administration of many multiples of the clinical dose to achieve the MTD.

As part of an ICH effort to develop an exposure (pharmacokinetic) based alternative to the MTD for high dose selection in carcinogenicity studies for drugs, the FDA examined carcinogenicity studies in FDA files (Contrera et al., 1995). Rodent and human pharmacokinetic exposure data were analysed to evaluate the relationship between the human maximum systemic exposure of drugs at the maximum therapeutic daily dose and rat systemic exposure achieved in carcinogenicity studies carried out at the MTD. The systemic exposure is equal to the area under the plasma concentration-time curve (AUC) for drug and or metabolites. Although carcinogenicity studies of drugs are carried out at the MTD, that often represents high multiples of the maximum human therapeutic dose, in a large proportion of these studies high multiples of the maximum human clinical systemic exposure were not attained. In about one third of the drugs tested at the MTD in rodents, systemic exposure in rodents was less than the human systemic exposure and 61% (20/33) attained a systemic exposure of less than 10-fold that in humans at the maximum therapeutic dose. A similar distribution was apparent when the rat/human body surface area (milligrams per square metre) dose ratio or mouse/human body surface area dose ratio was employed. When compared with the body surface area dose ratio, the milligrams per kilogram dose ratio usually overestimates the relative systemic exposure, and this has contributed to the false conclusion that excessively high and biologically irrelevant doses are routinely used in the carcinogenicity testing of pharmaceuticals. The MTD for pharmaceuticals in rodent carcinogenicity studies generally does not represent high multiples of the estimated human daily systemic exposure in part because drugs represent a class of compounds selected for high biological and pharmacological activity, which can produce adverse dose-limiting effects.

For use as a dose selection criterion, the magnitude of the relative systemic rodent/human exposure ratio (plasma AUC (rodent)/plasma AUC (human)) should be sufficiently high to detect known or probable IARC 1 and 2A carcinogenic pharmaceuticals and compounds with positive carcinogenicity findings in the FDA database. In order to be useful as a dose selection endpoint, an appropriate systemic exposure ratio should also be attainable by a reasonable proportion of compounds tested. On the basis of the current database, a minimum rodent/human systemic exposure ratio of 25 is sufficiently high to detect all IARC 1 and 2A carcinogenic pharmaceuticals and chemicals with positive carcinogenicity studies in the FDA database. On the basis of this data set a rodent/human systemic exposure ratio of 25 would be attained by approximately one in four nongenotoxic pharmaceuticals. A systemic exposure ratio of 25 thus represents an adequate margin of safety for rodent carcinogenicity studies, exceeding the systemic exposure currently attained by 75% of carcinogenicity studies carried out at the MTD in the FDA database. This ratio approach is considerd for all carcinogenicity studies irrespective of route of administration that meet the other criteria for use.

This approach to high dose selection in carcinogenicity studies can be used for nongenotoxic drugs with relatively low rodent toxicity that are similarly (at least qualitatively) metabolized in rodents and humans. In this context, genotoxicity is defined on the basis of a positive response in a standard battery of *in vitro* and *in vivo* tests used for pharmaceutical testing. Genotoxic compounds are excluded from the systemic exposure approach because of the presumption that members of this class may produce cancer after a single dose and tumours caused at greater than 25-fold the human exposure could be relevant. Ideally, all human metabolites identified by radioisotopic or equivalent methods should be present in the rodent strain used in a carcinogenicity study. High dose selection can be based on either the parent drug, parent plus major metabolite(s) or solely on a metabolite(s), depending on the degree of biotransformation and the degree of similarity to that which occurs in humans. A large difference in the pattern of biotransformation of a drug in a rodent test strain compared with humans would suggest that the compound is a poor candidate for high dose selection based on systemic exposure. Compounds with relatively high rodent toxicity would likely reach the MTD well before a relative systemic exposure ratio of 25 could be attained and available data suggests that this occurs in approximately 75% of drugs tested.

A Dose-limiting Pharmacodynamic Endpoint

For pharmaceuticals, dose may be limited by an extension of the primary pharmacodynamic properties of the drug. Hypotension, anorexia or inhibition of blood clotting are examples of dose-limiting pharmacodynamic effects that would be associated with antihypertensive drugs, appetite suppressants or anticoagulant drugs.

Saturation of Absorption

High dose selection for systemically active drugs may be based on saturation of absorption as measured by the systemic availability (e.g. plasma concentration) of drug-related substances. At saturation, further increases in administered dose produce no significant increase in plasma concentration and are considered to have no biological significance relevant to assessing carcinogenic potential. The guidance recommends that mid and low doses selected for the carcinogenicity study, however, should also take into account saturation of metabolic and elimination pathways, regardless of the method used for high dose selection.

Maximum Feasible Dose

Currently, the maximum feasible dose by dietary administration is 5% of the diet. When other routes of administration are appropriate, the high dose will be limited based on practical considerations such as dosing volume 10–20 ml/kg per day of a viscous suspension and local intolerance.

Limit Dose

For nongenotoxic compounds where the maximum human recommended daily dose does not exceed 500 mg/kg it may not be necessary to exceed a dose of 1500 mg/kg per day in a carcinogenicity study. This only applies provided there is an absence of evidence of genotoxicity in the comprehensive testing used for pharmaceuticals and assurance that the systemic exposure in the rodent exceeds that in human by greater than an order of magnitude. From available experience, this endpoint is rarely applicable either as a result of genotoxicity findings or because of an inability to ensure that the exposure multiple has been achieved.

The 'Weight of Evidence' Assessment of Carcinogenic Potential

An underlying principle in the application of ICH guidance's on carcinogenicity testing is the need to evaluate and consider all information on the pharmaceutical that may be relevant to the interpretation of tumour findings and their significance to humans. Clearly, the biological relevance and clinical implications of carcinogenic findings should not be based solely on the results of the rodent bioassay but must include consideration of other information about the pharmaceutical in the context of its clinical use. Even when it is concluded that potential carcinogenic risk to human is associated with a pharmaceutical, information on the intended use and patient population, anticipated therapeutic benefit and margin of safety considerations can play a major role in any regulatory actions. The strength and nature of the tumour findings (e.g. rare tumours, especially those histologically similar to human tumours), evidence of genotoxicity and the degree of similarity in drug metabolism and pharmacokinetics compared with humans all contribute to the weight of evidence approach for assessing potential human carcinogenic risk in the risk–benefit balance (**Figure 1**). The sources of this information and the types of information are many, but can generally be divided into that derived from the carcinogenicity study itself and that available from external information sources.

The severity and morbidity associated with the clinical indication and the availability and toxicity of alternative therapies are also important considerations for human pharmaceuticals that influence the overall assessment of acceptable risk.

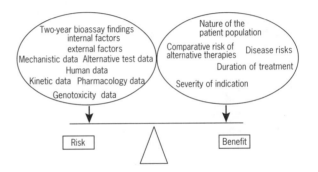

Figure 1 Summary assessment of carcinogenic risk and benefit for pharmaceuticals.

Carcinogenicity Study-derived Information

Study Acceptability

Adequacy of dose selection.

Appropriate route of administration relative to clinical route or other considerations.

Use of appropriate dose selection criteria as outlined in ICH guidance.

Adequate duration of dosing and study duration.

Adequate number of dose groups, animals/group and survival.

Appropriate selection and sampling of tissues and organs.

Scientific rationale for special design features (e.g. intermittent dosing, stop-dosing).

Scientific justification and rationale to support any alternative *in vivo* carcinogenicity studies.

Study Results

Organ- and tissue-specific tumour findings.

Magnitude and statistical significance of tumour findings compared with concurrent controls.

Malignant tumour incidence.

Benign tumour incidence.

Combined tumour incidence (e.g. McConnell *et al.*, 1986).

Common or rare tumour classification (spontaneous incidence rate 1% or < 1%, respectively).

Dose–tumour response relationship.

Presence or absence of preneoplastic lesions and related tumour site toxicity.

Body weight effects that may confound or mask tumour responses.

Tumour latency.

Tumour multiplicity (presence of multiple tumours at the same site).

Multiple-site tumours (presence of tumours at different tissue and organ sites).

External Supporting Information

Relevant biological and pharmacodynamic mechanisms. Examples of such mechanisms include hormonal alterations, receptor-mediated effects, immune suppression and cell proliferation linked toxicity.

Comparative rodent and human pharmacokinetic and metabolic profiles and consideration of the adequacy of the rodent model.

Relative systemic exposure in humans and animals and margin of safety.

Evidence of genotoxicity.

Evidence of epigenetic mechanisms.

Relevant findings from toxicity studies.

SAR (structure–activity relationship) relationship to known carcinogens.

Comparisons with contemporary historical tumour rate (derived from recent studies from the same laboratory).

Results of studies with similar findings or of related products.

Results of special studies, e.g. non-standard genotoxicity studies, novel alternative *in vivo* tumour assays.

Relationship of rodent tumour genotypes to human cancer genotypes.

Human epidemiology and clinical data, if available.

DISCUSSION

A sponsor must evaluate critical decision points in each of the ICH guidance's and choose appropriate assays and assay parameters, or risk conducting assays that are not considered acceptable assessments of carcinogenic potential by the regulatory authorities. As might be anticipated because of the many recent changes in carcinogenicity testing, there have been some problems with implementation of these new guidances. These arise both from an absence of specific information needed to address questions for a given pharmaceutical and from an incomplete understanding or an incomplete application of the guidances as written. In part, it was the intention in writing the guidances to avoid excess proscription and detail. This allows flexibility to accommodate changes in the state of the art of toxicology. One result is that few of the decision points in the guidances are written with definitive detailed explanatory text. Hence the guidances are subject to much individual interpretation without benefit of the extensive background dialogue that occurred when each guidance was written.

To decrease the potential for studies to fail to achieve regulatory acceptance and improve consistency in the interpretation of study findings, FDA/CDER established and expanded the role of the Carcinogenicity Assessment Committee (CAC) and has adopted a policy of centralized, tertiary review of both study protocols and completed studies. During 1999, approximately 130 protocols and completed carcinogenicity studies were evaluated for adequacy, including over 20 involving alternative carcinogenicity study models. CDER has found that an open dialogue with industry on the scientific merits of the study design and dose selection and interpretation of study results in relation to human risk is extremely beneficial to both agency staff and industry personnel. This dialogue, accomplished through the use of CDER's Carcinogenicity Assessment Committee, is especially useful in cases of divergent viewpoints related to the interpretation and significance of study results. Sponsors are invited to participate in discussions regarding their study proposals or study results. While this process has on occasion been criticized as lengthy, performance goals have been instituted to ensure communication within 45 days of receipt of a study protocol for consultation. This goal has been achieved in over 95% of the evaluations. This approach fosters greater mutual understanding of testing rationales and more consistent application of ICH guidances but, unfortunately, this process is generally only available for products where an Investigational New Drug (IND) application has been filed.

The ICH guidances on assessing the carcinogenic potential of pharmaceuticals have significantly changed the testing and evaluation process and have fostered research initiatives to improve test methods further. Given the rapid progress that is being made in developing new approaches and the changing scientific landscape upon which the regulatory evaluation process rests, a dialogue between the regulatory authorities and the regulated industry is essential if these science-driven guidances, requiring thoughtful consideration in their implementation, are to remain current. The outcomes of such discussions need to be shared broadly to achieve and maintain a harmonized understanding and consistent application of the guidances within the industry and between regulatory agencies. While this is being attempted within CDER with participation of the regulated industry, a forum for sharing information within the international drug regulatory arena has not yet arisen.

CONCLUSIONS

The 2-year rodent carcinogenicity study represented a pragmatic compromise, balancing factors such as test animal sensitivity, spontaneous tumour rate, lifespan and cost. To encourage the development of new assays that provide better information for evaluating human carcinogenic risk, special consideration is needed to foster progress by not prematurely demanding a higher degree of validation for new methods than has been attained by our current standard. A challenge for regulatory agencies and industry is to replace obsolete or redundant test requirements without compromising existing safety standards and while improving standards for the future. Promising transgenic rodent carcinogenicity models are currently being extensively characterized and many more will be developed in the future. Regulatory authorities can play an important role in fostering this process by demonstrating a willingness to consider and apply new scientifically acceptable methods through more flexible policies that accommodate improved, innovative approaches for assessing potential human carcinogenic risk.

The ICH process, based on mutual understanding and recognition of the available science, has resulted in guidances that have significantly changed and improved the process for assessing carcinogenic risk for humans for pharmaceuticals. A continued effort needs to be made to ensure further improvements in the future.

ACKNOWLEDGEMENT

This article is not an official FDA guidance or policy statement. No official support or endorsement by the Food and Drug Administration is intended or should be inferred.

REFERENCES

Ames, B. N. and Gold, L. S. (1990). Chemical carcinogenesis: too many carcinogens. *Proceedings of the National Academy of Sciences of the USA*, **87**, 7772–7776.

Barrett, J. C. and Wiseman, R. W. (1992). Molecular carcinogenesis in humans and rodents. In: Klein-Szanto, A. J. P., *et al.* (eds), *Comparative Molecular Carcinogenesis.* 1–30. (Wiley, New York).

Carr, C. J. and Kolbye, A. C. (1991). A critique of the maximum tolerated dose in bioassays to assess cancer risks from chemicals. *Regulatory Toxicology and Pharmacology*, **14**, 78–87.

Cogliano, V. J., *et al.* (1991). Carcinogens and human health: Part 3. *Science*, **251**, 606–608.

Contrera, J. F., *et al.* (1995). A systemic exposure based alternative to the maximum tolerated dose for carcinogenicity studies of human therapeutics. *Journal of the American College of Toxicologists*, **14**, 1–10.

Contrera, J. F., *et al.* (1997). Carcinogenicity testing and the evaluation of regulatory requirements for pharmaceuticals. *Regulatory Toxicology and Pharmacology*, **25**, 130–145.

De vries, A., *et al.* (1997). Spontaneous liver tumours and benzopyrene-induced lymphomas in XPA-deficient mice. *Molecular Carcinogenesis*, **19**, 46–53.

Dragani, T. A., *et al.* (1995). Genetics of liver tumour susceptibility in mice. *Toxicology Letters*, **82/83**, 613–619.

Drew, R. T., *et al.* (1983). The effect of age and exposure duration on cancer induction by a known carcinogen in rats, mice and hamsters. *Toxicology and Applied Pharmacology*, **68**, 120–130.

Dunnick, J. K., *et al.* (1997). Phenophthalein rapidly induces malignant hematopoietic tumours and loss of heterozygosity in p53 wild type allele in heterozygous p53 deficient mice. *Toxicologcial Pathology*, **25**, 533–540.

Everett, R. (1984). Factors affecting spontaneous tumour incidence rates in mice: a literature review. *CRC Critical Reviews in Toxicology*, **13**, 235–251.

Freedman, D. A., *et al.* (1996). Concordance between rats and mice in bioassays for carcinogenesis. *Regulatory Toxicology and Pharmacology*, **23**, 225–232.

Gold, L. S., *et al.* (1989). Interspecies extrapolation in carcinogenesis: prediction between rats and mice. *Environmental Health Perspectives*, **81**, 211–219.

Goldsworthy, T. L., *et al.* (1994). Symposium overview: transgenic animals in toxicology. *Fundamentals of Applied Toxicology*, **22**, 8–19.

Gray, G. M. *et al.* (1995). An empirical examination of factors influencing prediction of carcinogenic hazard across species. *Regulatory Toxicology Pharmacology*, **22**, 283–291.

Harris, C. C. (1995). Deichmann Lecture – p53 tumor suppressor gene: at the crossroads of molecular carcinogenesis, molecular epidemiology and cancer risk assessment. *Toxicology Letters*, **82/83**, 1–7.

Haseman, J. K. (1983). A re-examination of false-positive rates for carcinogenicity studies. *Fundamentals of Applied Toxicology*, **3**, 334–339.

Haseman, J. K. and Clark, A. (1990). Carcinogenicity results for 114 laboratory animal studies used to assess the predictivity of four *in vitro* genetic toxicity assays for rodent carcinogenicity. *Environmental and Molecular Mutagenesis*, **16, Suppl. 18**, 15–31.

Haseman, J. K. and Lockhart, A. (1993). Correlations between chemically related site-specific carcinogenic effects in long-term studies in rats and mice. *Environmental Health Perspectives*, **101**, 50–54.

Haseman, J. K., *et al.* (1986). Use of dual control groups to estimate, false positive rates in laboratory animal carcinogenicity studies. *Fundamentals of Applied Toxicology*, **7**, 573–584.

Huff, J. E. (1993). Issues and controversies surrounding qualitative strategies for identifying and forecasting cancer causing agents in the human environment. *Pharmacology and Toxicology*, **72, Suppl. 1**, 12–27.

Huff, J. and Haseman, J. (1991). Long-term chemical carcinogenesis experiments for identifying potential human cancer hazards: collective database of the National Cancer Institute and National Toxicology Program. *Environmental Health Perspectives*, **96**, 23–31.

IARC (1996). *IARC Monographs on the Evaluation of Carcinogenic Risks to Humans. Vol. 66. Some Pharmaceutical drugs.* (International Agency of Research on Cancer, Lyon).

Keenan, K. P., *et al.* (1992). The effect of diet and dietary optimization (caloric restriction) on survival in carcinogenicity studies. In: McAuslane, J., *et al.* (eds), *The Carcinogenicity Debate.* 77–102 (Quary Publishing, Lancaster).

Keenan, K. P. and Soper, K. A. (1995). The effects of ad libitum overfeeding and moderate dietary restriction on Sprague-Dawley rat survival, spontaneous carcinogenesis, chronic disease and the toxicologic response to pharmaceuticals. In: Hart, R. W., *et al.* (eds), *Dietary Restriction.* 99–126, (ILSI Press, Washington, DC).

Lai, D. Y., *et al.* (1994). Evaluation of reduced protocols for carcinogenicity testing of chemicals: report of a joint EPA/ NIEHS workshop. *Regulatory Toxicology and Pharmacology*, **19**, 183–201.

Lijinsky, W., *et al.* (1980). Liver tumours induced in rats by oral administration of the antihistamine methapyrilene hydrochloride. *Science*, **209**, 817–819.

Marselos, M. and Vainio, H. (1991). Carcinogenic properties of pharmaceutical agents evaluated in the *IARC Monographs* programme. *Carcinogenesis*, **12**, 1751–1766.

McConnell, E. E. (1989). The maximum tolerated dose: the debate. *Journal of the American College of Toxicology*, **8**, 1115–1120.

McConnell, E. E., *et al.* (1986). Guidelines for combining neoplasms for evaluation of rodent carcinogenesis studies. *Journal of the National Cancer Institute*, **76**, 283–394.

Perera, F. P. (1990). Carcinogens and human health: Part 1. *Science*, **250**, 1644–1645.

Rall, D. P. (1991). Carcinogens and human health: Part 2. *Science*, **251**, 10–13.

Rao, G., *et al.* (1990). Growth, body weight, survival and tumor trends in F344/N rats during an eleven-year period. *Toxicological Pathology*, **18**, 61–70.

Shelby, M. D. and Zeiger, E. (1990). The genetic toxicity of human carcinogens and its implications. *Mutation Research*, **234**, 83–115.

Spalding, J. W., *et al.* (1999). Development of a transgenic mouse model for carcinogenesis bioassays: evaluation of chemically induced skin tumours in TG. AC mice. *Toxicological Sciences*, **49**, 241–254.

Tarone, R. E., *et al.* (1981). Variability in the rates of some common naturally occurring tumours in Fischer 344 rats and (C57BL/6N X C3H/HeN)F1 mice. *Journal of the National Cancer Institute*, **66**, 1175–1181.

Tennant, R. W. (1993). Stratification of rodent carcinogenicity bioassay results to reflect relative human hazard. *Mutation Research*, **286**, 111–118.

Tennant, R. W., *et al.* (1995). Identifying chemical carcinogens and assessing potential risk in short-term bioassays using transgenic mouse models. *Environmental Health Perspectives*, **103**, 942–950.

Tennant, R. W., *et al.* (1996). Evaluation of transgenic mouse bioassays for identifying carcinogens and noncarcinogens. *Mutation Research*, **365**, 119–127.

Ward, J. M. and Vlahakis, G. (1978). Evaluation of hepatocellular neoplasms in mice. *Journal of the National Cancer Institute*, **61**, 807–810.

Yamamoto, S., *et al.* (1996). Rapid induction of more malignant tumors by various genotoxic carcinogens in transgenic mice harboring human prototype c-Ha-ras gene than in control nontransgenic mice. *Carcinogenesis*, **17**, 2455–2461.

FURTHER READING

Alison, R. H., *et al.* Neoplastic lesions of questionable significance to humans. *Toxicological Pathology*, **22**, 170–186.

Gold, L. S., *et al.* (1991). Target organs in chronic bioassays of 533 chemical carcinogens. *Environmental Health Perspectives*, **93**, 233–246.

Hart, R., *et al.* (1995). *Dietary Restriction: Implications for the Design and Interpretation of Toxicity and Carcinogenicity Studies.* (ILSI Press, Washington, DC).

Huff, J., *et al.* (1991). Scientific concepts, value, and significance of chemical carcinogenesis studies. *Annual Reviews of Pharmacology and Toxicology*, **31**, 621–652.

Huff, J., *et al.* (1991). Chemicals associated with site-specific neoplasia in 1394 long-term carcinogenesis experiments in laboratory rodents. *Environmental Health Perspectives*, **93**, 247–270.

ICCVAM (Interagency Coordinating Committee on the Validation of Alternative Methods) (1997). *Validation and Regulatory Acceptance of Toxicological Test Methods*. NIH Publication No. 97–3981. (National Institute of Environmental Health Sciences, Washington, DC).

McClain, R. M. (1984). Mechanistic considerations in the regulation and classification of chemical carcinogens. In: Kotsomis, F. N., *et al.* (eds), *Nutritional Toxicology*. 273–303. (New York, Raven Press).

Milman, H. A. and Weisburger, E. K. (eds). (1985). *Hand book of Carcinogen Testing*. (Noyes Publications, New Jersey).

National Research Council (1993). *Issues in Risk Assessment*. (National Academy Press, Washington, DC).

Office of Science and Technology Policy (1985). Chemical carcinogens: a review of the science and its associated principles. *Federal Register*, **50**, 10371–10442.

Vaino, H., *et al.* (eds) (1992). *Mechanisms of Carcinogenesis in Risk Identification*: IARC Scientific Publication No. 116. (International Agency of Research on Cancer, Lyon).

Chapter 27

Molecular Epidemiology of Cancer

Paolo Vineis
Institute for Scientific Interchange and University of Turin, Turin, Italy

CONTENTS

WHY MOLECULAR EPIDEMIOLOGY?

Epidemiology is the study of health and disease in populations, and of their determinants. The term molecular epidemiology may sound like an oxymoron, since it encompassess such different entities as molecules and populations. The aim of molecular epidemiology is to overcome some of the limitations of conventional epidemiology by linking research in the laboratory with research in free-living populations. In fact, rather than introducing an opposition between conventional and molecular epidemiology, it is more appropriate to consider the latter as a part of the first, involving the use of laboratory methods in order to overcome some of the methodological problems that are encountered in the study of the aetiology of human diseases.

The tools of molecular epidemiology include an appropriate study design, a specific attention to sources of bias and confounding and the development of markers that can be applied on a population scale. Study design is particularly important, because research that applied laboratory methods to human populations in the past was often based on 'convenience samples' that were affected by bias. Confounding, as we shall see, is a methodological problem that deserves special care.

Figure 1 is a simple representation of the goals of molecular epidemiology of cancer. Markers used in the molecular epidemiology of cancer are usually divided into the three categories of markers of internal dose, markers of early response and markers of susceptibility. In fact, each category includes subcategories. For example, protein adducts and DNA adducts are both markers of internal dose, but their biological meaning is different. 'Adduct' is a word that refers to the binding of an external compound to a molecule such as a protein or DNA. Whereas protein adducts are not repaired, i.e. they reflect external

exposure more faithfully, DNA adducts are influenced by the individual repair ability; in fact, if they are not eliminated by the DNA repair machinery, they will induce a mutation. Also markers of early response are a heterogeneous category, that encompasses DNA mutations and gross chromosomal damage. The main advantage of early response markers is that they are more frequent than cancer itself and can be recognized earlier, thus allowing researchers to identify earlier effects of potentially carcinogenic exposures. Finally, markers of susceptibility include several subcategories, in particular a type of genetic susceptibility that is related to the metabolism of carcinogenic substances, and another type that is related to the repair of DNA (see below).

The complexity of the processes that lead to cancer and the ensuing multifactorial nature of epidemiological investigations is depicted in **Figure 2**.

Technical advancements such as high-throughput technologies for the analysis of (single-nucleotide polymorphisms (SNPs)) (see below) will make molecular epidemiology more powerful in the future, but will also bring new scientific and ethical challenges.

In the following a few examples are described and some methodological issues related to molecular epidemiology are raised.

MARKERS OF INTERNAL DOSE: THE EXAMPLE OF HAEMOGLOBIN AND DNA ADDUCTS

Engine exhaust, tobacco smoke and other complex mixtures contain several groups of carcinogenic compounds, including arylamines, polycyclic aromatic hydrocarbons (PAHs) and nitrosamines, many of which are able to

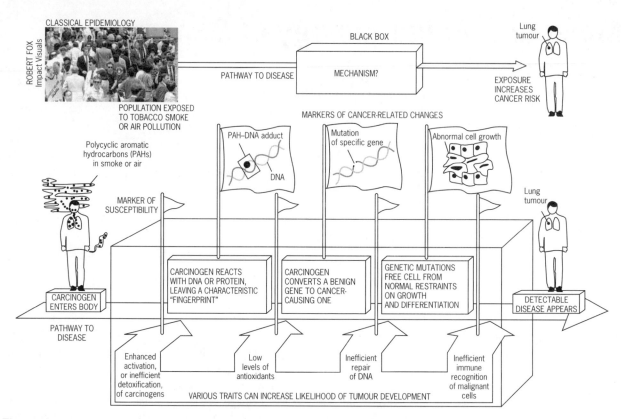

Figure 1   Uncovering new clues to cancer risk.

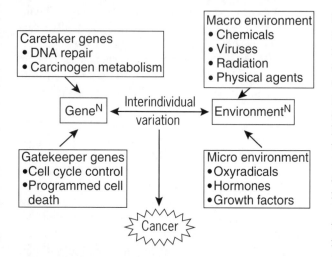

Figure 2   Many genes and environmental exposures contribute to the carcinogenic process. The effects can be additive or multiplicative, which are modifiable by interindividual variation in genetic function. It is proposed to include carcinogen metabolic activity and detoxification genes as caretaker genes involved in maintaining genomic integrity. (From Shields and Harris, 2000, *Journal of Clinical Oncology*, **18**, 2309-2315.)

form protein or DNA adducts after metabolic activation. The measurement of adducts is a method to partially overcome the inaccuracies inherent in traditional exposure assessment in epidemiology Different techniques have different biological meanings. Haemoglobin adducts have the advantage that large amounts of haemoglobin are available and well-established methods can lead to the identification of specific adducts, in particular from arylamines. The latter is a group of carcinogenic substances found in tobacco smoke, fried meat, car exhaust and some occupational environments. Arylamine–haemoglobin adducts have been shown to be associated with active and passive tobacco smoke (McLure *et al.*, 1989; Perera, 1996). The disadvantage of haemoglobin adducts is the short half-life (8 weeks), i.e. they reflect recent exposure.

White blood cell (WBC)–DNA adducts measured with the ^{32}P-postlabelling technique give an overall measurement of aromatic compounds, i.e. a large group of environmental contaminants. The half-life is months, i.e. such adducts express a cumulative exposure in the last several months. Different extraction methods give different fractions of compounds. The nuclease P1 technique, alone, is able to detect bulky adducts, such as those formed by the PAHs and by some arylamines bound to the exocyclic position of guanine or adenine, while extraction with butanol is effective for most of the aromatic amines bound to the C8 position of guanine and some low molecular weight alkylating agents.

Previous ^{32}P-postlabelling studies have reported conflicting results of the association between the adduct levels in peripheral WBCs and tobacco smoking. Discrepancies may depend on the marked interindividual variation in the metabolism of carcinogens, which results in different DNA adduct levels for similar degrees of exposure (Perera, 1996).

In addition to tobacco smoke, other exposures have been considered. Several studies in Europe, for example, have shown that the levels of WBC–DNA adducts were higher among subjects heavily exposed to air pollutants. This observation has been made among police officers (Peluso *et al.*, 1998a), newspaper vendors exposed to urban traffic (Pastorelli *et al.*, 1996), residents in a highly industrialized area in the United Kingdom (Farmer *et al.*, 1996) and bus drivers in Denmark (Nielsen *et al.*, 1996). In all these cases the more exposed subjects had significant differences from those less exposed, with WBC–DNA adducts of the order of about 3×10^8 for the relative adduct labelling (RAL) in the former and 1 in the latter. Benzo[*a*]pyrene is frequently used as a model compound for the class of PAHs. Benzo[*a*]pyrene is metabolically activated to benzo[*a*]pyrene diolepoxide (BPDE), the ultimate carcinogenic metabolite known to bind to DNA and blood proteins.

Lewtas *et al.* (1997) observed that human populations exposed to PAHs via air pollution show a non-linear relationship between levels of exposure and WBC–DNA adducts. Among highly exposed subjects, the DNA adduct level per unit of exposure was significantly lower than that measured for environmental exposures. The same exposure–dose non-linearity was observed in lung DNA from rats exposed to PAHs. One interpretation proposed for such an observation (Lutz, 1990; Garte *et al.*, 1997) is that saturation of metabolic enzymes or induction of DNA repair processes occurs at high levels of exposure (see below). Also in humans occupationally exposed to PAHs a less than linear relationship between external exposure and WBC–DNA adducts was observed.

Dietary habits may also influence DNA adducts. The relationship between fruit and vegetable consumption and DNA adduct formation has been examined in a case-control study of bladder cancer. The level of WBC–DNA adducts measured by the ^{32}P-postlabelling method was strongly associated with the case/control status. The age-adjusted odds ratio (OR) for a level of adducts greater than the median was 3.7 (95% confidence interval = 2.2–6.3), and a dose–response relationship with quartiles of adducts was apparent. The level of WBC–DNA adducts decreased with increasing levels of fruit and vegetable consumption (Peluso *et al.*, 2000). The association between the case/control status and the level of WBC–DNA adducts (below or above the median value) was stronger in the subjects who consumed less than two portions of vegetables per day (OR = 7.80; 95% confidence interval = 3.0–20.3) than in heavy consumers (OR = 4.98 for consumers of two portions per day; OR = 2.0 for consumers of three or more portions per day) (OR measures the extent of the risk increase in the exposed compared with the unexposed subjects).

MARKERS OF EARLY RESPONSE: THE EXAMPLE OF *p53* MUTATIONS

There is growing interest in the study of the relationship among carcinogenic exposures, the risk of cancer at specific sites and mutation spectra in relevant cancer genes (i.e. oncogenes and tumour-suppressor genes). One current theory is that specific carcinogens or carcinogenic mixtures (such as tobacco smoke) would leave a fingerprint (characteristic mutation spectrum) in relevant cancer genes.

Many *in vitro* and *in vivo* experimental studies have been conducted to elucidate carcinogenic mechanisms, with particular reference to mutation spectra in cancer genes. The fact that mutagens do not act randomly was already noted 30 years ago by Benzer, and then in a classical series of papers by Miller on the *lacI* gene, regarding mutational specificity in bacteria (see, for example, Coulondre *et al.*, 1977; Miller *et al.*, 1979). Denissenko *et al.* (1996, 1997, 1998) published some of the most interesting recent studies. They showed a strong and selective formation of adducts by the PAH 7,8,9,10-tetrahydrobenzo[*a*]pyrene at guanines in CpG sequences of codons 157, 248 and 273 of the *p53* gene, the major mutational hotspots in lung cancer. They concluded that methylated CpG dinucleotides are a target for chemical carcinogens in cancer genes.

An early example of a characteristic mutation spectrum in the human *p53* gene involved hepatocellular carcinoma in South Africa and China, and exposure to aflatoxins, a well-known dietary carcinogen. In early studies it was observed that about 50% of the patients in those areas had a relatively rare mutation, a G to T transversion at codon 249 (Bressac *et al.*, 1991; Hsu *et al.*, 1991). This mutation was deemed to be rare because it was not previously observed in patients living in areas where food contamination by aflatoxins is not common; furthermore, the same mutation could be induced experimentally by aflatoxin B$_1$ *in vitro*. On the contrary, *p53* mutational spectra induced by aflatoxin were not observed in rats (Hulla *et al.*, 1993; Tokusashi *et al.*, 1994). Another well-known example is represented by the characteristic C–T mutations induced by ultraviolet (UV) radiation at dipyrimidine sequences in the *p53* gene (Brash *et al.*, 1991).

Some difficulties should be considered in the study of human cancer gene 'fingerprints,' such as (1) the multi-factorial nature of human cancers, which hampers their attribution to single carcinogenic agents and/or the identification of common pathogenetic pathways; (2) the high genetic instability of cancer cells that may increase the frequency of mutations in certain cancer genes regardless of exposure factors; (3) the importance of DNA repair mechanisms and of the corresponding degree of population variation; (4) tissue selection bias that may affect the results, although its extent is difficult to establish; (5) the simultaneous presence of clinical (i.e. treatment) and biological factors (i.e. stage, grading or unknown factors) related to the exposure and to the frequency of mutations that may confound its association; and (6) the need for a consideration of temporal sequences in the activation/ deactivation of cancer genes.

Tumours are extremely dynamic entities and selection of tumour cell subpopulations is a continuous process. Mutations found in an advanced tumour may not be representative of the type of damage created by an agent in the DNA of the original target cell, since only those genetic changes that confer a growth advantage are selected in the course of the carcinogenic process. Certain mutations may provide sensitivity to the effects of tumour promoters, whereas others may not, thus resulting in the selective expansion of the former rather than the latter; this complicates the interpretation of the association between the genetic end-product and exposure to carcinogens.

Specific characteristics of bias and confounding in studies on mutational spectra should be considered. The size of the biopsies that are selected for investigation provides a prominent example of the types of selection bias that can occur in studies on cancer genes. In bladder cancer, for example, it is likely that early-stage tumours are too small to allow the urologist to obtain a biopsy sufficiently large for both research and clinical purposes. However, large biopsies tend to correspond to more advanced cases, which in turn may show a higher proportion of mutations in certain genes (Yaeger *et al.*, 1998).

Another kind of bias that is particularly difficult to characterize and quantify is publication bias. Publication bias refers to the greater probability that positive studies (i.e. those showing an association for example between *p53* spectrum and exposure) become published. A way to identify publication bias is to plot the result of each study (expressed, for example, as an OR) against their size. In the absence of publication bias, the plot is expected to show great variability with small samples and lower variability with large samples, around a central value of the true OR. If publication bias occurs, negative results are not published, particularly if they arise from small investigations, and their results do not appear in the plot (Begg and Berlin, 1988). For example, in the large database available at the International Agency for Research on Cancer on *p53* mutations (Hainaut *et al.*, 1998), the distribution of the proportion of mutations from different studies is skewed: all the studies with a proportion greater than 50% had less than 50 cases, while lower proportions were found in both small and large studies. This distribution does not necessarily imply that publication bias occurred; it might also suggest that large studies were based on heterogeneous populations, with a variable prevalence of mutations, while small studies refer to small subgroups with specific exposures to carcinogens and a genuinely high proportion of mutations.

Information bias is related to material mistakes in conducting laboratory or other analyses, or in reporting mutations; for example, a distortion arose from incorrect reporting of the *p53* sequence in an early paper, which influenced subsequent reports (Lamb and Crawford, 1986). However, this causes a genuine bias if the mistaken frequency is nonrandomly distributed in the categories that are compared.

Confounding occurs when a third variable creates a spurious association between the exposure at issue and the mutation spectrum. Several variables may act as confounders, for example if they modify the expression of oncogenes or tumour-suppressor genes. One such variable is chemotherapy: for example, cytostatic treatment for leukaemia induces characteristic cytogenetic abnormalities in chromosomes 5 and 7. Confounding arises if, for some reason, therapy is related to the exposure at issue. Stage is also a potential confounder. Therefore, studies that aim to determine the expression of cancer genes in humans should be restricted to untreated patients or specific stages, or statistical analyses should be stratified according to treatment/stage.

MARKERS OF SUSCEPTIBILITY

Metabolic polymorphisms

The human genome contains approximately 3 500 000 000 base pairs; of these, 10 000 000 are likely to differ among different individuals. Such variants in single base pairs are called single nucleotide polymorphisms (SNPs) and are potentially responsible for susceptibility to disease. It is becoming clear that only a minority of cancers have a frank genetic origin, in the sense that they are due to a highly penetrant gene (e.g. 5–10% of breast cancers occur in women carrying mutations of the *BRCA1* gene, which confers a risk of breast cancer of about 50–60% in the carriers). At the other extreme of the scale, there are diseases that are entirely due to the environment, with no role for genetic predisposition (this is the case with 15 workers who were exposed to β-naphthylamine in the British chemical industry in the 1950s: all of them developed transitional-cell bladder cancer, with no role for individual susceptibility) (Case *et al.*, 1954). Most cancers, however, are likely to be in the middle, i.e. to be due to an interaction between external exposure and genetic susceptibility caused by a low penetrance gene. One type of such susceptibility is related to the metabolism of carcinogens. Subjects with an SNP at a particular gene locus have a defect in the enzyme involved in the metabolism of a carcinogen, and therefore develop cancer more easily if they are exposed to the substance.

Enzymes involved in the metabolism of carcinogens belong to two categories, Phase I and Phase II enzymes, the former being involved in activation (usually by oxidation) and the latter in the inactivation of carcinogens (usually by conjugation). Examples of Phase I enzymes are cytochromes P450 involved in the activation of nitrosamines, and examples of Phase II enzymes are glutathione-*S*-transferases or *N*-acetyltransferase, involved in the deactivation of arylamines. Such enzymes can be less active because of genetic polymorphisms, i.e. common variants due to SNPs. **Figure 3** is an example of a meta-analysis that has been prepared for an IARC Publication on metabolic polymorphisms (Vineis *et al.*, 1999) and shows that, overall, the *N*-acetyltransferase slow genotype is associated with a 40% increase in the risk of bladder cancer. The vertical lines correspond to different studies, in which the effect of *N*-acetyltransferase has been measured by an OR and the corresponding confidence interval, while at the extreme right the overall OR (deriving from the meta-analysis) is reported. In fact, the risk was much higher in populations occupationally exposed to arylamines; an interaction with tobacco smoke has also been shown in a different meta-analysis (Marcus *et al.*, 2000). One aspect that deserves a comment is the heterogeneity of the effects shown in **Figure 3**, suggesting that the interaction between the genetic trait and environmental exposures is important indeed, depending on the specific populations investigated.

Methodological Issues in the Study of Metabolic Polymorphisms

One issue that is relevant to all epidemiological investigations aimed at interactions between exposures and genetic traits (gene–environment interactions) is statistical power (sample size). Statistical power is usually inadequate in most studies on this subject, and appropriate *a priori* calculations of the size required to detect an interaction are needed. A second, related issue is subgroup analysis: statistically significant associations may arise by chance when multiple comparisons are made within a single study. This problem is not only a statistical issue, i.e. one that can be solved with mathematical tools. Rather, the best way to avoid the pitfalls associated with subgroup analysis, multiple comparisons and publication bias is to define sound scientific hypotheses *a priori*. This goal can be accomplished by ensuring a strong cooperation among all the figures involved, i.e. geneticists, biochemists, molecular biologists, epidemiologists and biostatisticians. A sound *a priori* hypothesis implies (1) that evidence has been provided that a genetic polymorphism is implicated in the metabolism of a given carcinogen, (2) that the polymorphism can be measured with a reasonably small degree of misclassification and (3) that epidemiological tools

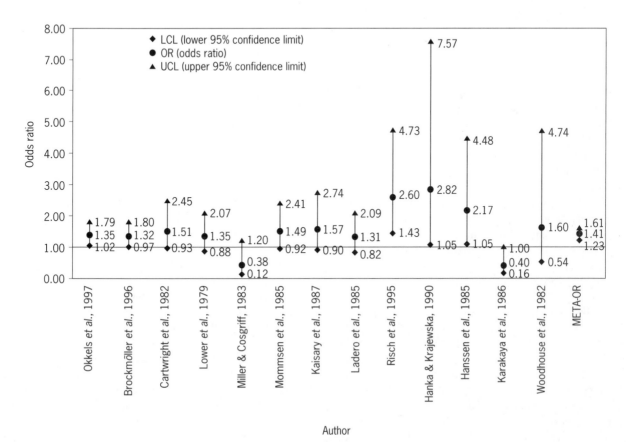

Figure 3 Meta-analysis of studies on NAT2 polymorphism and bladder cancer (caucasians). Note that the authors given are not cited in the present reference list. (From International Agency for Research on Cancer, 1998.)

allow the researcher to identify the exposed subjects with sufficient accuracy (i.e. exposure assessment is sound).

Cause–Effect Relationships

The *a posteriori* evaluation of published studies, in order to assess cause–effect relationships, is a difficult task that can only be accomplished by consensus in the context of Working Groups. I will not try to identify those gene–environment interactions that are more likely to be causal, but only suggest a method to accomplish this goal. Such a method is derived from the guidelines developed by Sir Bradford Hill to evaluate cause–effect relationships in observational studies (Hill, 1965):

- Strength of association (weak associations are more likely to be explained by bias, including publication bias, or confounding).
- Dose–response relationship (a criterion that applies to both genotyping, when two mutations are more effective than one, and to phenotyping, when the association with cancer risk is proportional to enzyme activity).
- Reproducibility of the association (in studies conducted in different populations with a different design).
- Internal coherence (for example, the association is observed in both genders, unless there is some biological explanation to justify gender differences).
- Biological plausibility (see above about the need for sound biological hypotheses; a particularly important issue is knowledge of the relevant carcinogens metabolized by the enzyme involved in the polymorphism).
- Specificity of the association (for example, the *N*-acetyltransferase polymorphism is associated with bladder cancer, a target site for arylamines).
- Animal models (which are expected to become available for metabolic polymorphisms with the development of the transgenic mice technology).
- Time sequence: although the genotype does not change with time, and its measurement within a cross-sectional design is meaningful, there are subtle problems of interpretation. For example, there is evidence that some polymorphisms influence the survival of cancer patients (Kelsey *et al.*, 1997); therefore, measurement of the genotype within a cross-sectional design may simply imply the observation of a survival effect.

To mention some examples, on the one hand we have the very well-established association between bladder cancer, arylamine exposure and the *N*-acetyltransferase (NAT) polymorphism. In this case, all Hill's criteria are met: the carcinogens metabolized are known, they induce the type of cancer (bladder) that has been associated with the NAT polymorphism, the association has been found in different populations with different study designs, the association is strong in at least a few of the studies and animal models are available. At the other extreme we have the CYP2D6 polymorphism, whose role in carcinogenesis

is still doubtful because of unresolved issues (the carcinogens metabolized are not known, and potential confounding due to genetic linkage has not been ruled out).

Public Health Applications

Ethical issues, related to the potential application of metabolic polymorphisms in a public health context, go far beyond the obtainment of informed consent. The use of metabolic polymorphisms to identify highly susceptible individuals has several implications that should be discussed thouroughly before any field application is approved: (1) the distribution of polymorphisms is uneven according to ethnic groups, which means that any job-related selection – on the basis of genetic susceptibility – would imply ethnic discrimination; (2) the role of insurances must be clarified if personal information on genetic susceptibility to cancer is released; and (3) metabolic susceptibility to cancer is such a complex issues that it can be hardly used to select the susceptible individuals for any meaningful purpose.

DNA Repair

In addition to polymorphisms in carcinogen metabolism, a potentially important source of variability is also DNA repair capability, including the genetic instability syndromes. These are rare, recessive traits that include ataxia-telangiectasia, Fanconi anaemia and Bloom syndrome, all characterized by both chromosome instability and high risk of cancer, and xeroderma pigmentosum, characterized by extreme susceptibility to UV radiation-induced skin cancer (Friedberg *et al.*, 1995). In addition to these rare syndromes, individuals differ for their capability in repairing DNA damage. At least part of such inter-individual differences are likely to have a genetic origin. A number of studies have been conducted on the subject, based on comparisons between cancer cases and healthy controls for their supposed DNA repair function. A variety of tests to measure DNA repair have been developed. In fact, these studies can be broadly grouped into three categories, depending on the tests used. The first category includes tests based on DNA damage (usually chromosome breaks) induced with chemical (bleomycin) or physical (radiation) mutagens; mutagen sensitivity assay, Unscheduled DNA synthesis, [^{3}H]thymidine incorporation or count of pyrimidine dimers are examples. In this category of tests DNA repair is simply inferred by the different frequency of DNA damage induced in cancer cases and controls, without direct evidence of repair. The second category encompasses tests based on some direct evidence of repair, e.g. the plasmid *cat* gene test, the ADPRT modulation test or immunoassays based on antigenicity of thymidine dimers. The third category is represented by genotype-based tests, in which the distribution of polymorphic alleles is the object of the test.

A systematic review on the subject has been published (Berwick and Vineis, 2000). According to this, all studies based on tests belonging to the first category showed highly statistically significant results; when ORs were available they were between 2.8 (Spitz *et al.*, 1994) and 10.3 (Spitz *et al.*, 1989), suggesting a fairly intense association. Concerning the second category, two of the eight studies belonging to it, and included in the review (Berwick and Vineis, 2000), did not attain statistical significance. The only investigation based on genotyping at the time of the review (Hu *et al.*, 1997) did not find a statistically significant association with breast cancer, although the phenotypic expression (oligonucleotide-induced PARP activity) showed a weak association with cancer. (See also chapter *Genomic Instability and DNA Repair*.)

Methodological Issues

Only one study had a population-based design and, ironically, this was the only clearly negative study (Hall *et al.*, 1994). One possible explanation is that all other studies are affected by selection bias. However, plausible reasons for the negative result have been given by the authors and may differ from the lack of selection bias. It is hard to conceive that selection bias affected all the positive studies (i.e. the vast majority), since they were based on different series of controls sampled from different populations. In addition, to justify ORs of in the order of four the bias should have been very important.

Confounding is related to the possibility that some exposure or characteristic of the patients is associated with DNA repair and is a risk factor for cancer, thus creating a spurious relationship between DNA repair and the disease. Repair enzymes can be induced in several ways by stresses that damage DNA, e.g. pro-oxidative stress. According to recent investigations based on microchip technology, in yeast treated with an alkylating agent, the expression of over 200 genes was upregulated, whereas that of nearly 100 genes was downregulated. However, no information is available on the persistence of gene induction (P. Hanawalt, personal communication).

In studies in humans, several tests of DNA repair were affected by characteristics such as age, sunlight, dietary habits (with a relationship between carotenoids and repair proficiency), exposure to pro-oxidants and cancer therapies. While age and therapies were usually controlled for in most studies, dietary habits might have acted as confounders, since both the intake and the plasma level of carotenoids and other antioxidants have been shown to be lowered in cancer patients compared with healthy controls. The extent of such potential confounding is hard to estimate. In one study (Schantz *et al.*, 1997), dietary habits were not associated with mutagen sensitivity in controls; rather, vitamins seemed to act as effect modifiers, not as confounders. How persistent the effect of potential confounders could be is unknown, although it has been suggested (Paleologo *et al.*,

1992) that DNA damage induced by coal tar treatment of psoriasis could persist for more than 3 months.

Biological Plausibility

A major limitation of many tests (those belonging to the first category as defined above) is that DNA repair is only indirectly inferred from DNA damage. The only investigation based on genotyping considered in the review (Hu *et al.*, 1997) did not find a statistically significant association with breast cancer, although the phenotypic expression (oligonucleotide-induced PARP activity) showed a weak association with cancer. This is an example of lack of phenotype-genotype correlation.

To draw firm conclusions about a cause–effect relationship, therefore, more evidence about the biological meaning of tests is needed. In particular, evidence has not been provided that many of these tests really express DNA repair. One possible interpretation is that some tests refer to a general and aspecific impairment of the DNA repair machinery, whereas others would explore more specific segments of it. However, this working hypothesis requires further evidence.

CONCLUSIONS

Gene–Environment Interactions and Cumulative DNA Damage

As a rule of thumb, there is an inverse proportionality between the frequency of at risk alleles and the risk of cancer (penetrance) (**Figure 4**). In particular, single highly penetrant mutations in cancer genes explain a small proportion of cancers (Vogelstein and Kinzler, 1998). This consideration arises both from empirical observation and from general scientific knowledge. Highly penetrant gene mutations, which confer an exceptionally high risk of

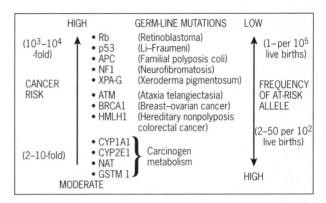

Figure 4   Examples of the inverse correlation between allelic frequency and cancer risk associated with selected cancer susceptibility genes. (From Hussain and Harris, 1998, *Cancer Research*, **58**, 4023-4037.)

cancer in the carriers, represent the tail of a distribution that includes (1) more common mutations in the same cancer genes (polymorphisms), that have a less disruptive effect on the protein function, or (2) rare or common mutations in genes that are less directly involved in the cancer process. There is increasing evidence in favour of both categories. Shen *et al.* (1998) have shown that even genes involved in rare and disruptive conditions such as xeroderma pigmentosum show common polymorphisms whose effects on the protein function (a DNA repair enzyme) are probably mild.

Concerning category (2), many metabolic polymorphisms are a clear example. Subjects with the *GSTM1* null genotype are frequent (about 50% of the caucasian population), have a serious genetic change (a deletion of the entire gene), but a slightly increased risk of some forms of cancer. In addition, many investigations (Berwick and Vineis, 2000) have been conducted on the greater susceptibility of cancer patients to DNA damage in comparison with controls. Most of these studies are based on the treatment of WBCs from cases and controls with a mutagen or a clastogen and on the observation of the frequencies of the induced DNA damage. The differences between cases and controls are interpreted as suggesting a greater susceptibility of cancer cases. As we have seen, the interpretation of such studies is not completely straightforward. In particular, the meaning of mutagen sensitivity tests is uncertain. Although virtually all studies show a greater sensitivity of cases, one cannot rule out that the apparent sensitivity is not due to a susceptibility factor, but is a consequence of cancer itself. Cancer is characterized by such a genetic instability that a mutagen-sensitive phenotype does not necessarily indicate a pre-existing susceptibility factor. In spite of such uncertainties, and of the aspecificity of mutagen sensitivity tests, the burden of investigations suggesting a greater sensitivity of some subjects to DNA damaging agents is impressive. Furthermore, the credibility of the observation is enhanced by the fact that in some investigations also healthy relatives of cancer patients, belonging to high-risk families, showed increased mutagen sensitivity or impaired DNA repair.

In addition to such studies, several investigations on DNA adducts (see the first section) suggest that cancer patients have a higher level of adducts after adjustment for relevant exposures. For example, in a study on bladder cancer we found that, after adjustment for smoking and dietary and occupational exposures, the level of WBC–DNA adducts was the variable that had the strongest association with the case vs control status (Peluso *et al.*, 1998b). Similar observations have been made by others (Perera, 1996). In fact, adducts can be seen both as markers of cumulative internal dose and as markers of susceptibility.

Epidemiological studies have shown that in many instances duration of exposure is more important than the daily dose in increasing the risk of cancer. The paradigm for this general relationship is represented by smoking and lung cancer, but also experimental evidence has been produced. In the case of smoking, the incidence of lung cancer increased with the fourth power of duration and the second power of daily dose in one study (Doll and Peto, 1978). Other investigations did not find such a strong discrepancy between dose and duration, but the latter was nevertheless more relevant. Duration is mainly due to age at start; classical epidemiological studies have shown a very strong association between earlier age at start of smoking and the risk of lung cancer. In animals, fractionated and repeated doses induced tumours more frequently than the same total amount administered as a single dose (Lee and O'Neill, 1971; Lee *et al.*, 1977). The latter observation is at odds with the general mechanisms of toxicity, according to which heavy exposure in a single administration has more devastating effects than repeated small doses (there are, however, some notable exceptions: not all carcinogens follow the rule suggested above).

In the light of such observations, a possible interpretation of the higher levels of adducts among cancer cases compared with controls is the concept of cumulative unrepaired DNA damage. What causes cancer, roughly speaking, would be the total burden of genotoxic chemicals that bind to DNA overcoming the repair processes. Such a burden may be higher because DNA repair is impaired (for genetic or acquired reasons) or because repeated exposures to the same agent occur.

Practical Consequences

If the premises are correct, important practical consequences follow. First, the contribution of genetic screening of populations is doomed to be rather limited. Genetic screening is sensible if at least two conditions are met: that the identification of a mutation is followed by effective preventive/therapeutic measures, that prolong survival and improve the quality of life; and that the population examined shows a high concentration of mutants so as to achieve a high predictive value of the screening test. If the prevalence of the mutation in the population is low, even in the case when we have effective preventive/therapeutic means, a screening strategy is unrealistic, since we have to screen hundreds of thousands to find one true positive plus (usually) a large number of false positives. Hence rare mutations can be reasonably sought in families, not in the general population.

Conversely, if the mutation is frequent (a polymorphism), its penetrance is likely to be very low and its effects to depend on interaction with external exposures. In such a case, even if the predictive value of the test is high, the success of screening is low: how can we deal effectively with 50% of the population (those with the *GSTM1* null genotype) who have a 30–40% excess risk of lung cancer? The best action is to advise them not to expose themselves to carcinogens, e.g. not to smoke, but such advice should be obviously extended to the remaining 50% of the population. Another even better reason why genetic screening for common polymorphisms is not feasible is that multiple polymorphisms (tens or even hundreds) are involved in modulating the risk of cancer. Therefore, it makes little sense to identify a *GSTM1* null individual if the same person is at low risk for other metabolizing enzymes. It is obvious that for polymorphic conditions that interact with external exposures the only reasonable approach is avoidance of exposure.

The preceding considerations will be clearer with a quantitative example, based on the concept of 'number needed to treat' (NNT) (**Table 1**). Let us imagine that we have two different genetic traits, (A) one with low penetrance (1.4% cumulative lifetime risk in the carriers) and (B) the other with high penetrance (37% cumulative risk). Let us suppose that screening allows us to reduce the risk of cancer by 58% in both cases. This means that the absolute risk goes down to six per thousand in category A and to 15.5% in category B, with an absolute reduction of eight per thousand and 21.5%, respectively. The NNT is the inverse of such figures, i.e. 125 in category A and 4.5 in category B. This means that we have to screen 125 subjects to prevent one cancer in category A (even with a relative effectiveness of the intervention as high as 58%), whereas it is sufficient to screen 4.5 individuals in category B to achieve the same result.

In conclusion, what practical strategies can be proposed? If we accept that genetic screening should be limited to high-risk families, and that, apart from these, the risk of cancer depends on the total cumulative unrepaired DNA damage, then avoidance of exposure is the only realistic approach, even for low exposures. Low exposures have two properties that make them potentially highly relevant to the population cancer risk: they are frequent or even ubiquitous (e.g. dietary components, air or water pollution) and they are prolonged rather than limited in time. The average person in Western societies is exposed to low-level genotoxic pollutants for all their life. Such low-level exposure starts at a very young age and induces cumulative DNA damage which, if unrepaired, will be able to increase the cancer risk. Although many controversies have arisen about thresholds for carcinogens, little attention has been paid to long-lasting exposures.

Advantages and Disadvantages of Molecular Epidemiology

Conventional epidemiology, based on simple tools such as interviews and questionnaires, has achieved extremely important goals, including the discovery of the causal relationships between smoking and lung cancer or asbestos and mesothelioma. Even a difficult issue such as the relationship between air pollution and chronic disease has been successfully dealt with by time-series analysis and other methods not based on the laboratory. Therefore, the use of molecular epidemiology should be carefully considered to answer specific scientific questions. The following are examples: (1) a better characterization of exposures, particularly when levels of exposure are very low or different sources of exposure should be integrated in a single measure; (2) the study of gene–environment interactions; and (3) the use of markers of early response, in order to overcome the main limitations of cancer epidemiology, i.e. the relatively low frequency of specific forms of cancer and the long latency period between exposure and the onset of disease. Limitations of molecular epidemiology should also be acknowledged: the complexity of many laboratory methods, with partially unknown levels of measurement error or interlaboratory variability; the scanty knowledge of the sources of bias and confounding; in some circumstances, the lower degree of accuracy (for example, urinary nicotine compared with questionnaires on smoking habits); and the uncertain biological meaning of markers, as in the case of some types of adducts or some early response markers (typically mutation spectra).

Table 1   Calculation of the number needed to treat for a genetic test involving a highly penetrant gene or a low-penetrance gene

	Genotype	
	Low penetrance	High penetrance
Risk of cancer without screening (U)	0.014	0.37
Risk reduction due to screening ((U − T)/U)	58%	58%
Risk of cancer in the screenees (T)	0.006	0.155
Absolute reduction of risk (U − T)	0.008	0.215
NNT to prevent one cancer 1/ (U − T)	1/0.008 = 125	1/0.215 = 4.5

ACKNOWLEDGEMENTS

This work was made possible by a grant from the Associazione Italiana per le Ricerche sul Cancro and a grant from the European Union to P.V. for the project Gen-Air (QRLT-1999-00927)

REFERENCES

Begg, C. B. and Berlin, J. A. (1998). Publication bias: a problem in interpreting medical data. *Journal of the Royal Statistical Society*, **151**, (Part 3), 419–463.

Berwick, M. and Vineis, P. (2000). DNA repair in human cancer: an epidemiologic review. *Journal of the National Cancer Institute*, **92**, 874–897.

Brash, D. E., *et al.* (1991). A role for sunlight in skin cancer: UV-induced *p53* mutations in squamous cell carcinoma. *Proceedings of the National Academy of Sciences of the USA*, **88**, 10124–10128.

Bressac, B., *et al.* (1991). Selective G to T mutations of *p53* gene in hepatocellular carcinoma from southern Africa. *Nature*, **350**, 429–431.

Case, R. A. M., *et al.* (1954). Tumours of the urinary bladder in workmen engaged in the manufacture and use of certain dye-stuff intermediates in the British chemical industry. I. The role of aniline, benzidine, alpha-naphthylamine and beta-naphthylamine. *British Journal of Industrial Medicine*, **11**, 75–212.

Coulondre, C. and Miller, J. A. (1977). Genetic studies of the lac repressor. IV. Mutagenic specificity in the *lacI* gene of *Escherichia coli*. *Journal of Molecular Biology*, **117**, 577–606.

Denissenko, M. F., *et al.* (1996). Preferential formation of benzo[*a*]pyrene adducts at lung cancer mutational hotspots in *P53*. *Science*, **274**, 430–432.

Denissenko, M. F., *et al.* (1997). Cytosine methylation determines hot spots of DNA damage in the human *P53* gene. *Proceedings of the National Academy of Sciences of the USA*, **94**, 3893–3898.

Denissenko, M. F., *et al.* (1998). Slow repair of bulky DNA adducts along the nontranscribed strand of the human *p53* gene may explain the strand bias of transversion mutations in cancers. *Oncogene*, **16**, 1241–1247.

Doll, R. and Peto, R. (1978). Cigarette smoking and bronchial carcinoma: dose and time relationships among regular smokers and lifelong non-smokers. *Journal of Epidemiology and Community Health*, **32**, 303–313.

Farmer, P. B., *et al.* (1996). Biomonitoring human exposure to environmental carcinogenic chemicals. *Mutagenesis*, **11**, 363–338.

Friedberg, E. C., *et al.* (1995). *DNA Repair and Mutagenesis*. (ASM Press, Washington, DC).

Garte, S., *et al.* (1997). Gene–environment interactions in the application of biomarkers of cancer susceptibility in epidemiology. In: Toniolo, P., *et al.* (eds), *Application of Biomarkers in Cancer Epidemiology*. IARC Scientific Publication No. 142. (IARC, Lyon).

Hainaut, P., *et al.* (1998). IARC database of *p53* gene mutations in human tumors and cell lines: updated compilation, revised formats and new visualization tools. *Nucleic Acids Research*, **26**, 205–213.

Hall, J., *et al.* (1994). DNA repair capacity as a risk factor for non-melanocytic skin cancer – a molecular epidemiological study. *International Journal of Cancer*, **58**, 179–184.

Hill, A. B. (1965). The environment and disease: association or causation? *Proceedings of the Royal Society of Medicine*, **58**, 295–300.

Hsu, I. C., *et al.* (1991). Mutational hotspots in the *p53* gene in human hepatocellular carcinomas. *Nature*, **350**, 427–428.

Hu, J. J., *et al.* (1997). Poly(ADP-ribose) polymerase in human breast cancer: a case-control study. *Pharmacogenetics*, **7**, 309–316.

Hulla, J. E., *et al.* (1993). Aflatoxin B1-induced rat hepatic hyperplastic nodules do not exhibit a site-specific mutation within the *p53* gene. *Cancer Research*, **53**, 9–11.

Kelsey, T. K., *et al.* (1997). Glutathione-*S*-transferase class mu deletion polymorphism and breast cancer: results from prevalent versus incident cases. *Cancer Epidemiology Biomarkers and Prevention*, **6**, 511–516.

Lamb, P. and Crawford, L. (1986). Characterization of the human *p53* gene. *Molecular Cell Biology*, **6**, 1379–1385.

Lee, P. N. and O'Neill, J. A. (1971). The effect of both time and dose on tumour incidence rate in benzopyrene skin painting experiments. *British Journal of Cancer*, **25**, 759–770.

Lee, P. N., *et al.* (1977). Fractionation of mouse skin carcinogens in cigarette smoke condensate. *British Journal of Cancer*, **35**, 730–742.

Lewtas, J., *et al.* (1997). Air pollution exposure–DNA dosimetry in humans and rodents: evidence for non-linearity at high doses. *Mutation Research*, **378**, 51–63.

Lutz, W. K. (1990). Dose–response relationship and low-dose extrapolation in chemical carcinogenesis. *Carcinogenesis*, **11**, 1243–1247.

Marcus, P., *et al.* (2000). NAT2 slow acetylation and bladder cancer risk: a meta-analysis of 22 case-control studies conducted in the general population. *Pharmacogenetics*, **10(2)**, 115–122.

McLure, M., *et al.* (1989) Elevated blood levels of carcinogens in passive smokers. *American Journal of Public Health*, **79**, 1381–1384.

Miller, J. A., *et al.* (1979). Genetic studies of the lac repressor. IX. Generation of altered proteins by the suppression of nonsense mutations. *Journal of Molecular Biology*, **131**, 191–222.

Nielsen, P. S., *et al.* (1996). Environmental air pollution and DNA adducts in Copenhagen bus drivers: effect of GSTM1 and NAT2 genotypes on adduct levels. *Carcinogenesis*, **17**, 1021–1027.

Paleologo, M., *et al.* (1992). Detection of benzo(*a*)pyrene-diol-epoxide–DNA adducts in white blood cells of psoriatic patients treated with coal tar. *Mutation Research*, **281**, 11–16.

Pastorelli, R., *et al.* (1996). Hemoglobin adducts of benzo(*a*)-pyrene diolepoxide in newspaper vendors: association with traffic exhaust. *Carcinogenesis*, **17**, 2389–2394.

Peluso, M., *et al.* (1998a). 32P-postlabelling detection of aromatic adducts in the white blood cell DNA of nonsmoking police officers. *Cancer Epidemiology Biomarkers and Prevention*, **7**, 3–11.

Peluso, M., *et al.* (1998b). White blood cell DNA adducts, smoking, and NAT2 and GSTM1 genotypes in bladder cancer: a case-control study. *Cancer Epidemiology Biomarkers and Prevention*, **7**, 341–346.

Peluso, M., *et al.* (2000). White blood cell DNA adducts and fruit and vegetable consumption in bladder cancer. *Carcinogenesis*, **21**, 183–187.

Perera, F. P. (1996). Molecular epidemiology: insights into cancer susceptiblity, risk assessment, and prevention. *Journal of the National Cancer Institute*, **88**, 496–509.

Schantz, S. P., *et al.* (1997). Genetic susceptibility to head and neck cancer: interaction between nutrition and mutagen sensitivity. *The Laryngoscope*, **107**, 765–781.

Shen, I. M., *et al.* (1998). Nonconservative amino acid substitution variants exist at polymorphic frequency in DNA repair genes in healthy humans. *Cancer Research*, **58**, 604–608.

Spitz, M. R., *et al.* (1989). Chromosome sensitivity to bleomycin-induced mutagenesis, an independent factor for upper aerodigestive tract cancers. *Cancer Research*, **49**, 4626–4628.

Spitz, M. R., *et al.* (1994). Mutagen sensitivity as a risk factor for second malignant tumors following malignancies of the upper aerodigestive tract. *Journal of the National Cancer Institute*, **86**, 1681–1684.

Tokusashi, Y., *et al.* (1994). Absence of *p53* mutations and various frequencies of Ki-ras exon 1 mutations in rat hepatic tumours induced by different carcinogens. *Molecular Carcinogenesis*, **10**, 45–51.

Vineis, P., *et al.* (1999). *Metabolic Polymorphisms and Susceptibility to Cancer*. IARC Scientific Publication No. 148. (IARC, Lyon).

Vogelstein, B. and Kinzler, K. W. (1998). *The Genetic Basis of Human Cancer*. (McGraw-Hill, New York).

Yaeger, T. R., *et al.* (1998). Overcoming cellular senescence in human cancer pathogenesis. *Genes and Development*, **12**, 163–174.

FURTHER READING

In General on Molecular Epidemiology

Bartsch, H. (2000). Studies on biomarkers in cancer etiology and prevention: a summary and challenge of 20 years of interdisciplinary research. *Mutation Research*, **462**, 255–279.

Hulka, B., *et al.* (1990). *Biological Markers in Epidemiology*. (Oxford University Press, New York).

Perera, F. P. (2000). Molecular epidemiology: on the path to prevention? *Journal of the National Cancer Institute*, **92**, 602–612.

Schulte, P. and Perera, F. (1993). *Molecular Epidemiology. Principles and Practice*. (Academic Press, San Diego).

On Cancer Mechanisms

Hanahan, D. and Weinberg, R. A. (2000). The hallmarks of cancer. *Cell*, **100**, 57–70.

Vogelstein, B. and Kinzler, K. W. (1998). *The Genetic Basis of Human Cancer*. (McGraw-Hill, New York).

On DNA Adducts

Denissenko, M. F., *et al.* (1996). Preferential formation of benzo[a]pyrene adducts at lung cancer mutational hotspots in *P53*. *Science*, **274**, 430–432.

Phillips, D. H. (1996). DNA adducts in human tissues: biomarkers of exposure to carcinogens in tobacco smoke. *Environmental Health Perspectives*, **104, Suppl. 3**, 453–458.

Vineis, P. and Perera, F. (2000). DNA adducts as markers of exposure to carcinogens and risk of cancer. *International Journal of Cancer*, **88**, 325–328.

On *p53*

Hussain, S. P. and Harris, C. C. (1998). Molecular epidemiology of human cancer: contribution of mutation spectra studies of tumor suppressor genes. *Cancer Research*, **58**, 4023–4037.

On Individual Susceptibility

Berwick, M. and Vineis, P. (2000). DNA repair in human cancer: an epidemiologic review. *Journal of the National Cancer Institute*, **92**, 874–897.

Shields, P. G. and Harris, C. C. (2000). Cancer risk and low-penetrance susceptibility genes in gene–environment interactions. *Journal of Clinical Oncology*, **18**, 2309–2315.

Vineis, P., *et al.* (1999). *Metabolic Polymorphisms and Susceptibility to Cancer*. IARC Scientific Publication No. 148. (IARC, Lyon).

Chapter 28

Dietary Genotoxins and Cancer

Takashi Sugimura and Keiji Wakabayashi
National Cancer Center Research Institute, Tokyo, Japan

Minako Nagao
Tokyo University of Agriculture, Tokyo, Japan

CONTENTS

- Introduction
- Microcomponents Affecting Carcinogenesis
- Macrocomponents Affecting Carcinogenesis
- Integration and Recommendation

INTRODUCTION

With regard to cancer causation, tobacco smoking, diet and infections/inflammation are three major factors (Doll and Peto, 1981). Cancer cells have multiple gene alterations (Sugimura, 1992), most of which occur owing to exposures encountered under life-style related conditions, although some of them are inherited through the germ-line. There are numerous genotoxic agents produced exogenously and endogenously. For instance, cigarette smoke contains many different types of genotoxic agents, and infection and inflammation yield reactive oxygen species and nitric oxide-related agents.

Dietary genotoxins exist in several situations: (1) as contaminants due to mould growth; (2) as edible plant components; (3) as substances formed during storage and fermentation of food, some of which are nitrosatable substances; (4) as products of cooking; and (5) as food additives, mainly of the preservative type.

Since the diet is one of three major cancer causative factors, it might be expected that large amounts of genotoxic substances are included. However, contrary to expectation, many kinds of genotoxic substance that do exist are present at very low levels, the only exception being aflatoxin B_1, where a positive association between exposure through the diet intake and liver cancer development is evident in epidemiological studies.

Nevertheless, diet is clearly of importance to human cancer occurrence. In addition to genotoxic agents present as microcomponents, macrocomponents such as fatty acids, salts and fibres have been indicated to be associated with human cancer. At the same time, many anti-carcinogenic compounds are included in the diet. This chapter mainly deals with genotoxic substances and macrocomponents in the diet related to carcinogenesis. In the concluding comments, the significance of these dietary substances is described from the viewpoint of their contribution to human carcinogenic risk. (See also chapter *Mechanisms of Chemical Carcinogenesis*.)

MICROCOMPONENTS AFFECTING CARCINOGENESIS

Mycotoxins

Mycotoxins are toxic compounds produced by fungi. Typical examples are aflatoxins, metabolites formed by *Aspergillus flavus*. In 1960, numerous turkeys died in the UK, and the aetiological factor was found to be a contaminant in their diet, subsequently identified to be aflatoxins. Similarly, rainbow trout were reported to have died due to aflatoxin contamination of their diet. Among aflatoxins, aflatoxin B_1 (AFB$_1$), G_1 and M_1 are frequently detected in foods. The structure of AFB$_1$, the most potent carcinogen and mutagen of this family, is shown in **Figure 1**. AFB$_1$ induces hepatocellular carcinomas in

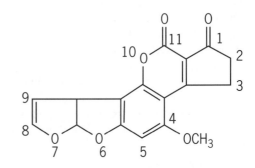

Figure 1   Structure of AFB$_1$.

many species of experimental animals, such as rats, monkeys and trout.

AFB$_1$ is metabolically activated to form its 8,9-epoxide derivative by cytochrome P-450s including CYP3A4 and 1A2, and the epoxide binds to guanine residues in DNA to produce 8,9-dihydro-8-(N^7-guanyl)-9-hydroxy-aflatoxin B$_1$. AFB$_1$ preferentially induces GC to TA transversions. In addition, G to T transversions in the third position of codon 249 of the *p53* tumour-suppressor gene in hepatocellular carcinoma have frequently been noted in inhabitants in Qidong, China and southern Africa, exposed to high levels of AFB$_1$. The data suggest that AFB$_1$ is involved in hepatocarcinogenesis in humans by inducing mutations in the *p53* gene. AFB$_1$ has been classified as a group 1 human carcinogen by the International Agency for Research on Cancer (IARC) (IARC, 1987). In the USA, the allowed levels of contamination of AFB$_1$, AFB$_2$ AFG$_1$ and AFG$_2$ in the diet are < 20 μg/kg. In Japan, AFB$_1$ contamination is limited to < 10 μg/kg in the diet.

Sterigmatocystin is a toxic metabolite produced by moulds in the genera *Aspergillus* and *Penicillium* and is detected in various foods. This mycotoxin is mutagenic to *Salmonella* strains and induces hepatomas in rats when administered orally.

Pyrrolizidine Alkaloids

Mutagenic and carcinogenic pyrrolizidine alkaloids are distributed in a variety of plant species. Humans are exposed to some of them in foods and herbal remedies. Petasitenine is present in coltsfoot, *Petasites japonicus* Maxim, the young flower stalks of which have been used as a food and a herbal remedy in Japan. Senkirkine, also having an otonecine moiety, is present in another kind of coltsfoot, *Tsussilago farfara* L., the dried buds of which are taken as a herbal remedy for coughs in China and Japan. Petasitenine and senkirkine are mutagenic to *S. typhimurium* TA100 with S9 mix, and carcinogenic in rats, inducing liver tumours (Hirono *et al.*, 1977). Petasitenine and senkirkine are responsible for tumour-induction by the two kinds of coltsfoot, *P. japonicus* Maxim and *T. farfara* L., respectively. The structures of petasitenine and senkirkine are shown in **Figure 2**.

Symphytine was isolated as a major alkaloid in comfrey, *Symphytum officinale* L., the leaves and roots of which are used as a green vegetable and a tonic. This alkaloid is mutagenic to *S. typhimurium* TA100 and carcinogenic in rats. Heliotrine similarly shows mutagenicity in *S. typhimurium* TA100 and causes tumours in rats. An outbreak of veno-occlusive disease which occurred in Afghanistan was due to intake of wheat flour heavily contaminated with seeds of a plant of the *Heliotropium* species containing heliotrine.

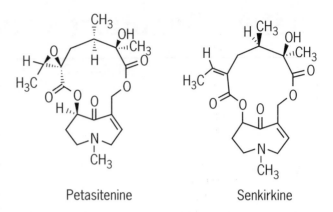

Petasitenine   Senkirkine

Figure 2   Structures of petasitenine and senkirkine.

Aquilide A/Ptaquiloside

The bracken fern, *Pteridium aquilinum*, is grown in many areas of the world and is eaten by residents of some countries, including Japan. However, haematuria with tumours of the urinary bladder are frequently observed in cows ingesting bracken fern in the fields in Turkey. Moreover, rats fed bracken fern develop tumours in the ileum, urinary bladder and mammary glands (Evans and Mason, 1965). It is also reported that a combination of papilloma virus and bracken fern could be involved in the development of the alimentary tract cancer in Scottish cattle.

The mutagenic principle in bracken fern was isolated and identified as a novel norsesquiterpene glucoside of the illudane type, named aquilide A (van der Hoeven *et al.*, 1983). Since aquilide A itself is not mutagenic to *Salmonella*, but only after alkaline treatment, an aglycone of aquilide A was suggested to be the mutagenic component. By monitoring the carcinogenicity of various fractions from bracken fern in rats, the same compound was identified as the active agent and termed ptaquiloside. This substance induces multiple ileal adenocarcinomas and mammary carcinomas at high incidence in rats. The carcinogenicity of bracken fern was found to be reduced after boiling, and exposure levels of humans to aquilide A/ptaquiloside in cooked bracken fern could be small. The structure of aquilide A/ptaquiloside is shown in **Figure 3**.

Cycasin

Cycad is a plant which grows in the tropics. The inhabitants in some areas, including the Amami Oshima and Miyako Islands of Japan and Guam, have employed its nuts as a source of starch for food, but this practice is now very limited. Cycad nuts induce cancers in the liver, kidney and colon of rats when given in the diet. Cycasin, the β-D-glucoside of methylazoxymethanol, is also carcinogenic, inducing cancers in the same organs as cycad nuts (Laqueur *et al.*, 1963). Cycasin is in fact not carcinogenic

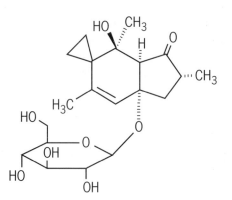

Figure 3   Structure of aquilide A/ptaquiloside.

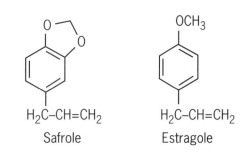

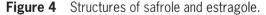

Safrole   Estragole

Figure 4   Structures of safrole and estragole.

in germ-free rats and β-glucoside hydrolysis in the intestinal microflora is necessary to produce the aglycone, methylazoxymethanol, as the proximate carcinogenic form.

Alkenylbenzenes

Safrole (1-allyl-3,4-methylenedioxybenzene), a major component of sassafras oil, has been used as a fragrance in soft drinks and soaps. Estragole (1-allyl-4-methoxy-benzene) is present in tarragon oil and sweet basil and is used as an essence. The structures of safrole and estragole are shown in **Figure 4**. These two alkenylbenzenes are carcinogenic in mice, and their 1′-hydroxy derivatives are mutagenic in *Salmonella* (Miller *et al.*, 1983). In addition, three naturally occurring alkenylbenzenes, iso-safrole (3,4-methylenedioxy-1-propenylbenzene), methyl-eugenol (1-allyl-3,4-dimethoxybenzene) and β-asarone (*cis*-1-propenyl-2,4,5-trimethoxybenzene), have been shown to be carcinogenic in rodents.

Mushroom Hydrazines

The cultivated edible mushroom *Agaricus bisporus* contains agaritine, β-N-[γ-L(+)-glutamyl]-4-hydroxy-methyl-phenylhydrazine, and its decomposition products. Three hydrazine derivatives (the N'-acetyl derivative of 4-hydroxymethylphenylhydrazine, 4-methylphenylhy-drazine hydrochloride and the tetrafluoroborate form of 4-(hydroxymethyl) benzenediazonium ion), derived from agaritine, are carcinogenic in mice. Moreover, uncooked cultivated *Agaricus bisporus* itself is carcinogenic in mice (Toth and Erickson, 1986). Agaritine is also present in the shiitake (*Cortinellus shiitake*), which is a popular edible mushroom in Japan. Another edible mushroom, false morel (*Gyromitra esculenta*), contains gyromitrin (acetaldehyde methylformylhydrazone). This compound is converted into the mutagenic and carcinogenic N-methyl-N-formyl-hydrazine and methylhydrazine under acidic conditions such as those prevailing in the stomach.

Flavonoids

Numerous kinds of flavonoids are present in plants. Among those, quercetin and its glycosides are the most common flavonoids, distributed in vegetables and fruits. Their daily intake by humans is estimated to be more than 100 mg per person. Many flavonoids including quercetin, kaempferol and isorhamnetin show mutagenicity in *Salmonella* with and without metabolic activation systems, but this is not the case with their glycoside compounds, which require digestion by glycosidase for mutagenic activity (Nagao *et al.*, 1978).

Quercetin is mutagenic not only in bacteria *Salmonella* strains but also in some *in vitro* mutation test systems with Chinese hamster V79 cells and Chinese hamster lung cells. However, many studies have shown no carcinogenicity of quercetin in rodents such as rats, mice and hamsters, even with 10% in the diet. Moreover, the conclusion of the NTP Technical Report on toxicology and carcinogenesis studies of quercetin in F344 rats was that there is no clear evidence of carcinogenic activity of quercetin, the reported increased incidence of renal tubular cell adenomas being possible due to involvement of α_{2u}-globulin in male rats (NTP, 1991; http://ntp-server.niehs.nih.gov/htdocs/LT-studies/tr409.html). This is not considered relevant to human carcinogenesis, and therefore the risk potential of quercetin for human cancer must be negligible. These studies with quercetin offer a very important warning: it is not necessarily the case that mutagens are carcinogens.

Nitrosamines and Nitrosatable Mutagens and Carcinogen Precursors

Sodium nitrite has been used as a food preservative and colouring substance in meat. Severe liver disease was encountered in sheep fed a diet containing fishmeal preserved with nitrite and subsequently the toxic principle was identified as N-nitrosodimethylamine (Sakshaug *et al.*, 1965). Vegetables are a major source of nitrite. Nitrite is also produced from nitrate by bacteria in the oral cavity. Under gastric acidic conditions, nitrite reacts with secondary amines to produce mutagenic and carcinogenic N-nitrosodialkylamines. Moreover, reactive nitric oxide produced from L-arginine by nitric oxide synthase in inflammatory processes is involved in the generation of N-nitroso compounds. It has been reported that beer may contain N-nitrosodimethylamine. Oxides of nitrogen are produced during direct-fire drying of barley malt, and react with the barley malt alkaloids gramine and hordenine, both of which have a dimethylamine moiety as a common structure. However, improvements in drying malt have significantly decreased the levels of N-nitrosodimethyl-amine in beer.

In addition to secondary amines, nitrite reacts with indole and phenol derivatives to produce mutagenic compounds under acidic conditions (Wakabayashi et al., 1989). 1-Methyl-1,2,3,4-tetrahydro-β-carboline-3-carboxylic acid in soy sauce and 4-chloro-6-methoxyindole in fava beans are examples of nitrosatable indole compounds, but carcinogenicity has not been proved. Tyramine, present in various fermented foods such as soy sauce, cheese and soybean paste, gives rise to 4-(2-aminoethyl)-6-diazo-2,4-cyclohexa-dienone (3-diazotyramine) after nitrite treatment. 3-Diazotyramine is mutagenic in Salmonella and carcinogenic in rats. Relatively large amounts of nitrite are required for the formation of diazo compounds in vitro and presumably also in vivo in the stomach.

Polycyclic Aromatic Hydrocarbons

Polycyclic aromatic hydrocarbons (PAHs), which have been identified as carcinogenic compounds in coal tar, are in fact widely distributed in our environment such as in cigarette smoke, exhaust gas and cooked foods. The presence of PAHs including benzo[a]pyrene in charred parts of biscuits, roasted coffee beans and broiled steak has been reported. The average levels of benzo[a]pyrene is 8 ng per gram of broiled steak (Lijinsky and Shubik, 1964). Benzo[a]pyrene is converted into the ultimate diol epoxide derivative by metabolic activation, producing adducts at the N^2 position of the guanine residue in DNA. A high frequency of mutations in the p53 tumour-suppressor gene due to G to T transversion is characteristic of mouse skin tumours induced by benzo[a]pyrene. Moreover, the aryl hydrocarbon receptor is required for its tumour induction. (See chapter on Mechanisms of Chemical Carcinogenesis.)

Heterocyclic Amines

Humans have used heat for cooking foods for over 500 000 years. Widmark (1939) reported carcinogenic activity of a solvent extract of broiled horse meat, with induction of mammary tumours in mice by painting on the skin. Production of mutagens by heating meat and fish was established in the 1970s by the use of bacterial mutagenesis assays (Sugimura et al., 1977). Methanol extracts from charred parts of grilled sun-dried sardine, beefsteak and hamburger were found to contain mutagens. Subsequent studies clarified that the mutagenic activity is mainly

derived from heterocyclic amine (HCA) compounds which are produced during cooking from the meat constituents, creatin(in)e, amino acids and sugars.

Structures of mutagenic HCAs in cooked foods and preparations of heated food protein (soybean globulin) and heated amino acids have been determined. All have nitrogen(s) within aromatic rings and exocyclic amino groups, and they can be divided into five groups based on their structures: imidazoquinolines, imidazoquinoxalines, phenylimidazopyridines, pyridoindoles and dipyridoimidazoles (**Figure 5**).

Mutagenic activities of HCAs together with other typical carcinogens to S. typhimurium TA98 and TA100 are summarized in **Table 1**. 2-Amino-1-methyl-6-phenylimidazo-[4,5-b]pyridine (PhIP), 2-amino-3,8-dimethylimidazo[4,5-f]quinoxaline (MeIQx), 2-amino-3,4-dimethylimidazo[4,5-f]quinoline (MeIQ), 2-amino-3-methylimidazo[4,5-f]quinoline (IQ) and 2-amino-9H-pyrido[2,3-b]indole (AαC) also proved to be mutagenic in vivo in lacI or lacZ transgenic animals that were established by introducing the gene on a lambda shuttle vector. Some of these HCAs are mutagenic in mammalian cells, including human fibroblasts in vitro.

HCAs are N-hydroxylated by cytochrome P-450s, mainly CYP1A2, and esterified by acetyltransferase, sulfotransferase and others. All of the eight HCAs so far examined form DNA adducts by covalent binding to the C8 position of guanine. There is a linear correlation between DNA adduct levels and exposure in experimental animals, and guanine adducts of PhIP and MeIQx have been detected in human samples. These adducts result in mutations on cell division. (See chapter on Mechanisms of Chemical Carcinogenesis)

Carcinogenicities of these compounds in rodents are summarized in **Table 2**, along with TD$_{50}$s, the daily amounts required for induction of tumours with 50% prevalence per kilogram. It is worth noting that HCAs induce tumours in various organs, including the colon, mammary glands, lung, liver, bladder, prostate, blood vessels, haematopoietic system, forestomach and skin (Sugimura, 1997). Different species of animals and different strains of the same species show different susceptibilities of the various organs. PhIP and MeIQx are most abundant HCAs in foods, followed by AαC, average human daily intakes of these HCAs being around 1 µg per person per day. It is evident that HCAs may not be sufficient to induce cancers in humans by themselves. However, some epidemiological studies have indicated higher relative risks for colon, breast and bladder cancer in consumers of well-done meat, although contradictory data are also available. Production of mutations involved with any genomic instability may play an important role in carcinogenesis. Collaborative effects with other genotoxic agents may result in effective accumulation of mutations in cells.

HCA carcinogenesis is modified by various food factors, such as soybean isoflavonoids, chlorophyllin, diallyl

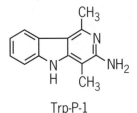

Trp-P-1

3-Amino-1,4-dimethyl-5*H*-pyrido[4,3-*b*]indole

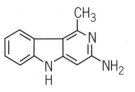

Trp-P-2

3-Amino-1-methyl-5*H*-pyrido[4,3-*b*]indole

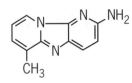

Glu-P-1

2-Amino-6-methyldipyrido[1,2-*a*:3′,2′-*d*]imidazole

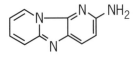

Glu-P-2

2-Aminodipyrido[1,2-*a*:3′,2′-*d*]imidazole

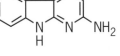

AαC

2-Amino-9*H*-pyrido[2,3-*b*]indole

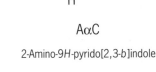

MeAαC

2-Amino-3-methyl-9*H*-pyrido[2,3-*b*]indole

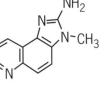

IQ

2-Amino-3-methylimidazo[4,5-*f*]quinoline

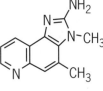

MeIQ

2-Amino-3,4-dimethylimidazo[4,5-*f*]quinoline

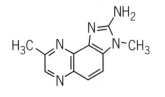

MeIQx

2-Amino-3,8-dimethylimidazo[4,5-*f*]quinoxaline

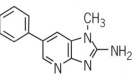

PhIP

2-Amino-1-methyl-6-phenylimidazo[4,5-*b*]pyridine

Figure 5   Structures of HCAs.

disulfide, docosahexaenoic acid, indole-3-carbinol tea cathechin and conjugated linoleic acids (CLAs). Since smaller amounts of HCAs are produced at lower cooking temperatures, a decrease in HCA exposure can be attained by modification of the way of cooking.

Dioxins

Contamination of food by dioxins, polychlorinated dibenzo-*p*-dioxins (PCDDs) and polychlorinated dibenzofurans (PCDFs), has received much attention from the general public. 2,3,7,8-Tetrachlorodibenzo-*p*-dioxin (2,3,7,8-TCDD) is recognized as the most toxic compound among 210 congeners of PCDDs and PCDFs. To aid in the interpretation of the complex database and evaluation of the risk of exposure to mixtures of structurally related PCDDs and PCDFs, the concept of toxic equivalency factors (TEFs) is widely used, and exposure levels are frequently expressed as toxic equivalents (TEQ). TCDD itself is not genotoxic and its lethal toxicity and teratogenicity emerge through binding to the Ah receptor which is expressed in the liver and other organs in adults of various animals and during embryonic development in mice. Lethal doses in 50% of the animals tested (LD_{50} values) for 2,3,7,8-TCDD in the guinea pig and C57BL/6 and DBA2/2J mice are 0.6, 181 and 2570 $\mu g \, kg^{-1}$, respectively. Guinea pig is among the most sensitive species to 2,3,7,8-TCDD.

2,3,7,8-TCDD induces cancers in the skin, liver, haematopoietic system and lung of mice, the hard palate, nasal turbinates, tongue, liver, thyroid and lungs of rats and the skin of hamsters. Dose-related trend was observed with oral administration of 2,3,7,8-TCDD twice a week for 104 weeks at 0.01, 0.05 and 0.5 µg kg^{-1} body weight (bw) in mice and rats (IARC, 1997).

2,3,7,8-TCDD accumulates mainly in the liver and the fat tissue. Its half-life in humans is about 10 years. Daily intakes of Europeans and Japanese are estimated to be around 120–160 pg TEQ, the major sources being fish and dairy products. Based on the data from animal experiments and considerations of mechanism of action, and epidemiological data from accidental exposure of humans to TCDD, the IARC concluded that 2,3,7,8-TCDD is 'carcinogenic to humans with only limited evidence.'

The ligand (TCDD)-activated Ah receptor forms complexes with the Arnt protein and functions as a transcription factor by binding to DNA. The enzymes CYP1A1, 1B1 and 1A2 that are involved in metabolic activation of chemical carcinogens and metabolism of hormones which have promotive effects on cancer development are among those genes that are transcriptionally activated by the Ah receptor. The activated Ah receptor also functions without DNA binding, activating the signal pathway of Src, with increased expression of *ras*, *erbA*, c-*fos*, c-*jun* and AP-1 which may result in cell growth. It also inhibits apoptosis and suppresses immune surveillance, resulting in expansion of preneoplastic cell populations. Mechanisms of TCDD carcinogenicity thus appear complex (IARC, 1997).

Table 1 Mutagenicities of HCAs and typical carcinogens in *Salmonella typhimurium* TA98 and TA100

Compound	Revertants (per µg)	
	TA98	TA100
MeIQ	661000	30000
IQ	433000	7000
MeIQx	145000	14000
Trp-P-2	104200	1800
Glu-P-1	49000	3200
Trp-P-1	39000	1700
Glu-P-2	1900	1200
PhIP	1800	120
AαC	300	20
MeAαC	200	120
Aflatoxin B$_1$	6000	28000
Benzo[a]pyrene	320	660
MNNG	0.00	870
N-Nitrosodimethylamine	0.00	0.23

MNNG: N-Methyl-N'-nitro-N-nitrosoguanidine.

MACROCOMPONENTS AFFECTING CARCINOGENESIS

Total Calories

Nutrition plays important roles in carcinogenesis through a variety of mechanisms. It is well established that excess calorie intake results in high incidences of spontaneously and chemically induced tumours in various organs in rats and mice, including the mammary glands, colon, lung, haematopoietic system and skin. Similar effects have also been suggested in humans by epidemiological studies, e.g. regarding incidence and mortality rates for cancers of the breast, colon, rectum, uterus and kidney in women and

Table 2   TD$_{50}$ and target organs of HCA carcinogenesis in mice and rats

	Mice (CDF$_1$)		Rats (F344)	
	TD$_{50}$ (mg kg^{-1} per day)	Target organ	TD$_{50}$ (mg kg^{-1} per day)	Target organ
IQ	14.7	Liver, forestomach, lung	0.7	Liver, small and large intestines, Zymbal glands, clitoral gland, skin
MeIQ	8.4	Liver, forestomach	0.1	Zymbal glands, large intestine, skin, oral cavity, mammary glands
MeIQx	11.0	Liver, lung, haematopoietic system	0.7	Liver, Zymbal glands, clitoral gland, skin
PhIP	64.6	Lymphoid tissue	2.2	Large intestine, mammary glands, prostate
Trp-P-1	8.8	Liver	0.1	Liver
Trp-P-2	2.7	Liver	–	Urinary bladder, lymphoid tissue
Glu-P-1	2.7	Liver, blood vessels	0.8	Liver, small and large intestines, Zymbal glands, clitoral gland
Glu-P-2	4.9	Liver, blood vessels	5.7	Liver, small and large intestines, Zymbal glands, clitoral gland
AαC	15.8	Liver, blood vessels	–	
MeAαC	5.8	Liver, blood vessels	6.4	Liver

cancers of the colon, rectum, kidney and central nervous system in men.

Furthermore, delay in tumorigenesis by energy restriction has been observed in many models including nullizygous *p53* knockout mice, which show high rates of spontaneous neoplastic changes. Oestrogen-induced pituitary tumours were abolished by 40% energy restriction in F344 rats. However, no such effects were observed with ACI rats, suggesting that the antitumorigenic actions of energy restriction are strongly affected by the genetic background.

Through induction of a nitric oxide synthase isoform, energy restriction results in reduced generation of nitric oxide (NO), which is converted to reactive nitrogen oxide species (RNOS) such as N_2O_3 and peroxynitrite, by reaction with oxygen or superoxide. RNOS or NO induce(s) DNA strand breaks, 8-nitroguanine formation and deamination of guanine, cytosine and adenine in DNA. Peroxynitrite and NO are mutagenic, and RNOS inhibit various enzymes including DNA repair enzymes by reacting with their cysteine residues. Calorie restriction also reduces chemical induction of somatic mutations *in vivo*, although effects on oxidative DNA damage are limited.

Another mechanism of action involves suppression of cell proliferation with decrease in serum level of insulin-like growth factor I (IGF-I), and expression levels of EGF and cyclin D1, as well as upregulation of the cell-cycle growth arrest factor p27. The fidelity of DNA polymerases is also up-regulated and the decrease in cellular DNA repair capacity which occurs with ageing is to some extent prevented. All of these effects are highly implicated in suppression of tumour development.

Fat Intake

Dietary fat is thought to be one of the main risk factors for cancer development on the basis of positive correlations observed between intake and incidences of tumours of the breast, colon and prostate (Schottenfeld and Fraumeni, 1996). Enhancing effects of fat could be partly explained by the included calories, but many experiments under isocaloric conditions have demonstrated an importance of fats themselves as genotoxic and cell-proliferation stimulating agents.

Experimental animal studies have demonstrated that high intake of dietary fat increases the incidence of cancer of the breast, colon and prostate, with influences on many steps in the tumorigenic process, including initiation, promotion and metastasis. In general, the ω-6 polyunsaturated fatty acids (PUFAs), such as linoleic acid (C18:2) and arachidonic acid (C20:4), strongly and the saturated fats weakly enhance tumour development. However, ω-3 PUFAs such as docosahexaenoic acid (DHA, C22:6), eicosapentaenoic acid (EPA, C20:5) and α-linolenic acid (C18:3) generally have a tumour-protective effects while monounsaturated fats, such as oleic acid

(C18:1 ω-9), have no significant influence. It is noteworthy, however, that several chemopreventive agents such as α-tocopherol and various classes of phenolics showing potent antioxidant activities are included as major components of the main source of ω-9 fatty acids, olive oil. Conjugated linoleic acid (CLA), present in dairy products, prevents mammary and colon cancer development in experimental animals. Linoleic acid has two double bonds at the 9 and 12 and CLA at the 9 and 11, 10 and 12 or 11 and 13 positions, being mainly present in the 9 and 11 form in food.

In fat-related carcinogenesis, induction of DNA damage by peroxidation products of PUFAs is one mechanism of action. This involves the generation of reactive α,β-unsaturated aldehydes. Thus, linoleic acid and arachidonic acid are sources of the major reactive aldehydes, *trans*-4-hydroxy-2-non-enal and malondialdehyde, which can form promutagenic exocyclic DNA adducts, such as M_1G (3-(2'-deoxy-β-D-*erythro*-pentofuranosyl)pyrimido[1,2-*a*]purin-10(3*H*)-one). *trans*-4-Hydroxy-2-non-enal is readily oxidized by fatty acid peroxides to form 2,3-epoxy-4-hydoxynonanal and the latter compound modifies DNA by forming etheno adducts such as 1,N^6-ethenoadenine, N^2,3-ethenoguanine and 3,N^4-ethnocytosine, which are highly miscoding.

The essential fatty acid linoleic acid is converted into arachidonic acid and then, with the aid of cycloxygenase and lipoxygenase, into prostaglandins, thromboxanes and leukotrienes that show hormone-like activity. One of them, prostaglandin E_2 (PGE$_2$), was recently shown to be involved in colon carcinogenesis using knockout mice for EP$_1$, one of the receptors for PGE$_2$. ω-6 PUFAs induce ornithine decarboxylase activity in colonic mucosa, activation of protein kinase C in mammary glands, and increases in number of oestrogen receptor binding sites, resulting in cell proliferation.

Oleic acid and ω-3 PUFAs, and specifically EPA, block the Δ^6-desaturase reaction, the first step from linoleic acid to eicosanoids. EPA, DHA and CLA suppress the arachidonic acid pathway by inhibiting cyclooxygenase activity. Stimulation of genotoxic NO production in a murine macrophage cell line with lipopolysaccharide is also suppressed by DHA, EPA and α-linolenic acid. Inhibition of inducible nitric oxide synthase gene expression may thus contribute to the cancer preventive activity of ω-3 PUFAs.

Sodium Chloride

A positive correlation between daily salt intake and gastric cancer incidence was noted by epidemiologists some time ago and urinary sodium chloride concentrations are well correlated with stomach cancer mortality. In experimental animal model systems, *N*-methyl-*N*'-nitro-*N*-nitrosoguanidine (MNNG) induces gastric cancers and this is enhanced by salt administration. High doses of salt disrupt the mucin layer covering and protecting the gastric epithelium and further damage epithelial cells by generation of a high osmotic pressure. This in turn stimulates proliferation of stem cells of the gastric epithelium, providing favourable conditions for the occurrence of mutations. Prolonged damage results in chronic atrophic gastritis and intestinal metaplasia, both of which are understood to be precursor lesions for intestinal-type gastric cancer.

INTEGRATION AND RECOMMENDATION

It is very clear that genotoxic substances in the diet are related to human cancer development. Laboratory data offer particularly strong support.

In this chapter, information on genotoxic carcinogens in the diet and the significance of other nutritional factors have been concisely summarized. Carcinogenesis is due to the accumulation of multiple genetic changes in a cell, implying multiple steps. Each step could be caused by exposure to a minute amount of a genotoxic substance in the diet. Amounts of individual substances are generally not sufficiently high to induce human cancer alone, one exception being human exposure to contaminant mycotoxins in limited regions of the world. However, since many kinds of genotoxic compounds exist in the diet, efforts to lessen their combined impact should be made wherever possible. Since mutations may result in genomic instability, even a single such genetic alteration, for example, in a gene involved in DNA repair could produce spontaneous accumulation of further mutations with time.

Endogeneous genotoxic agents (autobiotics) such as reactive oxygen species are produced in line with the calorific intake. Consumption of appropriate amounts of substances working as radical scavengers, such as vitamin E, is essential for protection from carcinogenesis. Over-intake of calories, fat and salt may act to enhance carcinogenesis through various pathways, while more fibre in the diet can suppress colon carcinogenesis. By integrating information described in this chapter, recommendations can be given with reference to eight of the 12 proposals from the National Cancer Center, Tokyo (Sugimura, 1986). These are: (1) have a nutritionally balanced diet, (2) eat a variety of types of food, (3) avoid excess calories, especially as fat, (4) avoid the excessive drinking of alcohol, (5) take vitamins in appropriate amounts and eat fibre and green and yellow vegetables rich in carotene, (6) avoid drinking fluids that are too hot and eating foods that are too salty, (7) avoid the charred parts of cooked food and (8) avoid food with possible contamination by fungal toxins. Similar recommendations were also proposed by the World Cancer Research Fund and the American Institute for Cancer Research (1997). It is noteworthy that, even for cancer-preventive compounds, the amount of intake should be appropriate, because it is reported that over-intake of β-carotene enhances carcinogenesis (The Alpha-Tocopherol, Beta Carotene Cancer Prevention Study Group, 1994).

REFERENCES

Doll, R. and Peto, R. (1981). The causes of cancer: quantitative estimates of avoidable risks of cancer in the United States today. *Journal of the National Cancer Institute*, **66**, 1191–1308.

Evans, I. A. and Mason, J. (1965). Carcinogenic activity of bracken. *Nature*, **208**, 913–914.

Hirono, I., *et al.* (1977). Carcinogenic activity of petasitenine, a new pyrrolizidine alkaloid isolated from *Petasites japonicus* Maxim. *Journal of the National Cancer Institute*, **58**, 1155–1157.

IARC (1987). *IARC Monographs on the Evaluation of Carcinogenic Risks to Humans; Overall Evaluations of Carcinogenicity: An Updating of IARC Monographs Volumes 1 to 42.* IARC Scientific Publications Supplement 7, 83–87 (IARC, Lyon).

IARC (1997). *IARC Monographs on the Evaluation of Carcinogenic Risks to Humans; Polychlorinated Dibenzo-para-dioxins and Polychlorinated Dibenzofurans*, Vol. 69. (IARC, Lyon).

Laqueur, G. L., *et al.* (1963). Carcinogenic properties of nuts from *Cycas circinalis* L. indigenous to Guam. *Journal of the National Cancer Institute*, **31**, 919–951.

Lijinsky, W. and Shubik, P. (1964). Benzo[*a*]pyrene and other polynuclear hydrocarbons in charcoal-broiled meat. *Science*, **145**, 53–55.

Miller, E. C., *et al.* (1983). Structure–activity studies of the carcinogenicities in the mouse and rat of some naturally occurring and synthetic alkenylbenzene derivatives related to safrole and estragole. *Cancer Research*, **43**, 1124–1134.

Nagao, M., *et al.* (1978). Environmental mutagens and carcinogens. *Annual Review of Genetics*, **12**, 117–159.

NTP (1991). *NTP Technical Report (No. 409) on the Toxicology and Carcinogenesis Studies of Quercetin in F344/N Rats*. NIH Publication No. 92-3140. (US Department of Health and Human Services, Public Health Service, National Toxicology Program, Research Triangle Park, NC).

Sakshaug, J., *et al.* (1965). Dimethylnitrosamine: its hepatotoxic effect in sheep and its occurrence in toxic batches of herring meal. *Nature*, **206**, 1261–1262.

Schottenfeld, D. and Fraumeni, J. F., Jr. (1996). *Cancer Epidemiology and Prevention*. (Oxford University Press, New York).

Sugimura, T. (1986). Studies on environmental chemical carcinogenesis in Japan. *Science*, **18**, 312–318.

Sugimura, T. (1992). Multistep carcinogenesis: a 1992 perspective. *Science*, **23**, 603–607.

Sugimura, T. (1997). Overview of carcinogenic heterocyclic amines. *Mutation Research*, **376**, 211–219.

Sugimura, T., *et al.* (1977). Mutagen–carcinogens in foods, with special reference to highly mutagenic pyrolytic products in broiled foods. In: Hiatt, H. H., *et al.* (eds). *Origins of Human Cancer*. 1561–1577 (Cold Spring Harbor Laboratory, New York).

The Alpha-Tocopherol, Beta Carotene Cancer Prevention Study Group (1994). The effect of vitamin E and beta carotene on the incidence of lung cancer and other cancers in male smokers. *New England Journal of Medicine*, **330**, 1029–1035.

Toth, B. and Erickson, J. (1986). Cancer induction in mice by feeding of the uncooked cultivated mushroom of commerce *Agaricus bisporus*. *Cancer Research*, **46**, 4007–4011.

van der Hoeven, J. C. M., *et al.* (1983). Aquilide A, a new mutagenic compound isolated from bracken fern (*Pteridium aquilinum* (L.) Kuhn). *Carcinogenesis*, **4**, 1587–1590.

Wakabayashi, K., *et al.* (1989) Mutagens and carcinogens produced by the reaction of environmental aromatic compounds with nitrite. *Cancer Surveys*, **8**, 385–399.

Widmark, E. M. (1939). Presence of cancer-producing substances in roasted food. *Nature*, **143**, 984.

World Cancer Research Fund and American Institute for Cancer Research (1997). *Food, Nutrition and the Prevention of Cancer: A Global Perspective*. (American Institute for Cancer Research, Washington, DC).

FURTHER READING

Nagao, M. and Sugimura, T. (eds) (2000). *Food Borne Carcinogens, Heterocyclic Amines*. (Wiley, Chichester).

Sugimura, T. (2000). Nutrition and dietary carcinogens. *Carcinogenesis*, **21**, 387–395.

Wakabayashi, K. and Sugimura, T. (1998). Heterocyclic amines formed in the diet: carcinogenicity and its modulation by dietary factors. *Journal of Nutritional Biochemistry*, **9**, 604–612.

Chapter 29

Tobacco Use and Cancer

Stephen S. Hecht
University of Minnesota Cancer Center, Minneapolis, MN, USA

CONTENTS

INTRODUCTION

Worldwide tobacco use is staggering. According to estimates by the World Health Organisation (WHO), there are about 1100 million smokers in the world, representing approximately one-third of the global population aged 15 years or older (WHO, 1997). China alone has approximately 300 million smokers, about the same number as in all developed countries combined. **Table 1** summarizes the estimated number of smokers in the world, according to data available in the early 1990s. Globally, about 47% of men and 12% of women smoke. Smoking prevalence varies widely by country. For example, in Korea, 68% of men smoke daily, whereas the corresponding figure for Sweden is 22%. Male smoking prevalence varies from < 30% in the African Region (as defined by WHO) to 60% in the Western Pacific Region. Among women, the highest smoking prevalence is in Denmark, where 37% of women smoke, whereas in many Asian and developing countries, prevalence is reported to be < 10%. Smoking among women is common in the former socialist countries of Central and Eastern Europe (28%), countries with established market economies (23%) and Latin American and Caribbean countries (21%) (WHO, 1997). **Figure 1** summarizes data on the number of cigarettes smoked per day per daily smoker in different regions of the world. Although smoking prevalence is lower in the less developed countries in general, it is expected that this will increase markedly as smoking takes hold and larger numbers of young smokers grow older.

Cigarettes are the main type of tobacco product worldwide (WHO, 1997). Manufactured cigarettes are available in all countries, but in some areas of the world roll-your-own cigarettes are still popular. Other smoked products include 'kreteks,' which are clove-flavoured cigarettes popular in Indonesia, and 'sticks' which are smoked in Papua New Guinea. '*Bidis*,' which consist of a small amount of tobacco wrapped in temburni leaf and tied with a string, are very popular in India and neighbouring areas, and have recently taken hold in the USA. Cigars are currently increasing in popularity, and pipes are still used. A substantial amount of tobacco is consumed worldwide in the form of smokeless tobacco products. These include chewing tobacco, dry snuff used for nasal inhalation, moist snuff which is placed between the cheek and gum, a popular practice in Scandinavia and North America, and '*pan*' or betel quid, a product used extensively in India. **Table 2** summarizes the estimated annual global consumption of various types of tobacco products. About six $\times 10^{12}$ cigarettes were consumed annually in the period 1990–1992 worldwide (WHO, 1997).

Most global tobacco manufacturing is controlled by a small number of state monopolies and multinational

Table 1 Estimated number of smokers (in millions) in the world (early 1990s) (from WHO, 1997)

Countries	Males	Females	Total
Developed countries	200	100	300
Developing countries	700	100	800
World	900	200	1100

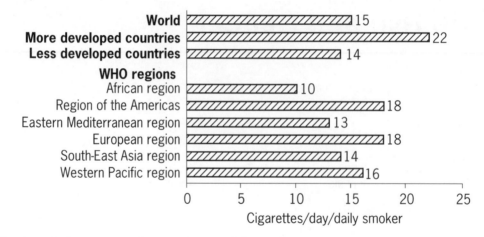

Figure 1   Number of cigarettes smoked per day per daily smoker, by region.

Table 2   Estimated annual global consumption of various types of tobacco products, 1990–1992 (from WHO, 1997)

Type of tobacco product	Estimated annual global consumption, 1990–1992 (kg $\times$ 10^9)	Estimated proportion of total global consumption (%)
All cigarettes, consisting of:	4.2-5.5	65-85
Manufactured cigarettes and kreteks	3.9-5.2	60-80
Bidis	0.2	3
Roll-your-owns	0.1	2
All other tobacco products	1.0-2.3	15-35
Al tobacco products	6.5	100

Table 3   Estimated percentage of deaths caused by smoking in 1995, all developed countries, by gender, age and major cause of death groupings (from WHO, 1997)

Gender	Age (years)	All causes	All cancer	Lung cancer	Upper aerodigestive cancer[a]	Other cancer	Chronic obstructive pulmonary diseases	Other respiratory diseases	Vascular diseases	Other causes
Men	35-69	36	50	94	70	18	82	29	35	35
	70+	21	36	91	59	13	73	11	12	12
	All ages	25	43	92	66	15	75	14	21	18
Women	35-69	13	13	71	34	2	55	16	12	15
	70+	8	13	74	38	2	54	7	5	6
	All ages	9	13	72	36	2	53	7	6	7
Both	35-69	28	35	89	65	10	73	25	28	27
	70+	13	25	86	52	7	65	9	8	8
	All ages	17	30	87	60	8	66	10	13	12

[a] Cancers of the mouth, oesophagus, pharynx and larynx.

corporations (WHO, 1997). The largest state monopoly is in China, where 1.7×10^{12} cigarettes were sold in 1993. This represents about 31% of the global market, about the same as the three largest multinational tobacco corporations combined. China produces about 36% of the world's tobacco, and the USA about 11%.

Worldwide, smoking is estimated to have caused about 1.05 million cancer deaths in 1990 (WHO, 1997). About 30% of all cancer deaths in developed countries are caused by smoking (**Table 3**). The corresponding figure for developing countries is 13%. Lung cancer is the dominant malignancy caused by smoking, with 514 000 lung cancer deaths attributed to smoking in developed countries in 1995 (WHO, 1997). Smoking also causes other types of cancer. This is discussed further below. Lung cancer was rare at the beginning of the twentieth century (Anonymous,

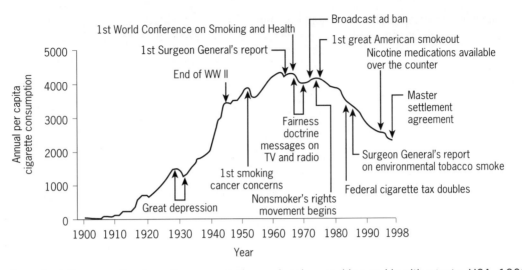

Figure 2   Annual adult per capita cigarette consumption and major smoking and health events, USA, 1900-1988.

1999). However, the incidence and death rates increased as smoking became more popular. In the USA, the lung cancer death rate in 1930 for men was 4.9 per 100 000. By 1990, this had increased to 75.6 per 100 000. The lung cancer death rate can be shown to parallel the curves for cigarette smoking prevalence, with an approximate 20-year lag time. In 1964, the first Surgeon General's report on the health consequences of cigarette smoking was published. Following this landmark report, smoking prevalence began to decrease in the USA. **Figure 2** summarizes annual adult per capita cigarette consumption and major smoking and health events in the USA in the twentieth century. Although smoking prevalence in the USA decreased from 1964 to 1990, there has been no overall change since then. There are still 48 million adult smokers in the USA (Anonymous, 1999).

EPIDEMIOLOGY OF TOBACCO AND CANCER

How do we know that smoking causes cancer? The strongest evidence comes from prospective epidemiological studies. The prospective study design is powerful. Individuals are asked questions about their lifestyle and other factors, then followed for long periods of time. Cancer deaths are recorded and relative risks are determined with respect to the answers given on the questionnaires. Therefore, the answers cannot be influenced by disease state, bias and many other confounding factors. Large studies of this type conclusively demonstrate that all three main types of lung cancer – squamous cell, small cell and adenocarcinoma – are caused mainly by tobacco smoking (IARC, 1986; Shopland, 1995; Blot and Fraumeni, 1996). These studies have consistently demonstrated a dose–response relationship between numbers of cigarettes consumed daily and relative risk of lung cancer. These data, which are based on over 20 million person

years of observation, are summarized in **Table 4** (IARC, 1986; Shopland, 1995; Blot and Fraumeni, 1996).

Case-control epidemiological studies ask questions of people with lung cancer and corresponding matched controls without cancer. Although this study design is not as powerful as the prospective method, it is more economical. Hundreds of case-control studies consistently demonstrate a higher risk for lung cancer in smokers than non-smokers.

The incidence of lung cancer also depends on the duration of smoking (IARC, 1986; Shopland, 1995; Blot and Fraumeni, 1996). The greatest risk is among those who start smoking in adolescence and continue throughout their lives. Cessation of smoking gradually decreases the risk of lung cancer, but no change is seen during the first 4 years. Data on the relative risk of developing lung cancer by time since stopping and total duration of smoking are summarized in **Table 5** (Blot and Fraumeni, 1996).

While cigarette smoking has been definitively established as the major cause of lung cancer, a number of issues remain to be investigated (Wynder and Hoffmann, 1994). Since 1975, the incidence of adenocarcinoma has greatly increased in the USA. The ratio of adenocarcinoma to squamous cell carcinoma was 1 : 2.3 among white males in 1969–1971, whereas it was 1 : 1.4 in 1984–1986. Adenocarcinoma now exceed squamous cell carcinoma of the lung in the USA. This changing histology of cigarette smoke-induced lung cancer is due to changes in cigarette design, particularly the introduction of lower nicotine and higher N-nitrosamine-containing cigarettes. There are important geographical and ethnic differences in lung cancer which require investigation. Lung cancer incidence in Japan is considerably lower than would be expected by comparison with US rates in spite of a dramatic increase in smoking. Diet may be one factor which enhances risk in the USA; laboratory studies have shown that a high-fat diet similar to that consumed in the USA can enhance lung cancer induction by constituents of tobacco smoke. In the

Table 4   Lung cancer mortality ratios in men and women, by number of cigarettes smoked daily, major prospective mortality studies. (From Shopland, 1995, *Environmental Health Perspectives*, **103**, 131–142.)

Study, population	Men Cigarettes/day	Ratio	Women Cigarettes/day	Ratio
American Cancer Society 25-State study, 1 million	Nonsmokers	1.00	Nonsmokers	1.00
	All smokers	8.53	All smokers	3.58
	1-9	4.62	1-9	1.30
	10-19	8.62	10-19	2.40
	20-39	14.7	20-39	4.90
	40+	18.7	40+	7.50
British Physicians' Study, 40 000	Nonsmokers	1.00	Nonsmokers	1.00
	All smokers	14.9	All smokers	5.00
	1-14	7.50	1-14	1.28
	15-24	14.9	15-24	6.41
	25+	25.4	25+	29.7
US veterans study, 290 000	Nonsmokers	1.00		
	All smokers	11.3		
	1-9	3.89		
	10-19	9.63		
	21-39	16.7		
	40+	23.7		
Japanese study, 270 000	Nonsmokers	1.00	Nonsmokers	1.00
	All smokers	3.76	All smokers	2.03
	1-9	2.06	1-9	2.25
	10-19	4.00	10-19	2.56
	20+	6.24	20+	4.47
American Cancer Society 50-State Study, 1.2 million	Nonsmokers	1.00	Nonsmokers	1.00
	All smokers	22.4	All smokers	11.9
	1-20	18.8	1-10	5.50
	20+	26.9	11-19	11.2
			20	14.2
			21-30	20.4
			31+	22.0

Table 5   Relative risk of developing lung cancer according to years since quitting smoking among males in three cohort studies of smokers[a]. (From Blot and Fraumeni, 1996, *Cancer Epidemiology and Prevention*, **637–665**, Oxford University Press, New York.)

Cohort	Years since quitting smoking					
	0	1–4	5–9	10–14	15–19	20+
British physicians	15.8	16.0	5.9	5.3	2.0	2.0
US veterans	11.3	18.8	7.5	5.0	5.0	2.1
American Cancer Society[b]	13.7	12.0	7.2	1.1	1.1	1.1

[a]All risks relative to lifelong nonsmokers.
[b]Excludes those who smoked less than one pack of cigarettes per day.

USA, lung cancer rates among African-Americans are substantially higher than among Caucasians in spite of the fact that African-Americans smoke less. Some evidence suggests that ethnic differences in the metabolism of tobacco smoke carcinogens may be involved in these differences. Recent studies have also indicated that there are gender differences in susceptibility to cigarette smoke, with women apparently being at greater risk than men, for a given level of cigarette consumption. It has been proposed that hormonal effects may mediate these differences.

In addition to its firmly established and widely recognized role as a major cause of lung cancer, cigarette smoking is also an important cause of bladder cancer, cancer of the renal pelvis, oral cancer, oropharyngeal cancer, hypopharyngeal cancer, laryngeal cancer, oesophageal cancer and pancreatic cancer (IARC, 1986). Other cancers that may be caused by smoking include renal adenocarcinoma, cancer of the cervix, myeloid leukaemia and stomach cancer (Doll, 1996). Relative risks for major smoking-related cancers are summarized in **Table 6** (Shopland, 1995). In the USA, about 30% of all cancer deaths are caused by smoking, similar to worldwide estimates for developed countries (**Table 7**; Shopland, 1995).

Establishing whether cause and effect exists between environmental tobacco smoke and lung cancer has been more difficult, given the limitations of conventional epidemiological studies (EPA, 1992; Boffetta *et al.*, 1998).

Environmental tobacco smoke is mainly a composite of the smoke generated between puffs, called sidestream smoke, and a minor portion of mainstream smoke constituents that are exhaled by a smoker. Although the levels of certain carcinogens in environmental tobacco smoke are greater than in mainstream smoke per gram of tobacco burned, environmental tobacco smoke is diluted by air. Therefore, the carcinogen dose received by a nonsmoker exposed to environmental tobacco smoke may be only 1% of that received by an active smoker and the risk of cancer will be less. Epidemiological studies of environmental tobacco smoke and lung cancer have typically found relative risks between 1 and 2 for exposed versus non-exposed people (EPA, 1992; Boffetta *et al.*, 1998). Several panels, including the National Research Council, the US Surgeon General and the Environmental Protection Agency, have concluded that environmental tobacco smoke is a cause of lung cancer.

Unburned tobacco is a cause of oral cavity cancer (IARC, 1985). The annual mortality from tobacco chewing in southern Asia, where it is used primarily in the form of betel quid, is estimated to be of the order of 50 000 deaths per year (WHO, 1997). Oral cavity cancer is the leading cancer killer in India. Snuff-dipping, as practised in North America, is also an accepted cause of oral cavity cancer. The prevalence of snuff-dipping has increased markedly in the USA, especially among young males (Hatsukami and Severson, 1999).

TUMOUR INDUCTION IN LABORATORY ANIMALS

Experimental studies evaluating the ability of cigarette smoke and its condensate to cause cancer in laboratory

Table 6 Relative risks for major smoking-related cancer sites among male and female smokers: American Cancer Society 50-State study, 4-year follow-up. (From Shopland, 1995, *Environmental Health Perspectives*, **103**, 131–142.)

Gender	Cancer site	Current smokers	Former smokers
Male	Lung	22.4	9.36
	Oral	27.5	8.80
	Oesophagus	7.60	5.83
	Larynx	10.5	5.24
	Bladder	2.86	1.90
	Pancreas	2.14	1.12
	Kidney	2.95	1.95
Female	Lung	11.9	4.69
	Oral	5.59	2.88
	Oesophagus	10.3	3.16
	Larynx	17.8	11.9
	Bladder	2.58	1.85
	Pancreas	2.33	1.78
	Kidney	1.41	1.16
	Cervix	2.14	1.94

Table 7   1995 US cancer deaths caused by cigarette smoking. (From Shopland, 1995.)

Gender	Site and ICD disease category	1995 cancer deaths expected	Smoking attributable risk (%)	Estimated deaths due to smoking
Male	Oral, 140-149	5480	90.6	4965
	Oesophagus, 150	8200	76.6	6282
	Pancreas, 157	13200	25.9	3419
	Larynx, 161	3200	79.6	2547
	Lung, 162	95400	89.4	85288
	Bladder, 188	7500	43.8	3285
	Kidney, 189	7100	45.1	3202
	Total cancer deaths expected	289000		108988
Female	Oral, 140-149	2890	58.5	1691
	Oesophagus, 150	2700	71.5	1931
	Pancreas, 157	13800	31.0	4278
	Larynx, 161	890	85.5	761
	Lung, 162	62000	76.1	47182
	Cervix, 180	4800	30.6	1469
	Bladder, 188	3700	34.2	1265
	Kidney, 189	4600	10.7	492
	Total cancer deaths expected	258000		159069
	Total male and female cancer deaths expected in 1995			547000
	Total excess deaths due to cigarette smoking			168057
	Percentage of cancer deaths due to cigarette smoking in 1995			30.7

animals have collectively demonstrated that there is sufficient evidence that inhalation of tobacco smoke as well as topical application of tobacco smoke condensate cause cancer in experimental animals (IARC, 1986; Hecht, 1998b). The Syrian golden hamster has been the model of choice for inhalation studies of cigarette smoke because it has a low background incidence of spontaneous pulmonary tumours and little interfering respiratory infection. Inhalation of cigarette smoke has repeatedly caused carcinomas in the larynx of hamsters and this model system has been widely applied. It is the most reliable model for induction of tumours by inhalation of cigarette smoke. Studies in mice, rats and dogs have been less frequent.

There are a number of operational problems inherent in inhalation studies of cigarette smoke (IARC, 1986; Hecht, 1998b). The smoke must be delivered in a standardized fashion and this has been accomplished in different ways. Both whole-body exposure and nose-only exposure designs have been used. Generally, a 2-s puff from a burning cigarette is diluted with air and forced into the chamber. Animals will undergo avoidance reactions and will not inhale the smoke the way humans do. Thus, the dose to the lung is less than in humans, and this partially explains the occurrence of larynx tumours rather than lung tumours in hamsters. Unlike humans, rodents are obligatory nose breathers. Their nasal passages are more complex than those of humans, thereby affecting particle deposition in the respiratory tract. Tobacco smoke is irritating and toxic, creating further problems in inhalation studies with rodents.

Inhalation studies have reproducibly demonstrated that cigarette smoke, especially its particulate phase, causes laryngeal carcinomas in hamsters (IARC, 1986; Hecht, 1998b, 1999). Some experiments with mice resulted in low incidences of lung tumours, in tests of both mainstream smoke and environmental tobacco smoke. Respiratory tract tumours were produced in one long-term exposure of rats to cigarette smoke. Studies in rabbits and dogs were equivocal. Treatment-related tumours other than those of the respiratory tract have not been consistently observed.

Cigarette smoke condensate (CSC) has been tested extensively for tumour induction (IARC, 1986; Hecht, 1998b). CSC is produced by passing smoke through cold traps and recovering the material in the traps by washing with a volatile solvent which is then evaporated. Some volatile and semivolatile constituents may be lost during this process. CSC is roughly equivalent to cigarette total particulate matter (TPM), the material collected on a glass-fibre filter which has had smoke drawn through it. The term 'tar,' which is often used in official reports on cigarette brands, is equivalent to TPM but without nicotine and water.

CSC generation and collection techniques have been standardized (IARC, 1986; Hecht, 1998b). The most widely used test system for carcinogenicity of CSC is mouse skin. Consistently, CSC induces benign and malignant skin tumours in mice. This test system has been employed to evaluate the carcinogenic activities of cigarettes of different designs and to investigate mechanisms of carcinogenesis by cigarette smoke. For example, mouse skin studies led to the identification of carcinogenic polycyclic aromatic hydrocarbons (PAHs) in cigarette smoke as well as the demonstration that CSC has co-carcinogenic and tumour-promoting activity. The overall carcinogenic effect of CSC on mouse skin appears to depend on the composite interaction of the tumour initiators such as PAH, tumour promoters and co-carcinogens.

There are drawbacks to the mouse skin assay (Hecht, 1998b). Since CSC lacks volatile and semivolatile components, contributions of these compounds to total activity is lost. Furthermore, mouse skin is insensitive to certain carcinogens in tobacco smoke, such as nitrosamines, which show high selectivity for tissues such as lung. Mouse skin is on the other hand a relatively sensitive tumour induction site for PAHs. Mouse skin studies also ignore the complexity of the respiratory system, where different cell types are known to respond differently to various carcinogens in tobacco smoke. CSC has also been tested by direct injection into the rodent lung, generally in a lipid vehicle. This caused squamous cell carcinomas of the lung in rats. Tumours were not observed in rats treated with the vehicle (IARC, 1986; Hecht, 1998b).

Many studies have evaluated tumour induction in rodents by extracts of unburned tobacco (IARC, 1985). Although some positive results have been obtained, there is currently no widely accepted and reproducible model for the induction of oral cavity cancer in rodents by tobacco extracts, in spite of the strong human data. There are probably cofactors that contribute to human oral cancer upon tobacco use, which are not reproduced in animal studies.

CHEMISTRY OF TOBACCO SMOKE

When cigarette tobacco is burned, mainstream smoke and sidestream smoke are generated (IARC, 1986; Hecht, 1998b). Mainstream smoke is the material drawn from the mouth end of a cigarette during puffing. Sidestream smoke is the material released into the air from the burning tip of the cigarette plus the material which diffuses through the paper. The material emitted from the mouth end of the cigarette between puffs is sometimes also considered as sidestream smoke.

The mainstream smoke emerging from the cigarette is an aerosol containing about 1×10^{10} particles ml^{-1}, ranging in diameter from 0.1 to 1.0 µm (mean diameter 0.2 µm) (IARC, 1986; Hecht, 1998b, 1999). About 95% of the smoke is made up of gases, mainly nitrogen, oxygen and carbon dioxide. For chemical analysis, the smoke is arbitrarily separated into a vapour phase and a particulate phase, based on passage through a glass-fibre filter pad called a Cambridge filter. This retains 99.7% of all particles with diameters of $\geq 0.1 \, \mu m$. Individual smoke components, of which more than 50% appear in the vapour phase of fresh mainstream smoke, are considered volatile smoke components whereas all others are considered particulate phase components. The particulate phase contains more than 3500 compounds, and most of the carcinogens. Standardized machine smoking conditions have been used for measurement of cigarette smoke constituents. These conditions are also arbitrary and it is recognized that each smoker may puff in ways that are widely different from the standardized conditions, thereby changing the yield of individual smoke constituents. In addition to nitrogen, oxygen and carbon dioxide, the gas phase contains substantial amounts of carbon monoxide, water, argon, hydrogen, ammonia, nitrogen oxides, hydrogen cyanide, hydrogen sulfide, methane, isoprene, butadiene, formaldehyde, acrolein, pyridine and other compounds. Some major constituents of the particulate phase include nicotine and related alkaloids, hydrocarbons, phenol, catechol, solanesol, neophytadienes, fatty acids and others. Many of the components are present in higher concentration in sidestream smoke than in mainstream smoke; this is especially true of nitrogen-containing compounds. However, a person's exposure to sidestream smoke is generally far less than to mainstream smoke because of dilution with room air.

Among the many compounds in tobacco smoke are carcinogens, which are agents capable of inducing cancer in laboratory animals or humans. There are 55 carcinogens in cigarette smoke that have been evaluated by the International Agency for Research on Cancer (IARC) and for which there is 'sufficient evidence for carcinogenicity' in either laboratory animals or humans (Hecht, 1999). The types of carcinogens, based on their chemical classes, are listed in **Table 8**. Carcinogens specifically associated with lung cancer are listed in **Table 9**. The 20 compounds included in this list have been found convincingly to induce lung tumours in at least one animal species and

Table 8 Summary of carcinogens in cigarette smoke. (From Hecht, 1999, *Journal of the National Cancer Institute*, **91**, 1194–1210.)

Type	No. of compounds
Polycyclic aromatic hydrocarbons (PAHs)	10
Azaarenes	3
N-Nitrosamines	7
Aromatic amines	3
Heterocyclic aromatic amines	8
Aldehydes	2
Miscellaneous organic compounds	15
Inorganic compounds	7
Total	55

have been positively identified in cigarette smoke. The structures of the organic compounds are shown in **Figure 3**. These compounds are most likely involved in lung cancer induction in people who smoke.

PAHs are condensed ring aromatic compounds that are formed during all incomplete combustion reactions, such as occur in the burning cigarette. Among the PAHs, benzo[*a*]pyrene (BaP) is the most extensively studied compound. Its ability to induce lung tumours upon local administration or inhalation is well documented (Hecht, 1999). It causes lung tumours in mice, but not in rats, when administered systemically. In studies of lung tumour induction by implantation in rats, BaP is more carcinogenic than several other PAHs of tobacco smoke. In analytical studies, it has often been used as a surrogate for other PAHs and extensive data on its occurrence in cigarette smoke are available (IARC, 1986; Hecht, 1999). Thus BaP is a potent lung carcinogen, the occurrence of which is well documented. The vast literature on BaP tends to distract attention from other PAHs. However, PAHs such as dibenz[*a*, *h*]anthracene, 5-methylchrysene and dibenzo[*a*, *i*]pyrene are substantially stronger lung tumorigens than BaP in mice or hamsters, although the levels of these compounds in cigarette smoke are lower than those of BaP (Hecht, 1999).

Azaarenes are nitrogen-containing analogues of PAHs. Two azaarenes, dibenz[*a*,*h*]acridine and 7*H*-dibenzo-[*c*,*g*]carbazole, are pulmonary tumorigens when tested by implantation in the rat lung and instillation in the hamster trachea, respectively (Hecht, 1999). The activity of dibenz[*a*,*h*]acridine is significantly less than that of BaP, whereas that of 7*H*-dibenzo[*c*, *g*]carbazole is greater than BaP. The levels of both compounds in cigarette smoke are relatively low.

N-Nitrosamines are a large group of potent carcinogens formed by nitrosation of amines. Among the N-nitrosamines, N-nitrosodiethylamine (NDEA) is an effective pulmonary carcinogen in the hamster, but not the rat (Hecht, 1999). Its levels in cigarette smoke are low compared with those of other carcinogens. The tobacco-specific N-nitrosamine 4-(methylnitrosamino)-1-(3-pyridyl)-1-butanone (NNK) is a potent lung carcinogen in rats, mice and hamsters (Hecht, 1998a, 1999). NNK is called a tobacco-specific N-nitrosamine because it is a chemical derivative of nicotine, and thus occurs only in tobacco products. It is the only compound in **Table 9** which induces lung tumours systemically in all three commonly used rodent models. The organospecificity of NNK for the lung is remarkable; it induces tumours of the lung, mainly adenoma and adenocarcinoma, independent of the route of administration and in both susceptible and resistant strains of mice (Hecht, 1998a, 1999). The systemic administration of NNK to rats is a reproducible and robust method for the induction of lung tumours. Cigarette smoke contains substantial amounts of NNK (IARC, 1986; Hecht, 1998b) and the total dose experienced by a smoker in a lifetime of

Table 9 Pulmonary carcinogens in cigarette smoke. (From Hecht, 1999, *Journal of the National Cancer Institute*, **91**, 1194–1210.)

Carcinogen class	Compound	Amount in mainstream cigarette smoke (ng/cigarette)	Sidestream/ mainstream ratio	Representative lung tumorigenicity in species
PAHs	Benzo[a]pyrene (BaP)	20-40	2.5-3.5	Mouse, rat, hamster
	Benzo[b]fluoranthane	4-22		Rat
	Benzo[j]fluoranthane	6-21		Rat
	Benzo[k]fluoranthane	6-12		Rat
	Dibenzo[a, i]pyrene	1.7-3.2		Hamster
	Indeno[1,2,3-cd]pyrene	4-20		Rat
	Dibenz[a,h]anthracene	4		Mouse
	5-Methylchrysene	0.6		Mouse
Azaarenes	Dibenz[a,h]acridine	0.1		Rat
	7H-Dibenzo[c,g]carbazole	0.7		Hamster
N-Nitrosamines	N-Nitrosodiethylamine	ND-2.8	< 40	Hamster
	4-(Methylnitrosamino)-1- (3-pyridyl)-1-butanone (NNK)	80-770	1-4	Mouse, rat, hamster
Miscellaneous organic compounds	1, 3-Butadiene	$(20\text{-}70) \times 10^3$		Mouse
	Ethyl carbamate	20-38		Mouse
Inorganic compounds	Nickel	0-510	13-30	Rat
	Chromium	0.2-500		Rat
	Cadmium	0-6670	7.2	Rat
	Polonium-210	0.03-1.0 pCi	1.0-4.0	Hamster
	Arsenic	0-1400		None
	Hydrazine	24-43		Mouse

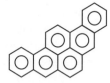

Dibenzo[a,i]pyrene

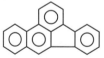

Dibenz[a,h]acridine

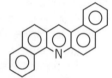

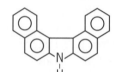

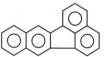

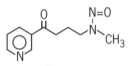

Benzo[a]pyrene (BaP)   Benzo[b]fluoranthene   Benzo[j]fluoranthene   Benzo[k]fluoranthene

Dibenzo[a,i]pyrene   Indeno[1,2,3-cd]pyrene   Dibenz[a,h]anthracene   5-Methylchrysene

Dibenz[a,h]acridine   7H-Dibenzo[c,g]carbazole   N-Nitrosodiethylamine   4-(Methylnitrosamino)-1-(3-pyridyl)-1-butanone (NNK)

$CH_2{=}CH{-}CH{=}CH_2$
1,3-Butadiene

$H_2N{-}\overset{\overset{O}{\|}}{C}{-}OCH_2CH_3$
Ethyl carbamate

Figure 3 Structures of organic pulmonary carcinogens in tobacco smoke.

smoking is remarkably close to the lowest total dose shown to induce lung tumours in rats (Hecht, 1998a). Levels of NNK and total PAHs in cigarette smoke are similar (IARC, 1986; Hecht, 1998b).

Lung is one of the multiple sites of tumorigenesis by 1,3-butadiene in mice, but is not a target in the rat (Hecht, 1999). 1,3-Butadiene is a component of the vapour phase of cigarette smoke, but in most inhalation studies, the particulate phase shows more overall carcinogenic activity. Ethyl carbamate is a well established pulmonary carcinogen in mice but not in other species (Hecht, 1999). Nickel, chromium, cadmium and arsenic are all present in tobacco and a percentage of each is transferred to mainstream smoke; arsenic levels have been substantially lower since discontinuation of its use as a pesticide in 1952 (Hecht, 1999). Metal carcinogenicity depends on the valence state and anion; these are poorly defined in many analytical studies of tobacco smoke. Thus, although some metals are effective pulmonary carcinogens, the role of metals in tobacco-induced lung cancer is unclear. Levels of polonium-210 in tobacco smoke are not believed to be great enough to impact lung cancer significantly in smokers (Hecht, 1999). Hydrazine is an effective lung carcinogen in mice and has been detected in cigarette smoke in limited studies (Hecht, 1999).

Considerable data indicate that PAHs and NNK play very important roles as causes of lung cancer in people who smoke. The other compounds discussed above may also contribute, but probably to a lesser extent.

PAHs and N-nitrosamines such as NNK and N'-nitrosonornicotine (NNN) are probably involved as causes of oral cavity cancer in smokers (Hoffmann and Hecht, 1990). N-Nitrosamines such as NNN and NDEA are likely causes of oesophageal cancer in smokers (Hoffmann and Hecht, 1990). The risk of oral cavity cancer and oesophageal cancer in smokers is markedly enhanced by consumption of alcoholic beverages. NNK is also believed to play a prominent role in the induction of pancreatic cancer in smokers, whereas aromatic amines such as 4-aminobiphenyl and 2-naphthylamine are the most likely causes of bladder cancer (Hoffmann and Hecht, 1990).

Cigarette smoke is also a tumour promoter (Hecht, 1998b). The majority of the activity seems to be due to uncharacterized weakly acidic compounds. Substantial levels of cocarcinogens such as catechol are present in cigarette smoke (Hecht, 1998b). Co-carcinogens enhance the activity of carcinogens when administered simultaneously. Other co-carcinogens in tobacco smoke include methylcatechols, pyrogallol, decane, undecane, pyrene, benzo[e]pyrene and fluoranthene. In addition, cigarette smoke contains high levels of acrolein, which is toxic to the pulmonary cilia, and other agents such as nitrogen oxides, acetaldehyde and formaldehyde that could contribute indirectly to pulmonary carcinogenicity through their toxic effects (Hecht, 1998b, 1999).

Whereas cigarette smoke is extraordinarily complex, unburned tobacco is simpler. With respect to carcinogens, the tobacco-specific nitrosamines NNK and NNN are the most prevalent strong cancer-causing agents in products such as smokeless tobacco (IARC, 1985). A mixture of NNK and NNN induces oral tumours in rats, and consequently these compounds are considered to play a significant role as causes of oral cavity cancer in people who use smokeless tobacco products (IARC, 1985; Hecht, 1998a).

MECHANISMS OF TUMOUR INDUCTION

The mechanisms by which tobacco causes cancer can best be illustrated by considering the relationship between cigarette smoking and lung cancer, because it is here that the most information is available. The overall framework for discussing this information is illustrated in **Figure 4** (Hecht, 1999). Carcinogens form the link between nicotine addiction and cancer. Nicotine addiction is the reason why people continue to smoke. While nicotine itself is not considered to be carcinogenic, each cigarette contains a mixture of carcinogens, including a small dose of PAHs and NNK among other lung carcinogens, tumour promoters and co-carcinogens (Hecht, 1999). Carcinogens such as NNK and PAHs require metabolic activation, that is, they must be enzymatically transformed by the host into reactive intermediates, in order to exert their carcinogenic effects. There are competing detoxification pathways which result in harmless excretion of the carcinogen. The balance between metabolic activation and detoxification differs among individuals and will affect cancer risk.

We know a great deal about mechanisms of carcinogen metabolic activation and detoxification (Hecht, 1999). The metabolic activation process leads to the formation of

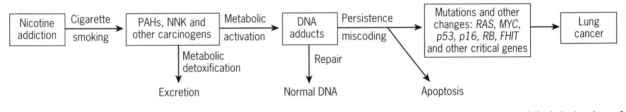

Figure 4 Scheme linking nicotine addiction and lung cancer via tobacco smoke carcinogens and their induction of multiple mutations in critical genes. PAHs = polycyclic aromatic hydrocarbons; NNK = 4-(methylnitrosamino)-1-(3-pyridyl)-1-butanone.

DNA adducts, which are carcinogen metabolites bound covalently to DNA, usually at guanine or adenine. There have been major advances in our understanding of DNA adduct structure and its consequences in the past two decades and we now have a large amount of mechanistic information (Hecht, 1999). If DNA adducts escape cellular repair mechanisms and persist, they may lead to miscoding, resulting in a permanent mutation. This occurs when DNA polymerase enzymes read an adducted DNA base incorrectly, resulting in the insertion of the wrong base, or other errors. As a result of clever strategies that combine DNA adduct chemistry with the tools of molecular biology, we know a great deal about the ways in which carcinogen DNA adducts cause mutations. Cells with damaged DNA may be removed by apoptosis, or programmed cell death (Sekido et al., 1998). If a permanent mutation occurs in a critical region of an oncogene or tumour-suppressor gene, it can lead to activation of the oncogene or deactivation of the tumour-suppressor gene. Oncogenes and tumour-suppressor genes play critical roles in the normal regulation of cellular growth. Changes in multiple tumour-suppressor genes or oncogenes lead to aberrant cells with loss of normal growth control and ultimately to lung cancer. Although the sequence of events has not been well defined, there can be little doubt that these molecular changes are important (Sekido et al., 1998). There is now a large amount of data on mutations in the human K-ras oncogene and p53 tumour-suppressor gene in lung tumours from smokers (Hecht, 1999).

Blocking any of the horizontal steps in **Figure 4** may lead to decreased lung cancer, even in people who continue to smoke. In the following discussion, some of these steps will be considered in more detail.

Upon inhalation, cigarette smoke carcinogens are enyzmatically transformed to a series of metabolites as the exposed organism attempts to convert them to forms that are more readily excreted. The initial steps are usually carried out by cytochrome P450 (CYP) enzymes which oxygenate the substrate (Guengerich and Shimada, 1998). These enzymes typically are responsible for metabolism of drugs, other foreign compounds and some endogenous substrates. Other enzymes such as lipoxygenases, cyclooxygenases, myeloperoxidase and monoamine oxidases may also be involved, but less frequently. The oxygenated intermediates formed in these initial reactions may undergo further transformations by glutathione-S-transferases, uridine-5′-diphosphate glucuronosyltransferases, sulfatases and other enzymes which are typically involved in detoxification (Hecht, 1999). Some of the metabolites produced by the CYPs react with DNA or other macromolecules to form covalent binding products known as adducts. This is referred to as metabolic activation (see **Figure 4**). Metabolic pathways of BaP and NNK, representative pulmonary carcinogens in cigarette smoke, have been extensively defined through studies in rodent and human tissues. The major metabolic activation

pathway of BaP is conversion to a reactive diol epoxide metabolite called BPDE; one of the four isomers produced is highly carcinogenic and reacts with DNA to form adducts with the N^2-atom of deoxyguanosine (Hecht, 1999). The major metabolic activation pathways of NNK and its main metabolite, 4-(methylnitrosamino)-1-(3-pyridyl)-1-butanol (NNAL), occur by hydroxylation of the carbons adjacent to the N-nitroso group (α-hydroxylation), which leads to the formation of two types of DNA adducts: methyl adducts such as 7-methylguanine or O^6-methylguanine, and pyridyloxobutyl adducts (Hecht, 1998a, 1999).

Considerable information is available on pulmonary carcinogen metabolism in vitro, in both animal and human tissues, but fewer studies have been carried out on uptake, metabolism and adduct formation of cigarette smoke lung carcinogens in smokers (Hecht, 1999). Various measures of cigarette smoke uptake in humans have been used, including exhaled carbon monoxide, carboxyhaemoglobin, thiocyanate and urinary mutagenicity. However, the most specific and widely used biochemical marker is the nicotine metabolite cotinine (IARC, 1986; Hecht, 1999). While continine and other nicotine metabolites are excellent indicators of tobacco smoke constituent uptake by smokers, the NNK metabolites NNAL and its O-glucuronide (NNAL-Gluc) are excellent biomarkers of tobacco smoke lung carcinogen uptake (Hecht, 1999). NNAL is a potent pulmonary carcinogen like NNK, whereas NNAL-Gluc is a detoxified metabolite of NNK (Hecht, 1998a, 1999). Since NNK is a tobacco-specific carcinogen, its metabolites NNAL and NNAL-Gluc are found only in the urine of individuals exposed to tobacco products. Urinary NNAL and NNAL-Gluc have been quantified in several studies of smokers and in nonsmokers exposed to environmental tobacco smoke. The latter results demonstrate that uptake of NNAL-Gluc is 1–3% of that in smokers, consistent with the weaker epidemiological evidence for a role of environmental tobacco smoke, compared with mainstream cigarette smoke, as a cause of lung cancer (Hecht, 1999).

BaP has been detected in human lung; no differences between smokers and nonsmokers were noted (Hecht, 1999). 1-Hydroxypyrene and its glucuronide, urinary metabolites of the noncarcinogen pyrene, have been widely used as indicators of PAH uptake. 1-Hydroxypyrene levels in smokers are generally higher than in nonsmokers (Hecht, 1999). Overall, there is considerable evidence that pulmonary carcinogens in cigarette smoke are taken up and metabolized by smokers as well as by nonsmokers exposed to environmental tobacco smoke.

Less than 20% of smokers will get lung cancer (IARC, 1986). Susceptibility will depend in part on the balance between carcinogen metabolic activation and detoxification in smokers. This is an important area requiring further study. Most investigations have focused on the metabolic activation pathways by quantifying DNA or protein adducts. There are considerable data demonstrating activation of BaP to DNA adducts in the lungs of smokers. Earlier investigations demonstrated that cigarette smoke induces aryl hydrocarbon hydroxylase (AHH) activity and proposed a relationship between AHH activity and lung cancer (IARC, 1986; Hecht, 1999). AHH metabolizes BaP to 3-hydroxyBaP, and is equivalent to CYP 1A1. Cigarette smoking induces expression of this enzyme. Cancer patients who stopped smoking within 30 days of surgery had elevated levels of AHH activity compared with non-smoking cancer patients (Hecht, 1999). Lung tissue from recent smokers with elevated AHH activity also metabolically activated BaP to a greater extent than lung tissue from nonsmokers or ex-smokers. DNA adduct levels correlated with AHH activity in the same samples. Collectively, these results support the existence of a cigarette smoke-inducible pathway leading to BaP–DNA adducts in smokers' lungs, as illustrated in **Figure 4**.

A large number of studies have used immunoassays and ^{32}P postlabelling, which are sensitive but relatively non-specific techniques, to estimate levels of 'PAH–DNA adducts' or 'hydrophobic DNA adducts' in white blood cells and other human tissues including lung (Hecht, 1999). Many of these have shown elevated adduct levels in smokers. However, none of the studies using immunoassays and ^{32}P postlabelling has identified the structures of the compounds leading to DNA adduct formation. Probably some are PAHs, but individual PAH–DNA adducts have not been characterized in these studies.

Several studies have detected 7-methylguanine in human lung (Hecht, 1999). Levels were higher in smokers than in nonsmokers in two studies, suggesting that NNK may be one source of these adducts. While 7-methylguanine is not generally considered as an adduct that would lead to miscoding in DNA and the introduction of a permanent mutation, other methyl adducts which do have miscoding properties such as O^6-methylguanine are formed at the same time, but at lower levels. Pyridyloxobutylated DNA also has been detected in lung tissue from smokers in one study, reflecting metabolic activation of NNK or NNN. The detection of methyl and pyridyloxobutyl adducts in DNA from smokers' lungs is consistent with the ability of human lung tissue metabolically to activate NNK, but the quantitative aspects of the relationship of metabolism to DNA adduct levels are unclear (Hecht, 1998a, 1999).

DNA repair processes are important in determining whether DNA adducts persist. Because smoking is a chronic habit, one would expect a steady-state DNA adduct level to be achieved by the opposing effects of damage and repair. There are three mechanisms of DNA repair: direct repair, base excision repair and nucleotide excision repair. With respect to smoking and lung cancer, direct repair of O^6-methylguanine by O^6-methylguanine–DNA alkyltransferase and nucleotide excision repair of PAH–DNA adducts would appear to be the most relevant processes (Hecht, 1999).

As indicated in **Figure 4**, the direct interaction of metabolically activated carcinogens with critical genes such as the *p53* tumour-suppressor gene and the K-*ras* oncogene is central to the hypothesis that specific carcinogens form the link between nicotine addiction and lung cancer (Hecht, 1999). The *p53* gene plays a central role in the delicate balance of cellular proliferation and death. It is mutated in about half of all cancer types, including over 50% of lung cancers, leading to loss of its activity for cellular regulation. Point mutations at guanine (G) are common. In a sample of 550 *p53* mutations in lung tumours, 33% were G $\rightarrow$ T transversions, and 26% were G $\rightarrow$ A transitions. (A purine $\rightarrow$ pyrimidine or pyrimidine $\rightarrow$ purine mutation is referred to as a transversion, and a purine $\rightarrow$ purine or pyrimidine $\rightarrow$ pyrimidine mutation is called a transition.) A positive relationship between lifetime cigarette consumption and the frequency of *p53* mutations and of G $\rightarrow$ T transversions on the nontranscribed DNA strand has also been noted. These observations are generally consistent with the fact that most activated carcinogens react predominantly at G, and that repair of the resulting adducts would be slower on the nontranscribed strand, and thus support the hypothesis outlined in **Figure 4**.

Mutations in codon 12 of the K-*ras* oncogene are found in 24–50% of human primary adenocarcinomas but are rarely seen in other lung tumor types (Hecht, 1999). When K-*ras* is mutated, a complex series of cellular growth signals are initiated. Mutations in K-*ras* are more common in smokers and ex-smokers than in nonsmokers, which suggests that they may be induced by direct reaction with the gene of an activated tobacco smoke carcinogen. The most commonly observed mutation is GGT $\rightarrow$ TGT, which typically accounts for about 60% of the codon 12 mutations, followed by GGT $\rightarrow$ GAT (20%), and GGT $\rightarrow$ GTT (15%).

The *p16^{INK4a}* tumour-suppressor gene is inactivated in more than 70% of human non-small cell lung cancers, via homozygous deletion or in association with aberrant hypermethylation of the promoter region (Hecht, 1999). In the rat, 94% of adenocarcinomas induced by NNK were hypermethylated at the *p16* gene promoter. This change was frequently detected in hyperplastic lesions and adenomas which are precursors to the adenocarcinomas induced by NNK. Similar results were found in human squamous cell carcinomas of the lung. The *p16* gene was coordinately methylated in 75% of carcinoma *in situ* lesions adjacent to squamous cell carcinomas which had this change. Methylation of *p16* was associated with loss of expression in tumours and precursor lesions indicating functional inactivation of both alleles. Aberrant methylation of *p16* has been suggested as an early marker for lung cancer. The expression of cell cycle proteins is related to the *p16* and retinoblastoma tumour-suppressor genes; NNK-induced mouse lung tumours appear to resemble human non-small-cell lung cancer in the expression of cell cycle proteins. The oestrogen receptor gene is also inactivated through promoter methylation. There was concordance between the incidence of promoter methylation in this gene in lung tumours from smokers and from NNK-treated rodents.

Loss of heterozygosity and exon deletions within the fragile histidine triad (*FHIT*) gene are associated with smoking habits in lung cancer patients and have been proposed as a target for tobacco smoke carcinogens (Hecht, 1999). However, point mutations within the coding region of the *FHIT* gene were not found in primary lung tumours.

Collectively, the evidence favouring the sequence of steps illustrated in **Figure 4** as an overall mechanism of tobacco-induced cancer is extremely strong, although there are important aspects of each step that require further study. These include carcinogen metabolism and DNA binding in human lung, the effects of cigarette smoke on DNA repair and adduct persistence, the relationship between specific carcinogens and mutations in critical genes and the sequence of gene changes leading to lung cancer.

Using a weight-of-the-evidence approach, specific PAHs and the tobacco-specific nitrosamine NNK can be identified as probable causes of lung cancer in smokers, but the contribution of other agents cannot be excluded (**Table 9**). The chronic exposure of smokers to the DNA-damaging intermediates formed from these carcinogens is consistent with our present understanding of cancer induction as a process which requires multiple genetic changes. Thus, it is completely plausible that the continual barrage of DNA damage produced by tobacco smoke carcinogens causes the multiple genetic changes that are associated with lung cancer. While each dose of carcinogen from a cigarette is extremely small, the cumulative damage produced in years of smoking will be substantial.

Aspects of the scheme illustrated in **Figure 4** are well understood for PAHs and NNK. A great deal is known about the metabolic activation and detoxification of these compounds. There is a good general understanding of the mechanisms by which they interact with DNA to form adducts and considerable information is available about the repair, persistence and miscoding properties of these adducts. There are many aspects of these processes that require further study, however. In particular, little is known about the levels, persistence, and repair of specific carcinogen DNA adducts in the lungs of smokers or the effects of chronic smoking on these factors. The location of carcinogen adducts at specific sites in human DNA has not been studied, mainly owing to limitations on sensitivity. Nevertheless, one can reasonably conclude that metabolically activated tobacco smoke carcinogens directly cause mutations observed in tumour-suppressor genes and oncogenes, although details remain elusive since numerous DNA-damaging agents in tobacco smoke cause similar mutations. (See also chapter *The Formation of DNA Adducts*.)

CHEMOPREVENTION OF TOBACCO-RELATED CANCER

Avoidance of tobacco products is clearly the best way to prevent tobacco-related cancers. Smoking cessation programmes have enjoyed some success in this regard, particularly with the advent of the nicotine patch. Political pressure, especially related to the potentially harmful effects of environmental tobacco smoke, has also had an impact on decreasing smoking. However, approximately 25% of the adult population in the USA continues to smoke, and many of these people are addicted to nicotine. For the addicted smoker who has failed smoking cessation, and for the ex-smoker, chemoprevention may be a way to reduce the risk for cancer (Hecht, 1998b). Chemoprevention involves administration of a non-toxic agent capable of blocking or reversing any of the steps illustrated in **Figure 4**.

Chemoprevention of lung cancer and other tobacco-related cancers in humans is attractive because epidemiological studies have consistently demonstrated a protective effect of vegetables and fruits against these cancers (Hecht, 1998b). This indicates that there are compounds in vegetables and fruits which can inhibit carcinogenesis by NNK, PAHs and other carcinogens. There are already a substantial number of compounds that have been shown to inhibit lung carcinogenesis induced by NNK and BaP in rats and mice, and many of these are naturally occurring (Hecht, 1998b). Phenethyl isothiocyanate (PEITC) is a relatively nontoxic compound which occurs in cruciferous vegetables as a thioglucoside conjugate. It is released upon chewing of the vegetable. PEITC is an effective inhibitor of lung cancer induced by NNK in both rats and mice (Hecht, 1998b). Its major mode of action is inhibition of metabolic activation of NNK by selectively inhibiting cytochrome CYP enzymes of the lung. PEITC does not inhibit carcinogenesis by BaP, but a related naturally occurring isothiocyanate, benzyl isothiocyanate (BITC), is a good inhibitor of BaP-induced lung tumorigenesis in mice (Hecht, 1998b). Other isothiocyanates are known inhibitors of tumour development at other sites. Notable among these is sulforaphane, a constituent of broccoli.

Some of the other compounds which have been shown to inhibit lung carcinogenesis by NNK include butylated hydroxyanisole, an antioxidant used in food preservation, (+)-limonene, a constituent of orange juice and other citrus products, and diallyl sulfide, a constituent of garlic. Inhibition of NNK carcinogenesis has also been observed in animals treated with green and black tea, as well as its major polyphenolic constituents. Inhibitors of lung tumorigenesis induced by BaP include β-naphthoflavone, butylated hydroxyanisole, ethoxyquin, diallyl sulfide and *myo*-inositol. It seems likely that properly designed combinations of some of these inhibitors will be effective chemopreventive agents against lung cancer in humans.

A number of human trials are already in progress, and several of these have centred on β-carotene as a potential chemopreventive agent for lung cancer. The results have not been encouraging, as β-carotene had an enhancing effect on lung cancer, and vitamin E and a combination of β-carotene and vitamin E had no inhibitory effect (Hecht, 1998b). However, it should be noted that animal studies have not demonstrated efficacy against lung cancer for these two agents. In future trials, it will be important to select chemopreventive agents carefully based on their effectiveness in animal studies and on known mechanisms of action that would be applicable to smokers and ex-smokers. In addition, subjects may need to be selected based on intermediate biomarker profiles and smoking history.

CONCLUSION

The sheer magnitude of the tobacco and cancer problem is difficult to grasp because the numbers are so large. While significant progress has been made in tobacco control, especially in the USA and some other developed countries, the worldwide problem is still immense. Tobacco products cause about 30% of all cancer deaths in developed countries. The epidemic of lung cancer, while possibly starting to abate in the USA and UK, is only beginning to develop fully in other parts of the world such as China. Oral cavity cancer due to tobacco products is a major cause of cancer deaths in parts of Asia. Tobacco products play a significant role as causes of cancers of the upper respiratory and digestive tract, pancreas, bladder and kidney. Three general strategies can be envisioned to decrease tobacco-related cancer death: (1) prevent people from starting to use tobacco; (2) if they do start, find ways to treat their dependence resulting in cessation; and (3) develop ways to decrease the risk of cancer in people who continue to use tobacco products. The first two approaches are likely to be the most effective, but they may not be universally successful. Taking the USA as an example, there has been no change in smoking prevalence since 1990. The third approach depends on an understanding of mechanisms of tobacco-induced cancer, as discussed here. Blocking any of the horizontal steps in **Figure 4** should result in decreased cancer incidence. This can potentially be achieved by identifying particularly susceptible individuals and by developing effective chemoprevention strategies. Even if these approaches are only partly successful, they would significantly impact overall cancer death rates.

REFERENCES

Blot, W. J. and Fraumeni, J. F. Jr (1996). Cancers of the lung and pleura. In: Schottenfeld, D. and Fraumeni, J. F., Jr (eds), *Cancer Epidemiology and Prevention*. 637–665 (Oxford University Press, New York).

Boffetta, P., *et al.* (1998). Multicenter case-control study of exposure to environmental tobacco smoke and lung cancer in Europe. *Journal of the National Cancer Institute*, **90**, 1440–1450.

Doll, R. (1996). Cancers weakly related to smoking. *British Medical Journal*, **52**, 35–49.

EPA (1992). *Respiratory Health Effects of Passive Smoking: Lung Cancer and Other Disorders*. Report No. EPA/600/6-90/006F. (Environmental Protection Agency. Office of Health and Environmental Assessment, Office of Research and Development, Washington, DC).

Guengerich, F. P. and Shimada, T. (1998). Activation of procarcinogens by human cytochrome P450 enzymes. *Mutation Research*, **400**, 201–213.

Hatsukami, D. K. and Severson, H. H. (1999). Oral spit tobacco: addictions prevention and treatment. *Nicotine and Tobacco Research*, **1**, 21–44.

Hecht, S. S. (1998a). Biochemistry, biology, and carcinogenicity of tobacco-specific *N*-nitrosamines. *Chemical Research in Toxicology*, **11**, 559–603.

Hecht, S. S. (1998b). Cigarette smoking and cancer. In: Rom, W. N. (ed.), *Environmental and Occupational Medicine*. 1479–1499. (Lippincott-Raven, New York).

Hecht, S. S. (1999). Tobacco smoke carcinogens and lung cancer. *Journal of the National Cancer Institute*, **91**, 1194–1210.

Hoffmann, D. and Hecht, S. S. (1990). Advances in tobacco carcinogenesis. In: Cooper, C. S. and Grover, P. L. (eds), *Handbook of Experimental Pharmacology*, 94/I. 63–102 (Springer, Heidelberg).

IARC (1985). Tobacco habits other than smoking: betel quid and areca nut chewing and some related nitrosamines. In: *Monographs on the Evaluation of the Carcinogenic Risk of Chemicals to Humans*, Vol. 37 (International Agency for Research on Cancer, Lyon).

IARC (1986) Tobacco smoking. In: *Monographs on the Evaluation of the Carcinogenic Risk of Chemicals to Humans*, Vol. 38 (International Agency for Research on Cancer, Lyon).

Sekido, Y. *et al.* (1998). Progress in understanding the molecular pathogenesis of human lung cancer. *Biochimica Biophysica Acta*, **1378**, F21–F59.

Shopland, D. R. (1995). Tobacco use and its contribution to early cancer mortality with a special emphasis on cigarette smoking. *Environmental Health Perspectives*, **103** (**supplement 8**), 131–142.

WHO (1997). *Tobacco or Health: A Global Status Report*. 1–48 (World Health Organization, Geneva).

Wynder, E. L. and Hoffmann, D. (1994) Smoking and lung cancer: scientific challenges and opportunities. *Cancer Research*, **54**, 5284–5295.

FURTHER READING

Blot, W. J. and Fraumeni, J. F., Jr (1996) Cancers of the lung and pleura. In: Schottenfeld, D., and Fraumeni, J. F., Jr (eds),

Cancer Epidemiology and Prevention. 637–665 (Oxford University Press, New York).

Hecht, S. S. (1998a). Biochemistry, biology, and carcinogenicity of tobacco-specific *N*-nitrosamines. *Chemical Research in Toxicology*, **11**, 559–603.

Hecht, S. S. (1998b). Cigarette smoking and cancer. In: Rom, W. N. (ed.), *Environmental and Occupational Medicine.* 1479–1499 (Lippincott-Raven, New York).

Hecht, S. S. (1999). Tobacco smoke carcinogens and lung cancer. *Journal of the National Cancer Institute*, **91**, 1194–1210.

IARC (1986). Tobacco smoking. In: *Monographs on the Evaluation of the Carcinogenic Risk of Chemicals to Humans*, Vol. 38 (International Agency for Research on Cancer, Lyon).

Sekido, Y., *et al.* (1998). Progress in understanding the molecular pathogenesis of human lung cancer. *Biochimica Biophysica Acta*, **1378**, F21–F59.

WHO (1997). *Tobacco or Health: A Global Status Report.* 1–48 (World Health Organization, Geneva).

Chapter 30

Occupational Causes of Cancer

Harri Vainio
International Agency for Research on Cancer, Lyon, France

Tony Fletcher
London School of Hygiene and Tropical Medicine, London, UK

Paolo Boffetta
International Agency for Research on Cancer, Lyon, France

C O N T E N T S

HISTORICAL AND CURRENT PATTERNS ON OCCUPATIONAL CANCER RISKS

Exposures encountered at the workplace are a substantial source of cancer, as has been known for over 200 years (Pott, 1775). Occupational cancers were initially detected by clinicians. From early findings of Pott of scrotal cancer among chimney sweeps in 1775 to Creech and Johnson's identification of angiosarcoma of the liver among vinyl chloride workers in 1974, unusual cancer patterns among persons with unusual occupations amounted to sufficient evidence to judge that the occupational exposure had caused the cancer (Creech and Johnson, 1974). Pott was a physician treating chimney sweeps and Creech was a physician who treated vinyl chloride monomer workers. The era of initial identification of occupational cancer by clinicians extended into the last quarter of the twentieth century. The period of formal epidemiological assessment of the occurrence of cancer in relation to workplace exposures started after the Second World War, and knowledge of the occupational and other environmental causes of cancer then grew rapidly in the next few decades. It has been clear for about 20 years that it should be possible to reduce the incidence of cancer in middle and old age by 80–90% (Doll and Peto, 1981); however, the precise means of how to bring about such a large reduction were not known. It might be helpful to recall here that most known occupational carcinogens were identified in the 1950–1970s, with few carcinogens identified later. Cancer hazards in the workplaces in the earlier decades of the twentieth century were substantial, causing, in the extreme case, all the most heavily exposed workers to develop cancer, as occurred in some groups of manufacturers of 2-naphthylamine and benzidine, while coal tar fumes and asbestos were so widespread that many thousands of skin and lung cancers were produced. Although the remainder of these cases are now starting to disappear through elimination of these substances and/or exposure to them, some of the consequences of the earlier exposure are still evident. Most estimates of the burden occupational cancer in industrialized countries are around 5% overall, with higher proportions among subgroups (Doll and Peto, 1981; Tomatis, 1990; Boffetta and Kogevinas, 1999). Mesotheliomas due to exposure to asbestos are typical examples of persisting occupational risks.

The workplace is an environment that provides unusual opportunities for the causation and thus the prevention and control of cancer. Occupational exposures tend to be greater, sometimes by orders of magnitude, than exposures in the general environment. This chapter provides a brief review of the occurrence and causes of occupational cancer based on epidemiological studies in humans and characteristics of occupational exposures. (See also chapter on *Identifying Cancer Causes through Epidemiology*.)

KNOWN AND SUSPECTED OCCUPATIONAL CARCINOGENS

The International Agency for Research on Cancer (IARC) has established, within the framework of its Monographs programme, a set of criteria to evaluate the evidence for carcinogenicity of specific agents. The IARC Monographs programme represents one of the most comprehensive efforts to review cancer data systematically and consistently, and is highly reputed in the scientific community (IARC, 1972–2000). It also has an important impact on national and international occupational cancer control activities. Agents, mixtures and exposure circumstances are evaluated within the IARC Monographs if there is evidence of human exposure, and data on carcinogenicity (either in humans or in experimental animals) are available.

The evaluation of carcinogenicity within the IARC Monographs programme includes several steps. First, the evidence for the induction of cancer in humans, which obviously plays an important role in the identification of human carcinogens, is reviewed and is classified into one of the following categories:

Sufficient evidence of carcinogenicity: a causal relationship has been established between exposure to the agent, mixture or exposure circumstance and human cancer. That is, a positive relationship has been observed between the exposure and cancer in studies in which chance, bias and confounding could be ruled out with reasonable confidence.

Limited evidence of carcinogenicity: a positive association has been observed between exposure to the agent, mixture or exposure circumstance and cancer for which a causal interpretation is considered to be credible, but chance, bias or confounding could not be ruled out with reasonable confidence.

Inadequate evidence of carcinogenicity: the available studies are of insufficient quality, consistency or statistical power to permit a conclusion regarding the presence or absence of a causal association, or no data on cancer in humans are available.

Evidence suggesting lack of carcinogenicity: there are several adequate studies covering the full range of levels of exposure that human beings are known to encounter, which are mutually consistent in not showing a positive association between exposure to the agent and the studied cancer at any observed level of exposure.

Second, studies in which experimental animals (mainly rodents) are exposed chronically to potential carcinogens and examined for evidence of cancer are reviewed and the degree of evidence of carcinogenicity is then classified into categories similar to those used for human data.

Third, data on biological effects in humans and experimental animals that are of particular relevance are reviewed. These may include toxicological, kinetic and metabolic considerations and evidence of DNA binding, persistence of DNA lesions or genetic damage in exposed humans. Toxicological information, such as that on cytotoxicity and regeneration, receptor binding and hormonal and immunological effects, and data on structure–activity relationship are used when considered relevant to the possible mechanism of the carcinogenic action of the agent.

Finally, the body of evidence is considered as a whole, in order to reach an overall evaluation of the carcinogenicity to humans of an agent, mixture or circumstance of exposure. The agent, mixture or exposure circumstance is described according to the wording of one of the following categories:

Group 1: The agent (mixture) is carcinogenic to humans. The exposure circumstance entails exposures that are carcinogenic to humans. This evaluation is mainly reached when the evidence in humans is considered sufficient.

Group 2A: The agent (mixture) is probably carcinogenic to humans. The exposure circumstance entails exposures that are probably carcinogenic to humans. Agents classified in this category are typically experimental carcinogens for which there is either limited epidemiological evidence in humans or mechanistic data suggesting that they also operate in humans.

Group 2B: The agent (mixture) is possibly carcinogenic to humans. The exposure circumstance entails exposures that are possibly carcinogenic to humans. Agents in this group are mainly experimental carcinogens with no or inadequate data in humans.

Group 3: The agent (mixture, exposure circumstance) is not classifiable as to its carcinogenicity to humans. Agents is this category are typically suspected experimental carcinogens with no or inadequate human data.

Group 4: The agent (mixture, exposure circumstance) is probably not carcinogenic to humans. This category includes agents with evidence suggesting lack of carcinogenicity.

At present, 26 chemicals, groups of chemicals and mixtures for which exposures are mostly occupational are established human carcinogens (**Table 1**). Whereas some agents such as asbestos, benzene and heavy metals are currently widely used in many countries, other agents are of mainly historical interest (e.g. mustard gas and 2-naphthylamine).

Twenty-six additional agents are classified as probably carcinogenic to humans (Group 2A): they are listed in **Table 2**, and include exposures that are currently prevalent in many countries, such as formaldehyde and buta-1,3-diene. A large number of important occupational agents are classified as possible human carcinogens (Group 2B), e.g. acetaldehyde, carbon black, chloroform, chlorophenoxy herbicides, DDT, dichloromethane, mineral wools, inorganic lead compounds, polychlorophenols and styrene. The complete list can be found at the IARC website (www.iarc.fr).

The distinction between occupational and environmental carcinogens is not always straightforward. Several of the agents listed in **Tables 1** and **2** are also present in the general environment, although exposure levels tend to be higher at the workplace. This is the case, for example, with 2,3,7,8-TCDD, diesel engine exhaust, radon and asbestos. On the other hand, there are agents that have been evaluated in IARC Group 1 or 2A for which exposure is not primarily occupational, but which are often

Table 1 Agents, groups or agents and mixtures classified as established human carcinogens (IARC group 1) for which exposure is mainly occupational

Exposure	Target organ/cancer	Main industry or use
4-Aminobiphenyl	Bladder	Rubber
Arsenic and arsenic compounds	Lung, skin	Glass, metals, pesticides
Asbestos	Lung, pleura	Insulation, construction
Benzene	Leukaemia	Solvent, fuel
Benzidine	Bladder	Pigment
Beryllium and beryllium compounds	Lung	Aerospace, metals
Bis(chloromethyl) ether[a]	Lung	Chemical
Chloromethyl methyl ether[a]	Lung	Chemical
Cadmium and cadmium compounds	Lung	Pigment, battery
Chromium(VI) compounds	Nasal cavity, lung	Metal plating, pigment
Coal-tar pitches	Skin, lung, bladder	Construction, electrodes
Coal-tars	Skin, lung	Fuel
Ethylene oxide	Leukaemia	Chemical, sterilant
Mineral oils, untreated and mildly treated	Skin	Lubricant
Mustard gas (sulfur mustard)[a]	Pharynx, lung	War gas
2-Naphthylamine[a]	Bladder	Pigment
Nickel compounds	Nasal cavity, lung	Metal, alloy
Radon and its decay products	Lung	Mining
Shale-oils	Skin	Lubricant, fuel
Silica, crystalline (inhaled in the form of quartz or cristobalite)	Lung	Construction, mining
Soots	Skin, lung	Pigment
Strong inorganic acid mists containing sulfuric acid	Larynx, lung	Chemical
Talc containing asbestiform fibres	Lung	Paper, paint
2,3,7,8-Tetrachlorodibenzo-p-dioxin	Several	Chemical
Vinyl chloride	Liver	Plastic
Wood dust	Nasal cavity	Wood

[a]Agent mainly of historical interest.

encountered in the occupational environment. They include the following:

- drugs, such as cyclophosphamide, combined chemotherapy including alkylating agents such as MOPP, and cyclosporin: occupational exposure can occur in pharmacies and during their administration by nursing staff;
- food contaminants, such as aflatoxins, to which food processors can be exposed;
- biological agents, such as hepatitis B virus, hepatitis C virus and human immunodeficiency virus, to which medical personnel can be exposed;
- environmental agents, in particular solar radiation (exposure in agriculture, fishing and other outdoor occupations);
- environmental tobacco smoke, deriving from smoking by fellow employees or by the public in bars, restaurants and other public settings.

Polycyclic aromatic hydrocarbons (PAHs) represent a specific problem in the identification of occupational carcinogens. This group of chemicals include several potent experimental carcinogens, such as benzo[a]pyrene, benz[a]anthracene and dibenz[a,h]anthracene. However, humans are always exposed to mixtures of PAHs (several of which are listed in **Tables 1** and **2**, e.g. coal-tars,

soots, creosotes) and an assessment of the carcinogenicity of individual PAHs in humans cannot be done at present.

Current understanding of the relationship between occupational exposures and cancer is far from complete; in fact, only 26 individual agents are established occupational carcinogens (**Table 1**) and for many more experimental carcinogens no definitive evidence is available from exposed workers. In some cases, there is considerable evidence of increased risks associated with particular industries and occupations, although no specific agents can be identified as aetiological factors. **Table 3** reports occupations and industries which entail (or are suspected to entail) a carcinogenic risk on the basis of the IARC Monograph programme.

Constructing and interpreting lists of chemical or physical carcinogenic agents and associating them with specific occupations and industries is complicated by a number of factors: (1) information on industrial processes and exposures is frequently poor, not allowing a complete evaluation of the importance of specific carcinogenic exposures in different occupations or industries; (2) exposures to well-known carcinogenic agents, such as vinyl chloride and benzene, occur at different intensities in different occupational situations; (3) changes in exposure

Table 2 Agents, groups or agents and mixtures classified as probable human carcinogens (IARC group 2A) for which exposure is primarily occupational

Exposure	Suspected target organ/cancer	Main industry or use
Acrylamide	–	Plastic
Benzidine-based dyes	Bladder	Pigment, leather
Buta-1,3-diene	Leukaemia	Plastic, rubber
Captafol	–	Pesticide
α-Chlorinated toluenes (benzal chloride, benzotrichloride, benzyl chloride, benzoyl chloride)	–	Pigment, chemical
p-Chloro-o-toluidine	Bladder	Pigment, textile
Creosotes	Skin	Wood
Diesel engine exhaust	Lung	Transport, mining
Diethyl sulfate	–	Chemical
Dimethylcarbamoyl chloride	–	Chemical
1,2-Dimethylhydrazine	–	Research
Dimethyl sulfate	–	Chemical
Epichlorohydrin	–	Plastic
Ethylene dibromide	–	Fumigant
Formaldehyde	Nasopharynx	Plastic, textile
Methyl methane-sulfonate	–	Chemical
4,4'-Methylenebis2-chloroaniline (MOCA)	Bladder	Rubber
Non-arsenical insecticides	Leukaemia	Agriculture
Polychlorinated biphenyls	Liver, lymphoma	Electrical components
Styrene-7,8-oxide	–	Plastic
Tetrachloroethylene	Oesophagus, lymphoma	Solvent
Trichloroethylene	Liver, kidney lymphoma	Solvent, dry cleaning
Trichloropropane	–	Solvent
Tris(2,3-dibromopropyl) phosphate	–	Plastic, textile
Vinyl bromide	–	Plastic, textile
Vinyl fluoride	–	Chemical

Table 3 Industrial processes and occupations evaluated in IARC Monographs Volumes 1–78 (IARC 1972–2001)

Industry/occupation	Target organs/cancer[a]
Group 1	
Aluminium production	Lung, bladder
Auramine manufacture	Bladder
Boot and shoe manufacture and repair	Nasal cavity, leukaemia
Coal gasification	Skin, lung, bladder
Coke production	Skin, lung, kidney
Furniture and cabinet making	Nasal cavity
Haematite mining (underground) with exposure to radon	Lung
Iron and steel founding	Lung
Magenta manufacture	Bladder
Painter	Lung
Propan-2-ol manufacture (strong-acid process)	Nasal cavity
Rubber industry	Bladder, leukaemia
Group 2A	
Art glass, glass containers and pressed ware, manufacture of	(Lung, stomach)
Hairdressers or barbers	(Bladder, lung)
Petroleum refining	(Leukaemia, skin)
Group 2B	
Carpentry and joinery	(Nasal cavity)
Dry cleaning	(Oesophagus, bladder)
Printing processes	(Lung, bladder)
Textile manufacturing industry	(Nasal cavity, bladder)

[a]Suspected target organs are given in parentheses.

occur over time in a given occupational situation, either because identified carcinogenic agents are replaced by other agents or (more frequently) because new industrial processes or materials are introduced; and (4) any list of occupational exposures can only refer to the relatively small number of chemical exposures which have been investigated with respect to the presence of a carcinogenic risk. (See also chapter on *Mechanisms of Chemical Carcinogenesis*.)

ESTIMATES OF THE BURDEN OF CANCER ATTRIBUTABLE TO OCCUPATION

It is instructive to estimate the number of cancers that might be prevented by avoiding workplace exposure to carcinogens. In practice this is most readily estimated in terms of the number of cancers which can be attributed to past exposures to workplace carcinogens. Estimating the total proportion of cancers attributable to occupation involves some extrapolation, and there are essentially two approaches which may be taken. One method draws on studies of specific occupational groups (usually 'cohort studies') in which the numbers of attributable cases can be estimated. Along with some estimate of the total number of exposed workers, the total burden can thus be estimated. This approach is somewhat uncertain as there is usually very limited quantitative information on the extent and level of exposure across occupational groups collected in a comparable way to the specific epidemiological studies from which risk estimates derive.

A more satisfactory approach is to estimate the attributable fraction directly from case control studies in communities. This fraction is, of course, specific to the community where the study was conducted, but if there are a number of such studies which can be synthesized, then a global estimate may be made. There are now a wealth of occupational case-control studies and the proportions summarized here derive from these types of studies.

The sites of cancer which contribute most numbers to the estimated burden of occupational cancer include mesothelioma, lung, bladder, sinonasal and laryngeal cancers. Estimated burdens in terms of the proportions of cases attributable to occupation are summarized here.

Mesothelioma

Pleural mesothelioma death rates are rising in several European countries where surveillance is most effective, in particular Finland, UK and The Netherlands. Extrapolation of current trends suggests that death rates will continue to rise, reaching a peak around 2018, before falling again. Asbestos is the overwhelming cause of mesothelioma and the proportion attributable to asbestos may be considered to be over 80%. Some of these are not directly occupational (e.g. children exposed while living adjacent to asbestos factories or family members exposed to dust brought home by asbestos workers), but most are due to occupational exposures. As a proportion of cancers, the approximately 1200 per year in the UK amount to about 0.5% of all cancers per annum and this is expected to rise to 2% of cancers at the mortality peak in 20–30 years time. In terms of absolute numbers it has been projected that asbestos-related mesothelioma deaths will amount to 250 000 in total in Western Europe alone over the next 35 years (Albin et al., 1999; Peto et al., 1999).

Lung Cancer

Case control studies in different communities show a range of estimates of proportions of lung cancers attributable to known occupational carcinogens. Two recent studies have looked at very large populations to overcome the small numbers inherent in individual studies. One is a four-country analysis of the entire Nordic population followed prospectively for cancer incidence from the 1970 censuses, and using exposures inferred from the occupation reported at the census. From this, 18% of male lung cancers and <1% of female lung cancers are attributed to occupational exposures. This compares with an estimate derived from a reanalysis of eight case-control studies in five European countries of 13% for male cancers and 3% for females. Both values are close to the earlier estimate for the USA of 15% for males, although lower than that estimate of 5% for females. Overall, an estimate of 15% for males and

2–3% for females would seem reasonable (Doll and Peto, 1981; Vineis and Simonato, 1991; Boffetta and Kogevinas, 1999).

Bladder

For cancer of the bladder, a pooled reanalysis of 11 case control studies of occupational risks for males found an overall attributable fraction for known occupational risks of 4%. The Nordic study found 2%. These are both somewhat lower than the 10% estimated by Doll and Peto (1981) for the USA. For females, both studies estimated the attributable fractions overall as very low.

Sinonasal Cancers

While most adenocarcinomas of the nose are caused by occupational exposures, the attributable fraction for all sinonasal cancers together is estimated as 30–41% for males by the Nordic and European pooled reanalysis of eight case control studies, respectively. For females the results are less consistent, with the equivalent estimates being 2% and 7% of all sinonasal cancers.

Laryngeal Cancers

The attributable fraction for laryngeal cancers together is estimated as 6–8% for males by the Nordic and European pooled reanalysis of six case control studies. For females, the attributable fraction was close to zero in both cases.

In summary, estimates for Europe of the proportion of cancers attributable to occupation varies between cancer site, from close to 100% for mesothelioma, close to 50% for sinonasal cancers among males, around 15% for male lung cancer and a little under 10% for larynx and bladder cancer, again among males. For females the risks are generally lower (apart from mesothelioma, which as for males is attributable entirely to asbestos), with attributable fractions under 1% except for lung cancer, which is around 1–2%, and sinonasal cancer, between 2 and 7%. For most other cancer sites, the attributable fractions calculated in this way are lower. Summing across all sites to estimate the total proportion of cancers which may be attributable to occupational exposures has led to estimates around 5%.

Cigarette smoking has been dealt with to an extent in these studies, in that in virtually all of them active smoking was assessed in cases and controls and controlled for in the analysis. However, in most cases these studies were conducted before awareness had grown about environmental tobacco smoke (ETS), and they focused on other occupational carcinogens. Thus, if the contribution of ETS exposure at the workplace were included, the attributable fraction of workplace exposures would need to be revised upwards, especially for lung cancer. As tobacco cessation programmes at workplaces are a relatively recent phenomenon, the health impact of ETS exposure at work will take some years before its impact on occupational cancers will have waned.

Recent studies of occupational cancer estimate the burden on current disease of past exposures. The burden on future disease due to current exposure would be expected to fall in countries where controls on occupational carcinogens have been successful. However, estimates of the total numbers of workers exposed to carcinogens at work remain high. Recent work carried out in the European Union to estimate these numbers has led to a European database on occupational exposures in the workplace, CAREX (available at http://www.occuphealth.fi/list/data/CAREX/). This is based on a systematic estimate in each country of the numbers of employees exposed to a defined list of established carcinogens at work. The grand total is 32 million, representing 23% of the working population, estimated for the early 1990s. The most important contributions come from solar radiation (from working outdoors) and environmental tobacco smoke (8.8 and 7.1 million exposed, respectively), followed by more classical occupational pollutants such as silica, diesel exhaust, radon decay products and wood dust (about 3 million each). These are very substantial numbers, emphasizing the remaining scope for primary prevention.

Outside Europe, the burden of occupational cancer may be different. Recent epidemiological studies of occupational cancer risk in developing countries revealed situations where exposures and risks might be much higher than currently found in Northern countries (Kogevinas et al., 1994). Some carcinogens are being substantially phased out, in some but not all countries. For example, asbestos use in Europe has fallen dramatically over the last 20 years and is now negligible in some countries, e.g. 0.004 kg per person per year in the Nordic countries in 1996, although in other countries consumption remains high, e.g. 2.4 kg per person per year in the former Soviet Union in 1996 (Albin et al., 1999). Therefore, the proportions of cancers attributable to occupation estimated above for Europe would underestimate the proportions in more poorly regulated developing country contexts.

PREVENTION OF OCCUPATIONAL CANCER

Primary prevention of occupational cancer is defined as aetiological prevention – prevention is directed against the source of the disease. Primary prevention contrasts with later (secondary and tertiary) forms of prevention that involve, respectively, the early detection of disease and treatment of disease to prevent death and reduce disability. Primary prevention is inherently more effective than secondary and tertiary prevention. Several avenues exist for the prevention of occupational cancer.

Legal Initiatives

Restriction of the use of carcinogens at the workplace, after they have been identified, is the simplest but bluntest tool available for risk reduction. Banning the use of a substance has been successfully used with occupational carcinogens.

Regulation is different from restriction. Regulation requires that anyone who deals with the substance should keep to certain minimum standards to minimize the exposure and consequently the toxic effects. Known carcinogens are strictly regulated at workplaces, through standards, at least in industrialized countries.

Industrial Hygiene

Industrial hygiene, workplace technology and general knowledge on the safety issues have been continuously improving in industrialized countries over the last 30 years. As a consequence, exposures in the workplace are now less intense than in the past. However, the possibility of low-level exposures exists, sometimes to a multitude of chemicals or mixtures of chemicals with possibilities for various types of interactions.

The most efficient of the industrial hygiene tools is the substitution of a new, less hazardous material for a material of known carcinogenicity. It is important, however, to ensure the new material is indeed less hazardous than that which is replaces. Other approaches include process enclosure or isolation, or use of ventilation.

Use of Personal Protective Equipment

Respirators, gloves and other forms of protective clothing are all common forms of protective equipment in use throughout industry. They can be important in reducing carcinogenic exposures provided that carefully designed equipment is in use and that equipment is properly used and maintained.

Cancer Surveillance and Monitoring at the Workplace

Biological monitoring and medical screening of workers uses information from health history and results from periodical physical and laboratory examinations to estimate the levels of exposure and to assess the early health effects. Surveillance of workers is useful for identifying unforeseen hazards and to protect workers who are at increased risk – with the idea of detecting the cancer in its presymptomatic stages when it still can be controlled or cured. Screening for occupational cancer in exposed populations for purposes of early diagnosis is rarely applied, but has been tested in some situations. Medical surveillance of populations at risk of getting cancer is only effective in the following situations: (1) if the screening test is easy to perform and sensitive, (2) if it detects pre-malignant abnormalities or tumours at an early stage and (3) if there is an effective intervention that reduces morbidity and mortality when applied to early tumours.

Cancer surveillance at the workplace has been explored, e.g., for bladder cancer among people exposed to 2-napthylamine and to benzidine, and for lung cancer among workers exposed to asbestos. Chest X-rays, cytology and urinalysis have been proposed (Schulte *et al.*, 1990). Urine cytology has good sensitivity and specificity for invasive bladder cancer, but no survival advantage has been demonstrated. Also, chest X-rays and cytological examination of sputum has not reduced mortality from lung cancer significantly. Judgments on the value of screening depend also on the intensity of exposure: it may be more justified in small groups exposed to high levels of carcinogens than among large groups exposed to low levels.

PROSPECTS FOR CANCER PREVENTION

In the future, new technology and molecular biomarkers (of exposure, effect and susceptibility) promise to revolutionize the practice of cancer prevention and provide new tools for screening and prevention of occupational cancer. Lung cancer remains the leading cause of death from cancer, and recent developments have generated substantial interest in the use of spiral computed tomography (CT) to screen for lung cancer. The use of lung cancer biomarkers to identify the early clonal phase of progression of lung cancer in high-risk populations has also been proposed, enabling cancers to be detected earlier than is possible with spiral CT, since the latter is not as sensitive for small central cancers as it is for small peripheral cancers. A hybrid CT–biomarker approach may improve the robustness with which lung cancer of any type can be detected early (Mulshine and Henschke, 2000). The high-risk populations screened for lung cancer will generally include large numbers of people who share risks of other, possibly coexisting, smoking- and/or asbestos-related disorders. Spiral CT is being used routinely in the investigation of emphysema and asbestosis. Simultaneous screening for coexisting disorders would be of great public health value. A rational integrated use of spiral CT and biomarkers in lung cancer screening is a research priority. However, for the purposes of practical prevention at workplaces, the avoidance of exposure remains the main and the primary means for occupational cancer prevention.

REFERENCES

Albin, M., *et al.* (1999). Asbestos and cancer: an overview of current trends in Europe. *Environmental Health Perspectives*, **107**, Suppl. 2, 289–298.

Boffetta, P. and Kogevinas, M. (1999). Introduction: epidemiologic research and prevention of occupational cancer in Europe. *Environmental Health Perspectives*, **107**, Suppl. 2, 229–231.

Creech, J. L. Jr and Johnson, M. N. (1974). Angiosarcoma of liver in the manufacture of polyvinyl chloride. *Journal of Occupational Medicine*, **16**, 150–151.

Doll, R. and Peto, R. (1981). The causes of cancer: quantitative estimates of avoidable risks of cancer in the United States today. *Journal of the National Cancer Institute*, **66**, 1191–1308.

IARC (1972–2000). *IARC Monographs on the Evaluation of Carcinogenic Risks to Humans*, Vols 1–78 (International Agency for Research on Cancer, Lyon).

Kogevinas, M., *et al.* (1994). *Occupational Exposure to Carcinogens in Developing Countries*. IARC Scientific Publication No. 129. 63–95 (International Agency for Research on Cancer, Lyon).

Mulshine, J. L. and Henschke, C. L. (2000). Prospects for lung-cancer screening. *Lancet*, **355**, 592–593.

Peto, J., *et al.* (1999). The European mesothelioma epidemic. *British Journal of Cancer*, **79**, 666–672.

Pott, P. (1775). *Chronological Observations Relative to the Cataract, the Polypus of the Nose, the Cancer of the Scrotum, the Different Kinds of Ruptures, and the Mortification of the Toes and Feet* (Clarke and Collins, London).

Schulte, P., *et al.* (1990). Final discussion: where do we go from here? *Journal of Occupational Medicine*, **32**, 936–945.

Tomatis, L. (1990). *Cancer: Causes, Occurrence and Control*. IARC Scientific Publication No. 100 (International Agency for Research on Cancer, Lyon).

Vineis, P. and Simonato, L. (1991). Proportion of lung and bladder cancers in males resulting from occupation: a systematic approach. *Archives of Environmental Health*, **46**, 6–15.

FURTHER READING

Andersen, A., *et al.* (1999). Work-related cancer in the Nordic countries. *Scandinavian Journal of Work and Environmental Health*, **25**, Suppl. 2, 1–116.

Boffetta, P. and Merler, E. (1999). Occupational cancer in Europe. *Environmental Health Perspectives*, **107**, Suppl. 2, 227–298.

Boffetta, P., *et al.* (1998). Occupational carcinogens. In: Stellman, J. M. (ed.), *Encyclopedia of Occupational Health and Safety*, 4th edn, Vol 1, 2.4–2.8 (International Labour Office, Geneva).

Stellman, J. M. and Stellman, S. D. (1996). Cancer and the workplace. *CA Cancer Journal for Clinicians*, **46**, 70–92.

Websites

http://www.occuphealth.fi/list/data/CAREX/. Exposure information on occupational carcinogens.

http://www.monographs.iarc.fr/. Information about carcinogens.

Chapter 31

Antigenotoxins and Cancer

Wilbert H. M. Peters and Esther M. M. van Lieshout
St Radboud University Hospital, Nijmegen, The Netherlands

CONTENTS

- Introduction
- Antigenotoxins
- Test systems for Antigenotoxins
- Mechanisms by which Antigenotoxins may Act
- Different Classes of Antigenotoxins
- Conclusions and Future Perspectives

INTRODUCTION

It is now widely accepted that the bulk of all cancer is related to environmental factors such as lifestyle practices; smoking, dietary habits, physical exercise, etc. In addition, cancer is one of the degenerative diseases of old age and increases dramatically with age. In a minority of cases, varying between 5 and 30%, depending on the type of cancer, genetic factors may contribute to cancer development, and in certain rare forms of human cancer hereditary factors play a decisive role. Now that such knowledge is becoming increasingly available, it is encouraging that theoretically most cancers could be prevented. Recent (epidemiological) studies have identified many factors that are likely to reduce cancer rates, and many others will follow. Therefore, prevention of cancer is the main goal for many researchers and clinicians in this new era (Anonymous, 1999).

The first method of choice in cancer prevention is to reduce exposure to potentially DNA-damaging sources by changing the lifestyle with respect to smoking, sun exposure, physical activity, diet, etc. Dietary factors alone have been estimated to account for approximately 30% of cancer risk, especially for cancers of the gastrointestinal tract. Two different types of dietary factors should be clearly discerned: those which initiate or promote carcinogenesis and those which are preventive against cancer. Of course, our diet should be formulated such that the latter substances dominate. Therefore, it is of utmost importance to gain more knowledge about both types of factors in order to be able eventually to modify our diets in favour of preventive substances and thus reduce cancer incidence in the future. In this chapter we will focus on factors (antigenotoxins) that are preventive in carcinogenesis.

According to the stage in the carcinogenic process at which they are effective, Wattenberg (1985) classified preventive compounds into three different categories: (1) compounds that prevent the formation of carcinogens, (2) compounds that inhibit carcinogenesis by preventing carcinogens from reaching and reacting with critical targets such as DNA (these inhibitors were called 'blocking agents') and (3) compounds acting subsequent to exposure to carcinogens. These compounds appear to inhibit the carcinogenic process after initiation, and were called 'suppressing agents' since they act by suppressing neoplasia in the exposed tissues. In **Table 1** some examples of these three classes of inhibitors are shown.

Before a normal cell is transformed into a cancer cell, it has to be irreversibly damaged, e.g. by a genotoxin. A genotoxic substance can be defined as a compound that is damaging to DNA and thereby may cause a mutation or cancer. Consequently, an antigenotoxin prevents or restores damage to DNA, and therefore substances stimulating DNA repair mechanisms may also be considered as antigenotoxins. In a strict sense, 'suppressing agents' should be called anticarcinogens rather than antigenotoxins. However, since the mechanism of many anticarcinogens, compounds preventing cancer, is still unclear, we will use the words antigenotoxin and anticarcinogen interchangeably. Adding to this complexity is the occurrence of species and test system dependences with respect to antigenotoxic properties of a certain compound, i.e. a particular substance has antigenotoxic characteristics in test system A but not in test system B; it will still be denoted an antigenotoxin. Several test systems derived from a variety of species will be discussed later.

ANTIGENOTOXINS

Antigenotoxins can be divided into endogenous and exogenous antigenotoxins according to whether they can be formed somewhere in the human body or are taken up from outside, such as food constituents or food additives.

Table 1   Inhibitors of carcinogen-induced neoplasias. (Adapted from Wattenberg, 1985.)

Category of inhibitor	Chemical class	Inhibitory compound
Compounds preventing formation of carcinogen	Reductive agents	Vitamin C[a]
	Tocopherols	α-Tocopherol[a], γ-tocopherol[a]
	Phenols	Caffeic acid[a], ferulic acid[a], gallic acid[a]
Blocking agents	Phenols	t-Butylhydroxyanisole[b], butylated hydroxytoluene[b], ellagic acid[a], caffeic acid[a], ferulic acid[a]
	Indoles	Indole-3-acetonitrile[a], indole-3-carbinol[a]
	Coumarins	Coumarin[a], limettin[a]
	Flavones	Quercetin[a], rutin[a], catechin[a]
	Aromatic isothiocyanates	Benzyl isothiocyanate[a], phenyl isothiocyanate[a]
	Dithiolthiones	Oltipraz[b]
Suppressing agents	Retinoids and carotenoids	Retinyl palmitate[a], retinyl acetate[a], β-carotene[a]
	Protease inhibitors	Soybean protease inhibitors[a]
	Inhibitors of arachidonic acid metabolism	Indomethacin[b], aspirin[b]
	Phenols	t-Butylhydroxyanisole[b],
	Methylated xanthines	Caffeine[a]
	Plant sterols	β-Sitosterol[a]
	Selenium salts	Sodium selenite[a], selenium dioxide[a], selenious acid[a]

[a]Naturally occurring compound present in food or formed during digestion.
[b]Synthetic compound.

Endogenous Antigenotoxins

Evidence is increasing that DNA damage can occur as a result of normal cellular functions. There are three main sources of DNA damage. (1) many cellular processes require or consume oxygen. Sometimes oxygen and other small molecules such as hydroxyl (OH) groups become electron deficient and may escape normal cellular pathways such as those of the respiratory chain, and these oxygen radicals can react with DNA and may cause mutations or cancer. (2) A second very important source of oxygen radicals in the body is the normal burst of free radicals generated by neutrophils, in order to kill bacteria, viruses, etc., entering the body, as part of the normal defence against such intruders. (3) In the normal metabolism of endogenous or exogenous molecules, often very reactive metabolites are formed intracellular by cytochrome P450-mediated reactions. Sometimes such metabolites may be mutagenic or carcinogenic and need to be further metabolized or detoxified by appropriate endogenous systems.

Most organisms have endogenous systems that prevent DNA damage caused by mechanisms as mentioned above. Such systems and their enhancers may belong to the class of antigenotoxins.

Some endogenous antigenotoxins, as outlined above, often have antioxidant or radical-scavenging properties.

These can be relatively simple molecules or very complex proteins or enzyme systems. (See also chapter on *Mechanisms of Chemical Carcinogenesis*.)

Simple Molecules

Relative simple endogenous molecules with antioxidant and potential antigenotoxic properties include the metabolites uric acid, porphyrins and bilirubin. The most important endogenous antigenotoxin, however, is probably the tripeptide glutathione and to a lesser extent other thiols such as cysteine and cysteinylglycine. These molecules are able to scavenge free radicals or other oxidative compounds directly. In addition, glutathione is an important cofactor in many enzymatic detoxification reactions.

Complex Molecules

More complex endogenous antigenotoxins include the proteins or enzymes that are involved in the rapid detoxification of reactive metabolites resulting from oxidative stress or from phase I enzyme-mediated reactions (cytochrome P450). Important enzymes are glutathione peroxidase, glutathione S-transferase (GST), catalase and superoxide dismutase, but many others can also be involved.

Exogenous Antigenotoxins

Exogenous antigenotoxins can be divided into synthetic and naturally occurring substances present in food or food constituents or additives.

Synthetic Antigenotoxins

Most antigenotoxins are taken up via consumption of food, and more especially from fruit and vegetables as part of the diet. Recently however, synthetic antigenotoxins such as nonsteroidal anti-inflammatory drugs (NSAIDs) such as aspirin, indomethacin, sulindac and oltipraz have been recognized. Also food supplements in the form of tablets containing vitamins, minerals, trace elements and other additives can be included in this group. NSAIDs have been shown to prevent the growth and formation of colon adenomas or carcinomas in several epidemiological and intervention studies. The mechanism of this protective effect may be very complex and multifactorial but enhancement of detoxification enzymes by NSAIDs was evident. Oltipraz, which is both an inhibitor of activating systems and an enhancer of detoxification enzymes, was shown to have strong antigenotoxic potential by preventing aflatoxin B_1-induced DNA damage (**Figure 1**). Aflatoxin B_1 is a fungal toxin, thought to be the cause of many liver cancers in China and other parts of the world.

Naturally Occurring Antigenotoxins from Food

From epidemiological studies it has now been firmly established that individuals who consume diets rich in fruits and vegetables have a reduced cancer risk (Steinmetz and Potter, 1991). Many chemical substances from fruits and vegetables with antigenotoxic or antimutagenic properties have been identified, but the bulk of the potential anticarcinogens from these sources remain to be identified. Since the mechanism of most of these food-derived anticarcinogens is not known in detail, it cannot be clearly established which compound has purely antigenotoxic properties or is an otherwise cancer-preventive compound, such as a stimulator of apoptosis, inhibitor of cell proliferation, inhibitor of metastasis, etc.

Antigenotoxins from fruit and vegetables can be divided into vitamins, minerals and trace elements, and other compounds based on their putative working mechanism.

Vitamins (see Odin, 1997)

Several vitamins have been shown to have antigenotoxic potential, including vitamins A, C, E, B_2, B_6, B_{11} and B_{12}.

Vitamin A (retinol) and its related structures are constituents of many orange- and red-coloured fruits and vegetables. They have shown antigenotoxic properties in many different test systems and experiments, mainly owing to their free radical scavenging properties. However,

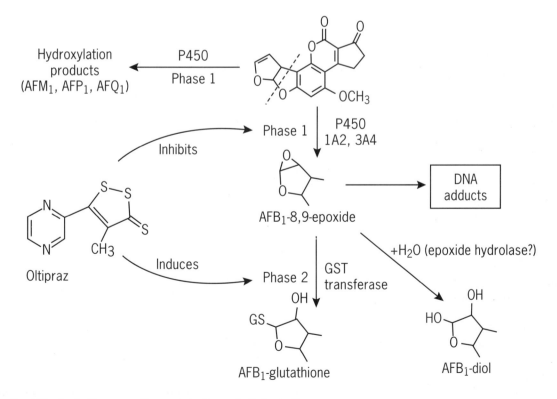

Figure 1   Effect of oltipraz on the metabolism of aflatoxin B_1.

it should be mentioned that vitamin A and other retinoids appear to have genotoxic properties, as was shown in some test systems. In addition, high doses of vitamin A may be toxic owing to hepatic storage, and these latter properties may possibly explain the disappointing results so far in cancer chemoprevention trials using high doses of this vitamin (see the chapter *Intervention and Chemoprevention of Cancer*).

Vitamin C or ascorbic acid is also a constituent of many fruits and vegetables. In analogy with vitamin A, the anti-genotoxic properties of vitamin C are mainly due to the scavenging of radicals, and high concentrations have also been to have mutagenic properties in some test systems. It is now generally accepted that this water-soluble vitamin is beneficial unless very high doses (up to 10 g daily) are consumed.

Vitamin E. The fat-soluble vitamin E is a naturally occurring mixture of several tocol derivatives among which α-tocopherol is the most biologically active. The basic function of vitamin E in all living organisms is as an antioxidant in protection against oxidative damage of hydrophobic molecules or structures, generated either by free radicals or by radical-inducing radiation. Thus, by preventing radical-induced damage, vitamin E was shown to be an antimutagen or antigenotoxin in many experimental studies.

Folic acid or vitamin B_{11}. Dietary factors which directly influence methyl group availability, in particular folic acid and the essential amino acid methionine, may also be associated with cancer incidence. Folic acid, which is a component of many green vegetables such as beans, spinach and Brussels sprouts, appears to be an important antigenotoxin. Several epidemiological studies have shown that people consuming large amounts of folic acid are better protected against cancer of the colon and possibly also of the smoking-related cancers of the lungs, head and neck area than people with a low intake (Glynn and Albanes, 1994). Folic acid is an essential factor in a number of critical pathways in the cell that involves the transfer of one-carbon groups, such as methyl groups, e.g. in the biosynthesis of DNA building blocks. In this way folic acid plays a key role in DNA replication and cell division and sufficient levels of folate do prevent mutations in DNA and thus may prevent cancer.

Vitamin B_2 or riboflavin has been shown to prevent binding of metabolically activated and highly carcinogenic aflatoxins to DNA. It also inhibits the damaging or mutagenic effects of irradiation or cigarette smoke condensate in *in vitro* test systems.

Vitamins B_6 and B_{12} have an important role in the conversion of homocysteine into methionine and in other steps of the folate metabolism pathway, ultimately leading to an optimal supply of methyl groups, which is essential for prevention of DNA damage.

Minerals and Trace Elements

Minerals such as calcium and phosphorus and trace elements such as zinc, selenium and molybdenum have important functions in the synthesis of biomolecules and tissue structures, and are essential in numerous cellular and enzymatic processes. Antigenotoxic properties of these minerals and trace elements have attracted little attention. In many studies, however, deficiencies of the trace element selenium have been associated with an increased cancer risk. Since selenium is an essential component of the selenium-dependent glutathione peroxidases, which detoxify highly reactive peroxides and thus may prevent oxidation and damage to DNA, it may be considered an antigenotoxin.

Other Compounds

Most antigenotoxins cannot be categorized into the above-mentioned groups. Several hundred agents have been identified as anticarcinogens with potential antigenotoxic properties, mainly based on data derived from one of the following study categories: (1) basic mechanism; (2) observational studies in laboratory animals; (3) studies in humans; and (4) selective screening systems. With the exception of antipromoter, antiprogression or tumour cell-killing activity, most anticarcinogens are antigenotoxins.

Apart from vitamins and trace elements, plant foods such as fruits, vegetables and cereals contain many bioactive compounds with antigenotoxic properties. Since these constituents do not belong to the classes of proteins, fats or carbohydrates, they are often called non-nutrients, microconstituents, phytochemicals or phytoprotectants. Exogenous antigenotoxins of plant origin can be roughly categorized as follows:

- Sulfides present in the allium vegetables which include onions, garlic and chives.
- Dithiolthiones, which are also sulfur-containing compounds of a more complex structure, are found in cruciferous vegetables such as cauliflower, cabbage and Brussels sprouts.
- Glucosinolates are also found in cruciferous vegetables. During cooking and chewing these glucosinolates are converted into the bioactive metabolites isothiocyanates and indoles.
- Terpenoids such as (+)-limonene, which are components of citrus fruits.
- Phyto-oestrogens including isoflavones and lignans. Isoflavones are found in cereals and pulses such as soy bean. The main dietary sources of lignans are wholegrain products, seeds, fruits and berries.
- Flavonoids such as quercetin, kaempferol, rutin, tangeritin and myricetin are widely distributed in fruits and vegetables. Rich sources are berries, potatoes, tomatoes, onions, broccoli, beans and citrus fruits.
- Other phenols and polyphenols, such as ellagic acid, caffeic acid, ferulic acid, resveratrol are found in nuts, fruits, wine and tea.

4 Inherited Predispositions to Cancer

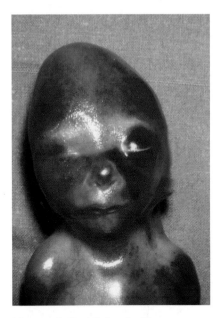

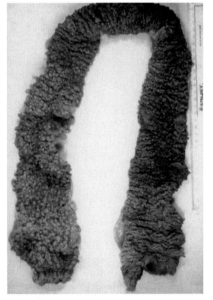

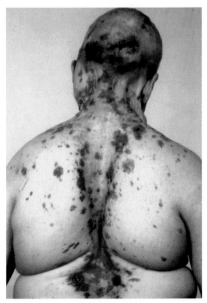

Figure 2 Familial retinoblastoma due to an unbalanced chromosome rearrangement. Retinoblastoma occurring in foetal life.

Figure 3 Colectomy specimen showing multiple adenomatous polyps in a patient with FAP.

Figure 6 Multiple basal cell carcinomas in the periphery of the radiotherapy field in a patient with Gorlin syndrome.

18 Cell Proliferation in Carcinogenesis

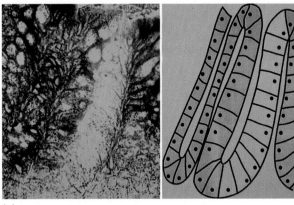

(a)

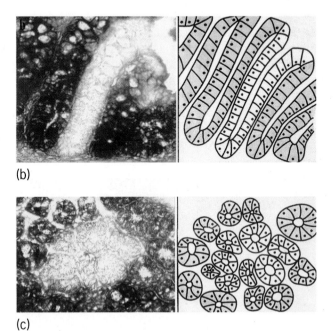

(b)

(c)

Figure 2 Sections from the colon of a mouse treated with a single injection of a mutagen (ethylnitrosourea) and histochemically stained for glucose-6-phosphatase dehydrogenase activity: (a) a partially negative crypt, where only a portion of the crypt is positive, and (b) a wholly negative crypt without any positive cells; (c) a patch of negative-staining crypts. (Figure courtesy of Dr Hyun Sook Park.)

34 Skin

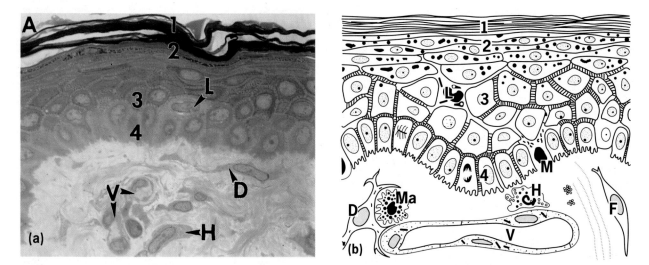

Figure 1 Normal histology of human skin. (a) Light photomicrograph. (b) Schematic representation. The epidermal layer is composed of cells termed keratinocytes and is divided into four strata: 1, the stratum corneum, keratin-filled lamellae which forms the surface scale; 2, the granular cell layer, which gives rise to the stratum corneum; 3, the spinous layer, which accounts for most of the epidermal thickness and which is recapitulated by many squamous cell carcinomas; and 4, the most primitive, basal cell layer, which provides cell division and, along with similar basal cells in the hair bulb, is recapitulated by most basal cell cancers. Melanocytes (M, see panel b) are pigment-producing cells that reside in the basal cell layer and that give rise to moles and melanomas. Langerhans cells (L) within the spinous layer are clear, immunologically-competent cells which interact with migrant T lymphocytes in many forms of skin allergy as well as in earlier stages of cutaneous T cell lymphoma (mycosis fungoides). Within the underlying dermal layer are blood and lymphatic vessels (V) from which benign haemangiomas and more aggressive vascular proliferations such as Kaposi sarcoma and angiosarcoma may arise. Dermal dendrocytes (D) are a family of relatively newly recognized cells responsible for benign dermatofibromas and more aggressive spindle cell tumours such as dermatofibrosarcoma protuberans. In addition to dermal dendrocytes, the perivascular space is also home to histiocytes (H) which take up pigments and particulate material, mast cells (Ma) which contain histamine and other biological mediators that regulate vessel function and small nerve fibres (not shown). Most of the dermis, however, is composed of tough and resilient acellular collagen and elastin fibres produced by cells termed fibroblasts (F, panel b).

35 Oral Cavity and Major and Minor Salivary Glands

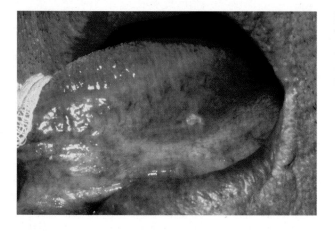

Figure 2 This small white patch (leukoplakia) at the junction of the tongue and floor of mouth histologically showed carcinoma *in situ*. This is one of the 'high-risk' sites that shows a much greater proportion of premalignant and malignant lesions than most of the oral mucosa.

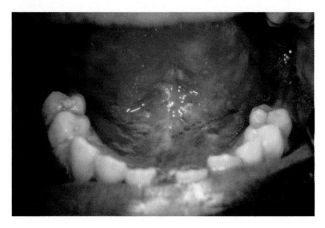

Figure 3 Oral mucosal lesions with a red component are much more likely to be premalignant or malignant than purely white lesions. On microscopic examination this lesion demonstrated early invasive squamous cell carcinoma.

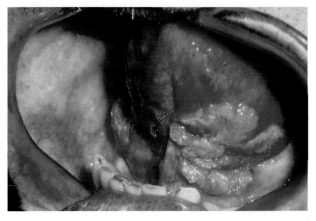

Figure 4 Squamous cell carcinoma. Although this example has a predominantly exophytic appearance clinically, histologically the neoplasm invaded underlying fibrous connective tissue and skeletal muscle.

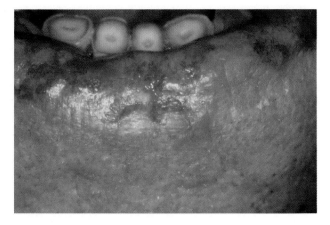

Figure 5 Actinic cheilitis. Non-healing, irregular ulcerations in this patient revealed carcinoma *in situ* microscopically. The poorly delineated vermilion border of this patient's lip typically follows long-term overexposure to sunlight and indicates tissue damage.

Figure 6 Epithelial dysplasia. The morphologically normal epithelium is seen on the right and the dysplastic epithelium on the left. The dysplastic cells are more haphazardly arranged and the normal pavement-like appearance is disrupted.

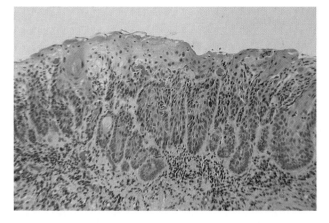

Figure 7 Early invasive squamous cell carcinoma. The morphologically abnormal epithelial cells have developed elongated rete pegs and several small islands of malignant epithelium extend into the lamina propria.

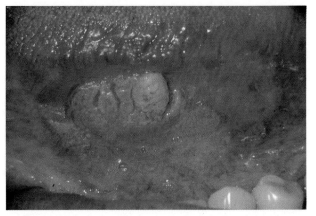

Figure 8 An irregular, diffuse, white plaque has slowly spread along the mucosal surface of the floor of the mouth and ventral surface of the tongue. Such lesions often involve multiple sites and have the potential to develop into verrucous carcinoma or conventional, invasive squamous cell carcinoma.

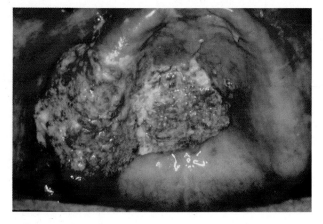

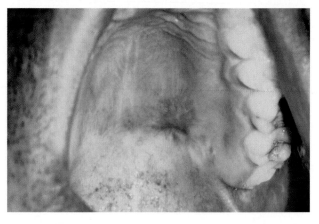

Figure 9 Verrucous carcinoma. The patient with this extensive, asymptomatic, papillary lesion of the hard palate, alveolar ridge, and vestibule sought treatment because of interference with a denture.

Figure 11 Mucoepidermoid carcinoma. A bluish, symptomatic slightly raised lesion of the palate was found during a routine dental examination. Such lesions are often thought to represent vascular lesions or mucoceles.

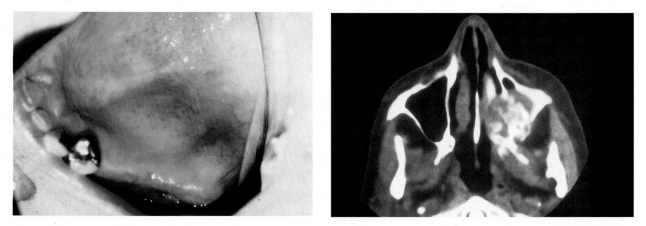

Figure 12 A diffuse swelling of the hard palate was biopsied and revealed adenoid cystic carcinoma. Computerized tomography showed that the tumour had perforated the maxilla and extended into the maxillary sinus and nasal cavity, destroying portions of their bony walls.

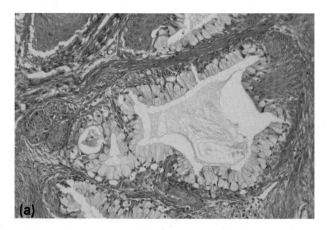

(a)

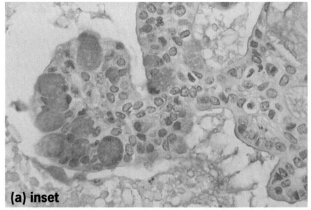

(a) inset

(figure continued on opposite page)

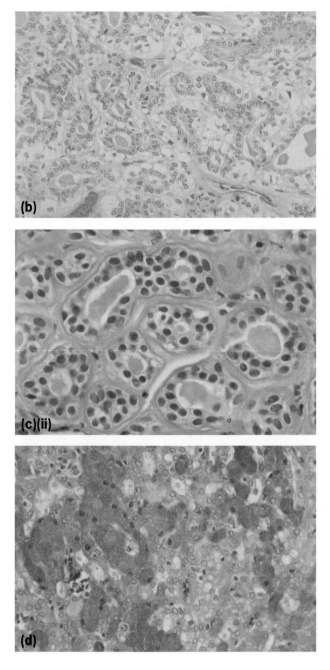

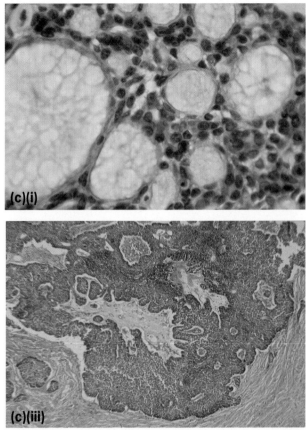

Figure 13 (a) This mucoepidermoid carcinoma forms small cysts and islands composed of mucous and squamous cells. The inset is of a different example in which a mucicarmine stain was needed to highlight the mucous cells. (b) In this acinic cell adenocarcinoma large acinar cells are seen with abundant, granular cytoplasm and are surrounded by cells that resemble intercalated duct cells. Sometimes such tumours are initially misinterpreted as normal glands because of their acinar differentiation. (c) Many of the 23 types of salivary gland carcinomas themselves have several subtypes. For instance, adenoid cystic carcinoma may have (i–iii) a predominant cribriform, tubular, or solid pattern. The solid type is the most aggressive form. (d) Epithelial-myoepithelial carcinoma is characterized by having a biphasic appearance of clear cells surrounding darkly staining ductal cells that line small lumens.

36 Respiratory System

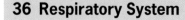

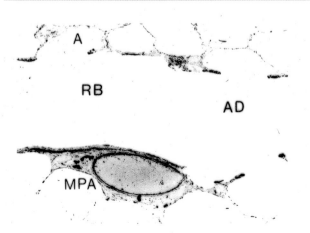

Figure 3 Photomicrograph of respiratory bronchiole (RB) with alveoli (A) branching from it and extending into the alveolar ducts (AD). MPA = muscular pulmonary artery.

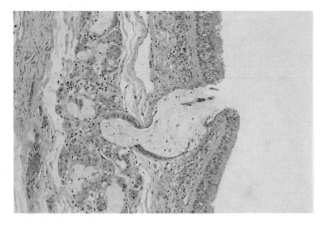

Figure 4 Bronchial wall showing a mucous gland opening to the surface and some mucous and serous glands beneath the epithelium.

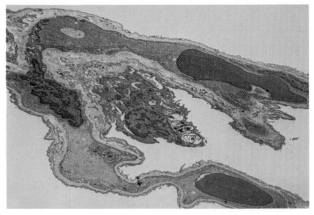

Figure 5 Electron micrograph of alveolar wall showing a large type II cell with lamellar bodies lying in the corner of the alveolus. On either side there are attenuated type I cells with a thin cytoplasm. Several red blood corpuscles can be seen in the capillaries and there is also an endothelial cell.

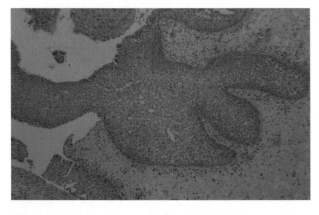

Figure 6 Photomicrograph of a Schneiderian papilloma of the nose showing hyperplastic squamous epithelium but no evidence of invasion.

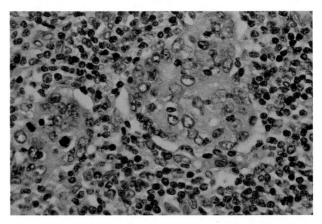

Figure 7 Lymphoepithelioma of the nasopharynx showing several clusters of poorly differentiated carcinoma surrounded by many lymphocytes. Some of these lymphocytes are infiltrating into the squamous components of the tumour. (Photograph courtesy of Professor L. Weiss.)

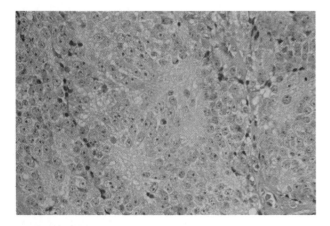

Figure 8 Olfractory neuroblastoma showing cells with a faintly eosinophilic cytoplasm. (Figure courtesy of Dr S. S. Banerjee, Christie Hospital, Manchester.)

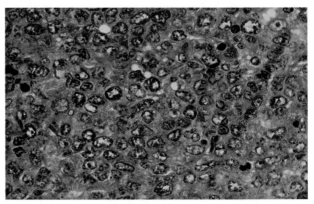

Figure 9 Non-Hodgkin lymphoma of the oropharynx, showing large cells with nuclear crenation. (Figure courtesy of Professor L. Weiss.)

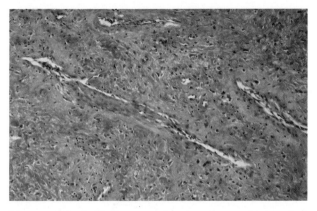

Figure 10 Angiofibroma showing large thick-walled blood vessels set in a fibrous stroma.

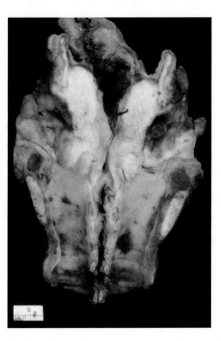

Figure 11 Bisected laryngectomy specimen showing advanced squamous cell carcinoma.

Figure 12 Intrapulmonary hamartoma showing a lobulated, glistening, well circumscribed tumour.

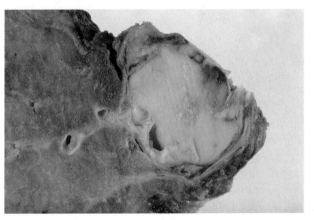

Figure 14 Intrabronchial carcinoid, which is distending the bronchus and has a grey appearance on cut surface.

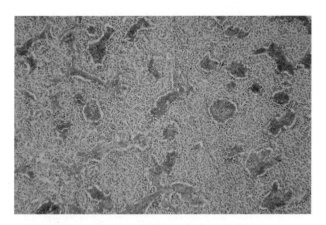

Figure 15 Typical carcinoid with a tendency to an insular pattern. The tumour is extremely vascular, due to TGF-α expression by the tumour cells. The cells are small, regular and show no mitoses or evidence of necrosis.

Figure 16 Carcinoma *in situ* of the bronchial wall. There is inflammation in the subepithelial tissues and marked dysplasia with mitoses and some focal individual cell keratinization in the epithelium.

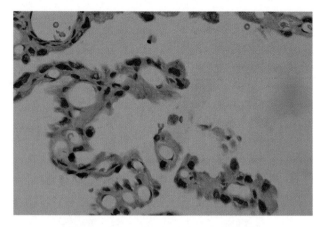

Figure 17 Atypical alveolar hyperplasia. There are hyperchromatic cells lining the alveolar wall with a marked increase in nuclear/cytoplasmic ratio.

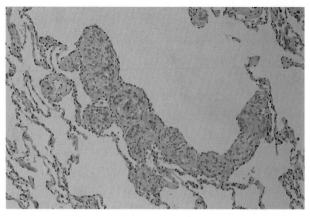

Figure 18 Diffuse neuroendocrine hyperplasia. The neuroendocrine cells are growing along alveolar walls. Note that there is no underlying interstitial pulmonary fibrosis. In other areas the bronchiolar lumina were occluded in areas by neuroendocrine cells.

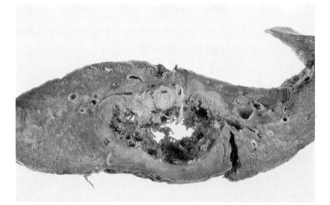

Figure 19 Cavitating squamous cell carcinoma. The central area has undergone necrosis and the firm grey tissue on the periphery is more likely to contain viable tumour tissue. It is difficult to discern, at the very periphery of the tumour, the difference between inflammation, collapsed lung and tumour.

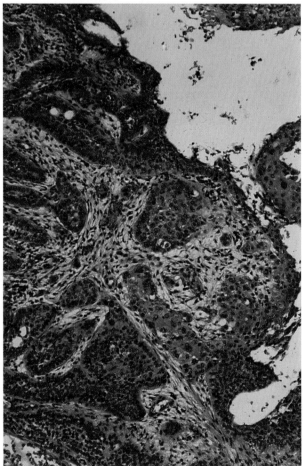

Figure 20 Moderately differentiated, invasive, squamous cell carcinoma.

Figure 21 Adenocarcinoma of lung. There is a large, fairly well-defined, lobulated tumour. Cut surface is glistening owing to the mucus.

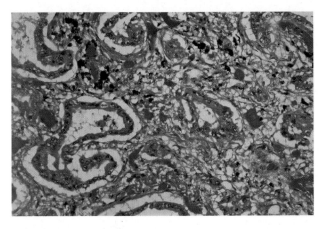

Figure 22 Well-differentiated adenocarcinoma of lung lying in a fibrous stroma.

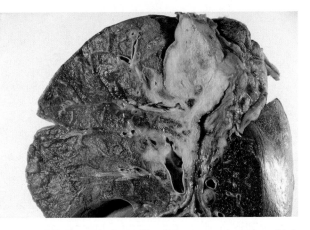

Figure 24 A central small-cell lung carcinoma, which has almost totally obliterated a main bronchus but can be seen involving nodes around the pulmonary artery and extending along some lymphatics.

Figure 23 Alveolar cell carcinoma showing grey 'consolidation' involving one lobe and extending into an adjacent lobe.

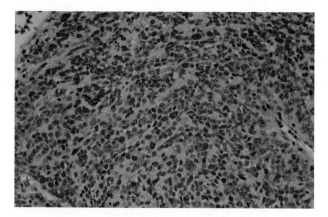

Figure 25 Small-cell lung cancer, showing small nuclei, little cytoplasm, evidence of some nuclear moulding and some intranuclear vacuoles. This magnification is too low to be able to discern the salt and pepper nature of the nuclear chromatin.

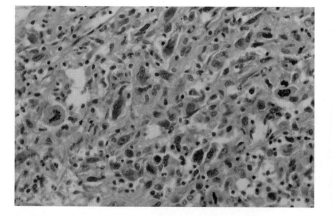

Figure 27 Pleomorphic carcinoma showing bizarre tumour cells with some abnormal mitoses, a large amount of nuclear chromatin and some cells with very marked increase in nuclear/cytoplasmic ratio. There is no discernible squamous, small-cell or adenocarcinomatous pattern in this field.

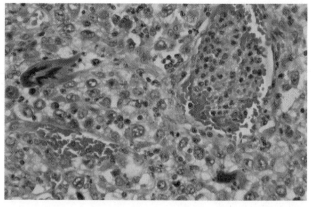

Figure 26 Large-cell lung cancer showing tumour cells with very prominent nuclei, a large amount of cytoplasm and a tumour giant cell. This is a diagnosis by exclusion and no mucin should be identified. In addition there should not be the typical pallisaded pattern of a large-cell neuroendocrine carcinoma. Many pathologists would use the term non-small-cell lung cancer on a small biopsy in a case such as this.

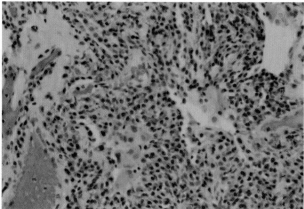

Figure 28 Non-Hodgkin lymphoma which has grown predominantly along the alveolar septae, expanding them. There are some paler cells in the alveolar lumina, which are macrophages.

40 Pancreas

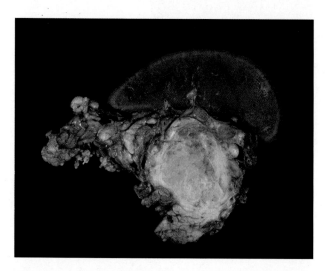

Figure 3 Gross photograph of an infiltrating carcinoma in the tail of the pancreas adjacent to the spleen. (Photograph courtesy of Mark Li-cheng Wu.)

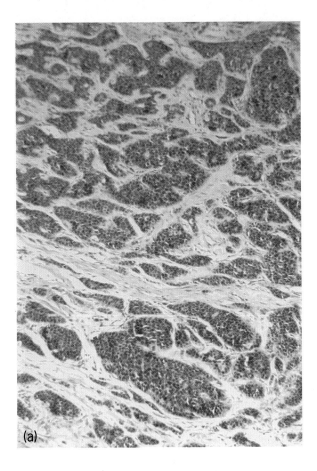

(a)

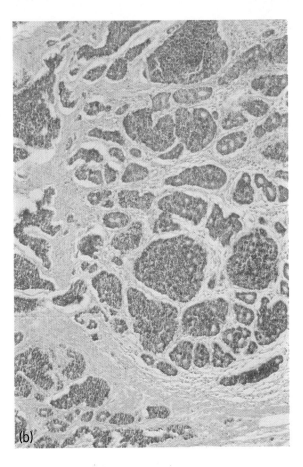

(b)

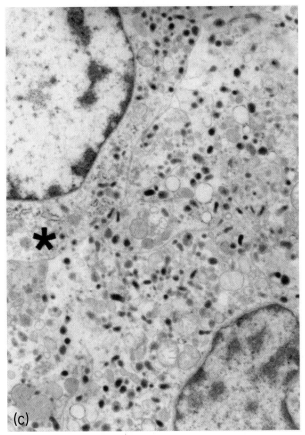

(c)

Figure 1 (a) Tumours of the neuroendocrine system, such as this gut endocrine carcinoma, are composed of nests, cords and sheets of epithelial cells in a fibrovascular stroma. They have monotonous nuclei but their infiltrative nature indicates malignancy. (b) These lesions stain for synaptophysin, one of the most sensitive and specific markers of neuroendocrine differentiation. (c) The ultrastructure of these lesions is characterized by the presence of rough endoplasmic reticulum (*) and numerous membrane-bound secretory granules that have variable size, shape and electron density. In this tumour, the pleomorphism of granules and peripheral halos is characteristic of phaeochromocytoma.

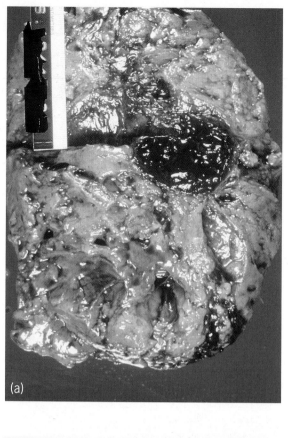

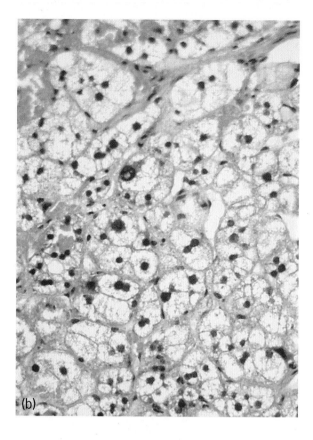

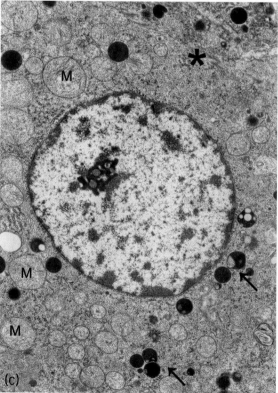

Figure 2 (a) Tumours of steroid hormone-secreting cells are generally bright yellow, reflecting the accumulation of carotene pigment in the fat of these lipid-rich hormones. This adrenal cortical carcinoma is very large and has areas of haemorrhage. (b) The histological appearance of adrenal cortical carcinoma is characterized by nests of large cells with clear cytoplasm. Nuclear pleomorphism is not a reliable indicator of malignancy. (c) By electron microscopy, steroid hormone-secreting cells have abundant smooth endoplasmic reticulum (*), dense lipid droplets (arrows) and numerous mitochondria (M) with tubulovesicular cristae.

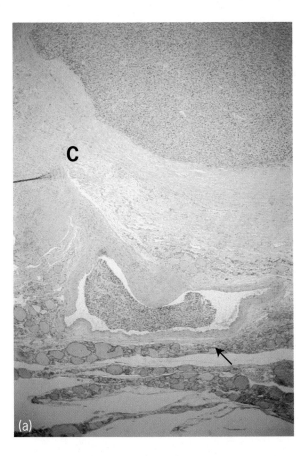

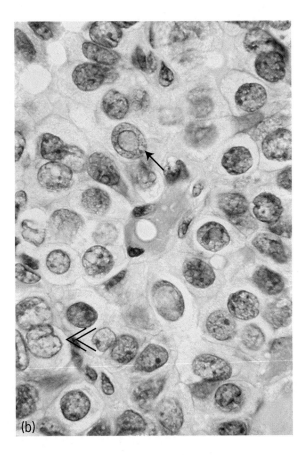

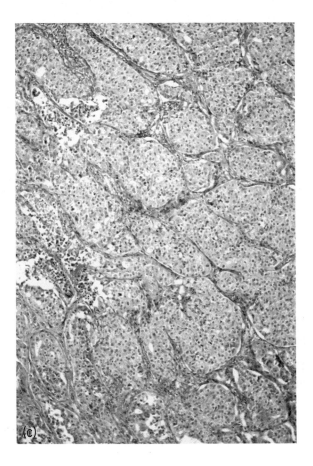

Figure 3 (a) Follicular carcinomas of thyroid are usually encapsulated cellular nodules that exhibit invasion of their thick fibrous capsule (C) and/or vascular invasion (arrow). (b) The diagnosis of papillary carcinoma of thyroid is based on the nuclear features shown in this photomicrograph: clearing of nucleoplasm and peripheral margination of chromatin, irregular nuclear contours with grooves (arrowheads) and inclusions (arrow). (c) In contrast to well differentiated papillary or follicular carcinoma, insular carcinoma is a poorly differentiated lesion. Although it is derived from follicular epithelial cells, it is composed of solid nests of cells that resemble neuroendocrine carcinoma. There is focal tumour cell necrosis.

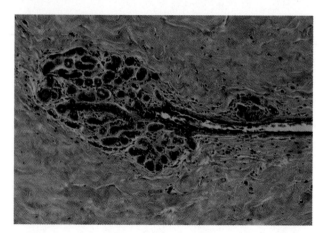

Figure 2 Low-power histology of a TDLU.

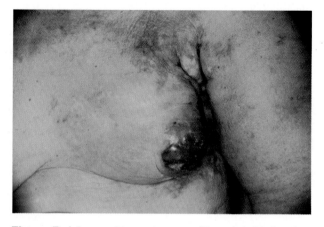

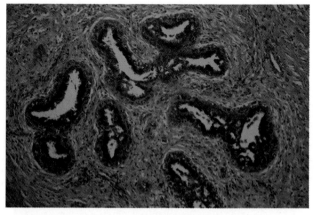

Figure 4 Example of hand-held 'gun' apparatus for FNA (left). Cytological material containing malignant epithelial cells consistent with breast carcinoma (intermediate power), obtained by FNA (right).

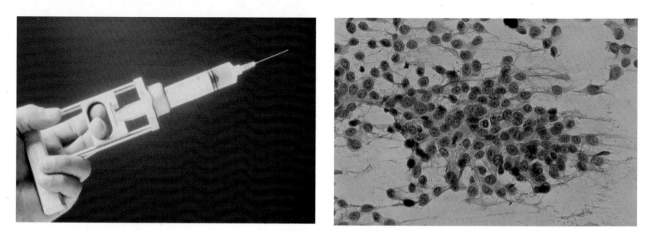

Figure 5 Advanced breast cancer. Note the skin involvement and ulceration, along with extensive deformity of the breast.

Figure 6 Fibroadenoma (intermediate power), containing epithelial and stromal components.

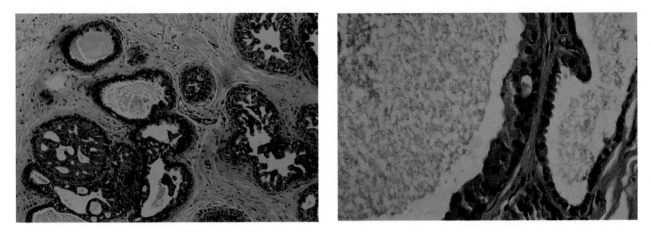

Figure 7 Fibrocystic changes. Note the alternating areas of stromal fibrosis and cystic ductal dilation, with focal ductal hyperplasia (low power) (left). Apocrine metaplastic ductal epithelial cells lining a cyst (high power) (right).

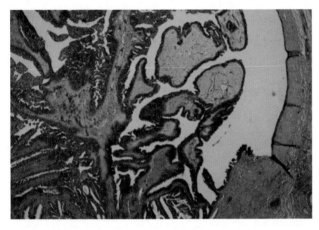

Figure 8 Intraductal papilloma (low power). Note the epithelial-lined fibrovascular stalks protruding into the dilated duct space.

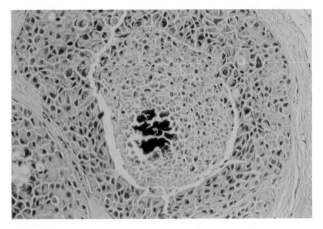

Figure 9 Comedo DCIS. Note the high-grade cancer cells filling the duct and surrounding the necrotic material, which is partially calcified (dark area) (intermediate power).

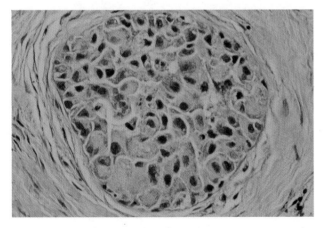

Figure 10 Solid DCIS. Note the high-grade cancer cells completely filling the ductal lumen (high power).

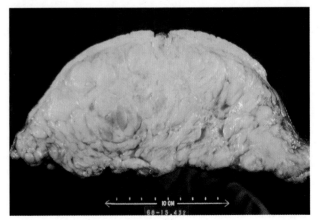

Figure 11 Mastectomy specimen: advanced infiltrating ductal carcinoma. The tumour has diffusely replaced the majority of the normal breast tissue, giving it a rigid consistency.

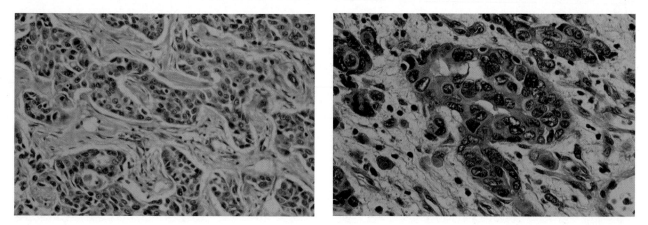

Figure 12 Infiltrating poorly differentiated ductal carcinoma, NOS. The image on the left shows infiltrating, anastomosing nests of pleomorphic, mitotically active cancer cells (intermediate power). Right, higher power of the same lesion.

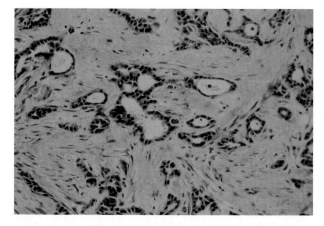

Figure 13 Tubular carcinoma. The tumour is composed of malignant, infiltrating cells in well-formed gland structures with open lumens (intermediate power).

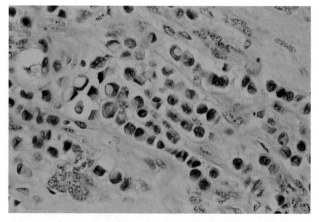

Figure 14 Infiltrating lobular carcinoma. Note the small, round tumour cells infiltrating in a single-file manner (high power). Signet-ring cells are also present.

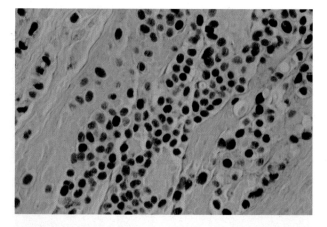

Figure 15 Immunohistochemical staining for oestrogen receptors. Note the diffuse, intense staining for oestrogen receptors on the cancer cell nuclei (high power).

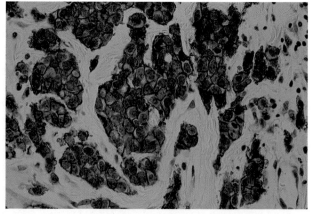

Figure 16 Immunohistochemical staining for Her-2/neu/c-erbB-2. Note the diffuse, intense cytoplasmic membrane staining on the cancer cells (intermediate power).

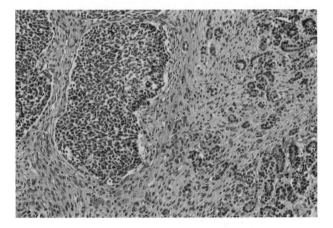

Figure 2 Nephroblastoma (Wilms tumour). Photomicrograph showing all three tumour elements. There is a nest of blastema on the left, with epithelial elements and intermingled stroma on the right.

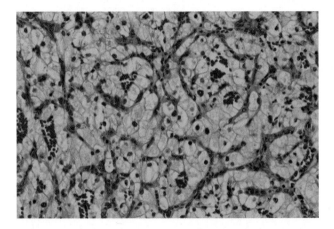

Figure 4 Conventional (clear cell) renal cell carcinoma. Cells with clear cytoplasm are arranged in nests, which are separated by a network of delicate, interconnecting blood vessels.

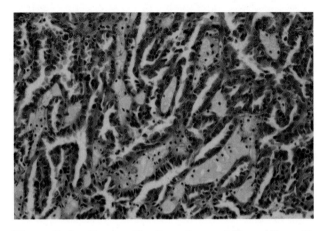

Figure 5 Papillary renal cell carcinoma. Thin papillae with a central fibrovascular core lined by low cuboidal epithelial cells with scant cytoplasm and dark nuclei. Groups of foamy macrophages, with pale voluminous cytoplasm, are present in the centre of most fibrovascular stalks.

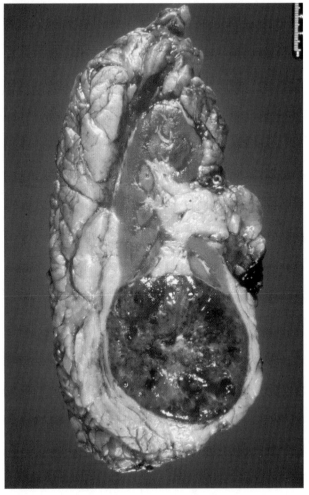

Figure 3 Renal cell carcinoma (gross photograph). Large tumour at the lower pole of the kidney.

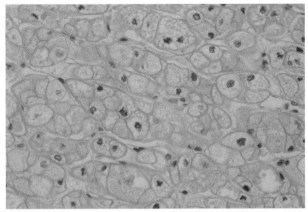

Figure 6 Chromophobe renal cell carcinoma. A broad sheet of tumour cells with abundant frothy, vacuolated cytoplasm (soap bubble appearance) and prominent cell membranes. The nuclei are hyperchromatic, and some have a wrinkled nuclear membrane.

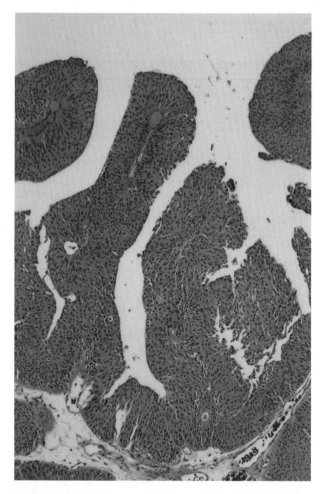

Figure 7 Low-grade papillary urothelial carcinoma of the urinary bladder. The tumour has delicate papillae with a central fibrovascular stalk.

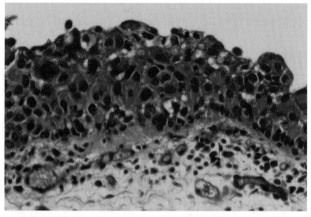

Figure 8 Urothelial carcinoma *in situ* of the urinary bladder. A 'flat tumour' of the urothelium, with most cells showing enlarged hyperchromatic nuclei and prominent nucleoli. A mitosis is present in the upper left corner of the urothelium.

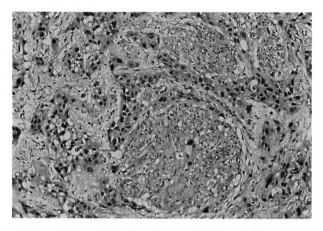

Figure 9 High-grade urothelial carcinoma of the urinary bladder invasive into muscularis propria. Single malignant cells and cords of malignant cells split the muscularis propria.

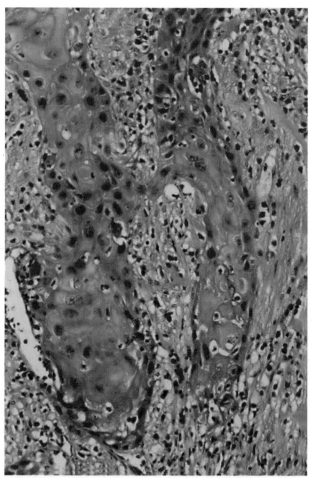

Figure 10 Squamous cell carcinoma of the urethra. Nests of malignant cells invade deep into the stroma.

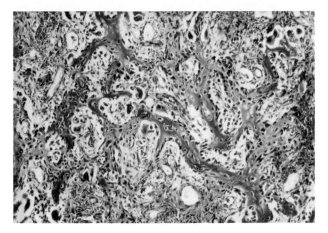

Figure 1 Osteoid osteoma. Mature bone formation is seen. The intervening cells are benign.

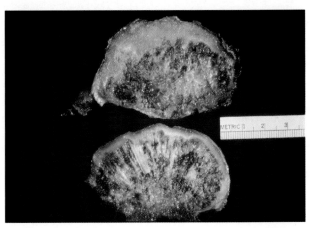

Figure 2 Osteochondroma. Note the grey cartilaginous cap.

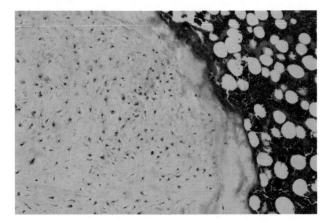

Figure 3 Chondroma. Benign cartilaginous tissue forms a nodule with adjacent normal bone marrow.

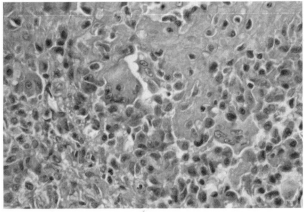

Figure 4 Chondroblastoma. A mixture of chondroblasts, giant cells and immature cartilage is seen.

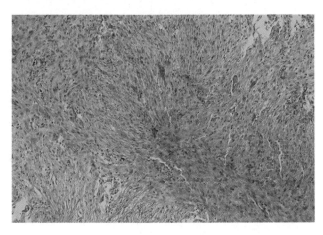

Figure 5 Nonossifying fibroma. A bland spindle cell proliferation is seen, with scattered giant cells.

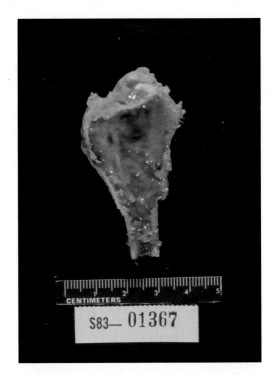

Figure 6 Giant cell tumour. A gelatinous tumour is seen replacing the epiphyseal end of the bone.

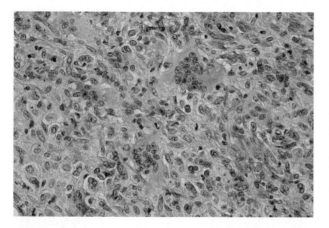

Figure 7 Giant cell tumour. There are numerous giant cells seen. Note the similarity of the nuclei of the giant cells with the nuclei in the adjacent stromal cells.

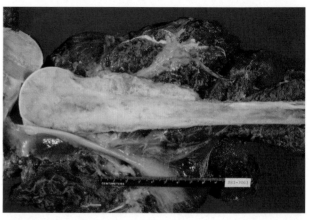

Figure 8 Osteosarcoma. This case shows a sclerotic white appearance in the metaphysis of the femur. Note the large soft tissue component extending out of the bone.

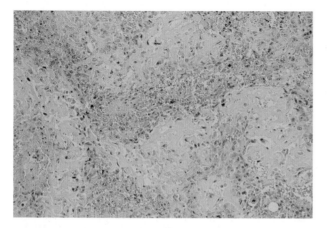

Figure 9 Osteosarcoma. There is abundant osteoid formation.

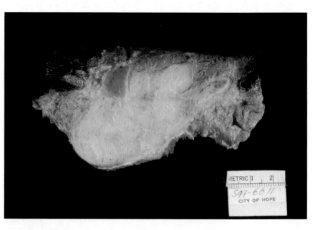

Figure 10 Chondrosarcoma. There is a white multi-nodular mass arising from the scapula.

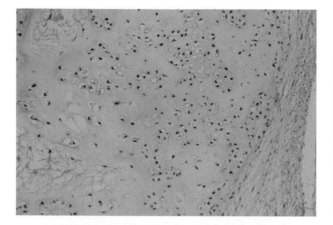

Figure 11 This low-grade chondrosarcoma shows an appearance similar to the benign chondroma seen in Figure 3. The radiological appearance is often the best way to establish the correct diagnosis in a low-grade chondrosarcoma.

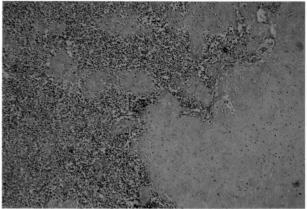

Figure 12 Mesenchymal chondrosarcoma. There is a biphasic appearance, with areas of small, round blue cell tumour alternating with ill-formed cartilage.

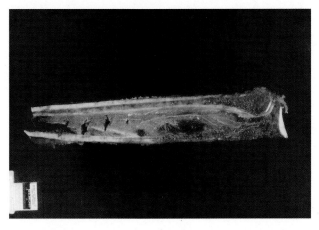

Figure 13 Ewing sarcoma/PNET. There is an extensive haemorrhagic soft tissue component, seen between the two bones.

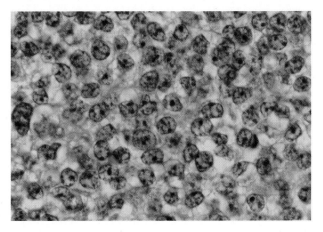

Figure 14 Ewing sarcoma/PNET. A typical appearance of a small, round blue cell tumour is seen, without any differentiating features.

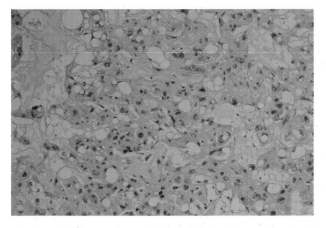

Figure 15 Chordoma. Cords of cells with vacuolated cytoplasmic inclusions are seen.

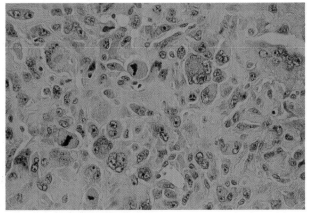

Figure 16 Malignant fibrous histiocytoma. Highly anaplastic cells are present. Note the numerous mitotic figures.

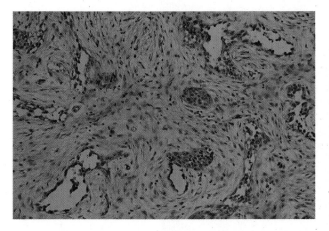

Figure 17 Adamantinoma. Islands of epithelial cells are present in a spindle cell stroma.

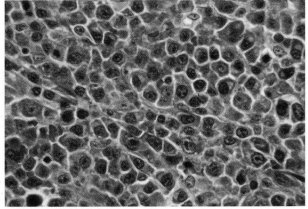

Figure 18 Multiple myeloma. Sheets of plasma cells of varying degrees of atypia are seen. Note the paranuclear cytoplasmic clearing, typical of plasma cells.

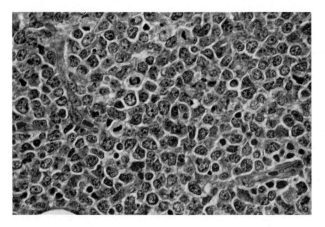

Figure 19 Malignant lymphoma, diffuse large B cell type. This lymphoma is a proliferation of large lymphoid cells.

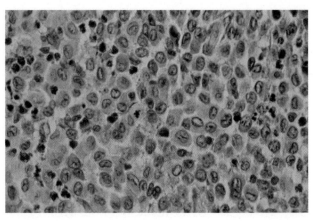

Figure 20 Langerhans cell histiocytosis. A mixture of Langerhans cells, histiocytes and eosinophils (bilobed cells with grainy red cytoplasm) are seen. Note the linear grooves present in many of the Langerhans cell nuclei.

49 Pleura and Peritoneum

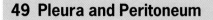

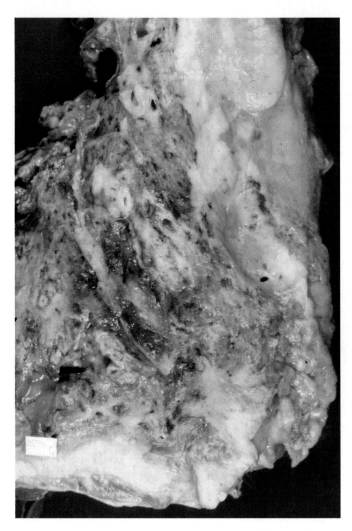

Figure 1 The gross appearance of pleural mesothelioma is characterized by pleural-based, diffuse thickening as demonstrated by the band of white tissue at the periphery of a cross-section of lower lobe. Mesothelioma, in advanced stages, may traverse the lung parenchyma along septae and involve peribronchial regions as illustrated here by white streaks in the parenchyma and thickened airway structures. This pattern of growth accounts for restrictive physiological features, which are often noted clinically.

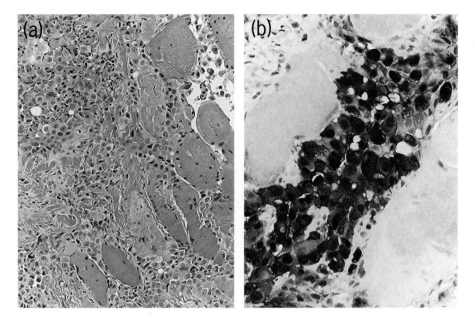

Figure 2 Epithelial-type mesothelioma is characterized by a uniform neoplastic epithelioid cell population. One feature enabling distinction from reactive mesothelial hyperplasia is invasion into the surrounding tissue, such as skeletal muscle, as demonstrated here (a). Differential diagnosis between mesothelioma and adenocarcinoma may be extremely difficult, but the immunohistochemical demonstration of calretinin in this context is highly specific for mesothelial differentiation (b).

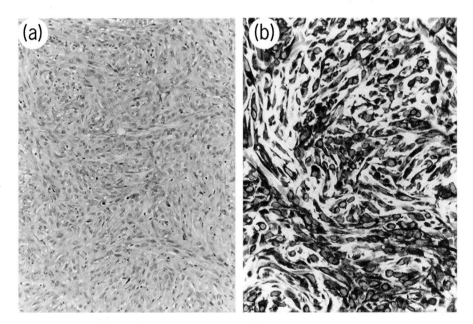

Figure 3 Sarcomatoid mesothelioma is characterized by neoplastic spindle cell proliferation in a variety of patterns ranging from swirling (so-called storiform) to herringbone (so-called fascicular), and making distinction from other spindle cell neoplasms difficult (a). The immunohistochemical detection of keratin intermediate filaments is useful in identifying sarcomatoid mesothelioma, but is not specific as other tumors such as monophasic synovial sarcoma may also demonstrate keratin filaments (b).

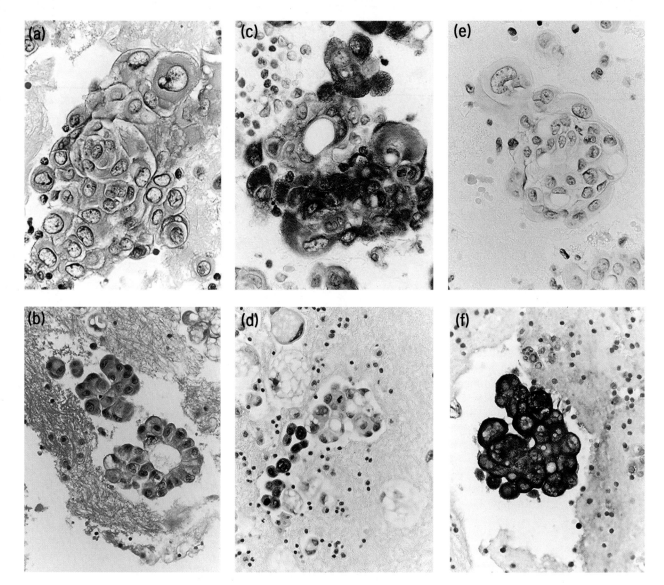

Figure 4 Distinction between mesothelioma and pulmonary adenocarcinoma in pleural fluid cytological evaluation may be difficult, and at times impossible, based on morphological features. Acini and glandular structures are more frequently seen in adenocarcinoma, but may also be found in mesotheliomas ((a) mesothelioma, (b) adenocarcinoma, cell block preparations). Various immunocytochemical panels have been proposed to assist in this differential diagnosis, all of which aim for maximum specificity and sensitivity. Calretinin is a recent addition to these panels and is one of the few immunocytochemical assays that are positive in mesothelioma but not in adenocarcinoma in this setting ((c) mesothelioma, calretinin-positive, (d) adenocarcinoma, calretininnegative with adjacent calretinin-positive reactive mesothelial cells). As one of the original immunohistochemical assays, carcinoembryonic antigen remains useful in this differential diagnosis but is not as specific as calretinin. It is usually detected in adenocarcinoma, but may be seen in a minority of mesotheliomas ((e) mesothelioma, carcinoembryonic antigen-negative, (f) adenocarcinoma, carcinoembryonic antigen-positive).

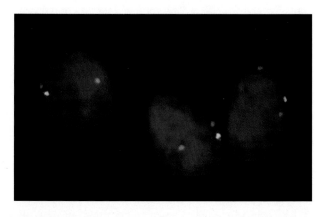

Figure 7 Fluorescence *in situ* hybridization with probes to chromosome 3 centromere (red) and chromosome 3p deletion region (green–blue) revealing clonal deletion in mesothelioma cytology preparation.

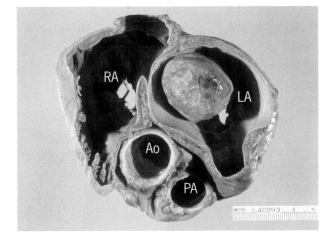

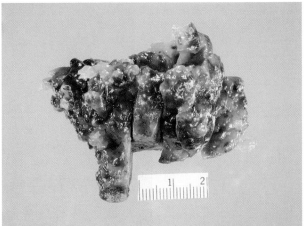

Figure 3 Cardiac myxoma, gross appearance. A typical smooth-surfaced cardiac myxoma. The heart is seen from above, with the atrial cavities exposed. The myxoma is attached at the level of the oval fossa. Symptoms may occur because of obstruction of blood flow into the left ventricle (similar to mitral stenosis); some myxomas prolapse into the ventricle during diastole. Chronically, this obstruction of blood flow can result in chronic pulmonary hypertension.

Figure 4 Cardiac myxoma, surgically excised specimen. This tumour had an irregular surface. It was removed from a patient who experienced neurological symptoms of cerebral embolization (transient ischaemic attacks).

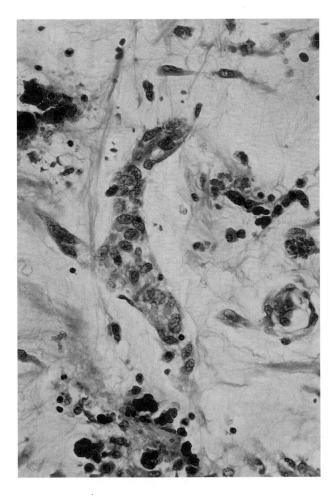

Figure 5 Cardiac myxoma, histological appearance. In the centre of the photomicrograph is an island of myxoma cells forming an elongated, vessel-like structure. The acellular 'empty' areas of the tumour are composed of myxoid ground substance (proteoglycans), inflammatory cells, including haemosiderin-laden macrophages, and isolated spindle and dendritic cells.

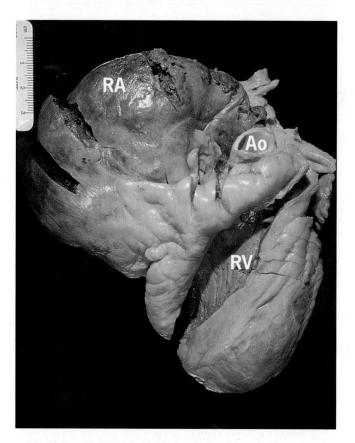

Figure 9 Cardiac angiosarcoma, right atrium. The right atrium (RA) is massively dilated by a haemorrhagic tumour. The right ventricle (RV) is opened and was free of tumour. The aorta (Ao) is seen posterior to the pulmonary valve.

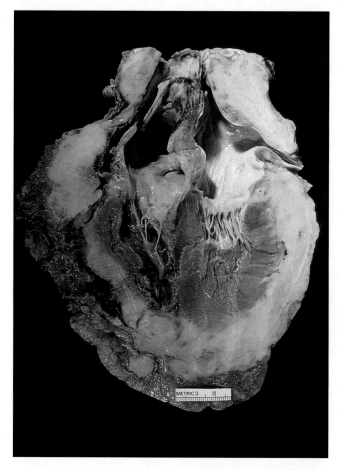

Figure 10 Pericardial mesothelioma. The heart is nearly encased in a firm, white mass which obliterates the pericardial space.

Figure 41 Isochromosome 17q in cells of a primitive neuroectodermal tumour is demonstrated here by FISH. In this FISH, each chromosome 17 is labelled by a green probe (on 17p) and a red probe (on 17q). The green dot and one of the red dots belong to one chromosome 17 that has no deletion. The other chromosome is an isochromosome 17q (i.e. deletion of both 17p and fusion of 17q) and therefore have two red dots. (Courtesy of DrJaclyn Biegel, Childrens Hospital of Philadelphia.)

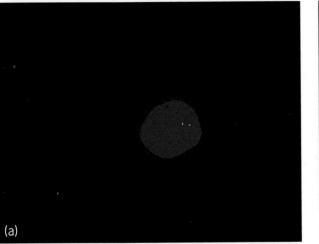

(a)

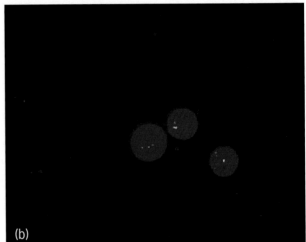

(b)

Figure 42 (a) Homogeneous deletion of chromosome 22q in ATRT. The two chromosomes 22 are labelled by a green probe (labelling EWS gene) and a red probe (labelling INI1 gene). EWS gene is located closer to the telomere than the INI1 gene. Normal karyotype should show two green dots and two red dots. Homogeneous deletion of the distal arm deleted both INSI gene (red dots) but preserves the EWS gene (green dots). (b) In heterozygous deletion, only one chromosome 22q is deleted. Therefore, one red dot (INI1 gene) and two green dots (EWS gene) are present. (Courtesy of Dr Jaclyn Biegel, Childrens Hospital of Philadelphia.)

52 Eye and Ocular Adnexa

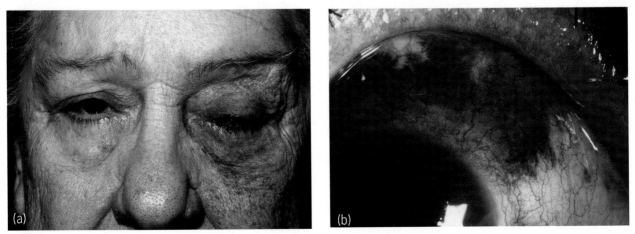

(a)

(b)

Figure 1 (a) Periocular skin pigmentation in oculodermal melanocytosis. (b) Slate gray episcleral pigmentation in oculodermal melanocytosis.

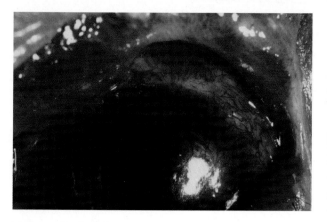

Figure 3 Sebaceous carcinoma masquerading as blepharoconjunctivitis.

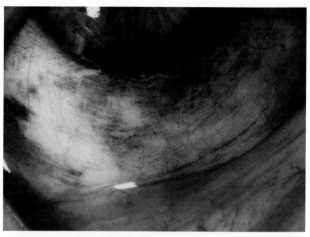

Figure 5 Clinical appearance of primary acquired melanosis of the conjunctiva.

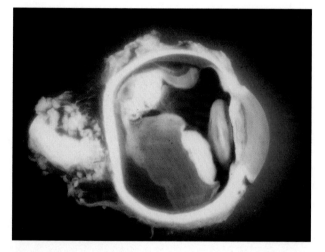

Figure 7 Two distinct foci of exophytic retinoblastoma with retinal detachment.

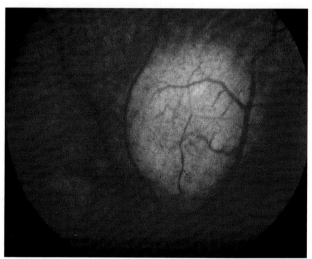

Figure 8 Exophytic retinoblastoma. Fundus photograph showing subretinal mass with retinal vessels coursing over the tumour (courtesy AFIP).

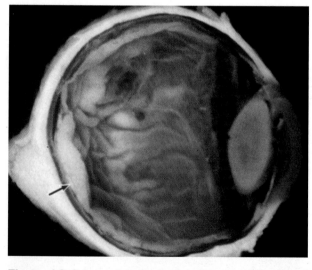

Figure 12 Primary intraocular lymphoma: thickening of the retina with focally haemorrhagic infiltrate. A mound of subretinal pigment epithelial infiltrate is also present (arrow) (courtesy AFIP).

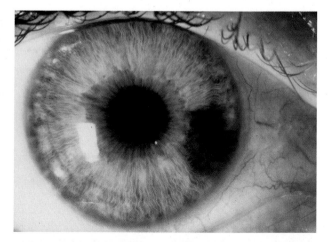

Figure 13 Iris naevus.

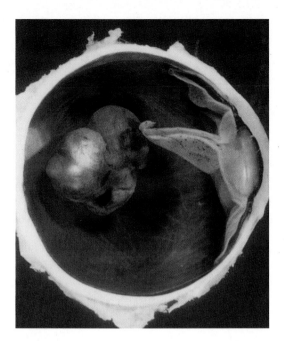

Figure 16 Malignant melanoma. Mushroom-shaped choroidal tumour has ruptured through Bruch's membrane and is growing in the subretinal space (courtesy AFIP).

53 Ear

Figure 1 The histological diagnosis of cholesteatoma is primarily based on the presence of a stratified keratinizing squamous epithelium.

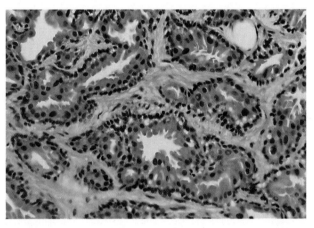

Figure 2 Ceruminal gland adenoma is characterized by well-formed glandular spaces lined by an inner layer of cuboidal to columnar cells and an outer layer of small compressed cells.

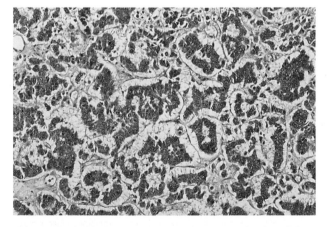

Figure 3 Middle ear adenoma is composed of a diffuse proliferation of gland-forming neoplasm.

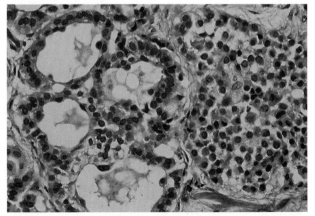

Figure 4 Middle ear adenoma composed of glands and an adjacent solid cellular focus. The neoplastic cells in both the glands and solid area are similar showing plasmacytoid features.

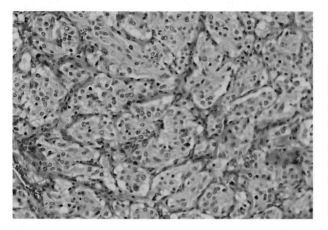

Figure 5 Jugulotympanic paraganglioma showing an organoid or the cell nest growth pattern. This tumour lacked gland formation; the chief cells were immunoreactive with neuroendocrine cell markers (e.g. chromogranin and synaptophysin) and the peripherally situated sustentacular cells were reactive with S100 protein.

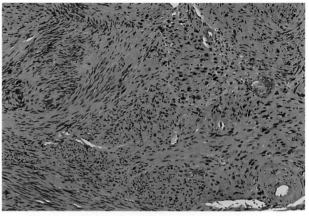

Figure 6 Acoustic neuroma composed of a neoplastic cellular infiltrate of elongated and twisted hyperchromatic nuclei and indistinct cytoplasmic borders. Vascular hyalinization is present. The neoplastic cells were diffusely and intensely reactive with S100 protein.

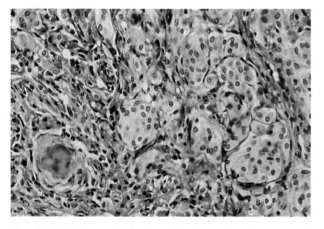

Figure 7 This meningioma of the internal auditory canal showing a cell nest or lobular growth separated by fibrovascular tissue. The cells are composed of round to oval or spindle-shaped nuclei with pale staining cytoplasm and indistinct cell borders; the nuclei show characteristic punched-out or empty appearance due to intranuclear cytoplasmic inclusions. At the lower left is a psammoma body that is a helpful diagnostic feature in this tumour.

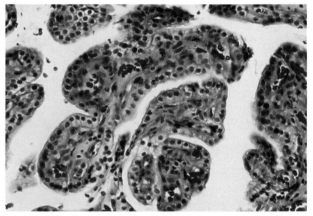

Figure 8 Endolymphatic sac papillary tumour showing a papillary growth pattern with a vascularized stroma. The epithelial component along the periphery is fairly distinct but at times may not be readily apparent and the overall process may be mistaken for granulation tissue.

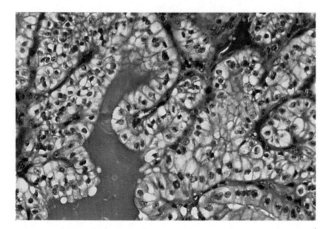

Figure 9 This endolymphatic sac papillary tumour has the morphological appearance of thyroid papillary-carcinoma, including the presence of colloid-like material and irregular appearing nuclei. Thyroglobulin staining was not present.

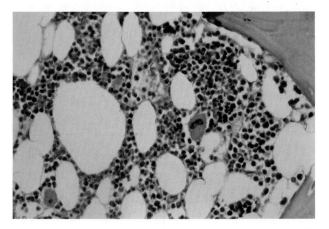

Figure 1 A normal adult marrow cellularity is seen, with about 50% fat cells, and 50% cells of various haematopoietic lineages.

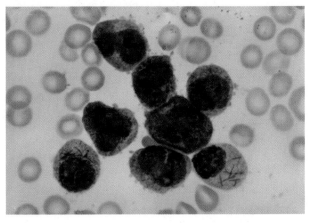

Figure 2 Acute promyelocytic leukaemia. Note the numerous red granules. At least two cells contain numerous Auer rods.

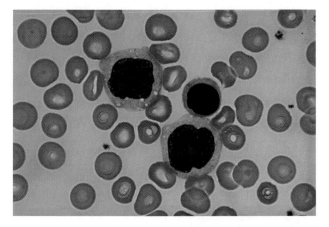

Figure 3 Acute myeloid leukaemia, not otherwise categorized. This case would have previously been classified as acute monocytic leukaemia, because the two blasts (the large cells) have nuclei with folded contours.

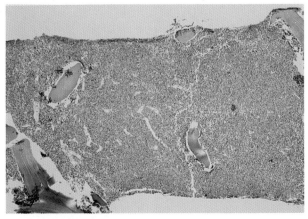

Figure 4 Myeloproliferative syndrome. Note the marked hypercellularity in comparison to Figure 1.

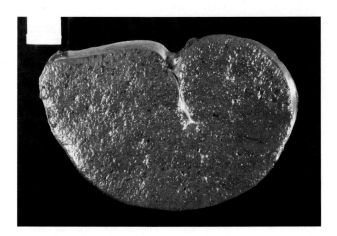

Figure 5 Chronic myeloid leukaemia. This spleen weighed 5000 grams (in comparison to the normal 50–150 grams. The sinuses are packed with leukaemic cells.

Figure 6 Chronic idiopathic myelofibrosis. Instead of its normal beefy red colour, this vertebral column shows a tan fibrous appearance.

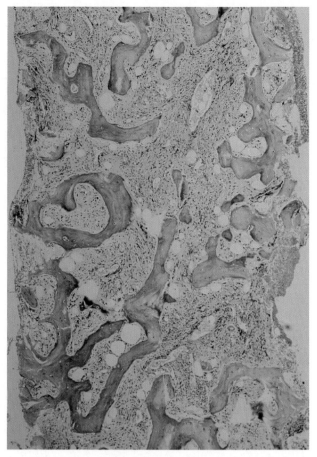

Figure 7 Chronic idiopathic myelofibrosis: The marrow is replaced by a fibrous proliferation. The bone also shows an increase in formation.

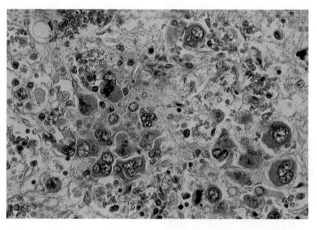

Figure 8 Myelodysplastic syndrome. This cluster of megakaryocytes shows abnormal lobulation of the nuclei.

TEST SYSTEMS FOR ANTIGENOTOXINS

In the search for and characterization of antigenotoxic, substances, both *in vitro* and *in vivo* test systems can be used. *In vitro* test systems can be divided into (1) tests with bacterial cultures such as the Ames test (Ames *et al.*, 1973), (2) tests with stable cell lines of animal or human origin, (3) short-term organ or cell cultures of both animal and human origin and (4) *in vivo* experiments, which include laboratory animal and human clinical trials or intervention studies. **Figure 2** shows a schematic overview of the strategy for detecting antigenotoxins.

There are two main problems with these studies: (1) data obtained in bacterial or animal test systems (both *in vitro* and *in vivo*) cannot automatically be extrapolated to humans; and (2) human studies are difficult to perform since the potential anticarcinogenic/genotoxic test compounds may themselves be toxic or mutagenic.

In Vitro Test Systems

In general, a substance selected on promising epidemiological data is tested at first using *in vitro* systems, since these tests are most easiest to interpret, the most readily available and the cheapest.

The most common test employed is the Ames test, where the effects of added substances on bacterial mutation rates are tested (see later).

Another category of *in vitro* tests use cell lines, which most often are derived from human or animal tumour cells, but sometimes originate from foetal cells or virus-transformed and thereby immortalized 'normal' cells. By adding the substance of interest to the culture medium the eventual antigenotoxic effect can be studied at several levels as outlined later.

In vitro test systems based on short-term cultures of slices of normal tissue or freshly isolated cells from patients or controls have been helped by the development of very sensitive detection methods for monitoring changes in DNA, RNA or other important biomolecules. Since such studies use normal human tissues, misinterpretation of data extrapolated from results in abnormal cells such as tumour-derived cell lines is avoided as much as possible.

In Vivo Test Systems

Next, when the *in vitro* data on compound efficacy combined with toxicity data are convincing, *in vivo* testing in laboratory animals is generally performed. Preferentially, different species should be used in parallel, in order to exclude incidental positive or negative results in one strain of animals.

Traditionally, laboratory animals are treated with various chemical carcinogens generating tumours at most common epithelial sites and used for the evaluation of antigenotoxic or anticarcinogenic test agents. Potential antigenotoxic test compounds can be added before, during or after the exposure to the carcinogen and in this way information on the working mechanism is also obtained.

More recently, genetically modified animal models that mimic specific characteristics of human risk groups or diseases have been used, specifically, transgenic animals, in which new properties have been introduced into the genome by genetic engineering, and gene knockout animals in which specific genes, and consequently specific functions, have been knocked out. Key aspects in evaluating the use of these experimental animals in chemoprevention research is the match between the (modified) animal model and the human disease entity: the closer the match, the more reliable the information obtained will be for transfer to the human situation.

There are two types of human *in vivo* study: (1) human clinical trials and (2) human intervention studies. Human clinical trials with antigenotoxic substances, owing to their high costs, intensive preparation, guidance and long duration, have rarely been performed (see the chapter *Intervention and Chemoprevention of Cancer*). In addition, there are often ethical problems due to the unknown properties of the test compounds with respect to short- or long-term toxicity. There are very few human intervention studies of short-term dietary supplementation with potential anticarcinogens which have examined biomarkers for genetic damage.

MECHANISMS BY WHICH ANTIGENOTOXINS MAY ACT

Many carcinogens are not directly active in their parental form but are metabolically activated to highly reactive

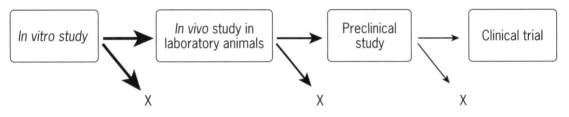

Figure 2   Common strategy for detecting and testing potential antigenotoxic compounds. X = compounds not suitable. (Adapted from Ito and Imaida, 1992.)

intermediates, which are the ultimate carcinogenic species (Miller and Miller, 1977). These compounds have gained the ability to react with DNA and to cause mutations that subsequently might lead to cancer. Approximately 90% of the chemical compounds that are mutagenic are also carcinogenic (Ames *et al.*, 1973). The ultimate carcinogens are electrophilic molecules that bind to electron-rich DNA, forming covalently bound adducts. Since this modified DNA is error-prone, subsequent replication can result in mutations, which are structural changes in the genetic material that are inherited by the daughters of these damaged cells. Different kinds of mutations can be discriminated: substitution of an incorrect base, the so-called point mutation; addition or deletion of genetic material, the so-called frameshift or missense mutation; or even DNA strand breakage with resultant aberrations in the pattern and organisation of the chromosomes, such as karyotypic abnormalities, sister chromatid exchange or micronucleus formation. When repair of the damage does not occur, replication of DNA may lead to permanent DNA lesions. In the presence of a tumour promoter these cells may change into pre-neoplastic cells and eventually neoplastic cells and may subsequently gain the potential to metastasize.

There are many ways of assessing genotoxicity. For example, one can extract DNA from tissues or cells and quantify the amount of DNA adducts formed. Mutations, chromosomal aberrations and DNA strand breaks can be examined at the DNA level by polymerase chain reaction, DNA sequencing and several other methods. Another two examples of genetic alterations are sister chromatid exchange and micronucleus formation. Sister chromatid exchange takes place due to crossing-over events during both mitosis and meiosis and results in two chromatids that no longer contain the same genes. Several techniques allow the visualization of this exchange on a cellular base.

Micronucleus formation reflects the amount of DNA damage. Using staining techniques it is possible to visualize gross changes in number and sizes of individual chromosomes.

In addition to genetic changes, it is also important to study proliferation rates of cell populations. The proliferating cell fraction can be determined by bromodeoxyuridine (BrdU) incorporation and by immunostaining for MIB-1, Ki-67 or proliferating cell nuclear antigen (PCNA), three antigens that are present during different phases of the cell cycle. Proliferation is also reflected in nucleolar organizer regions (NORs), which are loops of DNA that contain ribosomal RNA genes that are involved in protein synthesis. The proteins that are associated with these NORs can be visualized using a silver staining technique. The resulting silver reaction products (AgNORs) are visible as black dots. The number and size of AgNOR dots in a nucleus reflect cell proliferation. Several studies have demonstrated that AgNOR and PCNA both increase during the progression from normal epithelium to hyperplasia, dysplasia and carcinoma *in situ*. More specifically, they may be indicative of the stage of the carcinogenesis process. To gain more objective results, computer programs have been designed to analyse staining results.

The parameters mentioned above are generally not direct targets for antigenotoxins, but can be used to assess the beneficial effects of antigenotoxic compounds.

A large number of antigenotoxic and anticarcinogenic agents have been detected, some of which have proved effective in clinical trials. The multistage nature of carcinogenesis offers the possibility for intervention at each stage of the process, as shown in **Figure 3**. At the initiation stage chemoprevention can be accomplished by inhibition of metabolic activating enzymes or the enhancement of detoxification enzymes, radical scavengers and binding

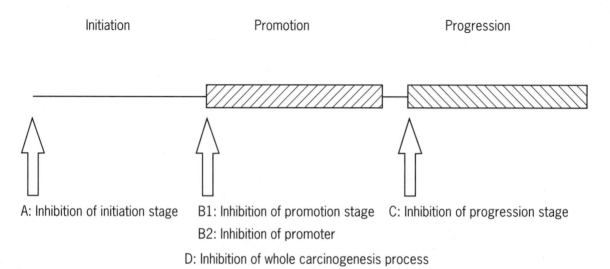

Figure 3 Classification of antigenotoxins and anticarcinogens based on the stage where they exert their protective effects. (Adapted from Ito and Imaida, 1992.)

capacity to active chemical carcinogens (A). At the promotion stage proposed mechanisms for chemoprevention include inhibition of DNA synthesis, cell proliferation and alteration of cell differentiation and communication as well as signal transduction pathways (B). At the progression stage, inhibition of cell proliferation has been proposed (C). Further, some compounds have chemopreventive capacity over the whole carcinogenic process (D). Potential antigenotoxic compounds need to be tested extensively before conclusions with respect to their suitability and applicability as antigenotoxin can be drawn, as was described in the previous section. Many of the target molecules by which antigenotoxins and anticarcinogens act are described below.

DIFFERENT CLASSES OF ANTIGENOTOXINS

Inhibitors of Carcinogen Formation

With the exception of preventing intake, preventing carcinogen formation is by far the most effective and desirable way of controlling cancer, e.g. preventing the formation of nitrosamines from secondary amines and nitrite in an acid environment, such as present in the stomach. Ascorbic acid, ferulic acid, gallic acid, caffeic acid, N-acetylcysteine, proline and thioproline can all exert antigenotoxic effects by inhibiting carcinogen formation.

Blocking Agents

Many procarcinogens need metabolic activation in order to react with DNA. Chemoprevention can be accomplished by interfering with the metabolism of carcinogens or mutagens. This process of biotransformation can be divided into phase I and phase II reactions. In phase I metabolism, oxidation, reduction or hydrolysis reactions transform endogenous or exogenous molecules into more hydrophilic compounds that are readily accessible for phase II reactions. The most important phase I biotransformation enzymes are the cytochromes P450 (Guengerich, 1988). In phase II, parent molecules or their derivatives are conjugated with endogenous compounds such as UDP-glucuronic acid and glutathione, catalysed by the phase II enzymes GSTs and UDP-glucuronyltransferases, respectively. The net result of biotransformation is a polar and water-soluble compound that is readily excreted in urine or faeces and unable to bind covalently with DNA. **Figure 4** shows a schematic overview of the biotransformation of procarcinogens. The antigenotoxins that prevent the carcinogens from reaching and reacting with critical targets such as DNA are called blocking agents. Most blocking agents can be assigned to one or more of the following major categories (**Table 2**).

Inhibitors of Cytochrome P450 Enzymes

Inhibitors of cytochrome P450 enzymes will reduce the activation of procarcinogens (Rendic and Di Carlo, 1997).

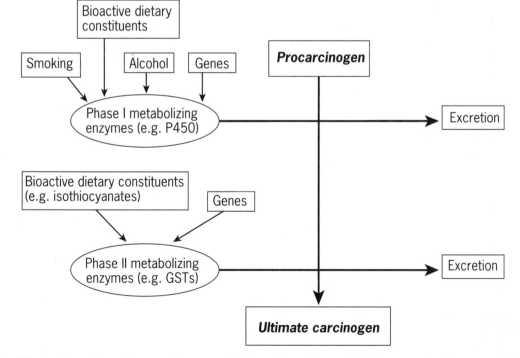

Figure 4 Biotransformation of procarcinogens. (Adapted from *Food, Nutrition and the Prevention of Cancer: A Global Perspective*. American Institute for Cancer Research/World Cancer Research Fund, Washington, DC, 1997.)

Table 2 Working mechanisms and examples of blocking agents. (Adapted from Stoner *et al.*, 1997.)

Mechanism	Examples
Inhibition of cytochrome P450	Ellagic acid, diallyl sulfide, isothiocyanates
Induction of cytochrome P450	Indole-3-carbinol
Induction of phase II enzymes:	
Glutathione S-transferase	Allyl sulfides, dithiolthiones, isothiocyanates
UDP-glucuronyltransferase	Polyphenols
Glutathione peroxidase	Selenium
Scavenging of electrophiles	Ellagic acid, N-acetylcysteine, glutathione
Scavenging of free radicals	Glutathione, polyphenols, vitamin E
Increased overall levels of DNA repair	Vanillin
Increased poly(ADP-ribosyl) transferase	N-Acetylcysteine
Suppression of error-prone DNA repair	Protease inhibitors

As a consequence, less genetic damage will occur. This category of blocking agents consists mainly of dietary anticarcinogens such as ellagic acid, diallyl sulfide and isothiocyanates.

Inducers of Cytochrome P450 Enzymes

Inducers of cytochrome P450 such as indole-3-carbinol may increase the metabolic activation of procarcinogens (Rendic and Di Carlo, 1997). Ironically, this often is a necessary step in the detoxification process. In other words, more ultimate carcinogenic derivatives are formed, but they are constructed in such a way that phase II biotransformation enzymes can dispose of them.

Inducers of Phase II Enzymes

Inducers of phase II detoxification enzymes might be more beneficial over inducers of cytochrome P450 because inducers of phase II systems are less likely to result in highly bioactive compounds. Of utmost importance are enhancers of GST activity (Hayes and Pulford, 1995). GSTs catalyse the conjugation between electrophilic highly reactive compounds with glutathione, giving rise to a conjugate that can be excreted via urine or faeces. Many dietary anticarcinogens such as vitamins, indole-3-carbinol, limonene and phenyl isothiocyanate are inducers of GSTs in the gastrointestinal tract (Van Lieshout *et al.*, 1996, 1998), but also NSAIDs such as aspirin, sulindac and indomethacin have this capacity (Van Lieshout *et al.*, 1997).

Other important phase II enzymes include the glutathione peroxidases, which can be divided into selenium-dependent and non-selenium-dependent enzymes (Mannervik, 1985). Selenium is a biological trace element that is necessary for cell growth. Selenium has preventive potential in carcinogenesis: it may stimulate the immune system, effect carcinogen metabolism, inhibit protein synthesis, induce apoptosis and protect against oxidative damage. Selenium-dependent glutathione peroxidases catalyse the rapid detoxification of very reactive peroxides such as hydrogen peroxides and lipid peroxides. The non-selenium-dependent activity mainly involves the GSTs.

Under some circumstances, phase II enzymes can have a stimulating effect on carcinogenesis. For example, some products of N-acetyltransferase-, sulfotransferase- and GST-mediated reactions have been associated with a higher cancer risk, mainly from epidemiological studies.

Scavengers of Electrophiles and Free Radicals

Free radicals may damage lipids, proteins, DNA and other important biomolecules and thereby contribute to the initiation of cancer. Free radicals may arise exogenously, e.g. in cigarette smoke, or endogenously as a consequence of inflammation or as a by-product of normal respiration. Scavengers or trapping agents are compounds that physically react with electrophilic forms of carcinogens and oxygen free radicals, preventing them from damaging DNA or other molecules. Vegetables and fruit contain natural antioxidants such as vitamin C and E, carotenoids and flavonoids, which appear to be good radical scavengers. Oxidative damage can be detected in the form of oxidized bases in the DNA. A common example is the formation of 8-oxodeoxyguanosine (8-oxo-dG) from its parent compound deoxyguanine in human DNA.

Inducers of DNA Repair

If a procarcinogen has been metabolically activated into an electrophilic ultimate carcinogen, the latter compound can initiate carcinogenesis by forming DNA adducts and subsequent somatic alterations of oncogenes, tumour-suppressor genes and DNA repair genes (**Figure 5**). Damaged DNA can be repaired to prevent the formation of (pre)neoplastic cells. There are three possible chemopreventive mechanisms that involve DNA repair. The first is an increase in the overall level of DNA repair enzymes, e.g. by vanillin. Second, the enzyme poly(ADP-ribosyl) transferase is involved in modulation of DNA damage and the level of this enzyme is reduced by chemical carcinogens, but may be stabilized by antigenotoxins. N-Acetylcysteine is an example of this group of antigenotoxins that act by preventing the decrease in poly(ADP-ribosyl) transferase. A third mechanism is found in bacteria, where proteases specifically activate error-prone repair systems, and in this respect protease inhibitors such as soy bean trypsin inhibitors may be shown beneficial in the future.

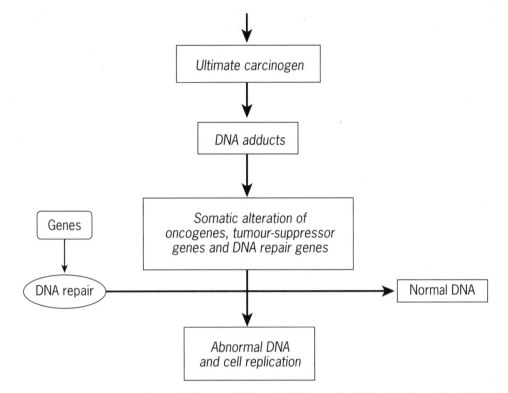

Figure 5 Initiation of carcinogenesis and the possibility of DNA repair. (Adapted from *Food, Nutrition and the Prevention of Cancer: A Global Perspective*. American Institute for Cancer Research/World Cancer Research Fund, Washington, DC, 1997.)

Suppressing Agents

Classification of suppressing agents is more difficult because the critical events and their exact sequence in the process of tumour promotion and progression are not yet well understood. However, the classification proposed by Kelloff *et al*. (1994) (**Table 3**) is generally accepted. After completion of the initiation phase, tumour cells have gained the ability to replicate uncontrolled. **Figures 6** and **7** show schematic overviews of the effects of antigenotoxic and anticarcinogenic compounds on the promotion and progression phases of the carcinogenic process, respectively.

Inhibitors of Polyamine Metabolism

Polyamines play an important role in the regulation of cell proliferation and differentiation. A key enzyme in the polyamine biosynthetic pathway, ornithine decarboxylase (ODC), catalyses the conversion of ornithine to the polyamine putrescine. The levels of ODC and polyamines are frequently elevated in tumour tissues compared with their normal counterparts, indicating the role of ODC in stimulating or maintaining high proliferation rates. Owing to the rapid turnover of ODC of several minutes, high levels of an ODC inhibitor must remain present in the target organ to achieve the desired antiproliferative activity. Examples of this group of anticarcinogens are α-difluoromethylornithine (DFMO) and polyphenols.

Inducers of Terminal Cell Differentiation

Terminal differentiation is one of the steps in the normal, regulated cell proliferation of epithelia. Cancer cells often have lost the ability to differentiate. The carcinogenic process may be stopped by substances which restore the ability of abnormal proliferating cells to differentiate, such as calcium, retinoids and vitamin D_3.

Modulators of Signal Transduction

Signal transduction is a very complex cascade of events leading to a cellular response on extracellular signals. The components of signal transduction pathways are attractive sites for chemopreventive activity since they can result in restoration of normal cellular growth control. For example, one of the steps in signal transduction involves activation of protein kinase C by diacylglycerol. Several chemopreventive agents such as the flavonoids and glycyrrhetinic acid cause inhibition of protein kinase C activity, which leads to suppression of carcinogenesis.

Modulators of Hormonal/Growth Factor Activity

This group of chemopreventive agents inhibit neoplastic cell proliferation by directly regulating the levels and biological activity of specific hormones and growth factors. As a result of specific binding of these hormones and

Table 3 Working mechanisms and examples of suppressing agents. (Adapted from Stoner *et al.*, 1997 and Kelloff *et al.*, 1994.)

Mechanism	Examples[a]
Inhibit polyamine metabolism	DFMO, polyphenols, substituted putrescines, ellagic acid, curcumin
Induce terminal cell differentiation	Calcium, retinoids, vitamin A and D_3
Modulate signal transduction	Glycyrrhetinic acid, NSAIDs, polyphenols, retinoids
Modulate hormonal/ growth factor activity	NSAIDs, retinoids, tamoxifen
Inhibit oncogene activity	Genistein, NSAIDs, monoterpenes, (+)-limonene, retinoic acid
Promote intracellular communication	Carotenoids, polyphenols, retinoids
Restore immune response	NSAIDs, selenium, vitamin E
Induce apoptosis	Butyric acid, genistein, selenium, sulindac sulfone, retinoids
Correct DNA methylation imbalances	Folic acid, choline, methionine, vitamin B_{12}
Inhibit basement membrane degradation	Protease inhibitors
Inhibit arachidonic acid metabolism	Glycyrrhetinic acid, N-acetylcysteine, NSAIDs, polyphenols, flavonoids, vitamin E

[a]DFMO, α-difluoromethylornithine; NSAIDs, nonsteroidal anti-inflammatory drugs.

growth factors to their receptor, very distinct signal transduction pathways will be started. For example, transforming growth factor-β has antiproliferative activity in both normal and neoplastic cells *in vitro* and *in vivo*. In addition, overexpression of the epidermal growth factor receptor, a product of the *erb* oncogene, may be involved in the pathogenesis of certain epithelial neoplasms (Shin *et al.*, 1994). For many growth factor receptors, antibodies are available that can be used for immunohistochemical staining and subsequent qualitative and quantitative analysis. NSAIDs and retinoids are among the compounds that have beneficial effects by modulating the activity of hormones or growth factors, e.g. by competing for binding sites to their receptors.

Inhibitors of Oncogene Activity

Protein inhibitors and retinoids exert their chemopreventive action by inhibiting oncogene expression. Oncogenes are genes that may cause cancer. Present in the genome as proto-oncogenes, they are not harmful as such. However, they can be converted to oncogenes when they acquire specific mutations. The *ras* oncogene protein, which plays a role in cell growth and differentiation, has been extensively studied. To be activated, the Ras protein must be farnesylated. The enzyme farnesyl protein transferase

(FPTase) catalyses farnesylation of Ras precursors in a critical step during post-translational modification of Ras oncoproteins, resulting in their anchorage to the plasma membrane. FPTase inhibitors therefore inhibit Ras-induced colonic tumorigenesis. Singh *et al.* (1998) demonstrated that ingestion of a high amount of corn oil enhances FPTase expression. This in turn leads to increased levels of functional Ras and promotes chemically induced colon carcinogenesis. Dietary fish oil, on the other hand, suppresses FPTase expression and causes decreased production of biologically active Ras, thereby inhibiting colon tumorigenesis. FPTase and type I and type II geranylgeranyl-protein transferases (GGTases) catalyse protein prenylation reactions. As much as 2% of the cellular proteins are isoprenylated in certain cell types. Some of these proteins perform basic cellular functions, whereas others may be involved in the signal transduction pathways that regulate cell proliferation, cell differentiation and cell death. Several isoprenylated proteins, including Ras, which is a substrate of FPTase, RhoA and Rac1 (two substrates of type I GGTase), were shown to have transforming properties. Chemoprevention by interfering with prenylation reactions effects proliferation, differentiation and cell death. Examples of compounds capable of such activity are genistein, NSAIDs, (+)-limonene and retinoic acid.

Promoters of Intercellular Communication

Communication between cells is mediated through gap junctions. Gap junctions are pores or channels in the cell membrane, which join channels of adjacent cells and allow the passage of molecules up to approximately 1000 Da in size. Growth regulatory signal molecules are among the molecules that move between cells. It has been postulated that inhibition of gap junctional communication between cells occurs during carcinogenesis. Several carotenoids, such as β-carotene and canthaxanthine, and several retinoids, such as vitamin A, enhance gap junctional communication *in vitro* and inhibit cell transformation.

Restorers of Immune Response

The immune system may also be a target for chemopreventive agents. For example, retinoic acid increases natural killer cell cytotoxicity which can be involved in eliminating (pre)cancerous cells. Retinoids can also cause leukaemic promyelocytes to differentiate into mature granulocytes, which behave normally. Compounds, as mentioned above, that stimulate the elimination of transformed or otherwise abnormal cells may prove to be chemopreventive.

Inducers of Apoptosis

Apoptosis or programmed cell death has an important function in preventing cells from changing into cancer cells. A desirable way of chemoprevention is by stimulating specific

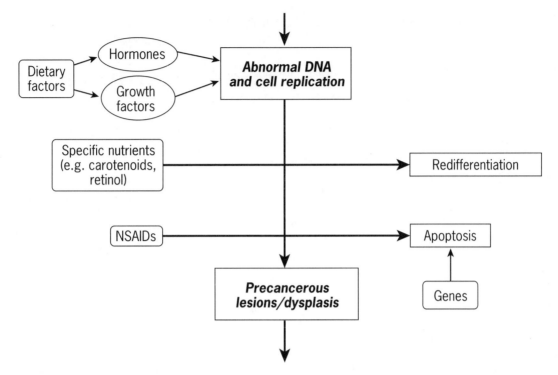

Figure 6   Promotion. (Adapted from *Food, Nutrition and the Prevention of Cancer: A Global Perspective.* American Institute for Cancer Research/World Cancer Research Fund, Washington, DC, 1997.)

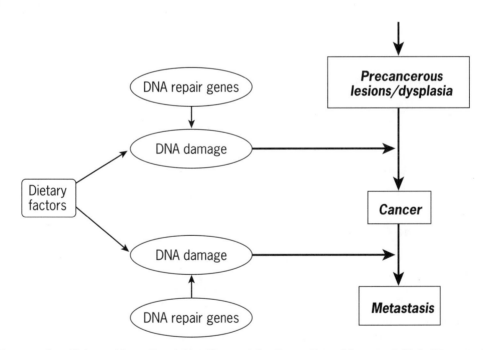

Figure 7   Progression. (Adapted from *Food, Nutrition and the Prevention of Cancer: A Global Perspective.* American Institute for Cancer Research/World Cancer Research Fund, Washington, DC, 1997.)

elimination of potential cancerous cells by apoptosis. Tumour-suppressor proteins such as wild-type p53, and growth factors such as TGF-β have been implicated as inducers of apoptosis. The regulation of apoptosis is very complex. This complexity, on the other hand, also presents many options for interfering with apoptotic pathways. NSAIDs such as sulindac have been demonstrated to be powerful stimulators of apoptosis. Other compounds capable of such activity include butyric acid, genistein, selenium and several retinoids.

Correctors of DNA Methylation Imbalances

A significant loss of methyl groups in DNA appears to occur very early in colorectal tumorigenesis; the smallest adenomas examined (a few millimetres in diameter) have already lost approximately 10–15 million methyl groups, compared with a similar amount of normal colon mucosa cells (Goelz *et al.*, 1985). Hypomethylated DNA may cause undercondensation of chromosomes during mitosis, which may lead to aneuploidy. Aneuploid cells contain an abnormal number of chromosomes, which enhances the cancer risk. Hypomethylation generally coincides with increased proto-oncogene expression and decreased expression of growth factors and their receptors. These observations imply that compounds such as folic acid are likely to be chemopreventative and indeed it has been shown that certain compounds that serve as methyl group donors inhibit tumorigenesis (see earlier). In addition, a number of studies have shown that methyl-deficient diets increase cell turnover and promote the development of carcinogen-induced liver tumours in rats and mice, whereas methyl-rich diets containing high levels of choline and of the amino acid methionine prevent or reduce these effects. Vitamin B_{12} is involved in the intracellular methyl metabolism and is therefore also considered an anticarcinogen.

Inhibitors of Basement Membrane Degradation

Cancer cells contain several enzymes that digest the basement membrane, allowing invasion through to normal tissues. Examples of these enzymes are the proteases collagenase, hyaluronidase, cathepsin B, elastase and plasminogen activators. Therefore, inhibitors of these proteases may prove to be effective in chemoprevention.

Inhibitors of Arachidonic Acid Metabolism

Among the multiple events that occur during experimentally induced tumour promotion is an increased metabolism of arachidonic acid, which contributes to an overall inflammatory response. Arachidonic acid, a fatty acid, is one of the components of the phospholipids, the normal building blocks of cellular membranes. The cyclooxygenase pathway converts arachidonic acid into prostaglandins, prostacyclins and thromboxanes, whereas lipoxygenase converts arachidonic acid into leukotrienes and hydroxyeicosatetraenic acids. During these processes, reactive oxygen and alkylperoxy species are formed, which may damage cellular structures or molecules such as DNA. Cyclooxygenase inhibitors such as the NSAIDs aspirin, indomethacin, ibuprofen and piroxicam and also certain antioxidants such as flavonoids are effective inhibitors of carcinogenesis, since they prevent the formation or cause the elimination of reactive oxygen species.

CONCLUSIONS AND FUTURE PERSPECTIVES

Although encouraging progress in identifying potential cancer chemopreventive or antigenotoxic compounds has been made, this field is in its earliest stages of development. The overview presented above is intended to give a general idea on what antigenotoxins are, how they can be discovered, selected and tested and how they work. However, one has to realize that (1) many potential antigenotoxins have so far only been tested in animals or animal cells, and care has to be taken in extrapolating these data to the human situation, (2) effects found may be strictly specific for a particular tissue or even for a particular type of cell or type of cancer, and thus an antigenotoxin with proven efficacy for prevention of colon cancer may be of no use at all in preventing gastric or oesophageal cancer, and (3) cancer can develop through a wide variety of mechanisms or by a cascade of events, and therefore chemoprevention may be most effective by using a combination of antigenotoxic substances. It will not be as simple as adding fluoride to drinking water for prevention of caries or adding iodine to bread for prevention of struma.

Figure 8 gives an overview of several aspects of the carcinogenic process, and also shows that antigenotoxins or anticarcinogens may interfere at many different levels, indicating once more that chemoprevention of cancer will be achieved most efficiently when a combination of different antigenotoxins is applied. This is probably why chemopreventive human trials performed until now have shown somewhat disappointing results. Another reason may be that the doses of the antigenotoxins used were inappropriate; for example, it has been shown many times in many different test systems that high doses of a particular compound can have deleterious effects, where low doses were beneficial.

Consuming a diet that contains a wide variety of fruits and vegetables provides a broad range of antigenotoxins and this may be the main reason why these diets have been associated with the prevention of a wide variety of different cancer types.

In conclusion, the search for and testing of chemopreventive compounds is a very promising activity which will lead to further reductions in cancer death rates by prevention of the disease, possibly when combinations of different antigenotoxins at low concentrations, are used. However, such research is time consuming, expensive and requires broad knowledge and intensive cooperation of specialists from several disciplines such as epidemiologists, tumour biologists, biochemists, clinicians and many others.

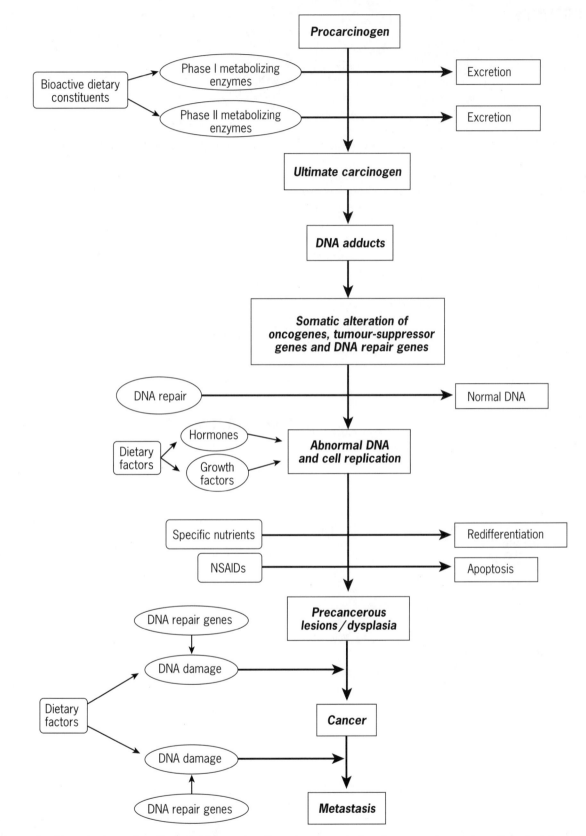

Figure 8   Target sites of antigenotoxins and anticarcinogens during the cancer process. (Adapted from *Food, Nutrition and the Prevention of Cancer: A Global Perspective.* American Institute for Cancer Research/World Cancer Research Fund, Washington, DC, 1997.)

REFERENCES

Ames, B. N., et al. (1973). Carcinogens are mutagens: a simple test system combining liver homogenates for activation and bacteria for detection. *Proceedings of the National Academy of Sciences of the USA*, **70**, 2281–2285.

Anonymous (1999). Prevention of cancer in the next millennium: report of the chemoprevention working group to the American Association for Cancer Research. *Cancer Research*, **59**, 4743–4758.

Glynn, S. A. and Albanes, D. (1994). Folate and cancer: a review of the literature. *Nutrition Cancer*, **22**, 101–119.

Goelz, S., et al. (1985). Hypomethylation of DNA from benign and malignant human colon neoplasms. *Science*, **288**, 187–190.

Guengerich, F. P. (1988). Roles of cytochrome P-450 in chemical carcinogenesis and cancer chemotherapy. *Cancer Research*, **48**, 2946–2954.

Hayes, J. D. and Pulford, D. J. (1995). The glutathione *S*-transferase supergene family: regulation of GST and contribution of the isoenzymes to cancer chemoprevention and drug resistance. *Critical Reviews in Biochemistry and Molecular Biology*, **31**, 445–600.

Ito, N. and Imaida, K. (1992). Strategy of research for cancer-chemoprevention. *Teratogenesis Carcinogenesis and Mutagenesis*, **12**, 79–95.

Kelloff, G. J., et al. (1994). Mechanistic considerations in chemopreventive drug development. *Journal of Cellular Biochemistry* **20**, (Supplement), 1–24.

Mannervik, B. (1985). Glutathione peroxidase. *Methods in Enzymology*, **113**, 490–495.

Miller, J. A. and Miller, E. C. (1977). Ultimate chemical carcinogens as reactive mutagenic electrophiles. Cold Spring Harbor Conference. *Cell Proliferation*, **4**, 604.

Odin, A. P. (1997). Vitamins as antimutagens: advantages and some possible mechanisms of antimutagenic action. *Mutation Research*, **386**, 39–67.

Rendic, S. and Di Carlo, F. J. (1997). Human cytochrome P450 enzymes: a status report summarizing their reactions, substrates, inducers and inhibitors. *Drug Metabolism Reviews*, **29**, 413–580.

Shin, S. Y., et al. (1994). Structure activity relationships of human epidermal growth factor (hEGF). *Life Sciences*, **55**, 131–139.

Singh, J., Hamid, R. and Reddy, B. S. (1998). Dietary fish oil inhibits the expression of farnesyl protein transferase and colon tumor development in rodents. *Carcinogenesis*, **19**, 985–989.

Steinmetz, K. A. and Potter, J. D. (1991). Vegetables fruit and cancer I. Epidemiology. *Cancer Causes and Control*, **2**, 325–357.

Stoner, G. D., et al. (1997). Perspectives in cancer chemoprevention. *Environmental Health Perspectives*, **105** (Supplement 4), 945–954.

Van Lieshout, E. M. M., et al. (1996). Effects of oltipraz, α-tocopherol, β-carotene and phenyl isothiocyanate on rat oesophageal, gastric, colonic and hepatic glutathione, glutathione *S*-transferase and peroxidase. *Carcinogenesis*, **17**, 1439–1445.

Van Lieshout, E. M. M., et al. (1997). Effects of nonsteroidal antiinflammatory drugs on glutathione *S*-transferases of the rat digestive tract. *Carcinogensis*, **18**, 485–490.

Van Lieshout, E. M. M., et al. (1998). Effects of sulforaphane analog compound-30, indole-3-carbinol, D-limonene or relafen on glutathione *S*-transferases and glutathione peroxidase activity. *Biochimica Biophysica Acta*, **1379**, 325–336.

Wattenberg, L. W. (1985). Chemoprevention of cancer. *Cancer Research*, **45**, 1–8.

FURTHER READING

Brugge, J., et al. (eds) (1991). *Origins of Human Cancer. A Comprehensive Review*. Cold Spring Harbor Laboratory Press, Cold Spring Harbor, NY).

Food, Nutrition and the Prevention of Cancer: A Global Perspective. (1997). (American Institute for Cancer Research/World Cancer Research Fund, Washington, DC).

Fourth international conference on prevention of human cancer: nutrition and chemoprevention controversies, Tucson, Arizona (1992). *Preventive Medicine*, **22**, 629–811.

Verhoeven, D. T. H., et al. (1997). A review of mechanisms underlying anticarcinogenicity by brassica vegetables. *Chemico-Biological Interactions*, **103**, 79–129.

Chapter 32

Intervention and Chemoprevention of Cancer

Gary J. Kelloff
National Cancer Institute, National Institutes of Health, Rockville, MD, USA

Caroline C. Sigman
CCS Associates, Mountain View, CA, USA

CONTENTS

INTERVENTION AND CHEMOPREVENTION OF CANCER – TREATMENT OF CARCINOGENESIS

Carcinogenesis is a several years to decades long process expressed in progressive genetic changes and corresponding increasingly severe tissue damage (**Figure 1**). Cancer prevention is intervention in this process before invasive disease develops, when it is potentially reversible, often asymptomatic, easier to control medically and associated with less morbidity. During the last half century, our understanding of carcinogenesis has grown enormously owing largely to technology allowing exploration of molecular pathways, cancer-associated genes and tissue architecture. This knowledge provides the basis for most cancer-preventive intervention strategies and, particularly for one of these strategies, chemoprevention – the use of drugs, biologicals and nutrients to treat precancer (i.e. to inhibit, delay or reverse carcinogenesis) (Sporn, 1976; Wattenberg, 1985; Kelloff *et al.*, 1995a, 1996a; Hong and Sporn, 1997; Lippman *et al.*, 1998; AACR Chemoprevention Working Group, 1999; Kelloff, 2000; Sporn and Suh, 2000).

Just as for cancer treatment drugs, the discovery and development of chemopreventive agents is mechanistically driven, focusing on modulating molecular targets associated with carcinogenesis (also called carcinogenesis biomarkers). This approach holds even more promise for chemoprevention than for treatment since molecular targets are more available and normal cell function and structure are less disrupted and, hence, easier to control in precancer than in cancer. Clinical cancer is in fact characterized by unregulated proliferation, cellular heterogeneity and, consequently very few sites and processes responsive to therapeutic intervention.

This chapter is an overview of strategies for chemoprevention. First, the principles of molecular target-based chemopreventive drug discovery and early development are described. Then a sequential drug development programme is described, which is translational in nature and builds on the rational mechanism-based and empirical agent discovery approach described, and leads to Food and Drug Administration (FDA) approvals for chemopreventive uses. An important aspect of this programme is identification of precancers (particularly intraepithelial neoplasia (IEN)) and early biomarkers of carcinogenesis, which can serve as surrogate endpoints for cancer incidence in chemoprevention studies. The material covered is drawn from and presented comprehensively in the references cited following the text.

MOLECULAR TARGETS AND CHEMOPREVENTION DRUG DISCOVERY AND EARLY DEVELOPMENT

Mechanisms of Chemopreventive Activity and Potential Chemopreventive Drugs

Basic research in carcinogenesis has identified enzymes, genetic lesions and other cellular components associated with the initiation and progression of precancers to invasive disease. Possible mechanisms for chemoprevention involve interfering with the expression and/or activity of these molecules; examples of the mechanisms, their possible molecular targets and agents that act at these targets

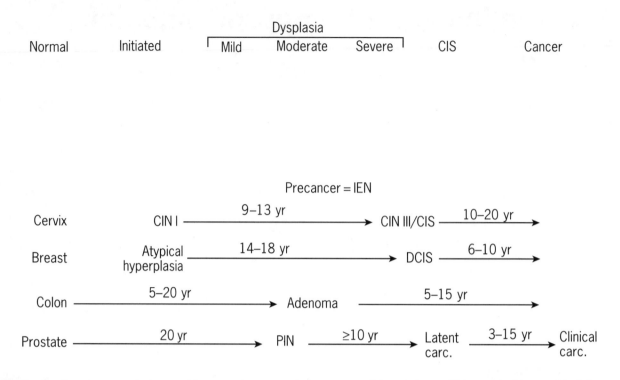

Figure 1 Carcinogenesis is a multiyear and progressive process. Abbreviations: CIN, cervical intraepithelial neoplasia; CIS, carcinoma *in situ*; DCIS, (breast) ductal carcinoma *in situ*; IEN, intraepithelial neoplasia; PIN, prostatic intraepithelial neoplasia. See also Kelloff, 2000, *Advances in Cancer Research*, **278**, 199–334 and Kelloff, *et al.*, 1996, *Oncology*, **10**, 1471–1484.

are listed in **Table 1** (Wattenberg, 1978; De Flora and Ramel, 1998; Hartman and Shankel, 1990; Kelloff *et al.* 1995b; Hong and Sporn, 1997; Singh and Lippman, 1998a,b; Kelloff, 2000).

Genetic progression models have been developed for many cancer sites, including colon, head and neck, bladder, brain, lung and cervix. (See the section on *In Vitro and Animal Models for Human Cancer*.) These models map the appearance of the specific molecular lesions and/or more general genotypic damage in their temporal association with increasingly severe precancer. In many cases early critical steps include inactivation of tumor suppressor genes, such as *APC* or *p53*, activation of oncogenes such as *RAS*, and damage to DNA repair mechanisms, such as by mutations in *MSH* and *MLH* (mismatch repair genes) and in *BRCA* (so named because it is mutated in some women at high risk of breast cancer). (See the section on *The Molecular Basis of Cell and Tissue Organisation*.) These models confirm that changes in specific biomarkers of carcinogenesis may be useful measures of potential chemopreventive activity.

Experimental and epidemiological carcinogenesis studies have associated >90% of cancers with exposure to mutagens and mitogens (agents which enhance cell proliferation). Mutagenesis can damage the cell and disrupt normal growth controls, resulting in loss of programmed cell death (apoptosis) and maturation pathways and increased (hyper)proliferation. Thus, inhibitors of mutagenesis and proliferation and inducers of apoptosis and differentiation are potential chemopreventives. There are also cell and tissue-based processes that are related to carcinogenesis, namely inflammation and oxidation. Hence, anti-inflammatories and antioxidants are possible chemopreventives. In this regard, experimental, epidemiological and clinical studies have demonstrated chemopreventive activity for agents that interfere with either the inflammatory or oxidating activities associated with arachidonic acid (AA) metabolism, for example nonsteroidal anti-inflammatory drugs (NSAIDs), polyphenols (tea, resveratrol) and vitamin A derivatives (retinoids).

Carcinogen-blocking Activities (Antimutagenicity)

Inhibition of carcinogen uptake into cells, inhibition of carcinogen formation or activation, carcinogen deactivation or detoxification, preventing carcinogen binding to DNA, and enhancing the level or fidelity of DNA repair are all carcinogen-blocking activities and potential chemopreventive mechanisms (Wattenberg, 1978; Kelloff *et al.*, 1995b). (See the chapter on *Antigenotoxins and Cancer*.)

Table 1 Mechanisms for chemoprevention with possible molecular targets[a]

Mechanism	Possible molecular targets	Representative agents
Inhibit carcinogen uptake	Bile acids (bind)	Calcium
Inhibit formation/activation of carcinogen	Cytochromes P450 (inhibit)	PEITC, tea, indole-3-carbinol
	PG synthase hydroperoxidase, 5-lipoxygenase (inhibit)	NSAIDs, COX-2 inhibitors, LOX inhibitors, iNOS inhibitors
	Bile acids (inhibit)	Ursodiol
Deactivate/detoxify carcinogen	GSH/GST (enhance)	Oltipraz, NAC
Prevent carcinogen-DNA binding	Cytochromes p450 (inhibit)	Tea
Increase level or fidelity of DNA repair	Poly(ADP–ribosyl)transferase (enhance)	NAC, protease inhibitors
Modulate hormone/growth factor activity	Oestrogen receptor (antagonize)	SERMs, soy isoflavones
	Androgen receptor (antagonize)	Bicalutamide, flutamide
	Steroid aromatase (inhibit)	Exemestane, vorozole, letrozole
	Steroid 5-reductase (inhibit)	Finasteride
	IGF-I (inhibit)	SERMs, retinoids
Inhibit oncogene activity	Farnesyl protein transferase (inhibit)	Perillyl alcohol, limonene, DHEA, FTI-276
Inhibit polyamine metabolism	ODC activity (inhibit)	DFMO
	ODC induction (inhibit)	Retinoids
Induce terminal differentiation	TGF (induce)	Retinoids, vitamin D, SERMs
	PPAR (activate)	GW7845
Restore immune response	COX (inhibit)	NSAIDs
	T, NK lymphocytes (enhance)	Selenium, tea
	Langerhans cells (enhance)	Vitamin E
Increase intercellular communication	Connexin 43 (enhance)	Carotenoids, retinoids
Restore tumour-suppressor function	p53 (stabilize)	CP-31398
Induce apoptosis	TGF (induce)	Retinoids, SERMs, vitamin D
	RAS farnesylation (inhibit)	Perillyl alcohol, limonene, DHEA, FTI-276
	Telomerase (inhibit)	Retinoic acid
	AA (enhance)	NSAIDs, COX-2 inhibitors, LOX inhibitors
	Caspase (activate)	Retinoids
	PPAR (activate)	Phenylacetate
	PPAR (inhibit)	NSAIDs
Inhibit angiogenesis	FGF receptor (inhibit)	Soy isoflavones, COX-2 inhibitors
	Thrombomodulin (inhibit)	Retinoids
Correct DNA methylation Imbalances	CpG island methylation (enhance)	Folic acid
	GSH/GST (enhance)	Oltipraz, NAC
Inhibit basement membrane degradation	Type IV collagenase (inhibit)	Protease inhibitors
Inhibit DNA synthesis	Glucose 6-phosphate dehydrogenase (inhibit)	DHEA, fluasterone

[a]Abbreviations: AA, arachidonic acid; COX, cyclooxygenase; CpG, cytosine–guanosine; DFMO, 2-difluoromethylornithine; DHEA, dehydroepiandrosterone; GSH, glutathione; GST, glutathione-S-transferase; FGF, fibroblast growth factor; IGF, insulin-like growth factor; iNOS, inducible nitric oxide synthase; LOX, lipoxygenase; NAC, N-acetyl-L-cysteine; NK, natural killer; NSAID, nonsteroidal anti-inflammatory drug; ODC, ornithine decarboxylase; PEITC, phenylethyl-isothiocyanate; PG, prostaglandin; PPAR, peroxisome proliferator-activated receptor; SERM, selective oestrogen receptor modulator; TGF, transforming growth factor.
See also Kelloff, G. J. (2000). *Advances in Cancer Research*, **278**, 199–334.

Inhibition of Carcinogen Uptake

Agents which inhibit carcinogen uptake appear to react directly with putative carcinogens, both initiators and promoters. For example, calcium inhibits the promotion of carcinogen- and dietary fat-induced colon tumours in rats. It also inhibits carcinogen-induced hyperproliferation induced in rat and mouse colon, including that induced by a Western 'stress' diet, i.e. a diet low in calcium and vitamin D and high in fat and phosphate. A partial explanation of these effects is that calcium binds to excess bile and free fatty acids that irritate the colon lumen and promote the formation of tumours. Such data suggest a potential for other sequestering and chelating agents as chemopreventives, particularly in the colon.

Inhibition of Carcinogen Formation/Activation

Vitamin C prevents the biosynthesis of carcinogenic N-nitroso compounds. Other chemopreventive antioxidants such as vitamin E prevent the formation of nitrosamines from their precursors by scavenging nitrite. Many putative chemopreventive agents interfere with metabolic activation of a procarcinogen (Wattenberg, 1978; De Flora and Ramel, 1998; Hartman and Shankel, 1990; Kelloff *et al.*, 1995b). Examples are allylic sulfides, arylalkyl isothiocyanates, carbamates and flavonoids and other polyphenols. Usually this activity involves inhibition of the cytochrome P-450 enzymes responsible for activating various classes of carcinogens such as polycyclic aromatic hydrocarbons (PAHs).

Steroid aromatase, a cytochrome P-450-dependent enzyme, catalyses the first step in oestrogen biosynthesis in humans: C19 hydroxylation and subsequent oxidative cleavage of the androgens androstenedione and testosterone to oestrone and oestradiol, respectively. Both steroidal (e.g. 4-hydroxyandrostenedione) and nonsteroidal (e.g. vorozole) aromatase inhibitors also inhibit carcinogenesis in oestrogen-sensitive tissues.

Enhancement of Carcinogen Deactivation/Detoxification

Enhancement of carcinogen deactivation/detoxification is potentially a very important strategy for chemoprevention (De Flora and Ramel, 1998; Kelloff *et al.*, 1995b). Two metabolic pathways are critical. The first is the introduction or exposure of polar groups (e.g. hydroxyl groups) on procarcinogens/carcinogens via the phase I metabolic enzymes, which are primarily the microsomal mixed-function oxidases. These polar groups become substrates for conjugation. The second pathway is via the phase II metabolic enzymes responsible for conjugation and the formation of glucuronides, glutathione (GSH) conjugates and sulfates. In both cases, the conjugates are more likely to be excreted from the body than they are to reach sensitive tissues in activated form. Agents that affect phase II enzymes probably hold more promise than those which induce phase I enzymes, since phase I oxidation also can result in carcinogen activation. (See the chapter on *Mechanisms of Chemical Carcinogenesis*.)

GSH is a prototype carcinogen scavenger (see also under the more general mechanism of electrophile scavenging below). It reacts spontaneously or via catalysis of GSH-S-transferases with numerous activated carcinogens including some N-nitroso compounds, aflatoxin B_1 (AFB$_1$) and PAHs. GSH protects against mouse skin tumours induced by PAHs, rat forestomach tumours induced by nitrosamines and rat liver tumours induced by AFB$_1$. A number of promising chemopreventive agents are potent inducers of GSH and GSH-S-transferases, including allylic sulfides, which are natural products found in onion, garlic and other members of the *Allium* genus as well as the sulfur-containing compounds found in cruciferous vegetables. Oltipraz (a dithiolthione similar to those found in cruciferous vegetables) is a potent GSH-S- transferase inducer with a wide spectrum of chemopreventive activity. Sulforaphane, an isothiocyanate

found in broccoli sprouts, induces phase II enzymes and has chemopreventive activity in rat colon (prevents formation of nitrosamine-induced ACF) and mammary gland (PAH-induced carcinoma). N-Acetyl-L-cysteine (NAC) is essentially a precursor of GSH. NAC shows inhibitory activity in mouse lung and bladder and rat colon and mammary gland against nitrosamine-induced tumours.

GSH-peroxidases (GSH-Px) catalyse the reduction of hydrogen peroxide (H$_2$O$_2$) and organic hydroperoxides; the antioxidant effects of selenium may be related to its function in the enzyme's active site. Although several studies show that the anticarcinogenic activity of selenium in mouse and rat mammary glands is not mediated by GSH-Px, in tissues such as colon, glandular stomach and skin, GSH-Px are thought to play a role.

Another type of carcinogen deactivation is modulation of the mixed-function oxidases involved in the metabolism of oestrogens. Indole-3-carbinol, a compound which occurs naturally in cruciferous vegetables, inhibits the induction of mammary tumours in rats and induces mixed-function oxidases. Particularly, it induces the activity of the enzymes responsible for 2-hydroxylation of oestradiol, leading to increased excretion of oestradiol metabolites.

Inhibition of DNA–Carcinogen Adduct Formation

DNA–carcinogen adduct formation can be considered a biomarker of carcinogen exposure. In most cases, it is probably secondary to other mechanisms of carcinogenesis, such as carcinogen activation and formation. Likewise, inhibition of DNA adduct formation is typically an indirect measure of other mechanisms of chemoprevention, particularly inhibition of carcinogen formation and activation and enhancement of carcinogen detoxification (Hartman and Shankel, 1990; Kelloff *et al.*, 1995b). For example, oltipraz prevents the formation of AFB$_1$–DNA adducts, an effect which has been attributed to increased rates of aflatoxin detoxification by GST. Nonetheless, inhibition of DNA adduct formation is a convenient assay for screening potential chemopreventive agents which are expected to modulate carcinogen metabolism. There is also limited evidence of chemopreventive agents directly obstructing adduct formation. For example, ellagic acid appears to inhibit the carcinogen adduct formation by itself binding to the duplex form of DNA. (See also chapter on *The Formation of DNA Adducts*.)

Enhancement of DNA Repair

There are three possible chemopreventive mechanisms that involve DNA repair (Kelloff *et al.*, 1995b). First is an increase in the overall level of DNA repair. Second, the enzyme poly(ADP-ribosyl)transferase (ADPRT) is known to be involved in modulation of DNA damage, and the level of this enzyme is decreased in the presence of carcinogens. The chemopreventive agent NAC prevents carcinogen-induced decreases in ADPRT. The third mechanism is suppression of error-prone DNA repair. It is known that protease inhibitors depress error-prone repair in bacteria, and it has been suggested that they might prevent carcinogenesis by inhibiting an error-prone repair system activated by proteases that, in turn, are induced by tumour promoters. The protease inhibitor best studied as a chemopreventive is Bowman–Birk soybean trypsin inhibitor (BBI), which inhibits nitrosamine-induced tumours in mouse colon and liver and in rat oesophagus.

Antiproliferative Activity via Signal Transduction Pathways

Much is now known about the biochemical control mechanisms involved in regulating cell growth and development. Cells respond to signals from extracellular stimuli via a complicated network of highly regulated events collectively referred to as signal transduction pathways. Stimulation of these pathways results in changes in transcriptional activity. While normal cells respond appropriately to extracellular stimuli, many precancerous and cancerous cells have lost this ability and display aberrant signalling.

Molecular targets on these pathways that allow interference with the deregulated signalling are potential sites for chemopreventive intervention (Powis, 1994; Powis and Workman, 1994). For example, key components of these pathways are growth factors such as epidermal growth factor (EGF), insulin-like growth factor (IGF) and transforming growth factor (TGF) and protein tyrosine kinases which catalyse the transfer of the phosphate of ATP to the hydroxyl group of tyrosine on numerous proteins. Many growth factor receptors (e.g. EGFR) and oncogenes are tyrosine kinases, and loss of tyrosine kinase regulatory mechanisms has been implicated in neoplastic growth.

Invocation of signal transduction pathways also provides a mechanistic rationale for the multiple chemopreventive effects of some classes of agents. For example, chemopreventive agents such as retinoids, antihormones and protein kinase inhibitors which affect activities at the cell membrane level and cytoplasmic and nuclear receptor levels can also affect other connected events. It is evident that many of these activities are interrelated, e.g. effects on the proliferation associated enzyme ornithine decarboxylase (ODC), AA metabolism, protein kinase C (PKC), IGF-I and TGF may be pleiotropic results of activity at single locus on signal transduction pathways. It is also clear that a single activity may not be the most important or the only one required for carcinogenesis. (See section on *The Molecular Basis of Cell and Tissue Organisation*.)

Modulate Hormonal/Growth Factor Activity

Chemicals may inhibit the proliferation associated with carcinogenesis by directly regulating the induction and activity of specific hormones and growth factors that initiate steps in signal transduction (Kelloff *et al.*, 1995b). This regulation may occur at membrane level receptors (for growth factors, peptide hormones and neurotransmitters) or via cytoplasmic and nuclear receptors (for the steroid superfamily consisting of oestrogen, progesterone, retinoid, glucocorticoid, vitamin D and thyroid receptors). For example, antioestrogens such as tamoxifen bind to nuclear oestrogen receptors, preventing the binding and activity of oestrogens. Tamoxifen inhibits carcinogen-induced, oestrogen-sensitive tumours in rat mammary glands and hamster kidney. Most importantly, tamoxifen has been shown to lower the risk of breast cancer in women at high risk. Phyto-oestrogens, such as the isoflavone genistein, have anti-oestrogenic activity. Studies in human breast cancer cells indicate that the anti-oestrogenic effect may result from slowed translocation of genistein-bound receptor from the cytoplasm to the nucleus compared with that of oestradiol-bound receptor.

TGFβ has antiproliferative activity in both normal and cancer cells. These observations suggest that chemicals that activate TGFβ could also control proliferation in carcinogenesis. In this regard, breast cancer cells normally produce only small amounts of activated TGFβ, but treatment with tamoxifen increases production up to 20-fold. Retinoic acid, which inhibits chemical carcinogenesis, particularly tumour promotion in mouse skin, induces TGFβ_2 in mouse skin after topical application. In vitamin A-deficient rats treated with retinoic acid, the level of expression of TGFβ correlates with levels of retinoids in skin, intestine and respiratory tract tissue.

There is also evidence of cross-regulation among membrane and nuclear receptors. For example, IGF-I stimulates cell replication in various tumours. Particularly, human breast cancer cells have membrane receptors for and excrete IGF-I. Tamoxifen lowers blood concentrations of IGF-I in breast cancer patients, suggesting that part of its antitumour activity is inhibition of IGF-I.

Other aspects of receptor activity are possible mechanisms for chemopreventive activity. Generally, receptors are phosphoproteins, and phosphorylation appears to play a role in receptor activation. Thus, chemopreventive agents which inhibit phosphorylation, e.g. inhibit protein kinases, may influence cell proliferation by effects on receptors. An example is the isoflavone genistein, which is a specific inhibitor of tyrosine kinase and other flavonoids.

Deactivation of steroids may prevent hormone-stimulated carcinogenesis. In this regard, aromatase inhibitors and modifiers of steroid hydroxylation have been described above under inhibition of carcinogen formation/activation and carcinogen deactivation/detoxification, respectively.

Inhibit Oncogene Activity

During the course of cell proliferation in carcinogenesis, numerous oncogenes are expressed abnormally, possibly as intermediates in the signal transduction pathways. The evidence for oncogene activity in signal transduction pathways is based on the similarity of some of their products (protein kinases) to other intermediates in these pathways (Kelloff *et al.*, 1995b). There are several points during activation at which the *ras* oncogene can be inhibited, and there are data relating this inhibition to chemopreventive activity.

First, a membrane receptor-linked tyrosine kinase is involved in Ras activation, and kinase inhibitors would be expected to prevent Ras activation. Particularly interesting are compounds such as genistein which specifically inhibit tyrosine kinase, and thus do not interfere with normal cellular processes mediated by other kinases.

To be activated, the Ras protein must first be farnesylated. *Ras* oncogenes are involved in rat mammary gland carcinogenesis. D-Limonene inhibits the progression of carcinogen-induced mammary tumours induced in rats, and it also inhibits the farnesylation of small G proteins (21–26 kDa); these experimental data suggest that D-limonene could be preventing oncogene activation by inhibiting post-translational farnesylation of the p21 Ras protein. Perillyl alcohol is an even more potent inhibitor of farnesyl–protein transferase. Recently, several specific farnesylation inhibitors have been described which are structural analogues of the C-terminal tetrapeptide of farnesyl–protein transferase and inhibit the growth of *ras*-dependent tumours.

Further, farnesyl pyrophosphate, the substrate for farnesyl–protein transferase, is an intermediate in the synthetic pathway from hydroxymethylglutaryl coenzyme A (HMG CoA) reductase to cholesterol. Inhibitors of HMG CoA reductase, e.g. lovastatin, and probably inhibitors of other enzymes along the synthetic route to cholesterol, have been shown to inhibit Ras farnesylation.

Cyclooxygenase (COX) catalyses the synthesis of prostaglandins (PGs) from AA. COX inhibitors also might inhibit proliferation in carcinogenesis by inhibition of oncogene expression, although the evidence is less direct than for other effects of AA metabolism inhibitors. Expression of the oncogene c-*myc* occurs early in EGF-induced cell proliferation. PGs are required but not sufficient for c-*myc* expression and DNA synthesis stimulated by EGF. The NSAID indomethacin inhibits both EGF-induced DNA synthesis and oncogene expression; this inhibition is reversed by addition of PGG_2.

Studies *in vitro* indicate inhibition of oncogene expression as a mechanism for chemopreventive activity of protease inhibitors and retinoids. For example, the protease inhibitors inhibit transformation of cells transfected with activated H-*ras* oncogene, suppress c-*myc* expression in mouse fibroblasts and inhibit carcinogen-induced tumours in rat colon, mouse lung and mouse skin. Retinoic acid also inhibits H-*ras*-induced transformation in cancer cells and mouse skin carcinogenesis.

Inhibit Polyamine Metabolism

Polyamines play a significant role in cell proliferation, differentiation and malignant transformation. The mode of action is not yet known, but it has been suggested that polyamines stabilize DNA structures; they have been shown to affect DNA and protein synthesis. A critical step in polyamine biosynthesis is the synthesis of putrescine from ornithine that is catalysed by ODC. There is ample evidence that ODC participates in carcinogenesis – the enzyme is induced during cell transformation by chemical carcinogens, viruses and oncogenes.

Association with cell proliferation during carcinogenesis is also well established. TPA and other tumour promoters increase ODC activity in skin, colon, bladder and liver. In mouse skin, topically applied TPA causes an approximately 200-fold increase in ODC activity within 4.5 h after treatment. The increase is dose dependent and correlates with the ability of the TPA dose to promote skin tumours. Also, the increased ODC activity has been proposed to be specific to tumour promotion, since most carcinogens that are not tumour promoters do not induce ODC.

Likewise, chemicals that inhibit induction of or deactivate ODC also inhibit carcinogenesis. Some of the most convincing results demonstrating that inhibition of ODC prevents cancers come from studies with DFMO. DFMO is a specific, mechanism-based irreversible inhibitor of ODC – that is, DFMO is activated by ODC into a form that reacts with the enzyme to inactivate it. DFMO inhibits carcinogen-induced tumours in mouse and rat colon and bladder, rat mammary glands and mouse skin.

ODC induction by TPA is regulated at the transcription level. Regulation occurs in part via signal transduction events at the membrane. For example, PKC appears to be involved, as are diverse signal transduction intermediates induced by TPA, including PGs, other products of AA metabolism and free radicals. Chemicals that inhibit PKC and AA metabolism and those that scavenge free radicals also may inhibit the induction of ODC, hence they may be chemopreventives by this mechanism. In this regard, several of the PKC inhibitors, including glycyrrhetinic acid, inhibit ODC induction and tumour promotion in mouse skin. AA metabolism inhibitors also inhibit both ODC induction and TPA-promoted mouse skin tumorigenesis, as do free radical scavengers such as GSH, flavonoids and green tea polyphenols.

Vitamin A (retinol) and its derivatives (i.e. retinoids) inhibit carcinogenesis specifically during promotion. There is evidence that the cancer inhibitory activity of these compounds may be mediated partially by regulation of ODC induction. One of the most active retinoids is fenretinide. This compound is a potent inhibitor of ODC induction as well as TPA promotion in mouse skin. It also inhibits carcinogen-induced mammary gland tumours in rats and bladder tumours in mice.

Inhibition of S-adenosyl-L-methionine (SAM) decarboxylase is another mechanism for inhibiting polyamine biosynthesis that may prove useful in chemoprevention. This enzyme, like ODC, is highly regulated in mammalian cells and catalyses the formation of the polyamines spermidine and spermine from putrescine.

Induce Terminal Differentiation

Terminal differentiation is one of the steps in normal, regulated cell proliferation in epithelial tissues. Proliferating cancer cells often have lost the ability to differentiate. These cancer cells are either deficient in or incapable of responding to differentiation signals. Abundant evidence demonstrates that restoring the ability of abnormally proliferating cells to differentiate suppresses carcinogenesis. Several classes of chemopreventives also induce differentiation. Retinoids are the best-studied example (Singh and Lippman, 1998a). For many years it has been known that vitamin A deficiency causes squamous metaplasia and hyperkeratinization – both are signs of excessive tissue. Studies in hamster trachea and various cancer cells show that the differentiated phenotype can be restored by treatment with retinoids. Evidence indicates that retinoids control differentiation via intracellular binding proteins (cellular retinol-binding protein and cellular retinoic acid-binding protein) and nuclear receptors.

Calcium and vitamin D_3 are well-known differentiating agents that also inhibit carcinogenesis. Calcium induces differentiation in epithelial tissues including rat oesophagus, mouse skin and human mammary gland and colon. Vitamin D_3 induces differentiation in human colon, human and mouse myeloid leukaemia cells, mouse skin cells, mouse melanoma cells and other cells. It has been suggested that the effects of the two chemicals on differentiation may be mediated by the same signal transduction pathway, involving the vitamin D_3 nuclear receptor with calcium as the messenger.

Restore Immune Response

Antibodies to oncogene products are important in the inhibition of cell transformation and tumour growth. PGE_2 is known to suppress immune response in certain tumour cells. COX inhibitors diminish the immune suppression, and it has been suggested that this effect on immune suppression may be part of the mechanism by which COX inhibitors reduce tumour growth, as seen in several animal tumour models including colon and Lewis lung carcinoma.

Retinoids also are known to be immunostimulants. Retinoic acid increases cell-mediated and natural killer (NK) cell cytotoxicity; retinoids also cause some leukaemia cells to differentiate to mature granulocytes comparable to mature neutrophils. These effects might be partially responsible for the activity of retinoids against established tumours.

Pharmacological doses of vitamin E fed with normal, well-balanced animal diets increase humoural antibody production, especially IgG; this effect has been observed repeatedly in chickens, mice, turkeys, guinea pigs and rabbits. Vitamin E also stimulates cell-mediated immunity, as evidenced by enhanced mitogenesis and mixed lymphocyte response in spleen cells from mice fed the vitamin. In particular, vitamin E prevents the carcinogen-induced decrease in the density of macrophage-equivalent cells (Langerhans cells) in the buccal pouch of carcinogen-treated hamsters. Likewise, vitamin E inhibits the induction and causes regression of tumours in hamster buccal pouch.

The role of selenium in mediating immune responses suggests that the broad spectrum activity of selenium in inhibiting chemical carcinogenesis may be attributed partially to stimulation of the immune system. In general, selenium deficiency causes immunosuppression, while supplementation with low doses of selenium restores and increases immune response. Perhaps most important in inhibiting tumorigenesis is the effect of selenium on the cytotoxicity of immune system cells. Compared with normal cells, both T and NK lymphocytes from selenium-deficient mice have decreased ability to destroy tumour cells in vitro. Supplementation with selenium enhances the ability of rat NK cells to kill tumour cells. The role of immunostimulation in carcinogenesis inhibition by selenium has been studied to only a limited extent and has not been confirmed. However, the potent inhibitory activity of selenium compounds against DMBA-induced tumors in rat mammary glands is suggestive, since the immunosuppressive effects of DMBA are well documented.

Increase Intercellular Communication

Gap junctions are the cell components that coordinate intercellular communication. They are composed of pores, or channels, in the cellular membranes that join channels of adjacent cells; these pores are regulated and, when open, allow passage of molecules up to about 1000 D in size. Gap junctions may allow growth regulatory signals to move between cells. There is evidence from studies in vitro that inhibition of gap junctional intercellular communication occurs in the proliferative phase of carcinogenesis. In in vitro studies, enhancement of communication correlates to inhibition of cellular transformation.

To date, only limited data suggest the potential for inhibiting chemical carcinogenesis by the other antiproliferative/antiprogression mechanisms listed in **Table 1**, but the possibilities exist and warrant consideration here.

Restore Tumour-suppressor Function

Many so-called 'tumour-suppressor' genes have been found that may be involved in controlling proliferation and differentiation in cells. Particularly, their function is associated with control of abnormal growth in carcinogenesis. Several of these genes have been identified and implicated in pathogenesis by the presence of mutated or otherwise dysfunctional forms in specific cancers. For example, the tumour suppressor *Rb* is involved in retinoblastoma, osteosarcoma and tumours in lung, bladder, prostate and breast; *p53* in adenocarcinomas in colon and breast, human T cell leukaemias, glioblastomas, sarcomas, and tumours in lung and liver; *WT* in Wilm tumour; and *DCC* (Deleted in Colorectal Cancer) in colon tumours. There is potential for treating cancer patients with exogenous functional tumour-suppressor genes to inhibit tumour growth and spread. Possibly, it also will be found that chemicals can modulate the expression and activity of tumour suppressors and inhibit carcinogenesis by this mechanism. CP-31398 stabilizes the DNA binding domain of both normal and mutant p53 in an active conformation, induces the $p21^{WAF1}$ cell cycle regulatory protein in the absence of normal p53 and inhibits growth of human tumours with p53 mutated tumours in a mouse model.

Induce Programmed Cell Death (Apoptosis)

Apoptosis is a well-regulated function of the normal cell cycle requiring gene transcription and translation. Tumour suppressors, such as p53 and certain regulatory growth factors, particularly TGFβ1, have been implicated as inducers of apoptosis. Programmed cell death has been described as the complement to mitosis in the maintenance, growth and involution of tissues; it is the process by which damaged and excessive cells are eliminated. Apoptosis is inhibited by tumour promoters such as TPA and phenobarbital and other chemicals that stimulate cell proliferation such as hormones. These data suggest that induction of apoptosis may inhibit tumour formation and that agents which inhibit tumour promotion may act by inducing or preventing inhibition of apoptosis through any one of several signal transduction pathways. For example, hamster pancreatic cancers regress when apoptosis is induced, and many potential chemopreventive agents (e.g. tamoxifen, NSAIDs, retinoids) induce programmed cell death in precancerous and cancer cells.

Correct DNA Methylation Imbalances

Changes in DNA methylation patterns appear to be involved in carcinogenesis. (See the chapter on *Non-Genotoxic Causes of Cancer*.) Methyl-deficient diets cause fatty livers, increased cell turnover and promote the development of carcinogen-induced liver tumours in rats and mice. Conversely, methyl-rich (fortified with choline and methionine) diets prevent or reduce these effects. Changes in gene expression, such as increased expression of oncogenes, appear in animals on methyl-deficient diets. These effects are similar to those seen in rodents given

tumour-promoting chemicals and they are reversible on methyl replacement. Hypomethylation is also associated with hyperproliferation in colon tissue. Methionine, which is involved with choline, folic acid and vitamin B_{12} in regulating intracellular methyl metabolism inhibits carcinogen-induced mammary gland cancers in rats. Also, folic acid inhibits carcinogen-induced lung tumours in mice. Conversely, methylation of CpG islands in the promoter regions of tumour-suppressor and *GST* genes has been seen in cancers of several major target organs including colon, prostate, breast and lung. This methylation prevents gene expression and provides a rationale for the chemopreventive activity of agents which induce GST and tumour-suppressor activity.

Inhibit Angiogenesis

Angiogenesis is the process leading to the formation of new blood vessels. In normal tissue, it is a highly regulated process essential to reproduction, development and wound repair. In carcinogenesis, it is required in tumour growth and involved in metastasis, and there is evidence that angiogenesis also may occur early in carcinogenesis. There is indirect evidence that certain chemicals that inhibit carcinogenesis may inhibit angiogenesis. For example, PGs E_1 and E_2 are angiogenic. Therefore, agents that inhibit PG synthesis may inhibit carcinogenesis by inhibiting angiogenesis. Similarly various growth factors and, particularly, vascular endothelial growth factor (VEGF), increase angiogenesis by activating signal transduction pathways. Inhibition of angiogenesis may be a chemopreventive mechanism for agents which affect these pathways.

Inhibit Basement Membrane Degradation

Tumour cells produce various enzymes that destroy the basement membrane which acts as a barrier against malignant cancer cells and prevents cancer spread. These enzymes include, among others, the proteases collagenase, cathepsin B, plasminogen activators and prostate-specific antigen (PSA). Protease inhibitors are known to act against thrombin and type IV collagenase, which are among the proteases hypothesized to participate in the destruction of basement membranes during cancer invasion. Proteases are also involved in angiogenesis. Thus, protease inhibitors that slow carcinogenesis may derive their effects, in part, by inhibiting basement membrane degradation or by inhibiting angiogenesis.

Antioxidant/Anti-inflammatory Activity

Many classes of antioxidants and anti-inflammatories have shown chemopreventive activity in animal models (Wattenberg, 1978; Kelloff *et al.*, 1995b; Singh and Lippman, 1998a,b). Those with activity derived by inhibition of AA metabolism are among the most promising chemopreventive agents. AA is metabolized to PGs, thromboxanes, leukotrienes and hydroxyeicosatetraenoic acids (HETEs) via oxidative enzymes. Activated oxygen species and alkylperoxy species are formed throughout this process; AA metabolism is increased during inflammation. Two aspects of AA metabolism are associated strongly with carcinogenicity

· The first is the PG synthetic pathway, involving the enzyme PG H synthase (PHS). This enzyme has two activities – COX, which catalyses the formation of PGG_2 from arachidonic acid, and hydroperoxidase, which catalyses the reduction of PGG_2 to PGH_2. To return to its native state, the hydroperoxidase requires a reducing cosubstrate; procarcinogens, e.g. arylamino and arylnitro compounds, are such substrates. According to the model proposed, the carcinogens are activated (oxidized) during catalysis to free radicals and electrophiles that can form adducts with DNA and initiate carcinogenesis. This process can be stopped in four ways: (1) at formation of PGG_2 via inhibition of COX, (2) by inhibition of peroxidase activity, (3) by preventing formation of reactive intermediates and (4) by scavenging reactive intermediates (e.g. by GSH conjugation). Relevant to these potential mechanisms, COX inhibitors such as NSAIDs and certain antioxidants (e.g. flavonoids) are effective inhibitors of carcinogenesis. Additionally, PGH_2 itself breaks down to form a known direct-acting mutagen, malondialdehyde. Thus, inhibition of COX may directly prevent the formation of a potential carcinogen.

NSAIDs, which are COX inhibitors have demonstrated potent activity against colon cancer in epidemiological and animal studies and against bladder cancer in animal models. They have also shown chemopreventive activity in skin, oesophagus, lung and breast in animal studies. However, PGs and other PHS products such as thromboxanes have multiple activities, some of which are beneficial and tissue-specific. For example, PGE_2 in the gut promotes protective mucosal secretions; lowered gut PG levels resulting from NSAID administration are associated with one of the major side effects of long-term NSAID treatment, gastrointestinal ulceration and bleeding. Likewise, PGs in the kidney and thromboxanes in platelets are important to normal physiological function. Their inhibition is associated with renal tubule toxicity and excessive bleeding, respectively. The development of chemopreventive agents which retain the ability to inhibit the carcinogenesis-associated activities of PGs without depressing protective effects is an attractive strategy. The discovery of an inducible form of COX, COX-2, which is predominant at inflammation sites, in macrophages and in synoviocytes, suggested that such an approach is feasible. In contrast to COX-2, constitutive COX-1 predominates in the stomach, gastrointestinal tract, platelets and kidney. Traditional NSAIDs inhibit both forms of the enzymes, but other compounds inhibit COX-2 selectively – glucocorticoids such as dexamethasone (which, for example, has chemopreventive activity on topical application to mouse skin) and newer NSAIDs such

as celecoxib and rofecoxib. Moreover, COX-2 regulates or participates in a number of different cellular pathways and biological processes important in carcinogenesis. Expression of COX-2 is increased in many types of human cancers (e.g. colon, oesophagus, lung, breast, pancreas, prostate) and precancers. COX-2 inhibitors have potent chemopreventive activity in animal models of colon, bladder and skin carcinogenesis. In a recent clinical study the COX-2 inhibitor celecoxib significantly reduced the number of colorectal adenomas (which are precancers) in patients with familial adenomatous polyposis (FAP), supporting the concept that COX-2 inhibitors may have therapeutic utility against colorectal cancer and gaining FDA approval for celecoxib use in treatment of FAP (see the chapter *Chemoprevention*).

The second aspect of AA metabolism associated with carcinogenesis is the burst of PHS and lipoxygenase activity that is seen during inflammation and is stimulated by the tumour promoter TPA. The available evidence suggests that the immediate products of lipoxygenase activity, the HETEs and their hydroperoxy precursors (HPETEs), are more important to tumour promotion than are PGs. Compounds that inhibit lipoxygenase, such as aesculetin, inhibit carcinogenesis in animal models.

Evidence of Chemopreventive Potential Derived from Studies at Molecular Targets

In evaluating the potential efficacy of chemopreventive agents, several molecular target parameters are weighed: (1) number of chemoprevention-related pharmacological activities, (2) impact of the agent on likely carcinogenesis pathways to the targeted cancer, (3) pharmacodynamics and (4) specificity for chemopreventive activity compared with effects on normal cellular function. These data are important throughout the development process for chemopreventive agents, and they are particularly important in the earlier phases of identifying promising candidate agents and characterizing efficacy. *In vitro* molecular target assays are a first step in evaluating chemopreventive potential.

However, given today's state of knowledge, activity at molecular targets alone may be inconclusive. Carcinogenesis can take multiple paths and be multifocal (not all cancers in a given tissue or all cells in a given cancer may ultimately contain the same molecular lesions); only a few early molecular lesions will progress. Progression can be influenced by factors specific to the host tissue's environment, such as the action of hormones. Further, although the progression models suggest that there is a rough order in which the various types of changes appear; until the time comes (which may be relatively soon) when the progression models are worked out in fine detail supported by functional genomic/proteomic analyses, the accumulation of multiple effects as evidenced in phenotypic changes at the cellular and tissue level can be more reliable measures of carcinogenesis and their inhibition or reversal, of chemopreventive potential. Hence, the early development of chemopreventive drugs also uses short-term *in vitro* assays that measure changes in cell proliferation and cell proliferation kinetics, other parameters of malignant transformation and even animal models of carcinogenesis in which tissue characteristics associated with precancer are measured. Nonetheless, effects on molecular targets are also useful in defining the most appropriate animal efficacy models and in interpreting the results of assays in these models.

EVALUATING CHEMOPREVENTIVE EFFICACY

In developing chemopreventive agents a sequential approach is used to evaluate potential efficacy – starting with *in vitro* and cell-based mechanistic assays and efficacy screening tests, then screens *in vivo* in animal carcinogenesis models with cancers and precancerous lesions as endpoints, and finally the most promising agents are characterized more fully in animal carcinogenesis models (e.g. dose–response and dosing regimens are evaluated, combinations with other agents are tested).

Mechanistic Assays

Agents not previously tested are put first into mechanistic assays to determine their potential range of chemopreventive activities (**Table 2**). Many of the mechanistic endpoints are described above in relation to characterizing various classes of chemopreventive agents. The battery of assays used is continually evolving and is designed to address various specific activities associated with general

Table 2   Representative assays of chemopreventive mechanisms[a]

Assays	Cell substrate	Mechanism measured
Antimutagenesis		
B(*a*)P-DNA adduct formation (inhibition)	Human bronchial epithelial cells (BEAS2-B)	DNA damage inhibition
NAD(P)H:quinone reductase (induction)	Human (Chang) liver cells	Carcinogen detoxification
GSH *S*-transferase (induction)	Human (Chang) liver cells	Carcinogen detoxification
GSH synthesis and GSSG reduction (induction)	Buffalo rat liver (BRL-3A) cells	Carcinogen detoxification
Antiproliferation		
TPA-induced ODC (inhibition)	Rat tracheal epithelial cells (2C5 cell line)	Antiproliferative activity
Normal epithelial cell proliferation (inhibition)	Primary human keratinocytes	Antiproliferative activity
Poly(ADP–ribose)polymerase (inhibition)	Primary human fibroblasts	Error-prone DNA repair inhibition (DNA damage inhibition)
Calmodulin-regulated phosphodiesterase (inhibition)	Human leukaemia (HL60) cells	Signal transduction regulation
TPA-induced tyrosine kinase (inhibition)	Human leukaemia (HL60) cells	Signal transduction regulation
EGFR (inhibition)	Human A431 and mouse 3T3 cells	Signal transduction regulation
ras farnesylation (inhibition)	Rat brain farnesyl transferase	Signal transduction regulation
HMG–CoA reductase (inhibition)	Rat liver HMG–CoA reductase	Signal transduction regulation
Steroid aromatase (inhibition)	PMSG-stimulated rat ovary aromatase	Antioestrogenic activity
Oestrogen receptor (antagonism of binding and expression)	MCF-7 cells	Antioestrogenic activity
5-reductase (inhibition)	Rat prostate 5-reductase	Antiandrogenic activity
Cellular differentiation characteristics (modulation)	Human leukaemia (HL60) cells	Differentiation
DNA fragmentation (induction)	Human leukaemia (HL60) or U937 cells	Apoptosis
Antioxidant/anti inflammatory activity		
AA metabolism: micronuclei in keratinocytes (inhibition)	P388 macrophages/human keratinocytes	Anti-inflammatory activity
TPA-induced active oxygen (inhibition)	Human leukaemia (HL60) cells	Free radical scavenging
COX-2 (inhibition)	Sheep placenta COX-2	Anti-inflammatory activity
LOX (inhibition)	Rat RBL-1 cell LOX (for 5-LOX)	Anti-inflammatory activity

[a]Abbreviations: AA, arachidonic acid; B(*a*)P, benzo[*a*]pyrene; COX, cyclooxygenase; EGFR, epidermal growth factor receptor; GSH, glutathione; GSSG, glutathione disulfide; GST, glutathione-*S*-transferase; HMG-CoA, hydroxymethylglutaryl coenzyme A; LOX, lipoxygenase; ODC, ornithine decarboxylase; TPA, tetradecanoyl phorbol acetate.

See also Kelloff, 2000, *Advances in Cancer Research*, **278**, 199–334.

Table 3 *In Vitro* Assays of Chemopreventive Efficacy[a]

Assay	Cell system	Carcinogen
Morphological transformation (inhibit)	Rat tracheal epithelial cells	Benzo[a]pyrene
Hyperplastic nodules (inhibit)	Mouse mammary gland organ culture	7,12-dimethylbenz[a]anthracene tetradecanoylphorbol acetate
Anchorage independence	Human lung tumour (A427) cells	None

[a]See also Steele *et al.*, 1996, *Journal of Cellular Biochemistry*, Suppl. 26, 29–53.

categories of chemopreventive activity – carcinogen blocking (antimutagenicity), antiproliferation and antioxidation/antiinflammation. As the molecular bases of carcinogenesis become better known, additional mechanistic activities appropriate to chemoprevention are identified. Examples of those in the early stages of investigation are inhibition of cell cyclins, telomerase and angiogenesis, as well as binding to peroxisome proliferator-activated receptors (PPARs) (Kelloff, 2000).

Cell-based Assays

Selected cell-based assays have been used routinely to screen the efficacy of potential chemopreventive agents (**Table 3**) (Steele *et al.*, 1996). Initial criteria for selecting the *in vitro* tests include (1) efficiency in terms of time and cost, (2) sensitivity and ease of quantitation, (3) controlled test conditions, (4) relevance to organ systems of interest, (5) use of epithelial cells and (6) if possible, use of human cells. In each assay, the agents are tested over a wide range of concentrations, and IC_{50}s are determined. New cell and organ culture technology is being used to design assays of chemopreventive efficacy, e.g. raft cultures (allowing evaluation of stromal–epithelial interactions), cells from transgenic mice and human cells carrying known cancer-predisposing genes (e.g. *p53* mutations characterizing Li–Fraumeni syndrome).

Inhibition of Carcinogenesis in Animal Models

Prevention of Cancers in Carcinogen-induced Animals

Numerous animal models are used to study inhibition of chemical carcinogenesis (**Table 4**). (See the section on *In Vitro and Animal Models for Human Cancer.*) Typically, a carcinogen is administered to the animal at a dose level high enough to induce a significant incidence of tumours in a specific target tissue. The carcinogen dose and treatment schedule are selected to ensure that the tumour incidence is not so high as to mask the potential of the inhibitor to reduce tumour incidence. The inhibitor is administered before, at the same time, after or in any combination of these times relative to the administration of the carcinogen. The relative timing of the administration of

the carcinogen and the inhibitor is useful in interpreting the mechanism of inhibition. For example, a compound that inhibits when it is administered before the carcinogen, but not when it is given after carcinogen treatment is completed, most likely affects carcinogen blocking activities.

Studies typically last as long as required for the carcinogen to induce a high tumour incidence. Because the activity of most of the carcinogens used is well known, these tests are usually shorter than chronic carcinogenicity studies, i.e. they last 6–12 months. Inhibition is usually measured as the percentage by which the inhibitor lowers the incidence, multiplicity or total number of tumours, or increases the latency of tumour induction. Sometimes such factors as tumour size and degree of invasiveness are considered. Results are usually based on microscopic evaluation of the target tissues, although gross pathology also may be used. For example, rat mammary gland tumours often are detected by palpation, and mouse skin tumours are determined visually. Some general guidelines have been suggested for interpreting the results of testing a potential inhibitor of carcinogenesis (**Table 5**) (Steele *et al.*, 1994).

Inhibition of Carcinogenesis in Transgenic and Gene Knockout Mice

Animal models which mimic specific characteristics of human carcinogenesis are valuable for fully evaluating chemopreventive efficacy and for determining appropriate carcinogenesis biomarkers for measuring chemopreventive activity. Transgenic and gene knockout mice which carry one or more well-characterized gene mutations predisposing to carcinogenesis are appropriate models (**Table 6**) (Kelloff, 2000).

CHEMOPREVENTIVE AGENT DEVELOPMENT

A collaboration between the USA National Cancer Institute (NCI) and the FDA resulted in conceptual and practical guidelines for developing cancer chemopreventive drugs (Kelloff *et al.*, 1995a; Kelloff *et al.*, 1997). These strategies are outlined in **Table 7**. First the efficacy of candidate drugs is characterized using epidemiological

Table 4   Carcinogen-induced animal models for chemoprevention efficacy studies[a]

Organ model	Species	Carcinogen	Endpoint: inhibition of
Buccal pouch	Hamster	DMBA	Squamous cell carcinoma, papilloma
Colon	Mouse	AOM, DMH, MAM	Adenocarcinoma, adenoma, aberrant crypt foci
	Rat	AOM, DMH, MAM, MNU	Adenocarcinoma, adenoma
Oesophagus	Rat	Nitrosamines	Squamous cell carcinoma, papilloma
Forestomach	Mouse	B(a)P	Squamous cell carcinoma, papilloma
Intestines[b]	Rat	AOM, DMH	Adenocarcinoma, adenoma
Liver	Mouse	Various	Hepatocellular carcinoma, adenoma
	Rat	AAF, DEN, DMN, me-DAB	Hepatocellular carcinoma, adenoma
Lung	Mouse	B(a)P, DMBA, NNK, urethane	Adenoma
	Hamster	DEN, MNU (trachea)	Squamous cell carcinoma, adenosquamouscarcinoma
Mammary glands	Mouse	DMBA	Adenocarcinoma, adenoma
	Rat	DMBA. MNU	Adenocarcinoma, adenoma
Pancreas	Hamster	BOP	Ductal adenocarcinoma, adenoma
	Rat	L-Azaserine	Acinar cell carcinoma
Skin	Mouse	UV radiation, B(a)P, B(a)P/TPA, DMBA, DMBA/TPA,	Carcinoma, papilloma
Stomach (and glandular stomach)	Rat	MNNG	Adenocarcinoma
Urinary bladder	Mouse	OH-BBN	Transitional cell carcinoma
	Rat	MNU, OH-BBN	Transitional cell carcinoma

[a]Abbreviations: AAF, 2-acetylaminofluorene; AOM, azoxymethane; B(a)P, benzo[a]pyrene; BOP, N-nitrosobis(2-oxopropyl)amine; DEN, N,N-diethylnitrosamine; DMBA, 7,12-dimethylbenz[a]anthracene; DMH, dimethylhydrazine; DMN, N,N-diethylnitrosamine; MAM, methylazoxymethyl acetate; me-DAB, 3'- methyl-N,N-dimethylaminoazobenzene; MNNG, N-methyl-N'-nitro-N-nitrosoguanidine; MNU, N-methyl-N-nitrosourea; NNK, N-nitrosonornicotine; OH-BBN, N-butyl-N-(4-hydroxybutyl)nitrosamine;TPA, tetradecanoylphorbol acetate.
[b]Small or large intestine not specified.
See also Steele et al., 1994, Journal of Cellular Biochemistry, Suppl. 20, 32–54.

Table 5   Criteria for evaluating chemopreventive efficacy in animal carcinogenesis models

Conclusive evidence of chemopreventive effect:

Agent must cause a statistically significant (p<0.05) decrease in tumour incidence, multiplicity, size or invasiveness, or a statistically significant increase in tumour latency (time to appearance of first tumour or time to 50% incidence) compared with carcinogen controls

In the absence of statistics, a twofold decrease in incidence, multiplicity, size, or invasiveness, or a similar increase in latency, is required to confirm a chemopreventive effect

The criteria above are for a single-dose level of agent. If at least three doses are tested and a dose–response inhibition or increase in latency is observed, the result may be considered chemopreventive, even if the effect is not statistically significant or of twofold magnitude at any dose tested

Suggestive evidence of chemopreventive effect:

No statistical analyses are performed, but the inhibition ranges from 35 to 50%

Other factors considered in determining adequacy of the test, regardless of the magnitude of the effect:

The numbers of animals in the treatment and control groups are sufficient to demonstrate statistical significance

Survival in both test and control groups is adequate to allow statistical evaluation, i.e. the toxicities observed due to carcinogen or chemopreventive agent treatment should not be so severe as to compromise the results of the study

Evidence of carcinogenicity is established in concurrent carcinogen-treated control animals

Body weight in animals treated with chemopreventive agent are not statistically significantly lower than those of carcinogen controls (body weight is a particularly meaningful and confounding factor in inhibition experiments, since decreased or delayed weight gain can be a measure of slowed growth. Slowed growth alone can depress tumorigenicity without other specific effects of a chemopreventive agent)

Tumour incidence in the carcinogen control group is significantly lower than expected

Table 6   Representative transgenic/gene knockout mouse models for chemoprevention studies[a]

Transgenic Mouse model	Target	Genetic lesions	Histological lesions
Min	Colon	Heterozygous Apc2549	Adenomas, adenocarcinomas, some CIS
Apc	Colon	Heterozygous Apc1638	Adenomas, adenocarcinomas
MLH1/Apc1638	Colon	Heterozygous MLH1 and Apc1638	Adenomas, carcinomas
MSH2/Min	Colon	Heterozygous MSH2 and Apc2549	Adenomas, carcinomas
pim	Lymphatic system	Amplified pim-1	T-cell lymphomas
TG.AC	Skin	Ha-ras mutation	Papillomas, possible carcinomas
TSG-p53	Skin	Heterozygous p53 deficient	Papillomas, possible carcinomas
A/JxTSG-p53	Lung	Heterozygous p53 deficient	Adenomas
A/JxUL53	Lung	Heterozygous p53 mutant	Adenomas
TGFβ1	Liver, lung	Heterozygous TGFβ1 mutant	Adenomas, carcinomas
v-Ha-ras	Skin	Ha-ras + human keratin K-1	Hyperplasia, hyperkeratoses, squamous papillomas
K14-HPV16	Skin	HPV-infected (K14-HPV16 heterozygote), oestradiol-treated + SV40T-antigen	Papillomas, condylomas
K14-HPV16	Cervix	HPV-infected (K14-HPV16 heterozygote), oestradiol-treated + SV40T-antigen	Cervical dysplasia
C3(1)-SV40	Prostate	Heterozygous rat prostatic steroid binding gene [C3(1)] + SV40 T-antigen	Dysplasia, adenoma, adenocarcinoma
C3(1)-SV40	Mammary glands	Heterozygous rat prostatic steroid binding gene [C3(1)] + SV40 T-antigen	Adenocarcinomas

[a]Abbreviations: HPV, human papilloma virus; TGF, transforming growth factor
See also Kelloff, 2000, *Advances in Cancer Research*, **278**, 199–334.

Table 7   FDA/NCI guidance on approaches to the development of chemopreventive drugs[a]

I. Preclinical efficacy studies recommended for initiation of phase I/II clinical trials for chemopreventive investigational drugs are (1) + (7), (2) + (4 or 5) + (8), (3) + (4 or 5) + (8), (6):
1. *In vivo* tumour modulation with (statistically significant) reduced tumour incidence or multiplicity or increased latency
2. *In vivo* tumour modulation with (statistically nonsignificant but dose-associated positive trend) reduced tumour incidence or multiplicity or increased tumor latency
3. *In vivo* surrogate endpoint modulation (statistically significant)
4. *In vitro* transformation modulation
5. *In vitro* chemoprevention-related mechanistic studies
6. Epidemiological study demonstrating a cancer-inhibitory effect of the specific agent in the target tissue
7. *In vivo* concentration–effect relationship
8. *In vitro* concentration–effect relationship

II. Preclinical safety studies for initiation of phase I/II clinical trials for chemopreventive investigational drugs are:
1. General toxicity studies conducted in two species, rodent and nonrodent, of equal or greater duration than the proposed clinical trial or up to 6 months in rodents and 12 months in dogs. Route of administration should be equivalent to the intended clinical route, and drug substance should be that prepared for clinical trials (preferably the clinical formulation)
2. Genotoxicity assessed in a battery of assays [Ames *Salmonella typhimurium*, gene mutation in mammalian cells *in vitro* (either L5178Y mouse TK$^{+/-}$ lymphoma cells or another cell line with an autosomal locus with documented sensitivity to mutagenic chemicals, such as Chinese hamster ovary AS52 cells), and cytogenetic damage *in vivo* (mouse bone marrow micronucleus and/or mouse or rat chromosomal aberration tests)]
3. Segment I reproductive performance/fertility in rat and Segment II teratology in rat and rabbit should be conducted as early as possible, prior to large clinical trials or trials of long duration, and in accordance with the ICH and the Guideline for the Study and Evaluation of Gender Differences in the Clinical Evaluation of Drugs
4. Combinations of chemopreventive drugs should be evaluated in at least one general toxicity study of appropriate duration in the most appropriate species for interactions in pharmacokinetics, toxicity, enzyme effects or other relevant parameters
   (Pharmacokinetics and metabolite profiles should be examined in conjunction with toxicity studies to aid in interpretation of findings and evaluation of relevance to humans)

(Continued)

Table 7   (*Continued*)

Required before clinical studies >1 year's duration (large phase II and phase III)
  1. Completion of general chronic toxicity studies in two species (6 months in rodent, 12 months in non-rodent)
  2. All special toxicity studies (assessing neurotoxicity, cardiotoxicity, etc., as appropriate) before phase III
  3. Initiation, preferably completion, of at least one of the rodent carcinogenicity bioassay prior to initiation of large phase III studies

Required for new drug application
  1. Segment III perinatal and postnatal development study in rats
  2. Completion of two rodent carcinogenicity bioassays.

III. Phase I–III clinical studies for chemopreventive investigational drugs

Required phase I
  1. Single-dose studies in both fasting and nonfasting normal subjects to characterize single-dose pharmacokinetics (i.e. absorption, distribution, metabolism, elimination) and acute toxicity
  2. Repeated daily dose studies using multiple dose levels for a period of 1–3 months in normal subjects **or** up to 12 months in subjects at increased risk to cancer(s), for which the drug demonstrates efficacy in preclinical evaluation, to assess multiple dose pharmacokinetics and chronic toxicity. Participation of normal subjects for more than 1 month is considered based on available information (toxicity, clinical experience, etc.) for each drug on a case-by-case basis

Recommended phase I
  Under III 1 above, include placebo control and pharmacodynamic evaluation of dose–response for modulation of selected drug effect or surrogate endpoint biomarkers. Subject follow-up upon completion of treatment will include evaluation of modulation of marker status

Phase II
  1. *Phase IIa.* In the event that a clearly defined and standardized surrogate endpoint biomarker is not identified, then a randomized, blinded, parallel dose–response chronic dosing study will be conducted for 3 months or more in subjects at high risk of cancer at the site of investigation using dosing levels shown to be safe in prior Phase I studies. As a basis for the phase IIb study, the objectives are to evaluate measurements of candidate biomarkers (drug effect and/or surrogate endpoint) and the dose–response relationship of biomarker modulation and tolerance to modulation, to standardize assays and quality control procedures and to characterize chronic dosing toxicity
  2. *Phase IIb.* Randomized, blinded, placebo-controlled chronic dosing study for 3 months or more in subjects at high risk of cancer at the site of investigation at one or more dosing levels shown to be safe and effective in modulating biomarkers. Study objectives are to establish dose–surrogate endpoint marker response and chronic dosing toxicity and to select a safe and effective dose based on surrogate endpoint marker response and chronic dosing toxicity

Phase III
  Randomized, blinded, placebo-controlled clinical trials with the following objectives:
  1. Demonstrate a significant reduction in incidence or delay in occurrence of cancer
  2. Validate surrogate endpoints
  3. Assess drug toxicity
  4. Characterize the relationship of dose and/or pharmacokinetics to efficacy and toxicity
  5. In case of formulation differences, establish the bioequivalence between the to-be-marketed formulation and the formulation used in pivotal clinical trials

[a]See also Kelloff *et al.*, 1995, *Cancer Epidemiological Biomarkers and Prevention*, **4**, 1–10.

data, and the mechanistic assays, *in vitro* efficacy tests and animal models of carcinogenesis just described. The most promising candidates are evaluated for preclinical toxicity and pharmacokinetics as needed. Clinical development is then planned and implemented for those agents that meet the criteria for acceptable toxicity as well as efficacy. Often, additional efficacy and toxicity testing are done to test alternative routes of agent delivery, dosage regimens, new target tissues, combinations of agents for increased efficacy and decreased toxicity, and to evaluate toxicities seen in early clinical studies.

Clinical development of chemopreventive agents, as for other pharmaceuticals, is carried out primarily in phases I, II, and III trials. Phase I clinical trials are safety and pharmacokinetics studies. These trials include single-dose studies in both fasting and nonfasting normal subjects to characterize single dose pharmacokinetics and acute toxicity. Also, repeated daily dose studies to assess multiple dose pharmacokinetics and chronic toxicity are conducted using multiple dose levels for a period of 1–3 months in normal subjects or up to 12 months in subjects at increased risk of cancer(s), for which the drug demonstrates efficacy in preclinical evaluation. Participation of normal subjects for more than 1 month is considered based on available information (toxicity, clinical experience, etc.) for each drug on a case-by-case basis. In most cases, the phase I studies evaluate agent effects as well as agent serum (and, sometimes, tissue) levels. Agent effects measured are those believed to be potentially associated with chemopreventive activity. For example, in studies of NSAIDs serum and tissue levels of PGE_2 would be measured. In studies with the ODC inhibitor, DFMO, tissue levels of polyamines are measured.

Considerations and current progress in clinical development of chemopreventive agents are described fully in the chapter Chemoprevention. (See also the rest of the section on *The Treatment of Human Cancer*.) Briefly, phase II trials are initial efficacy studies. These randomized, double-blind, placebo-controlled trials emphasize the evaluation of biomarkers of carcinogenesis that are highly correlated to cancer incidence and that may serve as surrogate endpoints for cancer incidence reduction. Phase III studies are randomized, blinded, placebo-controlled clinical efficacy trials. These studies are typically large and have the objectives of demonstrating a significant reduction in incidence or delay in occurrence of cancer, validating surrogate endpoints, further assessing drug toxicity and further characterizing the relationship of dose and/or pharmacokinetics to efficacy and toxicity.

Role of Biomarkers of Carcinogenesis

Because of cancer's long latency, reduced cancer incidence is an impractical endpoint for clinical evaluation of chemopreventive agents. Thus, biomarkers of carcinogenesis are being evaluated and validated as surrogate endpoints for chemoprevention trials. These biomarkers are addressed in both preclinical and clinical studies. The criteria for surrogate endpoint biomarkers are that they fit expected biological mechanisms (i.e. differential expression in normal and high-risk tissue, on or closely linked to the causal pathway for the cancer, modulated by chemopreventive agents and short latency compared with cancer), may be assayed reliably and quantitatively, may be measured easily and correlate with decreased cancer incidence). They must occur in sufficient incidence to allow their biological and statistical evaluation relevant to cancer.

The rationale for the testing done during chemopreventive agent development is described below (Kelloff, 2000).

Preclinical Efficacy Development

Efficacy testing starts with a battery of mechanistic assays representing a wide range of chemopreventive activities. Positive agents may then be screened in a battery of *in vitro* cell-based efficacy assays. Positive agents are then moved on to animal models – typically, the models used are selected based on clues provided by the mechanistic and cell-based assays. Translational research is carried out to prepare agents for clinical development. These studies include evaluating new animal carcinogenesis models, agent-delivery mechanisms,

potential synergy of efficacy and safety by the use of agent combinations and rational approaches to the development of defined mixtures as the best means to further test and verify hypotheses being generated by epidemiology data on diet and cancer.

A recent example confirmed the chemopreventive potential of aerosolized steroids in lung and the possible advantage of topical drug delivery. In this study, carcinogen-induced mice were treated with aerosol budesonide. This approach is particularly promising for preventing lung carcinogenesis, but is applicable to several target organs, the primary advantage being to improve therapeutic index. That is, relatively low doses of drug are required to reach the cancer target directly, and the toxicity in non-target organs seen on systemic absorption after oral doses is reduced. A phase II clinical study of aerosol budesonide is now in progress in patients with precancerous lesions in the bronchus (see also the chapter *Chemoprevention*).

Agent Combinations

Another strategy to improve efficacy and lessen toxicity is combinations of agents. In some combinations of two agents with different presumed mechanisms of activity, synergistic or additive efficacy is seen. Such improved activity may allow either or both the agents to be administered at lower doses, thereby reducing potential toxicity. For example, synergistic activity has been observed in rat colon studies with combinations of DFMO and the NSAID piroxicam and in rat mammary with combinations of retinoids and antiestrogens, and these strategies are now being tested clinically. Another combination strategy uses a second agent to counter the toxicity of a known effective chemopreventive agent. An example is coadministration of the PGE_2 analogue misoprostol to counter the gastrointestinal toxicity associated with administration of NSAIDs.

Development of Dietary Components

Dietary components with chemopreventive activity typically start as complex mixtures from which optimal standardized mixtures and purified active substance are prepared and characterized. For example, two soy isoflavone mixtures containing genistein (the presumed active substance), other isoflavones (primarily daidzein), fat and carbohydrate are being developed in parallel. One is nearly 'pure,' containing 90% genistein; the second more closely resembles a natural soy product, containing less than 50% genistein. Both mixtures will continue in development until one proves to have superior efficacy or practicality. Alternatively, the two may be developed for different chemoprevention uses. Similarly, well-characterized tea polyphenol extracts have been evaluated in preclinical studies, and epigallocatechin gallate (EGCG), which appears to be a primary active component, is being developed in parallel. The effort to confirm dietary leads is expected to burgeon over the next few years. For example, the FDA has proposed guidelines for the identification and evaluation of heterogeneous botanicals such as the tea and isoflavone mixtures, and the number of publications on chemopreventive effects of characterized dietary components is increasing (e.g. many on tea polyphenols, curcuminoids, selenized garlic/selenomethylcysteine, conjugated fatty acids, and broccoli compounds (sulforaphane)). Increasingly sophisticated analyses of epidemiological dietary data could produce many more new chemopreventive hypotheses regarding dietary components.

Toxicology and Pharmacology

As for other pharmaceuticals, the FDA requires sufficient preclinical toxicity and phase I clinical safety and pharmacokinetics testing to ensure that an investigational chemopreventive agent will not jeopardize the health of patients in efficacy trials. Because they are intended for chronic use in relatively well subjects, the safety criteria are more stringent for chemopreventives than for many other classes of pharmaceuticals (Kelloff *et al.*, 1995a).

Preclinical Toxicity and Pharmacokinetics

Preclinical safety studies for chemopreventive drugs are generally the same as for other drugs and include acute and subchronic toxicity (incorporating pharmacokinetic measurements), reproductive performance and genotoxicity. Generally included are single-dose, acute toxicity study and an absorption–elimination study in rats, and subchronic repeated daily dosing studies in rodents and dogs. Combinations of chemopreventive drugs are evaluated in the species most closely related to humans in terms of metabolism in at least one study of appropriate duration (generally studies greater than 90 days are not needed) to determine interactions in pharmacokinetics, toxicity, enzyme effects, or other relevant parameters.

Preclinical efficacy studies also incorporate limited toxicity evaluations that may help identify appropriate doses for the formal toxicity studies. For example, most animal efficacy screens include a preliminary 2–6-week study to determine the maximum tolerated dose (MTD) of the test agents. Blood levels of test agent are usually obtained during animal studies designed to characterize more fully the efficacy of an agent or agent combination.

Pharmacokinetic data help in the development of a phase I clinical dose escalation strategy. Absorption–elimination studies in rats are used to develop analytical methods for drug monitoring, which can be standardized and used in the clinic. These studies also provide other information on agent behaviour (e.g. protein binding). Single-dose pharmacokinetics are also assessed at the initiation of the repeated daily dosing studies in dogs, and measurements of plasma drug levels at steady state are performed in these studies in rodents and dogs (pharmacokinetic studies using radioactive drug to quantify tissue distribution and metabolism are performed later in development). The information developed at this stage (e.g. maximum and minimum blood levels, elimination time) is evaluated with information from efficacy studies in order to provide a dose–concentration–effect profile of the test agent and to estimate a margin of safety; the relationship of dose to effectiveness and toxicity is then used to refine dosing strategies and regimens. For example, if a promising chemopreventive agent has slight toxicity with daily dosing it might be evaluated in further phase I trials using intermittent dosing schedules chosen to induce or inhibit a drug-effect enzyme over the whole treatment period while not reaching blood concentrations that may cause side effects.

As needed, a battery of three genotoxicity tests is performed. Chronic toxicity, carcinogenicity and reproductive toxicity tests are undertaken later in development, prior to or during phase III development. Special toxicity studies are also undertaken, as appropriate, in response to safety issues arising on clinical use of the agent. One example of special studies recently pursued is for DFMO which is now in phase II/III clinical trials. In previous clinical studies, this agent had shown significant ototoxicity. The mechanism appeared to be destruction of cochlear cilia. Thirteen-week studies in dogs were undertaken to evaluate the effect quantitatively. At clinical doses no effects were seen on cochlear hair cell measurements, brainstem auditory evoked responses (including histology of auditory nuclei) or observed response to auditory stimuli such as clapping and calling.

For most investigational drugs used chronically to treat disease states, carcinogenicity studies are required prior to petitioning the FDA for approval to market the drug. Generally one rodent carcinogenicity study is initiated prior to initiation of large phase III clinical studies. However, for drugs under development for cancer prevention, where the agent is to be used prophylactically in essentially well people, completion of one carcinogenicity study prior to conduct of sizable long-term trials is considered based on the expected toxicity of the drug, the population, the planned clinical trial duration, the trial design and other factors.

Phase I Clinical Safety and Pharmacokinetics

Phase I single-dose studies are designed to characterize agent pharmacokinetics and tolerability. The dose and schedule of administration are based initially on pre-clinical toxicity and efficacy and are selected to achieve safe and effective plasma agent levels in humans. As is typical for other pharmaceuticals, the maximum initial dose in humans is a mg kg^{-1} dose that is the lower of one-tenth the highest no observed adverse effect dose (NOAEL) in rodents or one-sixth the highest NOAEL in mg kg^{-1} in nonrodents. The NOAEL is based on toxicity studies of equal or greater duration than the proposed clinical trial. The *in vitro* inhibitory concentration and *in vivo* plasma drug levels from efficacy testing may be used as a relative guide to the needed concentration, i.e. within an order of magnitude, but are not easily quantitatively extrapolated due to the conditions used in screening tests (i.e. the high dose of carcinogen). Ordinarily the human dose, usually in mg kg^{-1}, is not escalated above the animal NOAEL,

but this could depend on the nature of the adverse effect. Higher human doses may be justified based on pharmacokinetic or pharmacodynamic differences between humans and animals or clinical experience at lower doses. Where possible the dose escalation strategy uses pharmacokinetic parameters across species. After a cautious initial dose, further escalation is based on blood levels compared with those associated with toxicity in animals. Differences in the pharmacokinetic profile after acute and chronic dosing are also evaluated. Dose selection is, of course, ultimately controlled by emphasis on empirical clinical safety and toxicity observations.

Consistent with current FDA regulatory practice, normal subjects are used in studies 1–3 months in duration; participation of normal subjects for more than 1 month is considered based on available information (toxicity, clinical experience, etc.) for each drug on a case-by-case basis. When longer phase I studies are undertaken (up to 12 months), subjects at increased risk for cancer(s) are enrolled. Longer studies are designed not only to obtain pharmacokinetic and safety information after chronic administration but also to develop and evaluate effects on drug activity and carcinogenesis biomarkers.

Table 8 Requirements for successful phase II clinical chemoprevention trials

Agent
Experimental and/or epidemiological data supporting chemopreventive activity (efficacy)
Safety on chronic administration at multiple of efficacious dose
Mechanistic rationale for chemopreventive activity

Cohort
Suitable for chemopreventive activity of agent
Suitable for measurement of biomarkers
Risk/benefit analysis acceptable

Biomarkers
Fits expected biological mechanism
 – differentially expressed in normal and high-risk tissue
 – on or closely linked to causal pathway for cancer (e.g. expression increases/decreases with severity of precancer; intraepithelial neoplasia is the most promising in this regard)
 – modulated by chemopreventive agents
 – latency is (relatively) short compared with cancer
Biomarker and assay provide acceptable sensitivity, specificity, and accuracy
 – assay for biomarker is standardized and validated
Sampling is reliable
 – dose-related response to the chemopreventive agent is observed
 – statistically significant difference is seen between levels in treatment groups and controls
Biomarker is easily measured
 – biomarker can be obtained by noninvasive or relatively noninvasive techniques
 – assay for biomarker is not technically difficult
Biomarker modulation correlates to decreased cancer incidence (i.e. the biomarker can be validated as a surrogate endpoint for cancer incidence)

Clinical Efficacy

Clinical trials that support claims of chemopreventive efficacy can be designed using biomarkers as surrogate endpoints for cancer incidence. At each major target site, three components govern the design and conduct of these trials – well-characterized agents, reliable biomarkers for measuring efficacy and suitable cohorts (**Table 8**) (Kelloff, 1996b; Kelloff, 2000; Kelloff *et al.*, 2000).

The promise of chemoprevention is evidenced by the increasing number of clinical strategies and studies in the major cancer target organs – prostate, breast, colon, lung, head and neck, bladder, oesophagus, cervix, ovary, skin, liver (**Table 9**). In these organ systems cancer is associated with earlier, well-defined precancers (usually intraepithelial neoplasia) that may serve as biomarkers of carcinogenesis and surrogate endpoints for cancer incidence, as well as targets for treatment in their own right. Some examples are colon adenomas, bronchial dysplasia (lung), prostatic intraepithelial neoplasia (PIN), cervical intraepithelial neoplasia (CIN), actinic keratoses (skin), oral leucoplakia and ductal carcinoma *in situ* (breast). The remarkable progress that has been made in chemoprevention of cancer is evidenced by FDA approvals for the use of tamoxifen to reduce the risk of breast cancer in high-risk women and of celecoxib in the treatment of colorectal adenomas in patients with FAP. This progress is described fully in the chapter Chemoprevention. (See also the rest of the section on *The Treatment of Human Cancer*.)

Table 9 Aspects of chemoprevention at major cancer target sites[a]

	Prostate	Breast	Colon	Lung	Head and neck
Risk factors/markers	Age >50 years; familial history of prostate cancer; high serum testosterone; high-fat diet/high red meat consumption; population/geographical background (highest incidences in Canada and northwest Europe); genetic polymorphisms (e.g. in SRD5A2, gene for steroid 5-reductase); low micronutrient levels (e.g. selenium, carotenoids, vitamin D)	Age >50 years, familial history of breast cancer or genetic syndrome (e.g. Li-Fraumeni, BRCA1), previous breast, endometrial or ovarian cancer, atypical hyperplasia, DCIS, LCIS; oestrogen exposure (e.g. early menarche, late menopause, late age at first full-term pregnancy); life-style factors (e.g. diet)	High-fat/low-fibre diet, low fresh fruit, vegetable intake, low calcium and vitamin D intake; familial history of genetic syndrome (e.g. FAP, HNPCC); familial/past history of colorectal cancer or adenomatous polyps; past history of breast or endometrial cancer; inflammatory bowel disease	Tobacco use (smoking, chewing); alcohol consumption, especially combined with tobacco use; occupational exposure (e.g. asbestos, nickel, copper); cytochrome P-450 genetic polymorphisms (e.g. CYP1A1, GSTM2); low fruit, vegetable consumption; previous oral, laryngeal, lung cancer	Tobacco use (smoking, chewing); alcohol, especially combined with tobacco use; males, 50–70 years
Promising agents	Steroid 5-reductase inhibitors (e.g. finasteride); retinoids (e.g. 9-cis-retinoic acid; RAMBA; antiproliferatives (e.g. DFMO, DHEA analogues); differentiating agents (e.g. vitamin D analogues); antioxidants (e.g. vitamin E, selenium, lycopene); GSH-enhancing agents (e.g. oltipraz); antioestrogens (e.g. toremifene, tamoxifen, raloxifene and other SERMs); aromatase inhibitors (e.g. vorozole); antiandrogens (e.g. leuprolide, flutamide); angiogenesis inhibitors (e.g. linomide); signal transduction regulators (e.g. soy isoflavones), Anti-inflammatories (e.g. lipoxygenase inhibitors, selective COX-2 inhibitors)	Antioestrogens (e.g. tamoxifen, raloxifene and other SERMs); aromatase inhibitors; antiproliferatives (e.g. DFMO); soy isoflavones; fluasterone; retinoids (e.g. fenretinide, 9-cis-retinoic acid); monoterpenes (e.g. limonene, perillyl alcohol)	Anti-inflammatories (e.g. sulindac, piroxicam, aspirin, selective COX-2 inhibitors, curcumin, iNOS inhibitors, ASA derivatives); antiproliferatives (e.g. calcium, DFMO, ursodiol)	Retinoids, (e.g. vitamin A, 13-cis-retinoic acid, fenretinide, all-trans-retinoic acid); antimutagens (e.g. oltipraz, anethole trithione, PEITC); anti-inflammatories (e.g. aerosolized corticosteroids, lipoxygenase inhibitors, COX-2 inhibitors)	Retinoids/carotenoids (e.g. vitamin A, 13-cis-retinoic acid, fenretinide, β-carotene); anti-inflammatories (e.g. tea, curcumin)

Intermediate biomarkers	Histological: PIN (nuclear morphometry, nucleolar morphometry, nuclear texture, DNA ploidy); proliferation: loss of high molecular weight cytokeratins (50–64 kDa), altered blood group antigens (e.g. Lewis^Y antigen), vimentin; genetic/regulatory: c-erbB-2, TGF, P53, bcl-2/bax, pc-1 chromosomal loss or gain (e.g. 8p, 9p AND 16q), TGF, IGF-1; biochemical: PSA levels, PAP levels; angiogenesis: microvessel density, VEGF	Atypical hyperplasia, DCIS, nuclear morphometry, ploidy, c-erbB-2 amplification, p53 mutation, IGF-I	Adenomas (recurrence, regression); ACF; nuclear and nucleolar morphometry; apoptosis; proliferation indices (PCNA, Ki-67); crypt proliferation kinetics; differentiation indices (Lewis blood group antigens, sialyl-Tn antigen)	Cellular atypia in sputum, bronchial atypical metaplasia/dysplasia, increased cytokeratin 19 expression, PCNA, blood group-related antigens, p53 mutation; RAR induction	Leucoplakia with dysplasia, erythroplakia, GGT, keratins, c-erbB-1 amplification; LOH; proliferation indices (PCNA, Ki-67)
Clinical cohorts: Phase II	Patients scheduled for radical prostatectomy; patients with PIN; patients with cancer on biopsy, treated by watchful waiting; patients at high risk of biochemical failure or rising PSA postradical prostatectomy; subjects with positive family history	Patients scheduled for breast cancer surgery, patients with LCIS or mammographically detected calcifications/DCIS, high risk with multiple biomarker abnormalities	Patients with previous colon cancer or adenomatous polyps, FAP patients; HNPCC patients/carriers	Patients with recently resected stage I lung or laryngeal cancer, chronic smokers with squamous metaplasia/dysplasia	Patients with dysplastic leucoplakia; patients with previous head and neck cancers
Clinical cohorts: phase III	HGPIN; men at high risk (e.g. PSA >4 ng ml^{-1} and negative biopsy); men from general population, age ≥55 years, normal PSA and DRE	Women ≥60, or 35–59 years old with risk factors for 60 years old, patients with previous breast cancer	Patients with previous colon cancer or adenomatous polyps, FAP patients; HNPCC patients/carriers	Men exposed to asbestos or patients with asbestosis, chronic or heavy cigarette smokers, patients with previous lung, head or neck cancers	Patients with previously treated head and neck cancer; subjects at high risk (e.g. smokers, tobacco chewers)

(Continued)

Table 9 (Continued)

	Bladder	Oesophagus	Cervix	Skin	Liver
Risk factors/ markers	Males, age>55 years, cigarette, pipe, and cigar smoking; occupational exposures to aromatic amines; metabolic polymorphism: slow N-acetyltransferase phenotype; chronic cystitis or urinary tract infections; coffee drinking; chlorinated tap water	Alcohol and tobacco use; poor diet (e.g. lacking fresh fruit and vegetables); chronic gastro-oesophageal reflux disease (GERD) for the cancer, as well as for Barrett oesophagus; genetic syndrome (e.g. tylosis); Barrett oesophagus	HPV infection; early age at first intercourse; multiple sexual partners; oral contraceptive use; immunodepression; smoking	Dermatological factors (e.g. fair skin, freckling); genetic susceptibility (e.g. xeroderma pigmentosum, basal cell nevus syndrome, albinism, epidermodysplasia verruciformis); environmental exposures (e.g. UV radiation, cigarette smoke, tanning booths, PAH); lupus; immunosuppression	Alcohol consumption; smoking; HBV and HCV infection
Promising agents	Anti-inflammatories (e.g. sulindac, piroxicam, aspirin, ibuprofen); antiproliferatives (e.g. DFMO); retinoids (e.g. fenretinide)	Antiproliferatives (e.g. DFMO, BBI, selenium); antioxidants (e.g. tea polyphenols, PEITC, diallyl sulfide); anti-inflammatories (e.g. NSAIDs, selective COX-2 inhibitors); vitamins (e.g. vitamin E, nicotinic acid, riboflavin)	Retinoids (e.g. vitamin A, fenretinide, 9-cis-retinoic acid); antiproliferatives (e.g. DFMO), folic acid	Anti-inflammatories (e.g. piroxicam, curcumin, selective COX-2 inhibitors); antimutagens (e.g. oltipraz, diallyl sulfide); antiproliferatives (e.g. DFMO); retinoids (e.g. fenretinide, 13-cis-retinoic acid, retinyl palmitate, vitamin A); antioxidants (e.g. tea polyphenols, selenium, carotenoids)	Antimutagens (e.g. oltipraz); retinoids (e.g. polyprenoic acid)
Intermediate biomarkers	TIS, dysplasia, DNA content, LOH, Rb, blood group-related antigens, F- and G-actins, integrins	Barrett's oesophagus (area and grade of dysplasia); nuclear/nucleolar polymorphism; DNA ploidy; proliferation indices (Ki-67); apoptosis; p53; EGFR, EGF, TGFα, LOH (e.g. chromosome 17); microsatellite instability; iNOS expression	CIN (grade); aneuploidy; nuclear polymorphism; proliferation indices (e.g. PCNA, EGFR, TGFα, TGFβ) differentiation markers (e.g. involucrin) ras oncogene expression	Actinic keratosis; proliferation indices (e.g. PCNA, IGF-I/ IGFR, EGFR cyclin D1, ODC); TGFβ; differentiation indices (e.g. integrins); genetic/ regulatory biomarkers (e.g. c-fos, c-myc, c-jun)	Carcinogen-DNA adducts

Clinical cohorts: phase II	Patients with previous resected superficial transitional cell carcinoma (TA/T1 with or without TIS), patients with previous resected superficial transitional cell carcinoma treated with BCG	Patients with low-grade, intestinal-type Barrett's oesophagus with or without dysplasia	HPV-negative patients with CIN III	Patients with actinic keratosis	Subjects with environmental exposure (e.g. carcinogen or HBV)
Clinical cohorts: phase III	Subjects at high risk (e.g. occupational exposure to aromatic amines)	Patients at high risk of oesophageal cancer (e.g. GERD, smokers, geographic/ethnic, such as Linxian, China)	Patients with CIN I, II; patients with HPV infection	Patients with previous BCC or SCC; subjects with previous intense chronic or episodic sun exposure; patients with pre-existing dermatological disorders; patients with actinic keratosis; subjects with dysplastic naevi	Patients with previous hepatoma

[a]Abbreviations: ASA, acetylsalicylic acid; BCC, basal cell carcinoma; BBI, Bowman–Birk protease inhibitor; BCG, *Bacillus Calmette Guerin*; CIN, cervical intraepithelial neoplasia; COX, cyclooxygenase; DCIS, (breast) ductal carcinoma *in situ*; DFMO, 2-dimethylfluorornithine; DHEA, dehydroepiandrosterone; EGF, epidermal growth factor; EGFR, epidermal growth factor receptor; FAP, familial adenomatous polyposis; GERD, gastro-oesophageal reflux disease; GGT, γ-glutamyltransaminase; HBV, hepatitis B virus; HCV, hepatitis C virus; HNPCC, hereditary nonpolyposis colorectal cancer (syndrome); HPV, human papilloma virus; IGF, insulin-like growth factor; iNOS, inducible nitric oxide synthase; LCIS, (breast) lobular carcinoma *in situ*; LOH, loss of heterozygosity; NSAID, nonsteroidal anti-inflammatory drug; ODC, ornithine decarboxylase; PAHs, polycyclic aromatic hydrocarbons; PAP, prostatic acid phosphatase; PCNA, proliferating cell nuclear antigen; PEITC, phenylethyl isothiocyanate; PIN, prostatic intraepithelial neoplasia; PSA, prostate-specific antigen; RAMBA, retinoic acid metabolism blocking agent; RAR, retinoic acid receptor; SCC, squamous cell carcinoma; SERM, selective oestrogen receptor modulator; TGF, transforming growth factor; TIS, transitional cell carcinoma *in situ*; VEGF, vascular endothelial growth factor. See also Kelloff, 2000, *Advances in Cancer Research*, **278**, 199–334.

REFERENCES

AACR Chemoprevention Working Group (1999). Prevention of cancer in the next millenium: report of the chemoprevention working group to the American Association of Cancer Research. *Cancer Research*, **59**, 4743–4758.

De Flora, S and Ramel, C. (1988). Mechanisms of inhibitors of mutagenesis and carcinogenesis. Classification and overview. *Mutation Research*, **202**, 285–306.

Hartman, P. E. and Shankel, D. M. (1990). Antimutagens and anticarcinogens: a survey of putative interceptor molecules. *Environmental Molecular Mutagenesis*, **15**, 145–182.

Hong, W. K. and Sporn, M. B. (1997). Recent advances in chemoprevention of cancer. *Science*, **278**, 1073–1077.

Kelloff, G. J. (2000). Perspectives on cancer chemoprevention research and drug development. *Advances in Cancer Research*, **278**, 199–334.

Kelloff, G. J., *et al.* (1995a). Approaches to the development and marketing approval of drugs that prevent cancer. *Cancer Epidemiology Biomarkers and Prevention*, **4**, 1–10.

Kelloff, G. J., *et al.* (1995b). Inhibition of chemical carcinogenesis. In: Arcos, J., *et al.* (eds), *Chemical Induction of Cancer: Modulation and Combination Effects*. 73–122 (Birkhäuser Boston, Boston).

Kelloff, G. J., *et al.* (1996a). Strategy and planning for chemopreventive drug development: clinical development plans II. *Journal of Cellular Biochemistry*, Suppl. 26, 54–71.

Kelloff, G. J., *et al.* (1996b). Strategies for identification and clinical evaluation of promising chemopreventive agents. *Oncology*, **10**, 1471–1484.

Kelloff, G. J., *et al.* (1997). Progress in clinical chemoprevention. *Seminars in Oncology*, **24**, 241–252.

Kelloff, G. J., *et al.* (2000). Perspectives on surrogate endpoints in the development of drugs that reduce the risk of cancer. *Cancer Epidemiology Biomarkers and Prevention*, **9**, 127–134.

Lippman, S. M., *et al.* (1998). Cancer chemoprevention: progress and promise. *Journal of the National Cancer Institute*, **90**, 1514–1528.

Powis, G. (1994). Recent advances in the development of anticancer drugs that act against signalling pathways. *Tumori*, **80**, 69–87.

Powis, G. and Workman, P. (1994). Signalling targets for the development of cancer drugs. *Anticancer Drug Design*, **9**, 263–277.

Singh, D. K. and Lippman, S. M. (1998a). Cancer chemoprevention part 1: retinoids and carotenoids and other classic antioxidants. *Oncology*, **12**, 1643–1660.

Singh, D. K. and Lippman, S. M. (1998b). Cancer chemoprevention part 2: hormones, nonclassic antioxidant natural agents, NSAIDs and other agents. *Oncology*, **12**, 1787–1803.

Sporn, M. B. (1976). Approaches to prevention of epithelial cancer during the preneoplastic period. *Cancer Research*, **36**, 2699–2702.

Sporn, M. B. and Suh, N. (2000). Chemoprevention of cancer. *Carcinogenesis*, **21**, 525–530.

Steele, V. E., *et al.* (1994). Preclinical efficacy evaluation of potential chemopreventive agents in animal carcinogenesis models: methods and results from the NCI chemoprevention testing program. *Journal of Cellular Biochemistry*, Suppl. 20, 32–54.

Steele, V. E., *et al.* (1996). Use of *in vitro* assays to predict the efficacy of chemopreventive agents in whole animals. *Journal of Cellular Biochemistry*, Suppl. 26, 29–53.

Wattenberg, L. W. (1978). Inhibition of chemical carcinogenesis. *Journal of the National Cancer Institute*, **60**, 11–18.

Wattenberg, L. W. (1985). Chemoprevention of cancer. *Cancer Research*, **45**, 1–8.

FURTHER READING

Crowell, J. A., *et al.* (1994). Chronic toxicity studies of the potential cancer preventive 2-(difluoromethyl)-*dl*-ornithine. *Fundamentals of Applied Toxicology*, **22**, 341–354.

Fabian, C. J., *et al.* (2000). Short-term breast cancer prediction by random periareolar fine-needle aspiration cytology and the Gail risk model. *Journal of the National Cancer Institute*, **92**, 1217–1227.

Fearon, E. R. and Vogelstein, B. (1990). A genetic model for colorectal tumorigenesis. *Cell*, **61**, 759–767.

Fisher, B., *et al.* (1998). Tamoxifen for prevention of breast cancer: report of the National Surgical Adjuvant Breast and Bowel Project P-1 Study. *Journal of the National Cancer Institute*, **90**, 1371–1388.

Harris, C. C. (1991). Chemical and physical carcinogenesis: advances and perspectives for the 1990s. *Cancer Research*, **51**, 5023S–5044S.

Hawk, E., *et al.* (1999). Chemoprevention in hereditary colorectal cancer syndromes. *Cancer (Supplement)*, **86**, 2551–2563.

Henderson, B. E., *et al.* (1992). Environmental carcinogens and anticarcinogens. In: Wattenberg, L., *et al.* (eds), *Cancer Chemoprevention*. 3–17 (CRC Press, Boca Raton, FL).

Ilyas, M., *et al.* (1999). Genetic pathways in colorectal and other cancers. *European Journal of Cancer*, **35**, 335–351.

Kelloff, G. J., *et al.* (1996). Clinical development plan: tea extracts, green tea polyphenols, epigallocatechin gallate. *Journal of Cellular Biochemistry*, Suppl. 26, 236–257.

Kelloff, G. J., *et al.* (1996). Epidermal growth factor receptor tyrosine kinase inhibitors as potential cancer chemopreventives. *Cancer Epidemiology Biomarkers and Prevention*, **5**, 657–666.

Kelloff, G. J., *et al.* (1997). Farnesyl protein transferase inhibitors as potential cancer chemopreventives. *Cancer Epidemiology Biomarkers and Prevention*, **6**, 267–282.

Kelloff, G. J., *et al.* (1998). Aromatase inhibitors as potential cancer chemopreventives. *Cancer Epidemiology Biomarkers and Prevention*, **7**, 65–78.

Kelloff, G. J., *et al.* (1999). Cancer chemoprevention: progress and promise. *European Journal of Cancer*, **35**, 1755–1762.

Lipkin, M. (1992). Prototypic applications of intermediate endpoints in chemoprevention. *Journal of Cellular Biochemistry*, **16** (Suppl. G), 1–13.

Marnett, L. J. (1992). Aspirin and the potential role of prostaglandins in colon cancer. *Cancer Research*, **52**, 5575–5589.

Moon, R. C., *et al*. (1992). Chemoprevention of MNU-induced mammary tumors in the mature rat by 4-HPR and tamoxifen. *Anticancer Research*, **12**, 1147–1153.

Moon, R. C., *et al*. (1993). Chemoprevention of OH-BBN-induced bladder cancer in mice by piroxicam. *Carcinogenesis*, **14**, 1487–1489.

Oshima, M., *et al*. (1996). Suppression of intestinal polyposis in *Apc* 716 knockout mice by inhibition of cyclooxygenase 2 (COX-2). *Cell*, **87**, 803–809.

Rao, K. V. N., *et al*. (1996). Differential activity of aspirin, ketoprofen, and sulindac as cancer chemopreventive agents in the mouse urinary bladder. *Carcinogenesis*, **17**, 1435–1438.

Reddy, B. S., *et al*. (1990). Chemoprevention of colon carcinogenesis by concurrent administration of piroxicam, a nonsteroidal antiinflammatory drug, with D,L-α-difluoromethylornithine, an ornithine decarboxylase inhibitor, in diet. *Cancer Research*, **50**, 2562–2568.

Reddy, B. S., *et al*. (1996). Evaluation of cyclooxygenase-2 inhibitor for potential chemopreventive properties in colon carcinogenesis. *Cancer Research*, **56**, 4566–4569.

Schipper, H., *et al*. (1996). A new biological framework for cancer research. *Lancet*, **348**, 1149–1151.

Smalley, W. E. and DuBois, R. N. (1997). Colorectal cancer and nonsteroidal anti-inflammatory drugs. *Advances in Pharmacology*, **39**, 1–20.

Steele, V. E., *et al*. (1999). Lipoxygenase inhibitors as potential cancer chemopreventives. *Cancer Epidemiology Biomarkers and Prevention*, **8**, 467–483.

Steinbach, G., *et al*. (2000). The effect of celecoxib, a cyclooxygenase-2 inhibitor, in familial adenomatous polyposis. *New England Journal of Medicine*, **342**, 1946–1952.

Taketo, M. M. (1998). Cyclooxygenase-2 inhibitors in tumorigenesis (Part I). *Journal of the National Cancer Institute*, **90**, 1529–1536.

Taketo, M. M. (1998). Cyclooxygenase-2 inhibitors in tumorigenesis (Part II). *Journal of the National Cancer Institute*, **90**, 1609–1620.

Wattenberg, L. W., *et al*. (1997). Chemoprevention of pulmonary carcinogenesis by aerosolized budesonide in female A/J mice. *Cancer Research*, **57**, 5489–5492.

Zenser, T. V. and Davis, B. B. (1992). Arachidonic acid metabolism. In: Steele, V. E., *et al*. (eds), *Cellular and Molecular Targets for Chemoprevention*. 225–243 (CRC Press, Boca Raton, FL).

Part C
Systemic Oncology

Chapter 33
Introduction to the Diagnosis of Cancer

Sharon Poltis Wilczynski

City of Hope National Medical Center, Duarte, CA, USA

CONTENTS

INTRODUCTION TO THE DIAGNOSIS OF CANCER

One of life's most horrifying experiences is to be told that you or someone you love has cancer. Unfortunately, each year over 1.2 million individuals in the United States alone are diagnosed with serious invasive cancers. The life of the individual diagnosed with cancer is profoundly altered spiritually and emotionally as well as physically by both the disease and the treatment, which is itself often life threatening. The impact of a cancer diagnosis is so great that it must be made with absolute certainty. For most, the road to the diagnosis starts with unexplained bleeding, pain or the presence of a lump somewhere in or on the body. After numerous medical tests, a piece of the abnormal tissue or some cells are removed by biopsy or fine needle aspiration. In the laboratory the tissue/cells are examined by a pathologist, a physician who specializes in the diagnosis of disease. The interpretation of the morphology along with incorporation of pertinent clinical and laboratory data are integrated into a final diagnosis, a task that is both art and science. Simply rendering a diagnosis of benign or malignant is far from sufficient. The tumour must be given an exact histological classification and if the tumour is removed surgically, the extent of spread is determined by a detailed examination of the specimen. Based on accumulated experience with previous patients having similar tumours with similar spread, the natural course of the disease is predicted and appropriate therapy initiated.

The word tumour originally meant 'swelling' caused by inflammation but now generally means a 'new growth' or neoplasm. A variety of reactive processes can simulate neoplasms but these are usually polyclonal and eventually respond to endogenous homeostatic mechanisms and cease to proliferate. By definition a neoplastic process is an abnormal growth of cells and implies a clonal proliferation in which all the tumour cells are descendants of a single cell that gained the ability to replicate autonomously. A benign tumour will grow at the site of origin usually as an expansile mass without infiltration into adjacent normal tissue and does not have the capability to spread to distant sites. Generally, benign tumours can be surgically removed and do not kill the patient, but if they originate in critical areas such as the brain, blood vessels or in the airway they too can be lethal. Malignant tumours or cancers, on the other hand, infiltrate and destroy surrounding tissue and have the ability to disseminate to distant organs, often even when the primary tumour is small. In general, the pattern of spread is somewhat predictable for each given tumour type, e.g. most epithelial cancers first spread to the regional lymph nodes via lymphatics. Most sarcomas (cancers arising in mesenchymal tissue), however, spread by the vascular system to distant sites and less commonly involve the lymph nodes. This ability of malignant cells to metastasize is the greatest obstacle to the successful treatment of cancer.

There are some tumours that are difficult to pigeonhole neatly as benign or malignant. For example, basal cell carcinomas of the skin aggressively infiltrate surrounding tissue but rarely metastasize to distant sites. Borderline ovarian tumours (also called ovarian tumours of low malignant potential) will widely disseminate in the peritoneal cavity but have limited ability to invade into the abdominal organs. Unfortunately, there are no markers (morphological, molecular or otherwise) that denote malignant cell populations regardless of morphology, clinical setting or anatomic location. It is unlikely that such markers exist but if one should ever be identified it would be equivalent to finding the 'holy grail' of pathology.

Pathology is the branch of medicine that studies the mechanisms of cell/tissue/organ injury and the structural changes that underlie disease processes. The surgical pathologist is a physician who specializes in the examination of tissue from living patients, diagnosing diseases and guiding management of the patient. The surgical pathologist usually examines tissue sections while the cytopathologist specializes in the study of cells in smears, aspirates and fluids. This chapter concentrates on the process by which a pathological diagnosis is made in an academic medical centre in the United States with a discussion of the basic histological and immunological methods that are commonly available for routine diagnosis and clinical management. Experimental techniques that are likely to be in routine practice in the next few years are also briefly included. It is hoped that the reader will get a flavour of how surgical pathologists and cytopathologists interpret histological images and incorporate clinical and molecular findings to arrive at cancer diagnoses.

SCREENING AND EARLY DETECTION

Unfortunately, only a few cancers are detected by screening programmes and most are still found only after patients seek medical attention for symptoms related to their tumours. The underlying premise for successful cancer screening is that treatment improves outcome if the malignancy is detected before it is clinically evident. This is an assumption and must be validated for each tumour type that is targetted. Slow-growing tumours that metastasize late in their course and tumours which are resistant to any treatment are not good candidates for a screening programme. In the first case, the late-metastasizing tumours may be effectively treated when they become clinically obvious and in the second case, if there is no effective treatment for a specific type of cancer, even when small, screening serves no useful purpose.

There are three primary types of screening programmes, based on the stage of malignancy that is targetted. Some screening programmes are designed to detect precursor lesions, before they become invasive cancers and are very effective when removal of the pre-invasive lesion is curative. The Papanicolaou (PAP) test for cervical cancer is the model for this type of cancer screening and has significantly contributed to reduction in death from cervical cancer in developed countries by identification and treatment of the preinvasive lesion (cervical intraepithelial neoplasia) (Miller *et al.*, 2000). 'Organ-confined' invasive cancer screening is exemplified by detection of prostate cancer by elevated levels of serum prostate-specific antigen (PSA). Screening for breast cancer by mammography detects both small invasive breast cancers that cannot be identified by physical examination as well as the preinvasive ductal carcinoma *in situ*. As our understanding of cancer on the molecular level increases, a third type of screening programme is becoming available that identifies predispositions to certain types of cancer by genetic testing. For example,

individuals with strong family histories of cancer can be tested for genetic mutations in relevant genes such as *BRCA 1* (breast and ovarian cancer) or *DCC* (colon cancer). To be beneficial, therapeutic interventions or prevention strategies that are inexpensive and have little if any morbidity in a currently healthy population must be available for patients with such predispositions. Clinical testing for predisposition to cancer has huge emotional costs to patients and their families and it is essential that high-quality genetic counselling be given before the tests are ordered as well as at the time the results are discussed with the patient. Finally, the ethical and legal implications (such as effects on insurability) of identifying at risk populations have yet to be resolved.

Screening tests are not diagnostic, but rather identify asymptomatic, apparently healthy individuals that may have the disease from those that probably do not have it. The qualifiers 'may' and 'probably' reflect the sensitivity and specificity of the screening test. The sensitivity is defined as the percentage of individuals with the disease that the test was able to identify correctly while the specificity is defined as the percentage of individuals who are free of disease that are identified correctly (**Table 1**). Some other independent method must be used to make the final determination of who has disease and who does not in order to calculate these values. Ideally a screening test should be 100% specific and 100% sensitive, but in reality, the sensitivity and specificity are usually inversely related. A screening test that is highly sensitive identifies most of the individuals with disease but will often have a high percentage of false positives that lowers its specificity. Another critical factor in evaluating the effectiveness of a screening test is the prevalence of the disease in the population screened. If the disease is rare, even a screening test with excellent specificity and sensitivity will give a large number of false positives because of the many non-diseased individuals tested. This is usually expressed as 'low predictive value' for a positive test. In general, the positive predictive value of a screening test is high only if the disease is common in the population screened. Thus, limiting screening to a population at high risk due to age, family history or some other clinical variable is often necessary.

Further evaluation of all individuals who test positive in a screening programme is mandatory. Facilities for diagnosis and treatment must be available as well as resources to follow individuals that test positive until it is clear that they are cured or are truly without disease and not just in a period in which the cancer is so small that it is undetectable with current technology. Detection of presymptomatic cancers is often very difficult and requires expensive imaging tests and uncomfortable procedures. The monetary costs of screening programmes are substantial particularly when diagnostic medical procedures, lost work time and follow-up for individuals without disease are included in the calculations. The anxiety and stress of being told that a cancer screening

Table 1 Basic terms for evaluating screening tests

	Disease	*No disease*
Screening test positive	True positive (TP)	False positive (FP)
Screening test negative	False negative (FN)	True negative (TN)

Term	Definition	Calculation
Sensitivity	Percentage of individuals with the disease who are correctly identified by the test	$100 \times TP/(TP + FN)$
Specificity	Percentage of individuals without disease who are correctly identified by the test	$100 \times TN/(TN + FP)$
Per cent false negative	Percentage of individuals with the disease who were not detected by the test	$100 \times FN/(TP + FN)$
Per cent false positive	Percentage of individuals without disease who tested positive	$100 \times FP/(TN + FP)$
Positive predictive value	The likelihood that the individual who tests positive has the disease	$TP/(TP + FP)$
Negative predictive value	The likelihood that the individual who tests negative does not have the disease	$TN/(TN + FN)$

Table 2 Example of the results of a screening test with 95% sensitivity and 95% specificity for a cancer that is present in 1% of a population[a]

	Individuals with cancer	Individuals without cancer
Screening test positive	950 (true positive)	4950 (false positive)
Screening test negative	50 (false negative)	94050 (true negative)
Total	1000	99000

[a]In this example, in a population of 100 000 individuals, 5900 individuals will test positive, but only 950 have the cancer, a positive predictive value of 16%, while 50 of those with the cancer will be missed. This example is a 'best case' as most cancers will be less prevalent in the population screened and few tests are this sensitive and specific.

test is positive are considerable even when ultimately the individual is found to be free of disease. It is also inevitable that any screening test for cancer will miss a few individuals that actually have cancer and in our legalistic environment that can be a tragedy for all involved. As demonstrated in the example presented in **Table 2**, the evaluation of any cancer screening test must consider the disadvantages of applying additional medical tests to a large number of people who never had or never will develop the cancer for which they are screened.

With all these issues, it is no wonder that the concept of cancer screening is widely embraced but that there are only a few cancers for which it is actively pursued and shown to be effective in lowering the incidence of cancer death. The cost and infrastructure necessary to maintain screening programmes has been beyond the economic resources of many countries and even in the developed world the expense is staggering. It is beyond the scope of this chapter to discuss in detail specific cancer screening programmes and for a discussion the reader is referred to the published

literature. (See also chapter on *Inherited Predispositions to Cancer*.)

ROUTINE DIAGNOSIS

To make a diagnosis is to recognize a disease process, distinguish if from all others and assign it a name. This requires, as King stated over 30 years ago (King, 1967), both knowledge and judgement. Knowledge is information acquired from text books, personal experience or journal articles. Knowledge is dynamic and always in a state of flux both for the profession as new information is acquired and for individuals as we learn or forget. Yet application of that knowledge to a specific patient biopsy requires inference and judgment, qualities that reflect both reality and a perception of reality. It is easy to determine knowledge by testing, but judgment is a much more elusive and subjective quality yet essential for the intellectual process of rendering a diagnosis.

The initial pathological assessment of any tumour in the body is to differentiate a reactive process from benign or malignant growths. In most cases this can be accomplished by morphological evaluation of a tissue section stained with haematoxylin and eosin (H&E). As we enter the twenty-first century, the visual interpretation of the H&E slide by a surgical pathologist is still the primary means by which almost all patients are diagnosed with cancer. In this age of incredible technology the method is archaic but in most cases it is efficient, economical and conclusive. Furthermore, the easily performed H&E stain is universally available in hospitals worldwide, so that a biopsy prepared in a remote corner of the globe can be easily transported and interpreted by experts in distant cities or across oceans. The knowledge obtained through interpretation of the H&E slide by generations of pathologists and clinicians is amazingly concordant with the molecular abnormalities that underlie the malignant process being deciphered in laboratories today. Although this may seem surprising, it should not be as the visual interpretation of the architectural and cytological features in the H&E slide is based on the interactions of the chemical dyes with thousands of gene products that are a reflection of the distinctive differentiation state of the tissue.

H&E stands for haematoxylin and eosin, the most universally used histological stain. Haematoxylin is a dye extracted from the heartwood of a Central American legum tree, *Haematoxylin campechianum*, and was widely used in the 1800s in the textile industry for dying calico and woolen goods in shades of lavender and purple, and it was also used to colour wine. In the 1860–1870s it was adapted as a histological stain along with the xanthene dye eosin. Haematoxylin itself has little affinity for tissue, but with oxidation to haematein and in the presence of metal mordants (usually aluminium or iron) it binds to nucleoproteins, probably though electrostatic interactions. Eosin, a potassium salt of tetrabromofluorescein, was first synthesized by Baeyer in 1871. It stains cytoplasm and connective tissue a variety of shades of red and pink by chemical reactions with proteins, particularly those with basic amino acids such as arginine, lysine and histidine. Haematoxylin and eosin were combined by Busch in 1878 and over a century later the combination is still the most common means by which tissue sections are examined. A myriad of cellular substances interact with these two chemical compounds to produce patterns that convey an enormous amount of information that reflects the underlying biochemical and molecular processes occurring in the cells and tissue. With the aid of a microscope and this simple cellular stain, the surgical pathologist can diagnose almost all pathological processes from infectious diseases to cancer.

Most cancers are detected when they have grown large enough to interfere with the function of a specific organ or to cause pain or other physical symptoms. The patient, after reporting symptoms to a physician, usually will have numerous radiological and other studies to localize and characterize the process, but eventually a tissue biopsy (either surgical or fine needle aspiration) is required before therapy for cancer can be initiated. To prevent autolysis and to keep the cells in as close to their living state as possible, the tissue is 'fixed.' Although a large number of substances have been and are used, 10% neutral buffered formalin (with an actual working concentration of about 4% formaldehyde) is still the most widely used fixative. The chemistry of formalin fixation is complex and still not completely understood, but proteins and nucleic acids are reversibly cross-linked through the addition of methylene groups. Before microscopic sections can be prepared, thin pieces of the fixed tissue must be permeated by a supporting medium such as paraffin. First most of the water is removed from the fixed tissue by dehydration through graded alcohols. The tissue is then 'cleared' by removal of the dehydrant with a substance that is miscible with paraffin. Traditionally xylene was used but newer, less toxic and more environmentally friendly agents are now available. Finally, the tissue is permeated by the embedding agent, almost always paraffin. This process is automated and computer-controlled instruments move the tissue in cassettes from one solution to the next at preset times and often with applications of heat and vacuum to speed the process. Before the tissue can be sectioned it is removed from the cassette and must be oriented in the final block so that tissue relationships such as the junction between epithelium and stroma are preserved. This is a critical step that requires skill and a great deal of manual dexterity from the technician. After hardening, the tissue is now ready to be sectioned using a microtome, an instrument that has a very sharp knife and can advance the tissue block precisely to give sections 6–8 μm thick. Sections are floated on warm water to remove wrinkles and then picked up on glass microscope slides. After baking to adhere the tissue to the glass, the slides are now ready for staining. Since most histological stains are aqueous, the embedding process must be reversed to rid the tissue of paraffin. After running through xylene (or substitute), graded alcohols to water the section is finally ready for the H&E stain.

After staining, the H&E slide is examined under the microscope by a surgical pathologist and the tumour is characterized by its morphological phenotype as expressed in tissue architecture and cytological appearance. The process by which the slide is evaluated and the findings translated into a diagnosis is subjective and no two pathologists approach or 'see' the slide in exactly the same way. Usually it is examined first at low power (4×) to discern the overall pattern and to detect areas that have abnormalities. Once the overall pattern is appreciated and specific areas of the slide identified as worthy of additional study, the pathologists will look at the cells on medium and high power (20 or 40×). Any identified abnormal cell population is further examined for uniform or variable nuclear features, the size and shape of the nuclei and features of the nuclear membrane, the chromatin pattern, the degree of staining (hyperchromatic or hypochromatic), mitoses (number and abnormalities), the quantity and quality of cytoplasm, and the shape and pigmentation of the cells and their relationship to each other and to stromal cells. The type and extent of inflammatory or stromal reaction is also noted. A wide variety of 'special stains' can be performed in the histology laboratory to identify substances produced by the malignant cells, such as mucin (for epithelial mucins), PAS (distinguishes neutral polysaccharides and glycoproteins from sialic acid containing muco-substances) or Alcian blue (acid muco-substances). Other histochemical stains such as reticulum or trichrome are useful for evaluating the relationship of the tumour to the stroma. Although many of these substances are now defined antigenically and are detected by immunohistochemistry, these special staining techniques are still useful, inexpensive and can be performed in most histology laboratories on the same day as the initial H&E section.

The experienced histopathologist collects the visual information from the H&E slide almost subliminally, analysing and comparing with a set of internalized patterns that have been accumulated in memory from personal experience. The diversity of the histological features in human tumours is great and rarely does a pattern conform to the idealized description and no two tumours are ever exactly alike. Before a final diagnosis is reached, the pathologist must be methodical in eliminating histological mimics and consider unusual entities that may show similar morphological features. They also must determine if the biopsy is representative of the clinical lesion and if the diagnosis 'fits' with the clinical setting. No diagnosis can be made without knowledge of the clinical setting, including the age and sex of the patient, the anatomical site, previous histological and/or radiological findings and past surgical, chemotherapy or other medical interventions. Changes that would indicate malignancy in a brain biopsy from a 40-year-old man may be normal if from a 2-week-old baby.

In surgical specimens, the extent of the tumour is determined by the involvement of specific anatomical structures leading to a pathological stage. Particularly important is the presence or absence of tumour metastasis in regional lymph nodes. Margins of resection are carefully evaluated and prognostic markers are assessed. In some settings the decision for additional therapy is based on the findings in the resected specimen. For example, osteosarcomas are often treated with chemotherapy prior to resection and the presence and amount of viable tumour in the specimen dictates whether or not additional chemotherapy is given. All of this information is communicated by the pathologist to the clinician in a formal written report. There is growing support for the utilization of standardized surgical pathology reports so that the pathological characteristics of a tumour resection specimen are recorded in a complete and consistent manner (Rosai *et al.*, 1993).

The pathologist is ever more called on to render precise diagnoses on smaller and smaller fragments of tissue. Still, in most cases, the distinction between benign and malignant, and the classification and grade of the tumour can be determined solely by morphological evaluation of the H&E slide. Ancillary studies on the tissue such as immunohistochemistry and molecular analysis as discussed below can refine the diagnosis and contribute clinically useful information.

Tumour Classification

All tumour classification schemes are by their nature artificial and arbitrary as biological processes are generally continua. Yet specific landmarks can often be used to define boundaries not only in the spectrum from benign to malignant but also through the grades of malignancy and among the types of tumours. For example, the presence of stromal invasion is a critical parameter that separates carcinoma *in situ* of the cervix, a lesion with no metastatic potential, from an invasive cervical cancer that has the potential to metastasize and kill the patient. However, many of the boundaries are less clear and they can be very difficult to interpret in an individual case whether from inherent properties of the lesion or from inadequate tissue sampling. It is not surprising that pathologists will often vary in their thresholds for recognizing some specific diagnostic entities. However, meaningful reproducible criteria have been identified and are generally recognized for the diagnosis of most human cancers. With some exceptions, the most universally accepted classification schemes for human tumours are published in a series of monographs by the World Heath Organisation and in the systemic series of fascicles developed for the United States Armed Forces Institute of Pathology.

Currently tumours are classified based on their histogenesis, or the cell of origin for the neoplastic proliferation. Tumours that arise from the glandular epithelial cells of the body are called adenomas if benign or carcinomas if malignant. Malignant tumours from the supporting tissues derived from the embryonic mesodermal layer are sarcomas. Haematopoietic cells give rise to leukaemias and lymphomas. Tumours are thought to arise from stem cells, those cells that have retained the ability to replicate and differentiate into specialized tissues. Neoplasms are classified based on the type of differentiation the specific tumour cells display. Carcinomas with a glandular growth pattern are adenocarcinomas whereas those that have recognizable squamous differentiation are squamous cell carcinomas. Angiosarcomas have vascular channels whereas a chondrosarcoma will show cartilaginous differentiation. Identification of specific cellular products either morphologically by light or electron microscopy or by immunohistochemical detection is frequently helpful in the determination of the lineage of a tumour. For example, a squamous cell carcinoma can be recognized by the presence of intercellular bridges, an adenocarcinoma by the presence of acinar formation and/or mucin and a rhabdomyosarcoma by immunoreactivity with desmin. Although the classification of tumours is still primarily morphological, it has become more sophisticated and biologically more meaningful by incorporating immunohistochemical techniques that recognize specific proteins expressed by the tumour cells and by molecular studies that identify tumour-specific genetic changes.

By assigning a name to a tumour the probable behaviour and clinical implications are communicated. A diagnosis of cancer of the testis is essentially meaningless, but to call a testicular mass a seminoma indicates that the tumour is probably localized and cured by surgery or if spread to lymph nodes it is treatable by radiation therapy. On the other hand, a diagnosis of embryonal or choriocarcinoma of the testis implies a more ominous prognosis and the likelihood of distant spread is high and aggressive chemotherapy is needed to control the disease.

Electron Microscopy in Tumour Classification

Ultrastructural analysis of a tumour was for many years the primary means by which a poorly differentiated tumour was classified. For example, using transmission electron microscopy, malignant nerve sheath tumours could be recognized by their long cytoplasmic processes, primitive cell junctions and fragmented external basal lamina. Rhabdomyosarcomas had 6-nm (actin) and 15-nm (myosin) filaments associated with Z discs. Identification of subcellular structures such as desmosomes (epithelial tumours), neurosecretory granules (neuroendocrine tumours) or melanosomes (malignant melanoma) are also examples of how the electron microscope was applied in diagnostic pathology. Although immunohistochemistry has replaced electron microscopy for many of these applications, it is still useful in some cases and ultrastructural localization of specific antigenic substances may be a powerful tool in the future (Herrera *et al.*, 2000).

Immunohistochemistry in Tumour Classification

The diagnosis of tumours as benign or malignant is primarily based on morphological features, but immunohistochemistry is a powerful and complementary aid in classifying tumours and in identifying markers that have prognostic significance. The basic premise of classification by immunoreactivity is that malignant cells, even when very undifferentiated, continue to make antigenic substances that characterize the cell or tissue from which they arose. The same antigenic substance is present in normal, benign and malignant cells so that the expression of an antigen by itself is not usually diagnostic for cancer. It is absolutely essential that immunohistochemical analysis of a tumour be interpreted in the context of a carefully selected differential diagnosis based on the clinical setting and morphologic features of the tumour. To do otherwise is to invite diagnostic disaster.

One of the most challenging problems to a surgical pathologist is the diagnosis of a poorly differentiated tumour when no primary site is clinically evident. From a therapeutic perspective, it is most critical to correctly identify those tumours for which there is effective specific systemic chemotherapy or hormonal therapy, such as for lymphomas and metastatic carcinomas of the breast, prostate and ovary. Although extensive radiological and endoscopic work-ups can be done, these are often uninformative, expensive and may have significant morbidity. Frequently the use of antigenic markers can be helpful in narrowing the possibilities and a likely site can be suggested based on clinical setting, subtle morphological features of the tumour combined with a limited immunohistochemical panel of antibodies. Among the most useful antigens in this setting are the intermediate filaments that composed the cell's cytoskeletal framework (**Table 3**).

There is lineage-dependent expression of these proteins that is maintained even in very undifferentiated tumours. Immunohistochemical typing with appropriate antibodies can be very helpful in differentiating epithelial (expressing keratin filaments) from mesenchymal tumours (expressing vimentin filaments). Metastatic melanoma and lymphoma are also usually in the differential of a poorly differentiated tumour and the addition of antibodies to S100 and CD45 can be useful in recognition of these tumours. S100 is a calcium-binding protein that is strongly expressed in melanomas although it can also be seen in neural tumours, histiocytic lesions and some carcinomas. This demonstrates that no single antibody can be interpreted in isolation and evaluation by a panel of antibodies is necessary. A melanoma should also stain strongly with vimentin and will be negative for keratin and lymphoid

Table 3 Intermediate filaments

Intermediate filament	Location	Tumours
Keratin	Epithelial cells	All carcinomas, adenocarcinomas, squamous cell carcinomas, mesotheliomas
Desmin	Muscle tissue, smooth, skeletal and cardiac	Tumours derived from muscle such as leiomyosarcoma, rhabdomyosarcomas
Vimentin	Mesenchymal cells, fibroblasts, endothelial cells, muscle cells	Sarcomas including fibrosarcoma, liposarcomas, angiosarcomas, also lymphomas, melanomas
Neurofilament	Neural tissue, both central and peripheral, cells derived from neural crest	Adrenal and extra-adrenal pheochromocytomas, neuroblastomas
Glial fibrillary acidic protein	Glial cells, astrocytes, ependymal cells	Astrocytomas, ependymomas, gliomas

markers. Melanocytic differentiation can be confirmed by reactivity to premelanosome markers such as HMB45 or Mel-A.

Immunophenotyping of lymphomas is essential for their classification. A family of membrane protein tyrosine phosphatases, recognized by the antibody cluster CD45, is present on most haematolymphoid cells and their tumours. Membrane positivity for CD45 in an undifferentiated malignant neoplasm is virtually diagnostic of lymphoma. Most non-Hodgkin lymphomas have immunophenotypes that correspond to stages in the normal development of lymphoid cells. The current classification of lymphomas (Revised European–American Classification of Lymphoid Neoplasms (REAL)) depends heavily on the integration of morphological features with clinical, immunophenotypic and genetic features (Jaffe, 1999).

The cytokeratins have a diverse and unique expression pattern that has been found to be useful in identification of the site of origin for many epithelial tumours. The cytokeratins consist of a family of at least 20 different polypeptide chains and two-dimensional gel electrophoresis studies showed that these are more or less distributed in a tissue-specific manner. Tumours tend to retain the cytokeratin profile of the epithelial tissue from which they arose (Chu et al., 2000). About 95% of colonic carcinomas are keratin 7 negative and keratin 20 positive whereas the majority of adenocarcinomas in the differential such as endometrioid ovarian adenocarcinoma and most adenocarcinomas of the lung are keratin 7 positive and keratin 20 negative. **Table 4** lists the keratin 7/20 profile of some common epithelial cancers that are frequently in the differential of metastatic carcinoma of unknown origin.

Table 4 Use of keratin 7 and keratin 20 in the differential diagnosis of common epithelial cancers

Keratin 7	Keratin 20	Tumours
Positive	Positive	Transitional cell Ovarian cancer (mucinous) Pancreatic cancer
Positive	Negative	Breast (lobular and ductal) Lung (adenocancer, non-small cell) Ovarian cancer (serous) Endometrial adenocancer Epithelial mesothelioma Thymoma
Negative	Positive	Colorectal adenocancer
Negative	Negative	Hepatocellular cancer Renal cell cancer Prostatic cancer Squamous cell cancer Small cell (neuroendocrine)

A large number of antibodies that are helpful in the characterization of tumours include a few that are relatively tissue specific. For example, the antibody to PSA is relatively sensitive and specific for prostate tissue as is thyroglobulin for thyroid. Neuroendocrine tumours will react with markers for neurosecretory granules such as synaptophysin and chromogranin. Immunoreactivity for desmin is strong evidence that the tumour is of muscle derivation and only glial tumours (or some germ cell tumours differentiating into glial tissue) will express GFAP. For further reading on the role of immunohistochemistry in tumour diagnosis, the readers are referred to an excellent recent issue of *Seminars in Diagnostic Pathology* (Suster et al., 2000).

Although expression of a specific antigen is usually not diagnostic for malignancy, finding aberrant expression at a site that does not normally have immunoreactive cells can be diagnostically significant. For example, finding malignant glandular cells in an abdominal lymph node that express PSA is good evidence for metastatic prostate cancer. Similarly, keratin-positive cells are not usually found in bone marrow, and in a patient with breast cancer the presence of cells that react with keratin antibodies is evidence for metastatic disease. Morphologically atypical cells can be found in ascites and pleural fluids as a result of a reactive or malignant process. If the atypical cells in the fluids express epithelial antigens such as CEA, B72.3, CD15 or BerEP4, a malignant process is likely as these markers are not found on reactive mesothelial or inflammatory cells. Also, aberrant expression of antigens can be extremely helpful in establishing the diagnosis of lymphoma. Demonstration of a lymphoid population that co-expresses CD20 (a B cell marker) as well as CD43 (a T cell marker) is very strong evidence for malignant lymphoma.

Immunohistochemical identification of specific gene products in a patient's tumour is increasingly being used as an aid in the selection of therapy. Breast cancers expressing oestrogen and/or progesterone receptors respond to hormonal therapy and for the last decade immunohistochemistry has been the standard for determination of steroid receptor status. With the development of Herceptin® treatment for metastatic breast cancer, the immunodetermination of Her2/neu overexpression is also routinely performed.

Immunohistochemistry is based on a series of biochemical reactions that start with an antibody recognizing a specific tissue epitope and end with the visual detection of the antibody–antigen complex. Antibodies generally recognize a specific shape of an epitope formed either by continuous amino acid sequences or discontinuous residues that are conformationally folded into the recognized epitope. Detection of specific proteins/polypeptides in denaturing gels such as Westerns or sodium dodecyl sulfate (SDS) polyacrylamide gel electrophoresis (PAGE) often employs antibodies raised against polypeptides and which are usually continuous epitopes. However, many of these antibodies will not recognize the same antigen in tissue sections and may actually have unexpected reactivity with unrelated molecules. In tissue sections, diagnostically useful antibodies often recognize spatially related conformational epitopes that are lost when proteins denature. Most primary antibodies for diagnostic immunohistochemistry are murine monoclonals, but several monoclonal antibodies recognizing different epitopes on the same antigen can be combined into a cocktail.

For the detection of the antigen–antibody complex, hetero-antisera are raised against species-specific epitopes on the immunoglobulin protein. The oldest immunopathological method was to visualize the antigen using a secondary antibody labelled with a fluorescent dye that emits visible light after exposure to ultraviolet (UV) radiation. Although this method is suitable for virtually any antigen, it requires a specialized microscope and the immunostain is not permanent. More useful for tumour pathology are the detection systems in which a bridging antibody links the primary antibody to an antibody that reacts with a enzyme that precipitates a chromogen at the site such as the peroxidase–antiperoxidase (PAP) system (**Figure 1**). Another common detection system is the avidin–biotin peroxidase complex (ABC). Here the biotinylated secondary antibody links the primary antibody to a large preformed complex consisting of avidin, biotin and peroxidase. Large lattice-like complexes are formed so that several active peroxidase molecules are linked to each biotin binding site increasing the sensitivity of the system (**Figure 2**). With this system, endogenous biotin must be blocked or nonspecific background staining can be high, particularly in kidney, stomach or liver. The visual detection of specific antigen–antibody complexes in tissue sections depends on many factors including the nature of the antigenic determinants recognized, how well they survived tissue fixation and processing, the type of antibody used and the sensitivity of the detection system. There are now numerous commercial systems available for automation of immunohistochemical staining, but careful attention to technical details is still necessary for optimal results.

Loss of antigenicity during the fixation process is a major source of false negatives, but with the development of antigen retrieval methods, this is less of a problem than

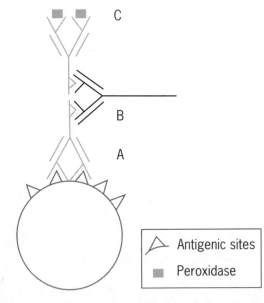

Figure 1 A secondary antibody (B) is directed against the immunoglobulins of the species producing the primary antibody which interacts with the antigen (A) and the antibody of the enzyme immune complex (C). The secondary antibody must be added in excess so that the FAB portions can bind to both antibodies. The substrate for the peroxidase enzyme – a chromogen (often 3,3'-diaminobenzidine tetrahydrochloride (DAB) – is added and an insoluble coloured precipitate is deposited at the site of the complex. This is referred to as the peroxidase-antiperoxidase (PAP) method.

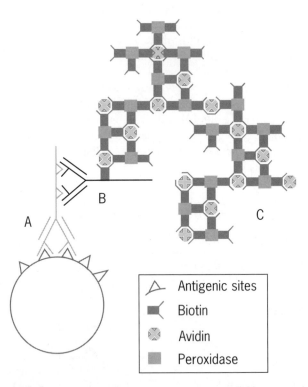

Figure 2 The avidin–biotin complex (ABC) method consists of a primary antibody (A) that interacts with the antigen. Its immunoglobulin portion is recognized by a biotinylated secondary antibody (B). A preformed avidin–biotin–peroxidase complex (C) binds to the biotin on the linked antibody. The peroxidase enzyme reacts with a chromogen (such as DAB) and a visual precipitate is produced. The high affinity of avidin for biotin (dissociation constant of 10^{-19}) contributes to the sensitivity of this method.

it once was. Enzymatic digestion of the tissue with proteinases was first found to be helpful in detecting a few antigens in formalin fixed tissue, but heat-induced epitope retrieval (HIER) has been shown to be more effective for a wider spectrum of antigens. The mechanism by which exposure of formalin-fixed sections in an aqueous medium to high temperatures reconstitutes epitopes is only partially understood. Fixatives such as formalin probably cross-link adjacent proteins in association with calcium. This cage-like complex is disrupted by heat and hydrolysis, aided by calcium chelation and/or precipitation by agents in the buffers. During the cooling phase, antigenic sites can be reformed. Small solubilized proteins that sterically inhibit the binding of antibodies may also be released during the process. A variety of means have been utilized to supply heat, including microwave, hot water baths, autoclaves, pressure cookers and rice steamers. Other variables include the temperature, duration of heating, pH, concentration and the buffers (citrate, borate, EDTA and several proprietary solutions). The exact conditions to release a specific antigenic site are variable and must be empirically determined for each antibody. However, using antigen retrieval methods, a wide variety of antibodies that were once restricted to analysis of only frozen sections are now determined in routinely processed formalin-fixed material.

When interpreting immunostains, it is critical that the pattern of reactivity be consistent with the known distribution of the cellular antigen. Antibodies to the intermediate filaments should give a fibrillary cytoplasmic staining pattern and if the staining is granular or muddy, or is present only in the Golgi region, artifactual staining should be suspected. S-100 is relatively unique in that it has both nuclear and diffusely cytoplasmic staining. p53 and the hormone receptors oestrogen and progesterone should be nuclear. Many of the lymphoma markers are membrane specific, such as CD45 and CD20. A common source of false-positive errors is the failure to recognize an aberrant cellular distribution pattern.

Both positive and negative controls are critical in preventing interpretation errors in histological material. Known positive and negative tissue samples must be analysed with every run, and if at all possible, internal controls in the same tissue should also be scrutinized. Immunohistochemical studies have a number of potential problems with both false negatives and false positives that may lead to diagnostic errors. Tumours are heterogeneous and irregular expression is a major source of false negatives, especially on small biopsies that are not representative. It is becoming increasingly clear that tumours can have aberrant antigen expression and few if any markers are specific to one or to a small group of tumours. Sarcomas such as leiomyosarcoma can express keratins and for some sarcomas such as synovial sarcomas and epithelioid sarcomas keratin expression is a diagnostic feature. Vimentin expression in carcinomas is not at all unusual either and it is actually expected in some such as

endometrial, renal and most carcinomas growing in body fluids. A few years ago CD99 was thought to be relatively specific for Ewing sarcoma/PNET, but reactivity is now appreciated in a wide variety of sarcomas and lymphoid malignancies. Although reactivity to the leucocyte common antigen (CD45) is characteristic of haemato-lymphoid cells, some lymphomas with plasmacytoid differentiation or large cell anaplastic lymphomas are negative. False positives due to aberrant expression of antigens can also be a source of errors, emphasizing the need to interpret immunohistochemistry results in the context of the clinical and morphological features.

Molecular Studies in Tumour Classification

At the present time, the majority of cancers can be routinely classified in a clinically useful manner by morphology with immunohistochemistry as an important accessory technique. The current classification schemes for tumours based on histogenesis and differentiation, however, have limitations and depend on subjective characteristics interpreted by individual pathologists. At least theoretically, a classification scheme based on molecular characteristics should be more objective, measurable and reproducible with the biological behaviour of an individual tumour better predicted. The application of molecular and genetic techniques to the classification schemes based on a comprehensive molecular profile of tumours is just beginning but will be a major thrust for translational research in the future.

Although studies on the molecular classification of tumours are in their infancy, perhaps the most reassuring finding has been that the molecular and/or cytogenetic alterations identified in research laboratories substantially agree with the traditional morphological classifications. This has been particularly true for mesenchymal and haematopoietic tumours that have specific cytogenetic and chromosomal translocations. For example, fatty tumours are among the more common mesenchymal tumours in adults and most show cytogenetic abnormalities that segregate them into categories similar to standard histopathology (**Table 5**) (Fletcher et al., 1996). Myxoid and round cell liposarcomas have been suspected to be closely related tumours and this is supported by the cytogenetic observation that both are characterized by the same translocation, t(12;16)(q13p11), involving a breakpoint in the CHOP gene on chromosome 12. Ring or giant marker chromosomes with consistent involvement of chromosome 12 are found in well-differentiated liposarcomas. The more aggressive dedifferentiated liposarcomas that mimic malignant fibrous histiocytoma are probably related, as they often have additional complex chromosomal alterations superimposed on ring and giant chromosomes. Benign fatty tumours also have specific molecular changes and the ordinary and innocuous lipoma has numerous cytogenetic abnormalities. These too tend to correlate well

Table 5   Cytogenetic and molecular alterations in fatty tumours

Histological type	Translocation	Genes
Myxoid liposarcoma	t(12;16)(q13;p11)	TLS/CHOP
	t(12;22)(q13;p12) (rare)	EWS/CHOP
Round cell liposarcoma	t(12;16)	TLS/CHOP
Atypical lipomatous tumours	Ring and giant chromosomes, often with abnormalities of 12q13–q15	
Lipoma	Abnormalities of 12q, 6p,13q	HMGIC/LPP
Lipoblastoma	8q rearrangements	
Spindle cell and pleomorphic lipomas	Aberrations of 16q and/or 13q	
Angiolipoma	Normal	

Table 6   Translocations used in the diagnosis of sarcomas

Sarcoma	Translocation	Genes involved	Available molecular test
Ewing sarcoma	t(11;22)	Fli1/EWS	PCR, FISH
Clear cell sarcoma	t(12;22)	ATF1/EWS	PCR, FISH
Myxoid chondrosarcoma	t(9;22)	CHN/EWS	PCR, FISH
Desmoplastic round cell tumour	t(11;22)	WT1/EWS	PCR, FISH
Synovial sarcoma	t(X;18)	SSX1/SYT	PCR, FISH
Alveolar rhabdomyosarcoma	t(2;13)	PAX3/FKHR	PCR
	t(1:13)	PAX7/FKHR	

with the previous morphological classification schemes. Of the common types of lipomas only angiolipomas have a normal karyotype. The common fatty lipomas of adults often have rearrangements involving 12q13–15. The breakpoint on chromosome 12 involves a gene, *HMGIC*, that codes for a member of the high-mobility group of proteins. These are small, acidic, nonhistone chromatin associated proteins that bind to AT-rich regions of the DNA. They have no inherent transcriptional activity but function by altering the nuclear chromatin, probably through interactions with other proteins. This alters the DNA structure and facilitates the assembly of transcriptional complexes. Spindle cell/pleomorphic lipomas usually have abnormalities of chromosome 16q or 13q, validating their histological separation from common lipomas and atypical lipomatous tumours.

Characteristic translocations have also been found by cytogenetic and molecular methods in a number of sarcomas (Ladanyi and Bridge, 2000) that are concordant with morphological and immunohistological categorization (**Table 6**). In some cases, a better understanding of the molecular defects found in a tumour have led to more accurate recognition of these rare tumours. For example, identification of the characteristic translocation t(X;18) in poorly differentiated spindle cell lesions by FISH analysis helps to discriminate monophasic and poorly differentiated synovial sarcomas from other spindle cell sarcomas.

Unfortunately, none of the common epithelial tumours of adults have simple genetic or cytogenetic changes underlying the malignant transformation. These tumours often have multiple changes in multiple pathways with no simple association with the current histological classifications. Microarray technology permits the expression of thousands of genes to be analysed simultaneously in a single tumour. The beginning of a molecular non-morphological classification of tumours is seen in the pioneering work of Alizadeh *et al*. (Alizadeh *et al*., 2000). Diffuse large cell lymphoma is a common type of non-Hodgkin lymphoma of adults and is clinically a heterogeneous group with some patients responding well to chemotherapy and others rapidly dying of their disease. Using a DNA array constructed primarily from B cell libraries, they demonstrated that two distinct subgroups could be identified by differential expression patterns. One group expressed genes characteristic of germinal centre B cells and had a 76% survival after 5 years whereas the other group had an expression pattern resembling activated B cells with only 16% survival after 5 years. Golub and colleagues (Golub *et al*., 1999) developed an expression-based microarray technology that discriminates and correctly classifies acute lymphoid and acute myeloid leukaemia without morphological evaluation. These are among the first but undoubtedly not the last examples of tumour classifications by gene expression profiles and the application of this technology to the common epithelial malignancies is to be expected in the near future.

Tumour Grading

The grade of a cancer is a reflection of how closely the tumour cells resemble their normal counterparts both morphologically and functionally. Malignant cells in well differentiated cancers can usually be readily recognized as having a histiogenic relationship to their cell of origin, i.e., they look like the tissues from which they arose. In some cases, e.g. very well-differentiated follicular cancers of the thyroid, the cells cannot be recognized as malignant until they demonstrate invasion. At the other extreme, some very undifferentiated tumours can only be assigned a lineage after exhaustive immunohistochemical or molecular studies and occasionally the cell of origin is never identified. In general, poorly differentiated cancers have a more aggressive behaviour than well-differentiated tumours of the same histological type.

For most tumours there are specific morphological criteria for assignment of grade and these have been shown to correlate with clinical behaviour. By evaluating architecture, presence or absence of specialized structures, the degree of cellular anaplasia and mitotic activity, many tumours are graded I–III with grade I tumours well differentiated and grade III poorly differentiated. This rather simplistic approach conveniently separates those tumours that are expected to do better (grade I) from those that are more deadly (grade III) than the majority of tumours in the middle. However, for some organs, more formalized grading systems are widely used such as the combined histological grade (modified Bloom–Richardson criteria) for breast carcinomas and Gleason's grading system for prostate cancers. These assign a numerical value to specific features. For example with breast cancer, a value of 1–3 is assigned for each of the degrees of gland formation, the nuclear features of anaplasia and the mitotic activity. The sum of these values (between 3 and 9) determines the tumour grade. In the prostate, architectural features are graded between 1 and 5 and the sum of the predominate and secondary patterns gives a score. Both of these systems have been shown to be reasonably reproducible and to correlate strongly with prognosis. Such grading systems are necessary for comparing results in therapeutic studies.

Tumour Staging

It is essential to have a uniform standardized system for classifying the extent of disease (staging) in order to compare therapeutic intervention and estimate outcome. One of the most widely used staging systems to describe the anatomic extent of neoplastic diseases has been developed by The American Joint Committee on Cancer (AJCC) (American Joint Committee on Cancer, 1997) in cooperation with the TNM Committee of the International Union Against Cancer. For most organs, the size of the tumour at its primary site and/or the involvement of local structures describe the tumour topography (T). The presence and extent of regional lymph node involvement (N) and whether or not there is documented evidence of distant metastasis (M) indicate spread of the tumour. These variables are incorporated into a shorthand notation called the TNM staging system. For most anatomical sites there are at least four categories for T, three for N and two for M, so that for some purposes the TMN groupings are condensed into stages (0, I–IV). Carcinoma *in situ* at all sites is Stage 0 while metastasis to distant sites is Stage IV and Stages I–III indicate increasingly greater extent of tumour spread. Staging can be clinical (cTMN), determined prior to initial therapy from the physical examination and imaging studies. The pathologic stage (pTMN) is assigned with information obtained from the surgical pathologist's assessment of the initial surgical resection of the primary tumour and regional lymph nodes. If the tumour recurs after treatment, the patient can be assigned a recurrent tumour stage (rTMN) and finally if a post mortem examination is performed, an autopsy stage (aTMN) may be assigned.

For common epithelial malignancies of adults (breast, colon, lung, prostate), lymph node status is probably the single most important standard risk factor for recurrence and a few additional comments should be made about their assessment. Extensive lymph node dissection has been the norm for cancer surgery and is responsible for much of the morbidity of the operations. Particularly for breast cancer and melanoma, sentinel lymph node biopsy is emerging as a technique to separate patients who have clinically occult lymph node metastasis from those whose tumours have not spread, sparing the latter group from the complications associated with radical lymph node dissection.

The first lymph node to receive lymphatic drainage from a tumour bed is termed the 'sentinel lymph node' (although it is often two or three nodes) and should be the first lymphatic tissue to be colonized by metastatic carcinoma spreading by lymphatics. A few hours before surgery, dyes or weak radioactive compounds are injected into the tumour bed, enter the lymphatics and are transported to the draining lymph nodes. At surgery these are identified visually or with the use of a hand-held Geiger counter and are selectively removed. Usually a frozen section is done during surgery and if micrometastases are found, a full regional lymph node dissection is performed. If no tumour is seen during intraoperative examination, the tissue is subjected to an extensive histological and immunohistochemical study to find tiny (even single cell) metastasis. For epithelial tumours and melanoma, immunohistochemistry for keratins and S100, respectively, is often used for identification of metastatic foci that could be easily missed by morphological examination only. Identification of tumour cell DNA or mRNA by PCR-mediated amplification can also be done but is still primarily a research technique reserved for patients on clinical protocols. If occult tumour is identified in these lymph nodes, the patient can then be taken back to the operating room for removal of the regional lymph nodes. For breast cancer, if the sentinel lymph node(s) is negative, there is less than a 2% chance that a full axillary dissection would reveal a positive node (reviewed by Beechey-Newman, 1998). The procedure, however, can be technically challenging for both the surgeons and the pathologist and considerable experience is necessary to achieve this success rate.

Tumour Markers and Prognostic Markers

In a broad sense, tumour markers are molecules or substances that are produced by tumours or in response to tumours that can be used for early detection, diagnosis, prediction of disease progression and monitoring response to therapy. Many tumour markers are substances normally produced by the tissue of origin such as prostate specific antigen (prostate) or α-fetoprotein (liver and germ cell tumours) and can be elevated in both benign and malignant processes. A great number of tumour markers have been

proposed as clinically useful but only a few are in routine clinical practice (**Table 7**). Ultimately a tumour marker is routinely evaluated if the results alter therapy and this improves clinical outcome. One of the most useful prognostic indicators for breast cancer is expression of oestrogen and progesterone receptors. Not only is the expression a favourable prognostic marker, effective antioestrogenic therapy is available for women whose tumours express the receptors. In the early 1990s immunohistochemical detection of oestrogen and progesterone receptors in breast cancer essentially replaced the dextran-coated charcoal biochemical analysis. This eliminated the need for frozen tissue and now the status can be obtained for very small tumours or even in fine needle aspiration specimens.

Markers are most useful when linked to specific pharmacological therapy or other forms of intervention based on the results. Her2/neu amplification in breast cancer predicting responsiveness to therapy with Herceptin® has already been mentioned and is now also being evaluated in other cancers such as lung and prostate. Similarly for lymphomas that express CD20 antigen, antibody therapy with Rituximab® is effective. On an investigational basis,

Table 7 Commonly used tumour markers

Tumour marker	Elevated	Comments
α-Fetoprotein (AFP)	Germ cell tumours Hepatocellular carcinomas	Glycoprotein synthesized by yolk sac and fetal liver. Usually measured in serum but can be detected by immunohistochemistry in the tumour tissue
CA125	Ovarian Cancer	Glycoprotein is elevated in sera of ovarian cancer patients, but also in many benign and reactive processes affecting the peritoneal lining
Carcinoembryonic antigen (CEA)	Gastrointestinal tumours, lung cancers, some breast cancers	Family of cell-surface glycoprotein that is elevated in a wide variety of carcinomas
Calcitonin	Medullary carcinoma of the thyroid	Approximately 80–90% of medullary carcinomas of the thyroid secrete calcitonin and serum elevation can be used to identify individuals at risk in families with an inherited form of multiple endocrine neoplasias
Her2/neu	Breast cancer	Amplification of gene associated with response to Herceptin therapy
Human chorionic gonadotropin (HCG)	Trophoblastic tumours	Glycoprotein secreted by placenta and is elevated in germ cell tumours with a trophoblastic component. Usually measured in serum but can be detected by immunohistochemistry in the tumour tissue
n-Myc	Neuroblastoma	Amplification of the gene is a poor prognostic indicator
Prostate-specific antigen (PSA)	Prostate cancer, some hindgut carcinoids	Produced by epithelial cells of the prostate gland and can be elevated in prostate cancer as well as by some benign prostate conditions

many markers are associated with biological behaviour but they are not routinely assessed as the marker result does not lead to changes in therapy or outcome. Small blood vessel density has prognostic value in breast cancer, but it is not routinely evaluated. Drugs that block angiogenesis first have to be proved effective in clinical trials and then the method for assessment of neovascularization also has to be proved to be predictive of response to therapy.

To be useful in determining successful treatment of cancer, a marker must be elevated prior to the initiation of therapy and then has to fall to a normal range when the tumour is surgically removed or is shrunken by therapy. Any elevation in subsequent measurements is evidence that the tumour has returned. Measurement of serum α-fetoprotein and/or β-HCG has been used very successfully in this manner for assessment of response to chemotherapy in germ cell tumours. A rise in these markers after a patient has been rendered free of disease by surgery or chemotherapy is an indication for treatment regardless of whether the recurrence can be detected by radiographic or other means.

Many markers show good predictive value in univariant analysis, but each new prognostic marker must be evaluated against well-established markers using appropriate multivariant statistical analysis. Many have shown strong correlation with traditional prognostic factors such as tumour stage, lymph node status, histological type of tumour, mitotic activity and histological grade. For example, p53 mutations occur in about 50% of breast cancers and these appear to be more aggressive than those with normal *p53* genes. However, the predictive value was much weaker in multivariant studies as the tumours with p53 mutations tended to be hormone receptor negative and had a high nuclear grade with more lymph node metastasis (Barbareschi, 1996). It is relatively easy by routine histology to separate well-differentiated tumours with an excellent prognosis from the aggressive poorly differentiated tumours, but there remains a large group of women who have tumours with intermediate histological features. Markers are needed that can segregate these tumours into those that are likely to have a good outcome from those that will do badly, so that aggressive therapy is given only to patients who are likely to benefit and the rest of the patients can be spared the toxicity and unpleasant side effects. Although a number of markers such as p53 mutational status and DNA ploidy are often considered in the clinical decision-making process, none has been shown to predict outcome reliably enough to be the sole or even a major criterion for management decisions.

Therapy

Unfortunately, most cancers are currently still treated by the relatively crude methods aimed at removal or ablation of malignant cells by surgery, chemotherapy or radiation therapy. Hormonal therapy is of value for the few cancers that are responsive. However, despite the tremendous amount of research, numerous press releases and scientific publications, immunotherapy and gene therapy have had little impact on routine clinical cancer care. Both of these therapies are likely eventually to find a niche and will be helpful for treatment of restricted tumours, but neither is likely to revolutionize cancer therapy in the near future.

Molecular pharmacogenomics may improve cancer therapy by predicting disease response to specific drug regimens and in reducing side effects and toxicity. The customization of therapy based on molecular targets is exemplified by the treatment of patients with acute promyelocytic leukaemia with all-*trans*-retinoic acid. This form of acute myeloid leukaemia is characterized by a t(15;17) translocation that involves the retinoic acid receptor-α and treatment with *trans*-retinoic acid induces differentiation with the majority of patients cured of their leukaemia (Slack and Rusiniak, 2000). Analysis of patient's enzyme systems or genes for drug metabolism and detoxification as well as tumour-specific factors such as the presence or absence of multiple drug-resistant genes may lead to improvements in selection of active drugs, their dosage and timing of therapy. However, the molecular foundations for determination of a tumour's resistance or sensitivity to specific chemotherapies is still not yet understood on either an empirical or a scientific basis and unfortunately there are still few, if any, applications in routine cancer care. (See the section on *The Treatment of Human Cancer*.)

MOLECULAR DIAGNOSTICS

The first use of molecular techniques in diagnostic pathology was the determination of clonality of haemato-lymphoid proliferations and this is still a potent tool for the diagnosis of lymphomas. The immunoglobulin genes and T cell receptor genes undergo unique somatic rearrangements during lymphocyte maturation. In reactive processes there are expansions of many clones of lymphocytes but in neoplastic proliferations the tumour is descendent from a single lymphoid cell. Originally, Southern blot analysis was used to detect these gene rearrangements, but now robust polymerase chain reaction (PCR) assays are available. Many lymphomas and leukaemias have specific characteristic translocations that can be identified by cytogenetics and/or molecular methods (Medeiros and Carr, 1999; Willman, 1999). **Table 8** lists some of the more common molecular abnormalities used in the diagnosis of lymphomas and leukaemias.

Identification of specific translocations by molecular tests in some of the sarcomas can also be diagnostically useful, especially in cases that are difficult to classify on morphological criteria, have aberrant immunohistochemical profiles or that occur at unusual sites (**Table 6**). These

Table 8 Some common molecular abnormalities of lymphomas and leukaemias

Lymphoma/leukaemia	Molecular defect	Genes involved
Follicular lymphoma	t(14;18)	IgH/bcl-2
Mantle cell lymphoma	t(11;14)	CCND-1 (bcl-1)/IgH
Burkitt lymphoma	t(8;14)	c-myc/IgH
Anaplastic large cell lymphoma	t(2;5)	npm/alk
Lymphoplasmacytoid lymphoma	t(9;14)	pax-5/IgH
B cell chronic lymphocytic lymphoma	t(14;19)	IgH/bcl-3
Acute lymphoblastic leukaemia		
Pre B	t(1;19)	E2A/PBX-1
B-cell	t(9;22) and others	BCR/ABL
Acute myeloid leukaemia		
M0 AML with minimal differentiation	−5/del, −7/del, +8	
M1 AML without differentiation	−5/del, −7 del, t(3;3), t(9;22)	
M2 AML with differentiation	t(8;21)	AML/ETO
M3 acute promyelocytic leukaemia	t(15;17)	PML-Rar-α
M4 acute myelomonocytic leukaemia	inv (16)	CBDF-β
M5 acute monocytic leukaemia	t(9;11)	MLL/AF9

are for the most part rare tumours and most are reliably diagnosed using morphological and immunohistological criteria, so that molecular testing is rarely required.

The difficulty in obtaining relatively pure tumour samples for analysis has hindered the widespread application of molecular techniques to solid tumours. Unlike the lymphomas and many sarcomas that grow as relatively pure tumour masses, for most epithelial cancers there is an intimate intermingling of tumour cells with stromal tissue and inflammatory cells. Separation of the malignant cell population by laser-capture microdissection is one method for the isolation of a relatively pure tumour cell population for study (Simone *et al.*, 1998). However, this technique still depends on the morphological recognition of the malignant cells and is very labour intensive, which will limit its use in routine diagnostic practice.

The inherent increased cost of sophisticated technology is justified if it can reduce total disease management by eliminating unnecessary diagnostic procedures and ineffective treatment. However, billing and reimbursement issues as well as the costs of required licensure are major obstacles for implementation of the current technology in many hospital settings. In addition, any one assay is required for clinical care relatively infrequently and the expense of training and maintaining personnel and equipment in a small laboratory is prohibitive. For most institutions, selected cases that have specific indications for molecular testing will be referred to a reference laboratory.

MINIMAL RESIDUAL DISEASE (MRD)

Failure of primary surgical treatment of cancer is usually attributed to the presence of undetected metastatic disease

(minimal residual disease). The goal of adjuvant chemotherapy or radiation therapy is the elimination of occult micrometastatic disease before it becomes clinically evident. For most oncology patients, the decision to add systemic therapy to surgical treatment is based on the staging parameters of the patient's tumours (tumour size, lymph node status and, to some extent, the histological type and grade of the tumour). A statistical analysis of accumulated data from similar patients with the same type and extent of disease is in most cases used to assess the likelihood that the disease will recur and whether additional therapy is given or withheld. However, conventional histological and clinical staging systems are limited. For example, with breast cancer patients who have small tumours and no lymph node metastasis, there is still a 15–25% chance of distant metastasis and no current histological or molecular marker identifies this population. This is far from ideal and there is a real need for markers that will unequivocally segregate patients into those whose tumours have already metastasized from those whose tumours have not metastasized. If a patient does not have metastatic disease, surgical removal is curative and cytotoxic therapy and all its negative side effects can then be reserved for those patients who may actually benefit.

Bone marrow is an accessible and frequent site for tumour metastasis and it is becoming increasingly common to examine bone marrow for the presence of metastatic tumour cells from patients with solid tumours. Immunohistochemical detection of micrometastasis is currently the standard method for the detection of the disseminated tumour cells. The identification of minimal residual disease depends on recognizing specific characteristics of the tumour cells that are not found in the surrounding tissue to which it has presumably metastasized. For example, haematopoietic cells rarely express epithelial antigens such as keratins and occult epithelial tumour cells in the bone marrow can be assessed using immunohistochemistry for cytokeratins. As few as one or two tumour cells in 10^6 bone marrow cells can be detected by cytokeratin immunohistochemistry and enrichment techniques can increase that sensitivity by a factor of 10 (Osborne et al., 1991).

Increasingly, molecular methods are used to assess the presence or absence of micrometastatic disease. PCR amplification of tumour-specific abnormalities present either in the DNA or mRNA of the tumour cells or, alternatively, amplification of tissue-specific mRNA can identify individual patients who have metastatic disease at the time of diagnosis and are most or least likely to benefit from the added therapy. In haematological malignancies, the identification of tumour-specific abnormalities at metastatic sites has been very useful for the detection of MRD. For example, primers can be made that span the t(14;18) translocation in the majority of follicular lymphomas, and amplification occurs only if DNA with the translocation is present in the sample. A few solid tumours, primarily sarcomas, have similar characteristic translocations, and similar methods have been used to identify MRD in patient with Ewing sarcoma or alveolar rhabdomyosarcoma.

Unfortunately, the genetic abnormalities are much more heterogeneous in the common malignancies of adults such as breast, prostate, lung and colon cancers. However, these malignant cells continue to express markers characteristic of their cell of origin and identification of a tissue-specific mRNA can be used to recognize MRD. For example, even very poorly differentiated metastatic prostate cancer to lymph nodes often express PSA mRNA, sometimes even when no protein is detectable by antigenic methods. Detection of micrometastasis by molecular methods is likely to have a profound impact on how cancer patients are treated and monitored in the future. For further information, the reader is referred to a recent review (Ghossein et al., 1999).

The process of metastasis is poorly understood, but malignant tumour cells leave the primary site and gain access to the lymphatic or vascular system. After transportation to a new organ they adhere to the walls of the vessels, transverse them, implant and eventually grow. Even less understood is the observation that malignant cells can become dormant for months, years or even decades at a distant site only to wake up and renew growth with a vengeance. In this dormant or nondividing state, malignant cells are unlikely to be killed by cytotoxic chemotherapy directed against replicating cells. Understanding and developing strategies either to eliminate the dormant tumour cells by novel immunotherapies or to prevent their regrowth by inhibiting angiogenesis are just two means under intense investigation.

THE FUTURE

Most of us who have spent our professional lives diagnosing cancer recognize that we are at the beginning of a revolution that is not just going to have a technical impact but that is also fundamentally challenging our traditional concepts of tumour classification by histogenesis and morphology. It is likely that the H&E section will be the cornerstone of diagnosis for the near future, but it is being and increasingly will be challenged. There will be re-evaluation and redefinition of many diagnostic entities as our knowledge and understanding of the underlying alterations in DNA and RNA expression becomes increasingly sophisticated. The transfer to clinical medicine of this new technology and the information it generates will not be quick, easy or painless and diagnostic anatomical pathology will be in a transition state for many years. It will take time to determine what information is therapeutically applicable and cost effective and how it should be obtained. Application of this knowledge to individual patients will still require physicians, whether traditional pathologists or specialists in the new molecular pathology, to exercise judgment and insight. However, in the end the hope is that the process will open up new areas of treatment options that can be individualized for each patient based on the inherent characteristics of the tumour.

REFERENCES

Alizadeh, A. A., et al. (2000). Distinct types of diffuse large B-cell lymphoma identified by gene expression profiling. Nature, 403, 503–511.

American Joint Committee on Cancer (1997). AJCC Cancer Staging Manual, 5th edn. (Lippincott Williams and Wilkins, Philadelphia, PA).

Barbareschi, M. (1996). Prognostic value of the immunohistochemical expression of p53 in breast carcinomas: a review of the literature involving over 9,000 patients. Applied Immunohistochemistry, 4, 106–116.

Beechey-Newman, N. (1998). Sentinel node biopsy: a revolution in the surgical management of breast cancer? Cancer Treatment Reviews, 24, 185–203.

Chu, P., et al. (2000). Cytokeratin 7 and cytokeratin 20 expression in epithelial neoplasms: a survey of 435 cases. Modern Pathology, 13, 962–972.

Fletcher, C. D. M., et al. (1996). Correlation between clinicopathological features and karyotype in lipomatous tumors: a report of 178 cases from the chromosomes and morphology (CHAMP) collaborative study group. American Journal of Pathology, 148, 623–630.

Ghossein, R. A., et al. (1999). Molecular detection of micrometastases and circulating tumor cells in solid tumors. Clinical Cancer Research, 5, 1950–1960.

Golub, T. R., *et al.* (1999). Molecular classification of cancer: class discovery and class prediction by gene expression monitoring. *Science*, **286**, 531–537.

Herrera, G. A., *et al.* (2000). Immunoelectron microscopy in the age of molecular pathology. *Applied Immunohistochemistry and Molecular Morphology*, **8**, 87–97.

Jaffe, E. S. (1999). Hematopathology: integration of morphologic features and biologic markers for diagnosis. *Modern Pathology*, **12**, 109–115.

King, L. S. (1967). What is a diagnosis? *Journal of the American Medical Association*, **202**, 154–157.

Ladanyi, M. and Bridge, J. A. (2000). Contribution of molecular genetic data to the classification of sarcomas. *Human Pathology*, **31**, 532–538.

Medeiros, L. J. and Carr, J. (1999). Overview of the role of molecular methods in the diagnosis of malignant lymphomas. *Archives of Pathology and Laboratory Medicine*, **123**, 1189–1207.

Miller, A. B., *et al.* (2000). Report on consensus conference on cervical cancer screening and management. *International Journal of Cancer*, **86**, 440–447.

Osborne, M. P., *et al.* (1991). Sensitivity of immunocytochemical detection of breast cancer cells in human bone marrow. *Cancer Research*, **15**, 2706–2709.

Rosai, J., *et al.* (1993). Standardized reporting of surgical pathology diagnoses for the major tumor types. *American Journal of Clinical Pathology*, **100**, 240–255.

Simone, N. L., *et al.* (1998). Laser-capture microdissection: opening the microscopic frontier to molecular analysis. *Trends in Genetics*, **14**, 272–276.

Slack, J. L. and Rusiniak, M. E. (2000). Current issues in the management of acute promyelocytic leukemia. *Annals of Hematology*, **79**, 227–238.

Suster, S., *et al.* (guest eds) (2000). Immunohistochemistry in tumor diagnosis. *Seminars in Diagnostic Pathology*, **17**, 169–256.

Willman, C. L. (1999). Acute leukemias: a paradigm for the integration of new technologies in diagnosis and classification. *Modern Pathology*, **12**, 218–228.

FURTHER READING

Cancer Screening

Smith, R. A., *et al.* (2000). American Cancer Society guidelines for the early detection of cancer. *Cancer*, **50**, 34–49.

Cuzick, J. (1999). Screening for cancer: future potential. *European Journal Cancer*, **35**, 685–692.

Diagnostic Surgical Pathology

Silverberg, S. G. (ed.) (1997). *Principles and Practice of Surgical Pathology and Cytopathology*, 3rd edn (Churchill Livingston, New York).

Classification of Cancer

Kleihues, P. and Sobin, L. H. (series eds) (2000). *World Health Organization Classification of Tumours* (IARC Press, Lyon).

Rosai, J. and Sobin, L. H. (eds) (2000). *Atlas of Tumor Pathology, Third Series* (American Registry of Pathology, Washington, DC).

Histotechnology

Prophet, E. B., *et al.* (eds) (1992). *Laboratory Methods in Histotechnology* (American Registry of Pathology, Washington, DC).

Sheehan, D. C. and Hrapchak, B. B. (1980). *Theory and Practice of Histotechnology*, 2nd edn. (C. V. Mosby, St. Louis, MO).

Immunohistochemistry

Taylor, C. R. (1986). *Immunomicroscopy: A Diagnostic Tool for the Surgical Pathologist* (W. B. Saunders, Philadelphia, PA).

Molecular pathology

Hammond, M. E., *et al.* (2000). College of American Pathologists Conference XXXV: solid tumor prognostic factors – which, how and so what? Summary document and recommendations for implementation. Cancer Committee and Conference Participants. *Archives of Pathology and Laboratory Medicine,* **124**, 958–965.

Wilczynski, S. P. (2001). Molecular biology. In: Weidner, N., *et al.* (eds), *Modern Surgical Pathology* (W. B. Saunders, Philadelphia, PA).

Websites

http://www.oncolink.upenn.edu. Oncology site at the University of Pennsylvania. Has a large number of links for information on cancers at specific sites and also for general oncology. Designed for both the medical professional and patients.

http://www-medlib.med.utah.edu/WebPath/ webpath.html. Large number of digital images for basic pathology and neoplastic diseases. It also has mini-tutorials on specific topics.

http://edcenter.med.cornell.edu/CUMC_PathNotes/ Neoplasia/Neoplasia. Descriptions of the pathology, aetiology and clinical aspects of a variety of neoplastic processes with links to images and further information.

Chapter 34

Skin

Vania P. Rudolf and George F. Murphy
Jefferson Medical College, Philadelphia, PA, USA

CONTENTS

NORMAL DEVELOPMENT AND STRUCTURE

The human integument is an extraordinarily versatile organ composed of tissue that is in a state of constant self-renewal and differentiation. In adults, the skin is the largest and most massive organ of the body, accounting for a $1.2–2.3 \, m^2$ of surface, 16% of body weight and a plethora of protective functions. Human skin provides protection, sensation, thermoregulation, biochemical, metabolic, and immune functions. It is composed of tissue that grows, differentiates and renews itself constantly. The skin is a complex organ system and there are both benign and malignant tumours described for each and every component. The benign tumours usually present as isolated, relatively stable skin nodules; the malignant lesions, on the other hand, form a complete spectrum from slowly growing tumours, which tend to invade only locally, to aggressive, rapidly growing and metastasizing lesions.

In utero, the skin forms from ectoderm and mesoderm, giving rise to the most superficial epidermal layer and the underlying dermal layer, respectively. Appendages results from down growths of specialized epidermal cells, which differentiate to become hair follicles, eccrine sweat glands and apocrine sweat glands. The epidermis is composed primarily of a continuum of four layers which represent a maturation sequence which produces tough, flattened cells filled with the structural protein keratin at the skin surface (**Figure 1; see colour plate section**). The basal cell layer, a reservoir for proliferating cells, takes part in maintaining a rate of epidermal turnover that is sufficient to maintain an effective environmental interface. Basal cell carcinoma (BCC) is an example of a tumour composed of cells with morphological resemblance to basal keratinocytes and basaloid hair matrix epithelial cells. The spinous layer contains larger polyhedral cells and is a site for active synthesis of keratin proteins. Usually, squamous cell carcinoma (SCC) recapitulates the spinous layer. The uppermost granular and cornified layers, representing either nucleated cells with keratohyaline granules or anucleated cells, are sites of terminal differentiation of the epidermal cells. Therefore, tumours, like some squamous cell carcinomas, that form keratin in association with granular layer differentiation show primarily epidermal-type differentiation, e.g. invasive squamous cell carcinoma. In addition, the epidermis contains two minority populations of dendritic cells, one (melanocytes) producing brown photoprotective melanin pigment, and the other (Langerhans cells) partly responsible for immune surveillance against environmental pathogens and proteins perceived as foreign. The dermis contains nutrient blood vessels, sensory and afferent nerve fibres, immune cells, dermal dendritic cells and fibroblasts which produce a tough leathery enveloping matrix termed collagen and more resilient elastin fibres which impart stretch and recoil upon exposure to mechanical stress. Tumours of the dermis may arise from any one of its cellular components e.g. the blood vessels, nerve cells, fibrilasts or smooth muscle. Usually, such tumours tend to be nonspecific cutaneous nodules and histological examination determines their origin. Metastatic skin cancer is relatively rare, but again diagnosis depends on histological analysis.

Specific anatomical features of skin structure and related function are described in **Figure 1**. As will be described below, understanding of the basic oncology of the skin depends heavily on appreciation of normal structure, since most tumours recapitulate to varying degrees their normal cellular counterparts.

TUMOUR PATHOLOGY

Tumour pathology of the skin involves literally hundreds of benign and malignant neoplasms derived from epidermal cells (true epithelial cells, termed keratinocytes, and melanocytes) and dermal cells (endothelial cells, nerve cells, immune cells and fibroblasts). The primary goals of diagnostic tumour pathology are to utilize gross and microscopic examination (1) to classify neoplasms according to histogenesis, (2) to make some prediction concerning anticipated biological behaviour and (3) to assess adequacy of surgical treatment. Classification generally depends on how closely given neoplasms recapitulate their 'cell of origin.' For example, the two most common forms of epidermal malignancy, the basal cell carcinoma and the squamous cell carcinoma, show differentiation features that most resemble cells of the normal stratum basalis and stratum spinosum, respectively. Tumours anticipated to behave in a benign manner possess a number of features, including slow growth, architectural symmetry and cellular uniformity. By contrast, aggressive tumours (i.e. those prone to produce damage to normal structures or to seed distant sites through metastasis) often grow in a rapid and destructive manner, demonstrate asymmetry of architecture and show considerable variability in cell size and shape. Exceptions exist, however, and in some instances the ability to predict biological behaviour based on tumour pathology is limited based on currently available methods of analysis.

AETIOLOGY

There are numerous environmental factors responsible for the genesis of skin cancer. Predisposing factors for squamous cell carcinoma include exposure to ultraviolet (UV) radiation, industrial carcinogens (tars and oils), chronic, draining ulcers potentially giving rise to free radical formation, old burn scars, arsenical ingestion, ionizing radiation, and tobacco and betel nut chewing in the case of perioral and intraoral cancers. Sun exposure, particularly UVB, is a primary cause of most basal cell cancers, and both UVB and UVA have been implicated in the cause of melanomas. Products that may activate the carcinogenic process may be generated as a consequence of UV radiation absorbed by epidermal melanin pigment. Because the relevant cellular targets of such carcinogens may reside in the basal cell layer, which is less accessible to their diffusion, the upper layers of the skin may actually be protective (Moan *et al.*, 1999). Prolonged exposure to UV radiation in the UVB part of the spectrum, 280–320 m, is a clearly established carcinogenic factor. Eye and hair colour, skin type and constitutive skin pigmentation also have a major role in cutaneous malignancies. Fair-skinned, blue-eyed individuals and lightly pigmented populations show a significantly higher number of cutaneous malignancies than more darkly pigmented populations, underscoring the importance of melanin pigment in protecting against UV radiation induced carcinogens. Individuals with darkly pigmented skin also selectively exhibit an increase in natural killer activity in response to irradiation with low-dose UVB, which could underlie at least partly their resistance to the development of photo dependent skin cancer (Matsuoka *et al.*, 1999). It has been postulated, however, that whereas melanin granules discharged by melanocytes into the uppermost epidermal layers may be photoprotective, those within the melanocytes, which normally reside in the basal cell layer, may actually be carcinogenic upon absorption of UV radiation. Evidence to support this includes the observation that certain albino Africans, as compared with normally pigmented Africans, appear to have a relatively smaller risk of developing melanoma as compared with nonmelanoma skin cancer (Moan *et al.*, 1999).

A corollary to understanding the roles effects of various environmental carcinogens on skin is the realization that breakdown in specific host defences may facilitate these processes. For example, defective melanin pigmentation or inability to develop photoprotective tanning, resulting in frequent sunburns, is associated with increased risk of developing skin cancer. Genetically determined predisposition to environmental carcinogens includes individuals with inborn errors in DNA repair after UV-induced damage, a condition termed xeroderma pigmentosum. Affected individuals cannot repair UV damage to the skin after exposure to UV radiation, and this leads to early development of cutaneous neoplasms – basal cell carcinoma, squamous cell carcinoma and malignant melanoma. Others suffer from gene mutations, which result in a tendency for dysregulated skin proliferation, resulting in numerous basal cell cancers at an early age (basal cell nevus or Gorlin syndrome). Exposure to ionizing radiation is an environmental factor that predisposes to cutaneous malignancy (X-irradiation, etc.). Immune deficiency may predispose to local defects in the body's ability to fend off deleterious mutations, thus producing an environment permissive to the genesis of skin cancer. Indeed, immune-suppressed populations experience higher rates of cutaneous malignancy than immunologically normal individuals. Moreover, certain viruses may incite altered cell proliferation in the setting of immune deficiency, as is the case of oncogenic human papilloma virus in the setting of renal transplantation and human herpes virus 8 in the setting of Kaposi sarcoma associated with acquired immunodeficiency syndrome (AIDS). In HIV infection, the risk of these cancers increases gradually, while the same risk increases fairly quickly among transplant patients (Mueller, 1999).

SCREENING AND PREVENTION

Environmental factors are potentially conspiring to produce increasing numbers of skin cancers, such as the progressive depletion of the photoprotective ozone layer by anthropogenic pollutants. Ozone depletion increases the amount of biologically harmful solar UV radiation that reaches the surface of the Earth, leading to an increased incidence of cutaneous neoplasms. Indeed, the incidence of malignant melanoma is increasing at an alarming rate, with an estimate of a 1 in 75 lifetime risk of developing this potentially lethal tumour for individuals born in 2000 (Brown and Nelson, 1999). The Caucasian population in Auckland, New Zealand, has the highest incidence of malignant melanoma in the world (Jones *et al.*, 1999); Kauai, Hawaii, on the other hand has one of the highest melanoma rates recorded in the United States (Chuang *et al.,* 1999). Accordingly, skin cancer prevention has become increasingly focused on public education regarding avoidance of sun exposure and the use of effective topical creams that significantly block the relevant portion of the UV spectrum. Such measures are particularly important in lightly pigmented individuals, or in those where genetic background or immune status could predispose to cancer formation. Health care professionals and patients alike also have been targeted for educational programmes that enhance early detection of both melanoma and nonmelanoma skin cancers. This approach is particularly important, since even malignant melanoma is 100% curable if it is surgically removed before the development of vertical growth within the dermal layers has occurred. Monitoring of patients with multiple pigmented spots representing potential precursors for or markers of malignant change has also been facilitated by the use of sensitive computerized image analysis approaches for digitized mapping of potentially changing lesions over time.

GROSS AND MICROSCOPIC PATHOLOGY

Precursors of Skin Cancer: Dysplastic Moles and Actinic (Solar) Keratoses

Although some skin cancers appear to develop '*de novo*' in normal skin, many others are preceded by proliferations termed atypical or dysplastic. These lesions have already begun to lose normal responsiveness to control mechanisms that determine the order and uniformity typical of normal skin and benign proliferations. In terms of malignant melanoma, the association of pigmented 'moles' (naevocellular naevi) with malignant melanoma was made over 160 years ago. However, it was not until 1978 that a genuine precursor of melanoma was described in detail. In that year, Clark and colleagues detailed the characteristics of lesions they termed 'BK' mole (a name derived

from the first letters of the last names of the initial two families studied) (Clark *et al.*, 1978).

Clinically, BK moles (today more often referred to as dysplastic naevi) are larger than most acquired naevi (often greater than 5 mm across) and may occur as hundreds of lesions on the body surface (**Figure 2a**, inset). They are flat to slightly raised, often with a 'pebbly' surface. Frequently they form target-like lesions, with a darker, raised centre and an irregular, flat periphery. In contrast to most benign moles, dysplastic naevi usually show variability in pigmentation (variegation) and borders that are irregular in contour. Unlike ordinary acquired moles, they have a tendency to occur both on non-sun-exposed and on sun-exposed body surfaces. Dysplastic naevi may occur in multiple members of families prone to the development of malignant melanoma (a condition therefore referred to as the heritable melanoma syndrome) (Reimer *et al.*, 1978). Dysplastic naevi also occur as isolated lesions not associated with the heritable melanoma syndrome. In this more common situation, the risk of malignant change appears to be low. Transitions from dysplastic naevi to early melanoma have been documented clinically and histologically within a period as short as several weeks, although the majority of such lesions are relatively stable.

Upon microscopic examination (**Figure 2a–c**), dysplastic naevi consist of compound naevi with both architectural and cytological evidence of abnormal growth. Unlike ordinary moles, where the neoplastic melanocytes tend to be arranged in orderly, small, discrete theques or nests (**Figure 2a**), dysplastic naevus cells form nests that tend to be enlarged and exhibit coalescence (**Figure 2b and c**). As part of this process, single naevus cells begin to replace the normal basal cell layer of the epidermis, producing so-called lentiginous hyperplasia. Cellular atypia, consisting of irregular, often angulated, nuclear contours and obliteration of nuclear detail by DNA-rich nuclear contents (hyperchromasia), is frequently observed. Associated alterations in the superficial dermis consist of a sparse inflammatory infiltrate, loss of melanin pigment from presumably destroyed naevus cells, with uptake of this pigment by dermal macrophages (melanin pigment incontinence), and a peculiar linear scarring surrounding the epidermal ridge-like downgrowths that are involved by the naevus (**Figure 2c**). All of these features are of assistance in the histological recognition of a dysplastic naevus.

Several lines of evidence support the belief that some dysplastic naevi are precursors of malignant melanoma. In one study (Greene *et al.*, 1985) it was shown that in a large number of families prone to the development of melanoma, over 5% of family members developed melanoma over an 8-year follow-up period. In addition, new melanomas occurred only in individuals with dysplastic naevi. From these and related studies, it has been concluded that the actuarial probability of persons with the dysplastic naevus syndrome developing melanoma is 56% at age 59.

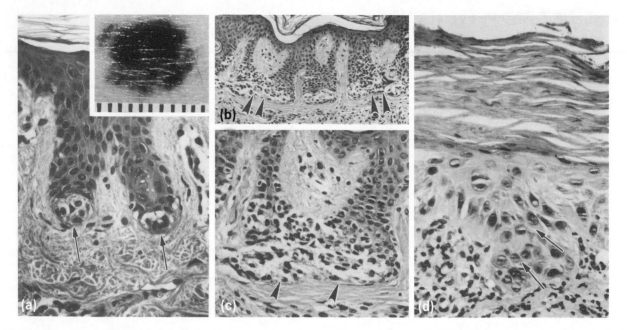

Figure 2   Premalignant dysplasia involving melanocytes and keratinocytes. (a) Unlike normal moles (also called melanocytic naevi) which grow as 'nests' of melanocytes at the tips of epidermal downgrowths called ridges (arrows), dysplastic naevi are characterized by abnormal patterns of growth, including readily recognized coalescence of adjacent melanocytic nests (b and c, arrowheads). The clinical result is a mole with irregular borders and non-uniform colouration (a, inset). Abnormal growth also is witnessed in a potentially premalignant dysplasia of epidermal keratinocytes termed an actinic keratosis (d). On comparison with **Figure 1a**, there is disordered growth of cells containing irregular nuclei within the basal and spinous cell layers (arrows), as well as abnormal formation of a thickened stratum corneum.

Further support of the relationship of melanoma to dysplastic naevi is the observation that the latter demonstrate expression of some abnormal cell surface antigens (Van Duinen *et al.*, 1994), chromosomal abnormalities (Caporaso *et al.*, 1987) and *in vitro* vulnerability to deleterious and mutagenic effects of UV radiation (Smith *et al.*, 1987).

Specific steps have been proposed (Clark *et al.*, 1985) whereby benign naevi may undergo aberrant differentiation to become dysplastic and eventually to evolve into melanoma. Parallels may be found in neoplasia involving other organ systems, such as uterine cervix, and thus dysplastic naevi are regarded by some as a paradigm for how certain malignant tumours develop from benign, albeit dysplastic proliferations of cells.

With regard to premalignant dysplasias of non-melanocytic epidermal cells, a series of progressively dysplastic changes typically occur in keratinocytes, a phenomenon analogous to the atypia that precedes carcinoma of the squamous mucosa of the uterine cervix. Excessive chronic exposure to sunlight can induce such premalignant lesions in the epidermis, causing histological changes in the normal keratinocyte maturation pattern and individual cell keratinization. Such a recognized condition is actinic keratosis, also termed solar keratosis. As would be expected, such lesions occur in particularly high incidence in lightly pigmented individuals. Exposure to ionizing radiation, hydrocarbons and arsenicals may induce lesions similar to or identical with actinic keratosis. Clinically, actinic keratoses are characterized by rough, scaling hyperpigmented plaques seen on the sun-exposed sites, especially the face, neck, upper trunk or extremities. Most lesions are usually less than 1 cm in diameter and may be tan–brown, red or skin-coloured. Some lesions may produce so much keratin that a 'cutaneous horn' develops, a phenomenon analogous to the formation of a true animal horn, which also originates from keratin-like protein. Because sites of predilection tend to be those prone to chronic UV damage, the lips may also develop similar lesions, and these are referred to as actinic cheilitis.

Cytologic atypia is seen in actinic keratosis in the lowermost layers of the epidermis and may be associated with increased numbers of basal cells (**Figure 2d**) or, alternatively, with thinning of the epidermis that results in a thin, semitransparent epidermal layer. The atypical basal cells usually contain enlarged, darkly stained nuclei. The superficial dermis contains thickened, blue–grey elastic fibres, a result of abnormal dermal elastic fibre synthesis by sun-damaged fibroblasts (Thielmann *et al.*, 1987). The stratum corneum is thickened and, unlike in normal skin, nuclei in the cells in this layer are often retained, a pattern termed 'parakeratosis' (**Figure 2d**).

It appears that not all actinic keratoses (perhaps the majority) do not evolve into skin cancers, and some may actually remain stable or disappear due to immune responses. However, enough do become malignant to warrant conservative local eradication of these potential precursor lesions. This can usually be accomplished by gentle scraping, freezing or topical application of chemotherapeutic agents, which destroy the dysplastic cells. Radical or extensive surgery is not warranted.

Squamous Cell Carcinoma

Squamous cell carcinoma is the most common tumour arising on chronically sun-exposed sites. As such, it is typically detected on facial, extremity and trunk skin of older people. Except for lesions that develop on the lower legs, these tumours have a higher incidence in men than in women. Industrial carcinogens (tars and oils), chronic ulcers and draining osteomyelitis, old burn scars, ingestion of arsenicals, ionizing radiation and in the oral cavity tobacco and betel nut chewing, immunosuppression and genetic factors (xeroderma pigmentosum) are all implicated in the pathogenesis of squamous cell carcinoma, in addition to exposure to sunlight. In the case of tumours induced by sunlight exposure, endogenous melanin pigment is believed to provide an important photoprotective effect. UV radiation is believed to damage DNA by directly forming photoadducts, which contribute to cell mutation and altered proliferation. Normally, many such altered cells may be eliminated by immunosurveillance mechanisms before tumours become clinically apparent. Accordingly, albinos with defective melanin pigment production, patients with xeroderma pigmentosum, an inborn enzyme defect in DNA repair, and those with immunosuppression all tend to have a high incidence of this neoplasm.

Histological variants of SCCs include various well- and poorly differentiated tumours, which may mimic various nonsquamous neoplasms (Murphy and Elder, 1991c). Immunohistochemistry may assist in evaluating antigenic parameters, useful to determine the cell lineage of such tumours. This is important, because poorly differentiated squamous cell carcinomas may occasionally be confused with malignant melanomas, certain lymphomas or even mesenchymal neoplasms. For example, a panel of antibodies to determine the presence of keratin protein (carcinoma), leucocyte common antigen (LCA) (haematopoietic cells), S-100 protein (neural and melanocytic cells) and desmin/vimentin (dermal spindle cell tumours) may be helpful in diagnosing poorly differentiated variants of squamous cell carcinoma.

Squamous cell carcinomas that have not invaded through the basement membrane of the dermoepidermal junction (carcinoma in situ) clinically appear as sharply defined, red scaling plaques. More advanced, invasive lesions are nodular, show variable keratin production appreciated clinically as hyperkeratosis and may ulcerate (**Figure 3c**). Well-differentiated lesions may be indistinguishable from keratoacanthoma, a potential variant form with a tendency to regress spontaneously, possibly as a consequence of immune-mediated mechanisms. When the mucosa is involved by squamous cell carcinoma, a zone of white thickening is seen, an appearance caused by a variety of disorders and referred to clinically as leucoplakia.

Unlike the potentially premalignant dysplasia, actinic keratoses (see above), squamous cell carcinoma in situ is characterized by cells with atypical (enlarged, angulated, and darkly stained) nuclei completely replacing all layers of the epidermis (**Figure 3a and b**). When over time these cells acquire the ability to break through the basement membrane and enter into the underlying dermis, the process has become invasive. Invasive squamous cell carcinoma (**Figure 3d and e**) exhibits variable differentiation, ranging from tumours formed by polygonal squamous cells resembling those of the stratum spinosum arranged in orderly lobules and exhibiting numerous large zones of keratinization, to neoplasms formed by highly anaplastic, rounded cells with foci of necrosis and only abortive, single-cell keratinization (keratin 'pearl' formation).

Unlike some advanced melanomas (see below), invasive squamous cell carcinomas are usually discovered at stages where complete resection results in permanent disease eradication (North et al., 1997; Rowe et al., 1992). Up to 5%, however, may metastasize to regional nodes, particularly deeply invasive tumours that involve skin of the head and neck (Friedman et al., 1985).

As indicated above, the most commonly accepted exogenous cause of squamous cell carcinoma is exposure to UV radiation light with subsequent DNA damage and associated mutagenicity. Individuals who are immunosuppressed as a result of chemotherapy or organ transplantation, or who have xeroderma pigmentosum, are at increased risk of developing malignant skin neoplasms (Penn, 1987). A considerable proportion of these tumours are squamous cell carcinomas, implicating aberrations in local immune networks in the skin in the production of an atmosphere permissive to neoplasia. Interestingly, sunlight, in addition to its effect on DNA, also seems to have a direct and at least a transient immunosuppressive effect on skin by influencing the normal surveillance function of antigen-presenting Langerhans cells in the epidermis (Cooper et al., 1985). For example, in experimental animals, it now appears that although Langerhans cells responsible for T lymphocyte activation are injured by UV radiation, similar cells responsible for the selective induction of suppressor lymphocyte pathways are resistant to UV damage (Granstein et al., 1987). Moreover, local exposure of the skin to UV radiation may also result in alterations in systemic immunity. Such phenomena could result in both systemic and local imbalances in T cell function that would favour tumour genesis and progression. DNA sequences of certain viruses

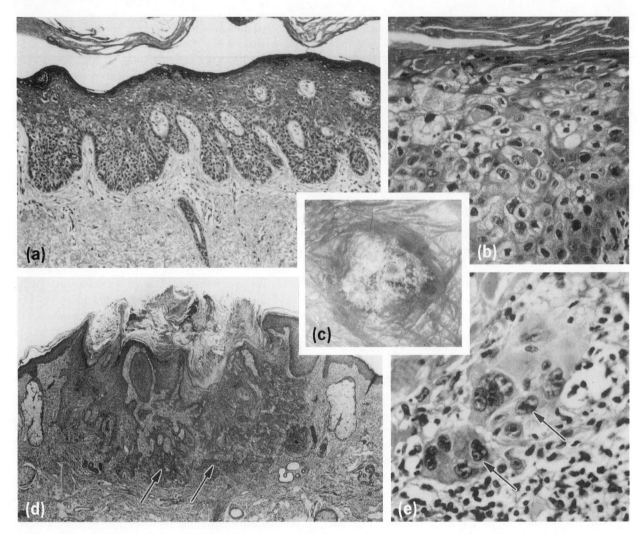

Figure 3 Squamous cell carcinoma. (a) and (b) malignant cells have not as yet invaded into the dermis, but have replaced most of the epidermal layer, a stage referred to as carcinoma *in situ*. (c) The clinical appearance of squamous cell carcinoma is characterized by a scaling, sometimes ulcerated nodule. (d) and (e) invasive squamous cell carcinoma differs from its earlier, *in situ* stage, by showing downward (invasive) growth of malignant cells into the dermis (arrows). These cells (e) have cytological features of malignancy, including enlarged, darkly staining, irregular nuclei (arrows).

(e.g. human papillomavirus HPV36) have been detected in DNA extracted from potential precursors of squamous cell carcinoma (Kawashima *et al.*, 1986). This suggests a role for these agents in the causation of these cutaneous epithelial neoplasms. Finally, certain chemical agents appear to have direct mutagenic effects on epidermal keratinocytes by producing DNA adducts with subsequent oncogene activation (Hochwalt *et al.*, 1988; Perez *et al.*, 1997).

Basal Cell Carcinoma

Basal cell carcinoma by far is the most frequent of all cutaneous cancers. Like squamous cell carcinoma, basal cell carcinomas are slow-growing tumours that rarely metastasize. They also have a tendency to occur at sites

subject to chronic sun exposure and in lightly pigmented people. Other predisposing factors include ionizing radiation, chronic scarring and arsenical exposure. As with squamous cell carcinoma, the incidence of basal cell carcinoma increases sharply with immunosuppression and in patients with inherited defects in DNA replication or repair (xeroderm pigmentosum). The rare, dominantly inherited basal cell naevus syndrome (Bale, 1997) is associated with the development of numerous basal cell carcinomas in early life, with abnormalities of bone, nervous system, eyes and reproductive organs, and with a specific gene mutation which now has been characterized.

Clinically, basal cell carcinomas present as smooth-surfaced, pearly papules often containing prominent, dilated subepidermal blood vessels termed telangiectasias

(**Figure 4b**). Some may contain melanin pigment and, as a consequence, may appear clinically similar to pigmented moles or melanomas. Chronic, large lesions may ulcerate (rodent ulcers), and extensive local invasion of bone, facial sinuses and deep subcutaneous nerves may occur after many years of neglect (Dixon *et al.*, 1989).

By light microscopy, tumour cells typically resemble those in the normal basal cell layer of the epidermis. Different histological variants of basal cell carcinoma can be distinguished according to the tumour growth pattern (e.g. nodular, sclerosing, cystic, pigmented). The earliest buds of basal cell carcinoma arise from the epidermis or follicular epithelium and do not characteristically occur on mucosal surfaces. Two patterns of growth include either multifocal origins from the basal cell layer of the epidermis and extending over several square centimeters or more of skin surface (**Figure 4a**), or nodular invasive lesions growing downward deeply into the dermis as cords and islands of darkly stained cells embedded in fibrotic matrix often with a pale blue hue as a consequence of associated mucin deposition (**Figure 4c–e**). Occasional tumours may appear cystic clinically and are found to contain large

cystic spaces upon histological examination (**Figure 4d**). The cells at the periphery of the tumour cell cords and islands tend to be arranged radially with their long axes in approximately parallel alignment, a characteristic feature also seen in the bulb of hair follicles and referred to as 'palisading.' The stroma shrinks away from the epithelial tumour nests (**Figure 4d** and **e**), creating clefts or 'separation artifacts' that assist in differentiating basal cell carcinomas from certain follicular appendage tumours also characterized by proliferation of basaloid cells (e.g. trichoepithelioma).

Mutations in the tumour-suppressor gene termed '*PATCHED*' (*PTC*) have been detected in human patients with the basal cell naevus syndrome. In this condition, multiple basal cell carcinomas as well as other anomalies develop according to an inherited pattern. Moreover, mice genetically engineered to overexpress the attachment site or ligand for PTC molecule, which is termed 'sonic hedgehog' or SHH and which mimics the loss of PTC function, develop basal cell carcinomas (Oro *et al.*, 1997). Thus, both SHH and PTC may have important roles in human skin carcinogenesis in the basal cell naevus

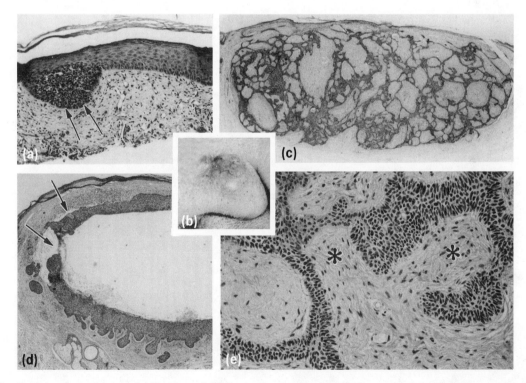

Figure 4   Basal cell carcinoma. (a) Tumours initially are formed by bud-like growth of darkly stained, 'basaloid' cells (arrows), here seemingly arising from the basal cell layer of the epidermis. (b) The clinical appearance of many basal cell carcinomas is that of a smooth-surfaced, 'pearly' nodule containing prominent superficial blood vessels. (c) Some nodular basal cell carcinomas may form an elaborate network of branching and anastomosing basaloid cells, while others (d) may have cystic spaces occupying their centres. (e) The cells forming these common tumours most resemble the epidermal basal cell layer and the basaloid cells that give rise to the hair follicle (matrix cells). The connective tissue that envelops the tumour cells (asterisks) resembles that of the bulb portion of the hair follicle, providing evidence that basal cell carcinoma is a tumour of follicular differentiation. Arrows in d indicate cleft-like spaces of artifactual stromal-epithelial separation.

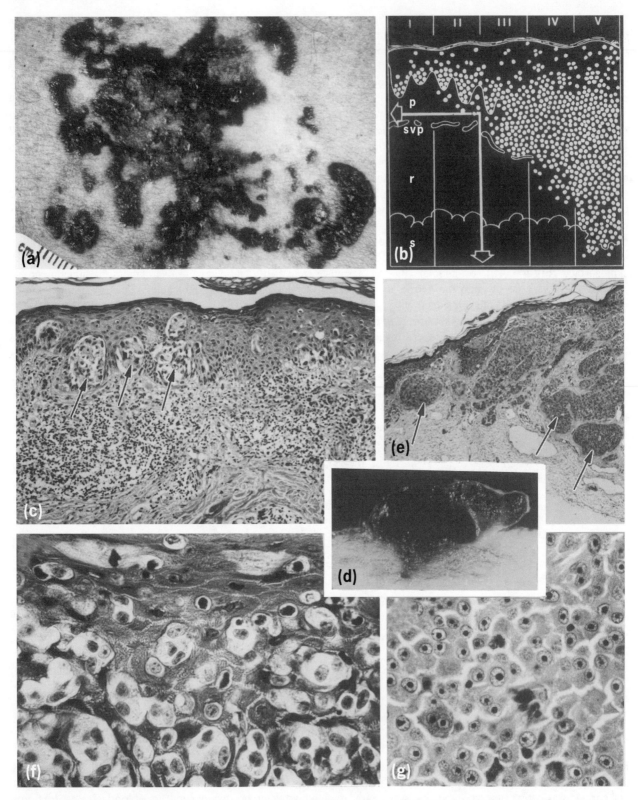

Figure 5   Malignant melanoma. (a) Clinically, melanoma is characterized by a diameter often greater than 1 cm, an irregular border and variation in colour. (b) Melanoma typically grows initially within the epidermal layer and as single cells within the superficial (papillary (p)) dermis, which is directly above an anatomic boundary called the superficial vascular plexus (svp). This early growth is generally curable with surgical excision and is termed the radial phase of growth (indicated by horizontal arrow). If untreated, the melanoma in time grows downward into the deeper (reticular (r)) dermal and subcutaneous (s) layers, an event termed vertical growth (signified by a vertical arrow). This stage carries with it the risk of metastatic spread which correlates with the depth and microanatomical levels of invasion, as

(*Continued*)

syndrome, although their precise roles in the majority of basal cell carcinomas unassociated with genetic patterns of inheritance remain to be elucidated.

Malignant Melanoma

Malignant melanoma is a relatively common neoplasm that as little as several decades ago was considered to be a potentially deadly form of skin cancer. The great preponderance of melanomas arise in the skin, although other sites of origin include the oral and anogenital mucosal surfaces, oesophagus, meninges and eye. All melanomas have the potential for metastasis if left untreated, and therefore the conventional modifier 'malignant' is really unnecessary. As a result of increased public awareness of the earliest signs of cutaneous melanomas, most are cured surgically in the early stages of their biological evolution (Mihm, 1971). Nevertheless, the incidence of malignant melanoma is on the rise, necessitating vigorous surveillance for its development.

As with epithelial malignancies of the skin (see above), sunlight appears to play an important role in the development of cutaneous melanoma. For example, men commonly develop this tumour on the upper back, whereas women tend have a relatively high incidence of melanoma on both the back and the legs. Lightly pigmented individuals are at higher risk for the development of melanoma than darkly pigmented individuals, an observation supported by epidemiological studies examining tumour incidence in equatorial regions versus those characterized by high latitudes. Sunlight, however, does not seem to be the sole predisposing factor for the development of melanoma, and the presence of a pre-existing naevus (e.g. a dysplastic naevus), hereditary factors or even exposure to certain carcinogens (as in the case of experimental melanomas in rodent models) may play a role in lesion development and evolution (Barnhill *et al.*, 1993).

Clinically, malignant melanoma of the skin is usually asymptomatic, although itching and focal bleeding may be early manifestations. The most important clinical sign of possible dysplastic or malignant degeneration is change in colour in a pigmented lesion. Unlike benign (nondysplastic) naevi, melanomas usually exhibit striking variations in pigmentation, appearing in shades of black, brown, red, dark blue and grey. Occasionally, regions of white or flesh-coloured hypopigmentation are also present. The borders of

melanomas are not smooth, round and uniform, as in naevocellular naevi; rather, they tend to be irregular and often 'notched' (**Figure 5a**). In conclusion, the clinical warning signs of melanoma are (1) enlargement of a pre-existing mole; (2) itching or pain in a pre-existing mole; (3) development of a new pigmented lesion during adult life; (4) irregularity of the borders of a pigmented lesion; and (5) variegation of colour within a pigmented lesion.

Crucial to understanding the complicated histology of malignant melanoma is the concept of radial and vertical growth. Simply described, radial growth indicates the tendency of a melanoma to grow horizontally within the epidermal and superficial dermal layers, often for a prolonged period of time (**Figure 5b**). During this stage of growth, melanoma cells do not have the capacity to metastasize and clinical cure is frequent. Specific types of radial growth phase melanoma are lentigo maligna, superficial spreading and acral/mucosal lentiginous. These can be defined on the basis of architectural and cytological features of growth within the epidermal layer as well as biological behaviour (e.g. lentigo maligna type of radial growth usually occurs on sun-damaged facial skin of the elderly and may continue for as long as several decades before the tumour develops the capacity to metastasize). With time, the pattern of growth assumes a vertical component. The melanoma now extends downward into the deeper dermal layers as an expansile growing mass lacking cellular maturation, without a tendency for the cells to become smaller as they descend into the reticular dermis (**Figures 5d, 5e**). Clinically, this event is heralded by the development of a nodule in the relatively flat radial growth phase, and correlates with the emergence of a clone of cells with true metastatic potential. The probability of metastasis in such as lesion may be predicted by simply measuring in millimeters the depth of invasion of this vertical growth phase nodule below the granular cell layer of the overlying epidermis (Breslow, 1970). Recently, prediction of clinical outcome has been improved further by taking into account factors such as number of mitoses and degree of infiltrative lymphocytic response within the tumour nodule (Clark *et al.*, 1989).

Individual melanoma cells generally are considerably larger than naevus cells. They contain large nuclei with irregular contours and have chromatin characteristically clumped at the periphery of the nuclear membrane with prominent red (eosinophilic) nucleoli (**Figures 5f, 5g**).

(**Figure 5** *caption continued*)
indicated by convention as levels I–V. (c) Histological presentation of an early radial growth melanoma, where most of the malignant cells are present as irregular nests within the epidermal layer (arrows). (d) and (e) gross pathological (cross-section) and low-magnification histological representations of a heavily pigmented melanoma that has progressed to the vertical stage of growth. Note in (e) the numerous large nests of darkly stained cells that have found their way into the deeper dermal layers (arrows). Melanoma cells, whether within the epidermis as part of early radial growth (f) or within the dermis as part of vertical growth (g), are distinguished from most naevus cells by their enlarged nuclei which generally contain conspicuous central nucleoli.

These tumour cells proliferate as poorly formed nests or as individual cells at all levels of the epidermis (**Figure 5b**) in the radial phase of growth and, in the dermis, as expansile, balloon-like nodules in the vertical phase of growth (**Figure 5e**). The nature and extent of the vertical growth phase determine the biological behaviour of malignant melanoma, therefore it is important to observe and record vertical growth phase parameters in a pathology report. (See the chapter on *Models for Melanoma and Sarcomas*.)

Mycosis Fungoides (Cutaneous T Cell Lymphoma)

Cutaneous T cell lymphoma (CTCL) represents a spectrum of lymphoproliferative disorders that affect the skin (Murphy and Mihm, 1999). Two types of malignant T cell disorders were originally recognized: mycosis fungoides (MF), which is a chronic proliferative process, and a nodular eruptive variant, mycosis fungoides d'emblée. It is now known that a whole variety of presentations of T cell lymphoma occur, including MF, the eruptive nodular type, and an adult T cell leukaemia or lymphoma type. The latter disorder may present with a rapid progressive downhill course.

Mycosis fungoides is a T cell lymphoproliferative disorder, arises primarily in the skin and may evolve into generalized lymphoma (Murphy, 1988). Most afflicted individuals have disease that remains localized to the skin for many years; a minority has rapid systemic dissemination. This condition may occur at any age, but most it affects persons over 40 years of age.

Clinically, lesions of the MF type of CTCL represent scaly, red–brown patches, raised, scaling plaques that may even be confused with psoriasis, and fungating nodules. Eczema-like lesions describe early stages of disease when obvious visceral or typical nodal spread has not occurred. Raised, indurated and irregularly outlined, erythaematous plaques may then supervene. Systemic spreading correlates with development of multiple, large (up to 10 cm or more in diameter), red–brown nodules. Sometimes plaques and nodules may ulcerate, as depicted in **Figure 6a**. Lesions may affect numerous body surfaces, such as the trunk, extremities, face and scalp. In some individuals, systemic spread and seeding of the blood by malignant T cells is accompanied by diffuse erythema and scaling of the entire body surface (erythroderma), a condition known as Sèzary syndrome.

Histologically, the identification of the Sèzary–Lutzner cells is the hallmark of CTCL of the mycosis fungoides type. These are T helper cells (CD4 antigen-positive), they form characteristically band-like aggregates within the superficial dermis (see **Figure 6b**) and invade the epidermis as single cells and small clusters (Pautrier microabscesses). The tumour cells have markedly infolded nuclear membranes, imparting a 'hyperconvoluted' or 'cerebriform' contour (see

Figures 6c, 6d). Patches and plaques show pronounced epidermal infiltration by Sèzary–Lutzner cells (epidermotropism), but in more advanced nodular lesions the malignant T cells often lose this epidermotropic tendency, grow deeply into the dermis and eventually seed lymphatics and the peripheral circulation.

The aetiology of CTCL is under active investigation. The discovery that a highly aggressive form of T cell lymphoma or leukaemia in adults is caused by infection of helper T cells by a specific retrovirus (human T cell leukaemia virus, or HTLV-I) (Murphy, 1988) promotes the possibility that conventional CTCL may also have an infectious causation. The proliferating cells in CTCL are clonal populations of lymphocytes of the CD4 subset; they often express aberrant cell surface antigens as well as clonal T cell receptor gene rearrangements, and detection of these features may be of diagnostic assistance in difficult cases (Bakels *et al.*, 1997).

Topical therapy with steroids or UV radiation is often delegated for early lesions of CTCL, while more aggressive systemic chemotherapy is indicated for advanced disease. In patients with circulating malignant cells, exposure of removed from the body blood cells to photosensitizing agents and UVA irradiation, followed by reinfusion into the patient (extracorporeal photopheresis; Rook *et al.*, 1991), has shown promise as a novel therapeutic approach to disseminated CTCL. (See also chapter *Lymph Nodes*.)

Angiosarcoma

Angiosarcoma is a rare malignant tumour showing variable degrees of vascular differentiation. It occurs primarily on the face and scalp, frequently in elderly people. The lesion presents as single or multiple plaques, may progress to become nodules, infiltrate the adjacent soft tissues and ulcerate. Histological examination shows diffuse dermal hypercellularity and irregular vascular spaces formed by malignant endothelial cells. These atypical neoplastic cells have hyperchromatic nuclei with irregular contours. The malignant cells of better differentiated tumours recapitulate vascular spaces, bulging into the vessel lumens and forming intraluminal tufts. Poorly differentiated tumours, on the other hand, often provide sheets composed of solid aggregates of tumour cells (Murphy and Elder, 1991a). Angiosarcoma can develop as a result of previous irradiation and in lymphedematous extremities, such as those produced after surgery for breast cancer or as a result of previous radiation therapy.

An angioproliferative disorder, which may show findings similar to angiosarcoma, is Kaposi's sarcoma. This vascular proliferative disorder occurs as two variant forms: an indolent cutaneous variety, seen in elderly individuals and common in Ashkenazi Jews and Southern Europeans, and a second form, characterized by an aggressive tumour that presents as a component of immunodeficiency states,

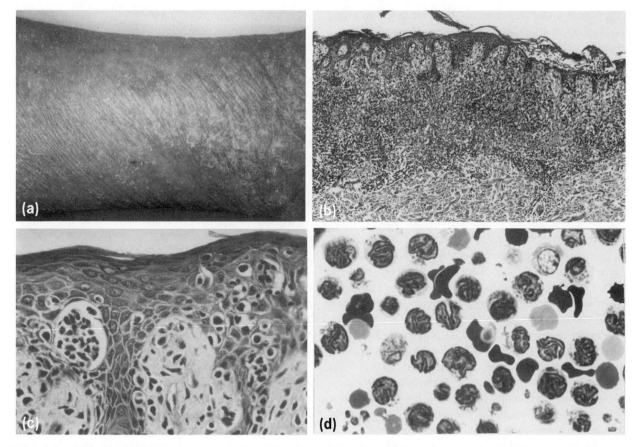

Figure 6   Mycosis fungoides (cutaneous T cell lymphoma). (a) Early lesions may present as pink–red, eczema- or psoriasis-like patches and plaques covered by adherent scales. (b) The biopsy at this stage may show a horizontal band of lymphocytes (many representing malignant T cells) within the upper dermis directly beneath the epidermal layer. (c) Inspection at higher magnification will often reveal large, darkly stained malignant lymphocytes abnormally collecting within the epidermis, where they tend to be found in association with Langerhans cells (see **Figure 1**). (d) Cytologically, the malignant T lymphocytes contain a nucleus with a characteristically infolded contour sometimes likened to the profile of a brain, and therefore referred to as 'cerebriform.'

especially in acquired immunodeficiency syndrome (AIDS). In this setting, its occurrence is associated with a new herpesvirus, human herpesvirus 8 (Murphy and Elder, 1991). Kaposi's sarcoma may begin as small solitary (isolated) purpuric papules, characterized by small zones of intracutaneous haemorrhage and comparable to bruises or petechiae (patch stage). Progression of Kaposi's sarcoma results in raised plaques and nodules, which are often large and destructive clinically. Advanced stage tumours frequently ulcerate. Histological examination during early phases demonstrates a multifocal angioproliferative process characterized by an increase in the number of spindle cells and thin-walled, poorly formed vessels within superficial vascular plexus, lymphoplasmocytic inflammatory infiltrates, and dilated lymphatics. Advanced lesions show expansive nodular growth of atypical spindle cells, containing hyperchromatic nuclei (Murphy and Elder, 1991). Such lesions may be confused with other malignancies of mesenchymal cells.

MOLECULAR GENETIC FINDINGS

In the case of the hereditary form of dysplastic naevi, genetic analyses have demonstrated the trait to be inherited as an autosomal dominant, possibly involving a susceptibility gene located on the short arm of chromosome 1, near the *Rh* locus (1p36) (Greene *et al.*, 1983). Other melanoma-susceptibility genes have been mapped to chromosomes 9p21 and 12q14 (Greene, 1997).

PROGNOSTIC FACTORS

The most common forms of skin cancer, namely squamous cell and basal cell carcinoma, are slowly growing, locally invasive, and tend not to exhibit metastatic behaviour. As mentioned earlier, some squamous cell carcinomas, particularly those that involve facial skin, may metastasize to local lymph nodes. Basal cell carcinomas rarely metasta-size, but when they do, large tumour size tends to be a constant feature. Locally aggressive basal cell carcinomas often will show a sclerosing or diffusely infiltrative pattern of dermal invasion.

Malignant melanoma, in contrast, shows a well-defined ability to metastasize once it has entered the vertical phase of growth. Numerous parameters have been defined which correlate with prognosis for such lesions. Negative attributes are represented by axial (versus acral) site of occurrence, male gender, progressive depth of dermal invasion, high mitotic count, absence of tumour infiltrating lymphocytes at the base of the tumour nodule, presence of regression and documentation of vascular invasion and microscopic satellite formation (Elder and Murphy, 1991). In lesions diagnosed unequivocally as vertical growth phase melanomas, such prognostic variables may be charted on multivariate databases, permitting prediction of 8-year survival with confidence intervals that demonstrate considerable accuracy.

A major drawback in predicting prognosis of melano-cytic tumours is represented by a recently recognized, relatively rare but genuine group of neoplasms that possess hybrid or intermediate characteristics between melanocy-tic naevi and fully evolved malignant melanoma. These tumours have been variously termed borderline melano-mas, minimal deviation melanomas, naevoid melanomas, severely atypical melanocytic naevi, severely atypical dermal and epidermal melanocytic proliferations and melanocytic tumours of uncertain malignant potential (MELTUPs) (Elder and Murphy, 1991). Depending on the designation, such problematic, grey-zone tumours may possess some or all of either the architectural or cytological features of melanoma, but do not qualify as fully evolved malignant lesions, leaving the prediction of their biological behaviour an open question. Diagnostic classification of such tumours, even among experts in dermatopathology (Farmer et al., 1996), has proven to be extremely prob-lematic. Accordingly, a pathologist has been astute to have identified such a lesion as at least representing significant melanocytic atypia. Often the best that one can do at this juncture is to relate concern regarding the hybrid nature of the histological features and to recommend complete excision, in addition to close clinical follow-up. Hopefully, as more of these problematic lesions are characterized, reproducible diagnostic criteria and prognostic attributes will be identified that will permit more accurate determi-nation of the likelihood of eventual metastasis.

OVERVIEW OF CLINICAL MANAGEMENT

Most squamous and basal cell carcinomas may be ade-quately treated by complete eradication either by excision or by destructive means, such as curretage, freezing or electrodesiccation. Excision has the advantage of providing for histological analysis to ensure negative margins, although the alternative modalities of local destruction have proven to be highly effective (Fitzpatrick et al., 1999), especially when lesions are small and bio-logically nonaggressive. In situations where tumours are present in close proximity to vital structures, particularly involving facial skin, a modified Mohs technique may be desirable (Leslie and Greenway, 1991). In this setting, multiple frozen sections of marginal tissue are examined at the time of the excision. Lymph node dissection in the case of invasive squamous cell carcinoma may be indicated when there exists suspicious clinical enlargement of draining lymph node chains.

The role of wide excision and lymph node dissection in the setting of vertical growth phase melanoma is potentially problematic. Primary lesions are generally recommended to be excised with a margin that will minimize the like-lihood of local recurrence. However, this recommendation is controversial, with some experts arguing that although wider excisions may decrease the incidence of local metastases, they fail to improve survival. This assumption is based on the contention that local metastases of mela-noma generally correlate with contemporaneous seeding of distant sites (Ackerman and Scheiner, 1983). In recent years, sentinel lymph node sampling has gained acceptance in the treatment of many vertical growth phase melanomas. In this procedure, a radiographically detectable dye is injected at the site of the primary tumour. This dye is taken up by draining lymphatic vessels and delivered physiolo-gically to regional lymph nodes. The first nodes to be detected by this method are presumed to be candidates for early metastases, and therefore they are surgically removed and studied extensively by histological and sometimes by immunohistochemical analysis for the presence of occult melanoma metastases. Occasionally, entire lymph node chains will be removed as part of a procedure termed prophylactic elective regional lymph node dissection. The clinical rationale for such procedures is to eradicate surgi-cally early metastases while they are theoretically confined to draining lymph nodes. This approach remains to be validated by prospective data. Moreover, it is complicated by the theoretical possibility that latent systemic metastases may occur synchronously with nodal ones, and by the notion that nodal deposits of tumour cells may in some instances eventuate in positive effects in terms of sensi-tizing the immune system against specific tumour-associated antigens.

In this regard, adjuvant therapy for melanoma has recently focused on immunoenhancing therapies, such as melanoma vaccines and treatment with proinflammatory mediators, such as interferon-α. Although these approa-ches have provided encouraging preliminary data in the treatment of clinically advanced melanoma metastases (Murphy et al., 1993), their role as adjuvants to ameliorate the potential for eventual metastatic spread is not as yet fully defined and awaits further experimental validation.

ACKNOWLEDGEMENT

This work was supported in part by grant CA40358 (G.F.M.) from the National Cancer Institute.

REFERENCES

Ackerman, A. B. and Scheiner, A. M. (1983). How wide and deep is wide and deep enough? A critique of surgical practice in excisions of primary cutaneous malignant melanoma. *Human Pathology*, **14**, 743–744.

Bakels, V., *et al.* (1997). Immunophenotyping and gene rearrangement analysis provide additional criteria to differentiate between cutaneous T-cell lymphomas and pseudo-T-cell lymphomas. *American Journal of Pathology*, **150**, 1941–1949.

Bale, A. E. (1997). The nevoid basal cell carcinoma syndrome: genetics and mechanism of carcinogenesis. *Cancer Investigations*, **15**, 180–186.

Barnhill, R. L., *et al.* (1993). Neoplasms: malignant melanoma. In: Fitzpatrick, T. B., *et al.* (eds), *Fitzpatrick's Dermatology in General Medicine* (Mcgraw-Hill, New York).

Breslow, A. (1970). Thickness, cross-sectional areas and depth of invasion in the prognosis of cutaneous melanoma. *Annals of Surgery*, **172**, 902–908.

Brown, T. J. and Nelson, B. R. (1999). Malignant melanoma: a clinical review. *Cutis*, **63**, 275–278, 281–284.

Caporaso, N., *et al.* (1987). Cytogenetics in hereditary malignant melanoma and dysplastic nevus syndrome: is dysplastic nevus syndrome a chromosome instability disorder? *Cancer Genetics and Cytogenetics*, **24**, 299–314.

Chuang, T. Y., *et al.* (1999). Melanoma in Kauai, Hawaii, 1981–1990: the significance of in situ melanoma and the incidence trend. *International Journal of Dermatology*, **38**, 101–107.

Clark, W. H. Jr, *et al.* (1978). Origin of familial malignant melanomas from heritable melanotic lesions: the BK mole syndrome. *Archives of Dermatology*, **114**, 732–738.

Clark, W. H., *et al.* (1985). A study of tumor progression: the precursor lesions of superficial spreading and nodular melanoma. *Human Pathology*, **15**, 1147–1165.

Clark, W. H., Jr, *et al.* (1989). Model predicting survival in stage I melanoma based on tumor progression. *Journal of the National Cancer Institute*, **81**, 1893–1904.

Cooper, K. D., *et al.* (1985). Effects of ultraviolet radiation on human epidermal cell alloantigen presentation: initial depression of Langerhans cell-dependent function is followed by the appearance of T6 Dr⁺ cells that enhance epidermal alloantigen presentation. *Journal of Immunology*, **134**, 129–137.

Dixon, A. Y., *et al.* (1989). Factors predictive of recurrence of basal cell carcinoma. *American Journal of Dermatopathology*, **11**, 222–232.

Elder, D. E. and Murphy, G. F. (1991a). Malignant melanoma. Fascicle 2, In: *Atlas of Tumor Pathology*, Fascicle 2, 3rd edn. 154–163 (Armed Forces Institute of Pathology, Washington, DC).

Farmer, E. R., *et al.* (1996). Discordance in the histopathologic diagnosis of melanoma and melanocytic nevi between expert pathologists. *Human Pathology*, **27**, 528–531.

Fitzpatrick, T. B., *et al.* (1999). Treatment of squamous and basal cell carcinoma, squamous cell carcinoma and basal cell carcinoma. In: Fitzpatrick, T. B., *et al.* (eds), *Fitzpatrick's Dermatology in General Medicine*, (5th edn) 852–862 (McGraw-Hill, New York).

Friedman, H. I., *et al.* (1985). Prognostic and therapeutic use of microstaging of cutaneous squamous cell carcinoma of the trunk and extremities. *Cancer*, **56**, 1099–1105.

Granstein, R. D., *et al.* (1987). Epidermal cells in activation of suppressor lymphocytes: further characterization. *Journal of Immunology*, **138**, 4055–4062.

Greene, M. H. (1997). Genetics of cutaneous melanoma and nevi [review]. *Mayo Clinic Proceedings*, **72**, 467–474.

Greene, M. H., *et al.* (1983). Familial cutaneous malignant melanoma: autosomal dominant trait possibly linked to the Rh flocus. *Proceedings of the National Academy of Sciences of the USA*, **80**, 6071–6075.

Greene, M. H., *et al.* (1985). The high risk of melanoma in melanoma prone families with dysplastic nevi. *Annals of the Internal Medicine*, **102**, 458–465.

Hochwalt, A. E., *et al.* (1988). Mechanism of H-ras oncogene activation in mouse squamous carcinoma induced by an alkylating agent. *Cancer Research*, **48**, 556–558.

Jones, W. O., *et al.* (1999). Incidence of malignant melanoma in Auckland, New Zeland: highest rates in the world. *World Journal of Surgery*, **23**, 732–735.

Kawashima, M., *et al.* (1986). Characterization of a new type of human papillomavirus (HPV) related to HPV5 from a case of actinic keratosis. *Virology*, **154**, 389–394.

Leslie, D. F. and Greenway, H. T. (1991). Mohs micrographic surgery for skin cancer. *Australasian Journal of Dermatology*, **32**, 159–164.

Matsuoka, L. Y., *et al.* (1999). Immunological responses to ultraviolet B radiation in black individuals. *Life Sciences*, **64**, 1563–1569.

Mihm, M. C. (1971). The clinical diagnosis, classification and histogenetic concepts of the early stages of cutaneous malignant melanomas. *New England Journal of Medicine*, **284**, 1078–1082.

Moan, J., *et al.* (1999). Epidemiological support for a hypothesis for melanoma induction indicating a role for UVA radiation. *Photochemistry and Photobiology*, **70**, 243–247.

Mueller, N. (1999). Overview of the epidemiology of malignancy in immune deficiency. *Journal of Acquired Immune Deficiency Syndrome*, **21**, 5–10.

Murphy, G. F. (1988). Cutaneous T cell lymphoma. In: Fenoglio-Preiser, C. M. (ed.), *Advances in Pathology*. 131–148 (Year Book Medical Publishers, Chicago).

Murphy, G. F. and Elder, D. E. (1991a). Angiosarcoma. In: *Atlas of Tumor Pathology*, (Fascicle 1, 3rd edn), 211–214 (Armed Forces Institute of Pathology, Washington, DC).

Murphy, G. F. and Elder, D. E. (1991b). Kaposi's sarcoma. In: *Atlas of Tumor Pathology*, Fascicle 1, 3rd edn, 214–219 (Armed Forces Institute of Pathology, Washington, DC).

Murphy, G. F. and Elder, D. (1991c). Non-melanocytic tumors of the skin. In: *Atlas of Tumor Pathology*, Fascicle 1, 3rd edn, 61–154 (Armed Forces Institute of Pathology, Washington, DC).

Murphy, G. F. and Mihm, M. C., Jr (1999). Mycosis fungoides (cutaneous T-cell lymphoma), the skin. In: Cotnar, R. S., Kumar, V. and Robbins, S. L. (eds), *Robbins' Pathologic Basis of Diseases*. 1190 (Saunders, Philadelphia).

Murphy, G. F., *et al.* (1993). Autologous melanoma vaccine induces inflammatory responses in melanoma metastases: relevance to immune regression and immunotherapy. *Journal of Investigative Dermatology*, **100**, 335–341.

North, J. H., Jr, *et al.* (1997). Advanced cutaneous squamous cell carcinoma of the trunk and extremity: analysis of prognostic factors. *Journal of Surgical Oncology*, **64**, 212–217.

Oro, A. E., *et al.* (1997). Basal cell carcinoma in mice over-expressing sonic hedgehog. *Science* **276**, 817–821.

Penn, I. (1987). Neoplastic consequences of transplantation and chemotherapy. *Cancer Detection and Prevention*, **1**, 149–157.

Perez, *et al.* (1997). P53 oncoprotein expression and gene mutations in some keratoacanthomas. *Archives of Dermatology*, **133**, 189.

Reimer, R. R., *et al.* (1978). Precursor lesions in familial melanoma: a new genetic preneoplastic syndrome. *Journal of the American Medical Association*, **239**, 744–746.

Rook, A. H., *et al.* (1991). Combined therapy of the Sezary syndrome with extra-corporeal photochemotherapy and low dose interferon alpha: clinical, molecular, and immunologic observations. *Archives of Dermatology*, **127**, 1535–1540.

Rowe, D. E., *et al.* (1992). Prognostic factors for local recurrence, metastasis, and survival rates in squamous cell carcinoma of the skin, ear, and lip. Implications for treatment modality selection. *Journal of the American Academy of Dermatology*, **26**, 976–990.

Smith, P. J., *et al.* (1987). Abnormal sensitivity to UV-radiation in cultured skin fibroblasts from patients with hereditary cutaneous malignant melanoma and dysplastic nevus syndrome. *International Journal of Cancer*, **30**, 39–45.

Starink, T. M., *et al.* (1985). The cutaneous pathology of Cowden's disease: new findings. *Journal of Cutaneous Pathology* **12**, 83–93.

Thielmann, H. W., *et al.* (1987). DNA repair synthesis in fibroblast strains from patients with actinic keratosis, squamous cell carcinoma, basal cell carcinoma, or malignant melanoma after treatment with ultraviolet light, *N*-acetoxy-2-acetylaminofluorene methyl methanesulfonate, and *N*-methyl-*N*-nitrosourea. *Journal of Cancer Research and Clinical Oncology*, **113**, 171–186.

Van Duinen, C. M., *et al.* (1994). The distribution of cellular adhesion molecules in pigmented skin lesions. *Cancer*, **73**, 2131–2139.

FURTHER READING

Bruce, A. J. and Brodland, D. G. (2000) Overview of skin cancer detection and prevention for the primary care physician. *Mayo Clinic Proceedings*, **75**, 491–500.

de Villiers, E. M., *et al.* (1999). Human papillomaviruses in non-melanoma skin cancer. *Seminars in Cancer Biology*, **9**, 413–422.

Hadshiew, I. M., *et al.* (2000). Skin aging and photoaging: the role of DNA damage and repair. *American Journal of Contact Dermatitis*, **11**, 19–25.

Hussain, S. P. and Harris, C. C. (2000). Molecular epidemiology and carcinogenesis: endogenous and exogenous carcinogens. *Mutation Research*, **462**, 311–322.

Leffell, D. J. (2000). The scientific basis of skin cancer. *Journal of the American Academy of Dermatology*, **42**, 18–22.

Murphy, G. F. and Mihm, M. C. (1999) Recognition and evaluation of cytologic dysplasia in acquired melanocytic nevi. *Human Pathology*, **30**, 506–512.

Tenkate, T. D. (1999) Occupational exposure to ultraviolet radiation: a health risk assessment. *Reviews on Environmental Health*, **14**, 187–209.

van Kranen, H. J. and de Gruijl, F. R. (1999). Mutations in cancer genes of UV-induced skin tumors of hairless mice. *Journal of Epidemiology*, **9**, S58–S65.

Woodhead, A. D., *et al.* (1999). Environmental factors in non-melanoma and melanoma skin cancer. *Journal of Epidemiology*, **9**, S102–S114.

Chapter 35

Oral Cavity and Major and Minor Salivary Glands

Paul L. Auclair
Maine Medical Center, Portland, ME, USA

Karen Rasmussen
Maine Center for Cancer Medicine, Scarborough, ME, USA

CONTENTS

NORMAL DEVELOPMENT AND STRUCTURE

During the third week of development of the human embryo, a deep groove develops below the forebrain that represents the future oral cavity. This groove is known as the primary oral fossa, or stomadeum, and it is lined by ectoderm that forms an additional ectodermal pouch, Rathke's pouch, that gives rise to the anterior lobe of the pituitary gland and to the dental organs that will form the enamel of the deciduous and permanent teeth. The stomadeum is separated from the endodermally lined foregut by the buccopharyngeal membrane that ruptures in the fourth week of development. In an adult the oral mucosa is covered by stratified squamous epithelium that is keratinized in areas exposed to masticatory forces, and is supported by fibrous tissue containing salivary glands, adipose tissue, skeletal muscle and bone. The red portion of the lips (vermilion) represents a transition zone from skin to mucosa but does not contain eccrine or sebaceous glands or hair follicles.

The salivary gland primordia develop as buds of primitive stomadeal epithelium that proliferate as strands into the underlying oral ectomesenchyme. This results in the formation of three pairs of major salivary glands the parotid, submandibular and sublingual glands and between 500 and 1000 lobules of minor salivary glands. Although the parotid is a single contiguous structure, the facial nerve courses through its centre, essentially dividing the gland into superficial (lateral) and deep (medial) lobes. The parotid gland is rich in lymphoid tissue, and normally contains from 3–24 lymph nodes, most in the superficial lobe (Ellis and Auclair, 1996). The minor glands are usually numerous in all oral mucosal sites except for the anterior hard palate and gingiva. The glands consist of secretory acini composed of mucous or serous acinar cells. Saliva then flows to the intercalated portion of the branching ductal system, lined by low cuboidal epithelium, then to the larger striated duct portion formed by columnar cells that have large numbers of mitochondria, and finally to the excretory ducts that are lined by stratified squamous epithelium where they merge with the oral epithelium. The acini are surrounded by myoepithelial cells that have ultrastructural features of both epithelium and smooth muscle.

TUMOUR PATHOLOGY: SQUAMOUS CELL CARCINOMA

Epidemiology

More than 90% of all cancers of the oral mucosa and lip vermilion are squamous cell carcinomas (epidermoid carcinoma). Although other forms of cancer, including sarcomas, melanomas and lymphomas, also affect the oral mucosa and jaws, only squamous cell carcinoma will be discussed in this section; adenocarcinomas that arise from the major and minor salivary glands will be discussed in the following section.

In the United States, squamous cell carcinomas of the oral mucosa and lip vermilion account for about 3% of all cancers of all sites, representing about 22 000 new cases each year. As shown in **Figure 1**, the incidence rates are strongly age-related. The death rate per 100 000 population

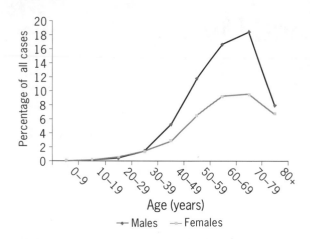

Figure 1 Age- and gender-specific incidence rates of oral and pharyngeal cancer. While the incidence rate for oral squamous cell carcinoma is greater in men than women, the rates in both increase dramatically with advancing age.

Table 1 Oral cancer death rates: selected countries[a]

Country	Male	Rank	Country	Female	Rank
Hong Kong	14.8	1	Singapore	4.8	1
France	14.3	2	Hong Kong	4.8	2
Singapore	12.8	3	Kuwait	2.4	3
Hungary	12.5	4	Cuba	1.8	4
Puerto Rico	9.0	5	Malta	1.7	5
Italy	6.4	11	Puerto Rico	1.4	11
Germany	6.0	13	United States	1.4	13
Spain	5.7	16	Canada	1.3	16
Canada	4.5	22	Luxembourg	1.2	22
Denmark	3.8	28	Belgium	1.0	28
United States	3.8	30	Germany	1.0	30
England and Wales	2.8	37	Netherlands	0.8	37
Venezuela	2.2	42	Finland	0.7	42
Mexico	1.7	45	Chile	0.7	45
Greece	1.6	46	Japan	0.6	46
Ecuador	0.9	50	Korean Republic	0.3	50

[a]*Source*: World Health Organisation data as adapted by the American Cancer Society, 1992.

for oral cancer (see **Table 1**) ranges in men from 0.9 in Ecuador to 14.8 in Hong Kong and in women from 0.3 in the Korean Republic to 4.8 in Singapore. In the United States the mortality rate ranges from 1.4 in Utah to 7.0 in the District of Columbia. In most populations males have an incidence rate about three times that of females and the incidence and mortality rates in the United States are greater among blacks than whites.

The tongue and floor of the mouth are the most commonly affected intraoral sites. There are exceptions, such as occurs in some Indian and South American cultures where carcinoma of the hard palate is endemic because of the custom of 'reverse' smoking (chutta). Women in particular hold the lit end of a slowly burning, hand-made cigarette inside the mouth in close proximity to the palatal mucosa, a site that rarely gives rise to carcinoma in most parts of the world.

Aetiology

It is estimated that about 90% and 60% of all deaths in males and females, respectively, caused by oral cancer can be attributed to cigarette smoking. Like cancers at other sites caused by smoking, the risk of developing cancer is dose related and is related to carcinogenic aromatic hydrocarbons. The relative risks are estimated to be at least five and as high as 10–24 for patients who smoke 40 cigarettes per day and this risk increases the longer one smokes. Pipe and cigar smoking appear to result in at least as great a risk. The association of the use of smokeless ('spit') tobacco with oral carcinoma is less clear. The prevalence of oral carcinoma is low in some countries where the use of smokeless tobacco far exceeds that of cigarette smoking (La Vecchia *et al.*, 1992; Vigneswaran *et al.*, 1995). On the other hand, some studies have shown that smokeless tobacco users are at increased risk and that about one-half of such cancers occur at the site where the tobacco is placed (Winn *et al.*, 1981). Another variation of topical use is seen in India and Southeast Asia where areca nut, tobacco and slaked lime are wrapped with betel leaf and chewed for long periods each day. This results in a precancerous scarring condition known as oral submucous fibrosis.

The fact that only a fraction of individuals with heavy exposure to tobacco and alcohol develop cancers of the upper aerodigestive tract suggests that there may be genetic differences between individuals that influence their susceptibility to these environmental agents. Heritable differences in head and neck cancer susceptibility have been found for nearly every step of tumorigenesis including carcinogen metabolism, DNA repair and progression as influenced by oncogenes and tumour-suppressor genes (Spitz, 1994; Khuri *et al.*, 1997; de Andrade *et al.*, 1998; Jahnke *et al.*, 1999). There is also increasing evidence to suggest that some of the population variance in response to therapy is due to interindividual genetic differences (Khuri *et al.*, 1997).

Because many heavy smokers are also heavy drinkers, it has been difficult to link alcohol use directly with oral cancer, but some investigators have estimated the relative risk at 2–6-fold. Alcohol acts synergistically with tobacco and together they increase a person's risk to 40-fold. Alcoholic beverages contain nitrosamines and hydrocarbons and, additionally, it has been proposed that contaminants or metabolites may promote malignant transformation (Blot, 1992). Malnutrition and vitamin deficiency may have a contributory role in oral cancers.

Vitamins A, B and C, are independently related to a reduced incidence of oral carcinoma and the risk of oral cancer in vitamin E users is half that of others according to one study (Gridley *et al.*, 1992).

Cancer of the lower lip is strongly related to excessive exposure to ultraviolet light with a wavelength range of 2900–3200 Å, especially in fair-skinned individuals. Actinic cheilitis, similar in name and biology to actinic keratosis of the skin, represents the premalignant clinical condition. Just as in the skin, extensive damage is done to the collagen in the lamina propria (solar elastosis), but whether or not this event has any influence on epithelial transformation is unknown. Exposure to therapeutic X-irradiation is associated with an increased risk for the development of both carcinomas and sarcomas. Evidence of infection with human papillomavirus (HPV) has been found in clinically normal oral mucosa, benign and malignant neoplasms that arise from it, and some of the metastatic tumours. About 35% of oral cavity tumours have been found to contain HPV, usually the 'high-risk' types of the virus. HPV positivity correlates with age (< 60 years) and gender (male), but not with tobacco or alcohol use (McKaig *et al.*, 1998). Nevertheless, its exact role remains elusive.

In summary, it appears that the pathogenesis of oral carcinomas is multifactorial with suppressor genes acting in association with growth factors, viruses, chemical carcinogens and oncogenes (Scully, 1993).

SCREENING AND PREVENTION: GROSS/ HISTOPATHOLOGY/PREINVASIVE

Lesions/Ultrastructure/ Immunohistochemistry

Squamous cell carcinoma (SCC) of the oral mucosa has numerous clinical appearances and is often preceded by premalignant lesions showing epithelial dysplasia or carcinoma *in situ*. The most common early form of premalignant or malignant disease, known as erythroplakia, is an asymptomatic, well-defined, erythematous macule or plaque that may have a finely granular surface texture. About 90% of erythroplakias show either dysplasia or carcinoma. SCC may also appear as a white patch but only between 5 and 25% of clinical white patches will show epithelial dysplasia or carcinoma, the remaining representing hyperkeratosis or other benign conditions. However, in sites designated 'high-risk,' including the ventral surface and lateral border of the tongue (**Figure 2; see colour plate section**), anterior floor of the mouth and soft palatal complex, the risk is much greater. Importantly, it is usually impossible to distinguish clinically between benign, premalignant and malignant disease. Often mucosal lesions show both red and white components (**Figure 3; see colour plate section**); the presence of

an erythematous area in a lesion for which an obvious source of irritation is not evident should be biopsied and reviewed microscopically.

Advanced tumours may present as exophytic masses that often have a papillary surface (**Figure 4; see colour plate section**) and as nonhealing ulcers that reveal an endophytic, indurated nodule on palpation. Carcinomas that involve the gingiva, alveolar mucosa and tooth extraction sockets may first be discovered as irregular radiolucencies; those of the vermilion of the lower lip typically present as crusted ulcers (**Figure 5; see colour plate section**).

The most important morphological alterations that indicate a premalignant condition of the oral mucosa involve the squamous cell nuclei. They are enlarged, more darkly stained then normal, have irregular shapes and large, dark nucleoli and reveal increased and abnormal mitotic figures (**Figure 6; see colour plate section**). Cells showing these features extend above the parabasal cell layer in a haphazard arrangement, are crowded and often form bulbous rete ridges. The term carcinoma *in situ* signifies that the entire thickness of the spinous cell layer demonstrate these changes, but invasion has not yet occurred.

Grossly, squamous cell carcinoma is firm, has a glistening, heterogeneous grey–white cut surface and is often poorly delineated. Microscopically, individual epithelial cells or cords or islands of cells showing dysplastic changes infiltrate the underlying connective tissue (**Figure 7; see colour plate section**). When the tumour cells show a striking resemblance to normal squamous cells and show prominent keratinization, the tumour is considered 'well differentiated.' 'Moderately differentiated' carcinomas show a greater degree of cellular variability, less resemblance to normal squamous cells and much less keratinization. 'Poorly differentiated' tumours show very limited, focal resemblance to their cell of origin. Two benign oral lesions that often show an epithelial proliferation known as pseudocarcinomatous hyperplasia that histologically mimics well differentiated squamous cell carcinoma are granular cell tumour and necrotizing sialometaplasia.

The tendency of a patient to develop more than one oral mucosal primary carcinoma is know as 'field cancerization.' In a study of over 21 000 patients the rate of development of second tumours was 3.7% per year and the risk of a second was 2.8 times greater than expected (Day and Blot, 1992). The risks are highest in patients who continue to smoke and persist for more than 5 years after diagnosis of the initial cancer. Frequent periodic follow-up oral examinations for this possibility are essential.

Field cancerization is believed to be the result of multiple related lesions that arise from a field defect. This situation is similar to that seen in bladder cancer (Sidransky, 1997) and diffuse gastric cancer, where a single transformed cell clonally propagates and then spreads throughout a region. Subsequently, independent additional mutations occur in the dispersed cells, giving rise to multiple malignancies over time, all of which share the original transforming mutations in common (Sidransky *et al.*, 1992; Sidransky, 1997). In head and neck squamous cell carcinoma (HNSCC), shared specific mutations in chromosomes 9p and 3p, as well as shared patterns of X-chromosome inactivation have been identified in synchronous and metachronous lesions along with independent mutations in each lesion (Nees *et al.*, 1993; Worsham *et al.*, 1995; Gauri *et al.*, 1996; Partridge *et al.*, 1997; Lydiatt *et al.*, 1998; Califano *et al.*, 1999). These findings indicate that multiple head and neck neoplasms may arise from a single clone which spreads, producing separate lesions that acquire additional mutations and progress individually.

There are several forms of squamous cell carcinoma that have important clinicopathological features different from the 'conventional' form previously described. Verrucous carcinoma is a low grade form that represents less than 10% of all oral squamous cell carcinomas. It most often occurs in patients who have used chewing tobacco for many years and appears as a white, papillary lesion that spreads slowly but progressively along the mucosal surface over one to several years (**Figure 8; see colour plate section**). Unlike conventional SCCs that may have a papillary configuration, the nuclear morphology is bland; characteristic architectural features, including broad, elongated, rounded rete ridges and papillary surface projections filled with parakeratin, facilitate the diagnosis. Invasive carcinomas develop in about 20% of cases mandating extensive tissue sampling. Proliferative verrucous leukoplakia is a term used to describe the white oral plaques that occur in some patients that, as they spread, change from having a smooth to fissured to granular to papillary surface texture (Hansen *et al.*, 1985). Some develop into verrucous carcinoma (**Figure 9; see colour plate section**) or conventional invasive SCC.

An aggressive variant is basaloid squamous carcinoma that most often occurs in the hypopharynx and base of the tongue. Histologically, the tumour is characterized by having well delineated nests of basaloid cells, some with hyaline cores and pseudoglandular structures, often resembling the solid variant of adenoid cystic carcinoma or small cell undifferentiated carcinoma. Weak immunoreactivity for neuron-specific enolase is seen in 75% of cases (Banks *et al.*, 1992) and ultrastructurally the basaloid cells reveal rare tonofilaments and varying numbers of desmosomes (Wain *et al.*, 1986). There is a poor prognosis; 40% of patients die within 17 months. Another variant is spindle cell carcinoma, a name chosen for the tumour's characteristic histopathological feature. The prominent spindle element resembles sarcomas but the focal presence of typical squamous cell carcinoma, dysplastic surface epithelium and immunoreactivity of the spindle cells for cytokeratin are all helpful in the distinction. These tumours are often clinically pedunculated, grow rapidly and about one-third are associated with prior therapeutic radiation.

Molecular Genetic Findings

Oral cavity and salivary gland neoplasms, like other solid tumours, arise from normal tissue that has undergone a series of genetic alterations. These changes include activating mutations of proto-oncogenes in addition to inactivation of tumour-suppressor genes, apoptotic genes and sometimes cell adhesion genes. For at least some cancers, tumour development also involves abnormalities in the cell's DNA repair system such that somatic mutations accumulate leading to malignancy (Sherbet and Lakshmi, 1997).

Investigations into the genetic-basis HNSCCs have resulted in a general molecular progression model for these neoplasms (**Figure 10**) (Califano *et al.*, 1996; Sidransky, 1997). This model resembles those developed by similar means for bladder cancer and non-small cell lung cancer (Sidransky *et al.*, 1992; Minna *et al.*, 1997) more than it corresponds to the colorectal cancer mutation paradigm (Fearon and Vogelstein, 1990). Whether this general progression model will hold true for all squamous cell

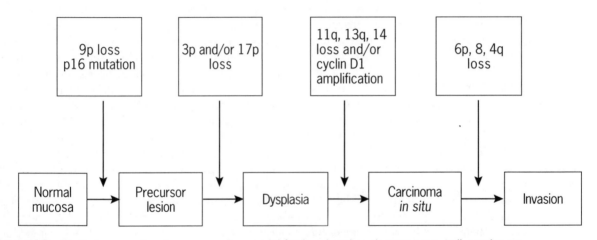

Figure 10 Preliminary molecular progression model for head and neck squamous cell carcinoma.

carcinomas of the head and neck remains to be seen. Some recent genetic evidence suggests that primary head and neck cancers arising in different locations are, in fact, separate clinical entities with independent genetic aetiologies and should be treated as such (Takes *et al.*, 1998; Gleich *et al.*, 1999).

Part of the rationale for grouping all head and neck cancers together, or at least all HNSCCs, has to do with shared aspects of disease management, their natural history (e.g. field cancerization and tendency for synchronous and metachronous lesions) and the common role of carcinogens in their origin, particularly the role of tobacco and alcohol exposure (Sidransky, 1997; Spitz, 1994). In molecular genetic studies, this tendency to group various head and neck cancers together makes it difficult to interpret the literature with regard to any particular subset, such as oral cavity lesions. Some research aimed at identifying specific genes involved in tumorigenesis and progression for head and neck cancers in general did not include oral cavity tumours in the study sample. A relatively small number of investigations focused on oral cavity lesions specifically. Therefore, it is unclear whether a conserved set of gene abnormalities is responsible for all head and neck cancers (or at least all HNSCCs) with minor variations on the theme, or whether each neoplasm has a distinct aetiology as has been suggested recently (Takes *et al.*, 1998; Gleich *et al.*, 1999)

Chromosomal changes detectable by cytogenetic methods provided the first clue to the identification of specific genes involved in tumorigenesis and progression. The chromosomal regions involved in rearrangement, deletion, amplification, etc., in tumour cells indicate sites where oncogenes, tumour-suppressor genes or other genes contributing to tumour development reside. The chromosomal changes most frequently reported for HNSCC include deletions of 3p, 5q, 8p, 9p, 18q and 21q (Sidransky, 1997), amplifications of 11q (Callander *et al.*, 1994; Sidransky, 1997) and breakpoints at 1p22, 3p21, 8p11 and 14q (Sidransky, 1997). These common abnormalities identify potential tumour-suppressor genes and oncogenes contributing to HNSCC progression. Their correlation with certain stages of tumour progression allowed for their relative placement, chronologically, in a preliminary genetic progression model (**Figure 10**) (Jares *et al.*, 1994; Sidransky, 1997). Multiple regions of deletion on chromosome arm 13q indicate the presence of a tumour-suppressor gene implicated specifically in oral cavity and supraglottal SCC (Gupta *et al.*, 1999).

Further refinement of the location of putative tumour-suppressor genes contributing to head and neck cancers is provided by loss of heterozygosity (LOH) analysis to define the minimal regions of loss within the larger common areas of chromosomal deletion. Correlation of these regions defined by molecular markers, with the known map position of various tumour-suppressor genes, reveals likely candidates for gene mutation (followed by loss of the corresponding normal allele on the deleted chromosome). Evidence from LOH analysis and direct mutational screening indicates that a number of tumour-suppressor genes play a role in HNSCCs, including *TP53*, *VHL*, *CDKN2/INK4/p16*, *p21/WAF/CIP* and *TGFβR* (Brachman, 1994; Sidransky, 1997). Molecular genetic studies on oral cavity lesions specifically have implicated *TP53*, cell cycle inhibitors *p16* and *p27* and a tumour-suppressor gene other than *RB* or *BRCA1* located on the long arm of chromosome 13 (Gupta *et al.*, 1999; Kanekawa *et al.*, 1999; Riese *et al.*, 1999; Venkatesan *et al.*, 1999).

Despite the abundance of characterized oncogenes believed to play a role in tumorigenesis in humans, relatively few have been convincingly linked to the progression of any primary tumour. In head and neck cancer, there are a few cases of direct alteration of an oncogene or its overexpression and stage-specific progression. Well documented examples of oncogene activation in HNSCCs and corresponding tumour-progression include *cyclin D1* and *EGFR* (Brachman, 1994; Sidransky, 1997). There is strong evidence that overexpression of *cyclin D1* and the ligand–receptor pair HGF–c-Met play a role in progression of oral cavity neoplasms (Marshall and Kornberg, 1998; Matthias *et al.*, 1998).

A variety of other genes have been identified that, when mutant, are involved in uncontrolled cell proliferation or the mechanisms by which benign lesions becomes invasive and metastatic. Some examples of additional genes that appear to promote development of various head and neck cancers including oral cavity tumours are *bcl-2*, *E-cadherin*, *EMS-1*, *telomerase*, *Ki-67*, *retinoic acid receptor*, *eIF4E*, *K19*, *GADD 153*, and *Cat D*, *B* and *L*. These genes encode apoptosis factors, cell adhesion molecules, translation initiation factors, cysteine proteases and other proteins for which the function of the altered gene product is unclear (Brachman, 1994; Kos *et al.*, 1996; Drachenberg, *et al.*, 1997; Friedman *et al.*, 1997; Takes *et al.*, 1998; Vo and Crowe, 1998; Crowe *et al.*, 1999; Los *et al.*, 1999; Nathan *et al.*, 1999).

Numerous investigators have attempted to determine the clinical relevance of specific gene mutations in terms of their value as diagnostic markers or their reliability in predicting outcome and likelihood of recurrence. Some genes believed to play a role in the development of oral cavity tumours show potential as prognostic indicators or molecular markers of response to therapy, most notably low levels of p27 protein and poor response to treatment (Venkatesan *et al.*, 1999), *GADD153* (growth arrest and DNA damage gene) mRNA levels as a predictor of response to cisplatin (Los *et al.*, 1999), overexpression of *bcl-2* and poor prognosis, and *cyclin D1* polymorphism as a predictor of clinical outcome (Friedman *et al.*, 1997). In addition, flow cytometric DNA content measurements (indicative of aneuploidy) can provide significant prognostic information, such as serving as an independent predictor of metastatic potential and clinical outcome

(Ensley and Maciorowski, 1994; Hemmer *et al.*, 1999). Abnormal chromosome copy numbers measured by FISH in exfoliated epithelial cells of tumours and clinically normal margins can detect subclinical tumorigenesis (i.e. chromosome imbalances indicative of preneoplastic cells in the 'field') (Barrera *et al.*, 1998).

Prognostic Factors

It has been shown that 14% of epithelial dysplastic lesions that were not excised progressed to invasive carcinoma within a follow-up period of 20 years, but 50% remained unchanged and 15% regressed (Lumerman *et al.*, 1995). Nonetheless, the potential progression of any dysplastic lesion to carcinoma must be presumed and, when possible, should be excised with microscopically uninvolved surgical margins. Only 6.2% of 65 patients who had excision developed SCC compared with 15.4% of 91 patients who received no treatment (Lumerman *et al.*, 1995).

Prognosis of oral squamous cell carcinoma is most directly related to the clinical stage of the tumour. The TNM staging system and Stage Grouping are shown in **Table 2**. Prior to 1992, 'fixation' of a node was considered in determining the N category, but now only the size of the node is evaluated, and bilateral nodal involvement is N2 rather than N3.

Most staging protocols do not include microscopic features. Nonetheless, some investigators have suggested that tumour thickness or depth of invasion independently correlates with patient outcome (Spiro *et al.*, 1986). One study, for instance, found that tumours that invaded less than 4 mm, 4–8 mm and more than 8 mm showed metastatic rates of 8.3, 35 and 83%, respectively (Shingaki *et al.*, 1988). Others have shown that tumour thickness correlates best with lesions of the vermilion border.

Overview of Present Clinical Management

Treatment failure most often is associated with uncontrolled regional disease. For most tumours, surgery with or without adjunctive postoperative radiotherapy is considered standard therapy, but patients with detectable distant metastases are usually treated palliatively. Radiation includes both external beam and interstitial brachytherapy. Local recurrence is more likely to follow excision of tumours with positive surgical margins so the goal is to establish tumour-free margins of 1–2 cm. The risks of occult cervical metastases in clinically negative necks is significant so elective neck dissections are often performed. Identification of positive lymph nodes in elective neck dissections has been reported to be 19, 40–50 and 25–54%, respectively, for tumours of the gingiva, floor of the mouth and oral tongue (de Braud *et al.*, 1989). Elective radiation to the regional lymph nodes of the neck is often performed instead.

Systemic and regional chemotherapy is used mainly for palliation of patients with tumours that can not be treated effectively with surgery or radiation, and to help improve regional control of aggressive tumours. The drugs used most often singly or in combination with others are methotrexate, bleomycin, *cis*-platinum and 5-fluorouracil.

Survival benefits with chemotherapy have not been demonstrated. Research and early clinical trials using monoclonal antibodies, such as antiepidermal growth factor antibody C225, are under way and, it is hoped, will offer effective additional treatment options in the future (Huang *et al.*, 1999).

It has only recently become possible to integrate information about an individual's genetic susceptibility and/or knowledge of specific genetic abnormalities in an individual's tumour with overall risk and response to particular therapies. Retinoid chemoprevention in head and neck cancers represents one of the most promising attempts at this sort of 'rational' intervention, in which levels of *RAR-B* expression in oral lesions predict response to intervention with retinoids (Khuri *et al.*, 1997). The mechanism of action of retinoids and role of *RAR-B* in tumorigenesis are becoming clear (Grandis *et al.*, 1996; Lotan, 1996; Cheng and Lotan, 1998; Vo and Crowe, 1998).

Gene therapy is also under exploration as a possible intervention for oral cavity and salivary gland cancers. This strategy provides a less invasive means of therapy compared with traditional management, and may prove particularly effective in combating aspects of recurrence associated with field cancerization. Adenovirus-mediated *p53* gene therapy has reached phase II clinical trials (Clayman *et al.*, 1999), and combination chemo- and gene therapy is under initial investigation in mice as a means of treating salivary gland tumours (O'Malley and Li, 1998).

TUMOUR PATHOLOGY: SALIVARY GLAND CARCINOMAS

Epidemiology

The annual incidence of both benign and malignant salivary gland tumours reported in most studies varies from 0.4 to 6.5 cases per 100 000 population. They account for about 2% of all neoplasms of the head and neck. Primary epithelial tumours comprise approximately 90% of the tumours seen, with most of the remaining cases being soft tissue tumours, lymphomas and metastatic tumours. Adenocarcinomas, on which this discussion is focused, represent between 21 and 45% of the primary tumours. Current classifications of salivary gland tumours include 23 different types of carcinomas, and all but one, primary squamous cell carcinoma, represent adenocarcinomas.

The average age of patients with salivary carcinomas is 47 years, but two of the most common types, mucoepidermoid carcinoma and acinic cell adenocarcinoma, have

Table 2   TNM staging system for oral squamous cell carcinoma[a]

T	*Primary tumour*
TX	Primary tumour cannot be assessed
T0	No evidence of primary tumour
TIS	Carcinoma *in situ*
T1	2 cm or less in greatest dimension
T2	More than 2 cm, but not more than 4 cm, in greatest dimension
T3	More than 4 cm in greatest dimension
T4 (lip)	Tumour invades adjacent structures such as cortical bone, inferior alveolar nerve, floor of mouth, skin of face
T4 (oral cavity)	Tumour invades adjacent structures such as cortical bone, muscle of tongue, maxillary sinus, skin. Superficial erosion alone of bone/tooth socket by gingival primary is not sufficient to classify as T4
N	*Regional lymph nodes*
NX	Regional lymph node cannot be assessed
N0	No regional lymph node metastasis
N1	Metastasis in a single ipsilateral cervical lymph node(s) less than 3 cm
N2	Metastasis in a single ipsilateral node more than 3 cm but not more than 6 cm in greatest dimension; or in multiple ipsilateral nodes, none more than 6 cm; or in bilateral or contralateral lymph nodes, none more than 6 cm
N2a	Metastasis in single ipsilateral lymph node 3–6 cm
N2b	Metastasis in multiple ipsilateral nodes, none more than 6 cm
N2C	Metastasis in bilateral or contralateral lymph nodes, none more than 6 cm
N3	Metastasis in a lymph node more than 6 cm in greatest dimension
N3a	Clinically palpable ipsilateral node(s), at least one more than 6 cm
N3b	Bilateral clinically palpable bilateral nodes
N3c	Clinically palpable contralateral nodes
M	*Distant metastasis*
MX	Distant metastasis cannot be assessed
M0	No distant metastasis
M1	Distant metastasis

Clinical stage – grouping of carcinoma of the oral cavity

Stage	T	N	M
Stage 0	Tis	N0	M0
Stage I	T1	N0	M0
Stage II	T2	N0	M0
Stage III	T3	N0	M0
	T1	N1	M0
	T2	N1	M0
	T3	N1	M0
Stage IVA	T4	N0	M0
	T4	N1	M0
	Any T	N2	M0
Stage IVB	Any T	N3	M0
Stage IVC	Any T	Any N	M1

[a] Adapted from American Joint Commission on Cancer, 1997, *AJCC Staging Manual*, 5th edn. 24–27 (Lippincott-Raven, Philadelphia).

a peak incidence in the third and fourth decades, unlike most of the other types. Females are more often affected than males but there is variation according to the tumour type. About 55, 10, 0.3 and 34% of the carcinomas occur in the parotid, submandibular, sublingual and minor glands, respectively. However, the proportion of all salivary gland tumours at a particular site that are malignant varies significantly. For instance, while less than 25% of parotid tumours are malignant, 45% of submandibular tumours, 50% of minor gland tumours and nearly 90% of sublingual gland tumours are carcinomas. Furthermore, in some minor gland sites, including the tongue, floor of the mouth and retromolar area, 80–90% are malignant. Most parotid gland tumours arise in the lateral (superficial) lobe and present as preauricular swellings. Those that develop in the deep lobe often expand into the parapharyngeal space and manifest as pharyngeal swellings.

Aetiology

Little is known about the cause of most salivary gland carcinomas, but there is a strong relationship with exposure to ionizing radiation. Studies of the survivors of the atomic bombings of Hiroshima and Nagasaki demonstrated an 11-fold increased risk for development of salivary carcinoma. The risk was greatest in patients closest to the hypocentre and during a period 12–16 years after exposure. Patients exposed to therapeutic radiation also appear to be at increased risk.

Although there is a strong association of cigarette smoking with the development of Warthin tumour, a benign neoplasm, no such association has been shown for salivary carcinomas. Occupations associated with increased risk of development of salivary gland carcinomas in a small number of cases include asbestos mining, industries with significant use of rubber products and plumbing (Auclair et al., 1991). A strong association of lymphoepithelial carcinoma, a rare salivary gland malignancy, with Epstein–Barr virus has been shown. Hamilton-Dutoit et al. (1991) found EBV genomes in all 18 such tumours removed from Greenlandic and Alaskan Eskimos that they studied.

Gross/Histopathology/Preinvasive Lesions/Ultrastructure/ Immunohistochemistry

Most patients with a salivary gland tumour, whether benign or malignant, present with an asymptomatic mass and both pain and rapid growth occur in both benign and malignant tumours (**Figures 11 and 12; see colour plate section**). However, facial paralysis occurs in about 12% of carcinomas but rarely in benign tumours and, when present, tumour fixation or ulceration suggest malignancy.

Most salivary gland carcinomas arise *de novo* rather than from morphologically recognizable premalignant disease. The most notable exception is carcinoma that arises from mixed tumours (carcinoma ex mixed tumour). The incidence of malignant transformation in mixed tumours, which is the most common of all benign salivary gland tumours, increases with duration. The incidence in tumours present for 5 years or less is 1.6% compared with 9.6% for those present more than 15 years (Eneroth and Zetterberg, 1974). Microspectrophotometric analysis has shown a similar tetraploid fraction in benign mixed tumours of long duration and in carcinomas.

Salivary gland carcinomas demonstrate extremely diverse cellular and architectural features (**Figure 13; see colour plate section**). Unlike carcinomas at many sites, most do not demonstrate a significant degree of nuclear pleomorphism and, therefore, their recognition as malignant is based on their characteristic growth patterns. Histological grading is based on one of four methods. For most salivary gland carcinomas there is a single grade determined by classification. For instance, acinic cell adenocarcinoma or basal cell adenocarcinoma are low grade whereas salivary duct carcinoma or undifferentiated carcinoma are high grade. The other three methods are uniquely applied to individual tumours: adenocarcinoma, not otherwise specified, is graded on its cytomorphological features, adenoid cystic carcinoma on the predominant growth either as cribriform-tubular (intermediate grade) or solid (high grade), and mucoepidermoid carcinoma on specific criteria that include the presence or absence of growth characteristics and cytomorphological features (Auclair et al., 1992).

Immunohistochemical staining shows that in normal gland, intercalated, striated and excretory ductal epithelium react strongly with antibodies for keratin intermediate filaments, but acinar and myoepithelial cells react weakly or not at all. Myoepithelial cells are reactive with smooth muscle actin antibodies and variably with antiglial fibrillary acidic protein antibodies. Immunoreactivity for S-100 protein is seen in intercalated duct and myoepithelial cells in glandular tissue that is next to tumour or severe inflammation but otherwise variable. The usefulness of immunohistochemical studies in diagnostic surgical pathology of salivary gland tumours is very limited. It is helpful in demonstrating neuroendocrine differentiation in small cell undifferentiated carcinoma. It is also invaluable in the identification of benign and malignant mesenchymal tumours and metastatic tumours such as malignant melanoma that involve the parotid glands.

Molecular Genetic Findings

Far fewer cytogenetic and molecular genetic studies have been carried out on salivary gland tumours than on SCCs of the oral cavity and, of those, most have investigated genetic alterations in pleomorphic adenoma and adenocarcinoma. For various salivary gland tumours, the most common chromosomal abnormalities reported are 11q;19p translocations (Martins et al., 1997), rearrangement at 6p23, amplifications and other abnormalities of 8q12 (Voz et al., 1998) and LOH at 3p, 6q, 8p, 8q and 12q (Gillenwater et al., 1997). The genetic lesions at 8q12 are associated with overexpression of *PLAG1*, the pleomorphic adenoma proto-oncogene which appears to be an early event in tumorigenesis (Voz et al., 1998). Tumour-suppressor genes involved in salivary gland tumorigenesis include *TP53*, *CDKN2/INK4/p16*, and an unidentified locus on 6q (Pignataro et al., 1998; Quemao et al., 1998; Suzuki et al.,

1998). Other genes that appear to play a role in development of salivary gland neoplasms include *TNF-α, bcl-2, MDM2* and the oncogenes *MYC* and *CDK4* which reside at 8q and 12 q (Rao *et al.*, 1998; Soini *et al.*, 1998). At present there is no genetic progression model for any salivary gland neoplasm or for salivary gland tumours in general.

Prognostic Factors

Clinical stage of disease correlates well with patient outcome for major gland disease. Staging largely depends on the size of the primary tumour and presence or absence of local neoplastic extension (**Table 3**). Local extension is the

Table 3   Staging system for major salivary glands[a]

Primary Tumour (T)

TX	Primary tumour cannot be assessed
T0	No evidence of primary tumour
T1*	Tumour 2 cm or less in greatest diameter without extraparenchymal extension
T2*	Tumour more than 2 cm but not more than 4 cm in greatest dimension without extraparenchymal extension
T3*	Tumour having extraparenchymal extension without seventh nerve involvement and/or more than 4 cm but not more than 6 cm in greatest dimension
T4	Tumour invades base of skull, seventh nerve, and/or exceeds 6 cm in greatest dimension

Regional lymph nodes (N)

NX	Regional lymph nodes cannot be assessed
N0	No regional lymph node metastasis
N1	Metastasis in a single ipsilateral lymph node, 3 cm or less in greatest dimension
N2	Metastasis in a single ipsilateral lymph node, more than 3 cm but not more than 6 cm in greatest dimension, or in multiple ipsilateral lymph nodes, none more than 6 cm in greatest dimension, or in bilateral or contralateral lymph nodes, none more than 6 cm in greatest dimension
N2a	Metastasis in a single ipsilateral lymph node more than 3 cm but not more than 6 cm in greatest dimension
N2b	Metastasis in multiple ipsilateral lymph nodes, none more than 6 cm in greatest dimension
N2c	Metastasis in bilateral or contralateral lymph nodes, none more than 6 cm in greatest dimension
N3	Metastasis in a lymph node more than 6 cm in greatest dimension

Distant metastasis (M)

MX	Presence of distant metastasis cannot be assessed
M0	No distant metastasis
M1	Distant metastasis

Clinical stage – grouping of carcinoma of the major salivary glands

Stage	T	N	M
Stage I	T1	N0	M0
	T2	N0	M0
Stage II	T3	N0	M0
Stage III	T1	N1	M0
	T2	N1	M0
Stage IV	T4	N0	M0
	T3	N1	M0
	T4	N1	M0
	Any T	N2	M0
	Any T	N3	M0
	Any T	Any N	M1

[a] Adapted from American Joint Commission on Cancer, 1997, *AJCC Staging Manual*, 5th edn. 53–55 (Lippincott-Raven, Philadelphia).

clinical or macroscopic evidence of invasion of skin, soft tissues, bone or nerve. Regional nodes are those within or immediately adjacent to the salivary gland and the deep cervical lymph nodes. There are no comparable staging criteria for intraoral minor gland tumours, but it has been shown that the criteria for intraoral squamous cell carcinoma can be applied successfully (Spiro *et al.*, 1991).

The grade of the tumour also influences the prognosis. For instance, in two recent studies, 3.3% of patients with low-grade mucoepidermoid carcinomas died of disease compared with 46.3% of those with high-grade tumours (Auclair *et al.*, 1991; Goode *et al.*, 1998). Tumour site also appears to affect biological behaviour with tumours of the submandibular gland of the same type and grade having the worst prognosis.

Overview of Present Clinical Management

The principal therapy for salivary gland carcinomas is surgical and the best results correlate with complete initial tumour resection. Partial parotidectomy, usually removal of the lateral lobe, with preservation of the facial nerve, if possible, is indicated for low-grade carcinomas whereas total parotidectomy is performed for high-grade carcinomas and recurrent low-grade tumours. Total removal of the submandibular or sublingual gland is indicated for carcinomas in those sites. Low-grade carcinomas of the minor glands are removed by wide local excision whereas high-grade tumours are more radically excised. For tumours of the hard palate, bone is not removed for low-grade carcinomas except for those exceptional cases that erode or infiltrate the palatal bone. For tumours of all sites, prophylactic neck dissection is indicated for high-grade carcinomas and in any patient in whom clinically suspicious lymph nodes are discovered. Radiotherapy is used postoperatively for some high-grade tumours and for treating residual tumour when positive surgical margins are found. Neutron beam therapy has shown promise in controlling locoregional disease but needs further study (Spiro, 1998). Chemotherapy is often used for palliation of patients with recurrent, unresectable disease.

REFERENCES

Auclair, P. L., *et al.* (1991). Salivary gland neoplasms: general considerations. In: Auclair, P. L., *et al.* (eds), *Surgical Pathology of the Salivary Glands*. 135–164 (W. B. Saunders, Philadelphia).

Auclair, P. L., *et al.* (1992). Mucoepidermoid carcinoma of intraoral salivary glands. Evaluation and application of grading criteria in 143 cases. *Cancer*, **69**, 2021–2030.

Banks, E. R., *et al.* (1992). Basaloid squamous cell carcinoma of the head and neck. A clinicopathologic and

immunohistochemical study of 40 cases. *American Journal of Surgical Pathology*, **16**, 939–946.

Barrera, J. E., *et al.* (1998). Malignancy detection by molecular cytogenetics in clinically normal mucosa adjacent to head and neck tumours. *Archives of Otolaryngology and Head and Neck Surgery*, **124**, 847–851.

Blot, W. J. (1992). Alcohol and cancer. *Cancer Research*, **52**, Suppl., 2119s–2123s.

Brachman, D. G. (1994). Molecular biology of head and neck cancers. *Seminars in Oncology*, **21**, 320–329.

Califano, J., *et al.* (1996). Genetic progression model for head and neck cancer. *Cancer Research*, **56**, 2488–2492.

Califano, J., *et al.* (1999). Second esophageal tumours in patients with HNSCC: an assessment of clonal relationships. *Clinical Cancer Research*, **5**, 1862–1867.

Callander, T., *et al.* (1994). PRAD-1(CCND1)/Cyclin D1 oncogene amplification in primary head and neck squamous cell carcinoma. *Cancer*, **74**, 152–158.

Cheng, Y. and Lotan R. (1998). Molecular cloning and characterization of a novel retinoic acid-inducible gene that encodes a putative G-protein coupled receptor. *Journal of Biological Chemistry*, **273**, 35008–35015.

Clayman, G. L., *et al.* (1999). Adenovirus-mediated wild-type p53 gene transfer as a surgical adjuvant in advanced head and neck cancers. *Clinical Cancer Research*, **5**, 1715–1722.

Crowe, D. L., *et al.* (1999). Keratin 19 downregulation by oral squamous cell carcinoma lines increases increases invasive potential. *Journal of Dental Research*, **78**, 1256–1263.

Day, G. L. and Blot, W. J. (1992). Second primary tumours in patients with oral cancer. *Cancer*, **70**, 14–19.

De Andrade, M., Amos, C. I. and Foulkes, W. D. (1998). Segregation analysis of squamous cell carcinoma of the head and neck: evidence for a major gene determining risk. *Annals of Human Genetics*, **62**, 505–510.

De Braud, F., *et al.* (1989). Metastatic squamous cell carcinoma of an unknown primary localized to the neck: advantages of an aggressive treatment. *Cancer*, **64**, 510–515.

Drachenberg, C. B., *et al.* (1997). Comparative study of invasive squamous cell carcinoma and verrucous carcinoma of the oral cavity: expression of bcl-2, p53 and Her-2/neu, and indexes of cell tunover. *Cancer Detection and Prevention*, **21**, 483–489.

Ellis, G. L. and Auclair, P. L. (1996). *Tumors of the Salivary Glands. Fascicle 17, Atlas of Tumor Pathology, 3rd Series. 1–8* (Armed Forces Institute of Pathology, Washington, DC).

Eneroth, C. M. and Zetterberg, A. (1974). Malignancy in pleomorphic adenoma. A clinical and microspectrophotometric study. *Acta Otolaryngologia (Stockholm)*, **77**, 426–432.

Ensley, J. F. and Maciorowski, Z. (1994). Clinical applications of DNA content parameters in patients with squamous cell carcinomas of the head and neck. *Seminars in Oncology*, **21**, 330–339.

Fearon, E. R. and Vogelstein, B. (1990). A genetic model of colorectal tumorigenesis. *Cell*, **61**, 759–767.

Friedman, M., *et al.* (1997). Prognostic significance of Bcl-2 expression in localized squamous cell carcinoma of the head and neck. *Annals of Otolaryngology, Rhinolaryngology and Laryngology*, **106**, 445–450.

Gauri, B., *et al.* (1996). Multiple head and neck tumours: evidence for a common clonal origin. *Cancer Research*, **56**, 2484–2487.

Gillenwater, A., *et al.* (1997). Microsatellite alterations at chromosome 8q loci in pleomorphic adenoma. *Archives of Otolaryngology and Head and Neck Surgery*, **117**, 448–452.

Gleich, L. L., *et al.* (1999). Variable genetic alterations and survival in head and neck cancer. *Archives of Otolaryngology and Head and Neck Surgery*, **125**, 949–952.

Goode R. K., *et al.* (1998). Mucoepidermoid carcinoma of the major salivary glands: clinical and histopathologic analysis of 234 cases with evaluation of grading criteria. *Cancer*, **82**, 1217–1224.

Grandis, J. R., *et al.* (1996). Retinoic acid normalizes increased gene transcription rate of TGF-alpha and EGFR in head and neck cell lines. *Nature Medicine*, **2**, 237–240.

Gridley G., *et al.* (1992). Vitamin supplementation and the reduced risk of oral and pharyngeal cancer. *American Journal of Epidemiology*, **135**, 1083–1092.

Gupta, V. K., *et al.* (1999). Multiple regions of deletion on chromosome arm 13q in head and neck squamous cell carcinoma. *International Journal of Cancer*, **84**, 453–457.

Hamilton-Dutoit, S. J., *et al.* (1991). Undifferentiated carcinoma of the salivary gland in Greenlandic Eskimos: demonstration of Epstein–Barr virus DNA by *in situ* nucleic acid hybridization. *Human Pathology*, **22**, 811–815.

Hansen J. L., *et al.* (1985). Proliferative verrucous leukoplakia: a long-term study. *Oral Surgery, Oral Medicine and Oral Pathology*, **60**, 285–290.

Hemmer, J., *et al.* (1999). DNA aneuploidy by flow cytometry is an independent prognostic factor in squamous cell carcinoma of the oral cavity. *Anticancer Research*, **19**, 1419–1422.

Huang, S. M., *et al.* (1999). Epidermal growth factor receptor blockade with C225 modulates proliferation, apoptosis, and radiosensitivity in squamous cell carcinomas of the head and neck. *Cancer Research*, **59**, 1935–1940.

Jahnke, V., *et al.* (1999). Genetic predisposition for the development of head and neck carcinomas. *Laryngorhinootologie*, **78**, 24–27.

Jares, P., *et al.* (1994). PRAD-1/Cyclin D1 gene amplification correlates with messenger RNA overexpression and tumour progression in human laryngeal carcinomas. *Cancer Research*, **54**, 4813–4817.

Kanekawa, A., *et al.* (1999). Chromosome 17 abnormalities in squamous cell carcinoma of the oral cavity, and its relationship with p53 and Bcl-2 expression. *Anticancer Research*, **19**, 81–86.

Khuri, F., *et al.* (1997). Molecular epidemiology and retinoid chemoprevention of head and neck cancer. *Journal of the National Cancer Institute*, **89**, 199–213.

Kos, J., *et al.* (1996). Prognostic significance of cathepsins D, B, H, and L and their protein inhibitors in breast, head and neck, and melanoma cancer (Meeting Abstract). *Proceedings of the Annual Meeting of the American Association of Cancer Research*, **37**, A622.

La Vecchia, C., *et al.* (1992). Trends of cancer mortality in Europe, 1955–1989: I. Digestive sites. *European Journal of Cancer*, **28**, 132–235.

Los, G., *et al.* (1999). Quantitation of the change in GADD153 mRNA levels as a molecular marker of tumour response in head and neck cancer. *Clinical Cancer Research*, **5**, 1610–1618.

Lotan, R. (1996). Retinoids and their receptors in modulation of differentiation, development, and prevention of oral premalignant lesions. *Anticancer Research*, **16**, 2415–2419.

Lumerman H., *et al.* (1995). Oral epithelial dysplasia and the development of invasive squamous cell carcinoma. *Oral Surgery Oral Medicine Oral Pathology, Oral Radiology and Endodontics*, **79**, 321–329.

Lydiatt, W. M., *et al.* (1998). Molecular support for field cancerization in the head and neck. *Cancer*, **82**, 1376–1380.

Marshall, D. D. and Kornberg, L. J. (1998). Overexpression of scatter factor and its receptor (c-met) in oral squamous cell carcinoma. *Laryngoscope*, **108**, 1413–1417.

Martins, C., *et al.* (1997). Cytogenetic characterisation of Warthin's tumour. *Oral Oncology*, **33**, 344–347.

Matthias, C., *et al.* (1998). Polymorphism within the cyclin D1 gene is associated with prognosis in patients with squamous cell cancer of the head and neck. *Clinical Cancer Research*, **4**, 2411–2418.

McKaig, R. G., *et al.* (1998). Human papilloma virus and head and neck cancer: epidemiology and molecular biology. *Head and Neck*, **203**, 250–265.

Minna, J. D., *et al.* (1997). Cancer of the lung. In: DeVita, V., *et al.* (eds), *Cancer: Principles and Practice of Oncology*. 849–857 (Lippincott-Raven, New York)

Nathan, C. A., *et al.* (1999). Expression of eIF4E during head and neck tumorigenesis: possible role in angogenesis. *Laryngoscope*, **109**, 1253–1258.

Nees, M., *et al.* (1993). Expression of mutated p53 occurs in tumour-distant epithelia of the head and neck cancer patients: a possible molecular basis for the development of multiple tumours. *Cancer Research* **53**, 4189–4196.

O'Malley, B. W. Jr and Li, D. (1998). Combination gene therapy for salivary gland cancer. *Annals of the New York Academy of Sciences*, **842**, 163–170.

Partridge, M., *et al.* (1997). Field cancerization of the oral cavity: comparison of the spectrum of molecular alterations in cases presenting with both dysplastic and malignant lesions. *Oral Oncology*, **33**, 332–337.

Pignataro, L., *et al.* (1998). p53 and cyclin D1 protein expression in carcinomas of the parotid gland. *Anticancer Research*, **18**, 1287–1290.

Quemao, L., *et al.* (1998). A refined localization of deleted regions in chromosome 6q associated with salivary gland carcinomas. *Oncogene*, **16**, 83–88.

Rao, P. H., *et al.* (1998). Nonsyntenic amplification of MYC with CDK4 and MDM2 in mixed tumour of the salivary gland. *Cancer Genetics and Cytogenetics*, **105**, 160–163.

Riese, U., *et al.* (1999). Tumor suppressor gene p16(CDKN2) mutation status and promoter inactivation in head and neck cancer. *International Journal of Molecular Medicine*, **4**, 61–5.

Scully, C. (1993). Oncogenes, tumour suppressors and viruses in oral squamous cell carcinoma. *Journal of Oral Pathology*, **22**, 337–347.

Sherbet, G. V. and Lakshmi, M. S. (1997). Clonal evolution of the metastatic phenotype. In: Sherbet, G. V. and Lakshmi, M. S. (eds), *The Genetics of Cancer – Genes Associated with Cancer Invasion, Metastasis and Cell Proliferation*. 4–20 (Academic Press, London).

Shingaki, S., *et al*. (1988). Evaluation of histologic parameters in predicting cervical lymph node metastasis of oral and oropharyngeal carcinoma. *Oral Surgery, Oral Medicine and Oral Pathology*, **66**, 683–688.

Sidransky, D. (1997). Cancer of the head and neck. In: DeVita, *et al*. (eds), *Cancer: Principles and Practice of Oncology*. 735–740 (Lippincott-Raven, New York).

Sidransky, D., *et al*. (1992). Clonal origin of bladder cancer. *New England Journal of Medicine*, **326**, 737–740.

Soini, Y., *et al*. (1998). Apoptosis is inversely related to bcl-2 but not bax expression in salivary gland tumours. *Histopathology*, **32**, 28–34.

Spiro, R. H. (1998). Management of malignant tumours of the salivary glands. *Oncology*, **12**, 671–680.

Spiro, R. H., *et al*. (1986). Predictive value of tumour thickness in squamous carcinoma confined to the tongue and floor of mouth. *American Journal of Surgery*, **152**, 345–350.

Spiro, R. H., *et al*. (1991). The importance of clinical staging of minor salivary gland carcinomas. *American Journal of Surgery*, **162**, 330–336.

Spitz, M. (1994). Epidemiology and risk factors for head and neck cancer. *Seminars in Oncology*, **21**, 281–288.

Suzuki, H. and Fujioka, Y. (1998). Deletion of the p16 gene and microsatellite instability in carcinoma arising in pleiomorphic adenoma of the parotid gland. *Diagnoses in Molecular Pathology*, **7**, 224–231.

Takes, R. P., *et al*. (1998). Differences in expression of oncogenes and tumour suppressor genes in different sites of head and neck squamous cell carcinoma. *Anticancer Research*, **18**, 4793–4800.

Venkatesan, *et al*. (1999). Prognostic significance of p27 expression in carcinoma of the oral cavity and oropharynx. *Laryngoscope*, **109**, 1329–1333.

Vigneswaran N., *et al*. (1995). Tobacco use and cancer. A reappraisal. *Oral Surgery, Oral Medicine, Oral Pathology, Oral Radiology and Endodontics*, **80**, 178–182.

Vo, H. P. and Crowe, D. L. (1998). Transcriptional control of retinoic acid responsive genes by cellular retinoic acid binding protein II modulates RA mediated tumour cell proliferation and invasion. *Anticancer Research*, **18**, 217–224.

Voz, M. L., *et al*. (1998). The recurrent translocation t(5;8)(p13;q12) in pleomorphic adenomas results in upregulation of the PLAG1 gene. *Oncogene*, **16**, 1409–1416.

Wain, S. L., *et al*. (1986). Basaloid-squamous carcinoma of the tongue, hypopharynx, and larynx: report of 10 cases. *Human Pathology*, **17**, 1155–1166.

Winn, D. M., *et al*. (1981). Snuff dipping and oral cancer among women in the southern United States. *New England Journal of Medicine*, **304**, 745–749.

Worsham, M., *et al*. (1995). Common clonal origin of synchronous primary head and neck squamous cell carcinomas. *Human Pathology*, **26**, 251–261.

FURTHER READING

McKinnell, R. G., *et al*. (eds) (1998). *The Biological Basis of Cancer*. (Cambridge University Press, New York).

Schantz, S. P., *et al*. (1997). *Tumors of the nasal cavity and paranasal sinuses, nasopharynx, oral cavity, and oropharynx*. In: DeVita, V. T., *et al*. (eds), *Cancer: Principles and Practice of Oncology*, 741–801 (Lippincott-Raven, Philadelphia).

Sessions, R. B., *et al*. (1997). Tumors of the salivary glands and paragangliomas. In: DeVita, V. T., *et al*. (eds), *Cancer: Principles and Practice of Oncology*. 830–847 (Lippincott-Raven, Philadelphia).

Silverman, S., Jr (1998). *Oral Cancer*, 4th edn (B.C. Decker, London).

Web Sites

http://rex.nci.nih.gov/NCI_Pub_Interface/raterisk
http://www.cancer.org
http://www.spohnc.org
http://cancernet.nci.nih.gov/canlit/canlit.htm
http://www3.ncbi.nlm.nih.gov/Omim/searchomim.html

Chapter 36

Respiratory System

Phillip S. Hasleton
Wythenshawe Hospital, Manchester, UK

CONTENTS

- Normal Upper Respiratory Tract
- Upper Respiratory Tract Tumours
- Lung
- Lung Tumours

The upper and lower respiratory tracts are the site of many common primary and secondary tumours. This area is exposed to many noxious influences, some environmental and others occupational.

NORMAL UPPER RESPIRATORY TRACT

The nose warms, humidifies and filters air via hairs and conchae (turnbinates) (**Figure 1**). These cause alterations in airflow, trapping particles larger than 6 μm in diameter in nasal mucus.

The nasal sinuses are collections of air cells called the frontal, sphenoidal, maxillary and ethmoid sinuses. The inner nasal cavity and sinuses, with their ostia in the lateral nasal walls, are lined by ciliated, pseudostratified columnar epithelium. A type of mucus cell called the goblet cell appears in the sinuses. Beneath the epithelium are seromucinous glands, which produce additional mucus, IgA and other immunoglobulins as defence mechanisms.

The epiglottis prevents aspiration of food and other materials into the respiratory tract. Because of the antigen load, in the nasopharynx there are large masses of lymphoid tissue – the adenoids, the palatine, tubal and lingual tonsils and aggregates of lymphoid tissue, which circle the pharyngeal wall (Waldeyer's ring). This forms part of a mucosa-associated lymphoid tissue (MALT), part of the immunological defence of the lung and gastrointestinal tract (**Figure 1**). With antigenic stimulation, especially in childhood, these areas enlarge. Any marked enlargement of the nasopharyngeal tonsil causes mouth breathing. This affects the efficiency of nasal function, impairing pulmonary function.

The larynx is divided into the supraglottis, glottis and subglottis (**Figure 2**). The larynx acts as a vibrator, via the vocal cords for speech. During normal breathing the cords are held wide open to allow air passage. With speech the folds close, so air causes vibrations. The intrinsic laryngeal muscles are innervated by the recurrent laryngeal branch

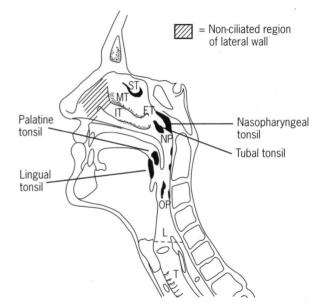

Figure 1 Diagram of nose, turbinates and larynx, showing relationships of the nasal cavity, nasopharynx (NP), oropharynx (OP), larynx (L) and distribution of lymphoid tissue (Waldeyer's ring). ST, MT and IT = superior, middle and inferior turbinates. ET = eustachian tube opening. Dotted line marks lower limit of the upper respiratory tract; below are the larynx (L), trachea (T) anteriorly and oesophagus (O) posteriorly. (Adapted from Jones, 1994.)

of the vagus nerve. Lung cancer metastases may entrap the vagus, causing hoarseness.

The epiglottis is lined by stratified squamous epithelium but in the lower half it gives way to a ciliated pseudostratified columnar type, characteristic of most of the larynx. The false cords enclose fibroadipose tissue, admixed with striated muscle and many seromucinous glands. The true cords are lined by stratified squamous epithelium and may contain some melanocytes along with elastic

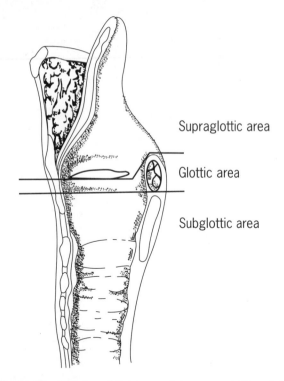

Supraglottic area

Glottic area

Subglottic area

Figure 2 Division of the larynx into supraglottic, glottic and subglottic areas. [From Gregor, 1998, Jones, Phillips and Hilgers (eds.) *Diseases of the Head and Neck, Nose and Throat* (Arnold, London).]

tissue. The larynx is supported by a cartilaginous framework, connected by ligaments.

The trachea has a series of C-shaped cartilages extending into the bronchi, joined by fibroelastic membranes forming a hollow tube. Posteriorly lies the trachealis muscle. The midline cervical trachea lies anterior to the oesophagus. Subglottic tracheal lesions may cause oesophageal problems and vice versa. The isthmus of the thyroid is anterior to the second to fourth rings.

The trachea divides into the main bronchi. The right follows the general direction of the trachea, the left diverges at a greater angle. Thus aspiration is commoner in the right lung. The trachea and main bronchi are conducting airways. Bronchial cartilage is progressively decreased with distance from the trachea. The airways continue dividing into respiratory bronchioles, alveolar ducts and finally alveoli (**Figure 3; see colour plate section**). The terminal bronchiole is the smallest airway lined by bronchial epithelial cells.

The trachea and main bronchi have an inner lining of immunoglobulin and mucus for protection. Beneath is a lining ciliated, pseudostratified epithelium with a variable number of goblet cells attached to a basement membrane.

The cilia maintain the mucociliary escalator, causing upward passage of mucus and entrapped organisms or particulate matter to be expectorated. The ciliary shaft or cilium is a cytoplasmic extension from the surface of the cell. Just above the basement membrane are Feyrter

cells [neuroendocrine (NE) cells], whose role in adults is unknown. They have clear cytoplasm and may occur as clusters, termed neuroepithelial bodies. NE cells contain dense core neurosecretory granules and secrete hormones. In the first 3 months of life, where there is relative hypoxia, they may act as chemoreceptors. These cells are the precursors of neuroendocrine tumours.

There is a surface, non-ciliated, bronchiolar secretory cell termed a Clara cell. These contain electron-dense membrane-bound inclusions and a few osmiophilic myelin bodies and produce surfactant apoprotein A.

In the subepithelial tissue there is collagen, elastin, nerves, lymphatics and small blood vessels. In addition there are serous and mucous glands (**Figure 4; see colour plate section**). The former produce lysozyme and if there is chronic cough they are converted to the mucous glands. The epithelium is regenerated by small pyramidal basal cells attached to the basement membrane.

Bronchus-associated lymphoid tissue (BALT) consists of subepithelial, mucosal, lymphoid follicles, containing both B and T lymphocytes. It develops at points of particle deposition, suggesting that it is stimulated as a response to inhaled particles. It is absent at birth and commoner in smokers.

The respiratory zone of the lung begins at the respiratory bronchiole and continues into alveolar ducts and alveoli. The alveolus is cup-shaped and thin-walled. Its cells can only be identified by electron microscopy. Up to 96% of the alveolar wall is covered by type I pneumocytes (**Figure 5; see colour plate section**). These are specialized cells, which cannot regenerate if damaged. The cytoplasm is thin to facilitate gas transfer between the alveolus and the pulmonary capillary. The edges of adjacent cells are bound by tight junctions, which restrict the movement of ions and water. These save the alveoli from flooding with water, as in pulmonary oedema.

Some 7% of the alveolar surface is covered with type II pneumocytes, which lie in the corners of alveolar walls. These cells form surfactant from their intracytoplasmic osmiophilic lamellar bodies. Surfactant is a phospholipid [dipalmitoylphosphatidylcholine (DPPC)]. This lowers the surface tension in the alveoli at the air/water interface. It acts similarly to a patch of oil on a road surface, repelling water. Any oedema can therefore be converted into droplets and they are removed by the pulmonary lymphatics.

The interstitial space is the part of the septal wall, which lies between the alveolar epithelial and capillary endothelial basement membrane. Normally it is inconspicuous but is distended in any form of alveolar damage. It contains macrophages, myofibroblasts, mast cells and occasional collagen and elastic fibres. Any thickening of this space causes alveolar diffusion problems. The interstitial connective tissue forms a continuous sheet with that surrounding blood vessels and bronchioles. This is efficient for removing fluid from alveoli into pulmonary lymphatics.

Pulmonary lymphatics aid the spread of infection and tumours. These are present around pulmonary blood vessels at an alveolar level and in the pleura. These drain directly into the mediastinal nodes, in the upper lobes especially. The lymphatics can be traced to the respiratory bronchioles and continue around small bronchi and bronchioles forming a plexus outside muscle. If the lymphatics are distended, Kerley B lines are formed on chest radiographs.

UPPER RESPIRATORY TRACT TUMOURS

These tumours are well documented in the book *Tumours of the Upper Aerodigestive Tract* (Mills *et al.*, 2000).

Tumours of the Nasopharynx

Clinical Features

Most nasal tumours cause nasal obstruction, occasionally epistaxis and facial pain, irrespective of their histology.

Squamous Papillomas

These are benign exophytic tumours with no association with human papillomavirus (HPV) and are seen in the oropharynx, larynx and trachea. They are covered by a bland, stratified, keratinizing squamous epithelium lining a fibrovascular core.

Schneiderian Papillomas

The ciliated columnar epithelium lining most of the nasal and paranasal cavity is called the Schneiderian membrane. The commonest tumour arising from this epithelium is the inverted Schneiderian papilloma, seen most commonly on the lateral nasal wall in the paranasal sinuses. They present as nasal polyps growing through the lateral wall within the maxillary or ethmoid sinuses. The nests of epithelium grow down into the underlying stroma with dilated ductal structures lined by multiple layers of epithelium. The epithelium may be squamous, ciliated, columnar or transitional and is often thick, being sometimes over 20 layers or more (**Figure 6; see colour plate section**). Mitoses are usually confined to the lower epithelial levels but nuclear pleomorphism may be identified. They may co-exist with a squamous cell carcinoma and any papillomas should be thoroughly sampled for evidence of carcinoma. These tumours have a recurrence rate of up to 75% when treated by local excision.

Fungiform Schneiderian papillomas are not associated with malignancy and arise predominantly from the nasal septum as polypoid tumours. The epithelium is similar to that of the inverted tumour but there are admixed mucous cells and little nuclear pleomorphism. Unlike papillary squamous cell carcinoma, there is no mitotic activity or dyskeratosis. They have a low recurrence rate.

Squamous Cell Carcinoma

These are relatively rare in the nasopharyngeal region. The distribution is maxillary antrum 58%, nasal cavity 30%, ethmoid sinuses 10% and frontal and ethmoid sinuses 1% each (Lewis and Castro, 1972). They are commonest on the lateral nasal wall. Tumours in the maxillary antrum may be misdiagnosed as chronic sinusitis, delaying treatment. Sinonasal squamous carcinomas occur predominantly in males, often in their 60s.

There is an association with cigarette smoking, nickel mining and refining and chromium exposure and, more recently, formaldehyde has been suggested as a carcinogen. HPV types 16 and 18 DNA have been found in 14% of sinonasal squamous cell carcinomas but the high sensitivity of polymerase chain reaction (PCR) suggests that contamination cannot be totally excluded (Furuta *et al.*, 1992).

The tumours are typically papillary, polypoid and are usually moderately or well differentiated squamous cell carcinomas. Nasal lesions spread to the submental and submandibular nodes and they enter the facial and superficial parotid deep cervical nodes. Spread of paranasal sinus carcinoma to regional nodes is uncommon when the tumour is confined to the sinus cavity.

Sinonasal Carcinoma

This is strongly associated with hardwood dust exposure but additional 'risk' occupations are logging, milling, exposure to leather dust and softwood dusts (Cecchi *et al.*, 1980). Most of these tumours occur in men, with origins in descending order of frequency in the ethmoid sinuses, nasal cavity, maxillary antrum and indeterminate. They present with the usual symptoms, as well as rhinorrhea or a mass in the cheek. The tumours mimic ulcerated or haemorrhagic inflammatory nasal polyps.

There is malignant, small and large intestinal type mucosa along with Paneth, goblet and argentaffin cells. These tumours do not usually express carcinoembryonic antigen (CEA), unlike metastatic small or large bowel carcinomas. Sinonasal adenocarcinomas are usually chromograninpositive, which is less common in colonic carcinomas.

The optimum treatment is surgical resection with radiation therapy to the region of the tumour. Grade and subtype correlate with survival. The better prognosis is with the papillary subtype as opposed to sessile or alveolar mucoid variants (Batsakis *et al.*, 1963). Woodworkers also appear to have a better survival than patients who present without this risk factor.

Nasopharyngeal Carcinoma

Nasopharyngeal carcinoma arises near the fossa of Rosenmuller (the internal opening of the middle ear canal) causes middle ear obstruction and involves the cervical nodes. These tumours are classified into keratinizing squamous cell carcinoma, nonkeratinizing carcinoma and undifferentiated carcinoma. These tumours affect a broad age range, including children. There is a distinct bimodal age distribution with peaks in the second and sixth decades of life.

Cigarette smoking may play a part in lymphoepithelial carcinoma but this cell type is especially predominant in Chinese patients, even when they emigrate to other countries. It is associated with Epstein–Barr virus (EBV). In Hong Kong it accounts for 18% of all malignancies compared with 2% in the United States (Digby *et al.*, 1941). Chinese patients in Singapore with lymphoepithelial carcinoma have an increased frequency of histocompatibility antigens HLA-A2 and HLA-BW46 (Simons *et al.*, 1976).

Clinically the nasopharynx may be normal, full or show surface granularity. An obvious carcinoma is uncommon. It is usually a poorly differentiated squamous cell carcinoma often with a marked inflammatory component, including lymphocytes, plasma cells and eosinophils (lymphoepithelioma) (**Figure 7; see colour plate section**). They may be confused with a lymphoma because of the prominent inflammation. Mitoses are typically numerous, ranging from 5 to 10 per 10 high power fields. The tumour cells have a syncytial growth pattern or form cohesive nests and cords. They tend to metastasize to regional nodes, where they may be first detected. Distant metastases to lung, brain, liver and bone are common. Lymphoepitheliomas are usually treated by radiation.

Other variants of squamous carcinoma are adenoid, angiosarcoma-like, papillary, spindle cell, basaloid and adenosquamous.

Squamous carcinoma also occurs in the oropharynx and hypopharynx. In both of these sites surgery is the mainstay of treatment followed by radiation.

Neural Tumours

Nasal glioma is a heterotopia due to failure of the developing frontal lobe to retract completely via the foramen caecum. They are therefore encephaloceles, not true tumours. Ectopic pituitary tissue may be seen in the same area and present as a pituitary adenoma.

Nasopharyngeal neurofibromas, neuromas and neurilemmomas are similar to those seen in other areas of the body.

Melanotic neuroectodermal tumour of infancy (MNTI) occurs in infants under the age of 1 year; 70% are seen in the anterior maxillary area. These are lobular, well-circumscribed, unencapsulated tumours, measuring up to 13 cm in diameter. They are grey/white to dark brown with nests of small neuroblastic cells, often surrounded by larger melanin-containing cells with an alveolar or tubular pattern. Nuclear pleomorphism, mitoses and necrosis are uncommon.

Paraganglioma (carotid body tumour) can be seen in the nasal cavity, paranasal sinuses, nasopharynx and larynx. They are no different from extra-adrenal paraganglial tumours of the autonomic nervous system in other parts of the body.

Olfactory Neuroblastoma

There are no known risk factors for this tumour, which has a bimodal distribution, at the ages of 15 and 55 years. In addition to the usual symptoms, headaches, visual disturbances and anosmia may also occur. The ethmoid sinus is often involved. Radiologically the tumour has a 'dumbbell' appearance extending across the cribriform plate (**Figure 8; see colour plate section**).

They are polypoid, vascular, red/tan masses set high in the nasal cavity. The tumour may have circumscribed nests of cells, which are small with round nuclei and little cytoplasm or grow as diffuse sheets of neoplastic cells set in a background of capillaries and little intervening stroma. There is a fibrillary cytoplasmic background in haematoxylin and eosin-stained sections. Necrosis is a poor prognostic indicator.

Most of these tumours stain positively for synaptophysin. Treatment is by surgical excision with adjuvant radiotherapy or chemotherapy.

Undifferentiated Sinonasal Carcinoma

This is rare but is seen in both young adults and the elderly. Typically it presents as a large fungating mass obstructing the nasal cavity and invading surrounding structures. There are nests, sheets, ribbons and trabeculae of polygonal cells, often with an organoid appearance. Mitoses are prominent and there is extensive vascular permeation. This tumour must be differentiated from a lymphoepithelioma.

Primary Small Cell Carcinoma

This is similar to that seen in the lung and may arise rarely in the sinonasal region. Malignant melanoma is rarely seen as a primary tumour developing in the nasal cavity or the paranasal sinuses.

Lymphoid Tumours

Non-Hodgkin Lymphoma (NHL)

Up to 10% of NHL may involve Waldeyer's ring (adenoids, oropharynx, tonsilar and lymphoid tissue at the base of the tongue). After gastrointestinal lymphomas, it is the commonest extranodal lymphoid tumour. Most involve the tonsil but 35% involve the nasopharynx. It is often difficult to determine if a lymphoma is strictly confined to the nose or paranasal sinuses. There is often involvement of multiple sinuses. They are usually localized, affecting a wide age span from the first to the tenth decades.

The tumours are greyish/white, firm and up to 10 cm in diameter. Under the REAL classification 85% are B cell lymphomas, half of which are diffuse large cell lymphomas (**Figure 9; see colour plate section**). There is a diffuse proliferation of large cells with immunoblastic features or diffuse mixed and large cells. Mantle cell and low-grade lymphomas also occur in Waldeyer's ring. A subset of nasopharyngeal lymphomas are of T/NK phenotype, especially in the Far East. These are probably human T cell leukaemia/lymphoma-virus induced, while others are more closely related to sinonasal T/NK cell lymphoma (Tomita *et al.*, 1996).

Radiation is the treatment of choice and chemotherapy is added for locally advanced or disseminated tumours. (See also chapter *RNA Viruses*.)

Sinonasal T/NK Cell Lymphoma

Virtually no B cells are seen in normal nasal epithelium but there are T cells. T helper cells outnumber the T cytotoxic/suppressor cells. T/NK cell lymphoma used to be termed midline malignant reticulosis, lethal midline granuloma and midfacial destructive lesion, amongst others. These terms are now no longer used. T/NK lymphoma is an angiocentric, immunoproliferative lesion. It is commoner in Asians. The disease can occur at any age with a median of 47 years with a male predominance (Aozasa *et al.*, 1995).

The patients present with mid-facial destruction, involving the nasal cavity, paranasal sinuses and in some cases the palate and other mid-facial structures. It may extend to involve the larynx. There is sometimes collapse of the nasal bridge, ulceration, necrosis, septal perforation, fever and weight loss. The tumour often spreads to other extranodal sites, such as skin, subcutaneous tissue, gastrointestinal tract and testis.

Histologically there is extensive necrosis, which may involve the cartilage and bone. Small lymphocytes, plasma cells, immunoblasts and some cytologically atypical lymphocytes, as well as polymorphs, eosinophils and histiocytes are seen. There is much angioinvasion, causing thrombosis. Mitoses are frequent. T/NK lymphoma is typically reactive for CD2, a T cell marker, and CD 56, a marker of NK cells. However, clonal T cell receptor gene rearrangements are absent in this lymphoma.

Other Lymphomas of the Sinonasal Tract

These include extramedullary plasmacytoma, post-transplant lymphoproliferative disorder (PTLD) and rare cases of Hodgkin's disease. The histology of these tumours does not differ from those elsewhere in the body.

Vascular Tumours

Haemangioma is a hamartoma. They are common in the nose.

Nasopharyngeal Angiofibroma

This usually arises in the posterior nasal cavity and nasopharyngeal wall. It is seen almost exclusively in male adolescents. The tumours have testosterone receptors (Gown *et al.*, 1993). Their vascularity can be reduced by oestrogen therapy. The mean age of the patients is 15 years and the presenting symptoms are those of any other nasal lesion. They are firm, sessile or polypoid tumours with a fleshy appearance. There is a fibrous stroma containing many vessels of varying sizes. Some are thick-walled with an obvious media (**Figure 10; see colour plate section**). The stroma consists of characteristic spindled and stellate shaped mesenchymal cells and haphazardly arranged collagen. Mitoses are rare. The deeper portions of an angiofibroma away from the central feeding vessels may be hypovascular. Angiofibromas lack the lobular arrangement of a capillary haemangioma. Treatment is by surgical excision but recurrence is common.

Glomus tumours, although rare, may occur in the nose.

Other Tumours

These include fibroma, solitary fibrous tumour, aggresive fibromatosis, osteoma, osteosarcoma, often involving the maxilla, teratoma involving the nasopharynx and metastatic tumours especially from breast, kidney and lung.

Other soft tissue tumours to involve the nasopharyngeal area are leiomyoma, chondroma, chondrosarcoma, rhabdomyosarcoma (nose) and leiomyosarcoma (nose).

Larynx

Squamous papillomas may arise from the true cords, at other sites in the larynx, the oropharynx and the trachea. They may be part of juvenile laryngeal papillomatosis, which may be single or multiple. 'Juvenile' is arbitrarily classified as presenting before the age of 20 years. Multiple is usually defined as more than three lesions.

Most laryngeal papillomas are probably caused by HPV, types 6 and 11 (Travis *et al.*, 1999). These tumours are glistening, nodular, exophytic masses and, depending on their site and size, cause hoarseness, stridor or respiratory distress. A rare complication is squamous cell carcinoma, which may develop in the larynx or lung.

Histologically there are multiple layers of orderly squamous epithelium with no atypia, covering a fibrovascular core. A few cases may show varying degrees of dysplasia. Prominent surface keratin or intraepithelial dyskeratosis suggests verruca vulgaris or veruccous carcinoma. Squamous carcinomas usually arise in the juvenile lesions. Treatment is by surgery but recurrence is frequent. Solitary adult and juvenile papillomas are often cured by surgery.

Keratosis and Dysplasia

Keratosis is an epithelial area with a marked degree of orthokeratosis or parakeratosis unassociated with underlying epithelial proliferation (AFIP). Typically keratosis is due to long-term tobacco abuse and affects the vocal cords. The mucosa is thickened and white. 'Leucoplakia' is a clinical term meaning 'white plaque' and not a pathological description. Keratotic epithelium usually separates from the vocal cords. This is helpful diagnostically since an intact basal layer helps exclude invasive carcinoma.

Non-dysplastic keratosis shows a normal or increased thickness of squamous epithelium with a prominent granular layer and overlying layers of orthokeratin admixed with parakeratosis. Maturation is orderly and mitoses are basal. If there is no dysplasia there appears to be only a minimal risk of developing a subsequent carcinoma.

Dysplasia is graded into mild, moderate and severe and has similarities to the system used in the cervix except that keratinization is more common in the larynx. Mild dysplasia involves the basal layer, moderate extends upwards to involve usually two-thirds but does not involve the superficial epithelium. Severe dysplasia shows increased mitoses and involves the full thickness of the epithelium. The more severe the dysplasia, the greater is the chance of an invasive carcinoma co-existing or developing in the larynx. Involvement of the underlying seromucinous glands by dysplastic epithelium is not considered to be evidence of invasion.

Invasive Squamous Cell Carcinoma

Squamous carcinoma of the larynx is associated with cigarette smoking and excess alcohol intake. 'Social' use of alcohol does not appear to cause an increased risk. There is no association between asbestos exposure and carcinoma of this site. Carcinoma of the larynx is divided into supraglottic, glottic and subglottic types. This division has relevance for surgical management. Transglottic carcinoma is a term applied to carcinomas bridging the laryngeal ventricle and involving both the vocal cord and supraglottic regions. Most are glottic carcinomas extending into the supraglottis.

Most carcinomas of the larynx are glottic, arising anteriorly on the mobile part of the cord. They cause hoarseness. The majority of the remaining laryngeal carcinomas are supraglottic and arise from the epiglottis, ventricles, false cords and aryepiglottic folds. These give rise to changes in voice quality and may cause difficulty in swallowing or the feeling of a mass in the throat. Subglottic carcinomas account for 5% or less of all laryngeal carcinomas.

The tumours are usually ulcerated and vary in size from small lesions to large masses, which may almost obstruct the laryngeal lumen (**Figure 11; see colour plate section**). There are varieties of squamous cell carcinoma, including spindle cell. Since the true cords have a limited lymphatic supply, tumours at this site have a good prognosis. Thus they are often cured by radiation or limited surgical resection. With an increase in size the cords become fixed and the tumour may extend outside the larynx, involving nodes. Subglottic carcinomas are often circumferential and extend beyond the larynx, penetrating the cricothyroid membrane. These cases are likely to involve cervical nodes.

Early carcinomas are usually cured with limited surgery or radiation but laryngectomy is one of the treatments for larger tumours. Recently chemotherapy has been shown to play a role. The size of the tumour and degree of differentiation are important factors in determining prognosis. Patients with laryngeal carcinoma have an increased risk of developing another tumour, especially in the lung or elsewhere in the head or neck.

Genetic Changes in Laryngeal Carcinoma

P53 status over-expression does not result in cell cycle arrest in some studies, although a correlation with this oncogene and early stage glottic cancer as well as those tumours recurring locally has been described (Narayana et al., 1998). It may also relate to decreased survival (Bradford et al., 1997). C-erbB-2 plays no part in prognosis in this tumour (Krecicki et al., 1999). Retinoblastoma protein, however, does relate to survival (Dokiya et al., 1998). Cyclin D1 overexpression identified patients with poor grade laryngeal carcinoma, tumour extension, lymph node involvement and poor histological differentiation (Bellacosa et al., 1996).

Adenosquamous Carcinoma

This may affect the larynx. These are usually high-grade tumours, similar to adenosquamous carcinoma in the lung. Adenocarcinoma is very rare in the larynx and the possibility of a secondary tumour should be considered.

Neural Laryngeal Tumours

Neurilemmomas, neurofibromas, granular cell tumour, paraganglioma, malignant melanoma and carcinoid tumour [this includes all neuroendocrine carcinomas (see the section on the lung) can all be identified in the larynx. These tumours are histologically identical with the pulmonary lesions described below.

Lymphoma

Localized laryngeal non-Hodgkin lymphoma is rare. Extramedullary plasmacytoma has been well described in the larynx, where it causes a subepithelial tumour.

Haemangiomas may arise in the larynx. In infants they present with respiratory distress and affect the subglottic region. Adult haemangiomas are commoner and usually affect the supraglottic and glottic areas. They may cause cough and haemoptysis, as well as hoarseness. Inflammatory myofibroblastic tumour may involve the larynx and in some cases it is caused by *Mycobacterium avium intracellulari*, often in HIV-positive or immunosuppressed patients. The commonest site is on the vocal cords, where they cause hoarseness and stridor.

Carcinomas may metastasize to the larynx, the commonest tumour is melanoma followed by breast, kidney, lung, prostate and gastrointestinal tract carcinomas. Soft tissue laryngeal tumours include liposarcoma, chondrosarcoma and rarely rhabdomyosarcoma, leiomyosarcoma and malignant fibrous histiocytoma.

Trachea

The trachea is rarely involved by tumours, the commonest being polyposis and adenoid cystic carcinoma but any of the neoplasms mentioned below may affect this area.

LUNG

Cigarette Smoking

This is one of the major causes of mortality and morbidity in the Western world. As some of the tobacco sales decline in this area, the producers are ensuring that Third-world countries are targetted.

Cigarette smoke yields more than 4000 constituents. These include carbon monoxide, hydrogen cyanide, aldehydes, cadmium, ammonia, nicotine and benz[a]anthracene, a potent carcinogen. In addition, there are aromatic hydrocarbons and other toxic substances, which may be tumour initiators, such as benzanthracenes and benzopyrenes. There are suspended water droplets, which vary in size and have central resinous cores. These smoke droplets are absorbed on bronchial walls and propelled on the mucociliary escalator back to the mouth; 98% of smoke particles landing in the bronchi are removed by cilia within 24 h. Smaller particles enter alveoli and, if undissolved, are ingested by macrophages and removed to lymphatics.

Nicotine makes cigarettes addictive. The faster a cigarette is smoked, the more nicotine is present in the mainstream smoke; 85% is absorbed in the lungs and it causes an increase in heart rate, blood pressure and cardiac output.

Cigarette smoking may be active or passive. The latter occurs in smokers and nonsmokers, in the same environment as a smoker. Passive smoking increases the risk of lung cancer by 26% and of ischaemic heart disease by 23%. In addition, passive smoking is linked with an increased incidence of asthma and chest infections in children.

This habit affects virtually every organ system, ranging from adenolymphoma of the parotid to peripheral vascular disease. (See the chapter *Tobacco Use and Cancer*.)

LUNG TUMOURS

These may be primary or secondary, benign or malignant. Because the lung receives the entire cardiac output, tumour metastases are common.

Classification of Lung Tumours

There has been an increase in new pulmonary lesions described in the last 18 years (Travis *et al.*, 1999). In addition to bronchial squamous dysplasia, the concept of atypical alveolar hyperplasia, as a precursor for adenocarcinoma of lung, is becoming well established. It is impossible in a chapter such as this to give a comprehensive description of all lung tumours and the reader is referred to specialist texts (Hasleton, 1996).

Benign Lung Tumours

These may be central or peripheral. Central indicates they involve main bronchi and peripheral, the lung parenchyma. The site of the neoplasm determines signs and symptoms. Central tumours cause collapse of a lobe or lung, with recurrent infections leading to bronchiectasis. All central lung tumours present with similar symptoms, i.e. cough, recurrent chest infections and haemoptysis, due to ulceration of the surface of the tumour.

Peripheral lung tumours are often detected as a chance radiological finding, known as 'a solitary pulmonary nodule.' As a rough guide, 40% of solitary nodules are malignant and 60% are benign. The benign lesions may well be inflammatory or non-neoplastic rather than benign tumours. For any individual patient these figures are meaningless and do not help with diagnosis. By convention a nodule is 4–6 cm in diameter; a larger lesion is termed a mass, often suggesting malignancy. The treatment options for a solitary nodule are outside the scope of this book but with computed tomography (CT) scans and fine-needle biopsy, some of the diagnostic responsibility rests with the histopathologist.

Radiologically benign lesions tend to have a smooth circumscribed periphery; malignant ones are larger with irregular margins. A calcified nodule can be followed up and is considered benign. If a nodule has been radiologically stable in size for 2 years and the patient is below 35 years of age, it is malignant in only 1–5% of cases. The widespread policy in remaining solitary nodules of unknown aetiology is resection.

It is unnecessary for anyone to memorize every benign lung tumour. If one remembers the normal bronchial wall components, i.e. epithelium, neuroendocrine cells, connective tissue, muscle, cartilage, fat and nerves, and the fact that the mucous and serous glands of the bronchial wall act as a minor salivary gland, the nature of the majority of benign tumours can be predicted. Only the important or commoner ones will be considered here.

Hamartoma

These tumours develop in adults and have an abnormal karyotype. The most characteristic aberration is a 6p21 rearrangement but a 12q14–15 rearrangement has also been identified. These molecular abnormalities indicate these 'hamartomas' are true neoplasms and a better term is 'mesenchymoma.' This tumour is twice as common in smokers and is associated with bronchial carcinoma. They are often peripheral and range from 1 to 4 cm in diameter. The cut surface is grey (**Figure 12; see colour**

plate section) but if fat is prominent it is yellow. If the tumour is central, there is distal bronchiectasis. They consist of cartilage, bone, fat, loose myxoid tissue and islands of ciliated or columnar epithelium.

Papilloma of the Bronchus

Papillomas are classified into solitary or multiple. The solitary lesions are rare, presenting in middle-aged smokers as a central tumour. It grows as a wart-like lesion into the bronchial lumen and consists of nonkeratinizing squamous epithelium. Papillomatosis is seen in children. HPV (human papillomavirus) types 6 and 11 can be identified in both solitary and multiple tumours. One-third show carcinoma *in situ* or invasive carcinoma and thus papillomas require at a minimum close follow-up.

Glandular and mixed squamous and glandular papillomas are solitary, benign central tumours.

Neuroendocrine Tumours

There are no real premalignant neuroendocrine lesions. DIPNECH (diffuse idiopathic pulmonary neuroendocrine hyperplasia) has been placed in the preinvasive section of the new WHO classification. The author has seen very rare cases, associated with tumourlets and typical carcinoids. However, DIPNECH is a nonspecific reaction to airway inflammation and/or fibrosis. There is neuroendocrine (NE) cell hyperplasia in association with peripheral carcinoid tumours. However, adjacent to central typical carcinoids there is a decrease in NE cells. No *in situ* lesion has been found in association with small cell carcinoma, although dysplastic squamous epithelium may lie over the tumour.

A tumourlet is defined by the WHO as 'a microscopic, peribronchiolar, nodular aggregate of uniform, round to oval or spindle-shaped cells with moderate amounts of cytoplasm and morphology similar to the cells of carcinoid tumours.' An arbitrary size of 0.5 cm or less is given for these lesions; larger tumours are termed bronchial carcinoids. Tumourlets usually occur with focal pulmonary fibrosis and bronchiectasis but not diffuse interstitial pulmonary fibrosis. They are found incidentally. They may be mistaken for small-cell carcinoma but lack this tumour's cytological features and have no mitoses.

Bronchopulmonary Carcinoid Tumours

As shown in **Figure 13** there is a spectrum of biological behaviour in these tumours, ranging from the 'benign' bronchopulmonary carcinoid to small-cell lung carcinoma (SCLC). The latter neoplasm accounts for 15–25% of all lung malignancies. This figure does not imply there is any transition from one tumour type to another. Typical carcinoid (TC), atypical carcinoid (AC) tumours and large-cell neuroendocrine carcinomas (LCNEC) are rare,

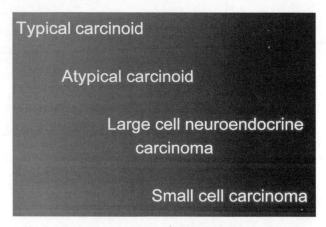

Figure 13 Diagram of neuroendocrine tumours of the lung, excluding non-small cell carcinomas with neuroendocrine features. This diagram does not imply that there is any biological transition from typical carcinoid into atypical carcinoid, etc. It merely depicts the increasing malignancy of these tumours with large-cell neuroendocrine tumours and small cell neuroendocrine carcinoma being the most malignant of the neoplasms.

together accounting for 2–3% of lung tumours. Nearly all patients with AC, SCLC and LCNEC are cigarette smokers. While TC and AC are morpologically similar to neuroendocrine tumours elsewhere in the body they do not always behave in a similar fashion. For example, the carcinoid syndrome is relatively rare in bronchial carcinoids but commoner with hepatic metastases from ileal tumours. Bone production is rare in gastrointestinal carcinoids but commoner in bronchial tumours.

TC may be central or peripheral. Central tumours give the signs and symptoms mentioned above but nearly 20% of cases may be asymptomatic. Endocrine manifestations are rare but hormones and peptides, including calcitonin, bombesin and cytokines are easily detectable immunohistochemically. This paradox may be due to the small tumour volume and the efficiency of endothelial cells in detoxicating such products. The tumours cause haemorrhage, due to the presence of many small blood vessels. These vessels are caused by TGF (transforming growth factor)-α formation by the tumour. Macroscopically they are yellow/white (**Figure 14; see colour plate section**) with foci of haemorrhage. Up to 30% of tumours contain bone, due to elaboration of osteogenic cytokines, including TGF-β and IGF-1.

TC has trabecular, insular or acinar growth patterns (**Figure 15; see colour plate section**). Other histological patterns have been documented. There should be fewer than two mitoses/2 mm^2/10 high-power fields (hpf) and no necrosis. These tumours may show cytological atypia, especially on frozen section (Sheppard, 1997), increased cellularity and lymphatic invasion. If there are tumour deposits in lymph nodes, the lesion may still be classed as typical if the histology is as described above. Special stains are not always necessary to confirm the diagnosis, since the histological pattern may be distinctive. Ultrastructurally they contain dense core neurosecretory granules, typical of NE cells.

AC may be central or peripheral, have the NE architecture as described above, and a mitotic rate of 2–10/ 2 mm^2/10 hpf and/or punctate necrosis.

LCNEC are usually peripheral, tan tumours with focal necrosis and haemorrhage. Histologically there is a neuroendocrine appearance, with large cells, irregular pleomorphic nuclei and low nuclear/cytoplasmic ratios. The cytoplasm is abundant, granular and eosinophilic. Necrosis is usually geographic and mitoses are frequent, with a mean of 75 per 2 mm^2 per 10 hpf. Prognosis is poor.

SCLC ('oat cell carcinoma') is described with malignant tumours.

Bax, bcl-2 and p53 in Neuroendocrine Tumours

The *bax* gene is one of the main effectors of apoptosis and can be considered a tumour suppressor gene. *Bcl-2* is an oncogene and can block both p53-mediated and p53-independent apoptosis. There is an inverse correlation between the scores of *Bax* and *bcl-2* expression in NE tumours. A predominant *Bax* expression is seen in low-grade NE tumours (TC or AC) and mainly *bcl-2* expression in small-cell and large-cell lung cancers. The p16-retinoblastoma pathway is normal in typical carcinoids but abnormal in the higher-grade NE tumours. (Dosaka-Akita *et al.*, 2000) P53 mutation or stabilization is absent in TC. AC may show focal (less than 10%) or patchy P53 positivity, are more aggressive and have significantly shorter survival times than those without P53 staining (Brambilla and Brambilla, 1999).

Carcinoma of Lung

Epidemiology

The lung is the commonest site of cancer worldwide and is in first place in all areas of Europe and North America. Lung cancer appears to be rising in incidence by 70% in women and 30% in men (Travis *et al.*, 1995). In the USA the largest percentage increases in age-adjusted rates are for small-cell carcinoma and adenocarcinoma (60% each) with a smaller change for the latter tumour (14%). In the EEC, lung cancer accounts for 21% of all cancer deaths in men and the corresponding figure for women is 4%. This latter figure is increasing and worldwide lung cancer is the fifth most frequent cancer in women. This is due to the social acceptability of smoking, the targeting of women in tobacco advertisements and appetite suppression caused by cigarettes. A decline in incidence in all cell types is predicted soon

in the USA. The rate in the West will probably continue to decrease balanced by an increase the Third-world countries, now targetted by tobacco companies. This proposed decrease does not take into account any drug habits of teenagers.

Tobacco is associated with most of the major histological types of lung cancer. The increase in lung cancer risk according to the number of cigarettes smoked appears stronger for squamous and small cell carcinomas than for adenocarcinoma. The increase in this latter cell type has yet to be explained. In the USA there has been a decline in tar and nicotine levels due to filter-tipped cigarettes. There has been a progressive introduction of specially processed tobacco and perforated cigarette paper. These changes may have altered the types of carcinogens in the cigarette smoke, affecting the histological type.

Aetiology

Cigarette Smoking

Cigarette smoking (see earlier) is the most important cause of lung cancer. With an increase in sales of cigarettes at the beginning of the 1900s, changes were made in the types of tobacco used. The smoke was milder and thus easier to inhale. pH was adjusted so that absorption did not occur across the oral mucosa. Subjects had to inhale smoke into the lung to absorb substantial amounts of nicotine. This deep inhalation and absorption of the tobacco's toxic and carcinogenic substances enhanced the lung cancer risk. The evidence linking cigarette smoking with lung cancer started to accumulate in the 1930s. Four retrospective studies showing the relationship between lung cancer and smoking were published in the 1950s, each showing a consistent statistically significant association. Relative risk increases in a stepwise fashion with the increased number of cigarettes smoked. The age at which the subject begins to smoke is also critical.

Other types of tobacco inhalation, ranging from pipes and cigars in the West to bidis in Asia, also correlate with a significant risk for lung cancer.

Involuntary (Passive) Smoking

This is a combination of sidestream smoke, emitted into the air from a burning cigarette between puffs and some of the mainstream smoke, exhaled by the smoker. The potential carcinogenicity of passive smoking was highlighted by the increased risk of lung cancer in nonsmoking women married to smokers. It is now estimated that in the USA at about 2000 deaths per year are due to passive smoking.

Genetic Predisposition

Some 85–90% of smokers who are consuming 20 or more cigarettes a day will not develop lung cancer. Therefore, host factors must be important in altering the risk/predisposition to the development of this disease. There is mounting evidence that some of the genetic changes predisposing to lung cancer are inherited in a mendelian character. First-degree relatives of lung cancer relatives have a 2.4-fold increased risk of lung cancer or other nonsmoking-related cancers. Patients treated for lung/laryngeal cancer have an increased risk of developing second lung tumours. More tangible evidence of linkage between hereditary and lung cancer has been shown in relatives of patients with retinoblastoma, with a 15-fold risk of lung cancer developing in carriers. Lung cancer is seen in some families with Li–Fraumeni syndrome. This is an inherited cancer-prone condition, due to mutation of the *p53* tumour-suppressor gene. Both the *RB* and the *p53* gene are mutated or inactivated in most small-cell and non-small-cell lung cancers.

Occupation

This is a complex subject since employees may be exposed to more than one potentially carcinogenic substance. The proportion of lung cancer attributable to a given occupational exposure has been estimated at 10–15%. Tobacco smoke acts as a strong confounder in the association.

A prime example of industrially induced cancer is asbestos. Cigarette smoke and asbestos have a multiplicative effect in increasing the incidence of lung cancer.

Metals and Gases

Arsenic and its compounds, chromates, nickel, beryllium and cadmium are associated with an excess of lung cancer deaths.

Hydrocarbons, derived from coal or petroleum and polycyclic aromatic hydrocarbons, such as dibenzanthracene and benzo[*a*]pyrene, are known carcinogens. Exposure to hydrocarbons with increased lung cancer risk is seen in coke oven workers, gas-house workers and aluminum workers, exposed to pitch volatiles (tar). Car and bus exhausts also contain hydrocarbons and truck and bus drivers have an increased risk of lung carcinoma.

Radiation

The increased risk of lung cancer in radiation was first shown in Schneeberg due to radon gas in the mines. Radon is a decay product of naturally occurring uranium. An increased risk of lung cancer is seen in uranium miners in Colorado and fluorspar miners in Newfoundland.

Pulmonary Fibrosis

An increased incidence of lung cancer complicates interstitial pulmonary fibrosis or other significant causes of pulmonary fibrosis and COPD. However, the earlier concept of pulmonary scar cancer is no longer regarded as valid since it has been shown that the fibrosis is a reaction to the tumour and not the cause. The increase in type III collagen in lung cancer is a host response (Madri and Carter, 1984).

Viruses and Cancer

The role of Herpes virus in the causation of papillomatosis has already been mentioned. Human immunodeficiency virus (HIV) infection is only seen as a cause of lung cancer in young individuals with a history of heavy tobacco smoking as well as a moderately advanced immunodeficiency status (Tirelli *et al.*, 2000). These patients were considerably younger than most patients with carcinoma at this location. Lymphoepithelioma-like carcinoma of lung is EBV-related in Asian patients, but not usually in Caucasians. This tumour is not usually related to cigarette smoking.

Chromosomal Changes in Lung Cancer

SCLC shows deletions on the short arm of chromosome 3, but this loss has also been observed in non-small-cell lung cancer.

Oncogenes regulate normal growth and development, but when activated promote tumour formation. Dominant oncogene mutations are seen in the *myc* family in SCLC and in the *ras* family in NSCLC (non-small-cell lung cancer). The *myc* family encode nuclear phosphoproteins, which bind to DNA and probably have transcriptional regulatory functions. Amplification of c-, N- and L-*myc* has been detected in SCLC.

The *ras* family of proto-oncogenes consists of H-*ras*, K-*ras* and N-*ras*. These encode related 21-kDa membrane-associated proteins, which probably have a role in transduction of growth signals. *Ras* gene mutations are found in 20–40% of NSCLC, especially adenocarcinomas. They are not seen in SCLC. K-*ras* mutations in NSCLC tumours is associated with shortened survival. K-*ras* mutations correlate with smoking in lung adenocarcinoma. This suggests that exposure to the carcinogens in tobacco smoke activate K-*ras* mutations.

The *C-ErbB-2* proto-oncogene encodes a transmembrane tyrosine-specific protein kinase, p185 neu, which acts as a putative growth factor receptor. Overexpression of p185 neu is common in NSCLC and adenocarcinoma and is associated with shortened survival.

p53 and the retinoblastoma (*RB*) gene are tumour suppressor genes. *RB* gene is always mutated in SCLC but in only 20% of NSCLC. p53 acts as a suppressor of cell division. p53 mutations are seen in 75% of SCLC and 50% of NSCLC. The commonest mutation is a guanine to thymine transversion.

Premalignant Lesions

Three types of the preinvasive epithelial lesions are documented in the new WHO classification. These are

1. squamous dysplasia and carcinoma *in situ*;
2. atypical adenomatous hyperplasia (AAH);
3. diffuse idiopathic pulmonary neuroendocrine hyperplasia (DIPNECH).

Preinvasive Squamous Lesions of the Bronchi

There is a great impetus in the United States and Japan, and beginning in Europe, to detect early bronchial carcinomas, so they may be resected early, hopefully producing a cure. LIFE (laser imaging fluorescence endoscopy) uses the different characteristics of malignant and premalignant tissues to enhance the bronchoscopist's ability to detect small neoplastic bronchial lesions. In high-risk groups, such as smokers, it is six times more sensitive than white light bronchoscopy in detecting preneoplasia (Lam *et al.*, 1998). One study spawned from this technique showed deletions of 8p21–23 commenced early during the multistage development of lung cancer, at the hyperplasia/metaplasia stage in smokers without cancer. Allelic deletions persisted for up to 48 years after smoking cessation (Witsuba *et al.*, 1999).

Auerbach *et al.* (1957) demonstrated a range of changes in smokers and patients with carcinoma of the lung, explaining the above molecular studies. These changes ranged from loss of normal ciliated lining cells with basal cell hyperplasia, low columnar nonciliated epithelium or squamous metaplasia and increasing degrees of dysplasia (**Figure 16; see colour plate section**) through to carcinoma *in situ* and invasive carcinoma. They meticulously blocked out entire bronchial trees and showed all these changes co-existed in any one cancerous lung.

Basal (reserve cell) hyperplasia, immature squamous hyperplasia and squamous metaplasia may be misdiagnosed as dysplasia by the unwary. As with any other dysplastic lesion elsewhere in the body, the diagnosis of preneoplasia should be made with great caution in the presence of active chronic inflammation, as well as adult respiratory distress syndrome (ARDS) (Hasleton and Roberts, 1999). Previous radiotherapy and/or chemotherapy may cause misdiagnosis. These two latter treatment modalities should be suspected if there are large, bizarre nuclei and plentiful cytoplasm.

Atypical Adenomatous Hyperplasia (AAH)

AAH is defined by the WHO as a focal lesion, often 5 mm or less in diameter, in which the involved alveoli and respiratory bronchioles are lined by monotonous, slightly atypical cuboidal to low columnar epithelial cells with dense nuclear chromatin, inconspicuous nucleoli and scant cytoplasm (**Figure 17; see colour plate section**). The size of the lesion, which is arbitrary, distinguishes it from bronchioloalveolar carcinoma (BAC). Other features delineating AAH from BAC are given below in the differential diagnosis.

Geographical Differences in Incidence of AAH and BAC

There appears to be a geographical difference in the incidence of AAH and BAC between Japan and the UK. Many papers relating to these two lesions originate from the East,

suggesting there are biological variations in the incidence of lung cancer between different continents. However, AAH has been described in the UK (Kerr *et al.*, 1994). There appears to be an increase in adenocarcinomas, both in the East and the USA (Travis *et al.*, 1995). This is not mirrored in the UK, where squamous cell carcinoma remains the predominant cell type in lung cancer.

Clinical and Pathological Considerations

AAH is asymptomatic and is an incidental pathological finding at lobectomy or pneumonectomy (Miller, 1990). It is found incidentally in up to 10% of surgically resected lungs for carcinoma (Kitamura *et al.*, 1996). AAH may co-exist with squamous carcinoma of the lung and metastatic colonic and renal cell carcinomas, but is seen most commonly with primary pulmonary adenocarcinoma.

The lesions are minute (smaller than 5 mm) white lesions, where the airways may still be identified, after magnification. Histologically there is a uniform proliferation of atypical cuboidal or low columnar epithelial cells with no mitoses growing along the alveolar septa. There are no admixed ciliated or mucus-secreting cells. There is variation in the cell density, with larger nuclei having increased variation in size, shape and nuclear hyperchromatism. Eosinophilic intranuclear inclusions may be seen. These are not specific for neoplastic cells, being present in reactive alveolar epithelium at times. The cells are ultrastructurally Type II pneumocytes or Clara cells. The alveolar septa may be thickened and infiltrated by lymphocytes.

Immunohistochemistry

Urine protein 1, which is identical with Clara specific 10-kDa protein, may be expressed in 70% of overt BAC but not in AAH lesions (Kitamura *et al.*, 1999). Ki-67, a marker of cell proliferation, has demonstrated AAH has a proliferative activity intermediate between normal cells and adenocarcinoma (Kitaguchi *et al.*, 1998). A useful marker may be cyclin D1. The frequency of lesions with this cell cycle control protein showing overexpression is high in AAH cycle (47–89%) but decreased in 'early' adenocarcinoma (28%) and overt adenocarcinoma (35%) (Kurasono *et al.*, 1998).

Molecular Studies

Both 3p and 9p deletions may be found in certain populations of AAH cells. In another study, 3p, 9p and 17p showed loss of heterozygosity (LOH) in 18, 13 and 66% of AAH cases, respectively. The corresponding carcinomatous lesions showed LOH in 67, 50 and 17%, respectively. This suggests that AAH lesions with moderate or severe atypia are a preneoplastic stage of lung adenocarcinoma.

There is allelic loss of tumour suppressor gene loci in the tuberous sclerosis complex-1 (TSC-1)-associated regions on the long arm of chromosome 9 (9q) and on the short arm of chromosome 16 (16p) in human lung carcinoma; 24% of adenocarcinomas show LOH on 9q and partial LOH on 9q.

The incidence of associated AAH is significantly higher in adenocarcinomas harbouring a partial LOH in the TSC-1-associated regions. These results suggest that TSC-1-associated regions are new candidate loci for tumour-suppressor genes in lung adenocarcinoma, especially when accompanied by multiple AAH lesions (Suzuki *et al.*, 1998).

Differential Diagnosis

In a small biopsy AAH or BAC may be part of an invasive adenocarcinoma or an intrapulmonary metastasis. The distinction of AAH from BAC has been considered above. AAH and multiple synchronous lung cancers may be part of the Li–Fraumeni syndrome, due to a constitutional mutation of the *p53* gene (Nadav *et al.*, 1998).

Alveolar or papillary adenomas may be misdiagnosed as AAH on small biopsy specimens. These two entities are solitary tumours.

Honeycomb lung (end-stage interstitial fibrosis) may show bronchiolar epithelial proliferation but the distribution of the epithelium is irregular. The epithelium does not grow along slightly thickened uniform alveoli with an intact architecture, as in BAC, but is part of an extensive fibroblastic process.

Organizing pneumonia is associated with Type II cell hyperplasia but there is intra-alveolar fibrosis.

Atypical type II proliferations suggest radiotherapy or chemotherapy-induced change, as with Busulphan or adult respiratory distress syndrome. In cytology specimens ARDS shows bizarre type II or bronchiolar cells. Typically the sheets or balls of cells in BAC are composed of monotonous cells, uniform in size and shape. They have round to oval nuclei and a finely granular chromatin. In ARDS there is group to group variability of cells, often with marked variation in the nuclear/cytoplasmic ratio.

Alveolar hyperplasia can be seen in lymphangioleiomyomatosis (Lantuejoul *et al.*, 1997).

Prognosis

There was no difference in the age, follow-up interval or survival rate in one study of 13 patients with no detectable nodules preoperatively compared with cases showing nodules on CT scan.

Some cases of BAC have a good prognosis (Logan *et al.*, 1996). The 5-year survival rate in stage 1 disease was 72.9% and stage 2 60.6%, falling to 27.1% in stage 3a and 0% in stages 3b and 4. The 5-year survival rate was higher (64.6%) in AAH associated with well-differentiated adenocarcinoma, as opposed to the presence of this lesion in adenocarcinoma with pulmonary metastases.

Tumourlets

Tumourlets are micronodular, neuroendocrine cell proliferations extending beyond the bronchial/bronchiolar walls, forming aggregates with organoid and nested patterns and measuring less than 0.5 cm in diameter. This measurement, like that of AAH, is purely arbitrary. Any lesion larger than 0.5 cm is diagnosed as a pulmonary carcinoid. Tumourlets are often associated with fibrosis in the walls of bronchiectatic cavities but are uncommon in interstitial pulmonary fibrosis, for some unknown reason. A possible explanation is the prominent inflammation seen in bronchiectasis, whereas in interstitial pulmonary fibrosis inflammation is an early event and is usually less prominent than the fibrosis at the time of biopsy. The differential diagnosis is considered under DIPNECH below but the unwary on a biopsy may suggest small cell lung carcinoma. It does not have the mitotic activity or the lack of cytoplasm of this tumour.

Diffuse Idiopathic Neuroendocrine Hyperplasia (DIPNECH)

DIPNECH is a proliferation of neuroendocrine cells limited to the bronchiolar epithelium (**Figure 18; see colour plate section**). There are increased numbers of scattered single cells, small nodules (neuroendocrine bodies) or linear proliferations of neuroendocrine cells within the bronchiolar epithelium. It is typically associated with obliterative bronchiolar fibrosis and co-existing interstitial or airway fibrosis or inflammation should be absent. This is because, especially with inflammation, there is a proliferation of NE cells.

DIPNECH is a rare condition and may be part of a diffuse neuroendocrine proliferation or identified adjacent to a peripheral carcinoid (Miller and Muller, 1995). DIPNECH may present as an interstitial disease (Armas *et al.*, 1995). Rare cases may show the full gamut with DIPNECH, tumourlets and peripheral typical carcinoid tumours (Miller *et al.*, 1978).

Differential Diagnosis

Minute meningiothelioid nodules are perivenular, interstitial aggregates of small regular cells with no airway contact. The cells often have a lobular, whorled arrangement, reminiscent of chemodectomas. Meningiothelioid nodules co-express vimentin and epithelial membrane antigen (EMA). DIPNECH is positive with neuroendocrine markers, such as NCAM (neural cell adhesion molecule), chromogranin and synaptophysin.

Carcinoma of Lung

All lung carcinomas show histological heterogeneity. If one accepts that there is a common stem cell, consequently there are mixtures of squamous and adeno or small cell carcinoma. However, major heterogeneity is found in only 5% of cases. The heterogeneity explains why after chemotherapy for SCLC a squamous or adenocarcinoma may develop at the site of the original tumour.

Synchronous tumours arise at the same time as a primary, while a metachronous one consists of a second tumour occurring after resection of the initial neoplasm. The incidence of synchronous and metachronous tumours is difficult to elucidate from the literature but approximately 1% of common lung neoplasms are multiple.

Classification of Lung Tumours

The WHO has now produced a new lung and pleural tumour classification (1999). The main tumour variants are given in **Table 1**.

Clinical Presentation Due to Local Disease

Central tumours cause obstructive symptoms, including cough, haemoptysis, wheezing and stridor, similar features to benign neoplasms. The haemoptysis is caused by bronchial ulceration but in a few cases there may be infiltration into a large pulmonary artery, causing life-threatening

Table 1 Classification of lung tumours

Epithelial tumours
  Benign
    Papilloma
    Adenoma
  – alveolar and papillary
      – salivary gland type
      – mucous gland
      – pleomorphic
      – mucinous
  Preinvasive lesions
    Squamous
    Atypical adenomatous hyperplasia
    Diffuse idiopathic pulmonary
      neuroendocrine cell hyperplasia
  Malignant
    Squamous cell carcinoma (and variants, including
      basaloid))
    Small-cell carcinoma (and variants)
    Adenocarcinoma (and variants)
    Large-cell carcinoma (and variants, including
      large-cell neuroendocrine carcinoma and
      lymphoepithelial carcinoma)
    Adenosquamous carcinoma
    Carcinomas with pleomorphic, sarcomatoid or
      sarcomatous elements (including carcinosarcoma and
      pulmonary blastoma)
    Carcinoid tumour – typical
              – atypical
    Carcinomas of salivary gland type
      (including mucoepidermoid and
      adenoid cystic carcinomas)
    Unclassified
    Soft tissue tumours
Mesothelial tumours
Miscellaneous tumours (including hamartoma and
    sclerosing haemangioma)
Lymphoproliferative disorders
Secondary tumours

haemorrhage. In addition, there may be bone pain, dyspnea, clubbing and dysphagia. More than 90% of patients with lung cancer are symptomatic at presentation, reflecting advanced disease. This is especially the case with SCLC, which is assumed to be a systemic disease at presentation by most oncologists. However, some patients have stage I disease and in some centres have been offered surgery and chemotherapy, although the role of surgery has yet to be established in patients with more extensive nodal disease (Lucchi *et al.*, 1997). Patients with general systemic symptoms or metastases in both small cell and non-small-cell lung cancer have a poor prognosis.

Pancoast tumours (superior sulcus tumours) are localized, arising posteriorly at the apex of the upper lobe near the brachial plexus. They infiltrate C8, T1 and T2 nerve roots, causing pain, temperature changes and muscle atrophy in the shoulder and arm innervated by these nerve roots. Horner's syndrome is caused by involvement of the sympathetic chain and stellate ganglion, giving unilateral enophthalmos, ptosis and miosis. Superior vena caval obstruction presents as oedema and plethora of the face, as well as dilated neck and upper torso veins. Hoarseness is due to recurrent laryngeal nerve entrapment, seen more frequently in left upper lobe tumours, as the left recurrent laryngeal nerve loops around the aortic arch. Tumour can involve the phrenic nerve, paralysing a hemi-diaphragm. The oesophagus may be infiltrated causing dysphagia and, if the pleura is involved, an effusion occurs.

Metastases are common in SCLC, with 20% of cases metastatic at presentation. Squamous cell carcinoma tends to remain intrathoracic whereas adeno- and large-cell carcinoma show metastases to regional nodes, liver, gut, adrenals, central nervous system and bone.

Paraneoplastic Syndromes
This term identifies symptoms and signs secondary to cancer, occurring at a site distant from the tumour or its metastases. They are caused by the production of products, such as polypeptide hormones, hormone-like peptides, antibodies, immune complexes, etc., by the tumour. Non-metastatic hypercalcaemia is commonest in squamous cell carcinoma. The squamous carcinoma cells secrete a parathormone-related protein (PTH-rP), which shows a limited sequence homology with parathyroid hormone. Cushing's syndrome, the commonest, is due to ectopic ACTH production, usually seen in SCLC. The syndrome of inappropriate antidiuretic hormone secretion (SIDDH) is seen mainly with SCLC. In half the cases there is ectopic vasopressin secretion from the tumour. In the remainder there is abnormal release of this peptide from the posterior pituitary because of altered or defective chemoreceptor control. Gynaecomastia develops because of increased levels of β-hCG (human chorionic gonadotrophin) produced by the tumour. This hormone is most commonly seen in germ cell tumours of the mediastinum and gonads and very rarely as a primary pulmonary tumour.

Neurological Syndromes

These are most often associated with an autoimmune reaction, in which the tumour shares antigens with normal nervous tissue. In recent years, antibodies reactive with nuclear and cytoplasmic antigens and neurons throughout the CNS and peripheral ganglia have been identified in patients with these syndromes. The Lambert–Eaton myasthenic syndrome is uncommon and is associated with SCLC. There is muscle weakness and fatigue and it is most pronounced in the pelvic girdle and thighs. There may be dysarthria, dysphagia and blurred vision. Hypertrophic osteoarthropathy is characterized by finger clubbing, periosteal bone formation (see below) and arthritis. Other neurological syndromes include autonomic neuropathy and subacute sensory peripheral neuropathy.

The enlargement of the distal phalanx of the digits due to an increase in the connective tissue in the nail bed is termed clubbing and is almost always a feature of hypertrophic osteoarthropathy. It is seen especially in squamous and adenocarcinomas but has also been documented in other diseases, including congenital cyanotic heart disease and cystic fibrosis. It may be neurogenic (vagally mediated), hormonal owing to a high oestrogen or growth hormone or vascular owing to arterio-venous shunts.

For treatment purposes lung carcinomas are divided into SCLC and NSCLC, the former only rarely having surgery. The commonest non-small-cell carcinomas are squamous, adeno- and large cell.

Squamous Cell Carcinoma

These are often central, in main or segmental bronchi, or peripheral. They may show an endobronchial growth pattern or infiltrate between the cartilaginous rings initially, in time destroying them to invade surrounding tissue. The tumour is solid, grey/white but may show cavitation (**Figure 19; see colour plate section**). Such cavity formation may cause clinical misdiagnosis as apical cavitating tuberculosis. Very rarely both diseases may co-exist. There is often related bronchiectasis and obstructive pneumonitis, due to bronchial obstruction. The pneumonitis causes both radiological and macroscopic problems in definition of the true extent of the tumour. This problem may be accentuated if there is a prominent inflammatory component to the tumour.

Adjacent to the tumour there may be carcinoma *in situ* as well as chronic bronchitic changes. In addition, there is squamous metaplasia and reserve cell hyperplasia. The tumour shows varying degrees of squamous differentiation, lying in a fibrous stroma with a varying amount of acute and chronic inflammation. Foci of recent and old haemorrhage are seen. Well-differentiated tumours show keratin pearls and keratinization (**Figure 20; see colour plate section**). Intercellular bridges should be sought and paradoxically can be best identified with a mucin stain. Rarely mucin can be seen in the malignant cells but more than 10% of the tumour should show a distinctive

glandular component before an adenosquamous carcinoma is diagnosed. Tumour giant cells imply a poor prognosis. Clear cell change, due to glycogen accumulation, is also a feature of some tumours but has no prognostic connotation. The nuclei are hyperchromatic and may show prominent nucleoli. The tumour may encircle the bronchus and a fibre-optic biopsy may only reveal fibrosis.

Squamous cell carcinomas manifest earlier than other types of pulmonary malignancy because of obstructive symptoms. They may involve lymph nodes by direct spread. There may be lymphatic and vascular invasion, but the prognostic significance of vascular invasion in non-small-cell carcinoma is uncertain. Some studies suggest that vascular invasion indicates a poor prognosis, others show it has no effect on survival, since the tumour-associated desmoplasia causes occlusive intimal fibrosis in thin walled pulmonary arteries and veins.

A small subgroup of squamous carcinomas is termed basaloid carcinoma. This tumour grows exophytically in proximal bronchi. Mediastinal pleura or adipose tissue are often invaded. There is a solid lobular or anastamotic trabecular pattern with small, moderately pleomorphic, cuboidal or fusiform cells. There is peripheral pallisading and a high mitotic rate. Other subtypes of squamous carcinomas are clear cell, not to be confused with adenocarcinoma, papillary, pleomorphic and spindle cell and small cell variant of squamous.

Differential Diagnosis

Conditions to be considered in the differential diagnosis are florid squamous metaplasia in the bronchus or states associated with an inflammatory process, dysplasia, which if high grade can be very difficult to distinguish on a small biopsy, any benign lung tumour with squamous metaplasia on the surface, especially granular cell myoblastoma, benign squamous cell papilloma, tumours with a squamous component, such as carcinosarcoma, spindle cell sarcomas, metastatic tumours with a squamous appearance, including sarcomas, which can be primary or secondary, and mesothelioma. Special stains, including mucins and cytokeratins, are often helpful in determining the cell of origin and in some cases the site.

It may be difficult with poorly differentiated tumours to differentiate squamous from adenocarcinoma. In such cases if mucin stains are diffusely negative the term 'non-small cell carcinoma' is used. This enables medical oncologists to give appropriate treatment, as they need to distinguish this tumour from small-cell lung carcinoma.

Treatment and Prognosis

Treatment depends on the stage of the disease. Cases with stage IIIA disease or less are treated by surgery though the role of surgery has yet to be established in N2 and N3 disease. Other options for more advanced disease are radiotherapy, either direct beam or intraluminal, brachytherapy and chemotherapy.

Prognosis depends on the stage. Five-year survival rates are stage I, 50%, stage II, 30% and stage IIIA, approximately 10% (Mountain, 1988).

Adenocarcinoma

It is often impossible to distinguish a bronchial primary from secondary pulmonary tumour. If an adenocarcinoma is thought to be secondary, a primary should be sought in the stomach, colon, pancreas, breast, ovary, prostate or kidney. Special stains, such as cytokeratins 7 and 20, TTF-1 (thyroid transcription factor 1, but commonly expressed in lung cancer), PSA (prostate-specific antigen), ER (oestrogen receptor) and PR (progesterone receptor) may help in identifying the site of the primary tumour.

Adenocarcinomas are usually peripheral, well-circumscribed masses (**Figure 21; see colour plate section**). If the pleura is involved there is fibrosis and puckering. These tumours may be central, arising from bronchial mucous glands. The peripheral tumours usually occur in females while the bronchial gland type tends to have a male predominance. There is no significant survival difference between the two variants. Adenocarcinomas vary in size and may occupy an entire lobe. They sometimes contain carbon pigment and may show marked scarring. The term 'scar carcinoma' is no longer used, since the stroma is a desmoplastic response to tumour rather than arising in a pulmonary scar (pulmonary fibrosis). Adenocarcinomas may be single or multiple and this may create confusion with metastases. Pleural seeding is common and may mimic a mesothelioma.

Histologically there are different growth patterns with tubular, papillary, acinar, signet ring and solid variants (**Figure 22; see colour plate section**). It is common to have a mixture of the above patterns in any one tumour. The cells are large, polygonal and tend to be discohesive with a high nuclear/cytoplasmic ratio. Some cases have mucin vacuoles. However, 30% of adenocarcinomas show no mucin on special stains. Spindle cell and giant cell foci may be identified. The tumour spreads aerogenously and may show a peripheral bronchioloalveolar pattern. This should not be diagnosed as bronchioloalveolar carcinoma. It rapidly invades lymphatics, blood vessels and the pleura and spreads to distal sites.

Differential Diagnosis

This includes any secondary adenocarcinoma, as detailed above, adenosquamous carcinoma, muoepidermoid tumour of the bronchus, germ cell tumours, carcinoid tumours with glandular foci, pulmonary blastoma and in the case of a pleural biopsy, mesothelioma. The stains mentioned above will help to differentiate *some* primary pulmonary tumours from secondary ones.

Trainee pathologists may misdiagnose benign lesions, such as radio or chemotherapy-induced change, type II cell hyperplasia associated with interstitial pulmonary fibrosis and resolving ARDS, alveolar adenoma, sclerosing haemangioma and atypical adenomatous hyperplasia.

Treatment and Prognosis

Surgery is the most appropriate treatment option. Survival is related to stage, stage I has a 50% 5-year survival rate, stage II approximately 25%, and stages IIIA and B, less than 10% (Mountain, 1988). These figures are pre-CT scans and the Japanese literature suggests they are detecting earlier tumours with this modality.

Bronchioloalveolar Carcinoma (BAC) (Alveolar Carcinoma)

This is a subtype of adenocarcinoma. It is the commonest tumour in North American women. There are greyish/white nodules with a central scar in some cases. If close to the pleura there is puckering and fibrosis, as in adenocarcinoma, but the tumour does not usually infiltrate this layer. Mucinous tumours have a glistening appearance. The tumour may involve an entire lobe (**Figure 23; see colour plate section**) or lung, often giving bronchorrhoea.

There are two main subtypes, mucinous and nonmucinous. Nonmucinous consist of Clara or type II cells and mucinous have goblet or mucin-producing cells. Both grow along intact alveolar walls as a single layer or occasionally forming papillae. If stromal invasion is identified, the tumour is classified as adenocarcinoma. In nonmucinous BAC, the cells are cuboidal with an eosinophilic, ciliated cytoplasm and prominent nuclei. In mucinous BAC there are tall columnar, mucinous cells that are well differentiated and lack cilia. The nuclei are uniform and show varying degrees of hyperchromasia. The cells produce much mucin. Discrete satellite nodules are seen in either type.

The differential diagnosis is similar to adenocarcinoma as detailed above. It is impossible on a small biopsy to differentiate invasive adenocarcinoma from BAC or AAH.

Treatment and Prognosis

The optimum treatment is resection and the 5-year survival rate is 42.1%, with a higher survival rate for stage I disease.

Small-cell Lung Carcinoma (SCLC)

This tumour grows rapidly and may occasionally present as metastases without any visible primary tumour. A primary tumour in the upper respiratory tract, oesophagus or cervix may metastasize to the lung. This tumour is responsive to chemotherapy. It presents as hilar masses with extension into lymph nodes (**Figure 24; see colour plate section**). The tumour is soft, white and shows extensive necrosis. In advanced cases the bronchial lumen is obstructed by extrinsic compression. There are two main histological variants.

The first is 'classical' small cell carcinoma (**Figure 25; see colour plate section**) and the second a combined small cell carcinoma. In classical SCLC there are sheets of small, hyperchromatic nuclei with nuclear moulding and little cytoplasm. There is a high mitotic rate. Because of the high cell turnover and necrosis, DNA leaches out and is taken up by blood vessels ('Azzopardi effect'). A combined SCLC has the above pattern and adeno-, large-cell or squamous carcinomatous components.

This tumour stains positively with NCAM (neural cell adhesion molecule), synaptophysin and chromogranin. Lymphovascular invasion occurs early and distant metastases are common. These are seen in bone marrow, liver, kidney, adrenals, cerebrum, cerebellum, meninges, regional and cervical lymph nodes. After chemotherapy, recurrent tumour may be predominantly squamous or adenocarcinoma.

Differential Diagnosis

Benign lesions may be confused with SCLC, especially if there is crush artifact. In the presence of this, a diagnosis of SCLC should never be made, since any chronic inflammatory condition, such as tuberculosis, may have crush artifact. Tumours that may be confused with SCLC are tumourlets, other neuroendocrine tumours, on a small biopsy, squamous, large-cell and adenocarcinomas, which may have an SCLC component, metastatic carcinomas and lymphomas.

Treatment and Prognosis

This is neoplasm is usually treated with chemotherapy, since cases with stage I disease are rare. There is an approximately 10% 5-year survival after treatment.

Large-cell Carcinoma

Large-cell carcinomas are large necrotic masses, which frequently invade the overlying pleura and grow into adjacent structures. This is a diagnosis of exclusion since no acinar or squamous differentation or mucin production are seen. Large-cell carcinomas have sheets and nests of large cells with prominent vesicular nuclei and nucleoli (**Figure 26; see colour plate section**). The cell borders are easily visualized. Necrosis and haemorrhage are frequent and there may be acute and/or chronic inflammation.

There are several variants. These include clear cell carcinoma, composed entirely of clear cells, basaloid carcinoma and lymphoepithelioma (lymphoepithelial-like carcinoma). Lymphoepithelial-like carcinoma has a marked lymphoplasmacytic infiltrate admidst large cell carcinoma. Epstein–Barr virus genome may be identified in this tumour. It is commoner in the Far East.

The differential diagnosis is similar to pleomorphic carcinoma, described below. It includes all the carcinomas, primary or secondary, described above, as well as large cell neuroendocrine carcinoma, primary or metastatic sarcoma, anaplastic large cell lymphoma and melanoma.

The prognosis is grim, with an approximately 1% 5-year survival.

Adenosquamous Carcinoma

These are usually peripheral tumours. There must be definite squamous and adenocarcinomatous components, one of which must comprise more than 10% of the tumour.

Pleomorphic Carcinoma of Lung

This entity was first described by Fishback *et al.* (1994), who studied 78 cases of this entity, with a male to female ratio of 2.7 : 1. About 80% of the patients had thoracic pain, cough and haemoptysis but 18% were asymptomatic. Foci of squamous cell carcinoma were present in 8%, large cell in 25% and adenocarcinoma in 45%. The remaining 22% of tumours were completely spindle and/or giant-cell carcinomas. Spindle and giant-cell carcinomas were found together in 38% of patients. Nodal metastases were the most significant single prognostic factor. Only 1% of cases had SCLC foci; such cases are classified as combined small-cell carcinoma.

The malignant spindle cell component consists of fusiform cells with eosinophilic cytoplasm (**Figure 27; see colour plate section**). The spindle cells vary from an epithelioid appearance to a slender banal morphology. The chromatin is frequently vesicular or coarse and hyperchromatic. Giant-cell carcinoma, with multiple tumour giant cells, covered by neutrophil polymorphs (emperopolesis), is a variant of pleomorphic carcinoma. However, tumour giant cells are an integral component of pleomorphic carcinoma. There is a mild to moderate inflammatory component, predominantly lymphocytes. As in mesothelioma, separation of spindle cell carcinoma from a desmoplastic stroma is often difficult.

Molecular techniques have shown that K-*ras*-2 showed mutations in fewer pleomorphic carcinomas than adenocarcinomas. Pleomorphic carcinomas also showed fewer *p53* point mutations than adenocarcinoma or squamous carcinoma. The *p53* point mutations in pleomorphic carcinoma were commoner exon 7 than those of squamous and adenocarcinoma, which were exon 8 (Pryzygodzki *et al.*, 1996).

The differential diagnosis is largely described above under Large-cell Carcinoma. In addition, any spindle cell lesion has to be considered. The WHO recommends epithelial markers, such as keratin or epithelial membrane antigen, as useful in confirmation of the carcinomatous differentiation in the spindle cell component. However, if these markers are negative the tumours are classified as pleomorphic carcinomas, assuming the neoplasm does not have the immunoprofile of one of the tumours noted in the differential diagnosis, especially a soft tissue sarcoma. Heterologous elements are necessary for the diagnosis of carcinosarcoma.

Keratin may be positive in synovial sarcoma, meso-thelioma, epithelioid haemangioendothelioma, rarely in leiomyosarcoma, anaplastic large cell lymphomas and occasionally in malignant peripheral nerve sheath tumours. Therefore, reliance on a single cytokeratin will cause problems. In such problematic pulmonary tumours a battery of immunostains may be useful.

Pulmonary Lymphomas

Pulmonary lymphoid proliferations may occur in rheu-matoid disease and in Sjogren's syndrome. Lymphomas in the lung are classified as lymphoid interstitial pneu-monia, non-Hodgkin lymphomas, primary pulmonary Hodgkin disease, plasma cell neoplasms and leukaemic infiltration.

Lymphoid interstitial pneumonia (LIP) consists of a diffuse infiltrate with small lymphocytes and plasma cells affecting large areas of the lung. There may be reactive lymphoid follicles and it may be associated with auto-immune disease and poly- or monoclonal gammopathy. Cases with monoclonal light-chain restriction probably represent 'MALT' lymphomas. Some cases have polytypic light-chain expression and have been classed as non-neoplastic.

Primary Pulmonary Non-Hodgkin Lymphoma

These are similar to non-Hodgkin lymphomas elsewhere, most being B cell in origin. Patients are middle-aged with respiratory and systemic symptoms. There may be lobar consolidation as well as skin, renal and central nervous system involvement. About 50% of patients are asympto-matic, the rest having a variety of respiratory and con-stitutional symptoms. In the T cell lymphomas there is often a vasculitic (**Figure 28; see colour plate section**) and granulomatous pattern, with necrosis.

Sarcomas

Primary pulmonary sarcomas are rare. Epithelioid hae-mangioendothelioma is a low-grade vascular sarcoma, occurring more commonly in young women. There is chest pain, dyspnea, mild cough and multiple bilateral nodules. It can also affect liver, bones and soft tissues. The tumour may resemble a mesothelioma. Kaposi sarcoma may be seen in HIV-positive patients and is described elsewhere.

Carcinosarcomas have a mixture of sarcomatous and carcinomatous elements.

Secondary Tumours

The lung is frequently the site of secondary adeno-carcinomas and sarcomas, especially osteogenic and chondrosarcoma. Because of advances in chemotherapy it may be beneficial to treat these patients with localized resection. In the case of secondary adenocarcinomas,

as mentioned above, TTF-1 and cytokeratins can be useful in determining whether a tumour is primary or secondary.

REFERENCES

Aozasa, K., *et al.* (1995). Polymorphic reticulosis is a neoplasm of large granular lymphocytes with CD3 plus phenotype. *Cancer*, **75**, 894–901.

Armas, O. A., *et al.* (1995). Diffuse idiopathic pulmonary neuroendocrine cell proliferation presenting as interstitial lung disease. *American Journal of Surgical Pathology*, **19**, 963–970.

Auerbach, O., *et al.* (1957). Changes in the bronchial epithelium in relation to smoking and cancer of the lung. *New England Journal of Medicine*, **256**, 97–104.

Batsakis, J. G., *et al.* (1963). Adenocarcinoma of the nasal and paranasal cavity. *Archives of Otolaryngology*, **77**, 625–633.

Bellacosa, A., *et al.* (1996). Cyclin D1 gene amplification in human laryngeal squamous cell carcinomas; prognostic sig-nificance and clinical implications. *Clinical Cancer Research*, **2**, 175–180.

Bradford, C. R., *et al.* (1997). P53 mutation as a prognostic marker in advanced laryngeal carcinoma. Department of Veterans Affairs Laryngeal Cancer Cooperative Study Group. *Archives of Otolaryngology and Head Neck Surgery*, **123**, 605–609.

Brambilla, C. and Brambilla, E. (1999). *Lung Tumors; Funda-mental Biology and Clinical Management* (Marcel Dekker, New York).

Cecchi, F., *et al.* (1980). Adenocarcinoma of the nose and para-nasal sinuses in shoemakers and woodworkers in the province of Florence, Italy (1963–77). *British Journal of Industrial Medicine*, **37**, 222–225.

Digby, K. H., *et al.* (1941). Nasopharyngeal malignancy. *British Journal of Surgery*, **28**, 517–537.

Dokiya, F., *et al.* (1998). Retinoblastoma protein expression and prognosis in laryngeal cancer. *Acta Otolaryngolica*, **118**, 759–762.

Dosaka-Akita, H., *et al.* (2000). Differential retinoblastoma and p16 (INK 4A) protein expression in neuroendocrine tumors of the lung. *Cancer*, **88**, 550–556.

Fishback, N. F., *et al.* (1994). Pleomorphic (spindle/giant cell) carcinoma of lung: A clinicopathologic correlation of 78 cases. *Cancer*, **73**, 2936–2945.

Furuta, Y., *et al.* (1992). Detection of human papilloma virus DNA in carcinomas of the nasal cavities and paranasal sinuses by polymerase chain reaction. *Cancer*, **69**, 353–357.

Gown, A. M., *et al.* (1993). Androgen receptor expression in angiofibromas of the nasopharynx (abstract). *Modern Pathology*, **6**, 81a.

Hasleton, P. S. (1996). *Spencer's Pathology of the Lung*, 5th edn. 896–897 (McGraw-Hill, New York).

Hasleton, P. S and Roberts, T. E. (1999). Adult respiratory distress syndrome: an update. *Histopathology*, **34**, 285–294.

Kerr, K. M., *et al.* (1994). Atypical alveolar hyperplasia: relationship with pulmonary adenocarcinoma, p53 and *C-erb* B2 expression. *Journal of Pathology*, **174**, 249–256.

Kitaguchi, S., *et al.* (1998). Proliferative activity, p53 expression and loss of heterozygosity on 3p, 9p and 17p in atypical adenomatous hyperplasia of the lung. *Hiroshima Journal of Medical Science*, **47**, 17–25.

Kitamura, H., *et al.* (1996). Atypical adenomatous hyperplasia and bronchoalveolar lung carcinoma: analysis of morphometry and the expressions of p53 and carcinoembryonic antigen. *American Journal of Surgical Pathology*, **20**, 553–562.

Kitamura, H., *et al.* (1999). Atypical adenomatous hyperplasia of the lung. Implications for the pathogenesis of peripheral lung adenocarcinoma. *American Journal of Clinical Pathology*, **111**, 610–622.

Krecicki, T., *et al.* (1999). c-erb B-2 immunostaining in laryngeal cancer. *Acta Oto-Laryngologica*, **119**, 392–395.

Kurasono, Y., *et al.* (1998). Expression of cyclin D1, retinoblastoma gene protein and p16 MTS-1 protein in atypical adenomatous hyperplasia and adenocarcinoma of the lung: An immunohistochemical analysis. *Virchows Archiv*, **432**, 207–215.

Lantuejoul, S., *et al.* (1997). Multifocal alveolar hyperplasia associated with lymphangioleiomyomatosis in tuberous sclerosis. *Histopathology*, **30**, 570–575.

Lam, S. T., *et al.* (1998). Localisation of bronchial intraepithelial neoplastic lesions by fluorescence bronchoscopy. *Chest*, **113**, 696–702.

Lewis, J. S. and Castro, E. B. (1972). Cancer of the nasal cavity and paranasal sinuses. *Journal of Laryngology and Otology*, **86**, 255–262.

Logan, P. M., *et al.* (1998). Bronchogenic carcinoma and coexistent bronchoalveolar cell adenomas: assessment of radiological detection and follow-up in 28 patients. *Chest*, **109**, 713–717.

Lucchi, M., *et al.* (1997). Surgery in the management of small cell lung cancer. *European Journal of Cardiothoracic Surgery*, **12**, 689–693.

Madri, J. A. and Carter, D. (1984). Scar cancers of the lung: origin and significance. *Human Pathology*, **15**, 625–631.

Miller, M. A., *et al.* (1978). Multiple peripheral carcinoids and tumorlets of carcinoid type, with restrictive and obstructive lung disease. *American Journal of Medicine*, **65**, 373–378.

Miller, R. R. (1990). Bronchioloalveolar cell adenomas. *American Journal of Surgical Pathology*, **14**, 904–912.

Miller, R. R. and Muller, N. L. (1995). Neuroendocrine cell hyperplasia and obliterative bronchiolitis in patients with peripheral carcinoid tumours. *American Journal of Surgical Pathology*, **19**, 653–658.

Mills, S. E., *et al.* (2000). *Tumors of the Upper Aerodigestive Tract. Atlas of Tumor Pathology* (Armed Forces Institute of Pathology, Bethesda, MD).

Mountain, C. F. (1988). Prognostic implications of the of the International Staging System for Lung Cancer. *Seminars in Oncology*, **15**, 236–245.

Nadav, Y., *et al.* (1998). Multiple synchronous lung cancers and atypical adenomatous hyperplasia in Li Fraumeni syndrome. *Histopathology*, **33**, 52–54.

Narayana, A., *et al.* (1998). Is p53 an independent prognostic factor in patients with laryngeal carcinoma? *Cancer*, **82**, 286–291.

Pryzygodzki, R. M., *et al.* (1996). Pleomorphic (giant and spindle cell) carcinoma cell carcinoma by K-ras-2 and p53 analysis. *American Journal of Clinical Pathology*, **106**, 487–492.

Sheppard, M. N. (1997). Nuclear pleomorphism in typical carcinoid tumours of the lung: problems in frozen section interpretation. *Histopathology*, **30**, 478–480.

Simons, M. J., *et al.* (1976). Immunogenetic aspects of nasopharyngeal carcinoma in young patients. *Journal of the National Cancer Institute*, **57**, 977–980.

Suzuki, K., *et al.* (1998). Loss of heterozygosity in a tuberous sclerosis gene-associated region in adenocarcinoma of the lung accompanied by multiple atypical adenomatous hyperplasia. *International Journal of Cancer*, **79**, 384–389.

Tirelli, U., *et al.* (2000). Lung carcinoma in 36 patients with human immunodeficiency virus infection. The Italian Cooperative Group on AIDS and Tumors. *Cancer*, **88**, 563–569.

Tomita, Y., *et al.* (1996). Non-Hodgkins lymphoma of the Waldeyer's ring as the manifestation of human T-cell leukaemia virus type I-associated lymphoproliferative diseases in South West Japan (abstract). *Modern Pathology*, **9**, 12a.

Travis, W. D., *et al.* (1995). Lung cancer. *Cancer*, **75**, 191–202.

Travis, W. D., *et al.* (1999). *Histologic Typing of Lung and Pleural Tumors*, 3rd edn, (World Health Organization, Springer, Berlin).

Witsuba, I. I., *et al.* (1999). Allelic losses at chromosome 8p 21–23 are early and frequent events in the pathogenesis of lung cancer. *Cancer Research*, **59**, 1973–1979.

FURTHER READING

Brambilla, C. and Brambilla, E. (eds) (1999). *Lung Tumors: Fundamental Biology and Clinical Management* (Marcel Dekker, New York).

Churg, A. and Green, F. H. Y. (1998). *Pathology of Occupational Lung Disease*, 2nd edn. (Williams and Wilkins, Baltimore).

Colby, T. V., *et al.* (1995). *Tumors of the Lower Respiratory Tract. Atlas of Tumor Pathology* (Armed Forces Institute of Pathology, Washington, DC).

Dail, D. H. and Hammar, S. P. (1988). *Pulmonary Pathology*, 2nd edn (Springer, New York).

Gregor, R. T. (1998). *Diseases of the Head and Neck, Nose and Throat* (Arnold, London).

Hasleton, P. S. (1994). Histopathology and prognostic factors in bronchial carcinoid tumours. *Thorax*, **49**, (Suppl.), S56–S62.

Hasleton, P. S. (ed.) (1996). *Spencer's Pathology of the Lung*, 5th edn (McGraw-Hill, New York).

Parkes, W. P. (1994). *Occupational Lung Disorders*, 3rd edn. Park, W. P. (ed.) (Butterworth-Hernemann Ltd, Oxford).

Roggli, V. L., *et al.* (1992). *Pathology of Asbestos-associated Diseases* (Little Brown, Boston).

Samet, J. M. (1994). *Epidemiology of Lung Cancer* (Marcel Dekker, New York).

Websites

The websites given are those of predominantly pulmonary journals, since there is no purely pulmonary pathology journal. These pulmonary journals feature good review articles, especially the *European Respiratory Journal* and the *American Review of Critical Care and Respiratory Care Medicine*. Pathology journals also carry original pulmonary articles. The recommended ones are *Modern Pathology*, *American Journal of Pathology*, *Laboratory Investigation*, *American Journal of Clinical Pathology*, *Histopathology* and *Journal of Pathology*. The *New England Journal of Medicine* has an excellent weekly clinicopathological conference with many pulmonary topics. Most of these journals require subscriptions/passwords, etc., to obtain full text but most libraries will be able to provide access.

American Journal of Respiratory and Critical Care Medicine http://intl-ajrccm.atsjournals.org/.

Chest http://www/chestjournal.org/.

European Respiratory Journal http://195.226.52.174/ers/issue-list.html.

Thorax http://thorax.bmjjournals.com/.

Cancer http://www3/interscience.wiley.com/cgi-bin/jtoc?ID=28741.

Chapter 37

Upper Gastrointestinal Tract

Grant N. Stemmermann, Amy E. Noffsinger and Cecilia M. Fenoglio-Preiser
University of Cincinnati School of Medicine, Cincinnati, OH, USA

C O N T E N T S

- Introduction
- Normal Development and Structure
- Epidemiology
- Aetiology
- Screening and Prevention
- Pathology
- Treatment
- Molecular Genetic Findings
- Conclusion

INTRODUCTION

Worldwide, oesophageal and gastric cancers are very common tumours, accounting for 6–34% of cancer-related deaths (Aoki *et al.*, 1992). Variations in carcinogen exposures account for striking geographical differences in the frequency of both tumours. Oesophageal and gastric cancers have decreased in both incidence and mortality rates in economically prosperous populations but their incidence remains high in less prosperous countries. This chapter will summarize the current status of our knowledge of the origin, pathology, molecular biology and behaviour of upper gastrointestinal tumours. We will also describe methods used to prevent and treat these malignancies.

NORMAL DEVELOPMENT AND STRUCTURE

General Organisation

The gastrointestinal tract is divided into several major anatomical regions, each with its own unique physiological functions and structure. The various regions share a basic structure. The inside has a mucosal lining beneath which is a thin muscular layer known as the muscularis mucosae. The mucosa serves many of the digestive and absorptive functions of the gastrointestinal tract. Beneath the muscularis mucosae is the submucosa. The next layer is the muscularis propria, which is responsible for propelling gastrointestinal contents forward throughout the gut.

Oesophagus

The oesophagus develops from the cranial portion of the primitive foregut, becoming recognizable at the 2.5-mm stage of development (approximately the third gestational week) as an annular constriction located between the stomach and pharynx (Fenoglio-Preiser *et al.*, 1999). The oesophagus elongates, growing in a cephalad direction and becoming increasingly tubular. Early in development, the cephalad portions of both the oesophagus and trachea lie within a common tube. When the oesophagus and trachea divide, the oesophagus comes to lie dorsal to the trachea. The oesophageal mucosal lining progresses through a series of epithelial changes before attaining the appearance of the glycogenated, nonkeratinized, stratified squamous epithelium present in the adult.

The mucosal lining of the oesophagus consists of stratified layers of squamous cells resembling those found in the skin (**Figure 1**). These stratified cells show an orderly progression of differentiation from the bottom of the epithelium to its surface. This squamous cell lining regularly renews itself. New cells form from progenitor cells at its base just above the basement membrane. The basement membrane is a linear structure lying under the epithelium; it serves as a boundary between the epithelium and its underlying tissues. Old, nonfunctional cells are shed from the mucosal surface. Newly formed epithelial cells pass upward in the mucosa, becoming increasingly more mature as they do so. At the surface they are held tightly together by intercellular junctions. This mucosal layer protects underlying tissues from damage by abrasion from food passing over it and from damage induced by the chemical contents of material in the oesophageal lumen.

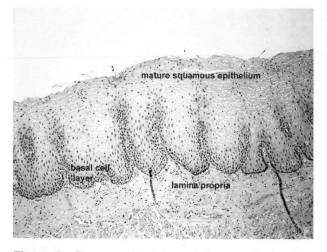

Figure 1 The normal histology of the oesophagus. The oesophagus consists of squamous epithelium arranged in stratified layers. The cells at the bottom (basal layer) are small and these cells represent the proliferative compartment. They give rise to daughter cells which pass upward into the overlying epithelium, becoming increasingly mature as they do so. As a result, the amount of cytoplasm relative to the nucleus, the nuclear : cytoplasmic ratio decreases. The basement membrane separates the basal cell layer from the underlying lamina propria.

The oesophageal lining is lubricated by mucus derived from the salivary glands and from oesophageal submucosal mucus glands. Passage of food and liquid through the oesophagus into the stomach is accomplished by contraction of its thick muscular coat. A muscular sphincter, known as the lower oesophageal sphincter, acts as the gateway to the stomach, controlling the passage of food forward and preventing reflux of gastric acid and digestive enzymes back into the oesophagus.

Stomach

The stomach is a bag-like structure lying between the oesophagus and the intestines. It develops from a fusiform swelling of the foregut at approximately 4 weeks gestation. During the sixth to seventh fetal week the gastric curvature develops. In the ninth week, a diverticulum appears in the upper stomach, which subsequently merges with, and lengthens, the greater curvature. The stomach is initially lined by stratified or pseudostratified epithelium. Later, it is replaced by cuboidal cells. As secretions accumulate, droplets and vacuoles coalesce to form the gastric lumen. The first differentiated cell types to appear are mucous neck cells that act as progenitors for other cell types. Gastric glands grow by progressively branching, a process that continues until birth.

Food reaching the stomach is mixed with acid and digestive enzymes to accelerate the digestive process. The muscles of the stomach wall help mix and churn the gastric contents increasing the contact between food and the digestive mixture and grinding the food into smaller particles.

The stomach has three functionally and anatomically distinct parts: the cardia, the corpus and the pyloric antrum (**Figure 2**) (Fenoglio-Preiser et al., 1999). These three areas are covered by a mucosa that contains a lining epithelium composed of gastric pits and gastric glands. The histological features of the lining epithelium of the gastric pits (**Figure 3**) is similar in all three areas, although the lengths of the pits differ in different gastric regions. In contrast, gastric glands differ in their histological features in the three anatomical regions. The cardia, a 1-cm segment of the stomach lying at its junction with the oesophagus, consists of mucus-producing glands resembling oesophageal mucus glands. The corpus normally constitutes approximately two-thirds of the gastric surface area. Its glands are lined by two major cell types. Chief cells produce pepsin, a digestive enzyme, from its precursor, pepsinogen. Parietal cells have several functions. They act as proton pumps that secrete hydrochloric acid into the stomach lumen, lowering the pH of gastric juice to 1.5. They also serve as the source of intrinsic factor which modulates small intestinal absorption of vitamin B_{12}. Autodigestion of the stomach by pepsin and hydrochloric acid is prevented by a thick mucus coat elaborated by mucosal surface cells. The pyloric antrum constitutes the distal third of the stomach. As in the corpus, its surface cells produce a thick layer of protective mucus. Antral glands contain chief cells that, like those in the corpus, secrete pepsin. Pepsinogen occurs in two forms. Pepsinogen group I (PGI) occurs only in the corpus, while pepsinogen group II (PGII) is made in all three parts of the stomach. The gastric epithelium in all three regions of the stomach maintains a dynamic equilibrium between cell production and cell loss. Cell proliferation increases any time that there is an excessive loss of gastric cells due to any mucosal injury (**Figure 4**).

The gastric mucosa also contains a diverse endocrine cell population. The predominant antral endocrine cell is the gastrin-producing G cell. The G cell is part of a physiological negative feedback loop. When acid secretion is low, gastrin stimulates acid secretion by parietal calls, followed by inhibition of gastrin release. Acid secretion also follows neural stimulation. Prolonged acid suppression induced by drugs, vagus nerve denervation or atrophy of the corpus mucosa leads to an increase in the G cell population and hypergastrinaemia (**Figure 5**). Hypergastrinaemia stimulates the growth of corpus ECL cells which may develop into small localized growths. Gastrin also functions as a general mucosal growth factor. Other gastric endocrine cells produce substances such as serotonin and somatostatin. Hormones produced by all gastric endocrine cells integrate physiological communications between the

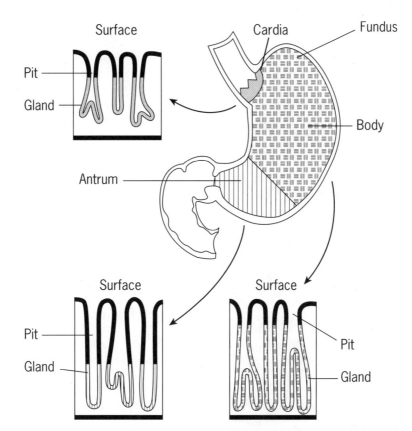

Figure 2   Diagrammatic representation of the stomach. The stomach is divided into four areas: the cardia, fundus, body and antrum. In each of these areas, the stomach is lined by surface epithelium which extends down into the gastric pits. Underlying the gastric pits are the gastric glands. The gastric glands of the fundus and body resemble one another and are sometimes referred to as oxyntic glands. These glands differ from those seen in the cardia and the antrum.

central and peripheral nervous system and the cells in the gastric mucosa and the muscle layers.

EPIDEMIOLOGY

Oesophageal Cancer

There are two major types of oesophageal cancer, squamous cell carcinoma (SCC) and adenocarcinoma, each with different risk factors and epidemiologies. SCC arises from the squamous cells lining the oesophagus. Adenocarcinomas arise in areas of metaplasia known as Barrett oesophagus.

Squamous Cell Carcinoma

The geographical distribution of oesophageal cancer shows wide variations within and between countries, in both mortality and incidence (Munoz and Day, 1996). As much as a 500-fold incidence difference can exist between the most and least affected areas of the same country and between different countries. SCC is virtually nonexistent in western and northern Africa. It also remains relatively rare in most of North America and Western Europe. In contrast, a high-risk zone extends from eastern Turkey through the southern former Soviet Union, Iraq, and Iran to northern China. High-risk areas also include Chile, the Transkei region of South Africa, Japan and regions of France and Brazil. Even in China, where 60% of oesophageal cancers develop, widespread differences in incidence and mortality exist. These high-risk foci have been explained on the basis of local food preservation practices that favour the generation of carcinogenic nitroso compounds from mould growing in pickled vegetables. Familial clusters of SCC of the oesophagus have been observed in Chinese high-risk areas. This can be attributed to shared environmental hazards, or to a common genetic influence.

Adenocarcinoma

Adenocarcinomas, cancers that form glands, constitute a relatively small proportion of oesophageal cancers worldwide, but among white males in the United States

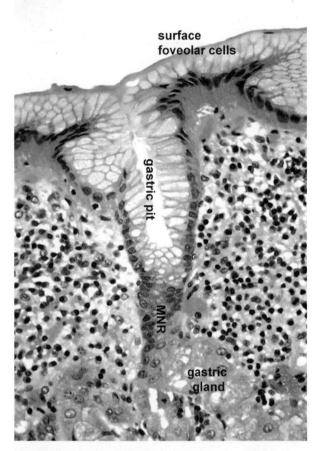

Figure 3 Photograph of the superficial portion of the gastric mucosa showing the surface foveolar epithelium extending into the gastric pit. Cell replication occurs in the mucous neck region (MNR), which is the area of junction betweem the pit and the underlying glands.

they are now more frequent than SCC (Zheng *et al.*, 1993). Indeed, most affected patients are white males. Oesophageal carcinomas share many clinical features with cancers of the gastric cardia, and it may be difficult to determine whether a cancer involving the gastro-oesophageal junction originates from the oesophagus or the stomach. Thus, it is likely that epidemiological studies of oesophageal adenocarcinomas include some cancers of the cardia, and vice versa. This may explain why both cancers share similar time trends and a predisposition to affect white men. Both tumours have increased in incidence between 1975 and 1995, but the increased incidence of oesophageal adenocarcinoma in white males is especially strong, rising from 0.7 to 3.2 per 100 000, an increase of more than 350%. A diet characterized by a high intake of meat, fat and calories, but a low intake of fruits and vegetables, has also been identified as a risk factor for this tumour.

Stomach Cancer

As in the oesophagus, there is more than one form of gastric cancer and the epidemiology of the various forms differs.

Intestinal-type Gastric Cancer

The most common form of stomach cancer in high-risk populations is a gland-forming tumour that arises in the pyloric antrum and is preceded by the appearance of mucosal glands that resemble those in the intestine – a condition called intestinal metaplasia. The tumours that develop in the intestinalized mucosa are termed intestinal-type gastric cancers. Intestinal-type tumours account for almost two-thirds of the gastric cancers in the high-risk areas of northeast Asia, central America and eastern Europe. They arise after long-term infection with

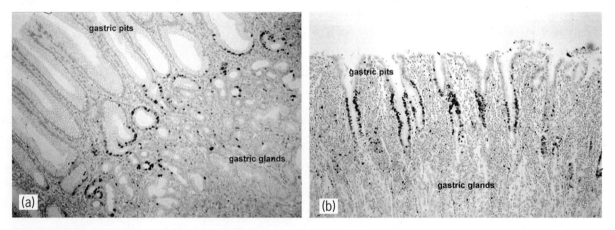

Figure 4 The area of the gastric pits which lies between the surface cells and the underlying gastric glands represents the proliferative zone of the stomach. (a) Under normal circumstances, isolated replicating cells are present, as indicated by the darkly stained cells. (b) When the mucosa becomes damaged, the number of brown staining cells increases and the gastric pits shorten. These changes indicate increased proliferation in response to mucosal injury.

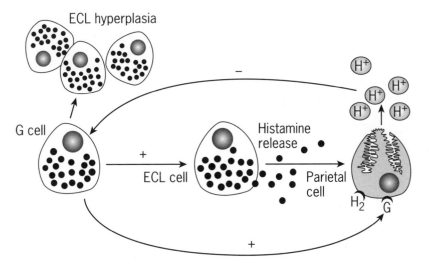

Figure 5 A feedback loop exists between parietal cells and G cells that secrete gastrin. When acid is secreted, the acid suppresses G cell function. In situations of hypochlorhydria, G cells increase their gastrin output. This serves directly to stimulate gastrin receptors on the surfaces of parietal cells. Gastrin also acts indirectly by stimulating ECL cells to release histamine. The histamine then binds to histamine receptors on the parietal cells. The binding of both gastrin and histamine to their respective receptors on parietal cells causes the acid secretion. In situations of prolonged G cell secretion, ECL hyperplasia develops.

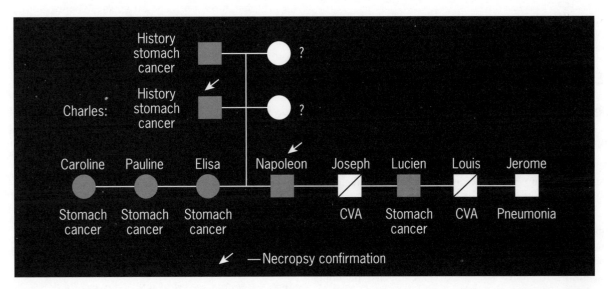

Figure 6 Diagram of the Bonaparte family tree indicating the presence of gastric cancer in several generations of the family.

Helicobacter pylori in persons whose diet is deficient in antioxidant vitamins (Correa, 1988; Nomura, 1996). Intestinal-type gastric cancer has shown a dramatic decrease in frequency in Western Europe and North America since 1940. This rapid decline in tumour incidence in westernized countries, and the persistence of high incidence rates in developing countries, suggest that gastric cancer risk is closely tied to socioeconomic status.

It is well recognized that the first-degree relatives of stomach cancer patients are at increased risk of developing gastric cancer, perhaps because the patients share common risk factors such as diet and *H. pylori* infections or because they share genetic factors that increase their risk of developing gastric cancer, or both. The Bonaparte family is a good example of a familial gastric cancer cluster (**Figure 6**) (Sokoloff, 1939). Napoleon and his father had autopsy-confirmed antral cancers. Four of his seven siblings were diagnosed with gastric cancer. Subsequently, there were 30 offspring from Napoleon's generation, and none developed gastric cancer. This and other similar familial kindreds suggest a pattern of weak genetic penetrance modulated by environmental factors. Napoleon's brothers and sisters were raised in rural Corsica under less than ideal living conditions imposed by the hand to mouth existence of parents who, for many years, were active participants in a guerilla war against the French. The small size of the Bonaparte families after the move to the European mainland is typical of migrants who improved their economic status. The children were now housed in palaces and probably escaped *H. pylori* infection. They would have had an improved diet as well, that could have accounted for the absence of stomach cancer in subsequent generations.

Diffuse Gastric Cancer

Diffuse tumours preferentially arise in the corpus of patients <50 years of age who have severe superficial gastritis due to *H. pylori* infection (Nomura and Stemmerman, 1993). The appearance of these cancers in younger individuals without atrophic gastritis suggests the presence of a genetically driven increase in vulnerability to environmental carcinogens. Two observations support this concept. The first is the fact that patients with diffuse gastric cancers are more likely than the general population to have blood type A (Correa *et al.*, 1973). Second, families with clusters of stomach cancer usually have diffuse-type carcinomas (Lehtola, 1978).

AETIOLOGY

Oesophagus

Squamous Cell Carcinoma

Oesophageal SCCs can be divided into two major risk groups: those tumours associated with tobacco and alcohol consumption and those occurring in populations consuming a poor, generally monotonous diet that lacks green, leafy vegetables, citrus fruits, micronutrients such as zinc, riboflavin and vitamin A and other unknown factors. These circumstances render the oesophageal mucosa more susceptible to injury by various carcinogens, including mycotoxins in the Transkei, substituted hydroxyphenanthrenes (a strongly mutagenic form of opium) in Iran, and *N*-nitroso compounds in China.

Heavy alcohol and cigarette consumption are recognized risk factors for oesophageal SCC, especially in Western populations. The increased risk with increasing alcohol consumption is exponential while the increase in risk from tobacco is linear (Tyuns *et al.*, 1977). The strong association of oesophageal cancer with alcohol helps explain the especially high rates of oesophageal cancer in calvados-producing regions of northern France. Alcohol may contribute to an increased oesophageal cancer risk by reducing nutrient intake and by displacing protective dietary micronutrients (Ziegler, 1986). In addition, alcoholic beverages may contain carcinogens, or facilitate the

transport of tobacco-associated carcinogens across the oesophageal lining. It may also impair the ability of the liver to detoxify carcinogens. In contrast, there appears to be a strong protective effect between the consumption of antioxidant vitamins and fresh fruits in areas at high risk for SCC.

Human papillomavirus (HPV) associates with the development of squamous cell carcinomas at many sites, including the oesophagus. There are approximately 70 distinct HPV strains, two of which, types 16 and 18, have been identified in oesophageal SCC. The frequency of HPV in oesophageal cancer varies from country to country, and appears to be most common in South Africa (Lewin and Appleman, 1996). HPV is probably not involved in the evolution in all oesophageal SCCs since it is absent from the majority of oesophageal cancers in Asia and Europe. When present, viral genetic sequences are present in nonneoplastic, dysplastic, invasive and metastatic lesions.

Motility disorders that delay oesophageal emptying increase the exposure of oesophageal squamous cells to ingested carcinogens. One such disorder, achalasia, results from impaired relaxation of the lower oesophageal sphincter and absent motility in the oesophageal wall. It is usually diagnosed after age 60 years. A population-based study showed that during the 24 years of follow-up, the risk increased more than 16-fold (Sandler *et al.*, 1995). Fortunately, achalasia is uncommon.

Adenocarcinoma

The lining of the lower oesophagus can be injured if it is exposed to prolonged reflux of gastric acid and digestive enzymes. As a result, the normal squamous epithelium may change into a glandular lining resembling that of the stomach or intestines, producing the lesion known as Barrett metaplasia or Barrett oesophagus (Jankowski *et al.*, 2000). Barrett oesophagus is a precursor to the development of oesophageal adenocarcinoma. Barrett oesophagus associates with decreased oesophageal sphincter resistance and increased gastric acid production, both of which lead to severe reflux oesophagitis. Obesity is also a risk factor, since it too predisposes to reflux disease.

Stomach Cancer

Intestinal-type Cancers

Intestinal metaplasia first appears in foci of atrophic mucosa at the antral–corpus junction (**Figure 7**). These foci ultimately fuse as the process progresses along the lesser curvature (Stemmerman, 1994). Further progression may result in the replacement of the entire antral mucosa by intestinal type glands and by proximal extension into the corpus. In late stages of the process all but a small portion of the corpus mucosa may be replaced by intestinal-type glands. In high-risk populations intestinalization of the stomach begins in adolescence, initiating a

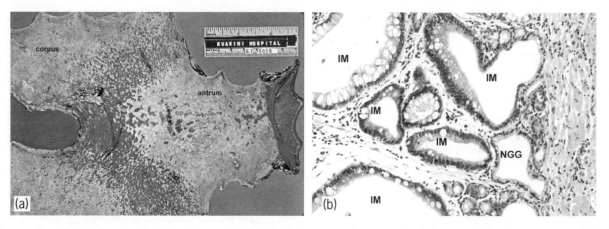

Figure 7   Intestinal metaplasia in the stomach. (a) This gross photograph of the stomach shows areas of dark staining. The stomach was immersed in a solution of alkaline phosphatase. This preferentially stains areas of intestinal metaplasia, resulting in the dark, inverted V-shaped pattern at the junction of the corpus and antrum. The duodenum located at the right hand edge of the photograph also intensely stains with the enzyme. (b) Histological features of intestinal metaplasia (IM) showing replacement of the normal gastric glands (NGG) with intestinalized glands.

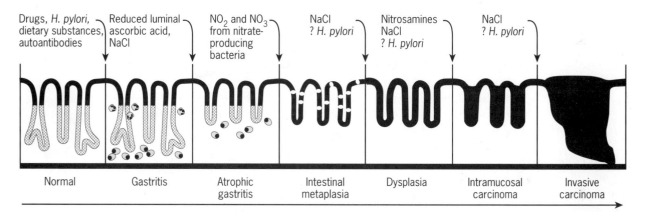

Figure 8   Diagram of the sequential abnormalities occurring in the development of intestinal-type cancers in the stomach. The individual steps are listed along the arrow at the bottom of the photograph. Substances thought to play a role in the progression of these steps are indicated above the diagram. This process is multifactorial and involves the presence of *H. pylori*, dietary substances and autoantibodies which produce gastritis and atrophy of the gastric glands that then lead to intestinal metaplasia. As a result of the atrophic gastritis and the replacement of gastric mucosa by mucosa resembling the intestine, the parietal cells decrease in number and as a result hydrochloric acid production decreases or ceases, allowing bacterial growth. These bacteria then serve to metabolize gastric contents into additional carcinogens. Additionally, the bacteria elicit an inflammatory response that generates genotoxic damage, further contributing to the molecular alterations occurring within the stomach and the genesis of a progressively abnormal gastric mucosa.

progressive expansion of the metaplasia. By the seventh decade, the metaplastic process may reduce the parietal cell volume to a level insufficient for maintaining gastric acid production. Loss of corpus chief cells results in low serum levels of PG I. As a result, tests that measure gastric acid production and serum PG I levels can identify persons who are at an increased risk for developing stomach cancer. Unfortunately, these tests do not identify individuals destined to develop stomach cancer before the

intestinal metaplasia is sufficiently advanced to affect gastric function.

The sequential, multifactorial steps in the development of intestinal-type cancers seen in high-risk populations are shown in **Figure 8**. The gastritis results from the combined effects of *H. pylori* infection (**Figure 9**), high salt and nitrate intake, smoking and a diet deficient in fresh vegetables and protective antioxidant vitamins. Prospective studies have shown that 95% of persons who

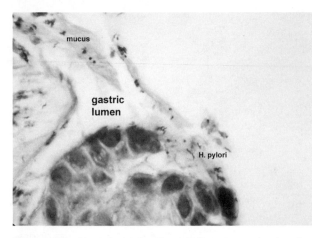

Figure 9 *H. pylori* infection of the stomach showing the presence of numerous *Helicobacter* attached to the surface epithelium. Alcian yellow stain of *H. pylori* infection showing the presence of numerous corkscrew-shaped organisms in the mucus overlying the gastric epithelial cells.

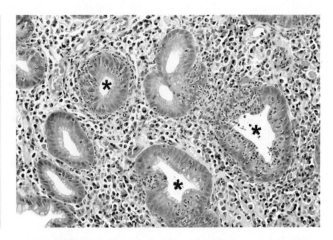

Figure 10 (a) Active chronic gastritis due to *H. pylori* infection. (b) Note the presence of large numbers of acute inflammatory cells in the starred glands.

develop cancer were infected with *H. pylori*. However, although at least 75% of persons in high-risk areas are infected with *H. pylori*, only 5% actually develop stomach cancer (Nomura and Stemmerman, 1993). Whether or not an infected person develops cancer probably depends upon their genetic predisposition to develop cancer, their level of exposure to other risk factors and possibly to the strain of *H. pylori* infecting them.

H. pylori Infection

H. pylori infection is most frequent in large families occupying crowded living quarters and lacking hot water. The infection is usually acquired during childhood, is related to birth order; the highest incidence affects the youngest children of large families (Goodman and Correa, 1995). *H. pylori* infection is most common among those with the shortest duration of schooling. The smaller families and improved housing that typify a prosperous economy in developed countries may explain, at least in part, the decrease in their gastric cancer rates.

   H. pylori infection increases gastric cancer risk via several pathways. The infection causes epithelial cell damage and the rate of cell proliferation increases in response to the cell loss. As the cells proliferate, the DNA unwinds, increasing the number of gastric cells vulnerable to genotoxic damage and subsequent genetic instability. Additionally, *H. pylori* infections generate a brisk inflammatory response with invasion of the replicating epithelium by white blood cells (**Figure 10**). Two types of inflammatory cells, neutrophils and monocytes, generate the toxic molecule, nitric oxide (NO) (**Figure 11**). In addition, other toxic molecules can be generated from NO including nitrosamines. Nitrosamines induce mutations in bacteria and are gastric carcinogens in many animal

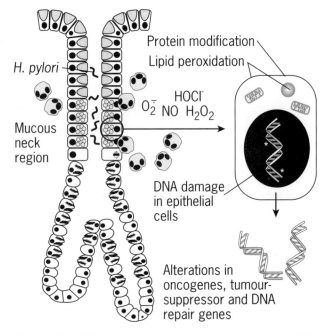

Figure 11 Diagram of the injury induced by neutrophils in the mucous neck region.

models. The local production of these compounds near the replicating gastric epithelium exposes them to an increased risk of DNA damage. The inflammatory cells also induce free radical damage due to the formation of NO and its oxidative byproducts. Vitamin C (ascorbic acid), an antioxidant, protects the gastric mucosa against oxidative stress. However, *H. pylori* infections decrease ascorbic acid concentrations in the gastric juice. Not all *H. pylori* are equally efficient in inducing the changes noted above. The most virulent of the bacteria contain a gene known as *cag* (Blaser *et al.*, 1995).

Diet and Stomach Cancer

Dietary patterns were once thought to be *the* most important basis of gastric cancer induction, and although diet has recently conceded the pride of place to *H. pylori* infection, diet still retains a major role in the cause and prevention of this tumour. Strong experimental and epidemiological evidence links salt intake to gastritis, intestinal metaplasia and gastric cancer. Evidence that dietary nitrite and nitrate play a direct role in gastric carcinogenesis is inconclusive, but these substances do induce intestinal metaplasia. Foods with high salt and nitrate concentrations, such as dried and salted fish or pickled vegetables, predispose to stomach cancer in many studies. Such foods constituted a major portion of the diet prior to the almost universal ownership of household refrigeration in Western countries and the availability of fresh or frozen fruits, vegetables, fish and meat. The decrease in gastric cancer rates in Western countries since 1945 is attributable to altered dietary habits with decreased consumption of the potential carcinogens in smoked, salted and pickled foods.

Autoimmune Gastritis

Autoimmune gastritis is a precursor to both benign and malignant stomach tumours. It is less common than multifocal gastritis and it develops when patients generate antibodies against their own parietal and chief cells. Cell proliferation in the corpus increases in response to the antibody-mediated cell loss. However, because cell destruction proceeds faster than cellular replacement, the mucosa of the corpus becomes atrophic. Loss of parietal cells results in a reduction in gastric acid production and a compensatory increase in antral gastrin secretion. The increased gastric cancer risk in this condition results from several synchronous events: (1) a bacterial flora emerges in the stomach which can generate potential carcinogens from dietary amines; (2) endogenous production of mutagens may follow NO production by reacting white cells in the stomach lining; (3) the increased cell turnover puts more cells at risk of accumulating genetic damage; and (4) gastrin functions as a growth promoter of gastric lining cells.

The diagnosis of autoimmune gastritis is confirmed by demonstrating low or no stomach acid and very low serum levels of pepsinogen group I (Samloff *et al.*, 1975). As in multifocal gastritis, the gastric mucosa of patients with autoimmune gastritis may develop intestinal metaplasia. The increased gastrin production stimulates gastric mucosal growth, sometimes contributing to the development of gastric polyps and gastric carcinoma (**Figure 12**). The risk of developing carcinoma with autoimmune gastritis varies from 2.1 to 5.6 times that of persons without the condition. The cancers arise in the antrum as well as in the corpus.

Previous Surgery

The risk of developing stomach cancer complicates previous ulcer surgery (Fisher *et al.*, 1993). Bleeding from

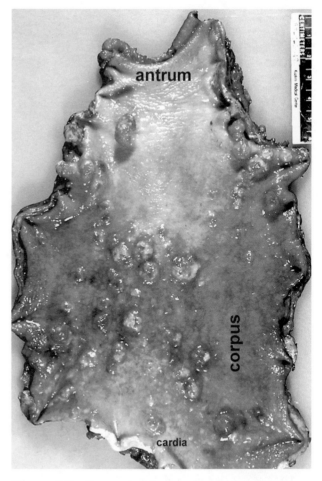

Figure 12 Gross photograph of a stomach from a patient with autoimmune gastritis showing the presence of numerous gastric polyps, as well as a gastric carcinoma. They mainly arise in the corpus. The surrounding mucosa is atrophic.

antral or duodenal peptic ulcers historically required the removal of these segments of the gastrointestinal tract, and also the nerves that stimulate acid secretion. The gastric remnant was often joined to a small intestinal loop, resulting in reflux of intestinal and pancreatic juices into the gastric remnant. This reflux of digestive enzymes into the denervated gastric remnant causes a gastritis resembling multifocal or autoimmune gastritis, increasing the gastric cancer risk. The elevation of risk becomes apparent 20 years after the resection and increases thereafter. The younger the patient at the time of surgery, the greater the risk of ultimately acquiring a carcinoma.

Radiation

The stomach is sometimes in the radiation field in patients with abdominal tumours, especially certain forms of lymphoma occurring in young people. A small number of these patients have an increased risk of developing stomach cancer. The tumours derive from X-ray-induced mutations in the gastric mucosa. Japanese victims of the

Hiroshima/Nagasaki atomic bomb explosions also had an increased incidence of gastric cancer.

Diffuse Cancer

The aetiology of diffuse gastric cancer is poorly understood, although *H. pylori* infections appear to play a role in their genesis.

SCREENING AND PREVENTION

Oesophagus

Squamous Cell Carcinoma

Patients with SCC present with dysphagia (difficulty swallowing) or with odynophagia (pain). Initially, symptoms only occur with the consumption of solid foods, but as the tumour progresses even liquids are swallowed with difficulty. Severe weight loss results from decreased food intake. Many cancers ulcerate, resulting in upper gastrointestinal bleeding. The bleeding is usually inconspicuous and is not noticed by the patient. Fatal internal bleeding may occur if a deeply invasive cancer erodes a major blood vessel. The only way to avoid these dire consequences is to screen populations at risk for the disease. The intent of screening programmes is to detect tumours while they are still curable. This is possible because cancers develop over a period of time, usually evolving over a decade or more.

The study of oesophageal lining cells that are dislodged by the passage of a brush or a balloon (cytological examination) allows the discovery of cancerous cells in early phases of tumour progression (**Figure 13**). Cytology screening programmes form the basis of community

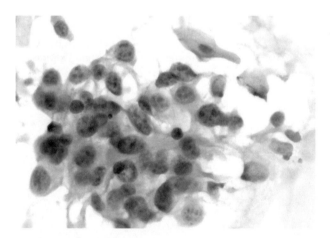

Figure 13   Cytological preparation of a carcinoma of the oesophagus. These cells were brushed off the surface of the oesophagus. They preferentially dislodge because of their malignant qualities. They have enlarged nuclei and small amounts of cytoplasm. There is cytologic atypia.

screening programmes in the high-risk areas of central China where up to 50% of the resected oesophageal cancers are noninvasive or early invasive tumours (Qui and Yang, 1988). In contrast, SCC is too uncommon in Western populations to justify community screening programmes. Rather, diagnostic procedures in most Western, low-risk countries are designed to explain the symptoms of late-stage disease and to estimate the extent of the cancer that caused them. The diagnosis is usually made on tissue obtained from an endoscopic biopsy.

Suggested guidelines for endoscopic surveillance of the oesophageal mucosa in patient populations with a high risk of developing squamous cell cancer areas are as follows: biopsy specimens should be obtained from all plaque-like, nodular, erosive and friable areas; normal areas, including mildly wrinkled mucosa and isolated small white patches, need not be sampled; and biopsy specimens should be obtained from diffusely irregular (prominently wrinkled) mucosa and distinct areas of focal reddening at the endoscopist's discretion.

It remains unclear as to whether these recommendations should be applied to patients in non-high-risk areas, although they may be a desirable addition to the examination of patients entering an alcohol abuse treatment programme.

Adenocarcinoma

The symptoms associated with progression of oesophageal adenocarcinomas are essentially similar to those associated with SCC – difficulty swallowing, obstruction of the passage of solid foods, weight loss and dissemination to other sites. As is the case of SCC, long-term survival requires diagnosis at a preinvasive or early invasive stage. This is most likely to occur if patients known to have Barrett change are screened on a regular basis in order to detect progression of the process to the level of high-grade dysplasia.

The following management approach is that recommended by the 1990 Barrett's Esophagus Working Party of the World Congress of Gastroenterology (Dent, 1989):

- A programme of regular endoscopic surveillance for dysplasia and early carcinoma is recommended for patients with Barrett oesophagus unless contraindicated by comorbidity. For patients who have no dysplasia or cancer, endoscopy (with procurement of biopsy and brush cytology specimen(s) from the Barrett's epithelium) is performed every other year.
- If dysplasia is detected, the finding should be confirmed by at least one other expert pathologist. If any doubt remains, the endoscopic examination is repeated immediately to obtain more biopsy and cytology specimens for analysis.
- For patients confirmed to have multiple foci of high-grade dysplasia, surgery is advised to resect all of the oesophagus lined by columnar epithelium.

- For patients confirmed to have low-grade dysplasia, intensive medical antireflux therapy (including omeprazole) should be given for 8–12 weeks, at which time endoscopic examination is repeated to obtain multiple oesophageal biopsy and cytology specimens.
- For patients whose specimens show histological improvement, intensive surveillance (e.g. endoscopic examination every 6 months) is recommended until at least two consecutive examinations reveal no dysplastic epithelium.
- For patients with persistent low-grade dysplasia, continued intensive treatment and surveillance are recommended.

Stomach

The nature of the symptoms depends upon the site and growth pattern of the tumour. Bulky tumours may erode and cause bleeding, while diffuse tumours may restrict the expansion of the stomach, causing early satiety and severe weight loss due to decreased food intake. It is not unusual for the first symptoms to be caused by metastases in sites remote from the stomach. In young women, the spread of gastric cancer to the ovaries produces so-called Krukenberg tumours that may reach the size of a grapefruit. Other symptoms caused by metastases include spread of the cancer to the lymph nodes of the lower neck and to the accumulation of excess fluid in the abdominal cavity. The configuration and mode of progression of stomach cancer depend upon the age and sex of the patient, the subsite of its origin within the stomach and its histological type.

The Japanese, in response to the high incidence of gastric cancer in their country, have introduced community screening to detect cancers early in their development. As a result, 50–60% of stomach cancers are discovered while still limited to the stomach lining or to the tissues immediately beneath it. Recent Japanese studies have also assessed the effectiveness of radioimmunoassays to determine the serum pepsinogen group I level (PG I), and the ratio between PG I and PG II in predicting the presence of stomach cancer in participants in an endoscopic screening programme (Kitahara et al., 1999). However, the sensitivity of this approach is not sufficient to detect all tumour cases. Additional variables must be identified before a focused screening programme can be used to identify high-risk subjects in low-risk Western settings. These might include two or more of the following: (1) first-generation migrants from countries with high rates of gastric cancer; (2) a high H. pylori antibody level; (3) persons with a strong history of stomach cancer among close family relatives; (4) smokers with a history of stomach ulcer; (5) persons who have had a partial resection of the stomach 17 or more years previously; and (6) persons who have received radiation treatment to the upper abdomen prior to age 30. Japanese studies of patients with untreated early cancer suggest that re-examination need not be performed more frequently than every 5 years.

PATHOLOGY

Oesophageal Carcinoma

Squamous Cell Carcinoma

As the oesophageal lining passes through a series of sequential steps that eventually result in the development of invasive SCC, it becomes progressively abnormal, a change that can be seen both by gross examination and by examination under the microscope. These steps include the presence of varying degrees of intraepithelial (non-invasive) neoplasia, termed dysplasia, finally ending in an invasive carcinoma that has the ability to spread and kill the patient (**Figure 14**).

Gross Appearance

The gross appearance of oesophageal neoplasia varies with the stage of neoplasia present. The earliest lesions may

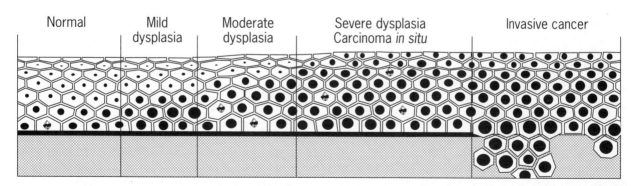

Figure 14 Diagrammatic summary of the progression of squamous cell neoplasia. As the disease progresses, more and more of the thickness of the oesophageal mucosa becomes replaced by neoplastic cells. These eventually invade through the area of the basement membrane into the underlying lamina propria and then into the submucosa. From here they can metastasize to sites distant from the oesophagus.

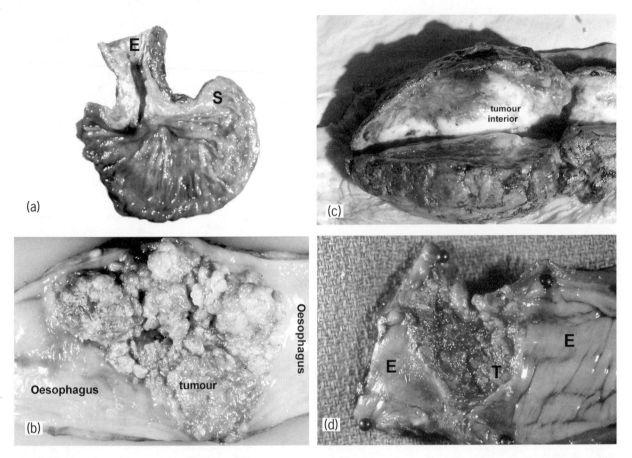

Figure 15   Gross appearances of oesophageal cancers. Oesophageal squamous cell cancers may assume a variety of gross appearances. (a) Diffuse infiltration of the oesophageal wall causes thickening of the distal end of the oesophagus (E). The line shows the area of the tumour. The stomach (S) is also present. (b) An exophytic papillary tumour rises above the surrounding oesophageal mucosa. (c) A large, bulky, polypoid growth. The tumour has been cut in half. (d) An ulcerating oesophageal cancer (T) is surrounded by normal oesophagus (E).

appear completely normal to the naked eye or to the endoscopist. (The endoscopist is the clinician who examines the oesophageal mucosa with a magnifying camera inserted into the oesophageal lumen). Alternatively, the oesophageal mucosa may appear reddened owing to inflammation and vascular congestion induced by the presence of neoplastic cells. Early lesions (intraepithelial or minimally invasive lesions) may also appear as areas of superficial erosion and/or as whitish plaques. Such lesions may be single or multiple. Invasive carcinomas usually arise from these erosive or plaque-like lesions. Invasive SCC usually arise in the distal half of the oesophagus, although they can occur anywhere. Grossly, invasive oesophageal squamous cell cancers assume various growth patterns (**Figure 15**). They may be large bulky polypoid lesions growing into and obstructing the oesophageal lumen. Other tumours grow as flat lesions or they grow into the oesophageal wall, creating oesophageal ulcers. Still other tumours diffusely infiltrate the oesophageal wall, causing oesophageal strictures. These growth patterns can occur alone, or they can associate with one

another. The extent and configuration of an invasive tumour partly determines how a patient presents. Patients with bulky polypoid lesions, or with areas of stenosis, are more likely to experience difficulty in swallowing than those with ulcerating or flat tumours.

Microscopic Appearance

As indicated in an earlier section, the oesophageal mucosal lining consists of an orderly arrangement of squamous epithelial cells that regularly renew themselves. Progenitor cells lying in the basal zone give rise to new cells that become increasingly mature as they pass upward in the mucosa. As part of their maturation, the cells progressively enlarge acquiring a smaller nuclear–cytoplasmic ratio as they do so. When the cells become neoplastic, they lose this orderly pattern of growth and maturation and proliferation no longer remains restricted to the basal cell layer. The cells appear disorganized and jumbled, and depending on the degree of change that is present, mitotic activity appears at various levels in the epithelial layer. This earliest form of neoplasia is called dysplasia and implies the presence of an unequivocally neoplastic epithelium.

Historically, dysplasia came in several grades, ranging from mild to moderate to severe (**Figure 16**). When the entire epithelial thickness is replaced by neoplastic cells, the process may be termed carcinoma *in situ* (CIS). Today there is a tendency to place intraepithelial neoplasias into two grades, high- and low-grade dysplasias. Using such a two-tier system, CIS falls into the category of severe dysplasia. Progression of squamous cell neoplasia beyond CIS is recognized by the presence of disruption of the basement membrane and penetration of the tumour into the underlying tissues. The term microinvasive carcinoma can be used if the invasive tumour tongues are minute, penetrating only a few millimetres into the underlying tissues. Once invasion has occurred, the tumour may spread horizontally beneath the intact squamous cell lining adjacent to the cancer, or it may variably penetrate through the oesophageal wall, eventually reaching its external surface and potentially entering contiguous structures. If that structure is the trachea, ingested food can be aspirated into the lungs via the fistula created by the tumour. If the adjacent structure is the aorta or pulmonary artery, massive and fatal internal haemorrhage will result. If the patient is spared either of these devastating events, the tumour may find its way into the lymph channels that drain the wall of the oesophagus. Tumour cells in these lymphatics may then spread to regional lymph nodes and then disseminate to more distant sites causing metastases in other organs.

Invasive squamous cell carcinomas exhibit varying degrees of cellular differentiation. If they closely resemble the squamous cells from which they arose, they are termed well-differentiated squamous cell carcinomas. Tumours composed of cells difficult to recognize as being squamous in nature are termed poorly differentiated. Tumour cells whose degree of differentiation is intermediate between these two extremes are said to be moderately differentiated.

Adenocarcinoma of the Oesophagus

As indicated above, oesophageal adenocarcinomas do not arise from the native squamous epithelium. Rather, they arise from areas of Barrett oesophagus which is a metaplastic epithelium consisting of glandular cells. As with squamous cell carcinomas, the epithelial lining of Barrett oesophagus becomes progressively abnormal as it passes through a series of sequential steps that eventually result in the development of invasive adenocarcinoma (**Figure 17**). These steps include the development of glandular dysplasia followed by the appearance of an invasive malignancy.

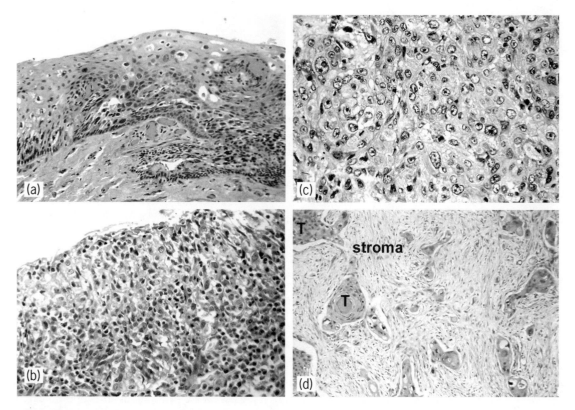

Figure 16 Histological features of the progression of oesophageal squamous cell neoplasia. (a) Low-grade dysplasia. (b) High-grade dysplasia. (c) Carcinoma *in situ*. (d) Invasive cancer. The tumour nests (T) are surrounded by a desmoplastic stroma.

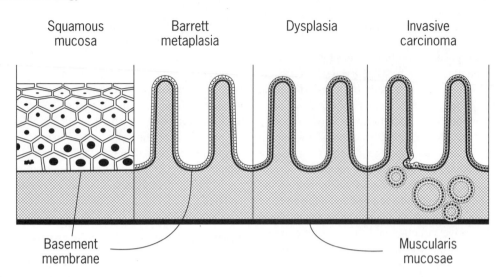

| Squamous mucosa | Barrett metaplasia | Dysplasia | Invasive carcinoma |

Basement membrane

Muscularis mucosae

Figure 17 Diagrammatic representation of the progression of the normal oesophagus to an adenocarcinoma arising in the background of Barrett oesophagus.

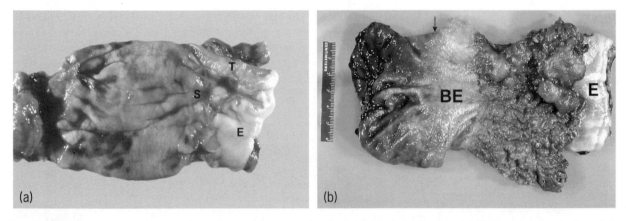

Figure 18 Gross appearance of adenocarcinoma arising in Barrett oesophagus. (a) Note the irregularity of the squamocolumnar junction. Normally, there should be a sharp demarcation with the distal stomach. The stomach (S) ends near the S. The smooth, lighter coloured mucosa represents the normal colour of the oesophagus (E). A small tumour is present beneath the T. (b) This photograph shows a large, fungating neoplasm arising in an area of Barrett oesophagus. The gastric folds terminate at the area of the arrow. The area above this is replaced by Barrett oesophagus (BE). Above that is the tumour, and the smooth, lighter coloured area of the mucosa represents normal oesophagus (E). The oesophagus has been extensively replaced by glandular epithelium and by the neoplasm.

Gross Appearance

The gross appearance of oesophageal glandular neoplasia varies, depending on the stage in the process at which it is examined (**Figure 18**). The lower end of the oesophagus loses its normal pinkish tan smooth appearance, typical of the native squamous mucosa, and instead it becomes reddened and less smooth. This is the earliest change and it is seen in patients with Barrett oesophagus. The mucosal alterations may make it difficult to determine where the original gastro-oesophageal junction lay before the Barrett oesophagus developed. The best way of determining the proximal extent of the stomach is to identify the termination of the gastric folds. The dysplasias that develop in the areas of Barrett oesophagus may be flat or polypoid. Those that are flat may be completely invisible to the naked eye and to the endoscopist. Some areas of dysplasia may appear slightly depressed or ulcerated. As invasive cancers develop, they tend to invade both laterally and into the oesophageal wall. Such lesions may be more visible when the cut surface of the oesophagus is examined or if the tissues are palpated for areas of firmness. It is very common for adenocarcinomas to extend underneath adjacent normal tissues. When the tumours become large, bulky polypoid or ulcerating lesions, it may be impossible to tell whether they arose in the distal oesophagus or in the cardia of the stomach. These are sometimes referred to as tumours of the oesophageal–gastric junction The majority of these cancers are flat or ulcerated, although in a third of the cases they may form elevated masses – polypoid cancers.

Microscopic Appearance

Disordered cell growth, called dysplasia, constitutes the first step in the progression of Barrett change into cancer. Dysplasia is recognized by the appearance of an increased nuclear–cytoplasmic ratio and loss of nuclear polarity. Initially, the metaplastic glands are lined by cells that become pseudostratified, somewhat resembling colonic adenomas. As the degree of dysplasia progresses, the cells become increasingly disorganized and the nuclei lose their pseudostratified appearance. Invasive cancer becomes recognizable once the tumour cells extend through the muscularis mucosae into the underlying submucosa. The evolution from low-grade dysplasia through moderate- to high-grade dysplasia and invasive cancer is shown in **Figures 17 and 19**. Overall, many invasive tumours appear to be very well differentiated because they make clearly identified glands. Other tumours are poorly differentiated and it is difficult to identify glandular structures. Even well-differentiated tumours have the tendency to undermine adjacent non-neoplastic tissues and to invade the lymphatics of the oesophageal wall at an early stage. As a result, most cancers arising at the cardio-oesophageal junction are late-stage tumours, with dissemination to lymph nodes on both sides of the diaphragm at the time of diagnosis. Spread of these tumours to the liver is also fairly common. Oesophageal cancers that have progressed to the point of causing symptoms carry an extremely poor prognosis. The majority of symptomatic oesophageal cancers are unresectable, and the average life expectancy of untreated patients is less than 10 months.

Stomach Cancer

Gross Appearance

The gross appearance of early gastric cancers tumours is shown in **Figure 20**. Protruded, type 1, early cancers are most likely to occur in the antrum of older male patients with diffuse intestinal metaplasia of the stomach. Flat or ulcerated type 2 and 3 early tumours are more likely to occur in younger patients and may arise in the mucosa at the junction of the antrum and corpus of a stomach showing minimal or no intestinal metaplasia.

The appearance of advanced tumours is shown in **Figures 21 and 22**. Cancers that arise in the corpus are usually type IV tumours, as are most cancers that occur in women <50 years old. All other growth patterns preferentially affect antral tumours, and they are most frequent in older men from high-risk populations.

Microscopic Appearance

Gastric cancer presents a complex variety of growth patterns, and one cancer may assume several forms. Lauren, a Finnish pathologist, devised a simplified classification of these tumours (Lauren, 1965), which subsequently proved helpful to epidemiologists studying the origins of stomach cancer. This system is based on the observation that many stomach cancers form rudimentary glands that superficially resemble intestinal glands; these are termed intestinal in type (**Figure 23**). Others consist of discohesive cells that form no distinct structures and stimulate an overgrowth of the supporting connective tissues (**Figure 24**). These are termed diffuse tumours and their cells may be so widely separated from one another that that they are difficult to identify. The antral tumours in older men with extensive multifocal gastritis generally are intestinal in type, whereas the cancers that arise in the corpus of younger men and women are usually diffuse in type. In addition, most stomach cancers arising in high-risk areas are intestinal in type. It is not unusual for gastric cancers to show both patterns of growth and these can be called mixed tumours. A committee of World Health Organisation pathologists devised another classification scheme, that identifies the many variants of stomach cancer (**Table 1**). Classifying gastric cancer is difficult by either system, and interobserver differences lessen their value as prognostic markers for individual cases.

TREATMENT

Oesophagus

Squamous Cell Carcinoma

Surgical treatment of SCC is most likely to be successful when the tumour is confined to the lining of the oesophagus or when the invasive tumour is limited to the most superficial portion of the oesophageal wall. The extent of the tumour may be estimated through the use of endoscopic sonography, which uses echoes of ultrasonic pulses at the time of endoscopy to measure the depth of tumour penetration into the oesophageal wall and to identify metastases into the regional lymph nodes. This procedure allows the physician to assign a stage to the tumour and to plan patient treatment. The standard staging method employed is termed the TNM system, where T indicates the extent of tumour penetration, N indicates the presence or absence of lymph node metastases and M indicates the presence or absence of distant metastases. The TNM staging criteria for oesophageal cancer are shown in **Table 2**.

The treatment of the late-stage oesophageal cancer that typically confronts the physician in most Western countries is more likely to be palliative than curable. Surgery may resect or bypass the tumour, ionizing radiation may be used to shrink or destroy it and chemotherapy may be used

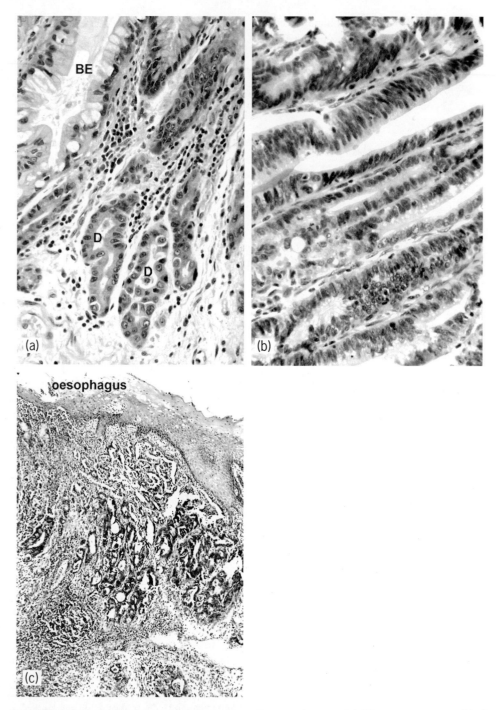

Figure 19 Evolution of the neoplastic changes in Barrett oesophagus. (a) The squamous epithelium has been replaced by glandular epithelium. One gland is a non-neoplastic gland representing Barrett oesophagus (BE). The majority of the glands that are present show evidence of low-grade dysplasia (D). (b) Further progression of the dysplasia with the presence of large numbers of cells showing nuclear palisading. (c) An invasive adenocarcinoma undermining the normal squamous mucosa of the oesophagus.

to control its growth. These approaches may be used alone or in combination with one another, depending upon the stage of the tumour and the physical condition of the patient. For example, the presence of cirrhosis of the liver, a not uncommon condition among heavy alcohol users

with advanced oesophageal cancer, may preclude the use of many chemotherapeutic agents. In contrast, an early cancer in an otherwise healthy patient may be treated by surgical resection alone. Radiation or chemotherapy may be used prior to surgery (so-called neoadjuvant therapy) in

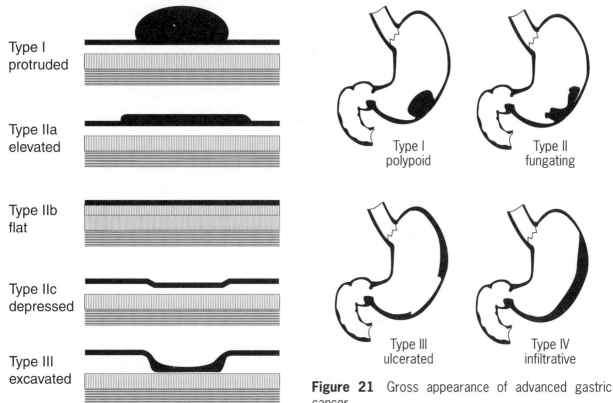

Type I
protruded

Type IIa
elevated

Type IIb
flat

Type IIc
depressed

Type III
excavated

Type I
polypoid

Type II
fungating

Type III
ulcerated

Type IV
infiltrative

Figure 21 Gross appearance of advanced gastric cancer.

Figure 20 Gross appearance of early gastric cancer.

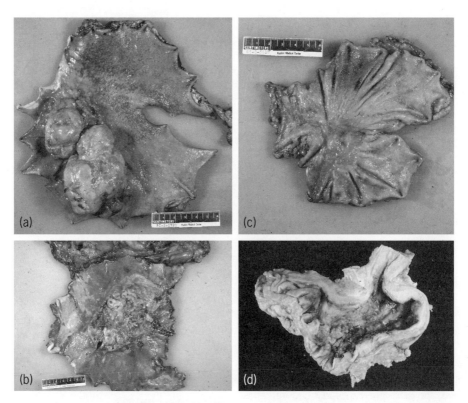

Figure 22 Gross appearance of gastric cancer. (a) Borman type I gastric carcinoma is a bulky tumour protruding into the gastric lumen. (b) A Borman type III lesion shows a heaped-up, ulcerated lesion. (c) A Borman type II gastric carcinoma shows a fungating tumour. (d) Linitis plastica with diffuse thickening of the gastric wall.

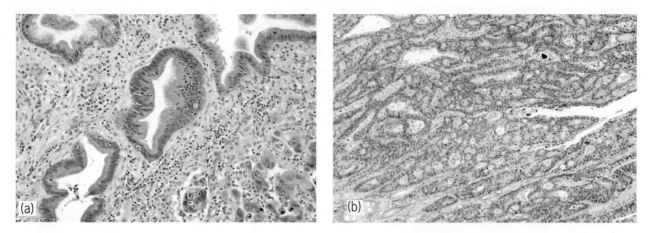

Figure 23 Gastric cancer of the intestinal type. (a) A combination of well- and poorly-differentiated carcinoma. The tumour forms reasonably intact glands everywhere except in the lower right-hand corner where they are discohesive. (b) Back-to-back glands in a moderately differentiated intestinal-type carcinoma.

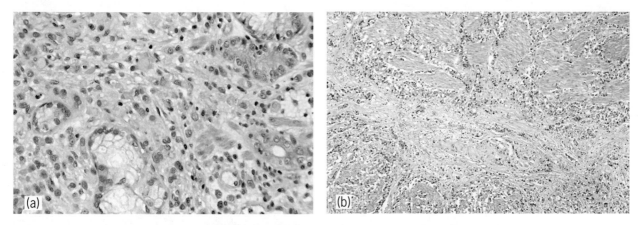

Figure 24 Diffuse gastric carcinoma. In contrast to the cancers illustrated in Figure 23, glandular formations are not present. (a) The tumour cells diffusely infiltrate the intestinal wall. (b) Infiltration of these same cells through the deeper layer of the stomach.

Table 1 World Health Organization classification of histological types of epithelial tumours of the stomach

Adenocarcinoma	Adenosquamous carcinoma
Papillary	Squamous cell carcinoma
Tubular	Undifferentiated carcinoma
Mucinous	Unclassified carcinoma
Signet ring cell carcinoma	

order to reduce the tumour to manageable proportions or may be used to supplement a surgical procedure so as to diminish the risk of early recurrence, so-called adjuvant therapy. Radiation may also be used alone to palliate symptoms in treating patients with inoperable disease.

The relative 5-year survival with oesophageal cancer in the United States for the year ending 1988 was only 8.1%. This is a measure of the grim prognosis that accompanies the late-stage cancers that prevail in that country. Fewer than 3% of patients with late-stage tumours survive for 5 years after diagnosis.

Table 2 TNM classification of oesophageal tumours

Primary tumour (T)	
T1	No obstruction or circumferential involvement
T2	Obstruction and/or circumferential involvement
T3	Extraesophageal spread
Nodal involvement (N) (surgical evaluation)	
N0	No involvement
N1	Positive nodes
Distant metastases (M)	
M0	None
M1	Present
Stage I	T1, N0, M0
Stage II	T1, N1, M0T2, N0, M0
Stage III	Any T3
	Any M1

Adenocarcinoma

Adenocarcinomas extensively infiltrate the oesophageal wall and often show lymphatic and vascular involvement, as well as direct extension through the oesophageal wall. Both regional and distant metastases develop. Primary oesophageal adenocarcinomas rarely spread distally into the stomach, whereas proximal spread commonly occurs.

About 33% of intramucosal tumours, 67% of intramural and 89% of transmural oesophageal adenocarcinomas metastasize to the regional lymph nodes; 60% of patients with nodal recurrence have recurrence at sites outside the resection margins. Patients with lymphatic metastases can be cured, particularly if fewer than four nodes are involved.

Stomach

The microscopic measurement of the depth of tumour penetration of the stomach wall and quantification of the number of regional lymph nodes involved by cancer are the most consistent methods for predicting the subsequent course of gastric cancer. This method is called the TNM system, as in the oesophagus, and is used to identify the stage of the tumour at the time of diagnosis. This staging system is summarized in **Table 3**. A British study of 31 716 gastric cancers showed that as stomach cancers advance from stage I to IV, the 5-year survival drops from 80% to less than 3%. These data reflect the experience of gastric cancer patients in most Western countries prior to the development of modern diagnostic and therapeutic methods (Craven, 1993). The cancers in this series were so far advanced that only 20% were considered suitable for curative resections. More recent Japanese experience reflects the advantage of making a diagnosis in early stage disease, of more extensive surgery and of adjuvant chemotherapy for advanced disease. A report of 2824 patients treated between 1979 and 1990 noted that 95% were considered suitable for surgical resection, that half of the patients were at Stage 1 and that their overall 5-year survival was 72% (Kinoshita *et al.*, 1993).

Surgery remains the principal treatment for gastric cancer; the extent of surgery depends upon tumour stage. Japanese surgeons who have had the opportunity to treat many early cancers have used sonographic techniques to assess the depth of tumour invasion and have excised the tumour from the stomach lining endoscopically, leaving the stomach intact. Unfortunately, this procedure is not applicable to the late-stage tumours typically found in Western patients. Resection of all, or part, of the stomach is required for all advanced, operable tumours. As in the oesophagus, surgery may be supplemented by neoadjuvant or adjuvant radiation and chemotherapy. The relative 5-year survival of stomach cancer patients in the United States, treated in the years 1983–1989 was only 16.9%, reflecting the late stage of the great majority of these cancers at the time of presentation.

Table 3 TNM classification of gastric cancers

1. Primary tumour (T)

The principal factor is the degree of penetration of the stomach wall by carcinoma.

TX Primary tumour cannot be assessed
T0 No evidence of primary tumour
Tis Carcinoma *in situ*: intraepithelial tumour without invasion of the lamina propria
T1 Tumour invades lamina propria or submucosa
T2 Tumour invades the muscularis propria or subserosa
T3 Tumour penetrates the serosa (visceral peritoneum) without invasion of adjacent structures
T4 Tumour invades adjacent structures (spleen, transverse colon, liver, diaphragm, pancreas, abdominal wall, adrenal gland, kidney, small intestine and retroperitoneum)

2. Nodal involvement (N)

The regional nodes include the perigastric nodes along the lesser and greater curvatures and the nodes along the left gastric, common hepatic, splenic and coeliac arteries. Involvement of other intraabdominal nodes represents distant metastasis.

NX Regional lymph nodes cannot be assessed
N0 No regional lymph node metastasis
N1 Metastasis in perigastric lymph nodes within 3 cm of the edge of the primary tumour
N2 Metastasis in perigastric lymph nodes greater than 3 cm from the edge of the primary tumour, or metastasis in lymph nodes along the left gastric, common hepatic, splenic and coeliac arteries

3. Distant metastasis (M)

MX Presence of distant metastasis cannot be assessed
M0 No distant metastasis
M1 Distant metastasis

MOLECULAR GENETIC FINDINGS

Oesophageal Cancer

Squamous Cell Carcinoma

A condition known as tylosis accounts for some forms of familial SCC. This autosomal dominant genetic disorder associates with oesophageal cancer in 90% of affected persons. The cancers usually appear during middle age, but are presaged in early life by marked thickening and fissuring of the palms of the hands and soles of the feet. Tylosis results from a mutation in the *TOC* (tylosis oesophageal cancer) gene on chromosome 17.

Molecular alterations are more commonly investigated in patients with sporadic oesophageal SCC and a number of abnormalities have been detected. These include the accumulation of p53 protein in aggressive cancers. The p53 protein is overexpressed in more than 75% of oesophageal SCC and it may associate with dietary factors. It may also predict responsiveness to chemotherapy. (The *p53* gene is important in regulating the cell cycle and it plays a critical role in protecting the cell from acquiring genetic damage that can be passed on to daughter cells. When the gene is overexpressed it is usually due to the presence of a mutation that potentially makes the protein nonfunctional and therefore predisposes the altered cells to genetic instability.) Another gene that is commonly abnormal in oesophageal SCCs is the *Cyclin D1* gene (another cell-cycle regulator) which is frequently amplified and overexpressed. Allelic loss on chromosome 13q12–13 may associate with lymph node metastasis in these patients.

Adenocarcinoma

Oesophageal adenocarcinomas associate with a number of molecular abnormalities, some of which resemble those seen in other gastrointestinal adenocarcinomas. Abnormalities in the expression of growth factors and their receptors, especially epidermal growth factor receptor, epidermal growth factor and transforming growth factor alpha, occur commonly and may contribute to nonregulated cell growth. These three substances are overexpressed in Barrett oesophagus and in oesophageal adenocarcinomas and may play a role in the progression of Barrett oesophagus to carcinoma, perhaps by providing a proliferative advantage to metaplastic cells overexpressing the proteins. Another protein related to cell proliferation that becomes abnormal in Barrett oesophagus and the cancers associated with it is p27, which is a cyclin-dependent kinase inhibitor and a negative regulator of cell cycle division. It is found that p27 is inactivated in many Barrett oesophagus-associated cancers and its loss associates with an aggressive tumour behaviour and unfavourable outcome. Other genes that may also be abnormal in patients with oesophageal adenocarcinomas are those which are often altered in colon cancer. These include the *p53* gene mentioned above for oesophageal SCC, the *APC* gene (a gene that predisposes to colon cancer) and the *DCC* (deleted in colon cancer) gene.

Gastric Cancer

There are several forms of hereditary gastric cancer in which the genetic makeup of the patient and the patient's family strongly favour the development of gastric cancer.

Germ-line mutations account for a small proportion of familial gastric cancer clusters, some of which may also be influenced by environmental factors. The hereditary nonpolyposis colon cancer (HNPCC) syndrome is an autosomal dominant disease that carries an increased risk of stomach and colon cancer. It results from a germ-line mutation in one of a number of DNA mismatch repair genes. Affected cells are susceptible to an accelerated accumulation of mutations.

Familial adenomatous polyposis (FAP) resulting from germ-line mutations in the *APC* gene on the long arm of chromosome 5 predispose patients to intestinal polyposis and cancer. In addition, the stomach develops adenomas that may evolve into carcinomas. An environmental influence on the underlying genetic alteration is suggested by the observation that Japanese patients with FAP more frequently have gastric adenomas and carcinomas than Westerners with this trait, reflecting the higher risk of gastric cancer experienced by all Japanese (Utsonomiya *et al.*, 1994).

A newly recognized autosomal dominant mutation in the E-cadherin gene was first found in a familial cluster of poorly differentiated gastric cancers in a Maori, New Zealand family. This observation was quickly followed by the observation of other gastric cancer families with germ-line E-cadherin mutations in Europe, Korea and Japan (Gayther *et al.*, 1998). The gastric cancer resulting from this defect develops in early life and is diffuse in type. E-cadherin is an adhesion molecule, and loss of its function might explain the discohesive growth pattern of these diffuse tumours.

Genetic polymorphisms may also contribute to gastric cancer risk. Inherited differences in the ability to detoxify potential carcinogens, and inherited variations in the ability to induce transcription or programmed cell death might explain some familial clusters of gastric cancer. The glutathione *S*-transferase enzyme system represents an example of a polymorphism that may favour the development of gastric cancer. These enzymes catalyse the conjugation of numerous carcinogens. Persons lacking the mu form of this enzyme (GSTM1) constitute 40% of the Japanese population and absence of this form of the enzyme increases the risk of developing gastric cancer (Katoh *et al.*, 1996). A similar finding has been noted in an English study. Smoking increases the risk of both gastric cancer and its precursor lesion, intestinal metaplasia of the stomach lining. The null variant of this enzyme may contribute to the increased gastric cancer risk associated with smoking due to alterations in the production of potential gastric carcinogens present in tobacco smoke. These interactions may be further modulated by dietary influences.

Polymorphisms present at codon 72 of the *p53* gene may also be important in the development of gastric cancer. Ethnic differences occur in the frequencies of different forms of this codon. The majority of people of European origin are *p53* arginine homozygotes, as are patients with cancer of the cardia of the stomach. Whether the predilection for cardia cancers to occur among white males is due to excess vulnerability derived from *p53* arginine homozygosity, or only reflects parallel, unrelated traits, remains to be determined. The same observation applies to the association of blacks with the presence of a proline allele at codon 72 and antral GC.

CONCLUSION

It is apparent that environmental hazards account for most oesophageal and stomach cancers worldwide. Both tumours are closely related to a poor economic status. Prevention of these cancers is a socioeconomic rather than a medical problem, and should include improved housing, raised living standards, better education and a food distribution system that makes fresh fruit and vegetables available on a year-round basis to all levels of society. Medical intervention is necessary when these ideals are not achieved, but this will only produce a major reduction in mortality rates if the proportion of patients who are treated in the early stages of tumour progression is greatly increased. The Japanese and Chinese community screening programmes for stomach and oesophageal cancer have achieved this result and they are clearly adaptable to other high-risk societies, and the development of focused, tumour-specific, screening programmes is necessary where these cancers are less common. These should be given high priority since the late stages of these tumours have not proved amenable to currently available therapeutic strategies.

REFERENCES

Aoki, K., *et al.* (1992). Death rates for malignant neoplasms for selected sites by sex and five year age group in 33 countries, 1953–57 to 1983–87. *70–155. UICC* (University of Nagoya Press, Nagoya).

Blaser, M., *et al.* (1995). Infection with helicobacter pylori strains possessing cag A is associated with increased risk of adencarcinomas of the stomach. *Cancer Research*, **55**, 2111–2115.

Correa, P. (1988). A human model of gastric carcinogenesis. *Cancer Research*, **48**, 3554–3560.

Correa, P., *et al.* (1973). Pathology of gastric carcinoma in Japanese populations: comparison between Miyagi Prefecture, Japan and Hawaii. *Journal of the National Cancer Institute*, **51**, 1449–1459.

Craven, J. L. (1993). End results of surgical treatment: British experience. In: Nishi, M., *et al.* (eds), *Gastric Cancer*. 341–348 (Springer, Berlin).

Dent, J. (1989). Approaches to oesophageal columnar metaplasia (Barrett's esophagus). *Scandinavian Journal of Gastroenterology*, **168**, 60.

Fenoglio-Preiser, C. M., *et al.* (1999). *Gastrointestinal Pathology, an Atlas and Text*. Oesophageal structure and development, 15–29; gastric structure and development, 133–151 (Lippincott-Raven, Philadelphia).

Fisher, S. G., *et al.* (1993). A cohort study of stomach cancer in men after gastric surgery for benign disease. *Journal of the National Cancer Institute*, **85**, 1303–1310.

Gayther, S. A., *et al.* (1998). Identification of germline E-cadherin mutations in gastric cancer families of European origin. *Cancer Research*, **58**, 4086–4089.

Goodman, K. J. and Correa, P. (1995). The transmission of *Helicobacter pylori*. A critical review of the evidence. *International Journal of Epidemiology*, **24**, 875–887.

Jankowski, J. A., *et al.* (2000). Barrett's metaplasia. *Lancet*, **356**, 2079–2085.

Katoh, T., *et al.* (1996). Glutathione S-transferase M1 (GSTM1) and T1 (GSTT1) genetic polymorphism and susceptiblity to gastric and colorectal adenocarcinoma. *Carcinogenesis*, **17**, 1855–1859.

Kinoshita, T., *et al.* (1993). Treatment results of gastric cancer patients: Japanese experience. In: Nishi, M., *et al.* (eds) Gastric Cancer. 319–330 (Springer, Berlin).

Kitahara, F., *et al.* (1999). Accuracy of screening for gastric cancer using pepsinogen concentration. *Gut*, **4**, 693–697.

Lauren, P. (1965). The two histologic main types of gastric carcinoma: diffuse and so-called intestinal type carcinoma. An attempt at a histo-clinical classification. *Acta Pathologica Microbiologica Scandinavica*, **64**, 31–49.

Lehtola, J. (1978). Family study of gastric carcinoma. *Scandinavian Journal of Gastroenterology*, **13** (Suppl. 50), 1–54.

Lewin, K. and Appleman, H. (1996). Tumors of the esophagus and stomach. In: Rosai, J. (ed.), *Atlas of Tumor Pathology*. 43–144 (Armed Forces Institute of Pathology, Washington, DC).

Munoz, N. and Day, N. E. (1996). Esophageal cancer. In: Schottenfeld, D. and Fraumeni, J. E., Jr (eds), *Cancer Epidemiology and Prevention*. 681–706 (Oxford University Press, New York).

Nomura, A. M. Y. (1996). Stomach cancer. In: Schottenfeld, D. and Fraumeni, J. E., Jr (eds), *Cancer Epidemiology and Prevention*. 707–724 (Oxford University Press, New York).

Nomura, A. M. Y. and Stemmermann, G. N. (1993). *Helicobacter pylori* and gastric cancer – a review article. *Journal of Gastroenterology and Hepatology*, **8**, 294–303.

Qiu, S. and Yang, G. (1988). Precursor lesions of esophageal cancer in high risk populations of Henan Province China. *Cancer*, **62**, 551–557.

Samloff, I. M. and Liebman, N. M. (1973). Cellular localization of group II pepsinogens in human gastric mucosa by immunofluorescence. *Gastroenterology*, **65**, 36–42.

Samloff, I. M., *et al.* (1975). A study of the relationship between serum group I pepsinogen and gastric acid secretion. *Gastroenterology*, **66**, 494–502.

Sandler, R. S., *et al.* (1995). The risk of esophageal cancer in patients with achalsia. *Journal of the American Medical Association*, **274**, 1359–1362.

Sokoloff, B. (1939). Predisposition to cancer in the Bonaparte family. *American Journal of Surgery*, **40**, 673–678.

Stemmermann, G. N. (1994). Intestinal metaplasia of the stomach, a status report. *Cancer*, **74**, 556–564.

Tyuns, A. J., *et al.* (1977). Le cancer de l'oesophage en Ille-et Vilaine en fonction des niveaux de consommation de alcool et tabac. Des risques qui se multiplient. *Bulletin du Cancer*, **64**, 45–60.

Utsonomiya, J., *et al*. (1994). Hereditary gastric cancer. *Surgical Clinics of North America*, **3**, 545–562.

Zheng, T., *et al*. (1993). The time trend of age-period cohort effects on the incidence of adenocarcinoma of the stomach in Connecticut from 1955–1989. *Cancer*, **72**, 330–340.

Ziegler, R. G. (1986). Alcohol–nutrient interactions in cancer etiology. *Cancer*, **58**, 1942–1958.

Smalley, S. R. and Williamson, S. K. (1996). Radiation and combined modality therapy for stomach cancer. In: Wanebo, H. J. (ed.), *Surgery for Gastrointestinal Cancer: a Multidisciplinary Approach*. 363–369 (Lippincott-Raven, Phildelphia).

Weber, W., *et al*. (1996). *Familial Cancer Management* (CRC Press, Boca Raton, FL).

FURTHER READING

Powell, S. M. (1997). Stomach cancer. In: Vogelstein, B. and Kinzle, K. W. (eds), *The Genetic Basis of Human Cancer*. 647–650 (McGraw-Hill, New York).

Chapter 38

Lower Gastrointestinal Tract

Jeremy R. Jass

University of Queensland, Brisbane, Australia

C O N T E N T S

NORMAL DEVELOPMENT AND STRUCTURE

Development

The foregut, midgut and hindgut are derived from the embryonic yolk sac, which is of endodermal origin. During embryogenesis, the midgut communicates with the remains of the yolk sac via the vitello-intestinal duct. The midgut is supplied by the superior mesenteric artery and from it develop the third and fourth parts of the duodenum, jejunum, ileum, caecum, appendix, ascending colon and transverse colon. As the midgut lengthens, it becomes coiled and this promotes the development of its dorsal mesentery containing the superior mesenteric artery. Eventually, the midgut can no longer be accommodated in the abdominal cavity and it is extruded into the umbilical cord as a physiological hernia. A process of rotation occurs before the gut is restored to the abdominal cavity and takes up its normal anatomical position.

The hindgut is suspended by a shorter mesentery through which passes the inferior mesenteric artery to supply the descending colon, sigmoid colon and upper rectum. The superior, middle and inferior rectal arteries are derived from the inferior mesenteric, internal iliac and internal pudendal arteries, respectively. At 5 weeks, the distal hindgut, allantois and urogenital tract end in a common cloaca. Downward growth by the urorectal septum occurs until it fuses with the cloacal membrane. Two anal tubercles arise from adjacent ectoderm to fuse with the urorectal septum, forming the proctodeum where ectoderm and endoderm are in direct contact. The proctodeum then fuses with the rectum and canalizes during the third month to become the anus.

Gross Appearance

The small intestine is approximately 500 cm in length (shorter in life owing to tone in the longitudinal muscle coat) and lacking obvious features on external examination apart from its mesentery (the duodenum is retroperitoneal). The large intestine (colon and rectum) is 150 cm in length and variably covered by peritoneum in its different regions. The longitudinal muscle is arranged in three continuous bands (taeniae coli) which fuse into a continuous sheet at the junction of sigmoid colon and rectum. The taeniae coli shorten the colon and produce the characteristic sacculations or haustra. The colon is also distinguished from the small intestine on external inspection by the rows of fat tags called epiploic appendages. The superior and inferior mesenteric arteries anastomose via a continuous marginal artery along the mesenteric border of the colon (**Figure 1**).

Histology

The layers of the intestinal wall from within outwards comprise mucosa, submucosa, muscle coat and serosa or peritoneum (**Figure 2**). The mucosa consists of columnar

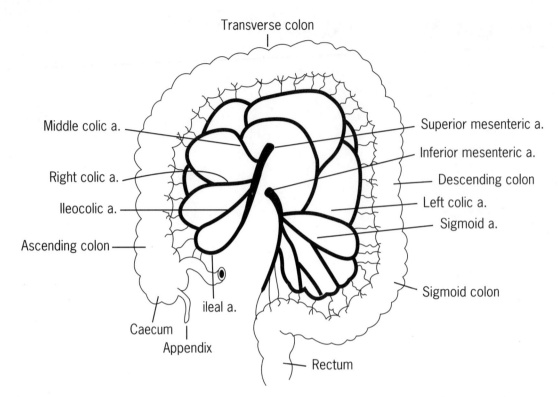

Transverse colon

Middle colic a.

Right colic a.

Ileocolic a.

Ascending colon

ileal a.

Caecum

Appendix

Superior mesenteric a.

Inferior mesenteric a.

Descending colon

Left colic a.

Sigmoid a.

Sigmoid colon

Rectum

Figure 1 Transverse colon lifted to show arterial blood supply to the large intestine. (a. = artery)

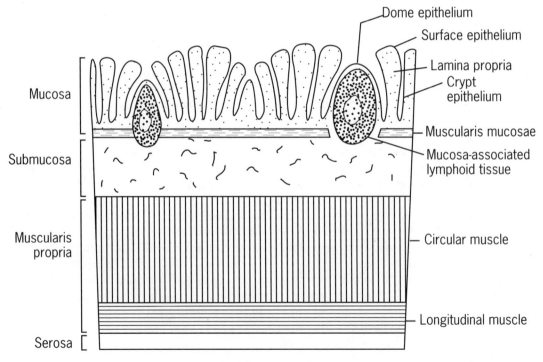

Dome epithelium

Surface epithelium

Lamina propria

Crypt epithelium

Muscularis mucosae

Mucosa-associated lymphoid tissue

Mucosa

Submucosa

Muscularis propria

Circular muscle

Longitudinal muscle

Serosa

Figure 2 Layers forming wall of large intestine.

epithelium, a delicate connective tissue or lamina propria and a thin sheet of muscle called the muscularis mucosae. The epithelium comprises secretory crypts and an absorptive surface layer. In the small intestine, but not the colon or rectum, the area of the surface epithelium is greatly increased by the formation of finger-like villi.

The columnar epithelium comprises columnar cells, goblet cells, endocrine cells and Paneth cells (the latter are limited to the small intestine and proximal colon). These cells are derived from a common precursor or stem cell. The lower crypt includes the replicative compartment. Maturing cells migrate up the crypt and reach the surface epithelium within a matter of days where they undergo apoptosis.

TUMOUR PATHOLOGY

In this section, a brief overview will be given of the types of tumour that may occur in the lower intestinal tract, both cancerous and benign. The rest of this chapter will focus upon the most common and important cancer: carcinoma of the colon and rectum.

Types of Tumour

The types of tumour reflect the normal tissues that contribute to the structure of the intestinal tract (Jass and Sobin, 1989).

Epithelial Tumours

The columnar or glandular epithelium of the intestinal tract gives rise to benign and malignant neoplasms termed adenoma and adenocarcinoma, respectively. The colon and rectum are by far the most common sites of both adenoma and adenocarcinoma in the lower intestinal tract. Most adenocarcinomas arise in a pre-existing adenoma and these lesions may be viewed as a neoplastic continuum. However, only about 5% of adenomas will transform into adenocarcinomas. Multiple adenomas occur in the colon, rectum,

duodenum and appendix in the rare autosomal dominant condition familial adenomatous polyposis (FAP) which is caused by mutation of the Adenomatous Polyposis Coli (*APC*) gene.

Certain types of epithelial polyp that have traditionally been regarded as non-neoplastic may occur in the intestinal tract. They are noted here (**Table 1**) because it is now appreciated that these lesions may show clonal genetic alterations and under certain circumstances may be precancerous. These polyps may be either single, occur in small numbers or be so numerous that the term polyposis is used. The commonest epithelial polyp is the hyperplastic polyp and occurs principally within the distal colon and rectum. These small polyps are characterized histologically by a saw-tooth or serrated crypt outline. While regarded as innocuous lesions, colorectal cancer has been associated with the rare condition hyperplastic polyposis in which the polyps are large and distributed throughout the colorectum.

Two types of epithelial polyp are classified as hamartomas (a maldevelopment in which epithelial and connective tissues are arranged in a haphazard manner). One of these occurs as part of the autosomal dominant Peutz–Jeghers syndrome (germ-line mutation of *STK11*). Peutz–Jeghers polyps are multiple and tend to be most numerous within the small intestine. Juvenile polyps are the second type of hamartoma and occur in the colon and rectum either singly, in small numbers or multiply in the autosomal dominant condition juvenile polyposis (germ-line mutations identified in *DPC4/Smad4*). Both Peutz–Jeghers syndrome and juvenile polyposis are associated with an increased risk of intestinal cancer. Endocrine cell tumours are considered in the chapter Systemic Oncology of the Endocrine Organs.

The lower anal canal is lined by squamous epithelium. Squamous cell carcinoma may arise from this site. Although uncommon, the frequency of this cancer is increasing in both males and females. Human papillomavirus (types 16 and 18) has been implicated in the aetiology; risk factors and mechanisms are similar to those underlying squamous cell carcinoma of the female genital tract (see the chapter *Systemic Oncology of the Female Reproductive System*).

Table 1   Nature and distribution of epithelial polyps of the intestinal tract

| Type | Nature | Site[a] | | | |
		Small intestine	Appendix	Colon	Rectum
Adenoma Tubular Tubulovillous Villous	Neoplastic	S	S	U	U
Hyperplastic	Unknown	N	S	S	U
Peutz-Jeghers	Hamartoma	U	N	S	S
Juvenile	Hamartoma	S	N	U	U
Inflammatory	Inflammatory	N	N	U	S

[a]U = usual site; S = site of occurrence; N = not found (or uncommon).

Lymphoid Tumours

Lymphoid tissue is distributed throughout the intestinal tract with notable collections in the terminal ileum known as Peyer's patches. Mucosa-associated lymphoid tissue (MALT) is organized differently from nodal lymphoid tissue in terms of both structure and function. Lymphoid neoplasms are malignant by definition and those arising in MALT are known as MALTomas and are derived from B-lymphocytes. The stomach does not normally contain lymphoid tissue, yet MALTomas are more common in this organ than the intestine (see the chapter *Systemic Oncology of the Upper Gastrointestinal Tract*). A special type of MALToma occurs in the small intestine and affects populations around the Mediterranean and in the Middle East. The neoplastic B-lymphocytes secrete α heavy chains (a component of immunoglobulin class A) and the lymphoma is also known as α heavy chain disease or immunoproliferative small intestinal disease (IPSID). Two additional B-lymphocyte lymphomas of the intestinal tract are Burkitt lymphoma occurring mainly in Africa and principally affecting the ileocaecal region and mantle cell lymphoma presenting as multiple mucosal polyps throughout the gastrointestinal tract. There is also a rare T-cell lymphoma which mainly affects the proximal jejunum and is most common in people of Northern Europe. Many of these lymphomas are associated with gluten-sensitive enteropathy or coeliac disease.

Stromal Tumours

Despite the large amount of smooth muscle and connective tissue in the wall of the intestinal tract, stromal tumours are uncommon. Gastrointestinal stromal tumours (GISTs) were considered to be tumours of smooth muscle in the past, but most are now known to express the phenotype of a pacemaker cell found in the muscle coat (interstitial cell of Cajal). Behaviour is unpredictable but large size and a high mitotic rate are markers of malignancy. Bona fide smooth muscles occur in the rectum; most are small and benign.

Secondary (Metastatic) Cancer

The intestinal tract is not a common site of metastatic cancer. The small intestine is the main site for metastases and melanoma, breast and lung cancer are the principal primary sources.

EPIDEMIOLOGY

Colorectal cancer is a leading cause of cancer death, second only to lung cancer in the West. It is responsible for 55 000 deaths per year in the USA. There were around 875 000 new cases worldwide in 1996, accounting for 8.5% of all cancers diagnosed in that year. Incidence rates vary by at least a factor of 20 between countries, with the highest rates being found in the West and the lowest in the developing world (Potter, 1999). Although these differences are exaggerated by competing causes of mortality in developing countries, such as infectious disease and other types of cancer, age-adjusted statistics show that the low incidence is genuine. Colon and rectal cancers share many environmental risk factors, but differences exist also. Colonic cancer occurs with approximately equal frequency in males and females whereas rectal cancer is at least twice as common in males.

Time trends indicate rapid increases in incidence in countries or populations that have adopted Western lifestyles in recent years. Examples include Japan, urban China and male Polynesians in Hawaii. Colonic cancer seems to be more sensitive to these changes than rectal cancer. Migrant studies have shown that populations migrating from low-risk to high-risk countries rapidly acquire the incidence rates of the adopted country, sometimes within the migrating generation. For example, one of the highest rates in the world is seen among Hawaiian Japanese (Haenszel, 1961).

Colorectal cancer is age related, colonic cancer more so than rectal. There will be competing causes of mortality in ageing populations and the mean age at presentation in most hospital series falls within the range 65–75 years. The age relationship, common to many types of solid cancer, is a reflection of the time-related multistep evolution of cancer. The stepwise accumulation of genetic errors in somatic cells requires a particular passage of time. In individuals who inherit one of the causative genetic errors, each somatic cell is already primed (or one step ahead). Such individuals develop multiple neoplasms and at an early age. This is observed in several forms of hereditary colorectal cancer (see below).

AETIOLOGY

The aetiology of colorectal cancer is not known but the brief account of descriptive epidemiology given above indicates the involvement of both environmental influences and genetic factors. The major shifts in incidence following migration were once taken as evidence of the overwhelming importance of the environment. Nevertheless, individuals inhabiting high-risk areas may live to advanced years without even developing a minute adenoma (the earliest visible signs of colorectal neoplasia). Conversely, an inherited genetic mutation may lead to early onset disease in an inhabitant of a low-risk area. The modern approach to unravelling the aetiology of colorectal cancer integrates lifestyle factors and genetic constitution within the discipline of molecular epidemiology.

Dietary and Lifestyle Factors

Vegetables and Fibre

Particular dietary practices have been associated with colorectal cancer in defined groups of subjects (cohort studies) or comparing affected cases with matched controls (case-control studies) (Trock *et al.*, 1990). However, these studies demonstrate associations rather than specific causality. Diets high in vegetables (raw, green or cruciferous) are protective although the nature of the specific agent is unclear. High on the list is fibre (the complex carbohydrate constituent of plant cell walls), which could act by diluting or binding potential carcinogens in the lumen of the bowel. Fibre is poorly digested in the small intestine but is fermented by bacteria in the proximal colon to generate short-chain fatty acids, notably butyrate. Resistant starch (that is not digested in the small bowel) is another source of butyric acid. Butyrate serves as an essential respiratory nutrient for colonic epithelium and its lack may be a factor in the aetiology of colorectal cancer. Butyrate may also serve as a protective factor in its capacity as a differentiating agent. Vegetables are high in folate and absence of this vitamin may also serve as a risk factor.

Meat and Fat

Estimates of risk of colorectal cancer have been either increased or null in cohort and case-control studies examining the role of dietary meat and fat. It appears that total protein consumption is relatively unimportant whereas meat preparation (processing or heavy cooking) may generate carcinogens such as heterocyclic amines. Additionally, saturated fat of animal origin may be associated with increased risk (Potter, 1999).

Calcium and Bile Acids

Epidemiological studies and intervention data indicate a protective role for dietary calcium. A possible mechanism may be the conversion of ionized fatty acids and faecal bile acids into insoluble salts. Deoxycholic and lithocholic acid are bacterially deconjugated bile acids that have been shown to serve as promoters or co-mutagens in experimental studies of colonic carcinogenesis. Faecal bile acid levels have in turn been correlated with meat consumption.

Selenium

This essential trace element is a component of the enzyme glutathione peroxidase which catalyses the removal of intracellular hydrogen peroxide. Deficiency of selenium occurs when diets lack whole grains and vegetables or when soil levels are low. A protective role is supported by epidemiological and intervention studies.

Smoking and Alcohol

Higher risks of colonic (not rectal) cancer and adenomas have been associated with a long history of smoking. The association with alcohol is less clear, beer being implicated in rectal cancer in males.

Non-steroidal Anti-inflammatory Drugs (NSAIDS)

NSAIDS, including aspirin, have been shown to lower the risk of colorectal cancer in cohort and case-control studies. Sulindac causes adenomas to regress in FAP and stabilizes the disordered apoptotic ratio that occurs in the normal colorectal mucosa of subjects with FAP. (See the chapter *Dietary Genotoxins and Cancer*.)

Genetic Factors–High-prevalence Polymorphisms

N-Acetyltransferases (NAT1, NAT2) and Cytochrome P450 (CYP) Enzymes

The weak effects of diet upon cancer risk might be increased by genetic factors. For example, at least three enzymes (NAT1, NAT2 and CYP1A2) influence the metabolism of heterocyclic amines produced in the course of cooking meat at high temperatures and hydrocarbons contained in tobacco smoke. Particular genetic polymorphisms affect the activities of these enzyme systems, but consistent correlations between genotypes, lifestyle factors and risk have not been demonstrated to date (Potter, 1999).

Methylenetetrahydrofolate reductase (MTHFR)

Folate may serve as a protective factor through influencing methylation of DNA and the size of the nucleotide pool required for DNA synthesis and repair. The polymorphic enzyme MTHFR appears to increase the risk of colorectal neoplasia in subjects with a particular genotype (TT) and a low-folate diet (Potter, 1999). Some tumour suppressor genes are silenced through hypermethylation of the promoter region. However, this mechanism applies mainly to the subset of colorectal cancers showing DNA microsatellite instability (MSI).

Genetic Factors–Rare Inherited Syndromes

Familial Adenomatous Polyposis (FAP)

About 1 in 8000 individuals carries a mutation in the tumour suppressor gene *APC*, either inherited (75%) or acquired as a new mutation (25%). The disease manifests as an autosomal dominant trait in which affected individuals develop many hundreds and usually thousands of colorectal adenomas in their teens. By the age of 50, one or more of these polyps is likely to have transformed into a carcinoma. The severity of the disease in terms of polyp numbers depends upon the nature of the germline mutation and modifying influences of other genes. Extracolonic manifestations occur, notably duodenal adenoma and carcinoma, fibromatosis (aggressive but non-metastasizing tumour composed of fibroblasts), benign bone tumours, sebaceous cysts of the skin, pancreatic cancer, thyroid cancer, hepatoblastoma (primary liver tumour recapitulating embryonic liver) and tumours of the central nervous system.

Inactivation of the normal or wild-type *APC* gene, by either mutation or loss, is sufficient to initiate and allow further growth of adenomas. The germ-line mutation leads to subtle growth disturbance of the normal colorectal mucosa by a dominant negative effect (not requiring mutation or loss of the normal copy of the gene). These changes include an increased rate of crypt fission and a disordered distribution of cells undergoing apoptosis (more in the crypt base and less on the epithelial surface) (Wasan *et al.*, 1998; Keller *et al.*, 1999). The *APC* gene mediates its normal function (the control of growth, differentiation and proliferation) through the *wnt* signalling pathway.

I1307K Mutation of APC

This mutation, found only in Ashkenazi Jews, creates a repetitive poly-A sequence that is subject to replication error, in turn causing protein truncation. Small numbers of adenomas and cancers occur in affected family members.

Hereditary Non-Polyposis Colorectal Cancer (HNPCC)

This autosomal dominant condition is caused by mutation of one of a family of DNA mismatch repair genes. The most frequently implicated are *hMLH1* and *hMSH2* followed by *hMSH6*, *hPMS1* and *hPMS2*. The germ-line mutation is nearly always inherited rather than new to an individual. Nevertheless, an obvious family history may not be apparent in small families as penetrance (the extent to which a mutated gene is expressed phenotypically) is not 100%. The frequency of disease causing mutations in particular populations may be exaggerated by founder effects (where a particular affected individual has been succeeded by multiple, large generations within a relatively sparsely populated region). Approximately 2% of individuals developing bowel cancer in the West do so on the basis of HNPCC. Since around one in 20 individuals will develop colorectal cancer, the population frequency of disease-causing mutations must be around 1 in 1000.

The first step leading to neoplasia in HNPCC is somatic mutation or loss of the second (wild-type) mismatch repair gene. Some genes, such as *TGFβRII* and *BAX*, contain short repetitive tracts that serve as targets for mismatch errors occurring during DNA replication. If the DNA repair mechanism is not operating adequately, the mismatch mutations will not be repaired. Particular mutations, for example in *TGFβRII*, will initiate the development of a neoplastic clone. Most mismatch errors, however, occur in non-coding repetitive tracts or microsatellites. The resulting microsatellite instability does not drive carcinogenesis but is a useful biomarker for HNPCC.

Approximately 70% of subjects carrying an HNPCC germ-line mutation will develop colorectal cancer by the age of 65 years and at a mean age of 45 years. Extracolonic cancers may develop in the uterus (endometrium), ovary, stomach, small intestine, central nervous system and urinary tract (pelviureter). Benign sebaceous gland adenomas may occur in the facial skin (the combination of sebaceous adenoma and colorectal cancer has been called Muir–Torre syndrome but is part of the HNPCC spectrum). The majority of colorectal cancers arise in adenomas. Although adenomas do not occur in large numbers in HNPCC, an individual adenoma carries a high risk of progressing to cancer and does so within a short timeframe. This accounts for cancer multiplicity and the clinical impression of *de novo* origin of cancer. Paradoxically, the colorectal cancers in HNPCC are relatively non-aggressive in terms of their potential for metastasis. Around 60% of colorectal cancers arise in the proximal colon (caecum, ascending or transverse colon) (Lynch *et al.*, 1996).

Germline Mutation of TGFβ Type II Receptor

This is a rare cause of familial colorectal cancer.

Chronic Inflammation

The risk of colorectal cancer is increased in subjects with chronic or longstanding inflammation of the large intestine, notably due to ulcerative colitis and Crohn's disease. A possible mechanism may be genetic damage by reactive oxygen species (superoxide, H_2O_2 and hydroxyl radicals), in turn generated by the inflammatory mediators released by inflammatory cells such as neutrophils and macrophages. Cycles of inflammatory damage and healing may also increase the rate of epithelial proliferation or change the microenvironment so that cells are more susceptible to the effects of luminal carcinogens.

SCREENING AND PREVENTION

The prevention of colorectal cancer may be achieved by primary means including lifestyle adjustments or taking preventive medication (chemoprevention) or by screening asymptomatic subjects for risk factors that can be reduced or neutralized. The concept of prevention can be broadened to include the prevention of radical surgery (since early stage colorectal cancer can be cured by local or conservative surgery) or prevention of death (since advanced cancer can be cured if it is treated at a sufficiently early stage). Screening can result in unnecessary investigation and promote needless anxiety if the test lacks specificity and is therefore associated with a high false-positive rate. Furthermore, if a cancer is detected earlier than it would otherwise have been but not early enough to allow spread and death to be prevented, the test will not have improved mortality rates. The resultant increase in survival is apparent only. Bringing forward the diagnosis of cancer in this way is known as lead time bias. The main approaches to screening include: (1) testing faeces for occult blood, (2) endoscopic examination of the mucosal lining of the large bowel and (3) demonstration of a high-risk genetic mutation.

Faecal Occult Blood Testing

The premise underlying this test is that larger adenomas and early cancers may bleed to a minor extent that goes unnoticed but is identified by a sensitive test for haemoglobin. A positive result is followed by a colonoscopy and removal of small lesions. Larger lesions may require surgery. Cancers detected in asymptomatic subjects are relatively early (in terms of their limited extent of spread) and the net result of removing adenomas and early cancers is a reduction in mortality in the study group as compared with a matched unscreened group. The reduction in mortality from colorectal cancer in randomized controlled trials has ranged from 15% to 33%. Amongst fully compliant participants the mortality reduction is of the order of 40% (Hardcastle et al., 1996; Kronborg et al., 1996).

Occult blood is not specific for neoplasia and neoplasms may not necessarily bleed. Specificity and sensitivity might be increased by testing for other products such as mutated DNA. K-ras mutations can be detected in stool samples but only a subset of colorectal cancers has K-ras mutation. One would need to test for a range of mutations to pick up all cancers, but the laboratory costs would be considerable.

Endoscopy

There is retrospective evidence as well as evidence from prospective adenoma follow-up trials that adenoma removal prevents colorectal cancer. Endoscopy allows precancerous adenomas to be visualized and removed before they can transform into cancers. Since no more than 5% of adenomas will become cancerous, it is necessary to destroy or remove 20 to prevent one cancer. The cost effectiveness is increased by offering endoscopy only to subjects at moderate to high risk (e.g. by virtue of a positive family history). However, most colorectal cancers occur in subjects without a strong family history. At least 50% of

colorectal cancers occur within the range of the flexible sigmoidoscope. It has been suggested that a single sigmoidoscopic examination between the ages of 55 and 64 years would have an important impact on morbidity and mortality due to cancer of the rectum and sigmoid colon (Atkin et al., 1998). Retrospective data suggest that subjects with small adenomas in the distal colon and rectum are at little risk of developing further neoplasms or of having more proximal adenomas. However, subjects with larger and/or multiple adenomas would require a full colonoscopy and additional colonoscopic surveillance (Atkin et al., 1992).

Some would argue that screening only the rectosigmoid region is unacceptable and that a full screening colonoscopy should be offered as the first step in screening. The drawbacks are that colonoscopy is more expensive and technically demanding and proximal cancers are less aggressive and more age-related. An alternative approach is 'virtual colonoscopy' achieved by computed tomography colonography which can detect remarkably small lesions. Colonoscopy would then be required to biopsy and treat the lesion.

Colonoscopic surveillance is also offered to subjects with chronic inflammatory bowel disease, particularly ulcerative colitis. The precancerous lesion is known as dysplasia, which appears macroscopically as a flat, velvety area or a raised sessile mass or may be invisible. The risk of associated or subsequent cancer is then high and colectomy is indicated.

Genetic Screening and Predictive Testing

This is offered to subjects with autosomal dominant syndromes predisposing to colorectal cancer: familial adenomatous polyposis (FAP) and hereditary non-polyposis colorectal cancer (HNPCC). The steps are similar in both conditions. After counselling and obtaining consent the causative mutation is detected in an affected family member. This is achieved in about 70% of FAP families and 50% of HNPCC families. After counselling, DNA samples from at-risk family members are screened for the mutation. Mutation-negative subjects are at no increased risk compared with the general population and require no further preventive management. Prophylactic surgery is required for FAP and this is generally performed in the mid-teens. The operative approach is either total colectomy with ileorectal anastomosis or proctocolectomy with construction of an ileo-anal pouch anastomosis. The former is preferred unless there is an extensive carpet of rectal adenomas, but the rectum will then require endoscopic surveillance. Rectal excision with ileo-anal pouch anastomosis will often be performed in later years. At-risk or mutation positive members of HNPCC families require one- to two-yearly colonoscopic surveillance from the third decade. If surgery is undertaken for a large adenoma or cancer, a total colectomy is the preferred option because of the high risk of developing additional cancers.

Dietary Intervention

A measure that is likely to be associated with general compliance is the addition to the diet of a cheap and palatable ingredient, particularly if this can be added safely to a product that is widely consumed anyway. Of the possible protective dietary factors that have been identified so far, resistant starch would be one of the easiest to accommodate in the diet. A rich natural source is unripe bananas, but resistant starch can be added to bread or sprinkled on food without altering its taste.

Chemoprevention

Cohort and case-control studies have demonstrated the protective role of aspirin and other non-steroidal anti-inflammatory drugs (NSAIDS) (Potter, 1999). These are believed to act through the inhibition of cyclo-oxygenase (COX) which is involved in the synthesis of prostaglandin (converts arachidonic acid to prostaglandin G_2). The more specific COX antagonists (sulindac) have been shown to cause adenomas to regress in FAP and to restore the altered apoptotic index in the normal-appearing mucosa of FAP subjects to normal. The molecular mechanisms underlying these interesting observational data are unknown. A drawback of NSAIDs is their gastrointestinal side-effects. COX-2 is not expressed by normal colonic epithelial cells but is upregulated in cancer cells. The latest generation of selective COX-2 antagonists was developed in order to achieve therapeutic or preventive effects without accompanying gastrointestinal disturbance. At this stage it is not known if the more selective components will be as effective as their broad-spectrum counterparts, but preliminary data are encouraging.

The most obvious use of chemoprevention is in subjects at high risk of colorectal cancer. Cost, safety and efficacy will determine if such an approach to cancer prevention can be generalized. Subjects with FAP have been observed to develop bowel cancer while taking sulindac.

PREINVASIVE LESIONS

Adenoma

The most important preinvasive lesions in the colorectum in terms of frequency and potential for malignant change are the benign neoplasms or adenomas (Muto *et al.*, 1975). The evidence is as follows: (1) adenomas show a spectrum of changes ranging from low-grade dysplasia through to high-grade dysplasia (or carcinoma-*in-situ*), (2) longitudinal studies demonstrate malignant transformation with time (in situations where the adenoma is not removed), (3) adenoma and carcinoma share similar demographic data and risk factors, (4) removal of adenomas reduces the frequency of cancer and (5) the genetic changes in adenomas are also present in carcinomas.

Macroscopic Features

Adenomas mainly present as polypoid growths that may be sessile or pedunculated. They are usually sessile elevations when less than 5 mm but increasing growth is associated with the formation of a stalk composed of normal mucosa and submucosa. A minority remain as flat or even depressed lesions which may be difficult to detect at colonoscopy without the use of dye spraying and high-resolution magnification. The head is darker than the surrounding normal mucosa in larger adenomas and becomes lobulated, resembling a baby cauliflower. A rare presentation is as a large sessile (broad-based) mass with a soft, shaggy surface. These are described as villous adenomas, although the finger-like villi seen in two-dimensional sections are in reality leaf-like folds.

Microscopic Features

Adenomas are typed as tubular, tubulovillous and villous according to the predominant architectural pattern (**Figure 3**) (Jass and Sobin, 1989). Tubules are lined by columnar epithelium and embedded within lamina propria where they proliferate by branching. Villi (in reality leaves) comprise a covering of columnar epithelium and a core of lamina propria. By forming complex, brain-like folds of epithelium, the surface area of a villous adenoma may be considerable and lead to significant loss of fluid and electrolytes. Tubulovillous adenomas combine both architectural patterns.

The morphological changes that distinguish adenoma from normal include disordered architecture, cytological atypia and abnormal differentiation. The combination of changes has been described as dysplasia and may be graded as mild, moderate and severe or (in a two-grade system) low grade and high grade (**Figure 4**). Mild or low-grade dysplasia deviates little from the normal whereas severe or high-grade dysplasia approximates to carcinoma-*in-situ*. The terms intra-epithelial neoplasia and dysplasia are synonymous. Because of its aggressive connotation the term 'carcinoma-*in-situ*' is generally omitted from diagnostic reports. The risk of cancer developing in an adenoma is associated with architecture (extent of villosity), grade of dysplasia and size of the adenoma (Muto *et al.*, 1975).

For the purposes of drawing a diagnostic distinction between adenoma and adenocarcinoma, a rule has been developed that is unique to the lower intestinal tract. In order to diagnose cancer there must be invasion across the line of the muscularis mucosae into the underlying submucosa. For other epithelial surfaces, cancer is diagnosed when there is invasion across the basement membrane. The reasons for this difference in approach are pragmatic and practical. First, the potential to metastasize is not realized

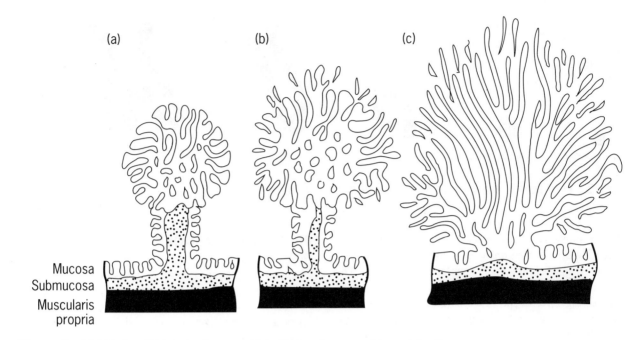

Figure 3   (a) Tubular, (b) tubulovillous and (c) villous adenoma of large intestine.

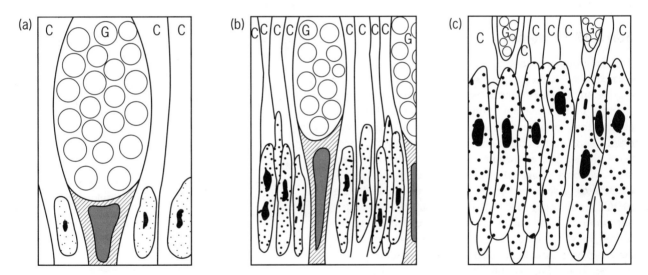

Figure 4   Normal epithelium of (a) large bowel, (b) low-grade dysplasia and (c) high-grade dysplasia. There is progressive loss of differentiation of goblet cells (G) and columnar cells (C) accompanied by nuclear enlargement, crowding, stratification and hyperchromatism.

until there has been submucosal invasion. Second invasion across the basement membrane into surrounding lamina propria is both unusual and difficult to diagnose at the light microscopic level. Invasion across the basement membrane is generally apparent only in the case of poorly differentiated adenocarcinoma, but it is unusual for early cancer arising in an adenoma to be poorly differentiated.

Early Morphogenesis

In squamous and transitional epithelial surfaces, a neoplastic clone is conceived as arising within and replacing the normal epithelium by lateral spread. While such a process may also occur within columnar epithelium, at least some if not the majority of colorectal adenomas originate through a different mechanism. Micro-reconstruction studies in the normal-appearing mucosa from subjects with familial adenomatous polyposis have demonstrated neoplastic crypts occurring as a bud from the side of a normal crypt, in other words recapitulating the normal process of crypt fission (Nakamura and Kino, 1984). The bud forms a tubule as it migrates up the crypt column to open finally on to the epithelial surface. This unicrypt adenoma then undergoes fission to form a microadenoma (**Figure 5**).

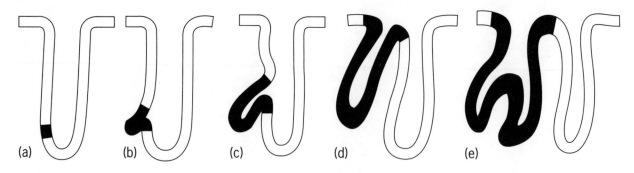

Figure 5   Formation of adenoma as an outpouching from normal crypt.

It is possible to identify microscopic epithelial lesions by their abnormal crypt openings using a combination of dye and magnification of the surface epithelium. The choice of dye will depend on whether this is performed by dissecting microscope *in vitro* (e.g. methylene blue) or during colonoscopy (e.g. indigo carmine). These microscopic lesions are known as aberrant crypt foci. A minority are microadenomas; most are minute hyperplastic polyps.

Serrated Adenomas

This subgroup of adenomas is distinguished from the usual adenoma by combining the serrated or saw-tooth crypt outline of the hyperplastic polyp with the cytological changes of an adenoma. Additionally, the proliferative compartment of a serrated adenoma remains in the lower crypt whereas proliferative cells are found within the upper crypt and surface epithelium in the usual adenoma. Serrated adenomas are also characterized by an over-expression of secretory or gel-forming mucins including MUC2 (intestinal) and MUC5AC (gastric). Serrated adenomas are probably more closely related to hyperplastic polyps than adenomas. Mixed polyps including both hyperplastic and serrated adenomatous components may be found. Furthermore, microsatellite markers have demonstrated clonal relationships between the two components. The high frequency of DNA microsatellite instability also distinguishes serrated adenomas from traditional adenomas (Iino *et al.*, 1999).

Dysplasia

In inflammatory bowel disease, dysplasia occurs as an ill-defined or diffuse lesion that may be flat or raised as a sessile mass but lacking the sharp demarcation of an adenoma. Although the term dysplasia has been applied to both the diffuse lesions found in inflammatory bowel disease and the circumscribed neoplasia of an adenoma, differences between the two forms of dysplasia exist with respect to histological appearances, molecular genetics and natural history.

GROSS APPEARANCES

Colorectal cancers are relatively well circumscribed with little growth beyond their macroscopically visible borders. A cancer may appear as a mass protruding into the bowel lumen, as an ulcer with a raised edge or as a band-like stricture causing narrowing of the bowel. Protuberant masses are more common in the caecum and ascending colon. The bowel contents are fluid in this region and obstruction is uncommon. Chronic bleeding from the ulcerated surface leads to the symptoms of iron deficiency anaemia and palpation of a mass in the right iliac fossa will point to the likely diagnosis. Cancers arising in the splenic flexure and left colon are often associated with stricturing that leads to the symptoms of partial or complete bowel obstruction. Cancers of the rectum are often ulcerating and may present with the passage of bright red blood per rectum or the sensation of incomplete evacuation. On section the cancer appears as a mass of relatively firm, pale tissue replacing the normal bowel wall structures. The mucinous subset has a grey, gelatinous cut surface reflecting the accumulated secretory mucin.

HISTOPATHOLOGY

Type

About 90% of colorectal cancers are adenocarcinomas composed of glandular structures containing variable amounts of mucin. About 10% secrete large amounts of mucin (constituting at least 50% of the tumour volume) and are known as mucinous adenocarcinomas. The signet ring cell carcinoma is a rare form of mucinous carcinoma in which the cells are discohesive and contain abundant intracellular mucin which pushes the nucleus towards the cell membrane (giving a signet ring appearance) (**Figure 6**). Loss of the adhesion molecule E-cadherin is responsible for the discohesion of signet ring cells. Undifferentiated carcinoma is exceedingly uncommon.

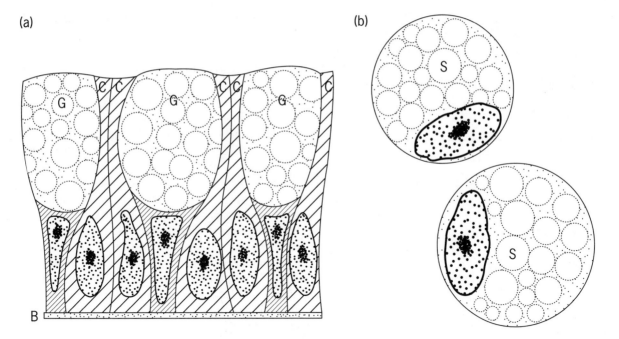

Figure 6 (a) Normal colorectal epithelium and (b) signet ring cell carcinoma. G = goblet cell and C = columnar cell in normal epithelium; S = signet ring cell carcinoma cells; B = basement membrane.

Grading

The grading of adenocarcinoma as well (grade 1), moderately (grade 2) and poorly (grade 3) differentiated is based primarily on the extent to which recognizable glands are formed (**Figure 7**). In well-differentiated adenocarcinoma, the glands are regular and the epithelium resembles adenomatous tubules. In moderately differentiated adenocarcinoma, the glands show complex budding, irregular outpouching or gland-within-gland structures. In poorly differentiated adenocarcinoma, glands are highly irregular or distorted. Cells may be arranged in solid clusters or cords. Undifferentiated carcinomas are graded as 4.

Invasive Margin

About 80% of colorectal cancers have a reasonably well circumscribed invasive margin whereas 20% show widespread dissection of normal structures and often extensive invasion around nerves and within small vessels (**Figure 8**).

Venous Invasion

The presence of tumour within large venous channels increases the risk of metastatic spread to the liver via the portal vein.

Immune Response

Lymphocytes may be conspicuous as part of a band-like arrangement of inflammatory cells at the growing margin

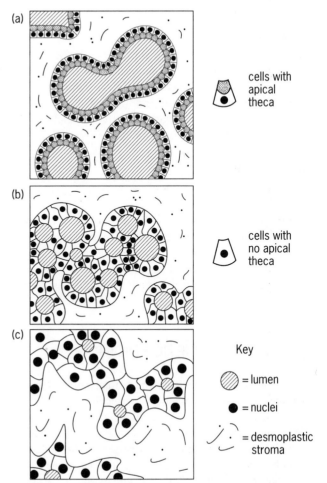

cells with apical theca

cells with no apical theca

Key

⊘ = lumen

● = nuclei

= desmoplastic stroma

Figure 7 (a) Well, (b) moderate and (c) poor differentiation in adenocarcinoma of the large intestine.

(a)

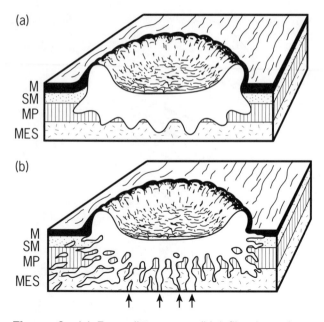

(b)

Figure 8 (a) Expanding versus (b) infiltrating adenocarcinoma of the large intestine. M = mucosa; SM =
submucosa; MP = muscularis propria; MES = mesentery. Arrows indicate points of surgical transection of
cancer.

(B and T cells), as nodular aggregates (B cells with a cuff
of T cells) in the surrounding submucosa or serosa, within
the tumour stroma (B and T cells) or infiltrating the
malignant epithelium (tumour infiltrating T lymphocytes).
These patterns often co-exist and are associated with
hyperplasia of the regional lymph nodes.

Ultrastructure and Immunohistochemistry

In general these do not provide diagnostically or prognostically useful information but immunohistochemistry
combines with the molecular genetic approach (see
below) to generate key insights into basic biological
mechanisms. The diagnostic use of antibodies to the
DNA mismatch repair proteins is described below.

MOLECULAR GENETIC FINDINGS

Colorectal cancer has provided more fundamental insights
than any other solid tumour in the search to uncover the
genetic basis of cancer. The well-documented adenoma–
carcinoma sequence provides a simple model that is
accessible to observation and investigation. Additionally,
the two major forms of hereditary colorectal cancer, FAP
and HNPCC, were directly responsible for the discovery of
important cancer genes through classical linkage studies
and positional cloning (*APC* and the DNA mismatch repair

genes, respectively). (See also the chapter *Inherited Predispositions to Cancer.*)

Genetic Instability

Molecular genetics is a rapidly expanding field. One of
its major contributions to date has been the realization
that colorectal cancer is not a single disease, but multiple
diseases driven by separate molecular pathways. The
impact of this realization upon epidemiology, aetiology,
prognosis and treatment is only just being appreciated.
The pathways are at least in part determined by the
nature of the primary fault that drives carcinogenesis:
the state of genetic instability. This state is caused by the
disruption of checkpoint mechanisms in the cell cycle
that normally ensure the maintenance of genomic fidelity
during cell division. Genetic instability occurs in at least
two major and distinct forms in colorectal cancer:
chromosomal instability and DNA instability (Lengauer
et al., 1998).

Chromosomal Instability

The majority (70%) of colorectal cancers arise through this
pathway. An early genetic change is disruption of the Wnt
signalling pathway, generally through biallelic inactivation of *APC* which explains the initiation and early growth
of adenomas. K-*ras* mutation occurs in a subset and drives
further clonal expansion. The key transition from adenoma
to carcinoma is driven in many cases by biallelic inactivation of *TP53*. Other tumour suppressor genes on 18q, 1p
and 8p are implicated (hence suppressor pathway). Aneuploidy is acquired around the transition from adenoma to
carcinoma suggesting that chromosomal instability is the
mechanism for overcoming this rate-limiting step in the
evolutionary sequence. DNA microsatellite instability is
not present, hence these cancers have been termed
microsatellite stable (MSS).

DNA Instability and MSI-H Cancers

This mechanism is implicated in HNPCC in which there is a
germ-line mutation of a DNA mismatch repair gene (see
above). DNA instability also occurs on a sporadic basis in
about 15% of colorectal cancers. The usual mechanism is
silencing of the DNA mismatch repair gene *hMLH1*
through methylation of its promoter region. The biomarker
for this subtype is widespread DNA microsatellite instability
(MSI) or MSI-high (MSI-H). Other genes are methylated
also, but the mechanism underlying the methylator phenotype is unknown. Breakdown of the DNA mismatch repair
mechanism results in mutation of genes with short mononucleotide repeats in their coding sequences: *TGFβRII*,
BAX, *IGF2R*, *caspase 5*, *Tcf-4*, *axin*, *CDX-2* and *BCL-10*
(hence mutator phenotype). Involvement of *APC*, K-*ras* and

TP53 is uncommon in sporadic MSI-H cancers. MSI-H cancers show a predilection for the proximal colon and a tendency to occur in elderly women. They are more likely to be mucinous and to express the secretory mucin core proteins MUC2 and MUC5AC (like serrated adenomas). They are also more likely to be poorly differentiated, have a well circumscribed invasive margin and show an enhanced immune reaction including tumour-infiltrating lymphocytes (TIL) (Jass *et al.*, 1998).

Loss of expression of DNA mismatch repair proteins can now be demonstrated with antibodies to hMLH1, hMSH2, hMSH6 and hPMS2. This will greatly assist in the management of HNPCC and identification of MSI-H cancers.

Mild Mutator Pathway

It has been suggested that all colorectal cancers will show minor microsatellite instability if a sufficient number of microsatellite markers is used to test for the mutator phenotype. Nevertheless selected dinucleotide and tetra-nucleotide markers are sensitive to cancers with low levels of MSI (MSI-L). These cancers differ from MSS cancers in their lower frequency of BCL2 expression, nuclear expression of β-catenin and 5qLOH and higher frequency of K-*ras* mutation, DNA methylation (for example the DNA repair gene *MGMT*) and lymphocytic infiltration. MSI-L cancers are in other respects like MSS cancers, showing high frequencies of APC mutation and allele loss at 17p and 18q (Jass *et al.*, 1999). In view of the multiple differences between MSS, MSI-L and MSI-H cancers, it is prudent to distinguish them carefully as a primary step in the characterization of colorectal cancer. Indeed, the failure to do so has led to oversimplification and confusion that is only now beginning to be resolved.

Pathways in Inflammatory Bowel Disease

Mutation of *TP53* and aneuploidy occur in early stages of neoplastic progression in ulcerative colitis (Potter, 1999).

PROGNOSTIC FACTORS

The outcome for a patient with colorectal cancer will depend upon (1) clinical factors such as age, gender, health status and mode of clinical presentation, (2) the extent of spread of cancer at the time of diagnosis and (3) biological properties of the cancer, both histopathological and molecular. Of these, staging classifications based upon the extent of spread cancer (**Figure 9**) provide the most reproducible and important guide to prognosis.

TNM Classification of Colorectal Cancer

Definitions of T, N and M categories are shown in **Table 2**. The data may be converted into four stages

Table 2 TNM Classification (American Joint Commission on Cancer/Union Internationale Contra Cancre, 1997)

Primary tumour (T)

TX	Primary tumour cannot be assessed
T0	No evidence of primary tumour
Tis	Carcinoma-*in-situ* or high-grade dysplasia
T1	Tumour invades submucosa
T2	Tumour invades muscularis propria
T3	Tumour invades through the muscularis propria into subserosa or into non-peritonealized pericolic or perirectal tissue
T4	Tumour directly invades other organs or structures and/or perforates visceral peritoneum

Regional lymph nodes (N)

NX	Regional lymph nodes cannot be assessed
N0	No regional lymph node metastasis
N1	Metastasis in 1–3 regional lymph nodes
N2	Metastasis in four or more regional lymph nodes

Distant metastasis (M)

MX	Distant metastasis cannot be assessed
M0	No distant metastasis
M1	Distant metastasis

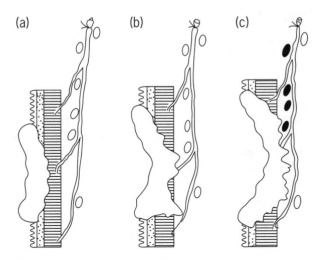

Figure 9 Dukes classification of rectal cancer.

(with the equivalent Dukes pathological stage) as follows:

1. Stage I (Dukes A, Fig. 9(a)): cancer confined to bowel wall (T1 or T2) with no spread to lymph nodes (N0) or distant spread (M0).
2. Stage II (Dukes B, Fig. 9(b)): cancer extends beyond muscle coat (T3 or T4) with no spread to lymph nodes (N0) or distant spread (M0).
3. Stage III (Dukes C, Fig. 9(c)): cancer (any T) spreads to lymph nodes (N1 or N2) with no distant spread (M0).
4. Stage IV (no Dukes equivalent but called D subsequently): cancer (any T and any N) involving distant sites (M1).

The 5-year survival (non-cancer deaths excluded) is around 100% for stage I, 80% for stage II, 50% for stage III and 10% for stage IV. Distribution of cancers by stage is around 15% stage I, 35% stage II, 40% stage III and 10% stage IV. Prognosis is therefore uncertain (50% 5-year survival) for 40% of patients with stage III disease.

Histopathological Factors

Tumour type, grade, invasive margin, venous invasion and immune response (see above) have all been shown to be of prognostic significance. In multivariate (Cox regression) analyses only invasive margin, venous invasion and immune response have been shown to provide additional (independent) prognostic data beyond that achieved by staging alone. The Jass prognostic classification developed for curative cases of rectal cancer (**Table 3**) utilizes invasive margin and peritumoral lymphocyte infiltration in addition to direct spread and lymph node spread. The Jass system minimizes the number of uncertain prognostic cases (Jass *et al.*, 1987). However, histopathological features are subjective and prone to interobserver variation.

Molecular and Genetic Factors

Microsatellite Status

Sporadic MSI-H cancers are associated with a good outcome and an independent prognostic effect has been demonstrated for stage III colorectal cancer. This will explain, at least in part, the adverse effects associated with molecular and genetic changes found in non-MSI-H cancers. These include K-*ras* mutation, 17p and 18q loss and increased expression of COX-2 and VEGF. The classification of colorectal cancer as MSS, MSI-H and MSI-L must precede the exploration of other prognostic markers, the effects of which could well be subsidiary to or explained by the major molecular pathways.

Other Prognostic Markers

The classes of molecule that have been linked to prognosis include enzymes involved in matrix degradation and their inhibitors (cathepsin L, urokinase, tissue-type plasminogen activator, tissue inhibitors of metalloproteinases), gene products involved in apoptosis (BCL2, survivin), cell surface molecules (CD44, ICAM1, galectin 3) and a variety of metabolic enzymes (GLUT1 glucose transporter, manganese–superoxide dismutase, thymidylate synthetase, ornithine decarboxylase).

CLINICAL MANAGEMENT

Initial Consultation and Diagnosis

The management of colorectal cancer begins with a process of consultation. This will vary according to the mode of presentation. The consultation may be motivated by altered bowel habit, present as an acute abdominal emergency due to obstruction or perforation or be precipitated by the diagnosis of cancer in an asymptomatic subject participating in a screening program. Regardless of the mode of presentation, frequent, clear and instructive communication is necessary to ensure the best outcome for the patient.

The main approach to treatment is a surgical one, but this is preceded by preoperative assessment to establish the diagnosis and provide information on the stage of the disease. A mass in the lower rectum need not always be a carcinoma. It could be a variety of benign lesions, a lymphoma or an upward-spreading squamous cell carcinoma of the anal canal (lesions that are not usually treated by rectal excision). Therefore, biopsy and a histopathological diagnosis are mandatory steps in the case of rectal masses and highly desirable for colonic tumours. The methods of investigation to achieve a diagnosis include digital examination, sigmoidoscopy, barium enema and colonoscopy.

Table 3 Jass prognostic classification for curative rectal cancer (UICC/TNM stages I–III): (A) scores for variables and (B) derivation of prognostic groups from total score

A		B			
Variable	Score	Total score per case (0–5)	Prognostic group (I–IV)	5-year survival (%)	Frequency (%)
Spread beyond rectal wall (muscularis propria)	1	0–1	I	95	30
Infiltrative growth pattern	1	2	II	80	30
No lymphocytic response (peritumoral at deep margin)	1	3	III	50	20
Lymph node metastasis	1	4–5	IV	25	20
>4 lymph nodes with metastasis	1				

Preoperative Staging

Colonic Cancer

Most patients with a colonic cancer do not require preoperative staging; the extent of tumour spread is better evaluated during laparotomy and by pathological examination of the resected specimen. A preoperative computerized tomography (CT) scan will occasionally be useful for identifying the extent of locally advanced disease.

Rectal Cancer

Preoperative staging is important for both planning surgery and establishing the need for preoperative adjuvant chemoradiotherapy. Apart from digital examination, the most important investigative technique is endorectal ultrasound, which provides a high-resolution image of the individual layers of the rectal wall and the destruction of one or more of these layers by tumour.

Distant Metastases

Routine chest X-ray, liver scanning by CT or ultrasound and serum levels of the tumour marker carcinoembryonic antigen (CEA) are used to gauge the presence of distant spread. This may assist in determining prognosis.

Early Colorectal Cancer

There is no strict definition in terms of extent of spread. The term refers to cancer that is sufficiently small and localized to be safely managed by conservative surgery, namely local excision as opposed to the radical approach required for advanced cancer. In practice, most early colorectal cancers have spread no further than the submucosa. An early cancer may be a small focus of malignancy within an adenoma which can be treated by simple polypectomy at the time of colonoscopy. It may also be a small ulcerating cancer in the lower rectum where the alternative to a disc excision of the rectal wall is radical excision of the rectum and anus (abdominoperineal excision) and establishment of a permanent colostomy. Local excision of a cancer is a safe and curative option provided that the excision is complete (there is no cancer at the surgical margin), the cancer is not poorly differentiated and there is no invasion of vascular spaces. Malignant adenomas with unfavourable features may warrant further treatment but this is individualized on the basis of the health, age and wishes of the patient.

Surgery for Colon Cancer

The principle underlying surgical treatment is to resect the segment of bowel bearing the cancer together with the mesentery carrying the blood supply and lymphatic drainage. The feeding arteries are ligated as close as possible to their sites of origin. For a cancer of the right colon, the right colic, ileocolic and right branch of the middle colic vessels are ligated and divided close to their origins and the proximal colon is then resected. For cancers of the left colon, the inferior mesenteric and ascending left colic vessels are ligated and a left hemicolectomy is performed. Intestinal continuity is restored by anastomosis using sutures or staples.

Surgery for Rectal Cancer

In the past this was often treated by an abdominoperineal excision of rectum and anus and the construction of a permanent colostomy. It is now often possible to resect most of the rectum and anastomose the proximal colon to the distal rectum or even to the upper anal canal, a procedure called an anterior resection. When the anstomosis is very low in the pelvis, it is usual to divert the faeces from it temporarily by fashioning a proximal loop ileostomy that is closed after around 12 weeks. It is still necessary to perform an abdominoperineal excision if the cancer is poorly differentiated, a distal margin of clearance of at least 2 cm cannot be achieved or the anal sphincter mechanism is not adequate for continence.

Adjuvant Therapy for Colon Cancer

Approximately 50% of subjects with stage III or Dukes C colon cancer will relapse with distant metastases and die within 5 years of surgery. This is explained by the presence of occult hepatic metastases at the time of surgical treatment. The aim of an adjuvant approach is to destroy these metastases at a time when they are of microscopic dimensions and therefore more amenable to cytotoxic therapy. Randomized controlled trials have to date demonstrated significant improvements in survival with the combination of 5-fluorouracil and leucovorin (folinic acid) that have not been bettered by any alternative regimen. A 6-month course is recommended.

Adjuvant Therapy for Rectal Cancer

Two major adverse outcomes are observed in rectal cancer: distant metastases (as for colon cancer) and local recurrence of the disease within the pelvic cavity. Recurrent pelvic cancer is incurable and will spread within the pelvis to cause pain, bleeding and urinary tract obstruction. Factors influencing local recurrence are the extent of spread of cancer beyond the rectal wall and the competence of the surgeon. Unacceptably high levels of variation in outcome have been demonstrated between surgeons (McArdle and Hole, 1991). Sharp dissection of the mesorectum ensuring that its thin fascial (connective tissue) covering is not breached is advocated as a measure to reduce the risk of incomplete removal of cancer. However, local recurrence will continue to be a problem for the more locally advanced cancers regardless of surgical skills. For this reason, radiotherapy is recommended for locally advanced rectal cancer and this has been shown to reduce the incidence of local recurrence in randomized controlled trials. It is therefore usual to offer combined radiotherapy and chemotherapy (e.g. 5-fluorouracil) to patients with stage II and III rectal cancer.

Radiotherapy may damage normal tissues, causing long-term complications. The risks of damaging the small intestine are reduced if radiotherapy is given preoperatively. Preoperative radiotherapy (combined with chemotherapy) can be offered selectively on the basis of preoperative staging. The advantages of this approach are that the cancer may be downstaged (partially eradicated) and sometimes completely eradicated. Preoperative radiotherapy may also render surgery less technically difficult and may even convert an apparently incurable cancer to a curable one. Pathological staging of the resected specimen will be less reliable owing to destruction of both tumour and lymphoid tissue (Wheeler *et al.*, 1999).

Recurrent and Distant Disease

This is usually incurable although patients with only a few hepatic metastases have been cured by excising the deposits of tumour with a clear margin. Local recurrence is also salvageable on occasion, particularly if it is at the site of the anastomosis. Local recurrence is otherwise managed by palliation with radiotherapy and/or chemotherapy as well as adequate pain relief.

The Future

In addition to the development of more effective cytotoxic compounds (e.g. Oxaliplatin and CPT-11), immunotherapy and gene therapy offer new hope for the future. These approaches depend on an understanding of cancer biology and must overcome the problems posed by tumour heterogeneity and drug resistance. Until we learn how to prevent the disease altogether, surgery will continue as the main treatment option for advanced colorectal cancer. Despite this, modern management of colorectal cancer is increasingly viewed as a team exercise involving oncologists, radiotherapists, radiologists, endoscopists, geneticists, pathologists and stoma therapists as well as surgeons. The informed participation of the patient is also integral to successful management.

REFERENCES

Atkin, W. S., *et al.* (1992). Long-term risk of colorectal cancer after excision of rectosigmoid adenomas. *New England Journal of Medicine*, **326**, 658–662.

Atkin, W. S., *et al.* (1998). Uptake, yield of neoplasia, and adverse effects of flexible sigmoidoscopy screening. *Gut*, **42**, 560–565.

Haenszel, W. (1961). Cancer mortality among the foreign born in the United States. *Journal of the Natural Cancer Institute*, **26**, 37–132.

Hardcastle, J. D., *et al.* (1996). Randomised controlled trial of faecal-occult-blood screening for colorectal cancer. *Lancet*, **348**, 1472–1477.

Iino, H., *et al.* (1999). DNA microsatellite instability in hyperplastic polyps, serrated adenomas and mixed polyps: a mild mutator pathway for colorectal cancer? *Journal of Clinical Pathology*, **52**, 5–9.

Jass, J. R. and Sobin, L. H. (1989). *WHO International Histological Classification of Intestinal Tumours.* (Springer, Berlin).

Jass, J. R., *et al.* (1987). A new prognostic classification of rectal cancer. *Lancet*, **i**, 1303–1306.

Jass, J. R., *et al.* (1998). Morphology of sporadic colorectal cancer with DNA replication errors. *Gut*, **42**, 673–679.

Jass, J. R., *et al.* (1999). Characterisation of a subtype of colorectal cancer combining features of the suppressor and mild mutator pathways. *Journal of Clinical Pathology*, **52**, 455–460.

Keller, J. J., *et al.* (1999). Rectal epithelial apoptosis in familial adenomatous polyposis patients treated with sulindac. *Gut*, **45**, 822–828.

Kronborg, O., *et al.* (1996). Randomised study of screening for colorectal cancer with faecal-occult-blood test. *Lancet*, **348**, 1467–1471.

Lengauer, C., *et al.* (1998). Genetic instabilities in human cancers. *Nature*, **396**, 643–649.

Lynch, H. T., *et al.* (1996). Overview of natural history, pathology, molecular genetics and management of HNPCC (Lynch syndrome). *International Journal of Cancer*, **69**, 38–43.

McArdle, C. S. and Hole, D. (1991). Impact of variability among surgeons on postoperative morbidity and mortality and ultimate survival. *British Medical Journal*, **302**, 1501–1505.

Muto, T., *et al.* (1975). The evolution of cancer of the rectum. *Cancer*, **36**, 2251–2276.

Nakamura, S. and Kino, I. (1984). Morphogenesis of minute adenomas in familial polyposis coli. *Journal of the Natural Cancer Institute*, **73**, 41–49.

Potter, J. D. (1999). Colorectal cancer: molecules and populations. *Journal of the Natural Cancer Institute*, **91**, 916–932.

Trock, B., *et al.* (1990). Dietary fiber, vegetables, and colon cancer: critical review and analyses of the epidemiologic evidence. *Journal of the Natural Cancer Institute*, **82**, 650–661.

Wasan, H. S., *et al.* (1998). APC in the regulation of intestinal crypt fission. *Journal of Pathology*, **185**, 246–255.

Wheeler, J. M. D., *et al.* (1999). Preoperative radiotherapy for rectal cancer: implications for surgeons, pathologists and radiologists. *British Journal of Surgery*, **86**, 1108–1120.

FURTHER READING

American Joint Committee on Cancer (1997). *AJCC Cancer Staging Manual*, 5th edn. (Lippincott-Raven, Philadelphia).

Baba, S. (1996). *New Strategies for Treatment of Hereditary Colorectal Cancer*. (Churchill Livingstone, Tokyo).

Hermanek, P. and Sobin, L. H. (1995). Colorectal cancer. In: Hermanek, P., *et al*. (eds), *Prognostic Factors in Cancer*. 64–79 (Springer, Berlin).

Isaacson, P. G. and Norton, A. J. (1994). *Extranodal Lymphomas*. (Churchill Livingstone, Edinburgh).

Kune, G. (1996). *Causes and Control of Colorectal Cancer: A Model for Cancer Prevention*. (Kluwer, Boston).

Medical Research Council Rectal Cancer Working Party (1996). Randomised trial of surgery alone versus radiotherapy followed by surgery for potentially operable locally advanced rectal cancer. *Lancet*, **348**, 1605–1610.

Medical Research Council Rectal Cancer Working Party (1996). Randomised trial of surgery alone versus surgery followed by radiotherapy for mobile cancer of the rectum. *Lancet*, **348**, 1610–1614.

Phillips, R. K. S., *et al*. (1994). *Familial Adenomatous Polyposis and Other Polyposis Syndromes*. (Edward Arnold, London).

Sircar, K., *et al*. (1999). Interstitial cells of Cajal as precursors of gastrointestinal stromal tumors. *American Journal of Surgery and Pathology*, **23**, 377–389.

Vogelstein, B., *et al*. (1988). Genetic alterations in colorectal tumor development. *New England of Journal of Medicine*, **319**, 525–532.

Website

http://www.health.gov.au/nhmrc/

Chapter 39

Liver, Gall Bladder and Extrahepatic Bile Ducts

Peter Paul Anthony

Royal Devon and Exeter Hospitals and University of Exeter, Exeter, UK

CONTENTS

NORMAL DEVELOPMENT AND STRUCTURE

Elements of the liver first appear at the beginning of the fourth week of gestation and its development is largely complete by the twelfth week. The parenchymal component (hepatocytes, biliary system and gall bladder) derive from the liver bud or hepatic diverticulum of the endodermal intestinal canal and the connective tissue framework and vessels from the mesenchyme of the septum transversum. The liver is also a major site for haematopoiesis throughout intrauterine life. Hepatocytes produce α-fetoprotein during the first trimester, after which they gradually switch to albumin. These events are, to a varying extent, reproduced in certain tumours: the morphological changes in hepatoblastoma, haematopoiesis in angiosarcoma and, most important, a switch back to α-fetoprotein in hepatocellular carcinoma.

The liver lies almost completely under the protection of the rib cage on the right and is firmly attached to the diaphragm above and loosely to the stomach and duodenum below by the lesser omentum. It is traditionally divided into right, left, caudate and quadrate lobes, which are visually recognizable, but, if one considers vascular supply and biliary drainage, it consists of nine autonomous segments, the limits of which guide the surgeon when carrying out partial hepatectomy or resection. The liver receives a dual blood supply: venous blood from the portal vein and arterial blood from the hepatic artery.

Some tumours are predominantly supplied via the portal vein (e.g. angiosarcoma) and others via the hepatic artery (e.g. hepatocellular carcinoma). Blood flows out of the liver via the hepatic veins into the inferior vena cava, close to the heart. Branches of the intrahepatic bile duct system join up to form the main hepatic duct which, when it receives the cystic duct of the gall bladder, becomes the common bile duct and this drains bile into the second part of the duodenum.

Concepts of the microscopic structure of the liver have progressed from the purely anatomical, the portal 'lobule' of Mall described in 1906, to the functional unit or 'acinus' of Rappaport which was defined in 1954; the latter makes more sense. **Figure 1** shows a simplified view of the arrangement of the various components. The centre of the acinus is the portal tract which carries the smallest branches of the portal vein and of the hepatic artery. These flow into specialized vascular channels called sinusoids which run between plates of hepatocytes and are lined by endothelium. They contain phagocytic Kupffer cells. The sinusoids are separated from the liver cells themselves by the space of Disse which, in turn, contains perisinusoidal or Ito cells and scanty Type I and III collagen which constitutes the connective tissue (reticulin) framework of the liver. The main function of the perisinusoidal cells is the production of extracellular matrix proteins. The sinusoids drain into the terminal hepatic venules which unite to form the hepatic veins. The third structure in the portal tract is the first, smallest branch of the intrahepatic bile duct

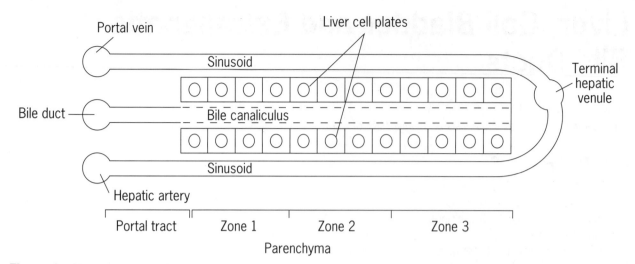

Figure 1 Microanatomy of the liver, showing portal tract with bile duct, hepatic artery and portal vein, liver cell plates with intervening sinusoids and the terminal hepatic vein.

Note: A two-dimensional diagram does not allow for the display of three-dimensional arrangements, e.g. both portal veins and hepatic arteries drain into the same sinusoids.

system which drains bile from the intercellular canaliculi between hepatocytes towards segmental bile ducts and, eventually, the common bile duct. Hepatocytes are roughly four-sided and are arranged in complex, continuous plates, being joined on two sides by other hepatocytes; the other two sides face the sinusoids or form the bile canaliculi.

Our understanding of the structure and function of the microscopic organisation of the liver is still evolving and there are several modifications and refinements. For example, the cells of the plates can be divided into Zones 1, 2 and 3 from those closest to the portal tracts (Zone 1) to those nearest to the terminal hepatic venules (Zone 3). Hepatocytes in Zone 1 are the youngest and those in Zone 3 the oldest: they proceed in this direction from birth to death by apoptosis in approximately 200 days. This is the concept of the 'streaming liver' created by Zajicek in 1985. As hepatocytes move they also display differences in function, suffer a fall in the supply of oxygen and nutrients and become more vulnerable. The site of origin of both hepatocytes and bile duct cells lies between the portal tract and liver parenchyma, the domain of stem cells.

Hepatocytes are the most complex cells in the body. They have a centrally placed nucleus and a cytoplasm rich in organelles and are capable of performing many storage, metabolic, synthetic, detoxifying and excretory functions. Bile ducts not only conduct bile but also modify it to its final effective form. The endothelial cells of the sinusoids are fenestrated, which allows the transport of nutrients to the hepatocytes. Kupffer cells and liver-specific lymphocytes are part of the mononuclear phagocytic system of the body and perisinusoidal Ito cells are capable of fibrogenesis.

This account is only a brief outline of the development, structure and function of the liver to allow the reader to relate specific tumours at this site to their cell of origin and

to normal structures which they recapitulate albeit in an aberrant fashion. For a comprehensive account, refer to MacSween and Scothorne (1994).

PATHOLOGY: TUMOURS OF THE LIVER

The term 'hepatoma' is often used loosely to describe any primary tumour in the liver but it has no precise meaning. Many different types arise which are designated by their cell of origin (Anthony, 1994). The commonest is liver cell or hepatocellular carcinoma, followed by bile duct or cholangiocarcinoma and various sarcomas, of which angiosarcoma is the most important. Benign tumours are uncommon. **Table 1** shows a detailed classification of liver tumours but only those that are common and/or are of interest will be discussed and the rest referred to only briefly.

Our knowledge of the world-wide distribution of tumours is based on data derived from cancer registries in many countries. These have been published in successive volumes of the series *Cancer Incidence in Five Continents*, the latest of which appeared in 1997 (Parkin *et al.*, 1997). The variability in incidence of liver tumours is almost entirely due to the large numbers of hepatocellular carcinoma in tropical Africa and South-East Asia. Cholangiocarcinoma is less common and occurs with much the same frequency everywhere except in South-East Asia. Other tumour types are rare. Overall, malignant liver tumours rank eighth in the list of all cancers, sixth in men and eleventh in women. Hepatocellular carcinoma accounts for most cases and kills around one million people in the world every year.

The outlook for hepatocellular carcinoma, cholangiocarcinoma and angiosarcoma is poor and nearly all patients die unless the tumour is detected early. Results

Table 1 Abbreviated WHO Classification of primary tumours of the liver

Type	Benign	Malignant
Epithelial tumours	Hepatocellular adenoma Bile duct adenoma Bile duct cystadenoma Biliary papillomatosis	Hepatocellular carcinoma Cholangiocarcinoma Bile duct cystadenocarcinoma Hepatoblastoma
Non-epithelial tumours	Haemangioma Angiomyolipoma Other benign tumours	Haemangiosarcoma Malignant epithelioid haemangioendothelioma Embryonal sarcoma Rhabdomyosarcoma Other sarcomas, lymphoma
Tumour-like lesions	Cysts Focal nodular hyperplasia Mesenchymal hamartoma Peliosis Inflammatory myofibroblastic tumour	

are improving with hepatoblastoma and the childhood sarcomas.

HEPATOCELLULAR (LIVER CELL) CARCINOMA

Hepatocellular carcinoma is defined by the World Health Organisation as a malignant tumour composed of cells resembling hepatocytes but abnormal in appearance; a plate-like organisation around sinusoids is common and is nearly always present somewhere in the tumour (Ishak et al., 1994).

Epidemiology

The remarkable geographical variability in the frequency of this tumour has attracted the attention of epidemiologists since the middle of the twentieth century. The data have been regularly summarized and updated over the years (Simonetti et al., 1991; Okuda, 1993; Anthony, 1994; Akriviadis et al., 1998; Bosch et al., 1999). Yearly incidence rates and mortality figures are almost the same as patients, other than those whose tumour is detected at an early stage by screening, die within a few weeks or at most months. In broad terms, countries may be divided into three groups: those with low, intermediate and high incidence rates. The highest frequencies are seen in South-East Asia and tropical Africa where the tumour is the commonest or next commonest of all cancers. The lowest rates are found in Western countries, South America and the Indian subcontinent. Intermediate rates prevail in Japan, the Middle East and the Mediterranean area. The possible role of racial and genetic factors has been examined and discounted in favour of environmental factors, notably chronic infections with the hepatitis B and C viruses and

exposure to aflatoxin. The incidence of the tumour appears to be rising in many areas, e.g. USA, Japan and Southern Europe.

Males predominate over females in a ratio of 2–4 to 1; generally, the higher the incidence, the higher is the rate between the genders. The mean age in high-incidence areas is in early to middle adulthood and Africans develop the tumour earlier than Asians. This is largely due to the acquisition of hepatitis B virus infection at or near birth. Patients in low- and intermediate-incidence areas are in late adulthood or old age. Cirrhosis of the liver is often associated with the tumour and is considered to be the greatest risk factor.

Whites, wherever they live, have a low incidence, even in Africa and South-East Asia, where hepatocellular carcinoma is rampant in the native population. They appear to be protected by maintaining the life style of their home countries. The same is not true of Indians who have settled in Singapore or Hong Kong since the end of the nineteenth century: their incidence rate is roughly double that in their home country. Chinese are at high risk wherever they live, e.g. in Europe or North America, but this decreases after the second generation as they adopt the environment of their new countries. The black population of the USA, West Indies and Brazil shows an incidence that is only marginally above that of whites amongst whom they have lived since the beginning of the slave trade in the seventeenth century. All of these phenomena can be explained by the prevalence rates of chronic infection with hepatitis B and, to a lesser extent, hepatitis C viruses. Small variations in tumour incidence have been observed in racially homogeneous countries such as Greece, Spain and Switzerland, which are due to differences in rates of alcoholic cirrhosis, smoking and exposure to chemicals. It is interesting to note that, although over 100 compounds, both man-made and naturally occurring, are known to be carcinogenic to rodents, few of these seem to affect humans, with the exception of aflatoxin, which is an important risk factor in Kenya and Swaziland.

Aetiology

The list of aetiological agents is long and is shown in **Table 2**, but some are more important than others. This is indicated in terms of the prevalence of the agent and the magnitude of the risk attached to it. The effect of most of them is to proceed from the normal state of the liver to the cancerous through cirrhosis, but the likelihood of this varies (Simonetti *et al.*, 1991; Okuda, 1993; Akriviadis *et al.*, 1998). Chronic hepatitis B and C account for four-fifths of cases of hepatocellular carcinoma followed by aflatoxin, chronic alcoholism, smoking and a number of other aetiologies in a minority (Anthony, 1994; Bosch *et al.*, 1999). However, a few metabolic disorders such as haemochromatosis and tyrosinaemia carry a surprisingly high risk. Also, the presence of more than one agent greatly increases the likelihood of malignancy.

Hepatitis B Virus (HBV)

HBV is one of a group of viruses known as Hepadnaviruses which affect humans (HBV) and certain animals such as the woodchuck (WHV), ground squirrel (GSHV) and duck (DHV). All of these cause liver disease: acute and chronic hepatitis, cirrhosis and hepatocellular carcinoma, in their respective hosts. In humans, transmission is mainly via blood or blood products, contaminated instruments, male homosexual contact and, most important, from mother to infant at birth. HBV is a partly double-stranded DNA virus possessing a genome consisting of four open reading frames which encode for four different proteins, surface

Table 2 Aetiology of hepatocellular carcinoma (male : female=2–4 : 1)

Agent	Prevalence	Magnitude of risk
HBV	High	High
HCV	High	High
Alcohol	High	Low
Chemicals and drugs	High	Low
Aflatoxin	Low	Moderate
Membranous obstruction of IVC	Low	Moderate
Haemochromatosis	Moderate	Moderate
AAT deficiency	Low	Low
Tyrosinaemia	Low	High
Glycogen storage disease	Low	Low
Porphyria	Low	Low

(HBsAg) and core (HBcAg) antigens, DNA polymerase and the X protein. The 'e' antigen (HBeAg) is closely associated with HBcAg. Replication takes place through reverse transcriptase and the virus is capable of integration into the host cell's genome. Most of the antigens and antibodies directed against them are demonstrable in the serum at one time or another during acute and chronic infections and the pattern of their presence is predictive of course, stage of disease and outcome. Levels of these 'marker' proteins decline in time as replication ceases and the virus becomes undetectable, but it remains in an integrated form in the nuclei of liver cells. The risk of malignant transformation relates both to the infective, replicative phase when continuing liver cell damage leads to hepatitis and cirrhosis, and to the non-replicative, inte-grated phase when carcinogenic events occur (Idilman *et al.*, 1998; Chen and Chen, 1999; Schafer and Sorrell, 1999).

Chronic HBV infection is common in tropical Africa, South-East Asia and Oceania; it is uncommon in Western Europe, North America and Australia and an intermediate prevalence is seen in the Mediterranean countries, the Middle East and India. Indeed, maps can be constructed to show almost identical frequencies of HBV carriage rates and incidence of hepatocellular carcinoma, as this virus accounts for up to two-thirds of all cases of the tumour and more in some areas. It is generally accepted that a particu-larly high risk of chronic infection, with the subsequent development of cirrhosis and hepatocellular carcinoma, is associated with infection at or near birth or in childhood, which happens in tropical Africa and South-East Asia. Elsewhere, those most commonly affected are adults in high-risk groups, e.g. intravenous drug addicts, homo-sexuals, prostitutes and inmates of prisons or mental institutions. Individuals who received transfusions of blood and blood products prior to the institution of effect-ive screening of donors in the 1980s are also at risk. Most of those who have chronic infection remain symptomless for many years and are known as carriers.

The strength of the association of HBV and hepato-cellular carcinoma, however, rests on multiple lines of evidence which are listed in **Table 3**. Numerous case-control studies were carried out in the 1970s and 1980s to show a much higher prevalence of HBV markers in the blood of patients with hepatocellular carcinoma than in controls, whether these were healthy individuals or hos-pital patients with other types of diseases including cancer. Infection precedes the development of the tumour by two to three decades on average and long-term follow-up studies established the measure of the risk. The best known of these was carried out on government employees in Taiwan, a high-incidence area for both HBV infection and hepatocellular carcinoma. They were chosen because all had life insurance policies provided by the State and an accurate record of causes of illness and death was readily available. The relative risk of developing the tumour, by

Table 3 Hepatitis viruses and hepatocellular carcinoma

	HBV	HCV
Infection is associated with tumour (case/control)	Yes	Yes
Infection precedes tumour (follow-up)	Yes	Yes
Tumour DNA contains viral genomic element (integration)	Yes	No
Tumour in culture produces viral component	Yes	No
Virus transforms cells in culture	No	No
Virus produces tumours in transgenic mice	Yes	Yes
Virus induces tumours in animals	Yes	No
Eradication of virus leads to decrease of tumour	Yes	Not known

those who tested positive for HBV markers at the outset over those who did not, turned out to be nearly 100-fold 10 years later (Beasley, 1988), a much higher figure than the relative risk of lung cancer in smokers over non-smokers. Replicative HBV is not detectable in hepatocellular carcinoma tissue or cell lines but antigenic components such as HBsAg rarely are. The virus is not directly oncogenic in the sense that it does not transform cells in culture. However, it does produce hepatocellular carcinomas when its genome is incorporated in the germ line of mice in transgenic experiments. HBV-like hepadnaviruses also produce the tumour in their respective hosts, particularly the woodchuck. The most important event in hepatic carcinogenesis by HBV is its integration in the DNA of liver cell nuclei. No consistent site exists and it appears to be random and multiple. However, insertion of HBV in the genome leads to its destabilization and chromosomal abnormalities are common, a process known as insertional mutagenesis. In addition, two transactivating proteins have been identified; one is encoded for in the pre-S2 region of the gene coding for HBsAg and the other is the HBX protein. Of the two, the latter is of greater interest (Feitelson and Duan, 1997; Idilman et al., 1998; Chen and Chen, 1999). Transactivation in this context means the ability to modify the action of host genes at a distance from the integration site. Most hepatocellular carcinomas contain oncogenes (e.g. ras, myc, fos) and/or anti-oncogenes or tumour suppressor genes (e.g. p53, Rb) which have been made by HBX to be overexpressed or inactivated. These events, in turn, lead to changes in growth factors, cell cycle regulators and DNA repair which are relevant to carcinogenesis but no coherent pathway has yet been elucidated. Mass vaccination of infants against HBV in high-risk areas such as Taiwan and the Gambia began in the mid-1980s and has proved to be effective in preventing chronic infection, with a fall in the number of childhood hepatocellular carcinomas to a quarter of the previous level. (See the chapter *Human DNA Tumour Viruses*.)

Hepatitis C Virus (HCV)

HCV is a single-stranded RNA virus which shows marked genetic heterogeneity and at least six major subtypes are known, of which Ib is thought to be the most likely to lead to chronic liver disease. Whilst it is associated with only about one-sixth of all cases of hepatocellular carcinoma world-wide, this proportion is higher and rising in some areas, notably Japan and, to a lesser extent, Spain, Italy and the Middle East (Idilman et al., 1998; Bosch et al., 1999; Colombo, 1999). The infection is usually acquired in adult life via transfusion of blood and blood products or by the use of contaminated instruments and syringes by intravenous drug abusers. Perinatal and sexual transmission are unimportant. The onset of malignancy is preceded by cirrhosis in 90% of cases. The course is long, 20–40 years from infection to tumour, and patients are affected in late middle to old age. **Table 3** shows that HCV is definitely associated with hepatocellular carcinoma in case-control and follow-up studies, but the pathogenesis is unknown. As it is an RNA virus, which does not possess a reverse transcriptase enzyme, it cannot integrate into the nuclei of liver cells. Instead, the risk of malignancy is associated with continued viral replication, liver cell death and stimulus to proliferation which lead to cirrhosis. However, hepatocellular carcinoma develops in a minority of cases without preceding cirrhosis and, therefore, a direct oncogenic effect cannot be ruled out. Accumulation of HCV core protein is thought to be the most likely mechanism. The co-existence of chronic HBV infection and alcoholism greatly increases the risk of malignancy. Attack rates of HCV infection have been reduced by screening of blood donors and the widespread use of disposable syringes but no vaccine is available and, because of the antigenic versatility of the virus, it may take many years yet to develop.

Other Hepatotropic Viruses

Hepatitis A, E, G and TT viruses are not associated with hepatocellular carcinoma, nor are herpes and other viruses that may rarely cause hepatitis. The delta agent (hepatitis D virus) can only co-infect with HBV and has no independent role.

Alcohol

A history of chronic alcohol abuse is frequently obtained in patients with cirrhosis and hepatocellular carcinoma, particularly in Europe, North America and Japan. Alcohol is not, by itself, a carcinogenic agent and it only exerts an effect through inducing cirrhosis. The risk is increased by concomitant HBV or HCV infection and, to a lesser extent, by smoking (Simonetti et al., 1991; Okuda, 1993; Bosch et al., 1999).

Chemicals and Drugs

Hundreds of chemicals – some purely experimental, others industrial – can produce liver tumours in rodents but epidemiological studies have shown that few, if any, are relevant to humans. Those that have caused most concern are nitrites, hydrocarbons, solvents, organochlorine pesticides and polychlorinated biphenyls (International Agency for Research on Cancer, 1972–1999). Tumours that develop after the administration of high doses of chemicals in short-term animal experiments may represent false-positive results for carcinogenicity because they produce a rapid mitogenic response. Damage to nuclear DNA is not repaired in the circumstances and it is 'fixed' by mitosis, leading to permanent mutation. The same chemicals in low doses do not stimulate mitosis in humans and therefore no harm results. Studies of occupational hazards have also produced inconclusive results. Therapeutic drugs are introduced after stringent testing procedures and few have proved to be carcinogenic and only in a small number of cases. They include oral contraceptives and anabolic–androgenic steroids, danazol and cytoproterone acetate. The radiological contrast agent thorium dioxide (Thorotrast) and the industrial contaminant vinyl chloride monomer (VCM) can be added to the list.

Aflatoxins

A hot, humid climate and prolonged storage encourage the growth of moulds on foodstuffs, notably of *Aspergillus fumigatus*, which produces toxic metabolites known as aflatoxins. Dietary exposure over long periods of time has led to an increased incidence of hepatocellular carcinoma in parts of sub-Saharan Africa and Southern China. The risk is increased by concomitant infection with HBV but aflatoxins are, by themselves, carcinogenic. A specific G to T mutation at the third base of codon 249 of the *p53* gene is a hallmark of exposure and it is seen in a high proportion of cases of hepatocellular carcinoma in these areas (Simonetti *et al.*, 1991; Bosch *et al.*, 1999; Wogan, 1999). (See the chapter *Mechanisms of Chemical Carcinogenesis*.)

Membraneous Obstruction of the Inferior Vena Cava

Reports have appeared from South Africa, Japan and Taiwan of an association between abnormalities of the inferior vena cava and hepatocellular carcinoma. The incidence of the lesion, which may be either congenital or acquired, is difficult to assess as it is seldom sought and is easily overlooked (Anthony, 1994).

Congenital Abnormalities and Metabolic Disorders

A large number of inherited conditions have been recognized as possible causes of hepatocellular carcinoma. These include Alagille's syndrome, ataxia–telangiectasia, familial polyposis of the colon, hereditary haemorrhagic telangiectasia, familial cholestatic cirrhosis, neonatal hepatitis/biliary atresia, neurofibromatosis and Soto syndrome. All of these are rare and some cases may have been pure chance associations (Anthony, 1994).

Inborn errors of metabolism are not all rare and some carry a surprisingly high risk of hepatocellular carcinoma (European Association for the Study of the Liver, 1999). It is interesting that this tumour is the only malignancy that complicates these disorders regularly. Genetic haemochromatosis is an autosomal recessive iron storage disorder associated with two mutations in the *HFE* gene: *C282Y* and *H63D*. The frequency in the general population is 0.5–1.0% in Northern Europe but lower elsewhere. The accumulation of iron leads to cirrhosis which then may be complicated by hepatocellular carcinoma, especially in males. The relative risk is about 100 over that of normal individuals. α-1-Antitrypsin deficiency is associated with neonatal jaundice and cirrhosis in early childhood and with emphysema and cirrhosis in adult life. Inheritance is under the control of *Pi* (protease inhibitor) genes of which the Z variant is the most important. Male adults with cirrhosis are at an increased risk of developing hepatocellular carcinoma but the magnitude of this is debated. Tyrosinaemia carries an almost 100% risk of hepatocellular carcinoma by the age of 10 years if patients survive that long. It is now recommended that hepatectomy and liver transplantation be carried out by 2 years of age. Glycogen storage disease and porphyria syndromes are rare and the risk of malignancy is low.

Precancerous Changes in the Liver, Screening and Prevention

Cirrhosis itself is a precancerous condition but the magnitude of the risk varies with aetiology, i.e. it is high with HBV and HCV but low with alcohol. Sustained proliferation of liver cells consequent upon chronic hepatitis B and C or the daily ingestion of a hepatoxic agent such as alcohol over many years seems to be the most likely mechanism of carcinogenesis as it predisposes the cell to accumulate DNA abnormalities. Proliferation prevents the repair of any damage to DNA and it is then 'fixed' and transmitted to the progeny. The 'right' combination of sites of damage that results in neoplastic transformation is a rare event, hence it takes time for the tumour to develop.

In addition, several microscopic and architectural abnormalities have been described and assigned a precancerous role (Anthony, 1994). Cellular changes such as large-cell dysplasia (meaning liver cells with enlarged, hyperchromatic, polyploid nuclei) have been held to be associated with an increased risk of malignant change for many years, especially in studies from Africa, Italy and France. Structurally abnormal and often large liver nodules in cirrhosis have been termed macroregenerative nodule, adenomatous hyperplasia and dysplastic nodule (**Figure 2**). These, especially when associated with cytological atypia (nuclear enlargement, prominent nucleoli, increased nucleo-cytoplasmic ratio), acinar, gland-like structures, nodules within nodules, and growth into areas of fibrosis, have been held to be directly precancerous lesions. Small-cell dysplasia has also been described in these nodules. However, dysplastic nodules may be difficult to distinguish from early, small hepatocellular carcinomas.

It must be pointed out that hepatocellular carcinoma does not always develop from cirrhosis with or without large nodules and dysplastic changes and, therefore, these abnormalities do not constitute obligate and exclusive pathways of liver carcinogenesis in humans. They are clinically useful, however, as they indicate an increased risk and the need for close supervision, which allows early intervention before overt development of tumours in cirrhotic patients (Okuda, 1993; Schafer and Sorrell, 1999; Hirohashi et al., 2000).

The best preventive measure for hepatocellular carcinoma is elimination of the causative agent (primary prevention). Vaccination against HBV is highly effective in reducing chronic infection with this virus and has resulted in a reduction of tumour incidence in countries with nation-wide programmes such as Taiwan. A vaccine against HCV is not yet available but the virus has now been eliminated from blood used for transfusion by screening of donors. It is also possible to reduce exposure to aflatoxin by improving conditions of food storage. However, hundreds of millions of people remain for whom such measures are too late.

Secondary prevention means the identification of individuals considered to be at highest risk. In practice, this means those with cirrhosis due to chronic infection with HBV and HCV and large nodular lesions with or without dysplastic changes. The most effective means are regular ultrasound examination and estimation of serum levels of α-fetoprotein, the role of repeat liver biopsies being more controversial. Individuals with early, small tumours can then successfully be treated by surgery: resection or transplantation.

Macroscopic and Microscopic Pathology

These have been described in detail over the years (Craig et al., 1989; Anthony, 1994; Ishak et al., 1994; Kojiro et al., 2000).

The Macroscopic Pathology of Hepatocellular Carcinoma

Most early tumours detected by screening with ultrasound and estimation of serum α-fetoprotein levels are small, usually <2 cm, solitary, and histologically well differentiated. Tumours that present with symptoms are > 2–3 cm and usually much larger and are increasingly less well differentiated as they grow. A classification devised in the early twentieth century distinguishes three forms. The most common is multinodular in which more or less rounded, sharply demarcated, yellow–green nodules of tumour are scattered throughout the liver which is usually cirrhotic. Massive tumours are large, solitary, necrotic masses, sometimes with small, satellite nodules in the vicinity, often in an otherwise normal liver. Partial or complete encapsulation may be seen. Diffuse tumours replace the entire liver without the formation of a discrete mass. At autopsy, these patterns frequently co-exist (**Figure 3**). Rarely, the tumour is pedunculated or even outside the liver: these arise from accessory lobes or from ectopic liver tissue.

Hepatocellular carcinomas have an arterial blood supply but both portal and hepatic veins proliferate alongside, resulting in arterio-venous communications. Consequently, intra- and extrahepatic spread can take place in all directions, commonly to all parts of the liver, via the hepatic veins to the inferior vena cava and the right atrium of the heart and to the stomach and the oesophagus. This vascular spread is characteristic of hepatocellular carcinoma and is always seen in advanced cases at autopsy (**Figure 3**). Lymphatic spread to portal lymph nodes and beyond occurs in about one-third of cases. Involvement of major bile ducts and dissemination within the peritoneal cavity are much less common. Distant metastases are usually found in the lungs, adrenals, pancreas, kidney, ovary and bone.

A frequently debated issue is multicentricity of hepatocellular carcinoma, namely the simultaneous development of separate primary tumours, usually in a cirrhotic liver. This undoubtedly occurs as evidenced by studies of differences in patterns of HBV DNA integration and in

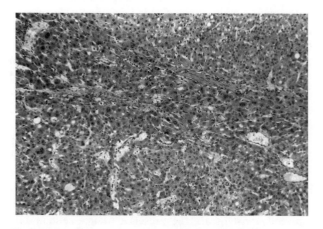

Figure 2 The interior of a cirrhotic 'dysplastic' nodule. Liver cell plates vary in thickness, their arrangement is disorganized and those in the middle of the field show nuclear enlargement.

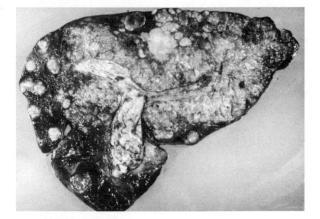

Figure 3 Cut surface of advanced hepatocellular carcinoma at autopsy. Most of the liver is replaced by tumour nodules. The triangular structure in the middle is the main portal vein and its two branches which are filled with tumour.

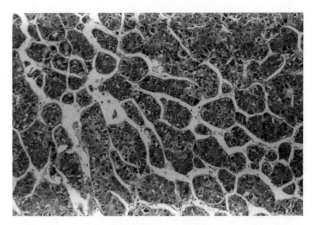

Figure 4 The microscopic appearances of hepatocellular carcinoma resemble those of the normal liver. The tumour is arranged in thick plates which are separated by sinusoids. Malignancy is manifested by the thickness of the plates and the variability in size and shape of nuclei.

dissimilar mutations of oncogenes and tumour-suppressor genes. However, separate tumours can also develop by vascular spread from the same primary source.

Microscopic Features: Histological Patterns and Cytological Variants, Ultrastructure and Special Techniques

The main microscopic characteristic of hepatocellular carcinoma is its resemblance to the normal liver, both in its plate-like growth pattern separated by sinusoids and its cytological appearances (**Figure 4**). Certain architectural and cytological variants have been recognized in the World Health Organisation classification (Ishak *et al.*, 1994) which are helpful for diagnosis but have no other, i.e. clinical or biological, significance.

The commonest architectural pattern is the plate-like or, as seen in two-dimensional histological sections, trabecular. Tumour cells grow in cords that vary in thickness from two to three to many cells. These are separated by sinusoids lined by flat endothelial cells. Kupffer cells are absent or reduced in number. Collagen fibres are increased in Disse's space surrounding the sinusoids and a basement membrane forms, i.e. they become 'capillarized'. The pseudoglandular pattern may result from dilatation of bile canaliculi or from central breakdown of cells in otherwise solid trabecula; the contents are bile or proteinaceous fluid. Compact, solid or scirrhous patterns are rare and develop from compression, scarring and chemo-radiotherapy. The term 'sclerosing hepatic carcinoma' has been applied to tumours associated with hypercalcaemia.

The commonest cytological variant is hepatic or liver-like. Tumour cells are polygonal, with vesicular nuclei and prominent nucleoli. The cytoplasm is finely granular and more basophilic than that of normal liver cells. Bile

canaliculi may be seen. Pleomorphic cells show marked variation in nuclear size, shape and staining. Clear cells have a seemingly empty cytoplasm. This may be due to accumulation of water, fat or glycogen. Sarcomatoid tumours form spindle and giant cells. Recently, a small-cell variant has also been described. Recognition of these cytological variants is diagnostically important so that they can be distinguished from metastatic tumours of similar appearance: renal cell carcinoma, soft tissue sarcoma and carcinoma of the lung, respectively.

A number of intracellular inclusions may be seen. Globular hyaline bodies are small, round and often acidophilic. They usually consist of α-1-antitrypsin. Mallory bodies, similar to those seen in alcoholic liver disease, are made up of altered cytokeratins.

Grading of hepatocellular carcinoma into well-, moderately and poorly differentiated tumours is traditional but it is less important than stage for prognosis.

Special staining techniques commonly employed include silver impregnation, which demonstrates the deficiency of the reticulin framework in hepatocellular carcinoma in contrast to normal or cirrhotic liver and hepatocellular adenoma in which it is normal or increased (**Figure 5**). Others are the PAS reaction for the demonstration of glycogen and trichrome methods for cytoplasmic inclusions.

Electron microscopy is relatively little used nowadays owing to the need for fresh tissue, long time of preparation and expense. However, the ultrastructural features of hepatocellular carcinoma are useful for diagnosis. Numerous mitochondria, a well-developed endoplasmic reticulum and, most of all, the presence of intercellular bile canaliculi are pathognomonic.

Immunocytochemistry, however, has replaced electron microscopy in the investigation of liver tumours. It can be done on formalin-fixed, paraffin-embedded tissues and it

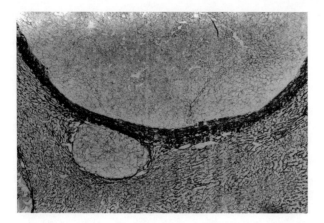

Figure 5 The curved band in the middle is the capsule of a hepatocellular carcinoma. The normal connective tissue framework of the non-tumorous liver is present below whilst it is almost completely absent in the tumour above. Note also that the tumour has broken through the capsule.

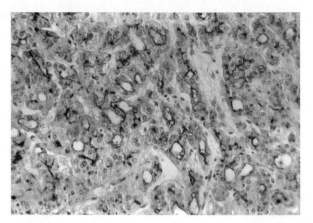

Figure 6 The darkly staining irregular circles and branching structures are bile ductules, stained by peroxidase-labelled polyclonal antisera against CEA/ biliary glycoproteins.

is quick and cheap. The demonstration of normal 'export' proteins such as α-1-antitrypsin, albumin, fibrinogen, ferritin and methallothionein is useful in identifying a tumour as being of liver cell origin. Normal adult liver cells express cytokeratins Nos 8 and 18 as defined in Moll's catalogue whereas bile duct cells contain these and Nos 7 and 19 in addition. The latest addition to liver cell markers is Hep Par1 (Leong *et al.*, 1998). The specificity of α-fetoprotein is high but its sensitivity is low. It is usually only demonstrable in tumour tissue when the serum levels are high, in excess of $5000 \, \text{ng mL}^{-1}$. Carcinoembryonic antigen is widely distributed in glandular tissues in the body and polyclonal antibodies raised against it react with biliary glycoproteins. This allows the demonstration of bile canaliculi without recourse to electron microscopy (**Figure 6**).

Fine needle aspiration cytology is a useful diagnostic aid in expert hands, especially when smears are combined with histology of centrifuged needle washings which may contain tiny tissue fragments.

Molecular Genetic Findings

Hepatic carcinogenesis has been extensively studied for many years in experimental animals, usually rodents, by the use of chemicals. Results have led to the concept of multi-step neoplastic development from initiation through promotion to progression. This is summarized in **Table 4**. Most of the chemicals used are not likely to play a part in the pathogenesis of human hepatocellular carcinoma, the experiments were short term and the phenotypic changes seen in animals are not definitely identified in humans. As evidence for the causative role of viruses began to emerge, attention has switched to mechanisms of viral carcinogenesis. These are presented in **Figure 7**. The possible

pathways of hepatitis B and C viruses and of aflatoxin have been discussed already. Both **Tables 4** and **Figure 7** are somewhat wishful and idealized since such evidence as we have is patchy. Broadly speaking, the genetic changes in carcinogenesis at any site are multiple and cumulative and their phenotypic expressions are not easily identified. What we have at present is an incomplete mosaic from which most of the pieces are missing. However, they can be broken down into alterations in cell cycle regulation, growth factors, oncogenes, tumour-suppressor genes and epigenetic changes, such as telomerase activity. All of these have been investigated in hepatocellular carcinoma and found to be acting abnormally in a varying proportion of cases (Feitelson and Duan, 1997; Geissler *et al.*, 1997; Idilman *et al.*, 1998; Chen and Chen, 1999; Hirohashi *et al.*, 2000).

Completion of the cell cycle requires the successive activation of cyclin-dependent protein kinases which are opposed by their inhibitors. The latter allow for DNA repair. Altered expression leads to the uncontrolled growth of liver cells. Growth factors are generally polypeptides that act at short range via signal transduction pathways across cell membranes. Insulin-like growth factor II (IGF-II) may be an early marker of malignant transformation whilst transforming growth factor α (TGFα) may play a role in its maintenance. Transformed hepatocytes are resistant to transforming growth factor β (TGFβ), which inhibits cell proliferation. In human hepatocellular carcinoma, oncogene (*ras*, *myc*, *fos* families) activation is a rare and tumour-suppressor gene (*p53*, *Rb*) activation is a late event. The most important epigenetic change perhaps is increased telomerase activity which immortalizes the cell.

None of these changes are 'stand-alone' events: they interlock and co-act to produce genomic instability which is amply supported by many chromosomal abnormalities found in hepatocellular carcinoma.

Table 4 Chemical hepatic carcinogenesis (multistep neoplastic development)

Initiation	Metabolic conversion of proximate to ultimate carcinogen
	Damage to DNA, organelles, membranes
	Fixation of abnormality by cell proliferation
Promotion	Inhibition/selection: clonal expansion
	Altered cell populations:
	Enzyme changes
	Hyperplastic nodules
	Autonomous neoplastic nodules
Progression	Metastases and death
	Increased cell turnover all-important

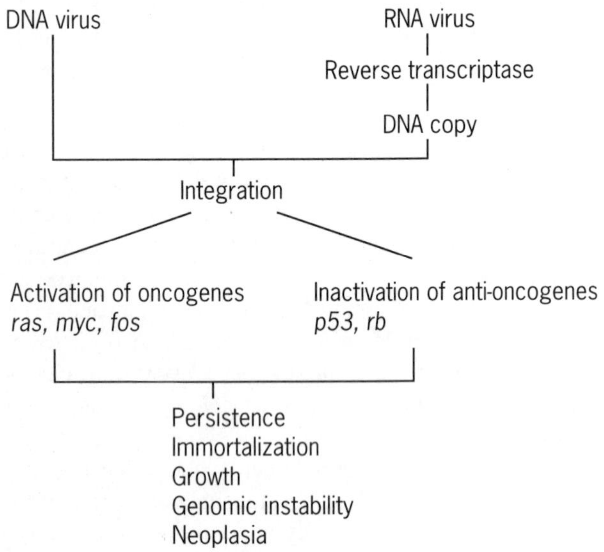

Figure 7 Viral hepatic carcinogenesis

Prognostic Factors

The outlook for hepatocellular carcinoma patients presenting with symptoms is poor, most specialized centres reporting a <5% survival rate amongst those considered suitable for treatment. Better results can be obtained in patients with small, asymptomatic tumours. Good prognostic indicators are a serum α-fetoprotein level below $100\,\mathrm{ng}\,\mathrm{mL}^{-1}$, a solitary tumour, size <5 cm and preferably < 2 cm, lack of portal or hepatic vein involvement, early stage in terms of the TNM classification and well-preserved liver function (Okuda, 1993; Akriviadis et al., 1998; Schafer and Sorrell, 1999).

Presentation, Clinical Diagnosis and Management

In Western countries and particularly in Japan, patients are middle aged or elderly, have had cirrhosis for years and the onset of malignancy is heralded by a sudden deterioration of their condition. In tropical Africa and Asia, patients are often young adults and cirrhosis is first discovered at the same time as the tumour, which is often large and the course is fulminant. Common presenting features are lethargy, pain, hepatomegaly or a mass, fever, weight loss and, in the case of large tumours, rupture and intraperitoneal haemorrhage. Some patients experience a variety of paraneoplastic syndromes such as hypoglycaemia, erythrocytosis and hypercalcaemia.

The most useful laboratory test is a serum α-fetoprotein level over $2-400\,\mathrm{ng}\,\mathrm{mL}^{-1}$, which is found in $\sim$80% of cases. Frequently used imaging methods are ultrasound, computed tomography and magnetic resonance imaging (Okuda, 1993; Akriviadis et al., 1998; Curley, 1998).

Treatment modalities include surgical resection, hepatic artery embolization or chemotherapy, percutaneous injection of alcohol and total hepatectomy followed by liver transplantation. The respective roles of local attempts at tumour removal or destruction and hepatectomy with transplantation have not been finally determined yet and each has its advocates. Once the tumour has spread outside the liver, no form of therapy is effective.

An intriguing aspect of hepatocellular carcinoma is spontaneous regression which has been reported on occasions over the years.

Fibrolamellar Carcinoma

This is a distinctive type of hepatocellular carcinoma that affects adolescents and young adults of either gender. It is not associated with cirrhosis, serum α-fetoprotein is seldom raised and <10% of patients show evidence of HBV or HCV infection. Despite all this, fibrolamellar carcinoma is of liver cell origin (Anthony, 1994; Ishak et al., 1994; Hirohashi et al., 2000).

Patients present with malaise, weight loss and a palpable mass, which is usually solitary and often large, 5–25 cm. The tumour cells are large, with vesicular nuclei and granular, pink cytoplasm, due to the presence of numerous mitochondria. Cytoplasmic globules and 'pale bodies' commonly represent α-1-antitrypsin and fibrinogen, respectively. Bile droplets, copper and copper-associated protein may be present. Bile canaliculi may be difficult to demonstrate. An abundant fibrous stroma, arranged as lamellae of coarse collagen is characteristic and is a *sine qua non* requirement for diagnosis. This fibrous incarceration of the tumour has been held to be responsible for its slow growth and favourable prognosis.

The surgical resectability rate is high and the 5-year survival figures are in the region of 50%.

HEPATOBLASTOMA

This is the most frequently occurring liver tumour in children with a peak incidence in the second year of life. A few present at birth or develop in early adolescence. Males are twice as commonly affected as females. Hepatoblastoma consists of immature liver cells in varying stages of development and a mesenchymal component that is frequently osteoid (Anthony, 1994; Ishak *et al.*, 1994; Stocker and Conran, 1997). One-third of patients with hepatoblastoma have a congenital anomaly (hemihypertrophy, cleft palate, talipes, cardiac or renal malformation), a syndrome (Beckwith–Widemann and Down) or other childhood tumour (nephroblastoma). There is also an increased incidence in familial adenomatous polyposis. Chromosomal abnormalities are common.

The usual presentation is with failure to thrive, loss of weight and a rapidly enlarging abdominal mass. The serum α-fetoprotein level is almost invariably high. Virilization is seen in a small minority, due to production of chorionic gonadotrophin by the tumour. Increased urinary excretion of cystathionine occurs in about half of cases.

Hepatoblastoma usually forms a single mass and is often large when first detected, up to 25 cm. It is well circumscribed, with a thin capsule and a partly solid, partly cystic, fibrous, gelatinous or haemorrhagic cut surface. The epithelial component consists of embryonal, foetal, occasionally adult-like liver cells or glandular structures and keratinizing squamous cells. The commonest mesenchymal elements are undifferentiated spindle cells and osteoid but cartilage, bone and striated muscle may be seen. Rarely, anaplastic small cells, neuroendocrine differentiation and melanin production are present. Extramedullary haematopoiesis is common. Immunocytochemistry shows a wide range of differentiation pathways.

Most hepatoblastomas fall into the epithelial or mixed epithelial and mesenchymal categories (**Figure 8**) but a more detailed classification defines six categories: epithelial (pure foetal, combined foetal and embryonal, macrotrabecular, small cell undifferentiated), mixed epithelial and mesenchymal and mixed with teratoid features (Stocker and Conran, 1997). These categories have limited prognostic significance.

Although half of patients are inoperable at presentation and one-fifth have pulmonary metastases, pre-operative

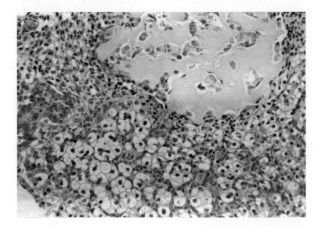

Figure 8   Dark and clear foetal-type cells of hepatoblastoma, mesenchymal spindle cells and structureless osteoid (bone matrix).

chemotherapy allows local resection or total hepatectomy followed by transplantation to be carried out in > 90% of cases. The overall survival rate is 65–70%. A rapid fall of serum α-fetoprotein levels after surgery is a particularly good prognostic sign.

CHOLANGIOCARCINOMA (INTRAHEPATIC AND HILAR BILE DUCT CARCINOMA)

Cholangiocarcinoma is a malignant tumour composed of structures resembling bile ducts (Ishak *et al.*, 1994). It may be intrahepatic, arising from small bile ducts within the liver or hilar, arising from large bile ducts near the porta hepatis. The clinical presentation is somewhat different according to location. The pathology is simple: all these tumours are mucus secreting adenocarcinomas (Anthony, 1989, 1994; Nakanuma *et al.*, 2000).

Epidemiology

Cholangiocarcinoma is much less common than hepatocellular carcinoma and constitutes about 15% of all liver cancers (Parkin *et al.*, 1997). It is distributed equally throughout the world except in South-East Asia, particularly Thailand, Laos, Korea, Hong Kong and Canton, where its incidence is increased. This is due to the high prevalence of liver fluke infestation in these areas. Patients are middle aged to elderly, there is no gender difference and the tumour is not associated with cirrhosis.

Aetiology

Liver Fluke Infestation

Infestation with the liver flukes *Opistorchis viverrini* in Thailand and Laos and *Clonorchis sinensis* in

Korea, Hong Kong and Canton is the major cause of cholangiocarcinoma in these high-incidence areas. The life cycle of liver flukes requires poor environmental conditions with infested human waste discharged into stagnant water, take-up by snails as intermediate hosts and the habit of eating raw or undercooked fish which themselves have become infested. A heavy parasite load is acquired over many years and results in cholangitis, liver abscess and cholangiocarcinoma. The presence of liver flukes may not, in itself, be carcinogenic and nitrosamines, derived from diet, may act as cofactors.

Hepatolithiasis

Intrahepatic biliary stones are frequently associated with clonorchiasis but not with opistorchiasis. Cystic lesions of bile ducts may also be complicated by stones.

Chronic Inflammatory Bowel Disease

Cholangiocarcinoma is a significant complication of long-standing ulcerative colitis commonly preceded by sclerosing cholangitis.

Congenital Anomalies of the Biliary Tree

These include cystic dilatation of the biliary tree or Caroli disease, choledochal cysts, biliary microhamartomas and anomalies of the union between the main pancreatic and common bile ducts.

Thorotrast

This once commonly used radiological contrast medium is best known for causing angiosarcoma of the liver but, in recent years, cholangiocarcinomas have also been observed.

Precancerous Changes, Screening and Prevention

The best studied precancerous changes are those associated with liver flukes and biliary stones (**Figure 9**). These consist of adenomatous hyperplasia, dysplasia with multilayering, nuclear enlargement and hyperchromasia and carcinoma-*in-situ* without invasion (Nakanuma *et al.*, 2000). Cell kinetic studies have shown increasing proliferative activity along this sequence and the acquisition of genetic abnormalities.

There is no effective screening method for cholangiocarcinoma and prevention consists of reducing the incidence of liver fluke infestation, surveillance of individuals with known high-risk factors and surgical removal of choledochal cysts which carry a particularly high risk of malignant change.

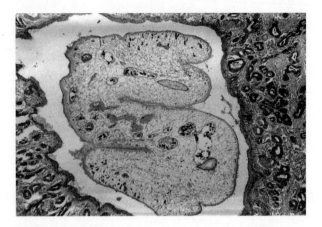

Figure 9   A female *Clonorchis sinensis* fluke lying in a bile duct, the lining of which shows glandular adenomatous hyperplasia. The small, dark, oval objects in the worm's body are eggs.

Macroscopic and Microscopic Pathology

The Macroscopic Pathology of Cholangiocarcinoma

The gross appearance of intrahepatic tumours is of a grey–white, tough, scirrhous type of growth which is often solitary but may be multinodular, or a combination of both. Central necrosis, scarring and calcification may be seen. Finger-like extensions around the main mass represent spread along portal tracts. Metastatic spread is common, to regional lymph nodes, lungs and the peritoneum. Tumours in the hilum present as ill-defined nodules, strictures or, rarely, as an intraductal papillary growth. The flow of bile from the liver is often obstructed and the liver is stained green whilst the gall bladder and common bile ducts are empty.

Microscopic Features: Histological Patterns, Ultrastructure and Special Techniques

Most cholangiocarcinomas are mucus-secreting adenocarcinomas of a tubular pattern and an abundant fibrous stroma is characteristic (**Figure 10**) (Colombari and Tsui, 1995). PAS diastase-resistant or mucicarmine-positive mucus is readily demonstrable and tumour cells express carcinoembryonic antigen in their cytoplasm as well as on their luminal border. The tumour may also grow in solid cords and form papillae. Rarely, it is of signet ring or clear cell type. Large amounts of extracellular mucus are sometimes formed in which tubulopapillary fragments of tumour appear to float freely. Tumours associated with stones, cysts or bile duct anomalies may be adenosquamous or purely squamous. Sarcomatoid cholangiocarcinoma is rare.

Electron microscopy is seldom used in the diagnosis of cholangiocarcinoma. It shows glandular characteristics: lack

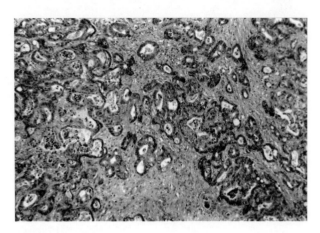

Figure 10 Cholangiocarcinoma made up of abnormally branching bile duct-like structures, separated by a dense fibrous stroma.

of organelles, presence of tonofilaments and a basal lamina.

Immunocytochemistry is used mainly to distinguish cholangiocarcinoma from metastatic adenocarcinoma and, less commonly, from hepatocellular carcinoma. The most useful are demonstration of different cytokeratin patterns for the former and Hep Par 1 for the latter (Leong *et al.*, 1998).

Molecular Genetic Findings

Mutations of the *ras* oncogene and the *p53* tumour-suppressor gene are the most common genetic abnormalities in cholangiocarcinoma followed by over-expression of c-*erbB-2* (Nakanuma *et al.*, 2000).

Prognostic Factors

Early detection of cholangiocarcinoma is difficult and most patients present with advanced tumours. Lymph node involvement, positive margins and bilobar distribution are associated with high recurrence rates after surgical resection. Patients with unrelieved obstruction of major hepatic ducts and those with cysts and stones may die of complications, e.g. sepsis or liver failure, before the tumour itself becomes evident.

Presentation, Clinical Diagnosis and Management

Malaise, abdominal pain and weight loss are common symptoms of intrahepatic tumours whilst hilar tumours cause unremitting obstructive jaundice. Ultrasound and computer-assisted tomography show the location of the tumour which can then be biopsied for a definitive diagnosis. Only a small minority of patients are suitable for surgical resection and other forms of treatment, e.g. radio- or chemotherapy, are ineffective.

BILIARY CYSTADENOMA AND CYSTADENOCARCINOMA

These are rare tumours. Their pathology is virtually identical with that of similar tumours seen in the ovary and, occasionally, in the pancreas. Most are mucinous and a minority are serous. Patients present with solitary masses which may be fairly large but they are usually amenable to surgical resection and the results are good.

MIXED HEPATOCELLULAR CARCINOMA AND CHOLANGIOCARCINOMA

The presence of both bile secretion and mucus production must be present, supported by appropriate immunocytochemical markers, for such a diagnosis to be made. Effective treatment is seldom possible and the prognosis is poor.

METASTATIC TUMOURS

These are nearly always secondary carcinomas and the common primary sites are the colon, rectum, upper gastrointestinal tract, pancreas, lung and breast. Liver metastases indicate advanced disease and most patients die within a few weeks or at most months. Colonic and, especially, rectal carcinoma metastases may be solitary or few in number and worthwhile results have been achieved by partial hepatectomy.

SARCOMAS OF THE LIVER

These are all rare but angiosarcoma, childhood sarcomas and malignant lymphoma are the most important (Ishak, 1997).

Angiosarcoma

The cause of this tumour is unknown in most cases but a minority are associated with exposure to the once popular radiological contrast agent Thorotrast (thorium dioxide), arsenic and the industrial contaminant vinyl chloride monomer. Thorium is radioactive with a half-life of approximately 400 years and, when injected, most of it is taken up by the liver. In addition to angiosarcoma, hepatocellular carcinoma and cholangiocarcinoma have also been observed. Particles of Thorotrast are readily visualized in histological sections as coarse, pink–brown granules (**Figure 11**).

Angiosarcoma of the liver is always fatal and at autopsy it appears as ill-defined, spongy and haemorrhagic, or greyish–white fibrous nodules which replace the entire

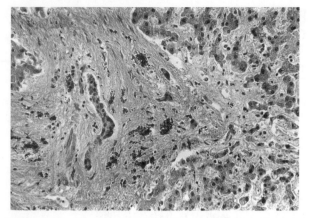

Figure 11 The dark granular material next to a portal bile duct is Thorotrast. There is much fibrosis, separating the liver cell plates around but angiosarcoma has not yet developed.

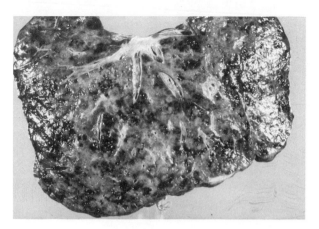

Figure 12 Reddish, dark and white (fibrous) angiosarcoma replaces the entire liver.

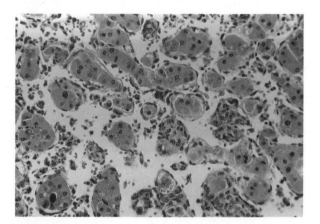

Figure 13 Dark, spindle and polygonal cells of angiosarcoma grow over the surface of liver cell plates in a scaffold-like or tectorial fashion.

liver (**Figure 12**). The histological appearances are variable but the most characteristic is a scaffold-like or tectorial growth of spindle cells on the surface of liver cell plates which eventually atrophy and disappear (**Figure 13**). Immunocytochemistry shows that tumour cells react with endothelial markers such as CD31, CD34 and Factor VIII related antigen or von Willebrand factor.

Another, distinctive form of malignant vascular tumour is epithelioid haemangioma, which occurs in the liver, lung, skin and bone and has a much better prognosis than angiosarcoma.

Childhood Sarcomas

These are embryonal sarcoma and rhabdomyosarcoma. They are much less common than hepatoblastoma. Their prognosis has been hopeless until recently but aggressive treatment combining surgical excision, chemotherapy and radiation has led to 5-year survival rates of around 15%.

Primary Malignant Lymphoma

All types of lymphoma may secondarily involve the liver in their advanced stage and the prognosis is then poor. However, it is increasingly recognized that lymphoma can also be primary in the liver and the outcome, with appropriate treatment, is much more favourable. They are all non-Hodgkin lymphomas of B or T cell lineage. Some have been associated with HBV or HCV infections and AIDS.

BENIGN TUMOURS AND TUMOUR-LIKE LESIONS

The most important benign tumour of the liver is hepatocellular adenoma. The majority of cases occur in young to middle-aged women who have taken oral contraceptive steroids for years or in individuals of either gender on long-term treatment with androgenic/anabolic steroids. Hepatocellular adenoma is often symptomatic, may grow to a large size, and rupture, giving rise to life-threatening intraperitoneal haemorrhage. The relationship of focal nodular hyperplasia to oral contraceptive steroids is much less certain and is often an asymptomatic, incidental finding. Inflammatory myofibroblastic tumour is an intriguing entity, the nature of which is not fully understood, i.e. whether inflammatory or neoplastic, but surgical excision is curative. Many other types of benign tumour have been described but they are all rare or clinically unimportant (Anthony, 1994).

TUMOURS OF THE GALL BLADDER

Nearly all tumours at this site are mucus secreting adenocarcinomas (Albores-Saavedra and Henson, 1986).

The incidence of carcinoma of the gall bladder is variable in different parts of the world and amongst ethnic groups. Overall, it ranks fourth amongst cancers of the digestive tract, after those of the colo-rectum, stomach and pancreas. The highest frequency is seen in South West American Indians and it is also common in Mexico, Chile, Bolivia and Israel.

South West American Indians apart, who seem to have a genetic predisposition to gall bladder carcinoma, the most important predisposing factor in most countries is chronic inflammation of the gall bladder associated with stones (cholelithiasis). Secondary factors are old age, female gender, obesity, abnormalities of bile and lipoprotein metabolism and multiple pregnancies which, themselves, predispose to gall stone formation. There is also a link with chronic inflammatory bowel disease, anomalous pancreaticobiliary duct union and the typhoid carrier state.

Carcinoma of the gall bladder is commonly preceded by epithelial hyperplasia, dysplasia and carcinoma-in-situ. Malignant change may also develop in tubular or villous adenomas. Rarely, biliary papillomatosis affects the gall bladder, the intra- and extrahepatic bile ducts and even the pancreatic duct system and carcinomas can arise at any of these sites.

There is no effective screening method for gall bladder carcinoma and the only means of prevention is prophylactic cholecystectomy which has been advocated for high-risk groups such as American Indian females beyond middle age.

Carcinoma of the gall bladder is often a silent disease and the tumour is discovered incidentally at cholecystectomy or else the symptoms are those of cholecystitis or cholelithiasis. These include intolerance of fatty meals, right upper quadrant abdominal pain and intermittent nausea or vomiting. Weight loss and jaundice are indicative of advanced disease. Ultrasonography and computed tomography are used in the assessment of patients with symptoms attributable to gall bladder disease.

Macroscopically, carcinoma of the gall bladder may appear as diffuse thickening of the wall, an ill-defined nodule or a polyp. Microscopically, most tumours are well to moderately differentiated adenocarcinomas with a tubular or tubulo-papillary pattern. Mucus secretion is nearly always demonstrable. Intestinal (with endocrine, Paneth and goblet cells), mucinous (with much extracellular mucin), signet ring, clear and small-cell variants are recognized. Ultrastructural or immunocytochemical studies are not particularly useful for diagnosis: the features are those of an adenocarcinoma occurring at many sites.

The majority of gall bladder carcinomas express mutated *p53* tumour-suppressor gene. *Ras* and other oncogene mutations are late events. Amplification of the c-*erbB-2* gene has also been found.

Surgical excision is the only effective method of treatment. The best results are obtained before the gall bladder wall has been breached. Direct extension into the liver and regional lymph node metastasis are indicators of a poor prognosis. Ultimately, patients die of disseminated disease with direct, lymphatic and blood-borne spread to many possible sites in the body.

TUMOURS OF THE EXTRAHEPATIC BILE DUCTS

As in the gall bladder, the commonest tumour in the extrahepatic bile ducts is an adenocarcinoma. About half arise in the common hepatic, cystic and upper common bile ducts, one quarter in the middle and one-tenth in the lower common bile duct; the rest are diffuse or multiple tumours. In general, the prognosis is worse for carcinomas of the proximal than of the middle or distal segments of the extrahepatic biliary tree. Most patients are elderly and males are more commonly affected than females, in contrast to carcinoma of the gall bladder. Cholelithiasis is not a risk factor. Ulcerative colitis, malunion of the main pancreatic and common bile ducts, congenital malformations such as choledochal cyst, pre-existing adenomas and papillomas are well-known predisposing factors. The onset of invasive malignancy may be preceded by dysplasia and carcinoma-in-situ, which are sometimes seen next to it in operative specimens. Most patients present with obstructive jaundice, some with ascending cholangitis and a few with blood in the bile (haemobilia). At laparotomy, extrahepatic bile duct carcinoma appears as a polyp, a stricture or a diffuse thickening. Histologically, most are tubular or tubulo-papillary adenocarcinomas with a fibrous stroma. A good histological grade has been claimed to confer a prognostic advantage but this is not universally accepted. Spread to adjacent structures or lymph node metastasis are indicative of a poor prognosis. The only effective treatment is complete surgical excision.

REFERENCES

Akriviadis, E. A., *et al*. (1998). Hepatocellular carcinoma. *British Journal of Surgery*, **86**, 1319–1331.

Albores-Saavedra, J. and Henson, D. E. (1986). *Tumors of the Gall Bladder and Extrahepatic Bile Ducts, Atlas of Tumour Pathology*, 2nd Series, Fascicle 22. (Armed Forces Institute of Pathology, Washington, DC).

Anthony, P. P. (1989). Epidemiology, aetiology and pathology of bile duct tumours. In: Preece, P. E., *et al*. (eds), *Cancer of the Bile Ducts and Pancreas*. 1–26 (Saunders, Philadelphia).

Anthony, P. P. (1994). Tumours and tumour-like lesions of the liver and biliary tract. In: MacSween, R. N. M., *et al*. (eds), *Pathology of the Liver*. 635–711 (Churchill Livingstone, Edinburgh).

Beasley, R. P. (1988). Hepatitis B virus. The major etiology of hepatocellular carcinoma. *Cancer*, **61**, 1942–1956.

Bosch, F. X., *et al.* (1999). Epidemiology of primary liver cancer. *Seminars in Liver Disease*, **19**, 271–285.

Chen, P.-J. and Chen, D. S. (1999). Hepatitis B virus infection and hepatocellular carcinoma: molecular, genetic and clinical perspectives. *Seminars in Liver Disease*, **19**, 253–262.

Colombari, R. and Tsui, W. M. S. (1995). Biliary tumours of the liver. *Seminars in Liver Disease*, **15**, 402–413.

Colombo, M. (1999). Hepatitis C virus and hepatocellular carcinoma. *Seminars in Liver Disease*, **19**, 263–269.

Craig, J. R., *et al.* (1989). *Tumors of the Liver and Intrahepatic Bile Ducts, Atlas of Tumor Pathology*, 2nd Series, Fascicle 26. (Armed Forces Institute of Pathology, Washington, DC).

Curley, S. A. (ed.) (1998). *Liver Cancer*. (Springer, New York).

European Association for the Study of the Liver. (1999). The liver in systemic diseases. *Journal of Hepatology*, **30** (Supplement 1).

Feitelson, M. A. and Duan, L.-X. (1997). Hepatitis B virus X antigen in the pathogenesis of chronic infections and the development of hepatocellular carcinoma. *American Journal of Pathology*, **150**, 1141–1157.

Geissler, M., *et al.* (1997). Molecular mechanisms of hepatocarcinogenesis. In: Okuda, K. and Tabor, E. (eds), *Liver Cancer*. 59–88 (Churchill Livingstone, New York).

Idilman, R., *et al.* (1998). Pathogenesis of hepatitis B and C-induced hepatocellular carcinoma. *Journal of Viral Hepatology*, **5**, 285–299.

International Agency for Research on Cancer (1972–1999). *IARC Monographs on the Evaluation of Carcinogenic Risks to Humans and Supplements to the Monographs*, Vols 1–71 and Supplements 1–8 (International Agency for Research on Cancer, Lyon).

Ishak, K. G. (1997). Malignant mesenchymal tumours of the liver. In: Okuda, K. and Tabor, E. (eds), *Liver Cancer*. 291–314 (Churchill Livingstone, New York).

Ishak, K. G., *et al.* (1994). *Histological Typing of Tumours of the Liver*, 2nd edn. (Springer, Berlin).

Hirohashi, S., *et al.* (2000). Hepatocellular carcinoma. In: Hamilton, S. R. and Aaltonen, L. A. (eds), *Pathology and Genetics of Tumours of the Digestive System. WHO Classification of Tumours*. 159–183. (International Agency for Research on Cancer, Lyon).

Leong, A. S.-Y., *et al.* (1998). Hep Par 1 and selected antibodies in the immunohistological distinction of hepatocellular carcinoma from cholangiocarcinoma, combined tumours and metastatic carcinoma. *Histopathology*, **33**, 318–324.

MacSween, R. N. M. and Scothorne, R. J. (1994). Developmental anatomy and normal structure. In: MacSween, R. N. M., *et al.* (eds), *Pathology of the Liver*. 1–49 (Churchill Livingstone, Edinburgh).

Nakanuma, Y., *et al.* (2000). Intrahepatic cholangiocarcinoma. In: Hamilton, S. R. and Aaltonen, L. A. (eds), *Pathology and Genetics of Tumours of the Digestive System. WHO Classification of Tumours*. 173–180. (International Agency for Research on Cancer, Lyon.)

Okuda, K. (1993). Epidemiology and clinical aspects of hepatocellular carcinoma. *Journal of Gastroenterology and Hepatology*, **8** (Supplement 1), S1–S4.

Parkin, D. M., *et al.* (eds) (1997). *Cancer Incidence in Five Continents*, Vol. VII (International Agency for Research on Cancer, Lyon).

Schafer, D. F. and Sorrell, M. F. (1999). Hepatocellular carcinoma. *Lancet*, **353**, 1253–1257.

Simonetti, R. G., *et al.* (1991). Hepatocellular carcinoma. A worldwide problem and the major risk factors. *Digestive Disease Science*, **36**, 962–972.

Stocker, J. T. and Conran, R. M. (1997). Hepatoblastoma. In: Okuda, K. and Tabor, E. (eds), *Liver Cancer*. 263–278. (Churchill Livingstone, New York).

Wogan, G. N. (1999). Aflatoxin as a human carcinogen. *Hepatology*, **30**, 573–575.

FURTHER READING

Bannasch, P., *et al.* (eds) (1989). *Liver Cell Carcinoma*. Falk Symposium 51. (Kluwer, Dordrecht).

Boyer, J. L. and Ockner, R. K. (eds) (1997). *Progress in Liver Diseases*. (Saunders, Philadelphia).

Clavien, P.-A. (ed.) (1999). *Malignant Liver Tumors*. (Blackwell, Oxford).

Curley, S. A. (ed.) (1998). *Liver Cancer*. (Springer, New York).

Goldin, R. D., *et al.* (eds) (1998). *Pathology of Viral Hepatitis*. (Arnold, London).

MacSween, R. N. M., *et al.* (eds) (1994). *Pathology of the Liver*. (Churchill Livingstone, Edinburgh).

Okuda, K. and Tabor, E. (eds) (1977). *Liver Cancer*. (Churchill Livingstone, New York).

Phillips, M. J., *et al.* (1987). *The Liver: an Atlas and Text of Ultrastructural Pathology*. (Raven Press, New York).

Preece, P. E., *et al.* (eds) (1989). *Cancer of the Bile Ducts and Pancreas*. (Saunders, Philadelphia).

Zakim, D. and Boyer, T. D. (eds) (1996). *Hepatology*. (Saunders, Philadelphia).

Chapter 40

Pancreas

Ralph H. Hruban, Robb E. Wilentz and Michael Goggins

Johns Hopkins Medical Institutions, Baltimore, MD, USA

CONTENTS

NORMAL DEVELOPMENT AND STRUCTURE

As is true for many organs, an understanding of the embryology of the pancreas can lead to a better understanding of the diseases that affect the gland. The five parts of the pancreas (head, uncinate, neck, body and tail; **Figure 1a**) develop from two separate outpouchings of the embryological foregut (Solicia *et al.*, 1997). The first outpouching, called the 'ventral anlage,' will give rise to most of the head and uncinate process of the pancreas. The second outpouching, called the dorsal anlage, will form the tail, body and inferior (lower) portion of the head of the gland.

These two anlages and their duct systems normally fuse by the eighth week of gestation to form a single organ. The main pancreatic duct, called the 'duct of Wirsung,' is normally formed when the duct in the dorsal anlage fuses with the duct in the ventral anlage at a point close to the duodenum. Because the ventral anlage also forms the common bile duct, the main pancreatic duct usually drains into the duodenum in conjunction with the common bile duct (**Figure 1b**). A remaining portion of the dorsal duct forms the accessory pancreatic duct, called the 'duct of Santorini' and this accessory duct usually drains separately into the duodenum.

The adult pancreas comes to rest in the centre of the abdomen, housed between the duodenum and spleen. The head of the pancreas is closely associated with the duodenum. The uncinate process forms a groove above which important blood vessels, the superior mesenteric artery and vein, pass. The neck, body and tail comprise the parts of the pancreas that are successively closer to the spleen (see **Figure 1a**).

Macroscopically, the pancreas is a single organ. Microscopically, however, the pancreas contains two distinct components, each with an important function (**Figure 2**). The 'exocrine' pancreas secretes digestive enzymes into the duodenum, while the 'endocrine' portion of the pancreas secretes hormones, such as insulin, into the

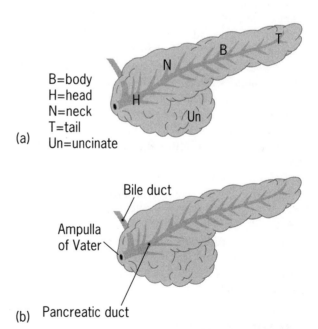

B=body
H=head
N=neck
T=tail
Un=uncinate

(a)

Bile duct

Ampulla of Vater

(b) Pancreatic duct

Figure 1 Structure of the adult pancreas. The head is that portion of the pancreas closest to the duodenum, the tail the portion closest to the spleen (a). Note that the main pancreatic duct joins the distal common bile duct at the ampulla of Vater (b). (Adapted from an original medical illustration by Jennifer Parsons, with permission.)

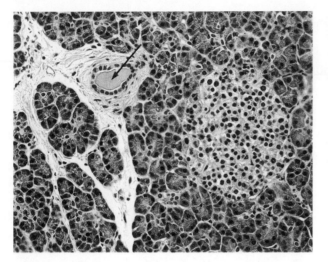

Figure 2   Microscopic section of normal pancreas. The acini comprise the bulk of the exocrine pancreas. The acini produce digestive enzymes which are released into small ductules (arrow) and from there the enzymes travel into the duodenum. The islets of Langerhans (nodule on right) form the endocrine pancreas. They release hormones such as insulin directly into the bloodstream.

bloodstream. The pancreas has cells specialized for each of these tasks, as well as the cells needed to support and nourish the organ (connective tissue, blood vessels).

The exocrine structures of the pancreas include the acini and ducts (**Figure 2**). Acini, which comprise over 80% of the pancreatic mass, are lobular units that secrete fluids rich in bicarbonate and enzymes into small ductules. These small ductules merge to drain their contents into larger ducts, which in turn merge into even larger ducts. This arborizing pattern continues to the level of the main and accessory pancreatic ducts, and the digestive enzymes of the exocrine pancreas are thereby released into the duodenum.

The endocrine portion of the pancreas consists of the islets of Langerhans (**Figure 2**). Although a normal pancreas contains over one million of these islets, they comprise only 1–2% of the organ mass (Solcia *et al.*, 1997). Approximately 70% of the cells in normal islets are α cells, 20% are β cells and 10% are δ cells. The α cells secrete the hormone glucagon, the β cells secrete the hormone insulin and the δ cells secrete the hormone somatostatin.

The various neoplasms of the pancreas can be best understood if one keeps these structures of the normal pancreas in mind.

TUMOUR PATHOLOGY

Cancer of the pancreas is not one disease. Instead, it is a number of different diseases broadly classified under one umbrella term (Klöppel *et al.*, 1996; Solcia *et al.*, 1997). For example, primary, metastatic and systemic tumours can all involve the gland. Primary cancers arise in the

pancreas. Metastatic cancers originate in other organs and spread to the pancreas secondarily. Systemic malignancies derive from the blood or lymph nodes and, by definition, simultaneously involve multiple sites, one of which may be the pancreas.

This section provides an overview of the many types of neoplasms that can arise in or spread to the pancreas. It focuses on primary pancreatic neoplasms, which can be benign (tumours which usually do not spread and which usually will not lead to a patient's death), borderline (tumours for which behaviour is difficult to predict) or malignant (tumours which, if untreated, will spread beyond the gland and lead to the patient's death). Not surprisingly, if we remember the dual composition of the normal pancreas, primary pancreatic neoplasms can show either endocrine or exocrine (non-endocrine) differentiation. The non-endocrine neoplasms can be further subclassified into solid or cystic. For example, ductal adenocarcinoma, the most common primary pancreatic malignancy, is a non-endocrine, solid neoplasm. Needless to say, each of the various pancreatic neoplasms is grossly, microscopically and clinically distinct. Therefore, understanding the pathology of pancreatic cancer forms the cornerstone for rational patient diagnosis, treatment and prognostication.

The following sections will describe the most common types of tumours of the pancreas. Wherever possible, the classification systems published by the Armed Forces Institute of Pathology (AFIP) and by the World Health Organisation (WHO) will be followed (see **Table 1**) (Klöppel *et al.*, 1996; Solcia *et al.*, 1997).

Solid Non-endocrine Neoplasms

Ductal Adenocarcinoma

Gross and Microscopic Features

Ductal adenocarcinoma is the most common malignancy of the pancreas, accounting for almost three-quarters of all primary cancers (Solcia *et al.*, 1997). Most, but not all, ductal adenocarcinomas arise in the head of the pancreas (Solcia *et al.*, 1997; Hruban *et al.*, 2000). These tumours are infiltrative (**Figure 3; see colour plate section**), firm masses. Those that arise in the head of the pancreas often obstruct and dilate the distal common bile and pancreatic ducts. As a result, many patients with pancreatic cancer develop jaundice, a yellowish discoloration of the skin and eyes caused by obstruction of the flow of bile. Microscopically, ductal adenocarcinomas are composed of infiltrating glands of various shapes and sizes surrounded by reactive connective tissue (**Figure 4a**). The cancer cells may contain abnormal mitotic figures and the nuclei of these cells can show marked pleomorphism (variation in size and shape) and hyperchromasia (increased nuclear staining).

Most ductal adenocarcinomas grow into nerves (**Figure 4b**) and blood vessels, and it is therefore

Table 1   Histological classification of tumours of the pancreas. (Adapted from Solcia *et al.*, 1997.)

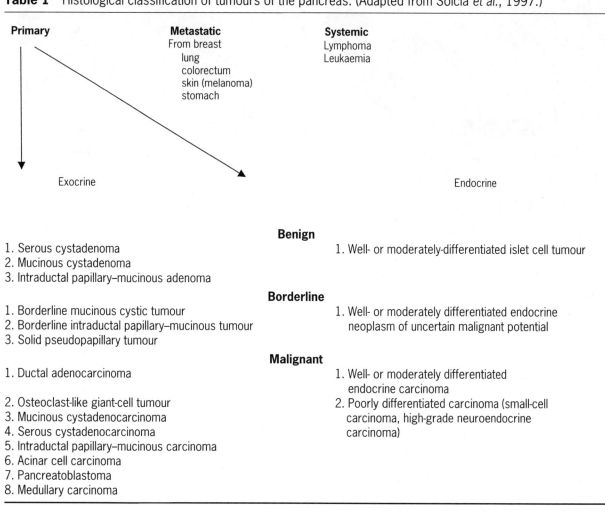

Primary	Metastatic	Systemic
	From breast	Lymphoma
	lung	Leukaemia
	colorectum	
	skin (melanoma)	
	stomach	

Exocrine   Endocrine

Benign

1. Serous cystadenoma	1. Well- or moderately-differentiated islet cell tumour
2. Mucinous cystadenoma	
3. Intraductal papillary–mucinous adenoma	

Borderline

1. Borderline mucinous cystic tumour	1. Well- or moderately differentiated endocrine
2. Borderline intraductal papillary–mucinous tumour	neoplasm of uncertain malignant potential
3. Solid pseudopapillary tumour	

Malignant

1. Ductal adenocarcinoma	1. Well- or moderately differentiated endocrine carcinoma
2. Osteoclast-like giant-cell tumour	2. Poorly differentiated carcinoma (small-cell carcinoma, high-grade neuroendocrine carcinoma)
3. Mucinous cystadenocarcinoma	
4. Serous cystadenocarcinoma	
5. Intraductal papillary–mucinous carcinoma	
6. Acinar cell carcinoma	
7. Pancreatoblastoma	
8. Medullary carcinoma	

not surprising that many patients with pancreatic cancer develop severe back pain. In addition, most ductal adenocarcinomas spread to lymph nodes (Solcia *et al.*, 1997). Ductal adenocarcinomas also frequently spread to other organs ('metastasize') (Solcia *et al.*, 1997; Hruban *et al.*, 2000). This spread to lymph nodes and other organs greatly reduces the effectiveness of surgery in the treatment of pancreatic cancer and, not unexpectedly, patients with metastases do significantly worse than do patients without them (Yeo *et al.*, 1995; Solcia *et al.*, 1997; Hruban *et al.*, 2000). Unfortunately, most patients with pancreas cancer do not come to clinical attention until after their cancers have spread. Overall survival from ductal adenocarcinoma is therefore extremely poor, with average survival time of about 6 months.

Special Features: Histological Precursors

One of the more important findings in the pathology of ductal adenocarcinoma of the pancreas has been the identification of the morphological precursors to invasive cancer. Called 'pancreatic intraepithelial neoplasias' (or

PanINs for short), these precursors arise in the small pancreatic ducts and ductules, and they are composed of mucin-producing cells with varying degrees of nuclear and architectural atypia. A complete description of the various PanINs as well as numerous examples can be found on the Web (http://pathology.jhu.edu/pancreas_panin). As shown in **Figure 5**, PanINs progress from flat lesions to papillary lesions to atypical papillary lesions to carcinomas *in situ* (non-invasive carcinoma) and finally to invasive cancers (Cubilla and Fitzgerald, 1976; DiGiuseppe *et al.*, 1996; Hruban *et al.*, 2000).

Several lines of evidence suggest that PanINs are the precursors of infiltrating pancreatic ductal adenocarcinoma, just like adenomas are the precursors of infiltrating cancer in the colon. First, PanINs are frequently found in pancreata adjacent to infiltrating cancers (Cubilla and Fitzgerald, 1976). Second, isolated clinical case reports have suggested that PanINs can progress to infiltrating cancer over time (Brat *et al.*, 1998). For example, Brat *et al.* reported three patients who developed infiltrating ductal adenocarcinomas months to years after high-grade PanINs

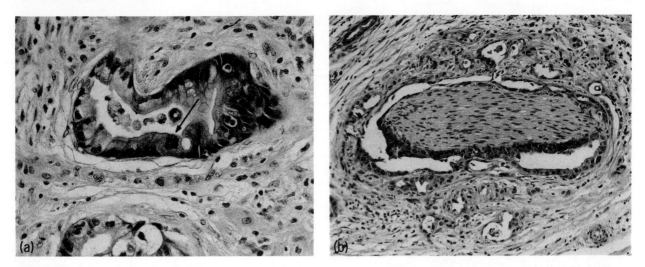

Figure 4   Microscopic section of infiltrating ductal adenocarcinoma. Note how the cancer cells form irregular glands and note the presence of an atypical mitotic figure (arrow) (a). Ductal adenocarcinomas often invade around nerves (b).

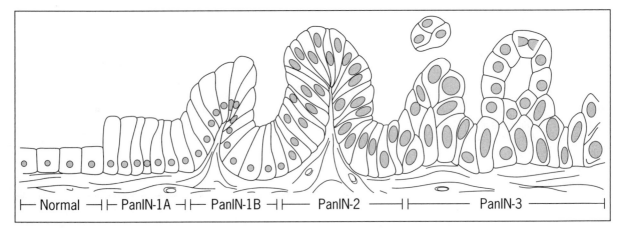

| ⊢— Normal —⊣ | ⊢— PanIN-1A —⊣ | ⊢— PanIN-1B —⊣ | ⊢——— PanIN-2 ———⊣ | ⊢——————— PanIN-3 ———————⊣ |

Figure 5   Illustration depicting the progression from normal pancreatic duct (left), to flat duct lesion without atypia (PanIN-1A), to papillary duct lesion without atypia (PanIN-1B), to papillary duct lesion with atypia (PanIN-2), to carcinoma-*in-situ* (PanIN-3). (Adapted from an original medical illustration by Jennifer Parsons, with permission.)

were identified in their pancreata. Third, PanINs display many of the same fundamental genetic changes (mutations in the K-*RAS*, *HER-2/neu*, *BRCA2*, *p16*, *p53* and *DPC4* genes) as do infiltrating adenocarcinomas (Caldas *et al.*, 1994; DiGiuseppe *et al.*, 1994a, b; Day *et al.*, 1996; Moskaluk *et al.*, 1997; Willentz *et al.*, 1998) (see Molecular Genetics).

An understanding of PanINs and the development of this progression model is important because it suggests that the detection of precursor lesions and curable early pancreatic cancers should one day be possible (Caldas *et al.*, 1994). Early detection is especially important in the case of ductal adenocarcinoma of the pancreas because, as mentioned earlier, most pancreatic cancers have already spread beyond the pancreas when they come to clinical attention.

Medullary Carcinoma

Gross and Microscopic Findings

Although historically grouped with ductal adenocarcinomas, medullary carcinomas are a newly recognized subtype of pancreatic cancer with distinct gross and microscopic appearances. Grossly, these neoplasms may be relatively well circumscribed. Microscopically, they have poorly defined cellular boundaries ('syncytial growth pattern') and expanding, rather than infiltrating, tumour borders (Goggins *et al.*, 1998). Most also have extensive necrosis.

Special Features: Genetics

Medullary carcinomas are important to recognize because they are genetically distinct tumours, in that they frequently have 'microsatellite instability' (MSI) and wild-type K-*RAS* genes (Goggins *et al.*, 1998). (see Molecular Genetics). These data are atypical for the usual ductal adenocarcinomas, which nearly universally harbour K-*RAS* gene mutations and seldom if ever have MSI (Hruban *et al.*, 1993). In addition, the authors have recently shown that patients with medullary carcinomas often have a familial history of cancer and that medullary carcinoma may be a sign of an inherited propensity to develop cancer. Medullary carcinomas also may be associated with an outcome better than that for ductal adenocarcinomas, but more study is necessary (Goggins *et al.*, 1998).

Acinar Cell Carcinoma

Gross and Microscopic Findings

Acinar cell carcinomas are usually large and most arise in the head of the pancreas (Klimstra *et al.*, 1992; Solcia *et al.*, 1997; Hruban *et al.*, 2000). In contrast to the infiltrative appearance of ductal adenocarcinomas, acinar cell carcinomas typically have smooth borders. Microscopically, the neoplastic cells in acinar cell carcinomas form small glands, called acini. The cells are pink and granular. These carcinomas usually express the digestive enzymes trypsin, lipase, chymotrypsin and/or amylase, and staining for these substances may be helpful in distinguishing acinar cell carcinomas from other neoplasms that arise in the pancreas. Electron microscopy will reveal the presence of zymogen granules in the neoplastic cells (Klimstra *et al.*, 1995). Zymogen granules are the granules which hold or package the digestive enzymes in normal acinar cells.

Special Features: Clinical Presentation

While most patients with acinar cell carcinomas present with non-specific symptoms, as many as 20% develop the clinical syndrome of subcutaneous fat necrosis. This dramatic syndrome is characterized by a skin rash (erythema nodosum-like), peripheral eosinophilia (increased numbers of eosinophils in the blood) and/or polyarthralgias (joint pain involving multiple joints) (Solcia *et al.*, 1997). These latter signs and symptoms are caused by the release of massive amounts of the digestive enzyme lipase into the bloodstream by the neoplasm (Klimstra *et al.*, 1992). The mean survival for patients with acinar cell carcinoma of the pancreas is only 18 months (Klimstra *et al.*, 1992; Solcia *et al.*, 1997).

Osteoclast-like Giant-cell Tumour (OCGT)

Gross and Microscopic Findings

OCGTs are typically well circumscribed, yellow–pink and fleshy. By light microscopy these tumours are composed of striking giant cells containing multiple nuclei (multinucleated giant cells) dispersed among bland tumour cells with only one nucleus (mononuclear cells) (Solcia *et al.*, 1997; Hruban *et al.*, 2000). The multinucleated giant cells in OCGTs closely resemble osteoclasts, a type of cell found in resorbing bone. The multinucleated giant cells in OCGTs express the macrophage markers KP-1 and Mac-387, while the bland mononuclear tumour cells variably express the epithelial marker cytokeratin.

Special Features: Genetics

The striking resemblance of the multinucleated giant cells in OCGTs to the osteoclasts normally found in bone confused pathologists for years. Are these distinctive tumours ductal adenocarcinomas which had elicited an unusual reaction, or are OCGTs more closely related to bone tumours? The answer has come from genetic analysis. OCGTs frequently harbour activating point mutations in codon 12 of the K-*RAS* gene and, as discussed in the Molecular Genetics section, K-*RAS* gene mutations are one of the most common genetic alterations in ductal adenocarcinomas (Hruban *et al.*, 1993; Westra *et al.*, 1998). These data help establish that OCGTs are really carcinomas which elicit a non-neoplastic, giant-cell response (Westra *et al.*, 1998). Osteoclast-like giant cell tumours of the pancreas are unrelated to bone tumours. The survival rate from OCGTs is somewhat better than that for ductal adenocarcinoma (Solcia *et al.*, 1997).

Pancreatoblastoma

Gross and Microscopic Features

Pancreatoblastomas have striking gross and microscopic appearances. They are large, necrotic and white–grey (Klimstra *et al.*, 1995; Solcia *et al.*, 1997; Hruban *et al.*, 2000). Microscopically, pancreatoblastomas contain back-to-back, small cells with round nuclei (Klimstra *et al.*, 1995). In this sea of small cells are embedded nests of swirled cells, called 'squamoid corpuscles' (**Figure 6**).

Special Features: Clinical Presentation

This rare neoplasm occurs primarily in children, with an age range of 1–15 years (Klimstra *et al.*, 1995). It has therefore been referred to as 'pancreatic carcinoma of infancy.' The survival rate for patients with pancreatoblastomas is better than it is for patients with infiltrating ductal adenocarcinomas (Klimstra *et al.*, 1995). Unfortunately, very little is known about what causes these tumours to develop in children.

Cystic Non-endocrine Neoplasms

Serous Cystadenoma and Serous Cystadenocarcinoma

Gross and Microscopic Findings

Grossly, serous cystadenomas are large, spongy tumours filled with a watery fluid. They often contain a central, calcified scar (Compagno and Oertel, 1978a). By light microscopy, a layer of simple cuboidal (square-shaped) cells with uniform nuclei can be seen lining the cysts (**Figure 7**) (Solcia *et al.*, 1997; Hruban *et al.*, 2000).

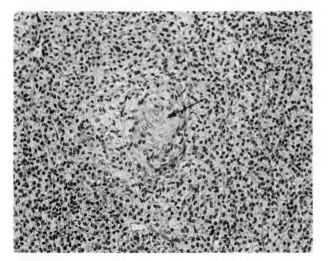

Figure 6   Microscopic section of a pancreatoblastoma. Note the prominent squamous corpuscle (arrow).

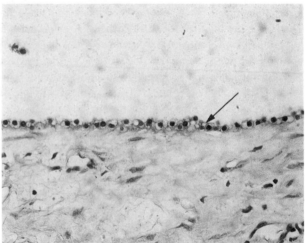

Figure 7   Microscopic section of a serous cystadenoma. The cysts (empty space at top of photograph) in serous cystadenomas are relatively small and are lined by cuboidal, cleared-out cells (arrow).

Because the cells contain large amounts of glycogen, they stain strongly with the periodic acid–Schiff (PAS) stain.

Special Features: Clinical Presentation and Prognosis

These neoplasms are more common in women than in men, and the average age at diagnosis is in the seventh decade. Patients with von Hippel–Lindau syndrome develop serous cystadenomas more frequently than the general population (Solcia *et al.*, 1997). The vast majority of serous cystic neoplasms are benign and patients with even very large (football-sized) serous cystadenomas can be cured of their disease if their tumours are surgically removed (Compagno and Oertel, 1978a; Solcia *et al.*, 1997). Recently, however, there have been a few isolated case reports of aggressive behaviour in serous cystic neoplasms ('serous cystadenocarcinomas').

Mucinous Cystic Neoplasms

Gross and Microscopic Findings

In contrast to the relatively homogeneous appearance and behaviour of serous cystadenomas, mucinous cystic neoplasms of the pancreas are morphologically and clinically heterogeneous (Albores-Saavedra *et al.*, 1987; Solcia *et al.*, 1997; Hruban *et al.*, 2000). Grossly mucinous cystic neoplasms are large tumours composed of cysts filled with tenacious fluid (mucin) (Compagno and Oertel, 1978b). The cysts are lined by tall, mucin-producing cells (**Figure 8**); expectedly, stains for mucin are positive. In some women a dense layer of spindle-shaped cells (stroma) resembling ovarian stroma surrounds the epithelial cells. The clinical significance of this finding is not clear, but it has been used to suggest a common origin for some neoplasms of the ovary and pancreas.

Figure 8   Microscopic section of a mucinous cystic neoplasm. The cysts (empty space at top of photograph) in a mucinous cystadenoma are larger than the cysts found in serous cystadenomas and the cysts in mucinous cystic neoplasms are lined by tall cells producing mucin (arrow). These cells sit on a dense stromal layer that resembles ovarian stroma (bottom portion of the figure).

Mucinous cystic neoplasms can be divided into three groups, mucinous cystadenomas, borderline mucinous cystic neoplasms and mucinous cystadenocarcinomas (Klöppel *et al.*, 1996; Solcia *et al.*, 1997). Mucinous cystadenomas contain a single layer of cells lacking significant atypia. In borderline mucinous cystic neoplasms, the cells may form finger-like projections (papillae) and complex architectural patterns. The cells in these tumours show significant atypia (e.g. loss of nuclear polarity and pleomorphism), but no carcinoma is seen. When an *in situ* carcinoma or an invasive carcinoma is present, the diagnosis of a 'mucinous cystadenocarcinoma' should be made. Importantly, otherwise benign-appearing mucinous cystic neoplasms may harbour small foci of invasive carcinoma (Compagno and Oertel, 1978b). Therefore, when possible, mucinous cystic neoplasms should be completely resected surgically, and the surgical pathologist should entirely submit and carefully examine the neoplasm. Failure to do so may explain the occasional reports of metastasizing 'mucinous cystadenomas' (Compagno and Oertel, 1978b; Wilentz *et al.*, 1999).

Special Features: Clinical Presentation and Prognosis

Mucinous cystic neoplasms are more common in women than they are in men and the mean age at diagnosis is in the late fifth decade (Compagno and Oertel, 1978b; Solcia *et al.*, 1997; Hruban *et al.*, 2000). The prognosis for patients with mucinous cystic neoplasms depends on the presence of invasive carcinoma. The authors recently showed that all patients with non-invasive mucinous cystic neoplasms are cured if their tumours are completely resected (Wilentz *et al.*, 1999). In addition, while invasive mucinous cystadenocarcinomas are fully malignant tumours, patients with these neoplasms usually live longer than do patients with typical solid infiltrating ductal adenocarcinomas (Wilentz *et al.*, 1999). In fact, approximately 50% of patients who have had an invasive mucinous cystadenocarcinoma completely resected will live at least 5 years. This survival rate is much better than the survival rate for infiltrating ductal adenocarcinomas of the pancreas, underscoring the importance of correct pathological classification in patient prognostication and treatment.

Intraductal Papillary Mucinous Neoplasm (IPMN)

Gross and Microscopic Findings

IPMNs are frequently papillary (finger-like) neoplasms that arise in the main pancreatic duct system. By light microscopy, dilated pancreatic ducts are lined by tall, mucin-secreting cells that form papillae (**Figure 9**). Approximately 25% of these tumours are associated with an invasive adenocarcinoma. These invasive cancers often show abundant extracellular mucin production and are called 'colloid' or 'mucinous' adenocarcinomas.

The WHO and the AFIP grading schemes include a three-tiered classification for IPMNs, similar to that for mucinous cystic neoplasms (Klöppel *et al.*, 1996; Solcia *et al.*, 1997). 'Intraductal papillary mucinous adenomas' are IPMNs without significant cytological or architectural atypia. 'Borderline IPMNs' show a moderate amount of atypia. Finally, 'papillary mucinous carcinoma' is the designation given to those tumours in which the intraductal lesion displays significant cytological and architectural

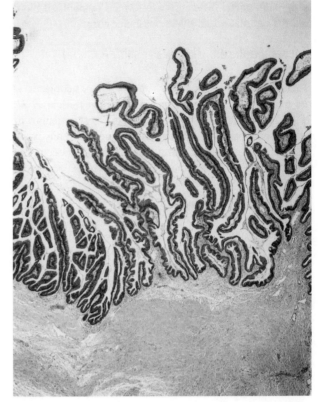

Figure 9   Microscopic section of an intraductal papillary mucinous neoplasm (IPMN). IPMNs are characterized by prominent papillary projections into the dilated pancreatic ducts.

atypia (carcinoma-*in-situ*) or in which an invasive cancer is identified (Klöppel *et al.*, 1996; Solcia *et al.*, 1997).

Special Features: Clinical Presentation and Prognosis

IPMNs occur with approximately equal frequency in both genders. Their origin in the main pancreatic duct or one of its branches helps distinguish IPMNs from mucinous cystic neoplasms, and it also helps explain why patients with IPMNs are often found to have mucin oozing from the ampulla of Vater, if they are examined endoscopically. The prognosis for patients with IPMNs is probably very similar to that of mucinous cystic neoplasms, but more study is needed (Solcia *et al.*, 1997; Hruban *et al.*, 2000).

Solid-pseudopapillary Neoplasm

Gross and Microscopic Findings

Solid pseudopapillary neoplasms form large, well-demarcated masses that are cystic, haemorrhagic and necrotic (Solcia *et al.*, 1997; Hruban *et al.*, 2000). Microscopically the tumour shows solid, cystic and papillary components. The solid areas are composed of nests of small, pink cells with bland nuclei. The cysts are formed by pools of blood and the papillae usually have vascular cores.

Special Features: Clinical Presentation and Prognosis

Remarkably, almost all solid-pseudopapillary neoplasms of the pancreas occur in women in their 20s (Solcia *et al.*, 1997; Hruban *et al.*, 2000). Fortunately, most patients with solid pseudopapillary neoplasms survive for many years after surgical resection; however, metastases do occur, and surgeons should try to remove these neoplasms completely.

Endocrine Tumours

Endocrine tumours, also known as islet cell tumours, account for only 1% of all pancreatic neoplasms (Solcia *et al.*, 1997; Hruban *et al.*, 2000). Unlike their exocrine counterparts, the majority of endocrine neoplasms of the pancreas are not easily divisible into distinct subtypes highly predictive of behaviour (Solcia *et al.*, 1997). Sometimes even a combination of gross, microscopic, immunohistochemical and clinical findings cannot definitively predict the overall malignant potential of one of these lesions. The exception is poorly differentiated endocrine carcinoma (high-grade neuroendocrine carcinoma, small-cell carcinoma), which is unequivocally malignant.

Well- and Moderately Differentiated Endocrine Neoplasms (Islet Cell Tumours)

Gross and Microscopic Findings

Well- and moderately differentiated endocrine neoplasms can be benign ('adenoma'), borderline ('neoplasm of uncertain malignant potential') or malignant ('carcinoma'). Grossly all three types of well- and moderately differentiated endocrine neoplasms are usually solid and well circumscribed. They contain uniform cells with granular nuclei (**Figure 10**). The cells can form ribbons, cords, tubules, sheets or nests. The tumours usually stain for the endocrine markers chromogranin, synaptophysin and neuron-specific enolase (NSE). Electron microscopy reveals 100–400-nm neurosecretory granules within the neoplastic cells. These granules are similar to the granules found in normal endocrine cells and they are easily distinguished from the much larger zymogen granules found in acinar cell carcinoma of the pancreas (Solcia *et al.*, 1997; Hruban *et al.*, 2000).

The best way to determine if a well- or moderately differentiated endocrine neoplasm is benign, borderline or malignant is to look at its behaviour. Microscopic findings such as cytological and architectural atypia are not as helpful. Therefore, well- and moderately differentiated endocrine tumours that show gross extension to other organs, that invade into large blood vessels or that metastasize are prima facie low-grade malignancies. Unfortunately, some endocrine neoplasms that do not

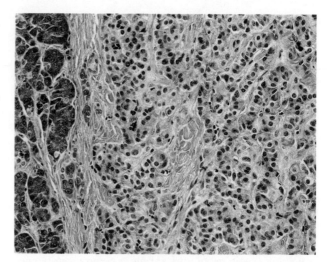

Figure 10 Well-differentiated neuroendocrine neoplasm. In this microscopic section the normal pancreas is to the left and the tumour to the right.

show these characteristics later behave in a malignant fashion. There has therefore been a great deal of interest in developing *indirect* markers of malignancy (Solcia *et al.*, 1997). When gross local extension, large-vessel invasion or metastasis is not seen, pathologists can apply these indirect markers (size of the tumour, mitotic rate, microscopic invasion of blood vessels and nerves) to assess whether a lesion is benign, borderline or malignant. These markers should be applied with the realization that indirect markers are imperfect markers of malignancy (Solcia *et al.*, 1997; Hruban *et al.*, 2000).

Special Features: Hormone Production

Remarkably, and often dramatically, endocrine neoplasms of the pancreas can produce excessive quantities of many of the same hormones normally produced in small quantities by the islets of Langerhans. Some patients with endocrine neoplasms therefore develop striking symptoms. For example, patients with insulin-producing tumours (insulinomas) can present with marked hypoglycaemia (low blood sugar), headaches, weakness, dizziness and/or seizures. Patients with tumours which produce the hormone gastrin (gastrinomas) can develop the Zollinger–Ellison (ZE) syndrome, characterized by gastric hyperacidity, multiple, recurrent peptic ulcers, gastro-oesophageal reflux and diarrhoea. Tumours that produce VIP (VIPomas) can lead to the Verner–Morrison or WDHA syndrome, which primarily results in watery diarrhoea, hypokalaemia (low potassium levels) and achlorhydria (or hypochlorhydria). Patients with glucagon-producing tumours (glucagonomas) experience a striking, symmetrical skin rash ('necrolytic migratory erythema') on their buttocks, groin, perineum, thighs and distal extremities. Patients with somatostatin-producing tumours (somatostatinomas) present with diabetes mellitus, cholelithiasis (gallstones), diarrhoea, hypochlorhydria, weight loss and anaemia.

Clinical presentation is very important in evaluating a well- or moderately differentiated endocrine neoplasm. Although 10% of glucagon-cell, somatostatin-cell, gastrin-cell and VIP-cell tumours discovered incidentally while the patient was being evaluated for some other problem are malignant, the majority of the *same* tumours are malignant if hormone production by the tumour produces a clinically recognizable syndrome (Solcia *et al.*, 1997). The exception is an insulin-producing tumour: only 10% of all insulin-producing neoplasms are malignant, regardless of clinical presentation.

Multiple Endocrine Neoplasia Syndrome, Type 1 (MEN1 Syndrome)

The multiple endocrine neoplasia syndrome, type 1 (MEN1), or Werner's syndrome, deserves special mention. This syndrome is characterized by concomitant multiple hyperplasias and neoplasias of the parathyroid gland (up to 97% of patients), pancreas (80%) and anterior pituitary (50%) (Solcia *et al.*, 1997). The MEN1 syndrome can be inherited in an autosomal dominant pattern or it can occur sporadically. The syndrome results from a germ-line mutation or deletion in the *MEN1* gene on the long arm of chromosome 11 (11q13) (Lubensky *et al.*, 1996).

As many as 80% of patients with MEN1 develop pancreatic tumours, most frequently gastrinomas, and it therefore should not be surprising that the Zollinger–Ellison syndrome occurs in at least one-third of MEN1 patients (Solcia *et al.*, 1997). Insulinomas (approximately 25% of MEN1 patients), VIPomas, glucagonomas and growth hormone-releasing tumours are less common in patients with this syndrome. (See also the chapter *Inherited Predispositions to Cancer*.)

Poorly Differentiated Endocrine Neoplasms (High-grade Neuroendocrine Carcinomas, Small-cell Carcinomas)

Gross and Microscopic Features
Poorly differentiated endocrine neoplasms account for only 2% of all pancreatic endocrine tumours (Solcia *et al.*, 1997; Hruban *et al.*, 2000). Grossly these tumours are infiltrative, haemorrhagic, necrotic and grey–white. The cells have extremely high nuclear-to-cytoplasmic ratios. Nuclear moulding, where nuclei wrap around one another, is prominent. The mitotic rate is extremely high (Solcia *et al.*, 1997).

Special Features: Prognosis
These tumours are unquestionably malignant, and patients with them have extremely poor survival rates.

Primary Mesenchymal Tumours

Benign and malignant mesenchymal (connective tissue) tumours of the pancreas are extremely rare. However, schwannomas (benign tumours of the nerve sheath), leiomyosarcomas (malignant tumours showing smooth muscle differentiation), liposarcomas (malignant tumours showing fat differentiation) and malignant fibrous histiocytomas (malignant tumours showing fibrous and histiocytic differentiation) of the pancreas have been reported. The diagnostic criteria for these neoplasms are the same as they are for mesenchymal tumours arising in other sites. Generally, survival rates for patients with sarcomas are low, as they are for sarcomas primary to other locations. (See also the chapter *Soft Tissues*.)

Metastatic Malignancies

Masses in the pancreas need not have arisen in the pancreas. They may arise in other organs and only later spread (metastasize) to the pancreas. The most common metastases to the pancreas originate in the breast (20%), lung (19%), colorectum (10%), skin (melanoma, 9%) and stomach (7%) (Solcia *et al.*, 1997).

Systemic Malignancies

Leukaemia and lymphoma simultaneously involve more than one site, one of which may be the pancreas. In fact, the pancreas is sometimes the presenting site for these malignancies. Of the 67 patients with systemic malignancies involving the pancreas reviewed by Cubilla and Fitzgerald (1976), three-quarters had lymphomas and one-quarter had leukaemias.

EPIDEMIOLOGY AND AETIOLOGY

Because ductal adenocarcinomas are the most common malignancy in the pancreas, and the most is known about ductal adenocarcinomas, the remainder of discussion in this chapter will centre around this type of cancer unless specified otherwise. As outlined in **Table 2**, a number of risk factors have been identified for the development of pancreatic cancer (Gold and Goldin, 1998). These include older age, cigarette smoking, family history of pancreas cancer, previous gastric surgery, chronic pancreatitis, diabetes mellitus, occupational exposure to certain chemicals, radiation exposure and a diet high in fat and low in fruits and vegetables (Gold and Goldin, 1998).

More than 80% of pancreatic cancers occur between the ages of 60 and 80, and cases before the age of 40 are rare (Solcia *et al.*, 1997; Gold and Goldin, 1998). Those that do occur at a younger age are usually special variants of pancreatic cancer, such as the pancreaticoblastoma, which occurs primarily in children (Klimstra *et al.*, 1995). Pancreatic cancer is more common in men than in women and in blacks than in whites (Solcia *et al.*, 1997). Of interest, pancreatic cancer may occur more frequently in individuals of Jewish descent (Gold and Goldin, 1998). As will

Table 2   Risk factors for pancreatic cancer

Patient characteristics
  Older age
  Male gender
  Black race
  Jewish ancestry
  Family history of pancreatic cancer
  Diabetes mellitus
  Chronic pancreatitis
Patient behaviour
  Cigarette smoking
  Diet low in fruits and vegetables
  Diet high in fat
  Occupational exposure to certain chemicals
  Radiation exposure

be discussed in greater detail in the Molecular Genetics section, this may be because of the high prevalence of inherited mutations in the second breast cancer gene (*BRCA2*) in Ashkenazi Jews (Ozcelik *et al*., 1997).

Cigarette smoking has been clearly established as a risk factor for pancreatic cancer. The increased risk of developing pancreatic cancer in smokers is 2–5-fold over non-smokers, and the risk increases with the number of cigarettes smoked. Importantly, those who stop smoking can quickly reduce their risk for developing pancreatic cancer. For example, Ghadirian *et al*. (1991a) conducted a population-based case-control study of pancreatic cancer in Montreal, Canada, and found that, depending on the number of cigarettes already smoked in a lifetime, patients can reduce their risk of pancreatic cancer as much as threefold by stopping smoking. Remarkably, Mulder *et al*., (1999) have estimated that a moderate reduction in smoking in Europe could save as many as 68 000 lives that will otherwise be lost to pancreatic cancer between 1999 and 2020. Clearly, smoking plays a major role in the development of pancreatic cancer.

While smoking is a habit we can control, family cancer history is something we cannot. Researchers at The Johns Hopkins Hospital and others have found that familial inheritance plays a significant role in the development of some pancreatic cancers (Hruban *et al*., 1998). The evidence for this comes from three areas. First, there have been a number of isolated case reports of pancreas cancer aggregating in certain families (Hruban *et al*., 1998). For example, one of former President Carter's parents, his brother and two of his sisters all died from pancreatic cancer. While these reports suggest that there is a genetic (inherited) basis for the development of pancreatic cancer, the occurrence of multiple cancers in a family could be just bad luck. A number of investigators have therefore conducted case-control studies of pancreatic cancer. For example, Ghadirian *et al*. (1991b) conducted a population-based case-control study of pancreatic cancer in the Francophone community of Montreal, Canada, and found

that 7.8% of the patients with pancreatic cancer reported a positive family history of pancreatic cancer, compared with only 0.6% of the controls. This 13-fold difference between cases and controls did not appear to be due to environmental factors such as smoking, strongly suggesting the genetic transmission of an increased risk of developing pancreatic cancer. The National Familial Pancreas Tumour Registry (NFPTR) at Johns Hopkins, and other registries like it, were therefore established to track families with multiple pancreatic cancers (Hruban *et al*., 1998). The NFPTR is perhaps the largest of these registries and it is truly an international registry with 719 kindred enrolled as of July 1, 2001. These kindred come from the United States, Europe and Australia, and include 284 families in which two or more first-degree relatives have been diagnosed with pancreatic cancer. This registry provides an invaluable resource to scientists studying the genetics of familial pancreatic cancer (see the Molecular Genetics section). Furthermore, a prospective study of the families enrolled in the NFPTR has demonstrated that the first-degree relatives of patients with familial pancreatic cancer have an increased risk of developing pancreatic cancer themselves. Tersmette *et al*. (2001) studied the families enrolled in the NFPTR. They found that if two family members had been diagnosed with pancreatic cancer at the time of enrollment into the NFPTR, then the risk of other previously healthy family members developing a new pancreatic cancer was 18-fold greater than expected. This risk increased to 56-fold when three or more family members had pancreatic cancer at the time the family enrolled in the registry. The *prospective* development of pancreatic cancer in these families clearly establishes that inherited susceptibility plays a significant role in the development of pancreatic cancer in some families.

Those wishing to learn more about the NFPTR and those wishing to register may contact the National Familial Pancreas Tumour Registry, c/o Dr Ralph Hruban, The Johns Hopkins Hospital, 401 N. Broadway, Baltimore, MD 21231, USA. E-mail: kbrune@jhmi.edu.

The final line of evidence establishing the genetic transmission of an increased risk of developing pancreatic cancer is the identification of some of the genes responsible for familial pancreatic cancer. These genes include *BRCA2*, *p16*, *STK11/LKB1* and *cationic trypsinogen* (Goggins *et al*., 1996; Whitcomb *et al*., 1996; Ozcelik *et al*., 1997; Su *et al*., 1999). These genes will be discussed in greater detail in the Molecular Genetics of Pancreatic Cancer section.

Previous gastric surgery has also been identified as a risk for pancreatic cancer. This association has been extensively studied by Offerhaus *et al*. (1998). They studied several groups of patients, both from the United States and from Europe, and found that patients who had peptic ulcer surgery have a 2–5-fold increased risk of developing pancreatic cancer, especially if the surgery was more than

20 years earlier. The reason for this increased risk is not clear, but it has been hypothesized that increased levels of cholecystokinin and the increased production of nitrosamines in the operated stomach may play a role.

Diet may also contribute to the development of pancreatic cancer (Gold and Goldin, 1998). Diets high in fruits and vegetables have shown to reduce the risk of pancreatic cancer, whereas diets high in fat increase the risk. The mechanism for this has not been established, however, Stolzenberg-Solomon et al. (1999) have shown that vitamins such as folate may play a role. They conducted a nested case-control study of a large cohort of male Finnish smokers and found that serum folate and pyridoxal-5′-phosphate concentrations have an inverse dose–response relationship with pancreatic cancer. Additional dietary factors that have been studied include alcohol and coffee consumption; however, there is insufficient evidence to support either as a causal factor in the development of pancreatic cancer (Stolzenberg-Solomon et al., 1999).

Finally, two medical conditions, diabetes mellitus and chronic pancreatitis, have also been implicated in the development of pancreatic cancer (Stolzenberg-Solomon et al., 1999). Both of these are complex factors to study. Not only have these factors been implicated in the development of pancreatic cancer, but cancer of the pancreas can also destroy normal pancreatic tissues and thus cause both diabetes and pancreatitis. The mechanism by which pancreatic cancer produces diabetes is not well defined; however, some have suggested that amylin production by pancreatic cancer may contribute to the development of diabetes. The increased risk of pancreatic cancer is, however, clear in familial pancreatitis (Whitcomb et al., 1996). Familial pancreatitis is caused by inherited mutations in the cationic trysinogen gene and affected family members develop severe recurrent bouts of pancreatitis at a young age. These patients have been shown to have a 40% lifetime risk of developing pancreatic cancer.

SCREENING AND PREVENTION

Screening

Population-based screening programmes have been shown to improve survival of breast, colon and cervical cancer. In contrast, the pancreas is a relatively inaccessible organ and current screening tests for pancreatic cancer are not effective. Nonetheless, there is an enormous need for such a test. Most patients with pancreatic cancer have a dismal prognosis because they do not come to clinical attention until after the disease has spread beyond the pancreas. This need for an effective screening test is perhaps felt most by those with an increased risk for developing pancreatic cancer, such as individuals with an inherited predisposition

to develop the disease. These would include individuals with inherited genetic abnormalities in cancer-causing genes, such as BRCA2, p16 and STK11/LKB1 and individuals with familial pancreatic cancer of unknown cause (Goggins et al., 1996; Hruban et al., 1998; Su et al., 1999). The importance of screening for pancreatic cancer can be seen in the survival statistics for pancreatic cancer surgery. Patients who have their cancer surgically resected and who are found to have small tumours confined to the gland ('node-negative disease, negative margins and tumours < 2 cm') have a 5-year survival of ~25% (Yeo et al., 1995). By contrast, most (~85%) patients with pancreatic cancer do not present to their doctor until after their cancers have grown so large that they are inoperable at the time of diagnosis, and patients with inoperable cancer have an average survival of only 6 months.

A great deal of effort is therefore being focused on research efforts for the early detection of pancreatic cancer in asymptomatic high-risk individuals. It is logical that with advances in the molecular genetics of pancreatic cancer and technological advances in endoscopy and radiology, more accurate screening tests for pancreatic cancer will soon become available.

Three groups of diagnostic tests could be applied to screening for pancreatic cancer: (1) radiological methods, (2) tumour markers and (3) endoscopic methods.

Radiological Methods

Radiological methods are the most commonly used methods to diagnose pancreatic cancer. The accuracy of radiology has improved in recent years. Computerized tomography (CT) scanning is commonly the first test used to image the pancreas (Bluemke et al., 1995). One recent advance in CT imaging has been the development of spiral or helical CT. This new imaging technique allows the radiologist to obtain higher resolution images in three dimensions. Currently, helical CT and magnetic resonance imaging (MRI) diagnose pancreatic cancer with a sensitivity of ~90%. The ~10% of cancers missed using CT scanning are often those tumours that cause mild diffuse enlargement of the pancreas rather than a discrete mass. In addition, the very small cancers, those less than 1–2 cm in diameter, are often not visible using CT or MRI.

Many pancreatic cancers that are not visualized on CT can be seen using endoscopic ultrasound (EUS). During EUS the endosonographer introduces an endoscope through the patients' mouth, through the stomach and into the duodenum. The tip of this endoscope contains an ultrasound transducer. The pancreas lies adjacent to the stomach and duodenum; this approach therefore allows the endosonographer to obtain close-up images of the pancreas. The main variable determining the quality of the EUS image obtained is the skill and experience of the endosonographer. The sensitivity of endoscopic ultrasound is at least as good as that of helical CT or MRI for visualizing pancreatic lesions. EUS has an advantage over CT in that the pancreas can also be biopsied using fine needle aspiration (FNA) techniques through the same endoscope, enabling multiple samples to be taken painlessly from any suspicious lesions encountered.

Endoscopic retrograde cholangiopancreatography (ERCP) is a valuable diagnostic and therapeutic tool for managing pancreatic diseases. During ERCP the gastroenterologist again passes an endoscope through the patient's mouth, through the stomach and into the duodenum. Once the tip of the scope is in the duodenum, the endoscopist can visualize the ampulla of Vater, the site where the pancreatic and bile ducts enter the duodenum. A small catheter is then placed through the endoscope and through the ampulla of Vater into the biliary and pancreatic ducts. By injecting radio-opaque dye into the catheter, abnormalities are accurately identified with ERCP. Unfortunately, small lesions in the parenchyma of the pancreas, especially those that have minimal effects on the duct system, can be missed at ERCP, and ERCP is not without risks. ERCP can be complicated by acute pancreatitis (~1/20 procedures), bleeding, complications of sedation, perforation and occasionally even death (< 1/500). The risks associated with undergoing an ERCP therefore preclude its use as a general screening test.

Other imaging modalities under investigation as tests for pancreatic cancer diagnosis include positron emission tomography (PET) scanning and intraductal ultrasound. While the availability of PET is limited, intraductal ultrasound is used to help interpret suspicious findings on ERCP. With the latter procedure, a catheter with an ultrasound probe at its tip is placed into the pancreatic or biliary duct during ERCP. Ultimately these probes may be helpful in identifying very early carcinomas.

In general, radiological imaging of the pancreas is useful in diagnosing pancreatic cancer in a patient for whom there is a high degree of suspicion. The methods are, however, either too expensive or too invasive to be used in the general population as screening tests. (See the section on *Diagnostic Imaging and Image-Guided Intervention*.)

Tumour Markers

Given the limitations of current radiological tools, much effort has been put into identifying molecular markers that have the potential to be sensitive and specific for pancreatic cancer.

An ideal marker would be both highly sensitive (it would correctly identify almost everyone who has pancreatic cancer) and specific (positive tests are only seen in patients with cancer) for pancreatic cancer and it could be applied to samples obtained relatively non-invasively. Although a large number of potential tumour markers have been evaluated, none of them yet have been shown to be sufficiently sensitive or specific for use in a screening setting for pancreatic cancer.

The tumour markers most studied are the carbohydrate antigen 19-9 (CA19-9), K-RAS and telomerase.

CA 19-9

CA19-9 is a valuable tumour marker for following the therapeutic response in patients who are being treated for pancreatic cancer (Ritts and Pitt, 1998). In this setting, CA19-9 levels correlate well with tumour volume and response to therapy. However, CA19-9 is not useful as a screening test for early pancreatic cancer. First, only patients with certain blood types are capable of making CA19-9. Approximately 10–15% of individuals do not secrete CA19-9 because of their Lewis antigen blood type. In addition, CA19-9 levels may be within the normal range while the cancer is still at a small and asymptomatic stage and conversely CA19-9 levels may be elevated in benign biliary or pancreatic conditions. These limitations also apply to related carbohydrate antigens such as CA-125, KAM17.1, CA2.2, CA-50 and CA-242.

K-RAS

K-*RAS* gene mutations are present in ~90% of pancreatic cancers (see Molecular Genetics below) and these mutations can be detected in specimens obtained distant from the cancer such as pancreatic juice, duodenal fluid, stool and blood using sensitive mutation assays (Hruban *et al.*, 1993; Caldas *et al.*, 1994). Unfortunately, a number of limitations preclude the use of K-*RAS* as a screening marker. First, K-*RAS* gene mutations are not specific for pancreatic cancer and also occur in the small non-invasive pancreatic duct lesions (PanINs) that are prevalent in individuals of increasing age. In autopsy series, PanINs can be found in as many as 10–30% of individuals, especially in smokers. Similarly, K-*RAS* gene mutations have also been reported in chronic pancreatitis (Caldas *et al.*, 1994). Clearly, mutant K-*RAS* is not a specific marker of pancreatic cancer. By contrast, circulating mutant K-*RAS* genes in the blood is much more specific for pancreatic cancer and is detectable in blood samples from 25 to 65% of patients with pancreatic cancer. However, the presence of mutant K-*RAS* in the blood may be a late event as it correlates with inoperable pancreatic cancer, with a poor prognosis and relapse after surgical resection.

Telomerase

Telomerase is an exciting new potential marker for pancreatic cancer. Telomerase is an enzyme which helps maintain the ends (telomeres) of chromosomes. Telomerase activity is lost in most normal cells after embryonic development while as many as 90% of cancers and some inflammatory cells express telomerase. Since telomerase is expressed in inflammatory cells, it may not be sufficiently specific for use as a cancer-screening marker. Nonetheless, several groups have reported that as many as 90% of patients with pancreatic cancer have measurable telomerase activity in their pancreatic juice (Suehara *et al.*, 1997), and telomerase may yet prove to be a relatively sensitive and specific marker for differentiating benign from malignant lesions of the pancreas.

Identifying New Markers

Several novel approaches have been used to identify new markers that might be specific for pancreatic cancer. One of these approaches that is particularly exciting is serial analysis of gene expression (SAGE). SAGE generates a quantitative list of the genes that are expressed by a tissue (Zhang et al., 1997). Using SAGE, comparisons can be made between the expression of genes in cancer and normal tissue and a list of genes can then be generated that are highly over-expressed in the cancer relative to the normal (Zhang et al., 1997). One marker identified using this approach is tissue inhibitor metalloproteinase 1 (TIMP-1). When used in combination with CA19-9, measurements of TIMP-1 levels in the blood can distinguish patients with pancreatic cancer from controls with greater sensitivity and specificity than CA19-9 alone. Recently, SAGE has been used to discover other additional exciting markers of pancreatic cancer, including prostate stem cell antigen (Argani et al., 2001).

Another powerful technology likely to enhance the prospects for finding cancer-specific markers is gene expression arrays. Gene expression arrays contain arrays of many thousands of genes gridded on to small templates such as a glass slide. Therefore, a tissue or sample can be probed to see if it contains any one of thousands of genes simultaneously using just one slide. It is therefore now easier to obtain gene expression profiles of cells from cancer and these profiles can be compared with the gene expression patterns of non-cancerous cells. For both SAGE and microarrays, complex analytical and statistical software programs are required to interpret complex gene expression data and results require confirmation using other experimental approaches. Nonetheless, both are exciting techniques which my help in the development of novel screening tests for early pancreatic cancer.

DNA Methylation

DNA is frequently methylated in mammalian DNA. Methylation refers to the addition of single carbon groups and methylation occurs at specific sites in DNA called CpG islands. Regions of DNA rich in CpGs are frequently found in the portion of genes which control the expression of the gene (the promoter). When CpG islands are methylated in a promoter of a gene, it can inhibit transcription of that gene by preventing RNA polymerase and the RNA transcription machinery from producing messenger RNA. Hence DNA methylation is a common mechanism for regulating gene expression. Both selective hyper- and hypomethylation of DNA are known to occur in cancer.

Several techniques have been used to screen cancers for methylation abnormalities. DNA methylation changes in cancer can be detected even when they are admixed with many more copies of normal DNA. DNA methylation is therefore being studied as a possible screening tool for the early detection of cancer. For example, DNA methylation of the *p16* gene has been found in the sputum of patients with early lung cancer (Belinsky et al., 1998).

Several genes (mostly tumour-suppressor genes) have recently been shown to be selectively hypermethylated in a subset of pancreatic cancers. These genes include *p16* and *hMLH1*.

Prevention

Unfortunately, there are no good published clinical trials for the prevention of pancreatic cancer. As the genetic and environmental factors responsible for pancreatic cancer have become more defined, so to has the need for preventive strategies become apparent.

Several approaches to prevention can be considered. First, general health measures are prudent such as avoiding smoking and alcohol consumption and maintaining a balanced diet. Balanced diets should be low in fat and high in fruits and vegetables. Second, groups with a high risk of developing pancreatic cancer can be enrolled into screening programmes as these programmes become available. Third, chemopreventive strategies should be tested on high-risk populations. For example, nonsteroidal anti-inflammatory drugs (NSAIDs) and COX-2 inhibitors have chemopreventive activity in a variety of animal and clinical studies, and epidemiological studies suggest that NSAIDs protect against colorectal, oesophageal and gastric cancer. Many cancers, including pancreatic cancer, over-express the enzyme COX-2, the likely target of NSAIDs, and COX-2 inhibitors have been shown to decrease the growth of pancreatic cancers in animal models (Molina et al., 1999). Finally, prophylactic pancreatic resection may be appropriate for a very few individuals at very high risk of developing pancreatic cancer (Brentnall et al., 1999). Two groups of individuals with the highest risk of developing pancreatic cancer are patients with hereditary pancreatitis (lifetime risk of pancreatic cancer 30–40%) and patients with idiopathic familial pancreatic cancer (individuals with three or more first-degree relatives with pancreatic cancer have a lifetime risk of pancreatic cancer of ~20%). To ensure protection against pancreatic cancer in this setting, prophylactic total pancreatectomy may be indicated, but this is a very high-risk procedure. Total pancreatectomy is associated with significant short-term and long-term morbidity and mortality, including brittle diabetes, and for this reason it is rarely performed.

MOLECULAR GENETICS

The last 10 years have seen a revolution in our understanding of the molecular genetics of pancreatic cancer. In

Table 3 Genes involved in the development of apparently sporadic pancreatic cancer

Gene	% of Cancers	Chromosome	Mechanism of alteration[a]
Oncogenes			
K-RAS	90	12p	Point mutation
AKT2	10–20	19q	Amplification
AIB1	65	20q	Amplification
HER/2-neu	70	17q	Overexpression
Tumour-suppressor genes			
p16	95	9p	HD, LOH and IM, PM
p53	50–70	17p	LOH and IM
DPC4	55	18q	HD, LOH and IM
BRCA2	5–10	13q	Germline with LOH
MKK4	4	17p	HD, LOH and IM
LKB1/STK11	5–6	19p	LOH and IM, HD
TGFβR1 and TGFβR2	4	9q, 3p	HD
DNA mismatch repair genes			
MSH2	<4	2p	Unknown
MLH1	<4	3p	Unknown

[a] HD = homozygous deletion; LOH = loss of heterozygosity; IM = intragenic mutation; PM = promoter hypermethylation.

a few short years, pancreatic cancer has gone from one of the most poorly understood diseases to one of the best. It is now clear that pancreatic cancer is a genetic disease. The genetic alterations which lead to the development of pancreatic cancer can be inherited (see Epidemiology and Aetiology section) or acquired and the genes affected can be classified into three broad groups: oncogenes, tumour-suppressor genes and DNA mismatch repair genes (see **Table 3**).

Oncogenes

Oncogenes are genes which, when *activated* by mutation or overexpression, possess transforming (cancer-causing) properties. The oncogenes which have been shown to play a role in the development of pancreatic cancer include the K-*RAS*, *HER2-neu*, *AKT2*, *AIB1* and *MYB* genes (Hruban *et al.*, 1993; 1998; Day *et al.*, 1996). The K-*RAS* gene resides on chromosome 12p and it is activated by point mutation in ~90% of the cancers (Hruban *et al.*, 1993). The *HER2-neu* gene on chromosome 17q is overexpressed in ~70% of pancreatic cancers and amplification of *AKT2* on chromosome 19q, *AIB1* on 20q and *MYB* on chromosome 6q has been reported in a smaller percentage of the tumours (Day *et al.*, 1996). The demonstration that these oncogenes are activated in pancreatic cancer is important for a number of reasons. First, these genes are potential targets for novel therapies. For example, in order for the K-*RAS* gene product to be functional, it must first be activated by the enzyme farnesyl transferase. Several groups have already developed farnesyl transferase inhibitors, some of which may be effective in treating pancreatic cancer. Similarly, mutated K-Ras peptides have been used as vaccines to treat pancreatic cancers. Second, as discussed in the section on tumour markers, activated oncogenes are

potential targets for gene-based screening tests for pancreatic cancer. For example, mutant K-*RAS* genes shed from a pancreatic cancer have been detected in pancreatic and duodenal fluids and in the stool of patients with pancreatic cancer (Caldas *et al.*, 1994; Brentnall *et al.*, 1999). Such gene-based screening tests are exciting because they could potentially detect as few as one mutant copy of a gene admixed with 10 000 normal copies of that same gene (see Screening and Prevention). Third, the patterns of alterations in oncogenes can provide a clue as to what caused the alterations and therefore what caused the cancer. For example, we and others have shown that activating point mutations in K-*RAS* are slightly more common in cancers obtained from smokers then they are in cancers obtained from non-smokers (Hruban *et al.*, 1993). This finding can be likened to finding the fingerprint of cigarette smoke in a cancer. It helps establish who the criminal is.

Tumour-suppressor Genes

The second class of genes which are altered in pancreatic cancer are the tumour-suppressor genes. Tumour-suppressor genes are genes which encode for proteins which normally function to restrain cell proliferation, so the *loss* of their activity may lead to unrestrained cell growth. The tumour-suppressor which have been shown to be inactivated in pancreatic cancer include *p16* (in 95% of the cancers), *p53* (in 75%), *DPC4* (in 55%), *BRCA2* (in 10%), *MKK4* (in 4%), *RB1* (in < 5%), *LKB1/STK11* (in 4%) and the transforming growth factor β receptor genes I and II (**Table 3**) (Schutte *et al.*, 1995, 1997; Goggins *et al.*, 1996; Hahn *et al.*, 1996; Ozcelik *et al.*, 1997; Rozenblum *et al.*, 1997; Hruban *et al.*, 1998; Wilentz *et al.*, 1998; Su *et al.*, 1999). Tumour-suppressor genes, like other autosomal

Table 4   Known causes of familial pancreatic cancer

Syndrome[a]	Gene	Chromosome	Familial characteristics
Breast cancer 2	BRCA2	13q	Breast cancer and pancreatic cancer
Peutz-Jeghers	STK11/LKB1	19p	Pigmented spots on lips
FAMMM	p16	9p	Multiple moles, melanoma and pancreatic cancer
HNPCC	Multiple	Multiple	Non-polyposis colon cancer, other cancers
Familial pancreatitis	Cationic trypsinogen	7q	Recurrent episodes of pancreatitis starting at a young age

[a] FAMMM = familial atypical multiple mole melanoma; HNPCC = hereditary non-polyposis colorectal cancer.

genes, are inherited in pairs; a maternal copy and a paternal copy. Both of these copies (called 'alleles') of a tumour-suppressor gene must be inactivated for there to be loss of function of the gene product, i.e. tumour-suppressor genes act as recessive genes. In pancreatic cancer, the inactivation of both alleles of a tumour-suppressor gene occurs by one of three mechanisms: (1) loss of one allele ('loss of heterozygosity') coupled with a mutation within (intragenic) the second allele; (2) loss of both copies of the gene ('homozygous deletions'); and (3) loss of one copy (LOH) coupled with epigenetic inactivation of the second copy (hypermethylation of the gene's promoter) (Schutte *et al.*, 1997).

The identification of the tumour-suppressor genes involved in the development of pancreatic cancer is important for a number of reasons. First, the identification of the pathways inactivated when a tumour-suppressor gene is mutated may provide new targets for treatment. For example, inactivation of the *DPC4* tumour-suppressor gene is relatively specific for pancreatic cancer and several potential targets within this pathway have been identified which could be used to develop new chemotherapeutic agents (Hahn *et al.*, 1996). Second, the demonstration that specific tumour-suppressor genes are inactivated in pancreatic cancers has proved a critical advance in our understanding of the causes of familial pancreatic cancers (Hruban *et al.*, 1998). To understand why this is true, one most go back over 20 years to Alfred Knudson's seminal research on retinoblastoma. He studied childhood eye cancers (retinoblastomas) and hypothesized that the gene that caused sporadic (non-familial) retinoblastoma also caused familial retinoblastoma. In the familial form of the cancer, affected family members inherit one defective copy of the gene. As a result, they have only one good copy of the gene remaining. If this second copy is inactivated (mutated) later in life, then the cancer develops. Cancers are therefore common in these families. This is analogous to going up in the space shuttle with one functioning computer and one broken computer. If something goes wrong with the good one, there is no backup. By contrast, in non-familial (sporadic) forms of the cancers, the patients inherit two good copies of the gene. Only the rare cases in which both copies are inactivated later in life does the cancer develop.

Knudson's hypothesis appears to operate for pancreatic cancer. Kern and colleagues at Johns Hopkins have demonstrated that some forms of familial pancreatic cancer are caused by germ-line (inherited) mutations in tumour-suppressor genes. As summarized in **Table 4**, the genes which are targeted in familial pancreatic cancer include *BRCA2*, *STK11/LKB1* and *p16* (Goggins *et al.*, 1996; Su *et al.*, 1999). Patients who inherit a defective copy of one of these genes are more likely to develop a cancer later in life because they begin life with only one, instead of the usual two, functional copies of the gene. Should that good copy be inactivated, gene function would be lost. For example, Goggins *et al.* (1996) studied a large series of patients with pancreatic cancer and found that 7% had a germ-line (inherited) mutation in the second breast cancer gene (*BRCA2*). These patients presumably developed their pancreatic cancer when a cell in their pancreas lost the second, only remaining, good copy of the *BRCA2* gene (Goggins *et al.*, 1996; Ozcelik *et al.*, 1997). Similarly, germ-line mutations in the *p16* gene predispose to both pancreatic cancer and melanoma (Hruban *et al.*, 1998); and germ-line mutations in the *STK11/LKB1* gene to pancreatic cancer and a rare syndrome called the 'Peutz–Jeghers' syndrome (Su *et al.*, 1999).

The discovery of the genes responsible for some forms of familial pancreatic cancer represents a critical advance, because it means that members of families in which there has been an aggregation of cancer can now be genetically tested. Those found to carry a mutation in one of these genes can be more carefully screened for cancer or may even choose prophylactic surgery, while those found not to carry of a mutation can be relieved of their anxiety.

Mismatch Repair Genes

The final class of genes which play a role in the development of pancreatic cancer are the DNA mismatch repair genes. The products of DNA mismatch repair genes function to ensure the fidelity of DNA replication. Inactivation of DNA mismatch repair genes can therefore be thought of as analogous to having a drunk mechanic inspect your car. The failure of this mechanic to fix problems can have a devastating long-term effect. Remember that every time a cell divides it must copy all three billion DNA base pairs. Errors are made, and if the enzymes which help repair these errors are inactivated, these errors will not be repaired. Over time, this will lead to the accumulation of mutations in both oncogenes and tumour-suppressor genes and therefore in the development of cancer. The inactivation of a DNA mismatch repair gene in a cancer produces a characteristic change in DNA called 'microsatellite instability', (MSI) and Goggins et al. (1998) have recently demonstrated MSI in ~4% of pancreatic cancers. These cancers are remarkable because as discussed in the section on tumour pathology, they appear to have a distinct microscopic appearance ('medullary phenotype') and because these cancers may have a different response to certain chemotherapeutic agents (Goggins et al., 1998).

Thus, there has been a revolution in our understanding of the molecular genetics of pancreatic cancer. This understanding is already being applied to the development of new screening tests for pancreatic cancer and new treatments for the disease, and it has led to a better understanding of why pancreatic cancer aggregates in some families.

PROGNOSTIC FACTORS

Overall, pancreatic cancer has the worst prognosis of all the common forms of cancer. Affected patients have a median survival of only ~6 months and less than 5% of patients live to 5 years. Given such dismal statistics, it is not surprising that few markers are available which can identify patients with a good prognosis. Among the subgroup of patients who undergo a surgical resection of the head of the pancreas (Whipple procedure, or pancreaticoduodenectomy), several prognostic factors influence outcome. The size of the carcinoma, the presence or absence of positive margins (cancer extending to where the surgeon cut), the histological grade (how closely it resembles normal tissue under the microscope) and the presence of lymph node metastases predict survival (Yeo et al., 1995). In addition, Allison et al. (1998) have shown that tumour DNA content (ploidy) also has prognostic significance and, as discussed in the Pathology section, histological classification can be an important predictor of prognosis. Finally, because of their late presentation, pancreatic carcinomas involving the tail and body of the pancreas have a poorer prognosis than cancers of the head of the pancreas.

OVERVIEW OF PRESENT CLINICAL MANAGEMENT

The management of pancreatic cancer depends on several factors, including the patient's symptoms, the performance status of the patient, the histological classification of the patient's tumour, the stage of the disease (whether or not it has spread beyond the gland) and the presence of complications. The diagnosis of pancreatic cancer is usually suspected from complaints of progressive obstructive jaundice (a yellow discoloration of the skin), profound weight loss and pain in the abdomen or mid-back. Less often patients can present with diabetes mellitus, thrombophlebitis migrans (blood clots developing at multiple sites), depression or evidence of metastatic disease. Generally, the diagnosis is established using CT (Bluemke et al., 1995), EUS or ERCP with histological (or cytological) confirmation. If curative resection is considered, staging investigations using EUS or angiography are performed, searching for evidence of spread to lymph nodes, to the peritoneum (the lining of the abdomen) or to the liver and for signs of large blood vessel involvement (invasion of the splenic or portal vein). Helical CT with contrast usually provides good assessment of the status of the blood vessels around the pancreas.

Pancreatic Adenocarcinoma

Surgery (Whipple resection) remains the only realistic curative modality for pancreatic cancer (Yeo et al., 1995). The Whipple procedure involves the resection of the head of the pancreas, the duodenum, lower common bile duct, local lymph nodes and peripancreatic tissue. This is not an easy operation. Operative mortality rates vary considerably with the experience of the surgeon, but mortality rates in expert centres are an acceptable 2–3%. Unfortunately, even this radical surgery is not curative in most cases. Most individuals who undergo Whipple operation will ultimately die of their disease with a median survival after surgery of ~18 months. Therefore, many patients who undergo a curative resection for pancreatic adenocarcinoma also receive adjuvant (post-operative) chemoradiotherapy (Yeo et al., 1995). Some centres are also investigating the potential benefit of neoadjuvant (preoperative) chemoradiotherapy.

There are few chemotherapeutic agents that are active against pancreatic cancer. Agents such as gemcitabine, taxotere, 5-fluorouracil and others are effective in only 10–20% of patients with the disease. A number of experimental approaches are therefore being tried, including herceptin to target overexpression of the ErbB2 receptor (Day et al., 1996), angiogenesis inhibitors and gene therapies which can deliver immunomodulators, prodrugs and tumour-suppressor genes. One of the more novel approaches is a vaccine approach developed by Jaffee et al. (2001) at Johns Hopkins, who have developed a pancreatic cancer vaccine that recruits the patients' own immune system to fight the cancer.

It is also important to consider the quality of life for patients with this disease. Pain control is important and can be achieved with the use of opiate analgesia, which can be given in the form of infusion pump. In addition, 'nerve blocks' may be effective in some patients. This procedure involves the destruction of the nerves around the pancreas ('coeliac axis nerve block') and it is achieved by injecting 100% alcohol percutaneously, intraoperatively or during EUS into the nerve bed.

Weight loss is also a common problem for patients with pancreatic cancer. Many patients lose their appetite and the normal taste of food as a result of byproducts (anorectic factors) released from the cancer. In addition, food may not be adequately digested if the pancreas fails to release sufficient pancreatic enzymes owing to pancreatic duct obstruction. Such patients may benefit from taking pancreatic enzyme supplements. However, most patients with pancreatic cancer will lose weight even if they are eating and digesting their food sufficiently. This may be because pancreatic cancers often release cachectic factors (tumour lipid mobilizing factors, proteolysis-inducing factors) which cause muscle and fat breakdown. Such profound weight loss causes weakness and can shorten survival. This cancer-related weight loss can be refractory to treatment, but appetite stimulants may help the anorexia and fish oil supplements appear promising for reversing the cachexia. In the laboratory, fish oils appear to block the effects of cancer on muscle and fat wasting.

Another frequent complication of pancreatic cancer is common bile duct obstruction. Biliary drainage can relieve symptoms of obstruction and it can be achieved with biliary stents introduced during ERCP or percutaneously (percutaneous transhepatic cholangiography (PTC)). Biliary stents can be placed as an outpatient procedure with minimal patient discomfort and they can provide good short-term palliation of symptoms. Unfortunately, such stents frequently block off due to progressive tumour growth.

Pancreatic Neuroendocrine Carcinoma

Patients with islet cell (or neuroendocrine) carcinomas usually present either with symptoms due to hormone hypersecretion or in the context of multiple endocrine neoplasia (MEN) type I or MEN type II. Common presentations are refractory peptic ulcer disease, hypoglycaemia (low blood sugar), carcinoid syndrome (flushing, diarrhoea and asthma), secretory diarrhoea, hypercalcoemia (elevated serum calcium levels) and bone pain and a necrolytic skin rash. These symptoms arise from oversecretion of gastrin, insulin, serotonin (and histamine and other peptides), vasoactive intestinal peptide (VIP), parathyroid hormone or glucagon, respectively. Rarely, other peptides are released, such as somatostatin, pancreatic polypeptide, CRF, GRF or neurotensin. With the appropriate clinical suspicion, diagnosis of the presence of a neuroendocrine carcinoma can be achieved by measuring the levels of the islet cell hormones in the blood. Because they can be small (1 cm or less), multiple and they may involve the duodenum, islet cell tumours can be hard to identify radiologically. EUS is the best test for localizing these tumours. When possible, surgical resection is performed to treat these tumours, but surgery may not be possible if the patient has multiple foci of metastatic disease. Somatostatin analogues are very effective in combating the release of secretory peptides usually observed with these tumours. Patients with gastrinomas usually undergo total gastrectomy, although proton pump inhibitor therapy has reduced the need for this operation. In addition to somatostatin analogues, hyperglycaemic agents such as diazoxide are used to limit hypoglycaemia in patients with inoperable insulinomas.

Finally, chemotherapeutic agents such as streptozocin, 5-fluorouracil and interferon are often used for patients with inoperable islet cell tumours.

CONCLUSIONS

Pancreatic cancer is one of the deadliest of all cancers. The average life expectancy for patients with pancreatic cancer is only 6 months. While there are no effective therapies or screening tests currently available, we believe that the revolution which has occurred in our understanding of the genetics of pancreatic cancer will soon be translated into new effective screening tests, novel treatments and a better understanding of why pancreatic cancer aggregates in some families.

REFERENCES

Albores-Saavedra, J., *et al.* (1987). Mucinous cystadenocarcinoma of the pancreas. Morphologic and immunocytochemical observations. *American Journal of Surgery and Pathology*, **11**, 11–20.

Allison, D. C., *et al.* (1998). DNA content and other factors associated with ten-year survival after resection of pancreatic carcinoma. *Journal of Surgical Oncology*, **67**, 151–159.

Argani, P., *et al.* (2001). Discovery of new markers of cancer through serial analysis of gene expression: prostate stem cell antigen is overexpressed in pancreatic adenocarcinoma. *Cancer Research*, **61**, 4320–4324.

Belinsky, S. A., *et al.* (1998). Aberrant methylation of p16(INK4a) is an early event in lung cancer and a potential biomarker for early diagnosis. *Proceedings of the National Academy of Sciences of the USA*, **95**, 11891–11896.

Bluemke, D. A., *et al.* (1995). Potentially resectable pancreatic adenocarcinoma: spiral CT assessment with surgical and pathologic correlation. *Radiology*, **197**, 381–385.

Brat, D. J., *et al.* (1998). Progression of pancreatic intraductal neoplasias (high-grade PanIN) to infiltrating adenocarcinoma of the pancreas. *American Journal of Surgery and Pathology*, **22**, 163–169.

Brentnall, T. A., *et al.* (1999). Early diagnosis and treatment of pancreatic dysplasia in patients with a family history of pancreatic cancer. *Annals of Internal Medicine*, **131**, 247–255.

Caldas, C., *et al.* (1994). Detection of K-*ras* mutations in the stool of patients with pancreatic adenocarcinoma and pancreatic ductal hyperplasia. *Cancer Research*, **54**, 3568–3573.

Compagno, J. and Oertel, J. E. (1978a). Microcystic adenomas of the pancreas (glycogen-rich cystadenomas). A clinicopathologic study of 34 cases. *American Journal of Clinical Pathology*, **69**, 289–298.

Compagno, J. and Oertel, J. E. (1978b). Mucinous cystic neoplasms of the pancreas with overt and latent malignancy (cystadenocarcinoma and cystadenoma). A clinicopathologic study of 41 cases. *American Journal of Clinical Pathology*, **69**, 573–580.

Cubilla, A. L. and Fitzgerald, P. J. (1976). Morphological lesions associated with human primary invasive nonendocrine pancreas cancer. *Cancer Research*, **36**, 2690–2698.

Day, J. D., *et al.* (1996). Immunohistochemical evaluation of HER-2/neu oncogene expression in pancreatic adenocarcinoma and pancreatic intraepithelial neoplasms. *Human Pathology*, **27**, 119–124.

DiGiuseppe, J. A., *et al.* (1994a). Detection of K-*ras* mutations in mucinous pancreatic duct hyperplasia from a patient with a family history of pancreatic carcinoma. *American Journal of Pathology*, **144**, 889–895.

DiGiuseppe, J. A., *et al.* (1994b). Overexpression of p53 protein in adenocarcinoma of the pancreas. *American Journal of Clinical Pathology*, **101**, 684–688.

DiGiuseppe, J. A., *et al.* (1996). Molecular biology and the diagnosis and treatment of adenocarcinoma of the pancreas. *Advances in Anatomical Pathology*, **3**, 139–155.

Ghadirian, P., *et al.* (1991a). Tobacco, alcohol, and coffee and cancer of the pancreas. A population-based, case-control study in Quebec, Canada. *Cancer*, **67**, 2664–2670.

Ghadirian, P., *et al.* (1991b). Reported family aggregation of pancreatic cancer within a population-based case-control study in the Francophone community in Montreal, Canada. *International Journal of Pancreatology*, **10**, 183–196.

Goggins, M., *et al.* (1996). Germline BRCA2 gene mutations in patients with apparently sporadic pancreatic carcinomas. *Cancer Research*, **56**, 5360–5364.

Goggins, M., *et al.* (1998). Pancreatic adenocarcinomas with DNA replication errors (RER+) are associated with wild-type K-ras and characteristic histopathology: poor differentiation, a syncytial growth pattern, and pushing borders suggest RER+. *American Journal of Pathology*, **152**, 1501–1507.

Gold, E. B. and Goldin, S. B. (1998). Epidemiology of and risk factors for pancreatic cancer. *Surgical Oncology Clinics of North America*, **7**, 67–91.

Hahn, S. A., *et al.* (1996). *DPC4*, a candidate tumor suppressor gene at human chromosome 18q21.1. *Science*, **271**, 350–353.

Hruban, R. H., *et al.* (1993). K-*ras* oncogene activation in adenocarcinoma of the human pancreas. A study of 82 carcinomas using a combination of mutant-enriched polymerase chain reaction analysis and allele-specific oligonucleotide hybridization. *American Journal of Pathology*, **143**, 545–554.

Hruban, R. H., *et al.* (1998). The genetics of pancreatic cancer: from genes to families. *Surgical Oncology Clinics of North America*, **7**, 1–23.

Hruban, R. H. and Wilentz, R. E. (2000) Pancreas. In: Weidner, N., Cote, R. J., Suster, S. and Weiss, L. M. (eds), *Modern Surgical Pathology*. (W.B. Saunders, Philadelphia).

Jaffee, E. M. (1998). A phase I clinical trial of lethally irradiated allogeneic pancreatic tumor cells transfected with the GM-CSF gene for the treatment of pancreatic adenocarcinoma. *Human Gene Therapy*, **9**, 1951–1971.

Jaffee, E. M., *et al.* (2001). Novel allogeneic granulocyte-macrophage colony-stimulating factor-secreting tumor vaccine for pancreatic cancer: a phase 1 trial of safety and immune activation. *Journal of Clinical Oncology*, **19**, 145–156.

Klöppel, G., *et al.* (1996). *World Health Organization International Histological Classification of Tumors*. (Springer, Berlin).

Klimstra, D. S., *et al.* (1992). Acinar cell carcinoma of the pancreas: a clinicopathologic study of 28 cases. *American Journal of Surgery and Pathology*, **16**, 815–837.

Klimstra, D. S., *et al.* (1995). Pancreatoblastoma. A clinicopathologic study and review of the literature. *American Journal of Surgery and Pathology*, **19**, 1371–1389.

Lubensky, I. A., *et al.* (1996). Allelic deletions on chromosome 11q13 in multiple tumors from individual MEN1 patients. *Cancer Research*, **56**, 5272–5278.

Molina, M. A., *et al.* (1999). Increased cyclooxygenase-2 expression in human pancreatic carcinomas and cell lines: growth inhibition by nonsteroidal anti-inflammatory drugs. *Cancer Research*, **59**, 4356–4362.

Moskaluk, C. A., *et al.* (1997). *p16* and K-*ras* gene mutations in the intraductal precursors of human pancreatic adenocarcinoma. *Cancer Research*, **57**, 2140–2143.

Mulder, I., *et al.* (1999). The impact of smoking on future pancreatic cancer: a computer simulation. *Annals of Oncology*, **10**, S74–S78.

Offerhaus, G. J. A., *et al.* (1988). Gastric, pancreatic and colorectal carcinogenesis following remote peptic ulcer surgery. Review of the literature with the emphasis on risk assessment and underlying mechanism. *Modern Pathology*, **1**, 352–356.

Ozcelik, H., *et al.* (1997). Germline BRCA2 6174delT mutations in Ashkenazi Jewish pancreatic cancer patients. *Nature Genetics*, **16**, 17–18.

Ritts, R. E. and Pitt, H. A. (1998). CA 19-9 in pancreatic cancer. *Surgical Oncology Clinics of North America*, **7**, 93–101.

Rozenblum, E., *et al.* (1997). Tumor-suppressive pathways in pancreatic carcinoma. *Cancer Research*, **57**, 1731–1734.

Schutte, M., *et al.* (1995). Identification by representational difference analysis of a homozygous deletion in pancreatic carcinoma that lies within the BRCA2 region. *Proceedings of the National Academy of Sciences of the USA*, **92**, 5950–5954.

Schutte, M., *et al.* (1997). Abrogation of the *Rb/p16* tumor-suppressive pathway in virtually all pancreatic carcinomas. *Cancer Research*, **57**, 3126–3130.

Solcia, E., *et al.* (1997). *Atlas of tumor pathology: Tumors of the pancreas*. (Armed Forces Institute of Pathology, Washington, DC).

Stolzenberg-Solomon, R. Z., *et al.* (1999). Pancreatic cancer risk and nutrition-related methyl-group availability indicators in male smokers. *Journal of the National Cancer Institute*, **91**, 535–541.

Su, G. H., *et al.* (1999). Germline and somatic mutations of the *STK11/LKB1* Peutz–Jeghers gene in pancreatic and biliary cancers. *American Journal of Pathology*, **154**, 1835–1840.

Suehara, N., *et al.* (1997). Telomerase activity in pancreatic juice differentiates ductal carcinoma from adenoma and pancreatitis. *Clinical Cancer Research*, **3**, 2479–2483.

Tersmette, A. C., *et al.* (2001). Increased risk of incident pancreatic cancer among first-degree relatives of patients with familial pancreatic cancer. *Clinical Cancer Research*, **7**, 738–744.

Westra, W. H., *et al.* (1998). K-*ras* oncogene mutations in osteoclast-like giant-cell tumors of the pancreas and liver: genetic evidence to support origin from the duct epithelium. *American Journal of Surgery and Pathology*, **22**, 1247–1254.

Whitcomb, D. C., *et al.* (1996). Hereditary pancreatitis is caused by a mutation in the cationic trypsinogen gene. *Nature Genetics*, **14**, 141–145.

Wilentz, R. E., *et al.* (1998). Inactivation of the *p16* (*INK4A*) tumor-suppressor gene in pancreatic duct lesions: loss of intranuclear expression. *Cancer Research*, **58**, 4740–4744.

Wilentz, R. E., *et al.* (1999). Pathologic examination accurately predicts prognosis in mucinous cystic neoplasms of the pancreas. *American Journal of Surgery and Pathology*, **23**, 1320–1327.

Yeo, C. J., *et al.* (1995). Pancreaticoduodenectomy for cancer of the head of the pancreas. 201 patients. *Annals of Surgery*, **221**, 721–733.

Zhang, L., *et al.* (1997). Gene expression profiles in normal and cancer cells. *Science*, **276**, 1268–1272.

FURTHER READING

Hruban, R. H., *et al.* (1997). Pathology of incipient pancreatic cancer. *Annals of Oncology,* **10**, S9–S11.

Hruban, R. H., *et al.* (1997). Pancreatic cancer. In: Vogelstein, B., Kinzler, K. W. (eds), *Genetic Basis of Human Cancer.* (McGraw-Hill, New York) 603–613.

Hruban, R. H., *et al.* (1998). The genetics of pancreatic cancer: from genes to families. *Surgical Oncology/Clinics of North America,* **7**, 1–23.

Hruban, R. H., *et al.* (1998). Tumor-suppressor genes in pancreatic cancer. *Journal of Hepatobiliary and Pancreatic Surgery,* **5**, 383–391.

Hruban, R. H., *et al.* (1999). Screening for pancreatic cancer. In: Kramer, B., *et al.* (eds) *Cancer Screening Theory and Practice.* 441–459 (Marcel Dekker, New York).

Hruban, R. H., *et al.* (1999). Molecular pathology of early pancreatic cancer. In: Shrivastava, D. E., *et al.*, (eds), *Molecular Pathology of Early Cancer.* 289–299 (IOS Press, Amsterdam).

Hruban, R. H. and Wilentz, R. E. (2001). Pancreas. In: Weidner, N., *et al.* (eds), *Modern Surgical Pathology.* (W.B. Saunders, Philadelphia).

Solcia, E., *et al.* (1997). *Atlas of Tumor Pathology: Tumors of the Pancreas.* (Armed Forces Institute of Pathology, Washington, DC).

Wilentz, R. and Hruban, R. H. (1998). Pathology of cancer of the pancreas. In: Pitt, H. A. (ed.), W.B. Saunders, Philadelphia, PA. *Oncology Clinics of North America,* **7**, 43–65.

Web Sites

The Johns Hopkins Pancreatic Cancer Web Site:
   http://pathology.jhu.edu/pancreas
The Lustgarten Foundation for Pancreatic Cancer Research:
   http://www.lustgartenfoundation.org
Pancreatic Cancer Action Network:
   http://info@pancan.org
American Cancer Society:
   http://www.cancer.org
National Cancer Institutes PDQ for Health Care Professionals:
   http://www.oncolink.upenn.edu/pdq_html/1/engl/

Chapter 41

Endocrine Organs

Sylvia L. Asa
University Health Network, Toronto, Canada

Shereen Ezzat
Freeman Centre in Endocrine Oncology, Mount Sinai Hospital, Toronto, Canada

CONTENTS

- Normal Development and Structure
- Tumour Pathology
- Epidemiology
- Aetiology
- Screening and Prevention
- Gross and Histopathology, Immunohistochemistry and Ultrastructure
- Molecular Genetic Findings
- Prognostic Factors
- Overview of Clinical Management

NORMAL DEVELOPMENT AND STRUCTURE

The endocrine organs represent a group of tissues that have, as their primary function, the production and secretion of hormones. They are generally classified into three broad categories:

1. peptide hormone-producing;
2. steroid hormone-producing;
3. thyroid hormone-producing.

Most endocrine cell types fall into the first category. This group of endocrine tissues is composed of cells that have a characteristic neuroendocrine morphology (DeLellis and Tischler, 1998). They have sufficient neural differentiation structurally and functionally that they have been called 'paraneurons' and have been classified as the APUD (amine precursor uptake and decarboxylation) system. In earlier literature it was suggested that they derive from the neural crest embryologically; however, this has not been proved for all members of this group of cells, many of which arise from the primitive endoderm. Nevertheless, functionally they act as neuron-like cells that secrete peptides that are often also produced by neurons. The relationship between these cells and neurons is rather like the comparison between wireless and conventional communication. Neurons produce messengers that are released at synapses and activate receptors in adjacent cells, while neuroendocrine cells produce the same types of messengers that are released into the bloodstream to activate cells throughout the body. The wide array of peptide hormones that they produce is essential for regulation of most metabolic and reproductive functions. These cells are found in classical endocrine organs, such as the pituitary, parathyroid and adrenal medulla, and as members of the dispersed endocrine system scattered within other organs, such as the calcitonin-secreting C cells of the thyroid and the endocrine cells of the lung, gut and pancreas.

The steroid hormone-producing cells are primarily found in the adrenal cortex and the gonads (Sasano, 1998). They also have a distinct morphology that reflects their primary function of conversion of cholesterol into the various mineralocorticoid, glucocorticoid, androgenic and oestrogenic hormones. They are of mesodermal origin arising from the coelomic epithelium that gives rise to the adrenal and the genital ridge.

The thyroid hormone-producing cells are modified epithelial cells derived from the oral endoderm that invaginate from the base of tongue (Murray, 1998). They are specifically involved in the synthesis of thyroglobulin and its iodination to form thyroid hormones.

TUMOUR PATHOLOGY

Tumours of the endocrine system reflect their origin in the three types of endocrine cells.

Tumours of neuroendocrine cells arise either in classical neuroendocrine tissues, such as pituitary, parathyroid or adrenal medulla, or in other tissues where the dispersed cells reside, such as thyroid, lung, gut or pancreas. These lesions exhibit a wide spectrum of biological behaviours. They may be slowly growing, well-differentiated neoplasms that are considered benign (adenomas), because they do not metastasize. The most aggressive neoplasms are poorly differentiated (small-cell) carcinomas that are rapidly lethal. Many tumours fall into intermediate categories and the prediction of outcome can be very difficult. The term 'carcinoid,' meaning 'carcinoma-like,' was originally introduced by Oberndorfer in 1907, and the terminology has been applied to well-differentiated neuroendocrine tumours and to tumours that result in the classical 'carcinoid syndrome' that results from serotonin excess. The use of this terminology, however, has caused great confusion because of the wide diversity of hormone activity and biological behaviour among these tumours that cannot all be conveyed by this classification. Since many of these ultimately prove to be malignant, this terminology has fallen out of favour. These tumours may be clinically silent in terms of hormone function, but they are almost always found to produce and store hormones. Some elaborate hormones that give rise to colourful clinical syndromes of hormone excess; the pattern of hormone production may be eutopic to the tissue of origin or ectopic, reflecting derepression of genes that are expressed in related cells.

Tumours of steroid hormone-secreting cells usually arise in the adrenals or gonads and very rarely arise in other sites where embryological remnants are found. They are generally classified as benign adenomas or malignant carcinomas based on features of differentiation, hormone production and invasion. Well-differentiated and generally benign tumours express mature steroid hormones. Tumours that are less well differentiated and exhibit malignant behaviour tend to lose the complex enzymatic pathways required for mature hormone production, but often produce hormone precursors of various types. Nevertheless, the functional behaviour of these tumours is not strict enough to allow classification as benign or malignant. These tumours are usually limited to the production of steroid hormones and almost never produce peptide hormones ectopically.

Tumours of thyroid follicular cell derivation are the most common neoplasms of the endocrine system. They include benign follicular adenomas, well-differentiated papillary or follicular carcinomas, poorly differentiated 'insular' carcinomas and dedifferentiated anaplastic carcinomas. Among human malignancies, they include the most benign and nonlethal occult papillary microcarcinomas that are found incidentally in up to 24% of the adult population, and one of the most rapidly lethal malignancies, the anaplastic carcinomas that frequently result in death by strangulation in less than 6 months.

EPIDEMIOLOGY

Tumours of endocrine differentiation are considered to be rare and, as such, the epidemiological data are weak. There are, however, several statistics of note.

Pituitary tumours are reported to be found in about 20% of the general population (Asa, 1998). Many of the studies have reported the identification of these lesions as incidental findings at autopsy, or as radiological findings in the asymptomatic 'normal' population. The true incidence of clinically significant lesions is not known. Some forms of pituitary neoplasia, including corticotroph adenomas causing Cushing's disease and prolactinomas, are more common in women than in men, but overall there is no sex predilection of pituitary neoplasia. These lesions tend to increase with age and are rare in children (Asa, 1998).

Primary hyperparathyroidism is most often due to parathyroid neoplasia and is reported to occur in 1% of the adult population (Apel and Asa, 2001). The true incidence of parathyroid adenomas is not known, however. Parathyroid carcinomas are rare. Benign lesions are more common in women than in men and are primarily found in middle-aged to elderly women. In contrast, carcinoma does not have a predilection for women and some studies indicate onset about one decade earlier than benign parathyroid tumours.

Pheochromocytomas of the adrenal medulla have a reported incidence of 2–8 per million per year and extra-adrenal paragangliomas are even rarer. These lesions have no sex predilection and are rare in children (Lack, 1997; Tischler, 1998).

Well-differentiated tumours of the dispersed endocrine system are rare. Tumors of thyroid C cells, medullary thyroid carcinomas, represent about 5% of thyroid cancers that predicts a prevalence of about 1–2 per 100 000 (LiVolsi, 1990; Moley, 2000). Tumours of the endocrine pancreas have an estimated prevalence of 1 in 100 000 (Klöppel et al., 1998). These lesions show no sex predilection and are very rare in children. Small-cell carcinoma of the lung, the most poorly differentiated endocrine neoplasm of this type, represents one of the four major types of lung cancer, the second most common cancer in men and women and the number one cancer mortality site (Greenlee et al., 2000); this variant has an annual incidence of almost 10 per 100 000 population.

Although adrenal cortical nodules are identified as incidental findings in 0.6–1.3% of asymptomatic individuals, clinically significant adrenal neoplasms are more rare and adrenal cortical carcinoma has an estimated incidence of only about 1 case per million population (Lack, 1997). There is a slight female preponderance. The incidence has a bimodal distribution in the first and fifth decades.

As indicated above, thyroid cancer is the commonest endocrine malignancy, representing 1–2% of all cancers

(LiVolsi, 1990; Murray, 1998; Asa and Bedard, 2000). It is about three times more common in women than in men and currently represents the tenth most common malignancy in women (Greenlee *et al.*, 2000).

AETIOLOGY

The aetiology of most endocrine tumours is not known. A small minority is due to inherited genetic defects. The genes responsible for the multiple endocrine neoplasia (MEN) syndromes, *MEN-1* and *MEN-2*, have been cloned and characterized, and the mutations have clarified our understanding of mechanisms of disease. MEN-1 is a classical example of germ-line inheritance of a mutant tumour-suppressor gene (TSG), menin (Komminoth, 1999). It is an autosomal dominant disorder with variable penetrance; the variability of tumour development in pituitary, parathyroids, pancreas and occasionally other sites of the dispersed endocrine system in individual patients is due to the requirement for loss of the intact allele encoding the tumour suppressor. In contrast, MEN-2 is the best example of inheritance of a mutant proto-oncogene. The gene responsible for this disease encodes the transmembrane receptor tyrosine kinase Ret (Mulligan and Ponder, 1995). The identification of an activating Ret mutation in members of kindreds is now accepted as an indication for prophylactic thyroidectomy in early childhood, since these individuals will develop medullary thyroid carcinoma that can metastasize and is lethal in more than half of patients. Moreover, distinct *ret* mutations are associated with distinct clinical phenotypes. Mutations in exons 10 and 11 that encode the extracellular domain of the Ret protein are implicated as the cause of familial medullary thyroid carcinoma alone. Specific mutations, usually in exon 11 involving codon 634, are associated with MEN-2A and specifically codon 634 mutations replacing cysteine with arginine are more often associated with parathyroid disease and pheochromocytoma that characterize this disease complex. Activating mutations in exon 16 that replace a codon 918 methionine with threonine alter the tyrosine kinase domain of Ret and result in MEN-2B, a more aggressive variant of MEN-2 with mucosal neuromas and a marfanoid habitus in addition to tumours of thyroid C cells, parathyroids and adrenal medulla.

The aetiology of thyroid carcinomas of follicular epithelial cells is not entirely known, but there is evidence of a causal role for radiation (LiVolsi, 1990; Murray, 1998; Asa and Bedard, 2000). This is true of radiation therapy, for example in patients who have received external beam radiotherapy for malignancies of the head and neck and also for cosmetic therapy for facial acne. It is also true in populations exposed to radioactive fallout from nuclear disasters, such as in Japan after the nuclear bomb disasters and in Ukraine and Belarus after the Chernobyl episode. The exposure to radioactivity has its highest impact in the young, and the disease is more often multifocal than in sporadic cases; however, the prognosis in patients who have been exposed to radiation does not appear to differ from those with no history of radiation (Brierley and Asa, 2001). Radiation has been implicated as causative of *ret/PTC* gene rearrangements that are thought to play a role in the genesis of thyroid carcinomas (Nikiforova *et al.*, 2000). Diet has also been implicated in the development of thyroid cancer; populations with low iodine intake develop goitres and have a higher incidence of follicular carcinoma, but most investigators now recognize dietary iodine insufficiency as the reason for a higher incidence of follicular as opposed to papillary carcinomas. In other words, there is no evidence that it increases the incidence of cancer; rather it alters the morphological variant of well-differentiated thyroid carcinoma.

SCREENING AND PREVENTION

Screening for endocrine tumours has really only been applied systematically in cases of familial disease. Members of kindreds have traditionally been screened using biochemical analysis of hormone hypersecretion. More recently, the addition of genetic information has allowed earlier and definitive identification of carriers in families with known mutations. Patients with MEN-1 have variable disease patterns, so that genetic identification results in continued and careful surveillance of affected family members. Patients with activating mutations of the *ret* proto-oncogene will almost certainly develop medullary thyroid carcinoma, a disease that is lethal if not detected early or prevented, and therefore current guidelines recommend prophylactic thyroidectomy in childhood, usually by age 5 years for those with MEN-2A or FMTC, and at or around age 1 year for those with the more aggressive mutation of MEN-2B. Some families have unidentified mutations and hormonal screening remains the standard mechanism of tumour detection, with the addition of radiological investigation where indicated.

Screening for thyroid tumours is usually part of the physical examination since the thyroid is readily accessible on palpation of the neck. When a thyroid nodule is detected, the most valuable technique to evaluate these lesions is the cytological examination of a fine-needle thyroid aspirate (Murray, 1998; Asa and Bedard, 2000). It can clearly identify some patients who will require surgery and most of those who are unlikely to require surgery. Cytological examination can very quickly impart a diagnosis of *papillary carcinoma, medullary carcinoma, lymphoma, anaplastic carcinoma* or *metastatic carcinoma*. In contrast to these clearly malignant lesions, the majority of thyroid aspirates yield a benign diagnosis, which is either *thyroiditis* or *colloid nodule*, a benign hyperplastic process with abundant colloid storage. Nevertheless, there is a population of patients whose thyroid aspirates yield abundant follicular epithelial cells, sometimes with atypia; these lesions cannot be classified based on cytology alone and surgery is required to allow thorough analysis of these *follicular lesions* to identify or exclude invasive behaviour that distinguishes benign from malignant neoplasms.

GROSS AND HISTOPATHOLOGY, IMMUNOHISTOCHEMISTRY AND ULTRASTRUCTURE

Tumours of Neuroendocrine Cells

The morphology of endocrine tumours varies with the type and location of the lesion.

Tumours of neuroendocrine cells are generally well-delineated but unencapsulated lesions that have a characteristic histopathology. They are composed of small nests, trabecula or sheets of epithelial cells in a highly vascular stroma (**Figure 1a; see colour plate section**). They occasionally form gland-like structures. The stroma may, in some instances, form amyloid. The tumour cells usually have poorly defined cell borders and abundant cytoplasm that may contain eosinophilic, amphophilic or basophilic granules. Characteristically, the nuclei of tumour cells are bland; nuclear pleomorphism that generally defines malignancy in other epithelial tumours is not a reliable indicator of aggressive behaviour. The more poorly differentiated carcinomas have less cytoplasm, lack granularity and have larger more hyperchromatic nuclei.

These lesions are readily classified by the immunohistochemical localization of common markers of neuroendocrine differentiation (**Table 1**) (Wick, 2000). They almost uniformly stain for synaptophysin, a 38-kDa molecule that is associated with synaptic vesicles of neurons and neuroendocrine cells (**Figure 1b; see colour plate section**). Most contain chromogranins, proteins associated with secretory granules. There are two families of chromogranins, A and B; to classify these lesions appropriately one needs to identify both chromogranins. Moreover, chromogranin immunoreactivity is directly related to the number of secretory granules that may be scarce in poorly differentiated tumours. Other markers of neuroendocrine differentiation

include CD57 (Leu7), neural cell adhesion molecule (NCAM; CD56), neuron-specific enolase (NSE) and Protein Gene Product 9.5 (PGP 9.5) that stain variable subpopulations of endocrine lesions and some, such as NCAM and NSE, also stain some non-endocrine tumours. Of course, the structure–function correlations of these lesions are best defined by their immunoreactivity for specific peptide hormones or, in the case of hormones that cannot be localized (such as adrenaline and noradrenaline), the enzymes involved in hormone production (such as tyrosine hydroxylase).

The ultrastructure of these lesions is highly characteristic (**Figure 1c; see colour plate section**). The tumour cells have well developed rough endoplasmic reticulum, reflecting the levels of peptide hormone synthesis, prominent Golgi complexes that are responsible for packaging of hormones for secretion and membrane-bound secretory granules that store hormones for secretion in response to stimulation. The development of these organelles varies with cell differentiation and hormonal activity; the numbers of secretory granules reflect the balance between synthesis, storage and secretion. The morphology of secretory granules is generally reflective of cell type and hormone content, and experts in the field of electron microscopy can classify neuroendocrine cells based on these ultrastructural parameters.

Pituitary tumours (Asa, 1998) and tumours of the adrenal medulla and extraadrenal paraganglia (Lack, 1997; Tischler, 1998) are generally considered benign unless there is evidence of metastatic spread. In contrast, tumours of the dispersed endocrine system, including medullary thyroid carcinomas and endocrine tumours of the lung and gut, are not reliably considered benign (Capella *et al.*, 1995); even in the absence of invasion, there may be delayed recurrence or metastasis. It can be difficult to distinguish tumours of the parathyroid glands from hyperplasia (Apel and Asa, 2001). In this tissue, the diagnosis of malignancy in a neoplasm usually relies on identification of vascular invasion or metastasis.

The current approach to the classification of tumours of the dispersed neuroendocrine system is based on three principles: (i) the diagnosis should be based on the microscopic features of the lesion but must incorporate useful immunohistochemical data; (ii) tumours should be distinguished according to the differentiated cell type and site of origin; and (iii) tumours should be subdivided based on biological behaviour, into benign, low-grade malignant and high-grade malignant lesions; the last include poorly differentiated endocrine carcinoma and the so-called 'small-cell' or 'oat-cell' carcinomas. The determination of malignant potential is based on architectural and cytological features including invasion as outlined below:

- cytological features;
- ploidy, proliferation markers;
- pattern of hormone production
  eutopic vs ectopic, α-subunit;

Table 1   Diagnosis of neuroendocrine tumours

General	Synaptophysin, chromogranins
	NSE, CD57,
	NCAM (CD56), PGP 9.5
	Hormones
	Specific
	Eutopic
	Ectopic

- invasion;

    capsular, adjacent tissues, perineural, vascular;

- metastases.

The location and hormone content of individual lesions are of importance, especially in the classification of tumours of histological low-grade malignancy, the 'well-differentiated endocrine carcinoma,' where these additional pieces of information aid in predicting the likelihood of metastatic behaviour.

The wide spectrum of clinical symptomatology associated with these lesions is attributed to the numerous peptide hormones that can be elaborated by the cells of the diffuse endocrine system. A limited example is included in **Table 2** that identifies some of the cell types, hormones and syndromes associated with tumours of the gastro-enteropancreatic system.

Tumours of Steroid-Hormone-Producing Cells

Tumours of steroid hormone-producing cells are usually solitary, bright-yellow lesions (**Figure 2a; see colour plate section**) with areas of haemorrhage and necrosis (Lack, 1997; Lack, 1998). They are composed of usually monotonous cells with well-defined cell borders and abundant clear cytoplasm (**Figure 2b; see colour plate section**). Immunohistochemistry does not play a major role in identifying these lesions; however, occa-

sionally it is not possible to confirm steroidogenic differentiation of poorly differentiated tumours on histological grounds alone. These lesions characteristically exhibit nuclear reactivity for the nuclear transcription factor steroidogenic factor-1 and cytoplasmic reactivity for inhibin-α. They also stain for various enzymes involved in the steroidogenic pathways. Ultrastructural examination can be helpful; the cells usually have very well developed smooth endoplasmic reticulum and cytoplasmic lipid droplets (**Figure 2c; see colour plate section**). In addition, the mitochondria have tubulovesicular cristae that are a hallmark of steroidogenic cells.

Nodules in the adrenal cortex are very common and may be hyperplastic or attributable to vascular insufficiency; it can be difficult to distinguish hyperplasia from neoplasia; the criteria for this distinction, although not always applicable, are outlined in **Table 3**. When dealing with unequivocal neoplasms, the diagnosis of malignancy can be very difficult. Cytological atypia is not an indicator of malignancy. Size is an important predictor of biological aggressiveness. Again, however, the distinction of benign from malignant lesions usually depends on the identification of invasion, with extension beyond a capsule into adjacent tissue, vascular invasion or metastasis as the features predicting malignant behaviour. These lesions may be associated with hormone excess syndromes; in some cases, hormonal activity can predict biology. It is, for example, extremely rare for adrenal cortical tumours associated with Conn's syndrome to be malignant. In contrast, adrenal tumours associated with feminization in males are invariably malignant. Most malignancies of these tissues are not associated with hormone excess as their primary manifestation; however, it is not unusual to identify production of steroid hormone precursors by tumour cells when this is examined.

Tumours of Thyroid Follicular Cell Derivation

Tumours of thyroid follicular cell derivation are common and are probably the best characterized endocrine neoplasms; however, in this field too there is controversy

Table 2 Classification of gastroenteropancreatic endocrine cells and tumours

Hormone	Cell type	Clinical syndrome
Insulin	B	Hypoglycaemia
Glucagon/glucagon-like peptides (GLP)	A/L	Diabetes mellitus; skin rash
Somatostatin	D	Somatostatinoma syndrome
Gastrin	G	Zollinger–Ellison syndrome
Pancreatic polypeptide	PP	?
Vasoactive intestinal peptide (VIP)	?	Verner–Morrison syndrome
Secretin	S	(watery diarrhoea hypokalemia achlorhydria (WDHA), pancreatic cholera)
Prostaglandins	?	?WDHA
Serotonin	EC	Carcinoid syndrome
Cholecystokinin (CCK)	I	?
ACTH/MSH; CRH	?	Cushing syndrome
Vasopressin	?	Diabetes insipidus
Growth hormone-releasing hormone (GRH); growth hormone (GH)	?	Acromegaly

Table 3 Hyperplasia vs Neoplasia in Endocrine Tissues

Hyperplasia	Neoplasia
Multiple	Solitary
Poorly encapsulated	Encapsulated
Architectural heterogeneity	Uniform architecture
Cytological heterogeneity	Cytological homogeneity
Comparable areas in adjacent gland	Different from surrounding gland
No compression of surrounding gland	Compresses surrounding gland

concerning diagnostic criteria (LiVolsi, 1990; Rosai *et al.*, 1992; Murray, 1998; Asa and Bedard, 2000).

Follicular Nodules of the Thyroid

Follicular nodules may be hyperplastic, benign follicular adenomas or malignant lesions which include follicular carcinoma and follicular variant papillary carcinoma.

Like in parathyroid and adrenal cortex, *hyperplasia* may be extremely difficult to distinguish from *neoplasia*. As shown in **Table 3**, there are rigid criteria for this distinction; however, in many instances the disease is not as defined as classical teaching has suggested. Generally, hyperplasia is a multifocal disorder in which lesions are poorly encapsulated. The nodules of nodular hyperplasia exhibit architectural as well as cytological heterogeneity and this is truly the hallmark of this disease. In contrast, a follicular neoplasm generally represents a solitary encapsulated lesion that is uniform both in cytology and architecture. Architecturally these lesions may be macrofollicular, in which case they are somewhat difficult to distinguish from hyperplastic nodules; microfollicular lesions are more cellular and worrisome but may also represent part of the spectrum of hyperplasia. Clonality studies have indicated that classical teaching may, in fact, be wrong. Although multinodular hyperplasia is expected to be a polyclonal disease, the dominant nodules in multinodular goitres are often monoclonal, raising serious doubts about our diagnostic criteria. Moreover, the evidence of clonal proliferation in sporadic nodular goitre indicates that the thyroid is a site for the hyperplasia–neoplasia sequence. Nevertheless, clinical experience has shown us that most of these lesions remain entirely benign.

The criteria for the diagnosis of *malignancy in a follicular neoplasm* require the presence of vascular or capsular invasion (**Figure 3a; see colour plate section**). Nuclear and cellular atypia and mitotic figures may be present in adenomas and also in carcinomas and therefore cytological characteristics are not helpful in this regard. Follicular carcinomas cannot, therefore, be distinguished from follicular adenomas by fine-needle aspiration cytology. However, there are additional tools that facilitate this diagnosis; for example, a novel marker of malignancy in these lesions is HBME-1, a monoclonal antibody directed against an unknown epitope that is expressed in malignancy but not benign thyroid follicular epithelial cells. More recently, another marker of follicular carcinoma is the detection of PPARγ that is aberrantly expressed due to a gene rearrangement that places PPARγ under the control of the thyroid transcription factor Pax 8 in follicular carcinoma (Kroll *et al.*, 2000).

Follicular carcinomas exhibit a wide range of biological behaviours that are reflected by morphological criteria. Capsular invasion is usually divided into two groups. *Widely invasive follicular carcinomas*, which are usually identifiable as invasive grossly, and certainly are not difficult to recognize as invasive microscopically, carry a poor prognosis with a 25–45% 10-year survival. In contrast, the more common scenario is that of minimal capsular invasion. This requires very careful and thorough examination of the entire capsule of the follicular neoplasm by the pathologist. *Minimally invasive follicular carcinoma* is identified by total thickness invasion through the capsule superficially into the adjacent parenchyma but not widely beyond the capsule. Borderline lesions include those with invasion into the capsule beyond the bulk of the lesion but not through the full thickness of the capsule or situations in which islands of tumour are trapped within a capsule, associated with perpendicular rupture of collagen. The finding of nests, cords or individual tumour cells within a tumour capsule leads some pathologists to the diagnosis of minimally invasive follicular carcinoma; however, this may represent an artifact in a patient who has undergone fine-needle aspiration biopsy, with trapping by fibrosis or displacement of tumour cells into the capsule. The pathologist is therefore advised to search carefully for evidence of fine-needle aspiration biopsy in the adjacent tissue. This would include finding focal haemorrhage, deposition of haemosiderin-laden macrophages and the presence of granulation tissue and/or fibrosis, all of which would indicate a needle biopsy site and the possibility of artifactual invasion rather than genuine invasion.

The careful search for minimally invasive carcinoma is time consuming and difficult for even the most diligent pathologist. Recent data suggest that this search may be unnecessary, since it would appear that patients with minimally invasive carcinoma have almost a 100% 10-year survival rates and therefore some argue that this disease does not need to be distinguished from follicular adenoma. Nevertheless, the investigators who have reported these data have treated their patients for carcinoma rather than for benign disease. Rather than endorsing a cavalier approach that would entail less work for the pathologist, it behoves us to recognize the presence of potential malignancy, to treat the patient appropriately, but also to identify the excellent prognosis that these lesions carry after appropriate management.

Vasculoinvasive follicular carcinomas are aggressive and require management accordingly.

The last few decades have seen a decrease in the incidence of follicular thyroid carcinoma, probably due to dietary iodine supplementation. However, misdiagnosis of this tumour continues. Benign lesions, such as partly encapsulated hyperplastic nodules or nodules exhibiting pseudoinvasion after fine-needle aspiration, are often overdiagnosed as malignant; papillary carcinomas with follicular architecture are often misinterpreted as follicular carcinoma. The clinical features, pathophysiology, and biological behaviour of follicular cancer differ significantly from those of the entities with which it is often confused. Only careful histopathological classification will allow correct evaluation of treatment options and prognosis.

Papillary Lesions

Papillary nodules of the thyroid are usually malignant but occasional benign papillary tumours are identified.

Papillary Hyperplasia

Papillary lesions are seen focally in *nodular goitre* with or without associated hyperfunction; 'hot' nodules are usually associated with increased uptake on radionucleotide scan.

The so-called *'papillary hyperplastic nodule'* most likely represents a benign neoplasm of the thyroid. These are said to occur most commonly in teenage girls. They present as solitary nodules and may be associated with clinical hyperfunction. *Benign papillary neoplasms* in adults may result in clinical toxicity and a 'hot' nodule on radionuclide scanning. These lesions are encapsulated, often show central cystic change and have subfollicle formation in the centres of broad oedematous papillae. They are distinguished from papillary carcinoma by lack of nuclear atypia (see below).

Papillary Carcinoma

Papillary carcinoma comprises more than 80% of thyroid epithelial malignancies in countries where goitre is not endemic. The name 'papillary carcinoma' is historic and often is misleading. In fact, the architecture of these neoplasms varies from an almost pure papillary pattern to a pure follicular pattern; many tumours have a mixed papillary and follicular pattern. It is now recognized that the diagnosis of papillary carcinoma is based on cytological criteria, as specified in the WHO classification on thyroid tumours, 'a distinctive set of nuclear characteristics' that can be listed as follows:

- crowded, overlapping 'shingle-tile' appearance;
- large, elongated nuclei;
- irregular nuclear outline;
- etched, folded or moulded nuclear membrane;
- nuclear grooves;
- pale vacuolated nucleoplasm;
- peripheral margination of chromatin;
- bare or marginated nucleoli; and
- nuclear cytoplasmic pseudoinclusions.

These characteristics are illustrated in **Figure 3b; see colour plate section**. No one specific feature is absolutely diagnostic of papillary carcinoma; usually, one relies on a constellation or combination of nuclear features for the diagnosis. These nuclear features may be accompanied by more easily recognized psammoma bodies and the presence of high molecular weight cytokeratins, which are readily localized in formalin-fixed paraffin-embedded tissue when microwave antigen retrieval is applied. Identification of high molecular weight cytokeratins confirms the suspected diagnosis of papillary carcinoma in approximately 60% of cases. Other markers of papillary carcinoma include HBME-1 (see Follicular Nodules of the Thyroid, above) and Ret. The Ret tyrosine kinase, that is expressed in thyroid C cells and exhibits somatic activating mutations in medullary thyroid carcinomas and germ-line activating mutations in MEN-2, is usually not expressed in thyroid follicular epithelial cells. However, there are several variants of gene rearrangements, known as *ret/PTC*, that result in expression of the C-terminus of Ret in papillary carcinoma. Detection of such a rearrangement by immunostaining for Ret can facilitate diagnosis in difficult cases.

Thyroid tumours exhibiting the nuclear characteristics of papillary carcinoma diffusely or multifocally should be diagnosed as papillary carcinoma rather than as follicular carcinoma. These lesions share certain clinical characteristics such as biological indolence and an excellent prognosis with a 20-year survival rate of 95% or better. Papillary carcinomas invade lymphatics, leading to a high percentage of regional lymph node metastases. Metastases beyond the neck are unusual in common papillary carcinoma and probably only occur in about 5–7% of cases.

Aggressive Tumours of Follicular Cell Derivation

Specific morphological features can identify tumours that are more aggressive than the usual well-differentiated follicular or papillary malignancies derived from follicular epithelial cells. For example, the *tall cell variant of papillary carcinoma* is recognized to behave in a much more aggressive fashion. These tumours have a height to width ratio that exceeds 3:1. Tumours that exhibit this feature in more than 30% of the tumour mass generally are found in older patients who have extrathyroidal extension and these patients have a guarded prognosis.

The identification of insular dedifferentiation marks a tumour that requires much more aggressive management. *Insular carcinoma*, also known as *poorly differentiated carcinoma*, is a tumour that exhibits a behaviour intermediate between well differentiated thyroid cancer and anaplastic carcinoma. These lesions are identified by their architectural growth pattern; they form solid nests of epithelial cells that resemble neuroendocrine carcinoma more than a follicular lesion (**Figure 3c; see colour plate section**), however, they generally contain thyroglobulin immunoreactivity to characterize their differentiation.

Anaplastic thyroid carcinomas are composed of undifferentiated cells that may exhibit three general patterns but most tumours manifest mixed morphology. The most common type is the *giant cell variant*; as the name suggests, these tumours are composed predominantly of large cells with abundant cytoplasm and bizarre, often multiple, hyperchromatic nuclei. The *squamoid variant* is composed of large cells that form nests, resembling squamous carcinoma. *Spindle cell anaplastic carcinomas* have a fascicular architecture and dense stromal collagen with spindle-shaped tumour that may resemble fibrosarcoma. In all three variants, mitotic figures and atypical mitoses are frequent. There is usually extensive necrosis and, in some cases, necrosis may be so extensive that the only viable tumour is around blood vessels. Anaplastic carcinomas are highly infiltrative, destroying thyroid tissue and invading skeletal muscle, adipose tissue and other perithyroidal structures. Blood vessel invasion and thrombosis with or without tumour cell involvement are frequent. These lesions usually have no immunoreactivity for markers of thyroid cells and are often a diagnosis of exclusion.

The reported association between well-differentiated thyroid carcinoma and anaplastic carcinoma ranges from 7 to 89% of cases; however, the lower figures are probably underestimates, attributable to inadequate sampling. The data suggest that anaplastic carcinoma originates most often in an abnormal thyroid; the tumour has a higher incidence in regions of endemic goitre and a history of goitre is reported in over 80% of cases. As stated above, nodular goitre is often the site of monoclonal proliferation, the first step in the hyperplasia–neoplasia sequence. However, it is difficult to document transformation of a benign lesion to a malignant tumour. Insular carcinoma appears to be intermediate in the spectrum, and may represent a transition form. The association of papillary carcinoma, particularly the more aggressive tall cell variant, with anaplastic tumours has also been described. The factors underlying dedifferentiation in thyroid tumours remain to be established; age and radiation have been implicated. Clearly, most well-differentiated thyroid lesions do not undergo such transformation. A pattern of genetic mutations resulting in oncogene activation or loss of tumour suppressor gene activity has been proposed to correlate with the stepwise progression from adenoma to carcinoma and through the dedifferentiation process in thyroid. The significance of microscopic anaplastic change is controversial; some people have suggested that focal microscopic anaplastic dedifferentiation does not alter prognosis, but others have shown that this finding alone is statistically significant as a marker of aggressive behaviour.

MOLECULAR GENETIC FINDINGS

The technique of clonality assessment using X chromosome inactivation patterns has evolved from the Lyon hypothesis, which states that only one X chromosome is active in any female somatic cell; the inactivation occurs early in embryogenesis and persists throughout the lifespan of the cell and its progeny. Traditionally, X chromosome inactivation was determined by the phenotypic expression of isoenzymes of glucose-6-phosphate dehydrogenase (G6PD), a protein encoded on that chromosome. Heterozygosity for this gene, however, is present in only a small proportion of black females, limiting the application of this technique. A molecular approach to the determination of clonality takes advantage of X chromosome inactivation patterns using DNA restriction fragment length polymorphisms (RFLPs). Activated genes can generally be distinguished from their inactive counterparts because of differences in the degree of methylation of cytosine (C) residues which are typically hypomethylated in active genes. X chromosome genes which have been utilized for these studies include hypoxanthine phosphoribosyltransferase (HPRT), phosphoglycerate kinase (PGK) and M27β. Molecular analyses have proved that most endocrine neoplasms are monoclonal.

Although the genetic basis of the inherited endocrine tumours is now understood, the genetic abnormalities underlying the far more common sporadic tumours are not clear (Asa and Ezzat, 1998). In fact, mutations of the common oncogenes and tumour-suppressor genes that have been implicated in other malignancies, such as *ras* and *p53*, are rare in endocrine tumours (Ezzat and Asa, 1998).

Proto-oncogenes are normal cellular genes that play an essential role in the proliferation and differentiation of normal cells. They function at each step of signal transduction pathways as growth factors (e.g. c-*sis*), membrane receptors (e.g. c-*erb*-B, c-*neu*, c-*fms*), GTP-binding proteins (e.g. *ras* family) and nuclear proteins (e.g. c-*myc*, c-*fos*). Proto-oncogenes may be activated by point mutations, translocations or increased expression. Genetic alteration in these genes leads to sustained activation of the gene product in the absence of the normal control mechanisms. Activated oncogenes have been associated with a large number of human tumours, e.g. N-*myc* amplification in neuroblastomas and K-*ras* point mutations in colonic carcinomas.

Ras proteins are involved in transducing signals from the cell surface to a number of ligand–receptor complexes. The commonest mutational sites alter the GTP-binding domain (codons 12/13) or more rarely the GTPase domain (codon 61). Point mutations of all three *ras* genes (H-, K- and N-) are rare in endocrine tumours of all kinds.

Although activating mutations of the *ret* proto-oncogene have been implicated as the cause of familial medullary thyroid carcinoma and MEN-2, activating *ret* mutations are not frequently identified as somatic events in sporadic tumours of the dispersed neuroendocrine system. They are found in a minority of sporadic medullary thyroid carcinomas and pheochromocytomas.

The only endocrine oncogene that has been proved in any consistent fashion in sporadic endocrine tumours is the α-subunit of the Gs protein (Lyons *et al.*, 1990). G-proteins are heterotrimeric membrane-anchored peptides that play a central role in transducing signals from the cell surface ligand–receptor complexes to the downstream effectors. The α-subunit dissociates from the β- and γ-subunits of Gs when GTP displaces its bound GDP, stimulates adenylyl cyclase to produce cyclic AMP from ATP. Cyclic AMP (cAMP) in turn activates c-AMP-dependent protein kinases, increases intracellular calcium transport and may potentiate the effect of activated inositol phospholipid-dependent protein kinases. The weak intrinsic GTPase activity of Gsα and the action of GTPase-activating peptides (GAPs) dissociates GTP from Gsα and terminates the response. Additionally, the multiple structural and functional isoforms of adenylyl cyclase underscore the complexity of this redundant system of signal transduction coupling and provides some insight into the array of potential sites of somatic mutations which could alter both cell division and hormone production. Indeed, one of the earlier and most exciting molecular defects to be described in endocrine tumours involved the single point mutations in two critical domains of the Gsα subunit of GTPase codon 201 where Arg is switched to a Cys or codon 227 where Gln is replaced with Arg. Substitutions at these codons (the *gsp* mutation) activate adenylyl cyclase by inhibiting the hydrolysis of GTP and thereby maintaining Gsα in a constitutively activated state. Activating mutations of this protein are reported to occur in 30% of pituitary growth hormone-producing adenomas (Spada *et al.*, 1992) and in a large proportion of hyperfunctioning thyroid adenomas (Suarez *et al.*, 1991; Goretzki *et al.*, 1992). Marked elevation in Gsα mRNA levels have been documented in insulin-secreting pancreatic endocrine tumorus. In all of these situations, they predict benign but endocrinologically hypersecretory lesions.

Over-expression of genes which act as inhibitors of the apoptotic process may also act as oncogenes. In some studies, the oncogenes c-*myc*, *bcl-2*, c-*erb*-B-2 and c-*jun* have been shown to be frequently expressed in human gastroenteropancreatic endocrine tumours. The expression of these oncogenes may represent pathogenic events in the generation, malignant transformation and progression of gastroenteropancreatic endocrine tumours.

Products of tumour-suppressor genes (TSGs) can alter transcription factor activity, thereby modulating physiological growth by arresting cell division in the G_1 phase. This delay may allow for repair of genomic damage or may trigger apoptotic cell death. Deletion or reduced expression of TSGs appear to be a commonly shared mechanism in human tumorigenesis.

The p53 protein plays a role in cell cycle regulation; point mutations, deletions or rearrangements in the *p53* gene which result in an altered protein are considered to be among the commonest genetic mutations in human neoplasms and have been implicated in tumour progression in several types of cancer. Progressive transformation to the malignant phenotype may be the result of mutational inactivation of the *p53* TSG. Indeed, p53 mutations appear

to play a role in the pathogenesis of some tumours of the dispersed endocrine system, including those arising from the appendix, and carcinomas of the parathyroids and adrenal cortex. They are a late event in thyroid cancer where they are found primarily in anaplastic carcinomas.

In patients with multiple endocrine neoplasia type 1, loss of heterozygosity (LOH) in tumours has been mapped to 11q13. The *MEN-1* tumour-suppressor gene was recently cloned at this chromosomal site. Mutations of menin are not found in most sporadic tumours of the tissues involved in MEN-1: pituitary, parathyroids and pancreas (Komminoth, 1999). *MEN-1* gene mutations have been found in some sporadic tumours of the dispersed endocrine system, primarily gastroenteropancreatic endocrine tumours including 44% of sporadic gastrinomas and 19% of insulinomas, but also in lung endocrine tumours. This region of 11q13 contains several other genes that are also known to be associated with tumorigenesis and may be implicated in the development of tumours that show a high frequency of LOH in this region.

The retinoblastoma (*Rb*) gene has been implicated in the pathogenesis of parathyroid carcinomas (Apel and Asa, 2001). Although animal models suggest that it should be important in pituitary tumorigenesis, there is no evidence for *Rb* loss or alteration in human pituitary adenomas (Asa and Ezzat, 1998). A small number of case reports have emerged describing deletions and possible rearrangements of the *Rb* gene in the very rare insulin-producing carcinomas. Deletions of the putative Wilms tumour and the transformation suppressor gene k-*rev*-1 have also been described in an insulinoma.

The gene conferring predisposition to familial adenomatous polyposis coli (FAP) has been identified (*APC*) and mapped to chromosome 5q21. Somatic mutations in *APC* have also been identified in sporadic pancreatic, colorectal and gastric carcinoma. This gene may play a role in the development of thyroid carcinomas in affected members of families with FAP; however, this remains unproved (Soravia *et al.*, 1999). There is no evidence for a pathogenetic role for APC in sporadic thyroid tumours.

Other genomic mutations that have been described in human endocrine tumorigenesis include chromosome 10 or 17 monosomy, and loss of the adhesion molecule DCC (deleted in colonic carcinoma).

Activating mutations of receptors that regulate hormone synthesis and secretion, long anticipated as the molecular solution to the problem of endocrine tumorigenesis, have been likewise disappointing (Ezzat and Asa, 1998). Only in some cases of hyperfunctioning thyroid adenomas have such activating mutations, in this case of the thyrotropin receptor (Porcellini *et al.*, 1994; van Sande *et al.*, 1995; Krohn *et al.*, 1998), proved to be associated with disease.

The molecular genetics of thyroid carcinoma are a model for understanding the role of genetic mutations in tumorigenesis and the application of that knowledge to diagnosis. The unique chromosomal rearrangements involving the *ret* proto-oncogene (*ret/PTC* gene rearrangements) are found in papillary carcinomas; however, these are early events, found most frequently in occult papillary microcarcinomas that are biologically insignificant lesions. Follicular carcinomas are now thought to involve another novel gene rearrangement involving the thyroid transcription factor Pax-8 and the *PPAR-γ* gene. However, the factors that predict growth and metastasis in these common well-differentiated malignancies are unknown and therefore the rational management of patients remains unscientific. Ras mutations are rare but their impact on biological behaviour is controversial; they may be involved in tumour progression. p53 mutations are late events that have been described only in anaplastic carcinomas.

The data indicate that endocrine tumorigenesis is the result of novel genetic events. The conventional approach of screening tumours for known oncogenes and TSGs has been attempted but with little success. Clearly, these tumours have the potential to clarify new mechanisms of tumour development.

PROGNOSTIC FACTORS

Prognostic factors in neuroendocrine tumours are generally extent of disease and sometimes involve patterns of hormone production. Some genetic factors are also predictive; for example, familial medullary thyroid carcinoma (FMTC), with or without the association of MEN-2A syndrome, has a better survival than that associated with MEN-2B syndrome and has been associated with better survival than sporadic medullary thyroid carcinoma. However, in patients matched for age, extent of tumour and lymph node involvement, survival is similar for those with the hereditary and sporadic medullary thyroid carcinomas. Any differences in survival of hereditary and sporadic cases may be due to earlier diagnosis in high-risk patients that are screened for hereditary medullary thyroid cancers. Although presenting at an earlier age, patients with MEN-2B have more advanced disease and poorer survival than those with MEN-2A. Younger age and female gender are generally reported as favourable prognostic indicators in this disease. The presence of lymph node involvement affects survival adversely, as does extension through the thyroid capsule. The most important predictive factor for survival is biochemical cure, measuring calcitonin after surgery. However, a decrease in the calcitonin level may indicate progression to a poorly differentiated tumour. Carcinoembryonic antigen (CEA) has also been used as a marker for disease progression in medullary thyroid carcinoma; a short CEA doubling time is associated with rapidly progressive disease.

Concerning the prognosis of tumours of steroid hormone-secreting cells, adrenocortical adenomas generally take longer to diagnose than carcinomatous counterparts. These adenomas usually cause Cushing syndrome, but can also result in virilization, Conn syndrome, or no endocrinological symptoms. 'Nonfunctional' tumours probably merely secreted insufficient steroids to cause signs and symptoms. Unfortunately, small tumour size and 'benign' histological features are not sufficient predictors of clinical behaviour. Among malignant tumours, a high proliferative index as identified by MIB-1 or Ki-67 labelling is thought to predict shorter disease-free survival.

The most useful prognostic markers in well-differentiated carcinomas of thyroid follicular epithelium are patient variables, tumour size and extent of disease. Age is the single most important prognostic factor. Patients under the age of 45 years usually have an excellent prognosis; in contrast, those over 45 years of age generally have a poorer outlook. Sex has also been said in the past to be an important determinant of tumour biology but more recent studies have suggested that there is no major difference in the behaviour of these carcinomas in men and women. Tumour size is exceedingly important. Tumours smaller than 1 cm are common and appear to be different biologically than larger tumours; a recent study has shown that occult papillary carcinomas are identified in up to 24% of the population in thyroids that are removed for non-malignant or unrelated disease. In contrast, tumours larger than 1 cm are thought to be of clinical significance and those larger than 3 cm generally have a poorer prognosis than do smaller tumours. The presence of cervical lymph node metastases, whether microscopic or identified clinically, is thought to increase the risk of recurrence of disease but has been shown to have no impact on mortality. Extrathyroidal extension, in contrast, predicts a worse prognosis and the presence of distant metastases is the hallmark of an aggressive tumour that will bear the potential for high mortality. In patients who have metastatic disease, the site of metastases, the size of metastases and the ability to take up radioiodine are important factors. The value of novel molecular markers in determining the prognosis of differentiated thyroid cancer remains to be established.

OVERVIEW OF CLINICAL MANAGEMENT

In most instances, the diagnosis of neuroendocrine tumours is based on the identification of hormone excess or radiographic identification of a mass lesion. Some neuroendocrine tumours can be difficult to localize and visualize. They have in common, however, the expression of somatostatin receptors as a distinguishing feature. While the subtype of the five distinct receptors varies among different endocrine tumours, they all bind somatostatin. This feature has provided a novel tool for the imaging of these lesions and their metastases, using a radiolabelled somatostatin analogue, [^{111}In]octreotide. It allows the diagnosis of neuroendocrine tumours and localization of occult metastases or, in some patients with metastatic disease, an occult primary lesion.

Surgery remains the treatment of choice for tumours of the dispersed endocrine system. In patients with localized disease, it can be curative.

In many cases, advanced neuroendocrine neoplasms follow an indolent course. Hepatic metastases are common, and although they can cause significant pain or, in some patients, incapacitating hormone hypersecretion, hepatic metastases are usually asymptomatic. The appropriate timing and efficacy of interventions, including hepatic artery embolization (HAE) and/or cytoreductive surgery remain controversial. While some studies have indicated that earlier resection of the primary tumour was associated with prolonged survival, those with liver involvement by tumour were least likely to benefit from surgical resection. Five-year survival rates range from 40 to 80%. Both HAE and surgical resection provide excellent palliation of hormonal and pain symptoms. In selected patients, surgical resection of hepatic metastases may prolong survival, but this is rarely curative.

The expression of somatostatin receptors by these lesions provides a therapeutic tool. Somatostatin tends to inhibit hormone synthesis and secretion, and there is evidence that it may also inhibit cell proliferation. Native somatostatin, however, has a short half-life and cannot be used therapeutically. Several years ago, a long-acting analogue, octreotide, became available for clinical use as a therapeutic tool; this agent required daily subcutaneous injection. More recently, a longer acting repeatable (LAR) preparation of the somatostatin analogue has been developed with activity lasting nearly 28 days. Its therapeutic efficacy, tolerability, and safety in patients with pituitary and gastro-enteropancreatic neuroendocrine tumours have been established. In patients with acromegaly due to pituitary growth hormone excess and in some with functional carcinoid tumour, Zollinger–Ellison syndrome and glucagonoma syndrome the analogue normalizes hormone levels and reduces symptoms. Tumour size does not change significantly and may increase in the rare patient on long-term therapy. The side-effect profile includes transient gastro-intestinal upset. Longer term complications include possible worsening of glucose intolerance into frank diabetes mellitus and/or gallstone formation. Another long-acting somatostatin analogue, lanreotide, has also been evaluated, and when compared with the older subcutaenous octreotide preparation, both agents appear to be equally efficacious in terms of symptom control. Thus, it appears that longer acting somatostatin analogues have good therapeutic efficacy, tolerability and safety in the treatment of neuroendocrine tumours. The current analogues, however, lack tumoricidal properties, which limits their overall impact on disease burden. The decision to incorporate this therapy in patients with symptoms related to neuropeptide hyersecretion is usually straightforward. The role of these agents alone or as part of chemotherapeutic agents in patients without neuropeptide hyersecretion symptoms is far less clear.

It has also been suggested that high activities of a radio-labelled somatostatin analogue may have a radiotherapeutic effect. In one recent study, patients with known disseminated neuroendocrine tumours were administered between 1.3 and 4.6 GBq of $[^{111}In]$octreotide for up to five doses over a 1-year period. The treatments were well tolerated. Further work with this and other radioisotopes including yttrium are now being performed to assess efficacy.

Neuroendocrine tumours are generally very resistant to chemotherapy and therefore chemotherapy is rarely recommended for control or palliation. A larger number of chemotherapeutic agents have been used as single agents or in combination. Streptozotocin (STZ), or glycosamine nitrosourea originally derived from streptomyces has been in use for three decades since initially being found to be active in pancreatic endocrine tumours. Current schedules in common use are the combination of STZ with doxorubicin or 5-fluorouracil (5-FU). Response rates vary according to the type of neuroendocrine malignancy; for example, rates as high as 80% have been reported with metastatic gastrinoma.

Second-line regimen incorporating VP-16 and cisplatin have also been evaluated with useful activity and palliation in some patients.

Tumours of steroid hormone-secreting cells are usually treated surgically. Patients with adrenocortical adenoma are generally cured by surgical tumour resection. Occasional patients with carcinoma experience long survival despite incomplete resection of their tumours, but most patients succumb to recurrent disease with metastases noted within the first 2 years following diagnosis. The adrenocorticolytic medication mitotane provides some temporary relief from cortisol excess in some patients.

Tumours of thyroid follicular epithelium are also most amenable to surgical resection but aggressive surgery is not usually indicated. These lesions have a unique affinity for iodine uptake and therefore microscopic residual disease is usually ablated by administration of radioactive iodine. As thyroid tumours lose their differentiation, one of the manifestations is reduction or loss of expression of the sodium iodide symporter that that is responsible for the success of this form of therapy. Therefore, lack of radioiodine uptake can occasionally mean that disseminated disease is of a less differentiated type. In patients with poorly differentiated or anaplastic carcinomas, or those with gross residual disease of differentiated carcinoma that is not amenable to complete surgical excision, there is a role for external beam radiotherapy.

REFERENCES

Apel, R. L. and Asa, S. L. (2001) The parathyroid glands. In: Barnes, L. (ed.), *Surgical Pathology of the Head and Neck.* 1719–1992 (Marcel Dekker, New York).

Asa, S. L. (1998). *Tumors of the Pituitary Gland. Atlas of Tumor Pathology*, Third Series, Fascicle 22 (Rosai, J., ed.) (Armed Forces Institute of Pathology, Washington, DC).

Asa, S. L. and Bedard, Y. C. (2000). Fine-needle aspiration cytology and histopathology. In: Clark, O. M. and Noguchi, S. (eds), *Thyroid Cancer. Diagnosis and Treatment.* 39–104. (Quality Medical Publishing, St. Louis, MO).

Asa, S. L. and Ezzat, S. (1998). The cytogenesis and pathogenesis of pituitary adenomas. *Endocrine Reviews*, **19**, 798–827.

Brierley, J. D. and Asa, S. L. (2001). Thyroid Cancer. In: Gospodarowicz, M. K. (ed.), *Prognostic Factors in Cancer.* 195–208 (Wiley-Liss, New York).

Capella, C., *et al.* (1995). Revised classification of neuroendocrine tumors of the lung, pancreas and gut. *Virchows Archiv, Abteiluns A: Pathologische Anatomie und Histopathologie*, **425**, 547–560.

DeLellis, R. A. and Tischler, A. S. (1998). The dispersed neuroendocrine cell system. In: Koracs, K. and Asa, S. L. (eds), *Functional Endocrine Pathology.* 529–549 (Blackwell, Boston).

Ezzat, S. and Asa, S. L. (1998). Molecular genetics of endocrine neoplasia. In: Koracs, K. and Asa, S. L. (eds.), *Functional Endocrine Pathology.* 967–983 (Blackwell, Boston).

Goretzki, P. E. *et al.* (1992). Mutational activation of RAS and GSP oncogenes in differentiated thyroid cancer and their biological implications. *World Journal of Surgery*, **16**, 576–582.

Greenlee, R. T., *et al.* (2000). Cancer statistics, 2000. *A Cancer Journal for Clinicians*, **50**, 7–33.

Klöppel, G. *et al.* (1998) The endocrine pancreas. In: Koracs, K. and Asa, S. L. (eds), *Functional Endocrine Pathology.* 415–487 (Blackwell, Boston).

Komminoth, P. (1999). Review: multiple endocrine neoplasia type 1, sporadic neuroendocrine tumors, and MENIN. *Diagnostic Molecular Pathology*, **8**, 107–112.

Krohn, D. *et al.* (1998). Clonal origin of toxic thyroid nodules with constitutively activating thyrotropin receptor mutations. *Journal of Endocrinology and Metabolism*, **83**, 180–184.

Kroll, T. G. *et al.* (2000). PAX8-PPARgamma1 fusion oncogene in human thyroid carcinoma. *Science*, **289**, 1357–1360.

Lack, E. E. (1997). *Tumors of the Adrenal Gland and Extraadrenal Paraganglia. Atlas of Tumor Pathology,* Third Series, Fascicle 19 (Rosai, J., ed.) (Armed Forces Institute of Pathology, Washington, DC).

Lack, E. E. (1998). The Adrenal Cortex. In: Koracs, K. and Asa, S. L. (eds), *Functional Endocrine Pathology.* 596–636. (Blackwell, Boston).

LiVolsi, V. A. (1990). *Surgical Pathology of the Thyroid* (W.B. Saunders, Philadelphia).

Lyons, J., *et al.* (1990). Two G protein oncogenes in human endocrine tumors. *Science*, **249**, 635–639.

Moley, J. F. (2000). Medullary thyroid carcinoma. In: Clark, O. H. and Noguchi, S. (eds), *Thyroid Cancer. Diagnosis and Treatment.*279–308 (Quality Medical Publishing, St. Louis, MO).

Mulligan, L. M. and Ponder, B. A. J. (1995). Genetic basis of endocrine disease. Multiple endocrine neoplasia type 2. *Journal of Clinical Endocrinology and Metabolism*, **80**, 1989–1995.

Murray, D. (1998). The thyroid gland. In: Koracs, K. and Asa, S. L. (eds), *Functional Endocrine Pathology.* 295–380 (Blackwell, Boston).

Nikiforova, M. N., *et al.* (2000). Proximity of chromosomal loci that participate in radiation-induced rearrangements in human cells. *Science*, **290**, 138–141.

Porcellini, A., *et al.* (1994). Novel mutations of thyrotropin receptor gene in thyroid hyperfunctioning adenomas. Rapid identification by fine needle aspiration biopsy. *Journal of Endocrinology and Metabolism*, **79**, 657–661.

Rosai, J., *et al.* (1992). *Tumors of the Thyroid Gland. Atlas of Tumor Pathology,* Third Series, Fascicle 5 (Rosai, J. ed.) (Armed Forces Institute of Pathology, Washington, DC).

Sasano, H. (1998) Steroid-producing tissues. In: Kovacs, K. and Asa, S. L. (eds), *Functional Endocrine Pathology.* 707–714. (Blackwell, Boston).

Soravia, C., *et al.* (1999). Familial adenomatous polyposis-associated thyroid cancer. *American Journal of Pathology*, **154**, 127–135.

Spada, A., *et al.* (1992). G protein oncogenes in pituitary tumors. *Trends in Endocrinology and Metabolism*, **3**, 355–360.

Suarez, H. G., *et al.* (1991). Gsp mutations in human thyroid tumors. *Oncogene*, **6**, 677–679.

Tischler, A. S. (1998). The adrenal medulla and extra-adrenal paraganglia. In: Kovas, K. and Asa, S. L. (eds), *Functional Endocrine Pathology.* 550–595. (Blackwell, Boston).

van Sande, J., *et al.* (1995). Genetic basis of endocrine disease. Somatic and germline mutations of the TSH receptor gene in thyroid disease. *Journal of Endocrinology and Metabolism*, **80**, 2577–2585.

Wick, M. R. (2000). Immunohistology of neuroendocrine and neuroectodermal tumors. *Seminars in Diagnostic Pathology*, **17**, 194–203.

FURTHER READING

Asa, S. L. (1998). *Tumors of the Pituitary Gland. Atlas of Tumor Pathology*, Third Series, Fascicle 22 (Rosai, J. ed.) (Armed Forces Institute of Pathology, Washington, DC).

Clark, O. H. and Noguchi, S. (eds) (2000). *Thyroid Cancer. Diagnosis and Treatment* (Quality Medical Publishing, St. Louis, MO).

DeLellis, R. A. (1993). *Tumors of the Parathyroid Gland. Atlas of Tumor Pathology*, Third Series, Fascicle 6 (Rosai, J. ed.) (Armed Forces Institute of Pathology, Washington, DC).

Kovacs, K. and Asa, S. L. (eds) (1998). *Functional Endocrine Pathology* (Blackwell, Boston).

Lack, E. E. (1997). *Tumors of the Adrenal Gland and Extra-adrenal Paraganglia. Atlas of Tumor Pathology,* Third Series, Fascicle 19 (Rosai, J., ed.) (Armed Forces Institute of Pathology, Washington, DC).

LiVolsi, V. A. (1990). *Surgical Pathology of the Thyroid* (W.B. Saunders, Philadelphia).

Rosai, J., *et al.* (1992). *Tumors of the Thyroid Gland. Atlas of Tumor Pathology*, Third Series, Fascicle 5 (Rosai, J., ed.) (Armed Forces Institute of Pathology, Washington, DC).

Chapter 42
Breast

Shahla Masood and Darian Kameh

University of Florida Health Science Center at Jacksonville, FL, USA

CONTENTS

NORMAL DEVELOPMENT AND STRUCTURE

The female breast (**Figure 1**) is a heterogenous structure which overlies the pectoralis major and minor muscles covering the chest wall. The resting mammary gland consists of 5–10 major duct systems which are arranged in a segmental, roughly radial pattern. These duct systems are subdivided into lobules, which are the functional units of the mammary parenchyma. Each ductal system drains through an individual lactiferous sinus. Successive branching leads to terminal ducts distally, which end blindly prior to puberty. With the onset of menarche (first appearance of the menstrual cycle), the terminal ducts proliferate distally, giving rise to lobules consisting of a cluster of epithelium-lined ductules or acini. Each terminal duct and its ductules compose the terminal duct lobular unit (TDLU) (**Figure 2; see colour plate section**) (Lawrence, 1992; Cotran *et al.*, 1999).

The majority of the breast stroma consists of dense fibroconnective tissue admixed with adipose fatty tissue, called interlobular stroma, containing elastic fibres supporting the large ducts. The lobules themselves are enclosed by loose delicate myxomatous stroma that is hormonally responsive and contains scattered lymphocytes (intralobular stroma) (Cotran *et al.*, 1999).

Histologically, the intact ducts are composed of an inner layer of cuboidal to low columnar epithelial cells, surrounded by a discontinuous layer of myoepithelial cells, enclosed by a basement membrane (**Figure 3**). It is the inner layer of epithelial cells within the TDLU that gives rise to the common forms of breast cancer.

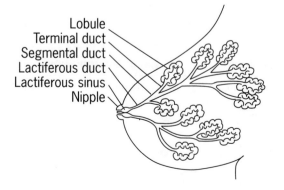

Lobule
Terminal duct
Segmental duct
Lactiferous duct
Lactiferous sinus
Nipple

Figure 1   Normal adult female breast (simplified).

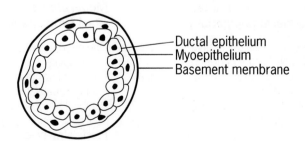

Ductal epithelium
Myoepithelium
Basement membrane

Figure 3   Breast duct histology (cross-section).

The lymphatic drainage of the breast is primarily to the axilla, while a minor portion of it courses to the internal mammary nodes (Lawrence, 1992).

EPIDEMIOLOGY AND RISK FACTORS

The incidence of breast cancer in developed countries is 200–250 per 100 000 women per year. One of nine women in the United States will develop breast cancer in her lifetime; one-third of these women will succumb to the disease, resulting in almost 50 000 deaths yearly (Cotran et al., 1999). The incidence increases with age with an average age at diagnosis of approximately 65 years. Age-adjusted incidence rates are rising, probably due in large part to an increase in mammographic screening and the changing epidemiological profile of women (White et al., 1990). Recognizing risk factors can help identify high-risk patients who need more intense monitoring as well as provide insight into the pathogenesis of the disease (Masood, 1996a). **Table 1** lists the best recognized risk factors. Women in North America and European countries have the highest rates of breast cancer, and those in Asian and African countries have the lowest (Kelsey and Horn-Ross, 1993). Breast cancer only rarely occurs in males.

About 10–15% of cases of breast cancer have a family history of breast or ovarian cancer (Thompson, 1994). With the identification of the breast cancer susceptibility genes BRCA1 and BRCA2 on chromosomes 17 and 13, respectively, a genetic predisposition clearly exists. However, many women with a family history of breast cancer do not carry mutations in one of these genes. The gene products of BRCA1 and BRCA2 are multifunctional proteins involved in maintaining genomic stability and the response to DNA damage, transcriptional regulation and cell proliferation (Unger and Weber, 2000; Welsch et al., 2000). Mutations in these genes are associated with a marked increase in the overall risk of developing breast cancer and a marked decrease in the age of onset. Specific mutations are more common in some ethnic groups (such as the Ashkenazi Jews) (Masood, 1996a; Cotran et al., 1999).

AETIOLOGY

Specific cellular changes occur in the progression to breast cancer. The earliest genetic lesions have been identified in morphologically normal breast epithelium near the site of a carcinoma, and usually large chromosomal deletions (Deng et al., 1996). In addition, one of the earliest detectable changes is the loss of normal regulation of cell number, resulting in epithelial hyperplastic lesions. Next, genetic instability occurs in multifocal small clonal populations of cells that can be recognized histologically as atypical hyperplasia. Complete replacement of the normal ducts by atypical cells characterizes carcinoma in situ; at this point, there are often (but not always) alterations in specific genes, such as the oestrogen receptor gene, TP53, HER-2/neu/erbB-2, and cyclin D (Devilee et al., 1994). Invasion of the surrounding stroma indicates an invasive neoplasm; although this process must be marked by alterations in specific genes leading to dysregulation of proteases, cell adhesion factors and angiogenic factors, the genetic lesions are not well understood. Similarly, the changes seen in breast cancer cells present in metastatic lesions are not well understood, although a recent report suggests that up-regulation of specific chemokines may account for specific organ propensities for harbouring metastases from breast carcinoma (Muller et al., 2001). It is hoped that microarray studies will shed light on these processes (Perou et al., 1999; Sgroi et al., 1999).

SCREENING

Education and diligent breast self-examination improve the possibility of early breast cancer detection. However, regular mammography is the cornerstone of effective screening for breast cancer. Early breast cancers have an excellent prognosis, with increased long-term survival. The American Cancer Society recommends an annual physical examination, beginning at age 40 years, accompanied by screening mammography at 1–2 year intervals until the age of 50, and yearly at age 50 and older (Masood, 1996a). Minimally invasive techniques such as fine-needle

Table 1   Risk factors for developing breast cancer

High risk (>4 times general population)	Moderate risk (2–4 times general population)	Slight risk (1–2 times general population)
Personal history of prior breast cancer	First-degree relative with history of breast cancer	Onset menarche <12 years of age
Family history of bilateral, premenopausal or familial cancer syndrome	Upper social/economic class	Moderate alcohol intake
	Prolonged uninterrupted menses	
	Postmenopausal obesity	
Proliferative breast disease with atypia	Personal history of prior carcinoma of ovary or endometrium	
	Proliferative breast disease with no atypia	

aspiration biopsy (FNAB) (**Figure 4; see colour plate section**) and core-needle biopsy can be used further to classify and assess lesions deemed radiographically 'suspicious' for malignancy. These procedures can be performed with or without radiographic guidance and can provide valuable information regarding which patients require surgical excision, radical treatment or simple follow-up (Masood, 1996b).

DIAGNOSIS

Generally, palpable breast lesions are felt by a patient or discovered by a physician during physical examination. Breast cancer often presents as an irregular, rock-hard mass with ill-defined margins that invade adjacent tissues (**Figure 5; see colour plate section**). The mass usually is not moveable and is inseparable from adjacent tissues. Rarely, patients may show diffuse induration of the breast skin due to the presence of tumour in dermal lymphatics; this is called inflammatory carcinoma. Non-palpable lesions are detected by imaging techniques (mammography with or without ultrasound). Physical exam and radiologic studies can, at best, establish a clinical suspicion of cancer; however, a firm diagnosis of cancer is made only by the pathologist. Pathologic studies include cytologic evaluation of FNAB material or histologic evaluation of tissue obtained by core needle biopsy or surgical excision (Lawrence, 1992; Masood, 1996a,b). (See also chapter *Breast Imaging and Diagnosis*.)

COMMON BENIGN LESIONS

Benign 'masses' or 'mass-like areas' occur far more frequently than cancer, at a rate of almost 10:1. Atypical clinical presentation of benign lesions leads to a clinical suspicion of carcinoma, for which pathological confirmation is warranted (Lawrence, 1992). Several benign lesions can mimic the clinical presentation of cancer, as follows.

Fibroadenoma

This is the most commonly occurring benign tumour of the female breast. These lesions are seen in women who are between the ages of 20 and 35 years, and are composed of hormonally sensitive glandular and stromal tissue. Grossly, these tumours are well circumscribed and have a solid, whorled, greyish white, bulging cut surface, with slit-like spaces. Histologically, these benign growths are composed of fibroblastic stroma resembling intralobular stroma, along with epithelial-lined ductal structures that tend to be cystic, elongated or flattened (**Figure 6; see colour plate section**). These tumours lead to a mild increase in the risk of subsequent breast cancer. Surgical

excision is curative (Rosai, 1989; Lawrence, 1992; Masood, 1996b; Cotran *et al.*, 1999).

Fibrocystic Change

This represents the single most common disorder of the breast and it accounts for more than half of all surgical operations on the female breast. It occurs most frequently between the ages of 25 and 45 years, with a peak incidence just before menopause, and rarely developing after menopause. Hormonal imbalances are considered to be basic to the development of this disorder. Grossly, the involved tissue has a whitish, poorly circumscribed fibrotic appearance, alternating with cystic structures. Histologically, there are alternating areas of fibrosis, cyst formation, apocrine metaplasia, ductal hyperplasia and adenosis (**Figure 7; see colour plate section**). In the absence of significant ductal hyperplasia (also termed proliferative breast disease), fibrocystic changes do not elevate the risk of developing cancer. Once there is histological confirmation of the diagnosis, no further treatment is warranted (Rosai, 1989; Lawrence, 1992; Masood, 1996b; Cotran *et al.*, 1999).

Other Benign Lesions

Between lesions such as fibroadenoma and fibrocystic change on the one hand and cancer on the other, there exists a range of breast lesions that impart an increased risk of subsequent carcinoma. These include proliferative breast disease (e.g. ductal epithelial hyperplasia), sclerosing adenosis and papillomatosis (**Figure 8; see colour plate section**), to name a few. These lesions are beyond the scope of this chapter and the reader is referred to the Further Reading section for further discussion of these entities.

DUCTAL CARCINOMA *IN SITU* (DCIS)

The number of cases of DCIS has increased rapidly over the past 20 years with the advent of mammographic screening. The lesion consists of a malignant population of epithelial cells that are confined by the basement membrane. However, these cells can spread throughout a regional ductal system, producing extensive segmental lesions, or later develop into invasive cancer. DCIS may or may not be grossly apparent (Rosai, 1989). Two general classes of DCIS are recognized, as follows.

Comedo DCIS

This is characterized by distended ducts, solid sheets of high-grade malignant cells and central necrosis (**Figure 9; see colour plate section**). The necrotic material often calcifies and is radiographically detectable. This form of DCIS has a greater malignant potential than other forms.

Non-comedo DCIS

This is the more common form and can have nuclear grades ranging from low to high. The malignant cells have a monomorphic appearance, necrosis and calcifications may be present. Histological variants include solid (**Figure 10; see colour plate section**), cribriform, papillary and micropapillary (Masood, 1996b; Cotran et al., 1999). For further discussion of these variants, see the Further Reading section.

PAGET DISEASE OF THE NIPPLE

This is a variant of carcinoma in situ in which the nipple skin is involved. Clinically, the patient often presents with a scaling or eczematous lesion of the nipple. Histologically, cancer cells are seen in between normal epithelial cells of the epidermis of the skin. Paget disease of the nipple is the result of intraepithelial spread from an underlying intraductal carcinoma in nearly all cases; in about half of cases there is an associated infiltrating carcinoma.

LOBULAR CARCINOMA *IN SITU* (LCIS)

LCIS is also known as lobular neoplasia. It usually is not grossly evident and is often an incidental finding in breast tissue removed for other reasons. Histologically, the lobules are distended and completely filled by relatively uniform, round, small- to medium-sized cells. Marked atypia, pleomorphism and mitotic activity are usually absent. LCIS is often multifocal in nature and is thought of more as a 'marker' of breast cancer rather than a direct precursor. This is due to the fact that women diagnosed with LCIS have a marked increase in the risk of developing invasive lobular or ductal carcinoma in their lifetimes (Rosai, 1989; Masood, 1996b; Cotran et al., 1999).

INVASIVE DUCTAL CARCINOMA, NOT OTHERWISE SPECIFIED (NOS)

This type of carcinoma represents the 'prototype' breast cancer and includes the majority of carcinomas (70–80%) that cannot be classified under any other subtype. Usually presenting as a fixed firm mass with a 'stellate' or 'spiculated' appearance on mammography, it grossly is tan-white with a firm, often gritty consistency and raggedly infiltrating, poorly defined borders (**Figure 11; see colour plate section**).

Histologically, the infiltrating edge of the tumour extends beyond what is visible grossly, warranting ample excision of normal tissue. The tumour itself consists of malignant ductal epithelial cells disposed in cords, solid nests, tubules, anastomosing masses and mixtures of all these patterns (**Figure 12; see colour plate section**).

The cells invade into the surrounding fibrofatty tissue and by elaborating certain chemical signals, stimulate the adjacent fibrous tissue to proliferate (desmoplastic response), giving the tumour its firm consistency. The histological grading of the tumour is based on mitotic count, cytological atypia and degree of tubule formation. Well-differentiated (low histological grade) tumours often display minimal atypia, low mitotic activity and have prominent tubule formation. Poorly differentiated tumours often have marked cytological atypia, prominent mitotic activity and a solid pattern of growth.

Other distinct histological variants of invasive ductal carcinoma include medullary carcinoma, colloid (mucinous) carcinoma, tubular carcinoma (**Figure 13; see colour plate section**) and papillary carcinoma (Rosai, 1989; Cotran et al., 1999). For further discussion of these variants, see the Further Reading section.

INVASIVE LOBULAR CARCINOMA

This type of invasive cancer comprises only 5–10% of primary breast carcinomas. It tends to be multicentric within the same breast, with a diffusely infiltrative pattern and tends to be bilateral far more frequently than other subtypes. Grossly, the tumour can be rubbery and poorly defined, or gritty hard with an infiltrating border, similar to ductal carcinoma. Histologically, the 'classical' appearance is that of small epithelial cells with little pleomorphism, that invade in strands only one cell thick (often referred to as 'Indian filing' (**Figure 14; see colour plate section**)). Signet ring cells (i.e. cells in which intracytoplasmic mucin pushes the nucleus to the periphery, resembling a signet ring) are common (Masood, 1996b; Cotran et al., 1999).

OTHER TUMOURS OF THE BREAST

Cystosarcoma phyllodes is a rare mixed stromal and epithelial neoplasm that may be benign or malignant. The size varies from 1 cm to >10 cm. The epithelial component is similar to that seen in fibroadenoma, whereas the stromal component is more cellular and has greater mitotic activity. The degree of malignancy is estimated by the degree of cellularity, mitotic rate and cytological atypia. Rarely, benign soft tissue tumours and sarcomas may occur as primary tumours in the breast. In addition, malignant lymphomas may present in the breast.

SPECIAL STUDIES/PROGNOSTIC INDICATORS

By far the most important prognostic indicator is the stage of the tumour, particularly the lymph node status. When axillary nodes are uninvolved, 10-year disease-free survival approaches 80%, but falls to as low as 10% if 10 or more nodes are involved. Increased size of the metastatic deposit and invasion of the metastasis through the lymph node capsule convey a worse prognosis. A poor prognosis is also associated with locally advanced disease (i.e. skin and skeletal muscle involvement), increased tumour size, histological evidence of lymphovascular invasion and high histological grade (more poorly differentiated) tumours. Some specific histological subtypes of invasive cancer (colloid, tubular, medullary, lobular and papillary) actually are associated with a better prognosis than the 'not otherwise specified' (NOS) subtype (Masood, 1996a; Cotran et al., 1999).

Special studies can be performed on cytological or solid tissue specimens submitted to the pathology laboratory. The proliferation rate can be assessed by flow cytometry to determine the fraction of cells actively synthesizing DNA and by immunohistochemistry to detect cellular proteins (such as Ki-67) expressed during the cell cycle. A higher proliferative rate is associated with tumours of more aggressive biologic behaviour. DNA content can be determined by flow cytometry analysis or image analysis. Aneuploid tumours have a slightly worse prognosis. The presence of oestrogen and progesterone hormone receptors within tumuor cells is associated with a better prognosis than those tumours that are receptor-negative. This is due to the high regression rate of receptor-positive tumours in response to hormonal manipulation (i.e. tamoxifen, discussed below). Hormone receptor studies can be performed by immunohistochemical methods (**Figure 15; see colour plate section**).

Loss of function of tumour-suppressor genes such as *TP53* (often detected by an increase in immunostaining of inactivated p53 protein) and increased expression of oncogenes such as *Her-2/neu* are commonly seen in association with other poor prognostic factors. Overexpression of *Her-2/neu* has been correlated with a shorter disease-free interval and shorter overall survival in node-positive or node-negative breast cancers. Patients can also be offered Herceptin (see below), based on *Her-2/neu* tissue studies. p53 and Her-2/neu testing can be performed by immunohistochemical methods (**Figure 16; see colour plate section**) or fluorescent *in situ* hybridization (FISH) studies (Rosai, 1989; Cotran *et al.*, 1999; Masood and Bui, 2000).

TREATMENT

Previously, the long-held theory of orderly regional to systemic progression resulted in aggressive local treatment, i.e. radical mastectomy (which included the resection of both pectoralis major and minor muscles). Now, a further understanding of the biology of breast cancer has supported an opposing theory, which states that breast cancer has a nonorderly progression to early systemic spread from inception (Lawrence, 1992). Studies have shown equivalent survival data when modified radical mastectomy (which only removes the pectoralis minor muscle) is compared with lumpectomy (excision of the lesion, with a surrounding rim of normal breast tissue) with or without adjuvant therapy (Masood, 1996a). That being said, surgical therapy still remains the foundation of breast cancer treatment. The extent of the initial surgical procedure is determined by the histological grade of the tumour, clinical stage at presentation and the patient's desire for breast conservation and reconstruction, if appropriate. Axillary nodes are routinely sampled or completely dissected to determine the presence of local–regional metastasis (Lawrence, 1992). Radiation therapy has been employed as a postoperative adjunct (especially in connection with the more limited surgical resections), sometimes as the primary treatment and for the control of locally advanced or recurrent disease (Rosai, 1989). Adjuvant chemotherapy is used in the control of regional (axillary) or systemic metastatic disease. Chemotherapy has also been used in the preoperative treatment of larger, high histological grade breast cancers with or without the presence of axillary metastasis. Tamoxifen, which functionally blocks oestrogen receptors in tumour cells which express them, is used in similar settings to other chemotherapeutic agents (Masood, 1996a; Lawrence, 1992). There also appears to be a role for tamoxifen even in the absence of nodal metastasis. The use of the drug herceptin, which targets cells that overexpress Her-2/neu, has found widespread use in patients with recurrent disease, whose tumours over express the *Her-2/neu* oncogene (Masood and Bui, 2000).

REFERENCES

Cotran, R. S., *et al.* (1999). *Robbins Pathologic Basis of Disease*, 6th edn. 1093–1119. (Lippincott-Raven, Philadelphia).

Deng, G., *et al.* (1996). Loss of heterozygosity in normal tissue adjacent to breast carcinomas. *Science*, **274**, 2057–2059.

Devilee, P., *et al.* (1994). Recent developments in the molecular genetic understanding of breast cancer. *Critical Reviews in Oncology*, **5**, 247–270.

Kelsey, J. L. and Horn-Ross, P. L. (1993). Breast cancer: magnitude of the problem and descriptive epidemiology. *Epidemiological Reviews*, **15**, 7–16.

Lawrence, P. F. (ed.) (1992). *Essentials of General Surgery*, 2nd edn. 272–283 (Williams and Wilkins, Baltimore).

Masood, S. (1996a). Breast health: challenges and promises. *Journal of the Florida Medical Association*, **83**, 459–465.

Masood, S. (1996b). *Cytopathology of the Breast*, 1st edn. 1–5, 78, 167–180, 203–271 (American Society of Clinical Pathologists, Chicago).

Masood, S. and Bui, M. (2000). Assessment of HER-2/neu overexpression in primary breast cancers and their metastatic lesions: an immunohistochemical study. *American Clinical Laboratory Science*, **30**, 259–265.

Muller, A., *et al*. (2001). Involvement of chemokine receptors in breast cancer metastasis. *Nature*, **410**, 50–56.

Perou, C. M., *et al*. (1999). Distinctive gene expression patterns in human mammary epithelial cells and breast cancers. *Proceedings of the National Academy of Sciences of the USA*, **96**, 9212–9217.

Rosai, J. (1989). *Ackerman's Surgical Pathology*, 7th edn. 1193–1267 (C.V. Mosby, St. Louis).

Sgroi, D. C., *et al*. (1999). *In vivo* gene expression profile analysis of human breast cancer progression. *Cancer Research*, **59**, 5656–5661.

Thompson, W. D. (1994). Genetic epidemiology of breast cancer. *Cancer*, **74**, 279–287.

Unger, M. A. and Weber, B. L. (2000). Recent advances in breast cancer biology. *Current Opinions in Oncology*, **16**, 69–74.

Welsch, P. L., *et al*. (2000). Insights into the functions of BRCA1 and BRCA2. *Trends in Genetics*, **16**, 69–74.

White, E., *et al*. (1990). Evaluation of the increase in breast cancer incidence in relation to mammography use. *Journal of the National Cancer Institute*, **82**, 1546–1552.

Fisher, E. R. (1984). The impact of pathology on the biologic, diagnostic, prognostic and therapeutic considerations in breast cancer. *Surgical Clinics of North America*, **64**, 1073–1093.

Hutter, R. V. P. (1984). Pathological parameters useful in predicting prognosis for patients with breast cancer. In: McDivitt, R. W., *et al*. (eds), *The Breast* (Williams and Wilkins, Baltimore).

Osborne, M. P. (1991). Breast development and anatomy. In: Harris, J. R., *et al*. (eds), *Breast Diseases*, 2nd edn. 1–13 (Lippincott, Philadelphia).

Page, D. L. and Anderson, T. J. (1988). *Diagnostic Histopathology of the Breast*, Churchill Livingstone (New York).

Romrell, L. J. and Bland, K. I. (1998). Anatomy of the breast, axilla, chest wall and related metastatic sites. In: Bland, K. I. and Copeland, E. M. (eds), *The Breast*, 2nd edn, Vol. 2 (W.B. Saunders, Philadelphia).

Rosen, P. P. (1979). The pathological classification of human mammary carcinoma: past, present and future. *Annals of Clinical Laboratory Science*, **9**, 144–156.

Rosenbloom, A. L. (1998). Breast physiology: normal and abnormal development and function. In: Bland, K. I. and Copeland, E. M. (eds), *The Breast*, 2nd edn, Vol. 2 (W.B. Saunders, Philadelphia).

Silverberg, S. G. and Masood, S. (1997). The breast. In: Silverberg, S. G., *et al*. (eds), *Principles and Practice of Surgical Pathology and Cytopathology*, 3rd edn, Vol. 2 (Churchill Livingstone, New York).

World Health Organization (1981). *International Histological Classification of Tumors, No. 2, Histologic Typing of Breast Tumors*, 2nd edn (WHO, Geneva).

FURTHER READING

Elston, C. W. and Ellis, I. O. (1998). *The Breast*, 3rd edn, Vol. 13 (Churchill Livingstone, Nottingham).

Chapter 43

Female Reproductive System

Beth Euscher, Carl Morisson and Gerard Nuovo
Ohio State University Medical Center, Columbus, OH, USA

CONTENTS

NORMAL DEVELOPMENT AND STRUCTURE

The female genital tract consists of the ovaries, fallopian tubes, surrounding adnexa, uterus, vagina, and vulva. Despite their proximity and their similarities in many aspects, such as response to oestrogen and progesterone, the female genital tract actually represents the combination of three distinct regions during embryogenesis. These include the ovaries, which begin as midline structures that migrate to the peritoneal cavity, the Mullerian system, which gives rise to the endometrium, myometrium, cervix and outer part of the vagina, and the ectodermal system, from which the vulva and part of the vagina originate. The mesonephric system, which plays a role in filtration of impurities in early foetal development, is also represented in the female genital tract as rests which are often found in the adnexa around the fallopian tube and in the lateral wall of the cervix; these rarely cause clinically relevant pathology.

PATHOLOGY OF THE CERVIX

Tumour Pathology

Squamous cell carcinoma is the most common tumour of the cervix, accounting for nearly 75% of the tumours from this region. This, of course, is consistent with the observation that the strong majority of premalignant lesions of the cervix are derived from squamous cells, termed squamous intraepithelial lesions (SILs). There are several histological subtypes within the category of squamous cell carcinoma of the cervix. The most common type is moderately well differentiated squamous cell carcinoma, where rare cells show the keratinization

diagnostic of this tumour. Less common is poorly differentiated squamous cell carcinoma, where keratin formation is very difficult to find with routine haematoxylin and eosin stain. Interestingly, extremely rare in the cervix is well differentiated squamous cell carcinoma, where keratin pearls and individual cell dyskeratosis are abundant. This is in sharp contrast to the vulva, where well differentiated squamous cell carcinoma is very common. In the vulva, this type is rarely associated with infection by human papillomavirus (HPV) (Nuovo *et al.*, 1991). This may explain why this type is so rare in the cervix for, as will be discussed below, over 98% of cervical cancers contain HPV DNA (Crum and Nuovo, 1991; Nuovo, 1994).

Another rare type of carcinoma found in the cervix is small cell carcinoma (**Figure 1**). This very rare variant has a poor prognosis, and is histologically equivalent to the very common small cell carcinoma of the lung. Such tumours are called neuroendocrine tumours, as they are commonly associated with the production of proteins that are part of the endocrine system, such as synaptophysin or chromogranin. (See also chapter *Endocrine Organs*.)

The other type of carcinoma found in the cervix is adenocarcinoma. About 25% of cancers of the cervix are of this type. Although the premalignant variant (adenocarcinoma *in situ*) is a well recognized entity, it is common to find SIL associated with adenocarcinoma of the cervix. This implies that the two entities share a common origin, which is indeed the case as will be discussed in the section Aetiology. Another important point that highlights the relatedness between adenocarcinoma and squamous cell carcinoma of the cervix is the fact that they both originate in the exact same location – the transformation zone of the cervix (Crum and Nuovo, 1991; Nuovo, 1994). There are several subtypes of adenocarcinoma of the cervix. The most common type is a moderately well differentiated

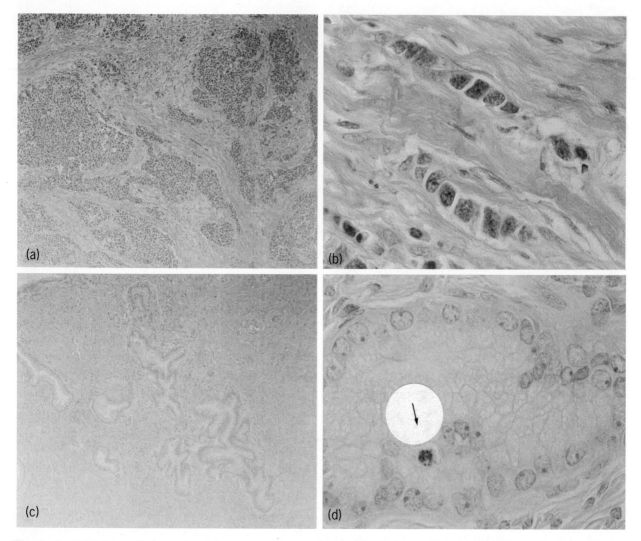

Figure 1 Histology of unusual carcinomas of the cervix. Panel (a) shows the pattern of growth of a small cell carcinoma. At higher magnification (b) note the lack of cytoplasm and nuclear molding. Panel (c) shows the well-formed glands which, however, are invading the underlying stroma. Note the mitotic figure ((d), arrow), characteristic of this tumour, called adenoma malignum. Both lesions contained HPV and showed areas of squamous cell dysplasia.

lesion in which mucous production is easily documented by special stains, such as the mucicarmine or PAS stain (**Figure 2**). At times, such tumours will show cribriform formation, similar to what is evident in endometrial adenocarcinomas. Further, like adenocarcinoma of the endometrium, squamous metaplasia is often identified. As might be expected, it may be difficult – indeed impossible – to differentiate a primary endocervical cancer from an endometrial cancer that has invaded into the endocervix. Similarly, it may be very difficult to differentiate a primary endometrial adenocarcinoma from an endocervical primary that has invaded into the endometrium. These are important clinical distinctions, as they relate to the stage of the disease, which ultimately is the most important indicator of the prognosis of the woman. There is, however, a very simple way to distinguish between endocervical and endometrial adenocarcinoma. This can reliably be done

with HPV testing, as endocervical cancer invariably contains HPV whereas endometrial cancer does not contain the virus (**Figure 2**). There are a few other types of endocervical adenocarcinoma to recognize. One is the clear cell variant, which looks histologically identical with the much more common renal cell carcinoma. Interestingly, this is the only type of adenocarcinoma of the cervix that is not found in the transformation zone or associated with HPV. It has been associated with DES exposure *in utero*; it is worth stressing that this is a very rare variant. Also, one should recognize the papillary variant of endocervical adenocarcinoma. On histological analysis, it looks identical with the common papillary serous carcinoma of the ovary (described later). It carries a poor prognosis. Finally, one should realize that the endocervix is the site of a rare variant of adenocarcinoma, very well differentiated, called adenoma malignum. The term adenoma stresses the

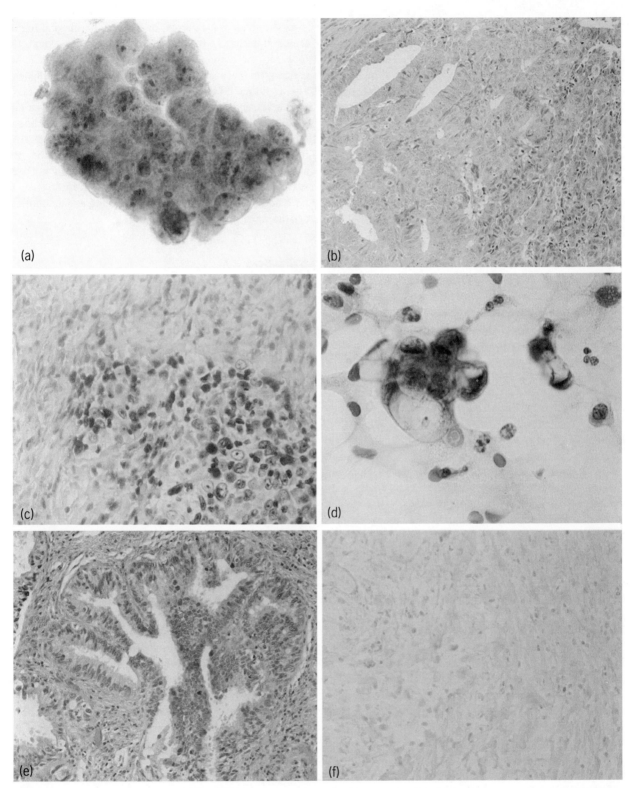

Figure 2 Differentiation between adenocarcinoma of the cervix and endometrium. Panel (a) shows the cytology of an adenocarcinoma from a Pap smear; note the variable cell density. The histology shows similar disorganisation (b); the lesion contains HPV 18 (panel (c), dark-staining cells are positive) confirming that the lesion is from the cervix. Compare this to the cytology ((d), Pap smear of the cervix) and histology (e) of a similar appearing tumour that was in the endometrium. HPV testing showed this to be HPV negative (f), confirming that it was an endometrial cancer.

fact that the glands are remarkably bland in appearance. Two features, mitotic activity (which is a very good marker of adenocarcinoma of the cervix) and branching, or claw-like glands infiltrating the stroma, are what allow one to differentiate adenoma malignum from normal endocervical glands (**Figure 1**).

Epidemiology

The cervix is unique in how well the epidemiology of cancers and precancers at this site are understood. Simply put, the epidemiological data for years have pointed to a sexually transmitted factor. Many years ago, before molecular techniques were so widely available, nearly every agent of sexually transmitted diseases (STDs) was implicated. In the early 1980s herpes simplex virus was a leading candidate (Crum and Nuovo, 1991; Nuovo, 1994). It would take the advent of molecular cloning and hybridization to realize that the actual agent was a virus, HPV. HPV is a small DNA virus – it contains only about 8000 base pairs – which cannot be grown in the laboratory. Its fastidious nature and small size are very well suited to study by molecular hybridization techniques. HPV will be discussed in detail in the Aetiology section. As noted above, it is well documented that the primary risk factor for a woman for developing cervical cancer is her number of sexual partners. This does not relate just to the actual number of her sexual partners, but also the number of female partners for the males with whom she has had sexual relations; this is the so-called 'high-risk male.' Clearly, if a man has had many partners this would put any given woman at higher risk of acquiring any sexual disease as compared with a man who has no other sexual partner. It also follows that groups where monogamy is strictly practiced, as is true of certain religious sects, or women who have not had sexual intercourse, such as nuns, are at very low if not zero risk for developing cervical cancer. Many other factors have been related to increased risk of SIL or cervical cancer, including cigarette smoking, but none has shown the strong correlation related to venereal transmission. It should be added that viruses related to HPV are common in many mammals, including monkeys, where a clear sexual spread has been documented (Crum and Nuovo, 1991; Nuovo, 1994).

Whereas HPV is very tropic for squamous epithelium and it cannot survive long without contact with such tissue, it follows that barrier methods of contraception may be useful in preventing the spread of this disease. Although this has been documented, the protection does not appear to be complete. Given the strong correlation between HPV infection and sexual transmission, an obvious question is whether any sites other than the genital tract show a high relationship between squamous tumours and HPV infection. Indeed, there are two other sites where the association is as strong as in the cervix, namely the periungual region (fingernail bed) of the fingers and, to a lesser extent, the toes and the conjunctiva (Eliezri et al., 1990). Whether cancers at these sites are acquired sexually is unclear, although they do contain the same HPV types as found in the cervix and cases of co-existent cervical dysplasia and periungual dysplasia have been documented. Although tumours of the oral cavity and head and neck region in general have been associated with HPV infection, the association is much less, as is the correlation between sexual risk factors (oral sex) and tumours at these sites. In head and neck tumours, cigarette smoking and alcohol use are the most important risk factors.

Aetiology

As indicated above, the aetiological agent of cervical cancers and SILs is HPV. Of course, not all women exposed to HPV develop cervical SILs or cancer, but infection by the virus is prerequisite for SILs (and ultimately cancer) to develop. A great deal of attention has been given to the function of the different genes (called open reading frames (ORFs)) of HPV, to understand better what is the actual mechanism whereby this virus induces cervical SILs and cancers. HPV, as noted above, is a small virus and has seven early ORFs (E1–E7) and two ORFs that appear later in the infectious cycle (L1 and L2). As might be expected, the late ORFs are involved with production of the protein capsid coat that covers the virus immediately before it leaves the cell. Several of the early ORFs have been shown to be essential for the oncogenic effects of HPV using in vitro models. Specifically, ORFs E6 and E7 are capable of transforming normal squamous cells into cells that look identical with dysplastic squamous cells. However, E6 and E7 are not capable of making the normal squamous cells become invasive, that is, malignant. For this to happen, other molecular events must occur, as will be discussed below under Molecular Genetic Findings. It is now clear how E6 and E7 function. They both are capable of binding to and thus inhibiting the action of two important tumour suppressor gene products, p53 and Rb. Both p53 and Rb function to keep a cell's growth in an organized mode. If these proteins are blocked, the cell starts to proliferate at a much higher rate, which is evident under the microscope as hyperplasia. Further, the cells show enlarged, hyperchromatic nuclei that are the features of dysplasia on microscopic examination (Crum and Nuovo, 1991; Nuovo, 1994).

As noted above, there are about 20 HPV types that may be found in cervical SILs. It can be seen from **Table 1** that these types predominate in low-grade SILs. Fewer HPV types are found in the high-grade lesions and invasive cancers. This has an important implication when analysing for HPV.

Table 1   Correlation of HPV type and histology (%)

	HPV 6/11	HPV 16	HPV 18	HPV 31/35/51	HPV other[a]
Cervix					
Low grade SIL	18	34	3	28	17
High grade SIL	0	77	2	18	3
Cancer:					
Squamous cell	0	55	30	10	5
Adeno	0	31	66	2	1
Vulva/penis					
Low grade	96	1	0	0	3
High grade	0	92	0	7	1

[a] HPV other refers to HPV 33, 40, 41, 42, 43, 44, 45, 51, 52, 56, 68 and 70.

Screening and Prevention

Screening for cervical SIL is an excellent example where routine prevention has greatly reduced the incidence of a cancer. In the United States where cytological screening is common, cervical cancer is a relatively rare disease, with an incidence of about 15 000 cases per year, which is far below the rate for other cancers in women, such as breast cancer and lung cancer. However, in other countries where routine cytological screening is not done, such as in Columbia, cervical cancer is the leading cause of cancer death in women. Of course, the screening test for cervical SILs is the Papanicolaou smear (Pap smear). However, a newer test has been proposed for the purpose of screening for cervical SILs, namely HPV testing (Crum and Nuovo, 1991; Nuovo, 1994).

The function of the Pap smear is to have a cytotechnologist examine under the microscope a large sample of the surface cells of the cervix. It is very important to understand the histology and dynamics of the cervix. The cervix contains two distinct types of epithelium, the squamous cell and the glandular cell. The glandular cell layer is one cell thick, whereas the squamous cell layer is many cells (usually around 10–15 layers) thick. The thicker the epithelium, the whiter it appears on gross or macroscopic examination, owing to the masking of the underlying blood vessels. Hence the outer portion of the cervix (called the ectocervix), lined by squamous cells, is white, whereas the inner portion of the cervix (called the endocervix), lined by glandular cells, is pink. The key concept to remember is the transformation zone, which is the area where the squamous epithelium and glandular epithelium meet. At the transformation zone, the squamous cells replace the glandular cells owing to a process called squamous metaplasia (**Figure 3**). In that HPV usually initially infects the metaplastic squamous cells, it follows that cervical SILs originate in the transformation zone. With this realization, one can see why it is so important that the clinician take a sample from the transformation zone when a Pap smear is done. To document that this has happened, the cytotechnologist looks for either the metaplastic squamous cells or the endocervical glandular cells, because if he/she sees the latter, it is assumed that the clinician must have also sampled the transformation zone. Failure to see either cell type raises the question of whether the transformation zone was not sampled, and if so it is more likely that if a SIL was present, it may have been missed (Crum and Nuovo, 1991; Nuovo, 1994).

Figure 3 depicts the normal epithelial cells that are seen on a Pap smear. These include two types of mature squamous cells, called the superficial and the intermediate cells. These terms refer primarily to cytoplasmic features, such as colour, which are under the influence of oestrogen and progesterone, in the cervix and to a greater degree in the vagina. The parabasal cell is rarely seen in the Pap smear, as in most cases it is not present near the surface and hence not likely to be sampled. The parabasal cell can be seen in atrophy, where the mature squamous cells are much reduced in number owing to the marked reduction in the amount of oestrogen and progesterone. The metaplastic squamous cell was described above. Finally, the glandular cells, often present in well-defined groups that resemble a honeycomb, should be evident on a Pap smear (**Figure 3**). Other cell types are commonly found in the Pap smear. These include several types of inflammatory cells, such as the neutrophil, lymphocyte and macrophage. Large numbers of neutrophils at times indicate acute cervicitis, which can be due to many causes including infection by *Candida* or *Trichomonas*. HPV does not cause an acute infection.

Most laboratories that deal with Pap smears taken as a screening test from primarily premenopausal women report that around 90% of the smears are within normal limits or negative for malignant cells. It is important to stress that findings such as inflammation and the associated squamous cell changes (**Figure 3**), often called reparative or reactive, are considered within normal limits at least in the context of precancers of the cervix (Crum and Nuovo, 1991; Nuovo, 1994). Of course, if there is severe inflammation and an organism such as *Trichomonas* or *Candida* is identified, this needs to be reported, but even such cases may be signed off as 'negative for malignant

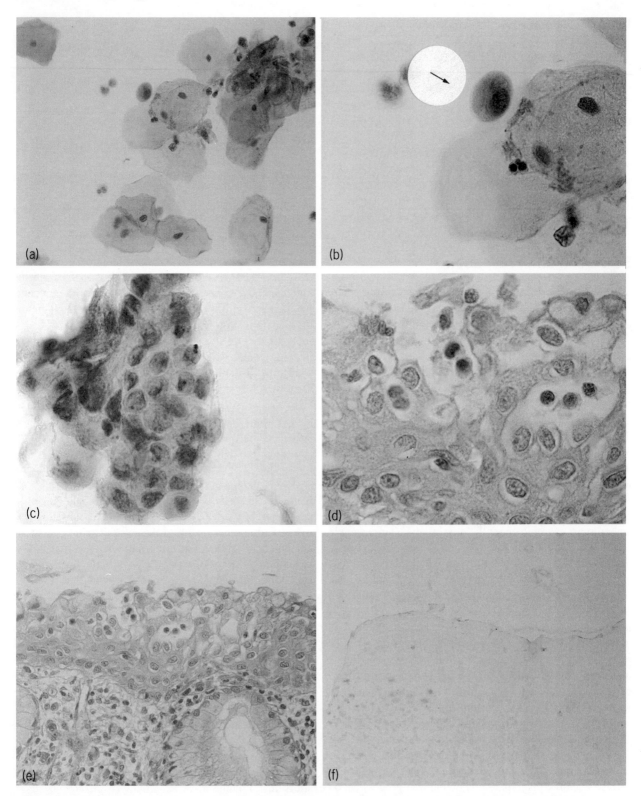

Figure 3   Morphological findings in the normal cervix. Panel (a) shows the squamous cells of a normal Pap smear; note the large amount of cytoplasm and small nucleus. Panel (b) shows the benign metaplastic cell with its small vacuoles (arrow). In panel (c), the honeycombed appearance of benign endocervical cells is apparent. The corresponding histology shows squamous metaplasia ((d) and, at lower magnification, (e)) which, as expected, are negative for HPV using *in situ* hybridization (f). Note that the nuclei are very uniform in squamous metaplasia.

cells,' with a comment that severe inflammation and a specific organism are identified. About 5–8% of Pap smears will be called ASCUS (atypical squamous cells of undetermined significance). This means that the cytological changes suggest but are not diagnostic of SIL. The remainder of Pap smears are diagnosed as SIL, most of these being low-grade SILs.

The diagnosis of low-grade SIL on a Pap smear is made on the basis of two cytological changes: (1) a large, well-defined perinuclear halo surrounded by a thin, clear-cut rim of cytoplasm; (2) enlarged nuclei that show hyperchromaticity (that is, increased darkness on the Pap stain). An example of low-grade SIL is provided in **Figure 4**. Note that the nucleus, although increased in size, is still surrounded by ample cytoplasm.

The diagnosis of high-grade SIL on a Pap smear is made on the basis of two cytological changes: (1) a high nuclear to cytoplasmic ratio (2) a marked increase in the chromaticity of the nucleus. An example of high-grade SIL is provided in **Figure 5**. Note that the nucleus shows an irregular distribution of chromatin and that, overall, there is a substantial increase in chromaticity. It should be added that irregularities in the contour of the nuclear membrane are also considered a diagnostic feature of high-grade SILs, and may also be seen in low-grade lesions. It is considered that the increased pressure that the cells are subjected to in the preparation of the ThinPrep makes such nuclear membrane irregularities common, including in many cases of cells that are clearly not SIL (G. J. Nuovo, unpublished observations). Hence, although abrupt changes or notches in the nuclear membrane are a feature of SIL in the conventional Pap smear, it is considered that they are not a reliable marker of such in the ThinPrep smear.

When the classical changes of low-grade or high-grade SIL are evident on a Pap smear, the diagnosis can be made easily and without equivocation. The difficulty arises when the Pap smear shows features suggestive but not diagnostic of SIL, i.e. ASCUS. There are four conditions which are the cause of most cases of ASCUS: reactive changes due to inflammation in mature squamous cells (mimic of low-grade SIL), reactive changes due to inflammation in immature metaplastic cells (mimic of high-grade SIL), SIL (usually low-grade) and atrophy. Let us examine each of these conditions.

Reactive changes in mature squamous cells are probably the most common cause of ASCUS. Inflammation in the cervix is common and can be due to many agents, such as *Candida* and *Trichomonas*, although in many cases a specific aetiological agent cannot be identified. Whenever there is inflammation, the mature squamous cells will usually demonstrate two cytological changes: a small perinuclear halo which does not show a clear-cut condensed rim of cytoplasm and a slightly enlarged nucleus. However, the enlarged nucleus does not show enough hyperchromaticity to warrant a diagnosis of low-grade SIL. Often, the nucleus will show a nucleolus and/or a

nuclear groove, which are useful clues that one is dealing with reactive changes and not true SIL. The difficulty arises when inflammation occurs in the setting of a SIL. It takes experience to be able to 'factor out' the reactive changes in the cells and decide if there still is adequate atypia to warrant a diagnosis of SIL.

Reactive changes in immature metaplastic cells are also a common cause of ASCUS, especially in the ThinPrep sample. It will be recalled that squamous metaplasia is a ubiquitous process in the cervix. When there is associated inflammation, which is also common, the metaplastic cells will demonstrate an increased nuclear to cytoplasmic ratio. It is important to realize that metaplastic cells commonly show darkened nuclei, which of course is also a feature of high-grade SILs. The most reliable way to differentiate high-grade SIL from reactive immature squamous metaplasia is to realize that the latter will show a strong uniformity in the nuclear chromaticity from one cell to the next (**Figure 3**). It is just as important to realize that there are cases when it can be difficult to decide whether the chromaticity is uniform or variable enough to warrant a diagnosis of high-grade SIL versus reactive squamous metaplasia – in such cases, of course, the diagnosis of ASCUS is completely appropriate.

Atrophy is characterized by an increase in the nuclear to cytoplasmic ratio, but not perinuclear halos. Thus, it can mimic a high-grade SIL. The key is to realize that atrophic cells will not have hyperchromatic nuclei.

A common cause of ASCUS is SIL. In some cases, there simply are not enough dysplastic cells for the cytopathologist to make an unequivocal diagnosis of SIL. This may well be a sampling issue, where either the lesion was too small and not enough cells were present for a definitive diagnosis or the SIL was not adequately scraped during the procurement of the Pap smear. In other cases, the cytological changes are not considered to be clear-cut enough for this diagnosis; this often is the case for low-grade lesions. Indeed, it has been well documented that low-grade SILs due to the so-called benign HPV types 6 and 11 often do not show the classical cytological features of low-grade SIL but rather may be interpreted as normal cells, or more commonly, ASCUS (Nuovo, 1994). How does one differentiate true SILs, either low or high-grade, from their mimics? Although some groups have tried to make this distinction on cytological criteria, or using immunohistochemistry for nonspecific markers of increased cell proliferation, in the authors' opinion these variables are not sensitive enough. There is a very sensitive and specific way to make the distinction of ASCUS – benign versus true SIL – namely by HPV testing.

HPV testing is often done with a method called the hybrid capture technique. This is a very sensitive test that is similar to the older dot blot hybridization assays. In these tests, the cells are destroyed and their DNA is retrieved. A sample of the DNA is then hybridized with HPV DNA or RNA probes, and the complex is detected in a variety of

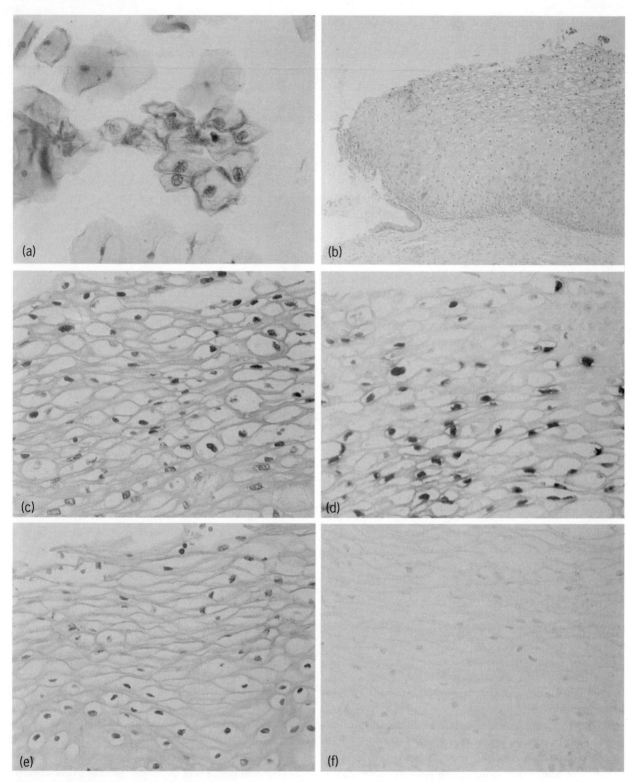

Figure 4 Morphological findings in low-grade SIL. Panel (a) shows the classical large, well-defined perinuclear halos and enlarged nuclei of a low grade SIL. Panels (b) and (c) (higher magnification) show the variable cell density, varying sized and shaped halos and nuclear variability towards the surface that are characteristic of the disease. The lesion contains a large amount of HPV 51 ((d), dark-staining cells mark HPV). Note the well-ordered appearance of the adjacent epithelium (e) that is HPV negative by *in situ* hybridization (f).

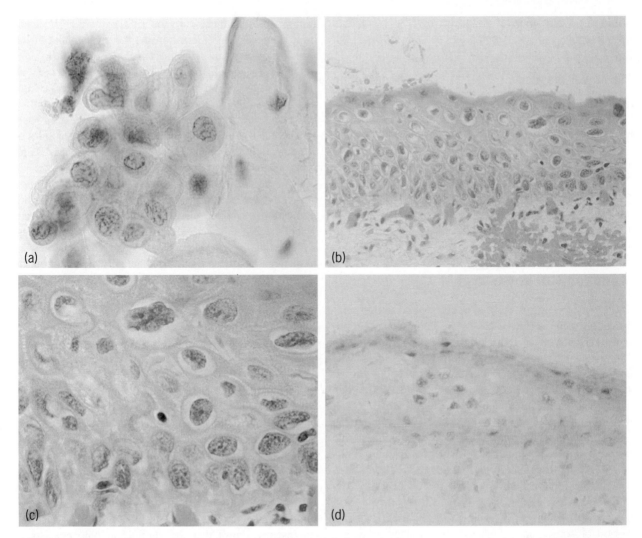

Figure 5   Morphological findings in high-grade SIL. Panel (a) shows the Pap smear; note the hyperchromaticity of the cells and the sharp, abrupt indentations in the nuclear membrane. The biopsy shows a relatively thin epithelium (b) that contains highly atypical cells showing variable cell density and concomitant nuclear atypia (c). HPV 16 is present (d), but in smaller numbers compared with the low-grade SIL (**Figure 4**).

ways (formerly using radioactivity, now more commonly using enzymes complexed to the HPV probes that either cause a colour or light emission to mark the presence of HPV in the sample) (Nuovo, 1997). If enough HPV probes are included to detect most of the 20 HPV types that can be found in the cervix (see **Table 1**), then this system will detect HPV in over 90% of cases of SIL, even if they are called ASCUS. The problem with this test is that they also detect HPV in the absence of ANY cytological changes. That is, about 15–20% of women will have HPV detected with this test, even if there Pap smears are completely normal. Thus, such tests have relatively low specificity. In that it is not clear what the significance is of detecting HPV in the setting of a normal cervix (i.e. a cervix without SIL), and most clinicians do not recommend treatment when HPV is found in this setting, it would be useful to have a test with high sensitivity, but better specificity so as not to detect HPV when no SIL is present.

HPV detection by *in situ* hybridization offers certain advantages over the more sensitive techniques of polymerase chain reaction (PCR) or dot blot hybridization/hybrid capture. First, the HPV is directly detected within intact cells, and thus one can correlate the cytological findings with the viral results. Second, with a probe cocktail that can detect most HPV types, over 90% of low-grade SILs will be positive. Finally, it is very rare (less than 1%) to detect HPV by *in situ* hybridization in a normal-appearing cell from the cervix (Crum and Nuovo, 1991; Nuovo, 1994). We undertook a study that tested all cases of ASCUS for HPV by *in situ* hybridization where there was a biopsy within 6 months of the Pap smear. The data are presented in **Table 2**. Note that the detection of HPV by *in situ* hybridization was an excellent way to differentiate cases of ASCUS associated with a biopsy where only benign reactive changes were seen (HPV negative) from those where an actual SIL was evident on biopsy (HPV positive).

Table 2 Correlation of detection of HPV by *in situ* hybridization with the cytology and, for cases of ASCUS, clinical outcome

Pap smear diagnosis	HPV detection
Normal	1/25 (4%)
SIL	22/25 (88%)
ASCUS (Total)	20/40 (50%)
ASCUS with biopsy proven SIL within 6 months	17/21 (81%)
ASCUS with biopsy negative for SIL within 6 months	3/19 (16%)

Gross/Histopathology/Immunohistochemistry/EM

The gross findings of the cervix are viewed under magnification using a device called the colposcope. Colposcopy typically involves looking at the cervix from 4× to 25× after applying a weak solution of acetic acid. The acetic acid solution will remove the mucous and highlight any areas where there is increased cellular density which will appear dark white (hence acetowhite lesions). Recall that the outer part of the cervix nearest the vagina (the portio) is white and the endocervix pink because the former is covered by a thick multilayer of squamous cells which masks the underlying blood vessels, which is responsible for the pink colour of the endocervix. It is important to realize that any process which causes a focal increased density of cells in the cervix, be it SIL, inflammation or squamous metaplasia, will produce an acetowhite patch. Hence the presence of such is simply an indicator for the colposcopist as to where to biopsy, and is not diagnostic of a SIL. To diagnose a SIL, a biopsy must be done.

The histological findings of low- and high-grade SIL are shown in **Figures 4** and **5**. Note that in either case, one uses the presence of a disorganized growth pattern (i.e. variable cell density, where some of the cells are closely packed and in other areas some of the cells are widely spread apart) as the most useful feature to diagnose a SIL on biopsy. It is important to stress that this is a low-power (4× or 10×) pattern to view under the microscope. Newcomers to the field often make the mistake of focusing their attention on the cytological details at high magnification. Although useful to see hyperchromatocity, one can usually make the diagnosis on histological grounds at low magnification, using the organisation of the cells as the key variable.

The immunohistochemical analysis of SILs is for the most part non-specific. That is, one can detect in greater number certain proteins that are indicative of the increased cellular proliferation evident in SILs, such as Ki-67. As indicated above, there is one highly sensitive and specific immunohistochemical stain for SILs, namely HPV detection. However, HPV detection via the protein coat of the virus is not very sensitive, as in many cases the virus does not produce enough of its capsid for detection by this method, especially in high-grade SILs and cancers (Crum and Nuovo, 1991; Nuovo, 1994). HPV DNA detection by *in situ* hybridization on biopsies, as on Pap smears, is very sensitive and specific. **Figures 4** and **5** show examples of the detection of HPV by *in situ* hybridization in SILs and cervical cancer. Two important points need to be stressed. First, there are cases where the histological changes are suggestive but not diagnostic of low-grade SIL. These are often biopsies where there is a lot of inflammation and where the Pap smear is called ASCUS. In these instances, HPV testing by *in situ* hybridization is a very reliable way to differentiate those tissues that actually are SIL from its mimics. The importance of this cannot be overstated, given that an over-diagnosis of SIL can cause serious emotional distress for the patient. In the authors' opinion, such equivocal cases should be signed off with the HPV *in situ* test; positive is low-grade SIL and negative is nonspecific reactive changes, negative for SIL (Crum and Nuovo, 1991; Nuovo, 1994). Second, the number of virus particles in high-grade SILs and, especially, invasive cancers is much reduced relative to low-grade SILs. To detect the virus reliably in invasive cervical cancer, one must use either PCR or, if one wishes to localize the virus to a specific cell type, PCR *in situ* hybridization.

Electron microscopy findings in SILs are often nonspecific; actual viral protein is detected occasionally in low-grade SILs as it is in this condition where numerous viral particles may be made. In low-grade SILs, electron microscopy shows that the perinuclear halo consists of a clear zone where the cytoplasm and cell organelles have been pushed to the outer aspect of the cell. Electron microscopy is not a useful method for detecting HPV infection of the cervix.

Molecular Genetic Findings

The molecular genetic findings of SILs centre around two important onco-proteins made by the virus, called E6 and E7. These proteins are capable of inhibiting two important proteins, specifically p53 and Rb, respectively. The E6 and E7 proteins from the oncogenic HPV types, such as HPV 16 and 18, are much more avid in their inhibition of p53 and Rb than the benign HPV types, such as HPV 6 and 11. However, it is now clear that other suppressor gene products, that are not apparently inhibited at all by HPV, are more commonly inhibited in the evolution of cervical cancer. Specifically, p16 is inactivated in nearly all cells in high-grade SILs and cancers, whereas such lesions contain many cells where p53 and Rb are still active, as the virus did not produce either E6 or E7 in those specific cells (Nuovo *et al.*, 1999). Finally, it is now clear that certain host RNAs are selectively increased or decreased in production as lesions progress from SIL to cancer, and again this appears to be independent of HPV interactions. Matrix metalloproteases (MMPs) are enzymes that help cells digest collagen, as is needed in healing of tissue damage. Cervical cancer cells make more MMPs and less of their inhibitors (TIMPS) as they progress from microinvasive cervical cancer (with its good prognosis) to invasive and metastatic cervical cancer (Crum and Nuovo, 1991; Nuovo, 1994).

Prognostic Factors

The primary prognostic marker of cervical cancer is its stage, which is how far it has infiltrated local tissues. It is important to stress that neither HPV type nor histological/cytological findings can accurately predict which SILs will progress and which will regress. The only exception to this statement is the observation that low-grade SILs that contain HPV 6 or 11 usually, if not always, regress.

Overview of Present Clinical Management

About 10 years ago, the treatment for cervical SILs was a simple office procedure called cryotherapy. The key clinical factor was whether the entire lesion could be visualized at colposcopy. If it could not, then the transformation zone of the cervix had to be removed surgically (called cone knife cone biopsy) to document that the lesion was not invasive in the canal and to remove it completely. However, if, as in most cases, the SIL could be seen in its entirety with the colposcope, then a simple 5-min office procedure could eradicate the virus and the lesion in about 90% of women. Over the last 10 years, this has shifted from cryotherapy to using laser ablation, which is equally effective but more expensive. Over the last several years, many gynaecologists have switched to a modified cone biopsy (usually smaller) using a metal loop and electrocautery procedure (LEEP). This procedure usually removes the entire lesion, but may have to be done in an operating room under general anaesthesia. The recurrence rates after LEEP are similar to those seen after cryo- or laser therapy (Crum and Nuovo, 1991; Nuovo, 1994).

The management of cervical cancer depends on stage. For microinvasive cancer, a cone biopsy or LEEP is curative. For more deeply invasive cancers, either surgery plus chemotherapy or, at times, radiotherapy are indicated. Death is usually due to renal failure secondary to obstruction of the ureters by the tumour. Studies using vaccines against HPV to treat cervical cancer are too preliminary but do not appear to be very effective, perhaps reflecting the decreased role of HPV at this advanced stage.

PATHOLOGY OF THE ENDOMETRIUM

This part of the chapter will focus on tumours of the endometrium and myometrium. In order to understand endometrial pathology, it is important to appreciate the effects of oestrogen and progesterone on the normal endometrium. It is the balance of these hormones that allows for normal function of the endometrium such as preparation for embryo implantation and normal menstrual cycles. Oestrogen stimulates proliferation (and thus mitotic activity) in the glands and stroma. Progesterone inhibits mitotic activity, and rather stimulates secretions in the glands and changes in the stroma called predecidualization, where the cells acquire more cytoplasm. The key point to remember is that unopposed oestrogen will induce continued mitotic activity and gland growth, which is a central point in the development of endometrial tumours (Deligdisch, 2000).

Tumour Pathology

A variety of tumours and tumour-like conditions can occur in the uterus. **Table 3** gives a list of the more commonly encountered tumours in the uterus.

Endometrial polyps are benign, localized lesions which protrude into the endometrial cavity (**Figures 6 and 7**) and represent focal hyperplasia of the endometrium. Variable amounts of endometrial glands, fibrous stroma and blood vessels will be present. If a significant amount of smooth muscle is present, the polyp is referred to as an adenomyomatous polyp. Polyps are common, occurring most frequently in women 40–50 years old; the presenting symptom is often abnormal uterine bleeding. Tamoxifen

Table 3   Commonly encountered uterine pathology

Benign endometrial lesions
  Endometrial polyp
  Tamoxifen-associated polyp
  Adenomyomatous polyp
  Decidual polyp
  Simple hyperplasia

Premalignant lesion
  Complex endometrial hyperplasia
  Malignant endometrial lesions
  Type I (oestrogen-associated)
    Endometrioid adenocarcinoma
  Type II (oestrogen-independent)
    Papillary serous carcinoma
    Clear-cell carcinoma

Benign myometrial tumour
  Leiomyoma

Uterine sarcomas
  Mixed mullerian tumour
  Leiomyosarcoma
  Endometrial stromal sarcoma

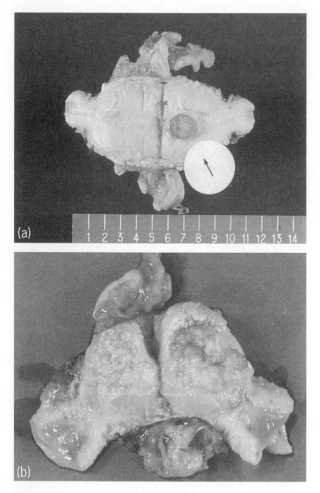

Figure 6 Macroscopic appearance of uterine polyps. Panel (a) shows the macroscopic appearance of a benign polyp (arrow). Panel (b) shows a polypoid endometrial adenocarcinoma that protrudes into the endometrial cavity. Note that the carcinoma is larger, has a less uniform appearance, and has foci of haemorrhage and necrosis.

(an antioestrogen used to treat breast cancer) is clearly linked to the development of endometrial polyps (Nuovo, 1994). Relative progesterone excess can cause a stromal proliferation evident clinically as a decidual polyp (**Figure 7**, which also shows the different histologic features seen in endometrial polyps).

While polyps represent a localized overgrowth of endometrium and stroma, certain precancerous lesions affect the endometrial cavity, diffusely leading to a thickened endometrium, which can simulate a tumour. Endometrial hyperplasia, a condition in which the proportion of endometrial glands is increased relative to endometrial stroma, is a well-defined step in the development of the most common types of endometrial cancer. Endometrial hyperplasia develops under conditions of oestrogen excess. The single most important factor in determining the likelihood of progression of hyperplasia to

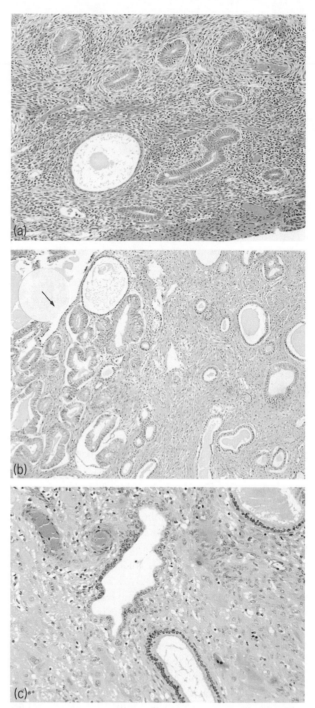

Figure 7 Microscopic appearance of uterine polyps. Note the fibrotic stroma, endometrial glands, which are relatively increased compared to the stroma, and the thick-walled blood vessels characteristic of a benign endometrial polyp (a). In panel (b) (an endometrial polyp from a woman taking tamoxifen for breast cancer), note that the glands are dilated and there is a small focus of endometrioid adenocarcinoma (arrow). This is a common finding in endometrial polyps associated with tamoxifen. Panel (c) shows a so-called decidual polyp, due to the effects of progesterone. Note how the stromal cells are large, plump with ample eosinophilic cytoplasm.

carcinoma is the presence of atypia, both cytological and architectural. Whereas hyperplasia-containing glands with simple architecture with normal gland cytology (simple hyperplasia) has been associated with a 1% cancer progression risk, hyperplastic glands with complex architecture and cytological atypia (complex atypical hyperplasia) has a 29% cancer progression risk (Burke *et al.*, 1996). **Figure 8** shows the histological spectrum of endometrial hyperplasia.

Tumours of the endometrium account for 95% of uterine neoplasms (Burke *et al.*, 1996). The endometrioid subtype of endometrial adenocarcinoma accounts for nearly 90% of endometrial carcinomas (Burke *et al.*, 1996). Endometrioid adenocarcinoma most commonly

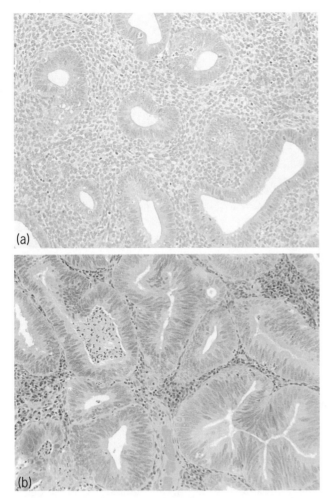

(a)

(b)

Figure 8 Histological appearance of endometrial hyperplasia. In simple hyperplasia, the endometrial gland to stroma ratio is increased. Glands have varying size, but maintain simple architecture and have no cytological atypia (a). Complex atypical hyperplasia has marked glandular crowding and, compared with (a), a markedly increased gland to stroma ratio. The important clues to the correct diagnosis include architectural atypia (glands within glands) and the associated nuclear atypia (b).

appears as a large polypoid lesion protruding into the endometrial cavity and may be detectable as an enlarged uterus on bimanual examination. There may be associated haemorrhage and necrosis (**Figure 6**). Histologically, well-differentiated tumours resemble normal endometrium but contain very complex glandular architecture, lack intervening endometrial stroma, and have cytological atypia. Areas of confluent, malignant cells may be seen as tumours become less well differentiated, and it is the percentage of these areas which are evaluated when assigning grade. Tumours with > 50% solid growth are considered poorly differentiated, or high grade. It is not uncommon for endometrioid adenocarcinomas to show areas of squamous or, less commonly, mucinous differentiation. It is important to realize that this does not adversely affect prognosis. Also, areas of squamous differentiation are not included when considering the percentage of solid growth within a tumour (Burke *et al.*, 1996). **Figure 9** shows the histological features of endometrioid adenocarcinoma and some of its variants/mimics.

Less common endometrial carcinoma histological subtypes include papillary serous carcinoma (3–10%) and clear cell carcinoma (0.8–5%). These patterns are histologically identical with their counterparts in the ovary and vagina/kidney, respectively. It is important to recognize these patterns as distinct entities because they tend to present at a more advanced stage and are associated with a more aggressive clinical course than endometrioid adenocarcinoma (Cirisano *et al.*, 1999). Because these histological patterns have not been associated with a clear premalignant condition or excess oestrogen, have clearly more aggressive behaviour, and have also been shown to have distinctly different molecular alterations compared with endometrioid carcinomas (see below), it is hypothesized that these tumour types have divergent patterns of development. Consequently, endometrial tumours are divided into Type I carcinomas encompassing endometrioid/ oestrogen-dependent cancer and Type II carcinomas encompassing those histological subtypes not associated with oestrogen (Cirisano *et al.*, 1999). **Figure 9** shows the histological features of Type II endometrial carcinomas.

Leiomyomas are the prototypical benign tumour of the uterine myometrium and are benign clonal neoplasms of smooth muscle. These tumours grossly appear as well-circumscribed, white, whorled nodules usually without haemorrhage or necrosis (**Figure 10**). Histologically, these tumours typically have uniform, bland spindle cells with few mitoses. This is in direct contrast to uterine sarcomas, which are usually large tumours with haemorrhage and necrosis displaying histological features of marked cellular pleomorphism and abundant mitoses. Uterine sarcomas represent only 5% of uterine malignancies. The malignant counterpart to leiomyoma is the leiomyosarcoma, which represent one third of uterine

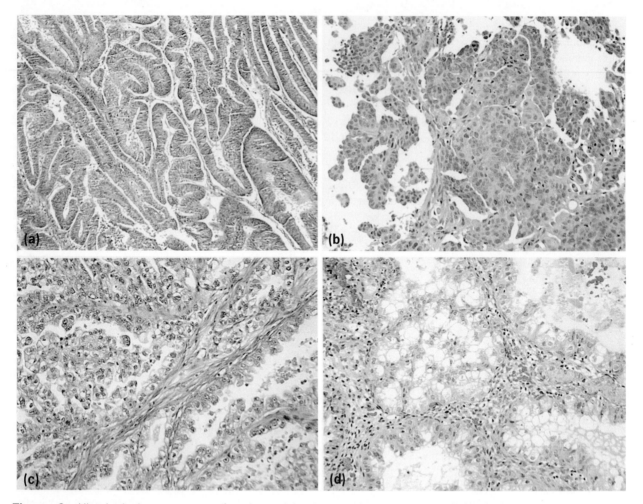

Figure 9 Histological appearance of endometrial adenocarcinoma. In well-differentiated endometrioid adeno-carcinoma (grade FIGO I), the tumour is comprised of well-formed glands without solid growth (a). Panel (b) shows a rare and aggressive variant of endometrial carcinoma, papillary serous carcinoma; note the multiple small detached groups of cells characteristic of this entity. A clear-cell carcinoma has in some areas clearing of the cytoplasm with marked cellular atypia; note the 'hobnail' appearance of the nuclei (c). A mimic of clear-cell carcinoma is the Arias Stella reaction (d), characteristic of pregnancy. These cells lack the cytological atypia of clear-cell carcinoma and have larger vacuoles reflecting active secretion.

sarcomas (Levenback, 1996). Other types of uterine sarcoma include the mixed mullerian tumour (most common uterine sarcoma) and endometrial stromal sarcoma. The malignant mixed mullerian tumour (MMMT) is characterized by the presence of a sarcomatous element intimately admixed with a malignant glandular component. This sarcomatous component may be composed of elements normally found in the uterus such as smooth muscle or endometrial stroma (homologous elements), or it may contain elements not present in the uterus such as cartilage and bone (heterologous elements). **Figure 10** shows a comparison of benign and malignant myometrial tumours. Endometrial stromal sarcomas usually show a more bland appearance than leiomyosarcoma or MMMT; they are characterized by increased mitotic activity and invasion of the uterine wall.

Epidemiology and Aetiology

Because endometrial carcinoma, particularly the endometrioid subtype, is by far the most common malignancy of the uterus, the discussion on epidemiology and aetiology will pertain most directly to these tumours. Endometrial cancer is the most common gynaecological malignancy and represents the fourth most common malignancy overall in American women while being the eighth most common cause of cancer death (Burke *et al.*, 1996). The incidence of endometrial cancer peaks at 70–74 years of age, and the lifetime risk of developing endometrial cancer is estimated to be 2%. Into the mid-1980s, the incidence of endometrial carcinoma increased. This has been attributed to increased use of oestrogen replacement therapy; increasing age of the population may also be

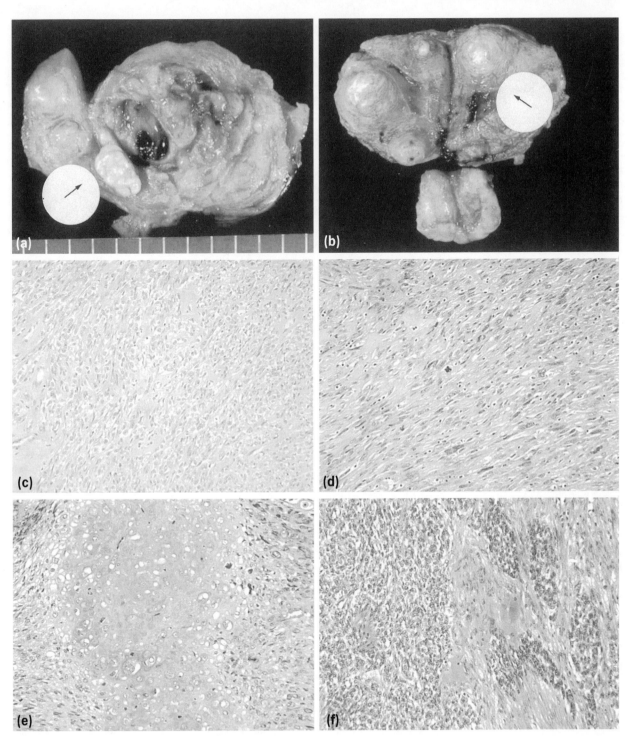

Figure 10   Stromal tumours of the endometrium. Panel (a) shows a benign leiomyoma with a smooth, well-defined tumour border. The cut surface is homogeneously white with a whorled texture (arrow). Panel (b) shows a leiomyosarcoma. In contrast, this tumour appears soft and friable with areas of haemorrhage and lacks a well-defined tumour border (arrow). The corresponding histology of the leiomyoma with bland spindled cells and no mitoses (c) is in contrast to the increased cellularity, marked cellular atypia, and the presence of mitoses of a leiomyosarcoma (d). A malignant mixed mullerian tumour with heterologous elements (cartilage) surrounded by malignant homologous stroma is shown in panel (e). Panel (f) shows an endometrial stromal sarcoma; such tumours usually show less cytological atypia than the other nonepithelial tumours of the endometrium.

related. More recently, a decline in incidence of endometrial carcinoma has been noted, which may be related to improved formulations in oral contraceptives with lower oestrogen content and to the addition of progesterone to menopausal hormonal replacement regimens (Burke *et al.*, 1996).

As previously discussed, a relationship between unopposed oestrogen and the development of endometrioid adenocarcinoma is well established. This was first suggested by the increased incidence of endometrial carcinoma with the advent of single-agent hormone replacement therapy with oestrogen. Other conditions that could expose the endometrium to unopposed oestrogen have been associated with an increased risk of developing endometrial cancer. Nulliparity is associated with the development of carcinoma, as are early menarche and late menopause. These three conditions allow for increased time of exposure of the endometrium to oestrogen. It is important to consider that nulliparity may be related to infertility due to anovulation. It is only after ovulation that progesterone impacts the endometrium. Therefore, anovulatory women have chronic overexposure to excess oestrogen. Obesity is a commonly cited risk factor and may be explained by an increased availability of unopposed oestrogen due to increased production of oestrone from androstenedione. Medical conditions such as diabetes and hypertension are also associated with increased cancer risk. It is not entirely clear whether they represent independent risk factors or whether their association with underlying morbid conditions such as obesity explains the association. A less common association with the development of endometrial cancer, secondary to the rarity of the tumour, is an oestrogen-secreting tumour such as a granulosa cell tumour of the ovary (Burke *et al.*, 1996). Finally, mention should be made of the association of tamoxifen with the development of endometrial carcinoma. Tamoxifen has an antioestrogenic effect in breast tissue and is therefore both a successful adjuvant therapy and a potential chemopreventive agent for breast cancer. In the uterus, however, tamoxifen is a partial oestrogen agonist leading to polyp formation, endometrial hyperplasia and carcinoma in some women (Nuovo, 1994).

Few risk modifiers have been described. Oral contraceptives with relative increased proportion of progestational agents may confer a decreased risk. Smoking has also been shown to decrease the risk of developing endometrial carcinoma and may be related to differences in oestrogen metabolism and earlier menopause (Burke *et al.*, 1996). It should be noted that the moderate decrease in endometrial cancer associated with smoking does not outweigh the risk of lung cancer, which is now the leading cause of cancer death in women in the United States.

The above discussion focused on endometrial cancers with Type I pathology. Cancers with Type II pathology do not have a relationship with unopposed oestrogen, and risk and lifestyle factors for these tumours have not been entirely elucidated. Precursor lesions to these cancer subtypes are currently being established, and certain oncogene mutations have been more strongly associated with the development of Type II than with Type I carcinomas. Family history with documented inherited predispositions to oncogene mutation is emerging as a risk factor for these tumour types.

Screening and Prevention

Although endometrial carcinoma is the most common gynaecological malignancy, no well-developed screening programme exists, as screening has not proven beneficial in the early detection of carcinoma. The majority of women present with postmenopausal bleeding or abnormal uterine bleeding if premenopausal and is subsequently discovered to have uterine carcinoma at an early stage (Burke *et al.*, 1996).

Some have attempted to detect preclinical disease in the asymptomatic patient and have suggested various screening options including the Pap smear, transvaginal ultrasound (TVUS) and endometrial biopsy (EMB). The sensitivity and specificity for the detection of endometrial carcinoma by Pap smear is low. In symptomatic patients, an abnormal Pap smear predicted correctly the presence of carcinoma in only 28% of patients (Nuovo, 1994). TVUS in the asymptomatic patient has no well established cutoffs for which a screen would be considered positive, although endometrial thickness < 4 mm usually results in tissue insufficient for diagnosis on subsequent biopsy and is less likely to be associated with significant uterine pathology. Important, too, is the cost of the equipment and time involved (Burke *et al.*, 1996). Endometrial biopsy in the asymptomatic patient may be problematic as many elderly patients have cervical stenosis and an office pipelle biopsy may be technically impossible (Burke *et al.*, 1996). It has been suggested that endometrial biopsy in patients without postmenopausal bleeding be limited to patients on postmenopausal hormone replacement therapy or in those patients with endometrial cells or ASCUS on Pap smear or who are taking tamoxifen. Some advocate the use of tumour markers to detect preclinical disease. The most commonly used marker in gynaecological malignancies is CA-125. Unfortunately, CA-125 may be elevated in inflammatory states and also in benign gynaecological conditions such as endometriosis. It has been reported as a useful marker to detect early disease recurrence in patients who have elevated CA-125 prior to definitive treatment. This is particularly true of papillary serous carcinoma (Kurman *et al.*, 1995).

In patients who have symptoms, i.e. abnormal bleeding, TVUS can be a useful tool. An endometrial stripe thickness of > 10 mm predicts the presence of significant uterine pathology in 10–20% of patients. When technically possible, EMB is most frequently performed to evaluate abnormal bleeding. It has the advantage of being an office procedure, and although only 5% of the endometrium is sampled, EMB has a 97% sensitivity and an 83% specificity (Chen *et al.*, 1999). The gold standard for the evaluation of symptomatic women remains hysteroscopy with D&C. However, this requires general anaesthesia. The advantage is that 60% of the endometrium is sampled and there is direct visualization of any polypoid lesions in the endometrial cavity (Chen *et al.*, 1999).

Little is written about prevention. Maintenance of ideal body weight and addition of progestational agents in hormone replacement regimens appear to be practical methods of prevention based on currently understood risk factors.

Gross/Histology/Preinvasive/ Immunohistochemistry

The gross and histological features of uterine tumour pathology and preinvasive lesions have been discussed in a previous section. This part of the chapter will focus on ancillary techniques of tumour diagnosis and histological mimics of uterine tumours.

Immunohistochemistry has become a useful tool in detecting markers of cellular differentiation in order to assign a histological subtype when the answer is not obvious by usual microscopic examination. Expression of immunohistochemical markers may also be used as prognostic indicators for tumour behaviour. Because the endometrium is a hormonally modulated by oestrogen and progesterone, it is logical that receptors for these hormones would be present. Oestrogen and progesterone receptors are abundant in benign endometrium but show a decreased presence in endometrioid malignancies by immunohistochemical analysis. This makes sense because malignancies are not under the same regulatory influences as benign tissues. Well-differentiated cancers are more likely to be receptor positive; they more closely resemble their tissue of origin. It has been suggested that progesterone receptor positivity is associated with better-differentiated tumours with less aggressive biological behaviour. In theory, progesterone administration as adjuvant therapy for patients with progesterone positive tumours could be useful in counteracting the effects of oestrogen as in the normal endometrium (Kurman *et al.*, 1995).

There are times when endometrial adenocarcinoma may be difficult to distinguish from endocervical adenocarcinoma, particularly when endometrial cancer extends into the cervix. In the past, some have used carcinoembryonic antigen (CEA) as a distinguishing tool, citing that there is positive staining in 80% of endocervical adenocarcinomas and 8% of endometrial carcinomas (Kurman *et al.*, 1995). The distinction is important because, of the two, endometrial carcinoma has a better prognosis. Recently,

because endocervical cancers have been associated with HPV (particularly subtype 18), studies have been made to determine whether there is a difference in HPV expression and determined that endometrial carcinoma is not associated with HPV, and is thus a more reliable way to differentiate endocervical from endometrial cancers, as discussed in detail above in the section on cervical cancer (Nuovo, 1994).

It is important to be aware of benign conditions that can simulate malignancy. The classical example is the Arias Stella reaction, which can look nearly identical with clear cell carcinoma (**Figure 9**). It is most commonly associated with pregnancy but has been reported to occur with use of certain medications (Kurman *et al.*, 1995). A good history and the presence of progesterone-related endometrial stromal changes (decidualization) are invaluable in making this distinction; if the Arias Stella reaction is due to miscarriage, villi may be present.

Molecular Genetic Findings

The molecular aspects of endometrial carcinogenesis continue to be elucidated. Endometrioid tumours are influenced by oestrogen and progesterone, and the development of endometrial hyperplasia is directly related to excess oestrogen. These hormones have effects on cellular proliferation; therefore, it is possible that molecular disturbances in the cell cycle contribute to the development of carcinoma. How transformation from premalignant lesions to cancer at the cellular level is still not known.

p53 has been studied extensively in the endometrium. It is involved in many crucial cellular functions such as cell cycle regulation, DNA repair, cellular differentiation and apoptosis (programmed cell death). It has been shown that there are alterations in the function of p53 in Type II, or nonoestrogen-dependent tumours, probably due to gene mutation. Oestrogen-dependent tumours (Type I) and their precursors rarely demonstrate *p53* mutations. The functional alteration of p53 in Type II tumours along with their lack of association with unopposed oestrogen suggests the existence of an oestrogen-dependent pathway in endometrial tumorigenesis. In non-endometrial tumours, *p53* mutation is associated with poor differentiation, aggressive clinical course and poor prognosis. The fact that most Type II tumours have altered p53 function explains at the molecular level why this subset of endometrial cancer has a more aggressive clinical course than Type I tumours.

Prognostic Factors

Endometrial cancer is currently surgically staged as anatomical extent of disease is felt to be an important indicator of prognosis and in directing adjuvant therapy. **Table 4** shows the current FIGO staging system. Additional

Table 4 FIGO* surgical staging for endometrial carcinoma

I		Tumour limited to the uterine fundus
	IA	No myometrial invasion
	IB	Myometrial invasion ≤ 50%
	IC	Myometrial invasion ≥ 50%
II		Tumour extends to the cervix
	IIA	Superficial glandular spread
	IIB	Stromal invasion
III		Regional tumour spread to the pelvis
	IIIA	Involvement of the uterine serosa, adnexa or positive peritoneal cytology
	IIIB	Vaginal metastases

Simplified Staging for Ovarian Carcinoma
Stage I Growth limited to the ovary/ovaries
Stage II Growth involving one or both ovaries, but limited to the true pelvis
Stage III Extension of tumour beyond the true pelvis, and/or positive pelvic lymph nodes or implants outside the pelvis
Stage IV Distant metastases

* Federation of International Gynecologic Oncologists.

features in determining prognosis and risk of recurrence include histological grade, histological subtype and age.

Studies of survival based on surgical stage have shown that depth of myometrial invasion is important with a 97% survival in patients with tumours confined to the inner third of the myometrium, decreasing to 70% with outer third involvement. The incidence of lymph node metastasis increases with depth of muscle invasion. Involvement of the cervix (stage II), particularly the cervical stroma, decreases the 5-year survival to 50%, probably related to the increased incidence of para-aortic lymph node metastases in these patients. Grade III histology is a sensitive indicator for poorer prognosis with a higher percentage of pelvic lymph nodes involved in these patients (Ludwig, 1995).

When one considers Type I versus Type II tumours, stage becomes a less important indicator of prognosis. Tumours with Type II histology do worse stage for stage than those with Type I histology. This is reflected in overall survival rates of 33% and 92%, respectively. These patients tend to present with more advanced disease than is initially suspected. Even when disease is at a very early stage, these tumours have a higher recurrence risk (Ludwig, 1995).

Clinically, age is considered to be an indicator of prognosis. Younger women tend to fare better than older women. Younger women who develop endometrial carcinoma usually do so in the context of complex atypical hyperplasia secondary to oestrogen excess. These malignancies tend to be better differentiated and less aggressive. Older women more often have tumours with poor differentiation and are at increased risk for developing tumours with Type II histology (Ludwig, 1995).

Clinical Management

The current first-line therapy for endometrial carcinoma is an exploratory laparotomy with a simple total abdominal hysterectomy/bilateral salpingo-oophorectomy. A lymph node dissection may also be performed as part of the staging procedure based on whether lymph nodes appear enlarged or firm, if high-grade or high-risk histology is known to be present, and when there is > 50% myometrial invasion (Chen *et al.*, 1999). The need for adjuvant therapy is based upon final surgical stage. Current modalities include radiation and chemotherapy.

UTERINE STROMAL TUMOURS

The most common benign stromal tumour in the uterus is a leiomyoma. In fact, it is one of the most common tumours encountered in gynaecological pathology with an estimated incidence of 20–40%. These tumours are benign proliferations of smooth muscle. Clinically, they tend to be less important as at least 50% are asymptomatic. Abnormal uterine bleeding (from submucosal leiomyomas) is the most common symptom and can be seen in one third of patients, and one third of patients may have pelvic pain. Local symptoms such as genitourinary and gastrointestinal compression and pelvic pressure may be seen when tumours reach a large size. These tumours may be detected incidentally in hysterectomies for other reasons, or may be discovered on routine bimanual examination. Treatment is often not indicated, but abnormal uterine bleeding, severe pelvic pressure or pain, infertility/habitual abortion due to uterine cavity distortion and compromise of adjacent organs (i.e. hydronephrosis) are all indications for therapy (Barbieri, 1999). Current therapeutic options include hysterectomy or myomectomy (local resection of the leiomyoma). Because these tumours are sensitive to oestrogen and progesterone, drugs to block the actions of these hormones have also been used with some success in an effort to treat these tumours (Deligdisch, 2000).

Uterine sarcomas are the least common uterine malignancy. In general, these tumours represent less than 5% of corpus cancers and have a poorer prognosis. The gross and histological subtypes have been discussed previously. Most patients present with abnormal uterine bleeding, and the tumour may be seen protruding through the cervix (classical for MMMT). The incidence tends to increase with age, and sarcomas may be more common in African Americans. Few risk factors are clearly defined. The most common histological subtype is the malignant mixed mullerian tumour. It also has the worst prognosis with an overall survival of 20%. Leiomyosarcomas account for 30% of sarcomas. It is important to note that most arise independently, and it is now no longer believed that they arise from pre-existing leiomyomas. Survival for patients with disease confined to the uterus approaches 30%. Endometrial stromal sarcomas are the least common subtype, but if the tumour is low-grade, the prognosis is good with 90% survival overall. The standard therapy for sarcomas is hysterectomy. The benefit of adjuvant therapy in extending survival has not been clearly proven (Levenback *et al.*, 1996).

PATHOLOGY OF THE OVARY

Tumour Pathology

Primary tumours of the ovary can be divided into three major groups that are based upon their presumed cell of origin. Tumours derived from the mesothelial-like lining of the ovary comprise the common group of epithelial ovarian tumours, which show various types of epithelial differentiation. Tumours derived from the germ cell elements are referred to as germ cell tumours, and encompass a wide variety of histological types. Tumours derived from the supporting elements of the ovary, which includes granulosa, theca and fibrous cells of the stroma, make up the group of tumours referred to as sex-cord stromal tumours. These tumours generally have less histological variety than germ cell tumours and are noted for their potential for hormonal production. A fourth group of tumours can be included that make up a wide variety of tumour types, including metastatic tumours, pseudoneoplastic tumours or tumour-like conditions, and a rare group of tumours of uncertain cell origin. For the purpose of simplicity, this last group of rare tumours will not be discussed.

Although ovarian tumours encompass a wide variety of neoplasms with numerous histological types and diverse clinicopathological features, general principles can be established regarding their presentation and outcome. In the premenopausal patient ovarian tumours must be distinguished from benign ovarian processes, including various benign types of cysts, endometriosis and inflammatory lesions whose mode of clinical presentation will often be identical with that for ovarian tumours and include vague abdominal symptoms, pelvic pain, urinary symptoms or abdominal distension. Rarely does either group present as dysfunctional uterine bleeding.

The presentation of epithelial ovarian tumours can best be explained by examining their natural course of spread. Tumour dissemination of ovarian carcinomas generally occurs by penetration of the ovarian capsule and seeding of peritoneal surfaces and by lymphatic invasion and spread to contiguous lymph nodes in the pelvic region. Spread by haematogenous routes to distant sites is a late manifestation and signals an ominous prognosis. Implantation of peritoneal surfaces is generally associated with relatively noninvasive growth, but increasing tumour size causes mechanical interference with other vital structures and organs such as the bowel and ureters. Because of this predictable route of dissemination, staging and prognosis of epithelial ovarian tumours can be divided into tumours confined to the pelvis and tumours that have spread beyond the pelvis. In contrast, germ cell tumours frequently disseminate to distant sites by haematogenous and lymphatic routes. Sex-cord stromal tumours, even when of a malignant nature, tend to be localized to the ovary, with metastases to distant sites noted many years after their removal.

Epidemiology

The incidence of ovarian cancer has remained relatively stable over the last 25 years. Ovarian cancer is the sixth most common form of cancer in women, the fourth leading cause of cancer death among women and the leading cause of death among gynaecological malignancies. The overall lifetime risk of a woman dying from ovarian cancer is approximately 1.5%, with ovarian cancer being the cause of death in one of every 90 women. Most malignant ovarian tumours occur in women over the age of 45 years where an ovarian mass has an approximately 30–40% chance of being malignant. Conversely, in women less than 45 years old, or premenopausal women, an ovarian mass is most likely to be a benign with malignant tumours making up less than 15% of this group. Thus, an ovarian mass in a premenopausal woman is approached much differently from an ovarian mass in a postmenopausal woman.

Certain generalizations can be made regarding the incidence of specific tumour types in pre- and postmenopausal woman. The most common ovarian tumour accounting for approximately one quarter of all ovarian tumours and one third of all benign ovarian tumours is the benign dermoid cyst (mature cystic teratoma), which belongs to the group of germ cell tumours. Germ cell tumours as a group are much more common in the first two decades of life. Conversely, the common group of epithelial ovarian tumours are rare in the first two decades of life and become much more prevalent with the onset of reproductive age and in postmenopausal women. Within these two groups, malignant epithelial ovarian tumours (carcinomas) tend to occur after the age of 60 years, whereas benign ovarian tumours and tumours of low malignant potential (borderline tumours) tend to occur in the 40–60 year age group. Sex-cord stromal tumours are most common in women from 40 to 60 years of age.

Most epidemiolgical factors of ovarian cancer relate to the common group of epithelial tumours. This group of tumours is uncommon before the age of 40 years, and peaks in the seventh to eighth decades of life. Most tumours in this group, 70–80%, are of a benign nature with the incidence of malignant tumours being closely related to age. Factors that have been associated with a higher risk of epithelial ovarian cancer include infertility, nulliparity, multiple miscarriages and the use of clomiphene (a fertility drug); factors associated with a lower risk include multiple pregnancies, breast feeding, tubal ligation and the use of oral contraceptives. Most of these factors can be explained by the hypothesis that ovulation induces an aberrant repair process, and factors which decrease ovulation decrease the incidence of this group of tumours. The use of oestrogen in postmenopausal women has not been shown to increase the risk of ovarian cancer.

Aetiology

Between 5 and 10% of women with ovarian cancer have a family history of ovarian cancer, and approximately half or less of this group have inherited disease. A woman with one affected first-degree relative has an approximately 5% lifetime risk of developing ovarian cancer, while two or more affected first-degree relatives confers a 30–50% lifetime risk of developing ovarian cancer. The most notable hereditary group is the breast–ovarian cancer group linked to *BRCA-1*, a probable tumour-suppressor gene. BRCA-linked ovarian cancer does not show distinct clinicopathological characteristics that distinguish it from sporadic ovarian tumours, although different studies have shown a significantly more favourable outcome. Owing to the much higher incidence of sporadic ovarian cancer versus inherited ovarian cancer, a routinely obtained family history is an unreliable way to identify patients who might be at high risk of developing ovarian cancer. Unlike *BRCA-1*, which confers a relatively high risk for breast and ovarian cancer, the incidence of ovarian cancer with *BRCA-2* appears to be much lower. Other inherited ovarian tumours are usually components of a multi-system genetic syndrome, and usually are not related to the common group of epithelial tumours. These syndromic complexes include Peutz–Jeghers syndrome (sex-cord stromal tumours), gonadal dysgenesis (gonadoblastomas), basal cell nevus syndrome (ovarian fibromas), ataxia telangiectesia, Muir–Torr syndrome, Li–Fraumeni syndrome and Cowden syndrome.

The effect of environmental factors on the incidence of ovarian cancer have been inconclusive with the exception of drugs used to enhance fertility or treat infertility, which generally increase the rate of epithelial malignancies. Factors which have shown conflicting results but may be possibly related to an increased rate of ovarian cancer include increased dietary fat, increased coffee consumption and the use of talc in the perineal area. The effect of oral contraceptive (OC) use has been extensively studied with results consistently showing a lower incidence of ovarian cancer in women who have used OCs for more than five consecutive years. A hypothetical analysis of the protective effect of OCs in nulliparous women with no family history of ovarian cancer has postulated that the risk of ovarian cancer in this group of women is reduced by more than 50% after 5 years of consecutive OC use and is less than the risk in parous women with a comparable family history and no history of OC use. (See also chapter *Inherited Predispositions to Cancer*.)

Screening and Prevention

Screening for ovarian cancer has primarily been directed towards the postmenopausal patient owing to the much higher incidence of malignant tumours in this group. Stage I ovarian carcinomas have a 90% cure rate, but only 25% of such tumours present as localized malignancies. Stage II ovarian carcinomas have an approximately 70% cure rate, while the prognosis for Stage III and IV carcinomas declines dramatically to 15–20%. Various screening tests that have been employed for the detection of ovarian cancer include tumour markers, ultrasound, rectovaginal or bimanual vaginal examination and Pap smears. All of these tests have various problems which has prompted many investigators to combine the various tests to increase sensitivity and specificity. Rectovaginal and bimanual vaginal examination is sensitive with experienced gynaecologists, but lacks specificity owing to the frequent occurrence of benign ovarian masses. Pap smears, although relatively specific, lack sensitivity as only 10–30% of ovarian cancers can be detected by this method (Nuovo, 1994).

Of the various tumour markers studied, including carcinoembryonic antigen, ovarian cyst adenocarcinoma antigen, lipid-associated sialic acid, NB/70K, TAG 72.3, CA 15-3 and CA 125, only the last has received widespread use. CA 125 is not specific for ovarian cancer and can be elevated in 5–40% of benign gynaecological masses including uterine leiomyomas and endometriosis. Other nongynaecological cancers, including those of the pancreas, stomach, colon, and breast, have been associated with elevated CA 125. Among gynaecological cancers other than ovarian cancers, elevated CA 125 has been reported in cervical and fallopian tube malignances. Although rare, elevated CA 125 has been reported in up to 1% of healthy women with no evidence of cancer. Problems with sensitivity also exist with CA 125 and must be considered with regards to quantitative parameters. CA 125 is determined by radioimmunoassay methods and is reported in units per millilitre, with levels $>35\,\mathrm{U\,mL^{-1}}$ being considered abnormal and levels $>65\,\mathrm{U\,mL^{-1}}$ being indicative of malignancy. CA 125 will be elevated above normal levels in 80–85% of women with Stage III or IV ovarian cancer, but varies in different studies from 30 to 50% in women with Stage I or II ovarian cancer. Most certainly it can be said that CA 125 is much more sensitive and reliable at detecting higher-stage ovarian cancer, but the lack of elevated CA 125 must be regarded cautiously in early ovarian cancer.

Owing to the lack of sensitivity of pelvic examination and serum CA 125 in detecting ovarian cancer a combination of these tests with ultrasonography has been advocated. A large study involving more than 22 000 postmenopausal women using a combination of CA 125 measurement and ultrasonography showed a specificity of greater than 99% for the detection of ovarian cancer but a positive predictive value of less than 30%. Others have advocated a more elaborate screening protocol first by transvaginal ultrasonography with abnormal results followed by pelvic examination, serum CA 125 determination, Doppler flow sonography and tumour morphological indexing by ultrasonography results. In these and numerous other studies the routine testing of asymptomatic women has shown limited utility in the prevention of ovarian cancer owing to the number of diagnostic laparotomies performed per cancer detected. It has been calculated that screening 100 000 asymptomatic women over the age of 45 years for ovarian cancer would detect 40 cases of ovarian cancer with 5398 false-positive results and 160 complications from diagnostic laparotomy. The NIH Consensus Development Panel in their most recent statement in 1995 concluded that there was no evidence to support routine screening in the general population and no convincing data even in high-risk patients.

Gross/Histopathology/Preinvasive Lesions/Ultrastructure/Immunohistochemistry

Among the three common groups of ovarian tumours, i.e. sex-cord stromal tumours, germ cell tumours and epithelial tumours, the last group accounts for over 90% of all malignant tumours of the ovary and approximately 60% of all ovarian tumours. The epithelial ovarian tumours are divided according to cell type and architectural pattern, with special reference given to any significant contribution by the surrounding ovarian stroma. If the tumour contains a prominent stromal component the suffix-fibroma is attached and the tumour is designated an adenofibroma rather than an adenoma, with this particular entity being almost invariably a benign proliferation. Architectural features are used in describing the location of the tumour as either on the surface or within the ovary, the degree of solid or cystic component, and are important in assessing the risk of benign or malignant behaviour. If the most prominent portion of the tumour is on the outer surface of the ovary, which almost invariably has papillary histological features, these are designated as surface papillary tumours. If the tumour contains a prominent cystic component the prefix cyst- is attached, such as cystadenoma, cystadenofibroma (**Figure 11**) and cystadenocarcinoma. A solid tumour with no cystic change would thus be called an adenoma, adenofibroma or adenocarcinoma. Adenofibromas and cystadenofibromas are generally solid tumours with the cystic component of cystadenofibromas only being recognized microscopically. The majority of

ovarian tumours of the epithelial type are grossly cystic and their distinction into specific type or prediction of their biological behaviour is limited by the gross examination. Most ovarian tumours in general cannot be distinguished from each other by their gross pathologic examination and require histologic examination for their final classification.

Architectural features are especially important in predicting the biological behaviour of a given tumour which is generally divided into three main categories of benign, borderline or malignant. Benign architectural features generally imply a tumour, whether it be solid or cystic, has a simple morphological pattern and shows no invasion of the surrounding stroma. Malignant architectural features are the opposite extreme with a complex morphological pattern and obvious invasion of the surrounding stroma. In between are borderline tumours. Each specific tumour type has its own specific criteria for what defines a borderline tumour, but the general concept is that borderline tumours exhibit a morphological pattern between simple and complex and can show minimal invasion of the surrounding stroma. Cytological features are also evaluated in placing a given tumour into one of these three specific categories of biological behaviour and include nuclear atypia, number of mitoses and other parameters such as multinucleation and the amount of cytoplasm present.

The most specific categorization of the epithelial ovarian tumours relates to the type of cellular component present, with the five major groups being serous (resembles fallopian tube), mucinous (resembles cervix), endometrioid (resembles endometrium), clear cell (resembles kidney tumour) and transitional cell (Brenner tumours, resemble urinary bladder). Not infrequently epithelial tumours of the ovary will be associated with numerous small foci of tumour spread throughout the peritoneal lining, which can be either totally benign or malignant. These peritoneal implants generally recapitulate the primary ovarian tumour and their origin is generally considered to be an example of independent primary tumours in a low-grade tumour, while in high-grade tumours they may be either true metastases or independent primary tumours. It is important to realize that these implants do not necessarily indicate malignant behaviour of the primary ovarian tumour and are not an unexpected finding.

The most common of all of the epithelial tumours are tumours of the serous type, which account for over half of this group and from 30 to 50% of all ovarian tumours. Over 70% of serous ovarian tumours are benign, with borderline tumours being relatively rare and malignant types accounting for the remaining 20–25% of these tumours. Serous tumours are usually cystic, generally of moderate size (less than 10 cm) and lined by an epithelium that mimics that of the fallopian tube being ciliated cuboidal or columnar. Microscopic features of benign tumours are single or multiple cysts with simple papillae projecting into the lumen (usually comprising less than 10% of the total cyst wall) that are lined by a single layer of serous

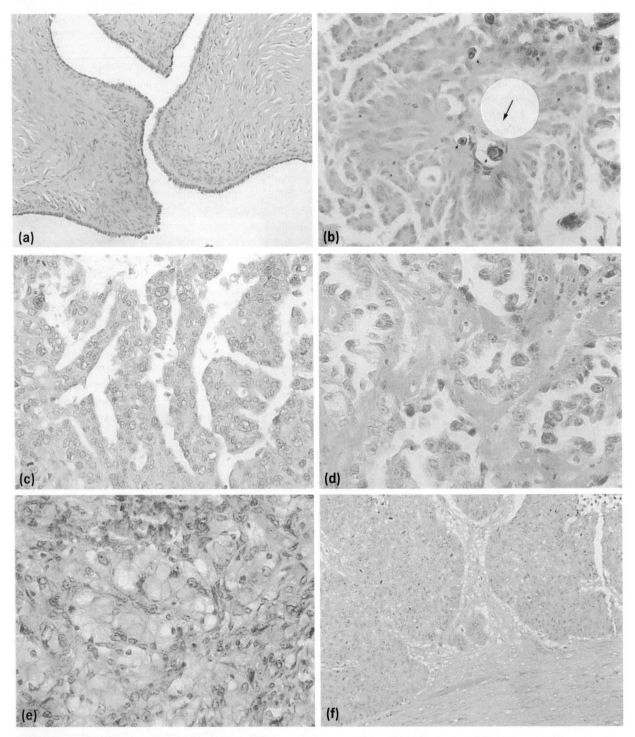

Figure 11   Epithelial tumours of the ovary. Panel (a) shows the large, broad papilla of a serous cystadenofibroma; the simple columnar lining indicates that this is a benign lesion. In panel (b), note that the papilla are more complex and that psammoma bodies are now evident (arrow); this is a serous cystadenoma of borderline malignant potential. In contrast, note the much more complex architecture of a serous cystadenocarcinoma (c). The other panels show other carcinomas of the ovary including clear cell carcinoma (d), note similarity to similar tumour of the endometrium), metastatic carcinoma from the stomach (Krukenberg tumour, where the malignant cells contain ample mucin (e)) and (f) endometrioid carcinoma of the ovary with its characteristic squamous metaplasia.

cells with no atypia. Borderline tumours show more complex papillae with a stratified layer of cells that usually show some atypia. Owing to the complex branching nature of the papillae and multiple layer of cells lining the papillae, histological sections will often show small clusters of cells that appear to be floating freely in the cystic space adjacent to the papillae. As these papillae become more complex they may become condensed into concentric concretions referred to as psammoma bodies, a characteristic feature of serous tumours (**Figure 11**). Some serous borderline tumours may show microinvasion of the surrounding stroma which has not been shown to have any prognostic significance. Serous borderline tumours frequently are associated with peritoneal implants that are generally of low grade and noninvasive. If these implants are benign they are often referred to as endosalpingiosis after their resemblance to fallopian tube epithelium.

Serous carcinomas are the most common malignant ovarian tumour and are most common in women after 65 years of age. They usually are grossly cystic but can appear solid owing to the greater degree of epithelial proliferation and their cystic nature is only recognized microscopically; when cystic most of their inner wall contains papillary structures. Serous carcinomas show more complex branching of the papillae and stratification of the epithelial lining to such a degree that crowding of the papillae results in a more solid appearing tumour with slit-like lumina (**Figure 11**) Areas of the tumour may show solid sheets of cells, making their distinction from endometrioid tumours difficult. Findings that may help in this instance are the presence of multinucleated cells and psammoma bodies and the absence of squamous differentiation and intracellular mucin, the latter two of which are often present in endometrioid carcinomas. Serous carcinomas show obvious stromal invasion and nuclear atypia.

Mucinous tumours represent approximately 25% of epithelial tumours and 15% of all ovarian tumours and are noted for the large size they commonly attain at presentation. Of all ovarian tumours, mucinous tumours are the type that can be most readily recognized grossly owing to their frequent multicystic appearance with prominent mucin production. The majority of mucinous tumours, (>75%), are benign with borderline tumours being extremely rare. As opposed to the fairly constant histological type seen in any given serous tumour, mucinous tumours are noted for histological variability. One histological section of a mucinous tumour may appear of borderline type, while an adjacent histological section shows invasive carcinoma. For this reason it is important to sample mucinous tumours well.

Mucinous tumours are lined by epithelium that resembles that of the endocervical canal and consists of mucin-filled columnar cells. Less often the epithelial lining resembles intestinal-type epithelium with prominent goblet cells. Low-grade mucinous tumours, or mucinous

cystadenomas, are generally cystic tumours lined by a single layer of endocervical-type mucinous epithelium. The criteria for endocervical-type borderline mucinous tumours closely resemble those of serous borderline tumours. Mucinous carcinomas vary greatly in their microscopic appearance in any given tumour and are not divided into endocervical or intestinal type, both of which are frequently seen in a single example. Mucinous carcinomas vary from solid nodules to glands, often with scant stroma.

Endometrioid tumours are usually carcinomas, with benign and borderline examples being very uncommon. Although endometrioid tumours comprise less than 5% of all ovarian tumours, they account for 15–20% of malignant ovarian tumours. Endometrioid carcinomas may be cystic or solid and lack gross features that distinguish them from other ovarian tumours. They are lined by epithelium that mimics the endometrium and are associated with endometriosis in 5–10% of all cases and a synchronous carcinoma of the endometrium in approximately 25% of cases. Endometrioid carcinomas classically are characterized microscopically by tubular glands lined by mucin-free psuedostratified epithelium as well as squamous metaplasia. Another feature commonly seen in endometrioid carcinomas is focal squamous differentiation (**Figure 11f**). Owing to their glandular appearance their distinction from metastatic carcinoma, particularly colonic adenocarcinomas, can be difficult. In the case of adenocarcinomas of the colon immunohistochemical stains can help in this distinction. Epithelial tumours of the ovary as a group are positive for cytokeratin 7 and negative for cytokeratin 20 whereas intestinal adenocarcinomas generally show the opposite pattern of immunoreactivity. Another common distinction is from metastatic breast cancers and again immunohistochemical stains can be helpful, with ovarian carcinomas staining positively for CA 125 and metastatic breast cancer staining for gross cystic disease fluid protein 15.

Clear-cell carcinomas represent approximately, 5% of all ovarian carcinomas. Like endometrioid carcinomas they are frequently associated with endometriosis, and in some reports up to 50% of clear-cell carcinomas show such an association. Clear-cell carcinomas, unlike other ovarian carcinomas, more frequently present as Stage 1 tumours prompting earlier investigators to suggest a better prognosis for this class of ovarian carcinomas, but if adjusted for stage at presentation clear-cell carcinomas have a worse prognosis than other epithelial ovarian carcinomas. Grossly, clear-cell carcinomas may be solid or cystic and typically show numerous nodules of solid tumour protuding into cystic cavities. Microscopically clear-cell carcinomas usually show a solid nest of clear cells mixed with small cysts lined by cells with a hobnail appearance (**Figure 11**).

Transitional cell tumours of the ovary are relatively rare, making up less than 2–3% of all ovarian tumours, and of this group practically all are benign. Often referred to as

Brenner tumours, these tumours show urothelial differentiation similar to the lining of the urinary tract. Grossly, Brenner tumours are usually solid tumours but may show cystic change. Microscopically, Brenner tumours are composed of sharply demarcated nests of transitional cells, often with small cysts in their central portion, in an abundant fibromatous stroma. Up to half of Brenner tumours are incidental findings in ovaries removed for other reasons, and are frequently associated with mucinous cystadenomas.

The other common group of epithelial tumours seen in the ovary are metastatic tumours. Owing to the rich vascularity of the ovarian stroma, 10–20% of all tumours of the ovary are metastatic. The clinical history is very valuable in such instances, but other findings that may help in such instances are the presence of bilateral tumours, numerous separate nodules within a single ovary and the presence of tumour on the ovarian surface without peritoneal involvement. The presence of bilateral involvement should be approached cautiously as only 75% or less of metastatic ovarian tumours are bilateral and 10–20% of primary ovarian carcinomas will present as bilateral masses with primary serous tumours being bilateral 50–75% of the time. Up to one third of breast cancer patients and one quarter of colon cancer patients will have ovarian metastases during the course of their treatment. Among metastatic ovarian tumours, those derived from signet ring cell carcinomas of the stomach, i.e. Krukenburg tumours, have received the most attention. Although not the most frequent metastatic tumour to the ovary, Krukenburg tumours have received such attention because they often occur in middle-aged to younger patients without a known primary. Krukenburg tumours can closely mimic clear-cell carcinomas and germ cell tumours owing to their histological appearance (**Figure 11**).

Sex-cord stromal tumours are relatively uncommon tumours that make up approximately 5% of all ovarian tumours. As a general rule this group of tumours occur in a slightly younger population than epithelial tumours and examples in paediatric populations are not rare. Derived from the stroma of the ovary this group of tumours is noted for their response to and production of hormones as they recapitulate their normal role in reproduction. Most ovarian sex-cord stromal tumours are oestrogenic but up to one quarter may be androgenic. The most general histological characteristic of this group of tumours is the presence or absence of the accumulation of lipid in the tumour cells which imparts a particular histological appearance. The most common tumours in this group include fibromas, thecomas and granulosa cell tumours. Grossly they are generally solid tumours but may be cystic, especially in the case of granulosa cell tumours. These tumours can occur in a mixed pattern and are usually solid nests of cells that vary from spindle-shaped cells to round or oval cells. Fibromas and thecomas are generally solid tumours and a sharp distinction between the two is often difficult to distinguish

as fibromas may undergo leutinization focally and are referred to as fibrothecomas. Whereas fibromas are generally spindle-shaped cells, thecomas undergo leutinization and classically have pale abundant cytoplasm (**Figure 12**). Granulosa cell tumours are divided into an adult and juvenile types, with the latter having a better prognosis, and both are characterized by round to oval cells with nuclear grooves surrounding small cystic spaces. In the case of adult granulosa cell tumours, these cystic spaces take on a microfollicular appearance classically referred to as Call–Exner bodies (**Figure 12**). Granulosa cell tumours generally present as Stage I tumours and have a 90% survival at 5 years, but are notorious for recurrence at distant metastatic sites 15–20 years later with a 50% mortality rate at this time. Other tumours in this group often referred to as steroid cell tumours, including Sertoli–Leydig cell tumours, are extremely rare.

Germ cell tumours account for approximately 30% of all ovarian tumours, and the dermoid cyst accounts for approximately 95% of this group of tumours. The remaining 5% of germ cell tumours are generally of a malignant tumour type and include dysgerminoma, yolk sac tumour, embryonal carcinoma, choriocarcinoma and immature teratoma. This latter group of tumours occurs almost exclusively in patients less than 20 years of age and as a group account for less than 1% of all ovarian tumours. Malignant germ cell tumours in general are most common in the paediatric population and young women. There are major differences between germ cell tumours occurring in very young female patients and those occurring in adolescents and adults. Germ cell tumours occurring in early childhood tend to be pure yolk sac tumours or teratomas, have no malignant non-neural epithelial components, are euploid or tetraploid and prior to puberty occur almost exclusively in extragonadal sites with primary germ cell tumours of the ovary being very rare. Germ cell tumours occurring in adolescents and adults are generally of mixed histological type or dysgerminomas, may have malignant epithelial components, commonly show isochromosome 12p and aneuploidy by cytogenetic studies and generally involve the ovary with extragonadal tumours being rare.

Germ cell tumours may be composed of a number of different tissue types or show a combination of different germ cell tumour types and are frequently complex histologically. It is the most malignant component present that determines the behaviour of these tumours. At one extreme of this complexity is the mature teratoma that contains tissue representing all three embryonic layers in a uniformly mature fashion. At the other end of the spectrum are immature teratomas and mixed malignant germ cell tumours which show a wide spectrum of histological types and degree of malignancy. In between these extremes of histological complexity are pure malignant germ cell tumours, with dysgerminoma being the most common example (**Figure 12**).

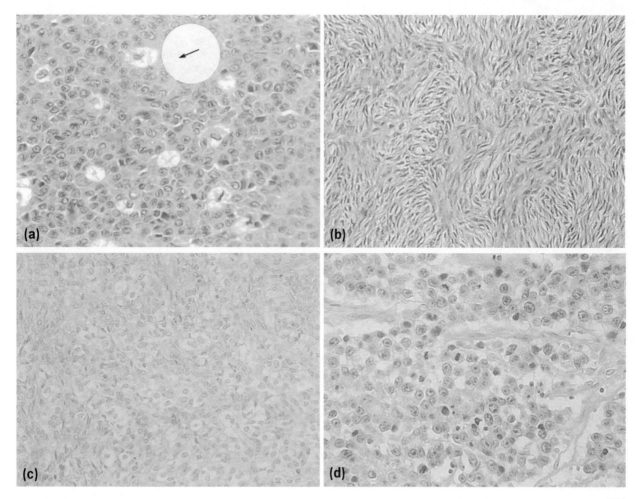

Figure 12 Stromal and germ cell tumours of the ovary. Panel (a) shows a granulosa cell tumour; note the nuclear grooves and the circular areas of degenerated material, called Call–Exner bodies (arrow). Panel (b) shows the interlacing fascicles of a fibroma whereas panel (c) demonstrates the prominent cytoplasm of a luteinized thecoma; this change often indicates hormonal production by the tumour. Panel (d) shows the large, polygonal cells of a dysgerminoma of the ovary; scattered lymphocytes are also characteristic of this tumour.

Molecular Genetic Findings

The most commonly identified gene conferring a high risk of epithelial ovarian cancer is *BRCA-1*, as discussed above. Among the sex-cord stromal tumours, molecular studies have generally been directed at adult-type granulosa cell tumours, where mutations have been identified in the G_I subunit of regulatory G proteins. Similar findings have been identified in individuals with the McCune–Albright syndrome, who show dysregulated ovarian function and isosexual precocity but no associated risk of ovarian cancer. Further studies are needed to identify the role of molecular alterations and the associated molecular genetic findings associated with regulatory G proteins.

The majority of molecular genetic findings in germ cell tumours have centred around cytogenetic findings with single gene mutations not being readily identified. The majority of mature teratomas have been shown to be karyotypically normal whereas immature teratomas show a high frequency of random nonrecurrent chromosomal abnormalities. Other adult germ cell tumours have frequently shown two copies of the short arm of chromosome 12, with this finding being rare in prepubertal patients with similiar tumours.

Prognostic Factors

The most reliable indicator of prognosis is stage at presentation. The overall 5-year survival rate for ovarian cancer confined to the ovary (Stage I) is approximately 75%. The rate declines to approximately 60% for pelvic extension of tumour beyond the ovary (Stage II) and 20% for metastatic disease (Stage III or IV). The size of the tumour in postmenopausal women has important prognostic implications, with tumours less than 5 cm usually being benign (95%), while tumours greater than 10 cm in size are often malignant (60%). Another prognostic factor at presentation is the presence or absence of ascites and the volume of fluid present, with high-volume ascites having a worse prognosis. Levels of CA 125 both preoperatively and postoperatively have prognostic significance. Older age at presentation is associated with a worse prognosis, although other medical factors associated with the elderly patient make this parameter difficult to judge. A large volume of residual tumour after initial surgery and adjuvant chemotherapy portend a poor prognosis. Histological type among epithelial tumours is most important for clear-cell carcinomas, which usually have a higher recurrence rate and lower survival rate for Stage I tumours than other ovarian epithelial carcinomas. The grade (or cytological details) of an ovarian epithelial carcinoma is generally only important in Stage I tumours, as poorly differentiated tumours as opposed to well or moderately differentiated have a worse prognosis (and thus higher stage) and often prompt more aggressive treatment.

Overview of Present Clinical Management

The initial management of a patient with an adnexal mass is directly related to the age of the patient and the size of the mass. An initial mass greater than 10 cm in any patient regardless of age will usually result in laparoscopy or an exploratory laparotomy. At the other extreme an adnexal mass slightly increased over normal ovarian size, or less than 5 cm, is approached differently in pre- and post-menopausal patients. In women of reproductive age the high incidence of cystic enlargement of one or both ovaries due to the process of ovulation and formation of corpora lutea allows a much more cautious approach. These patients will usually be re-evaluated after two menstrual cycles and if the mass persists will then be evaluated by transvaginal ultrasonography and CA 125 measurement. In the postmenopausal patient any ovarian enlargement will prompt transvaginal ultrasonography and measurement of CA 125. In these patients any abnormal findings by ultrasonography other than a simple cyst will prompt an exploratory laparotomy.

In the event that a primary ovarian cancer is found, the most important parameter that will influence future treatment is accurate surgical staging. A simplified view of ovarian cancer staging determines three basic parameters that include whether or not the tumour is confined to the ovary or ovaries (Stage I) and, if not, then whether the cancer is limited to the true pelvis (Stage II) or extends beyond the true pelvis (Stage III or IV). Generally, ovarian epithelial cancers limited to the ovary do not require adjuvant chemotherapy or radiation and reproductive sparing surgery may be performed with the exception of tumours that are poorly differentiated and clear-cell carcinomas. All other stages of ovarian epithelial cancers require at least a total abdominal hysterectomy and some form of adjuvant chemotherapy and radiation. Of special

note is that some borderline tumours, even if bilateral, can be treated with a reproductive sparing procedure.

Proper and accurate staging are particularly important in malignant germ cell tumours where reproductive sparing surgery is sufficent for Stage I tumours, which is the common presentation in this group. With the advent of multiagent chemotherapy, higher-stage germ cell tumours can be cured with a high rate of success (90%), and accurate staging can prevent significant morbidity and mortality in patients requiring such therapy, and just as importantly avoid undesirable side effects in those patients not requiring chemotherapy.

The management of sex-cord stromal tumours is not as well defined as for epithelial and germ cell tumours. Surgical treatment alone is often considered adequate treatment with the choice of adjuvant chemotherapy and/or radiation being of some debate. Historically, granulosa cell tumours have been treated with postsurgical radiation, but the recent recognition of their frequent recurrence 15–20 years later has prompted reconsideration of their treatment.

REFERENCES

Barbieri, R. (1999). Ambulatory management of uterine leiomyomata. *Clinical Obstetrics and Gynecology*, **42**, 197–205.

Burke, T., *et al*. (1996). Endometrial hyperplasia and endometrial cancer. *Obstetric and Gynecological Clinics of North America*, **23**, 411–455.

Chen, L., *et al*. (1999). Endometrial cancer: recent developments in evaluation and treatment. *Oncology (Huntington)*, **13**, 1665–1670.

Cirisano, F., *et al*. (1999). Epidemiologic and surgicopathologic findings of papillary serous and clear cell endometrial cancers when compared to endometrioid carcinoma. *Gynecology and Oncology*, **74**, 385–394.

Crum, C. P. and Nuovo, G. J. (1991). *Human Papillomavirus and Their Relationship to Genital Tract Neoplasms*. (Raven Press, New York).

Deligdisch, L. (2000). Hormonal pathology of the endometrium. *Modern Pathology*, **13**, 285–294.

Eliezri, Y., *et al*. (1990). The occurrence of human papillomavirus DNA in cutaneous squamous and basal cell neoplasms. *Archives of Dermatology*, **23**, 836–842.

Kurman, R., *et al*. (1995). Endometrial carcinoma. In: Kurman, R. (ed.), *Blaustein's Pathology of the Female Genital Tract*. 439–486 (Berlin, Springer).

Levenback, C., *et al*. (1996). Uterine sarcoma. *Obstetric and Gynecological Clinics of North America*, **23**, 457–473.

Ludwig, H. (1995). Prognostic factors in endometrial cancer. *International Journal of Gynaecology and Obstetrics*, 49, Suppl., S1–S7.

Nuovo, G. J. (1994). *Cytopathology of the Female Genital Tract: An Integrated Approach*. (Williams and Wilkins, Baltimore).

Nuovo, G. J. (1997). *PCR In Situ Hybridization: Protocols and Applications*, 3rd edn. (Raven Press, New York).

Nuovo, G. J., *et al.* (1991). Correlation of histology and detection of human papillomavirus DNA in vulvar cancers. *Gynecology and Oncology*, **43**, 275–280.

Nuovo, G. J., *et al.* (1999). *In situ* detection of the hypermethylation-induced inactivation of the *p16* gene as an early event in oncogenesis. *Proceedings of the National Academy of Sciences of the USA*, **96**, 12754–9.

FURTHER READING

Brown, F. M., *et al.* (1999). LSIL biopsies after HSIL smears. Correlation with high-risk HPV and greater risk of HSIL on follow-up. *American Journal of Clinical Pathology*, **112**, 765–768.

Lin, M. C., *et al.* (1998) Patterns of allelic loss (LOH) in vulvar squamous carcinomas and adjacent noninvasive epithelia. *American Journal of Pathology*, **152**, 1313.

Navarro, M., *et al.* (1997). Cytologic correlates of benign versus dysplastic abnormal keratinization. *Diagnostic Cytopathology*, **17**, 447–451.

Nuovo, G. J. (1997). *In situ* detection of PCR-amplified metalloprotease cDNAs, their inhibitors, and human papillomavirus transcripts in cervical carcinoma cell lines. *International Journal of Cancer*, **71**, 1056–1060.

Nuovo, G. J. (1999). Detection of human papillomavirus DNA in Papanicolaou smears: Correlation with pathologic and clinical findings. *Diagnostic Molecular Pathology*, **7**, 158–163.

Quade, B. J., *et al.* (1999). Frequent loss of heterozygosity for chromosome 10 in uterine leiomyosarcoma in contrast to leiomyoma. *American Journal of Pathology*, **154**, 945–950.

Chapter 44

Urinary Tract

Pheroze Tamboli
The University of Texas M. D. Anderson Cancer Center, Houston, TX, USA

Rafael E. Jimenez and Mahul B. Amin
Emory University Hospital, Atlanta, GA, USA

CONTENTS

INTRODUCTION

A myriad of tumours affect the urinary tract, including numerous benign and malignant types. These tumours arise from the different tissues that comprise the structures of the urinary tract. The malignant tumours originating from the epithelium are referred to as carcinomas and are the most common malignant tumours of the urinary tract (**Figure 1**). Only the most common malignant tumours of the urinary tract are discussed in this chapter. Sarcomas, lymphomas and other assorted tumours affecting the urinary tract are rare and are beyond the scope of this text.

NORMAL DEVELOPMENT AND STRUCTURE OF URINARY TRACT

Normal Development

The urinary tract is almost entirely derived from the mesoderm, except for the most distal part of the urethra, which develops from the ectoderm. The kidney and ureter develop from the intermediate mesoderm, while the urinary bladder and urethra are derived from the urogenital sinus.

Structure

The kidneys are paired organs located in the retroperitoneum, extending from the level of the twelfth thoracic vertebra to the third lumbar vertebra. Each kidney is surrounded by abundant adipose tissue that is covered by the membranous perirenal fascia of Gerota. The renal parenchyma is enveloped by a fibroelastic capsule, which acts as a barrier to the spread of cancer. The kidney is divided into 8–18 (average 14) lobes that are fused together. Each lobe is constituted by the outer cortex and inner medullary pyramid. The nephron is the functional unit, which is composed of the glomerulus and tubule. The tubules empty into collecting ducts that coalesce to form the terminal ducts of Bellini; the latter number 10–25 in each lobe. The ducts of Bellini open at the tip of the papilla, which is the apex of the medullary pyramid. The renal sinus is a concave space at the medial aspect of the kidney where the renal pelvis and calyces, blood vessels and nerves enter the kidney. It is filled with fibroadipose tissue that is continuous with the perirenal adipose tissue and has numerous lymphatic channels and blood vessels.

The renal pelvis is located at the renal hilum and consists of two or three major calyces and 8–18 minor calyces. The minor calyces surround the renal papillae. The ureters arise from the renal pelves, and both are hollow structures with similar features. Their walls are composed of four layers, which from inside out are the urothelium (transitional epithelium) lined mucosa, lamina propria, muscularis propria and adventitia.

The urinary bladder is also a hollow organ that is located deep in the pelvis, behind the pubic bone. The ureters traverse the wall of the urinary bladder to open in the inferior part referred to as the trigone. The superior portion is the dome. The wall of the urinary bladder is composed of four layers, starting from the inside with the urothelium (transitional cell) lined mucosa, followed by the lamina propria, muscularis propria, adventitia and

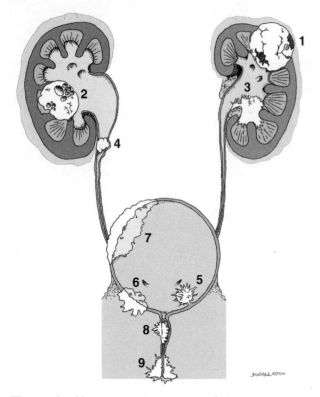

Figure 1 Most common cancers of the urinary tract and their locations. 1, Nephroblastoma (Wilms' tumour) and renal cell carcinoma; 2, collecting duct carcinoma; 3, urothelial carcinoma of renal pelvis; 4, urothelial carcinoma of the ureter; 5, papillary non-invasive urothelial carcinoma of the urinary bladder; 6, invasive urothelial carcinoma of the urinary bladder; 7, squamous cell carcinoma and adenocarcinoma of the urinary bladder; 8, papillary invasive urothelial carcinoma of the urethra; 9, squamous cell carcinoma and adenocarcinoma of the urethra. (Figure courtesy of Dr J. A. Gomez.)

perivesical adipose tissue. The muscularis mucosae is an interrupted layer of smooth muscle in the lamina propria, which needs to be distinguished from the muscularis propria as the staging of urinary bladder tumours is dependent on the depth of invasion.

The urethra is continuous with the neck of the urinary bladder. The male urethra is divided into the prostatic, membranous, penile and bulbar segments. Except for the distal end, which is lined by squamous epithelium, the urethra is also lined by urothelium. The female urethra is shorter and is roughly divided into the proximal one-third, which is lined by urothelium, and distal two-thirds lined by squamous epithelium.

KIDNEY

A variety of different benign and malignant tumours involve the kidney in children and adults, which are listed

Table 1 Tumours of the kidney

Benign tumours	Malignant tumours
Epithelial tumours	*Epithelial tumours*
Renal adenoma	Nephroblastoma
Renal oncocytoma	(Wilms tumour)[a]
Metanephric (embryonal)	Renal cell carcinoma
adenoma	Urothelial carcinoma of
Nephrogenic adenofibroma	renal pelvis
Mesenchymal tumours	*Mesenchymal tumours*
Angiomyolipoma	Clear cell sarcoma[a]
Mesoblastic nephroma[a]	Rhabdoid tumour[a]
Leiomyoma	Leiomyosarcoma
Juxtaglomerular cell tumour	
Renomedullary interstitial	
cell tumour	
Haemangioma	
Lymphangioma	
Lipoma	
Myxoma	
Neurogenic tumours	
Benign fibrous histiocytoma	
Solitary fibrous tumour	
Miscellaneous neoplasms	*Miscellaneous neoplasms*
Cystic nephroma	Lymphoma/leukaemia
Solid and cystic biphasic tumour	Plasmacytoma
	Secondary involvement
	Metastasis

[a] Tumours predominantly or exclusively affecting children.

in **Table 1**. These tumours arise from the different components that constitute the kidney. Malignant tumours arising from the epithelium of the kidney include nephroblastoma (Wilms' tumour), which is the most common renal tumour in children, and renal cell carcinoma, which is the most common renal cancer in adults. Urothelial carcinoma also affects the kidney, arising in the structures lined by urothelium, i.e. the renal pelvis. The discussion in this chapter will concentrate on the most common malignant tumours, i.e. nephroblastoma, renal cell carcinoma and urothelial carcinoma. The other less common tumours will not be described as they are beyond the scope of this text.

Nephroblastoma (Wilms' Tumour)

Tumour Pathology

Nephroblastoma (Wilms' tumour) is the most common primary renal tumour that affects children, accounting for more than of 80% of renal tumours in children. The eponym Wilms' tumour is used commonly in honour of Max Wilms, who reported seven tumours and reviewed the literature, although he was not the first to describe this tumour. The improvements in treatment and survival of nephroblastoma (Wilms' tumour) patients have in large part been due to the success of multidisciplinary cooperative groups such as the National Wilms' Tumor Study (NWTS) and the Société Internationale d'Oncologie Pédiatrique (SIOP). A large part of our knowledge of this disease is based on the findings of the NWTS and SIOP studies (Boccon-Gibod, 1998; Neville and Ritchey, 2000).

More than 90% of these tumours develop in children with no other known problems, while the remainder affect children with specific malformations. The presence of an abdominal mass is the most common presenting feature. Other signs and symptoms include pain, haematuria, hypertension, intestinal obstruction and sometimes problems related to distant metastasis.

There are two staging systems for nephroblastoma (Wilms' tumour) based on the extent of spread of tumour; these are listed in **Table 2**. The NWTS and SIOP staging systems are very similar, but the fundamental difference is that in the former the tumour is staged prior to chemotherapy.

Epidemiology

Nephroblastoma (Wilms' tumour) affects one in 8000–10 000 children (0–15 years of age), with over 90% tumours occurring in children under 6 years of age, most commonly between the ages of 3 and 4 years. Patients with unilateral tumours present at a mean age of 41.5 months for males and 46.9 months for females. In contrast, patients with bilateral tumours present at a younger age, with a mean of 29.5 months for males and 32.6 months for females. This tumour is very rare in neonates (0.1% of all nephroblastomas) and rarely affects adults. Girls are affected more commonly than boys, with a male to female ratio of 0.92:1 for unilateral tumours and 0.60:1 for bilateral tumours. In the United States this tumour is most common in African-Americans and least common in Chinese-Americans.

Aetiology

Nephroblastoma (Wilms' tumour) is associated with at least three well-defined congenital syndromes. The WAGR syndrome (Wilms' tumour, Aniridia, Genital abnormalities and mental Retardation) is associated with a deletion in the WT-1 gene located on chromosome 11p13. The Denys–Drash syndrome (glomerulonephritis, pseudohermaphroditism and nephroblastoma) is also associated with mutations of the WT-1 gene. Patients with Beckwith–Weidemann syndrome (hemihypertrophy, renal medullary cysts, adrenal cytomegaly and nephroblastoma) have abnormalities of the WT-2 gene located distal to the WT-1 gene on chromosome 11p15.5. In up to 1% of patients the tumours are familial. Other possible associations include renal malformations, cutaneous naevi, trisomy 18, genital malformations and neurofibromatosis.

Screening and Prevention

The use of abdominal ultrasound is recommended for routine screening of patients at high risk of nephroblastoma (Wilms' tumour), such as children with the three above-mentioned syndromes. Recommendations for screening include ultrasound examination every 3 months until the age of 7 years, followed by physical examination every 6 months. However, the efficacy of screening programme remains to be determined.

Gross Features

Nephroblastoma usually presents as a solitary tumour that is well encapsulated from the adjacent normal renal parenchyma. The tumour size varies, but the majority are larger than 5 cm and some may exceed 10 cm in greatest dimension. According to data from the NWTS the median weight of these tumours is 550 g. The cut surface shows a mainly

Table 2 Staging systems for nephroblastoma (Wilms' tumour)

Stage	NWTS[a]	SIOP[b]
I	Tumour confined to the kidney and completely resected without rupture	Tumour limited to the kidney and completely excised
II	Tumour extends beyond the kidney (by direct invasion of capsule, extrarenal vascular invasion or tumour spillage without peritoneal contamination), but is completely resected (includes biopsied tumour)	Tumour extending outside kidney, but completely excised, with or without regional lymph node invasion
III	Gross residual tumour, and/or involved surgical margin, and/or tumour in regional lymph nodes	Incomplete surgical excision, without haematogenous metastases, but including biopsy before or at surgery, preoperative rupture, peritoneal implants or nodal metastasis beyond regional lymph nodes
IV	Any local stage with haematogenous metastasis	Distant metastases
V	Bilateral renal tumours at time of diagnosis (tumour in each kidney is separately substaged)	Bilateral renal tumours at time of diagnosis

[a]National Wilms' Tumour Study: tumour staged following surgery and before chemotherapy.
[b]Société Internationale d'Oncologie Pédiatrique: tumour staged following surgery preceded by chemotherapy (unless metastases are present at time of presentation).

solid, uniform, soft, tan or grey tumour. Haemorrhagic and necrotic areas may be present. Cyst formation may be present, sometimes extensively involving the entire tumour.

Microscopic Features

Nephroblastoma (Wilms' tumour) has three components that are present in varying quantities, blastema, epithelium and stroma (**Figure 2, see colour plate section**). Blastema is composed of closely packed small cells without visible cell borders that are arranged as nodules, interconnecting cords or diffuse sheets (Schmidt and Beckwith, 1995). The epithelial component generally forms tubules, glands or glomeruloid structures. The stromal component is made of spindle cells that surround the blastema and epithelial components. The spindle cells may be set within a myxoid background resembling primitive mesenchyme or may have a fibroblastic appearance. The stromal cells may be differentiated into rhabdomyoblasts, bone, cartilage, adipose tissue, mature ganglion cells or neuroglia.

Anaplasia is one of the most important histological features that needs to be determined in every tumour. Anaplasia, which may be either focal or diffuse, is defined as the presence of multipolar mitotic figures and nuclei with increased chromatin that are at least three-fold larger than adjacent cells (Faria *et al.*, 1996). Diffuse anaplasia is the presence of anaplasia in more than one portion of the tumour or if found in any extrarenal or metastatic site.

Immunohistochemistry

There are no specific immunohistochemical stains for making the diagnosis of nephroblastoma (Wilms' tumour). The blastema component does stain with vimentin immunohistochemical stain.

Prognostic Factors

Tumour histology and stage are the most important prognostic factors in nephroblastoma (Wilms' tumour). Tumours are divided into those with favourable histology and those with unfavourable histology, depending on the presence or absence of anaplasia. Tumours with unfavourable histology account for 5–6% of all cases. Patients who have tumours with unfavourable histology have a worse prognosis, e.g. nearly half of the patients in the second NWTS who died of disease had unfavourable histology, although they numbered only 12% of all cases. Other prognostic factors that have limited success in predicting prognosis and that are still under investigation include DNA content measured by flow cytometry, nuclear morphometry, serum renin and erythropoietin.

Overview of present Clinical Management

A multimodal approach is used for treating patients with nephroblastoma (Wilms' tumour), which varies in different parts of the world. In most of the United States

and Canada the NWTS protocol is followed, which calls for radical nephrectomy (with rare exceptions) followed by chemotherapy and/or radiation therapy, based on the surgical and pathological findings. In most of Europe the SIOP protocols are followed, in which chemotherapy is given prior to nephrectomy.

Renal Cell Carcinoma

Tumour Pathology

Renal cell carcinoma is a malignant tumour that arises from the renal epithelium. The history of renal cell carcinoma is interesting in that it was not until 1960 that Oberling *et al.* laid to rest the controversy regarding the origin of renal cell carcinoma by providing conclusive electron microscopic evidence of its origin from renal tubular epithelium. Prior to the study by Oberling *et al.* there were certain schools of thought that considered renal cell carcinoma to be of adrenal origin. It was Grawitz in 1883 who put forth the theory of renal cell carcinoma originating from adrenal rests in the kidney, rather than from renal epithelium, because of its resemblance to the adrenal gland cortex. Therefore, in the past this tumour was referred to as Grawitz tumour or 'hypernephroma', the latter term being coined by Birch-Hirschfeld in 1892.

A number of renal cell carcinomas are detected incidentally when the patient is investigated for other medical conditions. The tumour may grow substantially before it induces any signs or symptoms. The so-called 'classical triad' of flank pain, flank mass and haematuria is now only seen with advanced-stage tumours, which occur rarely. In addition to the aforementioned, patients may have nonspecific complaints such as fever, weakness, malaise and weight loss. Renal cell carcinoma may also be associated with paraneoplastic syndromes such as polycythaemia, hypertension, Cushing syndrome and hypercalcaemia. In 25%–30% of patients metastasis may be the first indication of the presence of the cancer.

The classification of renal cell carcinoma has changed in the recent past to better embody our understanding of this disease. Two important workshops on the classification of renal tumours were held in 1996 and 1997. The first, entitled 'Impact of Molecular Genetics on the Classification of Renal Cell Tumours' was held in October 1996 in Heidelberg, Germany. The conclusions of this workshop are referred to as the Heidelberg classification of renal tumours (Kovacs *et al.*, 1997). The second, entitled 'Diagnosis and Prognosis of Renal Cell Carcinoma: 1997 Workshop', organized by the American Joint Committee on Cancer (AJCC) and Union Internationale Contre le Cancer (UICC), was held in March 1997 (Störkel *et al.*, 1997). These two classification systems are listed in **Table 3**. While these two classification systems at first glance may seem to be similar, and they are in the use of similar terms, the major difference is the Heidelberg classification's emphasis on genetic correlation. Both of these classification schemes are based on the light microscopic appearance of the tumour but are in keeping with our prevailing knowledge of the genetics of these cancers. The diagnostic terminology used is practical, concise and reflective of the morphologic appearance of the tumour; however, some of these terms are not descriptive and do not encompass all the morphologic patterns of a given tumour. There are numerous older classification schemes for subtyping renal cell carcinoma that use different terminology, including terms such as chromophil carcinoma (for papillary renal cell carcinoma), nonpapillary renal cell carcinoma, etc. It is preferable to avoid use of these terms as they may cause confusion.

All renal cell carcinomas are graded according to Fuhrman's nuclear grading system, which is divided into four grades based on the nuclear size, nuclear irregularity and nucleolar prominence (**Table 4**). The grade is based on the highest grade within the entire tumour, and not the predominant grade. It is evaluated at 100× and 400× magnification using a light microscope.

The tumour, nodes and metastasis (TNM) system is the most widely used system for staging renal cell carcinoma (**Table 5**). The other system that is used sometimes is the Robson staging system (**Table 5**). The staging systems are partly based on the extent of invasion by the tumour, with the lower stage tumours (pT1 and pT2) being confined to the kidney, whereas the higher stage tumours (pT3 and pT4) extend beyond the confines of the organ.

Epidemiology

Renal cell carcinoma affects approximately 1–3% of all patients with cancer worldwide (McLaughlin and Lipworth, 2000). The highest incidence of renal cell carcinoma is recorded in Scandinavia followed by other parts of northern Europe, the United States and Canada. The lowest incidence rates have been recorded in Central and South America and in Asia. It is estimated that 30 800 new cases of renal cell carcinoma will be diagnosed in the United States in the year 2001, constituting the ninth most common tumour in that country. An estimated 12 100 persons are expected to die of the disease in the United States in the year 2001. The incidence of renal cell carcinoma has been increasing every year in the United States since the 1970s, with a greater increase being noted in the African-American population as compared with Caucasians. This cancer more commonly affects men than women, with a male to female ratio of 2 : 1. Patients of renal cell carcinoma are more likely to be in the late sixth and early seventh decades of life, although these cancers have been reported to occur in children. In addition to the sporadic forms of the cancer, a small percentage are familial, these include renal cell carcinoma associated with Von Hippel–Lindau (VHL) syndrome, familial conventional (clear cell) carcinoma and familial papillary renal cell carcinoma. These cancers usually occur in younger patients, and show autosomal dominant inheritance.

Aetiology

Numerous agents (**Table 6**) are associated with development of renal cell carcinoma (McLaughlin and Lipworth,

Table 3 Classification of renal cell carcinoma

Heidelberg classification[a]	AJCC/UICC classification[b]
Benign tumours	*Benign tumours*
Papillary renal cell adenoma	Papillary adenoma
Renal oncocytoma	Renal oncocytoma
Metanephric adenoma	Metanephric adenoma
Metanephric adenofibroma	Metanephric adenofibroma
Malignant tumours	*Malignant tumours*
Common or conventional renal cell carcinoma	Conventional (clear) renal cell carcinoma
Papillary renal cell carcinoma	Papillary renal cell carcinoma
Chromophobe renal cell carcinoma	Chromophobe renal cell carcinoma
Collecting duct carcinoma	Collecting duct carcinoma
RCC, unclassified	Unclassified renal cell carcinoma

[a]Kovacs et al., 1997.
[b]Störkel et al., 1997.

Table 4 Fuhrman's nuclear grading for renal cell carcinoma

Grade	Nucleus	Nucleolus
1	Small (10-μm diameter), round, uniform, resembling nucleus of mature lymphocyte	Inconspicuous or absent nucleoli (viewed at 400× magnification)
2	Larger nuclei (15-μm diameter), with slight nuclear irregularity	Small nucleoli (only visible at 400× magnification)
3	Large nuclei (20-μm diameter), with obvious nuclear irregularity	Large, prominent nucleoli (visible at 100× magnification)
4	Same as grade 3 but more bizarre with multilobation and large clumps of chromatin	Large, prominent nucleoli (visible at 100× magnification)

Table 5   1997 TNM staging systems for renal cell carcinoma

Primary tumour (T)

TX	Primary tumour cannot be assessed
T0	No evidence of primary tumour
T1	Tumour 7.0 cm or less in greatest dimension, limited to the kidney
T2	Tumour > 7.0 cm in greatest dimension, limited to the kidney
T3	(a) Tumour invades adrenal gland or perinephric tissue, but not beyond Gerota's fascia
	(b) Tumour extension into renal vein(s) or vena cava below the diaphragm
	(c) Tumour invades vena cava above the diaphragm
T4	Tumour invades beyond Gerota's fascia

Regional lymph node (N)

NX	Regional lymph nodes cannot be assessed
N0	No regional lymph node metastasis
N1	Metastasis in a single regional lymph node
N2	Metastasis in more than one regional lymph node

Distant metastasis (M)

MX	Presence of distant metastasis cannot be assessed
M0	No distant metastasis
M1	Distant metastasis

Stage groupings

Stage I	T1	N0	M0
Stage II	T2	N0	M0
Stage III	T3	N0	M0
	T1-T3	N1	M0
Stage IV	T4	N0–N1	M0
	Any T	N2	M0
	Any T	Any N	M1

Robson staging system

I	Confined to kidney
II	Perinephric fat invasion but tumour completely resected
IIIa	Renal vein or vena cava involvement
IIIb	Lymph node involvement
IIIc	Vascular and lymphatic invasion
IV	Metastatic disease or involvement of adjacent organs other than the adrenal gland

2000). Cigarette smoking is the most prominent aetiological factor associated with renal cell carcinoma; 20–30% of all renal cell carcinomas affecting men and 10–20% affecting women are attributed to cigarette smoking. There is a strong dose–response relationship associated with cigarette smoking; the relative risk for smokers ranges from 1.2 to 2.3, with a relative risk from 1.9 to 2.5 for heavy smokers. In the familial forms of renal cell carcinoma, genetic alterations play an important aetiological role. Germ-line mutations of chromosome 3p are associated with the VHL syndrome; mutations of chromosome 3p are also associated with familial conventional (clear cell) carcinoma. Germ-line mutations of the *MET* proto-oncogene, located on chromosome 7, are associated with the familial form of papillary renal cell carcinoma. In women, there is a positive association with obesity, which may be hormonally related. Long-term haemodialysis used in the treatment of renal disease leads to an increased incidence of acquired cystic disease, which in turn leads to increased risk of renal cell carcinoma. Although use of the drug phenacetin has been related to urothelial carcinoma of the renal pelvis, there is a less consistent association with renal cell carcinoma. Association with the drug acetaminophen has not been proved, except in one study. Other possible aetiological factors include hypertension, diet, and exposure to asbestos and petroleum products.

Gross Features

Renal cell carcinoma most often occurs as a single solid tumour often located at the periphery of the renal parenchyma (**Figure 3; see colour plate section**). However, collecting duct carcinoma is located more centrally in the medullary region. A bright yellow or light orange colour is most characteristic of conventional (clear cell) renal cell carcinoma, which is the most common type of renal cell carcinoma. In addition, there may be areas of haemorrhage and necrosis resulting in a mottled

Table 6   Aetiological and putative aetiological factors in urinary tract tumours

Renal cell carcinoma	Urothelial carcinoma of renal pelvis and ureter	Urothelial carcinoma of urinary bladder
Cigarette smoking	Cigarette smoking	Cigarette smoking
Germ-line mutations (3p, MET proto-oncogene)	Phenacetin abuse	Arylamines
	Thorium exposure	Chemotherapeutic agents
Obesity (in women)	Balkan nephropathy	Radiation
Haemodialysis (long-term)	Urothelial tumours of the urinary bladder	Chronic infection
Hypertension		Schistosomiasis
Sickle cell trait		Bladder exstrophy
		Artificial sweeteners
		Human papillomavirus
		Gene mutation/deletions (*p15, p16, p53, ras, c-myc*)

appearance. Chromophobe renal cell carcinoma is relatively homogeneous with a light beige, tan–brown or brown colouration; however, higher grade tumours may have haemorrhage and necrosis. Papillary renal cell carcinoma is well circumscribed; it may have a similar colouration as the conventional (clear cell) type, or may be light tan to grey, depending on the number of foam cells in the stroma. Foci of necrosis, haemorrhage and cyst formation may be seen in any of the subtypes. Areas of sarcomatoid dedifferentiation are grey–white, more fleshy or firm. Pale yellow or pale tan firm areas of scar formation should not be confused for sarcomatoid dedifferentiation. Foci of calcification may also be present. The majority of the carcinomas are confined to the kidney, but some may show gross invasion into the perinephric adipose tissue or into the renal vein, rarely extending into the inferior vena cava and the right side of the heart.

Microscopic Features

Each of the different subtypes of renal cell carcinoma has distinct morphological features, which are detailed below.

Conventional (Clear Cell) Renal Cell Carcinoma
Conventional (clear cell) renal cell carcinoma is the most common subtype, representing 65–75% of renal cancer in most series. Tumour cells are arranged in sheets, nests, or tubules (**Figure 4; see colour plate section**). Uncommonly they may show a tubulocystic or, rarely, a papillary arrangement. Most tumour cells have clear cytoplasm; however, tumours can have a combination of cells with clear and granular eosinophilic cytoplasm. Tumours almost exclusively composed of cells with eosinophilic cytoplasm are rare. The clear cell appearance of conventional renal cell carcinoma is secondary to the lipid and glycogen content of the cells. The periodic acid Schiff (PAS) histochemical stain, with and without diastase, is the best method for demonstrating the cytoplasmic glycogen. One of the hallmark histological features is the delicate, interconnecting, sinusoidal-type of vasculature, sometimes likened to 'chicken wire' (**Figure 4**). This type of vascular pattern is generally not seen in the other subtypes of renal cell carcinoma and is a good clue to making the diagnosis of conventional renal cell carcinoma when cells with granular eosinophilic cytoplasm predominate. Thus, the diagnosis of conventional renal cell carcinoma is based on the architectural pattern and the vascular pattern, rather than the tinctorial properties of the cell cytoplasm.

Papillary Renal Cell Carcinoma
Papillary renal cell carcinoma accounts for about 10–15% of all renal carcinomas. Multifocal and bilateral tumours are more common in this subtype than any other subtype of renal cell carcinoma. Microscopically, it shows fibrovascular papillary cores lined by a single layer of low cuboidal epithelial cells that have scant pale cytoplasm and oval dark nuclei (**Figure 5; see colour plate section**). Some tumours have tall columnar pseudostratified cells with abundant eosinophilic cytoplasm. Tumour cells may have haemosiderin pigment within the cytoplasm. In addition to the papillae, tumour cells may form tubules, tubulopapillary structures and, rarely, solid nests. A characteristic feature, which may not be present in all tumours, is the presence of foamy macrophages within the fibrovascular stalks. Laminated calcifications (psammoma bodies) are also commonly present.

Chromophobe Renal Cell Carcinoma
Chromophobe renal cell carcinoma accounts for about 5% of all renal carcinomas and presents distinctive histological and ultrastructural features that clearly separate it from the other subtypes. There are two morphological variants, typical or classical chromophobe and the eosinophilic variant; this distinction is based on the tinctorial properties of the cytoplasm. These variants are not clinically important, but are important from the diagnosis point of view as the eosinophilic variant may be mistaken for renal oncocytoma, a benign tumour. Tumour cells are arranged in sheets, broad alveoli or nests. There are two types of cells, clear and eosinophilic (**Figure 6; see colour plate section**). Both types are usually present with one type predominating; if clear cells predominate, the tumour is referred to as typical or classical, and if the eosinophilic cells predominate, it is the eosinophilic variant. The clear cells have abundant clear cytoplasm with a frothy, vacuolated or bubbly appearance (soap bubble appearance) and prominent cell membranes, resembling plant cells. The cytoplasm typically forms a rim along the cell membrane that appears darker than the remainder of the cytoplasm. These cells also may have a perinuclear halo. The eosinophilic cells are smaller and have finely granular eosinophilic cytoplasm, with a variable degree of perinuclear clearing. The nuclei are hyperchromatic, frequently binucleate and have a wrinkled nuclear membrane. The nuclear features along with the perinuclear halo and the prominent cell membranes is referred to as 'koilocytoid atypia,' as it superficially resembles the changes seen in cells infected by the human papillomavirus. Hale's colloidal iron stain is the histochemical stain of choice for confirming the diagnosis of chromophobe renal cell carcinoma; this stain shows diffuse, reticular staining.

Collecting Duct Carcinoma
Collecting duct carcinoma is rare, accounting for about 1% of all renal cell carcinomas. Microscopically, three features characterize this renal cancer; a tubulo-papillary arrangement of cells, desmoplastic reaction of the stroma and dysplastic changes in the adjacent collecting ducts. Dilated tubules or solid areas may also be present. In

general, before making a diagnosis of collecting duct carcinoma, metastasis to the kidney should be excluded. Renal medullary carcinoma is a distinctive type of collecting duct carcinoma with an aggressive clinical course, which arises in the renal medulla and is associated with sickle cell trait. In addition to the typical morphological features of collecting duct carcinoma, these cancers have reticular, microcystic areas, which resemble yolk sac tumour. Collecting duct carcinoma shows variable areas of mucin formation, which stain with histochemical stains for mucin, such as mucicarmine and Alcian blue.

Renal Cell Carcinoma, Unclassified

Unclassified renal cell carcinoma is not a distinctive subtype, but rather represents renal cancers that do not fit into one of the above-mentioned categories. Renal cancers in this category include, but are not limited to, those not conforming to any of the known histological subtypes, composites of recognizable subtypes, cancers with extensive necrosis and minimal viable tumour, mucin-producing tumours that are not collecting duct carcinoma and tumours with sarcomatoid dedifferentiation that do not have an epithelial element that can be readily assigned to one of the above categories (Störkel *et al.*, 1997).

Renal Cell Carcinoma with Sarcomatoid Dedifferentiation

Sarcomatoid dedifferentiation is seen in approximately 1.5% of renal cell carcinomas. The term sarcomatoid dedifferentiation denotes anaplastic transformation of the renal cell carcinoma into a high-grade biphasic tumour that contains both malignant carcinomatous and mesenchymal elements. These tumours have been referred to in the past as carcinosarcoma or mixed mesodermal tumours. The incidence of sarcomatoid dedifferentiation, in our experience, varies amongst the different subtypes: 8% in conventional (clear cell), 3% in papillary renal cell carcinoma, 9% in chromophobe renal cell carcinoma, 27% in collecting duct carcinoma and 11% in renal cell carcinoma unclassified. The carcinoma component is usually high grade, at least a Fuhrman's nuclear grade 3, but may have any grade. The sarcomatous component may resemble pleomorphic malignant fibrous histiocytoma or an unclassified spindle cell sarcoma, or may show differentiation into bone, cartilage, skeletal muscle or blood vessels. It is important to differentiate a true sarcomatous component from benign spindle cells that are sometimes seen in renal cell carcinoma. The majority of these lesions are high stage at presentation and the prognosis is very poor. When reporting sarcomatoid dedifferentiation in renal cell carcinoma it is important to mention the percentage of the sarcomatoid component and the type of epithelial and sarcomatoid components. The percentage of the sarcomatoid component has been reported to be important for survival; patients with >50% sarcomatoid dedifferentiation in their cancer do poorly.

Immunohistochemistry

All renal cell carcinomas stain positive with immunohistochemical stains for cytokeratin cocktail (AE1/AE3 and CAM 5.2), low molecular weight cytokeratin and epithelial membrane antigen (EMA). Conventional (clear cell) and papillary renal cell carcinoma also stain with vimentin, which is an intermediate filament usually associated with mesenchymal structures. Chromophobe renal cell carcinoma, on the other hand, does not stain with vimentin, which may be utilized for distinguishing the eosinophilic variant of chromophobe renal cell carcinoma from conventional renal cell carcinoma with predominantly eosinophilic cells. Collecting duct carcinoma, however, has a unique staining pattern, reacting with both low and high molecular weight cytokeratins, peanut agglutinin, *Ulex europaeus* lectin and epithelial membrane antigen. This characteristic staining pattern is similar to that of the distal collecting tubule epithelium.

Electron Microscopy

Ultrastructurally, the cells of conventional (clear cell) renal cell carcinoma exhibit a brush border, tend to form microlumina and have a basal lamina that separates groups of cells from each other. Abundant glycogen and lipid are present in the cytoplasm. Chromophobe renal cell carcinoma has characteristic microvesicles, which are probably derived from the endoplasmic reticulum or from mitochondria. Mitochondria also impart the characteristic granularity to the cytoplasm seen by light microscopy.

Molecular Genetics

Sporadic conventional (clear cell) renal cell carcinoma typically (in approximately 80–90%) shows loss of genetic material from the short arm of chromosome 3, in the region 3p14–3p26 that harbours the *VHL* gene at 3p25.3. Mutations within the *VHL* gene region and inactivation of this gene by hypermethylation are common. Sporadic papillary renal cell carcinoma is characterized by trisomies, especially of chromosomes 7 and 17, and loss of the Y chromosome. Other chromosomes that may be involved include 3, 9, 11, 12, 16, and 20; some of these additional abnormalities are speculated to lead to progression to a more aggressive phenotype. Translocation between chromosomes X and 1 has also been reported, and is more common in children. As mentioned earlier, the familial cases of papillary renal cell carcinoma show germ-line mutations of the *MET* proto-oncogene. Chromophobe renal cell carcinomas are characterized by combined losses of multiple chromosomes including 1, 2, 6, 10, 12, 13, 14, 15 and 17. Polysomy of chromosome 7, trisomy 12, 16 and 19, telomeric associations and structural abnormalities of 11q have also been described in these cancers. Another important finding in chromophobe renal cell carcinoma is abnormalities of mitochondrial DNA, a feature not seen in the other subtypes. Collecting duct carcinoma does not have any distinct genetic alterations. Monosomy of chromosomes 1, 6, 14, 15 and 22, deletions of 8p and13q, and loss of heterozygosity (LOH) in 1q have all been reported in this cancer.

Prognostic Factors

The prognosis of renal cell carcinoma is heavily dependent on the TNM stage of the tumour (Rini and Vogelzang, 2000). The 5-year survival rate of all patients with renal cell carcinoma is 70–75%. The overall 5-year survival rate is ≤ 10% in patients with stage IV disease, 20–40% in patients with stage III tumours, 50–60% with stage II tumours and 60–90% with stage I tumours. The presence of sarcomatoid dedifferentiation also portends a poor prognosis, with disease-specific survival rates of 59 and 22% at 1 and 5 years, respectively. Fuhrman's nuclear grade has also been shown to have limited value in predicting prognosis. Up to 50% of patients with the VHL syndrome die of renal cell carcinoma. Newer markers that are under investigation for determining prognosis include DNA ploidy, proliferation marker MIB-1, p53, vascular endothelium growth factor (VEGF), *VHL* gene mutations, etc. None of these markers has so far been shown to be better at predicting tumour recurrence or death from disease, and all of these markers and molecular genetic alterations need to be studied further.

Overview of Present Clinical Management

Surgical resection in the form of radical nephrectomy remains the most effective treatment for clinically localized tumours. In recent years the use of nephron-sparing surgery has been gaining popularity for the treatment of small, localized tumours that can be easily resected (Wunderlich *et al.*, 1998). Solitary metastasis of renal cell carcinoma may be resected, but with limited success. Immunotherapy using interferon and/or interleukin 2 (IL-2) has had partial success in treating metastatic disease, as it remains resistant to systemic chemotherapy. Newer therapies for metastatic renal cell carcinoma that are currently undergoing investigation include tumour-specific vaccines, angiogenesis inhibitors, monoclonal antibodies and dendritic cell therapy.

RENAL PELVIS AND URETER

Tumours of the renal pelvis and ureter are uncommon. Urothelial carcinoma accounts for 90% of the malignant tumours, but represents less than 5% of all tumours arising from the urothelium. The remaining 10% include squamous cell carcinoma and adenocarcinoma. Urothelial carcinomas of the renal pelvis and ureter have epidemiological, clinical, morphological and prognostic features similar to those arising in the urinary bladder (Steffens and Nagel, 1988). There are significantly different aetiological factors (**Table 6**) associated with these tumours including phenacetin abuse, thorium (radiographic contrast medium) exposure and Balkan nephropathy. Another characteristic feature is the association with urothelial tumours of the urinary bladder, which may occur synchronously or metachronously. Tumours arising in the ureter may fill the lumen, leading to obstruction and possibly hydronephrosis. All the different morphological variants of urothelial carcinoma reported in the urinary bladder have also been reported in the renal pelvis and ureter. The grading system is similar to that of the urinary bladder urothelial carcinomas. Also like the urinary bladder, the TNM staging system is based on the depth of invasion (**Table 7**).

Table 7 1997 TNM staging system for urothelial carcinoma of renal pelvis and ureter

Primary tumour (T)

TX	Primary tumour cannot be assessed
T0	No evidence of primary tumour
Ta	Papillary noninvasive carcinoma
Tis	Carcinoma *in situ*
T1	Tumour invades subepithelial connective tissue
T2	Tumour invades the muscularis
T3	(For renal pelvis only): tumour invades beyond muscularis into peripelvic fat or the renal parenchyma
T3	(For ureter only): tumour invades beyond muscularis into periureteric fat
T4	Tumour invades adjacent organs, or through the kidney into the perinephric fat

Regional lymph nodes (N)[a]

NX	Regional lymph nodes cannot be assessed
N0	No regional lymph node metastasis
N1	Metastasis in a single lymph node, 2 cm or less in greatest dimension
N2	Metastasis in a single lymph node, 2 cm but not more than 5 cm in greatest dimension; or multiple lymph nodes, none more than 5 cm in greatest dimension
N3	Metastasis in a lymph node more than 5 cm in greatest dimension

Distant Metastasis (M)

MX	Distant metastasis cannot be assessed
M0	No distant metastasis
M1	Distant metastasis

Stage Groupings

Stage 0a	Ta	N0	M0
Stage 0is	Tis	N0	M0
Stage I	T1	N0	M0
Stage II	T2	N0	M0
Stage III	T3	N0	M0
Stage IV	T4	N0	M0
	Any T	Any N	M0
	Any T	Any N	M1

[a]Laterality does not affect the N classification.

Nephroureterectomy with a bladder cuff remains the treatment of choice for these cancers.

URINARY BLADDER

Up to 95% of urinary bladder tumours (**Table 8**) are of epithelial origin, of which 90% are urothelial neoplasms. The urothelium is a highly specialized epithelium that lines the entire urinary tract and has the ability to modify the number of layers forming it, depending on the level of distention of the organ wall. It has traditionally been referred to as the transitional cell epithelium, but urothelium is currently the preferred term (Epstein *et al.*, 1998).

Other types of epithelial tumours arise in the urinary bladder, including squamous cell carcinomas and adenocarcinomas. These are usually diagnosed when the entire tumour is entirely composed of malignant squamous or glandular elements, as foci of squamous or glandular differentiation can be seen in otherwise typical urothelial carcinomas, more commonly in high-grade tumours. Small

Table 8   Tumours of the urinary bladder

Benign tumours	Malignant tumours
Epithelial tumours	*Epithelial tumours*
Urothelial papilloma	Urothelial carcinoma
Urothelial inverted	(papillary noninvasive,
papilloma	papillary invasive, flat
Villous adenoma	noninvasive, flat invasive,
	invasive NOS, micropapillary,
	lymphoepithelioma-like,
	nested)
	Squamous cell carcinoma
	Adenocarcinoma
	Small cell carcinoma
	Undifferentiated carcinoma
Mesenchymal tumours	*Mesenchymal tumours*
Leiomyoma	Rhabdomyosarcoma
Neurofibroma	Leiomyosarcoma
Haemangioma	
Inflammatory	
myofibroblastic tumour	
	Miscellaneous neoplasms
	Lymphoma/leukaemia
	Plasmacytoma
	Malignant melanoma
	Paraganglioma
	Germ cell neoplasms
	Secondary involvement
	Direct extension from
	adjacent organs
	(rectum, bladder, uterus)
	Metastasis

cell carcinoma and other neuroendocrine carcinomas of the urinary bladder have also been reported.

Mesenchymal neoplasms, which range from benign proliferations to highly malignant and aggressive tumours, are much less common. The most common benign mesenchymal neoplasm is leiomyoma, while the most common sarcomas are rhabdomyosarcoma in children and leiomyosarcoma in adults. Lymphoma, plasmacytoma and infiltration by leukaemia rarely present in the urinary bladder without a previous history of the disease. Finally, secondary involvement of the urinary bladder by other tumours is rare, but when it occurs it is usually by direct extension from adjacent organs.

Urothelial Carcinoma

Tumour Pathology

Urothelial neoplasms arise by two distinct pathobiological pathways, resulting in the development of either papillary or nonpapillary tumours (see Molecular Genetics, below). Benign urothelial neoplasms, including exophytic and inverted urothelial papillomas, are much less frequent than carcinomas. Most urothelial carcinomas are preinvasive or early invasive papillary tumours. These tumours show a range of cytological and architectural atypia, which has been the basis for several proposed grading systems (see Microscopic Features, below). They are commonly multifocal, and may involve other sites along the urinary tract in addition to the urinary bladder. Papillary tumours tend to recur several times and eventually can invade the underlying lamina propria and muscularis propria. Less commonly, urinary bladder neoplasms start as nonpapillary or flat intraepithelial lesions, referred to as primary or *de novo* urothelial carcinoma *in situ*. These tumours also have the potential to invade the underlying wall. Up to 20% of urinary bladder neoplasms are diagnosed in an advanced stage, with invasion of the muscularis propria. When invasive, urothelial neoplasms have the potential to produce metastasis and death due to disease.

Epidemiology

It is estimated that 54 000 new cases of urinary bladder cancer will be diagnosed in the United States in the year 2001, constituting the fifth most common tumour in that country. Despite recent advances in treatment of both early and advanced urinary bladder tumours, an estimated 12 000 persons are expected to die of the disease in the United States in the year 2001. Urinary bladder cancer is more frequent in North America and Western Europe and uncommon in Japan. In the United States, it is twice as common in Caucasians as in African-Americans. It also has a 2.6-fold higher incidence in men than in women. Most tumours arise during late adulthood, with a median age at diagnosis of over 65 years.

Aetiology

Several aetiological factors have been associated with the development of urinary bladder cancer (Johansson and Cohen, 1997). This still growing list started in the nineteenth century when an increased incidence in urinary bladder tumours was noted among workers in the dye industry. Today, new data on the role of tumour-suppressor genes, oncogenes and other external influences have enhanced our knowledge of the pathogenesis of urinary bladder cancer (**Table 6**).

Tobacco

Approximately 33% of urinary bladder tumours (50–80% of tumours in men) are associated with smoking. The risk in smokers is increased 3–7-fold compared with non-smokers, depending on the number of pack-years and smoking habits. Ex-smokers have a reduced risk, but the period of time necessary for them to return to the same risk level as nonsmokers is unknown.

Arylamines

Occupational exposure to arylamines, which are widely used in the aniline dye and rubber industry, has been associated with up to one-third of urinary bladder cancers. The risk is dependent on the intensity and duration of the exposure, and tumours usually appear 15–40 years after the first exposure. The insult to the urothelium results when the urinary enzyme glucuronidase splits the nontoxic glucuronate conjugate previously formed in the liver, releasing an electrophilic reactant. The process is highly specific to humans, as we are one of the few species to possess glucuronidase.

Radiation

There is an increased risk of developing urothelial carcinoma in women treated with radiation for cervical carcinoma. The tumours usually develop many years after exposure and are usually of high grade and high stage at presentation.

Cyclophosphamide

Cyclophosphamide, an alkylating agent used as an immunosuppressant, is associated with up to a 10.7% cumulative risk of developing urinary bladder cancer after 12 years of exposure.

Urinary Tract Infection

Chronic urinary tract infection also appears to confer a significant risk for urinary bladder neoplasia, especially in women. This mechanism also explains the higher incidence of urinary bladder neoplasms in paraplegic patients with indwelling catheters. Urinary bacteria increase the levels of volatile nitrosamines, believed to be mediators in the development of neoplasia.

Other Aetiological Factors

Phenacetin has been linked to the development of urothelial carcinoma of the renal pelvis. In urinary bladder tumours, however, only a weak association has been demonstrated, except when high cumulative doses have been used. Artificial sweeteners have been associated with urinary bladder tumours in animal studies. A single case-control study in humans reported a 1.6-fold increase in risk for men who use saccharin. These findings, however, have not been confirmed by other studies, and thus the aggregate data appear to show no significant risk of urinary bladder cancer for persons using artificial sweeteners. Similarly, some studies have suggested an increased risk in coffee and tea drinkers, but based on the aggregate data the risk level appears to be weak to nonexistent. Although still limited, the overall data also show little if any role for human papillomavirus in urinary bladder neoplasia.

Screening and Prevention

Screening for urothelial cancer is usually done in one of three settings: (1) screening individuals at high risk for urinary bladder cancer (i.e., exposure to known carcinogens), (2) screening individuals with microscopic haematuria or irritative voiding symptoms, and (3) monitoring patients following diagnosis and conservative local therapy of urothelial carcinoma (i.e., for detection of recurrences).

A variety of methods have recently been developed, most of which target molecules that are present more frequently in the urine of patients with urothelial carcinoma than in that of patients without urothelial carcinoma (**Table 9**). As yet, none of these methods has replaced urine cytology, which is inexpensive, noninvasive and still considered the 'gold standard' screening method (Brown, 2000).

Urine Cytology

Urine cytology is still the most common screening method for diagnosing urothelial carcinoma. Although it is primarily used for the follow-up of patients with a diagnosis of urothelial carcinoma, it has value in the screening of

Table 9 Screening and monitoring methods for urothelial carcinoma

Urine cytology
Bladder tumour antigen
Nuclear matrix proteins
Fibrin/fibrinogen degradation products
Telomerase activity
Hyaluronic acid/hyaluronidase
Cystoscopy and biopsy
Cystogram and excretory urography

high-risk populations. The main limitations of urine cytology are its low sensitivity for low-grade lesions and that its accuracy is dependent on the experience of the pathologist reviewing the specimen. Sensitivity for low-grade tumours has ranged from 0 to 100%, with most studies reporting less than 50%. For high-grade tumours, including carcinoma *in situ*, sensitivity and specificity approach 90 and 100%, respectively.

Bladder Tumour Antigen

Urothelial neoplasms secrete enzymes that lyse the urothelial basement membrane, exposing antigens that can be detected in the urine by a latex agglutination reaction. Initial studies have suggested that this method has a higher sensitivity than urine cytology, but other studies have found conflicting results. Further, specificity is significantly reduced in patients who have urinary tract infections or urolithiasis or have undergone prior instrumentation.

Nuclear Matrix Proteins

Nuclear matrix proteins, the structural framework of the nucleus, are present at low levels in the urine of normal individuals and in increased quantity in patients with urothelial carcinoma. An immunoassay that quantifies the amount of nuclear matrix proteins has been developed. Its sensitivity and specificity are dependent on the cut-off value. An overall sensitivity of 66% has been reported. Specificity is significantly diminished in the presence of gross haematuria and prostate cancer, but even in optimal cases the test does not appear superior to urine cytology.

Fibrin/Fibrinogen Degradation Products

Increased vascular permeability induced by a urinary bladder tumour results in leakage of fibrinogen and plasminogen. The fibrinogen is converted into an extravascular fibrin clot but is degraded by plasmin, which is activated by the urinary enzyme urokinase. Thus, the presence of fibrin or fibrinogen degradation products is indicative of urinary bladder carcinoma. The currently available assay for detecting these products has an overall sensitivity in the range 48–68% and a specificity of around 80%, which is also diminished in patients with gross haematuria and prostate cancer.

Telomerase

Degradation of telomeres after several cell cycles is a cell death mechanism. Telomerase's primary function is to repair the telomeres at the end of each cell cycle, delaying their degradation. Thus, over-activity of telomerases, prolongs cell life and may turn cells immortal. The method for measuring telomerase activity has a sensitivity of 70% and a specificity of up to 99% for detecting urinary bladder cancer. However, the assay is not yet widely available and requires laboratories with well-established expertise. False-positive results may occur in patients with inflammatory conditions, and false negatives may occur in patients with gross haematuria.

Hyaluronic Acid/Hyaluronidase

High levels of hyaluronic acid in the urine of patients with urinary bladder cancer can be detected with a sensitivity and specificity of 92%. Further, patients with high-grade neoplasms have elevated urinary hyaluronidase activity that can be detected with a 100% specificity. These still rather preliminary data suggest that this assay could be used for the diagnosis of low-grade lesions and the early detection of tumour progression.

Cystoscopy and Biopsy

Cystoscopy allows the direct visualization of the urinary bladder mucosa and biopsy of suspicious lesions. Urinary bladder washings obtained at the time of cystoscopic examination also provide useful cytological material. Carcinoma *in situ* is not always identified by cystoscopic examination, and thus random urinary bladder biopsies are usually performed to identify this lesion.

Cystograms and Excretory Urography

These methods provide useful information regarding the presence of multifocal disease involving the upper urinary tract and the localization of large urinary bladder masses that produce filling defects.

Gross Features

Noninvasive papillary tumours are recognized by cystoscopy as exophytic papillary fronds in the mucosa, usually of varying size. Up to 40% of tumours may be multifocal. Tumours occur most often in the lateral and posterior walls of the urinary bladder and least often in the dome. Urothelial carcinoma *in situ* usually appears as an erythaematous area in the mucosa of the urinary bladder, but it can also be grossly inapparent. When invasive, urothelial carcinomas are usually bulging, nodular exophytic tumours, or ulcerated and indurated. A papillary component may still be present, albeit focally. Some tumours display diffuse infiltration of the urinary bladder wall with relatively unremarkable mucosa, analogous to the so-called linitis plastica of the stomach. Large, fleshy, polypoid tumours that fill the urinary bladder cavity usually exhibit sarcomatoid features.

Microscopic Features

Papillary urothelial neoplasms range from small and benign to large and aggressive tumours. The distinction is usually based on the degree of cytological and architectural atypia, which is the basis of the grading schemes used for these neoplasms. Recently, a new grading system, the one used in this discussion, was proposed by a conjoint effort of the World Health Organisation (WHO) and the

Table 10 World Health Organisation/International Society of Urologic Pathology grading scheme for urothelial neoplasia

Papillary lesions	Flat lesions
Papillary hyperplasia	Flat urothelial hyperplasia
Urothelial papilloma	Reactive atypia
Inverted papilloma	Atypia of unknown significance
Papillary urothelial neoplasm of low malignant potential	Dysplasia (low-grade intraurothelial neoplasia)
Papillary urothelial carcinoma, low grade	Carcinoma *in situ* (high-grade intraurothelial neoplasia)
Papillary urothelial carcinoma, high grade	

International Society of Urologic Pathology (ISUP) (**Table 10**) (Epstein *et al.*, 1998). In this system, benign papillary tumours are referred to as papillomas. They are usually small, delicate, papillary epithelial proliferations attached to the mucosa by a thin fibrovascular stalk. The urothelial lining is identical with that of the normal urinary bladder mucosa. Papillomas represent less than 1% of tumours and are usually seen in younger patients. These lesions can recur, although probably at a lower rate than other higher grade lesions. Tumours with slightly more complex architecture, of larger size and lined by cytologically normal or minimally abnormal urothelium are referred to as papillary urothelial neoplasms of low malignant potential. They have a tendency to recur but not invade or cause death. These tumours were previously referred to as transitional cell carcinomas, grade 1 (using the old WHO classification system). Papillary tumours containing cytologically malignant cells are currently classified as low-grade and high-grade papillary urothelial carcinomas (previously referred to as grade 2 and grade 3 transitional cell carcinomas, respectively). These tumours have a higher degree of nuclear pleomorphism and disorganisation of the epithelial cells, progressively losing their resemblance to normal urothelium (**Figure 7; see colour plate section**). High-grade tumours usually have less well-developed, blunt and fused papillae, with occasional solid areas.

Flat urothelial lesions also display a range of cytological changes, lesions at the lower end of the spectrum being referred to as urothelial dysplasia and at the higher end as carcinoma *in situ* (**Figure 8; see colour plate section**). As opposed to papillary lesions, however, only the high-grade lesions (i.e. carcinoma *in situ*) are known clinically significant, worthy of therapeutic intervention. As stated before, carcinoma *in situ* may be primary (i.e. arising *de novo*), or more commonly secondary (i.e. arising in association with previous or concurrent urothelial carcinoma). In the latter setting, its presence confers increased risk of progression to invasive disease.

Invasion into the underlying wall is most common in high-grade papillary tumours or in patients with carcinoma *in situ*. The extent of invasion ranges from microscopic foci of tumours invading the lamina propria to bulky tumours extending through the urinary bladder wall into the perivesical adipose tissue. The invasive components usually display high nuclear grade and may grow in nests, cords or trabeculae of neoplastic cells, which infiltrate the muscle bundles and adipose tissue (**Figure 9; see colour plate section**).

Sarcomatoid urothelial carcinoma is a high-grade neoplasm that has partially or totally lost its carcinomatous morphological phenotype and shows differentiation into spindle-cell mesenchymal elements. A well-defined malignant heterologous mesenchymal component, (e.g. leiomyosarcoma, osteosarcoma, rhabdomyosarcoma) may be present, but most often the mesenchymal component is relatively undifferentiated and high grade. Diagnosis of sarcomatoid carcinoma requires the presence of a focal, unequivocal, invasive or *in situ* epithelial component or evidence of epithelial differentiation either by immunohistochemistry (i.e. cytokeratin expression) or electron microscopy (i.e. presence of desmosomes or other epithelial elements). Differentiation between sarcomatoid carcinoma and sarcoma of the urinary bladder is clinically relevant, as the prognosis is significantly worse for sarcomatoid carcinomas.

Immunohistochemistry

The urothelium is a complex epithelium that expresses a wide variety of cytokeratin intermediate filaments. The urothelium and its neoplasms express both low and high molecular weight cytokeratin, and cytokeratin 7 and cytokeratin 20; however, up to 40% of high-grade urothelial cancers are negative for cytokeratin 20. Carcinoembryonic antigen (CEA) is expressed in approximately 60% of urothelial carcinomas, most frequently in those that show glandular differentiation. Cytokeratin 10 and 14 are frequently expressed in areas of squamous differentiation. The urothelium usually lacks vimentin expression. Expression of other epithelial markers, such as epithelial membrane antigen and Leu-M1, has also been reported. Uroplakin and thrombomodulin are newer markers that are also useful for staining urothelial tumours. Immunohistochemistry has also been used to identify a wide range of molecular markers, mostly for prognostic purposes (see Prognostic Factors, below, for a brief review of these markers).

Molecular Genetic Findings

The data from cytogenetic and molecular studies of urinary bladder carcinoma support the two-pathway mechanism seen morphologically (Cordon-Cardo *et al.*, 1997; Lee and Droller, 2000). Most low-grade papillary neoplasms that have been studied have been associated with deletions of chromosome 9, including monosomy of chromosome 9 and 9p and/or 9q deletions. Chromosome 9 deletions are the only genetic change consistently present in noninvasive and early invasive papillary tumours and are thus believed to be an initial step in the development of these neoplasms. The 9p deletions involve the tumour-suppressor genes *p15* and *p16*, which encode inhibitors of cyclin-dependent kinase. The 9q deletions also likely include multiple tumour-suppressor genes, most of which are yet to be identified. On the other hand, urothelial carcinoma *in situ* is usually associated with deletions of 14q and deletions of 17p or mutations of the *p53* gene. These alterations are rarely seen in noninvasive, low-grade papillary tumours. Invasive tumours are similarly associated with mutations of p53 and deletions of 13q, the site of the *RB* gene. Other alterations observed in invasive tumours, but seldom in papillary tumours, include deletions of 11p, 3p, 8p, 6q, 4p, and 5q and increased expression of Ras, c-Myc and epidermal growth factor receptors.

Hence, these data support two distinct molecular pathways for urothelial carcinoma. On one side, alterations of chromosome 9 induce the formation of papillary tumours, which have low potential for progressing. If additional molecular alterations are acquired (*p53* mutations, 17p−, 3p−, 5q−), the tumours progress to high-grade lesions and invasion. On the other hand, *p53* mutations, 14q deletions and possibly other mechanisms result in urothelial carcinoma *in situ* with a propensity for progressing and developing invasive disease upon acquisition of additional alterations. Molecular events correlating with development of advanced disease and metastasis are also likely to be identified in the future.

Prognostic Factors

Numerous factors are used for evaluating the prognosis of urothelial carcinoma (**Table 11**). The extent of disease is the most valuable prognostic information used for the

Table 11 Prognostic factors in urothelial carcinoma

Pathological factors
Depth of invasion (stage)
Tumour grade
Histological type
Vascular invasion
Tumour size
Multicentricity
Associated carcinoma *in situ*
Biological/molecular factors
Blood group antigens
DNA ploidy
p53 mutations
Proliferation markers
Retinoblastoma gene mutations
p21^{WAF1}

management of urothelial carcinoma. When dealing with noninvasive or at most lamina propria-invasive tumours, management is focused on local control of the disease and parameters in this setting are those that can predict the frequency of tumour recurrence and likelihood of progression to muscle-invasive disease. Once the tumour has invaded the muscularis propria layer (**Figure 9**), aggressive management (usually cystectomy or radiation) is usually indicated, and useful prognostic parameters are those that can help predict development of distant metastasis or local recurrence. Thus, the main prognostic indicator for urothelial carcinoma, and the one on which others are dependent, is tumour stage (Mazzucchelli *et al.*, 1994).

Tumour Stage

Tumour stage is important not only because of the powerful prognostic information it conveys but also because it defines the management of the patient. The TNM system (**Table 12**) is the most commonly used staging system. Five-year survival for patients with T1 tumours is approximately 90% but drops to 70% for patients with T2 tumours and to 35% for those with T3 and T4 neoplasms (Mazzucchelli *et al.*, 1994). Owing to the abrupt difference in clinical behaviour between tumours showing only lamina propria invasion and those showing muscularis propria invasion, there is a tendency to simplify the staging system into two categories: 'superficial' (i.e. pTa pTis, and pT1 tumours) and 'invasive' (i.e. pT2, pT3, and pT4 tumours). While this nomenclature identifies two subsets of urinary bladder cancer that are traditionally managed in substantially different fashion, it oversimplifies and diminishes the power of the staging system. Further, the inaccurate terminology is confusing and can lead to miscommunication between pathologists and clinicians.

Tumour grade

Prognostic significance of grading in urinary bladder tumours is mostly limited to noninvasive or early invasive papillary tumours. Carcinoma *in situ* is a high-grade lesion by definition, and flat lesions of lesser grade (i.e. dysplasia) imply urothelial instability, but do not warrant therapeutic intervention. In muscle-invasive disease, grade has not provided any more prognostic information than stage alone. However, grade has repeatedly been shown to predict tumour recurrence and progression in papillary neoplasia. Patients with papillary urothelial neoplasms of low malignant potential have a 98% 10-year survival, whereas high-grade tumours are associated with a 35% 10-year survival. High-grade tumours with invasion into the lamina propria account for 60% of tumours that progress to muscle invasion (Lapham *et al.*, 1997).

Histological Tumour Type

The histological type of urinary bladder tumour has also been shown to have significant prognostic value.

Table 12 1997 TNM staging system for the urinary bladder

Primary tumour (T)

TX   Primary tumour cannot be assessed
T0   No evidence of primary tumour
Ta   Papillary noninvasive carcinoma
Tis   Carcinoma *in situ* 'flat tumour'
T1   Tumour invades subepithelial connective tissue
T2   Tumour invades muscle
  T2a Tumour invades superficial muscle (inner half)
  T2b Tumour invades deep muscle (outer half)
T3   Tumour invades perivesical tissue
  T3a Microscopically
  T3b Macroscpocially (extravesical mass)
T4   Tumour invades any of the following:
       prostate, uterus, vagina,
       pelvic wall, abdominal wall
  T4a Tumour invades prostate, uterus, vagina
  T4b Tumour invades pelvic wall, abdominal wall

Regional lymph nodes (N)[a]

NX   Regional lymph nodes cannot be assessed
N0   No regional lymph node metastasis
N1   Metastasis in a single lymph node, 2 cm or less in greatest dimension
N2   Metastasis in a single lymph node, more than 2 cm but not more than 5 cm in greatest dimension; or multiple lymph nodes, none more than 5 cm in greatest dimension
N3   Metastasis in a lymph node more than 5 cm in greatest dimension

Distant metastasis (M)

MX Distant metastasis cannot be assessed
M0 No distant metastasis
M1 Distant metastasis

Stage groupings

Stage 0a	Ta	N0	M0
Stage 0is	Tis	N0	M0
Stage I	T1	N0	M0
Stage II	T2	N0	M0
Stage III	T3	N0	M0
	T4a	N0	M0
Stage IV	T4b	N0	M0
	Any T	Any N	M0
	Any T	Any N	M1

[a]Regional lymph nodes are those within the true pelvis; all others are distant lymph nodes.

Squamous and glandular differentiation have been associated with poor responses to radiotherapy and to chemotherapy, respectively. Both are associated with high-stage urinary bladder cancer. Certain histological types of carcinoma, such as sarcomatoid carcinoma, small cell carcinoma and the variant of urothelial carcinoma known as micropapillary carcinoma, usually present at an advanced tumour stage (Lapham *et al.*, 1997). A variant known as lymphoepithelioma-like carcinoma of the urinary bladder may be amenable to chemotherapy alone.

Vascular invasion

Vascular invasion in tumours with limited lamina propria invasion has been associated with worse prognosis. However, data on the impact of vascular invasion in urothelial carcinoma are conflicting and difficult to interpret, owing mostly to the fact that in the urinary bladder, vascular invasion is difficult to recognize histologically, is easily over-diagnosed and confirmation usually requires use of immunohistochemical stains for endothelium (Lapham *et al.*, 1997).

Multicentric Tumours and Tumour Size

Tumour size, as assessed at time of cystoscopy, is correlated with muscularis propria-invasive disease. Similarly, multicentric tumours (i.e. presence of multiple tumours at the time of cystoscopy) are more likely to both recur and progress (Lapham *et al.*, 1997).

Adjacent Carcinoma In Situ

In cases of papillary bladder tumours, the presence of carcinoma *in situ* in the adjacent mucosa has been associated with a higher risk of recurrence and progression than in tumours without carcinoma *in situ*. Thus, it is common practice to randomly biopsy urothelium that appears normal at the time of resection of a papillary tumor (Lapham *et al.*, 1997). Studies have also shown that dysplasia in the adjacent urothelium is associated with higher risk of recurrence and progression.

Biological Prognostic Factors

A growing list of biological/molecular prognostic markers has been studied in the literature (**Table 11**) (Stein *et al.*, 1998). Most of them, however, have not provided significant or consistent predictive power beyond traditional pathological parameters. Several of these markers are currently being evaluated in a prospective and/or randomized manner, in order to determine their true clinical significance.

Lack of expression of blood group antigens, which are commonly expressed in normal urothelium, has been associated with tumour progression in patients with urinary bladder neoplasms. DNA ploidy has been shown to predict recurrence and progression in stage Ta and T1 tumours, and aneuploidy has been associated with a better response to radiation therapy. Proliferation indexes, whether derived by DNA flow cytometry, thymidine labelling, Ki-67 immunohistochemical staining or other methods, are correlated with tumour grade, disease progression and poor survival. As stated before, p53 mutations have also been associated with progression of urinary bladder tumours and possibly with initiation of cancer via the carcinoma *in situ* pathway. Current data suggest that p53 status is most useful in the management of locally advanced urinary bladder neoplasms, by helping to select patients who would benefit most from urinary bladder preservation or chemotherapy. Other molecular/biological prognostic indicators suggested in urinary bladder cancer include mutations in oncogenes, epidermal growth factor receptors, growth factors, adhesion molecules, angiogenesis inhibitors, and other cell-cycle regulatory proteins, such as the gene products of the retinoblastoma tumour-suppressor gene and p21^{WAF1}. Analysis of these markers is beyond the scope of this discussion, but a recent comprehensive review is available (Stein *et al.*, 1998).

Overview of Present Clinical Management

As stated above, clinical management is highly dependent on the stage of disease and includes local resection of a surface tumour, intravesical therapy, radical resection, radiation therapy and systemic therapy.

Stage Ta tumours are treated mainly with transurethral resection and fulguration of visible tumours. Patients at high risk for recurrence or progression (i.e. those who have high-grade tumours, large tumours, associated carcinoma *in situ* or multiple tumours) also benefit from intravesical therapy, including immunotherapy (*Bacillus Calmette-Guérin*, interferon) and chemotherapy (thiotepa, mitomycin C, doxorubicin). These patients require close follow-up with repeat cystoscopy and urine or bladder-wash cytology every 3 months for 2 years, every 6 months for a further 2 years and subsequently every year for the rest of their lives. Stage Tis lesions are treated mainly with intravesical therapy and require close surveillance owing to the high rate of progression to invasive disease. Stage T1 tumours are most often treated conservatively with local resection and intravesical therapy, although some physicians advocate cystectomy for high-grade T1 tumours. Standard treatment for muscularis propria invasive tumours (i.e. stages T2, T3 and T4) is radical cystectomy or cystoprostatectomy. Radiation therapy is also an acceptable treatment and is standard therapy in some parts of the world. Local or distant metastatic disease is treated with adjuvant systemic chemotherapy; doxorubicin, cisplatin and methotrexate being the most commonly used agents.

Other Carcinomas of the Urinary Bladder

Squamous cell carcinoma accounts for up to 75% of urinary bladder cancers in areas where schistosomiasis is endemic. In the developed world they constitute less than 10% of all urinary bladder cancers. The mean age of presentation for these tumours is 46 years, almost 20 years younger than that for urothelial carcinomas in the Western world (Johansson and Cohen, 1997). Men are affected more often than women. Patients usually present with haematuria or irritative symptoms and most tumours are usually high stage at the time of presentation. Infection with *Schistosoma haematobium* is endemic to the Nile river valley in Egypt and other parts of Africa. Its eggs are deposited in the urinary bladder wall, eliciting a chronic granulomatous inflammatory response, fibrosis, calcification and squamous

or glandular metaplasia of the urothelium. Tumours associated with schistosomiasis are mostly squamous cell carcinomas (75%), with a smaller proportion of adenocarcinomas (6%). Schistosomiasis appears to induce urinary bladder neoplasia by promoting increased cell proliferation as a result of inflammation, which in turn provides an increased risk of spontaneous genetic mutations. High levels of nitrosamines have also been found in patients with schistosomiasis, as in patients with chronic urinary tract infections. In countries where schistosomiasis is not endemic, squamous cell carcinoma usually arises secondary to chronic irritation caused by factors such as calculi, urinary retention, indwelling catheters, etc. These tumours tend to be large and bulky, often necrotic, sometimes filling most of the lumen of the urinary bladder. Squamous cell carcinomas display similar histology to those occurring at other sites and include tumour islands of squamous cells showing intercellular bridges and keratinization. Typical areas of urothelial carcinoma are not present. Squamous metaplasia of the adjacent urothelium is usually present. Verrucous carcinoma is a variant of squamous cell carcinoma that rarely affects the urinary bladder. They are graded according to the amount of keratinization and degree of nuclear pleomorphism. The TNM staging system for urinary bladder tumours (**Table 12**) is also used for these tumours and is the most useful prognostic indicator. Radical cystectomy or cystoprostatectomy with or without radiation therapy is the mainstay of therapy for this tumour.

Adenocarcinomas of the urinary bladder are rare, forming less than 1% of urinary bladder cancers. There is a significant association between urinary bladder exstrophy and the development of urinary bladder adenocarcinoma, although the mechanism by which this occurs remains unknown. Adenocarcinomas may be classified according to their location into urachal and non-urachal types. Both types show a variety of histological patterns, including enteric (i.e. mimicking colonic adenocarcinoma), signet ring, mucinous (colloid), clear cell, mixed and not otherwise specified (NOS).

URETHRA

Tumours of the urethra are distinctly rare. Owing to their significant anatomical and pathological differences, tumours arising in the female urethra are discussed separately from those arising in the male urethra (Grabstald, 1973; Ray *et al.*, 1977; Amin and Young, 1997). In both settings, most tumours are epithelial neoplasms (**Table 13**), with only leiomyoma and melanomas of the urethra being common enough to deserve mention.

Carcinomas of the Female Urethra

Urethral carcinomas typically occur in the postmenopausal period. Clinically patients present with one or more of the following symptoms: vaginal or urethral bleeding, dysuria, urinary frequency, incontinence, urinary tract infection, perineal or introital mass or urinary obstruction. Associated aetiological factors include trauma and infection, human papillomavirus for squamous cell and urothelial carcinomas and urethral diverticula for clear cell adenocarcinomas.

The histological spectrum of urethral carcinomas is similar to that of the urinary bladder, although the histological type is highly dependent on the sites where they arise. Tumours involving the distal urethra and meatus (approximately 70% of tumours) are usually squamous cell carcinomas (**Figure 10; see colour plate section**). They are aggressive neoplasms that present at an advanced stage. Carcinomas of the proximal urethra are either urothelial carcinomas or adenocarcinomas. Urothelial carcinomas account for approximately 20% of tumours and exhibit the same diversity of histology as that seen in the urinary bladder, including papillary, flat, noninvasive and

invasive tumours. Frequently, they are preceded by, followed by or occur concurrently with a urinary bladder urothelial carcinoma. Adenocarcinomas account for approximately 10% of female urethral carcinomas. Approximately 40% of adenocarcinomas are clear cell adenocarcinomas and the remaining show colloid, signet ring or NOS histology. Clear cell adenocarcinomas are pathologically and clinically distinctive. Histologically, they display papillary, tubulocystic, tubular or solid patterns. The tubules are usually hollow or contain eosinophilic secretions. The lining cells show characteristic hobnail shape and typically display clear to eosinophilic cytoplasm. Patients with clear cell adenocarcinomas appear to have a slightly better prognosis than those with nonclear cell adenocarcinomas, with between 30% and 40% of patients dying within 24 months; the survival is significantly lower for other types of adenocarcinomas.

The prognosis of female urethral carcinomas is relatively poor. Location of the tumour and stage of the disease are the most important prognostic parameters. Between 18% and 50% of women will have metastasis at presentation. Tumours restricted to the anterior urethra are more amenable to local surgical excision and have a better outcome than those involving the posterior or entire urethra. In 1973, Grabstald proposed a staging system specific for female urethral carcinomas (Grabstald, 1973) (**Table 14**). Five-year survival when this system is used is roughly 45% for stage A, 40% for stage B, 25% for stage C, and 18% for stage D. The 1997 TNM staging system (**Table 15**) is applicable to both male and female urethral tumours.

Carcinomas of the Male Urethra

Tumours of the male urethra occur in the sixth and seventh decades and usually present with obstructive symptoms or

Table 13 Histological classification of carcinomas of the urethra

1. Primary Tumors
   a. Transitional cell carcinoma
   b. Squamous cell carcinoma
   c. Adenocarcinoma
      i. Clear cell carcinoma
      ii. Colloid (mucinous) carcinoma
      iii. Signet-ring cell carcinoma
      iv. Adenocarcinoma, not otherwise specified
   d. Adenosquamous carcinoma
   e. Undifferentiated carcinoma
2. Secondary Tumors
   a. Direct extension from adjacent organs
   b. Metastatic

Table 14 Staging systems in urethral carcinoma

Female urethral tumours: Grabstald system	1997 UICC/AJCC TNM system		Male urethral tumours: Ray system
	Ta	Noninvasive papillary, polypoid or verrucous carcinoma	
	Tis	Carcinoma *in situ*	
A Tumour invades submucosa	T1	Tumour invades subepithelial connective tissue	A Tumour invades lamina propria
B Tumour invades muscle	T2	Tumour invades corpus spongiosum, prostate or periurethral muscle	B Tumour invades substance of corpus spongiosum or prostate
C Tumour invades vagina, bladder, labia or clitoris	T3	Tumour invades corpus cavernosum, beyond prostatic capsule, anterior vagina or bladder neck	C Tumour invades into corpus cavernosum, fat or beyond the prostatic capsule
	T4	Tumour invades other adjacent organs	
D Metastatic disease	N1–3	Regional metastasis	D1 Regional metastasis
	M1	Distant metastasis	D2 Distant metastasis

Table 15   1997 TNM staging system for the urethra

Primary tumour (T)

TX   Primary tumour cannot be assessed
T0   No evidence of primary tumour
Ta   Noninvasive papillary, polypoid or verrucous
        carcinoma
Tis   Carcinoma *in situ*
T1   Tumour invades subepithelial connective tissue
T2   Tumour invades any of the following: corpus
        spongiosum, prostate, periurethral muscle
T3   Tumour invades any of the following: corpus
        cavernosum, beyond prostatic capsule, anterior
        vagina, bladder neck
T4   Tumour invades other adjacent organs

Regional lymph nodes (N)

NX   Regional lymph nodes cannot be assessed
N0   No regional lymph node metastasis
N1   Metastasis in a single lymph node, 2 cm or less in
        greatest dimension
N2   Metastasis in a single lymph node more than 2 cm
        greatest dimension, or in multiple lymph nodes

Distant metastasis (M)

MX   Distant metastasis cannot be assessed
M0   No distant metastasis
M1   Distant metastasis

Stage groupings

Stage	T	N	M
Stage 0a	Ta	N0	M0
Stage 0is	Tis	N0	M0
Stage I	T1	N0	M0
Stage II	T2	N0	M0
Stage III	T1	N1	M0
	T2	N1	M0
	T3	N0	M0
	T3	N1	M0
Stage IV	T4	N0	M0
	T4	N1	M0
	Any T	N2	M0
	Any T	Any N	M1

infection. Tumours of the posterior urethra are associated with haematuria, purulent discharge or urinary obstruction. Some patients present with a palpable mass. Other symptoms include painful priapism, penile erosion and impotence. Suggested aetiological factors include chronic irritation from strictures or infectious processes. Human papillomavirus has been documented in squamous and urothelial carcinomas.

Grossly, tumours appear as ulcerative, nodular, papillary, cauliflower-like or firm solid masses. About 75% of tumours are squamous cell carcinomas, with the remainder being urothelial carcinomas, adenocarcinomas or undifferentiated carcinomas. Squamous cell carcinomas arise in a background of metaplasia. Urothelial carcinomas are seen most frequently in the prostatic urethra but may also occur in the membranous or penile urethra. They display the same histological spectrum as those arising in the urinary bladder. As in the female urethra, there may be a synchronous or metachronous urinary bladder tumour. Adenocarcinomas are less common in the male than in the female urethra, and clear cell adenocarcinoma is an oddity in the male urethra.

Prognosis is similarly dependent on location and extent of the disease. A staging system specific for male urethral cancer was proposed in 1977 by Ray *et al.* (Ray *et al.*, 1977) (**Table 14**), but the TNM system (**Table 15**) is also applicable. Anterior tumours have a significantly better outcome than posterior tumours, as they can be managed successfully by surgery. Tumours of the anterior urethra generally metastasize to inguinal and external iliac lymph nodes, whereas posterior urethral tumours spread to internal iliac and hypogastric lymph nodes. Most often, the sign of treatment failure is patient's local recurrence, rather than distant metastasis.

Both male and female urethral tumours are initially treated for local excision if possible, including lymphadenectomy. Radiation therapy is indicated in cases that recur or in those not amenable to surgical excision. Adjuvant systemic therapy is indicated in metastatic disease.

REFERENCES

Amin, M. B. and Young, R. H. (1997). Primary carcinomas of the urethra. *Seminars in Diagnostic Pathology*, **14**, 147–160.

Boccon-Gibod, L. A. (1998). Pathological evaluation of renal tumors in children: international society of pediatric oncology approach. *Pediatric and Developmental Pathology*, **1**, 243–248.

Brown, F. M. (2000). Urine cytology. Is it still the gold standard for screening? *The Urologic Clinics of North America*, **27**, 25–37.

Cordon-Cardo, C., *et al.* (1997). Genetic studies and molecular markers of bladder cancer. *Seminars in Surgical Oncology*, **13**, 319–327.

Epstein, J. I., *et al.* (1998). The World Health Organization/ International Society of Urological Pathology consensus classification of urothelial (transitional cell) neoplasms of the urinary bladder. Bladder Consensus Conference Committee. *American Journal of Surgical Pathology*, **22**, 1435–1448.

Faria, P., *et al.* (1996). Focal versus diffuse anaplasia in Wilms tumor–new definitions with prognostic significance: a report from the National Wilms Tumor Study Group. *American Journal of Surgical Pathology*, **20**, 909–920.

Grabstald, H. (1973). Proceedings: tumors of the urethra in men and women. *Cancer*, **32**, 1236–1255.

Johansson, S. L. and Cohen, S. M. (1997). Epidemiology and etiology of bladder cancer. *Seminars in Surgical Oncology*, **13**, 291–298.

Kovacs, G., *et al.* (1997). The Heidelberg classification of renal cell tumours. *Journal of Pathology*, **183**, 131–133.

Lapham, R. L., *et al.* (1997). Pathologic prognostic parameters in bladder urothelial biopsy, transurethral resection, and cystectomy specimens. *Seminars in Diagnostic Pathology*, **14**, 109–122.

Lee, R. and Droller, M. J. (2000). The natural history of bladder cancer. Implications for therapy. *The Urologic Clinics of North America*, **27**, 1–13.

Mazzucchelli, L., *et al.* (1994). Invasion depth is the most important prognostic factor for transitional-cell carcinoma in a prospective trial of radical cystectomy and adjuvant chemotherapy. *International Journal of Cancer*, **57**, 15–20.

McLaughlin, J. K. and Lipworth, L. (2000). Epidemiologic aspects of renal cell cancer. *Seminars in Oncology*, **27**, 115–123.

Neville, H. L. and Ritchey, M. L. (2000). Wilms tumor. Overview of National Wilms Tumor Study Group results. *The Urologic Clinics of North America*, **27**, 435–442.

Ray, B., *et al.* (1977). Experience with primary carcinoma of the male urethra. *Journal of Urology*, **117**, 591–594.

Rini, B. I. and Vogelzang, N. J. (2000). Prognostic factors in renal carcinoma. *Seminars in Oncology*, **27**, 213–220.

Schmidt, D. and Beckwith, J. B. (1995). Histopathology of childhood renal tumors. *Hematology and Oncology Clinics of North America*, **9**, 1179–1200.

Steffens, J. and Nagel, R. (1988). Tumours of the renal pelvis and ureter. Observations in 170 patients. *British Journal of Urology*, **61**, 277–283.

Stein, J. P., *et al.* (1998). Prognostic markers in bladder cancer: a contemporary review of the literature. *Journal of Urology*, **160**, 645–659.

Störkel, S., *et al.* (1997). Classification of renal cell carcinoma: Workgroup No. 1. Union Internationale Contre le Cancer (UICC) and the American Joint Committee on Cancer (AJCC). *Cancer*, **80**, 987–989.

Wunderlich, H., *et al.* (1998). Nephron sparing surgery for renal cell carcinoma 4 cm. or less in diameter: indicated or under treated? *Journal of Urology*, **159**, 1465–1469.

FURTHER READING

Bostwick, D. G. and Eble, J. N. (eds) (1997). *Urologic Surgical Pathology*, 1st edn (Mosby, Philadelphia, PA).

Murphy, W. M., *et al.* (eds) (1994). Tumors of the kidney, bladder, and related urinary structures. *Atlas of Tumor Pathology*, third series, fascicle 11 (Armed Forces Institute of Pathology, Washington, D.C.)

Vogelzang, N. J., *et al.* (eds) (2000). *Comprehensive Textbook of Genitourinary Oncology*, 2nd edn (Lippincott Williams & Wilkins, Philadelphia, PA).

Walsh, P. C., *et al.* (eds) (1998). *Campbell's Urology*, 7th edn (W. B. Saunders, Philadelphia, PA).

Raghavan, D., *et al.* (eds) (1997) *Principles and Practice of Genitourinary Oncology*, 1st edn (1997). (Lippincott-Raven, Philadelphia, PA).

Chapter 45

Male Genital Tract

Thomas M. Ulbright

Indiana University School of Medicine, Indianapolis, IN, USA

CONTENTS

- Prostate
- Penis
- Seminal Vesicle
- Testis

PROSTATE

Normal Development and Anatomy

The prostate gland develops as outgrowths of epithelium from the urogenital sinus that are surrounded by primitive mesenchyme. This epithelial component forms the ducts and acini of the peripheral and transition zones of the prostate, and the mesenchyme differentiates into its fibromuscular stroma. The distal prostatic urethra, formed from the urogenital sinus, is thus in continuity with the prostatic ducts. The central zone glands and ducts may derive from mesonephric duct remnants, similar to the development of the proximal prostatic urethra.

The prostate gland in young men weighs about 20 g and is shaped like a truncated cone with its base along the neck of the urinary bladder and its blunt apex at the urogenital diaphragm. The prostatic urethra courses through the gland with an angulation occurring at its approximate mid-portion at the level of the verumontanum, a mound-like elevation on the posterior urethral surface. The two ejaculatory ducts penetrate the base of the prostate and run in an anteroinferior direction through the gland to empty into the prostatic urethra, just lateral to either side of the verumontanum.

The prostate gland is currently described in terms of its zonal anatomy according to the McNeal model (McNeal, 1981). In this model, there are three major prostatic zones (**Figure 1**). The central zone accounts for about 25% of the prostatic volume and occupies a pyramidal-shaped region with its base at the bladder neck and apex at the point of angulation of the prostatic urethra. The transition zone represents only about 5% of the prostatic volume and consists of two small lobes just lateral to the proximal prostatic urethra. The remainder of the glandular prostate (approximately 70%) is represented by the peripheral zone, which surrounds both the central and transition zones in the basal aspect of the gland and constitutes essentially all of the glandular prostatic tissue distal to the urethral angulation. The prostate is surrounded by a condensation of stroma along its peripheral and lateral aspects that blends, anteriorly, with the anterior fibromuscular stroma. No true capsule is present at the apex and bladder neck aspects of the gland.

The major blood supply to the prostate derives from the branches of the internal iliac arteries. These branches enter the gland with the major neurovascular pedicles at either superolateral aspect of the gland (**Figure 2**). Venous drainage occurs through a plexus of veins in the capsular region and into the internal iliac veins. The prostatic lymphatics mainly drain into the lymph nodes along the internal iliac vessels, but direct drainage into the external iliac nodes may also occur.

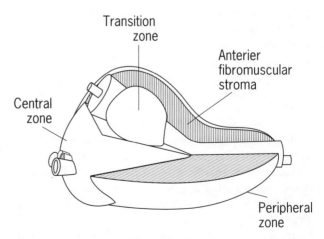

Figure 1 The McNeal model of prostatic anatomy. (Adapted from Lee *et al.*, 1989.)

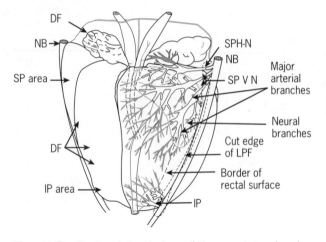

Figure 2   Posterolateral view of the prostate showing the major arterial and neural branches. (Adapted from McNeal, 1997.)

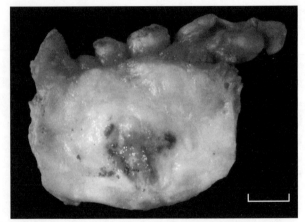

Figure 3   Cut surface of a prostate gland in the anterior–posterior plane shows yellow nodules of adenocarcinoma in the peripheral zone at bottom right. Bar, 1 cm.

Tumour Pathology

A diverse number of different types of neoplasm may occur in the prostate gland, but the overwhelming majority (>95%) of malignant tumours of the prostate are adenocarcinomas. With the elaboration of the McNeal model of prostatic anatomy (see above), it has become clear that different zones of the prostate have different propensities to develop adenocarcinoma. Accordingly, about 75% of adenocarcinomas develop in the peripheral zone, about 15% in the transition zone and the residual cases in the central zone (McNeal *et al.*, 1988). Because much of the peripheral zone abuts the anterior wall of the rectum, some prostate carcinomas, when sufficiently large, may present palpable abnormalities on digital rectal examination (DRE). However, DRE is not an especially sensitive or specific method for detection; it identified only 56% of patients who were ultimately diagnosed with prostate cancer in a screening programme and had a positive predictive value of 21% (Catalona *et al.*, 1994).

Prostatic adenocarcinoma may not be grossly apparent. In one series that examined radical prostatectomy specimens, 63% of tumours were correctly recognized on gross examination; no tumour was apparent in 22% of cases, and tumour was falsely identified in 19% of the cases (Renshaw, 1998). When they are recognizable, the tumours often have a yellow to grey solid character that contrasts with the frequently spongy appearance of the adjacent non-neoplastic prostatic parenchyma (**Figure 3**). Those tumours that develop in the transition zone may sometimes be grossly recognizable in prostate chips that have a tan to yellow discoloration.

Prostatic adenocarcinoma is recognized microscopically through a combination of architectural and cytological features. Typically, the malignant glands are smaller in size than the associated benign acini, and often, but not always, tend to be arranged in haphazard or infiltrative patterns that contrast with the more organized, lobular arrangement of benign glands and patterns that tend to be produced by benign pathological processes.

The grading of prostatic adenocarcinomas may be performed by utilization of a variety of schemes, but the one in most widespread usage is the Gleason method (Gleason, 1966; Gleason and Mellinger, 1974) that has been shown to be of significant prognostic value in a variety of studies (Thomas *et al.*, 1982; Gleason, 1992; Albertsen *et al.*, 1999). This system relies on the architectural assessment of tumour growth according to five histological grades (**Figure 4**). Those tumours whose growth is a well-circumscribed collection of uniform small glands are assigned a grade of 1 (**Figure 5**) and, on the other end of the scale, grade 5 tumours are those having a diffuse sheet-like arrangement of malignant cells, isolated single cells infiltrating the stroma (**Figure 6**), and/or nests with central necrosis (**Figure 7**). Tumours with features intermediate between these two extremes receive an intermediate grade. Since many prostatic adenocarcinomas are heterogeneous with respect to their growth patterns, the Gleason method furthermore sums the grades of the two most prominent patterns to arrive at a 'pattern score' that varies from 2 to 10. When there are two patterns of close to equal proportions that are in competition for the second grade, the one with the higher grade is chosen. If only one grade is present, its value is doubled to determine the pattern score. Recent research also demonstrates that even small amounts of grade 4 or grade 5 tumours are prognostically important, and there may be a role for the assessment of so-called 'tertiary grades' in prostate cancer (Pan *et al.*, 2000).

The Gleason method, in prostatectomy specimens, correlates with disease-free survival and overall survival

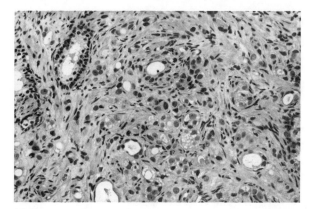

Figure 6 Atypical cells that infiltrate the stroma as irregular cords and single cells represent a grade 5 adenocarcinoma of the prostate. Note invasion between residual benign glands (left).

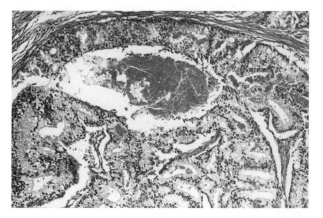

Figure 7 A cribriform pattern of adenocarcinoma of the prostate with zones of necrosis, a Gleason grade 5 tumour.

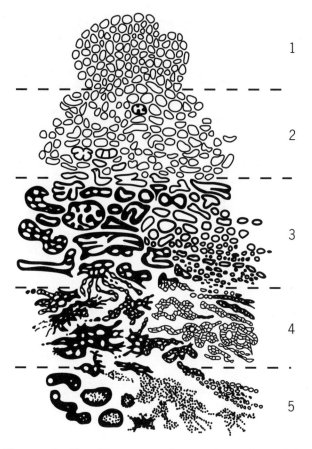

Figure 4 The Gleason grading system of prostate carcinoma. There are five grades based on the architectural pattern of tumour growth. (Adapted from Gleason, 1992.)

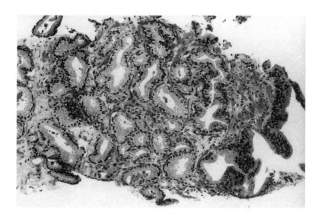

Figure 5 This well-circumscribed collection of relatively uniform-sized glands represents a Gleason grade 1 or grade 2 adenocarcinoma of the prostate.

(**Figure 8**). Because of sampling problems, needle biopsy specimens are subject to grading disparity with respect to prostatectomy specimens, most commonly undergrading secondary to failure to sample a high-grade component.

Such undergrading occurs in approximately 40% of the cases and most typically is a problem with small amounts of low-grade tumour on needle biopsy. Nevertheless, Gleason grading of needle biopsies and transurethral resectates does correlate with the final Gleason grade in prostatectomy specimens and also correlates with disease-free and overall survival.

In addition to the architectural patterns that are the initial basis for concern and that provide the Gleason pattern score, the diagnosis of cancer must be confirmed on cytological grounds. This is necessary because of several benign entities, such as atypical adenomatous hyperplasia (adenosis), sclerosing adenosis, prostatic extension of nephrogenic adenoma (nephrogenic metaplasia), meso-nephric remnant hyperplasia and verumontanum mucosal gland hyperplasia, that may mimic prostatic adenocar-cinoma on architectural grounds, particularly in small tissue specimens. There are several cytological features that, together, provide strong reassurance concerning the diag-nosis of carcinoma (**Figure 9**). These include nucleolar prominence (usually considered in excess of 1.5 μm in

Cause-specific survival (%)

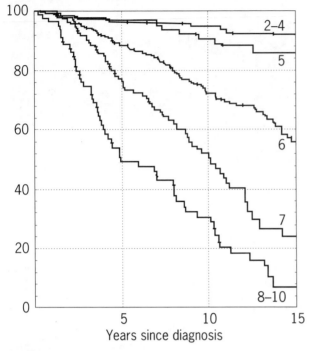

Figure 8   The relationship of Gleason pattern score to disease-specific survival in prostate adenocarcinoma. (Adapted from Albertsen *et al.*, 1999.)

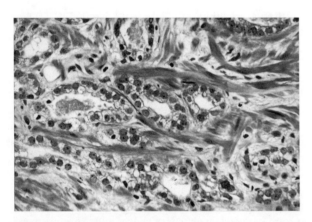

Figure 9   This adenocarcinoma of the prostate shows nuclear enlargement, hyperchromasia, prominent nucleoli and absence of a basal cell layer. The neoplastic glands intercalate between bundles of stromal collagen.

diameter), nuclear enlargement (compared with adjacent benign glands), nuclear hyperchromasia and irregularity, glands with an absence of basal cells and amphophilic cytoplasm (in contrast to the more pale cytoplasm of benign glands). Ancillary features that support a diagnosis of adenocarcinoma, but that are by no means specific for it,

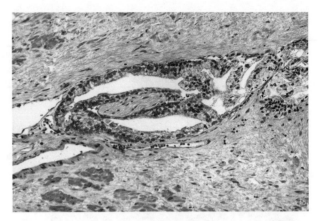

Figure 10   Circumferential perineural invasion in prostate adenocarcinoma, a finding considered pathognomonic of cancer.

include the presence of intraluminal acid mucins (usually visible as wispy, slightly basophilic intraluminal material on haematoxylin and eosin-stained sections) and the occurrence of intraluminal, eosinophilic, rod-shaped or polygonal crystalloids.

Only a few features are considered pathognomonic of carcinoma; these include huge nucleoli ($>3\,\mu m$), mucinous fibroplasia (also termed 'collagenous micronodules'), the occurrence of sieve-like, cribriform architectural patterns (**Figure 7**), and circumferential perineural invasion (**Figure 10**). The occurrence of any of these 'pathognomonic' features in biopsy material is rare, so the diagnosis of adenocarcinoma usually rests upon a constellation of features that vary in significance but that together permit its accurate and reproducible recognition.

There are two putative precursors for prostatic adenocarcinoma, one well established and the second of doubtful premalignant potential. The well-established precursor is now termed 'high-grade prostatic intraepithelial neoplasia' (PIN) (Bostwick and Brawer, 1987), although it has also been termed 'atypical hyperplasia' and 'intraductal dysplasia.' The poorly established possible precursor is known most commonly as either 'atypical adenomatous hyperplasia' or 'adenosis'.

PIN is considered a spectrum of atypical prostatic epithelial change that develops in pre-existing ducts and acini (**Figure 11**). Changes that include mild nuclear enlargement and stratification without nucleolar prominence characterize 'low-grade PIN,' a purely descriptive term that is not considered a diagnostic entity because of its unclear clinical significance and its poorly reproducible recognition. Cells resembling those of adenocarcinoma characterize high-grade PIN. Thus, on scanning magnification, one can appreciate the presence of a greater degree of basophilia in glands affected by high grade PIN than in normal glands (**Figure 12**). This reflects the cellular crowding, stratification, nuclear enlargement and nuclear hyperchromasia in these glands (**Figure 13**). As in

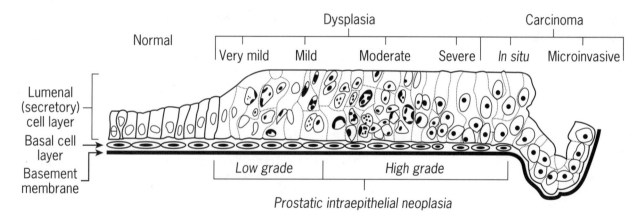

Figure 11 Drawing showing the spectrum of atypical epithelial changes in prostatic intraepithelial neoplasia (PIN), with final progression to invasive carcinoma. Cellular stratification and nucleolar prominence characterize high grade PIN. (Adapted from Bostwick, 1997.)

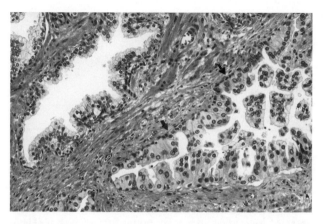

Figure 12 A normal prostate gland (left) contrasts with one having a papillary configuration of high grade PIN (right). The latter shows nuclear enlargement and cellular stratification, but there remains a basal cell layer (arrows).

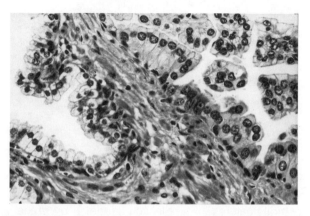

Figure 13 The nuclei in a gland with high-grade PIN (right) are focally stratified, have prominent nucleoli and are larger than those in an adjacent, normal gland (left). The gland with PIN still has an identifiable basal cell layer.

prostatic adenocarcinoma, nucleolar prominence is a key finding in high-grade PIN. In contrast to the acini of prostatic adenocarcinoma, the glandular structures of high-grade PIN have a residual basal cell layer, although it may be attenuated or focally absent. In the differential diagnosis of adenocarcinoma versus high-grade PIN, the absence or presence of a residual basal cell layer is thus a key finding. Several architectural patterns of high-grade PIN are common, caused by the piling up of increased numbers of epithelial cells in pre-existing duct/acinar units. Thus, tufted, papillary, cribriform and flat patterns occur, usually two or more together. Some authors have argued that the cribriform pattern of PIN is not a precursor to invasive adenocarcinoma, but reflects the growth of invasive adenocarcinoma into the duct/acinar system of the prostate, even though the invasive component may not be apparent in the available specimen (McNeal and Yemoto, 1996). This conclusion is based on the rare finding of cribriform 'PIN' in cancer-bearing prostates at sites remote from the tumour, whereas other patterns of 'PIN' are common at such foci.

There are numerous pieces of evidence that link high grade PIN with adenocarcinoma (**Table 1**). These include similar ploidy values, genetic and cytogenetic changes in high-grade PIN and the associated adenocarcinoma, the similar cytological appearance of both processes (as mentioned above), similar ultrastructure, morphometric values, topographical distribution in the prostate (i.e. almost always in the peripheral zone), lectin binding patterns and the occurrence of so-called transitive glands. The latter are adenocarcinomatous glands that appear to 'bud' from foci of high-grade PIN. There is a much higher frequency of high-grade PIN in prostates with cancer than in those without cancer (McNeal and Bostwick, 1986; Bostwick and Brawer, 1987). Most importantly, there is a significant risk for the subsequent identification of adenocarcinoma of the prostate in a patient who has

Table 1 Evidence for the association of high-grade prostatic intraepithelial neoplasia (PIN) and prostatic carcinoma. (Adapted from Bostwick, 1997.)

Histology
  Similar architectural and cytological features
Location
  Both are located chiefly in the peripheral zone
    and are multicentric
  Close spatial association of PIN and cancer
Correlation with cell proliferation and death (apoptosis)
  Growth fraction of PIN is similar to cancer
  Number of apoptotic bodies in PIN is similar
    to cancer
  Apoptosis-suppressing oncoprotein bcl-2 expression
    is increased in PIN and cancer
Loss of basal cell layer
  The highest grade of PIN has loss of basal
    cell layer, similar to cancer
Increased frequency of PIN in the presence of cancer
Increased extent of PIN in the presence of cancer
Increased severity of PIN in the presence of cancer
Immunophenotype
  PIN is more closely related to cancer than
    benign epithelium
  For some biomarkers there is progressive loss of
    expression with increasing grade of PIN and
    cancer, including prostrate-specific antigen,
    neuroendocrine cells, cytoskeletal proteins and
    secretory proteins

Immunophenotype (continued)
  For some biomarkers there is progressive increase in expression
    with increasing grades of PIN and cancer, including type IV
    collagenase, TGF-alpha, EGF, EGFR, Lewis Y antigen and c-erb-2
    oncogene
Morphometery
  High-grade PIN and cancer have similar nuclear area, chromatin
    content and distribution, nuclear perimeter, nuclear diameter
    and nuclear roundness.
  High-grade PIN and cancer have similar nucleolar number, size
    and location
DNA content
  High-grade PIN and cancer have similar frequency of aneuploidy
Genetic instability
  High-grade PIN and cancer have similar frequency of allelic loss
  High-grade PIN and cancer have similar foci of allelic loss
Microvessel density
  Progressive increase in microvessel density from
    PIN to cancer
Origin
  Cancer found to arise in foci of PIN
Age
  Age incidence peak of PIN precedes cancer
Predictive value of high-grade PIN
  PIN on biopsy has high predictive value for cancer on
    subsequent biopsy

high-grade PIN identified on needle biopsy. Several studies have shown up to a 50% frequency of invasive adenocarcinoma in second biopsy procedures of patients whose initial biopsy showed high-grade PIN. Whereas high-grade PIN and conventional acinar adenocarcinoma both occur disproportionately in the peripheral zone of the prostate, the other putative precursor for adenocarcinoma, atypical adenomatous hyperplasia (AAH), is usually seen in the transition zone. Hence AAH is sampled most commonly in transurethral resections specimens and is uncommon in needle biopsy material.

AAH is an architecturally worrisome lesion that consists of a circumscribed proliferation of tightly packed, relatively small glands, usually having abundant pale cytoplasm (**Figure 14**). Hence it is most likely to be confused with a Gleason grade 1 or grade 2 adenocarcinoma. Careful inspection, however, usually discloses that there is a greater variation in gland size and shape than in the typical low-grade adenocarcinoma, and many of the glands of AAH have an undulating border that contrasts with the straight luminal edges of adenocarcinoma. Most importantly, AAH lacks the cytological features of carcinoma, and basal cells are present, although frequently inconspicuous, often requiring high molecular weight cytokeratin immunostains for their demonstration.

Unlike high-grade PIN, the evidence linking AAH to adenocarcinoma is scant. One study identified a higher

rate of subsequent carcinoma in patients who were initially diagnosed with 'adenosis' (Brawn, 1982), but that study has been criticized for misinterpreting some cases of low-grade adenocarcinoma for 'adenosis.' There

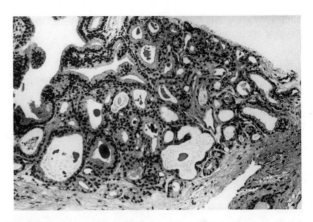

Figure 14 Atypical adenomatous hyperplasia consists of a collection of small glands that mimics the architectural features of a Gleason grade 1 or grade 2 adenocarcinoma. The close relationship to a 'parent' duct is a helpful distinguishing feature. At high magnification, these glands lacked the cytological features of adenocarcinoma.

is unquestionably a degree of morphological similarity between AAH and the typically low-grade adenocarcinomas that tend to occur in the transition zone of the prostate. Additionally, AAH, on average, tends to occur in patients who are 5–10 years younger than those with adenocarcinoma (Srigley, 1988; Amin *et al.*, 1993), supporting the evolution of the latter from the former. In addition, AAH has proliferation rates intermediate between those of normal prostate and adenocarcinoma. Disparate results have been obtained concerning cytogenetic abnormalities in AAH. One study found loss of heterozygosity (LOH) in 47% of cases by utilizing polymorphic microsatellite probes to chromosomes 7q, 8p, 8q and 18q (Cheng *et al.*, 1998). Another study, however, using probes to 1q, 6q, 7q, 8p, 10q, 13q, 16q, 17p, 17q and 18q, identified LOH that was confined to chromosome 8p in only 12% of AAH cases (Doll *et al.*, 1999). The former provided support for AAH as a neoplastic precursor but the latter questioned its neoplastic potential.

Immunohistochemistry may assist in the evaluation of prostatic adenocarcinoma. The secretory cells of the non-neoplastic prostate stain positively for prostate-specific antigen (PSA) and prostatic acid phosphatase (PAP), and these substances are also identified in all but a very small percentage of poorly differentiated adenocarcinomas of the prostate, although the staining can be focal in many tumours. Immunostains for PSA and PAP may therefore be of help in distinguishing prostatic carcinoma from transitional cell carcinoma that has extended from the bladder. In addition, certain mimics of adenocarcinoma, such as nephrogenic adenoma (nephrogenic metaplasia), hyperplasia of mesonephric remnants, adenotic seminal vesicle and prostatic xanthoma, are negative for PSA and PAP, so immunostaining can help in their differentiation from prostatic adenocarcinoma. Also helpful are immunostains using antibodies directed against high molecular weight cytokeratins, including the most commonly used one, clone 34βE12. Such stains highlight the basal cells that are present in non-neoplastic glands but that are absent in adenocarcinoma. In a worrisome lesion that is suspicious for adenocarcinoma by routine light microscopy, the absence of high molecular weight cytokeratin in the worrisome focus may provide sufficient additional evidence to permit the diagnosis of adenocarcinoma (**Figure 15**). Conversely, the presence of high molecular weight positive basal cells in the worrisome lesion is strong evidence that it does not represent invasive adenocarcinoma.

In addition to the usual form of adenocarcinoma, a number of specialized forms of prostatic carcinoma exist. One such type is the small cell carcinoma that, pathologically, resembles the much more common form of lung cancer. Unlike conventional adenocarcinoma, small cell carcinoma may not be associated with PSA elevations. For patients who have *de novo* small cell

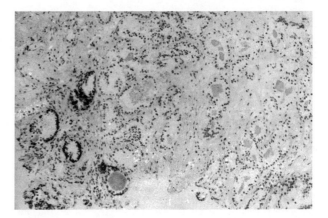

Figure 15   A high molecular weight cytokeratin immunostain is negative in a small acinar proliferation in the prostate, supporting that it is adenocarcinoma. A few non-neoplastic glands (left) show positively staining basal cells.

carcinoma, most have advanced stage disease at presentation. About half of small cell carcinomas are seen in patients who had a conventional acinar adenocarcinoma that failed hormonal or chemotherapeutic management, suggesting that many cases derive from therapy-resistant clones as a treatment selection phenomenon. The neuroendocrine nature of this tumour can be demonstrated with immunohistochemical markers, such as synaptophysin and chromogranin. Other types of prostatic carcinoma include prostatic duct, mucinous, signet-ring cell, adenosquamous, squamous, basaloid/adenoid cystic and transitional cell (i.e. of prostatic urethral or periurethral duct origin) types. It is controversial if the prostatic duct type of carcinoma merits separate classification since it is considered by some authorities to represent a conventional acinar adenocarcinoma with an unusual growth pattern caused by its extension into large periurethral ducts. Most continue to classify it separately but grade it using the Gleason method. In support of this approach, the clinical presentation is sometimes completely different from conventional adenocarcinoma. Patients with prostatic duct carcinoma may present with haematuria and, on cystoscopic examination, a mass may be seen protruding into the prostatic urethra. These features would not be expected with a conventional adenocarcinoma. The prior notion that prostatic duct carcinoma is derived from Mullerian tissues of the prostatic utricle (hence 'endometrioid' carcinoma of the prostate) is largely discredited on the basis of its positive staining with both of the usual markers of prostatic differentiation, PSA and PAP.

In addition to carcinomas, the prostate is also subject to much rarer mesenchymal tumours. Although virtually any form of sarcoma may be encountered in the prostate on occasion, only a select few merit special mention. Embryonal rhabdomyosarcoma of the prostate has an appearance similar to that seen in the soft tissues and tends to occur in children and young adult patients, but it may rarely be seen in older adults. There also occur mixed epithelial–stromal tumours of prostatic origin that have a histological appearance and spectrum similar to the much more common phyllodes tumours of the breast (Gaudin *et al.*, 1998) and the very rare, similarly named tumour of the seminal vesicle (see **Figure 23**). At the benign end of the spectrum, glands lined by bland epithelium are embedded in a cellular stroma, often with abundant stromal mucopolysaccharide. Cellularity, cytologic atypia and mitotic rate remain low. Malignant epithelial–stromal tumours of the prostate are characterized by increased stromal cellularity, stromal atypia and mitotic figures. Overgrowth of atypical stroma, to the exclusion of glands, remains an important malignant criterion. Between these two ends of the spectrum, there are tumours having intermediate features that are placed in a category of uncertain malignant potential. Benign tumours may recur locally, but do not metastasize, and this seems also to be the case with tumours thus far categorized as 'uncertain malignant potential,' although recurrence is more common than with unequivocally benign lesions. Malignant tumours are reported to metastasize.

Epidemiology and Aetiology

Apart from carcinomas of skin, prostate cancer is the most common malignant tumour of men. There is an estimated overall prevalence of 30% in men over 50 years of age, but the prevalence increases with age so that about 80% of men over 80 years old have prostate cancer based on autopsy studies. The apparent incidence of prostate cancer in the USA underwent a twofold increase from 1976 to 1994, but this observation may largely be attributable to better detection methods, including measurement of serum PSA levels and imaging the prostate with transrectal ultrasound (TRUS) (see chapter on *Ultrasound*). This viewpoint is supported by a decline in prostate cancer mortality rates by 0.5% per year between 1990 and 1994 that followed an increasing mortality rate from 1976 to 90. Nonetheless, prostate cancer currently ranks second only to lung cancer as a cause of cancer mortality in men in the USA. It therefore represents a major public health problem.

Epidemiological studies (see chapter on *Identifying Cancer Causes through Epidemiology*) demonstrate wide variations in the clinical incidence and mortality rates from prostate cancer in different countries. Low rates are seen in the Far East and many third-world countries, whereas there is a high incidence in Northern Europe, the USA, and Canada. Since migrated populations tend to acquire the prostate cancer rate of the new country of residence, environmental factors appear to have a major impact on prostate cancer incidence. Despite marked differences in the incidence of clinical carcinoma of the

prostate in different geographic locations, the frequency of detectable prostate cancer at autopsy in these different areas is similar. These observations suggest that in countries with a high rate of clinical carcinoma, there is an increased rate of conversion of 'latent' carcinoma to clinical carcinoma.

Ethnic factors also appear important in determining prostate cancer risk. In the USA, there is a significantly higher mortality rate among African Americans than in Caucasians, and Jewish populations have a lower mortality rate compared with non-Jewish men. It is often not clear if genetic factors account for such differences or if differences in cultural habits are largely responsible. Some have suggested that the higher incidence of clinical prostate cancer in African Americans can be at least partially attributed to their higher levels of serum testosterone compared with other ethnic groups. It is clear that androgen exposure is necessary for the development of prostate cancer since prepubertal castrates do not develop prostatic carcinoma.

Among the environmental factors that have been linked to prostatic carcinoma, high fat intake has one of the more consistent associations. Intake of saturated fat, rather than monounsaturated or polyunsaturated forms, largely correlates with this increased risk and may account for at least some of the difference in prostate cancer incidence between Western and Far Eastern countries. Other factors that have been linked to an increased risk of prostatic carcinoma include vitamin D deficiency (partially based on the higher incidence in northern latitudes and among darkly pigmented persons), exposure to cadmium, employment in the textile, rubber, drug, chemical and atomic energy industries, large body mass and high plasma levels of insulin-like growth factor 1. Decreased risk has been associated with high soy protein intake (perhaps related to the phyto-oestrogens that are present in soy), high selenium intake, increased serum levels of lycopene (a carotenoid found in tomatoes) and increased intake of α-tocopherol.

It is now clear that prostate cancer has a genetic component (see chapter on *Inherited Predispositions to Cancer*), but cases with a clear familial component represent a small minority of prostate cancers. In men who have a single first-degree relative (father or brother) with prostate cancer, there is a calculated twofold increased risk, whereas having two or more affected first-degree relatives has been associated with an increased risk of 5–11-fold. Younger age (<50 years) of onset in a first-degree relative also appears to convey an increased risk beyond that seen with an older first-degree relative having had prostate cancer. A putative prostate cancer susceptibility gene has been identified on the long arm of chromosome 1.

Despite these numerous observations concerning factors conveying increased or decreased risk of prostate cancer, the cause or causes of carcinoma of the prostate remain unknown. It is likely that environmental factors make certain important genetic mutations either more or less likely to occur in prostatic epithelial stem cells. One or more such mutations must be required for malignant transformation. It also seems likely that cases with a familial component represent tumours developing in patients with a germline mutation in one of the important genes for at least one of the pathways to malignant transformation. More specific information, however, is lacking at this time.

Screening and Prevention

The early detection of prostate cancer provides the best hope for its cure. The current screening recommendations are for men 50 years of age or older to have annual DRE and serum PSA measurements. Abnormal findings are typically followed by TRUS and, in some cases, biopsy. For men with a positive family history, it is recommended that screening begin earlier, at age 40 years. Unfortunately, neither PSA measurement nor DRE is entirely specific or sensitive. Benign prostatic hyperplasia and prostatitis can cause PSA elevations and abnormal DRE. The 'normal' PSA value is usually considered $<4 \, \mathrm{ng} \, \mathrm{mL}^{-1}$, and the positive predictive value of a PSA level exceeding $10 \, \mathrm{ng} \, \mathrm{mL}^{-1}$, is about 66%. A level of $4–10 \, \mathrm{ng} \, \mathrm{mL}^{-1}$, however, has one of only 22–35%. Furthermore, 22% of men with PSA values of $2.5–4.0 \, \mathrm{ng} \, \mathrm{mL}^{-1}$, generally considered in the 'normal' range, were found to have adenocarcinoma on prostate biopsy in one study (Catalona et al., 1997). A positive DRE has a positive predictive value of 21–39%.

In an effort to improve the specificity and sensitivity of PSA measurements, additional PSA measurements have been employed. Thus, the PSA density (total serum PSA per cubic centimetre of prostatic volume as determined by TRUS), PSA velocity (change in PSA value over time) and percentage of free (non-protein-bound) PSA improve the sensitivity and specificity for the detection of carcinoma and permit the avoidance of biopsy in some cases.

There have been no controlled trials to date that have documented a successful method of prostate cancer prevention. Potentially successful means might include drugs to decrease serum androgens or inhibit their tissue effects, a reduction in saturated fats in the diet and dietary supplements to provide increased amounts of phyto-oestrogens, vitamin E, selenium and/or lycopene. In one ongoing study looking at prostate cancer prevention with the 5-α-reductase inhibitor finasteride (which prevents the conversion of testosterone to its active metabolite, dihydrotestosterone), preliminary results showed no decrease in high-grade PIN among those receiving the drug, casting some doubt on its ultimate efficacy as a preventive measure.

Molecular Genetic Findings

A heterogeneous mixture of genetic alterations characterizes prostate cancers. Some of the most common abnormalities include loss of heterozygosity corresponding to loci on 7q, 8p, 10q, 13q, 16q and 18q. Loss of genetic material at these locations may well correspond to deletions of tumour suppressor genes that normally restrict cellular growth.

The association of prostate cancer with vitamin D deficiency has prompted the investigation of the role of genetic variation of the vitamin D receptor gene in prostate cancer. In one study of Japanese men with and without prostate cancer, one of three polymorphisms of the vitamin D receptor gene was associated with one-third the risk of prostatic cancer (Habuchi et al., 2000).

Because of the relationship of prostate cancer to androgen, studies of a gene (CYP3A4) that is normally involved in the deactivation of testosterone have been conducted and shown interesting results. A CYP3A4 variant has been linked to a higher frequency of prostate cancer and, more recently, this variant was found in a much higher proportion of African Americans, a group known to be at relatively high risk for prostatic carcinoma. Furthermore, African Americans with prostate cancer were homozygous for the variant gene significantly more frequently (46%) compared with a control group (28%) who did not have prostate cancer (Paris et al., 1999). Along similar lines, a missense mutation in the 5-α-reductase gene that is responsible for coding the protein that converts testosterone to its active metabolite was found to be associated with a much higher enzyme activity and was identified seven times more frequently in African Americans with prostate cancer compared with a healthy control population of African Americans (Makridakis et al., 1999).

A novel DNA transcript, designated DD3 and mapping to chromosome 9q, was recently shown to be overexpressed in 53 of 56 prostate tumours, but it was not identified in other tumours or non-neoplastic tissues other than prostate (Bussemakers et al., 1999). Another gene that appears important in prostate cancer progression is the androgen receptor gene located on Xq-12, which is amplified in one-third of hormone refractory prostate cancers (Nupponen and Visakorpi, 1999).

Prognostic Factors

A number of features impact on the prognosis of prostate cancer. Initial stage remains of paramount importance. Clinical stage correlates with overall survival (**Figure 16**) and pathological stage, as determined from the examination of the radical prostatectomy specimen, provides a stronger assessment of the prognosis (**Figure 17**). Patients with incidentally identified

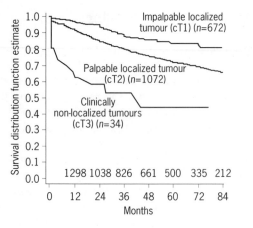

Figure 16 There is a decline in the survival of patients with prostate cancer treated by prostatectomy with advancing tumour stage as determined by clinical assessment. (Adapted from Catalona and Smith, 1998.)

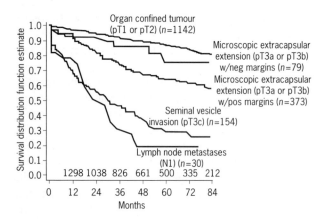

Figure 17 There is a decline in the survival of patients with prostate cancer treated by prostatectomy with advancing tumour stage as determined by pathological examination of the prostatectomy specimen and regional lymph nodes. (Adapted from Catalona and Smith, 1998.)

tumours in transurethral resectates (stage T1a) have a 95% 10-year survival, but there is a progressive decline in 10-year cancer-specific survival with advancing tumour stage; patients with T1b–T2 tumours have about an 80% 10-year cancer-specific survival, and those with T3–T4 tumours have a 60% 10-year cancer-specific survival. Patients who have nodal involvement at operation are rarely cured, but may have a prolonged survival, with a ten-year cancer-specific survival of about 40%.

In addition to stage, significant prognostic factors include pretreatment PSA levels (**Figure 18**), Gleason score (**Figure 8**) and, in patients treated by prostatectomy, tumour volume, margin status, the presence of perineural invasion and tumour ploidy in the prostatectomy specimen. These factors are not necessarily independent; some

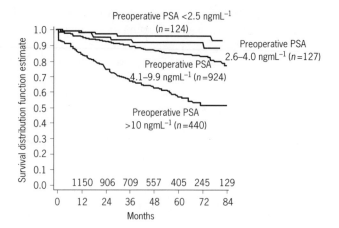

Figure 18 There is a decline in the survival of patients with prostate cancer treated by prostatectomy with increasing levels of serum PSA determined pre-operatively. (Adapted from Catalona and Smith, 1998.)

investigators, for instance, maintain that tumour volume provides no further prognostic information once Gleason score and margin status are determined.

Overview of Present Clinical Management

There are several treatment options for patients with carcinoma of the prostate. These include radical prostatectomy, radiation treatment by either external beam or radioactive seed implants (brachytherapy), anti-androgen treatment (orchiectomy or drug-induced androgen blockade) and so-called 'watchful waiting.' Patients with localized disease (T1–T2) are the best candidates for radical prostatectomy. Advanced prostate cancers (T3 and T4) are usually treated locally by radiation, whereas the primary approach for patients with metastatic disease is with androgen deprivation. Because many prostate cancers have an indolent course and do not affect the longevity of the patient, some have advocated no specific treatment for those with localized tumours. These patients receive periodic follow-up and may be treated if there is evidence of disease progression beyond a certain point. One problem with this approach is the reliable identification of those patients who will have a slowly progressive course versus those who are likely to experience rapid progression. For older patients with low-grade tumours that are predicted to be of small volume (based on TRUS and needle biopsy estimates), this may be a rational approach. T1a tumours (incidentally discovered in transurethral resectates) may be particularly amenable to this approach since they are often low-grade, low-volume lesions. Nonetheless, progression of the T1a tumours to high-stage lesions has been documented in up to 37% of patients who are followed beyond 10 years (Epstein *et al.*, 1986). In one Swedish study there was no difference in cancer-specific survival comparing treated versus untreated patients with localized tumours who had been followed for up to 15 years (**Figure 19**) (Johansson *et al.*, 1997).

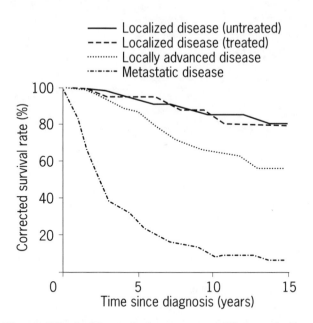

Figure 19 In this study there was no difference in the survival of patients with localized prostate cancer who received no treatment as compared to those who were treated. (Adapted from Johansson *et al.*, 1997.)

PENIS

Normal Development and Structure

The penis develops from the genital tubercle, a swelling at the superior aspect of the cloacal folds. Such development is dependent on stimulation by androgenic hormones of testicular origin *in utero*. The superior portion of the cloacal folds is segregated from the inferior and become the urethral folds, which become incorporated into the penis to form the urethra. The genital tubercle, with androgenic stimulation, enlarges and elongates to form the phallus. A plaque of ectoderm at the distal aspect of the phallus forms the glans and distal most portion of the urethra.

The distal penis consists of the glans, the coronal sulcus and foreskin (prepuce) (**Figure 20**). The glans consists of a layer of stratified squamous epithelium, a thin lamina propria and the erectile tissue of the corpus spongiosum that surrounds the distal most portion of the urethra. The body or shaft represents the majority of the penis. The shaft is composed of three cylinders of erectile tissue, the paired corpora cavernosa and the ventralmost corpus spongiosum that contains the urethra. Each of these structures is covered by the tunica albuginea, a dense layer of connective tissue, and is encased in a layer of fascia (Buck's fascia). The most proximal portion of the penis, the root, is located in the perineum. Here, the paired corpora cavernosa form the penile crura, which have ligamentous insertions on the ischial bones. The central corpus spongiosum is expanded into the penile bulb, which is penetrated by the membranous urethra.

The arterial supply to the penis is derived from the pudendal branches of the internal iliac arteries. These give

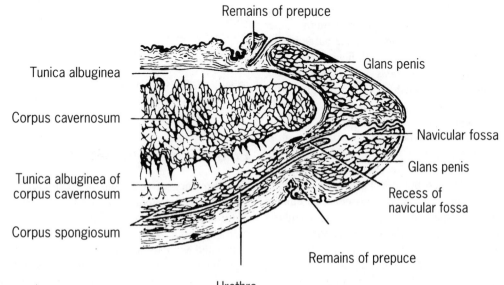

Figure 20 Sagittal section of distal penis, with foreskin removed. (Adapted from Romanes, 1986.)

rise to branches that run on the dorsal aspect, deep aspect, and bulb of the penis. The dorsal vein of the penis splits into two branches and drains into the prostatic plexus. The lymphatics that drain the glans and corpora cavernosa empty into superficial and deep inguinal nodes, whereas the skin of the shaft and foreskin empty into superficial inguinal lymph nodes.

Tumour Pathology

The overwhelming majority of penile cancers are squamous cell carcinomas. Most cases occur in older men (mean age, 58 years), but occasional younger patients may also be affected. The portions of penis that are most commonly affected are the glans (80%), foreskin mucosa (15%) and coronal sulcus (5%), but spread of tumours that originate in one of these locations to other penile components is common (Young et al., 2000).

Several subtypes of penile squamous cell carcinoma are described based on both the gross and histological appearances of these tumours. Young et al. (2000) have divided them into three major categories based on their grossly recognizable growth patterns: superficial spreading (35%), verruciform (25%) and vertical growth (20%), with the remainder having mixed patterns. The superficial spreading variant usually shows a plaque-like growth of white granular tissue that often spreads over large areas of the glans and foreskin. Verruciform tumours have an exophytic growth of white to grey tumour, typically with well-defined, circumscribed margins on cut surface. The vertical growth tumours are often ulcerated, deeply penetrating lesions with foci of haemorrhage, necrosis and cystic change.

Histologically, most tumours fall into the 'usual-type' squamous cell carcinoma category and are typically well differentiated and rarely poorly differentiated or sarcomatoid in type, with a spindle cell growth pattern. Other variants of squamous cell carcinoma include basaloid carcinoma (10%) (strongly associated with human papilloma virus (HPV; see chapter on *Infectious Agents and Cancer*)), papillary carcinoma (8%), which has a verruciform gross pattern but tends to have a jagged base composed of infiltrating nests of squamous cell carcinoma, warty carcinoma (6%) (**Figure 21**), which usually has a verruciform gross appearance and shows features related to HPV, and verrucous carcinoma (3%), which also has a verruciform appearance and pushing borders but lacks HPV-related features.

Preinvasive lesions of penile squamous carcinoma demonstrate the same spectrum of squamous cell dysplasia as is more commonly seen in the uterine cervix. For the high-grade dysplastic lesions, those affecting the glans may produce a diffusely erythematous clinical appearance, so-called 'erythroplasia of Queyrat.' 'Bowen disease' is the clinical term applied to high-grade squamous dysplasia that affects the penile shaft, producing a red or white elevated lesion. A third lesion, Bowenoid papulosis, typically

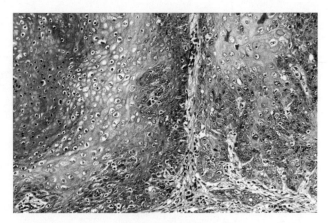

Figure 21 A portion of a 'warty' squamous cell carcinoma shows the nuclear enlargement and perinuclear clearing associated with the human papillomavirus (left) and an invasive growth of malignant-appearing squamous cells (right).

affects the shaft as small, multiple papules in younger patients (mean age 30 years) than those with erythroplasia of Queyrat or Bowen disease (mean age in the sixth decade). Most commonly, the lesions of Bowenoid papulosis undergo spontaneous regression, whereas those of erythroplasia of Queyrat or Bowen disease persist and occasionally progress to invasive carcinoma.

In addition to these variants of squamous cell carcinoma, some much more rare primary malignant tumours of the penis may also be seen. These include adenosquamous carcinoma, basal cell carcinoma, malignant melanoma, Paget disease, and various sarcomas. Of the sarcomas, those showing vascular differentiation are most common and include angiosarcoma, epithelioid hemangioendothelioma and Kaposi's sarcoma, the latter often occurring in patients with the acquired immunodeficiency syndrome. Other sarcomas include leiomyosarcoma, epithelioid sarcoma, malignant fibrous histiocytoma and embryonal rhabdomyosarcoma. Lymphoma may also rarely occur. Occasionally, metastatic tumours involve the penis, usually in patients with known advanced stage disease. The urinary bladder, prostate and kidney are the most common sources.

Epidemiology and Aetiology

The incidence of squamous cell carcinoma of the penis varies markedly around the world. It is common in Africa, Latin America and much of Asia, but rare in Europe and North America. Poor hygiene and phimosis are strongly associated with its development. Other features that are significantly associated with penile cancer include a history of HPV-related lesions, such as condylomata, and the absence of circumcision. It is likely that some forms are, like carcinoma of the uterine cervix, related to HPV infection given that HPV types can be identified in some tumours and there is an increased frequency of penile cancer in the sexual partners of women with cervical dysplasia and carcinoma. It seems likely that absence of circumcision may permit carcinogenic substances or agents to accumulate in smegma to initiate tumour development. This hypothesis is also consistent with the anatomical distribution of penile cancer, with a marked predominance on the glans, mucosa of foreskin and coronal sulcus. Perhaps, in addition, the development of a thickened keratin layer that follows circumcision is a protective factor.

Screening and Prevention

Because of the rarity of penile carcinoma in Europe and North America, no experience with screening programmes is available. It is likely that simple inspection of high-risk patients would suffice to identify early lesions at a curable stage. In theory, precursor lesions could likely be detected by cytological preparations similar to those employed for the uterine cervix.

Circumcision in the neonatal period is considered a simple and effective method for the prevention of penile cancer. Schoen (1997) reported that the incidence of penile cancer among circumcised men in the USA is essentially zero, whereas it is 2.2/100 000 among uncircumcised men. Among a historical series of more than 1600 penile cancers that occurred in the last 60 years in the USA, none of the patients had been circumcised in infancy (Schoen, 1991).

Molecular Genetic Findings

Because of the rarity of penile cancer in Europe and North America, relatively little information is available concerning the molecular genetic events in these tumours. In one study of 64 penile cancers, HPV DNA was found in 36 cases (56%) (most commonly HPV 16), and 26% had evidence of *p53* mutations (Levi *et al.*, 1998). An additional study identified c-Ha-*RAS* mutations in a metastasis of a penile squamous cell carcinoma that contained HPV 18 DNA. This mutation was not identified in the primary tumour or in an earlier metastasis, suggesting it was a late event involved in tumour progression (Leis *et al.*, 1998).

Prognostic Factors

A number of features of penile carcinoma have prognostic significance regarding the occurrence of metastasis. Tumours with a verruciform growth pattern (Cubilla *et al.*, 2000) have a better prognosis than those with a superficial spreading pattern which are, in turn, associated with a better outcome that those with vertical growth. Among the histological types, verrucous carcinoma has the best prognosis, warty and papillary squamous carcinomas have a good prognosis, but somewhat worse than the pure verrucous carcinomas, squamous cell carcinomas of the usual type have an intermediate prognosis and the most aggressive tumours are the basaloid (Cubilla *et al.*, 1998) and sarcomatoid variants. A further refinement in outcome can be obtained by defining the degree of tumour differentiation, although this seems to have been applied mostly for the 'usual' type of squamous cell carcinoma rather than the less common variants (Horenblas and van Tinteren, 1994). Maiche *et al.* (1991) have further refined the grading methodology by developing a scoring system that factors the degree of keratinization, mitotic rate, cytological atypia and inflammatory response. Young *et al.* (2000) found a good correlation between a prognostic index (based on the tumour grade and anatomical level of invasion) and subsequent metastasis and tumour-related death. This is in line with the work of McDougal (1995) regarding the importance of the depth of tumour invasion and metastasis.

Overview of Present Clinical Management

The mainstay of treatment for penile carcinoma is surgical excision with lymph node dissection. For tumours of the foreskin, circumcision without penectomy may be adequate if frozen section evaluation of the margins is negative. For cases involving the glans, partial penectomy is required. In some cases with extensive areas of involvement, total penectomy may be necessary. In some cases, sentinel lymph node sampling, if negative, may permit the avoidance of more extensive inguinal lymph node dissection, but occasional cases of 'skip' metastases do occur.

SEMINAL VESICLE

Normal Development and Structure

The seminal vesicles develop from outpouchings of the mesonephric ducts, which also form the vasa deferentia. They are normally located along the posterolateral aspect of the urinary bladder and superior to the prostate, although they are occasionally embedded within the prostatic capsule. The excretory ducts of the seminal vesicles empty into the vasa deferentia, with the resultant conjoined structure known as the ejaculatory duct. Each seminal vesicle consists of numerous branching ducts embedded in a smooth muscle stroma.

Tumour Pathology

Primary cancers of the seminal vesicle are extraordinarily rare and hence have no known epidemiological features. Most have occurred in older men, with a mean age of 62 years, but occurrence in the third decade is also reported. Patients typically present with symptoms of urinary

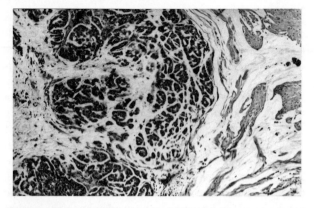

Figure 22 A mucinous carcinoma of the seminal vesicle has nests and cords of malignant epithelial cells in pools of extracellular mucinous secretion.

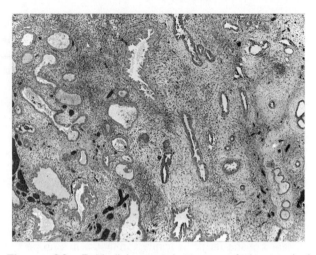

Figure 23 Epithelial–stromal tumour of the seminal vesicle. A cellular, neoplastic stroma surrounds numerous glands, some having a tufted epithelial lining. [From Young *et al.*, 2000, *Tumours of the Prostate, Seminal Vesicles, Urethra, and Penis*. 354 (Armed Forces Institute of Pathology, Washington, DC), by permission.]

obstruction, although haematuria and haemospermia also may occur. A palpable mass is present on digital rectal examination.

The tumours are usually multinodular, solid masses of grey–tan tissue. Microscopically, they are typically poorly differentiated adenocarcinomas. Papillary patterns are common, and clear cell carcinoma, similar to the tumour seen in the female genital tract, and mucinous carcinoma may also occur (**Figure 22**).

On immunohistochemical study, the primary carcinomas of the seminal vesicle are negative for PSA and PAP, assisting with the differential diagnosis of secondary involvement of the seminal vesicle by prostatic carcinoma, a much more common occurrence. In addition, seminal vesicle carcinomas may stain for carcinoembryonic antigen, CA-125 and cytokeratin 7, but are negative for cytokeratin 20 (Ormsby *et al.*, 2000).

In addition to the very rare primary carcinomas of the seminal vesicle, even more rare epithelial–stromal tumours also occur that are similar in appearance to those of prostatic origin. They typically occur in middle-aged to older patients who present with urinary retention. On gross examination, they are multicystic and may have solid foci. On microscopic examination, glandular structures, sometimes cystically dilated, are lined by cytologically benign cuboidal to columnar epithelium and surrounded by a variably cellular and atypical stroma that may show mitotic activity (**Figure 23**). Classification of the neoplasm as low or high grade depends on the stromal cellularity, atypia, mitotic activity and extent of stromal overgrowth. Immunostains for PSA and PAP are negative in the epithelial component, unlike the epithelial–stromal tumours of prostatic origin.

Rare sarcomas of the seminal vesicle origin are reported and include leiomyosarcoma, fibrosarcoma, malignant fibrous histiocytoma, liposarcoma and angiosarcoma.

Secondary spread of malignant tumours to the seminal vesicle is common. Overwhelmingly, these represent prostatic carcinoma or, less commonly, urothelial carcinoma from the bladder. Others include colorectal carcinoma, germ cell tumour and carcinoid. There is a significant decline in prognosis with secondary spread of prostatic carcinoma to the seminal vesicle as compared with otherwise similar tumours lacking such spread (**Figure 17**).

Prognostic Factors

Seminal vesicle carcinoma has a poor prognosis. Most of the reported patients have metastatic disease at the time of diagnosis; 95% of the patients with follow-up have survived less than 3 years. Of the few patients with survival of more than 1.5 years, all were treated with surgical excision (often requiring cystoprostatectomy) and anti-androgenic therapy, either with oestrogen, orchiectomy, or androgen inhibitors.

TESTIS

Normal Development and Structure

The testes develop initially as undifferentiated gonads represented by bilateral thickenings of mesenchyme between the mesenteric root and the mesonephros. The coelomic epithelium overlying these genital ridges proliferates and subsequently grows into the mesenchyme to form the primitive sex cords (**Figure 24**). The germ cells develop in the yolk sac but migrate along the midline to take residence in the gonads. The sex cord cells form the Sertoli cell component of the seminiferous tubules, which are also populated by the migrated germ cells. The Leydig cells differentiate from the primitive mesenchyme of the interstitium. Gradually the testis assumes its adult shape as a distinct ovoid structure and migrates caudally, eventually to descend into the scrotal sacs in association with a small tongue of pelvic peritoneum, the tunica vaginalis. The seminiferous tubules anastomose with mesonephric tubules that form the ductular system of the testis and

which empty into the mesonephric duct, the precursor of the vas deferens.

The ovoid testis is composed of numerous seminiferous tubules that anastomose with those of the rete testis and that, in turn, empty into the efferent ductules, which form the head of the epididymis, a structure closely applied to the external testicular surface (**Figure 25**). The testis is surrounded by a thick fibrous coating, the tunica albuginea, with a layer of mesothelium on its external aspect derived from the visceral layer of the tunica vaginalis.

The arterial supply to the testis and epididymis is from the testicular artery, usually a branch of the aorta, and from the artery of the vas deferens that derives from the superior vesical artery. The venous drainage exits the testis as a group of four to eight small veins at the hilum that invest the testicular artery in the spermatic cord as the pampini-form plexus. The lymphatics empty into the retroperitoneal lymph nodes.

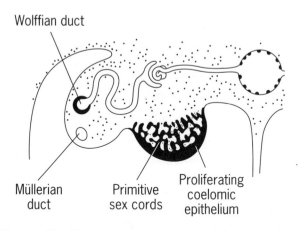

Figure 24   The primitive sex cords of the testis form from the proliferation of the coelomic epithelium that overlies the embryonic gonadal ridge. (Adapted from Langman, 1969.)

Tumour Pathology

Although testicular germ cell tumours can be divided into two main categories that are often treated differently – seminomas and non-seminomatous germ cell tumours – both tumour types are derived from a common precursor malignant germ cell. This cell resembles those of

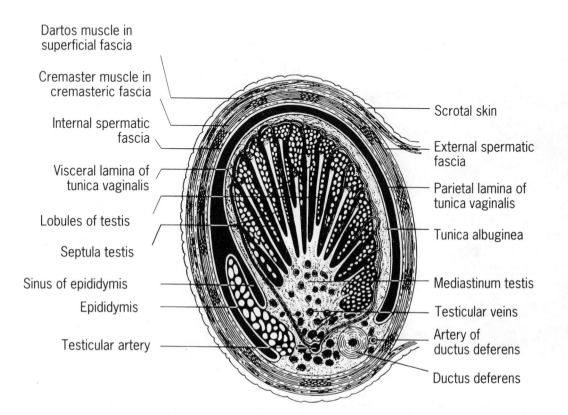

Figure 25   Cross-section of the testis and surrounding scrotum. (Adapted from Romanes, 1981.)

seminoma but also has the capacity to form non-seminomatous germ cell tumours. Such cells characteristically occur in the basal portion of seminiferous tubules that show decreased or absent spermatogenesis and have been termed 'carcinoma-*in-situ*' (**Figure 26**). However, since they can give rise to tumours that are not strictly 'carcinomas,' the term that a committee of pathologists recommended for this lesion is 'intratubular germ cell neoplasia, unclassified type' (IGCNU). Follow-up studies of patients who have had IGCNU identified on testicular biopsy verify

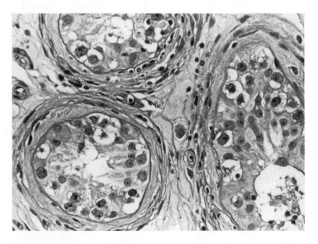

Figure 26 Intratubular germ cell neoplasia, unclassified type (also termed 'carcinoma-*in-situ*'). Note the basal proliferation of seminoma-like cells with clear cytoplasm and enlarged nuclei with prominent nucleoli in seminiferous tubules that lack spermatogenesis.

a high rate of progression to an invasive germ cell tumour of either seminomatous or non-seminomatous type. The estimated rate of progression is 50% at 5 years, but some experts feel that all cases of IGCNU will eventually progress to an invasive tumour if sufficient time is allowed. Occasional cases of invasive testicular germ cell tumour have been reported in patients 15–20 years after a biopsy showing IGCNU.

The evidence that IGCNU gives rise to testicular germ cell tumours is strong. Apart from the follow-up studies already mentioned, IGCNU is identified in the great majority of adult testes harbouring germ cell tumours (but, interestingly, not in prepubertal boys with testicular germ cell tumours). It also has the same immunohistochemical, ultrastructural and cytogenetic findings as are seen in seminomas, and it occurs with high frequency in patients who are known to be at increased risk for testicular germ cell tumours (see below).

Seminoma is the most common form of testicular germ cell tumour and occurs at an average age of 40 years. Most patients present with a testicular mass, but occasional patients present with metastatic tumour, most commonly manifest as vague abdominal or back pain because of retroperitoneal spread. A small group of patients actually have smaller than normal testes, reflecting pre-existing atrophy.

On gross examination, seminoma tends to have a fairly uniform, solid, white/grey to tan cut surface and a lobular outline (**Figure 27**). Some tumours, however, may diffusely replace the testis or show foci of haemorrhage or necrosis that produce a more variegated appearance.

On microscopic examination, the tumour cells are typically arranged in diffuse sheets in an overall lobulated configuration. The sheets are usually subdivided by fibrous septa that contain a lymphocytic infiltrate with occasional plasma cells (**Figure 28**). Some tumours may have a cord-like pattern of growth, especially at the tumour periphery.

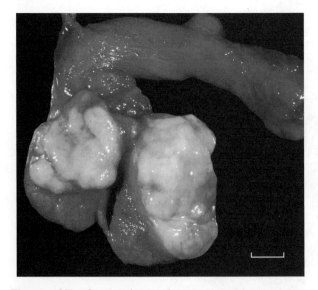

Figure 27 Cut surface of a testis with seminoma showing a solid, lobulated tumour with the typical, homogeneous, cream-coloured to light tan appearance. Bar, 1 cm.

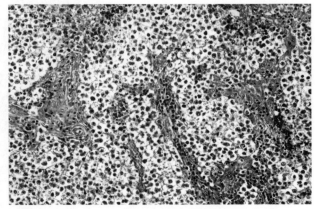

Figure 28 Typical seminoma, showing a sheet-like arrangement of cells with clear cytoplasm that is interrupted by fibrovascular septa with a lymphocytic infiltrate.

Occasional seminomas have a prominent interstitial growth pattern.

The tumour cells have round, often vesicular nuclei, with occasional flattened edges and one or more prominent nucleoli. They have polygonal shapes and generally abundant clear cytoplasm with well-defined cell membranes, although sometimes the cytoplasm is more dense and the nuclei more pleomorphic. The mitotic rate is usually brisk.

Small collections of epithelioid histiocytes occur in about 50% of seminomas, and rarely a similar granulomatous reaction may efface most of the tumour, making careful search for residual tumour cells necessary. Syncytiotrophoblast cells, usually multinucleated with eosinophilic cytoplasm, can be identified in about 10% of seminomas by light microscopy, but are more common if an immunohistochemical stain for human chorionic gonadotropin (hCG) is employed. They are often associated with small foci of haemorrhage, and their presence correlates with elevated levels of serum hCG.

Seminomas, like many other forms of testicular germ cell tumour, are cellular and friable, making artifactual tumour implants common on tissue surfaces and in vessels. Since these may lead to a false-positive diagnosis of extratesticular extension or lymphatic involvement, it is important to distinguish this phenomenon from legitimate examples of these processes. Artifactual implants on tissue surfaces occur at the periphery of tissue sections and in isolated tissue spaces that are discontinuous from clearly invasive tumour. The cells tend to have a poorly cohesive 'floating' arrangement and incite no tissue reaction. This is also true for artifactual vascular invasion, whereas true vascular invasion shows more cohesive cellular nests that conform to the shape of the vessel and may be attached to its wall and have an associated thrombus.

Spermatocytic seminoma is an entirely different entity from classic seminoma. It usually occurs in older men, with a mean age in the sixth decade, who present with testicular masses. Although it rarely 'dedifferentiates' into a sarcoma that behaves aggressively, the usual spermatocytic seminoma virtually never metastasizes; hence radical orchiectomy alone is adequate treatment. On gross examination, the tumours are often large, grey to haemorrhagic, multinodular, solid and cystic, and have a myxoid quality. Microscopically, the tumour cells are most typically arranged in sheets that are interrupted by oedema and have a paucity of lymphocytes and granulomas. The tumour cells vary in size from small, round, lymphocyte-like cells to intermediate-sized cells to giant cells that may be multinucleated. Despite the almost invariably benign biology of these cases, numerous mitotic figures, including abnormal forms, may be seen.

There are several types of non-seminomatous germ cell tumour; a detailed description of these tumours, however, is beyond the scope of this chapter and can be obtained from other sources (Ulbright et al., 1999). In general, the gross appearances of the non-seminomatous tumours are more heterogeneous than those of seminomas (**Figure 29**), reflecting the more common occurrence of haemorrhage, necrosis and cystic degeneration in the former.

Embryonal carcinoma, like the other forms of non-seminomatous germ cell tumour, tends to occur in patients who average 30 years of age. Although, like patients with seminoma, most present with testicular masses, a higher proportion have symptoms secondary to metastatic spread at presentation, reflecting the greater degree of aggressiveness of embryonal carcinoma. The tumour cells may be arranged in solid, glandular, and/or papillary patterns (**Figure 30**). They have large, pleomorphic, often irregularly shaped nuclei that appear crowded, with adjacent nuclei seeming to touch or even overlap. The

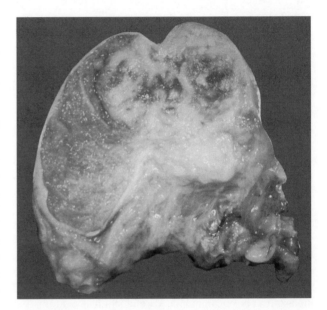

Figure 29   An embryonal carcinoma with a variegated, haemorrhagic appearance.

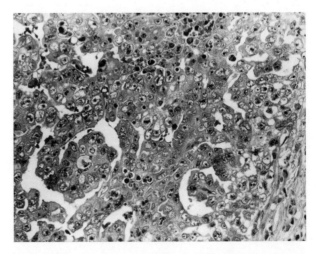

Figure 30   Papillary pattern of embryonal carcinoma. Note the crowded nuclei and indistinct cell borders.

cytoplasm is usually denser that that of seminoma cells and the cytoplasmic borders are ill-defined. The mitotic rate is brisk, and necrosis is frequent and often extensive. Intratubular embryonal carcinoma is often seen in the adjacent parenchyma and may be confused with intravascular tumour, although the more uniform size and shape of the rounded intratubular tumour and frequent comedo-type necrosis contrast with the features of intravascular tumour.

Yolk sac tumour is an uncommon form of pure non-seminomatous germ cell tumour in adult patients, but it represents about 70% of testicular germ cell tumours in children in whom it presents at an average age of 1.5 years. It is a common component of mixed germ cell tumours in postpubertal patients. Yolk sac tumour is the form of germ cell tumour that most consistently produces α-foetoprotein (AFP), which therefore serves as an extremely useful tumour marker. There are numerous yolk sac tumour patterns, and most tumours show several of them. The most common one is a microcystic arrangement wherein vacuolated tumour cells interconnect (**Figure 31**). Solid, myxoid, glandular, papillary, endodermal sinus-like (resembling structures normally identified in the placenta of rodents), macrocystic, hepatoid, sarcomatoid, polyvesicular vitelline, and parietal (basement membrane-rich) patterns also occur. In general, the neoplastic cells are less pleomorphic and atypical than those seen in embryonal carcinoma. The presence of hyaline, eosinophilic globules (**Figure 31**) and bands of basement membrane are helpful ancillary features for the recognition of yolk sac tumour.

Choriocarcinoma, as a pure tumour, is extremely rare and is even unusual as a component of mixed germ cell tumours. Unlike other forms of germ cell tumour, patients with choriocarcinoma usually present with metastatic tumour rather than a palpable mass. Even with known metastatic choriocarcinoma, careful clinical examination of the testes may fail to identify any testicular abnormality. This is because choriocarcinoma is the most common tumour to undergo regression in the testis, so that only foci

of scarring with haemosiderin deposits may be present as evidence of pre-existing tumour. Choriocarcinoma is consistently associated with very high levels of hCG, and this can lead to gynaecomastia and thyrotoxicosis, which may therefore be presenting features. On gross examination, a haemorrhagic nodule is typical. Microscopically, syncytiotrophoblast cells and cytotrophoblast cells are intermixed, almost always with associated haemorrhage. Angioinvasion is frequent.

Teratoma is uncommon as a pure tumour in adult patients, but it is the second type of germ cell tumour (in addition to yolk sac tumour) that occurs in children, representing about 30% of the total in paediatric patients. In children it is benign, but in adults it may be associated with metastases of either teratomatous or non-teratomatous germ cell tumours. The reason for this unexpected occurrence is that in postpubertal patients teratoma develops through a process of differentiation from an invasive malignant germ cell tumour, probably embryonal carcinoma most commonly. In postpubertal patients, therefore, teratoma has an aneuploid DNA content and cytogenetic abnormalities similar to those of other testicular germ cell tumours, whereas in prepubertal patients, it is diploid with a normal karyotype.

On gross examination, the tumours may be either solid or cystic. Microscopically, a large variety of tissues may be seen. Cartilage is common, as are enteric-type glands, squamous nests, and smooth muscle stroma. Immaturity is usually manifest as a cellular, mitotically active stroma or islands of neuroepithelium, but it is prognostically irrelevant, given the derivation of teratoma in postpubertal patients from an invasive malignant germ cell tumour and the benign outcome in prepubertal patients. Occasional overgrowth of primitive neuroepithelium or embryonic-appearing skeletal muscle is justification for a diagnosis of teratoma with a secondary malignant component (primitive neuroectodermal tumour or embryonal rhabdomyosarcoma, respectively).

Mixed germ cell tumours are fairly common and, by definition, represent those neoplasms having more than one of the types of tumours already discussed. Those cases with both seminoma and a non-seminomatous component are considered to be non-seminomatous in type because the latter component is most important in determining its behaviour.

Sex cord–stromal tumours of the testis are uncommon, representing about 5% of testicular tumours. They include Leydig cell tumour, Sertoli cell tumour, fibroma, granulosa cell tumour, mixed sex cord–stromal tumour, and unclassified variants. Most patients present with testicular masses, but some develop hormonal symptoms, which may be the presenting feature. This is particularly true for children who may develop pseudoprecocity or gynaecomastia. These tumours occur over a wide age range.

Grossly, sex cord–stromal tumours are usually solid, although cystic degeneration may be present. The colour

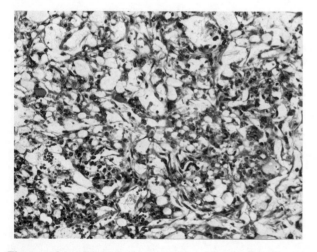

Figure 31 Typical microcystic pattern of yolk sac tumour. There are numerous hyaline globules.

varies from grey/white to tan to yellow. Microscopically, a variety of patterns may occur. Leydig cell tumours most commonly have a diffuse arrangement of cells with abundant eosinophilic cytoplasm and sometimes have intracytoplasmic crystals (crystals of Reinke). The hallmark of Sertoli cell tumours is tubule formation. The granulosa cell tumours may have the range of patterns as seen in the more common ovarian counterpart, including microfollicular, trabecular, diffuse and gyriform. Fibromatous tumours again resemble the much more common ovarian lesions composed of gonadal stromal cells arranged in short fascicles and storiform patterns. Those showing substantial amounts of two or more well-recognized lines of differentiation are placed in the mixed category, whereas those with poorly formed elements such that much of the tumour can no longer be recognized in a reliable fashion as having a particular line of differentiation are placed in the unclassified category.

Malignant behaviour can occur with tumours in the sex cord–stromal category and generally correlates with a number of features, including large tumour size (> 4–5 m), elevated mitotic rates, tumour necrosis, lymphovascular space invasion, significant cytological atypia and extratesticular growth. In general, about 10% of sex cord–stromal tumours are malignant.

A number of other malignant tumours may occur in the testis, but a detailed description of them is beyond the scope of this work, and most are similar to those occurring more commonly at other sites. These include malignant lymphoma, plasmacytoma, granulocytic sarcoma, leukaemic infiltrates, metastatic carcinoma and melanoma, malignant mesothelioma derived from the mesothelium of the tunica vaginalis, ovarian-type epithelial tumours of either 'borderline' or frankly malignant nature, the recently described desmoplastic round cell tumour and a variety of soft tissue sarcomas of paratesticular origin, including embryonal rhabdomyosarcoma in children.

Immunohistochemical stains are helpful in the evaluation of testicular tumours. Stains for placental alkaline phosphatase (PLAP) highlight the cytoplasmic membranes of most seminomas and are frequently positive in the other germ cell tumour types, with the exception of spermatocytic seminoma, although typically more focally. CD30 (BerH2) is a useful marker for embryonal carcinoma, but is virtually absent in other types. Epithelial membrane antigen is typically absent in germ cell tumours, with the exception of choriocarcinoma and teratoma. AFP is positive in yolk sac tumour and occasionally seen in embryonal carcinoma and teratoma, but it is absent in other types of germ cell tumours. hCG is present in syncytiotrophoblast cells, whether in choriocarcinoma or other types of germ cell tumour. Inhibin is a very useful marker for tumours in the sex cord–stromal category, typically staining most Leydig cell tumours diffusely and somewhat more than half of Sertoli cell tumours focally.

Epidemiology and Aetiology

Testicular cancer is overwhelmingly of germ cell origin and occurs predominantly in young men with a mean age of about 30 years (**Figure 32**). It is a disease that is most common in highly industrialized countries and in the Caucasian population. The highest incidence is reported from Denmark, Switzerland and Germany. Testicular cancer has increased in incidence over much of the twentieth century in those countries where it is common (**Figure 32**).

There are several well-recognized risk factors for testicular cancer (**Table 2**). Cryptorchidism remains one of the strongest associations. Some of the more recent studies suggest that patients with cryptorchidism have about a four times increased risk of testicular cancer that is not alleviated by orchiopexy, and that an elevated risk also applies to the non-cryptorchid testis. This risk, however, does not manifest until late adolescence. Swerdlow *et al.* (1997) presented data showing a higher relative risk, although the small number of abdominal testes in that study did not

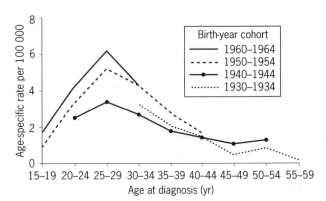

Figure 32 The incidence of testicular germ cell tumours with age in different birth cohorts in Ontario. Note the increasing incidence with later birth year. (Adapted from Weir *et al.*, 1999.)

Table 2 Risk factors for testicular germ cell tumours

Intersex syndromes
Prior testicular germ cell tumour
Familial history of testicular cancer
Testicular atrophy
Cryptorchidism
Infertility
Exposure to high levels of ostrogen *in utero*
Caucasian race
Young adult age

Table 3 Estimates of increased risk of cancer in testes associated with various forms of maldescent. (From Swerdlow et al., 1997, British Medical Journal, **314**, 1507–1511.)

Position of testes	No. of testes	Observed/expected No. of cancers	Relative risk (95% CI)
Descended opposite maldescended[a]	718	1/0.48	2.1 (0.1–9.2)
Unilaterally maldescended	697	4/0.47	8.5 (2.6–19.8)[*]
Maldescended opposite maldescended	708	7/0.49	14.4 (6.2–27.8)[**]
Abdominal maldescended[b]	199	0/0.13	0 (0–28.4)
Non-abdominal maldescended[b]	1206	11/0.84	13.0 (6.8–22.3)[**]
Maldescended[b]	1405	11/0.97	11.3 (5.9–19.4)[**]

[*]$P < 0.01$; [**]$P < 0.001$.
[a]Includes 21 descended testes for which the contralateral maldescended testis had been excised before the follow-up period.
[b]Regardless of position of other testis.

allow an accurate assessment of their potential for malignant change (**Table 3**).

Patients with certain intersex syndromes have a remarkably high incidence of gonadal germ cell tumours. These syndromes include two main types: gonadal dysgenesis in patients with a Y-chromosome and androgen insensitivity syndrome. Patients with the former often have ambiguous external genitalia and gonads with 'streak' morphology or containing mixtures of ovarian-type stroma and immature-appearing seminiferous tubules. They often develop germ cell tumours in childhood or adolescence; hence, gonadectomy is indicated shortly after the diagnosis is established. Patients with androgen insensitivity syndrome are phenotypic females but genetic males. They have maldescended testes that are at high risk of germ cell tumours after puberty. One study reported that 22% of patients with androgen insensitivity syndrome who were over 30 years of age had developed a germ cell tumour (Morris and Mahesh, 1963).

Patients with a history of testicular germ cell tumour have an increased risk of a second germ cell tumour in the remaining testis, especially if that testis is atrophic. Overall, about 5% of patients develop bilateral neoplasia (Dieckmann and Loy, 1998), but the frequency of contralateral neoplasia increases to about 20% if the remaining testis is atrophic. A similar frequency of contralateral neoplasia is also seen in patients who have a positive family history (see below). At minimum, therefore, continued follow-up of the contralateral testis is indicated for testicular cancer patients.

Males with a family history of testicular cancer are at increased risk (see chapter on *Inherited Predispositions to Cancer*). The risk is greater if the relative is a brother rather than a father. Overall, there is a 2.2% frequency of testicular cancer in the first-degree male relatives of patients with testicular cancer (Tollerud et al., 1985). As mentioned above, a family history also increases the risk of bilateral involvement. A recent study of a large group of testicular cancer families has, through linkage analysis, implicated a

testicular cancer gene with a dominant pattern of inheritance that is present on the X-chromosome (Rapley et al., 2000).

Despite these strong associations with testicular cancer, most cases do not occur in patients with well-recognized risk factors. Numerous epidemiological studies have found only weak associations with certain occupations or industrial exposures (see chapter on *Identifying Cancer Causes through Epidemiology*). More recently, a number of studies have implicated *in utero* exposure to high levels of circulating oestrogens as a significant factor for testicular carcinogenesis. Hence, there is increased risk in males born from first pregnancies, in those whose mothers had gestational hyperemesis and in those with a history of neonatal jaundice – all conditions associated with high oestrogen levels during foetal life. In addition, there are numerous factors that likely increase environmental oestrogen exposure, including the increased therapeutic use of oestrogenic substances, the oestrogenic supplementation of livestock and oestrogenic activity of some pesticides.

Molecular Genetic Findings

Most testicular germ cell tumours have a hyperdiploid to hypotriploid DNA content and, on cytogenetic study, they frequently have one or more copies of an isochromosome derived from the short arms of chromosome 12 (i (12p)). This distinctive marker chromosome is considered specific for germ cell tumours and can be used to establish a germ cell tumour diagnosis in problematic cases. Even in those germ cell tumours lacking i (12p), there is an increased amount of DNA derived from 12p, so this region of the genome appears to play a key role in the pathogenesis of germ cell tumours.

In addition to gain of 12p DNA, there are other non-random chromosomal changes. These include loss from 11p, 12q, 13, 18 and Y and gain of 7, 8, 21 and X. It has been noted that the DNA content of seminomas is greater than that of non-seminomatous tumours, and it has been hypothesized that the non-seminomatous tumours derive from seminomas as a consequence of gene loss. As mentioned in the discussion of familial testicular cancer, a putative testis cancer gene has recently been localized to the X-chromosome through linkage analysis (Rapley *et al.*, 2000).

Prognostic Factors

The great majority of testicular germ cell tumours are now curable through a combination of surgery, chemotherapy and/or radiation. Prior to the development of effective chemotherapy, many patients with metastatic seminoma could be effectively treated with radiation, but those with metastatic non-seminomatous tumours had a poor prognosis. Now, however, more than 80% of patients with metastatic non-seminomatous tumours are cured.

Stage remains of paramount prognostic importance. Patients with early stage tumours are almost uniformly cured, whereas those with bulky retroperitoneal disease experience about a 20% overall mortality. There are prognostic models to help divide patients into different categories that factor in features such as the levels of serum hCG and AFP, sites of involvement and size of metastatic lesions.

Occasional patients with early stage disease have an unexpectedly aggressive course or fail initial therapy for unclear reasons. It would be of great interest to identify such cases prospectively, but this goal has not yet been achieved.

Several investigators have attempted to define groups of testicular cancer patients who are at high or low risk for metastatic disease after an orchiectomy for clinical stage I tumour (i.e. having no clinical evidence of metastatic tumour after thorough staging, including radiographic evaluation of the retroperitoneum and chest and serum marker studies). Based on either follow-up studies or the results of retroperitoneal lymph node dissections, it is known that about 30% of such patients have occult retroperitoneal metastases. A successful division would permit simple follow-up for those patients at low risk, whereas high-risk patients could be recommended for staging retroperitoneal lymph node dissection (non-seminomatous patients) or adjuvant radiation (seminoma patients). Thorough pathological evaluation of the primary tumour for features such as lymphovascular invasion, extratesticular extension, percentage or volume of embryonal carcinoma and tumour size have shown strong correlations with either pathologically confirmed metastatic tumour or relapse. Alternative methods of evaluation, including flow cytometric studies for tumour S-phase and ploidy, and immunohistochemical staining for determination of proliferative fraction have also been applied with varying results.

Overview of Present Clinical Management

Patients with a clinical diagnosis of a testicular neoplasm receive radical orchiectomy. For those with seminoma, most receive adjuvant radiation to the retroperitoneum, although there is some interest in surveillance management (i.e. close follow-up but no adjuvant therapy) for clinical stage I patients with favourable pathological features. Radiation is usually given for those seminoma patients with small volume, retroperitoneal metastases, but cisplatin-based chemotherapy is used for those with bulkier disease or supradiaphragmatic spread. Patients with non-seminomatous tumours who are clinical stage I may either be placed on surveillance management or receive limited, nerve-sparing retroperitoneal lymph node dissection, again depending in part on pathological features. For those with known metastatic tumour, cisplatin-based chemotherapy is the mainstay followed by surgical excision of residual masses, if necessary. A patient with a teratomatous component in the testicular primary appears to be at higher risk of requiring post-chemotherapy resection because of the increased likelihood of teratomatous metastases and the non-responsiveness of teratoma to chemotherapy.

Patients who have sex cord–stromal tumours and who are clinical stage I may receive either surveillance management or retroperitoneal lymphadenectomy. It is sensible to manage patients whose tumours lack the features associated with malignant behaviour by surveillance and to reserve nodal dissection for those clinical stage I patients who have tumours with one or more of the pathological features that are associated with metastases. For patients with sex cord–stromal tumours that have metastasized, surgical excision by retroperitoneal lymphadenectomy or other procedures provides the best current approach. Chemotherapy and radiation have not proved effective for this situation.

REFERENCES

Albertsen, P. C., *et al.* (1999). Statistical considerations when assessing outcomes following treatment for prostate cancer. *Journal of Urology*, **162**, 439–444.

Amin, M. B., *et al.* (1993). Putative precursor lesions of prostatic adenocarcinoma: fact or fiction? *Modern Pathology*, **6**, 476–483.

Bostwick, D. G. and Brawer, M. K. (1987). Prostatic intra-epithelial neoplasia and early invasion in prostate cancer. *Cancer*, **59**, 788–794.

Brawn, P. N. (1982). Adenosis of the prostate: a dysplastic lesion that can be confused with prostate adenocarcinoma. *Cancer*, **49**, 826–833.

Bussemakers, M. J., *et al.* (1999). DD3: a new prostate-specific gene, highly overexpressed in prostate cancer. *Cancer Research*, **59**, 5975–5979.

Catalona, W. J., et al. (1994). Comparison of digital rectal examination and serum prostate specific antigen in the early detection of prostate cancer: results of a multicenter clinical trial of 6,630. *Journal of Urology*, **151**, 1283–1290.

Catalona, W. J., et al. (1997). Prostate cancer detection in men with serum PSA concentrations of 2.6 to 4.0 ng/mL and benign prostate examination. Enhancement of specificity with free PSA measurements. *Journal of the American Medical Association*, **277**, 1452–1455.

Cheng, L., et al. (1998). Atypical adenomatous hyperplasia of the prostate: a premalignant lesion? *Cancer Research*, **58**, 389–391.

Cubilla, A. L., et al. (1998). Basaloid squamous cell carcinoma: a distinctive human papilloma virus-related penile neoplasm: a report of 20 cases. *American Journal of Surgical Pathology*, **22**, 755–761.

Cubilla, A. L., et al. (2000). Warty (condylomatous) squamous cell carcinoma of the penis: a report of 11 cases and proposed classification of 'verruciform' penile tumours. *American Journal of Surgical Pathology*, **24**, 505–512.

Dieckmann, K. P. and Loy, V. (1998). The value of the biopsy of the contralateral testis in patients with testicular germ cell cancer: the recent German experience. *APMIS*, **106**, 13–20.

Doll, J. A., et al. (1999). Genetic analysis of prostatic atypical adenomatous hyperplasia (adenosis). *American Journal of Pathology*, **155**, 967–971.

Epstein, J. I., et al. (1986). Prognosis of untreated stage A1 prostatic carcinoma: a study of 94 cases with extended followup. *Journal of Urology*, **136**, 837–839.

Gaudin, P. B., et al. (1998). Sarcomas and related proliferative lesions of specialized prostatic stroma: a clinicopathologic study of 22 cases. *American Journal of Surgical Pathology*, **22**, 148–162.

Gleason, D. F. (1966). Classification of prostatic carcinomas. *Cancer Chemother. Rep., Part 1*, **50**, 125–128.

Gleason, D. F. (1992). Histologic grading of prostate cancer: a perspective. *Human Pathology*, **23**, 273–279.

Gleason, D. F. and Mellinger, G. T. (1974). Prediction of prognosis for prostatic adenocarcinoma by combined histological grading and clinical staging. *Journal of Urology*, **111**, 58–64.

Habuchi, T., et al. (2000). Association of vitamin D receptor gene polymorphism with prostate cancer and benign prostatic hyperplasia in a Japanese population. *Cancer Research*, **60**, 305–308.

Horenblas, S. and van Tinteren, H. (1994). Squamous cell carcinoma of the penis. IV. Prognostic factors of survival: analysis of tumour, nodes and metastasis classification system. *Journal of Urology*, **151**, 1239–1243.

Johansson, J. E., et al. (1997). Fifteen-year survival in prostate cancer. A prospective, population-based study in Sweden. *Journal of the American Medical Association*, **277**, 467–471.

Leis, P. F., et al. (1998). A c-rasHa mutation in the metastasis of a human papillomavirus (HPV)-18 positive penile squamous cell carcinoma suggests a cooperative effect between HPV-18 and c-rasHa activation in malignant progression. *Cancer*, **83**, 122–129.

Levi, J. E., et al. (1998). Human papillomavirus DNA and p53 status in penile carcinomas. *International Journal of Cancer*, **76**, 779–783.

Maiche, A. G., et al. (1991). Histological grading of squamous cell carcinoma of the penis: a new scoring system. *British Journal of Urology*, **67**, 522–526.

Makridakis, N. M., et al. (1999). Association of mis-sense substitution in SRD5A2 gene with prostate cancer in African-American and Hispanic men in Los Angeles, USA. *Lancet*, **354**, 975–978.

McDougal, W. S. (1995). Carcinoma of the penis: improved survival by early regional lymphadenectomy based on the histological grade and depth of invasion of the primary lesion. *Journal of Urology*, **154**, 1364–1366.

McNeal, J. E. (1981). The zonal anatomy of the prostate. *Prostate*, **2**, 35–49.

McNeal, J. E. and Bostwick, D. G. (1986). Intraductal dysplasia: a premalignant lesion of the prostate. *Human Pathology*, **17**, 64–71.

McNeal, J. E. and Yemoto, C. E. (1996). Spread of adenocarcinoma within prostatic ducts and acini. Morphologic and clinical correlations. *American Journal of Surgical Pathology*, **20**, 802–814.

McNeal, J. E., et al. (1988). Zonal distribution of prostatic adenocarcinoma. Correlation with histologic pattern and direction of spread. *American Journal of Surgical Pathology*, **12**, 897–906.

Morris, J. M. and Mahesh, V. B. (1963). Further observations on the syndrome, "testicular feminization". *American Journal of Obstetrics and Gynecology*, **87**, 731–748.

Nupponen, N. and Visakorpi, T. (1999). Molecular biology of progression of prostate cancer. *European Urology*, **35**, 351–354.

Ormsby, A. H., et al. (2000). Primary seminal vesicle carcinoma: an immunohistochemical analysis of four cases. *Modern Pathology*, **13**, 46–51.

Pan, C. C., et al. (2000). The prognostic significance of tertiary Gleason patterns of higher grade in radical prostatectomy specimens: a proposal to modify the Gleason grading system. *American Journal of Surgical Pathology*, **24**, 563–569.

Paris, P. L., et al. (1999). Association between a CYP3A4 genetic variant and clinical presentation in African-American prostate cancer patients. *Cancer Epidemiology Biomarkers Prevention*, **8**, 901–905.

Rapley, E. A., et al. (2000). Localization to Xq27 of a susceptibility gene for testicular germ-cell tumours. *Nature Genetics*, **24**, 197–200.

Renshaw, A. A. (1998). Correlation of gross morphologic features with histologic features in radical prostatectomy specimens. *American Journal of Clinical Pathology*, **110**, 38–42.

Schoen, E. J. (1991). The relationship between circumcision and cancer of the penis. *CA – A Cancer Journal for Clinicians*, **41**, 306–309.

Schoen, E. J. (1997). Benefits of newborn circumcision: is Europe ignoring medical evidence? *Archives of Disease in Childhood*, **77**, 258–260.

Srigley, J. R. (1988). Small-acinar patterns in the prostate gland with emphasis on atypical adenomatous hyperplasia and small-acinar carcinoma. *Seminars in Diagnostic Pathology*, **5**, 254–272.

Swerdlow, A. J., *et al*. (1997). Risk of testicular cancer in cohort of boys with cryptorchidism. *British Medical Journal*, **314**, 1507–1511.

Thomas, R., *et al*. (1982). Aid to accurate clinical staging-histopathologic grading in prostatic cancer. *Journal of Urology*, **128**, 726–728.

Tollerud, D. J., *et al*. (1985). Familial testicular cancer and urogenital developmental anomalies. *Cancer*, **55**, 1849–1854.

Ulbright, T. M., *et al*. (1999). *Tumours of the Testis, Adenexa, Spermatic Cord and Scrotum: Atlas of Tumour Pathology*, Third Series. (Armed Forces Institute of Pathology, Washington, DC).

Young, R. H., *et al*. (2000). *Tumours of the Prostate, Seminal Vesicle, Male Urethra and Penis: Atlas of Tumour Pathology*. (Armed Forces Institute of Pathology, Washington, DC).

FURTHER READING

Bostwick, D. G. (1997). Neoplasms of the prostate. In Bostwick, D. G. and Eble, J. N. (eds). *Urologic Surgical Pathology*. 349 (Mosby Year Book, St. Louis).

Bostwick, D. G. (1999). Prostatic intraepithelial neoplasia is a risk factor for cancer. *Seminars in Urology and Oncology*, **17**, 187–198.

Bostwick, D. G., *et al*. (2000). Prognostic factors in prostate cancer. College of American Pathologists Consensus Statement 1999. *Archives of Pathology and Laboratory Medicine*, **124**, 995–1000.

Catalona, W. J. and Smith, D. S. (1998). Cancer recurrence and survival rates after anatomic radical retropubic prostatectomy for prostate cancer: intermediate-term results. *Journal of Urology*, **160**, 2428–2434.

Cubilla, A. L., *et al*. (1998). Basaloid squamous cell carcinoma: a distinctive human papilloma virus-related penile neoplasm: a report of 20 cases. *American Journal of Surgical Pathology*, **22**, 755–761.

Cubilla, A. L., *et al*. (2000). Warty (condylomatous) squamous cell carcinoma of the penis: a report of 11 cases and proposed classification of 'verruciform' penile tumours. *American Journal of Surgical Pathology*, **24**, 505–512.

Kim, I., *et al*. (1985). Leydig cell tumours of the testis. A clinicopathological analysis of 40 cases and review of the literature. *American Journal of Surgical Pathology*, **9**, 177–192.

Langman, J. (1969). *Medical Embryology and Human Development – Normal and Abnormal*, 2nd edn. 164 (Williams and Wilkins, Baltimore).

Lee, F., *et al*. (1989). The role of transrectal ultrasound in the early detection of prostate cancer. *CA – A Cancer Journal for Clinicians*, **39**, 337–360.

McNeal, J. E. (1997). Prostate. In: Sternberg, S. S. (ed.). *Histology for Pathologists*, 2nd ed. 1001 (Lippincott-Raven, Philadelphia).

Randolph, T. L., *et al*. (1997). Histologic variants of adenocarcinoma and other carcinomas of prostate: pathologic criteria and clinical significance. *Modern Pathology*, **10**, 612–629.

Romanes, G. J. (1981). *Cunningham's Textbook of Anatomy*, 12th edn. 555 (Oxford University Press, Oxford).

Romanes, G. J. (1986). *Cunningham's Practical Anatomy, vol. 2: Thorax and Abdomen*, 15th edn. 110 (Oxford University Press, Oxford).

Ruijter, E., *et al*. (1999). Molecular genetics and epidemiology of prostate carcinoma. *Endocrine Reviews*, **20**, 22–45.

Ulbright, T. M. (1993). Germ cell neoplasms of the testis. *American Journal of Surgery and Pathology*, **17**, 1075–1091.

Ulbright, T. M. (1999). Testis risk and prognostic factors. The pathologist's perspective. *Urologic Clinics of North America*, **26**, 611–626.

Ulbright, T. M., *et al*. (1999). *Tumours of the Testis, Adenexa, Spermatic Cord and Scrotum: Atlas of Tumour Pathology*, Third series, Fascicle 25. (Armed Forces Institute of Pathology, Washington, DC).

Young, R. H., *et al*. (1998). Sertoli cell tumours of the testis, not otherwise specified: a clinicopathologic analysis of 60 cases. *American Journal of Surgical Pathology*, **22**, 709–721.

Young, R. H., *et al*. (2000). *Tumours of the Prostate, Seminal Vesicle, Male Urethra and Penis: Atlas of Tumour Pathology*, Third series, Fascicle 28. (Armed Forces Institute of Pathology, Washington, DC).

Weir, H. K., *et al*. (1999). Trends in the incidence of testicular germ cell cancer in Ontario by historic subgroup, 1964–1996. *Canadian Medical Association Journal*, **160**, 201–205

Web Sites with Information on Cancer of the Prostate, Testis and Penis

Prostate

http://www3.cancer.org/cancerinfo/load_cont.asp?ct= 36&prevURL=load_cont.asp&language=ENGLISH from http://www.cancer.org/

http://www.cancerlinksusa.com/prostate/index.htm

Testis

http://rex.nci.nih.gov/WTNK_PUBS/testicular/index.htm

http://www.cancerlinksusa.com/testicular/

Penis

http://www3.cancer.org/cancerinfo/load_cont.asp?ct=35

http://www.oncolink.upenn.edu/disease/penile/

Chapter 46

Lymph Nodes

Hans Konrad Müller-Hermelink and German Ott
University of Würzburg, Würzburg, Germany

CONTENTS

THE ANATOMICAL STRUCTURE OF THE LYMPH NODE

Lymph nodes are organs with highly organized compartments, the knowledge of which is a prerequisite for the recognition of reactive and neoplastic lymph node processes.

They are surrounded by a fibrous capsule, where afferent lymphatics penetrate and reach the subcapsular (marginal) sinus. Within the lymph node parenchyma, the cortex contains the B cell follicles, which are embedded in the interfollicular paracortex, organized into the T cell areas and the perisinusoidal and vascular zones. The vascular hilus, where arterial branches reach and efferent lymphatic and venous vessels leave the lymph node, is the localization of the central medulla containing collecting sinuses and the perisinusoidal pulp cords.

The **primary B cell follicle** is composed either of small lymphocytes of mantle zone type, in older patients (or in inactive conditions) or sometimes marginal zone lymphocytes (marginal zone cell nodules). When confronted with antigenic stimulation, germinal centres develop within the primary follicles at the interface of paracortical T cell areas, then called **secondary follicles**. They are surrounded by small lymphocytes of the follicular mantle zone. The germinal centres are usually sharply demarcated, and are composed of a network of follicular dendritic reticulum (FDC) cells, the professional antigen presenting cells of the B cell follicle. The B cells within the germinal centres have the appearance of either large transformed cells, the so-called centroblasts, and smaller to intermediate-sized cleaved cells, the centrocytes. Characteristically, centroblasts and centrocytes are not haphazardly distributed, but display a zonation phenomenon with the appearance of a 'dark' zone predominantly composed of centroblasts (the proliferative compartment of the germinal centre), and a 'light' zone containing centrocytes (which is normally oriented towards the marginal sinus). Within the dark zone, multiple mitotic figures are found, and there may be a prominent admixture of large histiocytes with pale cytoplasm, thus creating a 'starry sky' appearance. These macrophages may be densely packed with pyknotic nuclear debris ('tingible body macrophages'). Furthermore, a specific type of T cell is contained in germinal centres (the CD4 +, CD57+ T cell).

Reactive germinal centres, as a rule, are surrounded by the **follicular mantle zone**, composed of small lymphocytes with small cytoplasm and round inconspicuous nuclei. In some localizations, predominantly in abdominal (mesenteric) lymph nodes, and rarely also in superficial nodes after antigenic stimulation, another structural component of the follicular zone, termed the so-called **marginal zone** is present. This outermost part of the perifollicular B cell area may occasionally become apparent, but usually cannot be seen in all lymph nodes. Marginal zones, however, can be readily detected and form a characteristic part of the follicular B cell areas in the spleen. By morphology, the marginal zone, as compared with the 'dark' lymphocytes of the mantle zone, which are derived from germinal centre precursors or naive B lymphocytes, is composed of slightly larger cells with a broad pale cytoplasm, which represent different populations of memory B cells.

On immunohistochemistry, all these different components of the follicle are composed of B cells, and therefore stain strongly positive for B cell-associated antigens (see **Table 2**), but may be distinguished by their different phenotypes.

The **nodal paracortex** is composed of T cells areas (or nodules) and the perivascular (perisinusoidal) cortical pulp areas. The paracortical T zone, which may become a nodular structure after chronic (antigenic) stimulation, is composed of small T lymphocytes and intermingled, frequently pale-appearing, interdigitating reticulum cells (the professional antigen presenting cells for T cell activation). In the paracortical pulp, post-capillary high endothelial venules and some transformed (blastic) cells are found which are a mixture of T and B cells or plasma cell precursors. In the paracortex, CD4+ T cells normally are more numerous than CD8+ T cells.

The central portion of the lymph nodes, the **medulla**, contains the collecting sinuses, which are often filled with histiocytes and a special type of endothelial cells, the sinus lining cells. The perisinusoidal pulp cords contain the plasma cells, some T cells and macrophages.

A FUNCTIONAL APPROACH TO THE RECOGNITION OF REACTIVE AND NEOPLASTIC LYMPH NODE PATTERNS

Lymph nodes are filter organs of interstitial fluids and lymph, where circulating molecules, particles, cells and microorganisms are subjected to cognate cells and interaction with the phagocytic and immune systems, and major effector functions of these systems are initiated. In particular, immune stimulation and acceleration, where complex interactions of highly specialized cell types are needed to generate and regulate potentially dangerous effector functions, usually take place in the organized structures of the lymphoid organs (tonsils, Peyer's patches, lymph nodes, spleen). The lymph reaches the lymph nodes via afferent lymph vessels by the marginal sinus which acts like a sieve – there are only few shunts to the collecting ducts, so that everything has to pass through the meshwork of the interstitial reticular tissue and re-enter the collecting sinus. Macrophages take up particles or macromolecular constituents by pinocytosis. Dendritic cells and possibly also sinus lining cells may transport and present antigens to the organized T and B cell areas for further immune reactions.

The blood arteries enter the lymph node at the opposite medullary hilus and branch via lobular vessels to the capillary bed of the cortical lymphoid follicle, where fenestrated capillaries allow plasma proteins including antibodies to leave the circulation and attach to the

follicular dendritic cells. Migrating lymphocytes leave the blood stream after specific attachment to the high endothelial vessels penetrating the T and B cell areas and leave the lymph nodes via the collecting sinuses at the hilus through efferent lymph vessels, together with the veins.

Specific antigenic stimulation of naive reactive T and B cells takes place in the highly organized microenvironment of T and B cell areas by professional antigen presenting cells, the interdigitating cells of the T cell area and the follicular dendritic cells of the B cell follicle.

Within the germinal centre of the B cell follicle, antigenic stimulation of naive B cells leads to transformation of these resting B cells into highly proliferating centroblasts that mature into centrocytes. By antigen-dependent selection and somatic mutation of immunoglobulin receptor genes, cells with high receptor affinity become selected, whereas cells with low antigen reactivity die by apoptosis and become phagocytosed by the so-called starry sky macrophages. Selected B cells leave the germinal centre as memory B cells or plasma cell precursors. The T cell influence through different cytokines is crucial for these precursors. Somatic mutation is confined to the germinal centres, and stops in the emigrant cell population.

In the T cell areas, naive T cells become activated and either cooperate with B cells at the interface of T cell areas and B follicles to induce the germinal centre reaction by TH_2 cytokines, or T effector functions by TH_1 mediated macrophages and granulomatous reactions or MHC Class I restricted cytotoxic T cell responses. Effector T cells will leave the lymph node collecting medullary sinuses and form the recirculating lymphocyte pool.

REACTIVE PATTERNS OF THE LYMPH NODE

Table 1 gives an overview on major reactive patterns in lymph nodes. Some of them are described in greater detail, since they represent important differential diagnoses to malignant lymphomas.

Progressive transformation of germinal centres is a relatively rare, but distinct, condition in which in the background of reactive follicular hyperplasia few or many follicles are greatly enlarged. They are characterized by a prominent mantle zone and ill-defined germinal centres, mainly consisting of small lymphocytes. Remnants of germinal centre cells may be found, and are difficult to recognize. In some instances, epithelioid histiocytes are interspersed. This condition sometimes bears a close resemblance to nodular paragranuloma, but no lymphocytic and histiocytic (L&H) cells are present.

Castleman's disease of hyaline vascular type: in contrast to the lesions described above, Castleman disease (CD) represents a distinct clinicopathological entity.

Table 1 Reactive hyperplasias and reactions in different compartments in chronic lymphadenitis

B cell compartment
Follicular hyperplasia
Sinusoidal B cell reaction (immature sinus histiocytosis)
Marginal cell reaction/nodules
Plasmacytosis
Progressive transformation of germinal centres

T cell compartment
Paracortical nodular T zone hyperplasia
Diffuse cortical hyperplasia
Plasmacytoid monocyte reaction

Sinus reactions
Sinus histiocytosis
Foreign body reaction
Mastocytosis
Sinus lymphocytosis

Macrophage reactions
Foreign body reactions
Epithelioid cell reaction
Histiocytic-suppurative granulomas

Usually, this type of CD presents as a solitary lesion, most commonly found in the mediastinum, abdomen or cervical lymph nodes.

The morphological hallmarks of CD are regressively changed small follicles, increased vascularity in the interfollicular area and the presence of plasmacytoid monocytes. In addition, sinuses are lacking. Follicular centres frequently are 'onion skin' shaped with a predominance of follicular dendritic cells and few lymphocytes, and the mantle zone is prominent, sometimes exhibiting a curious 'Indian file' pattern with small lymphocytes being arranged in concentric circles. In the interfollicular areas, postcapillary venules of the high endothelial cell type are numerous, and sometimes one or more of these vessels are seen penetrating into the regressive germinal center. Usually, there is a mixture of lymphoid cells, histiocytes and few plasma cells present, and the so-called plasmacytoid monocytes are diffusely interspersed or may be recognized as small cell nests. They are of medium size and have round to oval nuclei with fine chromatin distribution and pale eccentric cytoplasm, reminiscent of plasma cells. On immunohistochemistry, they stain positive for CD68 and CD43.

In contrast, **multicentric Castleman's disease**, also called multicentric angiofollicular lymphoid hyperplasia, or plasma cell-rich variant of Castleman disease, consistently involves multiple peripheral lymph nodes and may also manifest in the bone marrow, liver, kidney and CNS. The germinal centres may be expanded, or regressively changed as in the hyaline-vascular variant. High endothelial venules are a prominent feature in the interfollicular tissues, as is an enormous proliferation of plasma cells. In most cases, these plasma cells are polyclonal;

however, they may be monoclonal in HIV-infected individuals in which the disease is associated with human herpes virus type 8 (HHV-8) infection.

In some patients, the so-called 'POEMS' syndrome may be diagnosed, the acronym summarizing the principal disease features of polyneuropathy, organomegaly, endocrinopathy, M proteins and skin lesions (Rosati and Frizzera, 1997).

ANCILLARY METHODS NECESSARY FOR THE DEFINITION OF MALIGNANT LYMPHOMAS

Immunophenotypic Studies

Immunohistochemistry has gained particular importance both with respect to the differentiation of the various subtypes of malignant lymphomas and in the differentiation of reactive versus neoplastic lymphoproliferative disorders. Immunophenotypic studies have also become accepted as a valuable help in the recognition of lymphoma entities, and have also contributed substantially to our understanding of the histogenesis and pathogenesis of haematopoietic neoplasms in general.

They are not only useful in the primary distinction of a neoplastic versus a benign lymphoid infiltrate, but are also important in the revelation of a preserved or destroyed normal architectural pattern. With the use of antibodies to kappa and lambda immunoglobulin light chains, and the determination of the light chain ratio, plasma cells or other immunoglobulin-producing lymphoid cells can be judged as polyclonal or monoclonal, the latter at least documenting a monoclonal expansion of a B cell population, if not its malignant nature.

By the application of other antibodies, certain biological features (e.g. the Ki67 antigen reflecting the proliferative index of a neoplasm) or prognostic features such as the atypical expression of tumour-suppressor genes (e.g. a mutated *p53* gene) or the formation of a fusion gene (e.g. *NPM-ALK*) may be determined.

Table 2 gives an overview of antibodies useful in the daily diagnostic practice of lymphoid neoplasms. This table lists antibodies to CD antigens and other antibodies reliably working on paraffin sections provided that antigen retrieval is performed. The specificity indicated represents only basic reactivity. Some of the antibodies, therefore, may have a broader spectrum of reactions.

It should be strictly kept in mind, however, that immunophenotypic studies can only be an adjunct to morphological diagnosis. For example, aberrant monoclonal B cell populations may be identified in non-neoplastic disorders, e.g. in certain autoimmune diseases. Therefore, 'monoclonality' by no means equates with 'malignancy'.

Table 2 Overview of antibodies useful in diagnosis of lymphoid neoplasms

Antigen	Specificity
CD2	T cells
CD3	T cells
CD4	Helper T cells
CD5	T cells, B cell subpopulation
CD8	Cytotoxic T cells
CD10	Germinal centre B cells
CD15	Neutrophils, Hodgkin and Reed–Sternberg cells
CD20	B cells
CD21	B cell subpopulation, follicular dendritic cells
CD23	Follicular mantle cells, follicular dendritic cells
CD30	Activated B and T cells, Hodgkin and Reed–Sternberg cells
CD34	Precursor myeloid and lymphoid cells
CD43	T cells, B cell subpopulation, myelomonocytic cells
CD45	Leukocyte common antigen
CD45RO	T cells
CD56	T/NK cells, NK cells
CD57	NK cells
CD68	Monocytes, macrophages
CD79a	B cells, plasma cells
CD138	Plasma cells
Others	**Specificity**
TdT	Precursor B and T cells
TIA 1, granzyme B	Cytolytic/cytotoxic cells
DBA44	Hairy cells
Bcl-2	Proto-oncogene product
p53	Suppressor gene product
p27	Cdk inhibitor
p21	Cdk inhibitor
Cyclin D1	Cdk activator
VS38c	Plasma cells

GENOTYPIC STUDIES

The detection of a clonal population of B or T cells refers to the capability of these cells to rearrange physically either their immunoglobulin heavy (IgH) and light (IgL) chain genes or their T cell receptor genes. Some other gene rearrangements, such as in chromosomal translocations, also alter the spatial arrangement of the DNA in the nucleus, thus being accessible to DNA rearrangement studies. The Southern blot technique as a means of determining clonality in a lymphocytic proliferation may detect clonal populations as low as 1–5% of cells relative to the total number of cells in a (fresh) specimen, thus clearly exceeding the threshold of pure morphological analysis. In addition to the detection of a clonal cell population represented by a non-germline band (or bands), the technique may also be used for distinguishing T or B lineage neoplasms.

The most important shortcoming of this technique, the requirement for fresh material, can be overcome by the use of the polymerase chain reaction (PCR) technique. The PCR, in its basic principle, represents a technique in which small amounts of DNA can be amplified *in vitro*, provided that the DNA sequences flanking the regions looked for are known. Because of the requirement of only minimal amounts of DNA (or small degraded DNA particles), this technique can be used for the detection of clonal cell populations or DNA rearrangements also in paraffin-embedded formalin-fixed material (in which the DNA normally is largely degraded). Because of this inherent advantage, the PCR may also be used in the monitoring of minimal residual disease, especially if clonotypic primers are used.

By DNA sequence analysis of Ig receptor genes, non-mutated (naive) prefollicular and mutated (memory) postfollicular B cells may be distinguished. In follicular cell populations, and some of their descendants, various 'ongoing' somatic mutations show a micropolymorphism of the B cell receptor repertoire. The detailed analysis of Ig receptor genes, therefore, permits conclusions on the status of antigen-dependent selection and mutation as well as the V_H gene repertoire.

Karyotypic Studies

Malignant lymphomas, especially the non-Hodgkin lymphomas of B type, are fairly well characterized – at least with respect to their primary genetic alterations – on the cytogenetic level. Mitelman's catalog of 'Chromosome aberrations in cancer' lists over 2000 lymphoid neoplasms on which conventional cytogenetic (banding) studies have been performed. Apart from proving the neoplastic nature of a lymphoid cell proliferation, the description of characteristic cytogenetic aberrations in certain types of malignant lymphomas has greatly added to our understanding of the biology of malignant lymphomas and has also influenced taxonomy, as may best be exemplified by the close association of mantle cell lymphoma to the translocation t(11;14)(q13;q32), the recognition of which ultimately led to the worldwide acceptance of mantle cell lymphoma as an entity on its own.

Table 3 lists the most common and characteristic chromosome aberrations in malignant lymphoma.

At present, malignant lymphoid tumours can not be classified according to their primary genetic aberrations alone, because (1) in some entities, no characteristic aberrations have been detected so far, and (2) because a recurring chromosomal translocation may be encountered in different lymphoma entities, e.g. the t(14;18)(q32;q21) in follicular lymphoma and diffuse large B cell lymphoma. In addition, cytogenetically detectable alterations are recognized only in a fraction of a given lymphoma entity.

More recently, the use of fluorescent dye-conjugated DNA probes in *in situ* hybridization has overcome some

Table 3   Characteristic chromosome aberrations in malignant lymphoma

Diagnosis	Chromosome aberration	Genes involved
Precurser B cell lymphoblastic lymphoma/leukaemia	t(1;19)(q23;p13)	c-ski (1q23)
	t(4,11)(q21;q23) del(6q)	c-ets1 (11q23-24)
	t(9;22)(q34;q11)	bcr-abl
B cell chronic lymphocytic leukaemia/small lymphocytic lymphoma	del(13)(q14)	
	Trisomy 12	
Mantle cell lymphoma	t(11;14)(q13;q32)	Cyclin D1
Follicular lymphoma	t(14;18)(q32;q21)	BCL-2
Extranodal marginal zone B cell lymphoma of MALT type	t(11;18)(q21;q21)	API2/MLT1
Splenic marginal zone B cell lymphoma	t/del(7)(q22-32) del(10)(q22-24)	
Lymphoplasmacytic lymphoma (immunocytoma)	t(9;14)(p13;q32)	PAX-5
Diffuse large B cell lymphoma	t(3;14)(q27;q32)	BCL-6
	t(14;18)(q32;q21)	BCL-2
Burkitt lymphoma	t(8;14)(q24;q32)	c-myc
	t(2;8)(p12;q24)	
	t(8;22)(q24;q11)	
Plasmacytoma	t(4;14)(p16;q32)	FGFR3
	t(6;14)(p25;q32)	MUM-1/IRF 4
Precursor T cell lymphoblastic lymphoma/leukaemia	14q11	TCR genes
	7p15 or 7q34-35	TCR genes
T cell prolymphocytic leukaemia	inv(14)(q11q32)	TCL-1
Angioimmunoblastic T cell lymphoma	+3, +5, +X	
Anaplastic large cell lymphoma	t(2;5)(p23;q35)	NPM/ALK
Hepatosplenic gd T cell lymphoma	i(7)(q10)	

limitations of conventional cytogenetics, i.e. the need for viable dividing cells. With the use of the fluorescence *in situ* hybridization (FISH) technique, cytogenetic investigations can today also be performed on interphase cells, thus allowing for the recognition of amplifications, deletions or even translocations without the need to cultivate cells. This technique is sometimes also referred to as 'molecular cytogenetics'. With the aid of the FISH technique, it has been possible to define independent prognostic parameters in certain lymphoma entities which, in some cases, may be equivalent to the items of the International Prognostic Index. *ATM* or *p53* deletions in B cell chronic lymphocytic leukaemia, for example, are strong negative prognostic indicators.

The comparative genomic hybridization (CGH) technique allows for an overview of genetic imbalances (over-representations and deletions) in malignant tumours and may be used to calculate the overall genomic instability, which appears to constitute a new important prognostic feature.

LYMPHOMA CLASSIFICATION

History

The history of the recognition and classification of tumours that today are called malignant lymphomas is long, controversial and complicated. In 1832, Sir Thomas Hodgkin first identified malignant tumours of lymph nodes. Among those were cases that we would now classify as Hodgkin lymphoma. The definition of 'leukaemia' followed in 1845 by Rudolf Virchow and in 1863 he laid down the concepts of lymphosarcoma and lymphoma. At the turn of the nineteenth century, Sternberg and Reed, in 1898 and 1902, defined morphologically the tumour cells of Hodgkin disease. About 25 years later, Brill and Symmers described follicular lymphoma and in 1948 Burkitt and in 1960 O'Connor and Davis described African lymphoma, now called Burkitt lymphoma. Within this short list, of course, only historical milestones have been cited, constituting only those steps that still remain valuable in the twenty-first century.

Since 1960, modern immunology has greatly influenced our knowledge of lymphoid tumours. The biology of lymphoma cells, reflecting the immunological activities of their normal counterparts, has been clarified to a great extent and has allowed the establishment of a biological basis for new and more comprehensive classification systems of malignant lymphomas. Two classification systems have been widely used until recently, the Kiel Classification of Non-Hodgkin Lymphomas (Stansfeld *et al.*, 1988; Lennert and Feller, 1992) and the Working Formulation for Clinical Usage (Non-Hodgkin's Lymphoma Pathologic Classification Project, 1982). The Kiel classification was based on the exact morphological description and immunological identification of the normal cellular counterparts of tumour cells and was updated several times, introducing new findings and more comprehensive knowledge. The so-called Working Formulation, on the other hand, was based on historical clinical survival data and, therefore, was not updated, although its usage was also adapted to modern findings. Of importance, there was a geographic split of categories in the diagnosis of lymphoid tumours, the Kiel classification in Europe and the Working Formulation in the USA.

An international group of experienced haematopathologists, the International Lymphoma Study Group (ILSG) formulated a new proposal for a modern lymphoma classification and published it as the so-called Revised European American Lymphoma (REAL) Classification (Harris *et al.*, 1994). In the following years, this proposal was tested for its applicability and reliability and then accepted worldwide. It is, therefore, largely identical (with some minor corrections and additions) with the now proposed WHO classification.

Basic Taxonomic Principles

The taxonomic unit of the new WHO classification is the **disease entity**. Distinct entities in malignant lymphomas can be recognized by pathologists and, ideally, are of clinical relevance. For each disease entity, a combination of morphological, immunophenotypic, genetic and clinical features is needed for its definition. The relative value of each of these features may vary among different disease entities. Variations in grade and aggressiveness, that may exist within a given disease entity, and may be related to patients' survival and treatment response, must be distinguished from 'different diseases' (Jaffe *et al.*, 1998; Harris *et al.*, 1999, 2000).

The basic rules for the definition of disease entities in this proposal are comparable to the general rules of tumour classification as used in many other organs and organ systems. A given lymphoma entity is defined in first line by recognition of the predominant differentiated cell type using morphological and immunological features, a principle that follows the rules of the Kiel classification. In addition, the importance of the primary site of involvement, which is not only a feature of staging, but also an easy, clinically relevant and important biological distinction, has been explicitly stated.

Second-line principles of classification are important for some entities. These are **aetiological features,** such as the association of certain infectious agents, like the Epstein–Barr virus, Helicobacter pylori or HTLV I, **primary cytogenetic abnormalities** or **specific clinical features**. Daily clinical and pathological experience shows minor or more evident exceptions to the proposed rules, leading to the well-recognized heterogeneity of each type of lymphoid neoplasia. Therefore, within many entities, specific morphological or clinical subtypes are mentioned which are of clinical importance. Morphological variants reflect the diagnostic spectrum of a disease, which is important to recognize in order to establish a correct differential diagnosis.

Table 4 lists the recent WHO classification of B and T cell lymphomas and of Hodgkin lymphoma.

The non-Hodgkin lymphomas are divided primarily into those of the B and the T cell system. In both lineages, there is a primary distinction of lymphomas that arise from precursor cells (the lymphoblastic lymphomas or acute lymphoid leukaemias) and from peripheral cells.

Clinical Relevance

The clinical relevance of the WHO proposal was intriguingly confirmed by the results of the Non-Hodgkin's Lymphoma Classification Project (1997), which involved the pathomorphological and immunophenotypic investigation of 1403 lymphomas in eight different sites around the world. These cases were taken from the years 1988–1990, and were reviewed by experienced haematopathologists attempting to compare different classification systems, the recognition of epidemiological variations in the occurrence of lymphomas and the correlation of treatment results with histological diagnoses. The results of this study clearly established that the criteria formulated in the REAL classification and applied in the WHO classification resulted in a high inter-observer accuracy and were of significant prognostic value for the recognition of diseases with different clinical courses and behaviour. It turned out that immunophenotyping was less important in some of the diseases (e.g. in follicular lymphoma), but absolutely essential in others (mantle cell lymphoma, T cell lymphomas). Some diseases were only reliably diagnosed if clinical data were available (e.g. mediastinal B cell lymphoma). In other cases, the differential diagnosis was at least greatly improved by the knowledge of clinical features and presentation (Armitage and Weisenburger, 1998).

For some disease entities and variants, however, diagnostic accuracy was less satisfactory. In particular, the distinction of Burkitt lymphoma and 'Burkitt-like' non-Hodgkin lymphoma involved a high inter-observer disagreement of more than 40%, clearly establishing that additional and better criteria will have to be proposed for the definition of certain disease entities. Similarly, the subclassification of peripheral T cell lymphomas showed high inter-observer variability.

Prognostic Factors

As was clearly shown by the international Non-Hodgkin's Lymphoma Classification Project (1997) and many other multicentre trials published in recent years, the most important prognostic factor today is the definition of the disease entity, that is, the exact type of non-Hodgkin lymphoma. Within these individual diseases, prognostic

Table 4 The WHO classification of lymphoid neoplasms

B cell neoplasms

Precursor B cell lymphoblastic leukaemia/lymphoma
(Precursor B cell acute lymphoblastic leukaemia)

Peripheral B cell neoplasms
B cell lymphocytic leukaemia/small lymphocytic lymphoma
B cell prolymphocytic leukaemia
Lymphoplasmacytic lymphoma
Mantle cell lymphoma
Follicular lymphoma
Cutaneous follicle centre lymphoma
Marginal zone B cell lymphoma of mucosa-associated
  lymphoid tissue (MALT type)
Nodal marginal zone B cell lymphoma (±monocytoid B cells)
Splenic marginal zone B cell lymphoma (±villous lymphocytes)
Hairy cell leukaemia
Diffuse large B cell lymphoma
  Variants: Centroblastic
       Immunoblastic
       T cell or histiocyte-rich
       Anaplastic large B cell
  Subtypes: Mediastinal (thymic) large B cell lymphoma
       Intravascular large B cell lymphoma
       Primary effusion lymphoma
Burkitt lymphoma
Plasmacytoma
Plasma cell myeloma

T cell neoplasms

Precursor T cell lymphoblastic leukaemia/lymphoma
(Precursor T cell acute lymphoblastic leukaemia)

Peripheral T cell and NK cell neoplasms
T cell prolymphocytic leukaemia
T cell large granular lymphocytic leukaemia
Aggressive NK cell leukaemia
NK/T cell lymphoma, nasal and nasal type
Sezary syndrome
Mycosis fungoides
Angioimmunoblastic T cell lymphoma
Peripheral T cell lymphoma (unspecified)
Adult T cell leukaemia/lymphoma (HTLV 1+)
Anaplastic large cell lymphoma (T and null cell types)
Primary cutaneous CD30 positive T cell lymphoproliferative
  disorders
  Variants: Lymphomatoid papulosis (Type A and B)
       Primary cutaneous ALCL
       Borderline lesions
Subcutaneous panniculitis-like T cell lymphoma
Enteropathy-type T cell lymphoma
Hepatosplenic γ/λ T cell lymphoma

Hodgkin lymphoma (Hodgkin disease)

Nodular lymphocyte predominance Hodgkin lymphoma

Classical Hodgkin lymphoma
Hodgkin lymphoma, nodular sclerosis
Classical Hodgkin lymphoma, lymphocyte-rich
Hodgkin lymphoma, mixed cellularity
Hodgkin lymphoma, lymphocyte depletion

factors may influence clinical outcome (Shipp *et al.*, 1993). Prognostic factors and variations in grades within diseases should be distinguished from different diseases. They may be histological, biological or clinical in nature, such as stage or the International Prognostic Index. Histological grading is one method to define types of prognostic factors. Usual approaches include the determination of cell size, nuclear features, mitotic rates and growth pattern. In recent years, biological markers, such as genetic features, have turned out to be important prognostic factors and may even be more powerful than clinical or morphological features. Some of them may be recognized today by interphase cytogenetics (such as *p53* and *ATM* deletions in B-CLL), or by immunohistochemistry (such as the presence of the t(2;5/ALK) rearrangement in anaplastic large-cell lymphomas of T and O cell types, or the determination of the proliferative index in mantle cell lymphomas using the Ki67 antibody). More recently, exciting new data have become available taking into account mutated or unmutated IgVH genes in B-CLL or the subdivision of diffuse large B cell lymphomas according to their mRNA expression profiles.

These examples show how dependent a given classification is on new facts and findings that may be used for the definition of diseases in the borderline and grey zone of different diseases. It does not need great fantasy to predict that the new approaches of molecular biology will further modify our concepts of the biology of malignant lymphoma, and that in the not too distant future our concepts of lymphoma classification will be stepwise modified and possibly reverted to a molecular definition of neoplastic processes in different lymphoma entities (Alizadeh *et al.*, 2000).

LYMPHOMAS OF B CELL LINEAGE

Precursor B Cell Lymphoblastic Leukaemia/Lymphoma (Precursor B Cell Acute Lymphoblastic Leukaemia)

Clinical Features

The peak incidence of lymphoblastic lymphomas, irrespective of B or T cell lineage, is in the second and third decades, and the male gender is over-represented in the range 2–10:1. The majority of patients are diagnosed with advanced disease stages, and central nervous system involvement is common. About 60% of patients with no obvious bone marrow infiltration at presentation are reported to develop marrow infiltration and leukaemic conversion. Only 20% of the so-called lymphoblastic lymphomas are of B cell lineage, in contrast to 80% of acute lymphoblastic leukaemias.

Morphology

Precursor B cell neoplasias, in most cases, show a diffuse infiltration and destruction of the normal tissue structure. The tumour cells are medium-sized with a scant cytoplasm and round to oval or convoluted nuclei, often with distinct nuclear membranes, a finely dispersed, sometimes 'dust'-like chromatin and inconspicuous nucleoli. In some cases, a 'starry sky' pattern may be seen due to the presence of tingible body macrophages. Usually, numerous mitotic figures are encountered with numbers of 10–20 per high-power field (HPF). Owing to their aggressive nature, they often infiltrate the lymph node capsule and invade the surrounding perinodal fatty or fibrous tissues.

Immunophenotype

The majority of precursor B cell lymphoblastic lymphomas express B cell antigens similar to or identical with B cell acute lymphatic leukaemia. They express HLA-DR antigens and B cell-associated antigens CD19 and/or CD22 and may be positive for IgM and Ig light chains. In paraffin sections, most of them are positive for CD20 and CD34, as well as for CD10 (cALLA). Of pivotal importance in the diagnosis of precursor B (and T) cell neoplasias is the detection of nuclear expression of the terminal deoxynucleotidyl transferase (TdT), thereby clearly differentiating these neoplasms both from chronic lymphocytic leukaemia/small lymphocytic lymphomas and diffuse large cell lymphomas.

Genetic Features

The majority of precursor B cell neoplasms express clonal IgH or IgL gene rearrangements. Characteristic cytogenetic abnormalities in precursor B cell neoplasias are numerical chromosome changes (hyperploidy), t(1;19) (q23;p13) involving c-*ski*, t(4;11)(q21;q23) involving c-*ets1*, del(6q), del(12p) and t(9;22)(q34;q11) involving *bcr-abl*.

PERIPHERAL B CELL LYMPHOMAS

Chronic Lymphocytic Leukaemia of B Type (B-CLL)/Small Lymphocytic Lymphoma (B-SLL)

Clinical Features

B-CLL comprises 90% of chronic lymphoid leukaemias in Europe and the USA. Most patients will present with generalized lymphadenopathy, bone marrow and blood involvement and enlarged spleen. Hepatomegaly is frequent. A minority of patients initially present with a leukaemic nodal involvement.

Morphology

Lymph nodes in patients with B-CLL show a characteristic infiltration pattern in roughly 90% of cases which may be recognized at low-power magnification. In most B-CLL, there is a so-called 'pseudo-follicular' growth pattern. In these pseudo-follicles (also termed proliferation centres), slightly larger lymphocytes (prolymphocytes and para-immunoblasts) are found in contrast to the majority of the infiltrate which consists of small lymphoid cells with scant cytoplasm and slightly clumped chromatin. In the proliferation centres, which only very occasionally show some remnants of follicular dendritic cells, the larger cells possess a small cytoplasmic rim and a lighter nuclear chromatin, so that these pseudo-follicles stand out, imparting 'light zones' to the infiltrate (**Figure 1**). Only about 10% of B-CLL/SLL are characterized by a diffuse infiltration without pseudo-follicles, and this represents the predominant pattern in extranodal infiltrates of the disease.

Variants include cases with a larger number of prolymphocytes and/or paraimmunoblasts (B-CLL/PL), tumours in which a sometimes marked nuclear irregularity can be seen (and which may be difficult to differentiate from mantle cell lymphomas), and cases with a secretory differentiation (monotypic cytoplasmic light-chain expression) corresponding to the lymphoplasmacytoid immunocytoma of the Kiel classification system.

Immunophenotype

The tumour cells of B-CLL are characteristically positive for B cell-associated antigens (CD19, CD20 (weak), CD79a) and IgM ± IgD, and express CD5, CD23, and CD43. Recognition of CD23 expression is important in the differential diagnosis of mantle cell lymphoma, in which CD23 (on paraffin or frozen sections) is not expressed. In B-CLL, CD23 expression may be pronounced in the proliferation centres, and it is also more often preserved than CD5 in transformed large B cell lymphomas having evolved from B-CLL.

Genetic Features

Ig heavy- and light-chain genes are rearranged. Of importance, recent studies have shown that, by the analysis of somatic mutations in IgVH genes, B-CLL is not a homogeneous disease, but may contain at least two important subentities. In roughly 50% of cases, the tumour cells do not display somatic mutations and hence may be referred to as derived from naive or virgin B cells. In the other 50% of cases, somatic mutations have occurred, indicating a germinal centre passage of the tumour cells. As judging from clinical data available to date, the mutated form of B-CLL may have a better prognosis.

In contrast to many other non-Hodgkin lymphomas, B-CLL is not characterized by a reciprocal chromosome

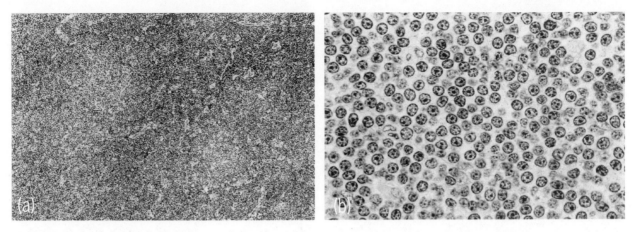

Figure 1 B cell chronic lymphocytic leukaemia. (a) The normal lymph node architecture is replaced by a pseudo-follicular infiltrate. (b) The infiltrate consists of small cells with round nuclei and few prolymphocytes.

translocation. The most common cytogenetic/molecular cytogenetic aberration is a deletion in chromosomal band 13q14 encountered in up to 40% of cases. Other recurring aberrations include trisomy 12, 6q deletions and deletions/ mutations in 17p13 and 11q22/23. Deletions in 17p frequently target the *p53* gene and 11q deletions commonly result in the loss of one copy of the *ATM* (mutated in Ataxia telangiectasia) gene. Both aberrations have been shown to be prognostically relevant in defining patient subgroups with inferior prognosis.

In B-CLL, prolymphocytoid transformation or transformation to large B cell lymphomas (Richter syndrome) may occur. Transformation to Hodgkin disease was also observed and should be distinguished – by the appropriate background infiltrate and the characteristic immunophenotype of Hodgkin and Reed–Sternberg cells – from the occasional occurrence of Hodgkin- and Reed–Sternberg-like cells in B-CLL.

B Cell Prolymphocytic Leukaemia (B-PLL)

Clinical Features

B-PLL is a rare disease, occurring in older patients over 60 years of age with a marked male predominance presenting with massive splenomegaly, bone marrow infiltration and marked lymphocytosis in the peripheral blood (>55% prolymphocytes). Lymph nodes are rarely involved. Anaemia and thrombocytopenia are frequent.

Morphology

The infiltrate in the bone marrow consists of diffusely infiltrating medium-sized prolymphocytic or paraimmuno-blastic cells with a small rim of slightly basophilic or pale cytoplasm, round to oval nuclei and a central prominent eosinophilic nucleolus. No pseudo-follicles are seen.

Immunophenotype

The tumour cells in B-PLL express pan B cell markers, IgM ± IgD and CD5 in a proportion of cases. CD23 usually is negative.

Genetic Features

Clonal rearrangements of IgH and IgL chain genes are found. Most of the tumours have been shown to carry somatic mutations. The occurrence of cases with t(11;14)(q13;q32) points to an overlap with mantle cell lymphoma ('mantle cell leukaemia').

Mantle Cell Lymphoma (MCL)

Clinical Features

MCL is a disease of middle-aged to older persons. Most patients present in stages III and IV. The tumour tends to involve lymph nodes and Waldeyer's ring. The bone marrow is often infiltrated, and a proportion of patients have prominent splenomegaly and peripheral blood involvement. The gastrointestinal tract is often infiltrated (lymphomatous polyposis). Sometimes, a high peripheral leukocyte count is found (mantle cell leukaemia). Blastic transformation may occur (blastoid MCL).

Morphology

Mantle cell lymphoma, in most cases, presents with diffuse lymph node infiltrates of monomorphic small to medium-sized cells with scant, barely recognizable cytoplasm and irregular or cleaved nuclei. The chromatin is slightly dispersed and inconspicuous nucleoli are found. In rare cases, the cells are nearly round, rendering a differential diagnosis to B-CLL. Two blastoid variants have been described, one with medium-sized nuclei with a more dispersed chromatin resembling lymphoblasts and a high proliferative index

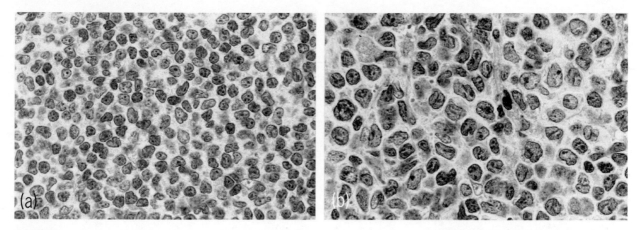

Figure 2   Mantle cell lymphoma. (a) In the classical variant, small- to medium-sized cells are seen, with small cytoplasm and irregular nuclei. (b) Pleomorphic variant of MCL. Cells are considerably larger and nuclei are deeply indented. The chromatin distribution is coarse.

(blastoid or lymphoblastoid type). Another variant variously termed as 'anaplastic,' 'large cell' or 'pleomorphic' is characterized by rather large cleaved cells with sometimes light or slightly basophilic cytoplasm and coarse chromatin distribution. This type obviously had been included in the Kiel classification as the 'centrocytoid' variant of centroblastic lymphoma (**Figure 2**).

In some cases, the infiltrate in mantle cell lymphoma may be found predominantly surrounding (partially) preserved germinal centres giving the impression of a 'mantle zone' pattern or may form sometimes vaguely circumscribed nodules.

Immunophenotype

The tumour cells of MCL are characterized by the expression, next to B cell antigens, of CD5 and CD43 in the absence of CD10 and CD23. Notably, the characteristic overexpression of Cyclin D1 can be recognized by suitable antibodies. Recently, it has been shown that the classical variant of MCL displays – in contrast to other non-Hodgkin lymphomas with comparably low proliferative indices – a marked down-regulation of nuclear p27 expression, a feature which is highly characteristic of and favours mantle cell lymphoma. Staining for follicular dendritic cells (using anti-CD21 or -CD23 antibodies) may show, especially in the cases with a nodular growth pattern, dispersed and disorganized meshworks of these cells.

Genetic Features

The cytogenetic hallmark of MCL is the chromosomal translocation t(11;14)(q13;q32), joining the Ig heavy-chain locus and the *BCL-1* locus and resulting in the overexpression of the cell-cycle protein Cyclin D1. It should be noted, however, that the t(11;14)/Cyclin D1 deregulation is not absolutely specific for mantle cell lymphomas, having also been described in plasmacytoma/multiple myeloma. Mantle cell lymphomas, in addition, show characteristic

secondary aberrations, many of them targeting other cell cycle-related genes such as *p16*, *p53* and the *ATM* gene. Blastoid MCL of the pleomorphic type frequently are characterized by tetraploid chromosome clones.

Follicular Lymphoma (FL)

Clinical Features

Follicular lymphomas represent, together with diffuse large B cell lymphomas, the most frequent type of B cell lymphoma in Western countries. Both genders are equally affected. Systemic disease at presentation is common, including involvement of lymph nodes, spleen, bone marrow and, rarely, extranodal sites. PB involvement is rare and tends to occur only in final stages. The disease follows an indolent course.

Morphology

In the most common type with an almost exclusive follicular growth pattern, neoplastic follicular structures are found throughout the lymph node and also frequently penetrate the capsule and invade the perinodal fatty tissue. In contrast to reactive follicles, they are uniform in size and lack a well-defined mantle zone. Cytologically, they are composed of centrocytes and centroblasts. Centrocytes represent medium-sized cells with a small, barely recognizable cytoplasm and irregular contoured and indented nuclei. The chromatin is irregular, and small inconspicuous nucleoli are present. In contrast, centroblasts are large cells with a usually small, moderately basophilic cytoplasm, and round nuclei with vesicular chromatin and 1–3 nucleoli commonly found adjacent to the nuclear membrane. Centrocytes and centroblasts are arranged haphazardly, and a well-formed dark and light zone as seen in reactive germinal centres structures is not found (**Figure 3**). Likewise, in most cases, no tingible body

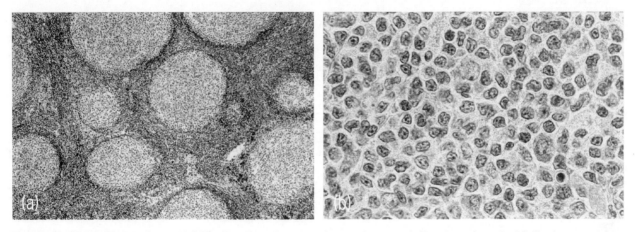

Figure 3 Follicular lymphoma. (a) The lymph node parenchyma shows an infiltration of atypical follicular structures. (b) On higher magnification, the neoplastic follicles are composed of small cleaved cells (centrocytes) with few interspersed blasts (centroblasts).

macrophages are present and the number of mitotic figures is low. Diffuse areas may be present in addition, and tumours may be classified as predominantly follicular (>75% follicular), follicular and diffuse (25–75% follicular) or predominantly diffuse (<25% follicular). Entirely diffuse follicular lymphomas, composed of centrocytes and centroblasts, are very rare neoplasms and caution has to be exerted in differentiating them from mantle cell lymphomas.

The WHO classification proposes a grading scheme for follicular lymphomas according to the content of centroblasts. Therefore, tumours with 0–50 centroblasts per 10 high-power fields (HPF) are grade 1, tumours with 50–150 centroblasts per 10 HPF are grade II and lymphomas with more than 150 centroblasts/10 HPF are grade III. Lymphomas with an exclusively follicular growth pattern and consisting entirely of centroblasts are very rare. They are more commonly found in association with a diffuse large B cell lymphoma and should be diagnosed as 'follicular lymphomas grade III with diffuse large B cell lymphoma'. There are some indications, however, that these tumours, on a genetic basis, are different from follicular lymphomas with varying centroblast content, but preserved maturation to centrocytes, being t(14;18) negative in 80% of the cases and more closely related to a 'follicular' variant of diffuse large B cell lymphomas. Follicular lymphomas grades I or II associated with a diffuse large cell component, in most cases, should be regarded as 'transformed' follicular neoplasias.

Some follicular lymphomas may show a more or less prominent 'marginal zone' differentiation, implying the occurrence of tumour cells slightly rounder than centrocytes and with a broad pale-staining cytoplasm reminiscent of monocytoid B cells. In most cases, these cells are accentuated in the outermost parts of the follicles, giving the impression of a marginal zone pattern. A differentiation to plasma cells (secretory differentiation) may be rarely seen in follicular lymphomas.

Immunophenotype

Most follicular lymphomas grades I and II express CD10 and show a nuclear reactivity for BCL-6, but lack CD5 and CD43 reactivity. In some tumours, CD23 may be expressed, and these lymphomas are frequently CD10-negative. One intriguing immunohistochemical finding in follicular lymphomas, and strongly suggesting a neoplastic process (in the differential diagnosis to reactive follicular hyperplasia), is the presence of CD10+ B cells in the interfollicular region. About 80–90% of follicular lymphomas express BCL2, a feature clearly differentiating them from reactive follicles which are always BCL2-negative. By staining of follicular dendritic cells using CD21 and/or CD23, FDC meshworks are usually dense and sharply demarcated. In BCL2-negative lymphomas, the diagnosis may require gene rearrangement studies.

Genetic Features

Apart from clonal rearrangements of (extensively hypermutated) IgH and IgL chain genes, follicular lymphomas are characterized by 'ongoing' somatic mutations, creating an intraclonal diversity. The cytogenetic hallmark of follicular lymphomas is the t(14;18)(q32;q21) chromosome translocation, that is found in 80–90% of grade I and II tumours. As already pointed out, follicular lymphomas grade III are t(14;18)-positive in only 50% of cases, and especially grade III lymphomas that are composed of centroblasts exclusively in the majority of cases are t(14;18) negative. On the molecular genetic level, the t(14;18) leads to the juxtaposition of the BCL2 oncogene to the IgH chain gene promoter region, thus overexpressing BCL2, which is, as already mentioned, not expressed in centroblasts and centrocytes of reactive follicles. Secondary chromosome aberrations are common and well-defined in follicular lymphomas. Especially trisomies for chromosomes 1q, 7, 12, 18 and X are found, while deletions are encountered in chromosome regions 1p and 6q.

Transformed follicular lymphomas frequently are characterized by deletions in the short arm of chromosome 17, the site of the *p53* tumour suppressor gene. The retained allele has been found to be mutated in a fairly large number of transformed follicular lymphomas.

Marginal Zone B Cell Lymphomas (MZBL)

Marginal zone B cell lymphomas (MZBL) are B cell neoplasias with a presumed origin from the marginal zone cells of the B cell follicle. Three variants are discerned: extranodal MZBL of MALT type, splenic and nodal MZBL. Whereas the REAL classification regarded nodal and splenic MZBL as provisional entities, the WHO classification, taking into account the immunophenotypic and genetic differences in MZBL, regards them as true lymphoma entities.

Extranodal MZBL of MALT Type

Clinical Features

MALT-type MZBL frequently arise in extranodal sites commonly devoid of a regular lymphatic parenchyma. Therefore, MALT has to be introduced in organs such as the stomach, the lungs, the thyroid and salivary glands, the ocular adnexa, the skin or the mammary gland (the most frequent localizations) by chronic inflammatory processes such as chronic infections or autoimmune diseases prior to the development of these enigmatic tumours. The gastrointestinal tract is the most common site of involvement. Gastric MALT-type MZBL frequently (in 90% of cases) arise in the background of a chronic *Helicobacter pylori* (HP) gastritis. Upon eradication of the bacterium, about 80% of MALT-type MZBL regress and hence patients may be cured by this antibiotic therapy. However, clonal rearrangements for the IgH and IgL chain genes may be demonstrated also after complete regression of the lymphoma, the prognostic significance of which is not yet entirely

understood. In rare cases, after eradication, a monoclonal plasma cell population may still be present in biopsies, representing a plasma cellular maturation of the tumour cells.

The majority of patients present with stage I or II disease, reflecting the particular feature of these tumours to be confined to their site of origin for long times.

Morphology

Extranodal MZBL, in early lesions, infiltrate the marginal zones of frequently preserved reactive follicular structures and, as a rule, present with an invasive and destructive growth potential forming so-called lymphoepithelial lesions (**Figure 4**). On the cytological level, marginal zone B cells are small- to medium-sized with a small to moderately broad, sometimes pale cytoplasm and slightly indented 'centrocytoid-like' nuclei. These tumours may be associated with a diffuse large B cell component and should then be designated as 'diffuse large B cell lymphomas with an extranodal MZBL of MALT-type component' (not as 'low- and high-grade MALT-type lymphoma' or 'transformed MALT-type lymphoma').

Immunophenotype

MALT-type MZBL are CD5−, CD10−, CD23−, CD43−/ + and IgD−. In contrast to mantle cell lymphomas (frequently presenting as primary gastrointestinal tumours, the so-called malignant lymphomatous polyposis), they are consistently cyclin D1 negative.

Genetic Features

The t(11;18)(q21;q21) chromosome translocation, juxtaposing the *API2* and *MLT1* genes, has been identified as the most common structural cytogenetic alteration in extranodal MZBL of MALT-type accounting for about 30% of cases (and even 50% of cases without any large-cell component). Interestingly, this translocation

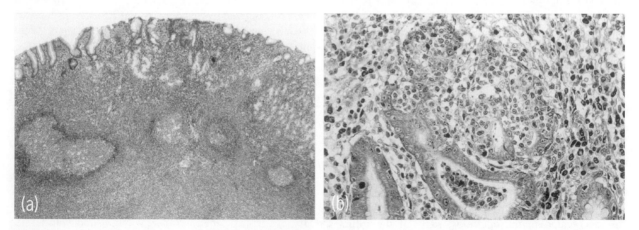

Figure 4 Extranodal marginal zone B cell lymphoma of MALT type. (a) Gastric lymphoma. The infiltrate colonizes the marginal zone areas of preserved follicles and spreads out into the mucosa and submocosa. (b) The tumour cells (centrocyte-like cells) invade and destroy epithelial structures, forming lymphoepithelial lesions.

has not been found in extranodal large B cell lymphomas with or without an extranodal MZBL MALT-type component.

Splenic MZBL (± Villous Lymphocytes)

Clinical Features

Splenic marginal zone lymphomas (SMZL), a distinctive type of primary splenic lymphoma, has to be differentiated from secondary splenic involvement occurring in B-CLL, B-PLL, mantle cell lymphoma, immunocytoma and follicular lymphoma. SMZL involves the spleen and frequently the bone marrow. Hilar splenic and abdominal lymph nodes may be infiltrated, and leukaemic dissemination often occurs. Peripheral lymphadenopathy is uncommon. SMZL is a rare disease and usually follows an indolent course.

Morphology

The tumour cells characteristically infiltrate the splenic marginal zone and, on the cytological level, resemble extranodal MALT-type MZBL cells. In most cases, the central parts of the splenic white pulp nodules are composed of small lymphoid cells with dark nuclei, and merge with surrounding, slightly larger, sometimes 'monocytoid-like' cells with a frequently pale and broader cytoplasm. Transformed blasts may be interspersed, and the splenic red pulp is involved to varying degrees. In splenic hilar lymph nodes, sinuses are generally preserved and distended, and the infiltrate surrounds germinal centres. About one third of cases may present with a leukaemic course and the appearance of 'villous' lymphocytes in the peripheral blood. Bone marrow infiltrates characteristically are found in an intertrabecular localization and sometimes sinusoidal infiltration may be encountered (**Figure 5**).

Immunophenotype

The tumor cells express pan B cell antigens and IgM, but are CD5−, CD10− and CD23−. In contrast to MALT-type MZBL, they are, in most cases, IgD-positive. Plasmacytic differentiation, as in other types of MZBL, may occur.

Genetic Features

On the cytogenetic level, splenic MZBL are consistently t(11;18)-negative, and some of the cases may show trisomy 3 and structural aberrations in 7q22–32 and 10q22–24. In fact, the apparent cytogenetic diversity of this neoplasm has elicited speculations on a different biological background of tumours designated as splenic MZBL.

Nodal MZBL

Clinical Features

Nodal marginal zone B cell lymphomas, by definition, are malignant lymphomas primarily manifesting in lymph nodes without extranodal or splenic involvement. It has been shown, however, that by careful clinical staging procedures, an occult extranodal manifestation may be present in a fraction of cases. Many patients present with advanced disease stages, but the disease is rather less aggressive.

Morphology

The small- to medium-sized tumour cells may resemble monocytoid B cells or centrocytoid B cells, and frequently show secretory differentiation with a plasmacytoid component. In most cases, large B cells are interspersed. In early stages, they colonize the perifollicular and interfollicular areas with remnants of germinal centres still being present (**Figure 6**). In later stages, however, these may be entirely destroyed and invaded by the tumour cells ('follicular colonization'). There may be cases in which the

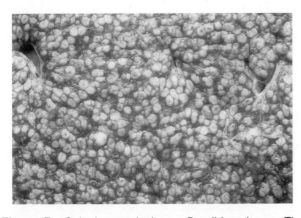

Figure 5   Splenic marginal zone B cell lymphoma. The cut surface of the spleen shows a prominence of tiny nodules representing infiltrated white pulp structures. Note that there is no merging of nodules in contrast to B-CLL splenic infiltrations.

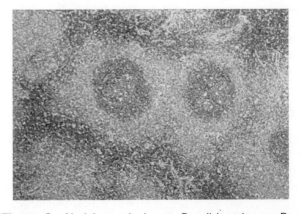

Figure 6   Nodal marginal zone B cell lymphoma. Preserved follicles are surrounded by neoplastic cells invading and broadening the perifollicular marginal zone.

tumour cells are entirely blastic in nature but with a pre-served marginal zone growth pattern; we tend to classify these cases as 'aggressive' MZBL rather than diffuse large B cell lymphomas. Recently, two different types of nodal MZBL have been described, a 'MALT' type and a 'splenic' type. Apart from subtle morphological differences, splenic-type MZBL, as a rule, express IgD, whereas MALT-type MZBL are IgD-negative. It should be noted, however, that the designations of MALT and splenic types of nodal MZBL, at present, are only descriptive terms and it is not expected that these tumours represent secondary lymph node involvement by a primary extranodal or primary splenic lymphoma. While no splenic involvement has been found in the splenic-type nodal MZBL, around 50% of nodal MZBL designated as MALT type have been shown to be associated with an extranodal component, thus illustrating the present difficulties in discriminating true primary nodal MZBL from secondary lymph node involvement by a MALT-type lymphoma. On the other hand, characteristic clinical features have been described differentiating those tumours.

Immunophenotype

Most nodal MZBL are comparable to MALT-type lymphomas; however, some express IgD.

Genetic Features

Only single cases of presumably true nodal MZBL have been characterized on the cytogenetic level, and no unifying aberrations are known.

Lymphoplasmacytic Lymphoma (LPL)

Clinical Features

LPL is a disease of older adults, with a male predominance. Lymphoplasmacytic lymphomas are neoplasms only rarely manifesting as nodal tumours. They most commonly present with bone marrow and splenic infiltrations clinically corresponding to most cases of Waldenstrom macroglo-bulinaemia. Monoclonal serum paraproteins (>3 g dL^{-1}), autoimmune phenomena, cryoglobulinaemia, and hyper-viscosity syndromes are frequent.

Morphology

This type of malignant lymphoma, by definition, lacks features of B-CLL, mantle cell, follicular, or marginal zone lymphomas. In the lymph node, there is a diffuse efface-ment of the normal architecture, sometimes however sparing preserved 'naked' germinal centres. The infiltrate consists of a mixture of small lymphocytes, plasmacytoid cells and mature plasma cells, and the demonstration of a monoclonal cytoplasmatic light chain is a *sine qua non* for the disease. Intranuclear immunoglobulin inclusions (Dutcher bodies) are frequently observed. In some cases,

sinuses are preserved and even wide. In rare cases, a pro-minent epithelioid cell reaction may be seen.

Immunophenotype

These lymphomas are IgM (rarely IgG and IgA) cyto-plasmic positive and IgD and CD5 negative. Some may express CD23. CD10 is always negative.

Genetic Features

A specific chromosome translocation, t(9;14)(p13;q32), has been demonstrated in 50% of cases, leading to the deregulation and over-expression of the *PAX 5* gene.

Diffuse Large B Cell Lymphomas (DLBL)

Clinical Features

Diffuse large B cell lymphomas constitute around 30–40% of adult non-Hodgkin lymphoma. Typically, patients pre-sent with a single, rapidly enlarging symptomatic mass at a single nodal or extranodal site. About one-third of DLBL are primary extranodal in origin, while the majority of cases arise in lymph nodes or other lymphatic organs, such as the tonsils or spleen.

Morphology

DLBL are principally composed of 'large' lymphoid cells, usually with nuclei at least twice the size of a small lym-phocyte. The cytoplasm is moderately to deeply baso-philic, and nuclei are large with a vesicular chromatin structure and prominent nucleoli. As can be seen from **Table 5**, diffuse large B cell lymphomas, in the WHO classification, are subdivided into distinct clinical subtypes and variants.

DLBL Variants

The **centroblastic** variant is characterized by a tumour cell population that may be either predominantly composed of cells with round to oval nuclei, a vesicular chromatin structure and membrane-bound nucleoli, or by a mixture of these centroblasts with immunoblasts. By convention, in the centroblastic variant, as much as 90% immunoblasts may be present (**Figure 7a**).

Table 5 Subtypes and variants in diffuse large B cell lymphomas

Variants:	Centroblastic
	Immunoblastic
	T cell- or histiocyte-rich
	Anaplastic large B cell
Subtypes:	Mediastinal (thymic) large B cell lymphoma
	Intravascular large B cell lymphoma
	Primary effusion lymphoma

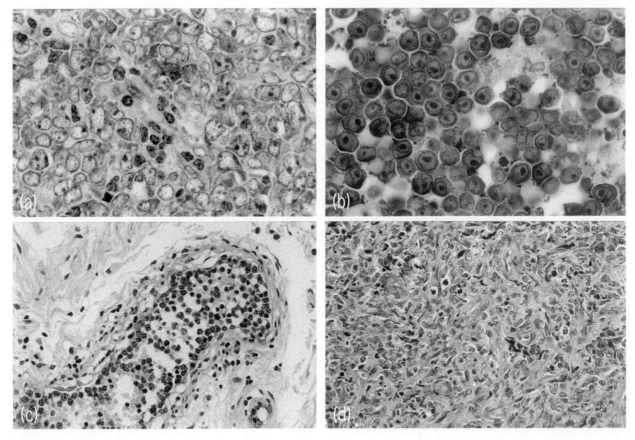

Figure 7   Diffuse large B cell lymphoma. (a) Centroblastic variant. Tumour cells are medium- to large-sized and possess a narrow rim of moderately basophilic cytoplasm. The nuclei are round to oval. Within the vesicular nuclear chromatin, 1–3 nucleoli are attached to the nuclear membrane. (b) Immunoblastic variant. Tumour cells are large with abundant cytoplasm, vesicular nuclei and single prominent central nucleoli. (c) DLBL, intravascular subtype. The blastic tumour cells are seen in the lumina of medium-sized vessels. (d) DLBL, mediastinal (thymic) large-cell subtype. Tumour cells of large size are embedded in a sclerosing stroma.

In the **immunoblastic** variant of DLBL, typical centroblasts comprise less than 10% of the total cellular infiltrate. The most cells are large with a central prominent nucleolus and a broad basophilic cytoplasm. Plasmablastic differentiation is common (**Figure 7b**).

The **anaplastic** variant comprises tumours with large, 'anaplastic,' oval or polygonal cells with pleomorphic, sometimes bizarre nuclei, sometimes reminiscent of Hodgkin or even Reed–Sternberg cells.

T cell- or **histiocyte-rich** large B cell lymphomas are characterized by a prominent reactive inflammatory infiltrate, comprising more than 90% of the total cell population.

Immunophenotype

Diffuse large B cell lymphomas, in all variants, consistently express B cell-associated antigens (CD20 and CD79a). Other B cell antigens are variably present. CD5 and CD23 immunoreactivity may be found in around 10% of cases, sometimes pointing to an underlying small lymphocytic lymphoma/B-CLL from which the diffuse large

B cell lymphoma had evolved. CD10 expression is more commonly found in centroblastic variants (30%). CD30 is expressed in the anaplastic variant, but may also be demonstrated in centroblastic or immunoblastic types.

Genetic Features

Diffuse large B-cell lymphomas have their IgH and IgL chain genes clonally rearranged in a high percentage of cases and show a high load of somatic mutations. DLBL, therefore, in most cases, represent germinal or post-germinal neoplasias, having undergone germinal centre passage (and possibly antigen selection).

Chromosomal aberrations involving chromosomal band 3q27, the localization of the BCL-6 gene, seem to constitute the most frequent recurring genetic alterations in DLBL. In 20–30% of DLBL, the t(14;18) is found, and these tumours may have evolved from an (occult) follicular lymphoma. Little is known on the significance of the so-called secondary chromosomal aberrations in DLBL, although these are definitely non-random and may even be different in different variants. The most common secondary aberrations involve deletions in the long arm of chromosome 6 and complete or partial trisomies for chromosomes 3, 5, 7, 11, 12, 18 and X. An exciting new finding in DLBL is the demonstration of different RNA expression profiles, delineating a 'germinal centre-like' and an 'activated B cell-like' subtype and, hence, possibly pointing to different transformation pathways. The recognition of these different pathways may even have profound prognostic importance.

DLBL subtypes

Primary mediastinal (thymic) B cell lymphoma is a tumour possibly derived from thymic B cells. The tumours commonly arise in the anterior mediastinum of younger, often female patients and frequently are characterized on the cytological level by large, clear cells. Prominent sclerosis is a characteristic structural feature.

Apart from the expression of B cell-associated antigens, these tumours are negative for immunoglobulins and may express CD30. The notion of a distinct biological entity has been further substantiated by the finding of characteristic chromosomal aberrations, namely a gain of material in the short arm of chromosome 9 and an amplification of the *REL* oncogene on chromosome 2p (**Figure 7d**).

Intravascular (angiotropic) B cell lymphoma is a rare disease characterized by the almost exclusive infiltration of small- to medium-sized blood vessels by large B blasts. Lymph nodes are rarely involved, and the diagnosis is commonly rendered in organ biopsies such as from the skin, the CNS or the renal parenchyma (**Figure 7c**).

Primary effusion lymphoma represents a rare body cavity-associated lymphoma and is constantly found in association with HIV and HHV8 (human herpes virus type 8) infection.

There are other characteristic clinico-pathological manifestations of diffuse large B cell lymphomas, at present regarded as provisional entities. Recognition as distinct entities is still pending and will require additional evidence for biological significance. Among those are **AIDS-associated primary CNS lymphomas**, which are consistently associated with Epstein–Barr virus (EBV) infection, **plasmablastic lymphomas**, frequently presenting in the oral cavity and, as a rule, evolving in the setting of HIV infection as well, and **primary extranodal DLBL**, e.g. primary gastric or intestinal lymphomas, or primary cutaneous DLBL.

It should be pointed out, however, that neither reliable pathological or biological criteria for the subclassification of DLBL nor distinctive therapies recommended for clinical practice are available at present. For these reasons, the Clinical Advisory Committee of the WHO agreed that the subclassification of DLBL should be optional at present. However, it was agreed that the site of involvement should be clearly stated in the pathology report.

Burkitt Lymphoma (BL)

There is an endemic form (EBV-associated African Burkitt lymphoma), a so-called sporadic form occurring in Western countries, and tumours that occur in the setting of HIV infection. (See the chapters *Human DNA Tumour Viruses* and *RNA Viruses*.)

Clinical Features

Burkitt lymphoma is most common in children (one-third of paediatric lymphomas in Western countries). In African cases, the jaws and other facial bones are frequently involved. In non-endemic cases, BL tends to occur in extranodal sites, most commonly in the distal ileum, caecum and/or mesentery. In rare cases, the tumour presents as acute leukaemia. BL is a specific type of HIV-associated non-Hodgkin lymphoma.

Morphology

The tumour cells of Burkitt lymphoma are medium-sized and are characteristically arranged in cohesive sheets. They possess a deeply basophilic cytoplasm and round, monomorphic nuclei with several, usually prominent, nucleoli. Large macrophages with a broad cytoplasm and ingested apoptotic tumour cells ('tingible body macrophages') are regularly present, thus imparting a characteristic 'starry sky' appearance of the tumour. The proliferation index as measured by the Ki67 antibody is very high ($>90–95\%$ of cells) (**Figure 8**).

Immunophenotype

The tumour cells express B cell-associated antigens and are characteristically CD10+, BCL-6+ and BCL-2−.

Genetic Features

The cytogenetic hallmark of Burkitt lymphoma is the translocation t(8;14)(q24.1;q32) or one of the related translocations t(2;8) or t(8;22). On the molecular level, these translocations invariably involve the c-*myc* locus in chromosome band 8q24.1, but different breakpoints in the IgH or IgL chain genes. In endemic (African) cases, the breakpoint in chromosome 14 involves the IgH joining region in contrast to non-endemic (Western) cases in which the IgH switch region is targetted.

The WHO Steering Committee, after thorough discussion, decided to remove the tumours that in the REAL classification proposal were termed 'high-grade B cell lymphoma, Burkitt-like' (and regarded as a provisional entity) from the category of diffuse large B cell lymphomas and include those as variants under the general term of (atypical) Burkitt lymphoma. These variants commonly show, in contrast to classical Burkitt lymphoma, some unusual features either related to cell size (slightly larger), or to immunohistochemical features (cytoplasmic Ig

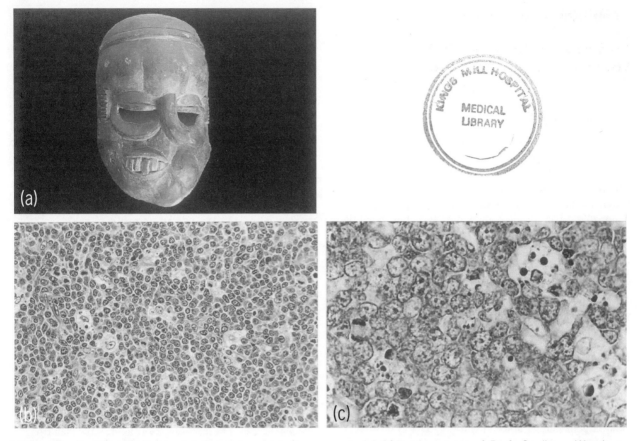

Figure 8 Burkitt lymphoma. (a) Gangoza mask from equatorial Africa (courtesy of Prof. Seeliger, Würzburg, Germany) illustrating the characteristic infiltration of the jaw bones and ensuing displacement of midfacial structures in endemic (African) cases. (b) Low-power view of a lymph node showing cohesive sheets of medium-sized blasts with interspersed macrophages imparting a starry sky pattern. (c) High-power view illustrating medium-sized blasts with round nuclei, coarsely reticulated chromatin and small nucleoli.

expression). Of note, extranodal 'Burkitt-like' lymphomas nevertheless frequently are t(8;14) positive and in the majority of cases are CD10+ and BCL2−. Therefore, these features, together with an exceedingly high proliferation index, should be considered when diagnosing 'Burkitt-like' lymphoma. The term for these tumours has now been changed to 'atypical Burkitt lymphoma'.

B Cell Lymphomas Rarely Infiltrating Lymph Nodes

Plasmacytoma rarely manifests in lymph nodes. In these cases, nodal infiltrates represent a secondary phenomenon in generalized multiple myeloma. Typically, the neoplastic plasma cells are diffusely infiltrating the lymphatic parenchyma without a lymphoid or lymphoplasmacytoid cell component. On immunohistochemistry, plasmacytomas are SIg−, CIg+ (G, A, rarely IgD or E or light chain only), CD20-negative and CD79a-positive in 50% of cases. VS38c and CD138 (syndecan) are expressed in the cytoplasm. Recently, the MUM-1 protein has been described as consistently expressed in the nucleus.

Plasmacytomas represent postfollicular neoplasms with somatic hypermutations of IgH and IgL genes, but without ongoing mutations. Some specific cytogenetic aberrations have been reported, such as the t(4;14)(q16;q32) involving *FGFR3*, the t(6;14)(p25;q32) involving the *MUM-1/IRF 4* gene locus and t(11;14)(q13;q32) deregulating cyclin D1.

Hairy cell leukaemia is diagnosed only rarely in lymph nodes. Tumour cells predominantly infiltrate the spleen and bone marrow, resulting in splenomegaly and pancytopenia. In the peripheral blood, circulating tumour cells may be present with circumferential 'hairy' projections. Splenic involvement occurs in the red pulp. In lymph nodes, this neoplasm may primarily invade the subcapsular and intertrabecular sinuses. On the cytological level small- to medium-sized monomorphic lymphoid cells with a rather broad, pale cytoplasm and dense, bean-shaped nuclei are seen. The characteristic immunophenotype, CD5−, CD23−, CD11c+, CD25+, CD103+, DBA44+, along with its unique clinical features (prominent splenomegaly and infiltration of the bone marrow), helps in the diagnosis. No consistent cytogenetic alterations have been described so far.

LYMPHOMAS OF T CELL LINEAGE

Precursor T Cell Lymphoblastic Leukaemia/Lymphoma (Precursor T Cell Acute Lymphoblastic Leukaemia)

Clinical Features

Patients are adolescents or young adults, with male predominance. T-LBL accounts for roughly 40% of childhood lymphomas. T-LBL constitute 20% of precursor cell acute lymphatic leukaemias. Clinically, patients may present with large thymic tumours or peripheral lymphadenopathy. The disease is aggressive, but potentially curable.

Morphology

The morphology of the tumour cells is virtually identical with that of precursor B-LBL (**Figure 9**).

Immunophenotype

Most cases will express T cell-associated antigens CD3 (cytoplasmic) and CD7. CD4 and CD8 may be double-positive or double-negative. Sometimes, expression of NK cell antigens can be noted. Typically, TdT is positive.

Genetic Features

TCR genes are clonally rearranged. A number of recurring cytogenetic aberrations have been described, frequently involving 14q11 and 7p15 or 7q34-36 (the chromosomal bands in which the T cell receptor (TCR) genes are located); 25% of tumours have been reported to carry *SCL/TAL-1* rearrangements.

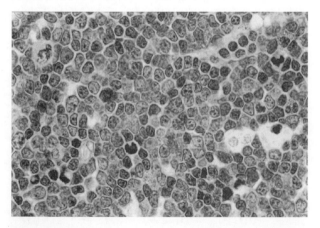

Figure 9 Precursor T cell lymphoblastic leukaemia/ lymphoma. The tumour cells have round to irregular nuclei, a faint dust-like chromatin and scant cytoplasm. Note some interspersed large macrophages.

Peripheral T and T/NK Cell Neoplasias

Peripheral T and T/NK cell lymphomas are rare neoplasms in Western countries, but, they are more frequent in Oriental and Asian countries. Although the Clinical Advisory Committee of the WHO classification did not recommend a clinical grouping of the various entities of NHL, peripheral T and T/NK neoplasias may be subdivided according to their predominant clinical features into those that are primarily leukaemic or disseminated, primary nodal or primary extranodal in origin (Chan, 1999).

PREDOMINANTLY LEUKAEMIC (DISSEMINATED) PERIPHERAL T AND T/NK CELL NEOPLASMS

T Cell Prolymphocytic Leukaemia (T-PLL)

Clinical Features

T-PLL is a disease of older adults comprising only 1% of CLL. Patients present with marked leukocytosis $(100 \times 10^9/1)$ and bone marrow, spleen, liver and lymph node infiltrates. Occasionally, cutaneous or mucosal involvement is seen. The disease is more aggressive than B-CLL.

Morphology

T-PLL diffusely infiltrates the paracortical lymph node areas, sometimes sparing pre-existing follicles. In contrast to B-CLL, no pseudo-follicular structures are present. Cytology is characterized by small- to medium-sized lymphocytes with scant cytoplasm and sometimes marked nuclear irregularity. One of the most powerful diagnostic hallmarks of T-PLL is the presence of numerous small high-endothelial venules. They often contain tumour cells, within both the lumens and vessel walls, so that the vessel walls appear to be transmigrated by the tumour (**Figure 10**). Splenomegaly is due to the infiltration of the splenic red pulp.

Immunophenotype

T-PLL cells display a mature T cell immunophenotype with positivity for CD2, CD3, CD5 and CD7. Most cases are CD4 +.

Genetic Features

The *TCR* genes are clonally rearranged. In around 80% of cases, a characteristic chromosomal aberration, inv(14)(q11;q32), is present involving the *TCL-1* oncogene in 14q32. Frequently, there is also a partial trisomy for the long arm of chromosome 8. Deletion of the *ATM* gene has been observed in a considerable portion of cases.

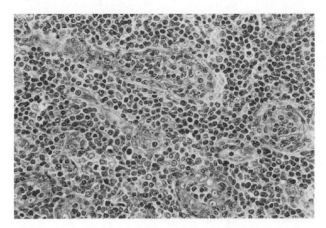

Figure 10 T cell prolymphocytic leukaemia. A characteristic hallmark of the disease is the transmigration of neoplastic cells through the walls of numerous high-endothelial postcapillary vessels.

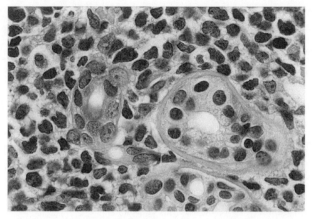

Figure 11 Aggressive NK cell leukaemia/lymphoma. Medium-sized blastic cells with irregular nuclear contours surround and invade adnexal structures in the skin. Note finely dispersed nuclear chromatin.

T Cell Large Granular Lymphocytic Leukaemia (T-LGL)

Clinical Features

T-LGL is a disease of adults frequently presenting with rheumatoid diseases and PB neutropenia and anaemia. Usually, there is mild leukocytosis (20×10^9/1) and mild to moderate splenomegaly. Although the clinical course of T-LGL is usually indolent, more aggressive types may be found with an NK cell phenotype. T cell types are usually indolent, with morbidity related to cytopenias.

Morphology

T-LGL only rarely involves lymph nodes. Generally, there is infiltration of the bone marrow and leukaemic dissemination. Splenic red pulp and hepatic sinus infiltrations are common. In peripheral blood smears, T-LGL cells usually are small and characteristically show a wide rim of eccentric pale blue cytoplasm and the presence of azurophilic granules. The nuclei are round to oval, sometimes with nucleoli.

Immunophenotype

Most frequently, there is a T cell-associated phenotype with CD2+, CD3+, CD7+, CD16−/+, CD56−, CD57+ marker constellation. In rarer cases, an NK cell phenotype may be present with CD2+, CD3-, CD16+, CD56+, CD57+/−.

Genetic Features

In most of the cases with T cell phenotype, clonal rearrangements of the TCR genes may be found. NK cell cases usually are germline. There may be an association with Epstein–Barr virus in Asian cases.

Aggressive NK Cell Leukaemia/Lymphoma

Clinical Features

This is an exceedingly rare neoplasm in Western countries, while most of the cases have been described in Orientals. There apparently is some overlap with nasal NK/T cell lymphoma, however, there is infiltration of the bone marrow and peripheral blood lymphocytosis.

Morphology

The cytological picture has been described as composed of monotonous-appearing medium-sized lymphoblastoid cells with small cytoplasm, round to oval vesicular nuclei and inconspicuous nucleoli. Numerous mitotic figures are present (**Figure 11**).

Immunophenotype

Tumour cells are usually CD2+, CD3−, CD3ε+, CD56+, TIA-1+, granzyme B+.

Genetic Features

No clonal rearrangements of the TCR genes are present. As a rule, there is an association with Epstein–Barr virus infection.

Adult T Cell Leukaemia/Lymphoma (ATL/L)

Clinical Features

ATL/L is a very rare neoplasm in Western countries, and most cases have been reported in patients from south western Japan and the Caribbean. Patients are HTLV1 retrovirus positive. Several clinical variants have been described with differing clinical presentations such as an 'acute', 'lymphomatous', 'chronic' and 'smoldering' form. The acute form with high peripheral blood count, hypercalcaemia, lytic bone lesions and hepatosplenomegaly is most common.

Morphology

Histology may vary with respect to the cytological composition of the infiltrate. In most cases, a mixture of small and large cells, sometimes pleomorphic in shape, can be seen. Also, multinucleated giant cells may be present, reminiscent of Reed–Sternberg cells.

Immunophenotype

The tumour cells usually express T cell-associated antigens CD2, CD3 and CD5, but characteristically lack CD7, but are CD25+. A CD4+ phenotype is much more common than CD7+ types.

Genetic Features

The prerequisite for the diagnosis of ATL/L is the demonstration of integrated HTLV-1 genomes in virtually all cases. TCR genes are clonally rearranged. Some recurring structural and numerical chromosome aberrations have been reported, among them trisomies 3 and 5 and structural alterations involving chromosomal band 14q11.

Hepatosplenic γ/λ T Cell Lymphoma

Clinical Features

This primary splenic T cell lymphoma is a rare, albeit distinct, form of primary splenic lymphoma with cytotoxic features. The disease rarely affects peripheral lymph nodes, but may be suspected in leukaemic cases owing to its classical immunophenotye. The spleen shows moderate to distinct enlargement.

Morphology

In the spleen, there is a diffuse infiltration of the red pulp with sinus involvement by small- to medium-sized cells with sometimes more abundant pale cytoplasm and usually small round to ovoid nuclei. The white pulp is atrophic and sometime entirely absent. In the bone marrow, the infiltrate may manifest purely intrasinusoidal, a feature which in fact is a diagnostic hallmark of the disease in trephine specimens.

Immunophenotype

The tumour cells are CD3+ and also other T cell-associated antigens positive (CD2, CD5, CD7); however, they do not express either CD4 or CD8. No expression of

$TCR\alpha/\beta$ receptor is present, but $TCR\gamma/\lambda$ markers are expressed. Most characteristically, the tumour cells express both cytolytic/cytotoxic proteins, such as TIA-1, perforin and granzyme B, as well as NK cell-associated antigen CD56.

Genetic Features

The $TCR\alpha/\beta$ chain genes are germ-line, but the $TCR\gamma$ and $-\lambda$ chain genes are clonally rearranged. A characteristic chromosomal abnormality, i(7)(q10), has been recognized, sometimes associated with trisomy 8. Interestingly, rare $TCR\alpha/\beta$ variants of the disease have been described with identical chromosome aberrations.

Primary Nodal T/NK Cell Lymphomas: Angioimmunoblastic T Cell Lymphoma (AIL-T)

Clinical Features

AIL-T is a T cell lymphoma that can be suspected by clinicians because of its characteristic features. Typically, there is a generalized lymphadenopathy, fever, weight loss, localized or generalized erythema and polyclonal hyper-gammaglobulinaemia. Interestingly, occasional spontaneous remissions have been reported. Disease course is aggressive. Infectious complications are common, and progression to aggressive lymphomas of T cell or, rarely, B cell type may occur.

Morphology

In most cases, the nodal architecture is diffusely effaced, although rare cases have been described in which secondary follicles are still present, presumably representing early stages of the disease. The subcapsular sinuses may be preserved. The lymphoid infiltrate usually is composed of a mixture of small- and medium-sized lymphocytes, some immunoblasts and in some cases there may be an admixture of clear cells with pale or clear cytoplasm and pleomorphic nuclei. Epithelioid histiocytes, plasma cells and sometimes large numbers of eosinophils may be interspersed. Characteristically, a proliferation of small arborizing high endothelial venules with PAS-positive vessel walls is present throughout the lymph node, and also extending beyond the capsule (**Figure 12**). Sometimes, in routine H&E sections, expanded aggregates of follicular dendritic cells may be seen, in some cases forming characteristic onion-shaped 'burned-out' germinal centre nodules.

Immunophenotype

The tumour cells express T cell-associated antigens and usually are CD4+. Expanded and loosely structured

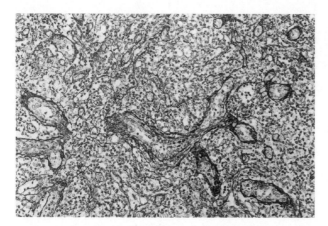

Figure 12 Angioimmunoblastic T cell lymphoma. The lymph node architecture is diffusely effaced. Note conspicuous proliferation of arborizing high-endothelial vessels.

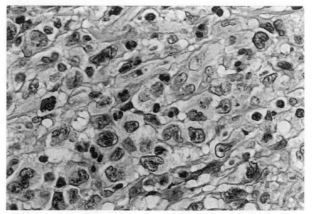

Figure 13 Peripheral T cell lymphoma (unspecified). There is a predominance of medium- to large-sized cells with moderate to broad cytoplasm and irregular nuclei varying in size and shape.

follicular dendritic cell clusters are recognized on staining with FDC markers such as CD21 or CD23. In rare cases, a prominent admixture of large atypical CD20+ B blasts may be present either haphazardly distributed in the infiltrate, or forming small to larger cell clusters. These cells, which often are reminiscent of Hodgkin and Reed–Sternberg cells, may either be CD30+, CD15+ or be CD20+, CD30+, and characteristically express LMP-1 due to Epstein–Barr virus infection.

Genetic Features

TCR genes are rearranged in most cases. Paradoxically, IgH rearrangements may be detected in 20–30% of cases. By *in situ* hybridization, EBV early repeat (EBER) transcripts have been noted, in varying numbers, in >95% of cases. Recurring chromosomal aberrations in AIL-T are trisomies 3 and 5 and, less frequently, an additional X chromosome.

Peripheral T Cell Lymphoma, Unspecified (PTCL-NOS)

This category comprises a large group of peripheral T cell neoplasms that cannot be subcategorized under one of the distinct, nodal or extranodal, entities. It comprises cases which in the Kiel classification have been described as T zone lymphoma, lymphoepithelioid (Lennert's) lymphoma, pleomorphic T cell lymphoma and T immunoblastic lymphoma. At present, it is not clear if this category contains several biological disease entities. The striking variability of the morphological picture, however, suggests that this could be in fact the case.

Clinical Features

PTCL-NOS is more frequent in advanced age groups. The disease is more common in Eastern countries, and in

Western countries it comprise only 10–15% of all lymphomas. Aside from lymph nodes, the disease may frequently also involve the skin, liver, spleen and bone marrow. The disease is aggressive, but potentially curable.

Morphology

In most cases, the lymph node architecture is completely destroyed. In rare cases, however, an interfollicular infiltration pattern may be present with sparing of B cell follicles. Cytologically, peripheral T cell lymphomas typically are characterized by a mixture of small and large atypical cells. The appearance of the cytoplasm is variable, but in contrast to B cell lymphomas, the neoplastic cells, as a rule, have more irregular nuclei and vary considerably in size and shape. In some cases, large blasts reminiscent of Hodgkin and Reed–Sternberg cells are present (**Figure 13**). The background infiltrate may be equally variable in its cytological composition. There may be eosinophils or epithelioid histiocytes and plasma cells present. The number of high endothelial venules is not as striking as in AIL-T. In contrast to angioimmunoblastic T cell lymphoma, expanded meshworks of follicular dendritic cells usually are absent.

Immunophenotype

Peripheral T cell lymphomas are positive for T cell-associated antigens, but they may display selective loss of expression for all T cell markers, especially for CD7. Most cases are CD4 + and CD8−, but rare CD8+, CD4− peripheral T cell lymphomas may be encountered, often with an associated expression of cytotoxic molecules. Others may be CD4−, CD8−.

Genetic Features

The TCR genes are clonally rearranged in most cases. Ig genes are germ line. No unifying cytogenetic aberration has been described in PCTL-NOS. Recurring chromosomal alterations involve chromosomes 7 and 14 (the bands in which the T cell receptor genes are localized). Recurring deletions have been described in the short arm of chromosome 1, the long arm of chromosome 6 and the short arm of chromosome 17. Gains are common in chromosomes 3, 7 and X. PTCL-NOS of the large cell type are frequently characterized by a tetraploid karyotype.

Anaplastic Large Cell Lymphoma (ALCL)

ALCLs were recognized in 1985 by their characteristic expression of the CD30 antigen. Although it soon became clear that other T cell or even B cell lymphomas may occasionally express CD30, the classical morphology of ALCL of T and null cell types justified its recognition as a distinct entity. CD30-positive B cell lymphomas with 'anaplastic' morphology have now been recognized as a variant of diffuse large B cell lymphoma.

Clinical Features

The majority of patients are children or adolescents, but a second peak in age distribution is seen in (older) adults. In the systemic form, lymph nodes and extranodal sites are involved, including the skin. The disease is moderately aggressive, but cure rates are high in the ALK + variants.

Morphology

The majority of anaplastic large cell lymphomas is composed of large blastic cells with a broad eosinophilic cytoplasm on H&E sections (and grey–blue cytoplasm on Giemsa stain). The nuclei are large with a vesicular chromatin structure and a single prominent or multiple nucleoli. They may be round or, more often, horseshoe-shaped or pleomorphic. In contrast to peripheral T cell lymphomas, unspecified (which in some cases may also be CD30+), the cell size at least in the 'common' variant shows relatively little variation. The tumour cells are often arranged in cohesive sheets and infiltration of the lymph node sinuses, at first glance suggesting involvement of a solid tumour, is a key feature of the disease (**Figure 14**). In addition to this common type, a small-cell variant and a so-called lymphohistiocytic variant have been described.

In the small-cell variant, the infiltrate is mainly composed of small- to medium-sized cells with irregular nuclei and pale cytoplasm. However, typically, the characteristic large 'anaplastic' blasts are also present. In the lymphohistiocytic variant of the disease, the tumour cells comprise only a minority of the infiltrate. There are numerous histiocytes present, frequently with a broad and foamy cytoplasm, greatly obscuring the neoplastic cells. Other variants, e.g. sarcomatoid, granulocyte-rich and giant-cell types, may be encountered.

There may be an overlap with tumour cell-rich or syncytial variants of Hodgkin lymphoma (sometimes termed 'grey zone' or 'borderline' cases), in which a clear decision may be difficult. However, with the description of more and more antigens that are differentially expressed in Hodgkin lymphoma and ALCL, such as ALK-1, LMP-1, CD15 and others, in most cases a clear diagnosis can be rendered (**Table 6**).

Immunophenotype

The tumour cells, by definition, are CD30 + , and in most cases also express the leukocyte common antigen. Irrespective of T or null cell origin, most of the tumours (roughly 75%) are positive for the epithelial membrane antigen (EMA) and CD25. Also, most cases of both T and null cell types express cytotoxic molecules (e.g. perforin, TIA-1 and granzyme B), pointing to the derivation of ALCL from cytotoxic cells. T cell-associated antigens may be variably present in T-ALCL. As a rule, CD20 and other B cell-associated antigens are negative.

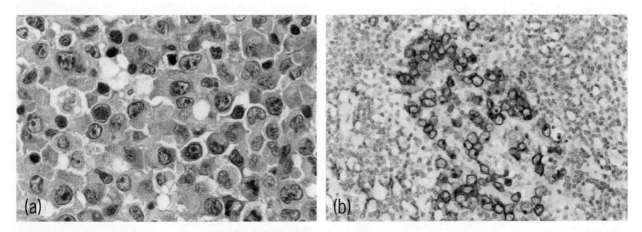

Figure 14 Anaplastic large cell lymphoma. (a) Diffuse proliferation of large cells with broad cytoplasm and round to oval nuclei and prominent nucleoli. (b) CD30 staining of the tumour cells highlighting the characteristic sinus infiltration pattern.

Table 6 Antigen expression patterns in classical Hodgkin lymphoma (cHL) and anaplastic large-cell lymphoma (ALCL)

	CD30	CD15	CD20	T cell markers	CD45	EMA	LMP	TIA1	ALK1
cHL	+	+/−	−/+	−	−	−/+	+/−	−/+	−
ALCL	+	−	−	+/−	+/−	+/−	−	+/−	+/−

Genetic Features

A reciprocal chromosome translocation, t(2;5)(p23;q35), has been detected in 40–60% of ALCL, generating a fusion protein that consists of the nucleophosmin (*NPM*) gene in 5q35 and the anaplastic lymphoma kinase (*ALK*) gene in 2p23. By virtue of the translocation, the ALK kinase is constitutively overexpressed and activated. After the generation of a monoclonal antibody directed against the kinase domain of the ALK protein, it became possible to detect the translocation even in paraffin sections. In cases with this classical translocation, the fusion protein is expressed both in the nucleus and the cytoplasm, while in rare variant translocations also involving ALK, but different fusion partners, the fusion protein is only seen in the cytoplasm. Although it was noted that ALK-positive ALCL comprise a wide morphological spectrum with common, lymphohistiocytic and small cell types being ALK-positive, it was shown that patients with ALK-positive ALCL are generally younger and predominantly of male gender. In comparison with ALK-negative ALCL, patients with tumours expressing the fusion protein show a distinctly favourable clinical course (with 10-year survival rates as high as 70–90%). Because of this important difference, ALK-positive anaplastic large-cell lymphomas are today regarded as a distinct disease entity.

PREDOMINANTLY EXTRANODAL T/NK CELL LYMPHOMAS

Primary Cutaneous Anaplastic Large Cell Lymphomas and Cutaneous CD30-positive Lymphoproliferative Disease (CD30 + LPD)

CD30-positive lymphoproliferative disorders in the skin represent a spectrum of diseases ranging from lymphomatoid papulosis to anaplastic large-cell lymphoma. Since a reliable distinction of these diseases on purely morphological grounds may be difficult, it was suggested to diagnose, in all of these cases, a primary cutaneous CD30-positive lymphoproliferative disease and to subcategorize lymphomatoid papulosis and primary cutaneous ALCL with respect to clinical features.

Morphology

In primary cutaneous CD30 + lymphoproliferative disease, the skin is infiltrated by sometimes cohesive sheets of large neoplastic cells with anaplastic morphology. In other cases, these cells are more loosely distributed, and there is a prominent reactive infiltrate of small lymphocytes and histiocytic cells rendering the differential diagnosis to lymphomatoid papulosis difficult. A single (large) tumour favours anaplastic large-cell lymphoma, while lymphomatoid papulosis tends to present with multiple, waxing and waning, small-sized lesions. By definition, primary cutaneous ALCL may only be diagnosed if the skin is the only site involved.

Immunophenotype

Primary cutaneous LPD express CD30, and frequently are positive for T cell-associated antigens. Cytotoxic markers (TIA1, perforin and/or granzyme B) are frequently found. In contrast to the systemic form, the epithelial membrane antigen is negative, and the cutaneous lymphocyte antigen HECA452 may be positive in most cases. Expression of the ALK kinase is an absolute rarity in this disorder. If ALK protein is expressed, one is more likely to be dealing with a cutaneous infiltration of primary systemic ALCL.

Genetic Features

TCR genes are clonally rearranged in most cases.

Nasal NK/T Cell Lymphoma and NK/T Cell Lymphoma of Nasal Type

Clinical Features

These tumours are rare in Western countries, but are more common in the East. They arise predominantly extranodal, in the nose, the nasopharynx and the paranasal sinuses. Because of their resemblance to nasal NK/T cell lymphoma, tumours with a similar morphology and immunophenotype in the skin, the soft tissue, the gastrointestinal tract or in other localizations, these tumours are diagnosed as 'of nasal type'. The most frequent manifestation of the disease, however, is in the midfacial structures, hence the old term of 'lethal midline granuloma'.

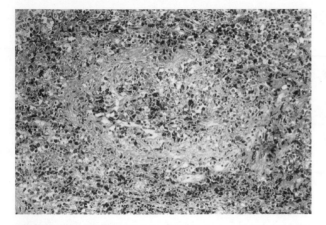

Figure 15 Nasal NK/T cell lymphoma. Tumour cells invade and destroy a larger blood vessel. Note necrosis of adjacent tissue compartments.

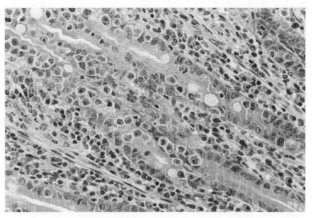

Figure 16 Enteropathy-type T cell lymphoma. The neoplastic cells invade preserved epithelial structures of the mucosa adjacent to a deeply ulcerated small intestinal tumour.

Morphology

Nasal and nasal type NK/T cell lymphomas are in many, but not all, cases characterized by a prominent angiocentric and angiodestructive growth pattern (**Figure 15**) leading to sometimes marked necrosis. The cytological spectrum may be variable with some tumours predominantly consisting of small cells, and some of medium- to large-sized cells. An admixed inflammatory infiltrate may be prominent. Frequently, the nuclei are irregular or pleomorphic, and the chromatin structure may be finely dispersed or granular. Because of their sometimes close similarity to T cell lymphomas, the immunophenotype plays a pivotal role in the diagnosis of the disorder.

Immunophenotype

Nasal NK/T cell lymphomas and NK/T cell lymphomas of nasal type invariably express the CD56 antigen and cytotoxic molecules. T cell-associated antigen CD2 is present in most cases, while CD3 is not found, but CD3ε(cytoplasmic) is expressed.

Genetic Features

Usually, no clonal rearrangements for TCR genes are found; however, in some cases they may be present pointing to a derivation of the tumour cells from T lymphocytes (hence the term NK/T cell lymphoma). In most cases, the tumour cells are infected with the Epstein–Barr virus, rendering EBER *in situ* hybridization an important diagnostic tool if the disease is suspected.

Enteropathy-Type T Cell Lymphoma

Clinical Features

Patients are adults, frequently with a history of gluten-sensitive enteropathy. In others, signs of enteropathy may only be observed in resection specimens, or be entirely absent. Disease course is aggressive. Most often, the disease manifests in the jejunal parts of the small intestine, and because of the difficult clinical diagnosis, may only be recognized if a small bowel segment is resected, frequently because of perforation. This disease was originally thought to represent a histiocytic disorder ('malignant histiocytosis of the intestine'), but has now been conclusively shown to be a T cell lymphoma.

Morphology

The tumours show a broad morphological spectrum ranging from small- and medium-sized to medium- and large-sized or anaplastic tumour cells. There may be diffuse infiltration throughout the bowel wall, and large ulcerations may be present. In the vicinity of these lesions (**Figure 16**), in preserved mucosal parts, there may be a characteristic infiltration of tumour cells into the crypt epithelium, sometimes reminiscent of lymphoepithelial lesions. The adjacent mucosa may or may not show villous atrophy, crypt hyperplasia and a high content of inter-epithelial T cells (which may be neoplastic as well).

Immunophenotype

T cell-associated antigens are usually expressed, as are cytotoxic molecules. A characteristic finding, which, however, is not present in all cases, is the expression of the mucosal homing receptor CD103 antigen. Some of the cases may be CD8+, and a rather monomorphic variant of small- to medium-sized tumour cells has been described with expression of CD56.

Genetic Features

The TCR genes are clonally rearranged in most cases.

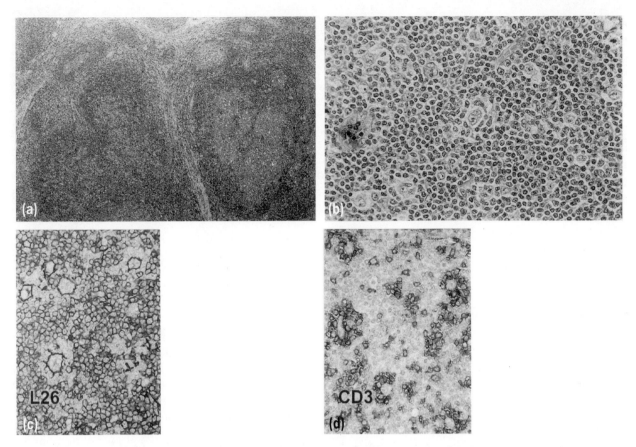

Figure 17   Nodular lymphocyte predominance Hodgkin lymphoma. (a) Low magnification showing large tumour nodules adjacent to areas of follicular hyperplasia. (b) High magnification illustrating lymphocytic and histiocytic (L&H) cells in a background of small lymphocytes. (c) L26 staining showing positivity of the L&H cells and of the background lymphoid cells for CD20. (d) CD3 staining illustrating 'rosetting' of T cells around the tumour cells.

HODGKIN LYMPHOMA

Hodgkin disease is histologically diverse and may be classified into two main entities, namely nodular lymphocyte predominance Hodgkin lymphoma (NLPHL or paragranuloma) and classical Hodgkin lymphoma.

Principally, the diagnosis of Hodgkin disease or Hodgkin lymphoma requires a malignant proliferation of Hodgkin and Reed–Sternberg cells (in the case of classical Hodgkin disease) or of the so-called lymphocytic and histiocytic cells (of NLPHD) and their variants in an 'appropriate background' of reactive, non-neoplastic bystander cells. The tumour cells as such comprise only a minority of the cellular infiltrate. The appropriate inflammatory background in the infiltrate, that is required for the diagnosis, varies widely in its structure and cytological composition and may contain variable numbers of small lymphocytes, eosinophils, histiocytes, plasma cells, neutrophils and epithelioid cells.

Nodular Lymphocyte Predominance Hodgkin's Disease (NLPHD, Paragranuloma)

Clinical Features

NLPHD occurs in all age groups. Usually, peripheral lymph nodes are involved. Often, the disease is localized (Stage I) at diagnosis. Prognosis, usually, is excellent, but transformation to DLBL may occur.

Morphology

NLPHD or paragranuloma mainly infiltrates the lymph nodes in a vaguely nodular pattern. Within this nodular proliferation, small lymphocytes, histiocytes and the characteristic tumour cells, the so-called lymphocytic and histiocytic or 'popcorn' cells, are seen (**Figure 17a and b**). The latter are large cells with a small- to medium-sized cytoplasm and large, usually folded or lobated, nuclei with a vesicular chromatin structure and a single to several medium-sized nucleoli. In some cases, they may resemble classical Hodgkin or Reed–Sternberg cells. Sometimes, the tumour cells are surrounded by (in comparison with normal lymphocytes) slightly larger cells (expressing the CD57 antigen).

Diffuse areas may be present. When these comprise more than 30% of the lymph node, the case should be classified as nodular paragranuloma with diffuse areas. Diffuse paragranulomas comprise cases in which less than 30% of the infiltrate show a nodular pattern. Rare, purely diffuse paragranulomas are virtually indistinguishable from T cell-rich B cell lymphoma. Adjacent to the tumour infiltrate, a reactive follicular hyperplasia, sometimes with progressive transformation of the germinal centres, may be present (Mason *et al.*, 1994).

Immunophenotype

The neoplastic cells in NLPHD constantly express B cell-associated antigens CD20 and CD79a and, in most cases, are positive for the J-chain. In roughly 60% of cases, the epithelial membrane antigen (EMA) is expressed; however, in contrast to classical Hodgkin disease, the tumour cells are negative for CD30, CD15 or the latent membrane protein (LMP-1) of the Epstein–Barr virus. In rare tumours, a monotypic immunoglobulin light-chain expression may be noted. In contrast to classical Hodgkin lymphoma, the small lymphocytes in the background infiltrate are also CD20-positive, and frequently coexpress IgD, like the cells of the normal perifollicular mantle zone. There is, however, a so-called 'rosetting' of CD3-positive T cells and CD57-reactive NK cells directly around the tumour cells of NLPHD (**Figure 17d**).

Genetic Features

By virtue of single-cell PCR analysis, a clonal rearrangement for IgH chain genes was found in all cases investigated. The finding of a high load of somatic mutations in the rearranged Ig genes and the presence of ongoing mutations suggests that NLPHD is derived from germinal centre B cells (Marafioti *et al.*, 1997).

Classical Hodgkin Lymphoma

Clinical Features

Hodgkin lymphoma of nodular sclerosis type is most common in adolescents and young adults. The mediastinum is frequently involved. HD, mixed cellularity is a disease of adults, and more widespread disease is common involving lymph nodes, spleen, liver or bone marrow. Lymphocyte-depleted HD is the least common variant, predominantly occurring in older patients and in HIV-infected individuals. In spite of advanced disease stages, HD of all types are curable.

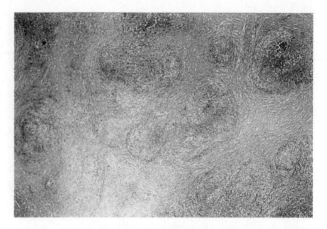

Figure 18 Classical Hodgkin lymphoma, nodular sclerosis type. Note cellular nodules surrounded by broad bands of densely packed collagen.

Morphology

Classical Hodgkin lymphoma is characterized by the presence of Hodgkin and Reed–Sternberg cells with a classical immunophenotype and an appropriate, albeit variable, background infiltrate. Several subtypes are now recognized, each presenting with a more or less unique infiltrate structure (Lukes and Butler, 1966).

Nodular sclerosing HL

Most Hodgkin lymphomas are of nodular sclerosis subtype, which is characterized by the formation of abundant collagen organized in broad bands surrounding cellular nodules (**Figure 18**). This collagen mantle shows birefringence on polarization and is PAS-positive. The thickened capsule normally is integrated into this fibrosing process, and even localized bands of fibrosis warrant the diagnosis of nodular sclerosis subtype, irrespective of the histological appearance of the remainder of the lymph node. The cellular nodules contain a sometimes wide morphological range of tumour cells, including Hodgkin, Reed–Sternberg and the so-called 'lacunar' cells. The lacuna-like appearance of these cells results from fixation artifacts. The reactive background is composed mainly of small lymphocytes and eosinophils. The so-called 'cellular phase' of nodular sclerosing Hodgkin lymphoma may be diagnosed if the capsule of the lymph node is thickened and tumour cells of lacunar type show a (frequently vague) nodular arrangement.

Classical Lymphocyte-rich Hodgkin Lymphoma, Nodular

Classical lymphocyte-rich Hodgkin lymphoma represents one end of a spectrum leading over mixed cellularity to lymphocytic depletion. In classical lymphocyte-rich Hodgkin lymphoma, the lymph-node structure is effaced and a varying degree of nodularity is present. The background infiltrate is mainly composed of lymphocytes, while eosinophils and neutrophils are only rarely found. In the (more common) nodular form the lymphocytes are mainly B cells and, sometimes, in the centre of the nodules, regressively changed germinal centres may be found (**Figure 19**). In contrast, in the diffuse form the background infiltrate is mainly composed of T lymphocytes. The distinction from NLPHD is not always possible on histological grounds alone; however, immunohistochemistry will as a rule help in this distinction.

Mixed Cellularity

This subtype is histologically intermediate between classical lymphocyte-rich Hodgkin lymphoma and lymphocytic depletion (**Figures 20 and 21**). The diagnosis in fact is made whenever in a case of Hodgkin lymphoma the criteria for the other subtypes are not fulfilled. Partial or interfollicular involvement of the lymph node, by definition, is classified as mixed cellularity.

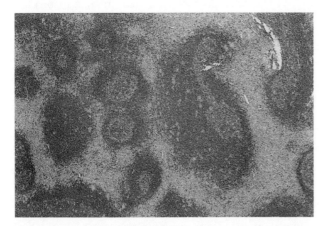

Figure 19 Classical Hodgkin lymphoma, lymphocyte-rich, nodular. The overview shows large tumour nodules with sometimes preserved germinal centres. Tumour cells are vaguely seen in the broadened follicular mantle zone.

Lymphocytic Depletion

Lymphocyte-depleted type Hodgkin lymphoma is rare (< 5% of all cases) and the diagnosis is often made in relapse or in patients with the acquired immunodeficiency syndrome. In lymphocytic depletion, there may be a diffuse fibrosis with the presence of disorderly orientated reticulin fibres that tend to surround individual cells. The overall cellularity is low, and diagnostic Reed–Sternberg cells may be rare. In the reticular variant, the key feature is the presence of numerous bizzare and anaplastic-appearing Hodgkin and Reed–Sternberg cells together with a depletion of small lymphocytes.

Immunohistochemistry

No significant differences in antigen expression are encountered between the subtypes of classical Hodgkin lymphoma. The tumour cells typically are positive for CD30, and in most of the cases also express CD15 and vimentin. In roughly 20% of the cases, CD20 may be positive, but usually is expressed only weakly and inconsistently in a part of the tumour cells. Other B cell-associated antigens (CD79a, J-chain) are absent. In 10–50% of cases (depending on the histological subtype), the latent membrane protein (LMP-1) of the Epstein–Barr virus is expressed. The positivity of the tumour cells for CD3 or cytotoxic proteins (TIA-1 or perforin) is a rarity. The cellular background is composed (with the exception of nodular lymphocyte-rich classical Hodgkin lymphoma) mainly of CD3-positive T cells and histiocytes. In contrast to paragranuloma, cytotoxic proteins are expressed in a significant number of the small background lymphocytes (**Table 7**).

Genetic Features

The cellular derivation of Hodgkin and Reed–Sternberg cells lymphoma remained enigmatic until, in 1994, by the use of single-cell PCR studies, both the clonal nature and

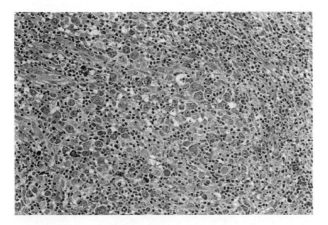

Figure 20 Classical Hodgkin lymphoma, mixed cellularity. Numerous Hodgkin and Reed–Sternberg cells are seen in a reactive background infiltrate.

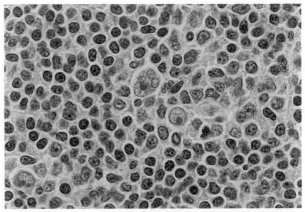

Figure 21 Classical Hodgkin lymphoma. One Hodgkin cell and one multinucleate Reed-Sternberg cell are seen embedded in a reactive background infiltrate.

Table 7   Antigen expression patterns in classical Hodgkin lymphoma (cHL), T cell-rich B cell lymphoma (TCRBCL) and nodular lymphocyte-predominant Hodgkin lymphoma (NLPHL)

	Tumour cells						Background	
	CD30	CD15	CD20	CD79a	J-chain	Vimentin	TIA/CD57 ratio	B cells
cHL	+	+/−	Weak, uneven	−	−	+	↑	↓
TCRBCL	−	−	+	+/−	−/+	−	↑	↓↓
NLPHL	−/+	−	+	−/+	+/−	−	↓	↑

B lymphocyte origin of Reed–Sternberg cells was revealed in over 95% of cases (Küppers *et al.*, 1994). More recent results indicate that a very small proportion of cases may actually be derived from T cells. As in nodular lymphocyte predominant Hodgkin's disease, the immunoglobulin genes in classical Hodgkin lymphoma are highly mutated, giving evidence for a germinal centre origin of the tumour cells. Although Hodgkin and Reed–Sternberg cells are derived from B cells, they are not able to express immunoglobulins. It has been suggested that this perplexing phenomenon was due to so-called 'crippling' mutations in Ig genes. However, more recent results suggest that the Ig promotor region is not active, thereby preventing the transcription of the Ig genes. The expression of several antiapoptotic proteins may be the reason why the cells are able to escape from apoptosis.

The role of the Epstein–Barr virus in the pathogenesis of classical Hodgkin lymphoma still remains to be elucidated. The virus is found, with slightly varying frequencies in the subtypes recognized, in 40–60% of HL. It has been suggested that the latent membrane protein 1, that posseses transforming capacities *in vitro*, may be involved in tumorigenesis via its homologies to members of the tumour necrosis factor receptor molecules. By complexing in the cell membrane, LMP-1, therefore, is able to activate intracellular signal transduction factors ultimately leading to the activation of the nuclear factor (NF) κB. However, the presence of the EBV in the tumour cells of Hodgkin lymphoma does not necessarily imply that the virus is directly involved in the pathogensis of the neoplasm. A strong argument in favour of a pathogenetic role of EBV in HL is the monoclonal origin of the virus in the tumour cells. Large population studies showed that patients who developed Hodgkin lymphoma had abnormally high titres of some anti-EBV antibodies in prediagnostic sera, indicating that infection occurred prior to clonal expansion of the tumour and was not just due to a manifestation of immunosuppression secondary to the emergence of the neoplastic clone.

Lymphoproliferations in Immunologically Compromised Patients

Lymphoproliferative disorders in the immunosuppressed patient represent a spectrum of diseases different from sporadic lymphomas. The pathogenetic concepts involved result in problems of classification and diagnosis of these tumours and also of treatment options (Knowles, 1999).

Post-transplantation Lymphoproliferative Disorders (PTLDs)

In PTLDs, the allograft type and immunosuppressive regimen applied are most important. The incidence of PTLDs is approximately 1% and 2% for renal and hepatic transplants, respectively, whereas it varies from 2 to 10% for heart, combined heart–lung and bone-marrow transplants. These differences, however, appear to be more related to different degrees of immunosuppression than to the organ itself. With increasing organ mass and tissue type, entirely different factors become more important, such as the number of allogeneic passenger lymphocytes, frequency of allograft rejection and graft versus host disease. PTLD in conventional immunosuppression (antilymphocyte immunoglobulin and azathioprin) is about 1–5% in cardiac transplants. After the introduction of cyclosporin A, initially much higher frequencies of PTLD were observed (9–13%). More recently, as a result of dose reduction and serum level monitoring of the drug, lower frequencies in the range 1–2% are observed.

The majority of PTLDs occur shortly after transplantation, in most instances at a mean time of 6 months, within the first 2 years after transplantation. However, a small but steady number of PTLDs continue to occur throughout the following years. Whereas EBV-positive cases are seen early after transplantation, EBV-negative PTLDs and T cell lymphomas tend to occur in the later post-transplant period.

Clinical Features

There is considerable variability in clinical presentations of PTLDs. Very often the disease starts, especially in younger patients, with mononucleosis-like symptoms (tonsillar enlargement, cervical lymphadenopathy), rapidly transforming into general lymphadenopathy. About half of these patients in a survey of the University of Minnesota took a rapidly fatal course whereas in the other half the disease was self-limiting. Another type of presentation consists of a localized tumour mass occuring very often at extranodal sites, such as the gastrointestinal tract, the central nervous system or unusual sites (liver, lung, oral cavity, skin or uterus). Involvement of the allograft itself is rare (10–15%) and in some cases was related to donor cell origin of the tumour. Donor cell origin is especially frequent in bone marrow transplantation and increased when T cell depletion of the graft had been performed in order to avoid graft-versus-host disease. Most other PTLDs are of host cell origin representing a reactivation or *de novo* infection by EBV.

PTLDs were considered in the early days as frankly malignant disease and treated (mostly unsuccessfully) by antitumoral combined cytostatic regimens. This view was challenged when spontaneous regression of tumours was reported upon reduction or discontinuation of immuno-suppressive therapy. A favourable response is seen in 31% of PTLDs. Early onset lesions and polymorphous rather than monomorphous lymphoproliferations are more likely to respond. However, exact predictive diagnosis has to take into account morphological, molecular and karyotypic as well as virological data.

Pathological Classification of Post-transplant Lymphoproliferative Disorders

Early lesions of mononucleosis-like type or plasmacytic hyperplasias are terms used for PTLD occuring early after organ transplantation (mean time 3–4 months) and fre-quently involving adenoids, tonsils and superficial nodes, but also extranodal localizations, in children or young adults. The histological pattern is overlapping, showing plasmacytic hyperplasia without destruction of the under-lying architecture of lymphoid or organ tissues. Plasma cells do not show light chain restriction. EBV can be demonstrated in most instances showing either a poly-clonal, oligoclonal or monoclonal type of infection. These lesions tend to regress spontaneously or after reduction of immunosuppressive treatment, but rarely can progress to higher histological grades, accompanied by more aggres-sive clinical behaviour or even be fatal, as can infectious mononucleosis in other conditions.

Polymorphic PTLDs are invasive and destructive lesions leading to the effacement of the underlying normal architecture of lymphoid tissues or involved organs. In con-trast to sporadic B cell lymphomas, these tumour masses consist of a mixture of cell types including the full range of B cell maturation from centroblasts to immunoblasts and plasma cells and a background inflammatory component of different T cell populations. There may be areas of necrosis, which may be prominent in some cases. The proliferative activity is high.

Immunophenotyping on paraffin sections reveals monotypic light-chain restriction and immunoglobulin secretion in some cases, but no immunoglobulin production in others. EBV may be detected in most cases, the antigen expression profile suggesting EBV latency type 2 or 3.

Polymorphic PTLDs may show partial or complete regression after discontinuation of immunosuppressive treatment or resolution with surgery, radiation therapy or chemotherapy less frequently. Other cases may progress in spite of therapy.

Most cases of **monomorphic PTLD** fulfil diagnostic criteria used for the designation of aggressive lymphomas on morphological grounds, and show a B cell phenotype. The designation of these lymphomas should follow the rules of the WHO classification, but include the term PTLD for clinical and prognostic reasons. Grossly, monomorphic PTLDs are aggressive and invasive tumours destroying the architecture of the lymph node or extranodal tissues. Most frequently these lymphomas are composed of large trans-formed immunoblasts or plasmablasts, with little or no differentiation toward plasma cells. The term also may be used in cases containing bizarre or multinucleated cells. Immunophenotyping reveals B cell-associated antigens in most cases. CD20 may be negative in plasmablastic lym-phoma or anaplastic myeloma which, however, are rarely seen as PTLD. If immunoglobulin production is detected, light-chain restriction is present. The proliferative fraction is high. Most monomorphic PTLDs representing malignant non-Hodgkin lymphomas or multiple myelomas after organ transplantation tend to occur in a higher age group (after the age of 50 years) and do not regress after discontinuation of immunosuppressive treatment or progress despite cyto-static treatment.

EBV Infection

EBV infection is detected in 90% of PTLDs by EBER *in situ* hybridization techniques. Plasmacytic hyperplasias and early lesions of mononucleosis-like type usually show polyclonal EBV infection patterns involving increased numbers of EBV-positive small lymphocytes or activated blast cells. Polymorphic PTLD and monomorphic PTLD show monoclonal EBV integration and a positive result of EBER *in situ* hybridization in most if not all tumour cells. These cases usually also show LMP1 expression in at least some tumour cells, but in fewer cells than detected by EBER *in situ* hybridization. Half of the cases of poly-morphic PTLD also express EBNA2, suggesting that these cases are latency type 3, while the others are of latency type 2. Latency type 1, lacking the expression of EBNA2 and LMP1, is seen in some of the malignant lymphomas or monomorphic PTLDs, respectively.

Clonality Studies

Using Southern blot hybridization techniques or PCR-based immunoglobulin heavy-chain CDRIII region amplification, early lesions of PTLDs usually show a polyclonal smear or, rarely, a weak clonal predominance. In polymorphic PTLD, clonality analyses usually demon-strates a monoclonal or oligoclonal result. The investiga-tion of multiple tumour nodules within one organ (e.g.

Table 8   Molecular genetic features in PTLD

Category	IgH clonality	EBV/clonality	Oncogene/tumour-suppressor gene alterations	Clinical course
Plasma cell hyperplasia	Polyclonal	Absent Polyclonal Clonal	Absent	Non-aggressive
Polymorphic PTLD	Monoclonal	Clonal	Absent	?
Monomorphic PTLD	Monoclonal	Clonal	Yes	Aggressive

gastrointestinal tract) may show different clones in each lesion. Malignant (monomorphic) lymphoma occuring as PTLD harbour monoclonal tumour cell populations (Knowles *et al.*, 1995).

Genetic Alterations

The status of proto-oncogenes and tumour suppressor genes has been intensively studied. Early lesions and polymorphic PTLD characteristically lack evidence of *BCL1*, *BCL2*, c-*MYC*, *RAS* and *p53* gene alterations, whereas monomorphic lymphomas after organ transplantation consistently contain structural alterations of one or more proto-oncogenes or tumour suppressor genes, most commonly involving *RAS*, c-*MYC* or *p53* genes. More recently, analysis of the *BCL-6* gene in these tumours revealed frequent mutations, the presence of which strongly predicted shorter survival and refractoriness to reduced immunosuppression and/or surgical excision (Cesarman *et al.*, 1998). An overview on these findings is summarized in **Table 8**.

Rare types of post-transplantation lymphoproliferative disorders include EBV-negative B cell-related PTLDs, classical Hodgkin lymphoma and peripheral T cell lymphoma.

Iatrogenic Non-transplantation-induced Lymphoproliferative Disorders

Clinical Features

Iatrogenic non-transplantation-induced lymphoproliferative disorders have been recognized only very recently. The most characteristic clinical setting for the occurrence of these disorders is represented by methotrexate treatment in rheumatological diseases, especially rheumatoid arthritis. In contrast to solid organ transplant recipients, where the occurrence of PTLD is considered to be related to the kind and severity of medical immunosuppression, it is usually not known whether and to what extent a state of immunosuppression exists or is active in patients with rheumatoid arthritis receiving methotrexate therapy. Clearly, not all malignant lymphomas that occur in patients with rheumatological diseases are related to their immunomodulatory treatment.

Lymphoproliferative disorders related to immunosuppressive or immunomodulatory treatment appear to comprise only a minority of lymphomas in these patients. Most lymphomas that occur are likely coincidental with rheumatological disease and not the effect of immunosuppression. Most lymphomas in patients with rheumatoid arthritis, similar to other autoimmune diseases, represent malignant lymphomas that are EBV negative and in their histology are similar to lymphomas seen in patients without rheumatological disease. Most iatrogenic lymphoproliferative disorders are EBV positive.

Morphology

The morphological features of iatrogenic lymphoproliferative disorders reported are seen in three main categories: **Atypical polymorphous lymphoproliferative disorders** occurring in lymph nodes or extranodal tissues tend to efface the organ architecture and contain a mixture of lymphoid cells at various stages of activation and maturation. These cases show clonal immunoglobulin gene rearrangement or light-chain restriction. Nevertheless, many of them regress after discontinuation of immunosuppressive treatment.

Diffuse aggressive non-Hodgkin lymphomas cytologically represent different types of diffuse large B-cell lymphomas either of large cell or of Burkitt-like type. Some of these proliferations reveal pleomorphic features and focally show Reed–Sternberg-like cells. EBV may be detected in almost all cases by EBER *in situ* hybridization in most, if not all, tumour cells.

Hodgkin lymphoma and lymphoproliferations resembling Hodgkin lymphoma show the most intriguing morphology in the group of iatrogenic lymphoproliferative disorders. The diagnosis of these tumors is difficult, since features of Hodgkin disease may be evident in one place and diffuse large B cell lymphoma in others. The immunophenotype of Hodgkin cells very often is positive for CD20 and CD30, which renders the distinction between classical Hodgkin lymphoma and lymphoproliferations resembling Hodgkin disease in this setting difficult. Hodgkin disease in iatrogenic lymphoproliferative disorders may show diagnostic features of mixed cellularity or nodular sclerosing variant of classical Hodgkin lymphoma including a typical phenotype of Hodgkin cells. The exact diagnosis requires morphological, immunophenotypic and detailed studies on EBV status, including the definition of the latency type.

'Sporadic' Atypical Lymphoproliferative Disorders

As has been pointed out, the pathological features of lymphoproliferative disorders after organ transplantation and/or immunomodulatory treatment differ from sporadic cases of malignant lymphoma. However, their morphology is by no means specific. Therefore, similar, if not identical, cases are also seen without a clinical report of the respective conditions. EBV is also found in 5–10% of aggressive non-Hodgkin lymphomas in the general population and polymorphic lymphoproliferations associated with EBV with or without Hodgkin disease-like features are definitely found outside manifest immunosuppression or immunomodulatory treatment.

Therefore, the question is still unresolved as to whether PTLD and iatrogenic lymphoproliferations represent the well-defined, quasi-experimental condition allowing one to recognize a specific morphology of immunodeficiency-related lymphomas and lymphoproliferative disorders which may also be seen in sporadic, less well-defined states of immunodeficiency or postchemotherapy immunosuppression in elderly patients predisposing to a so-far undefined type of 'sporadic' lymphoproliferative disorder.

REFERENCES

Alizadeh, A. A. *et al.* (2000). Distinct types of diffuse large cell lymphoma identified by gene expressing profiling. *Nature*, **403**, 503–511.

Armitage, J. O. and Weisenburger, D. D. (1998). New approach to classifying non-Hodgkin's lymphomas: clinical features of the major histologic subtypes. Non-Hodgkin's Lymphoma Classification Project. *Journal of Clinical Oncology*, **16**, 2780–2795

Cesarman, E. *et al.* (1998). BCL-6 gene mutations in posttransplantation lymphoproliferative disorders predict response to therapy and clinical outcome. *Blood*, **92**, 2294–2302.

Chan, J. K. (1999). Peripheral T-cell and NK-cell neoplasms. An integrated approach to diagnosis. *Modern Pathology*, **12**, 177–199.

Harris, N. L. *et al.* (1999). World Health Organization classification of neoplastic diseases of the hematopoietic and lymphoid tissues: report of the Clinical Advisory Committee meeting – Airlie House, Virginia, November 1997. *Journal of Clinical Oncology*, **17**, 3835–3849.

Harris, N. L. *et al.* (2000). Lymphoma classification – from controversy to consensus: the R. E.A. L. and WHO classification of lymphoid neoplasms. *Annals of Oncology*, **11**, Supplement 1, 3–10.

Harris, N. L. *et al.* (1994). A revised European–American classification of lymphoid neoplasms: a proposal from the International Lymphoma Study Group. *Blood*, **84**, 1361–1392.

Jaffe, E. S. *et al.* (1998). World Health Organization classification of lymphomas: a work in progress. *Annals of Oncology*, **9**, 25–31.

Knowles, D. M. *et al.* (1995). Correlative morphologic and molecular genetic analysis demonstrates three distinct categories of posttransplantation lymphoproliferative disorders. *Blood*, **85**, 552–565.

Knowles, D. M. (1999). Immunodeficiency-associated lymphoproliferative disorders. *Modern Pathology*, **12**, 200–217.

Küppers, R. *et al.* (1994). Hodgkin disease: Hodgkin and Reed–Sternberg cells picked from histological sections show clonal immunoglobulin gene rearrangements and appear to be derived from B cells at various stages of development. *Proceedings of the National Academy of Sciences of the USA*, **91**, 10962–10966.

Lennert, K. and Feller, A. C. (1992). *Histopathology of Non-Hodgkin's Lymphomas* (*Based on the Updated Kiel Classification*). (Springer, Berlin).

Lukes, R. J. and Butler, J. J. (1966). Natural history of Hodgkin's disease is related to its pathologic picture. *Cancer*, **19**, 317–344.

Marafioti, T. *et al.* (1997). Origin of nodular lymphocyte-predominant Hodgkin's disease from a clonal expansion of highly mutated germinal-center B cells. *New England Journal of Medicine*, **337**, 453–458.

Mason, D. Y. *et al.* (1994). Nodular lymphocyte predominance Hodgkin's disease. A distinct clinicopathologic entity. *American Journal of Surgery and Pathology*, **18**, 526–530.

Non-Hodgkin's Lymphoma Pathologic Classification Project (1982). National Cancer Institute sponsored study of classifications of non-Hodgkin's lymphomas: summary and description of a working formulation for clinical usage. *Cancer*, **49**, 2112–2135.

Non-Hodgkin's Classification Project (1997). A clinical evaluation of the International Lymphoma Study Group classification of non-Hodgkin's lymphoma. *Blood*, **89**, 3909–3918.

Rosati, S. and Frizzera, G. (1997). Pseudoneoplastic lesions of the hematolymphoid system. In: Wick, M. R., *et al.* (eds), *Pathology of Pseudoneoplastic Lesions*. 449–544 (Lippincott-Raven, Philadelphia).

Shipp, M. A. *et al.* (1993). A predictive model for aggressive non-Hodgkin's lymphoma. The International Non-Hodgkin's Lymphoma Prognostic Factors Project. *New England Journal of Medicine*, **329**, 987–994.

Stansfeld, A. G. *et al.* (1988). Updated Kiel classification for lymphomas. *Lancet*, **i**, 292–293 and 603.

FURTHER READING

Döhner, H. *et al.* (1999). Chromosome aberrations in chronic lymphocytic leukemia: reassessment based on molecular cytogenetic analysis. *Journal of Molecular Medicine*, **77**, 266–281.

Goossens, T. *et al*. (1998). Frequent occurrence of deletions and duplications during somatic hypermutation: implications for oncogene translocations and heavy chain disease. *Proceedings of the National Academy of Sciences of the USA*, **95**, 2463–2468.

Heim, S. and Mitelman, F. (1995). *Cancer Cytogenetics*, 2nd edn. (Wales, New York).

Hockenbery, D. *et al*. (1990). Bcl-2 is an inner mitochondrial membrane protein that blocks programmed cell death. *Nature*, **348**, 334–336.

Mason, D. Y. *et al*. (1998). Nuclear localization of the nucleophosmin–anaplastic lymphoma kinase is not required for malignant transformation. *Cancer Research*, **58**, 1057–1062.

Müller-Hermelink, H. K. and Greiner, A. (1998). Molecular analysis of human immunoglobulin heavy chain variable genes (IgVH) in normal and malignant B cells [comment]. *American Journal of Pathology*, **153**, 1341–1346.

Pulford, K. *et al*. (1997). Detection of anaplastic lymphoma kinase (ALK) and nucleolar protein nucleophosmin (NPM)–ALK proteins in normal and neoplastic cells with the monoclonal antibody ALK1. *Blood*, **89**, 1394–1404.

Rüdiger, T. *et al*. (1998). Differential diagnosis between classic Hodgkin's lymphoma, T-cell-rich B-cell lymphoma, and paragranuloma by paraffin immunohistochemistry. *American Journal of Surgical Pathology*, **22**, 1184–1191.

Johansson, B. *et al*. (1995). Cytogenetic evolution patterns in non-Hodgkin's lymphoma. *Blood*, **86**, 3905–3914.

Chapter 47

Bones

Lawrence M. Weiss

City of Hope National Medical Center, Duarte, CA, USA

CONTENTS

- Introduction
- Normal Development and Structure
- Epidemiology and Aetiology
- Pathology of Benign Tumours
- Giant Cell Tumour of Bones
- Osteosarcoma
- Chondrosarcoma
- Ewing Sarcoma/Peripheral Neuroectodermal Tumour of Bone (PNET)
- Chordoma
- Malignant Fibrous Histiocytoma and Fibrosarcoma
- Adamantinoma
- Angiosarcoma
- Multiple Myeloma
- Malignant Lymphoma Presenting in Bone
- Langerhans Cell Histiocytosis

INTRODUCTION

Bone tumours are relatively uncommon, but comprise an interesting group of neoplasms (**Table 1**). As a whole, these tumours occur in a younger age group than most other tumours, particularly frequent at the time of maximal bone growth in the teens. Recent advances in modern chemotherapeutic regimens have significantly improved the prognosis in selected types. The chapter will summarize the pertinent pathological features of the most common types of bone tumours. Excellent specialized tests are recommended for rare entities not covered in this chapter (Dahlin and Unni, 1986; Fechner and Mills, 1993; Unni, 1996; Dorfman and Czerniak, 1998).

NORMAL DEVELOPMENT AND STRUCTURE

The bones are derived from the mesenchyme of the mesoderm. They can be classified into three main types: the flat bones, including the skull, scapula, clavicle, pelvis and sternum; the tubular bones, including most of the bones of the extremities and the ribs; and epiphysioid bones, including the carpal (wrist) and tarsal (ankle) bones and the patella. The tubular bones grow until adulthood by virtue of a cartilaginous growth plate located near the ends

Table 1 Classification of common neoplasms of bone

Benign
   Osteoid osteoma
   Osteoblastoma
   Osteochondroma
   Enchondroma
   Chondroblastoma
   Chondromyxoid fibroma
   Fibrous dysplasia
   Osteofibrous dysplasia
   Nonossifying fibroma
   Benign fibrous histiocytoma
   Haemangioma/lymphangioma/angiomatosis

Locally aggressive
   Giant cell tumour

Malignant
   Osteosarcoma
   Chondrosarcoma
   Ewing sarcoma
   Chordoma
   Malignant fibrous histiocytoma
   Fibrosarcoma
   Adamantinoma
   Angiosarcoma
   Multiple myeloma and plasmacytoma of bone
   Malignant lymphoma
   Langerhans cell histiocytosis

of the bones. The region between the growth plate and the end of the bone is called the epiphysis, the region around the growth plate is called the metaphysis and the region between the metaphyses is known as the diaphysis. Different bone tumours often have distinct predilections for specific regions of the bone.

Mature bone is a combination of two main types of bone, including cortical bone, dense bone present at the exterior, and trabecular bone, a looser meshwork of bone enclosing the medullary cavity containing the bone marrow. The matrix of bone is composed of collagen, proteoglycans and calcium-containing hydroxyapatite. The cellular composition of bone includes osteoblasts, the specialized cells responsible for the synthesis of the bony matrix; osteocytes, osteoblasts that have been incorporated into the bony matrix and responsible for the maintenance and metabolic activity of bone; and osteoclasts, multinucleated cells of monocyte/macrophage lineage responsible for the resorption and remodelling of bone. Cartilage is present at the joint surfaces and the immature growth plate. It consists of S-100 protein-expressing, specialized cells called chondrocytes embedded in an avascular matrix rich in proteoglycans. The external lining of the bone is a fibrous membrane called the periosteum.

The tubular bones are usually formed by a process called endochondral ossification, in which a cartilaginous intermediary forms a scaffold for the deposition of bone. Growth of the bone occurs at the cartilaginous growth plate by calcification of the cartilaginous matrix accompanied by apoptosis of chondrocytes and osteoblastic differentiation, with conversion of the cartilage to immature bone. Flat bones are usually formed by a process called intramembranous ossification, in which fetal mesenchymal cells directly differentiate into osteoblasts without a pre-existing cartilage matrix. Immature bone that lacks a calcified matrix is known as osteoid. The first bone formed lacks normal organisation and is called woven bone. In time, woven bone is organized into concentric layers surrounding blood vessels (haversion canals) forming the osteons of mature lamellar bone.

EPIDEMIOLOGY AND AETIOLOGY

Bone tumours are relatively rare tumours, accounting for about 0.2% of all malignancies, or about 1 in 100 000 individuals (Dorfman and Czerniak, 1995). There has been no discernible trend toward a change in the frequency in recent years. In general, there is a bimodal age distribution, with one peak occurring in adolescence (at the time of greatest bone growth) and a second peak in patients older than 60 years. There is a slightly higher incidence of bone tumours in whites than blacks, and in males than females. However, each specific bone tumour has its own characteristic age, race and sex predilections. Since bone tumours are so rare, there are no effective programmes for screening and prevention.

Most bone tumours have no known aetiology. A small percentage of bone tumours are due to genetic predisposition. There are several well-known syndromes in which specific bone tumours are markedly increased in frequency. Multiple hereditary exostoses is a rare autosomal dominant disorder in which patients develop multiple osteochondromas associated with bone deformities of the affected sites. Some families with this syndrome have a genetic defect at a gene called EXT-1 present on chromosome 8q24.1 (Ahn et al., 1995). Other families have a different genetic defect at a gene called EXT-2 on chromosome 11p11-13, while still other families may have an abnormality on chromosome 19 (Strickens et al., 1996). About 20% of patients develop secondary malignancies, usually a chondrosarcoma arising in a previous osteochondroma. Ollier disease is a rare, nonhereditary congenital disorder characterized by multiple enchondromas. Malignant transformation, again usually with chondrosarcoma, occurs in about 20–25% of patients with Ollier disease (Goodman et al., 1984). Mafucci syndrome is similar to Ollier disease in the development of multiple enchondromas, but patients also have co-existing soft tissue angiomas (Bean, 1958). The incidence of complicating chondrosarcoma is even higher in these patients, at approximately 50%; in addition, a variety of other extraskeletal neoplasms have also been reported. Chondrosarcoma may also arise as a rare complication of solitary enchondromas and osteochondromas.

Patients with Li–Fraumeni syndrome carry a germline mutation in the TP53 gene, leading to an increase in the frequency of numerous neoplasms, including osteosarcoma. In addition, families carrying mutations in the retinoblastoma (RB) gene also have a greatly increased risk of osteosarcoma. In addition, there may be a familial osteosarcoma syndrome, independent of the above two disorders. Finally, Rothmun–Thomson syndrome is an extremely rare syndrome characterized by skin, endocrine and neural abnormalities, in which there is an increased incidence of squamous cell carcinoma of the skin and osteosarcoma, which may be multicentric (Vennos et al., 1992).

Nongenetic aetiological factors include pre-existing Paget disease of bone, which predisposes to a variety of high-grade sarcomas; osteomyelitis with sinus tract formation, which predisposes to squamous cell carcinoma; bone infarcts, which predispose to bone sarcoma, usually malignant fibrous histiocytoma; and radiation injury, which predisposes to a variety of bone sarcomas. Finally, some investigators have suggested that Kaposi sarcoma-associated human herpesvirus (HHV)-8 may be present in bone marrow antigen presenting cells in cases of multiple myeloma (Berenson and Vescio, 1999). HHV-8 produces viral interleukin-8, which may act as a stimulator of plasma cells, the precursor cells of multiple myeloma.

However, the issue is highly controversial at present, as the findings are inconsistent within the numerous laboratories that have attempted to confirm the original findings.

PATHOLOGY OF BENIGN TUMOURS

Osteoid osteoma and osteoblastoma are the two main benign bone-forming tumours (Healy and Ghelman, 1986). Osteoid osteoma usually occurs in patients between the ages of 5 and 25 years, with a male predilection. It is usually less than 1 cm in size and typically occurs in the tubular bones in the extremities. Histologically, bone formation by benign osteoblasts is seen (**Figure 1; see colour plate section**). Osteoblastoma usually occurs in patients between the ages of 10 and 40 years, with a male predilection. It is usually larger than 1.5 cm in size and typically occurs in the vertebral column. The histological features are very similar to those seen in osteoid osteoma. Osteochondroma is more a hamartomatous (developmental) anomaly than a true neoplasm (Milgram, 1983). It is a common lesion that has a peak incidence between 10 and 30 years of age, with a male predilection. It typically occurs on the surface of the metaphyseal region of the large tubular bones of the extremities. Pathologically, there is an external benign cartilage cap, usually less than 1 cm in thickness, with an underlying support of benign trabecular bone (**Figure 2; see colour plate section**). The histological features resemble the normal sequence of endochondral ossification.

Enchondroma, chondroblastoma and chondromyxoid fibroma are the three most common benign tumours of cartilage. Enchondroma is common neoplasm that occurs in patients of a wide age range, with no clear sex predilection (Mirra *et al.*, 1985). It usually occurs in the medullary cavity of tubular bones, particularly in the hands and feet. Clinically, it is usually unassociated with pain (in contrast to some other tumours of cartilage including chondrosarcoma), and histologically, it is composed of mature cartilage with a lobular architecture and containing chondrocytes with small nuclei that lack atypia (**Figure 3; see colour plate section**). Chondroblastoma is an uncommon neoplasm that typically occurs in patients between the age of 10 and 20 years, with a male predilection (Dahlin and Ivins, 1972). It usually occurs in the epiphysis of the large tubular bones of the extremities. It is often associated with pain clinically, and histologically consists of varying numbers of chondroblasts, chondrocytes and multinucleated giant cells in a matrix that varies from immature to mature cartilage, often with a distinctive 'chicken wire' pattern of calcification (**Figure 4; see colour plate section**). Chondromyxoid fibroma is a relatively rare neoplasm that typically occurs in patients between the age of 10 and 30 years, with a male predilection (Rahimi *et al.*, 1972). It usually occurs in the metaphysis of the large tubular bones of the extremities. It is usually associated with pain, and histologically shows areas of immature myxoid mesenchymal tissue with variable areas showing primitive cartilage formation.

Fibrous dysplasia is a dysplastic disorder of bone characterized by the inability to form mature lamellar bone (Reed, 1963). It occurs in two major forms. The monostotic form occurs as a single focus in one bone, while the polyostostic form occurs as multiple foci in several bones, either unilateral in one area (monomelic) or widespread (polymelic). The Albright–McCune syndrome is the combination of polyostotic fibrous dysplaia, with endocrine abnormalies (typically precocious puberty in females). Mutations of signal-transducing G proteins may underly this syndrome (Shenker *et al.*, 1994). Histologically, fibrous dysplasia displays abnormal immature woven bone with an intervening stroma of spindle cells. Osteofibrous dysplasia is a rare lesion that occurs in infants and children in the bones of the lower leg that histologically has a close resemblance to fibrous dysplasia.

Nonossifying fibroma (fibrous cortical defect) is a very common lesion that typically occurs in patients aged between 5 and 15 years, without a distinct sex predilection. It is often an incidental finding discovered during a radiological study, and usually occurs in the metaphyses of the long tubular bones. Histologically, a bland but cellular spindle cell proliferation is seen (**Figure 5; see colour plate section**). Left alone, most lesions regress spontaneously, evidence that nonossifying fibroma probably represents a developmental disorder due to incomplete ossification. Benign fibrous histiocytoma is a rare neoplasm that occurs in patients of all ages, with no sex predilection (Roessner *et al.*, 1981). It most commonly involves the pelvis and the ribs. The histological features are identical with those seen in nonossifying fibroma, with the distinction made on its clinical and radiological features; however, benign fibrous histiocytoma probably represents a true neoplasm.

Haemangioma is a benign tumour of blood vessels (Wold *et al.*, 1982). It most often occurs in adults, and is most commonly seen in the skull or the spine. Grossly, they are red–brown, well-demarcated, medullary lesions. Histologically, they are composed of capillary-sized (capillary haemangioma) or slightly larger (cavernous haemangioma) vessels lined by bland endothelial cells. Mixtures of the two patterns are most frequently seen. Lymphangioma is a rare benign tumour of lymphatics. Histologically, it consists of a dilated, thin-walled lymphatic filled with a proteinaceous fluid. Both haemangiomas and lymphangiomas may be multiple. Regional angiomatosis involves one or several bones in a single anatomical region, whereas disseminated (cystic) angiomatosis affects multiple sites within bones of the trunk. Multiple lymphangiomas are often asscoiated with soft tissue lymphangioma or systemic lymphangiomatosis. A rare sporadic syndrome known as Gorham disease is an aggressive form of angiomatosis in which massive osteo-lysis occurs which eventually effaces the normal bone architecture. The disease may stabilize or, in some cases, lead to death.

GIANT CELL TUMOUR OF BONES

In contrast to the preceding tumours, giant cell tumour of bone is a locally aggressive neoplasm with a high pro-pensity for local invasion, frequent recurrence and rare pulmonary metastases (Dahlin, 1985). It usually occurs in patients between 20 and 40 years of age, without a sex predilection, and it may have an increased incidence in Chinese patients. It typically affects the epiphyses of the large tubular bones (**Figure 6; see colour plate sec-tion**). Histologically, one sees sheets of plump, spindle cells in which numerous multinucleated giant cells are evenly interspersed (**Figure 7; see colour plate sec-tion**). The giant cells are distinctive and may have up to 100 nuclei, which are said to resemble the nuclei of the mononuclear spindle cells. The lineage of the mono-nuclear and giant cells is not yet entirely clear. The giant cells show some features of the monocyte/macrophage lineage, similar to benign osteoclasts, while the mono-nuclear cells have suggestive but not definite features of monocyte/macrophage lineage. Furthermore, it is not clear which cell population (or whether both) represents the neoplastic element. A high proportion of giant cell tumours are aneuploid, and the majority of cases show chromosome aberrations, particularly telomeric fusion. Patients with giant cell tumour are usually treated by thorough curettage and bone grafting. Rare cases of giant cell tumour may be complicated by secondary malig-nancy; many of these patients have received prior radio-therapy. Rarer cases represent *de novo* malignant giant cell tumour, characterized by overtly atypical histological features.

OSTEOSARCOMA

Osteosarcoma represents the most common sarcoma of bone, accounting for about one-quarter of all primary malignancies of bone and about one-third of all bone sar-comas (Dorfman and Czerniak, 1998). It is defined as a malignant mesenchymal neoplasm that shows differenti-ation towards bone formation. Osteosarcoma may be divided into the common intramedullary variant and the much rarer surface oestosarcomas. In conventional intra-medullary osteosarcoma, there is a bimodal age distribu-tion with a large peak in patients between the age of 10 and 20 years (corresponding to the peak of bone growth) and a second smaller peak in older patients; there is a male

predilection. The locations of the neoplasms in the peak in adolescence are those areas with the greatest growth rate; therefore, the metaphyses of the large tubular bones are the most commonly affected sites. On radiological studies, osteosarcomas may be lytic or sclerotic, depending on the amount of bone formation in the lesion. The borders of the lesion are usually ill-defined, and a soft tissue component is often seen. Grossly, the cut section of an osteosarcoma is variegated, with areas of bony, chondroid and soft tissue, usually with foci of haemorrhage and necrosis (**Figure 8; see colour plate section**). Histologically, a wide variety of patterns can be seen, united by the presence of malig-nant cells forming bone, even if very focal (**Figure 9; see colour plate section**) (Dahlin and Unni, 1977). Thus, although an osteoblastic pattern with obvious bone for-mation is most common, chondroblastic, fibroblastic, malignant fibrous histiocytoma-like, osteoblastoma-like, giant cell-rich, small-cell, epithelioid and telangiectatic variants occur, which have little to no impact on prognosis, but may cause great difficulty in differential diagnosis. Mixtures of several patterns are often seen in an individual case. One histological variant that may have an impact on prognosis is well-differentiated intramedullary osteo-sarcoma. Microscopically, this variant has deceptive bland cytological features combined with a relatively mature pattern of bone. Although most of the histological variants of osteosarcoma are considered to be of high grade, well-differentiated intramedullary osteosarcoma is the one exception that is of low grade when it is the only histolo-gical component present.

DNA ploidy studies have usually demonstrated highly aneuploid populations in osteosarcoma (Mandahl *et al.*, 1993). Classical cytogenetic studies confirm this, often showing grossly aneuploid karyotypes, with numerous extra chromosomes, marker chromosomes or loss of chromosomes, particularly loss of chromosomes 3, 10 and 12 (Mertens *et al.*, 1993). Even cases with a normal complement of chromosomes usually have evidence of structural rearrangements, particularly in chromosome 1q. On a molecular level, a high proportion of cases of osteosarcomas has mutations in the *RB* gene, similar to those seen in patients with familial retinoblastoma (and possibly explaining the high frequency of osteosarcoma in these patients) (Miller *et al.*, 1996). In addition, many cases also show mutations in the *TP53* gene (pos-sibly explaining the increased frequency of osteosarcoma in patients with the Li–Fraumeni syndrome). The double minute 2 (*MDM2*) gene is amplified in a high proportion of metastatic lesions, providing another mechanism of *TP53* gene inactivation in osteosarcoma (Ladanyi *et al.*, 1993).

Untreated, conventional osteosarcoma is always fatal, and if treated with surgery alone, patients with osteo-sarcoma have survival rates no higher than 10–20%. However, patients with resectable lesions and without evidence of metastases are now often treated with aggressive preoperative chemotherapy followed by complete surgical excision (often limb-sparing) followed by postoperative chemotherapy (Link *et al.*, 1986). These patients now have 5-year survivals greater than 50%. The degree of tumour necrosis observed in the resection specimen is of critical importance as patients with 90% or more necrosis in their tumours have survival rates greater than 80%, whereas patients with less than 90% necrosis have survival rates less than 20%. Other prognostic factors include the site of the neoplasm (patients with tumours in the long bones do better than those with tumours in the trunk), tumour size, the degree of aneuploidy, the status of the *TP53* gene and the status of the multidrug resistance gene (*MDRI*) (upregulation is associated with chemoresistance and decreased survival) (Baldini *et al.*, 1995). Metastases are most commonly seen in the lung and liver. Patients with solitary or even several metastases may benefit from surgical resection and adjuvant chemotherapy.

There are three main types of surface osteosarcoma: parosteal osteosarcoma, periosteal osteosarcoma and high-grade surface osteosarcoma. High-grade surface osteosarcoma is a rare type of high-grade osteosarcoma that develops on the surface of a long bone without the usual medullary involvement. Other than the lack of medullary involvement, it has an epidemiology, pathology and natural history similar to those of conventional osteosarcoma. However, parosteal osteosarcoma and periosteal osteosarcoma are distinctive low-grade forms of osteosarcoma. Parosteal osteosarcoma is a rare variant characterized by location on the surface of long tubular bones on top of the periosteum and a distinctive microscopic appearance (Unni *et al.*, 1976a). The peak incidence is between 20 and 30 years, with a female predilection. These neoplasms are characteristically located on the posterior aspect of the distal portion of the femur, just above the knee joint, or just opposite the knee joint in the posterior aspect of the proximal portion of the tibia. Grossly and radiologically, there is an exophytic (mushroom-like) growth on the periosteum, without elevation of the periosteum. Microscopically, there is a bland spindle-cell proliferation admixed with well-formed bony trabeculae. These tumours when pure have an excellent prognosis following radical surgical excision alone; however, the presence of focal areas of high-grade osteosarcoma seen microscopically is associated with a much higher incidence of metastases, and patients with such neoplasms are often treated with postoperative chemotherapy. Periosteal osteosarcoma is a rare low- to intermediate-grade variant of osteosarcoma that develops on the surface of long tubular bones, but in contrast to parosteal osteosarcoma, it occurs beneath the periosteum (Unni *et al.*, 1976b). It is also rare, with a peak occurrence between 10 and 30 years, with a female predilection. These tumours characteristically occur in proximal tibia or the distal femur. Grossly and radiologically, the lesion is present on the surface of

the cortex, with elevation of the periosteum above the tumour. This often induces periosteal reactive new bone formation as perpendicular striae within the tumour and parallel striae at the edges where it attaches to the cortex, the latter often forming a characteristic 'Codman triangle' that may be observed on radiographs. Histologically, one sees prominent cartilaginous differentiation, with only focal areas of bone formation, identifying the neoplasm as an osteosarcoma. The tumour nuclei are usually of intermediate to high grade. Patients with periosteal osteosarcoma are usually treated by radical surgical excision, with a survival of about 70%.

CHONDROSARCOMA

Chondrosarcoma of bone is the second most common sarcoma of bone, accounting for about one-fifth of all primary bone malignancies and about one-quarter of all bone sarcomas. It is defined as a malignant tumour forming cartilaginous matrix, without any evidence of bone formation directly synthesized by the neoplastic cells (Sanerkin, 1980).

Chondrosarcoma may be divided into the common conventional chondrosarcoma and the rarer dedifferentiated, clear-cell and mesenchymal variants. Conventional chondrosarcoma is a neoplasm of older adults, with an increasing incidence with increasing age; there is no sex predilection. It occurs most frequently in the pelvis, ribs and proximal extremities, and is very rare in the spine and craniofacial bones. Patients usually present with a dull aching pain (in contrast to most benign lesions of cartilage), often with local swelling due to a mass effect. Radiographically, it usually appears as a clearly demarcated radiolucent lesion with discrete calcified opacities originating in the medullary cavity. Rarely, the neoplasm may arise in a subperiosteal site on the bone surface, a variant termed juxtacortical chondrosarcoma. Grossly, chondrosarcoma usually consists of lobulated hyaline nodules, with areas of calcification, particularly at the periphery of the lobules (**Figure 10; see colour plate section**). An extraosseous component is often present, and high-grade lesions may show areas of haemorrhage and necrosis. Histologically, the hallmark of a chondrosarcoma is the presence of a hyaline cartilage matrix, usually in a lobulated architecture. There is often a variable degree of calcification in the cartilage matrix, and variable degrees of myxoid change (a loose, gelatinous matrix) may be present. Bone may be present in the lesion, but this bone arises from the cartilage via endochondral ossification, and not directly from the neoplastic cells; the presence of the latter would mandate a diagnosis of osteosarcoma.

The neoplastic cells in chondrosarcoma are chondrocytes of varying degree of atypia, graded I–III (Rosenthal *et al.*, 1984). Grade I chondrosarcomas have cells whose nuclei differ only subtly or not at all from the chondrocytes in benign enchondromas, with the distinction between the two neoplasms best made based on the radiological appearance rather than the pathological findings (**Figure 11; see colour plate section**). Grade II chondrosarcoma features chondrocytes with a greater degree of cytological atypia. Grade III chondrosarcomas are rare, but feature chondrocytes with overtly malignant nuclear features. Both grade I and grade II chondrosarcomas may progress to higher grade chondrosarcomas when recurrence (or metastasis) occurs. Similar to normal chondrocytes, the neoplastic cells in chondrosarcoma express S-100 protein.

Essentially all grade I, and many grade II, chondrosarcomas are diploid, while many grade II and essentially all grade III chondrosarcomas have an aneuploid DNA population. Classical cytogenetic studies reveal complex karyotypes, particularly in high-grade neoplasms, with nonrandom abnormalities in chromosome 1p. High-grade chondrosarcomas have been reported to have mutations or abnormal overexpression of the *TP53* gene in many cases (Nawa *et al.*, 1996).

The primary treatment for chondrosarcoma is complete surgical excision, with adjuvant chemotherapy and radiotherapy only effective in high-grade chondrosarcomas. Prognostic factors include histological grade, size, anatomical location, location (extremities better than axial skeleton), presence of aneuploidy, S-phase measurements and presence of TP53 mutation. In general, grade I chondrosarcoma has the potential to recur, but generally does not metastasize, while grade II chondrosarcoma has a higher potential to recur and metastasizes in 10–20% of cases. Overall, grade I and II chondrosarcomas have a 5-year survival greater than 80%, although the disease may recur years after treatment. Grade III chondrosarcoma is a high-grade tumour with a high propensity for recurrence and metastasis, and a 5-year survival of about 20%. Metastases most often occur in lungs and liver.

In about 10% of cases of chondrosarcoma, a phenomenon known as dedifferentiation may occur (McCarthy and Dorman, 1982). In a dedifferentiated chondrosarcoma, a grade I or grade II chondrosarcoma is associated with a distinct area of a high-grade sarcoma, with a clear demarcation between the two areas. Patients with dedifferented chondrosarcoma have similar epidemiological characteristics as those with conventional chondrosarcoma, but often give a clear history of an increase in pain, which may in about half of patients may represent a pathological fracture. The radiological and gross appearance usually shows an area characteristic of conventional chondrosarcoma with an adjacent lytic region corresponding to a fleshy mass. Microscopically, the high-grade sarcoma often has features of a malignant fibrous histiocytoma or osteosarcoma. DNA studies have shown that the low-grade component is usually diploid whereas the dedifferentiated component is aneuploid. Cytogenetic

studies have shown abnormalities common to both components, with additional abnormalities in the high-grade component, consistent with a common origin. The dedifferentiated areas consistently show overexpression of the p53 protein, consistent with mutations in the *TP53* gene (Simms *et al.*, 1995). In addition, loss of the *RB* gene and/or loss of Bcl-2 protein present in the low-grade component is seen in most cases. The prognosis of dedifferentiated chondrosarcoma is very poor, with few long-term survivors.

Clear-cell chondrosarcoma is a rare variant of chondrosarcoma with characteristic epidemiological and pathological features (Bjornsson *et al.*, 1984). It has a peak of incidence between 20 and 30 years, with a strong male predilection. It occurs most often at the proximal ends of the long tubular bones, usually extending to the articular cartilage. Radiologically, a lytic defect is usually seen. Grossly, it is usually a well-circumscribed soft, grey mass, often with focal calcifications. Histologically, one observes distinctive variants of chondrocytes with abundant clear cytoplasm in a loose cartilaginous matrix, often with varying foci of calcification. Ultrastructural and histochemical studies demonstrate that the clear cytoplasm is due to the presence of abundant glycogen. Preliminary cytogenetic studies suggest that clear-cell chondrosarcoma may possess a hypodiploid karyotype distinct from other forms of chondrosarcoma. Clear-cell chondrosarcoma is a low-grade malignancy, but metastasis may occur.

Mesenchymal chondrosarcoma is a very rare variant of chondrosarcoma that has a peak of incidence between 20 and 30 years with no sex predilection (Nakashima *et al.*, 1986). It usually affects the bones of the jaws, the vertebrae or the ribs. Radiologically, it most often is a lucent lesion with varying degrees of calcification, and grossly it is usually a well-circumscribed soft grey mass, with foci of calcification. Mesenchymal chondrosarcoma is defined by its characteristic histological appearance, with cellular areas of round to spindle cells and other areas showing cartilaginous differentiation of varying maturation, often with calcification (**Figure 12; see colour plate section**). The proportion of the two elements may vary widely from case to case. Only the cells in the cartiliginous component express S-100 protein. Mesenchymal chondrosarcoma is a high-grade neoplasm, with a propensity for recurrence and metastasis; the 5-year survival is under 50%.

EWING SARCOMA/PERIPHERAL NEUROECTODERMAL TUMOUR OF BONE (PNET)

Ewing sarcoma/PNET comprises about 15% of primary bone sarcomas. A similar neoplasm also occurs in soft tissue sites. In bone, it essentially occurs in patients under the age of 30 years with a peak between 10 and 20 years (Kissane *et al.*, 1983). There is a slight male predilection, and the neoplasm only rarely occurs in blacks. It occurs in all bones, but has a slight preference to involve the long tubular bones, pelvis and ribs; when it occurs in the ribs, it has been known as the Askin tumour. Radiologically, one sees an ill-defined, lytic lesion that involves the intramedullary spaces. When long bones are affected, the diaphysis is usually the site of origin. There is often an extensive soft tissue component. Grossly, the neoplasm is a grey–white tumour that fills the medullary cavity, permeates the cortex, grows subperiosteally and usually forms an extensive soft tissue mass (**Figure 13; see colour plate section**). Microscopically, Ewing sarcoma/PNET consists of a highly homogeneous population of small cells with a fine chromatin pattern, indiscernible nucleoli and a thin rim of cytoplasm; thus, it is the prototype of the 'small, round, blue cell tumour' (**Figure 14; see colour plate section**). The mitotic rate is generally high, and there is usually a high number of apoptotic cells. In a subset of cases, the cells focally form rosettes around stroma, a pattern termed the Homer–Wright rosette, which is suggestive evidence of neural differentiation. The ultrastructural correlate of the Homer–Wright rosette is the presence of cytoplasmic projections, with their organisation toward a central core. Other ultrastructural features that suggest neural differentiation in a subset of tumours is the presence of neurosecretory granules, neurofilaments or neurotubules. Ultrastructural and histochemical studies demonstrate that the cytoplasm contains abundant glycogen in most cases, whereas immunohistochemical studies demonstrate that the cell membrane has consistent (although not highly specific) strong staining for CD99, the *MIC2* gene product (Llombart-Bosch *et al.*, 1996). The neoplasm shows a spectrum of expression of neuroendocrine markers, including the chromogranin family of proteins, CD57, protein gene product 9.5 (PGP9.5), neurofilaments, S-100 protein, neuron-specific enolase and synaptophysin. Some pathologists consider neoplasms that possess two or more markers of neuroendocrine differentiation, Homer–Wright rosettes, or ultrastructural evidence of neural differentiation to represent PNET, while neoplasms that possess none or one neuroendocrine marker and lack ultrastructural markers of neural differentiation to represent Ewing sarcoma, whereas other pathologists prefer to consider all cases to represent one neoplasm regardless of the degree of neural differentiation, using the term Ewing's sarcoma/PNET for all tumours.

A characteristic molecular feature of Ewing sarcoma/PNET is the presence a translocation involving the *EWS* gene on chromosome 11 in over 90% of cases (Lopez-Terrada, 1996). A t(11;22)(q24;q12) occurs in about 90% of cases, and involves the *FLI-1* gene on chromosome 11, while the t(7;22)(p22;q12) and t(21;22)(q22;q12) are both rare, and involve the *ETV-1* gene on chromosome 7 and the *ERG-1* gene on chromosome 21, respectively. FLI-1, ETV-1 and ERG-1 are all transcription factors with DNA binding domains. In all three translocations, there is creation of a new fusion protein that uses the promoter of EWS to upregulate the transcription factor. Interestingly, a translocation has not been found in about 10% of cases of Ewing sarcoma. Additionally, there is a distinct soft tissue tumour, the small-cell desmoplastic tumour, that utilizes *EWS* in a distinct t(11;12)(p13;q12) involving another gene on chromosome 11, *WT-1*, that also codes for a transcription factor.

Ewing sarcoma/PNET is a highly aggressive tumour and, if untreated, will rapidly lead to death. Current treatment protocols include a combination of surgery, pre- and postoperative multidrug chemotherapy and radiotherapy, leading to a dramatic increase in survival, with 5-year survival rates of about 70% for those with resectable disease. Surgical removal of one to a limited number of lung metastases may improve overall survival. Prognostic factors include stage (particularly, the presence of metastases at diagnosis), tumour size, site (trunk lesions worse than extremity lesions) and the degree of necrosis in the resection specimen following preoperative chemotherapy (less than 90% necrosis worse than 90–100% necrosis). The presence or absence of neural differentiation is a controversial prognostic factor; some studies show the presence of neural differentiation to be associated with more aggressive tumours, when strict criteria are used.

CHORDOMA

Chordoma is a relatively uncommon neoplasm, representing about 5% of primary bone tumours, and about 8% of bone sarcomas. It is thought to originate from the remnants of the primitive notochord that is present in embryonal development and which forms the forerunner of the vertebral column. It occurs in all age groups, with a peak from 50 to 60 years (Dahlin and MacCarty, 1952). There is perhaps a slight male predominance and it is very rare in blacks. It almost always involves the axial skeleton, particularly the base of the skull and the sacrococcygeal region. Patients with chordoma usually present with pain or symptoms related to compression of adjacent structures. Radiologically, chordoma usually appears as a lytic lesion with scattered calcifications. Grossly, the tumours are grey–tan gelatinous multilobulated masses. Microscopically, chordomas have a resemblance to the normal notochord, with cords and nests of vacuolated cells in a myxoid matrix (**Figure 15; see colour plate section**). Immunohistochemical studies reveal differentiation similar to the cells of the primitive notochord with expression of S-100 protein and the epithelial markers keratin and epithelial membrane antigen. Cytogenetic studies have revealed abnormalities, most frequently involving chromosome 21.

Complete surgical excision is the treatment of choice. However, as these tumours frequently arise in the base of the skull, complete excision is not always feasible; in these cases, radiotherapy is often used after tumour debulking. Chordoma is a moderately aggressive tumour, marked by both recurrences and metastases, most commonly in the lung.

Dedifferentiated chordoma is a tumour consisting of conventional chordoma and a distinct adjacent component of a high-grade sarcoma, similar to that seen in dedifferentiated chondrosarcoma (Meis *et al.*, 1987). It may occur in primary or recurrent lesions of chordoma. Radiologically, the neoplasm appears as a destructive lytic lesion. Grossly, the dedifferentiated component is a fleshy mass adjacent to a gelatinous region typical of chordoma. Histologically and immunohistochemically, the sarcomatous component is undifferentiated. The prognosis of dedifferentiated chordoma is very poor, with widespread metastasis and few survivors.

Chondroid chordoma is a controversial entity that contains an admixture of chordoid and cartilaginous areas (Wojno *et al.*, 1992). It occurs in bones commonly affected by pure chordomas. Immunohistochemical studies usually show chordoid differentiation (keratin, epithelial membrane, and S-100 protein positive) in both areas of the tumour. Patients with these tumours appear to have a longer survival time than those patients with conventional chordoma.

MALIGNANT FIBROUS HISTIOCYTOMA AND FIBROSARCOMA

Malignant fibrous histiocytoma is a rare sarcoma of bone, comprising approximately 3% of all primary bone tumours and 5% of bone sarcomas. It is similar to the more common entity seen in the soft tissues now thought to be of myofibroblastic differentiation rather than derived from the monocyte–macrophage lineage. It occurs in all age groups, with an increasing incidence with age; there is no sex predilection (Capanna *et al.*, 1984). It may involve any bone, but there is a predilecton for the metaphyses of the long tubular bones. Radiologically, a lytic lesion is seen, usually with an associated soft tissue mass. The gross appearance is that of a sarcoma, with a fleshy grey mass, usually with haemorrhage and necrosis. Histologically, a spindle cell proliferation is seen, forming whorls and fascicles. Storiform–pleomorphic, giant cell and myxoid variants are recognized, but there is often intermixture of these components within a single case. Bone formation by the neoplastic cells is not present, as this would mandate the diagnosis of osteosarcoma. The individual cells vary from highly spindled to oval. Nuclear atypia is usually marked, but can show a spectrum from case to case and within a given case (**Figure 16; see colour plate section**). Immunohistochemical studies are commonly performed to rule out other entities, but there are no specific findings in malignant fibrous histiocytoma. Although expression of smooth muscle actin is often seen and used to support a myofibroblastic differentiation, many other sarcomas may also express this antigen. There have been no specific molecular abnormalities found in malignant fibrous histiocytoma; this is not surprising as the entity probably represents a 'waste-basket' of cases of bone sarcoma that do not show specific features of other sarcomas. It is usually treated by radical surgical excision followed by systemic chemotherapy and/or radiotherapy, although newer approaches are examining treatment protocols similar to those used for osteosarcoma. The prognosis is poor, particularly in those patients whose tumours have arisen as a transformation event in a lower grade sarcoma. Metastases most often occur in the lungs.

Some pathologists separate fibrosarcoma from malignant fibrous histiocytoma and regard it as a separate bone sarcoma, whereas other pathologists classify these cases within the category of malignant fibrous histiocytoma. The epidemiological, radiological and gross characteristics of fibrosarcoma are similar to those seen in malignant fibrous histiocytoma (Dahlin and Ivins, 1969). Histologically, those pathologists who distinguish fibrosarcoma from malignant fibrous histiocytoma look for a well-developed fascicular architecture, often with a 'herring-bone' pattern between the different fascicles. The fascicles are formed by spindled cells, without the oval cells typical of malignant fibrous histiocytoma. Collagen formation is variable. The immunohistochemical findings are similar to those seen in malignant fibrous histiocytoma, and the molecular findings are similarly nonspecific. The treatment is usually the same as that for malignant fibrous histiocytoma. The survival figures for patients with fibrosarcoma may be superior to those of patients with malignant fibrous histiocytoma, but this may be because a higher proportion of fibrosarcomas are of lower histological grade.

ADAMANTINOMA

Adamantinoma is a rare primary epithelial neoplasm of bone (Weiss and Dorfman, 1977). It is currently subdivided into classical and differentiated types. The classical type usually occurs in adults, without a sex predilection. It exclusively involves the tibia or, less often, the fibula, the long tubular bones of the lower leg. Patients present with pain in the involved site, often accompanied by a mass. Radiological studies show a mixed lytic and sclerotic mass that may either be intracortical or may show complete cortical disruption with involvement of the medullary cavity, soft tissue or both. Grossly, it appears as a fleshy mass. Histologically, adamantinoma features epithelial cells arranged in various patterns, including basaloid, spindle, tubular, squamoid and osteofibrous dysplasia-like (**Figure 17; see colour plate section**). The tumour cells in all patterns are keratin-positive on immunohistochemical studies, and ultrastructurally show prominent desmosomes and evidence of keratinization, consistent with epithelial cells. Cytogenetic studies have revealed complex chromosomal abnormalities. Classical adamantinomas are indolent tumours with a high recurrence rate; metastasis, mostly to lungs, occurs in about one-quarter of patients.

Differentiated adamantinoma is extremely rare and, in contrast to classical adamantinoma, usually in patients under the age of 20 (Baker and Coley, 1953). It also exclusively involves the tibia and the fibula, and synchronous lesions may occur. The radiological appearance is identical with that of the classical subtype. Grossly, the tumour appears fibrous rather than fleshy. Histologically, the tumour looks very similar to osteofibrous dysplasia (see above), with the exception that single epithelial cells and small nests of epithelial cells are present within the fibrous stroma. These cells are best identified by immunohistochemical studies for keratin. Cases of differentiated adamantinoma have not yet been reported to metastasize.

ANGIOSARCOMA

Angiosarcoma is a malignancy of endothelial cells. It is a rare primary sarcoma of bone, representing less than 1% of cases. It is separated into classical and well-differentiated epithelioid subtypes. Both classical and well-differentiated occur in all age groups, with a peak of incidence in young adulthood; there is a male predilection (Volpe and Mazabraud, 1982; Wold *et al.*, 1982). The long tubular bones of the lower extremity are most often involved, and multifocal lesions are frequent. Radiological studies show usually show a lytic lesion or multiple lesions. They are bright red on cut section. Histologically, classical angiosarcoma typically consists of irregular anastomosing channels lined by individual or heaped up masses of highly atypical endothelial cells. Solid sheets of these cells may also be present focally, extensively or comprising the entire lesion. In contrast, well-differentiated epithelioid angiosarcoma features plump (epithelioid) cells that form sheets, cords, and occasionally lines spaces. They are frequently vacuolated – the vacuoles representing abortive attempts at vessel formation. The nuclei usually show mild to moderate degrees of atypia. The proliferating cells of both subtypes of angiosarcoma express markers of vascular cells, including CD31, CD34 and factor VIII-related antigen. Expression of keratin and, occasionally, epithelial membrane antigen is seen in a subset of cases. Ultrastructural studies demonstrate Weibel–Palade bodies, cytoplasmic structures found in normal endothelial cells.

Classical angiosarcoma is a high-grade sarcoma, usually requiring radical surgery. The prognosis is poor, with a high propensity for metastasis, particularly to the lungs. In contrast, epithelioid angiosarcomas are indolent neoplasms, with local invasion and only occasional metastasis, (also to the lungs). They are usually treated by more conservative surgery with postoperative radiotherapy.

MULTIPLE MYELOMA

Multiple myeloma (plasma cell myeloma) represents a malignant neoplasm of plasma cells, the terminally differentiated cells of the B-lymphocyte lineage that secrete immunoglobulins (Bataille and Harousseau, 1997). Multiple myeloma is a relatively common tumour, occurring more frequently than all primary bone sarcomas combined. It occurs in adults, with an increasing frequency with age. There is a slight male predilection, and there is a higher incidence in blacks than whites. The spine, skull, pelvis and the ribs are most frequently involved. Patients typically present with bone pain and often have recurrent infections and symptoms of renal disease, either at presentation or during the course of the disease. Laboratory abnormalities include anaemia, hypercalcaemia, a monoclonal gammopathy in serum and/or urine and reduced levels of normal polyclonal immunoglobulins. The monoclonal gammopathy derives from the neoplastic plasma cells, and usually consists of IgG (about half of cases) or IgA (one-quarter of cases) in the serum and/or kappa or lambda light chains (called Bence Jones protein) in the urine. Radiological studies usually demonstrate multiple sharply delimited lytic lesions. Grossly, the lesions are usually soft and grey. Microscopically, a uniform proliferation of plasma cells is seen in biopsies from lesions, of varying levels of cytologic atypia (**Figure 18; see colour plate section**) (Bartl *et al.*, 1987). Plasma cells are distinctive cells with a round, eccentrically placed nucleus with a clumped chromatin pattern and abundant cytoplasm with a paranuclear pale zone. In addition, an atypical plasmacytosis may also be seen in random biopsies or aspirates from random sites of bone such as the iliac crest that do not appear to be radiologically involved. Immunohistochemical studies usually demonstrate lack of the leucocyte common antigen CD45 and the B-lineage markers CD20 and CD19, because these markers are usually absent on terminal differentiated B-lineage cells. However, there is positivity for the B cell marker CD79a, which is expressed throughout the complete gamut of B cell maturation. In addition, there is usually expression of the plasma cell marker CD38 and the adhesion markers CD138 (syndecan-1), CD56 and CD58. Most importantly, there is almost always monotypic expression of immunoglobulin light and heavy chains, usually of the IgG or

IgA class. Some myeloma cells may express the immature B cell antigen CD10 (common acute lymphoblastic leukaemia antigen (CALLA)), myelomonocytic antigens or T cell antigens. In general, multiple myeloma has a relatively low proliferative index, indicating that the primary abnormality in this neoplasm may be lack of cell death due to loss of cell death mechanisms rather than active proliferation due to loss of growth control mechanisms.

Molecular studies demonstrate monoclonal rearrangements of the heavy and light chain immunoglobulin genes. Classical cytogenetic studies reveal consistent clonal structural abnormalities in about 40% of cases. The most common abnormalities involve chromosomes 11, 13 and 14, with a t(11;14) involving the *BCL1/CCND1* gene on chromosome 11 and the immunoglobulin heavy chain gene on chromosome 14 have been seen in about 25% of cases. High levels of c-Myc have been reported in a subset of patients. Mutations of the *TP53* gene have also been reported in some patients. Alterations of the *PAX-5* gene have also been reported, and may account for the loss of B-lineage markers in multiple myeloma.

Malignant myeloma is usually treated by chemotherapy, although radiotherapy and even surgery may play a role in the treatment of individual lesions that are particularly symptomatic. Prognostic factors include tumour burden (tumour mass), cytological features, expression of CD10, high proliferative index, specific cytogenetic abnormalities and the presence of complications such as renal dysfunction or amyloidosis.

There are several uncommon variants of multiple myeloma. Plasma cell leukaemia is a rare variant with a dominant leukaemic component (Dahlin and Unni, 1986). Solitary myeloma (plasmacytoma of bone) is defined as a neoplastic plasma cell proliferation present in one site of bone (Woodruff *et al.*, 1979). Random bone marrow examinations lack plasmacytosis and a serum or urine gammopathy is usually absent. In the majority of cases, progression to multiple myelomas occurs within a few years. Smouldering myeloma lacks overt bone lesions but contains a moderate marrow plasmacytosis, while indolent myeloma has a lesser degree of marrow plasmacytosis but may have up to three bone lesions (Kyle and Griepp, 1980). Finally, monoclonal gammopathy of unknown significance is defined as the presence of a monoclonal gammopathy in the absence of bone lesions or significant marrow plasmacytosis (Kyle, 1978).

MALIGNANT LYMPHOMA PRESENTING IN BONE

Malignant lymphoma involves bones most commonly secondary to spread from other sites, but rarely may present as a primary lesion in bone (Baar *et al.*, 1994). Primary bone lymphoma usually represents non-Hodgkin

lymphoma. Most cases occur in adults with a slight male predilection. The large tubular bones, pelvis and the spine are most frequently involved, and multifocality may be seen (**Figure 19; see colour plate section**). About two-thirds of cases represent diffuse large B cell lymphoma, with peripheral T cell lymphoma, including cases of anaplastic large cell lymphoma being relatively rare. Hodgkin disease rarely presents in bone without extraskeletal involvement; it most commonly involves the lower spine or the pelvis (Gold and Mirra, 1979). The histological features of non-Hodgkin lymphomas and Hodgkin disease are identical with those seen in the more commonly involved sites.

LANGERHANS CELL HISTIOCYTOSIS

Langerhans cell histiocytosis (histiocytosis X) is a rare neoplastic proliferation of Langerhans cells (Lieberman *et al.*, 1996). Most cases occur in childhood, with a predilection for males. The disease is rare in blacks. There are three overlapping syndromes, all of which may involve bone: unifocal disease (solitary eosinophilic granuloma), multifocal, unisystem disease (Hand–Schuller–Christian disease) and multifocal, multisystem disease (Letterer–Siwe disease). In unifocal disease, a single bone is affected, most commonly the skull, femur, pelvic bones or ribs). In multifocal, unisystem disease, there is involvement of several bones, usually the craniofacial bones. In multifocal, multisystem disease, multiple organ systems are involved, but the bones are commonly included, usually in a diffuse fashion. In general, the younger the patient at diagnosis, the more extensive is the pattern of involvement. Histologically, one sees a proliferation of Langerhans cells, in a milieu which typically includes eosinophils, histiocytes, neutrophils and lymphocytes. Langerhans cells have a characteristic grooved nucleus and abundant histiocyte-like cytoplasm (**Figure 20; see colour plate section**). Langerhans cells express CD1 and S-100 protein, and ultrastructurally show characteristic organelles called Birbeck granules. There is a wide spectrum of clinical behaviour, with the number of organs affected at presentation being the critical factor. Survival is greater than 95% in patients with unifocal disease, 80% in patients with multifocal unisystem disease and poor in patients with multisystem disease. The last type of patients are typically treated with multidrug chemotherapy.

REFERENCES

Ahn, J., *et al*. (1995). Cloning of the putative tumour suppressor gene for hereditary multiple exostoses (EXT1). *Nature Genetics*, **11**, 137–143.

Baar, J., *et al.* (1994). Primary non-Hodgkin's lymphoma of bone: a clinicopathologic study. *Cancer*, **73**, 1194–1199.

Baker, H. and Coley, B. (1953). Chordoma of lumbar vertebra. *Journal of Bone and Joint Surgery*, **35A**, 403–408.

Baldini, N. *et al.* (1995). Expression of P-glycoprotein in high-grade osteosarcoma in relation to clinical outcome. *New England Journal of Medicine*, **333**, 1380–1385.

Bartl, R., *et al.* (1987). Histologic classification and staging of multiple myeloma: a retrospective and prospective study of 674 cases. *American Journal of Clinical Pathology*, **87**, 342–355.

Bataille, R. and Harousseau, J.-L. (1997). Multiple myeloma. *New England Journal of Medicine*, **336**, 1657–1664.

Bean, W. (1958). Dyschondroplasia and hemangiomata (Maffucci's syndrome). *Archives of Internal Medicine*, **102**, 544–550.

Berenson, J. R. and Vescio, R. A. (1999). HHV-8 is present in multiple myeloma patients. *Blood*, **15**, 3157–3159.

Bjornsson, J., *et al.* (1984). Clear cell chondrosarcoma of bone: observations in 47 cases. *American Journal of Surgical Pathology*, **8**, 223–230.

Capanna, R., *et al.* (1984). Malignant fibrous histiocytoma of bone: the experience at the Rizzoli Institute: report of 90 cases. *Cancer*, **54**, 177–187.

Dahlin, D. (1985). Caldwell Lecture: giant cell tumor of bone – highlights of 407 cases. *American Journal of Roentgenology*, **144**, 955–960.

Dahlin, D. and MacCarty, C. (1952). Chordoma: a study of fifty-nine cases. *Cancer*, **5**, 1170–1178.

Dahlin, D. and Ivins, J. (1969). Fibrosarcoma of bone: a study of 114 cases. *Cancer*, **23**, 35–41.

Dahlin, D. and Ivins, J. (1972). Benign chondroblastoma: a study of 125 cases. *Cancer*, **30**, 401–413.

Dahlin, D. and Unni, K. (1977). Osteosarcoma of bone and its important recognizable varieties. *American Journal of Surgical Pathology*, **1**, 61–72.

Dahlin, D. and Unni, K. (1986). *Bone Tumors: General Aspects and Data on 8,542 Cases*, 4th edn (Charles C. Thomas, Springfield, Il).

Dorfman, H. D. and Czerniak, B. (1995). Bone cancers. *Cancer*, **75**, 203–210.

Dorfman, H. D. and Czerniak, B. (1998). *Bone Tumors* (Mosby, St. Louis).

Fechner, R. and Mills, S. (1993). *Atlas of Tumor Pathology: Tumors of the Bones and Joints*, 3rd Series (Armed Forces Institute of Pathology, Washington, DC).

Gold, R. and Mirra, J. (1979). Case report 101: primary Hodgkin disease of humerus. *Skeletal Radiology*, **4**, 233–235.

Goodman, S., *et al.* (1984). Ollier's disease with multiple sarcomatous transformations. *Human Pathology*, **15**, 91–93.

Healy, J. and Ghelman, B. (1986). Osteoid osteoma and osteoblastoma: current concepts and recent advances. *Clinical Orthopaedics*, **204**, 76–85.

Kissane, J., *et al.* (1983). Ewing's sarcoma of bone: clinicopathologic aspects of 303 cases from the Intergroup Ewing's Sarcoma Study. *Human Pathology*, **14**, 773–779.

Kyle, R. (1978). Monoclonal gammopathy of undetermined significance: natural history in 241 cases. *American Journal of Medicine*, **64**, 814–826.

Kyle, R. and Griepp, P. (1980). Smoldering multiple myeloma. *New England Journal of Medicine*, **302**, 1347–1349.

Ladanyi, M., *et al.* (1993). MDM2 gene amplification in metastatic osteosarcoma. *Cancer Research*, **53**, 16–18.

Lieberman, P., *et al.* (1996). Langerhans cell (eosinophilic) granulomatosis: a clinicopathologic study encompassing 50 years. *American Journal of Surgical Pathology*, **20**, 519–552.

Link, M., *et al.* (1986). The effect of adjuvant chemotherapy on relapse-free survival in patients with osteosarcoma of the extremity. *New England Journal of Medicine*, **314**, 1600–1606.

Llombart-Bosch, A., *et al.* (1996). Histology, immunohistochemistry, and electron microscopy of small round cell tumors of bone. *Seminars in Diagnostic Pathology*, **13**, 153–170.

Lopez-Terrada, D. (1996). Molecular genetics of small round cell tumors. *Seminars in Diagnostic Pathology*, **13**, 242–249.

Mandahl, N., *et al.* (1993). Comparative cytogenetic and DNA flow cytometric analysis of 150 bone and soft-tissue tumors. *International Journal of Cancer*, **53**, 358–364.

McCarthy, E. and Dorman, H. (1982). Chondrosarcoma of bone with dedifferentiation: a study of eighteen cases. *Human Pathology*, **13**, 36–40.

Meis, J., *et al.* (1987). "De-differentiated" chordoma: a clinicopathologic and immunohistochemical study of three cases. *American Journal of Surgical Pathology*, **11**, 516–525.

Mertens, F., *et al.* (1993). Cytogenetic findings in 33 osteosarcomas. *International Journal of Cancer*, **55**, 44–50.

Milgram, J. (1983). The origins of osteochondromas and enchondromas. *Clinical Orthopaedics*, **174**, 264–284.

Miller, C., *et al.* (1996). Alterations of the p53, Rb and MDM2 genes in osteosarcoma. *Journal of Cancer Research and Clinical Oncology*, **122**, 559–565.

Mirra, J., *et al.* (1985). A new histologic approach to the differentiation of enchondroma and chondrosarcoma of the bones; a clinicopathologic analysis of 51 cases. *Clinical Orthopaedics*, **201**, 214–237.

Nakashima, Y., *et al.* (1986). Mesenchymal chondrosarcoma of bone and soft tissue: a review of 111 cases. *Cancer*, **57**, 2444–2453.

Nawa, G., *et al.* (1996). Prognostic significance of Ki67 (MIB1) proliferation index and p53 over-expression in chondrosarcoma. *International Journal of Cancer*, **69**, 86–91.

Rahimi, A., *et al.* (1972). Chondromyxoid fibroma: a clinicopathologic study of 76 cases. *Cancer*, **30**, 726–736.

Reed, R. (1963). Fibrous dysplasia of bone: a review of 25 cases. *Archives of Pathology*, **75**, 480–495.

Roessner, A., *et al.* (1981). Benign fibrous histiocytoma of bone: light- and electron-microscopic observations. *Journal of Cancer Research and Clinical Oncology*, **101**, 191–202.

Rosenthal, D., *et al.* (1984). Chondrosarcoma: correlation of radiological and histological grade. *Radiology*, **150**, 21–26.

Sanerkin, N. (1980). The diagnosis and grading of chondrosarcoma of bone: a combined cytologic and histologic approach. *Cancer*, **45**, 582–594.

Shenker, A., *et al.* (1994). An activating Gs alpha mutation is present in fibrous dysplasia of bone in Albright–McCune–Sternberg syndrome. *Journal of Clinical Endocrinology and Metabolism*, **79**, 750–755.

Simms, W., *et al.* (1995). p53 expression in dedifferentiated chondrosarcoma. *Cancer*, **76**, 223–227.

Strickens, D., *et al.* (1996). The EXT2 multiple exostoses gene defines a family of putative tumour suppressor genes. *Nature Genetics*, **14**, 25–32.

Unni, K. (1996). *Dahlin's Bone Tumors: General Aspects and Data on 11,087 Cases*, 5th edn (Lippincott-Raven, Philadelphia).

Unni, K., *et al.* (1976a). Parosteal osteogenic sarcoma. *Cancer*, **37**, 2644–2675.

Unni, K., *et al.* (1976b). Periosteal osteogenic sarcoma. *Cancer*, **37**, 2476–2485.

Vennos, E., *et al.* (1992). Rothmund–Thomson syndrome: review of the world literature. *Journal of the American Academy of Dermatology*, **27**, 750–762.

Volpe, R. and Mazabraud, A. (1982). Hemangioendothelioma (angiosarcoma) of bone: a distinct pathologic entity with an unpredictable course? *Cancer*, **49**, 727–736.

Weiss, S. and Dorfman, H. (1977). Adamantinoma of long bone: an analysis of nine new cases with emphasis on metastisizing lesions and fibrous dysplasia-like changes. *Human Pathology*, **8**, 141–153.

Wojno, K., *et al.* (1992). Chondroid chordomas and low-grade chondrosarcomas of the craniospinal axis: an immunohistochemical analysis of 17 cases. *American Journal of Surgical Pathology*, **16**, 1144–1152.

Wold, L., *et al.* (1982). Hemangioendothelial sarcoma of bone. *American Journal of Surgical Pathology*, **6**, 59–70.

Woodruff, R., *et al.* (1979). Solitary plasmacytoma. II. Solitary plasmacytoma of bone. *Cancer*, **43**, 2344–2347.

FURTHER READING

Dahlin, D. and Unni, K. (1986). *Bone Tumors: General Aspects and Data on 8,542 Cases*, 4th edn (Charles C. Thomas, Springfield, IL).

Dorfman, H. D. and Czerniak, B. (1998). *Bone Tumors* (Mosby, St. Louis, MO).

Fechner, R. and Mills, S. (1993). *Atlas of Tumor Pathology: Tumors of the Bones and Joints*, 3rd Series (Armed Forces Institute of Pathology, Washington, DC).

Huvos, A. G. (1991). *Bone Tumors: Diagnosis, Treatment, Prognosis* (W. B. Saunders, Philadelphia).

Jaffe, H. L. (1972). *Tumors and Tumorous Conditions of the Bones and Joints* (Lea and Febiger, Philadelphia).

Mirra, J. M. (1989). *Bone Tumors: Clinical, Radiologic and Pathologic Correlations* (J.B. Lippincott, Philadelphia).

Unni, K. (1996). *Dahlin's Bone Tumors: General Aspects and Data on 11,087 Cases*, 5th edn (Lippincott-Raven, Philadelphia).

Chapter 48

Soft Tissues

Andre M. Oliveira
Mayo Graduate School of Medicine, Rochester, MN, USA

Antonio G. Nascimento
Mayo Clinic, Mayo Medical School, Rochester, MN, USA

CONTENTS

DEVELOPMENT AND STRUCTURE OF SOFT TISSUES AND SOFT TISSUE NEOPLASMS

Soft tissue is a broad and poorly defined term that includes distinct tissue types, including connective or supporting tissues, vascular tissue and peripheral nerve tissue. Connective tissues develop from the embryonic mesoderm and are composed of mesenchymal cells. Connective tissues include cartilage, fat, ligaments, tendons, capsules, fasciae, aponeuroses, skeletal muscle, smooth muscle and bone. Bone is excluded from the definition of soft tissue because of its unique histological characteristics. Vascular tissue, which is composed of endothelial cells, is also a mesoderm-derived tissue, originating from primitive mesenchymal cells (angioblasts) during the third week of the embryonic development. Peripheral nerve tissue, in contrast to the other soft tissues, is an ectoderm-derived tissue predominantly originating from the neural crest.

New concepts on soft tissue oncogenesis are being advanced; to avoid misconceptions, we shall discuss some ideas briefly. First, soft tissue tumours currently are considered to be a group of distinct neoplasms showing predominantly mesenchymal differentiation. The word histogenesis will be abandoned, at least for the time being. The erroneous idea that soft tissue tumours are originated from well-developed adult tissue has little clinicopathological support in most cases. Two examples that challenge the concept of histogenesis are liposarcoma and rhabdomyosarcoma. These tumours frequently arise in areas devoid of adipose tissue and skeletal muscle, respectively. Mesenchymal cells are mesoderm-derived motile and nonpolarized embryonic connective tissue cells that can undergo differentiation into distinct cell types. Accordingly, the current hypothesis on soft tissue oncogenesis is that genetic alterations in mesodermal progenitor cells lead to many types of soft tissue tumours. The line of differentiation seems to depend mainly on two factors: the level of commitment of these mesodermal progenitors to development into a certain type of cell when the oncogenic events occur and on the differential pattern of gene expression during the clonal evolution of the tumour. However, it is important to note that even the concepts of mesoderm progenitors or cell of origin will not be blindly adopted or denied. Research has challenged traditional ideas of cell differentiation, dedifferentiation and transdifferentiation, finding a deeper phenotypic cellular plasticity than previously thought (Orkin, 2000). Furthermore, nothing precludes the possibility that oncogenic processes also occur in well-developed cells. Some tumours of smooth muscle and neural differentiation are examples of this point.

Second, soft tissue neoplasms are not necessarily restricted to the same patterns of development and differentiation as are normal tissues. In neoplasms, uncontrolled and cumulative genetic and epigenetic alterations result in cell phenotypes that are distinct from those of normal cells. Searching for counterparts in normal cell types is helpful mainly for classification purposes; this activity should not obligate us to current paradigms of differentiation.

Third, soft tissue neoplasms need not be exclusively restricted to mesenchymal differentiation. The same tumorigenic alterations described above may result in other cell phenotypes, such as epithelial. There are numerous examples of soft tissue neoplasms with a biphasic appearance, or aberrant differentiation; an example is the biphasic synovial sarcoma. Epithelial–mesenchymal and mesenchymal–epithelial transitions are well-known developmental processes that also can occur during tumorigenesis.

Fourth, the traditional and academic distinction between benign and malignant soft tissue tumours is blurred because many soft tissue tumours behave in a benign fashion despite malignant-like clinicopathological features. The reverse is also true. Examples that do not exactly fit the traditional view include deep fibromatoses (desmoid tumours) and metastasizing benign leiomyomata. Therefore, a spectrum of tumours ranging from the very benign to the fully malignant does exist.

Fifth, soft tissue tumour oncogenesis does not follow the current model of carcinogenesis. At our present level of knowledge, concepts of dysplasia or preneoplastic lesions do not readily apply in most cases of soft tissue sarcoma. Malignant transformation of benign soft tissue tumours into malignant tumours seems very rare; the best example is the malignant transformation of neurofibroma in malignant peripheral nerve sheath tumour in patients with neurofibromatosis.

Sixth, soft tissue sarcomas should not be regarded as rare tumours refractory to any kind of treatment. They comprise various neoplasms with distinct epidemiological, clinicopathological and genetic features that respond differently to various therapeutic modalities. Many advances in cancer genetics and treatment have come from basic and clinical research on soft tissue neoplasms.

In this chapter we discuss the general classification, epidemiology, pathogenesis, clinical features, histological features (including current grading systems), relevant immunohistochemical and ultrastructural findings, cytogenetics, molecular genetics and treatment of soft tissue sarcomas. Emphasis on the pathogenesis and molecular aspects of soft tissue sarcomas will fill the gap present in most textbooks on the subject. New and relevant concepts are discussed as appropriate. Owing to space limitations, clinicopathological features of exceedingly rare sarcomas arising in visceral locations and benign soft tissue tumours, including pseudosarcomatous lesions, are not discussed. The reader is referred to comprehensive reviews on the subject for additional information. For mesothelial tumours, including solitary fibrous tumours, see chapter on *Pleura and Peritoneum*.

CLASSIFICATION

The current World Health Organisation classification of soft tissue tumours is based primarily on clinicopathological features (Weiss and Sobin, 1994). The tumours are classified according to their resemblance to normal tissues or their line of differentiation and clinical behaviour (**Table 1**). The tumours are generally classified as benign or malignant (malignant tumours also are known as sarcomas, from the Greek words *sarx*, flesh, and *oma*, tumour). Many specific entities and variants exist within each category. Despite the efforts of several experts in soft tissue pathology to create a useful and rational classification, the current one, like any other, is not perfect. The field of soft tissue pathology is one of the most dynamic areas in diagnostic and experimental pathology and, because of tremendous technical advances in immunohistochemistry, cytogenetics and molecular genetics, previously unrecognized tumours have been described and fully characterized, and many similarities between apparently disparate entities have been identified. Therefore, future classifications are expected to incorporate this new information.

Table 1 World Health Organisation's histological classification of soft tissue tumours

1. Fibrous tissue tumour
　Benign
　　Fibroma
　　Keloid[a]
　　Nodular fasciitis[a]
　　Proliferative fasciitis[b]
　　Proliferative myositis[b]
　　Elastofibroma[b]
　　Fibrous hamartoma of infancy[c]
　　Myofibromatosis, solitary and multicentric[c]
　　Fibromatosis colli[c]
　　Calcifying aponeurotic fibroma[c]
　　Hyaline fibromatosis[c]
　Fibromatosis
　　Superficial fibromatosis
　　　Palmar and plantar fibromatosis[a]
　　Infantile digital fibromatosis (digital fibroma)[c]
　Deep fibromatosis　·
　　Abdominal fibromatosis (desmoid tumour)[a]
　　Extra-abdominal fibromatosis (desmoid tumour)[a]
　　Intra-abdominal and mesenteric fibromatosis[a]
　　Infantile fibromatosis[c]
　Malignant
　　Fibrosarcoma
　　Adult fibrosarcoma[b]
　　Congenital or infantile fibrosarcoma[c]

2. Fibrohistocytic tumours
　Benign
　　Fibrous histiocytoma
　　Cutaneous histocytoma (deramtofibroma)[a]
　　Deep histiocytoma[a]
　　Juvenile xanthogranuloma[c]
　　Reticulohistiocytoma[b]
　　Xanthoma[b]
　Intermediate
　　Atypical fibroxanthoma[b]
　　Dermatofibrosarcoma protuberans[a]
　　Pigmented dermatofibrosarcoma protuberans (Bednar tumour)[a]

Table 1   *(Continued)*

      Giant cell fibroblastoma[c]
      Plexiform fibrohistiocytic tumour[a]
      Angiomatoid fibrous histiocytoma[a]
  Malignant
    Malignant fibrous histiocytoma
    Storiform-pleomorphic[b]
    Myxoid[b]
    Giant cell[b]
    Xanthomatous (inflammatory)[b]

3. *Lipomatous tumours*
  Benign
    Lipoma[a]
    Lipoblastoma (foetal lipoma)[c]
    Lipomatosis[a]
    Angiolipoma[a]
    Spindle cell lipoma[b]
    Pleomorphic lipoma[b]
    Angiomyolipoma[a]
    Myelolipoma[b]
    Hibernoma[b]
    Atypical lipoma[b]
  Malignant
    Well-differentiated liposarcoma[b]
    Lipoma-like
    Sclerosing
    Inflammatory[b]
    Myxoid liposarcoma[a]
    Round cell (poorly differentiated myxoid) liposarcoma[b]
    Pleomorphic liposarcoma[b]
    Dedifferentiated liposarcoma[b]

4. *Smooth muscle tumours*
  Benign
    Leiomyoma[a]
    Angiomyoma[a]
    Epithelioid leiomyoma[a]
    Leiomyomatosis peritoneales disseminata[b]
  Malignant
    Leiomyosarcoma[b]
    Epithelioid leiomyosarcoma[b]

5. *Skeletal muscle tumours*
  Benign
    Rhabdomyoma
    Adult[b]
    Genital[a]
    Fetal[c]
  Malignant
    Rhabdomyosarcoma
    Embryonal rhabdomyosarcoma[c]
    Botryoid rhabdomyosarcoma[c]
    Spindle cell rhabdomyosarcoma[c]
    Alveolar rhabdomyosarcoma[c]
    Pleomorphic rhabdomyosarcoma[b]
    Rhabdomyosarcoma with ganglionic
      differentiation (ectomesenchymoma)[c]

6. *Endothelial tumours of blood and lymph vessels*
  Benign
    Papillary endothelial hyperplasia[a]
    Haemangioma

Table 1   *(Continued)*

    Capillary haemangioma[a]
    Cavernous haemangioma[a]
    Venous haemangioma[a]
    Epithelioid haemangioma (angiolymphoid hyperplasia,
      histiocytoid haemangioma)[a]
    Pyogenic granuloma
      (granulation tissue type haemangioma)[a]
    Acquired tufted haemangioma (angioblastoma)[a]
    Lymphangioma[a]
    Lymphangiomyoma[a]
    Lymphangiomyomatosis[a]
    Angiomatosis[a]
    Lymphangiomatosis[c]
  Intermediate: haemangioendothelioma
    Spindle cell haemangioendothelioma[a]
    Endovascular papillary angioendothelioma (Dabska
      tumour)[c]
    Epithelioid hemangioendothelioma[a]
  Malignant
    Angiosarcoma[b]
    Lymphangiosarcoma[b]
    Kaposi's sarcoma[b]

7. *Perivascular tumours*
  Benign
    Benign haemangiopericytoma[a]
    Glomus tumour[a]
  Malignant
    Malignant haemangiopericytoma[b]
    Malignant glomus tumour[b]

8. *Synovial tumours*
  Benign
    Tenosynovial giant cell tumour
    Localized[a]
    Diffuse (extra-articular pigmented villonodular synovitis)[a]
  Malignant
    Malignant tenosynovial giant cell tumour[b]

9. *Mesothelial tumours*
  Benign
    Solitary fibrous tumour of pleura and peritoneum
      (localized fibrous mesothelioma)[b]
    Multicystic mesothelioma[a]
    Adenomatoid tumour[b]
    Well-differentiated papillary mesothelioma[a]
  Malignant
    Malignant solitary fibrous tumour of pleura and
      peritoneum (malignant localized fibrous mesothelioma)
    Diffuse mesothelioma[a]
    Epithelial
    Spindled (sarcomatoid)
    Biphasic

10. *Neural tumours*
  Benign
    Traumatic neuroma[a]
    Morton neuroma[b]
    Neuromuscular hamartoma[c]
    Nerve sheath ganglion[a]
    Schwannoma (neurilemoma)[a]
    Plexiform schwannoma[a]

Table 1 (*Continued*)

Cellular schwannoma[a]
Degenerated (ancient) schwannoma[b]
Neurofibroma
Diffuse[a]
Pacinian[a]
   Plexiform[a]
   Epithelioid[a]
   Granular cell tumour[a]
   Melanocytic schwannoma[b]
   Neurothekeoma (nerve sheath myxoma)[a]
   Ectopic meningioma[a]
   Ectopic ependymoma[a]
   Ganglioneuroma[a]
   Pigmented neuroectodermal tumour of infancy (retinal enlarge tumour, melanotic progonoma)[c]
Malignant
   Malignant peripheral nerve sheath tumour (MPNST) (malignant shwannoma, neurofibrosarcoma)
   MPNST with rhabdomyosarcoma (malignant Triton tumour)[a]
   MPNST with glandular differentiation[a]
   Epithelioid MPNST[a]
   Malignant granular cell tumour[a]
   Clear cell sarcoma (malignant melanoma of soft parts)[a]
   Malignant melanotic schwannoma[a]
   Neuroblastoma[c]
   Ganglioneuroblastoma[c]
   Neuroepithelioma (peripheral neuroectodermal tumour, peripheral neuroblastoma)[a]

11. Paraganglionic tumours
Benign
   Paraganglioma[a]
Malignant
   Malignant paraganglioma[a]

12. Cartilage and bone tumours
Benign
   Panniculitis ossificans[b]
   Myositis ossificans[a]
   Fibrodysplasia (myositis) ossificans progressiva[c]
   Extraskeletal chondroma[a]
   Extraskeletal osteochondroma[a]
   Extraskeletal osteoma[a]
Malignant
   Extraskeletal chondrosarcoma[a]
   Well-differentiated chondrosarcoma
   Myxoid chondrosarcoma
   Mesenchymal chondrosarcoma
   Dedifferentiated chondrosarcoma
   Extraskeletal osteosarcoma[b]

13. Pluripotential mesenchymal tumours
Benign
   Mesenchymoma[a]
Malignant
   Malignant mesenchymoma[a]

14. Miscellaneous tumours
Benign
   Congenital granular cell tumour[c]
   Tumoural calcinosis[a]

Table 1 (*Continued*)

Myxoma
   Cutaneous[a]
   Intramuscular[b]
   Angiomyxoma[a]
   Amyloid tumour[b]
   Parachordoma[a]
   Ossifying fibromyxoid tumour[a]
   Juvenile angiofibroma[c]
Inflammatory myofibroblastic tumour (inflammatory fibrosarcoma)[a]
Malignant
   Alveolar soft part sarcoma[a]
   Epithelioid sarcoma[a]
   Extraskeletal Ewing sarcoma[a]
   Synovial sarcoma[a]
   Monophasic fibrous type
   Malignant (extrarenal) rhabdoid tumour[c]
   Desmoplastic small cell tumour of children and young adults[a]

15. Unclassified tumours

[a]Although this tumour is known to present more often in children than in adults, it is not strictly considered a neoplasm of either age group.
[b]More than 90% of cases present in patients beyond the third decade of life.
[c]Most tumours of this type present before the age of 20 years.
[From Weiss, 1994, *Histological Typing of Soft Tissue Tumours*, 2nd edn (Springer, Berlin), by permission of the publisher.]

EPIDEMIOLOGY, AETIOLOGY AND PATHOGENESIS

Soft tissue tumours are common if one considers the occurrence of benign and malignant tumours, the latter being 100 times less common than the former. Sarcomas represent approximately 1% of all malignant tumours in adults and 15% of all malignant tumours in children. According to a recent report, almost 8000 new cases of soft tissue sarcoma occur and more than 4000 patients die annually of this condition in the USA (Landis *et al.*, 1999). Soft tissue sarcomas are slightly more common in males and can occur anywhere in the body. The most common nonvisceral anatomical sites are the extremities and retroperitoneum.

The aetiology of soft tissue sarcomas is still largely unknown. Environmental and genetic factors have been associated with their development. Ionizing radiation for the treatment of other neoplasms, such as lymphomas and breast and cervical carcinomas, was found to induce high-grade sarcomas, most commonly osteosarcoma and malignant fibrous histiocytoma. Megavoltage and orthovoltage radiation have been implicated. Postradiation sarcomas usually arise 2–3 years after radiation therapy, and a higher risk is observed with cumulative doses greater than 10 Gy. The criteria proposed for the diagnosis of a postradiation sarcoma, which have been constantly modified over the years, require tumour development in a previously unaffected area within the radiotherapy field and a minimum latency period of 2–3 years. However, the risk of radiation therapy is very low; postradiation sarcoma develops in only 0.1% of patients with cancer who survive more than 5 years after diagnosis.

Many chemicals have been implicated in the aetiology of sarcomas, including thorotrast, poly(vinyl chloride), arsenic, alkylating agents, phenoxyacetic acids, chlorophenols and dioxin (2,3,7,8-tetrachlorodibenzo-*p*-dioxin, or TCDD). The causal role of the three last-mentioned agents in the development of soft tissue sarcomas is controversial. The associations between the development of hepatic angiosarcomas and thorotrast, poly(vinyl chloride) and arsenic are better established.

Viruses have been implicated in the aetiology of a few sarcomas. The best example is the association between Kaposi sarcoma and the human herpes virus 8 (also known as Kaposi sarcoma-associated herpes virus, KSHV). KSHV has been detected in more than 95% of Kaposi sarcomas in all clinical settings. KSHV encodes proteins that disrupt cell cycle and apoptosis control mechanisms. Interference with the normal function of the retinoblastoma and p53 tumour-suppressor proteins as well as derepression of the c-*MYC* oncogene are caused by KSHV-derived proteins (Antman and Chang, 2000). KSHV also has been implicated in the pathogenesis of primary effusion lymphoma and multicentric Castleman disease.

Epstein–Barr virus has also been implicated in the pathogenesis of some sarcomas. Sequences of Epstein–Barr virus have been found in smooth muscle tumours that arise in children with acquired immune deficiency syndrome (AIDS) (McClain *et al.*, 1995) and in the rare follicular dendritic cell sarcoma. More recently, the expression of the adenovirus early region 1A gene (*E1A*) in normal human fibroblasts and keratinocytes was found to induce the classical Ewing sarcoma translocation t(11;22)(q24;q12) with the formation of the fusion transcript *EWS/FLI1*. However, these intriguing results are unconfirmed.

A history of trauma is common in patients with soft tissue and bone sarcomas. However, the causal role of trauma is questionable. It is currently believed that trauma near or over the tumour area does not cause but rather leads to the discovery of the tumour. The short time between trauma and the diagnosis of sarcoma supports this view.

Chronic lymphoedema has been correlated with the development of lymphangiosarcoma (currently considered angiosarcoma) in different clinical settings. Stewart–Treves syndrome, the classical example, is characterized by the development of angiosarcoma in a lymphoedematous arm after radical mastectomy. Breast irradiation can also cause chronic arm lymphoedema and secondary angiosarcoma outside the irradiation field. Stewart–Treves syndrome is rarely observed today because of major modifications in the surgical and postsurgical management of patients with breast cancer. Filarial-induced

lymphoedema has also been implicated in the development of angiosarcoma.

Several genetic disorders have been associated with an increased risk for the development of soft tissue sarcomas (see Section B). Li–Fraumeni syndrome, neurofibromatosis type I (von Recklinghausen disease), Gardner syndrome, familial retinoblastoma and Beckwith–Wiedemann syndrome are well-known examples. Li–Fraumeni syndrome is a rare familial syndrome characterized by an inherited predisposition to epithelial and nonepithelial tumours, including soft tissue sarcomas, osteosarcomas, breast and lung adenocarcinomas, medulloblastomas, adrenal cortical tumours, leukaemias and others. In 75% of cases, Li–Fraumeni syndrome results from germline mutations of the *TP53* gene on chromosome 17q13. However, germline mutations of the *CHK2* gene (*CH*eckpoint *K*inase 2) have been described in a subset of patients with Li–Fraumeni syndrome (Bell *et al.*, 1999). Neurofibromatosis type I is characterized by germline mutations of the *NF1* (*N*euro*F*ibromin) gene on chromosome 17q11.1. The NF1 protein normally inhibits the protein product of the *RAS* proto-oncogene (*RAt Sarcoma* virus). Inactivation of *NF1* predisposes to neurofibromas, malignant peripheral nerve sheath tumours and glial tumours. Gardner syndrome is characterized by mutations of the *APC* gene (*A*denomatous *P*olyposis *C*oli) located on 5q21. Multiple intestinal adenomatous polyps develop in patients with Gardner syndrome; these patients have an increased risk for colon cancer and mesenteric fibromatosis (desmoid tumours). Patients with familial retinoblastoma carry a germline mutation in one of the *RB1* gene (*R*etino*B*lastoma *1*) alleles on chromosome 13q24. Loss of the wild-type allele on the homologous chromosome predisposes to retinoblastoma, osteosarcoma, pinealoma and soft tissue sarcomas. Beckwith–Wiedemann syndrome is a sporadic or autosomal-dominant disorder characterized by generalized overgrowth, hemihypertrophy and a tendency for neonatal hypoglycaemia, among other conditions, and an increased risk for Wilms tumour, adrenocortical carcinoma, hepatoblastoma and embryonal rhabdomyosarcoma. The syndrome seems frequently to be caused by loss of imprinting of the *IGFII* (*I*nsulin *G*rowth *F*actor-*II*) and *H19* genes on chromosome 11p15.5. Other disorders associated with an increased incidence of soft tissue sarcomas include tuberous sclerosis, Gorlin syndrome, Werner syndrome and Carney triad. (For additional information, see chapter on *Inherited Predispositions to Cancer*.)

GENETICS AND MOLECULAR BIOLOGY

Genetic alterations in soft tissue sarcomas can be tumour specific or nonspecific. Tumour-specific alterations include genetic alterations highly characteristic of certain soft tissue sarcomas and most commonly represented by chromosomal translocations (**Table 2**). Tumour-nonspecific alterations include genetic abnormalities seen

Table 2 Characteristic chromosomal and genetic abnormalities in sarcomas

Tumour type	Chromosomal abnormality	Fusion transcript or genetic abnormality	Prevalence (%)
Alveolar soft part sarcoma	t(X;17)(p11.2;q25)	TFE3/ASPL	>99
Alveolar rhabdomyosarcoma	t(2;13)(q35;q14)	PAX3/FKHR	75
	t(1;13)(p36;q14)	PAX1/FKHR	10
Angiomatoid fibrous histiocytoma	t(12;16)(q13;p11)	TLS/ATF1	?[a]
Clear cell sarcoma (malignant melanoma of soft parts)	t(12;22)(q13;q12)	EWS/ATF1	>85
Congenital fibrosarcoma/mesoblastic nephroma	t(12;15)(p13;q25)	ETV6/NTRK3	>99
Dermatofibrosarcoma protuberans /giant cell fibroblastoma	t(17;22)(q22;q13)	COL1A1/PDGFB	>99
Desmoplastic small round cell tumour	t(11;22)(p13;q12)	EWS/WT1	>99
Epithelioid hemangioendothelioma	t(1;3)(p36.3;q25)	varNOW	?
Ewing sarcoma/peripheral neuroectodermal tumour[b]	t(11;22)(q24;q12)	EWS/FLI1	95
	t(21;22)(q22;q12)	EWS/ERG	5
	t(7;22)(p22;q12)	EWS/ETV1	<1
	t(17;22)(q12;q12)	EWS/E1AF	<1
	t(2;22)(q33;q12)	EWS/FEV1	<1
	t(1;22)(p36.1;q12)	EWS/ZSG	<1
Extraskeletal myxoid chondrosarcoma	t(9;22)(q22;q12)	EWS/CHN	75
	t(9;17)(q22;q11)	RBP56/CHN	25
Inflammatory myofibroblastic tumour	2p23 rearrangements	TPM3/ALK	?
		TPM4/ALK	?
Malignant rhabdoid tumour	del(22q11.2)	hSNF/INI1 (deletion or mutation)	?
Myxoid/round cell liposarcoma	t(12;16)(q13;p11)	TLS/CHOP	95
	t(12;22)(q13;q12)	EWS/CHOP	5
Synovial sarcoma	t(X;18)(p11.2;q11.2)	SYT/SSX-1	65
		SYT/SSX-2	35
		SYT/SSX-4	<1

[a]Rearranged in a single case.
[b]Data from bone tumours.
Adapted from Ladanyi and Bridge, 2000, by permission of W. B. Saunders.

in various tumours and often associated with the clonal evolution of the tumour.

Since the discovery of the translocation t(11;22) (q24;q12) in Ewing sarcoma/peripheral primitive neuroectodermal tumour (PNET) in 1983 (Aurias *et al.*, 1983; Turc-Carel *et al.*, 1983), an explosion of new knowledge has contributed to our understanding of the molecular biology of soft tissue tumours. Many soft tissue sarcomas are characterized by specific, recurrent, balanced chromosomal translocations that result in the fusion of two constitutional genes into a new chimaeric aberrant gene. These chimaeric genes usually function as altered DNA transcription factors and seem to participate in the pathogenesis of these tumours. The fusion between the *EWS* gene (*EW*ing *S*arcoma) on chromosome 22q12 with the *FLI1* gene (*F*riend *L*eukaemia virus *I*ntegration *1*) on chromosome 11q24 is the best-known example (de Alava and Gerald, 2000). *EWS* encodes for a ubiquitously expressed protein involved in mRNA transcription. The structure of *EWS* protein includes an N-terminal domain homologous to the eukaryotic RNA polymerase II and a C-terminal domain that contains an RNA-binding sequence. *FLI1* encodes for a protein member of a large

family of DNA-binding transcription factors that contain a highly conserved amino acid sequence, the ETS domain (*E*rythroblastosis virus-*T*ransforming *S*equence), in the C-terminal end. During the translocation process, the 5' end of the *EWS*, which contains the *EWS* promoter region, fuses with the 3' end of the *FLI1*, which contains the ETS domain, resulting in a potent DNA transcription factor (Sandberg and Bridge, 2000) (**Figure 1**).

Similar translocation mechanisms occur in other sarcomas and often involve similar genes (**Table 2**). For example, *EWS* fuses with several ETS family members in other translocations observed in Ewing sarcoma/PNET and related tumours: *ERG* (*ETS*-*R*elated *G*ene), *ETV-1* (*ETS T*ranslocation *V*ariant-*1*), *E1AF* (*E1A F*actor), *FEV* (*F*ifth *E*wing *V*ariant) and *ZSG* (*Z*inc finger *S*arcoma *G*ene). In addition, *EWS* is fused with other gene partners in clear cell sarcoma (melanoma of soft parts), desmoplastic small round cell tumour, myxoid liposarcoma and extraskeletal myxoid chondrosarcoma (**Table 2**). Other genes involved in sarcoma and leukaemia chromosomal translocations show striking similarities to *EWS*. *FUS/TLS*, *RPB56/hTAFII68*, and *EWS* genes, which contribute their 5' end to many chimaeric

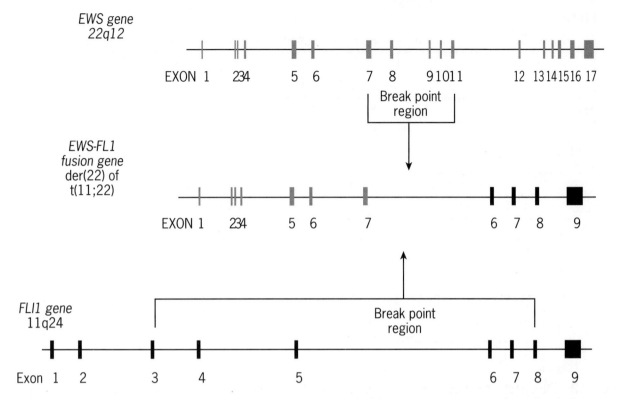

Figure 1 Schematic diagram representing the fusion of the *EWS* gene on chromosome 22q12 with the *FLI1* gene on chromosome 11q24. Fusions of exon 7 of *EWS* with exon 6 (type I) and exon 7 (type II) of *FLI1* occur in 70–75 and 15–25% of cases, respectively. *EWS/FLI* type I gene has been correlated with a low proliferative rate and prolonged survival in Ewing sarcoma. (Adapted from de Alava and Gerald, 2000.)

genes, have similar structures and seem to be originated from the same ancestor gene (**Figure 2**). *FUS/TLS* or *EWS* fuses with the *CHOP* gene in myxoid liposarcoma, and *EWS* or *RPB56/hTAFII68* fuses with the *CHN* gene in extraskeletal myxoid chondrosarcoma. *FUS/TLS* also fuses with the *ERG* gene in acute myeloid leukaemia. Other chromosomal translocations generate chimaeric proteins that function as growth factors (see Dermatofibrosarcoma Protuberans and Giant Cell Fibroblastoma, below) and tyrosine kinase proteins (see Congenital Fibrosarcoma, below).

The underlying mechanism responsible for the genesis of these translocations is still unknown. However, some clues have been found. DNA sequences near the breakpoints of the *FUS/TLS* and *CHOP* genes in myxoid liposarcoma and in the *PAX3* and *FKHR* in alveolar rhabdomyosarcoma are homologous to translin– and topoisomerase II–DNA binding sequences, suggesting the involvement of these proteins or their DNA binding sequences for the genesis of the translocations. In addition, a LINE-1 DNA sequence was found to be present in the translocation t(11;22)(p13:q24) breakpoint in desmoplastic small round cell tumour. It has been proposed that a series of constraint factors collaborate at the level of chromosomal rearrangements, gene expression and gene product function to determine the acquisition and maintenance of a specific translocation (Barr, 1998).

Inactivation of the tumour-suppressor gene *TP53* is commonly observed in soft tissue sarcomas. Loss of heterozygosity of 17p and missense mutations of the *TP53* are the most common mechanisms, occurring in 30–50% of cases. Overexpression of the p53 protein occurs after DNA damage and results in G1/S cell cycle arrest, induction of DNA repair systems, and apoptosis activation (see the chapters *Regulation of the Cell Cycle* and *Genetic Instability and DNA Repair*). Missense mutations of *TP53* result in an abnormal p53 protein that has a prolonged half-life and accumulates above the levels for immunohistochemical detection. Immunoreactivity for mutant p53 protein was found in approximately 27% of cases in a series of 211 soft tissue sarcomas and correlated with decreased survival (Cordon-Cardo, 1994). In the same series, mutant p53 protein expression did not always correlate with *TP53* mutation. Other studies have found a correlation between mutant p53 protein and high-grade histology or poor survival.

The tumour-suppressor gene *RB1* is commonly inactivated in soft tissue sarcomas. Normally, the hypophosphorylated Rb1 protein forms a complex with the transcription factor E2F, arresting the cell cycle in the G1/S checkpoint. Complexes of cyclins and cyclin-dependent kinases phosphorylate Rb1, releasing E2F and promoting cell cycle progression (see the chapter *Regulation of the Cell Cycle*). Loss of Rb1 protein

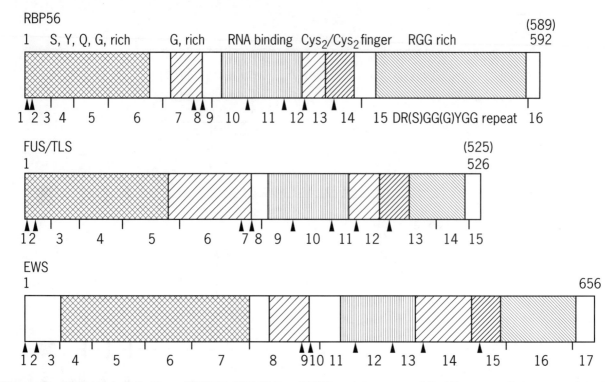

Figure 2   Structural similarities of RBP56, FUS/TLS and EWS proteins suggest that the respective genes originated from the same ancestral gene. *RBP56(hTAFII68)* is rearranged in extraskeletal myxoid chondrosarcoma. *TLS* is rearranged in myxoid liposarcoma and some acute leukaemias. A single case of angiomatoid malignant fibrous histiocytoma also showed a *TLS* rearrangement. *EWS* is rearranged in Ewing sarcoma, clear cell sarcoma, myxoid liposarcoma, extraskeletal myxoid chondrosarcoma and desmoplastic small round cell tumour. (From Morohoshi *et al.*, 1998, Genomic structure of the human RBP56/hTAFII68 and FUS/TLS genes. *Gene*, **221**, 191–198, copyright 1998, with permission from Elsevier Science.)

expression has been correlated with a worse prognosis in some (Cance *et al.*, 1990) but not all series of soft tissue sarcomas (see Prognostic Factors, below).

MDM2 (*Murine Double Minute 2*) gene amplification and protein overexpression are commonly observed in soft tissue sarcomas (Oliner *et al.*, 1992). *MDM2* is mapped on 12q13 and has its transcription regulated by the p53 protein in a negative feedback loop. Mdm2 protein seems to form a trimeric complex with both p53 and Rb1. Mdm2 protein inhibits apoptosis and stimulates cell cycle progression by inactivating the p53 protein. *MDM2* gene amplification is not always correlated with Mdm2 protein overexpression detected by immunohistochemical analysis. Overexpression of Mdm2 protein was correlated with a worse prognosis in large series of patients with soft tissue sarcomas.

Additional genetic alterations have been observed in soft tissue sarcomas. On the same region of *MDM2* (12q13-15), other genes, including *HMGI-C*, *SAS*, *GLI* and *CDK4*, were found to be amplified. The *HMGI-C* gene (*High Mobility Group Protein I-C*) encodes for a DNA transcription factor. *HMGI-C* has been found to be rearranged or amplified in lipomas and atypical lipomatous tumours (well-differentiated liposarcomas). The *SAS* gene (*Sarcoma Amplified Sequence*),

a member of the transmembrane 4 superfamily of proteins, is involved in cell growth regulation and was found to be amplified in malignant fibrous histiocytomas and liposarcomas. The *GLI* gene (*GLIoma*) encodes a transcription factor and is amplified in gliomas and high-grade childhood sarcomas. *CDK4* (*Cyclin Dependent Kinase 4*) encodes a cell cycle protein kinase, and its amplification may favour cell proliferation. Deletions or rearrangements, but not point mutations, of the genes *INK4A* (*INhibitor of Cyclin Dependent Kinase 4A*, which encodes for the cell cycle inhibitors p16 and p19ARF) and *INK4B* (which encodes for the cell cycle inhibitor p15) on the chromosome 9p21 were found in high-grade sarcomas and correlated with poor survival after adjustment for size and grade. Mutations of K-*RAS* (*Kirsten*) and H-*RAS* (*Harvey*) oncogenes were found in a few series of soft tissue sarcomas and were more common in malignant fibrous histiocytoma. Interestingly, these mutations are common in Korean patients and rare in American patients.

*HER2/*neu (*Human Epidermal growth factor Receptor 2*) gene amplification or protein overexpression as well as microsatellite instability seem uncommon in soft tissue sarcomas, but the data are limited. (See Synovial Sarcoma later in this chapter for additional information on HER2/neu).

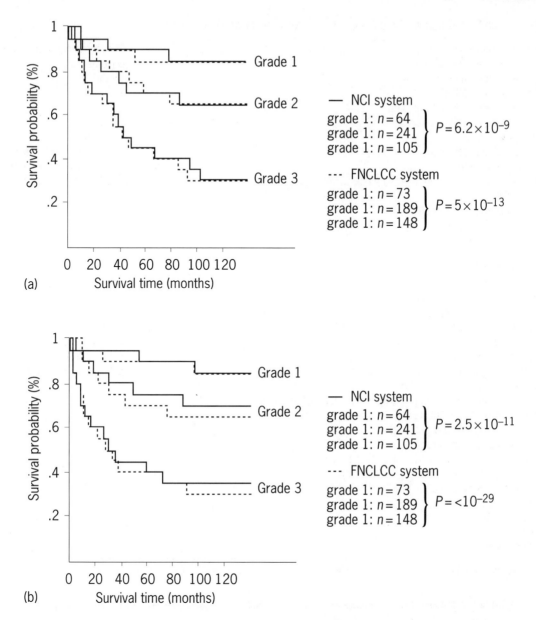

Figure 3 Survival curves according to histologic grade using the National Cancer Institute (NCI) and French Federation of Cancer Centres (FNCLCC) systems. (a) Overall survival; (b) metastasis-free survival. (From Guillou *et al.*, 1997, by permission of the American Society of Clinical Oncology.)

GRADING AND STAGING SYSTEMS

Many systems have been proposed for the grading and staging of soft tissue sarcomas. Their main goal is to identify patient groups with comparable clinicopathologic features for treatment optimization, prognostication and data comparison among cancer centres.

Histological grading has been considered the most powerful independent prognostic factor for soft tissue sarcomas and is based on the assessment of morphological features. Degree of tumour differentiation (resemblance to normal tissue counterparts), mitotic activity, necrosis and cellularity are histological variables commonly evaluated during the grading process. Currently, the French Federation of Cancer Centres (Trojani *et al.*, 1984) and the National Cancer Institute (Costa *et al.*, 1984) grading systems are the most commonly used and provide similar results (**Figure 3**) (Guillou *et al.*, 1997). The French Federation of Cancer Centres uses a 3-grade system that combines tumour differentiation, mitotic count, and necrosis to create a score (**Table 3**). The NCI also uses a three-grade system based on histological subtype and the amount of necrosis. The prognostic information obtained with each system has been validated in many reports but problems remain. Subjectivity on the assessment of some histologic variables, uneven representation of specific

Table 3   French Federation of Cancer Centres system for sarcoma grading

A. Tumour differentiation score[a]	B. Tumour necrosis score[b]
1 Well-differentiated liposarcoma	0 No necrosis
Well-differentiated fibrosarcoma	1 ≤50% tumour surface examined
Well-differentiated MPNST	2 >50% tumour surface necrosis
Well-differentiated leiomyosarcoma	
Well-differentiated chondrosarcoma	
2 Myxoid liposarcoma	C. Mitotic activity score
Conventional fibrosarcoma	1 0–9 mitoses/10 HPF
Conventional MPNST	2 10–19 mitoses/10 HPF
Well-differentiated malignant haemangiopericytoma	3 ≥20 mitoses/10 HPF
Myxoid MFH	
Typical storiform/pleomorphic MFH	
Conventional leiomyosarcoma	
Myxoid chondrosarcoma	
Conventional angiosarcoma	
3 Round cell liposarcoma	Final grade
Pleomorphic liposarcoma	Score A + score B + score C
Dedifferentiated liposarcoma	
Poorly differentiated fibrosarcoma	
Poorly differentiated MPNST	Score
Epithelioid malignant schwannoma	2–3 Grade 1 sarcoma
Malignant Triton tumour	4–5 Grade 2 sarcoma
Conventional malignant haemangiopericytoma	6–8 Grade 3 sarcoma
Giant cell and inflammatory MFH	
Poorly differentiated/pleomorphic/epithelioid leiomyosarcoma	
Synovial sarcoma (any subtype)	
Rhabdomyosarcoma (any subtype)	
Mesenchymal chondrosarcoma	
Poorly differentiated/epithelioid angiosarcoma	
Extraskeletal osteosarcoma	
Extraskeletal Ewing sarcoma/PNET	
Alveolar soft part sarcoma	
Malignant rhabdoid tumour	
Clear cell sarcoma	
Undifferentiated sarcoma	

[a]Tumours showing close similarity to normal adult tissue are scored 1, sarcomas of certain histological sybtype are scored 2 and sarcomas of uncertain histological subtype are scored 3.
[b]Estimated by microscopic review only.
HPF, high-power field (1 HPF = 0.174 mm^2); MFH, malignant fibrous histiocytoma; MPNST, malignant peripheral nerve sheath tumour; PNET, peripheral neurectodermal tumour.
Data from Trojani et al. (1984).
Adapted from Guillou et al., 1997, by permission of the American Society of Clinical Oncology.

sarcomas and lack of standardization of cutoff points among the reported series are factors that preclude universal acceptance of a particular grading system. Because soft tissue sarcomas are rare, prospective multicentre studies are needed to determine useful histological variables for each type of sarcoma.

The two most common staging systems are the American Joint Committee on Cancer/Union Internationale Contre le Cancer (AJCC/UICC) staging system (Fleming et al., 1997) (**Table 4**) and the Enneking system (Enneking et al., 1980). These systems are chiefly designed for the staging of adult soft tissue sarcomas. The AJCC/UICC system is a four-stage system based on tumour size, presence or absence of lymph node involvement and distant metastases and histological grade. Approximate 5-year overall

survival rates for patients with soft tissue sarcomas in stages I, II and III are 95, 80, and 45%, respectively (**Figure 4**) (Pisters and Brennan, 2000). Important limitations of the AJCC/UICC system are the inclusion of lymph node status and the noninclusion of the anatomic site or the adequacy of the surgical margins. The first is a limitation in that lymph node metastases occur infrequently (2.6–5.9%) in sarcomas, in contrast to epithelial tumours. However, epithelioid sarcoma, angiosarcoma and rhabdomyosarcoma often do metastasize to lymph nodes. Most sarcomas metastasize hematogenously, and distant metastases are often present when lymph node involvement is discovered. Anatomical site is omitted in the AJCC/UICC system. Retroperitoneal, visceral and head and neck sarcomas are less likely to be completely resected without affecting vital structures; these

Table 4   American Joint Committee on Cancer/Union Internationale Contre le Cancer Staging System (Fleming *et al.*, 1997)

Tumour (T)	
T1 tumours: ≤5 cm (T1a, T1b)	a, superficial to superficial fascia
T2 tumours: >5 cm (T2a, T2b)	b, deep to superficial fascia
Grade (G)	Stage I
G1: well-differentiated	IA: G1/G2 T1a/b N0 M0
G2: moderately differentiated	IB: G1/G2 T2a N0 M0
G3: poorly differentiated	
G4: undifferentiated	Stage II
	IIA: G1/G2 T2b N0 M0
Lymph nodes (N)	IIB: G3/G4 T1a/b N0 M0
N0: no involvement	IIC: G3/G4 T2a N0 M0
N1: involved	
	Stage III
Metastasis (M)	G3/4 T2b N0 M0
M0: no metastasis	
M1: metastasis present	Stage IV
	IVA: Any G Any T N1 M0
	IVB: Any G Any T Any N M1

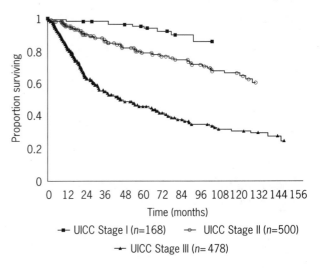

Figure 4   Overall survival for 1146 patients with primary soft tissue sarcoma according to the Union Internationale Contre le Cancer (UICC) staging system. Patients were treated at Memorial Sloan-Kettering Cancer Center, New York. (From Pisters and Brennan, 2000, by permission of Churchill Livingstone.)

sarcomas tend to be associated with a worse prognosis (see Treatment, below).

The Enneking system is surgical staging based on anatomical compartments and histological grade (Enneking *et al.*, 1980). The primary tumour is considered intracompartmental or extracompartmental according to its confinement within well-defined anatomic boundaries. Each of the system's three stages carries its own prognosis.

DIAGNOSIS

The diagnosis of soft tissue sarcoma requires a multidisciplinary approach. Physical examination, imaging studies, histological evaluation and ancillary techniques such as immunohistochemical analysis, electron microscopy, and cytogenetics molecular studies are important steps toward a correct diagnosis.

Clinical History and Physical Examination

Clinical findings alone are not specific for the diagnosis of a soft tissue tumour, but some clues point toward the possibility of a sarcoma. Information on age, sex, tumour location, the presence of genetic syndromes and the duration and quality of symptoms narrow the differential diagnosis substantially. In general, a soft tissue sarcoma presents as a painless mass of a few months' duration. Short duration of symptoms suggests a reactive process, such as that observed in nodular fasciitis (a pseudosarcomatous lesion commonly seen in the upper extremities of young patients). In contrast, long duration of symptoms suggests a benign tumour. Pain,

paresthesias and paresis are observed when there is direct involvement or compression of major neurovascular structures and can occur with benign and malignant tumours. Organ-specific dysfunction also may occur due to the same causes. For example, large retroperitoneal liposarcomas can lead to renal dysfunction due to ureter compression. Paraneoplastic syndromes are seen rarely; examples include fever, weight loss, anaemia and paraproteinaemia occasionally seen in angiomatoid fibrous histiocytoma (see Angiomatoid Fibrous Histiocytoma, below); increased hepatic transaminases in the absence of liver metastases in patients with malignant peripheral nerve sheath tumour (Stauffer syndrome); osteomalacia in patients with phosphaturic mesenchymal tumour; and hypoglycemia in patients with solitary fibrous tumour. Patients who present with metastatic disease have symptoms and signs according to the location of the metastases.

Imaging Studies

After the initial clinical assessment, imaging studies often are needed for better delineation of soft tissue masses and their relation to surrounding normal structures. Simple radiographs have a limited role in the evaluation of soft tissue masses. However, simple radiographs can detect a soft tissue calcification or ossification, involvement of adjacent bone, or a possible bone origin of a soft tissue tumour (Kransdorf and Murphey, 1997). Computed tomography (CT) has been largely replaced by magnetic resonance imaging (MRI) in the evaluation of soft tissue tumours. Nonetheless, CT remains the best imaging technique for detecting pulmonary metastases, providing essential information for staging and

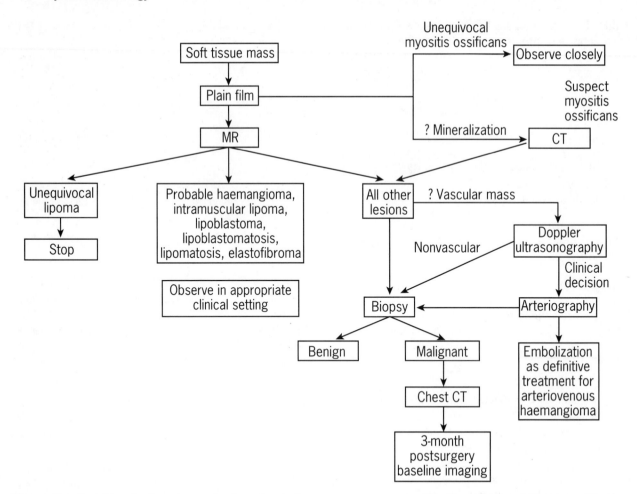

Figure 5　Algorithm for imaging evaluation of soft tissue masses proposed by Kransdorf and Murphey. CT, computed tomography; MR, magnetic resonance. (From Kransdorf and Murphey, 1997, by permission of WB Saunders.)

management. CT is superior in detecting calcification or ossification in soft tissue masses, such as zonal ossification in myositis ossificans, and has higher sensitivity than simple radiographs in detecting subtle bone involvement. Ultrasonography is useful for distinguishing between a solid and a cystic lesion and between soft tissue oedema and a soft tissue mass; it is also useful for guiding percutaneous biopsy. MRI is considered the gold standard because it provides precise information regarding tumour size, depth, local extension and relationship to normal structures such as vessels, bone and nerves. However, MRI is not usually diagnostic. Soft tissue lesions for which MRI can allow diagnosis include haemangioma, myositis ossificans, elastofibroma, fibromatosis, lipoma and liposarcoma, ganglion, haematoma, neurofibroma and malignant peripheral nerve sheath tumour (MPNST). Scintigraphy usually is not needed except to differentiate bone metastases from soft tissue tumours. Other imaging techniques are seldom used at present. An algorithm for imaging evaluation of soft tissue masses is shown in **Figure 5** (Kransdorf and Murphey, 1997). (Additional information can be found in the section on Diagnostic Imaging and Image-Guided Intervention.)

Biopsy and Basic Histological Assessment

Biopsy is usually the final step in the evaluation of soft tissue masses (see section on *Diagnostic Imaging*). It is generally advisable to perform a biopsy on any enlarging soft tissue mass (larger than 4–5 cm) with a median duration of 4–8 weeks in an adult patient (Pisters and Brennan, 2000). The biopsy can be closed or open. Closed procedures include core-needle biopsy and fine-needle aspiration (FNA). Open procedures include incisional and excisional biopsies. In incisional biopsies only part of the tumour is resected; in excisional biopsies the entire lesion is removed. Closed procedures, particularly core-needle biopsies, are the preferred method in most centres. FNA also is routinely used in many institutions and usually provides satisfactory results. In addition, ancillary techniques can be performed on FNA-obtained material. However, the most important role of FNA is documentation of tumour recurrence or metastasis. The major disadvantages of core biopsies and FNA are that tumour sampling is inadequate for precise histological analysis and, when preoperative treatment with radiotherapy or chemotherapy is contemplated, a limited amount of tumour material is available for future studies. In these latter cases, the tumour is often largely necrotic after preoperative treatment and has few or no viable cells. Open procedures, such as excisional biopsies, are sometimes indicated for small superficial lesions, usually smaller than 4–5 cm. Imaging techniques such as CT and ultrasonography are important for guiding biopsy procedures.

Assessment of tumour type and histological grade is performed on paraffin-embedded, formalin-fixed material stained with haematoxylin and eosin. However, frozen material stained with haematoxylin and eosin or toluidine blue is commonly used in some institutions for a fast preliminary diagnosis.

Immunohistochemical Analysis

Immunohistochemical analysis has been extensively used in the study of soft tissue tumours and is primarily based on enzymatic methods, which work well on formalin-fixed material. The avidin–biotin–enzyme complex is one of the most commonly used methods. More than 30 markers are routinely used to evaluate soft tissue tumours, mainly for diagnostic purposes. Vimentin is a 57-kDa cytoplasmic intermediate filament present in almost all soft tissue tumours but also in some carcinomas and melanomas. In the analysis of soft tissue tumours, vimentin primarily is used as an internal control marker; its presence indicates preservation of tissue antigenicity. It is important to emphasize that vimentin is not useful to distinguish between sarcomas and other tumour types.

Cytokeratins are much more useful than vimentin for differentiating soft tissue sarcomas from carcinomas. However, cytokeratin expression is found in up to 5% of soft tissue sarcomas and is considered diagnostic for certain sarcomas. Well-known examples of sarcomas that express cytokeratins are synovial sarcoma, epithelioid sarcoma, desmoplastic small round cell tumour, MPNST, angiosarcoma, leiomyosarcoma, epithelioid haemangioendothelioma and rhabdoid tumour.

Epithelial membrane antigen (EMA) is a complex of proteins isolated from the human milk fat globule membrane. EMA is commonly expressed in synovial sarcoma, epithelioid sarcoma, MPNST, and other soft tissue tumours.

Muscle markers include desmin, muscle-specific actin (MSA HHF35), alpha smooth muscle actin (SMA 1A4), MyoD1 (also known as Myogenic Factor 3), myoglobulin, myogenin, calponin and caldesmon. Desmin is a 52-kDa intermediate filament expressed in leiomyosarcoma, rhabdomyosarcoma and other tumours of muscle differentiation. MSA comprises alpha (skeletal, smooth and cardiac) and gamma smooth muscle actin. MSA is expressed in more than 90% of leiomyosarcomas and 95% of rhabdomyosarcomas. SMA also is expressed in smooth muscle neoplasms such as leiomyosarcoma but is seldom expressed in rhabdomyosarcoma (1–2%). SMA expression frequently indicates the presence of myofibroblastic or myoid differentiation in nonmuscle tumours. MyoD1 is a 45-kDa protein member of a group of myogenic regulatory nuclear proteins that also includes myogenin, myf5 and mrf4-herculin/myf-6. MyoD1 is expressed in an early stage of skeletal muscle differentiation and is found primarily in rhabdomyosarcoma. Myoglobulin is a highly specific but not sensitive marker for rhabdomyoblastic differentiation, considering that it is primarily expressed in more differentiated rhabdomyosarcomas.

CD31, Factor VIII-related antigen (Factor VIIIRa) and CD34 are commonly used markers for endothelial differentiation. CD31 (glycoprotein gpIIa) is a membrane protein from the immunoglobulin supergene family. CD31 shows the highest sensitivity and specificity for endothelial differentiation, being detected in more than 80% of angiosarcomas. Factor VIIIRa is less sensitive than CD31 but is a useful marker for endothelial differentiation. CD34 (also known as haematopoietic progenitor cell antigen) is a 110-kDa transmembrane protein primarily expressed by human haematopoietic stem cells and endothelial cells. CD34 is sensitive but not specific for endothelial differentiation. CD34 expression is also of diagnostic importance in nonendothelial tumours such as DFSP, giant cell fibroblastoma, solitary fibrous tumour, and gastrointestinal stromal tumour.

S-100 protein, which is principally expressed by melanocytic tumours, also is expressed by soft tissue tumours, such as clear cell sarcoma (malignant melanoma of soft parts; 90% of tumours) and MPNST (50–70% of tumours). Nonetheless, S-100 expression has also been identified in other soft tissue sarcomas. CD68 is a 110-kDa lysosomal glycoprotein found mainly in monocytes and macrophages. In the past, CD68 and Factor XIIIa were considered markers of histiocytic differentiation. However, studies have shown the lack of specificity of both markers for this aim, limiting their diagnostic applicability. In addition, expression of CD68 and factor XIIIa by tumour-infiltrating histiocytes can lead to false-positive results.

p30/32 MIC2 (*M*onoclonal *I*mperial *C*ancer Research Fund *2*) or CD99 is a 32-kDa cell membrane glycoprotein encoded by the *MIC2* pseudoautosomal gene located on chromosome Xpter-p22.32. MIC2 is expressed by more than 95% of Ewing sarcoma/PNET. However, MIC2 also is expressed by other neoplasms, such as lymphomas, rhabdomyosarcomas, synovial sarcoma and mesenchymal chondrosarcoma.

Recently, immunohistochemical techniques have been developed to detect abnormal chimaeric proteins or amino acid sequences associated with specific sarcomas. It is expected that they will be used commonly in the future. Prognostic markers detected by immunohistochemical analysis include Ki-67, p53, Mdm2, Rb1 and p-glycoprotein (see Prognostic Factors, below).

Ultrastructural Analysis

With the advent of immunohistochemical and molecular techniques, the role of ultrastructural analysis in the diagnosis of soft tissue tumours is more limited but still important. Generally, ultrastructural analysis is required when histological, immunohistochemical and cytogenetic and molecular studies are inconclusive. Ultrastructural studies are useful in the identification of poorly differentiated rhabdomyosarcoma, the differentiation of sarcomatoid carcinoma or spindle cell melanoma from spindle cell sarcomas such as MPNST and monophasic synovial sarcoma and the identification of atypical forms of alveolar soft part sarcoma. Electron microscopy remains an important research tool, however, providing ultrastructural support for new morphological and immunohistochemical findings in many of the previously and most of the recently recognized tumours. For example, neuroendocrine differentiation in extraskeletal myxoid chondrosarcoma was confirmed through detection of neurosecretory granules by electron microscopy.

Cytogenetics, Molecular Cytogenetics and Molecular Genetics

Cytogenetic and molecular techniques are important adjuvant tools in the diagnosis of soft tissue sarcomas. Traditional cytogenetic evaluation has provided fundamental information regarding chromosomal abnormalities in soft tissue sarcomas. However, this technique depends on the availability of fresh viable tumour material and is time- and labour-intensive. Therefore, it is of limited clinical use in many centres.

Fluorescence *in situ* hybridization (FISH) was a considerable technical advance for chromosomal analysis. FISH relies on the use of fluorochrome-labelled complementary DNA (cDNA) probes that hybridize to specific DNA sequences. FISH can be performed not only in fresh tumour material but also in frozen and paraffin-embedded tissue. Both metaphase chromosomal spreads and interphase cells can be studied. In addition, FISH provides direct cell visualization, allowing correlation between histological and cytogenetic features. *In situ* hybridization can also be performed using enzymatic methods, such as the colorimetric *in situ* histochemistry (CISH).

Another important technique in the diagnosis of soft tissue sarcomas is the reverse transcriptase–polymerase chain reaction (RT-PCR), a variant of PCR. RT-PCR is used for detecting abnormal chimaeric mRNA transcripts on frozen and paraffin-embedded material. RT-PCR is preferred to standard PCR because chimeric mRNAs have more structural consistency than native chimeric genes owing to splicing of intronic sequences. More recently, RT-PCR has been tested to detect minimal disease in the peripheral blood in patients with Ewing sarcoma/PNET, rhabdomyosarcoma and myxoid liposarcoma. Southern blot is occasionally used but requires large amounts of frozen material (Ladanyi and Bridge, 2000). Because these methods have advantages and disadvantages, they should be viewed as complementary diagnostic tools. **Table 2** lists some chromosomal and genetic abnormalities that can be investigated with the above techniques.

CLINICOPATHOLOGICAL FEATURES

In this section, we discuss clinicopathological, immunohistochemical, ultrastructural and genetic features of specific sarcomas following the same schema (with some modifications) as used by the World Health Organisation for classification of soft tissue tumours. Rare sarcomas are not discussed; the reader is referred to comprehensive references on the subject.

Tumours of Fibroblastic and Myofibroblastic Differentiation

Fibromatoses

Fibromatoses are locally aggressive lesions without metastatic potential. They are broadly divided into superficial and deep (desmoid type). The main types of superficial fibromatosis are palmar fibromatosis (Dupuytren disease), plantar fibromatosis (Ledderhose disease) and penile fibromatosis (Peyronie disease). Fibromatoses usually occur in adults and can be bilateral. They are characterized by slow nodular fibroblastic and myofibroblastic proliferations that arise in fascias and aponeuroses. Immunohistochemical analysis shows the expression of vimentin and actin. A weak association of Dupuytren disease with alcoholism and epilepsy has been suggested. Cytogenetic studies often show trisomies 7, 8 and 14.

Deep fibromatosis or desmoid tumours are divided anatomically into three main types: extra-abdominal, abdominal and intra-abdominal. They frequently occur in young adults, and there is a female predominance. These tumours can be sporadic or familial. Intra-abdominal (mesenteric) fibromatosis occurs in 5–15% of patients with Gardner syndrome. Abdominal desmoid tumours are more common in females and tend to occur during or after pregnancy. Desmoid tumours commonly present as large tumours, usually exceeding 5 cm. They are characterized by a fascicular fibroblastic and myofibroblastic proliferation with infiltrative borders. Desmoid tumours are considered clonal lesions. Trisomies 8 and 20 and deletion of 5q (region of the *APC* gene) are common cytogenetic abnormalities. Overexpression of β-catenin has been implicated in the pathogenesis of desmoid tumours and seems related to mutations in the *APC* gene. In addition, β-catenin gene mutations have been found in sporadic desmoid tumours.

Clinically, desmoid tumours are characterized by high rates of recurrence (40%; 90% in some old series). Surgical excision followed or not by radiotherapy has been

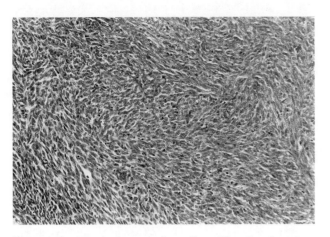

Figure 6   Fascicular spindle cell proliferation in a herringbone pattern is characteristic of but not specific for fibrosarcoma.

considered the therapy of choice. In a series including almost 200 patients, the overall 5- and 10-year relapse rates were 30 and 33%, respectively. Wide local excision with negative surgical margins provided the best results (Ballo *et al.*, 1999). However, the need for negative surgical margins to prevent recurrence is not universally accepted. Because desmoid tumours express oestrogen receptors, the use of tamoxifen and anti-inflammatory drugs has been suggested, but the efficacy of these treatments is questionable. Chemotherapy has been attempted in patients with progressive disease.

Fibrosarcoma

Fibrosarcoma was a commonly diagnosed soft tissue sarcoma before the 1980s. However, major advances in immunohistochemistry, electron microscopy, cytogenetics and molecular genetics resulted in the reclassification of most cases as monophasic synovial sarcoma or MPNST. Currently, fibrosarcoma represents less than 5% of soft tissue sarcomas and is considered a diagnosis of exclusion. Fibrosarcoma usually occurs between the fourth and sixth decades of life, and there is a slight male predominance. The lower extremities and the trunk are the most common locations. Histological analysis shows fascicular spindle cell proliferation in a herringbone pattern, which is characteristic but not specific (**Figure 6**). Collagen deposition is usually small, and the cellularity is higher than that observed in deep fibromatoses. However, a low-grade fibrosarcoma can be misdiagnosed as a desmoid tumour. Fibrosarcoma shows immunoreactivity for vimentin only. Cytokeratin, EMA, actins, desmin and S-100 protein must be absent to rule out other differential diagnoses. No specific cytogenetic or molecular findings have been described for the adult type of fibrosarcoma. A study of more than 100 patients from the late 1980s found a 5-year overall survival rate of 40% (Scott *et al.*, 1989).

Congenital Fibrosarcoma

Congenital or infantile fibrosarcoma (CF) occurs mainly during the first 2 years of life, has a male predominance and usually arises in the distal extremities. Histologically, it is characterized by a proliferation of oval to round cells with prominent mitotic activity arranged in shorter fascicles than the adult fibrosarcoma. A vascular pattern resembling that of haemangiopericytoma and a rich lymphocytic infiltrate are other frequently observed histological findings. The immunohistochemical profile of CF is similar to that of adult fibrosarcoma. The non-random chromosomal translocation t(12;15)(p13;q25) fusing the *ETV6* (*TEL*) gene (*ETS Variant 6*) on chromosome 12p13 and the *NTRK3*(*TRKC*) gene (*Neurotrophin TyRosine Kinase type-3* receptor) on chromosome 15q25 has been found in CF and the cellular variant of congenital mesoblastic nephroma, supporting the view that they have a common pathogenesis. Trisomy 11 is also common in both tumours. Interestingly, the same chimeric gene *ETV6/ NTRK3* is found in some cases of acute myelogenous leukaemia. Clinically, CF is characterized by its excellent prognosis (5-year survival rate >80%) and low metastatic potential (10%).

Fibrosarcoma Variants and Related Tumours

Some variants of fibrosarcoma or related lesions with distinct clinicopathologic features have been recognized. They include the low-grade fibromyxoid sarcoma, which should not be confused with myxofibrosarcoma (see Malignant Fibrous Histiocytoma below), the closely related hyalinizing spindle cell tumour with giant rosettes, sclerosing epithelioid fibrosarcoma, acral myxoinflammatory fibroblastic sarcoma and low-grade myofibroblastic sarcoma (myofibrosarcoma).

Inflammatory Myofibroblastic Tumour

Inflammatory myofibroblastic tumour (IMT) is also known as inflammatory pseudotumour, plasma cell granuloma, inflammatory myofibrohistiocytic proliferation, intra-abdominal myxoid hamartoma and inflammatory fibrosarcoma. IMT is a clonal disorder characterized by fascicles of deceptively bland myofibroblastic cells admixed with a prominent inflammatory infiltrate rich in plasma cells, lymphocytes and eosinophils. IMT occurs predominantly during childhood and is commonly associated with systemic symptoms. The abdominal cavity, retroperitoneum and lungs are commonly affected sites. IMT shows immunoreactivity for actin, which supports its myofibroblastic nature. Cytogenetically, recurrent rearrangements of the *ALK* gene (*Anaplastic Lymphoma Kinase*) on chromosome 2p23 with the tropomyosin genes *TPM3* and *TPM4* have been found in some cases of IMT (Lawrence *et al.*, 2000). Interestingly, the chimaeric *TPM3/ALK* gene also has been described in anaplastic large cell lymphoma. Expression of Alk protein can also be detected by immunohistochemical analysis. Clinically, IMT is characterized by local recurrence in up to 25% of cases and very low metastatic potential.

Tumours of Fibrohistiocytic Differentiation

The idea of fibrohistiocytic differentiation was introduced in the 1980s and was based on erroneous conclusions drawn from morphological, immunohistochemical and cell culture studies of poorly differentiated sarcomas. Currently, it is largely believed that most of these tumours show some degree of fibroblastic or myofibroblastic differentiation. In this chapter, the term fibrohistiocytic is used in accordance with the current literature and for purposes of classification only.

Atypical Fibroxanthoma

Atypical fibroxanthoma (AF) is a superficial fibrohistiocytic tumour with a bimodal age incidence. In older individuals, AF occurs in areas of solar exposure, such as the head and neck. In young patients, it commonly affects the trunk and extremities. However, it has been suggested that the pleomorphic variant of benign fibrous histiocytoma accounts for most cases of AF in young patients. Clinically, AF presents as small cutaneous nodules that sometimes ulcerate. Histologically, it is characterized by a storiform or fascicular proliferation of spindle and epithelioid cells exhibiting striking pleomorphism and high mitotic activity. Cellular lipidization is common. AF shows immunoreactivity for vimentin and other nonspecific markers. Actin has been detected in some cases, suggesting myofibroblastic differentiation. In a study using digital image analysis, the pleomorphic cells were shown to be aneuploid. In contrast, the spindle cells had a diploid DNA content. The prognosis is excellent, with very low recurrence rates (5%) and an exceedingly small metastatic potential. Local surgical excision using micrographic surgery (Mohs technique) seems to be the treatment of choice.

Dermatofibrosarcoma Protuberans and Giant Cell Fibroblastoma

Dermatofibrosarcoma protuberans (DFSP) and giant cell fibroblastoma (GCF) seem to represent two ends of the same spectrum of tumours. DFSP is a superficial sarcoma that occurs mainly during the third and fourth decades of life. The trunk and upper extremities are the most common locations. Histologically, DFSP is characterized by a storiform proliferation (resembling a rush mat) of spindle cells with minimal mitotic activity and infiltrative margins. The pigmented variant of DFSP, also known as Bednar tumour, is characterized by the presence of abundant melanin-pigmented dendritic spindle cells.

In contrast, GCF frequently occurs in male patients during the first decade of life. The thorax and lower extremities are the most common sites. Histologically, GCF is characterized by pseudovascular (angiectoid) spaces and solid areas where giant cell fibroblasts similar to florete cells are found in variable amounts. Mitotic activity is minimal. Immunohistochemistry shows that DFSP and GCF express vimentin and CD34. Neural, muscular and endothelial markers are usually absent. Ultrastructural analysis shows the presence of modified fibroblasts known as veil cells in both GCF and DFSP. Traditionally, cytogenetic studies have shown ring chromosome 17 in more than 75% of cases of DFSP. It has been further shown that these ring chromosomes harbour a nonrandom translocation t(17;22)(q22;q13) involving the *PDGFβ* gene (*Platelet-Derived Growth Factor β*-chain) on chromosome 22q13 and the *COL1A1* gene (*COL*lagen type *I Alpha 1*) on chromosome 17q22 in DFSP and GCF (Simon *et al.*, 1997). PDGFβ stimulates cell proliferation and transformation and COL1A1 is an important connective tissue matrix constituent. The chimaeric protein was shown to transform NIH3T3 fibroblast cell lines via an uncontrolled autocrine mechanism, reflecting its oncogenic ability. Clinically, DFSP is characterized by high recurrence rates (up to 75%) and low metastatic potential (1%). The presence of fibrosarcoma or malignant fibrous histiocytoma areas has been associated with higher metastatic rates (15%). This last impression, however, was questioned in one report. GCF also presents a high recurrence rate (up to 50%) but metastases have not been reported so far.

Plexiform Fibrohistiocytic Tumour

Plexiform fibrohistiocytic tumour (PFT) is a rare neoplasm that occurs predominantly in the dermis and subcutaneous tissue of the upper extremities during the first two decades of life. There is a strong female predilection. Histologically, PFT is composed of nodules of histiocyte-like and osteoclast-like giant cells (plexiform areas) separated by fascicles of spindle cells. Haemorrhage and haemosiderin deposition are common in the plexiform areas. Immunohistochemical studies have shown the presence of CD68 in the histiocyte-like and osteoclast-like giant cells and actin in the spindle cells. PFT shows a diploid DNA content. Cytogenetic studies are rare. PFT recurs locally in up to one-third of cases and metastasizes in one-fifth. Because of the tendency of PFT to recur locally, wide local surgical excision seems to be the treatment of choice.

Angiomatoid Fibrous Histiocytoma

Angiomatoid fibrous histiocytoma (AFH), previously known as angiomatoid malignant fibrous histiocytoma, is a rare subcutaneous tumour that arises predominantly in the extremities. AFH commonly occurs in the first three decades of life and does not show sex predilection. AFH may be associated with systemic symptoms, including fever, weight loss, anaemia and paraproteinaemia. These seem to be caused by cytokines released by the tumour or by the associated inflammatory cells. Histologically, AFH is characterized by a nodular proliferation of oval to spindle cells associated with pseudovascular spaces. A rich lymphoplasmacytic infiltrate often surrounds the lesion. Immunohistochemical studies have shown the presence of vimentin, CD68, actin and desmin, which suggests that AFH has a line of differentiation similar to that of myoid fibroblastic reticulum cells found in the connective tissue of lymph nodes. Ploidy studies have shown a diploid DNA content in most cases. The chromosomal translocation t(12;16)(q13:p11) involving the *ATF-1* gene (*A*ctivating *T*ranscription *F*actor-*1*; see Clear Cell Sarcoma, below) on chromosome 12q13 and the *FUS* gene (*FUS*ion; see Myxoid and Round Cell Liposarcomas, below) on chromosome 16p11 was found in a case of AFH. Despite the need for confirmatory studies, this finding opened new avenues for the understanding of the pathogenesis of this tumour. AFH is characterized by low rates of local recurrence (10–20%) and limited metastatic potential (<2%). Surgical excision is considered the treatment of choice.

Malignant Fibrous Hystiocytoma

Malignant fibrous histiocytoma (MFH) comprises a heterogeneous group of undifferentiated neoplasms characterized by high pleomorphism and cellular atypia. In the past, a fibrohistiocytic origin was attributed to these neoplasms on the basis of morphological and functional similarities to fibroblasts and histiocytes found in studies of cell cultures. This misinterpretation was supported by the detection of nonspecific histiocytic markers on MFH. With advances in the immunohistochemical techniques and careful tissue sampling, many cases diagnosed as MFH have been reclassified as other high-grade tumours, such as pleomorphic liposarcoma, dedifferentiated liposarcoma, pleomorphic rhabdomyosarcoma, pleomorphic leiomyosarcoma, undifferentiated carcinoma and anaplastic large cell lymphoma. However, there is still a group of tumours that lack specific features and thus remain unclassifiable. Therefore, MFH is currently regarded as a group of tumours with fibroblastic characteristics but undetermined or aberrant lines of differentiation as compared with normal cell types. MFH is considered a diagnosis of exclusion.

MFH was once the most common soft tissue sarcoma. MFH most commonly occurs between the fifth and eighth decades of life and usually arises in the lower extremities (particularly thigh), upper extremities and retroperitoneum (Weiss and Enzinger, 1978). Males are affected slightly more frequently than are females. Histologically, MFH is divided into four variants: storiform/pleomorphic, myxoid, giant cell and inflammatory. Storiform/pleomorphic MFH is characterized by a proliferation (in a pattern resembling a rush mat) of spindle to oval cells and bizarre multinucleated cells showing prominent mitotic activity (**Figure 7**) (Weiss and Enzinger, 1978). Myxoid MFH, also known as

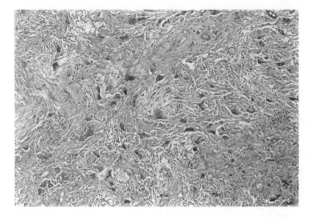

Figure 7 Malignant fibrous histiocytoma showing bizarre giant cells in a vague storiform pattern.

myxofibrosarcoma, has a multinodular and mucinous appearance and tends to be more superficial than the storiform/pleomorphic variant. Myxoid MFH is unusual in the retroperitoneum. Extensive myxoid areas characterize this histological variant; these areas are rich in hyaluronic acid, have high vascularization and contain lipoblast-like cells (pseudolipoblasts). It is currently believed that the giant cell variant of MFH probably encompasses a group of distinct neoplasms rich in osteoclast-like giant cells; this variant includes giant cell-rich extraskeletal osteosarcoma, giant cell-rich pleomorphic leiomyosarcoma, giant cell-rich undifferentiated tumours and the soft tissue counterpart of the giant cell tumour of bone. Inflammatory MFH, the least common variant (<5%), most commonly is found in the retroperitoneum and often is associated with peripheral leucocytosis and systemic symptoms. Histologically, it is characterized by the presence of an inflammatory infiltrate rich in neutrophils, xanthomatous histiocytes, lymphocytes and eosinophils among bizarre Reed–Sternberg-like cells. MFH has no specific immunohistochemical profile; cytogenetic studies have shown very complex karyotypes.

The prognosis of MFH is dictated primarily by its grade and stage. However, other clinicopathological features have been correlated with tumour aggressiveness. A retroperitoneal location and the inflammatory variant have been associated with a poor prognosis. In contrast, myxoid MFH tends to run a less aggressive clinical course. In a series of 216 patients with localized MFH, 5-year disease specific-free, metastasis-free and local recurrence-free survival rates were 70, 63 and 63%, respectively. The presence of high-grade histological features was considered the most important prognostic factor for metastasis-free and disease specific-free survival (Le Doussal *et al.*, 1996).

Sarcomas of Adipose Tissue Differentiation

Sarcomas of adipose tissue differentiation, or liposarcomas, are currently considered the most common soft tissue sarcoma. This group comprises four major variants with distinct clinicopathological and genetic features: well-differentiated, myxoid/round cell, pleomorphic and dedifferentiated.

Well-differentiated Liposarcoma

Well-differentiated liposarcoma arises most commonly in the extremities and retroperitoneum. Histologically, well-differentiated liposarcoma is divided into three major subvariants: lipoma-like (adipocytic), sclerosing and inflammatory. A spindle cell variant also has been recognized. The lipoma-like variant is the most common and is predominantly composed of uniloculated adipocytes and scattered atypical multivacuolated lipoblasts. The sclerosing variant, which occurs most frequently in the retroperitoneum, has extensive fibrillary fibrotic areas where scattered multivacuolated lipoblasts are found. The inflammatory (or lymphocyte-rich) variant is characterized by the presence of lymphoplasmacytic nodular aggregates and may be misdiagnosed as inflammatory myofibroblastic tumour or Castleman disease. This variant often arises in the retroperitoneum. Well-differentiated liposarcomas arising in superficial locations also are known as atypical lipomas because they have an excellent prognosis and no metastatic potential. However, controversies regarding this nomenclature remain. Cytogenetic studies frequently show rings or giant rods derived from chromosome 12 in all subtypes of well-differentiated liposarcomas. These structures contain amplified 12q13-15 sequences, which include the *MDM2*, *SAS*, *HMGI-C* and *CDK4* genes. The clinical course of well-differentiated liposarcomas is usually excellent, with overall 5-year survival rates >90%. However, a worse prognosis has been found in retroperitoneal and dedifferentiated tumours. Local recurrence seems to be prevented by wide local excision and is more common in the retroperitoneum.

Myxoid and Round Cell Liposarcomas

Myxoid liposarcoma is the most common subtype of liposarcoma, representing 35–45% of all liposarcomas. It occurs mainly during the fifth decade of life, has a male predilection, and most commonly arises in the lower extremities, particularly the thigh (Kilpatrick *et al.*, 1996). Histologically, myxoid liposarcoma is composed of spindle and stellate cells immersed in a myxoid matrix rich in hyaluronic acid. A chicken-wire pattern of vascularization is characteristic (**Figure 8**). Lipoblasts occasionally are found, and cystic degeneration of the matrix (resembling lymphangioma) is common.

Round cell liposarcoma is the cellular and poorly differentiated form of myxoid liposarcoma. Histologically, it is composed of round and larger cells with high mitotic and apoptotic activity. Cytogenetic and molecular studies have shown that myxoid and round cell liposarcomas share the same chromosomal translocations. The translocation

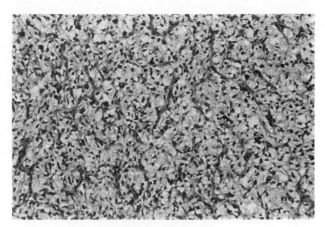

Figure 8   A chicken-wire pattern of vascularization is characteristic and almost diagnostic of myxoid liposarcoma.

t(12;16)(q13;p11) occurs in 95% of cases and involves the *TLS* gene (*T*ranslocated in *L*iposarcoma) or *FUS* gene (*FUS*ion) on chromosome 16p11 and the *CHOP* gene (*CCAAT/enhancer binding protein HO*mologous *P*rotein) or *DDIT3* (*D*NA-*D*amage-*I*nducible *T*ranscript *3*) on chromosome 12q13 (**Figure 9**) (Crozat *et al.*, 1993; Rabbitts *et al.*, 1993). *TLS* encodes for RNA-binding protein similar to the EWS protein (**Figure 2**). *CHOP* encodes for DNA-damage-inducible negative transcription regulator, which also is involved in adipocyte differentiation. In the second chromosomal translocation t(12;22)(q13;q12), which occurs in <5% of cases, the *EWS* gene on chromosome 22q12 fuses with *CHOP* (**Figure 9**). Both chimaeric proteins TLS/CHOP and EWS/CHOP can transform NIH3T3 fibroblasts, reflecting their oncogenic properties.

Myxoid liposarcoma has been associated with a relatively good prognosis, with a 5-year overall survival rate of 75%. Round cell differentiation has been considered the single most important adverse prognostic factor in myxoid liposarcoma (Kilpatrick *et al.*, 1996). More recently, expression of the cell cycle inhibitor $p27^{kip1}$ was associated with a prolonged metastasis-free and overall survival in myxoid/round cell liposarcoma (Oliveira *et al.*, 2000).

Dedifferentiated Liposarcoma

Dedifferentiated liposarcoma is traditionally defined as a well-differentiated liposarcoma showing an abrupt transition to areas of high-grade pleomorphic histological features, similar to storiform/pleomorphic MFH or fibrosarcoma. However, low-grade dedifferentiated areas also have been recognized. Dedifferentiated liposarcoma is predominantly found in the retroperitoneum and appears to occur as a *de novo* phenomenon in >90% of cases. Divergent differentiation to osteosarcoma, chondrosarcoma, rhabdomyosarcoma, leiomyosarcoma and neural-like areas have been described.

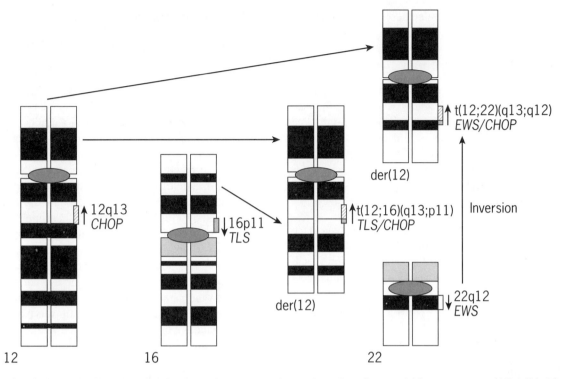

Figure 9   Schematic diagram showing two chromosomal translocations in myxoid liposarcoma: t(12;16)(q13;p11) and t(12;22)(q13;q12). The most common translocation (95% of cases) involves the fusion of the *CHOP* gene on chromosome 12q13 with the *TLS* gene on chromosome 16p11. Observe that the 5′ end of *TLS* gene on chromosome 16 fuses with the downstream sequences of the *CHOP* gene on the derivative chromosome 12. In the least common translocation (5% of cases), the 5′ end of *EWS* gene fuses with downstream sequences of *CHOP*. Observe that the *EWS* gene is read from centromere to telomere (c→t) on chromosome 22 and that the *CHOP* gene is read from telomere to centromere (t→c) on chromosome 16. This suggests that an inversion involving the *EWS* gene must occur before its fusion with the *CHOP* gene, which may explain the lower frequency of this second chromosomal translocation in myxoid liposarcoma. The derivative chromosomes 16 and 22 are not shown (arrowhead, 3′ end; arrow tail, 5′ end).

Immunoreactivity for S-100 protein, frequently found in liposarcomas, is not observed in the dedifferentiated areas. Mdm2 protein overexpression is common, and *TP53* gene mutations are rare. The amount and histological grade of the dedifferentiated component have not been correlated with outcome. In a large series of patients with dedifferentiated liposarcomas, the local recurrence, metastatic and disease-related mortality rates were 41, 17 and 28%, respectively. Overall 5-year survival rates of 50–70% have been estimated.

Pleomorphic Liposarcoma

Pleomorphic liposarcoma comprises <5% of the cases of liposarcoma and most frequently occurs in the extremities. Pleomorphic liposarcoma is a high-grade sarcoma showing MFH-like histological features, including the finding of scattered multiloculated lipoblasts. The incidence of pleomorphic liposarcoma is expected to increase because of ongoing reclassification of cases of MFH. The prognosis of pleomorphic liposarcoma parallels that of other high-grade sarcomas.

Sarcomas of Smooth Muscle Differentiation

Leiomyosarcoma is the single example of this group and probably represents 3–5% of soft tissue sarcomas. Leiomyosarcomas arising in soft tissues are clinically divided into four main types: cutaneous, subcutaneous and intra-muscular, vascular and intra-abdominal. All types are morphologically and immunohistochemically indistinguishable. They are characterized by a fascicular proliferation of eosinophilic spindle cells with cigar-shaped nuclei and perinuclear vacuolization. The tumour fascicles tend to cross each other obliquely, a feature not readily appreciated in pleomorphic variants. Immunohistochemical studies show smooth muscle actin (SMA) in >90% of cases and desmin in 50–70% of cases. Approximately 40% of leiomyosarcomas express cytokeratin and epithelial membrane antigen. Cytogenetic studies frequently show complex karyotypes, and no consistent recurrent chromosomal abnormality has been identified. It has been suggested that 1p36 and 8p21p-ter chromosomal losses may be associated with a more aggressive clinical course, but studies are needed to confirm these initial impressions.

Cutaneous Leiomyosarcoma

Cutaneous leiomyosarcoma occurs most frequently in the lower extremities of young adults. Clinically, they are painful tumours with almost no metastatic potential. Local recurrences occur in up to one-third of cases and seem strongly related to the adequacy of the surgical excision.

Subcutaneous and Intramuscular Leiomyosarcomas

Subcutaneous and intramuscular leiomyosarcomas occur more frequently in the thigh but the retroperitoneum also is a common site. In contrast to the cutaneous form, subcutaneous and soft tissue leiomyosarcomas frequently metastasize to the lungs. A 5-year overall survival rate of 64% was found in a large series of cases (Gustafson et al., 1992).

Vascular Leiomyosarcoma

Vascular leiomyosarcoma represents <5% of all cases of leiomyosarcoma. It arises most commonly in the inferior vena cava and in veins of the lower extremities (Enzinger and Weiss, 1995). There is no sex predilection except for those arising in the inferior vena cava, where a striking female predilection is observed. The pulmonary artery is the single most commonly affected arterial site. In a review of 144 cases of inferior vena cava leiomyosarcoma, radical tumour excision was associated with a better overall survival, despite high recurrence rates (50%) (Mingoli et al., 1991).

Intra-abdominal Leiomyosarcoma

Intra-abdominal leiomyosarcoma most commonly occurs in the retroperitoneum, omentum and mesentery and seems more common in females. These tumours can reach large sizes and often follow an aggressive clinical course. In a series of 44 cases, the overall 5-year survival rate was 21% (Hashimoto et al., 1985). However, with the advent of immunohistochemical analysis, some intra-abdominal leiomyosarcomas have been reclassified as extragastrointestinal stromal tumours (see the chapters *Upper Gastrointestinal Tract (Oesophagus, Stomach)* and *Lower Gastrointestinal Tract (Small Intestine, Appendix, Colon, Rectum, Anus)*.

Sarcomas of Skeletal Muscle Differentiation

Rhabdomyosarcoma and its subtypes comprise this group of sarcomas. However, rhabdomyoblastic differentiation may be observed in other soft tissue sarcomas, such as malignant peripheral nerve sheath tumour with rhabdomyoblastic differentiation (Triton tumour), dedifferentiated liposarcoma and others.

Rhabdomyosarcoma

Rhabdomyosarcoma is the most common peadiatric soft tissue sarcoma (Qualman et al., 1998). Classically, it is divided into the embryonal, botryoid, alveolar and pleomorphic types. However, modifications of this traditional classification are taking place and no schema is universally accepted. Currently, three histological variants are recognized: embryonal (50–60), alveolar (25–30) and pleomorphic (5%).

Embryonal rhabdomyosarcoma occurs most commonly in the first decade of life and is most commonly found in the head and neck area and in the genitourinary tract. It is characterized by a proliferation of small basophilic spindle cells associated with a variable number of rhabdomyoblasts (strap or tadpole cells) in a myxoid stroma. Variants of embryonal rhabdomyosarcoma include the spindle cell and botryoid. Spindle cell rhabdomyosarcoma occurs primarily in the paratesticular area and is associated with an excellent prognosis (5-year overall survival >85%). Botryoid rhabdomyosarcoma has a grape-like macroscopic appearance and most commonly occurs in the genitourinary tract. The characteristic histological finding is the condensation of the rhabdomyoblasts underneath the epithelial lining (cambium layer).

Alveolar rhabdomyosarcoma occurs more commonly in adolescents and frequently arises in the extremities, particularly in the distal segments of the upper extremities, and the trunk. It is characterized by nests of round basophilic cells separated by fibrous septa, simulating the pulmonary parenchyma. Osteoclast-like giant cells frequently are seen in the fibrous septa, and rhabdomyoblasts are scarce.

Pleomorphic rhabdomyosarcoma arises more commonly in the extremities of adults after the fourth decade of life and is associated with an aggressive clinical course. Histologically, it is similar to storiform/pleomorphic MFH and occasionally has large eosinophilic rhabdomyoblasts.

Two other rhabdomyosarcoma variants have been recognized: anaplastic and undifferentiated sarcoma. These terms are in the International Classification of Rhabdomyosarcoma (ICR). Anaplastic rhabdomyosarcoma is considered the pleomorphic variant of rhabdomyosarcoma that occurs in children. Undifferentiated sarcoma, which does not show any rhabdomyoblastic differentiation, is included in the ICR because it has a similar response to the chemotherapy used for other rhabdomyosarcomas (Qualman et al., 1998).

Immunohistochemical studies are important in the differential diagnosis of other tumours, such as Ewing sarcoma/PNET and desmoplastic small round cell tumour. Rhabdomyosarcoma cells express MSA (94%), desmin (80–95% of tumours), MyoD1 (90–95%) and myogenin (75–99%). Myoglobin is expressed in more differentiated rhabdomyoblasts and consequently is less sensitive (60–78%). SMA is present in a minority of cases (<5%).

Ultrastructural studies show the presence of thick myosin filaments associated with ribosomes and Z bands; this finding indicates muscle differentiation. Ultrastructural studies are particularly useful for the diagnosis of poorly differentiated rhabdomyosarcomas, such as pleomorphic and anaplastic rhabdomyosarcoma.

Cytogenetic and molecular studies have shown that alveolar rhabdomyosarcoma is associated with two chromosomal translocations. The translocation t(2;13) (q35;q14) occurs in 75% of cases and involves the fusion of the transcription factors *PAX3* gene (*PA*ired bo*X 3*) on chromosome 2q35 and *FKHR* gene (*ForKH*ead *R*elated) on chromosome 13q14 (Galili *et al.*, 1993). In the translocation t(1;13)(p36;q14), which occurs in approximately 10% of cases, *FKHR* is fused with another partner, *PAX7*. *PAX3* and *PAX7* are specifically expressed during the development of the dorsal neural tube and somites. *PAX3* is also important for the migration of myoblasts to the limbs. Gene expression analyses using cDNA microarrays in alveolar rhabdomyosarcoma have shown that the *PAX3/FKHR* fusion transcript induces the expression of several genes involved in myogenic differentiation, including *MyoD1* and myogenin. In addition, PAX3 protein and the chimaeric protein FKHR/PAX3 stimulate the expression of the antiapoptotic protein BCL-X_L and the *MET* proto-oncogene. PAX7/FKHR fusion transcript in alveolar rhabdomyosarcoma was associated with a younger age at presentation, extremity location, prolonged event-free survival and a trend for a prolonged overall survival in a small series of cases (Kelly *et al.*, 1997).

Embryonal rhabdomyosarcoma frequently shows loss of heterozygosity on 11p15, and this may contribute to the commonly observed overexpression of insulin-like growth factor-II (IGFII). The mechanism underlying this effect seems to result from loss of imprinting or loss of heterozygosity of the normally silent *IGFII* maternal-derived gene allele (see Epidemiology, Aetiology and Pathogenesis, above). Furthermore, loss of heterozygosity of the 11p15 locus can lead to loss of the tumour-suppressor gene *GOK*.

Three staging systems for rhabdomyosarcoma have been proposed: the Clinical Group System (CGS), the TNM system from the Union Internationale Contre le Cancer (UICC) and the TNM system from the American Joint Committee on Cancer (AJCC). The CGS is a surgico-pathological system based on the surgical resectability of the tumour. The TNM system proposed by the UICC is based on the invasiveness of the tumour according to the presence or absence of tumour confinement to a specific organ or muscular group. The TNM system proposed by the AJCC relies primarily on tumour size (Fleming *et al.*, 1997). In the Intergroup Rhabdomyosarcoma Study-V, the information provided by these three systems has been combined to establish prognostic groups (**Table 5**).

Table 5 Prognostic groups for rhabdomyosarcoma

Stage	Group[a]	Site[b]	Size[c]	Age (years)	Histology[d]	Lymph nodes[e]	Distant metastasis[e]	Disease-free survival
1	I	Favourable	a or b	<21	Embryonal	N0	M0	
1	II	Favourable	a or b	<21	Embryonal	N0	M0	
1	III	Orbit only	a or b	<21	Embryonal	N0	M0	Excellent (>85%)
2	I	Unfavourable	a	<21	Embryonal	N0 or NX	M0	
1	II	Favourable	a or b	<21	Embryonal	N1	M0	
1	III	Orbit only	a or b	<21	Embryonal	N1	M0	
1	III	Favourable (no orbit)	a or b	<21	Embryonal	Any	M0	
2	II	Unfavourable	a	<21	Embryonal	N0 or NX	M0	Very good (70–85%)
3	I or II	Unfavourable	a	<21	Embryonal	N1	M0	
3	I or II	Unfavourable	b	<21	Embryonal	Any	M0	
2	III	Unfavourable	a	<21	Embryonal	N0 or NX	M0	
3	III	Unfavourable	a	<21	Embryonal	N1	M0	
3	III	Unfavourable	a	<21	Embryonal	Any	M0	Good (50–70%)
1 or 2 or 3	I or II or III	Any	a or b	<21	Alveolar	Any	M0	
4	Any	Any	a or b	<10	Embryonal	N0 or N1	M1	
4	IV	Any	a or b	>10	Embryonal	N0 or N1	M1	Poor (<30%)
4	IV	Any	a or b	<21	Alveolar	N0 or N1	M1	

[a]Group I, localized tumour, completely excised; group II, total gross tumour excision with evidence of regional spread; group III, incomplete excision with gross residual tumour; group IV, distant metastasis present at onset.

[b]Favourable sites are orbit and eyelid, nonparameningeal head and neck and nonbladder and nonprostate genitourinary tract; unfavourable sites are bladder, prostate, extremity, parameningeal and others.

[c]a, tumour size ≤5 cm; b, tumour size >5 cm.

[d]Embryonal, including also botryoid and spindle cell variants; alveolar, including also solid alveolar, anaplastic, and undifferentiated variants.

[e]N0, regional lymph nodes not clinically involved; N1, regional lymph nodes clinically involved; NX, lymph node status unknown; M0, no distant metastases; M1, distant metastases present.

Adapted from Wexler *et al.*, 2000, Soft tissue sarcomas of childhood. In: Bust, R. C., Jr, *et al.* (eds), *Cancer Medicine*, 5th edn. 2198–2203. (B. C. Decker, Hamilton, ON), by permission of the publisher.

Treatment of rhabdomyosarcoma commonly entails chemotherapy, radiotherapy and surgical excision. Chemotherapy is indicated for unresectable tumours, to allow subsequent surgical excision, for elimination of microscopic disease after primary surgical excision and for metastatic disease. Radiation therapy is used to provide local tumour control after surgical excision or for metastatic disease. Vincristine, D-actinomycin, and cyclophosphamide are commonly used drugs (Arndt and Crist, 1999).

Clinical features and the histological subtypes of rhabdomyosarcoma seem the most important factors in predicting the overall prognosis (**Table 5**). The International Classification of Rhabdomyosarcoma divides rhabdomyosarcomas into those associated with a superior prognosis (botryoid and spindle cell variants of embryonal rhabdomyosarcoma), intermediate prognosis (embryonal rhabdomyosarcoma) and poor prognosis (alveolar and anaplastic or undifferentiated) (Newton *et al.*, 1995; Qualman *et al.*, 1998). In a large series of cases from the Intergroup Rhabdomyosarcoma Study, 5-year overall survival rates of 95, 88, 64 and 53% for botryoid, spindle cell, embryonal and alveolar subtypes, respectively, were found. By multivariate analysis, the histological categories retained their prognostic significance after adjustment for other prognostic factors in rhabdomyosarcoma, such as tumour sizes primary site, and clinical group (Newton *et al.*, 1995).

Sarcomas of Endothelial and Pericytic Differentiation

The three most important sarcomas showing endothelial differentiation are epithelioid haemangioendothelioma, Kaposi sarcoma and angiosarcoma. These sarcomas and haemangiopericytoma are discussed below.

Epithelioid Haemangioendothelioma

Epithelioid haemangioendothelioma is a rare vascular tumour that occurs most commonly in the superficial and deep soft tissues, liver and bone. The tumour affects mainly adults in the fourth to sixth decades of life. Approximately 60% of cases arise in a vessel, usually a vein of medium size or larger. Histologically, it is characterized by cords and nests of round to spindle eosinophilic cells arranged in a myxohyaline stroma. The cells commonly exhibit an intracytoplasmic vacuolization (signet ring-like cells) in which erythrocytes occasionally are found. Mitotic activity is usually very low. Immunohistochemical studies show the expression of vascular markers, such as factor VIIIRa, CD31 and CD34. Expression of cytokeratin and actin is frequently found. Ultrastructural studies support its endothelial differentiation. Cytogenetic and molecular studies are almost nonexistent, but the balanced chromosomal translocation t(1;3)(p36.3;q25) was recently found in two cases. Epithelioid haemangioendothelioma is less aggressive than angiosarcoma, but it metastasizes in 20% of cases and has a mortality rate of 17% when it occurs in soft tissues. Higher mortality rates are seen in hepatic and pulmonary tumours.

Kaposi Sarcoma

Kaposi sarcoma is a unique tumour showing features of lymphatic endothelial differentiation. Whether Kaposi sarcoma is a reactive process or a true neoplasm remains to be settled because monoclonality has been shown by some but not all investigators (Gill *et al.*, 1998). A multicentric clonal evolution has been proposed to explain the pathogenesis of Kaposi sarcoma. In this elegant model, Kaposi sarcoma arises from independent cells and acquires clonal characteristics during tumour progression (Gill *et al.*, 1998).

Kaposi sarcoma traditionally has been divided into four clinical variants: classical, endemic, post-transplant-associated or immunosuppression-associated and epidemic or acquired immunodeficiency syndrome (AIDS)-associated (Antman and Chang, 2000). The classical form is prevalent in Eastern Europe and the Mediterranean and typically presents as indolent purple–blue cutaneous nodules on the lower extremities of elderly men. An increased risk of haematological disorders, particularly Hodgkin lymphoma, has been attributed to this variant. The endemic form occurs in human immunodeficiency virus (HIV)-negative individuals and commonly manifests as indolent nodular lesions associated with localized or generalized lymphadenopathy. A more aggressive form is commonly found in children (Antman and Chang, 2000). The transplant-associated or immunosuppression-associated Kaposi sarcoma is an aggressive form that occurs months or years after transplantation or the beginning of immunosuppression. It often is characterized by lymphatic or visceral manifestations (Antman and Chang, 2000). The epidemic or AIDS-associated Kaposi sarcoma is a very aggressive form that involves the skin, mucosas, viscera and lymph nodes. It is more commonly seen in homosexual AIDS patients.

Independent of clinical presentation, all Kaposi sarcoma are histologically similar. The relationship between Kaposi sarcoma and Kaposi sarcoma-associated herpes virus is discussed above (see Epidemiology, Aetiology and Pathogenesis, above). Histologically, Kaposi sarcoma is characterized by a spindle cell nodular proliferation separated by slit-like thin-walled vascular channels. Extravasated erythrocytes, haemosiderin deposition and hyaline intracytoplasmic and extracytoplasmic PAS-positive globules are commonly seen. Immunohistochemical analysis shows CD31 and CD34 in most cases and variable expression for factor VIIIRa, consistent with Kaposi sarcoma endothelial differentiation. Treatment includes surgical excision (simple excisions), radiation therapy and single or multiple agent chemotherapy, including interferon-α (Antman and Chang, 2000).

Angiosarcoma

Known in the past as malignant haemangioendothelioma or lymphangiosarcoma, angiosarcoma is a highly malignant neoplasm of endothelial differentiation. The term angiosarcoma encompasses blood and lymphatic vascular tumours because no current technique reliably differentiates the two. However, new markers specific for the lymphatic endothelium, such as M2A oncofoetal antigen may shed some light on this issue. Aetiological factors associated with the development of angiosarcoma are discussed above (see Epidemiology, Aetiology and Pathogenesis).

Clinically, angiosarcomas are divided into four groups: cutaneous, soft tissue, postirradiation and visceral. Cutaneous angiosarcoma not associated with lymphoedema shows a predilection for elderly men and most frequently occurs in the head and neck region, particularly in the scalp. It is characterized by a haemorrhagic appearance and multinodularity. The prognosis is reserved, with 5-year overall survival rates <35%. Cutaneous angiosarcoma associated with chronic lymphoedema is discussed above (see Epidemiology, Aetiology and Pathogenesis).

Soft tissue angiosarcoma occurs predominantly in the abdominal cavity, including the retroperitoneum, and lower extremities of older men. As in the cutaneous form, the prognosis is very poor, with more than 50% of patients dying before 1 year after the diagnosis. In a large series of cases, older age, the presence of retroperitoneal tumours and high expression of the proliferative marker Ki-67 were associated with a more aggressive clinical course (Meis-Kindblom and Kindblom, 1998).

Postirradiation angiosarcoma is a highly aggressive tumour that tends to have a shorter latent period than other irradiation-induced sarcomas. Postirradiation angiosarcoma should not be confused with the cutaneous angiosarcoma associated with chronic lymphoedema. Visceral angiosarcoma often occurs in the liver, breast and spleen and is discussed in the respective chapters.

Histologically, all clinical types of angiosarcoma are characterized by an infiltrative proliferation of anastomosing irregular vascular spaces lined by atypical and pleomorphic endothelial cells. Immunohistochemical studies show the expression of Factor VIIIRa, CD31 and CD34 in most cases and the expression of cytokeratin in 35%. However, immunoreactivity for some endothelial markers tends to be lost in more undifferentiated areas. Cytogenetic and molecular studies are limited, and no specific abnormality has been found. *TP53* and *K-RAS2* gene mutations are common. A proliferative autocrine loop mediated by vascular endothelial growth factor (VEGF) and its receptor FLT has been proposed for the pathogenesis of angiosarcoma.

Haemangiopericytoma

Haemangiopericytoma has been considered a controversial entity since it was first described more than 50 years ago.

Its putative pericytic nature was suggested by its morphological similarities to normal pericytes. However, this analogy has not been confirmed by immunohistochemical analysis since most haemangiopericytomas do not express actin, which is normally expressed by pericytes. Most cases diagnosed as haemangiopericytoma have been reclassified as entities such as monophasic synovial sarcoma, mesenchymal chondrosarcoma and solitary fibrous tumour. Currently, the most prevalent opinion is that haemangiopericytoma is a morphological pattern shared by distinct entities, and only a few unclassifiable cases should be termed haemangiopericytoma. Moreover, the old subdivision of haemangiopericytoma into adult and infantile forms no longer holds because the latter has been reclassified as myofibroma. Cases that still deserve the label haemangiopericytoma are some soft tissue tumours that arise in the retroperitoneum and pelvis, meningeal haemangiopericytoma (previously known as angioblastic meningioma), and sinonasal haemangiopericytoma.

Histologically, haemangiopericytomas are composed of a vague nodular proliferation of basophilic oval cells arranged around dilated thin-walled vessels with a characteristic staghorn appearance. Nuclear atypia, high mitotic activity, high cellularity and necrosis and haemorrhage tend to be associated with a more aggressive clinical course. Immunohistochemical analyses show the expression of vimentin and CD34. Actin is expressed more consistently by sinonasal haemangiopericytomas. Clinically, some haemangiopericytomas are associated with hypoglycaemia, which seems to be caused by IGF and IGF receptor expression by the tumour. Meningeal haemangiopericytomas often are associated with an aggressive clinical course characterized by local recurrences and metastases. Sinonasal haemangiopericytomas tend to recur locally but do not mestastasize.

Sarcomas of Peripheral Neuroectodermic Differentiation

Extraskeletal Ewing Sarcoma and Peripheral Primitive Neuroectodermal Tumour (PNET)

Extraskeletal and skeletal Ewing sarcoma and peripheral primitive neuroectodermal tumour (PNET) (also known as neuroepithelioma) represent opposite ends of a continuum of primitive tumours showing various degrees of neuroectodermic differentiation. Ewing sarcoma is the more undifferentiated tumour and PNET the more differentiated tumour. In extraskeletal sites, they tend to occur in the paravertebral areas, thoracopulmonary region (Askin tumour) and lower extremities of adolescents and young adults. There is no sex predilection but African Americans are rarely affected.

Histologically, sheets or lobules of small round cells separated by strands of fibrous tissue are characteristic but not specific. Homer Wright rosettes frequently are found in PNET. Brisk mitotic activity and areas of confluent necrosis (filigree pattern) are found in both Ewing sarcoma and PNET. Immunohistochemical studies show the expression of the MIC2 protein in both tumours. Expression of neuron-specific enolase, synaptophysin, Leu-7 (CD57), neurofilament, S-100 protein and the protein gene product 9.5 (PGP 9.5) as well as the presence of Homer Wright rosettes have been suggested as diagnostic criteria for PNET because they indicate neuroectodermal differentiation. (See also the chapter *Bones*.)

Cytogenetic studies done mostly in skeletal tumours have shown the balanced translocations t(11;22)(q24;q12) and t(21;22)(q22;q12) in 95% and 5% of cases, respectively (Sandberg and Bridge, 2000). In these translocations, the *EWS* gene on chromosome 22q12 fuses with *FLI1* gene on chromosome 11q24 or *ERG* gene on chromosome 21q22, respectively. Other translocations have been identified involving the *EWS* gene in a minority of cases (**Table 2**). *EWS/FLI1* has been shown to transform mouse NIH3T3 fibroblasts in transfection experiments, which reflects its oncogenic properties. Among several types of *EWS/FLI1* transcripts, the fusion of the *EWS* exon 7 with the *FLI1* exon 6 is the most common (type I) (**Figure 1**) and has been associated with a more aggressive disease independent of stage, tumour location and age (de Alava *et al.*, 1998). However, the clinical significance of individual transcripts other than those of type I remains unknown. Other common cytogenetic abnormalities are trisomies 8 and 12, der(16)t(1;16)(q12;q11.2) and deletion 1p36. The first two appear to represent independent events during tumour evolution. The inactivation by distinct mechanisms of the tumour suppressor gene $p16^{INK4}$ has been correlated with a worse prognosis in Ewing sarcoma.

Many other prognostic factors have been suggested for Ewing sarcoma/PNET but detection of distant metastases at presentation, which occurs in approximately 25% of patients, is the most adverse (Terrier *et al.*, 1996). The value of neuroectodermal differentiation as a prognostic factor in Ewing sarcoma/PNET remains controversial. Treatment of localized skeletal Ewing sarcoma/PNET consists of a combination of surgical excision, radiotherapy and chemotherapy. The most commonly used agents are vincristine, doxorubicin, cyclophosphamide, D-actinomycin, etoposide and ifosfamide. The 5-year overall survival rate can reach 70% for patients with localized disease and 20–30% for those who presented with distant metastasis (Arndt and Crist, 1999). Treatment and survival data on extraskeletal Ewing sarcoma/PNET are limited, and the clinical course seems more aggressive. The overall 5-year survival rate appears to be <40%. Potential new treatments for Ewing sarcoma/PNET have been reported. The use of monoclonal anti-CD99 and nanocapsules with antisense *EWS/FLI1* were shown to inhibit Ewing sarcoma cells in both *in vitro* and *in vivo* experiments.

Malignant Peripheral Nerve Sheath Tumour

Malignant peripheral nerve sheath tumour (MPNST), formerly known as malignant schwannoma and neurofibrosarcoma, is divided into three clinical groups: neurofibromatosis type I-associated (40–50%), sporadic (40–50%) and postirradiation (5–10%). The lifetime risk for the development of MPNST in patients with neurofibromatosis type I (NF1) is estimated to be 2%. The anatomical distribution is wide, and there is a male predominance. The incidence of NF1-associated MPNST peaks during the fourth decade of life. The sporadic form occurs more often in the lower extremities, shows no sex predilection and peaks during the fifth decade of life. The postirradiation form is the least common and occurs up to 30 decades after the radiation therapy.

Histologically, MPNST is characterized by a fascicular spindle cell proliferation in which there is an abrupt transition from more cellular areas to more myxoid areas. Whorling of tumour cells around vascular spaces is another characteristic feature. In 10% of cases, rhabdomyoblastic differentiation is observed (Triton tumour), which portends a more aggressive clinical course. MPNST shows epithelioid phenotype in 5% of cases. This variant tends to be superficially located and is associated with a more favourable outcome. A pigmented variant also has been described. The traditional criteria for the diagnosis of MPNST relied on the presence of a spindle cell tumour with ultrastructural evidence of Schwann cell differentiation arising in association with a nerve or a benign peripheral nerve tumour (i.e. neurofibroma) in a patient with neurofibromatosis. However, better recognition of MPNST's morphological features and the advent of immunohistochemical analysis has changed this view. MPNST expresses S-100 protein in approximately 50% of cases.

Cytogenetic studies have shown complex karyotypes in most cases, but structural abnormalities involving chromosomes 17 and 22 are occasionally found. Accumulation of mutant p53 protein was found to be higher in MPNSTs than in neurofibroma, suggesting a role for *TP53* mutations in neurofibroma transformation to MPNST. In addition, the proliferative marker Ki-67 tends to be higher and the cell cycle inhibitor $p27^{kip1}$ lower in MPNST than in neurofibroma.

The overall 5-year survival rates for patients with MPNST are approximately 50% for those with the sporadic form, 25% for those with NF1 and 10% for those with postirradiation MPNST. In two large series of cases, tumour size larger than 5 cm, history of NF1 and incomplete surgical excision were associated with a worse prognosis.

Clear Cell Sarcoma (Malignant Melanoma of Soft Parts)

Clear cell sarcoma of tendons and aponeuroses, also known as malignant melanoma of soft parts, is a rare soft tissue sarcoma that tends to occur in adolescents and young adults. The foot and ankle, followed by the knee, are the most commonly affected sites, despite a wider anatomical distribution. Histologically, clear cell carcinoma is characterized by nests of polygonal or spindle cells separated by delicate fibrous septa. The cells have a clear or eosinophilic cytoplasm and prominent nucleolus. Mitoses are uncommon. Giant cells and melanin pigmentation are seen with some frequency. Ultrastructural studies show the presence of premelanosomes in approximately 50% of cases. Immunohistochemical analyses show expression of S-100 protein, HMB-45 and Melan A.

Cytogenetically, clear cell carcinoma is characterized by the chromosomal translocation t(12;22)(q13;q12), which results in the fusion of the DNA-binding domain of the *ATF-1* gene (*Activating Transcription Factor-1*) located on chromosome 12q13 with the 5′-end of the *EWS* gene. The chimaeric protein EWS/ATF-1 binds to ATF-DNA binding sites and leads to altered induction of cAMP-inducible promoters. Studies have shown that antibodies against the EWS/ATF-1 protein trigger tumour apoptosis. In addition, the somatostatin gene promoter may be a potential target for drug therapy.

Clear cell sarcoma is characterized by the development of metastasis in 50% of patients, most commonly to lungs and lymph nodes. The overall 5-year survival rate is 65% according to the results in one series. Factors associated with a more aggressive clinical course include larger tumour size, presence of necrosis and nondiploid DNA content. Local radiation therapy was associated with prolonged survival by univariate analysis in a series of 30 cases.

Sarcomas of Osseous or Cartilagenous Differentiation

Extraskeletal Osteosarcoma

Extraskeletal osteosarcoma (ESO) represents <1% of soft tissue sarcomas and occurs mainly after the sixth decade of life. Males are more commonly affected than females. The lower extremities, particularly the thigh, are more frequently involved. Histologically, ESO is similar to malignant fibrous histiocytoma, with a high degree of pleomorphism and brisk mitotic activity. Osteoid formation, present in ESO, differentiates it from malignant fibrous histiocytoma. Extensive areas of necrosis are also common. Immunohistochemical studies are largely nonspecific. However, the expression of osteocalcin and osteonectin, common bone proteins, by tumour cells and osteoid matrix can be used to differentiate ESO from other pleomorphic soft tissue sarcomas. Cytogenetic and molecular data are almost nonexistent, in contrast to data on bone osteosarcoma. Clinically, ESO follows an aggressive clinical course characterized by multiple local recurrences and metastases in >60% of patients. The 5-year overall survival rate is approximately 20–35%. Tumour size smaller than 5 cm, chondroblastic differentiation and a Ki-67 index <24% seem to be associated with a better survival.

Mesenchymal Chondrosarcoma

Mesenchymal chondrosarcoma occurs most often in bone (65%) and soft tissues (35%) of adolescents and young adults. In soft tissues, the most common anatomical sites are the head and neck region and the lower extremities. Histologically, it has a biphasic appearance in which islands of well-developed cartilage are intermixed with areas composed of primitive small ovoid cells. Haemangiopericytoma-like areas are also common. Immunohistochemical studies show expression of S-100 protein in the cartilage areas and MIC2 in the small round cells. Cytogenetic and molecular studies are rare. Investigation of the differential expression of collagen subtypes has suggested that mesenchymal chondrosarcoma has a line of differentiation consistent with premesenchymal chondroprogenitor cells. Mesenchymal chondrosarcoma is characterized by an aggressive clinical course with frequent lung metastasis. The overall 5-year survival rate is approximately 50%.

Extraskeletal Myxoid Chondrosarcoma

Extraskeletal myxoid chondrosarcoma (EMC) occurs predominantly in the lower extremities of individuals in the fifth to eighth decades of life. Histologically, EMC is a multilobular neoplasm composed of cords of small eosinophilic cells immersed in a myxoid matrix. Intracisternal bundles of parallel microtubules and scattered neurosecretory granules are characteristic but not specific ultrastructural findings. Immunohistochemical analysis shows the expression of vimentin and synaptophysin in most cases, indicating neuroendocrine differentiation, and S-100 protein in a minority of cases. Cytogenetic and molecular studies have shown the presence of the chromosomal translocations t(9;22)(q22;q12) and t(9;17) (q22;q11) in 75 and 25% of cases, respectively. In these translocations the *CHN* gene, a member of the steroid/thyroid receptor gene superfamily located on chromosome 9q22 is fused with either *EWS* on chromosome 22q12 or *RPB56/hTAF$_{II}$68* on chromosome 17q11, respectively. Clinically, EMC is characterized by an indolent clinical course in most but not all patients. Metastases, most commonly to the lungs, occur in up to 50% of patients. The 5 and 10-year overall survival rates are 90% and 70–80%, respectively.

Sarcomas of Uncertain Line of Differentiation

This group of sarcomas is mainly represented by synovial sarcoma, epithelioid sarcoma, alveolar soft part sarcoma, desmoplastic small round cell tumour and extrarenal rhabdoid tumour.

Synovial Sarcoma

Synovial sarcoma was placed in the category of sarcomas of uncertain line of differentiation because its putative synovial differentiation has not been confirmed. It represents approximately 10% of all soft tissue sarcomas, but this figure is expected to increase owing to better recognition of monophasic and poorly differentiated variants using immunohistochemical, cytogenetic and molecular techniques. Synovial sarcoma has a slight predilection for males and occurs at any age, particularly affecting adolescents and young adults. It can arise in any site but is more common in the lower extremities. Despite its common periarticular location, intra-articular synovial sarcoma is exceedingly rare.

Histologically, synovial sarcoma is classified into biphasic, monophasic and poorly differentiated variants. The biphasic variant is composed of epithelial and spindle cell components. The epithelial component has a glandular appearance; the spindle cell component comprises fascicles of spindle cells frequently arranged in a herringbone pattern similar to that in fibrosarcoma (**Figure 7**). Monophasic synovial sarcoma can be purely epithelial, which is very rare, or purely spindled. Areas with a haemangiopericytoma-like vascular pattern as well as mast cell infiltration are common. Calcification and metaplastic ossification are also frequent, being detected in plain films in up to 30% of cases. The undifferentiated form of synovial sarcoma has a round cell shape that may simulate Ewing sarcoma/PNET.

Immunohistochemical analysis shows expression for vimentin, epithelial membrane antigen (EMA) and cytokeratin. EMA and cytokeratin are commonly expressed by the epithelial component and only focally expressed by the spindle cell component. In addition, it has been shown that synovial sarcoma commonly expresses cytokeratins 7, 13 and 19 but not cytokeratins 8 and 18. S-100, MIC2, and the antiapoptotic protein Bcl-2 also are expressed in many cases. More recently, *Her-2/neu* gene amplification and protein overexpression were found in cases of synovial sarcoma.

With the use of modern cytogenetic techniques, the characteristic translocation t(X;18)(p11.2;q11.2) is found in most cases (>99%), including cases of poorly differentiated tumours (**Table 2**). This translocation results in the fusion of the *SYT* gene (*SY*novial sarcoma *T*ranslocation) on chromosome 18q11.2 with members of the *SSX* family of genes (*S*ynovial *S*arcoma *X* chromosome breakpoint) on chromosome Xp11.2 (*SSX-1*, *SSX-2*, and, more rarely, *SSX-4*; the other members, *SSX-3*, *SSX-5*, and *SSX-6* have not been detected in synovial sarcoma translocations) (Clark *et al.*, 1994). Whereas *SYT* encodes for a ubiquitously expressed nuclear protein that seems to function as a transcriptional coactivator, *SSX* encodes for transcription repressor proteins. The mechanism of action of the chimaeric protein remains unknown, but it has been suggested that it works through recruitment of the PcG complex of proteins involved in transcriptional repression.

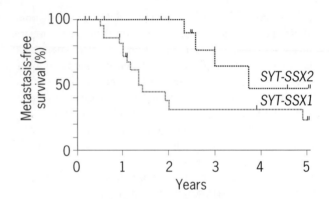

Figure 10   In synovial sarcoma, patients with the *SYT/SSX-1* fusion transcript had shorter metastasis-free survival than patients with the *SYT/SSX-2* fusion transcript (hazard ratio = 3; 95% confidence interval = 1.1–8; *P* = 0.03; Cox regression model). (From Kawai *et al.*, 1998, SYT-SSX gene fusion as a determinant of morphology and prognosis in synovial sarcoma. *New England Journal of Medicine*, **338**, 153–160, by permission of the Massachusetts Medical Society.)

It has also been shown that the *SYT/SSX-1* fusion transcript, which is detected in 65% of cases, is associated with biphasic histological findings, a high proliferation rate, and shorter metastasis-free survival (**Figure 10**). The specificity of the t(X;18) for synovial sarcomas has been questioned because it also has been found in some cases of MPNST, suggesting that MPNST and synovial sarcoma may be part of the same spectrum of tumours. However, these intriguing results need further confirmation.

Many adverse prognostic factors have been proposed for synovial sarcoma, including older age, larger tumour size, poorly differentiated histological features, nuclear grade, necrosis, mitotic activity, low mast cell infiltration, Ki-67 expression, *TP53* mutations, bone or neurovascular invasion, *SYT/SSX-1* chimaeric gene and hepatocyte growth factor. However, the clinical utility of most of these prognostic factors remains to be settled. Synovial sarcoma metastasizes in 50% of cases, most commonly to lungs and lymph nodes, and 5-year overall survival rates between 24 and 64% have been reported. Treatment involves surgical excision, radiotherapy and chemotherapy. Chemotherapy often includes ifosfamide because synovial sarcoma seems to be particularly sensitive to this drug.

Epithelioid Sarcoma

Epithelioid sarcoma is a rare soft tissue sarcoma that occurs predominantly in adolescents and young adults. It presents most commonly as dermal or subcutaneous nodules in the distal portions of the upper extremities, particularly the hands and wrists. However, its anatomical distribution is wider. Epithelioid sarcoma occurring around the pelvic region also has been termed proximal type and seems to follow a more aggressive clinical course. Histologically, epithelioid sarcoma has a multinodular architecture with a granuloma-like appearance. The nodules are composed of epithelioid or spindle cells often surrounded by an inflammatory infiltrate rich in lymphocytes. Necrotic areas are common, often assuming a map-like pattern. Immunohistochemical studies show the expression of vimentin, EMA and cytokeratin in most cases and CD34 in approximately half.

Cytogenetic studies show frequent rearrangements or deletions involving chromosome 22, particularly the band 22q11. Interestingly, this chromosomal band often is deleted or rearranged in rhabdoid tumour (see Extrarenal Malignant Rhabdoid Tumour, below), an entity that shares some degree of morphological overlap with epithelioid sarcoma. Epithelioid sarcoma has a high local recurrence rate, up to 80% in some series, owing to its extensively infiltrative margins along tendons and fascia, often well beyond the apparent clinical limits of the tumour. Metastases are very common, mostly to regional lymph nodes, lungs and scalp. The estimated 5-year survival rate is approximately 50–70%. Some prognostic factors associated with a worse outcome include tumour size larger than 5 cm, necrosis, vascular invasion, lymph node metastasis and proximal location.

Alveolar Soft Part Sarcoma

Alveolar soft part sarcoma (ASPS), also known as Christopherson tumour, represents <1% of soft tissue sarcomas and commonly occurs in lower extremities in patients between the second and third decades of life. In children, the head and neck are preferentially involved. Female patients are slightly more affected. Histologically, ASPS is characterized by a pseudoalveolar architecture composed of richly vascularized fibrous septa lined by polygonal cells with low mitotic activity and minimal pleomorphism. PAS-positive intracytoplasmic rod-like inclusions are common and are seen to have a characteristic crystalline rhomboid shape on ultrastructural analysis. The line of differentiation of ASPS is still subject to debate, and a putative skeletal muscle differentiation has been suggested. However, the expression of muscle markers, such as desmin and MyoD1, is inconsistently detected.

Cytogenetic and molecular studies have shown that the nonreciprocal translocation t(X;17)(p11.2;q25) is characteristic of ASPS (100% of cases) and results in the fusion of the transcription factor *TFE3* gene (*T*ranscription *F*actor binding to IGHM *E*nhancer *3*) on chromosome Xp11.2 with the *ASPL* gene (*A*lveolar *S*oft *P*art sarcoma *L*ocus) on chromosome 17q25. Interestingly, the *TFE3* gene commonly is rearranged in some cases of renal papillary carcinoma. ASPS is associated with a poor long-term prognosis, with 5- and 10-year overall survival rates of 46–67% and

38%, respectively. Metastases to lungs, brain and bone are common. Younger age and tumours smaller than 10 cm in diameter tend to be associated with a better prognosis.

Desmoplastic Small Round Cell Tumour

Desmoplastic small round cell tumour (DSRCT) is a highly malignant sarcoma that most commonly occurs in the peritoneal cavity of adolescents and young adults of the male sex. DSRCT usually forms large intra-abdominal whitish masses that are histologically characterized by nests or strands of small round cells surrounded by a dense desmoplastic stroma. Mitoses, apoptotic bodies, necrosis and lymphatic invasion are common. Immunohistochemical studies show the expression of several proteins, including cytokeratin, EMA, neuron-specific enolase and desmin, supporting its divergent differentiation. Desmin expression is usually paranuclear and of globular appearance. MIC2 expression is not uncommon and may cause problems in the differential diagnosis with Ewing sarcoma/PNET.

Cytogenetic analyses show the chromosomal translocation t(11;22)(p13;q12) in almost all cases of DSRCT. This results in the fusion of the tumour-suppressor gene *WT1* on chromosome 11p13 to the *EWS* gene on chromosome 22q12. The causal mechanism of this translocation is unknown but insertion of LINE-1 DNA sequences at the genomic breakpoint of DSRCT has been identified. The chimaeric product has oncogenic attributes and seems to activate the *IGF1* gene promoter with higher affinity that the WT1 protein alone. DSRCT follows a highly aggressive clinical course, often characterized by multiple local recurrences. Distant metastases are uncommon. Despite intensive chemotherapy regimens, radical surgical procedures and radiotherapy, most patients die less than 3 years after diagnosis.

Extrarenal Malignant Rhabdoid Tumour

Malignant rhabdoid tumour (MRT) used to be a highly controversial entity because the so-called rhabdoid phenotype can be found in several other tumours. However, recent findings have shed some light on this issue. Currently, it seems that renal MRT and extrarenal MRT are characterized by deletions or mutations of the chromatin remodelling gene *hSNF5/INI1* located on chromosome 22q11.2. In addition, germ-line mutations of the *hSNF5/INI1* gene also have been described, predisposing the carriers to renal MRT, extrarenal MRT and other tumours in the so-called rhabdoid predisposition syndrome. In soft tissues, MRT tends to occur in young patients and in a wide anatomical distribution. Histologically, MRT is characterized by sheets of polygonal cells with hyaline globular cytoplasmic inclusions and vesicular nuclei. By immunohistochemical analysis, the cells consistently express vimentin, cytokeratin and EMA. Ultrastructural analysis demonstrates that the cytoplasmic inclusions are composed of whorls of intermediate filaments. Clinically, soft tissue MRTs follow a very aggressive clinical course with higher rates of metastasis. Death usually occurs less than 2 years after diagnosis.

PROGNOSTIC FACTORS

Several prognostic factors have been proposed for soft tissue sarcomas, but only a few are universally accepted and routinely used. The large void between the identification and the clinical application of prognostic factors for soft tissue sarcoma exists for many reasons. First, the prognostic factors proposed so far have been incompletely validated. Theoretically, the validation of proposed prognostic factors is carried out in three major steps: exploratory studies, retrospective clinical studies and prospective clinical trials. The first step is the study of a plausible prognostic factor in relationship to outcomes and the predictive data available. This step is fundamental to hypothesis formulation. The second step confirms the initial observations through large studies in which multivariate analysis establishes the independence of the investigated prognostic factor in relation to known predictors. Definition and validation of cutoff points in two or more distinct data sets are tasks involved in the second step. The third step consists of well-designed multi-institutional prospective studies with a large number of patients using pre-established cutoff points (Hall and Going, 1999). Unfortunately, almost all studies of prognostic factors in soft tissue sarcomas have not gone beyond the second step.

Other important problems include (1) the uneven representation of specific sarcomas in heterogeneous series, (2) the number and type of variables included in multivariate analysis and how they are selected and modelled, including pre-establishment of cutoffs, (3) the statistical power of the study for detecting differences between groups of patients, (4) standardization of specific outcomes (local recurrence, metastasis, disease-free and overall survival) and (5) appropriateness of the statistical methods. In addition, the identification of a prognostic factor does not necessarily mean that it has clinical utility. A meaningful prognostic factor should also influence clinical decisions.

Despite numerous problems associated with histological grading systems, histological grade has been considered the most powerful prognostic factor in heterogeneous series of patients with soft tissue sarcoma (**Figure 3**) and frequently incorporates other factors such as mitotic count, necrosis and degree of differentiation (see Grading and Staging Systems, above). In a retrospective series involving more than 1000 cases of soft tissue sarcomas, the presence of high-grade histological features was the most powerful independent prognostic factor for metastasis-free survival ($P = 0.0001$; relative risk (RR) = 4.3; confidence interval (CI) = 2.6–6.9) and

disease-specific overall survival ($P = 0.0001$; RR = 4.0; CI = 2.5–6.6), but not for local recurrence-free survival (Pisters *et al.*, 1996). Tumour size has been considered an adverse prognostic factor in many but not all series including more than 100 patients. Standardization of cutoffs for tumour size and other problems already described partially explain these divergent results.

Several other prognostic factors have been evaluated. DNA ploidy, S-phase fraction, AgNORs (silver staining for nucleolar organizer regions; segments of DNA containing ribosomal genes whose expression reflects the proliferation activity of the tumour), Ki-67, Mdm2, p53, *RB1* gene product, c-Myc, PDGFβ (platelet-derived growth factor β) and Bcl-2 have been correlated with histological grade and decreased metastasis-free or overall survival in many but not all studies. Overexpression of the transmembrane p-glycoprotein, product of the multiple resistance gene 1 (*MDR-1*), has been correlated with decreased sensitivity to chemotherapy and survival. Specific chimaeric mRNA transcripts have been shown to have a prognostic role in synovial sarcoma and Ewing sarcoma (**Figure 9**) (see Extraskeletal Ewing Sarcoma and Peripheral Primitive Neuroectodermal Tumour, above, and Synovial Sarcoma, above).

TREATMENT

The treatment of soft tissue sarcomas commonly combines combination of surgical excision, radiation therapy and chemotherapy. The therapeutic approach is chosen after adequate imaging and pathological studies and determination of whether the patient has localized, locally recurrent or metastatic disease. With this information, a specific therapeutic plan is best chosen based on individual characteristics of the patient and results obtained in clinical trials.

Overview of Sarcoma Treatment

Surgical excision is used primarily for the treatment of localized or locally recurrent sarcoma and is the only potentially curative treatment at present. However, surgical excision also can be used for the treatment of metastatic sarcoma, particularly pulmonary metastasis (metastasectomies). Radiation therapy is used primarily as an adjuvant treatment for the control of localized or locally recurrent sarcoma. Chemotherapy is used for localized and metastatic sarcomas.

Treatment of Clinical Groups

Localized Sarcoma

Local disease is defined when a soft tissue sarcoma is confined to a certain anatomical site or compartment without clinicoradiological evidence of systemic disease (metastasis). In this situation, surgical excision is considered the mainstay therapy because it is the only potentially curative modality at present.

Surgical excision can be divided into five basic types: intralesional, marginal, wide, radical and amputation. In an intralesional excision (also known as curettage, debulking or incisional biopsy), the tumour is incompletely resected and gross disease is left behind. This surgical procedure is performed when broader excisions cannot be carried out without affecting vital structures. In marginal excisions, the tumour is excised through its pseudocapsule or perilesional reactive fibroinflammatory zone. Because there is a substantial risk for microscopic positive margins after this procedure, marginal excision is commonly indicated for benign soft tissue tumours or after successful preoperative radiotherapy or chemotherapy for sarcomas. Local recurrence rates of 60% or more have been reported with this type of resection alone.

Wide excision, which is currently the most common type of surgical excision performed, includes a rim of normal tissue surrounding the tumour. Wide excision is used for low-grade and high-grade sarcomas with or without adjuvant treatment. Local recurrent rates of up to 30% have been reported when wide excision is performed alone. Because of this, there is a general arbitrary recommendation that a surgical margin of at least 2 cm around the tumour be achieved. Radical excision involves the removal of the entire anatomical compartment, i.e. all tissues within the natural anatomical boundaries. Radical excision often is indicated for recurrent sarcomas or when imaging studies were inconclusive for defining the tumour's anatomical limits. Amputation, often used in the past, is performed uncommonly now because a limb-sparing operation followed by postoperative radiotherapy provide similar results. Amputation is indicated mainly (1) when it is impossible to obtain adequate margins without compromising vital structures in primary or locally recurrent disease, (2) when the dose and volume of adjuvant radiotherapy are likely to cause important local complications and (3) in certain situations when the use of a prosthesis will provide better postoperative results than a radical limb-sparing operation (O'Sullivan *et al.*, 1999).

Currently, radiotherapy commonly is used in combination with surgical excision for the management of localized soft tissue sarcoma. Radiotherapy can be delivered in the form of external-beam radiation or brachytherapy (from the Greek *brachys*, short). In the latter, the source of radiation is placed close to or in the tumour bed. Several retrospective and few prospective clinical trials have shown that the combination of radiotherapy and surgical excision provides better results than surgical excision alone in the management of localized soft tissue sarcoma. However, there is no clear evidence that local control of the disease automatically confers prolonged survival. Preoperative radiation therapy has the advantage of using smaller radiation fields and doses but has been associated with a higher risk of wound complications.

Postoperative radiation therapy decreases the latter risk. Advantages of brachytherapy include cost-effectiveness and a short interval between the surgical procedure and the beginning of radiation therapy. However, brachytherapy seems to provide results that are inferior to those of external-beam radiation for low-grade tumours.

Several other types of adjuvant radiotherapy have been used for local disease control, including a combination of brachytherapy and external beam radiation, intraoperative radiotherapy, hyperfractionation, the use of radiosensitizers, and others. However, none has been shown to be superior to external-beam radiation.

The role of adjuvant chemotherapy for localized soft tissue sarcoma remains controversial despite convincing evidence of its clear though modest benefit (Benjamin, 1999). Despite the lack of statistical significance, most randomized trials have shown a clear trend for prolonged disease-free survival and overall survival in patients who received adjuvant chemotherapy with multiple regimens. Moreover, meta-analysis of some reported series has confirmed these impressions (**Figure 11**) (Sarcoma Meta-analysis Collaboration, 1997). Reasons accounting for some of the persistent controversies include large variation in the criteria for patient enrollment (tumour location, histological subtype and grade, size and depth), follow-up periods and chemotherapy regimens used.

Neoadjuvant or preoperative chemotherapy has been advocated for treating localized soft tissue sarcomas based on three theoretical assumptions: (1) elimination of occult micrometastases present at diagnosis, before the development of chemoresistant tumour clones, (2) reduction of tumour volumes, to allow less radical surgical procedures and (3) clinical and pathological assessment of tumour chemoresistance by an *in vivo* test (Pisters and Brennan, 2000). Nonrandomized studies have shown complete and partial response rates between 3 and 64% with the use of neoadjuvant chemotherapy. However, these results did not translate into a better outcome (metastasis-free or overall survival) for responders as compared with nonresponders or patients treated with adjuvant chemotherapy. In spite of these findings, patients with large high-grade tumours should be considered for neoadjuvant chemotherapy because of a high risk of development of metastasis.

Locally Recurrent Sarcoma

Soft tissue sarcomas recur in up to 90% of cases according to the adequacy of the surgical margins. Because head and neck and retroperitoneal sarcomas are difficult to resect without affecting vital structures, local recurrence rates are much higher than those observed in extremity sarcomas. The treatment of locally recurrent soft tissue sarcoma should be highly individualized, but surgical re-excision of the recurrent tumour should be attempted when feasible because good long-term results have been obtained with this approach. Amputation is indicated especially when dealing with

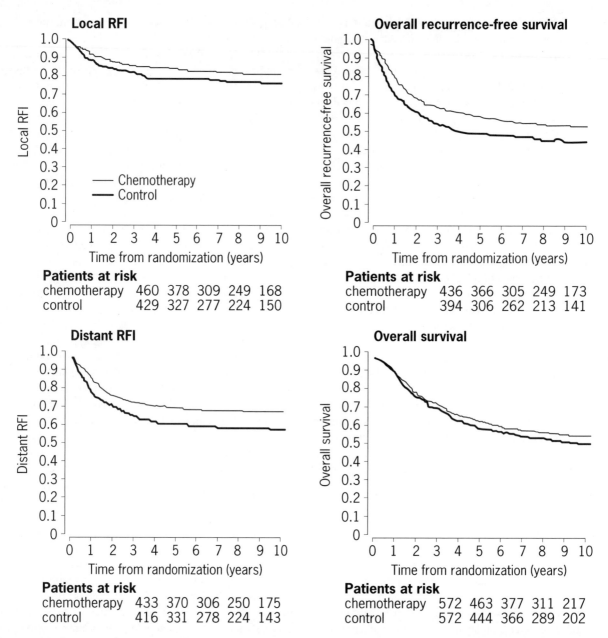

Figure 11   Kaplan–Meier curves obtained with a quantitative meta-analysis of data on 1568 patients from 14 clinical trials comparing doxorubicin-based adjuvant chemotherapy with control in localized soft tissue sarcoma. Prolonged local recurrence-free (hazard ratio (HR) = 0.73; 95% confidence interval (CI) = 0.56–0.94; P = 0.016), metastasis-free (HR = 0.70; 95% CI = 0.57–0.85; P = 0.0003), disease-free (HR = 0.75; 95% CI = 0.64-0.87; P = 0.0001) and overall survival (HR = 0.89; 95% CI = 0.76-1.03; P = 0.12) were observed. However, no statistical significance was reached for overall survival. RFI, recurrence-free interval. (From Sarcoma Meta-analysis Collaboration, 1999, Adjuvant chemotherapy for localized resectable soft-tissue sarcoma of adults: meta-analysis of individual data. *Lancet*, **350**, 1647–1654, by permission of The Lancet, Ltd.)

multiple local recurrences or tumour involvement of important neurovascular structures. The use of adjuvant radiation often is indicated if the tumour was not previously irradiated. Using this approach, local control was obtained in up to 80% of patients in some series. Additional radiation therapy in previously irradiated recurrent tumours should be evaluated on an individual basis, but local control can be attained in most patients. The role of chemotherapy for locally recurrent disease remains to be established.

Metastatic Sarcoma

Metastatic soft tissue sarcomas are primarily managed with chemotherapy or surgical excision (metastasectomy).

Chemotherapy is the main therapeutic modality and is indicated for nonresectable metastases. The most effective single agents are doxorubicin and ifosfamide. They induce objective response in more than 20% of patients and exhibit a dose–response relationship (O'Byrne and Steward, 1999). Doxorubicin-based combination regimens such as CYVADIC (cyclophosphamide, vincristine, doxorubicin (Adriamycin) and dacarbazine) and MAID (mesna, doxorubicin, ifosfamide and dacarbazine) have led to response rates in up to 70% of patients, but no improvement in overall survival has been demonstrated. Furthermore, no difference in terms of response rate, remission duration or overall survival was seen in a large prospective randomized phase III trial comparing CYVADIC, doxorubicin–ifosfamide, and doxorubicin alone for treatment of advanced soft tissue sarcoma. The concomitant use of recombinant human granulocyte macrophage colony-stimulating factor (hrGM-CSF) has been used by some investigators to allow more intensive chemotherapy regimens. Other treatments include hyperthermic isolated limb perfusion (HILP) using an antiangiogenic factor, such as recombinant tumour necrosis factor alpha (rTNFα), in combination with cytotoxic drugs and whole-body hyperthermia.

Surgical excision of metastatic disease has been investigated in several studies; the benefits are marginal. In a series of 135 patients who were treated at a single institution for metastatic sarcoma to the lungs, complete excision, incomplete excision and no excision of the metastatic sarcoma were associated with median survivals of 19, 10 and 8 months, respectively. However, the 3-year overall survival rate was only 23% for those in whom complete metastasectomy was achieved (Gadd et al., 1993). A series evaluating 230 patients with pulmonary and nonpulmonary metastasis found that unresectability of distant metastases correlated with a shorter survival by multivariate analysis ($P = 0.0001$; HR = 2.3; CI = 1.2–3.7; **Figure 12**) (Billingsley et al., 1999). Other investigations found similar numbers, with median survivals after development of pulmonary metastases ranging from 18 to 27 months. Comparison of surgical excision alone with the combination of surgical excision and chemotherapy has provided discordant results among studies. A prognostic system for use with patients who have pulmonary metastases has been proposed. It is based on the presence of metastases, number of metastases, metastasis-free period less than 18 months and size of the metastases larger than 2 cm (Choong et al., 1995). It seems that complete metastasectomy is the single most important factor for prolonged postmetastasis survival and that careful patient selection is critical for achieving good results. Four criteria for pulmonary metastasectomy have been suggested: ability to control the primary tumour, absence of extrathoracic metastases, clinical condition satisfactory for surgical excision and absence of a better treatment option (McCormack, 1990).

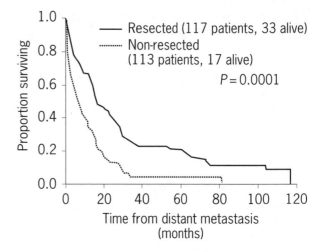

Figure 12   Overall survival curves comparing the effect of complete resection of metastatic soft tissue sarcoma with incomplete or no resection. Shorter overall survival was seen in patients with nonresected metastases (hazard ratio = 2.3; 95% confidence interval = 1.2–3.7; $P = 0.0001$). (From Billingsley et al., 1999, by permission of the American Cancer Society.)

Future Treatments

Alternative treatments for soft tissue sarcomas have been investigated with promising results. These treatments include use of the peroxisome proliferator-activated receptor-gamma ligand troglitazone to induce terminal adipocytic differentiation in liposarcomas, antisense *FLI/EWS* and anti-MIC2 (CD99) for Ewing sarcoma/PNET, tyrosine kinase inhibitors (STI-576) for c-*KIT* proto-oncogene product expressing tumours, angiogenesis inhibitors and others. Additional information on current clinical trials for the treatment of sarcomas can be found at http://clinicaltrials.gov.

Websites

http://www.cancerlinks.org/sarcoma.html.
http://www.cancernet.nci.nih.gov.

REFERENCES

Antman, K. and Chang, Y. (2000). Kaposi's sarcoma. *New England Journal of Medicine*, **342**, 1027–1038.

Arndt, C. A. and Crist, W. M. (1999). Common musculoskeletal tumors of childhood and adolescence. *New England Journal of Medicine*, **341**, 342–352.

Aurias, A., et al. (1983). Chromosomal translocations in Ewing's sarcoma (letter to the editor). *New England Journal of Medicine*, **309**, 496–497.

Ballo, M. T., *et al.* (1999). Desmoid tumor: prognostic factors and outcome after surgery, radiation therapy, or combined surgery and radiation therapy. *Journal of Clinical Oncology*, **17**, 158–167.

Barr, F. G. (1998). Translocations, cancer and the puzzle of specificity. *Nature Genetics*, **19**, 121–124.

Bell, D. W., *et al.* (1999). Heterozygous germ line hCHK2 mutations in Li–Fraumeni syndrome. *Science*, **286**, 2528–2531.

Benjamin, R. S. (1999). Evidence for using adjuvant chemotherapy as standard treatment of soft tissue sarcoma. *Seminars in Radiative Oncology*, **9**, 349–351.

Billingsley, K. G., *et al.* (1999). Multifactorial analysis of the survival of patients with distant metastasis arising from primary extremity sarcoma. *Cancer*, **85**, 389–395.

Cance, W. G., *et al.* (1990). Altered expression of the retinoblastoma gene product in human sarcomas. *New England Journal of Medicine*, **323**, 1457–1462.

Choong, P. F., *et al.* (1995). Survival after pulmonary metastasectomy in soft tissue sarcoma. Prognostic factors in 214 patients. *Acta Orthopaedic Scandinavica*, **66**, 561–568.

Clark, J., *et al.* (1994). Identification of novel genes, SYT and SSX, involved in the t(X;18)(p11.2;q11.2) translocation found in human synovial sarcoma. *Nature Genetics*, **7**, 502–508.

Cordon-Cardo, C., *et al.* (1994). Molecular abnormalities of mdm2 and p53 genes in adult soft tissue sarcomas. *Cancer Research*, **54**, 794–799.

Costa, J., *et al.* (1984). The grading of soft tissue sarcomas. Results of a clinicohistopathologic correlation in a series of 163 cases. *Cancer*, **53**, 530–541.

Crozat, A., *et al.* (1993). Fusion of CHOP to a novel RNA-binding protein in human myxoid liposarcoma. *Nature*, **363**, 640–644.

de Alava, E. and Gerald, W. L. (2000). Molecular biology of the Ewing's sarcoma/primitive neuroectodermal tumour family. *Journal of Clinical Oncology*, **18**, 204–213.

de Alava, E., *et al.* (1998). EWS-FLI1 fusion transcript structure is an independent determinant of prognosis in Ewing's sarcoma. *Journal of Clinical Oncology*, **16**, 1248–1255.

Enneking, W. F., *et al.* (1980). A system for the surgical staging of musculoskeletal sarcoma. *Clinical Orthopaedics*, **18**, 106–120.

Enzinger, F. M. and Weiss, S. W. (1995). *Soft Tissue Tumours*, 3rd edn (Mosby, St. Louis).

Fleming, I. D., *et al.* (1997). *AJCC Cancer Staging Manual. American Joint Committee on Cancer*, 5th edn (Lippincott-Raven, Philadelphia).

Gadd, M. A., *et al.* (1993). Development and treatment of pulmonary metastases in adult patients with extremity soft tissue sarcoma. *Annals of Surgery*, **218**, 705–712.

Galili, N., *et al.* (1993). Fusion of a fork head domain gene to PAX3 in the solid tumour alveolar rhabdomyosarcoma. *Nature Genetics*, **5**, 230–235.

Gill, P. S., *et al.* (1998). Evidence for multiclonality in multicentric Kaposi's sarcoma. *Proceedings of the National Academy Sciences of the USA*, **95**, 8257–8261.

Guillou, L., *et al.* (1997). Comparative study of the National Cancer Institute and French Federation of Cancer Centers Sarcoma Group grading systems in a population of 410 adult patients with soft tissue sarcoma. *Journal of Clinical Oncology*, **15**, 350–362.

Gustafson, P., *et al.* (1992). Soft tissue leiomyosarcoma. A population-based epidemiologic and prognostic study of 48 patients, including cellular DNA content. *Cancer*, **70**, 114–119.

Hall, P. A. and Going, J. J. (1999). Predicting the future: a critical appraisal of cancer prognosis studies. *Histopathology*, **35**, 489–494.

Hashimoto, H., *et al.* (1985). Malignant smooth muscle tumours of the retroperitoneum and mesentery: a clinicopathologic analysis of 44 cases. *Journal of Surgical Oncology*, **28**, 177–186.

Kilpatrick, S. E., *et al.* (1996). The clinicopathologic spectrum of myxoid and round cell liposarcoma. A study of 95 cases. *Cancer*, **77**, 1450–1458.

Kelly, K. M., *et al.* (1997). Common and variant gene fusions predict distinct clinical phenotypes in rhabdomyosarcoma. *Journal of Clinical Oncology*, **15**, 1831–1836.

Kransdorf, M. J. and Murphey, M. D. (1997). *Imaging of Soft Tissue Tumours*. (W. B. Saunders, Philadelphia).

Ladanyi, M. and Bridge, J. A. (2000). Contribution of molecular genetic data to the classification of sarcomas. *Human Pathology*, **31**, 532–538.

Landis, S. H., *et al.* (1999). Cancer statistics. *CA Cancer Journal for Clinicians*, **49**, 8–31.

Lawrence, B., *et al.* (2000). TPM3-ALK and TPM4-ALK oncogenes in inflammatory myofibroblastic tumours. *American Journal of Pathology*, **157**, 377–384.

Le Doussal, V., *et al.* (1996) Prognostic factors for patients with localized primary malignant fibrous histiocytoma: a multicenter study of 216 patients with multivariate analysis. *Cancer*, **77**, 1823–1830.

McClain, K. L., *et al.* (1995). Association of Epstein–Barr virus with leiomyosarcomas in children with AIDS. *New England Journal of Medicine*, **332**, 12–18.

McCormack, P. (1990). Surgical resection of pulmonary metastases. *Seminars in Surgical Oncology*, **6**, 297–302.

Meis-Kindblom, J. M. and Kindblom, L. G. (1998). Angiosarcoma of soft tissue: a study of 80 cases. *American Journal of Surgical Pathology*, **22**, 683–697.

Mingoli, A., *et al.* (1991). Leiomyosarcoma of the inferior vena cava: analysis and search of world literature on 141 patients and report of three new cases. *Journal of Vascular Surgery*, **14**, 688–699.

Newton, W. A. Jr, *et al.* (1995). Classification of rhabdomyosarcomas and related sarcomas. Pathologic aspects and proposal for a new classification – an Intergroup Rhabdomyosarcoma Study. *Cancer*, **76**, 1073–1085.

O'Byrne, K. and Steward, W. P. (1999). The role of chemotherapy in the treatment of adult soft tissue sarcomas. *Oncology*, **56**, 13–23.

Oliner, J. D., *et al.* (1992). Amplification of a gene encoding a p53-associated protein in human sarcomas. *Nature*, **358**, 80–83.

Oliveira, A. H., *et al*. (2000). p27^kipl protein expression correlates with survival in myxoid and round-cell liposarcoma. *Journal of Clinical Oncology*, **18**, 2888–2893.

Orkin, S. H. (2000). Stem cell alchemy. *Nature Medicine*, **6**, 1212–1213.

O'Sullivan, B., *et al*. (1999). The local management of soft tissue sarcoma. *Seminars in Radiative Oncology*, **9**, 328–348.

Pisters, P. W., *et al*. (1996). Analysis of prognostic factors in 1,041 patients with localized soft tissue sarcomas of the extremities. *Journal of Clinical Oncology*, **14**, 1679–1689.

Pisters, P. W. T. and Brennan, M. F. (2000). Sarcomas of soft tissue. In: Abeloff, M. D., *et al*. (eds), *Clinical Oncology*, 2nd edn. 2273–2313 (Churchill Livingstone, New York).

Qualman, S. J., *et al*. (1998). Intergroup Rhabdomyosarcoma Study: update for pathologists. *Pediatric Development Pathology*, **1**, 550–561.

Rabbitts, T. H., *et al*. (1993). Fusion of the dominant negative transcription regulator CHOP with a novel gene FUS by translocation t(12;16) in malignant liposarcoma. *Nature Genetics*, **4**, 175–180.

Sandberg, A. A. and Bridge, J. A. (2000). Updates on cytogenetics and molecular genetics of bone and soft tissue tumours: Ewing sarcoma and peripheral primitive neuroectodermal tumors. *Cancer Genetics and Cytogenetics*, **123**, 1–26.

Sarcoma Meta-analysis Collaboration (1997). Adjuvant chemotherapy for localised resectable soft-tissue sarcoma of adults: meta-analysis of individual data. *Lancet*, **350**, 1647–1654.

Scott, S. M., *et al*. (1989) Soft tissue fibrosarcoma. A clinicopathologic study of 132 cases. *Cancer*, **64**, 925–931.

Simon, M. P., *et al*. (1997). Deregulation of the platelet-derived growth factor B-chain gene via fusion with collagen gene COL1A1 in dermatofibrosarcoma protuberans and giant-cell fibroblastoma. *Nature Genetics*, **15**, 95–98.

Terrier, P., *et al*. (1996). Small round blue cell tumors in bone: prognostic factors correlated to Ewing's sarcoma and neuroectodermal tumours. *Seminars in Diagnostic Pathology*, **13**, 250–257.

Trojani, M., *et al*. (1984). Soft-tissue sarcomas of adults; study of pathological prognostic variables and definition of a histopathological grading system. *International Journal of Cancer*, **33**, 37–42.

Turc-Carel, C., *et al*. (1983). Chromosomal translocations in Ewing's sarcoma (letter to the editor). *New England Journal of Medicine*, **309**, 497–498.

Weiss, S. W. and Enzinger, F. M. (1978). Malignant fibrous histiocytoma: an analysis of 200 cases. *Cancer*, **41**, 2250–2266.

Weiss, S. W. and Sobin, L. H. (1994). *Histological Typing of Soft Tissue Tumours* (Springer, Berlin).

FURTHER READING

Bridge, J. A. and Sandberg, A. A. (2000). Cytogenetic and molecular genetic techniques as adjunctive approaches in the diagnosis of bone and soft tissue tumors. *Skeletal Radiology*, **29**, 249–258.

Delattre, O., *et al*. (1992). Gene fusion with an ETS DNA-binding domain caused by chromosome translocation in human tumours. *Nature*, **359**, 62–165.

Drobnjak, M., *et al*. (1994). Prognostic implications of p53 nuclear overexpression and high proliferation index of Ki-67 in adult soft-tissue sarcomas. *Journal of the National Cancer Institute*, **86**, 549–554.

Khan, J., *et al*. (1999). cDNA microarrays detect activation of a myogenic transcription program by the PAX3-FKHR fusion oncogene. *Proceedings of the National Academy Sciences of the USA*, **96**, 13264–13269.

Knezevich, S. R., *et al*. (1998). A novel ETV6-NTRK3 gene fusion in congenital fibrosarcoma. *Nature Genetics*, **18**, 184–187.

May, W. A., *et al*. (1997). EWS/FLI1-induced manic fringe renders NIH 3T3 cells tumorigenic. *Nature Genetics*, **17**, 495–497.

Ordonez, N. (1997). Application of immunohistochemistry in the diagnosis of soft tissue sarcomas: a review and update. *Advances in Anatomical Pathology*, **5**, 67–85.

Pisters, P. W. and Pollock, R. E. (1999). Staging and prognostic factors in soft tissue sarcoma. *Seminars in Radiative Oncology*, **9**, 307–314.

Rubin, B. P., *et al*. (1998). Congenital mesoblastic nephroma t(12;15) is associated with ETV6-NTRK3 gene fusion: cytogenetic and molecular relationship to congenital (infantile) fibrosarcoma. *American Journal of Pathology*, **153**, 1451–1458.

Somerhausen, N. S. A. and Fletcher, C. D. M. (1999). Soft-tissue sarcomas: An update. *European Journal of Surgical Oncology*, **25**, 215–220.

Shapiro, D. N., *et al*. (1993). Fusion of PAX3 to a member of the forkhead family of transcription factors in human alveolar rhabdomyosarcoma. *Cancer Research*, **53**, 5108–5112.

Zucman, J., *et al*. (1993). EWS and ATF-1 gene fusion induced by t(12;22) translocation in malignant melanoma of soft parts. *Nature Genetics*, **4**, 341–345.

Chapter 49
Pleura and Peritoneum

Jonathan A. Fletcher
Harvard Medical School, Brigham and Women's Hospital, Boston, MA, USA

Christopher N. Otis
Tufts University School of Medicine, Baystate Medical Center, Springfield, MA, USA

C O N T E N T S

INTRODUCTION

Primary cancers of the pleura and peritoneum arc uncommon in the general population. Nonetheless, such cancers – particularly those which arise from mesothelial cells and are therefore known as malignant mesothelioma – have commanded substantial attention in recent years. There are several reasons why mesotheliomas are subject to active discussion in the scientific and lay press. First, they often arise from exposure to asbestos fibres, and are thereby a public and occupational health concern. Second, they are a particularly deadly form of cancer. Third, diagnosis of mesothelioma is often difficult.

Malignant mesotheliomas are locally aggressive neoplasms in which the neoplastic proliferation originates from pleural, peritoneal or, rarely, pericardial mesothelial cells (Craighead and Mossman, 1982; Craighead, 1987; Antman, 1993). Mesotheliomas are linked epidemiologically to asbestos exposure and from that standpoint alone have been a major public health concern. Although mesotheliomas are often associated with extensive occupational asbestos exposure, a substantial 'bystander' risk has been documented, and as many as 50% of American patients have no history of known asbestos exposure (Craighead and Mossman, 1982). Advances in clinical recognition of mesothelioma have allowed the evaluation of additional risk factors. One known risk factor is inhalation of the airborne mineral dust erionite (Selcuk *et al.*, 1992), which is responsible for endemic mesothelioma in central Turkey. Another potential risk factor – albeit less convincingly implicated than asbestos – is exposure to

SV40 virus. Accordingly, accurate diagnosis of mesothelioma is a global concern, and this concern will certainly persist after the present wave of asbestos-associated cases peaks and subsides.

Many other types of cancer can involve the pleura or peritoneum, but discussion of these entities, individually, is beyond the scope of this chapter. Such cancers are occasionally primary and can be multifocal and/or associated with familial cancer syndromes, as in the case of papillary serous carcinoma of the peritoneum (Schorge *et al.*, 1998). However, nonmesothelial pleural and peritoneal tumours are more often metastatic from another tissue site. Pleural or peritoneal metastases are generally manifested by shortness of breath or abdominal swelling/discomfort due to fluid accumulation, and they are sometimes the only evident metastases in carcinomas arising from organs such as lung, large bowel, ovary or breast. Patients can come to medical attention because of symptomatic pleural or peritoneal metastases at a time when the primary carcinoma is not yet evident. These scenarios emphasize the importance of distinguishing histologically and immunohistochemically between epithelial-type mesothelioma and carcinoma.

NORMAL DEVELOPMENT AND STRUCTURE

Mesothelial cells derive from the mesoderm, and they form a single cell layer lining the pleural, peritoneal and pericardial spaces. They allow relatively frictionless movement of opposed surfaces, a function which is important for the organs they encompass. For example, they ease the motion of pleura and pericardial surfaces which is important during respiration and cardiac contraction/relaxation, respectively. Mesothelial cells also play vital roles in regulating transport of fluids and molecules across the pleural, peritoneal and pericardial spaces. The pleura and peritoneum proper include not only mesothelial cells but also fibrovascular connective tissue which provides support for the mesothelial cells. Cancers can arise from any of the cell types in the pleura and peritoneum, but this chapter will focus on those – malignant mesotheliomas – which originate from the mesothelial cells.

AETIOLOGY

Malignant mesothelioma was diagnosed infrequently prior to 1960, at which time Wagner *et al.* (1960) described a dramatically increased incidence in asbestos miners. Thereafter, mesothelioma was highly publicized owing, in part, to public health concerns. Subsequent epidemiological studies confirmed the striking association between asbestos exposure and mesothelioma. Mesothelioma was found to be common in groups as diverse as native Americans (occupational exposure during production of silver jewellery); carpenters, plumbers, and electricians (occupational exposure to asbestos insulation materials); and villagers of central Turkey (inhalation of the endogenous mineral erionite, a structural mimic of asbestos) (Craighead and Mossman, 1982; Craighead, 1987; Selcuk *et al.*, 1992; Antman, 1993). The latency period between asbestos exposure and presentation with mesothelioma is typically 30–45 years. Mesothelioma incidence will probably increase over the next several decades because asbestos use rose in most countries after the Second World War and was not regulated until 1970. A registry of mesothelioma deaths has been maintained in England, Wales and Scotland since 1968, and annual deaths from mesothelioma in these populations rose from 154 in 1968 to 1009 in 1991 (Peto *et al.*, 1995). Based on known occupational asbestos exposure in these countries, it is estimated that mesothelioma incidence will peak in year 2020 and will account for 1% of all deaths in the most highly exposed cohorts (men born during the 1940s) (Peto *et al.*, 1995).

Asbestos belongs to a family of magnesium and calcium silicates that withstand extremely high temperatures. The thermoresistant properties of asbestos have been appreciated for many millenia, and were evident to the ancient Greeks, who used asbestos in wraps for cremation. In recent times, asbestos has found widespread use as insulation material in the walls of buildings and as heat-resistant material in engine parts and brake linings, among

other applications. Asbestos fibres can be grouped into those which are wavy (serpentines) and straight (amphiboles), the latter being more often implicated in oncogenesis (Walker *et al.*, 1992). As discussed below, it is likely that the oncogenic potential of asbestos is multifactorial.

Several *in vitro* studies provide fascinating clues to the pathogenesis of tumorigenic chromosomal rearrangements in mesothelioma. Addition of asbestos fibres to non-neoplastic mesothelial cell cultures results in pronounced chromosome damage that is mediated by physical interactions between asbestos fibres and chromosomes (Lechner *et al.*, 1985; Ault *et al.*, 1995). Asbestos fibres 'snare' whole chromosomes, or break off pieces of chromosomes, during mitosis, and these chromosomes and chromosome fragments are separated from the normal mitotic spindle apparatus (Ault *et al.*, 1995). The end result is aberrant chromosome segregation with loss of a chromosome, or chromosome region, from one daughter cell. Therefore, these studies establish a scenario in which asbestos fibres are directly responsible for random chromosomal damage. Amongst the asbestos-exposed mesothelial cells are presumably those occasional cells in which the chromosomal damage results in loss of key tumour-supressor loci. These cells might represent the starting point for neoplastic mesothelial proliferation. *In vitro* models suggest that asbestos fibres also have a direct role in promoting mesothelial cell proliferation via nonmutational mechanisms (Pache *et al.*, 1998; Timblin *et al.*, 1998). Consequently, asbestos may inflict initial genotoxic damage, then promote proliferation of the damaged mesothelial cells, enabling them to acquire additional oncogenic mutations.

Considerable controversy attended recent reports that SV40 virus is found in many human mesotheliomas. The SV40 promoter is commonly used to drive expression of various genes which are introduced into mammalian cells as plasmid constructs for *in vitro* analyses. However, SV40 itself is generally nontransforming when expressed in human non-neoplastic cells. Nonetheless, there is substantial, although disputed, evidence that SV40 participates in the genesis of human mesotheliomas. Evaluation of human mesothelioma was prompted by the discovery, by Carbone *et al.*, (1994) that Syrian hamsters developed mesothelioma following injection of wild-type SV40 virus into the pleural space. The same group noted that SV40-like sequences were demonstrable by polymerase chain reaction (PCR) in primary human mesotheliomas (Carbone *et al.* (1994). Other groups did not confirm this finding, or noted that the ability to identify SV40-like sequences depended on the specific SV40 oligonucleotide primers used for the PCR (Strickler *et al.*, 1996). In addition, SV40 protein was not identified in human mesothelioma cell lines (Modi *et al.*, 2000), and immunohistochemical studies of primary mesothelioma tumours revealed a weak, non-nuclear, expression pattern of putative SV40, which was interpreted as inconsistent with a transforming role. These contrary findings raised the question of whether the apparent SV40 genomic sequences might represent trivial PCR contaminants, 'bystander' SV40 in non-neoplastic cells, or a closely related virus distinct from SV40. A follow-up, multi-instutional study again supported the presence of true SV40 DNA within primary human mesotheliomas, and recent studies show that SV40 synergizes with asbestos in transforming mesothelial cells *in vitro* (Bocchetta *et al.*, 2000). Nonetheless, it is unclear whether the neoplastic cells in primary human mesotheliomas express SV40 protein. It is important that these questions be resolved inasmuch as the possibility of an SV40 role is a substantial public health concern. Millions of individuals, in the United States and in other countries, were potentially exposed to SV40 in poliovirus vaccines administered between 1955 and 1963.

SCREENING AND PREVENTION

Malignant mesothelioma is an asbestos-associated neoplasm that has been diagnosed with increasing frequency over the past two decades. Contemporary regulations on asbestos constitute one key measure in preventing mesotheliomas, but these measures are not expected to eradicate the disease. Many mesotheliomas develop in persons with no evident exposure to asbestos, and whose lung tissue does not contain elevated levels of asbestos fibres. Furthermore, several non-asbestos risk factors have been identified, including radiation therapy to the chest or abdomen, inhalation of certain environmental dusts and, potentially, exposure to the SV40 virus.

One strategy for mesothelioma prevention would involve screening at-risk individuals so that mesotheliomas could be detected at their earliest, *in situ*, stages and be cured surgically. Indeed, it would seem that the unique epidemiology of mesothelioma, particularly its relationship to asbestos exposure, should permit the development of effective screening measures. However, that has not been the case, and timely diagnosis remains a challenge. Only a small subset of individuals, presumably less than 5%, develop mesothelioma even after occupational exposures to large amounts of asbestos (Ribak *et al.*, 1998). In addition, individuals exposed to asbestos develop benign pleural and peritoneal masses, known as 'plaques,' more often than they do malignant mesothelioma (Kannerstein *et al.*, 1977). The challenges for screening are compounded because the latency period between asbestos exposure and clinical manifestations of disease is long, commonly more than 30 years, and conventional radiological screening methods, such as plain radiographs and CAT scans, do not distinguish early mesothelioma from benign asbestos-mediated pleural and peritoneal thickening or effusions. Further, patients often present with nonspecific symptoms, leading to delays in diagnosis, and mesothelioma progresses rapidly once clinically apparent. Given these challenges, it is perhaps more realistic to expect that improved survival in mesothelioma patients will result from better therapies rather than earlier detection. Most mesotheliomas are probably beyond the reach of surgical cure long before they first manifest clinically and radiologically. This is because mesothelioma cell shedding, and resultant pleural or peritoneal dissemination, occur early in the course of the disease.

CLINICAL PRESENTATION AND PATHOLOGY

Although the accuracy of mesothelioma diagnosis has improved dramatically over the past 20 years, many potential pitfalls remain. Most patients with malignant mesothelioma present with discomfort and/or respiratory distress due to mesothelioma bulk tumour, pleural effusion or ascites (Craighead, 1987; Antman, 1993). However, some patients present only with nonspecific symptoms, such as weight loss, fevers and fatigue. The most common radiographic sign is that of pleural effusion with or without pleural plaques, and cytological examination of effusion or ascites fluid is often the initial diagnostic procedure. Cytological diagnosis is challenging as the morphological similarities between malignant mesothelioma and reactive mesothelial hyperplasia may preclude differentiating between the two in fluid cytology. When overt cytological features of malignancy are present, distinction from adenocarcinoma (primary to the lung or from a distant site) may be impossible without employing immunocytochemical studies. Cytological diagnosis of malignancy was achieved in 22–66% of mesothelioma patients in several large series, whereas the remaining cases could not be distinguished from reactive mesothelial hyperplasia (Scherman and Mark, 1990; Boutin *et al.*, 1993). Reactive mesothelial hyperplasia is a relatively nonspecific finding which can occur in response to almost any type of pleural or peritoneal insult. For example, pronounced mesothelial hyperplasia can be seen in association with pleural or peritoneal effusions secondary to infection, cirrhosis or rheumatoid arthritis. Although pleural or peritoneal thickening are demonstrated by computed tomography (CT) or magnetic resonance (MR) scanning in some patients with mesothelioma, these findings are also not conclusive for malignancy. Asbestos is well known to induce pleural or peritoneal plaques and/or diffuse thickening even in the absence of actual mesothelioma (Kannerstein *et al.*, 1977).

Only 50% of mesotheliomas are associated with asbestos exposure. Based on this statistic, it is obvious that the recent surge in diagnosed mesothelioma cannot be due entirely to changing trends in asbestos use. A minor factor is the growing number of cases occurring as second neoplasms after radiation therapy. A more significant variable, however, is the increasing sophistication of mesothelioma diagnosis. There is little question that many or most epithelial-type mesotheliomas were misdiagnosed as adenocarcinoma prior to 1970, whereas many or most spindle-cell mesotheliomas were misdiagnosed as sarcoma. Increased awareness of histological and immunohistochemical subtleties has allowed more accurate (and more frequent) diagnosis of mesothelioma over the past two decades. Accurate diagnosis of mesothelioma is of more than academic interest, because survival for patients with early-stage mesothelioma has improved with a combined approach of pleural or peritoneal stripping, multiagent chemotherapy and radiation to sites of bulky disease (Sugarbaker et al., 1999).

Histopathology

The gross appearance of mesothelioma often features numerous small nodules and plaques and/or generalized thickening of the pleura or peritoneum (**Figure 1; see colour plate section**) (Corson, 1997). As discussed above, there is invariably some degree of associated effusion. Invasion of the lungs proper (pulmonary parenchyma) is unusual in the early stages of pleural mesothelioma, whereas involvement of local lymph nodes is seen occasionally (Sugarbaker et al., 1993, 1999). Nonetheless, pulmonary function is often compromised by the combined restrictive effects of malignant pleural effusion and pleural encasement by the tumour (**Figure 1**). The histological appearance of malignant mesothelioma is variable. There are three major morphological presentations, which may be categorized into epithelial, biphasic and sarcomatoid types.

Most mesotheliomas are composed of round epithelial-like cells (**Figure 2; see colour plate section**), and such cases can be misdiagnosed as adenocarcinoma. Other mesotheliomas are composed of spindled cells (**Figure 3; see colour plate section**), and these tumours can be mistaken for various sarcomas, including monophasic synovial sarcoma, malignant peripheral nerve sheath tumour, solitary fibrous tumour and fibrosarcoma. Spindle-cell mesotheliomas can also be mistaken for epithelial cancers, which occasionally have a spindle-cell morphology. Furthermore, mesothelioma spindle cells can be innocent-looking in some cases, despite their invariably lethal behaviour, and can be mistaken for a non-neoplastic – or desmoplastic – spindle-cell proliferation. Immunohistochemistry and electron microscopy have been helpful in resolving these diagnostic considerations. A number of monoclonal antibodies facilitate differentiation of epithelial-type mesothelioma from adenocarcinoma, and other antibodies enable distinction of spindle-cell mesothelioma from sarcoma (Cagle et al., 1989; Brown et al.,

1993; Weiss and Battifora, 1993; Ordonez, 1999). Cytogenetic and molecular analyses are also helpful in some cases. For example, synovial sarcoma, malignant peripheral nerve sheath tumour and solitary fibrous tumour can generally be distinguished based on their respective expression of SYT–SSX fusion oncogenes, S100 protein and CD34 and their lack of expression for the calretinin mesothelioma marker. On the other hand, neither immunohistochemistry nor electron microscopy has been helpful in distinguishing malignant mesothelioma from reactive mesothelial hyperplasia (Crotty et al., 1992).

Immunohistochemistry

Although all aspects of the clinicopathological evaluation must be considered in arriving at a diagnosis of mesothelioma, most would agree that immunohistochemistry is the key adjunct to routine histology. Indeed, the immunohistochemical evaluation of mesothelioma receives considerable attention in the pathology literature, and a full account of this dynamic field is beyond the realm of this chapter. Only representative highlights will be mentioned, such as the recent discovery that calretinin, a calcium-binding protein, is expressed in virtually all mesothelial cells (**Figures 2** and **4**). Calretinin is expressed in both normal and malignant mesothelial cells, and therefore does not serve to distinguish mesothelioma from reactive mesothelial hyperplasia. However, calretinin is seldom expressed in mesothelioma histological mimics (Doglioni et al., 1996), including adenocarcinomas metastatic to pleura or peritoneum, or spindle-cell sarcomas and sarcomatoid carcinomas (Doglioni et al., 1996; Attanoos et al., 2000). There are many other antibodies which discriminate mesothelioma from histological mimics, and which are suitable for paraffin section immunohistochemistry. None of these reagents provides perfect specificity or sensitivity, and they are therefore applied as panels in which complementary antibodies provide a more convincing final answer. Examples of antibody targets useful in distinguishing mesothelioma from adenocarcinoma include (1) Ber-EP4, which is expressed diffusely and strongly in most bronchogenic adenocarcinomas but absent or only focal in most mesotheliomas, (2) CEA, which is expressed in most adenocarcinomas but rarely in mesothelioma (**Figure 4; see colour plate section**), and (3) Leu-M1, which is also expressed generally in adenocarcinoma but not in mesothelioma. Similarly, TAG-72 (recognized by the antibody B72.3) and thyroid transcription factor-1 (TTF-1) are observed in a large percentage of pulmonary adenocarcinomas, but not in mesotheliomas.

It is important to emphasize that specificity and sensitivity of immunohistochemical detection is influenced by the epitope against which the antibody was raised and the method – particularly monoclonal versus polyclonal – of antibody preparation. Not surprisingly, there are conflicting reports as to whether the above-mentioned antibodies are suitable for evaluation of mesothelioma. These discrepant results undoubtedly reflect both the use of different antibody preparations as well as the different techniques for immunohistochemical staining. CEA provides an illustrative example. It is well known that monoclonal antibodies to CEA vary in their sensitivity for detecting CEA in bronchogenic adenocarcinomas. Conversely, polyclonal antisera to CEA can recognize a nonspecific cross-reactive antigen which decreases their specificity. Preabsorption with mouse spleen powder is reported to decrease this nonspecific immunoreactivity but, nevertheless, a small percentage of malignant mesotheliomas are immunoreactive to antibodies directed against CEA. Further, immunohistochemical staining for CEA is less useful in evaluation of peritoneal mesothelioma, because a substantial number of ovarian carcinomas do not stain for this glycoprotein.

Keratin expression (**Figure 3**) is a near-universal finding in mesothelioma whereas it is uncommon and/or focal in some of the spindle-cell sarcomas which mimic sarcomatoid mesothelioma. Keratin staining is less useful in distinguishing epithelial-type mesothelioma from adenocarcinoma, although some observers report that the keratin staining pattern is diffuse and perinuclear in most epithelial-type mesotheliomas whereas it stains in a peripheral pattern, accentuating the cell membrane, in many adenocarcinomas (Corson, 1997).

Ultrastructure

Electron microscopy evaluation is less critical than immunohistochemistry in the diagnostic work-up of malignant mesothelioma. Nonetheless, there are characteristic ultrastructural differences – particularly between epithelial-type mesothelioma and adenocarcinoma – which can be useful in arriving at a diagnosis. Notably, epithelial-type mesotheliomas, and the epithelial-type components in mixed histology mesotheliomas, may often be distinguished from adenocarcinomas based on the size and number of microvilli which project from their cell surfaces (**Figure 5**). Epithelial-type mesotheliomas generally have numerous microvilli which are long, thin and branching, whereas adenocarcinomas typically have microvilli which are short and sparse (Corson, 1997).

CYTOGENETIC AND MOLECULAR GENETIC FINDINGS

There is experimental evidence that asbestos fibres are directly responsible for chromosomal damage in mesothelial cells. Also, there is evidence that the SV40 virus serves as an oncogenic cofactor in promoting the development of some mesotheliomas. Mesotheliomas differ

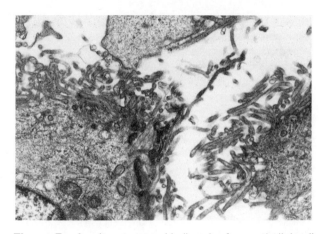

Figure 5   An ultrastructural hallmark of mesothelial cell differentiation is the finding of long branching microvilli at the cell surface (commonly referred to as bushy microvilli). In contrast, pulmonary and many extrapulmonary adenocarcinomas display short microvilli. In addition, perinuclear condensation of keratin intermediate filaments (tonofilaments) may be seen in mesothelial cells. Although ultrastructural examination remains useful in the diagnosis of mesothelioma, it is generally more cumbersome than immunohistochemical evaluation.

from many other solid tumours, however, in that the early, preinvasive, stages of the disease are rarely observed (Henderson *et al.*, 1998). In addition, it can be very difficult to distinguish *in situ* mesothelioma from non-neoplastic mesothelial hyperplasia. Therefore, the *in situ* stage of mesothelioma has not been readily available for comparison with invasive mesothelioma, and the molecular mechanisms responsible for mesothelioma initiation remain to be defined. On the other hand, various studies have shed light on cytogenetic, molecular and cell biology mechanisms in invasive mesotheliomas. Several of these mechanisms are discussed below.

Cytogenetic Alterations

Cytogenetic studies have revealed a characteristic profile of chromosomal deletions in most mesotheliomas. These cytogenetic findings implicate loss of several tumour-suppressor genes as a critical event in mesothelioma pathogenesis. Although mesothelioma karyotypes are often described as 'complex,' they are in fact less complex than those in many carcinomas. In particular, epithelial-type mesothelioma karyotypes often have fewer than five chromosomal abnormalities per cell (**Figure 6**), whereas bronchogenic adenocarcinomas typically have more than 20 chromosomal abnormalities per cell. Sarcomatoid mesotheliomas, on the other hand, have more complex karyotypes than do the epithelial-type cases. A rather detailed account of mesothelioma chromosomal aberrations has emerged over the past 10 years (Taguchi *et al.*, 1993), and it is clear that the nonrandom chromosomal

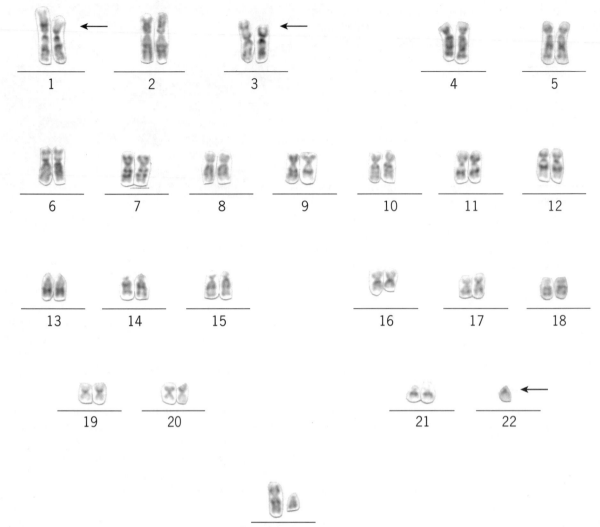

Figure 6   Noncomplex karyotype in an epithelial-type mesothelioma, showing characteristic losses of 1p, 3p and chromosome 22 (arrows).

deletions are found in mesotheliomas irrespective of histology (epithelial-type versus spindle-cell) or primary site (pleural versus peritoneal). The deletional hotspots are within the long arms of chromosomes 6 and 22 and within the short arms of chromosomes 1, 3 and 9 (**Figure 6**). Notably, the pathogenesis of some mesothelioma chromosome deletions may be directly attributable to asbestos-mediated chromosome damage (Lechner *et al.*, 1985; Ault *et al.*, 1995).

Molecular Alterations

Cytogenetic studies implicate loss of several tumour genes in the pathogenesis of virtually all mesotheliomas. However, the molecular targets for most of these chromosomal deletions are not yet known. Exceptions are the *CDKN2A* and *CDKN2B* genes, which are targetted by chromosome 9p deletions, and the *NF2* gene, which is targetted by chromosome 22q deletions (Cheng *et al.*, 1994). The *CDKN2A* and *CDKN2B* genes encode proteins which inhibit the CDK4 cell cycle checkpoint kinase and which thereby serve to block cell cycling. *CDKN2A* is targetted by chromosomal deletions in many human tumours, and *CDKN2A* genomic loss or functional inactivation, resulting in dysregulated cell cycling, is one of the more common tumour-suppressor mechanisms in human cancers. It is particularly interesting that *CDKN2A* mutations are often either/or in relationship to mutations of several 'downstream' effectors, including the CDK4 kinase and the retinoblastoma protein (Rb) (He *et al.*, 1995). CDKN2A inhibits the function of CDK4–cyclin D1 complexes, which, in turn, inactivate the Rb protein via phosphorylation. Hypophosphorylated Rb blocks cell entry into the S phase of the cell cycle, whereas phosphorylated Rb fails to block entry to S phase and thereby promotes cell proliferation. Hence CDKN2A, CDK and Rb are control points along a single biological pathway, and disruption of any one of these points can disable normal constraints on cell cycling. These either/or relationships also appear to hold in mesothelioma, where CDKN2A inactivation is nearly universal, but Rb or CDK4 mutations are very uncommon (Cheng et al., 1994; Shimizu et al., 1994).

The NF2 protein is inactivated in virtually all mesotheliomas with chromosome 22 deletions (Sekido et al., 1995), and these represent approximately 75% of all mesotheliomas. NF2 was identified originally through analyses of its tumour-suppressor role in the genetic cancer syndrome, neurofibromatosis type 2, and through study of the various tumours, particularly benign schwannomas, which are characteristic of that syndrome. The normal functions of NF2 are poorly understood but it belongs to a family of proteins, each of which contains a so-called 'ezrin–radixin–moesin' domain, which communicate signals between cell surface receptors and the cytoskeleton. Recent studies show that NF2 interacts with substrates of the Met receptor tyrosine kinase and with scaffolding proteins interacting with the platelet-derived growth factor receptor tyrosine kinase. These findings suggest that NF2 modulates signal transduction pathways downstream of Met, PDGFR and other cell surface receptors. Such findings are relevant clinically because inhibition of receptor tyrosine kinases, whether by immunological or small molecule methods, has proved very effective in treatment of some cancers.

p53 is a seminal tumour-suppressor protein, whose inactivation contributes to the development of many human cancers. Initial reports suggested that p53 mutation was commonplace in mesotheliomas. This impression was not confirmed in other studies, and it is unlikely that p53 mutation plays a major role in mesothelioma pathogenesis (Mor et al., 1997). Nonetheless, it is possible that the p53 pathway is inhibited by other oncogenic mutations, and just such a role has been proposed for SV40 oncoproteins in some mesotheliomas.

Diagnostic Relevance

Further characterization of mesothelioma chromosomal and molecular aberrations may lead to improvements in diagnosis of mesothelioma (Granados et al., 1994). For example, virtually all mesotheliomas contain clonal chromosomal deletions whereas such alterations are not found in reactive mesothelial hyperplasia. Cytogenetic and molecular assays can be useful diagnostically because neoplastic and reactive mesothelial proliferations cannot be distinguished consistently using histological adjuncts such as immunohistochemistry and electron microscopy. There is also evidence that molecular assays are useful in distinguishing mesothelioma from adenocarcinoma (Sekido et al., 1995). Certain of the cytogenetic methods can now be performed routinely in cytological preparations (**Figure 7; see colour plate section**),

and therefore should be useful in enabling a diagnosis of mesothelioma in pleural or peritoneal fluid specimens.

PROGNOSTIC FACTORS

Overall survival for patients with malignant mesothelioma is unquestionably poor. Nevertheless, intensive combined modality therapeutic strategies, as summarized below, have enabled a subgroup of patients to achieve 5-year survival. This accomplishment is striking, given that very few mesothelioma patients survive even 1 year when less intensive treatment methods are used. In the face of these therapeutic advances, it becomes more pressing to identify reliable prognostic factors. In particular, it is important to identify the subgroup of patients who will benefit from major surgical procedures, such as extrapleural pleuropneumonectomy.

Various potential prognostic variables have been evaluated in different mesothelioma series. Such studies have considered the prognostic implications of presenting symptoms (e.g. dyspnea, chest pain, cough), performance status, age, sex, histology, stage of disease and asbestos exposure. Tumour histology has been a major prognostic factor in all studies. Survival for patients who are untreated, or who receive single-modality therapy, is typically in the range of 4, 7 and 12 months depending on whether histology is sarcomatoid, mixed or epithelial-type, respectively (Fusco et al., 1993). The prognostic role of histology is also evident in patients receiving intensive treatment approaches, including the trimodality approach of extrapleural pleuropneumonectomy, chemotherapy and radiation therapy. In one such study, patients with epithelial-type mesothelioma had median survivals of 52 and 21% at 2 and 5 years, respectively, whereas only 16% of those with sarcomatoid mesothelioma survived for 2 years and none survived for 5 years (Sugarbaker et al., 1999). Primary site has also influenced prognosis in virtually all studies. Patients with peritoneal mesothelioma – with the exception of cases that are very well differentiated – have a median survival which is less than half of that in patients with pleural mesothelioma (Sridhar et al., 1992).

Although most mesotheliomas are disseminated locally at time of diagnosis, disease stage is nonetheless important prognostically (De Pangher Manzini et al., 1993). Not surprisingly, mediastinal lymph node involvement is an adverse prognostic factor in patients undergoing cytoreductive surgical approaches, such as extrapleural pleuropneumonectomy (Sugarbaker et al., 1993). Other prognosticators are undoubtedly influenced by the treatment approach. These include age less than 65 years, female gender, absence of pain, longer duration of symptoms, excellent performance status and absence of malignant cells in the associated effusion, all of which have been favourable prognostic factors in some studies but not in others (Fusco et al., 1993; Sugarbaker et al., 1993).

OVERVIEW OF PRESENT CLINICAL MANAGEMENT

Mesothelioma is relatively resistant to conventional chemotherapy and radiation therapy approaches. There are numerous reports, generally in small numbers of patients, which show impressive response rates – often in the range 25–50% for partial response – after single- or multiagent chemotherapy. Invariably, however, such findings have been refuted in follow-up studies, where the partial response rates prove to be well under 20%. Nonetheless, there are several chemotherapeutic agents, including doxorubicin and cisplatin, which unquestionably induce occasional partial responses, albeit typically lasting for no more than a few months (Taub and Antman, 1997). Multi-agent chemotherapy protocols, e.g. cisplatin + doxorubicin, may achieve partial response rates in 20–30% of patients (Chahinian et al., 1993). Radiation therapy as a single modality is relatively ineffective, with very few partial responders, although some patients receive temporary benefit in the form of symptomatic improvement (Gordon et al., 1982). Likewise, mesothelioma is rarely eradicated by surgery alone, although meaningful palliation can be achieved (Butchart et al., 1981). Even the more radical surgical approaches invariably leave tumour cells behind, and are therefore cytoreductive rather than curative.

Although single modality therapies – whether with chemotherapy, radiation therapy or surgery – have been relatively ineffective, the combination of these methods has been highly successful in certain subgroups of patients. In particular, cytoreduction by extrapleural pleuropneumonectomy, when followed by multiagent chemotherapy and radiation therapy, leads to 5-year survival in many patients with epithelial-type mesothelioma (Boutin et al., 1993). Unfortunately, only one-third of pleural mesothelioma patients are candidates for this radical surgical approach, which involves en bloc removal of the lung, pleura, pericardium and diaphragm from the involved side of the chest (Boutin et al., 1993). In addition, combined modality methods have been less successful in patients with sarcomatoid mesothelioma, very few of whom survive for 2 years. Another constraint is that postoperative mortality is high, typically in excess of 10%, in centres which do not specialize in the radical surgical methods needed for effective cytoreduction (Rusch, 1999). Survival after the combined approach of extrapleural pleuropneumonectomy, chemotherapy and radiation therapy has been particularly prolonged in patients with epithelial-type histology whose resection margins and mediastinal lymph nodes were free of apparent tumour. This subgroup, represented by 31 of 176 extrapleural pleuropneumonectomy patients in one study, had 2- and 5-year survivals of 68 and 46%, respectively, whereas those for the overall group were 38 and 15%, respectively

(Boutin et al., 1993). Similar trimodality approaches have also proved effective in pilot studies of peritoneal mesothelioma, where cytoreduction is accomplished by surgical debulking and then followed with chemotherapy and local irradiation to destroy residual tumour. Such studies often use intraperitoneal chemotherapy, which can be delivered readily using a Port-A-Cath set up. In one such study, with an intraperitoneal chemotherapy component of doxorubicin and cisplatin, three of five patients were disease-free at intervals of 46, 60 and 61 months after diagnosis (Lederman et al., 1988).

Despite the impressive advances provided by combined modality treatment, including a small but growing number of 10-year survivors, most mesothelioma patients do not survive past 2 years. This in part reflects the reality that many patients are fairly sick and/or inoperable at the time of diagnosis. Delays in diagnosis are common, particularly in those patients presenting with nonspecific symptoms, and many patients lose weight rapidly and develop significant respiratory compromise before therapy can be initiated. Therefore, improved survival for the overall group of mesothelioma patients probably depend on prompt diagnosis and development of more effective pharmacological interventions. Several novel therapies provide basis for optimism, although it is as yet unclear whether they will serve as effective solutions in their own right or as stepping stones in the quest for curative therapies. Examples include the intrapleural administration of immunomodulatory agents, such as interleukin-2 and γ-interferon, which have induced partial responses in up to 50% of patients with early-stage mesothelioma (Astoul et al., 1998). Beyond these tangible advances, it is certain that the growing understanding of mesothelioma biology, including oncogenes, tumour-suppressor genes and key growth factor signalling pathways, will translate in the near future to novel and biologically rational therapies.

REFERENCES

Antman, K. H. (1993). Natural history and epidemiology of malignant mesothelioma. Chest, **103**, 373S–376S.

Astoul, P., et al. (1998). Intrapleural administration of interleukin-2 for the treatment of patients with malignant pleural mesothelioma: a Phase II study. Cancer, **83**, 2099–2104.

Attanoos, R. L., et al. (2000). Anti-mesothelial markers in sarcomatoid mesothelioma and other spindle cell neoplasms. Histopathology, **37**, 224–231.

Ault, J. G., et al. (1995). Behavior of crocidolite asbestos during mitosis in living vertebrate lung epithelial cells. Cancer Research, **55**, 792–798.

Bocchetta, M., et al. (2000). From the cover: human mesothelial cells are unusually susceptible to simian virus 40-mediated transformation and asbestos cocarcinogenicity. Proceedings *of the National Academy of Sciences of the USA*, **97**, 10214–10219.

Boutin, C., *et al.* (1993). Thoracoscopy in pleural malignant mesothelioma: a prospective study of 188 consecutive patients. Part 2: Prognosis and staging. *Cancer*, **72**, 394–404.

Brown, R. W., *et al.* (1993). Multiple-marker immunohistochemical phenotypes distinguishing malignant pleural mesothelioma from pulmonary adenocarcinoma. *Human Pathology*, **24**, 347–354.

Butchart, E. G., *et al.* (1981). The role of surgery in diffuse malignant mesothelioma of the pleura. *Seminars in Oncology*, **8**, 321–328.

Cagle, P. T., *et al.* (1989). Immunohistochemical differentiation of sarcomatoid mesotheliomas from other spindle cell neoplasms. *American Journal of Clinical Pathology*, **92**, 566–571.

Carbone, M., *et al.* (1994). Simian virus 40-like DNA sequences in human pleural mesothelioma. *Oncogene*, **9**, 1781–1790.

Chahinian, A. P., *et al.* (1993). Randomized phase II trial of cisplatin with mitomycin or doxorubicin for malignant mesothelioma by the Cancer and Leukemia Group B. *Journal of Clinical Oncology*, **11**, 1559–1565.

Cheng, J. Q., *et al.* (1994). p16 alterations and deletion mapping of 9p21–p22 in malignant mesothelioma. *Cancer Research*, **54**, 5547–5551.

Corson, J. M. (1997). Pathology of diffuse malignant pleural mesothelioma. *Seminars in Thoracic and Cardiovascular Surgery*, **9**, 347–355.

Craighead, J. E. (1987). Current pathogenetic concepts of diffuse malignant mesothelioma. *Human Pathology*, **18**, 544–557.

Craighead, J. E. and Mossman, B. T. (1982). The pathogenesis of asbestos-associated diseases. *New England Journal of Medicine*, **306**, 1446–1455.

Crotty, T. B., *et al.* (1992). Desmoplastic malignant mesothelioma masquerading as sclerosing mediastinitis: a diagnostic dilemma. *Human Pathology*, **23**, 79–82.

De Pangher Manzini, V., *et al.* (1993). Prognostic factors of malignant mesothelioma of the pleura. *Cancer*, **72**, 410–417.

Doglioni, C., *et al.* (1996). Calretinin: a novel immunocytochemical marker for mesothelioma. *American Journal of Surgical Pathology*, **20**, 1037–1046.

Fusco, V., *et al.* (1993). Malignant pleural mesothelioma. Multivariate analysis of prognostic factors on 113 patients. *Anticancer Research*, **13**, 683–689.

Gordon, W., *et al.* (1982). Radiation therapy in the management of patients with mesothelioma. *International Journal of Radiation Oncology and Biological Physics*, **8**, 19–25.

Granados, R., *et al.* (1994). Cytogenetic analysis of effusions from malignant mesothelioma. A diagnostic adjunct to cytology. *Acta Cytologia*, **38**, 711–717.

He, J., *et al.* (1995). Lack of p16INK4 or retinoblastoma protein (pRb), or amplification-associated overexpression of cdk4 is observed in distinct subsets of malignant glial tumors and cell lines. *Cancer Research*, **55**, 4833–4836.

Henderson, D. W., *et al.* (1998). Reactive mesothelial hyperplasia vs mesothelioma, including mesothelioma in situ: a brief review. *American Journal of Clinical Pathology*, **110**, 397–404.

Kannerstein, M., *et al.* (1977). Pathogenic effects of asbestos. *Archives of Pathology and Laboratory Medicine*, **101**, 623–628.

Lechner, J. F., *et al.* (1985) Asbestos-associated chromosomal changes in human mesothelial cells. *Proceedings of the National Academy of Sciences of the USA*, **82**, 3884–3888.

Lederman, G. S., *et al.* (1988). Combined modality treatment of peritoneal mesotheliomas. *National Cancer Institute Monographs*, 321–322.

Modi, S., *et al.* (2000). Protein expression of the RB-related gene family and SV40 large T antigen in mesothelioma and lung cancer. *Oncogene*, **19**, 4632–4639.

Mor, O., *et al.* (1997). Absence of p53 mutations in malignant mesotheliomas. *American Journal of Respiratory Cellular and Molecular Biology*, **16**, 9–13.

Ordonez, N. G. (1999). Role of immunohistochemistry in differentiating epithelial mesothelioma from adenocarcinoma. Review and update. *American Journal of Clinical Pathology*, **112**, 75–89.

Pache, J. C., *et al.* (1998). Increased epidermal growth factor-receptor protein in a human mesothelial cell line in response to long asbestos fibers. *American Journal of Pathology*, **152**, 333–340.

Peto, J., *et al.* (1995). Continuing increase in mesothelioma mortality in Britain. *Lancet*, **345**, 535–539.

Ribak, J., *et al.* (1988). Malignant mesothelioma in a cohort of asbestos insulation workers: clinical presentation, diagnosis, and causes of death. *British Journal of Industrial Medicine*, **45**, 182–187.

Rusch, V. W. (1999). Indications for pneumonectomy. Extrapleural pneumonectomy. *Chest Surgery Clinics of North America*, **9**, 327–338.

Schorge, J. O., *et al.* (1998). Molecular evidence for multifocal papillary serous carcinoma of the peritoneum in patients with germline BRCA1 mutations. *Journal of the National Cancer Institute*, **90**, 841–845.

Sekido, Y., *et al.* (1995). Neurofibromatosis type 2 (NF2) gene is somatically mutated in mesothelioma but not in lung cancer. *Cancer Research*, **55**, 1227–1231.

Selcuk, Z. T., *et al.* (1992). Malignant pleural mesothelioma due to environmental mineral fiber exposure in Turkey. Analysis of 135 cases. *Chest*, **102**, 790–796.

Sherman, M. E. and Mark, E. J. (1990). Effusion cytology in the diagnosis of malignant epithelioid and biphasic pleural mesothelioma. *Archives of Pathology and Laboratory Medicine*, **114**, 845–851.

Shimizu, E., *et al.* (1994). RB protein status and clinical correlation from 171 cell lines representing lung cancer, extrapulmonary small cell carcinoma, and mesothelioma. *Oncogene*, **9**, 2441–2448.

Sridhar, K. S., *et al.* (1992). New strategies are needed in diffuse malignant mesothelioma. *Cancer*, **70**, 2969–2979.

Strickler, H. D., *et al.* (1996). Simian virus 40 and pleural mesothelioma in humans. *Cancer Epidemiology Biomarkers and Prevention*, **5**, 473–475.

Sugarbaker, D. J., *et al.* (1993). Node status has prognostic significance in the multimodality therapy of diffuse, malignant mesothelioma. *Journal of Clinical Oncology*, **11**, 1172–1178.

Sugarbaker, D. J., *et al.* (1999). Resection margins, extrapleural nodal status, and cell type determine postoperative long-term survival in trimodality therapy of malignant pleural mesothelioma: results in 183 patients. *Journal of Thoracic and Cardiovascular Surgery*, **117**, 54–63.

Taguchi, T., *et al.* (1993). Recurrent deletions of specific chromosomal sites in 1p, 3p, 6q, and 9p in human malignant mesothelioma. *Cancer Research*, **53**, 4349–4355.

Taub, R. N. and Antman, K. H. (1997). Chemotherapy for malignant mesothelioma. *Seminars in Thoracic and Cardiovascular Surgery*, **9**, 361–366.

Timblin, C. R., *et al.* (1998). Patterns of c-fos and c-jun proto-oncogene expression, apoptosis, and proliferation in rat pleural mesothelial cells exposed to erionite or asbestos fibers. *Toxicology and Applied Pharmacology*, **151**, 88–97.

Wagner, J. C., *et al.* (1960). Diffuse pleural mesothelioma and asbestos exposure in the North Western Cape Province. *British Journal of Industrial Medicine*, **17**, 26.

Walker, C., *et al.* (1992). Possible cellular and molecular mechanisms for asbestos carcinogenicity. *American Journal of Industrial Medicine*, **21**, 253–273.

Weiss, L. M. and Battifora, H. (1993). The search for the optimal immunohistochemical panel for the diagnosis of malignant mesothelioma. *Human Pathology*, **24**, 345–346.

FURTHER READING

Antman, K. H. (1993). Natural history and epidemiology of malignant mesothelioma. *Chest*, **103**, 373S–376S.

Ault, J. G., *et al.* (1995). Behavior of crocidolite asbestos during mitosis in living vertebrate lung epithelial cells. *Cancer Research*, **55**, 792–798.

Bocchetta, M., *et al.* (2000). From the cover: human mesothelial cells are unusually susceptible to simian virus 40-mediated transformation and asbestos cocarcinogenicity. *Proceedings of the National Academy of Sciences of the USA*, **97**, 10214–10219.

Corson, J. M. (1997). Pathology of diffuse malignant pleural mesothelioma. *Seminars in Thoracic and Cardiovascular Surgery*, **9**, 347–355.

Craighead, J. E. (1987). Current pathogenetic concepts of diffuse malignant mesothelioma. *Human Pathology*, **18**, 544–557.

Modi, S., *et al.* (2000). Protein expression of the RB-related gene family and SV40 large T antigen in mesothelioma and lung cancer. *Oncogene*, **19**, 4632–4639.

Ordonez, N. G. (1999). Role of immunohistochemistry in differentiating epithelial mesothelioma from adenocarcinoma. Review and update. *American Journal of Clinical Pathology*, **112**, 75–89.

Pache, J. C., *et al.* (1998). Increased epidermal growth factor-receptor protein in a human mesothelial cell line in response to long asbestos fibers. *American Journal of Pathology*, **152**, 333–340.

Sekido, Y., *et al.* (1995). Neurofibromatosis type 2 (NF2) gene is somatically mutated in mesothelioma but not in lung cancer. *Cancer Research*, **55**, 1227–1231.

Sugarbaker, D.J., *et al.* (1999). Resection margins, extrapleural nodal status, and cell type determine postoperative long-term survival in trimodality therapy of malignant pleural mesothelioma: results in 183 patients. *Journal of Thoracic and Cardiovascular Surgery*, **117**, 54–63.

Taguchi, T., *et al.* (1993). Recurrent deletions of specific chromosomal sites in 1p, 3p, 6q, and 9p in human malignant mesothelioma. *Cancer Research*, **53**, 4349–4355.

Taub, R. N. and Antman, K. H. (1997). Chemotherapy for malignant mesothelioma. *Seminars in Thoracic and Cardiovascular Surgery*, **9**, 361–366.

Chapter 50

Heart

Renu Virmani and Allen Burke
Armed Forces Institute of Pathology, Washington, DC, USA

CONTENTS

NORMAL DEVELOPMENT AND STRUCTURE

The heart forms as a tube which loops between 24 and 26 days postovulation. Ventricular and atrial septation occur by 39 and 43 days postovulation, respectively; at the latter time, the heart structure is generally complete. There is little information relating cardiac development and neoplasia of the heart, as cardiac embryology is studied primarily in the context of congenital cardiac malformations (Burke and Virmani, 1996). Cardiac masses that develop *in utero* include rare lesions such as rhabdomyomas (frequently seen in conjunction with extracardiac hamartomas as part of the tuberous sclerosis syndrome), cardiac fibromas, benign rests of endodermal tissues (primarily benign AV nodal tumours) and potentially malignant tumours derived from developmentally misplaced germ cells (cardiac teratomas and related lesions). Rhabdomyomas and fibromas are generally considered to be hamartomas, that is, they are benign growths, usually developmental, that are composed of cells native to the organ of origin. An AV nodal tumour is not strictly a tumour, in that it represents a cluster of misplaced cells that migrated incorrectly within the foetus. These three lesions (rhabdomyoma, fibroma and AV nodal tumour) are not, then, strictly tumours, and result in potentially lethal symptoms only because of their delicate location, often near the conduction system of the heart, and not in their capability to grow and metastasize, which is absent. Germ cell tumours of the heart and pericardial space occur as a neoplastic growth of germ cell rests that remained in the mediastinum due to arrested migration from the yolk sac to the gonads. Mediastinal germ cell tumours in themselves are fairly rare; nevertheless, they outnumber intrapericardial germ cell tumours by a large margin.

The cell of origin of the commoner heart tumours in adults, namely myxomas and sarcomas, is controversial, as is any potential relationship between these two entities. Cardiac myxoma arises almost exclusively in the endocardium of the atrial septum. This rare neoplasm is made of undifferentiated mesenchymal cells (derived from connective tissue) that elaborate a matrix rich in proteoglycans and inflammatory cells which release various growth factors and thrombogenic substances. The embryological origin of cells that become cardiac myxoma is unknown, but because of the location and myxoid appearance, it has been suggested that myxomas are derived from cells that make up the endocardial cushion. Cardiac sarcomas are a heterogeneous groups of tumours with presumably various cells of origin. The most common group appear to arise from the endocardial lining of the atria, often elaborate myxoid ground substance similar to cardiac myxomas, and generally demonstrate myofibroblastic differentiation. There is no evidence that they derive from the same cell as myxomas, however, in that they do not arise in benign myxomas, tend to originate in sites in the atrium away from the septum and are histologically similar to sarcomas that arise in the intima of great arteries (a site in which myxomas do not arise). The second most common group of cardiac sarcomas are angiosarcomas, which are histologically identical with angiosarcomas that arise in extracardiac sites, and arise from endothelial cells usually in the right atrium or pericardium. Despite the fact that the heart is comprised mostly of muscle, only a small fraction of cardiac sarcomas show characteristics of striated muscle (i.e. rhabdomyosarcomatous differentiation). Because working heart muscle cells are terminally differentiated and show little propensity to divide, it is perhaps not a surprise that neoplasms of the heart are more likely to derive from less committed stromal cells that line the endocardium.

TUMOUR PATHOLOGY (CLINICAL, GROSS AND HISTOLOGICAL FEATURES)

For the purposes of this review, only primary cardiac neoplasms will be addressed (**Table 1**). Neoplasms arising in the heart include cardiac myxoma (about 75%) and cardiac sarcomas (less than 25%); other neoplasms, such as paragangliomas and teratomas, are extremely rare and will not be discussed in detail. Cardiac sarcomas are heterogeneous, but will be grouped into endocardial-based sarcomas, or myofibroblastic intimal sarcomas, which usually arise in the left atrium; angiosarcomas, which generally arise in the right atrium and pericardium; and miscellaneous sarcomas.

Two additional malignancies that arise in or near the heart need brief mention here. Malignant mesotheliomas of the pericardium, or the serosal lining of the heart, are rare neoplasms that share many clinical and pathological features with the much more common mesothelioma of the pleura. Pericardial mesotheliomas are often extensions of pleural mesotheliomas, and share the same pathological and epidemiological features as pleural mesotheliomas. The second rare malignancy of the heart that needs mention is the malignant lymphoma. Lymphomas generally arise from haematopoietic tissues that reside in lymph nodes, the spleen or the bone marrow, but may occasionally arise in parts of the body that do not normally possess large numbers of lymphoid cells. These locations include the soft tissue and internal organs, including brain, liver, and heart. The incidence of extranodal lymphomas has recently increased, because of the large numbers of people with immune deficiency syndromes, either due to infection with human immunodeficiency virus or because of iatrogenic immunosuppression in patients with allografts. Malignant lymphomas and malignant mesotheliomas will

be discussed briefly in this chapter, but the reader is directed to other portions of this volume that address these neoplasms in greater detail. (See the chapters *Lymph Nodes* and *Pleura and Peritoneum*.)

Myxoma

Cardiac myxoma is a benign endocardial-based neoplasm that usually arises in the left atrium (70%) at the region of the oval fossa (**Figure 1**). About 20% of myxomas arise in the right atrium, also usually in the region of the atrial septum or, less commonly, in ventricular sites. Myxomas that originate on the valve surfaces are exceptionally rare, and many reported cases actually represent a different lesion, usually a papillary fibroelastoma, not a true neoplasm.

The mean age at presentation is 50 years in cases of sporadic myxoma (Burke and Virmani, 1996). Cardiac myxoma arises from the endocardial surface by a stalk, which may be either broad-based or pedunculated. There are two gross appearances which characterize the surface of cardiac myxoma. Approximately 70% of tumours have an intact, smooth, endothelialized surface, with no surface thrombus; these lesions appear to be quiescent, with little possibility for further growth. Such tumours cause symptoms generally by chronic obstruction of the mitral valve, often resulting in pulmonary hypertension and symptoms of congestive heart failure (**Figure 2**). Occasional tumours cause symptoms as a result of hormone-like substance (cytokines) that stimulate the immune system, causing fever, weight loss and other constitutional symptoms. Because cardiac imaging is becoming more sophisticated and commonplace, an increasing percentage of cardiac myxomas are being detected as incidental findings in asymptomatic patients. Although a routine chest X-ray is unlikely to detect a cardiac myxoma in the majority of cases, about 5% of left-sided myxomas and up to 50% of right-sided tumours, will be detected on the basis of tumour calcification. More non-specific findings, such as cardiomegaly or evidence of mitral valve obstruction, are common in left-sided myxomas.

The majority of cardiac myxomas have a smooth surface (**Figure 3; see colour plate section**). A small

Table 1   Classification of primary cardiac neoplasms[a]

Tumour type	Site in heart	Biological behaviour	Associations
Myxoma	Left atrium, right atrium	Benign	Myxoma syndrome (2%)
Sarcoma		Highly malignant	None
Myofibroblastic	Atria (left > right)		
Angiosarcoma	Right atrium, pericardium		
Other	Various		
Lymphoma	Atria, epicardium, ventricles	Malignant	Immunosuppression (50%)
Mesothelioma	Pericardium	Highly malignant	Asbestos (20–30%)

[a]Lesions that are variably considered hamartomas, such as rhabdomyoma, fibroma, haemangioma and papillary fibroelastoma, are not included. Likewise, primary neoplasms that are extremely rare, such as paraganglioma, are also not included.

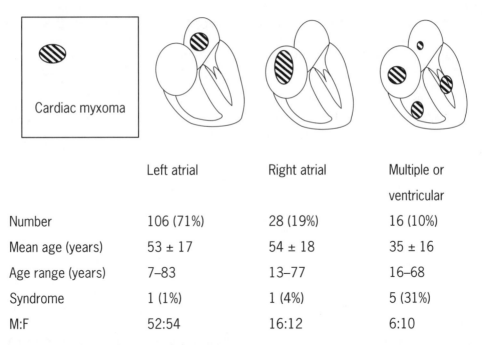

	Left atrial	Right atrial	Multiple or ventricular
Number	106 (71%)	28 (19%)	16 (10%)
Mean age (years)	53 ± 17	54 ± 18	35 ± 16
Age range (years)	7–83	13–77	16–68
Syndrome	1 (1%)	1 (4%)	5 (31%)
M:F	52:54	16:12	6:10

Figure 1 Sites of occurrence, cardiac myxoma (150 tumours seen by the authors). Multiple and ventricular cardiac myxomas demonstrate a clinically distinct clinical profile. They arise in younger patients and are more likely to be associated with extracardiac lesions (myxoma syndrome).

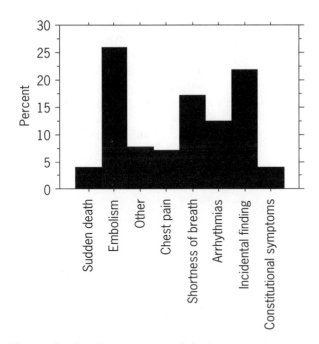

Figure 2 Cardiac myxoma, clinical symptoms at presentation. The most common single presentation relates to embolization. However, these tumours account for only 25% of cases. Sudden death may occur from cardiac myxoma by embolization to coronary vessels.

but significant proportion of cardiac myxomas (about 30%) have a rough, papillated surface partly covered by thrombus (**Figure 4; see colour plate section**). These tumours often cause symptoms because of embolization; that is, a portion of tumour or attached clot will break off and lodge somewhere in the patient's circulation. In most cases, the embolic site will be in the systemic circulation, as most cardiac myxomas are left-sided. Typical embolic sites are the brain, kidneys and arteries of the extremities. Emboli to the brain may be asymptomatic, or cause minor or even major strokes; if the retinal artery is involved, temporary blindness (amaurosis fugax) may ensue. Dislodged tumour is not synonymous with metastasis, as the myxoma does not seed organs and lymph nodes, forming new growths (metastatic deposits). However, embolic myxoma may occasionally cause weakness and aneurysm of the involved artery, especially in the cerebral circulation (Furuya *et al.*, 1995). These aneurysms may be detected by angiography, but their relationship to a patient's symptoms is often unclear and, after removal of the primary tumour, they tend to regress. If a cardiac myxoma dislodges into the arteries of the arm or legs, ischaemic symptoms may result, including muscle cramping and pain, and rarely even gangrene.

Other symptoms that can be precipitated by cardiac myxoma include palpitations, syncope and chest pain. Right-sided tumours may cause pulmonary embolism if they possess an irregular surface. Approximately 2% of cardiac myxomas occur in families, and are associated with noncardiac diseases, including skin lesions and tumours and endocrine abnormalities (Singh and Lansing, 1996). In these patients, tumours tend to cause symptoms at an early age (childhood to young adulthood), by embolization.

The microscopic features of cardiac myxoma are heterogeneous, often within a single tumour, explaining the diversity of imaging findings, especially with contrast media. The name 'myxoma' derives from the abundant myxoid ground substance which is produced by the tumour cells (**Figure 5; see colour plate section**). Unlike most neoplasms, the tumour cells themselves are often a minority of the total cells of the tumour, which include reactive vessels, inflammatory cells and reactive stromal cells. Unlike sarcomas, myxomas never infiltrate the cardiac muscle, and respect the borders of the endocardium. The tumour cells are primitive, undifferentiated cells that form syncytia shaped as cords and rings, and have a variety of cytological features. In general, the nuclei are round to ovoid without prominent nucleoli, although in some tumours, large nucleoli may be present. The cytoplasm is abundant and eosinophilic. In many areas, especially away from the attachment to the myocardium, the tumour cells are intimately related to endothelial cells and capillaries, and appear to give rise to vascular structures. In 2% of cardiac myxomas, the tumour cells exhibit glandular differentiation, similar to the lining of the gastrointestinal tract. The interstitium of the tumour often contains dendritic cells, macrophages, lymphocytes, haemorrhage and breakdown blood products in the form of haemosiderin. In about 10% of myxomas, large deposits of haemosiderin may precipitate in elastic tissue of the interstitium, forming calcified structures that may be seen on radiographs (gamna-gandy bodies). In general, however, the majority of the haemosiderin is found engulfed within foamy macrophages. Ossification is also not infrequently present in cardiac myxoma, often those arising on the right side; approximately 10% of myxomas demonstrate radiographically detectable calcification (Basso *et al.*, 1997).

Myofibroblastic (Intimal) Sarcoma

Myofibroblastic sarcomas are among the most common cardiac sarcomas, followed by angiosarcomas and undifferentiated sarcomas (**Figure 6**). Malignant neoplasms that occur in the atrial cavities are generally highly malignant myofibroblastic sarcomas grossly and clinically closely mimic the benign myxoma (Burke *et al.*, 1992; Burke and Virmani, 1996). The initial symptoms may be similar to those of myxoma, including shortness of breath, chest pain, signs and symptoms of mitral valve or tricuspid valve obstruction and symptoms resulting from tumour embolism. Cardiac sarcomas tend to embolize less frequently than myxoma, however. Like myxoma, atrial sarcomas are often pedunculated, but are more likely to arise in the wall of the atria, and not the atrial septum, and often invade the wall of the atrium, epicardium or mitral valve. Those sarcomas that demonstrate infiltrative characteristics are easily distinguished from myxomas, which always respect the endocardial boundaries of the heart. Imaging studies may not be able to differentiated myxoma from sarcoma, although certain features suggest a malignancy, i.e. attachment site in the wall of the atrium and infiltration of the atrial wall. Contrast techniques that take advantage of the heterogeneous vascularity of cardiac myxomas and imaging studies that detect the large amount of haemorrhage within myxomas may also prove to be helpful adjuncts in the differential diagnosis of atrial myxoma and sarcoma. A small proportion (less than 20%) of intimal sarcomas of the heart arise in the cardiac ventricles, where they occur as endocardial-based tumours that obstruct blood flow.

The histological features of intimal sarcoma are heterogeneous, and include sarcoma subtypes that would by roughly synonymous with fibrosarcoma, malignant fibrous histiocytoma, osteosarcoma and chondrosarcoma. The

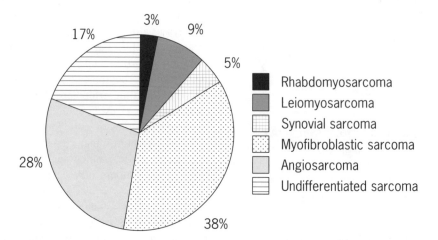

Figure 6   Histological types of cardiac sarcoma. In the authors' files, the majority of cardiac sarcomas include myofibroblastic, leiomyosarcomatous and undifferentiated tumours. Leiomyosarcomas are similar to myofibroblastic sarcomas, but are more purely smooth muscle cell in origin.

degree of osteo- or chondrosarcomatous differentiation is usually small, and it is rare to have a diffusely calcified sarcoma arising in the atrium. It must be kept in mind that ossifying tumours of the left atrium are usually malignant; small foci of ossification are not rare, however, in right atrial myxomas. The histological appearance of cardiac sarcomas is similar to that of sarcomas that arise in soft tissue and, overall, the full histological spectrum of soft tissue sarcomas may be encountered in the heart. However, those that arise within the atrium are primarily intracavitary. Because of their predominantly endoluminal growth, and because they are histologically very similar to sarcomas that arise within the great arteries (pulmonary artery and aorta), it is convenient for descriptive and taxonomic purposes to assume that they derive from the endocardium. Like the intima of arteries, the endocardium is composed of a layer of endothelial cells overlying an elastic layer, with a variable number of smooth muscle cells (or myofibroblastic cells) that occur sandwiched within. It is presumably these myofibroblastic cells, which are prone to proliferate, that undergo malignant transformation and result in the formation of sarcomas of the atria.

Angiosarcoma

Myofibroblastic sarcomas and angiosarcomas are the most common subtypes of cardiac sarcomas. The mean age at presentation for these sarcomas is 40 years (**Figure 7**). Angiosarcomas of the heart are one of the more common cardiac sarcomas and, for unknown reasons, usually arise in the right atrium (Putnam *et al.*, 1991; Burke *et al.*, 1992; Tazelaar *et al.*, 1992). There may be a slight bias for males over females (**Figure 8**). Unlike myofibroblastic sarcomas, they do not form pedunculated intracavitary masses, but invade early into the atrial wall and pericardium (**Figure 9; see colour plate section**). A few cardiac angiosarcomas are entirely confined to the pericardial space. The presenting symptoms of cardiac angiosarcomas, therefore, are typically related to pericardial disease, especially recurrent pericardial effusions or haemopericardium. A minority of cardiac angiosarcomas present with symptoms of obstruction of cardiac blood flow. Because cardiac angiosarcomas typically are right-sided, pulmonary metastases occur very early in the course of disease. In some patients, it is the presence of these lung lesions which cause the initial symptoms. The histological appearance of cardiac angiosarcoma is similar to that of soft tissue sarcomas. Rare examples of low-grade angiosarcomas (epithelioid haemangioendothelioma) have been described in the heart. However, epithelioid angiosarcomas, which are as lethal as histologically typical angiosarcomas, have not yet been reported to occur within the pericardium.

Miscellaneous Sarcomas

One would think initially that sarcomas with muscular differentiation (i.e. tumours composed of cells demonstrating features of striated muscle, or rhabdomyosarcomas) would predominate in the myocardium, as the bulk of the heart is composed of working muscle cells. However, cardiac muscle is terminally differentiated, with limited propensity for cellular division. Therefore, it makes sense that rhabdomyosarcomas are rare tumours, and make up less than 10% of all heart malignancies. As one would expect, the majority of these tumours occur in the walls of the heart, and they do not usually project into the lumen like intimal sarcomas, and rarely infiltrate the pericardium like angiosarcomas. Rhabdomyosarcomas of the heart are almost always of the embryonal type, and tend to occur in children and adolescents (Burke *et al.*, 1992). Histologically, they are similar to embryonal rhabdomyosarcomas of soft tissue, although the so-called 'alveolar' subtype of rhabdomyosarcoma is infrequently seen in the myocardium.

Another variety of sarcoma that makes up about 5% of heart sarcomas is the synovial sarcoma, which, in the soft tissue, generally arises at or near joint spaces (Burke *et al.*, 1992; Karn *et al.*, 1994; Iyengar *et al.*, 1995). The cell of origin of synovial sarcomas is unknown. These tumours typically demonstrate a biphasic histological growth pattern of spindle and glandular cells. In the heart, synovial sarcomas have a predilection for the pericardial space, but may occur in any cardiac site.

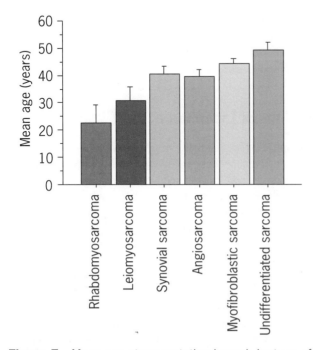

Figure 7   Mean age at presentation (years), by type of cardiac sarcoma. Rhabdomyosarcomas are tumours of adolescents and young adults. The overall mean age at presentation of cardiac sarcoma is 40 years.

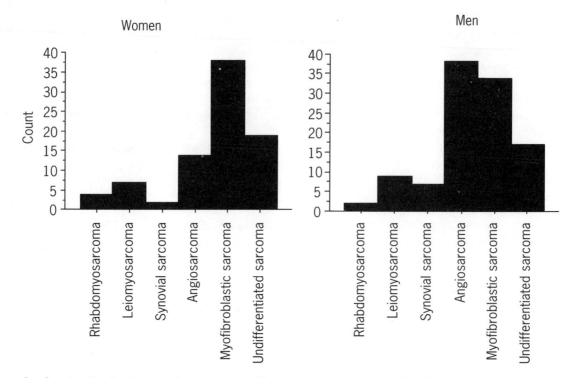

Figure 8 Gender distribution, cardiac sarcomas. There is no particular gender bias in cardiac sarcomas. In our experience, however, myofibroblastic sarcomas are slightly more common in women and angiosarcomas in men.

Sarcomas that are extremely rare in the cardiac location include liposarcomas, malignant localized fibrous tumours, malignant peripheral nerve sheath tumours and Ewing sarcoma (primitive neuroectodermal tumour). A fairly large proportion (up to 25%) of cardiac sarcomas defy classification, and represent a variety of undifferentiated spindle cell or small cell sarcomas.

Malignant Mesothelioma

Mesotheliomas are malignancies of the serosal lining tissues and, as such, may occur in the pleura, pericardium, peritoneum and inguinal sac. For reasons probably related to causation, they are most common in the pleura, which is at higher risk of exposure to inhaled asbestos than the other serosal sites. Pericardial mesotheliomas cause symptoms of chronic pericarditis, including pericardial pain, jugular venous distension, shortness of breath and eventually heart failure. The typical patient with pericardial mesothelioma may experience several episodes of pericarditis and pericardial effusion before a definitive diagnosis is made. The diagnosis may be confirmed only by biopsy sampling of pericardial tissue, and may be suggested by cytological analysis of pericardial fluid. Pericardial mesotheliomas, like angiosarcomas, often result in chronic effusion, but are much more likely to encase the heart in an unresectable constricting mass (**Figure 10; see colour plate section**). In early stages of disease, the primary differential diagnosis is chronic constrictive pericarditis, which is usually idiopathic, but may be related to autoimmune and other disorders (Burke and Virmani, 1996).

Pathologically, malignant mesotheliomas of the pericardium are identical with those of other sites. There is a bimodal appearance to these tumours microscopically, as there is for synovial sarcoma. However, the antigenic profile of mesothelioma is somewhat different from that of synovial sarcoma, and the latter tumour produces mucins not found in mesothelioma.

Malignant Lymphoma

Lymphomas arising in the heart are extremely uncommon; conversely, secondary involvement of the myocardium in patients with well advanced lymphomas arising in lymph nodes is not uncommon. Primary cardiac lymphomas are virtually all of B cell lineage, and may represent one of many histological subtypes, including low-, intermediate- and high-grade tumours (Burke and Virmani, 1996). For reasons that are not clearly understood, T cell lymphomas and Hodgkin disease are exceedingly rare as primary lesions within the heart or pericardium. The symptoms that cause lymphomas of the heart are varied, and depend on the site of origin within the myocardium. Typically, cardiac lymphomas arise within the walls of the organ, often in the atria with prominent epicardial involvement. There may be depressed cardiac function, obstruction to blood flow or pericardial effusions that produce the initial symptoms in patients with cardiac lymphoma.

Miscellaneous Neoplasms

Besides myxomas and sarcomas, primary neoplasms of the myocardium are vanishingly rare (Burke and Virmani, 1996). These include paragangliomas (phaeochromocytomas), neurofibromas and granular cell tumours. Cardiac paragangliomas generally occur in the atrial and atrial septum, where there are paraganglial tissues as a result of autonomic innervation of the heart. Cardiac paragangliomas may cause symptoms of hypertension. Rarely, cardiac paragangliomas may be malignant, and demonstrate the capability of developing distant metastases. However, in most patients, excision of the lesion is curative. The pathological and biological features of cardiac paraganglioma are similar to those that arise in paraganglial tissues elsewhere in the body, such as the adrenal gland and carotid bodies.

EPIDEMIOLOGY

Primary cardiac tumours are rare, so there are few accurate data to suggest their true prevalence. In general, it has been estimated that the incidence of cardiac neoplasms is approximately 0.01%, or one in 10 000 persons (Lam *et al.*, 1993; Burke and Virmani, 1996). Of these, the majority of adult tumours are myxomas and sarcomas, at a ratio of between 2 : 1 and 8 : 1. The incidence of surgically excised cardiac tumours is estimated at more than three per million population per year (Reyen *et al.*, 1998). There is no strong sex or racial predilection among primary heart tumours, although in some studies, more women than men suffer from cardiac myxomas, sometimes by a factor of 3 : 1 (Endo *et al.*, 1997). In our experience, women are more likely to develop myofibroblastic sarcomas and men angiosarcomas (**Figure 8**). Epidemiological studies demonstrate that there are a variety of environmental factors and hereditary conditions that predispose to extracardiac soft tissue sarcomas. In the case of mesothelioma, it has become clear that there is a strong association with pericardial mesothelioma and asbestos exposure, as had been demonstrated for pleural and abdominal mesotheliomas. Pericardial mesotheliomas are rare, account for 1% of all mesotheliomas, and it has been estimated that there were 140 cases reported in the world literature in 1994 (Kaul *et al.*, 1994), and fewer than 30 in the English literature (Thomason *et al.*, 1994).

AETIOLOGY

Cardiac myxoma

There is little known about the aetiology of primary cardiac tumours. The aetiology of the various types of primary cardiac tumours is presumably the same as that for histologically similar neoplasms that arise in extracardiac sites. In the case of cardiac myxoma, which is unique to the heart, the only clues to aetiology come from those cases that are familial and may have a genetic basis. In 1980, Atherton *et al.* described a patient with skin pigmentation, neurofibromas and cardiac myxomas (Atherton *et al.*, 1980). Later, the associations were refined to include lentigines, mucocutaneous myxomas and blue naevi, when it was recognized that the myxoid skin lesions were better classified as myxomas than myxoid neurofibromas. The list of associated conditions continues to grow, and includes Sertoli cell tumours of the testis, myxoid fibroadenoma of the breast, pituitary hyperactivity including growth hormone-producing adenoma, pigmented nodular adrenocortical disease and psammomatous melanotic schwannoma (Carney, 1995; Stratakis *et al.*, 1996). The genetic mode of transmission of myxoma syndrome has not been determined, but autosomal dominant transmission is favoured in most families. It has been shown by several investigators that familial cardiac myxomas are more often multiple, recurrent and right-sided than sporadic myxomas.

Cardiac Sarcoma

The aetiology of cardiac sarcoma is unknown, and is probably similar to that of soft tissue sarcomas. Angiosarcoma may be induced by ionizing radiation, especially those of the liver in patients having received injections of radiation contrast material. There is a case report of a primary cardiac (pericardial) angiosarcoma in a patient with prior radiation therapy for mediastinal seminoma (Killion *et al.*, 1996). In the majority of patients with cardiac angiosarcoma, however, there is no such prior history. Chromosomal and genetic defects have been described in soft tissue sarcomas but an extensive study of such defects in cardiac sarcomas has not been undertaken. It has been estimated that 7–33% of soft tissue sarcomas may have a genetic component (Hartley *et al.*, 1993). A variety of exposures have been associated with extracardiac sarcomas, including arsenical pesticides and medications, phenoxy herbicides, dioxin, vinyl chloride, immunosuppressive drugs, alkylating agents, androgen-anabolic steroids, human immunodeficiency virus and human herpes virus type 8 (Zahm and Fraumeni, 1997).

Pericardial Mesothelioma

The most common site of malignant mesothelioma is the pleura. A majority of patients with pleural mesothelioma have a history of asbestos exposure. There is increasing evidence that at least a large minority of patients with pericardial mesotheliomas also have a history of asbestos exposure, and pericardial mesothelioma may be experimentally induced by topical asbestos application (Burke and Virmani, 1996). The mechanism by which asbestos causes mesothelioma is uncertain, but it is known that certain forms of the inhaled element are more likely to result in malignancies than others. About 1% of asbestos-related mesotheliomas are pericardial and the rest are pleural and other sites. There are undoubtedly other stimuli for the development of mesothelioma, as some animals develop malignant mesothelioma of pericardium without any apparent asbestos exposure (Maltoni *et al.*, 1991; Chandra and Mansfield, 1999; Closa *et al.*, 1999). Simian virus induces pericardial mesotheliomas in hamsters, but a viral aetiology for human mesothelioma has not been demonstrated (Cicala *et al.*, 1993).

Cardiac Lymphoma

Approximately 50% of primary lymphomas of the heart arise in patients with acquired immunodeficiency, either iatrogenic (in cases of allograft recipients) or viral (in cases of AIDS) (Burke and Virmani, 1996). However, the heart is not a common site for the development of lymphomas in patients with AIDS or allografts (Tirelli *et al.*, 1994). The aetiology of immunosuppression-related lymphomas is believed related to infection by Epstein–Barr virus, which has the ability to transform B cells *in vitro*. In immunocompetent patients, Epstein–Barr virus is also associated with nasopharyngeal carcinomas and Burkitt lymphoma. Another virus which may have an aetiological role in immunosuppression-related lymphomas is another herpes virus, HHV-8, also known has Kaposi sarcoma-associated herpes virus. HHV-8-related lymphomas are often confined to serosal spaces without an identifiable contiguous tumour mass. The usual location for these lesions, however, is the peritoneum or pleura, with only rare examples occurring in the pericardium (Nador *et al.*, 1996).

The remaining 50% of primary cardiac lymphomas are not related to immunosuppression or herpes viruses (Bogaert *et al.*, 1995; Versluis *et al.*, 1995; Ito *et al.*, 1996). These tumours are fairly rare and aetiolgeal agents have not been identified. Presumably, the pathoaetiology of cardiac lymphoma is similar to that of nodal lymphomas.

SCREENING AND PREVENTION

Because of the rarity of primary cardiac neoplasms, there is little if any role for screening or attempts at prevention. The only possible exception to this rule would be in easily identifying individuals at greatly increased risk for the development of a primary cardiac myxoma. In cases of myxoma syndrome, family relatives should be aggressively evaluated for the presence of cardiac myxoma, as these can present with embolization and even sudden death. We are aware of a case of a young boy with

cutaneous features of the myxoma syndrome, whose father had a cardiac myxoma removed at a young age. The boy was not evaluated medically, and died suddenly due to coronary embolism from cardiac myxoma at a young age.

ULTRASTRUCTURE/AND IMMUNOHISTOCHEMISTRY

Cardiac Myxoma

The electron microscopic features of cardiac myxoma are of limited value in diagnosis, owing to the heterogeneous nature of cardiac myxoma and limited sampling afforded by ultrastructural techniques. Studies of myxoma have demonstrated myxoma cells to be primitive mesenchymal cells with intermediate filaments and cytoplasmic organelles. The cells are present either as single stellate cells, or groups, and have primitive tight intracellular junctions lacking desmosomes. Myxoma cells are best described ultrastructurally as embryonic cells that occasionally show features of myofibroblasts. The ground substance contains fine electron-dense granules which have been described as identical with the proteoglycan granules seen in the ground substance of cartilage (Feldman *et al.*, 1977; Goldman *et al.*, 1987).

The immunohistochemical features of cardiac myxoma indicate a pluripotent myxoma cell capable of divergent differentiation (Burke and Virmani, 1993, 1996; Berrutti and Silverman, 1996; Deshpande *et al.*, 1996). The most consistent antigenic type of cellular antigen expressed in myxomas is that of endothelial differentiation (Silverman and Berrutti, 1996). Other antigens found on myxoma cells have included smooth muscle cell antigens, neural antigens and epithelial antigens. The use of immunohistochemical techniques in the diagnosis of cardiac myxoma is limited. Recently, immunohistochemical data suggest that the myxoma is a weakly proliferative lesion without modulation of oncogene/tumour suppressor gene products (Suvarna and Royds, 1996).

Cardiac Sarcoma

Immunohistochemical studies are useful for distinguishing cardiac sarcomas from other processes, but are not particularly useful in subtyping the lesions (Burke *et al.*, 1992; Tazelaar *et al.*, 1992). An exception to this rule includes the diagnosis of rare types of sarcoma, such as malignant localized fibrous tumour (CD 34 positivity) and synovial sarcoma. Immunohistochemistry is currently of little use in providing prognostic data for cardiac sarcomas, which are uniformly lethal. In general, the immunohistochemical findings of cardiac sarcomas are similar to those of soft tissue sarcomas, and the reader is directed to relevant chapters in this volume. (See the chapter *Soft Tissues*.)

Cardiac Lymphoma and Pericardial Mesothelioma

The immunohistochemical and ultrastructural features of these neoplasms vary by cardiac or noncardiac origin. The reader is referred to other sections of this volume for immunohistochemical and ultrastructural characterization of lymphomas and mesotheliomas. (See the chapters *Lymph Nodes* and *Pleura and Peritoneum*.)

MOLECULAR GENETIC FINDINGS

Myxoma

Tissue cultures of cardiac myxoma cells have demonstrated chromosomal abnormalities both in familial and non-familial cases. A locus on chromosome 2p16 has been identified that may be involved in the regulation of genomic stability of dividing myxoma cells, in particular the structure of telomeres in replicating chromosomes (Stratakis *et al.*, 1996). Other studies have shown clonal and non-clonal abnormalities including dicentric chromosomes and telomeric associations, clonal telomeric associations between chromosomes 13 and 15 and nonclonal telomeric associations between chromosomes 12 and 17 (Richkind *et al.*, 1994; Dijkhuizen *et al.*, 1995).

Cardiac Sarcoma

Molecular genetic and chromosomal abnormalities are helpful in the classification of soft tissue sarcomas (Pollock, 1994; Mohamed *et al.*, 1997; Singer, 1999). In the heart, molecular diagnosis has been helpful in the classification of cardiac synovial sarcomas (Karn *et al.*, 1994; Iyengar *et al.*, 1995), specifically the X;18 translocation. The molecular aetiology of extracardiac soft tissue sarcoma involves growth factors and their receptors, nuclear and cytoplasmic oncogenes and tumour-suppressor genes (Pollock, 1994).

Cardiac Lymphoma

Most cardiac lymphomas are of B cell origin (Bogaert *et al.*, 1995; Chao *et al.*, 1995; Versluis *et al.*, 1995; Ito *et al.*, 1996; Chim *et al.*, 1997). Those that arise in immunocompromised patients are often associated with Epstein–Barr virus. The molecular genetics of nodal lymphomas have been extensively studied, and are covered in other areas of this volume.

Pericardial Mesothelioma

The karyotypes of malignant mesotheliomas are complex, and often preclude the identification of primary chromosome abnormalities. Recently, peritoneal mesothelioma with a balanced t(3;3)(p14;q29) translocation has been described. Molecular genetic abnormalities of pericardial mesotheliomas have not been described.

PROGNOSTIC FACTORS

Cardiac Myxoma

The prognosis for cardiac myxoma is excellent. With adequate surgical excision, the recurrence rate is vanishingly small. Patients with recurrent myxoma should be considered possible myxoma syndrome victims, especially if they are younger than 40 years of age. Alternatively, an incorrect diagnosis should be considered, as many recurrent cardiac sarcomas are initially misdiagnosed as myxomas. In the majority of a series of cardiac myxoma, surgical treatment is curative in virtually all cases (Lazzara *et al.*, 1991; Actis Dato *et al.*, 1993; Bastos *et al.*, 1995; Gawdzinski and Sypula, 1996; Bjessmo and Ivert, 1997). Reports of malignant myxoma should be regarded with suspicion. Rare well-documented examples of myxomas with embolization ('metastasis') to the cerebral vessels and skin have been reported (Reed *et al.*, 1989; Scarpelli *et al.*, 1997).

Cardiac Sarcoma

In stark contrast to cardiac myxoma, the prognosis of cardiac sarcoma is dismal, and generally measured in months. Although surgery is indicated for accurate diagnosis and palliation, and incurs a low mortality risk, the outcome is death within 2–3 years (Murphy *et al.*, 1990; Putnam *et al.*, 1991; Endo *et al.*, 1997; Centofanti *et al.*, 1999). The most important histopathological prognostic indicators are increased mitotic rate and the presence of necrosis (Burke *et al.*, 1992). In addition, patients with right-sided tumours and those presenting with metastatic disease have an especially poor prognosis. Even in patients with completely resectable tumours, most recur at a median time of 10 months. The median time to progression, in one series, was shorter in patients presenting a cardiac angiosarcoma than other histological types (3 vs 14 months, $P < 0.01$), with an overall 2-year survival rate of 26% (Llombart-Cussac *et al.*, 1998).

Pericardial Mesothelioma

The prognosis of pericardial mesothelioma is poor: 50% of patients are dead at 6 months, and an exceptional patient may live as long as 48 months. The mean survival of patients with pericardial mesothelioma is shorter than that of patients with pleural and peritoneal mesotheliomas (Hillerdal, 1983).

Cardiac Lymphoma

The prognosis of primary cardiac lymphoma is difficult to ascertain, because of the extreme rarity of the lesion, and concomitant diseases in patients who are immuno-suppressed. As with nodal lymphomas, the prognosis, and also the treatment, would vary by the grading of the lymphoma. As low-, intermediate- and high-grade lymphomas have all been described to arise in the heart, the prognosis would probably vary with the histological subtype.

OVERVIEW OF PRESENT CLINICAL MANAGEMENT

The clinical management of cardiac myxoma is that of surgical excision, which is curative (Mishra *et al.*, 1991; Actis Dado *et al.*, 1993; Castells *et al.*, 1993; Bjessmo and Ivert, 1997). Occasionally, a patch repair of the atrial septum is required and, rarely, valve reconstruction or repair.

The initial treatment of cardiac sarcoma is surgical excision. In many cases, the preoperative diagnosis is cardiac myxoma. However, complete excision is often difficult, unlike myxoma, and surgical margins for adequacy of excision should be ascertained by intraoperative consultation with the pathologist. The long-term management of cardiac sarcomas is difficult, as the use of radiation and chemotherapy is of limited benefit (Noirclerc *et al.*, 1997; Movsas *et al.*, 1998). However, many centres offer these modalities of treatment, which are similar to those administered for soft tissue sarcomas. The only chance at a cure in a patient with heart sarcoma is orthotopic heart transplantation (Noirclerc *et al.*, 1997); long-term survival has also been attained with fractionated radiation therapy (Movsas *et al.*, 1998). Adjuvant chemotherapy has been advised in high-grade cardiac sarcomas (Ceresoli *et al.*, 1999), although it has not been demonstrated to be effective (Llombart-Cussac *et al.*, 1998).

REFERENCES

Actis Dato, G. M. (1993). Long-term follow-up of cardiac myxomas (7–31 years). *Journal of Cardiovascular Surgery*, **34**, 141–143.

Atherton, D., *et al.* (1980). A syndrome of various cutaneous pigmented lesions, myxoid neurofibromata and atrial myxoma: the NAME syndrome. *British Journal of Dermatology*, **103**, 421–429.

Basso, C., *et al.* (1997). Cardiac lithomyxoma. *American Journal of Cardiology*, **80**, 1249–1251.

Bastos, P., *et al.* (1995). Cardiac myxomas: surgical treatment and long-term results. *Cardiovascular Surgery*, **3**, 595–597.

Berrutti, L. and Silverman, J. S. (1996). Cardiac myxoma is rich in factor XIIIa positive dendrophages: immunohistochemical study of four cases. *Histopathology*, **28**, 529–535.

Bjessmo, S. and Ivert, T. (1997). Cardiac myxoma: 40 years' experience in 63 patients. *Annals of Thoracic Surgery*, **63**, 697–700.

Bogaert, J., *et al.* (1995). High-grade immunoblastic sarcoma: an unusual type of a primary cardiac non-Hodgkin lymphoma. *RoFo. Fortschritte aut dem Gebiete der Röntgenstranlen under neuen bildgebenden Verfahren*, **162**, 186–188.

Burke, A. P., *et al.* (1992). Primary sarcomas of the heart. *Cancer*, **69**, 387–395.

Burke, A. P. and Virmani, R. (1993). Cardiac myxoma. A clinicopathologic study. *American Journal of Clinical Pathology*, **100**, 671–680.

Burke, A. P. and Virmani, R. (1996). Classification and incidence of cardiac tumours. In: *Atlas of Tumor Pathology. Tumors of the Cardiovascular System*. 1–12, 21–46, 127–170, 181–194. (Armed Forces Institute of Pathology, Washington, DC).

Carney, J. A. (1995). Carney complex: the complex of myxomas, spotty pigmentation, endocrine overactivity, and schwannomas. *Seminars in Dermatology*, **14**, 90–98.

Castells, E., *et al.* (1993). Cardiac myxomas: surgical treatment, long-term results and recurrence. *Journal of Cardiovascular Surgery*, **34**, 49–53.

Centofanti, P., *et al.* (1999). Primary cardiac tumors: early and late results of surgical treatment in 91 patients. *Annals of Thoracic Surgery*, **68**, 1236–1241.

Chandra, M. and Mansfield, K. G. (1999). Spontaneous pericardial mesothelioma in a rhesus monkey. *Journal of Medical Primatology*, **28**, 142–144.

Cicala, C., *et al.* (1993). SV40 induces mesotheliomas in hamsters. *American Journal of Pathology*, **142**, 1524–1533.

Closa, J. M., *et al.* (1999). Pericardial mesothelioma in a dog: long-term survival after pericardiectomy in combination with chemotherapy. *Journal of Small Animal Practice*, **40**, 383–386.

Deshpande, A., *et al.* (1996). Phenotypic characterization of cellular components of cardiac myxoma: a light microscopy and immunohistochemistry study. *Human Pathology*, **27**, 1056–1059.

Dijkhuizen, T., *et al.* (1995). Rearrangements involving 12p12 in two cases of cardiac myxoma. *Cancer Genetics and Cytogenetics*, **82**, 161–162.

Endo, A., *et al.* (1997). Characteristics of 161 patients with cardiac tumors diagnosed during 1993 and 1994 in Japan. *American Journal of Cardiology*, **79**, 1708–1711.

Feldman, P. S., *et al.* (1977). An ultrastructural study of seven cardiac myxomas. *Cancer*, **40**, 2216–2232.

Furuya, K., *et al.* (1995). Histologically verified cerebral aneurysm formation secondary to embolism from cardiac myxoma. Case report. *Journal of Neurosurgery*, **83**, 170–173.

Gawdzinski, M. P. and Sypula, S. (1996). The long term results of treatment of heart myxomas with special attention to very rare myxoma of the right ventricle. *Journal of Cardiovascular Surgery*, **37**, 121–129.

Goldman, B., *et al.* (1987). Glandular cardiac myxomas. Histologic, immunohistochemical, and ultrastructural evidence of epithelial differentiation. *Cancer*, **15**, 1767–1775.

Hartley, A. L., *et al.* (1993). Patterns of cancer in the families of children with soft tissue sarcoma. *Cancer*, **72**, 923–930.

Hillerdal, G. (1983). Malignant mesothelioma 1982: review of 4710 published cases. *British Journal of Diseases of the Chest*, **77**, 321–343.

Iyengar, V., *et al.* (1995). Synovial sarcoma of the heart. Correlation with cytogenetic findings. *Archives of Pathology and Laboratory Medicine*, **119**, 1080–1082.

Karn, C. M., *et al.* (1994). Cardiac synovial sarcoma with translocation (X;18) associated with asbestos exposure. *Cancer*, **73**, 74–78.

Kaul, T. K., *et al.* (1994). Primary malignant pericardial mesothelioma: a case report and review. *Journal of Cardiovascular Surgery*, **35**, 261–267.

Killion, M. J., *et al.* (1996). Pericardial angiosarcoma after mediastinal irradiation for seminoma. A case report and a review of the literature. *Cancer*, **78**, 912–917.

Lam, K. Y., *et al.* (1993). Tumors of the heart. A 20-year experience with a review of 12,485 consecutive autopsies. *Archives of Pathology and Laboratory Medicine*, **117**, 1027–1031.

Llombart-Cussac, A., *et al.* (1998). Adjuvant chemotherapy for primary cardiac sarcomas: the IGR experience. *British Journal of Cancer*, **78**, 1624–1628.

Lazzara, R. R., *et al.* (1991). Cardiac myxomas: results of surgical treatment. *Journal of Cardiovascular Surgery*, **32**, 824–827.

Mohamed, A. N., *et al.* (1997). Cytogenetic aberrations and DNA ploidy in soft tissue sarcoma. A Southwest Oncology Group Study. *Cancer Genetics and Cytogenetics*, **99**, 45–53.

Movsas, B., *et al.* (1998). Primary cardiac sarcoma: a novel treatment approach. *Chest*, **114**, 648–652.

Murphy, M., *et al.* (1990). Surgical treatment of cardiac tumors: a 25 year experience. *Annals of Thoracic Surgery*, **49**, 612–617.

Nador, R. G., *et al.* (1996). Primary effusion lymphoma: a distinct clinicopathologic entity associated with the Kaposi's sarcoma-associated herpes virus. *Blood*, **88**, 645–656.

Noirclerc, M., *et al.* (1997). Primary cardiac sarcoma treated by orthoptic cardiac transplantation. Apropos of a case. *Archives des Maladies du Coeur et des Vaisseaux*, **90**, 1539–1543.

Putnam, J. B., Jr, *et al.* (1991). Primary cardiac sarcomas. *Annals of Thoracic Surgery*, **51**, 906–910.

Reed, R. J., *et al.* (1989). Embolic and metastatic cardiac myxoma. *American Journal of Dermatopathology*, **11**, 157–165.

Reyen, K., *et al.* (1998). Heart operations for heart tumors in Germany – results of 1996 survey. *Zeitschrift für Kardiologie*, **87**, 331–335.

Richkind, K. E., *et al.* (1994). Cardiac myxoma characterized by clonal telomeric association. *Genes, Chromosomes and Cancer*, **9**, 68–71.

Scarpelli, M., *et al.* (1997). Cardiac myxoma with glandular elements metastatic to the brain 12 years after the removal of the original tumor. *Clinical Neuropathology*, **16**, 190–194.

Silverman, J. S. and Berrutti, L. (1996). Cardiac myxoma immunohistochemistry: value of CD34, CD31, and factor XIIIa staining. *Diagnostic Cytopathology*, **15**, 455–456.

Singer, S. (1999). New diagnostic modalities in soft tissue sarcoma. *Seminars in Surgical Oncology*, **17**, 11–22.

Stratakis, C. A., *et al.* (1996). Cytogenetic and microsatellite alterations in tumors from patients with the syndrome of myxomas, spotty skin pigmentation, and endocrine overactivity (Carney complex). *Journal of Clinical Endocrinology and Metabolism*, **81**, 3607–3614.

Suvarna, S. K. and Royds, J. A. (1996). The nature of the cardiac myxoma. *International Journal of Cardiology*, **57**, 211–216.

Tazelaar, H. D., *et al.* (1992). Pathology of surgically excised primary cardiac tumors. *Mayo Clinic Proceedings*, **67**, 957–965.

Tirelli, U., *et al.* (1994). Malignant tumours in patients with HIV infection. *British Medical Journal*, **308**, 1148–1153.

Thomason, R., *et al.* (1994). Primary malignant mesothelioma of the pericardium. Case report and literature review. *Texas Heart Institute Journal*, **21**, 170–174.

Versluis, P. J., *et al.* (1995). Primary malignant lymphoma of the heart: CT and MRI features. *RoFo. Fortschritte auf dem Gebiete der Röntgenstrahlen und der neuen bildgebenden Verfahren*, **162**, 533–534.

FURTHER READING

Actis Dato, G. M., *et al.* (1993). Long-term follow-up of cardiac myxomas (7–31 years). *Journal of Cardiovascular Surgery*, **34**, 141–143.

Bear, P. and Moodie, D. (1987). Malignant primary cardiac tumors. The Cleveland Clinic experience, 1956 to 1986. *Chest*, **92**, 860–862.

Bjessmo, S. and Ivert, T. (1997). Cardiac myxoma: 40 years' experience in 63 patients. *Annals of Thoracic Surgery*, **63**, 697–700.

Burke, A. P. and Virmani, R. (1993). Cardiac myxoma. A clinicopathologic study. *American Journal of Clinical Pathology*, **100**, 671–680.

Burke, A. P. and Virmani, R. (1996). In: *Atlas of Tumor Pathology. Tumors of the Cardiovascular System.* 1–12 (Armed Forces Institute of Pathology, Washington, DC).

Dijkhuizen, T., *et al.* (1995). Rearrangements involving 12p12 in two cases of cardiac myxoma. *Cancer Genetics and Cytogenetics*, **82**, 161–162.

Llombart-Cussac, A., *et al.* (1998). Adjuvant chemotherapy for primary cardiac sarcomas: the IGR experience. *British Journal of Cancer*, **78**, 1624–1628.

Movsas, B., *et al.* (1998). Primary cardiac sarcoma: a novel treatment approach. *Chest*, **114**, 648–652.

Murphy, M., *et al.* (1990). Surgical treatment of cardiac tumors: a 25 year experience. *Annals of Thoracic Surgery*, **49**, 612–617.

Putnam, J. B., Jr, *et al.* (1991). Primary cardiac sarcomas. *Annals of Thoracic Surgery*, **51**, 906–910.

Chapter 51

Neuromuscular System

Kar-Ming Fung
University of Texas, MD Anderson Cancer Center, Houston, TX, USA

John Q. Trojanowski
University of Pennsylvania, Philadelphia, PA, USA

C O N T E N T S

- Normal Development and Structure
- Tumour Pathology
- Epidemiology
- Aetiology
- Screening and Prevention
- Gross/Histopathology/Preinvasive lesions/Ultrastructure/Immunohistochemistry
- Molecular Genetics
- Prognostic Factors
- Overview of Present Clinical Management

NORMAL DEVELOPMENT AND STRUCTURE

The nervous system and skeletal muscular system are both electrically active and they have an intimate functional relationship. However, tumours that arise in these two systems are very different. Whereas primary tumours of neuroepithelial differentiation arising from the central nervous system (CNS) and peripheral nervous system (PNS) are common, primary tumours of skeletal muscular differentiation that arise from skeletal muscle are extremely rare. In contrast, most primary tumours in skeletal muscles have mesenchymal differentiation of other lineages and they presumably arise from nonmuscular tissue adjacent to or within the muscle. Interestingly, primary tumours with muscular differentiation (e.g. rhabdomyosarcoma) usually arise in soft tissue rather than skeletal muscle. Therefore, it is most appropriate to consider these tumours with other soft tissue tumours. The reader should refer to the chapter on soft tissue tumours in this section and the Further Reading section for further details.

Tumours of the nervous system display morphological, immunohistochemical and molecular features that recapitulate their normal developing and mature counterparts. Knowledge on normal development and anatomy of the nervous system is fundamental for the study of these tumours.

The mature nervous system is composed of neurons and their supporting cells. In the CNS, neurons and axons are supported by glial cells, namely astrocytes, oligodendrocytes, ependymal cells and microglia. Choroid plexus is neuroepithelial tissue specialized in the production of cerebral spinal fluid. Other supporting cells of the nervous system include the arachnoid cells and a variety of mesenchymal cells. Neurons and axons in the PNS are supported by Schwann cells that are of neuroepithelial (neurocrest) origin and other mesenchymal cells. Tumours of the nervous system can have features reminiscent of any or a combination of these components but they do not necessarily arise from these components.

Formation of the CNS and PNS is a highly organized process that involves induction, cell division, differentiation, migration and cell death. During early development, the ectoderm undergoes neural induction by the underlying chordamesoderm and becomes the neuroectoderm. The neuroectoderm becomes a thickened layer of cells and forms the neural plate that in turn folds into a tube that will eventually develop into the brain and spinal cord. Part of the neural plate will give rise to the neural crest cells that give rise to Schwann cells, adrenal medulla and cell types such as melanocytes, odontoblasts and many mesenchymal and musculoskeletal components of the head.

At the dawn of development, the neural tube is composed of a thick, pseudostratified, columnar neuroepithelium that is composed of primitive neuroepithelial cells. Then, these cells segregate into a highly cellular ventricular zone and the paucicellular marginal zone. The ventricular zone will give rise to all neurons and glial cells with the exception of microglial cells that belong to the mononuclear phagocytic cell lineage. Through the guidance of radial glia, developing neurons and glial cells migrate out from the ventricular zone and segregate into several foetal layers between the ventricular zone and marginal zone. Such foetal laminations will evolve into the six-layer adult cortex during maturation.

The maturation process involves interaction between many temporally and developmentally regulated genes. Young neurons will lose their ability to divide as they develop into mature neurons and over 50% of the young neurons will undergo apoptosis during maturation. Glial cells will develop into several specialized forms including astrocytes, oligodendrogliocytes, ependymal cells and epithelium of choroid plexus. In contrast to neurons, glial cells maintain their ability to divide in the mature nervous system.

In-depth discussion on development is beyond the scope of this chapter and the reader is referred to the Further Reading section.

TUMOUR PATHOLOGY

The central goal of tumour classification is to correlate pathological and biological properties with prognostic data. Classification of tumours of the nervous system, similar to tumours of other organ systems, is essentially based on a comparison of similarities between the neoplastic tissue and normal mature or developing counterparts. In the past 100 years or so, such comparison has been limited primarily to morphological features. In the recent past, comparison of the molecular phenotypes, mainly achieved by utilization of immunohistochemical techniques, *in situ* hybridization and cytogenetics have been used. The World Health Organisation (WHO) Classification of Tumours of the Nervous System (Kleihues and Cavenee, 2000) was formulated on the basis of such information (**Table 1**). In general, tumours are named according to the cell type that they most resemble. For example, an astrocytoma is a tumour that has features resembling astrocytes. Recent advances in molecular biology and cell biology and recognition of molecular signatures specific to particular types of tumour will presumably play a more important role in future classification systems.

Tumours of the Central Nervous System

The pathology of CNS tumours is a vast topic and it is not the intention of the authors to cover every aspect in this

Table 1   2000 WHO Classification of Tumours of the Nervous System

Tumours of neuroepithelial tissue
Astrocytic tumours
Diffuse astrocytoma
   Fibrillary astrocytoma
   Protoplasmic astrocytoma
   Gemistocytic astrocytoma
Anaplastic astrocytoma
Glioblastoma
   Giant cell glioblastoma
   Gliosarcoma
Pilocytic astrocytoma
Pleomorphic xanthoastrocytoma
Subependymal giant cell astrocytoma

Oligodendroglial tumours
Oligodendroglioma
Anaplastic oligodendroglioma

Mixed gliomas
Oligoastrocytoma
Anaplastic oligoastrocytoma

Ependymal tumours
Ependymoma
   Cellular
   Papillary
   Clear cell
   Tanycytic
Anaplastic ependymoma
Myxopapillary ependymoma
Subependymoma

Choroid plexus tumours
Choroid plexus papilloma
Choroid plexus carcinoma

Glial tumours of uncertain origin
Astroblastoma
Gliomatosis cerebri
Chordoid glioma of the 3rd ventricle

Neuronal and mixed neuronal–glial tumours
Gangliocytoma
Dysplastic gangliocytoma of cerebellum (Lhermitte–Duclos)
Desmoplastic infantile astrocytoma/ganglioglioma
Dysembryoplastic neuroepithelial tumour
Ganglioma
Anaplastic ganglioglioma
Central neurocytoma
Cerebellar liponeurocytoma
Paraganglioma of the filum terminale

Neuroblastic tumours
Olfactory neuroblastoma (aesthesioneuroblastoma)
Olfactory neuroepithelioma
Neuroblastomas of the adrenal gland and sympathetic nervous system

Pineal parenchymal tumours
Pineocytoma
Pineoblastoma
Pineal parenchymal tumour of intermediate differentiation

Embryonal tumours
Medulloepithelioma

Table 1   *(Continued)*

Ependymoblastoma
Medulloblastoma
   Desmoplastic medulloblastoma
   Large cell medulloblastoma
   Medullomyoblastoma
   Melanotic medulloblastoma
Supratentorial primitive neuroectodermal tumour (PNET)
   Neuroblastoma
   Ganglioneuroblastoma
Atypical teratoid/rhabdoid tumour

Tumours of peripheral nerves
Schwannoma (neurilemmoma, neurinoma)
Cellular
Plexiform
Melanotic

Neurofibroma
Plexiform

Perineurioma
Intraneural perineurioma
Soft tissue perineurioma

Malignant peripheral nerve sheath tumour (MPSNST)
Epithelioid
MPSNST with divergent
   mesenchymal and/or epithelial differentiation
Melanotic
Melanotic psammomatous

Tumours of the meninges
Tumours of meningothelial cells
Meningioma
   Meningothelial
   Fibrous (fibroblastic)
   Transitional (mixed)
   Psammomatous
   Angiomatous
   Microcystic
   Secretory
   Lymphoplasmacyte-rich
   Metaplastic
   Clear cell
   Chordoid
   Atypical
   Papillary
   Rhabdoid
   Anaplastic meningioma

Mesenchyma, nonmeningothelial tumours
Lipoma
Angiolipoma
Hibernoma
Liposarcoma (intracranial)
Solitary fibrous tumour
Fibrosarcoma
Malignant fibrous histiocytoma
Leiomyoma
Leiomyosarcoma
Rhabdomyoma
Rhabdomyosarcoma
Chondroma

Table 1   *(Continued)*

Chondrosarcoma
Osteoma
Osteochondroma
Osteosarcoma
Haemanagioma
Epithelioid haemangioendothelioma
Haemangiopericytoma
Angiosarcoma
Kaposi sarcoma

Primary melanocytic lesions
Diffuse melanocytosis
Melanocytoma
Malignant melanoma
Meningeal melanomatosis

Tumours of uncertain histiogenesis
Haemangioblastoma

Lymphomas and haematopoietic neoplasms
Malignant lymphomas
Plasmacytoma
Granulocytic sarcoma

Germ cell tumors
Germinoma
Embryonal carcinoma
Yolk sac tumour
Choriocarcinoma
Teratoma
   Mature
   Immature
   Teratoma with malignant transformation
Mixed germ cell tumours

Tumours of the sellar region
Craniopharyngioma
   Adamantinomatous
   Papillary
Granular cell tumour

Metastatic tumours

Source: Kleihues and Cavenee, 2000, *World Health Organisation Classification of Tumours – Pathology and Genetics, Tumours of the Nervous System* (International Agency for Research on Cancer, Lyon).

chapter. The reader should consult the Further Reading section for further details.

Tumours of the CNS can be separated into several major categories (**Table 2**). First and foremost, they can be separated into primary and secondary tumours. Primary tumours are those that arise within the central nervous system and can be categorized into several major groups.

The first category consists of tumours that have features of primitive neuroepithelium. In the WHO Classification (Kleihues and Cavenee, 2000), this category includes the embryonal tumours and pineoblastomas. Some tumours such as olfactory esthesioneuroblastoma also belong to this category, although they do not occur within the cranial cavity. Essentially, these tumours resemble the primitive neuroectoderm or primitive neuroepithelium.

Table 2 Major biological categories of tumours of the nervous system

---

Central nervous system (CNS)

Category 1: Primary tumour with features of primitive neuroepithelial cell

Category 2: Primary tumour with features of mature neuroepithelial cell

Category 3: Primary tumour with features of meninges and mesenchyme

Category 4: Primary tumour with features of tissue normally found outside the central nervous system

Category 5: Secondary (metastatic) tumour

Peripheral nervous system (PNS)

Category 1: Primary tumours with features of neuroblasts/mature neurons

Category 2: Primary tumours with features of mature supporting elements of the peripheral nervous system

Category 3: Primary tumours of paraganglia

Category 4: Secondary tumour

The second category consists of tumours which display features of mature neuroepithelial cells such as glial cells and neurons. These tumours are further separated into three major subcategories. The first subcategory has features of glial cells, the supporting elements of the CNS. These are among the most common primary tumours of the CNS and they are formed by cells that resemble astrocytes and/or oligodendrocytes and/or ependymal cells. They are, therefore termed astrocytoma, oligodendroglioma and ependymoma, respectively. Not infrequently, they may have features of more than one type of glial cell in which case they are termed mixed gliomas. The second subcategory contains a variable neuronal component. Tumours composed exclusively of neoplastic neurons are uncommon. Very often, the neoplastic neurons or ganglion cells are mixed with neoplastic glial cells, most often neoplastic astrocytes. This category constitutes the neuronal and mixed neuronal–glial tumours of the WHO Classification. The third subcategory consists of choroid plexus tumours. Although the choroid plexus is regarded as modified ependyma, it has features of epithelial cells rather than glial cells. Choroid plexus tumours also behave like epithelial tumours rather than glial tumours. For this reason, choroid plexus tumours are regarded as a separate category.

The third category consists of tumours that have features resembling meninges and other supporting mesenchymal components of the CNS. Meningiomas have features of arachnoid cells that cover leptomeninges. Tumours composed of other mesenchymal elements are named after the mature tissue they most resemble. Melanocytic tumours of the CNS arise most commonly from the leptomeninges.

The fourth category consists of primary tumours that resemble mature and developing tissue that may or may not be normally present in the cranial cavity, including germ cell tumours, primary haematopoietic tumours such as lymphoma and craniopharyngioma.

Secondary (metastatic) tumours are extremely common, primarily in adults. In fact, they are the most common tumour of the CNS. This should not be surprising since the brain consumes about 20% of the cardiac output but comprises only about 2% of the body mass. Secondary tumours of the CNS include metastatic carcinomas, malignant melanomas and sarcomas as well as secondary involvement of the CNS by haematopoietic tumours such as lymphomas and leukaemias.

Tumours of the Peripheral Nervous System

Tumours of the PNS can also be separated into several major categories (**Table 2**). Similar to CNS tumours, there are PNS tumours that recapitulate features of primitive neuroepithelial cells or neuroblasts and some of them contain mature neuronal elements. These tumours are classified under neuroblastic tumours in the WHO Classification.

The second major category consists of tumours that have features of the mature supporting elements of the PNS such as Schwann cells. These tumours are named after their normal counterparts and are termed schwannoma, neurofibroma and perineuroma. Some have aggressive biological properties and cannot be clearly identified phenotypically clearly as schwannoma or neurofibroma. Because of their malignant behaviour and mixed histological features, they are collectively termed malignant peripheral nerve sheath tumours (MPNSTs) and stand by themselves in a distinct subcategory.

The third major category has features of paraganglia. Paraganglia are widely dispersed collections of specialized neural crest cells that arise in association with the segmental or collateral autonomic ganglia throughout the body. Histologically, they have features of neuroendocrine cells.

Owing to the small size of the PNS, metastatic tumours limited strictly to the PNS are extremely rare, although they may occur theoretically. Direct invasion of peripheral nerve by malignant tumour is common and peripheral nerves are preferentially invaded by some primary tumours such as prostate carcinoma and adenoid cystic carcinoma of the salivary gland.

EPIDEMIOLOGY

The overall incidence of primary brain tumours is around 11.8 per 100 000 persons per year. Congenital brain tumours are rare. With the exception of meningioma that affects women twice as often as men, they are more prevalent in man. In the United States, the incidence of

Table 3 Incidence of CNS tumours

Tumour	Incidence/age
Primitive neuroectodermal tumours of posterior fossa (medulloblastoma)	*Incidence:* About 0.5 per 100 000 persons per year *Age:* Peak incidence during the 1st decade of life, a small number of them are seen in adults
Diffuse astrocytoma	*Incidence:* About 0.2 per 100 000 persons per year *Age:* Mean age of onset is 34 years. Peak incidence between 20 and 45 years of age. About 15% of them are seen in children under 10 years old
Anaplastic astrocytoma	*Incidence:* About 0.5 per 100 000 persons per year *Age:* Peak incidence in the 4th to 5th decade. Uncommon in children
Glioblastoma	*Incidence:* Most common malignant astrocytic tumour and the incidence is about 2.0–3.2 per 100 000 persons per year *Age:* Peak incidence in the 5th to 7th decades. They also comprise about 8.8% of all brain tumours in children
Pilocytic astrocytoma	*Incidence:* Most common glioma in children and 85% of them occur in the cerebellum. The incidence is about 0.3 per 100 000 persons per year *Age:* Peak incidence in the first two decades
Pleomorphic xanthoastrocytoma	*Incidence:* Exact incidence is not known. They account for less than 1% of all astrocytic tumours *Age:* Usually seen in young adults with peak incidence in the 2nd decade
Oligodendroglioma	*Incidence:* Usually seen in adults, although children are also affected. Peak incidence in the 5th to 6th decade. The incidence is about 0.3 per 100 000 persons per year *Age:* The peak incidence is in the 4th to 6th decades
Ependymoma	*Incidence:* They account for about 3–9% of all neuroepithelial tumours and are frequently seen in the spinal cord. The incidence is about 0.2–0.3 per 100 000 persons per year *Age:* The first peak of incidence is in the 1st decade and second peak of incidence is in the 4th decade
Choroid plexus tumour	*Incidence:* They account for about 0.4–0.6% of all brain tumours, about 2–4% of all brain tumours in children *Age:* Peak incidence in the 1st decade
Ganglioglioma and gangliocytoma	*Incidence:* They represent about 0.4% of all CNS tumours and 1.3% of all brain tumours *Age:* They can be seen in all ages but are most common in children and young adults
Meningioma	*Incidence:* The annual incidence is about 2.8–6.0 per 100 000 persons per year. They account for 13–26% of primary intracranial tumours *Age:* Most common in middle-aged and elderly patients, peak incidence in the 6th decade
Malignant lymphoma	*Incidence:* Relatively uncommon in the general population, marked increase in incidence in immunocompromised patients *Age:* For immunocompetent patients, the peak incidence is in the 7th decade. Occur in young patients who are immunocompromised
Germ cell tumours	*Incidence:* The incidence is less than 0.1 per 100 000 population per year. They account for about 0.3–2% of all primary intracranial tumours. The incidence is lower in the West and higher in Asia *Age:* Most common in the first two decades
Craniopharyngioma	*Incidence:* 0.05–0.25 per 100 000 persons per year *Age:* Most common in children and a second peak in the 6th decade
Schwannoma	*Incidence:* They are most commonly seen in peripheral nerves. About 8% of all intracranial tumours and 29% of all spinal tumours are schwannomas *Age:* Peak incidence in the 4th to 6th decades
Neuroblastic tumours of adrenal gland and sympathetic system	*Incidence:* 0.7–1.0 per 100 000 persons per year *Age:* 85% occur before the age of 5 years

Source: Kleihues and Cavenee, 2000, *World Health Organisation Classification of Tumours – Pathology and Genetics, Tumours of the Nervous System* (International Agency for Research on Cancer, Lyon).

brain tumours, with the exception of meningioma and craniopharyngioma, has been consistently higher in whites than in blacks. The overall incidence of brain tumours has a bimodal pattern. The first peak occurs in infants and children and the second peak occurs at the sixth to seventh decade. Each individual tumour, however, has its own pattern of age distribution (**Table 3**). Patients affected by hereditary cancer syndromes may develop neoplasms at an earlier age than sporadic cases. There is also a general tendency for high-grade glial tumours to occur in older patients. There is an apparent increase in the incidence of brain tumours both in the United States and in other countries. However, the increase in the early 1980s may partly reflect improved detection techniques, mainly the use of magnetic resonance image (MRI) and computed tomography (CT) scans. There also appears to be an increase in incidence of childhood brain tumours, most apparent in children under 5 years of age. Increase in the rate of primary CNS lymphomas is dramatic and correlates with the large population of patients with compromised immune system secondary to immune suppression, most often after solid organ transplantation, and human immunodeficiency virus (HIV). Some countries and geographic areas have higher incidences than others. The incidence of a particular tumour may be unusually high in some country. For example, germ cell tumour and craniopharyngioma are far more common in Japan than elsewhere. The overall survival of primary brain tumours varies significantly among the different histological types.

AETIOLOGY

Numerous epidemiological studies have been conducted in the search for risk factors and aetiological agents for brain tumours. Mutations of specific genes have been strongly associated with the development of brain tumours. Some of them are associated with hereditary cancer syndromes that involve the nervous system, others are found with increased frequency in some types of tumours. These genes will be discussed later.

It has been reported repeatedly that virus or virus-like particles have been observed in human cerebral tumours or tumour cell lines. Between 1955 and 1962, poliomyelitis vaccines were contaminated with Simian virus 40 (SV40), a member of the polyoma virus family. SV40 has been used to generate experimental choroid plexus tumour and primitive neuroectodermal tumours in transgenic mice. In addition, a partial genome of SV40 has been identified in a few ependymomas, meningiomas and primitive neuroectodermal tumours (also known as medulloblastomas). Despite these findings, there is no epidemiological evidence that the contaminated poliomyelitis vaccine is associated with any increase in incidence of primary brain tumours. JC and BK viruses, also members of the polyoma virus family, have been suspected for being tumorigenic in human brain tumours. To this date, however, there is no solid proof. The association of HIV infection and primary CNS lymphoma primarily rests on the destruction of immune tumour surveillance by HIV.

A wide variety of other physical and chemical agents have also been studied but ionizing radiation is the only proven risk factor for glial tumours and meningiomas. Children who receive therapeutic doses of X-rays (1.5 Gy) for treatment of tinea capitis have an overall increased relative risk of 8.4 for brain tumours. A correlation at higher dosages (1.0–6.9 Gy) is even stronger (Ron et al., 1988). Correlation between risk of brain tumours and low-dose X-rays has not been well established, although association between dental X-rays and possible increase in meningiomas has been reported. The tumorigenic effects of electromagnetic fields on brain tumours have been shown in industrial settings but the relationship with weaker electromagnetic fields has not been well established and the results of different studies have been inconsistent.

Numerous other aetiological agents and risk factors, including N-nitroso compounds, diet, tobacco, alcohol and occupational factors, have also been studied. No conclusive evidence of their association with brain tumours has been identified.

SCREENING AND PREVENTION

Many organs, such as the vagina, uterine cervix, peripheral blood, skin, oral cavity and gastrointestinal tract, are easily accessible. Cancer screening involves simple procedures and is highly effective. The situation is different for the CNS. Except for germ cell tumours that may secret markers detectable in the serum, there is no reliable marker in the blood for most primary brain tumours. The anatomical complexity and bony encasement of the central nervous system make biopsy-based screening impossible. The only reliable method for detecting an asymptomatic or presymptomatic brain or spinal cord tumour is a high-resolution imaging technique such as MRI. This method, however, is too expensive, time consuming and complicated to provide a practical screening test for the general population.

Early Recognition of Brain Tumours

Early recognition of brain tumours relies on astute clinical evaluation since there are no specific symptoms or signs of brain tumours. However, headache, new-onset seizures, hemiparesis and mental-status abnormalities are among the most common symptoms. Diagnosis is largely dependent on imaging techniques such as MRI or CT scan. These tools have revolutionized the diagnosis of CNS tumours and other intracranial and intraspinal conditions.

CNS tumours, like any intracranial and intraspinal space-occupying lesions, generate two major problems. The first is increased intracranial pressure because of oedema and mass effect caused by the tumour or obstruction of the flow of cerebrospinal fluid, a typical situation when the tumour is located in or around the ventricles. Increased intracranial pressure produces headache, vomiting and papilloedema; occasionally, it may cause paralysis of the sixth cranial nerve (abducens nerve) due to excessive stretching. Recognition of papilloedema, often an asymptomatic clinical sign, is important for pre-symptomatic recognition of brain tumours. Brain herniation is a life-threatening condition often associated with a severe increase in intracranial pressure.

Local effects of CNS tumours produce symptoms depending upon locations. For example, cortical lesions are prone to cause seizures. Tumours adjacent to the optic nerve often produce visual symptoms due to compression of the optic nerves and chiasma. Tumour masses compressing the cervical cord often cause hemiplegia or quadriplegia. The interested reader should refer to the Further Reading section for further details on clinical aspects of brain tumours.

High-risk Patients

Two major groups of patients have increased risk of developing brain tumours. The first includes those who have underlying nonhereditary conditions that predispose them to develop brain tumours, specifically patients with a primary carcinoma or melanoma in some other part of the body. Immune compromised patients also have an increased risk of developing primary CNS lymphoma.

Patients with hereditary syndromes that predispose them to develop tumours of the CNS comprise the second group. Typically, a variety of tumours from several organs occur in a syndromic manner. Recent advances in genetics and molecular biology have identified the genetic abnormalities in many of these syndromes (**Table 4**), and their molecular mechanisms will be discussed later. Well-structured periodic screening programmes have been invaluable in detecting and treating tumours in early stages. With these screening and treatment programmes, the expectancy and quality of life have been improved in these patients.

GROSS/HISTOPATHOLOGY/PREINVASIVE LESIONS/ULTRASTRUCTURE/ IMMUNOHISTOCHEMISTRY

Tumours of the CNS

Pathological features of brain tumours are diverse and fascinating. Pathological examination for diagnostic purposes must include a thorough macroscopic and microscopic evaluation that often includes utilization of immunohistochemical techniques. Occasionally, ultrastructural examination may be necessary. Molecular biology and/or cytogenetic studies may also provide crucial information for diagnostic and prognostic purposes in some cases. Although a full discussion of immunohistochemistry in CNS tumour is beyond the scope of this chapter, the reader should be familiar with a few commonly used diagnostic molecular markers such as Ki-67,

synaptophysin, neurofilament proteins (NFPs), glial fibrillary acidic proteins (GFAPs), vimentin, S-antigen and epithelial membrane antigen (EMA) (**Table 5**).

Primary Tumours of Primitive Neuroepithelial Tissue

This is a family of CNS tumours, two of which recapitulate the phenotypic features of the developing nervous system, i.e. medulloepithelioma, primitive neuroectodermal tumours (PNETs) and related tumours. The third tumour in this group, atypical teratoid/rhabdoid tumour, displays unique features and a remarkably consistent cytogenetic abnormality.

Medulloepithelioma
Medulloepithelioma is a tumour that recapitulates the neural tube stage of the developing CNS. These tumours are rare and predominantly seen in infancy and early childhood. Over half arise in the lateral ventricles, occasionally in the posterior fossa and other locations. Macroscopically, they are well-defined, often massive tumours with extensive haemorrhage and necrosis, and are typically associated with extensive cerebrospinal dissemination. The microscopic appearance is highly distinctive and composed of tubular or papillary structures that are morphologically and immunohistochemically similar to the primitive epithelium (**Figure 1**) of the neural tube. Cytologically, they have hyperchromatic nuclei and a high nuclear-to-cytoplasmic ratio. Sheets of patternless undifferentiated tumour cells are invariably present. Ultrastructural examination of these areas also discloses extensive primitive lateral cell junctions and basal lamina, both features of the neural tube. The tumour cells may also differentiate along neuronal, astrocytric, ependymal, oligodendroglial and, on rare occasions, mesenchymal lineage.

Primitive Neuroectodermal Tumours (PNETs) and Related Tumours
This is a family of tumours that phenotypically resembles the primitive neuroectoderm of developing CNS. PNET of the posterior fossa, also known as medulloblastoma, is the prototype and such tumours can also occur in any CNS locations. PNET is the most common malignant childhood brain tumour but sometimes they are seen in adults, particularly young adults. With adequate treatment, the 5-year survival rate is about 60–80% (Packer *et al.*, 1999). PNETs arising in the posterior fossa typically present in midline and involve the vermis. They project into the fourth ventricle and often extend into the leptomeninges (**Figure 2**). The strategic location in the posterior fossa often leads to hydrocephalus (i.e. pathological expansion of the ventricles). Macroscopically they often appear as soft to firm masses with well-demarcated margins. The cut surface has a pale pink to tan colour and there may be a variable amount of haemorrhage. PNETs are typically composed of

Table 4   Hereditary tumour syndromes

Syndrome	Pathology	Genetics	Reference
Tuberous sclerosis	*Nervous system:* Cortical hamartomas (tuber), subependymal hamartoma and subependymal giant cell tumour *Extraneural:* Adenoma sebaceum and other manifestations of skin, retinal astrocytoma, renal angiolipoma, cardiac rhabdomyoma and other systemic manifestations	*Inheritance:* Autosomal dominant *Prevalence:* Between 1 in 5 000 and 1 00 000 Gene: *TSC1* gene (tuberin) on chromosome 9q34 and *TSC2* gene on chromosome 16p13.3.	Kandt et al. (1992); van Slegtenhorst et al. (1997)
Neurofibromatosis type 1	*Nervous system:* Neurofibromas and malignant peripheral nerve sheath tumour of the peripheral nerve, gliomas of the brain *Extraneural:* Multiple café-au-lait spots, rhabdomyosarcoma, phaeochromocytoma, carcinoid tumour, juvenile chronic myeloid leukaemia, bone lesions and other manifestations	*Inheritance:* Autosomal dominant *Prevalence:* 1 in 3000–4000 of the general population Gene: *NF1* gene (neurofibromin) on chromosome 17q2	Seizinger et al. (1987); Pollack and Mulvihill (1997); Von Deimling, et al. (2000)
Neurofibromatosis type 2	*Nervous system:* Bilateral vestibular schwannomas, peripheral schwannomas, meningiomas and meningioangiomatosis, ependymomas, astrocytomas, glial hamartoma, and cerebral calcifications *Extraneural:* Posterior lens opacity	*Inheritance:* Autosomal dominant *Prevalence:* 1 in 50 000 of the general population Gene: *NF2* gene (merlin) on chromosome 22q12	Trofatter et al. (1993); Pollack and Mulvihill (1997)
Von Hippel–Lindau disease	*Nervous system:* Haemangioblastoma of the retina and CNS *Extraneural:* Renal cysts and renal cell carcinoma, pancreatic cysts, islet cell tumours, phaeochromocytoma, and other manifestations	*Inheritance:* Autosomal dominant *Prevalence:* 1 in 36 000 to 1 in 45 500 of the general population Gene: *VHL* gene is located on chromosome 3p25.3	Latif et al. (1993); Maddock et al. (1996)
Naevoid basal cell carcinoma syndrome (Gorlin syndrome)	*Nervous system:* PNET in the posterior fossa *Extraneural:* Multiple basal cell carcinoma and keratocyst of the jaw. Abnormal ribs and other skeletal abnormalities, epidermal cyst, ovarian cysts and other features	*Inheritance:* Autosomal dominant *Incidence:* 1 in 57 000 of the general population Gene: Human homologue of the *Drosophilia* segment polarity gene patched (*PTCH*) on chromosome 9q22.3	Hahn et al. (1996); Vorechovsky et al. (1999)

Syndrome	Features	Inheritance/Gene	References
Cowden disease	Nervous system: Dysplastic gangliocytoma of the cerebellum (Lhermitte–Duclos disease). Other pathologic changes include megalencephaly and heterotopic grey matter. Meningiomas and medulloblastomas have also been described Extraneural: Verrucous skin changes, papules and fibromas of oral mucosa, multiple facial trichilemmomas, hamartomas polyps of the colon, thyroid tumour and breast cancer	Inheritance: Autosomal dominant Gene: PTEN/MMAC1 gene on chromosome 10q23.	Sutphen et al. (1999); Robinson and Cohen (2000)
Turcot syndrome (type 1)	Nervous system: Usually glioblastoma Extraneural: Café-au-lait spots. Small number of large colorectal polyps and high incidence of colorectal carcinoma. Some patients are associated with hereditary non-polyposis colorectal carcinoma syndrome (HNPCC)	Inheritance: Autosomal dominant Gene: Several genes involved in mismatch repair including hMLH1 at chromosome 3p21, hMLH2 at 2p16, hMSH3 at 5q11-q13, hMSH6/GTBP at 2p16, hPMS1 at 2q32 and hPMS2 at 7p22	Paraf et al. (1997); Cavenee et al. (2000)
Turcot syndrome (type 2)	Nervous system: Usually PNET in the posterior fossa Extraneural: Associated with familial adenomatous polyposis syndrome (FAP). Patient has innumerable adenomatous colorectal polyposis and high incidence of colorectal carcinoma	Inheritance: Autosomal dominant Gene: APC gene on chromosome 5q21 that is associated with familial adenomatous polyposis syndrome (FAP)	Hamilton et al. (1995); Paraf et al. (1997); Cavenee et al. (2000)
Retinoblastoma (RB) gene deletion syndrome	Nervous system: Retinoblastoma in the retina with or without PNET in the pineal gland (pineoblastoma) Extraneural: Increased incidence of second malignancy, multiple congenital abnormalities and mental retardation	Inheritance: Autosomal dominant Gene: RB1 gene on chromosome 13q14.2	Sopta et al. (1992); Pratt et al. (1994)
Li-Fraumeni syndrome	Nervous system: Astrocytic tumour, oligodendroglioma, PNET within and outside the posterior fossa, and choroid plexus tumour Extraneural: Tumour in various organs including the breast, lung, stomach, colon, pancreas, skin and others	Inheritance: Autosomal dominant Gene: p53 on chromosome 17p13	Malkin et al. (1990); Tachibana et al. (2000)

Source: Kleihues and Cavenee, 2000, World Health Organisation Classification of Tumours – Pathology and Genetics, Tumours of the Nervous System (International Agency for Research on Cancer, Lyon).

Table 5   Diagnostic immunohistochemical markers for brain tumours

Protein	Properties	Application
Ki-67	Non-histone proteins that are present in all phases of the cell cycle, except G0 and the early G0–G1 transitional phase	Immunohistochemical recognition of Ki-67 is used to estimate the proportion of proliferating cells in brain tumours
Glial fibrillary acidic protein (GFAP)	This is a class III intermediate filament of 55 kDa. GFAP is expressed in mature astrocytes. It may co-express with other intermediate filaments in developing CNS	Expression of GFAP in a brain tumour is highly suggestive but not an absolute indicator of astrocytic differentiation
Synaptophysin	Synaptophysin is an acidic, N-glycosylated integral membrane glycoprotein of 38–42 kDa that is expressed in the CNS	Detection of neuroendocrine differentiation in CNS tumours
Chromogranin A	This is a 70–80-kDa protein that is found in neurosecretory granules. It is expressed in neuroendocrine cells outside the CNS	Detection of neuroendocrine differentiation in PNS tumours
Neurofilament proteins (NEPs)	Neurofilament proteins are class IV intermediate filaments that exist in three different isoforms (low, medium and high molecular mass) and different phosphorylation state	Expression of neurofilament proteins is highly suggestive but not an absolute indicator of astrocytic differentiation
Vimentin	This is class III intermediate filament of 56 kDa. It is widely expressed in the developing nervous system. It is not expressed in most mature neurons. It is co-expressed with GFAP in mature and developing astrocytes	Vimentin is strongly and extensively expressed by atypical teratoid/rhabdoid tumours. It is also variably expressed by many neuroepithelial tumours
S-antigen and rhodopsin	S-antigen and rhodopsin are proteins expressed by photoreceptor cells in the retina	Detection of photoreceptor differentiation in PNETs, retinoblastomas and pineal tumours
S-100	S-100 is an acidic protein that is widely expressed in the CNS, PNS and a variety of cells outside the nervous system	It is used in the diagnosis of tumours of the PNS and soft tissue
Cytokeratins	Cytokeratins are proteins of class I and II intermediate filaments. They are predominantly expressed by epithelial cells	Used in diagnosis of tumours with epithelial differentiation such as metastatic carcinomas and craniopharyngioma
Epithelial membrane antigen (EMA)	This is a group of high molecular mass molecules with a high carbohydrate content. They are widely expressed by many epithelial cells	Used in diagnosis of metastatic carcinomas. Some CNS tumours such as meningiomas, ependymomas and atypical teratoid/rhabdoid tumours also express EMA

solid sheets of small cells with an extremely high nuclear-to-cytoplasmic ratio and small hyperchromatic nuclei. The tumour cells inconstantly form Homer Wright rosettes (neuroblastic rosettes), but may arrange themselves in other patterns (**Figure 3**). Individual cell and small areas of necrosis are common but extensive necrosis is uncommon. The most common genetic aberration in PNETs arising from the posterior fossa is isochromosome 17 but other chromosomal abnormalities may also be found. Spinal leptomeningeal dissemination is common.

Desmoplastic medulloblastoma is a variant of PNET that tends to occur in cerebellar hemispheres rather than midline. They are also found in older patients. Histologically these tumours contain nodular, reticulin-free islands ('pale-islands') of tumour cells surrounded by densely packed PNET cells with dense intercellular reticulin deposition. The pale islands are usually less cellular and more differentiated than the surrounding cells. Medulloblastoma with extensive nodularity and advanced neuronal

differentiation is a variant that is associated with favourable prognosis and contains intranodular cells that resemble mature neurons. Large cell medulloblastoma is a variant in which the tumour cells have large, round and pleomorphic nuclei, prominent nucleoli and more obvious cytoplasm. They usually carry a grave prognosis.

PNETs typically contain numerous mitoses and apoptotic bodies. Depending on the studies, the proliferation rate based on Ki-67 labelling may range from 5 to 80% (**Figure 4**). Such a high proliferation rate has been confirmed by other labelling method such as iododeoxyuridine that discloses a range of 3.9–38.2% (Onda et al., 1996).

Immunohistochemically, PNETs frequently express synaptophysin, a marker indicative of neuroendocrine differentiation. Many PNETs also express nestin, a marker for primitive neuroepithelial cells. Although PNET cells appear histologically similar, they may express different developmentally regulated antigens that recapitulate different developmental stages of the CNS. While some PNETs may

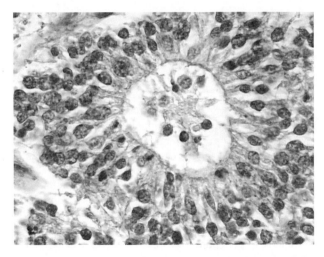

Figure 1 Medulloepitheliomas are characterized by small blue cells that arrange in glandular or tubular structures reminiscent of the primitive neuroepithelium. (Case courtesy of Dr Lucy B. Rorke, Children's Hospital of Philadelphia.)

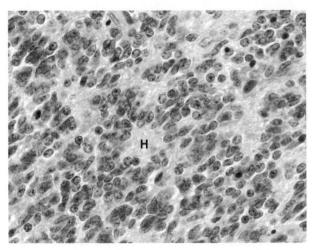

Figure 3 Homer Wright rosettes are formed by small islands of neoplastic neuropil surrounded by tumour cells. Same case as in **Figure 4**.

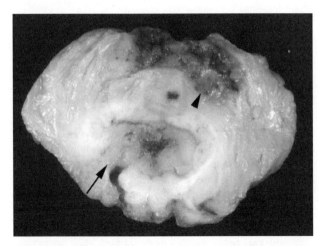

Figure 2 The fourth ventricle (arrow) is filled and expanded by this primitive neuroectodermal tumour. The haemorrhagic region (arrowhead) is in the leptomeningeal extension of the lesion.

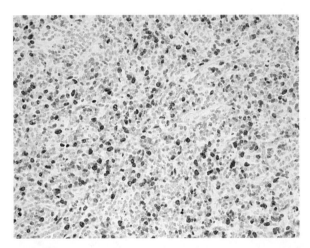

Figure 4 Proliferating cells express Ki67 strongly and comprise about 25% of the population in this primitive neuroectodermal tumour. Immunostaining for Ki-67, ABC peroxidase method.

express NFP indicative of neuronal differentiation, others may express GFAP indicative of glial differentiation and many PNETs express both. A small proportion of PNETs also express cytokeratins, intermediate filament proteins that are expressed in the very early stage of neural development. Ependymal differentiation can also be seen, in which case some investigators prefer to call them ependymoblastomas. Photoreceptor-specific proteins such as retinal S-antigen and rhodopsin are also expressed by a subpopulation of PNETs. Rarely, they express desmin or actually contain skeletal muscle cells in which case they are termed medullomyoblastoma. Melanotic medulloblastoma is the variant that contains melanin pigment. It is obvious that PNETs have the potential to differentiate along different lineages.

Ultrastructually, tumour cells may contain few, if any, specific ultrastructural features. Neurosecretary granules and synapses, an indication of differentiation towards neuronal lineage, may be seen in some tumours. Intermediate filaments are also common.

Less commonly, PNETs occur in supratentorial locations. In the WHO Classification, neuroblastoma and ganglioneuroblastoma are grouped under the heading of supratentorial PNET. These tumours are seen in early childhood. They occur most frequently in the frontal and frontoparietal regions but rare examples are seen in the spinal cord. Macroscopically, they are well-defined tumours. Histologically and immunohistochemically, they are very similar to if not identical to PNETs arising in the posterior fossa (medulloblastoma). Although infratentorial and supratentorial PNETs are given different names in the WHO Classification (i.e. medulloblastoma vs neuroblastoma), they are best regarded as part of the spectrum of PNETs.

Atypical Teratoid/Rhabdoid Tumour (ATRT)

This is a highly malignant embryonal CNS tumour that contains rhabdoid cells (**Figure 5**). They are predominantly seen in infants under 2 years of age and the mean postoperative survival is less than 1 year. ATRTs are equally frequent in both infratentorial and supratentorial locations. Dissemination throughout the CNS is seen in about one-third of the cases at initial presentation. Macroscopically, they are well-demarcated tumours. Rhabdoid cells are round to oval cells with medium to large nuclei and distinct nucleoli. About two-thirds of ATRTs also have a PNET component. In addition, they may contain epithelial (carcinomatous) and mesenchymal (sarcomatous) components. The tumour cells typically express vimentin, smooth muscle actin and epithelial membrane antigen, but may also express GFAP and NFP. They do not express germ cell markers such as α-fetoprotein, placental alkaline phosphatase or β-human chorionic gonadotrophin, nor do they express desmin. Ultrastructually, they are characterized by massive whorls of intermediate filaments. Characteristically, they show homozygous or heterozygous, complete or partial deletion of chromosome 22q and presumably are related to germline and somatic mutation of the *hSNF5/INI1* gene (Biegel *et al.*, 2000). Although ATRTs often contain a PNET component, their distinctive histology, characteristic chromosomal abnormality and aggressive clinical behaviour distinguish them from PNETs. The true nature of ATRT remains to be determined.

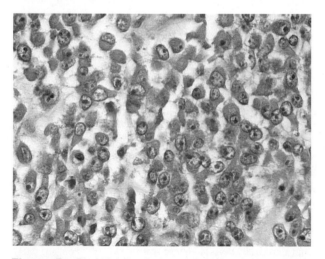

Figure 5   Rhabdoid cells in atypical teratoid/rhabdoid tumours are loosely arranged large egg-shaped cells with eosinophilic cytoplasm, large eccentrically located nuclei containing prominent nucleoli. (Case courtesy of Dr Lucy B. Rorke, Children's Hospital of Philadelphia.)

Primary Tumours of Mature Neuroepithelium

Tumours considered in this section are the most common primary tumours in the CNS. They display features of mature neuroepithelial cells although they do not necessarily arise from such cells. Rather, they may arise from primitive neuroepithelial cells that show differentiation during tumorigenesis. Three major categories will be considered here: glial tumours, glial–neuronal tumours and choroid plexus tumours.

Glial Tumours

Glial tumours, otherwise known as gliomas, are tumours that display features of mature glial cells specifically astrocytes, oligodendrogliocytes and ependymal cells. It is not unusual to have tumours composed of a mixture of these cells. In addition, they may also display a spectrum of biological aggressiveness, often reflected by their histology. In general, low-grade gliomas occur more commonly in younger patients whereas high-grade gliomas are more common in older adults.

Astrocytoma, Anaplastic Astrocytoma, Glioblastoma.
Astrocytic tumours are composed of cells that look like astrocytes and are by far the most common of all gliomas. They comprise about one-third of the gliomas in the cerebral hemispheres. Astrocytic tumours are separated into different histological grades that reflect their biological behaviour. Astrocytomas are histologically benign/low-grade tumours, anaplastic astrocytoma has features of a malignant tumour, and glioblastoma is the most malignant version.

Astrocytoma occurs in young adults with a peak incidence in the fourth decade and 15% are seen in children. They are most commonly located in the cerebral hemispheres with frontal and temporal regions as the most common site. They are also common in the spinal cord. In children, the optic nerve, diencephalon, brainstem and cerebellum are the most favoured locations.

Astrocytomas in adults and children behave differently. In adults, the survival rate of astrocytoma is variable and they are notorious for recurring as anaplastic astrocytoma or glioblastoma with a mean time interval of 4–5 years. This occurs more commonly in older patients.

MRI often discloses a poorly defined nonenhancing lesion with oedema. Macroscopically, they are poorly demarcated, soft, grey, expanding lesions that involve mainly the white matter (**Figure 6**). Tumours that arise from the brainstem often diffusely enlarge the latter. Hemispherical astrocytomas may involve the basal ganglia and thalamus. Degenerative changes and cyst formation are common. Histologically, they are composed of neoplastic astrocytes with variable morphology. The architecture ranges from streaming bundles of fibrillary astrocytes to a meshwork-like arrangement. Most often, the tumour cells have poorly defined cytoplasm and small and mature-looking nuclei (**Figure 7**). Some astrocytomas are composed of fibrillary astrocytes or polygonal to stellate neoplastic cells that arrange themselves into a fine cobweb resembling protoplasmic astrocytes. Gemistocystic forms which tend to be large oval with eosinophilic homogeneous cytoplasm and large nuclei, often binucleated, may also be seen. Often, all morphological subtypes of neoplastic astrocytes can be seen in the same tumour. Degenerative changes and formation of microcysts are very common. Features indicative of aggressive behaviour such as necrosis and mitoses are not present. The low proliferative rate is also reflected by a low Ki-67 labelling index of less than 4% in most cases. Astrocytes strongly express GFAP. These tumours also express other antigens such as S-100 proteins and vimentin, but these markers are not diagnostically useful. Onset at a young age and location at a site that allows gross total resection are two favourable prognostic indicators.

In contrast to astrocytomas occurring in adults, astrocytoma arising from cerebellum and midbrain in children have excellent prognosis. Childhood astrocytomas arising from pons often carry a grave prognosis.

Anaplastic astrocytomas are aggressive tumours with a peak age of occurrence about 10 years later than that of astrocytomas. MRI usually discloses an enhancing mass with its epicentre in the white matter. These tumours usually enhance with gadolinium. Macroscopically, the tumours have poorly defined borders and are friable, greyish and occasionally haemorrhagic. They are densely cellular, exhibit nuclear pleomorphism, are mitotically active (**Figure 8**) and show endothelial proliferation (**Figure 9**). In some cases, the bulk of the tumour may appear to be a low-grade astrocytoma but microscopic foci of anaplasia may be scattered around. GFAP is usually widely expressed by tumour cells. The brisk proliferative activity is well reflected by the presence of mitotic figures and a Ki-67 labelling index that is usually >5%.

Glioblastoma is the most aggressive astrocytic tumour and unfortunately the most common glial tumour in adults. They also occur in children. The peak incidence is around the sixth and seventh decade and they are 1.5 times more common in men than women. Glioblastoma may be present initially as such or evolve from low-grade glial

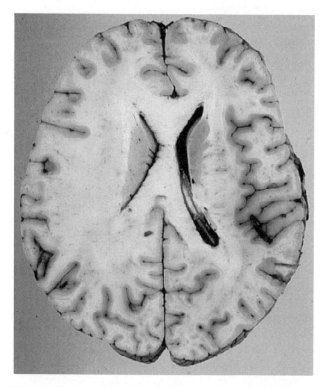

Figure 6 The left side of the brain is expanded by a diffusely infiltrating astrocytoma that also compresses the ventricle. The cut surface of the tumour is similar to normal white matter and no delineation between tumour and normal tissue in appearance. Attenuation of the gyral architecture, however, is obvious.

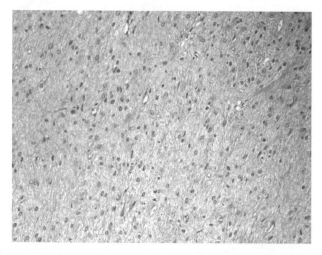

Figure 7 Astrocytoma cells have small hyperchromatic nuclei and a substantial amount of cytoplasm.

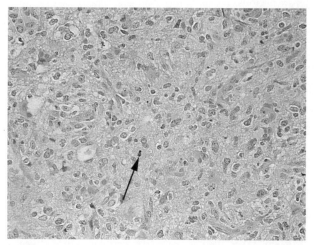

Figure 8 When compared with astrocytomas, cells in anaplastic astrocytocytomas are larger, more pleomorphic and mitotically active (arrow).

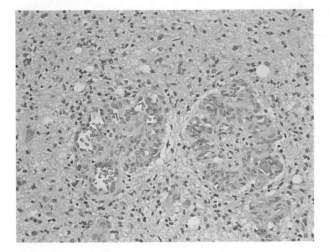

Figure 9   Endothelial proliferation is a hallmark of anaplastic astrocytoma and glioblastoma multiforme. Note glomeruloid architecture of the blood vessels with large and tombstone-like endothelial cells projecting into the lumen.

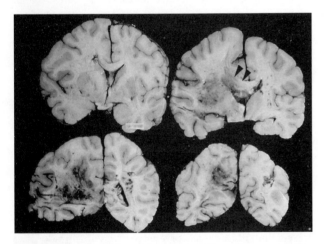

Figure 10   Four coronal sections of cerebrum showing large, poorly demarcated partially haemorrhagic glioblastoma multiforme. Note thickening of the corpus callosum due to tumour infiltration (arrow head).

tumours such as astrocytoma, oligodendroglioma or mixed astrocytoma–oligodendroglioma. The frontal half of the brain is more affected. The tumour may appear as an irregular to multinodular mass with heterogeneous signal and ring enhancement on MRI. They are often associated with a substantial amount of oedema.

Macroscopically, they are typically large hemispherical tumours that extend across the corpus callosum to involve the contralateral hemispheres, the so-called 'butterfly tumour.' They may be poorly demarcated or sharply demarcated; necrosis and haemorrhages are common (**Figure 10**). Histologically, the cellular morphology is highly diversified, as reflected by old term 'glioblastoma multiforme.' The salient histological features of glioblastoma include pseudopalisading necrosis (**Figure 11**),

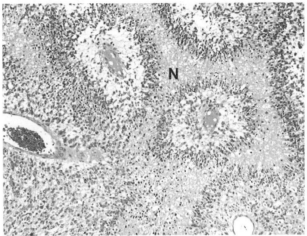

Figure 11   Pseudopalisading necrosis in GBM is composed of necrotic tissue (N) rimmed by viable tumour cells that arrange themselves in a palisading fashion.

striking endothelial proliferation, markedly anaplastic cells and prominent mitotic activity. Bizarre tumour cells and multinucleated giant cells are often seen adjacent to fields of densely packed small anaplastic cells. In general, expression of GFAP is inversely proportional to the degree of anaplasia. Although the majority of glioblastomas express GFAP, it is often expressed in a patchy manner. Ki-67 labelling may vary significantly in different areas of the same tumour and mean values of 15–20% have been reported.

Giant cell glioblastoma is a variant that contains a substantial number of giant cells; it has a slightly better prognosis than regular glioblastoma. Gliosarcoma is a variant that contains a glioblastoma component and sarcomatous component. In rare examples, the latter consist of osteosarcoma or chondrosarcoma.

Astrocytoma with Special Features. Pilocytic astrocytoma, pleomorphic xanthoastrocytoma, desmoplastic infantile astrocytoma and subependymal giant cell astrocytomas are tumours that exhibit distinct clinical and histological features.

Pilocytic astrocytomas are most commonly seen in the first two decades of life. They tend to remain histologically benign, i.e. they do not progress to high-grade gliomas. They are most common in the cerebellum as discrete, slow-growing lesions with or without cystic change. Other preferred sites include optic nerve, optic chiasma/hypothalamus and brainstem. Those that are located in a surgically accessible position can be totally resected and have an excellent prognosis, whereas locations in some sites may preclude such an approach. Hence prognosis in the latter instance is not so sanguine. In contrast to astrocytomas in adults that infiltrate the surrounding brain tissue in a sinister fashion, pilocytic astrocytomas especially in the cerebellum are often well demarcated. Histologically they are characterized by alternating densely packed and loosely packed areas (**Figure 12**). The densely packed

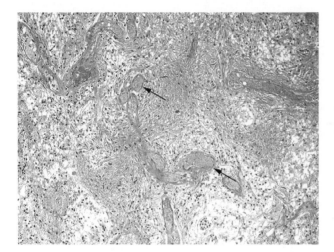

Figure 12 Pilocytic astrocytomas have alternating densely packed and loosely packed areas. Tumour cells in the densely packed areas are reminiscent of bundles of hair. Many thin-walled and dilated blood vessels are typically present (arrow).

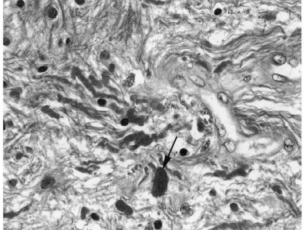

Figure 13 Rosenthal fibres are amorphous to fibrillary hyalinized eosinophilc structures that are intracytoplasmic components of glial processes (arrow). They are typical but not diagnostic for pilocytic astrocytoma.

areas are composed of elongated hair-like (piloid) astrocytes whereas the loosely packed areas are composed of astrocytes with small nuclei and stellate processes that branch and anastomose producing a 'chicken-wire' appearance. Pilocytic astrocytomas are usually vascular and contain peculiar glomeruloids of thin-walled blood vessels reminiscent of wickerwork. They must be distinguished from endothelial proliferation found in anaplastic astrocytoma and glioblastoma. Rosenthal material (**Figure 13**) and eosinophilic granular bodies are common and are most often seen in the densely packed areas. Mucoid and cystic degeneration are common. As expected, the tumour cells strongly express GFAP.

Pleomorphic xanthoastrocytoma and subependymal giant cell astrocytomas are two tumours that are classified as astrocytoma but should probably be in the category of neuronal–glial tumours as they often express both GFAP and NFP that indicate simultaneous glial and neuronal differentiation.

Pleomorphic xanthoastrocytoma is usually seen in children and young adults. They typically occur as supertentorial and superficial tumours that are attached to the leptomeninges and have cystic components. Histologically, they are composed of cells that show extreme variation in size and shape of both nuclei and cytoplasm, hence they are called 'pleomorphic.' Some cells may have foamy or xanthomatous cytoplasm. They contain a dense network of reticulin fibre and multinucleated giant cells are common. Admixed with these cells are also spindly cells. Collections of lymphocytes are often prominent. The large xanthomatous spindle cells express GFAP. Some also express NFPs and synaptophysin. The anaplastic variant exhibits significant mitotic activity and/or necrosis. Most pleomorphic xanthoastrocytomas carry a favourable

prognosis but a small proportion of them may progress to high-grade tumours.

Desmoplastic infantile astrocytoma will be discussed later together with desmoplastic infantile ganglioglioma. Subependymal giant cell tumour is almost always associated with tuberous sclerosis and will be discussed together with the latter.

Oligodendroglioma and Anaplastic Oligodendroglioma. Oligodendrogliomas are neoplasms composed of oligodendrocytes and uncommon. Most arise in hemispherical white matter of individuals in the fourth to sixth decades of life. Macroscopically, they display a relatively well-demarcated, soft, greyish pink appearance. Often, mucoid changes in the cells produce a translucent mucoid consistency. Microscopically they are moderately cellular tumours. The cells grow in solid sheets with delicate vascular networks. The cells are round to polygonal cells with a well-defined cytoplasmic membrane, clear cytoplasm and isomorphic round, small nuclei producing the so-called 'fried-egg' appearance (**Figure 14**). Calcified deposits are more common than other gliomas. The proliferation rate is low and mitotic figures are rare, if present at all; the Ki-67 labelling index is <5% (Coons *et al.*, 1997). Oligodendrogliomas may express small amounts of GFAP but no immunohistochemical marker is specific for these tumours. The mean survival time for oligodendrogliomas varies from 3.3 to 7.1 years and the 5-year survival rate varies from 38 to 54% (Dehghani *et al.*, 1998). The biological behaviour is not always predicted by histology and oligodendrogliomas without any anaplastic features can also behave aggressively.

Anaplastic oligodendrogliomas occur in a slightly older age group than do the histologically 'benign' type but the

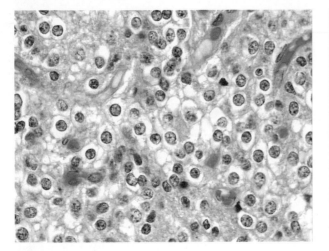

Figure 14 Oligodendrogliomas are characteristically composed of round to polygonal cells with clear cytoplasm and centrally located round nuclei. (Courtesy of Dr Lucy B. Rorke, Children's Hospital of Philadelphia.)

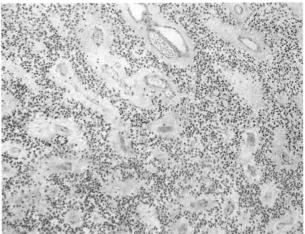

Figure 15 Ependymomas often appear as isomorphic cellular tumours with a rich vascular supply and pseudorosette formation.

preferred locations are similar. The histological features are similar to those of oligodendrogliomas but these tumour cells tend to contain amphophilic rather than clear cytoplasm. There is increased cellularity, a high nuclear-to-cytoplasmic ratio and variation in size and shape of nuclei. Endothelial proliferation and necrosis are often present and mitotic activity is usually brisk. It is not uncommon to find focal anaplastic changes in an otherwise oligodendroglioma, in which case the tumour behaves like an anaplastic oligodendroglioma. The survival rate of patients with anaplastic oligodendroglioma (median survival time 0.87–3.9 years) is overall worse than for its 'benign' counterparts (Shaw *et al.*, 1992; Dehghani *et al.*, 1998). Recent association of chromosome 1p and 19q deletion with improved responsiveness to chemotherapy in anaplastic oligodendrogliomas may improve survival of these patients (Cairncross *et al.*, 1998).

Ependymal Tumours. Ependymal cells are modified glial cells that line the ventricles. Although they have partial features of epithelial cells, they do not have a basement membrane. Ependymal tumours can be segregated into several clinically and pathologically distinct groups on the basis of pathology and clinical behaviour.

Ependymomas are seen in all age groups but most commonly in children, amongst whom they comprise 6–12% of all intracranial tumours in children and about 30% of them occur before the age of 3 years. Ependymomas may occur at any site along the ventricular system and in the spinal canal. In adults they are most common in the spinal cord; in children they are most common in the fourth ventricle. Hydrocephalus and increased intracranial pressure are common manifestations, particularly in tumours that arise in the fourth ventricles.

Ependymomas are grossly well demarcated. Tumours that arise within the fourth ventricle often expand through the foramina of Luschka and Magendie and extend caudally through the foramen magnum, making complete excision difficult. Ependymoma may also have spinal dissemination. They have diverse histological features. Classical ependymomas are composed of densely packed isomorphic cells that have a small amount of cytoplasm (**Figure 15**). The typical architecture is a perivascular distribution of cells forming pseudorosettes (**Figure 16**). Tumour cells have cytoplasmic processes that taper towards the blood vessel wall. Less frequently canals formed by ependymal cells (also known as ependymal

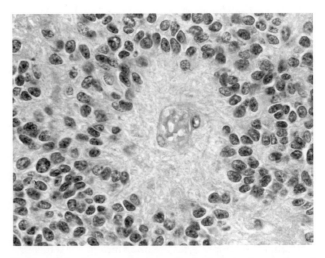

Figure 16 Pseudorosettes, the hallmark of ependymal tumours, are composed of small blood vessels rimmed by a nucleus free mantle of fibrillary cytoplasmic processes that are surrounded by tumour cells.

rosettes) of variable size may predominate in some tumours. A subtype called cellular ependymomas has paucity of pseudorosettes or ependymal canals. Clear cell ependymomas resemble oligodendrogliomas and central neurocytomas. Care must be taken not to confuse them. Papillary ependymoma is a rare variant that is composed of papillae and must be distinguished from choroid plexus papilloma. Tanycytic ependymomas histologically resemble the spindly bipolar tanycytic ependymal cells.

Myxopapillary ependymomas have a distinctive histology and carry an excellent prognosis if completely resected. They can be seen in all age groups but are most common in the fourth decade. These tumours occur almost exclusively in the conus medullaris, cauda equina and filum terminale. Rarely, they can be seen at other levels of the spinal cord or even in sacrococcygeal subcutaneous tissue. These tumours typically have a lobulated, soft, greyish appearance. Histologically, they consist of hyalinized or oedematous fibrovascular cores covered by variable amounts of ependymal cells (**Figure 17**). A mucoid matrix material between tumour cells and blood vessels is typically present. The tumour cells often express GFAP but not cytokeratin, a useful feature to differentiate them from metastatic papillary carcinomas.

Subependymoma is an uncommon, slow-growing, histologically benign periventricular tumour that is composed of cells resembling both ependymal cells and astrocytes. Such tumours are found predominantly in the lateral and fourth ventricles and all age groups are affected. Subependymomas often but not always remain asymptomatic. Clinical manifestations, when present, often result from ventricular obstruction and increased intracranial pressure. Macroscopically, they are sharply demarcated exophytic nodular masses arising from the ventricular wall. Histologically, they display features of both astrocytoma and

ependymoma. Sparsely cellular fibrillary astrocytes form a matrix throughout which ependymal cells are unevenly scattered. These cells may form hollow rosettes or perivascular pseudorosettes or may merely consist of small clumps of polygonal cells with no special orientation. Mitotic figures are not usually seen.

The majority of ependymal tumours express GFAP. EMA is also expressed and most often at the luminal border of the ependymal canal, the internal border of the perivascular pseudorosettes and luminal surface of papillary ependymoma. Cytokeratin is occasionally expressed. The ultrastructural characteristics of normal ependymal cells such as a $9+2$ arrangement of cilia, blepharoblasts and microvilli are well maintained by the tumour cells.

Anaplastic ependymoma is a tumour with histological features suggestive of aggressive behaviour and malignancy. These features included nuclear pleomorphism, high mitotic activity and necrosis.

However, the clinical behaviour of ependymomas is not well correlated with their histological features. In a series of 298 cases, survival of patients could not be correlated with the histopathological features of malignancy (Schiffer et al., 1991). On the other hand, Ritter et al. (1998) noted that onset at young age, a Ki-67 labelling index of >20% and anaplastic features are associated with aggressive behaviour.

Mixed Gliomas. Some gliomas contain more than one neoplastic component. Oligoastrocytoma, the prototype of mixed glioma, is composed of a substantial mixture of distinct components of astrocytoma and oligodendroglioma. When features indicative of malignant behaviour are present, they are termed anaplastic oligoastrocytoma. The median survival for low-grade mixed oligoastrocytoma is 6.3 years and for high-grade oligoastrocytoma it is 2.8 years (Shaw et al., 1994). Other mixed gliomas may contain ependymal and oligodendroglial components, less commonly astrocytic and ependymal components. Rarely, neoplastic components of all three lineages can be found.

Neuronal and Mixed Glial–Neuronal Tumours

Primary neuroepithelial tumours that contain mature neuronal elements are most common in children and young adults. Many are histologically and biologically benign tumours and often have features of hamartomas. While paraganglioma is included in this category of CNS tumour in the WHO Classification, it is best regarded as a neuroendocrine tumour that arises from the nerve roots and hence is discussed in the section 'Tumours of the PNS' (see later).

Ganglioglioma and Gangliocytoma. Ganglioglioma is composed of neoplastic ganglion (neuronal) cells and neoplastic glial cells. Symptoms vary according to location, but intractable epilepsy is the most common clinical manifestation. Indeed, total resolution or significant

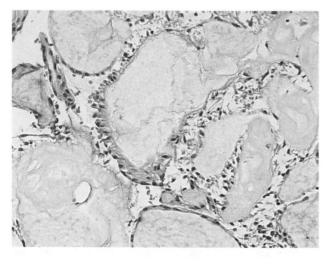

Figure 17 Myxopapillary ependymomas typically contain lakes of myxoid material bounded by a thin layer of cells.

improvement for control of epilepsy is often noted following removal of the tumour. They can occur anywhere in CNS but the temporal lobe is the preferred site.

Macroscopically, they consist of a well-circumscribed solid mass or cyst with a mural nodule; they are not usually associated with significant mass effect. Calcification is often present but haemorrhage and necrosis are rare. Neoplastic ganglion cells, the salient feature of these tumours, are moderate to large dysmorphic cells that resemble neurons. They have eccentrically placed, round nuclei containing small but distinct nucleoli; binucleated cells are common. Their cytoplasm is usually basophilic. The ganglion cells may be arranged in clusters in a neuropil-like or glial background.

The amount of glial component is variable. In some tumours there is no significant glial component, in which case the tumour is gangliocytoma (**Figure 18**). Gangliocytomas are almost always benign and can be cured by resection if in an accessible location. Rare anaplastic gangliocytomas have been reported.

Ganglioglioma, a far more common entity than gangliocytoma, is composed of neoplastic ganglion cells admixed with neoplastic astrocytes and enlarged or bizarre-shaped neurons (**Figure 19**). In unusual cases, the glial component may be oligodendroglial rather than astrocytic. Both gangliocytoma and ganglioglioma may contain reticulin around ganglion cells and/or perivascular lymphocytic infiltrations. Neoplastic ganglion cells express NFPs, synaptophysin and other neuronal markers in the neoplastic ganglionic cells, whereas the glial component expresses GFAP. At the ultrastructural level, neurosecretory granules are often seen in the neoplastic neurons; synaptic junctions may or may not be present.

Most gangliogliomas can be cured by resection but a minority of them recur and undergo malignant transformation. Only in exceptional conditions is the product of malignant transformation a high-grade glial neoplasm. Gangliogliomas in the brainstem and spinal cord are 3.5–5 times more likely to recur than cerebral gangliogliomas (Lang *et al.*, 1993).

Dysplastic Gangliocytomas of the Cerebellum (Lhermitte–Duclos Disease).
This interesting benign cerebellar lesion combines features of hypertrophy, congenital malformation and neoplasm. It is benign and often associated with Cowden disease (see below). Neurological manifestations include ataxia, mild mental retardation and a self-limited seizure disorder. They are most common in young adults and have a marked male preponderance. The lesion is characterized by diffuse hypertrophy of cerebellar folia. Histologically, the normal architecture of cerebellum is effaced. Instead, folia are composed of an outer layer of well-developed radial and more superficially distributed parallel myelinated nerve fibres, and an inner layer of abnormal neurons that contains both small hyperchromatic neurons and large polygonal neurons with prominent nucleoli. The large cells resemble Purkinje cells. The white matter is either absent or greatly reduced. It has been suggested that this is a hamartomatous lesion, a hypothesis supported by its frequent association with other malformations such as megalencephaly and heterotopic grey matter.

Dysembryoplastic Neuroepithelial Tumour (DNET).
DNETs are benign glial–neuronal neoplasms that are most commonly seen in children and young adults, often with a history of prolonged drug-resistant seizures. They are superficially located supratentorial tumours that frequently involve the temporal lobe. Macroscopically, they contain a central viscous mass associated with firmer nodules in the periphery. The affected cortex is expanded and foci

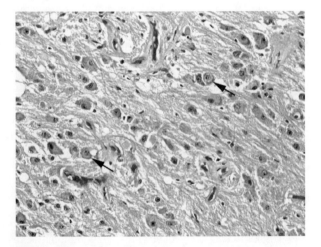

Figure 18 Photomicrograph of gangliocytoma showing tumour composed of abnormal ganglion (arrow) cells scattered through the neuropil.

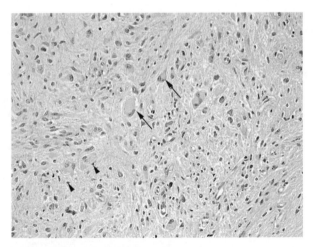

Figure 19 Gangliogliomas have a neuronal (ganglionic) component and an astrocytic component. Ganglionic cells (arrow) are usually much larger than astrocytic cells (arrow head).

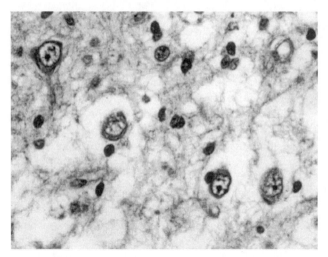

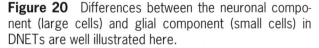

Figure 20 Differences between the neuronal component (large cells) and glial component (small cells) in DNETs are well illustrated here.

of cortical dysplasia (focally disorganized cortex) are invariably seen in the surrounding cortex. Such cortical topography is an important criterion for differentiating between DNETs and other gangliogliomas. Therefore, clinical imaging findings must be seriously examined in conjunction with the histological features. Classical DNETs contain a mucoid component composed of columns of axons perpendicularly oriented to pial surface and lined by small S-100-positive and GFAP-negative oligodendroglia-like cells. Suspended in between these bundles is mucoid material (**Figure 20**) that contains neurons with normal cytology and some GFAP-positive stellate astrocytes. This combination is termed 'specific glioneuronal elements' and is considered the histological hallmark of DNETs (Daumas-Duport, 1993).

Desmoplastic Infantile Ganglioglioma/Astrocytoma (DIG/DIA). Desmoplastic infantile ganglioglioma (DIG) and desmoplastic infantile astrocytoma (DIA) (also known as superficial cerebral astrocytoma or desmoplastic cerebral astrocytoma of infancy) are rare tumours that invariably arise in the supratentorial region and are almost exclusively seen in infants under 2 years of age, although noninfantile cases have been reported. They tend to be large and superficially placed cystic tumours that involve the leptomeninges and are often attached to the dura. The solid part of the tumour is firm or rubbery in consistency and grey or white in colour. Necrosis and haemorrhage are uncommon. They may casue cranial enlargement, tense and bulging fontanelles, downward ocular deviation ('sunset sign') and palsy of the sixth and seventh cranial nerve in infants. Hydrocephalus is common. Despite their large size and some suggestive malignant histological features, prognosis is favourable after surgical resection.

Histologically, DIGs are reticulin-rich astrocytic tumours with a variable neuronal component (DIG). There

is an often a sharp demarcation between the cortical surface and tumour. Neoplastic ganglion cells and astrocytes are found within a desmoplastic background. Reticulin stain characteristically discloses deposition of reticulin substance around individual tumour cells. Aggregates of poorly differentiated neuroepithelial cells are often found. The glial cell express GFAP and vimentin; the neuronal component expresses synaptophysin, NFPs and class III β-tubulin. The identity of the poorly differentiated cells is not well defined but is most likely primitive neuroepithelial cells. Mitotic activity in the differentiated component is usually rare, however, the poorly differentiated cases may display mitotic activity. DIA is a reticulin-rich desmoplastic astrocytic tumour with no neuronal component.

Central Neurocytoma. Central neurocytomas are typically seen in young adults with peak incidence in the third decade. They are uncommon tumours that are usually found in the lateral ventricles and/or third ventricle, a feature that often leads to increased intracranial pressure and hydrocephalus. The tumours are greyish and friable and may be calcified and occasionally haemorrhagic. Histological architecture may vary from place to place. Some tumour cells are round to polygonal, contain clear cytoplasm and have well-defined cytoplasmic margins. In fact, they were previously regarded as clear cell ependymoma of the foramen of Monro. They often have a honeycomb appearance that simulates oligodendrogliomas. In other areas, tumour cells may have a substantial amount of neuropils. Ganglioid cells and Homer Wright rosettes are rare findings. Although histologically similar, neurocytoma are separated from oligodendroglioma by immunohistochemical and ultrastructural features. The most useful diagnostic marker is synaptophysin, which is strongly expressed in both the cytoplasm and neuropil of these tumours but not in oligodendrogliomas. If synaptophysin is not detected, electron microscopy may be used to confirm the presence of neurosecretory granules. Synapses are also common but are not required for diagnosis. NFPs are usually not expressed except in ganglioid cells and GFAP is expressed by a small number of tumours. Neurocytomas usually behave in a benign fashion but a small number of them may exhibit increased proliferative activity, necrosis and other features indicative of aggressive behaviour.

Choroid Plexus Tumour

Choroid plexus has features of epithelial cells including tight junctions and basement membrane. Choroid plexus tumours, namely papilloma and carcinoma, are intraventricular tumours. Over 90% arise from the lateral and fourth ventricles while about 5% are found in the third ventricles. Although 80% of these tumours occur before the age of 20 years, most of them occur before the age of 2 years; congenital tumours have been described. They typically cause hydrocephalus by two mechanisms: obstruction and overproduction of spinal fluid.

Choroid plexus papilloma appears as a cauliflower-like mass that is adherent to the ventricular wall but well demarcated from the brain parenchyma. Histologically, there is recapitulation of normal choroid plexus structure. The tumours are composed of delicate, often oedematous, fibrovascular connective tissue fronds that are covered by single-layered columnar to cuboidal epithelium with basally located nuclei (**Figure 21**). A basement membrane can easily be demonstrated by a periodic acid–Schiff (PAS) stain. Pseudostratification may occur but multilayered epithelial cells are not seen in papilloma. A few mitotic figures may be present but, unless excessive and atypical, do not indicate malignancy. Brain invasion and necrosis are absent. Like their normal counterparts, the tumours express cytokeratins. Most express vimentin and S-100. Although GFAP is absent in normal choroid plexus, it is focally expressed in about 25–55% of choroid plexus papillomas. Transthyretin (prealbumin), a protein involved in the transport of thyroxine, is expressed in normal choroid plexus and papillomas. Expression of synaptophysin occurs in normal choroid plexus, choroid plexus papilloma and carcinoma but the significance is unclear.

Choroid plexus carcinomas show partial lost of papillary pattern with tumour cells arranged in solid sheets. There are numerous mitoses, nuclear pleomorphism, increased cellularity, necrosis and often extensive brain invasion. The pattern of antigen expression is similar to choroid plexus papillomas. Expression of transthyretin, however, may be reduced. Proliferative activity of the carcinoma (mean 13.8%, range 7.3–60%) is significantly higher than found in papillomas (mean 1.9%, range 0.2–6.0%) (Vajtai *et al.*, 1996). Choroid plexus carcinoma is rare in adults. Such a diagnosis should only be made when the possibility of metastatic papillary carcinoma is eliminated through thorough morphological and immunohistochemical study.

Choroid plexus tumours tend to spread throughout the cerebrospinal fluid. Whereas the carcinomas may produce frank metastases, papilloma with spinal dissemination may remain asymptomatic. The overall 5-year survival rate for choroid plexus papilloma is 100% and for choroid plexus carcinoma 40%. Choroid plexus carcinoma is one of the rare brain tumours that can metastasize to visceral organs.

Pineal Parenchymal Tumour

Pineocytoma is a rare neoplasm that can occur at all ages but older children and young adults are predominantly affected. They tend to be well-defined masses which are composed of solid sheets of small, uniform, mature cells that resemble pineocytes. Some have neuropil or are arranged in a circular pattern that looks like an enlarged Homer Wright rosette. These large rosettes are termed 'pineocytoma rosettes' as they are only seen in these tumours. A papillary subtype of pineocytoma has also been described. These tumours strongly express synaptophysin and variably express NFP and other neuronal markers such as class III β-tubulin. Expression of retinal S-antigen and rhodopsin indicating their photoreceptor lineage can often be demonstrated. The 5-year survival of patients with pineocytoma is about 86% (Schild *et al.*, 1996).

Pineoblastomas, in contrast, are highly malignant tumours and almost half of them occur within the first 10 years of life. They share many features of PNETs and are better regarded as PNETs with photoreceptor differentiation. Macroscopically, they are soft, friable, haemorrhagic and poorly demarcated tumours. Histologically, they are composed of small primitive cells with hyperchromatic nuclei and scant cytoplasm. Mitotic activity is brisk. They may contain rosettes that resemble those in PNETs in other locations (Homer Wright rosette) or in retinoblastoma (Flexner–Wintersteiner rosette). Dissemination through CSF is common. They are variably immunoreactive for synaptophysin, neurofilament proteins, class III β-tubulin, chromogranin A and retinal S-antigen.

The distinction between pineocytoma and pineoblastoma is blurred in a significant number of cases, in which event they are regarded as pineal parenchymal tumours with intermediate differentiation.

Primary Tumours of Meninges and Mesenchyme

This family of tumours arise within intracranial and intraspinal locations and recapitulate the normal supporting tissue of the CNS such as the leptomeninges and the surrounding mesenchyme.

Meningiomas

Meningiomas are tumours that consist of arachnoid (meningothelial) cells and are most commonly seen in

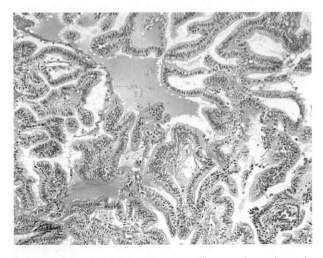

Figure 21 Choroid plexus papilloma show branching papillary structures covered by a single layer of epithelium.

the areas where arachnoid villi are most abundant, such as the parasagittal region and olfactory groove, and display features of mature meningothelial cells; sometimes they arise from intraventricular locations and are rare in tissue outside the cranium and spinal cord. These are common tumours and comprise 13–26% of all primary intracranial mass lesions. Meningiomas are essentially tumours of middle-aged and elderly individuals, and are only rarely seen in children and infants. They are twice as common in women than in men. These tumours are slow growing and many remain asymptomatic for years. However, local recurrence after surgery is not uncommon. The neurological manifestations are closely related to compression of adjacent structures and the specific neurologic deficits depend on the location of the tumour.

As noted, meningiomas are preferentially found over the cerebral convexity, olfactory groove, sphenoid ridge, parasellar regions, petrous ridge and tentorium cerebelli. Multiple tumours are not infrequent, particularly in patients with neurofibromatosis 2 (see below), and are not necessarily an indication of malignancy. On MRI, meningiomas typically appear as well demarcated masses that enhance homogeneously and may be associated with a variable amount of oedema in the surrounding brain. Grossly,

they are well-demarcated, round to lobulated, rubbery to firm masses (**Figure 22**). The cut surface is often homogeneous and tan and can be gritty when substantial calcification is present. Brain tissue is often compressed by the tumour. Intracranial meningiomas are typically attached to the dura whereas those in the vertebral canal are adhered to leptomeninges. These tumours may invade the skull bone and adjacent sinuses or may arise entirely within bone and be associated with osteoblastic activity.

Meningiomas are basically histologically benign tumours. They have the most diversified histopathological features and the histology is often variable within the same tumour. Nuclei of the tumour cells are small, round to oval, and display minimal pleomorphism; they may contain nuclear pseudoinclusions. Sporadic large and hyperchromatic nuclei can sometimes be seen. Proliferative activity, as measured by cell cycle labelling, is low; high proliferative activity may be correlated with an increased risk of recurrence. There is no significant pleomorphism, mitotic activity or necrosis.

Histological features of meningiomas are diverse. There are several common histological subtypes of meningiomas. The meningothelial type is composed of tumour cells that are arranged into sheets and lobules that are separated by thin collagenous septae (**Figure 23**). Cytologically they are benign looking and resemble arachnoid cells (**Figure 24**) and very often they arrange themselves into small whorls of cells resembling arachnoid granulations. The fibrous (fibroblastic) meningioma is composed of spindle-shaped cells with elongated cytoplasm that resemble fibroblasts (**Figure 25**). These cells are arranged in parallel and interlacing bundles intermingled with a variable amount of dense collagen. The transitional (mixed) type is essentially a hybrid that has features of both the meningothelial and fibroblastic types. Tumour cells of the psammomatous meningioma tend to arrange

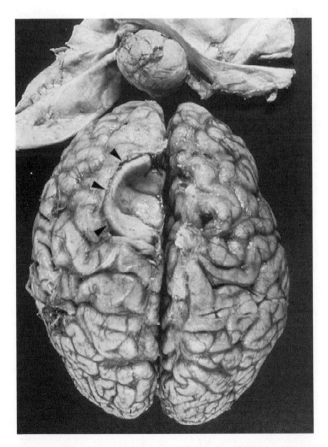

Figure 22 Parasagittal meningioma which has compressed but not invaded the surrounding gyri producing atrophy (arrow head).

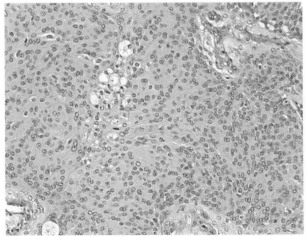

Figure 23 Typical field of meningotheliomatous meningioma showing sheets of arachnoid cells and a small focus of foamy macrophages.

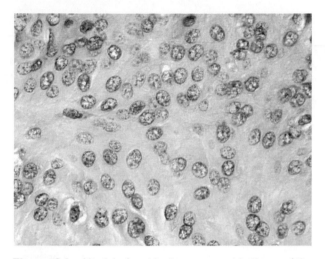

Figure 24 Nuclei of meningioma resemble those of the arachnoid cells and are round to oval and have a speckled chromatin pattern.

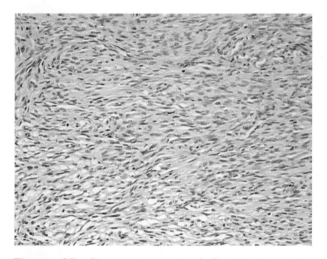

Figure 25 Photomicrograph of fibroblastic meningioma composed of enlarged spindle cells reminiscent of fibroblasts.

themselves into whorls that often contain psammoma bodies, a round to irregular, laminated calcified structure.

Less common types include angiomatous meningioma, microcystic meningioma, secretory meningioma, lympho-plasmacyte-rich meningioma and metaplastic meningioma.

While the aforementioned variants do not exhibit differences in their biological behaviour, papillary meningioma is a variant that behaves aggressively. These tumours are characterized by a perivascular pseudopapillary arrangement of tumour cells. They often have mitotic activity and pleomorphism and tend to recur locally and metastasize to other body regions. Clear cell and chordoid meningioma may also be associated with increased risk of recurrence and aggressiveness.

Immunohistochemically, most meningiomas express EMA in a patchy manner. Expression is less consistent in atypical and anaplastic meningiomas. Vimentin is seen in virtually all meningiomas. These tumours do not express GFAP, a useful feature for differentiating them from desmoplastic gliomas.

Characteristic ultrastructural features of meningiomas include interdigitations of the cytoplasmic membrane, hemidesmosones and desmosomes. They contain abundant amounts of intermediate filaments, sometimes with a pronounced whirling pattern. These filaments are also firmly anchored to the desmosomes, a feature that is also seen in normal arachnoid cells.

Atypical and Anaplastic Meningiomas

Atypical meningiomas display features that suggest aggressive biological behaviour including four mitotic figures per 10 high-power fields, uninterrupted patternless or sheet-like cell growth, increased pleomorphism and necrosis. Such atypical changes can occur with any of the histological variants.

Anaplastic (malignant) meninigiomas display more sinister histological features that far exceed those displayed by atypical meningiomas. Histologically, they are frankly malignant. Both atypical meningiomas and anaplastic meningiomas have a significantly higher proliferation rate than meningioma.

Brain invasion by meningioma is an indication of aggressive behaviour but not an equivalent to frank malignancy as histologically benign meningiomas may invade the brain. On the other hand, atypical and anaplastic meningiomas frequently invade the brain.

Mesenchymal Non-meningothelial Tumours

This is a family of rare tumours that arise within the intracranial and/or intraspinal cavity. They exhibit mesenchymal differentiation of various types including fat, fibrous tissue, muscle, bone, endothelial cells and others. This heterogeneous family includes benign tumours such as lipomas and highly malignant lesions such as mesenchymal chondrosarcomas. Some tumours, such as rhabdomyosarcoma, are preferentially seen in children, whereas other tumours such as chondrosarcoma are often seen in adults; no age group is spared. Only a few will be discussed here.

Vascular Tumours. Vascular lesions of the brain fall into three major groups. The most frequent type is malformative in nature and includes arteriovenous malformations, cavernous angiomas, venous angiomas and capillary telangiectases. These must be distinguished from true neoplastic vascular lesions. Interestingly, these vascular malformations are often associated with familial syndromes that involve malformations of the CNS and blood vessels.

The second type is a true neoplasm with the neoplastic cells displaying histological and immunohistochemical features of endothelial cells. The tumour cells express factor-VIII and CD31 and can also be identified with

Ulex europeus lectin. Haemangiomas are benign tumours. Epithelioid haemangioendotheliomas are rare vascular tumours of intermediate malignancy which arise from the skull base, dura or brain parenchyma. Angiosarcomas are rare but highly malignant vascular tumours. Kaposi sarcomas are only exceptionally encountered and almost always associated with acquired immune deficiency syndrome (AIDS).

In the third type, the tumours have such a rich vasculature to suggest a vascular tumour but the neoplastic cells do not exhibit features of endothelial cells. Examples include haemangiopericytoma and haemangioblastoma.

Haemangiopericytoma. Haemangiopericytoma is an uncommon tumour of intermediate-grade malignancy. The tumours are almost always dural-based and tend to occur in young adults. Macroscopically, they are dural-based solid masses well demarcated from the adjacent brain tissue, almost invariably solitary at initial presentation. Large, thin-walled and dilated blood vessels often with the appearance of a stag-horn are present. Haemangiopericytomas are highly cellular tumours composed of compactly arranged, monotonous polygonal cells with ill-defined cytoplasm and usually mitotically active. There are numerous small vascular channels between the tumour cells. The tumour cells arrange themselves in lobules separated by thin vascular spaces. The neoplastic cells are not immunohistochemically reactive for CD31, factor-VIII or *Ulex europeus*. Characteristically, reticulin material surrounds the individual cells. This is confirmed by ultrastructural demonstration of basal lamina-like amorphous material around the cells. Local recurrence is a rule.

Haemangioblastoma. Haemangioblastoma is a highly vascular tumour but the neoplastic cells do not express features of endothelium. In fact, their nature is poorly understood and, therefore, they are classified as tumours of uncertain histogenesis in the WHO Classification. For practical purposes, they are discussed with other vascular tumours. Haemangioblastomas are relatively common and about 25% of them are associated with von Hippel–Lindau disease. This is a biologically benign tumour and occurs most commonly in young and middle-aged adults; the cerebellum is the preferred site, although they can occur in any part of the CNS. Macroscopically, they are often well-circumscribed cystic tumours, and the strategic position in the posterior fossa often obstructs CSF flow. Histologically, they are highly vascular (**Figure 26**) and are composed of sheets and lobules of vacuolated large stromal cells, the histological hallmark of the tumour. This is combined with a rich capillary network (**Figure 27**). Immunohistochemically, they do not express markers of endothelial cells. The stromal cells contain lipid droplets, a feature best demonstrated by fat stains on frozen sections or electron microscopy, but do not express any marker of endothelial cells. Their nature remains a matter of dispute.

Chordoma. Chordomas are tumours of notochordal tissue that arise mainly at either end of the vertebral column. These tumours may involve the cranial base and extend into the middle and posterior fossae and penetrate the dura. Chordomas in the sacral region are more common, and rarely extend into the spinal canal. Most cases are seen after the age of 50 years (Dorfman and Czerniak, 1998). Although locally invasive, these tumours are histologically benign. Macroscopically, they are grey, bulky, soft to gelatinous masses in consistency. The histological hallmark of chordoma is the large and bubbly physaliferous cell (**Figure 28**) which has pale eosinophilic or amphophilic cytoplasm and a centrally located small-to medium-sized nucleus. These cells form cohesive sheets or nests and are embedded in a sea of strongly metachromatic acellular substances. Ultrastructurally, the tumour cells contain numerous desmosome-type

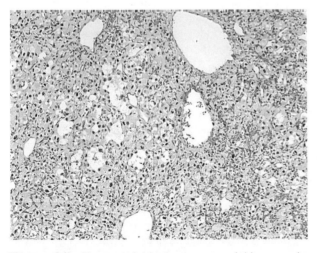

Figure 26 Haemangioblastomas are richly vascular and often have dilated blood vessels.

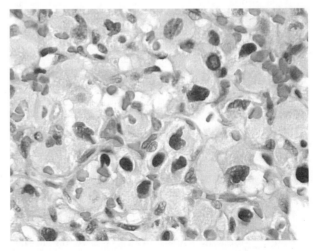

Figure 27 High-magnification photomicrograph of stromal cells in haemangioblastoma showing pale to vacuolated cytoplasm with centrally located nuclei.

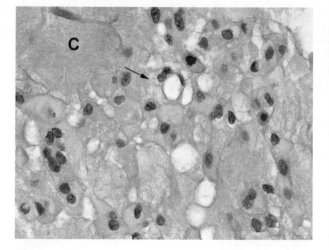

Figure 28 Photomicrograph of chordoma showing bubbly physaliferous cells (arrow) and metachromatic acellular material (C).

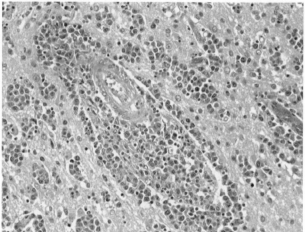

Figure 29 Neoplastic lymphoid cells demonstrating characteristic concentric perivascular arrangements.

intercellular junctions which tightly bond them to one another. These cells are immunohistochemically reactive for S-100 protein, EMA, vimentin and cytokeratin. These tumours must be distinguished from chondrosarcoma which they may mimic histologically.

Primary Tumours of Tissue Outside the CNS

These interesting primary tumours have no normal counterparts in the mature CNS. Three families of tumours comprise this group: tumours of the haematopoietic system, germ cell tumours and teratomas, and craniopharyngioma.

Primary Tumours of the Haematopoietic System

The CNS may be involved by both primary and secondary tumours of the haemotopoietic system. A variety of primary lymphoproliferative disorders, including intraparenchymal primary lymphoma, plasmacytoma and mucosal associated lymphoid tissue (MALT) lymphoma of the dura and post-transplantation lymphoproliferative disorder, can be seen in the CNS. Primary non-Hodgkin lymphoma is the most commonly seen entity. In contrast, primary Hodgkin disease of the CNS is exceedingly rare. Primary histiocytic tumours, predominantly Langerhans histiocytosis, are also seen in the CNS.

Primary non-Hodgkin lymphoma of the CNS was a rare disease until the epidemic of HIV infection and wide use of immunosuppression for organ transplantation. In immunocompetent patients, primary CNS lymphoma is seen mainly in elderly patients, but in immunodeficient patients, the age of onset is related to the time of onset of the immunodeficiency and all age groups are affected. Patients with hereditary immunodeficiency disorders have the lowest age of onset, followed by patients with acquired immunodeficiency such as AIDS, and then by patients with organ allograft transplantation. Symptoms and clinical

presentation are nonspecific. MRI may reveal solitary or multiple hyperdense or isodense lesions that may or may not enhance. Cystic change is not common. Macroscopically, these tumours are preferentially found in deep-seated brain tissue such as the basal ganglia and periventricular areas. Demarcation from the surrounding tissue can be variable and the consistency varies from soft to firm.

Classification of lymphomas changes frequently. The most recent system in use is the Revised European–American Lymphoma (REAL) classification (Harris *et al.*, 1994), which defines entities on the basis of morphological, immunological, genetic and clinical information. Over 98% of all primary CNS lymphomas are B cell lymphomas, predominantly the diffuse large B lymphoma. T cell lymphomas represent the other 2% of primary CNS lymphoma. Morphologically, the lymphomas are characterized by a multifocal, perivascular (**Figure 29**) and concentric infiltration by large, atypical and monotonous lymphocytes which extensively infiltrate brain tissue. Reticulin fibres around the blood vessels are typically layered and infiltrated by the neoplastic lymphocytes giving an 'onion bulb' appearance. Immunohistochemically, B cell lymphomas express pan-B markers such as CD20 and CD79a. They express monoclonal surface or cytoplasmic immunoglobulins with IgM and kappa light chain being the most common combination. Immunocompetent patients are usually responsive to therapy and the overall 5-year survival rate is about 25–45%. The prognosis in AIDS patients is much more ominous and their median survival rate is only 10–18 months when treated with multimodal therapy.

Germ Cell Tumours

Germ cells are not normal residents of the CNS. However, it is thought that a small number of primordial germ cells are disseminated along the migration trail from the yolk sac to the gonads during embryogenesis. These cells are the putative origin of germ cell tumours in the CNS. Some tumours are primarily seen in children and are more common in men than women. For unknown reasons, the prevalence in Asian countries is higher than that in the West. They typically occur along the midline with the pineal gland (**Figure 30**) being the most common site, followed by the suprasellar region. The third ventricle, optic chiasma and tectal plate are often affected. In consequence, they often cause hydrocephalus, precocious puberty, visual field defects and Parinaud syndrome.

Like other gonadal and extragonadal germ cell tumours, those arising in the CNS display a spectrum of differentiation. Germinoma, choriocarcinoma, yolk sac tumour, embryonal carcinoma, mixed germ cell tumour and immature and mature teratoma can all occur as primary tumours of the CNS. Pure germinoma and teratoma are, however, the most commonly seen entities. Their pathology is similar to that of other gonadal and extragonadal tumours. Germinomas are generally soft and friable. Histologically, they are composed of large, uniform cells with large vesicular nuclei containing a prominent nucleolus which resemble primitive germ cells. There is an admixture of lymphocytic cells. This is variable but sometimes intense. Placental alkaline phosphatase (PLAP) is expressed by germinoma cells and is helpful in diagnosis. Yolk sac tumours display histological features reminiscent of the embryonic yolk sac endoderm and are composed of primitive-appearing cells that arrange themselves into loosely packed, variably cellular retiform structures. When present, Schiller–Duval bodies are diagnostic. Yolk sac tumours characteristically contain eosinophilic hyaline globules that are PAS positive and immunoreactive for α-foetoprotein (AFP). The histology of embryonal carcinoma may be confused with that of yolk sac tumour. These tumours, however, are more monotonous in their patterns and are composed of sheets of undifferentiated epithelial cells. Embryonal carcinoma expresses cytokeratin and

carcinoembryonic antigen (CEA). Choriocarcinoma is a germ cell tumour that differentiates along the trophoblastic lineage and is characterized by the presence of cytotrophoblastic and syncytiotrophoblastic elements. These tumours are immunoreactive for β-human chorionic gonadotrophin.

Teratomas, in contrast to the aforementioned germ cell tumours, differentiate along ectodermal, endodermal and mesodermal lineages. Derivatives from all three germ layers such as neural tissue, respiratory epithelium, cartilage, bone, secretory glands and others may be found. In mature teratoma, all elements are fully differentiated 'adult-type tissue.' Immature teratomas contain elements that are not fully developed. Teratoma with malignant transformation refers to tumours that have a frankly malignant component, most often a rhabdomyosarcoma or undifferentiated sarcoma.

Because of the secretion of PLAP, AFP and β-HCG, germ cell tumours currently compose the only class of primary CNS tumours in which detection of primary and recurrent tumour can be easily assayed for oncoproteins in CSF and serum.

Craniopharyngioma

Craniopharyngiomas are biologically benign but locally invasive tumours. They have a bimodal distribution; the bulk of them are seen in children and young adults and the second peak occurs around the sixth decade. They occur in the suprasellar region (**Figure 31**), often have an intrasellar component and are presumably derived from Rathke's pouch. Their proximity to the optic chiasma and pituitary gland make visual disturbance, endocrine abnormalities of the anterior pituitary and diabetes insipidus the

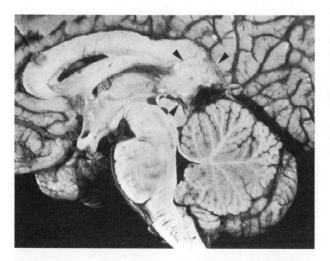

Figure 30 Sagittal section of brain showing yolk sac tumour (arrow head) arising from the pineal gland.

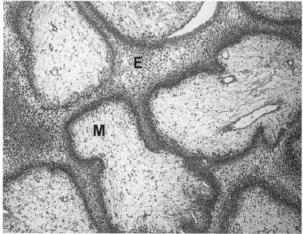

Figure 31 Photomicrograph of an adamantinomatous craniopharyngioma showing a complex pattern composed of anastomosing trabeculae of epithelial cells (E) with peripheral palisading. Supporting the epithelial cells is delicate mesenchymal tissue (M). This field is highly reminiscent of ameloblastomas that occur in the jaw.

most frequent clinical presentations. Compression of the third ventricle often causes hydrocephalus. Craniopharyngiomas are well-demarcated tumours that vary greatly in size and extent. They vary from solid to predominantly cystic. The cystic lesions often contain a cholesterol-rich, thick, brownish yellow fluid that looks like machine oil.

Two major histological variants, namely the adamantinomatous and papillary type, have been described. The adamantinomatous type is histologically very similar to if not identical with ameloblastoma or calcifying odontogenic tumour of the jaw. They are characterized by anastomosing trabeculae of stratified squamous epithelium with peripheral palisading of nuclei. Enclosed within these islands are loosely arranged stellate-shaped epithelial cells and nodular and often calcified masses of 'wet keratin,' a distinctive diagnostic feature of craniopharyngioma. These cell islands are held together and nourished by the vascularized connective tissue stroma. Substantial calcification is often associated with the components that resemble calcifying odontogenic tumour. The papillary craniopharyngioma is composed of pseudopapillae covered by keratinizing squamous cell epithelium. Craniopharygioma is a biologically benign but locally invasive tumour, often associated with substantial gliosis in the surrounding brain tissue. Surgical removal remains the most effective approach and they recur occasionally.

Secondary Tumours

Secondary neoplastic involvement of the CNS falls into two major groups, namely metastatic tumours and secondary involvement of the CNS by haematopoietic tumours such as lymphomas and leukaemias; both involve haematogenous spread. They may present as single or multiple lesions in the brain.

Carcinoma, malignant melanoma and germ cell tumours often produce metastases to the CNS. In contrast, metastatic sarcomas with the exception of alveolar soft part sarcoma are not as common. Metastatic tumours are typically associated with substantial oedema and the clinical symptoms may be disproportionate to the size of the metastases *per se*. The location and size of the metastasis but not the type of tumour dictate the type and nature of neurological abnormalities. Whereas metastases in the cerebral cortex may cause seizures, metastases to the posterior fossa structure often cause hydrocephalus by obstructing the flow of CSF. Metastasis to the spinal cord may compress the spinal cord and produce hemiplegia or quadriplegia, depending on the level of involvement.

Intracranial metastases are most frequently seen in the brain and occasionally in the dura. In the cerebrum, the tumours are most frequently located at the cortical–medullary junction where the calibre of the blood vessels abruptly changes from large to small; most of them are found in the arterial watershed areas of the cerebral hemispheres. In contrast, epidural metastases are most

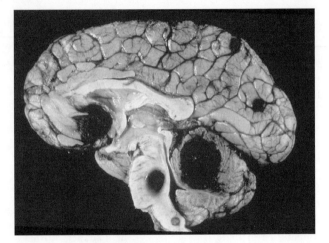

Figure 32 Multiple metastases from a peripheral malignant melanoma. Note the carbon black colour of the tumour.

commonly seen in the spinal cord although leptomeningeal and intramedullary (spinal cord) metastases can also occur.

Over 50% of all metastatic carcinomas originate from the respiratory tract. Adenocarcinoma, small cell and large cell carcinomas are far more likely to generate metastases than squamous cell carcinoma of the lung. Other common origins include carcinoma of the breast and malignant melanoma (**Figure 32**). Renal cell carcinoma has an unexplained high tendency to metastasize to the cerebellum and prostate carcinoma tends to generate epidural metastases that compress the spinal cord. Germ cell tumours of the testis metastasize to the brain in 15–25% of patients and in patients with choriocarcinoma the rate is 83%.

In most cases, the histopathology of the metastatic tumour is similar to the original tumour. The primary tumours in some cases are never found. In these cases, histology and immunohistochemistry may be helpful in identifying the tumour of origin, although this may not always be possible. The survival rate of patients with metastatic tumour in the brain varies greatly but those with single metastasis show the best survival.

Tumours of the PNS

Similar to the CNS, tumours of the PNS can also display features of embryonal and mature features of the PNS. The reader should refer to the Further Reading section for detailed discussion of PNS tumours.

Neuroblastic Tumours of the Adrenal Gland and Sympathetic Nervous System

Neuroblastic tumours are childhood tumours composed of immature neuroectodermal cells derived from the neural crest with or without associated mature ganglionic elements. Neuroblastic tumours are the most common extracranial malignant tumours during the first 2 years of life and they tend to metastasize widely. About half arise from the adrenal medulla whereas the remainder are associated with ganglia along the sympathetic chain. They typically present clinically as a palpable abdominal mass, hepatomegaly or a thoracic mass. They may compress the spinal cord and/or adjacent nerve roots and present with neurological symptoms. A small number may secrete vasoactive intestinal polypeptide and cause diarrhoea.

The International Neuroblastoma Pathology Classification by Shimada *et al.* (1999) provides a comprehensive approach in correlating the histopathology and clinical outcome of neuroblastic tumours. The neuroblastic cell nests may also display various degrees of differentiation. Neuroblastoma refer to a lesion that is composed exclusively of primitive neuroectodermal cells (**Figure 33**). Ganglioneuroblastoma is composed of nests and islands of neuroblastic cells embedded within a schwannian stroma that contains ganglionic cells (**Figure 34**). Ganglioneuroma is composed predominantly of mature ganglionic cells in a schwannian background, although a small amount of differentiating neuroblasts can be present. Grossly, they are encapsulated, soft, grey–tan tumours. Ganglioneuromas are firmer than neuroblastomas. Histologically, neuroblastomas are composed of neuroblastic cells that have small, hyperchromatic nuclei and minimal cytoplasm. Some of them may display features of differentiating neural cells with neuropil and Homer Wright rosettes. Adrenergic, cholinergic or mixed neurotransmitter enzyme and intracytoplastic catecholamines may be demonstrated histochemically. These tumours may also express chromogranin, gamma-subunit of neuron-specific enolase, neurofilament proteins and neuronal microtubule-associated proteins. The schwannian stroma expresses S-100 protein. The overall prognosis of neuroblastoma correlates with clinical staging, the histological grade of tumour, expression of TrkA and N-Myc amplification.

Olfactory Neuroblastoma (Esthesioneuroblastoma)

Olfactory neuroblastoma is a malignant tumour that is composed of primitive neuroepithelial cells and is assumed to arise from olfactory receptor cells in the nasal cavity. In contrast to neuroblastoma of the adrenal gland and sympathetic ganglia, olfactory neuroblastomas are fairly uncommon and occur predominantly in adults. They are slow-growing tumours and are often associated with long-standing symptoms. Invasion into the adjacent structures and metastasis, often to the cervical lymph nodes, is common. Macroscopically, they are soft and richly vascularized polypoid lesions. Histologically, they are composed of primitive neuroectodermal cells arranged in lobules and often form Homer Wright rosettes. Immunohistochemistry is often necessary to distinguish them from other primitive tumours.

Neurofibroma

Neurofibroma is a benign tumour that may occur in all age groups. The exact incidence of neurofibroma is unclear and they are often associated with neurofibromatosis 1 (NF1). They are most frequently found in the part of the PNS that is most distant from the spinal cord and brain; they are occasionally seen in spinal nerve roots and rarely seen in the cranial nerves. When neurofibromas arise from a small peripheral nerve, they characteristically diffusely infiltrate the nerve. They may be confined by the perineurium when they arise from medium-sized nerves but they tend to infiltrate into the surrounding soft tissue. Neurofibromas usually present as cutaneous nodules (localized cutaneous

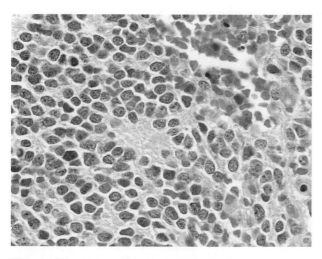

Figure 33 Neuroblastoma arising within the adrenal gland showing a Homer Wright (neuroblastic) rosette (centre of the figure). (Courtesy of Dr David Carpentieri, Children's Hospital of Philadelphia.)

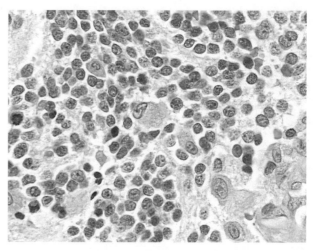

Figure 34 Ganglioneuroblastoma displaying neuronal differentiation (large cells). (Courtesy of Dr David Carpentieri, Children's Hospital of Philadelphia.)

neurofibroma) and less commonly as isolated, well-circumscribed masses (isolated intraneural neurofibroma) within nerves. In patients with NF1, they often present as plexiform neurofibromas that appear as diffuse enlargement of major nerve trunk and their branches. Macroscopically, they are firm and grey–tan tumours. While the isolated intraneural neurofibromas may be well demarcated, the plexiform neurofibroma typically appears like a string of sausages (**Figure 35**). Since they arise within the nerve and become an integrated part of it, they cannot be removed without sacrificing the nerve. Cells composing the tumour are fibroblasts, Schwann cells and perineural cells that are embedded within a collagenous and mucoid matrix (**Figure 36**). Most tumour nuclei are small and hyperchromatic; mitotic figures are rare. Axons and myelin

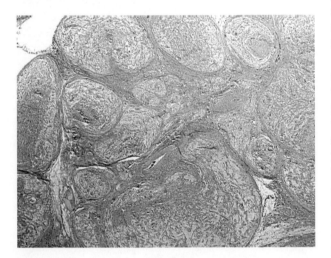

Figure 35 Plexiform neurofibroma showing variable enlargement of nerve bundles which completely obscure normal structure.

degenerate as a consequence of pressure on nerves by neoplastic cells. S-100 is invariably expressed in these lesions. Ultrastructural examination documents the presence of Schwann cells and perineural cells.

Schwannoma

Schwannomas are common benign tumours that are most frequently seen in middle-aged patients (fourth to sixth decades), although they are seen in all age groups. Unless associated with neurofibromatosis 2 (NF2) they are usually solitary. They arise most frequently from sensory branches of peripheral nerves of the head and neck region and extensor aspects of the extremities and are often asymptomatic. When they arise from the spinal nerve roots, they may have a dumbbell shape and compress the nerve root and spinal cord. The cochlear–vestibular nerve is also a common site, causing tinnitis and hearing loss. Rarely, these tumours may be found within the brain and spinal cord.

The majority are well-circumscribed, oval, solid to cystic, tan, rubbery tumours. In contrast to neurofibroma which diffusely infiltrates the nerve, schwannomas compress but do not excessively infiltrate the nerve. Thus, the nerve may be be salvaged during surgical excision of schwannomas. Histologically, schwannomas are composed of elongated spindle-shaped cells that exhibit a variety of patterns. The tumour cells often arrange into Antoni A and Antoni B patterns. The Antoni A pattern is characterized by compact spindle cells that may have nuclear palisading and whorling of cells. Verocay bodies (**Figure 37**) refer to structures formed by two compact rows of palisading nuclei separated by fibrillary cell processes. The nuclei of schwannoma are usually elongated. The Antoni B pattern consists of cells that are loosely arranged in a delicate and reticular pattern (**Figure 38**).

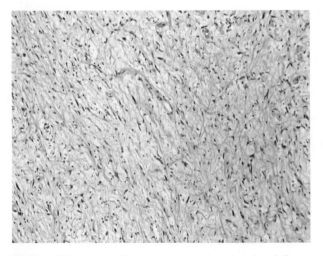

Figure 36 Neurofibromas typically contain delicate spindle cells and mucoid material.

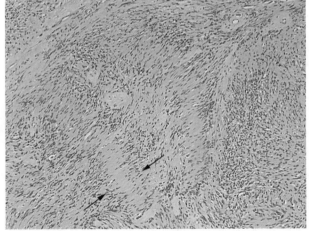

Figure 37 This photomicrograph shows the densely packed Antoni A areas and Verocay bodies formed by alternating palisading bands of nuclei and acellular tumour tissue (arrow).

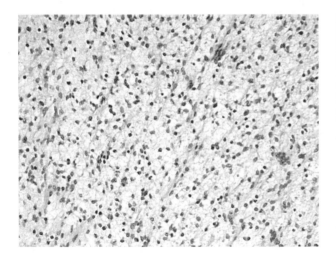

Figure 38 In Antoni B areas, the tumour cells are loosely packed and do not grow in any specific pattern.

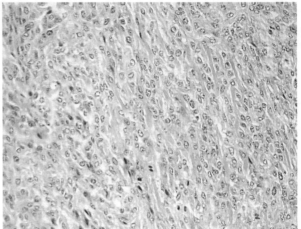

Figure 39 A malignant peripheral nerve sheath tumour can display densely packed and pleomorphic spindle cells. (Courtesy of Dr Paul Zhang, University of Pennsylvania.)

Lipid-laden macrophages and mucoid material are often present. Cellular schwannoma is a variant with increased cellularity. It is a benign variant of schwannoma, although recurrences have been reported. Melanotic schwannomas contain melanin and have immunohistochemical and ultrastructural features of both Schwann cells and melanocytes.

Malignant Peripheral Nerve Sheath Tumour (MPNST)

Malignant peripheral nerve sheath tumours (MPNSTs) are uncommon and over half occur in patients with neurofibromatosis 1. They most commonly arise from plexiform neurofibromas. Many have both features of neurofibroma and schwannoma but the preferred diagnostic classification is MPNST. This has been defined as 'any malignant tumour arising from a peripheral nerve or showing nerve sheath differentiation, with the exception of tumours originating from epineurium or the peripheral nerve vasculature,' according to the WHO Classification. The most common sites of MPNST are deep nerve branches in the buttock, thigh, brachial plexus and paraspinal areas. Cranial nerves are uncommonly involved. On gross examination they are medium-sized, firm, hard, pseudo-encapsulated tumours that are adherent to the nerve of origin. Necrosis is common. MPNSTs exhibit the most diverse histological features among all tumours of the PNS and soft tissue tumours. Significant portions may be undifferentiated (**Figure 39**). Diagnosis depends either on demonstration of tumour origin from a peripheral nerve trunk, a benign or malignant peripheral nerve tumour or immunohistochemical or ultrastructural features of Schwann or perineural cell differentiation.

Paraganglioma

This is a benign neuroendocrine tumour that arises in autonomic ganglia (paraganglia) throughout the body or within the adrenal medulla where this tumour is known as a phaeochromocytoma. Within the CNS, paragangliomas are restricted to the cauda equina and filum terminale. Paragangliomas usually occur in adults and some are endocrinologically active. These well-differentiated tumours are composed of large polygonal chief cells (type I cells) arranged in lobules (zellballen architecture) delimited by reticulin fibres and a single layer of inconspicuous sustentacular cells (type II cells). The relationship between these two types of cells is progressively lost with reduction of the sustentacular component as the tumour increases in malignancy. The chief cells are immunoreactive to synaptophysin and chromogranin whereas the sustentacular cells express S-100 protein and GFAP. The chief cells may also express other neuropeptides. Ganglionic differentiation is seen in over half of the paragangliomas arising within the cauda equina.

MOLECULAR GENETICS

Recent advances in molecular genetics have greatly improved our understanding of the aetiology of brain tumours. At the same time, such knowledge has been used to screen high-risk patients, to confirm diagnosis and to plan treatment. Limitation of space allows discussion of only a few examples.

Familial Tumour Syndromes Involving the Nervous System

This is a consortium of syndromes characterized by a combination of malformations, hamartomas and tumours of the nervous system with systemic neoplastic and non-neoplastic conditions. Many are associated with other conditions which facilitate early clinical recognition (**Table 4**). Some have characteristic skin lesions and are known as neurocutaneous syndromes, phakomatoses or ectomesodermal syndromes, the most common of which are discussed.

Tuberous Sclerosis

Tuberous sclerosis involves multiple organs but the brain is most frequently affected. It is relatively common, the incidence being between 1 in 6000–10 000. Multiple hamartomas or slowly growing tumours involve the CNS, retina, skin, heart and kidney. This is an autosomal dominant condition with high penetrance. It is unusual to observe affected siblings of apparently normal parents. The *TSC1* gene on chromosome 9q34 that encodes hamartin and and *TSC2* gene on chromosome 16p13.3 that encodes tuberin have been identified. Hamartin is strongly expressed in organs that are affected by tuberous sclerosis such as brain, kidney and heart. Tuberin is also widely expressed and its pattern of expression overlaps that of hamargin. Although mutations of both *TSC1* and *TSC2* have been described in patients with tuberous sclerosis, genotype–phenotype correlation has not been well established.

Clinical manifestations are mostly related to the slowly growing tumours or hamartomas, and are highly variable. Severity is related to the extent of involvement and age of onset. In classical cases patients have seizures, are often mentally retarded and have adenoma sebacum; however, clinical manifestations can be extremely variable. Tuberous sclerosis can be separated into definitive, provisional and suspect category on the basis of specific clinical criteria. The pathology of tuberous sclerosis is diverse (**Table 6**), and only features pertinent to the CNS will be discussed.

Cortical tubers consist of pale, firm, cortical nodules that expand the gyri and blur the margin between grey and white matter. Calcification is common and can transform the tuber into a stony-hard structure. The number and location of tubers varies and they are scattered throughout the brain and they often act as epileptic foci. Histologically, the normal cortical architecture is effaced by collections of large bizarre cells that are haphazardly arranged within a gliotic background. These bizarre-looking cells have a amphophilic to slightly eosinophilic homogeneous cytoplasm and well-defined cytoplasmic borders. They also have stout processes, peripheral vacuolation, eccentric nuclei and prominent nucleoli. It is often difficult to determine whether they are glial cells or neurons by routine histological criteria. These cells often express tuberin, vimentin, nestin and some may express GFAP and neurofilament.

Subependymal nodules are often described macroscopically as 'candle-gutterings' which consist of variably sized nodules that protrude into the ventricle, most often the lateral ventricle. Histologically, they are composed of large, bizarre cells with pale amphophilic cytoplasm and large nuclei, often more than one in each cell. Scattered clusters of primitive neural cells may be seen in neonates. Subependymal nodules are often calcified. Vimentin is usually strongly expressed and, since both GFAP and NFP are also expressed in an irregular manner, it is difficult to define these cells as glial cells or neuronal cells. In contrast to the bizarre cells in cortical tubers, cells in the white matter and subependymal nodules express tuberin weakly or not at all. In some cases, these nodules continue to expand and give rise to a true neoplasm called 'subependymal giant cell astrocytoma' (**Figure 40**). Although this tumour is called an astrocytoma, it displays both glial and neuronal phenotypes and should more correctly be simply termed 'subependymal giant cell tumour.'

Table 6 Manifestations of tuberous sclerosis

Brain	Cortical tuber
	Subependymal nodule
	Subependymal giant cell tumour
	Heterotopic grey matter
Skin	Adenoma sebacum (facial angiofibroma)
	Hypomelanotic macule
	Peri- or subungal fibroma
	Shagreen patches (fibrous hamartomas of dorsal surfaces, rarely seen before puberty)
	Poliosis and leucotrichia
Eye	Retinal giant cell astrocytoma
	Hypopigmented iris spot
	White eyelashes
	Hamartomata of eyelids and conjunctivae
Kidney	Angiolipoma
Heart	Single or multiple rhabdomyoma
Other organs affected	Bone, lung, liver, adrenals, gonads, thyroid, teeth and gingival tissue

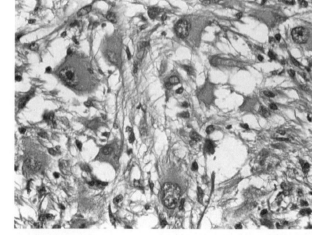

Figure 40 Large atypical cells characteristic of subependymal giant cell tumour. Note the fibrillary component and large cells with a resemblance to ganglion cells.

Table 7   Diagnostic criteria for neurofibromatosis

Neurofibromatosis 1
The criteria for making a diagnosis of NF1 are met if
a patient has two or more of the following:
1. Six or more café-au-lait macules that have a maximum
   diameter over 5 mm in prepubertal patients and
   over-15 mm in postpubertal patients
2. Two or more neurofibromas of any type or one
   plexiform neurofibroma
3. Freckling in the axillary or inguinal regions
4. Optic nerve glioma
5. Two or more Lisch nodules (iris hamartomas)
6. A characteristic osseous lesion, such as sphenoid
   wing dysplasia or thinning of the long bone cortex
   with or without pseudoarthrosis and deformity of long
   bone
7. A first-degree relative (i.e. parent, sibling or offspring)
   with NF1 by the above criteria

Neurofibromatosis 2
The criteria for making a diagnosis of NF2 are met if a
patient has one of the following:
1. Bilateral vestibular schwannomas
2. A first-degree relative with NF2 and either
   • Unilateral vestibular schwannoma or
   • Two of the following: neurofibroma, meningioma,
     schwannoma, glioma, juvenile posterior lenticular
     opacity

(Adapted from the National Institutes of Health Consensus Development Conference, 1988, Neurofibromatosis. *Archives of Neurology*, **45**, 575–578.)

Table 8   Manifestations of NF1

Skin	Café-au-lait macules
Neurofibromas	Plexiform
	Dermal
	Nodular
Sarcomas	Malignant peripheral nerve sheath tumour
	Rhabdomyosarcoma
	Triton tumour
Neoplastic CNS lesions	Optic tract/hypothalamic glioma
	Brainstem glioma
	Astrocytoma
	Anaplastic astrocytoma
	Glioblastoma
Non-neoplastic CNS conditions	Unidentified bright objects (UBO) on MRI
	Learning problem
	Epilepsy
	Neuropathy
	Hydrocephalus
	Hamatomatous glial proliferation
Osseous lesions	Sphenoid wing dysplasia
	Pseudoarthrosis
	Macrocephaly
	Scoliosis
Ocular	Lisch nodules
Other tumours	Phaeochromocytoma
	Carcinoid
	Juvenile chronic myeloid leukaemia

Neurofibromatosis Type 1 (NF1)

NF1, also known as von Recklinghausen disease and peripheral neurofibromatosis, is a pleiotropic congenital
multiple dysplasia syndrome characterized by multifocal
hyperplasia and neoplasia in the supportive tissue
throughout the entire nervous system. It is not a homogeneous syndrome and many clinical variants exist. The
NF1 gene is located on 17q11.2 and it encodes neurofi-
bromin, a classical tumour-suppressor gene. Whole gene
deletion, single- and multiple-exon deletions and insertions comprise about 50% of all the mutations.

The syndrome is defined by clinical criteria (**Table 7**).
Clinical manifestations of NF1 are diverse (**Table 8**) and
only those pertinent to the nervous system are discussed.
The cardinal sign of NF1 is multiple neurofibromas. Some
unusual variants of neurofibromas such as dermal neurofibroma and plexiform neurofibroma are characteristically
seen in NF1 patients. Malignant transformation of neurofibromas in NF1 patients most frequently occurs in a pre-
existing plexiform neurofibroma and they usually do not
occur until middle or late adult age. The transformation
may occur as a progression in anaplasia over a period of
years. The reported incidence of malignant transformation
varies widely but a rate of 3–5% may be a good estimate.
The resultant malignant tumour is usually a malignant
peripheral nerve sheath tumour (MPNST).

NF1 patients are also prone to develop gliomas. Those
which develop in the optic nerve, hypothalamic region and
brainstem are usually pilocytic astrocytomas and may
remain static for many years and, in fact, some may even
regress. Astrocytomas that arise in the cerebral and cerebellar hemispheres, however, may progress to anaplastic
astrocytomas and glioblastoma multiforme.

Neurofibromatosis 2 (NF2)

Similarly to NF1, the cardinal changes of NF2 are multifocal hyperplasia and neoplasia in the supportive tissue
throughout the entire nervous system. The elements being
affected, however, are different.

NF2 is also an autosomal dominant disorder but its prevalence is only one-tenth of that of NF1. It is also defined by
clinical criteria (**Table 7**). The gene is on chromosome
22q12 and encodes the protein merlin or schwannomin,
most likely a tumour-suppressor gene. Nonsense and frameshift mutations are often associated with a more severe
phenotype while missense mutations that preserve the carboxyl terminus of the protein result in milder phenotypes.

Schwannoma, particularly arising in the eighth cranial
nerve, is the most frequent manifestation but malignant

transformation is extremely uncommon. Schwannomatosis, essentially pathological proliferation of Schwann cells, is often found in the dorsal spinal nerve roots and also in the perivascular space of the spinal cord. Meningiomas are seen in about half of NF2 patients and they are often multiple. Interestingly, they have a tendency to arise from the stroma of choroid plexus, an otherwise unusual site.

Meningioangiomatosis, a rare hamartomatous lesion of the leptomeninges, is far more commonly seen in NF2 patients than in general population. NF2 patients also have an increased incidence of glial tumours. Over 80% of them are in the spinal cord and of the rest 10% are in the medulla. Ependymomas are common and often occur as multiple intramedullary masses. Ependymal ectopias have also been described in NF2 patients and may represent the cell of origin of the ependymomas.

Von Hippel–Lindau Syndrome

Von Hippel–Lindau syndrome is an autosomal dominant heriditary syndrome characterized by multiple cysts and benign and malignant neoplasms involving the brain, retina, kidney, pancreas, adrenal glands, inner ear and other organs. The incidence is about 1 in 36 000 to 1 in 45 000 in the general population. This results from germ-line mutations of the *VHL* tumour-suppressor gene that is located on chromosome 3p25.3; a missense mutation is the most common. The *VHL* gene is involved in cell cycle regulation and angiogenesis.

Haemangioblastomas must be present in order to make a diagnosis of von Hippel–Lindau syndrome. Although haemangioblastomas can occur sporadically, they are seen in younger age groups when associated with von Hippel–Lindau syndrome. Most commonly, they occur in the cerebellum but they can also occur in other parts of the brain and in the retina. Other manifestations of von Hippel–Lindau syndrome include renal cysts and renal cell carcinoma, pancreatic cysts and islet cell tumours, phaeochromocytoma and endolymphatic sac tumour of the inner ear. Other organs may also be affected. The occurrence of phaeochromocytoma and renal cell carcinoma, interestingly, is correlated with specific mutations.

Basal Cell Naevus Syndrome

Basal cell naevus syndrome, also known as naevoid basal cell carcinoma syndrome, is transmitted in an autosomal dominant pattern and is typically caused by a germ-line mutation of the *PTCH* gene on chromosome 9q22.3. The majority of the mutations are frameshift or nonsense mutations that lead to truncated proteins. This gene is involved in the Sonic hedgehog signalling pathway. Mutations of the *PTCH* gene and Sonic hedgehog signal pathway are also related to holoprosencephaly.

Basal cell naevus syndrome is characterized by multiple basal cell carcinomas of the skin, odontogenic keratocysts, palmar and plantar dyskeratotic pits and CNS abnormalities including intracranial calcifications, macrocephaly and PNETs of the posterior fossa (medulloblastoma). Other less common clinical manifestations such as ophthalmic abnormalities, cardiac fibromas and cleft palate may also be present. Histological features of the PNETs that occur in patients with basal cell naevus syndrome are similar to those that occur sporadically, although the majority are the desmoplastic variant.

Cowden Disease

One of the major manifestations of Cowden disease is dysplastic gangliocytoma of the cerebellum (Lehmitte–Duclos disease). It is associated with a variety of mucocutaneous lesions that include verrucous skin changes, fibroma of the oral mucosa, multiple facial tichilemmomas, hamartomatous polyps and cancer of the colon and tumours of the breast and thyroid. It is an autosomsal dominant disorder and is frequently caused by a germ-line mutation of the *PTEN/MMCA1* gene on chromosome 10q23. In addition to dysplastic gangliocytoma of the cerebellum, Cowden disease can also be associated with heterotopic grey matter, hydrocephalus, mental retardation and seizures. (See also chapter *Inherited Predispositions to Cancer*.)

Cytogenetics and Fluorescent *In Situ* Hybridization (FISH)

Cytogenetics is the study of karyotypes and allows the detection of structural changes of chromosomes, namely deletion, inversion, translocation, trisomy and polysomy, and microsatellites. Since all chromosomes are visualized at the same time, it is a good screening test for chromosomal abnormalities. A variety of chromosomal abnormalities have been identified in human brain tumours using cytogenetics. Although cytogenetic techniques allow visualization of the entire karyotype, culture of tumour cells is required. In addition, they cannot detect microdeletions that are beyond resolution by banding techniques. Fluorescent *in situ* hybridization (FISH) can be used in paraffin-embedded tissue and in cultured cells. By using an appropriate fluorescent probe, a particular chromosome can be visualized or the visualization can be limited to a small region that allows the detection of microdeletions. Gene amplifcation in the form of double minutes can also be seen. FISH, however, cannot visualize all chromosomes at the same time and is more appropriate for confirmation of a specific chromosomal change.

Although many genetic abnormalities have been identified in brain tumours, most of them do not have a consistent pattern of chromosomal abnormalities. However, some genetic abnormalities are more often seen than others. One of the best examples is the association of isochromosome 17q with primitive neuroectodermal tumours of the posterior fossa (medulloblastoma) (**Figure 41; see colour plate section**). Another example is atypical teratoid rhabdoid tumour, which is associated with monosomy or deletion of chromosome 22 (**Figure 42; see colour plate section**) in over 80% of cases, a useful diagnostic feature.

Molecular Genetics and Progression of Brain Tumours

Astrocytic tumours often progress from a low-grade tumour to anaplastic astrocytomas and finally become the highly malignant glioblastoma multiforme, the so-called secondary glioblastoma. This type of tumour progression is a multistep process driven by sequential alternations of specific genes or chromosomal loss. On the other hand, glioblastoma may also arise *de novo* without a precursor low-grade astrocytoma. Interestingly, the genetic changes in these tumours, also known as primary glioblastoma, are not the same as the secondary glioblastoma. Similar sequential genetics have also been observed in the progression of oligodendrogliomas. A variety of mutations have also been observed in other tumours.

PROGNOSTIC FACTORS

It cannot be overemphasized that tumours of the CNS are heterogeneous in clinical and biological behaviour. In general, the type of the tumour and its biological grade dictate the clinical outcome. In the WHO Classification (Kleihues and Cavenee, 2000), CNS tumours are separated into four grades. Grades I and II are low-grade tumours and that behave either in a benign fashion or as slow growing lesions; prolonged survival is possible. Grades III and IV are high-grade tumours, behave aggressively (**Table 9**) and are associated with short survival.

Location of a tumour in an inaccessible site such as the deeper parts of the cerebrum (such as basal ganglia and thalamus) or brainstem often precludes the benefits of surgical resection. The general condition of a patient also affects the clinical outcome. Younger patients with high-grade astrocytic tumours, in general, have a better survival than older patients. Other favourable prognostic factors for prolonged survival for patients with glioblastoma include long preoperative duration of symptoms, high Karnofsky Performance Status score, extensive surgical resection, use of postoperative radiation therapy and use of adjuvant chemotherapy.

Multiple prognostic indices are often present for one particular type of tumour, e.g. PNETs. Diagnosis at over 4 years of age is a favourable prognostic sign in PNETs arising from the cerebellum (medulloblastoma). In addition, limited extent of local disease, extensive surgical resection and no dissemination within the CNS are also good prognostic signs. The large cell variant of PNET has a worse prognosis; c-*myc* amplification and expression of GFAP are unfavourable. On the other hand, expression of Trk C receptor, a high-affinity neurotrophin receptor, is associated with improved survival.

Table 9 WHO grades of different brain tumours

Grade I
Pilocytic astrocytoma
Subependymoma
Choroid plexus papilloma
Ganglioglioma
Desmoplastic ganglioglioma/astrocytoma (DIG/DIA)
Dysembryoplastic neuroepithelial tumour (DNET)
Paraganglioma
Schwannoma
Neurofibroma
Perineuroma
Meningioma (variant dependent)

Grade II
Diffuse astrocytoma
Pleomorphic xanthoastrocytoma
Oligodendroglioma
Oligoastrocytoma
Ependymoma
Ganglioglioma
Central neurocytoma
Pineocytoma
Meningioma (variant dependent)

Grade III
Anaplastic astrocytoma
Anaplastic oligodendroglioma
Anaplastic oligodendroglioma
Anaplastic ependymoma
Choroid plexus carcinoma
Anaplastic ganglioglioma
Malignant peripheral nerve sheath tumour (MPNST)
Meningioma (variant dependent)
Anaplastic meningioma

Grade IV
Glioblastoma
Giant cell glioblastoma
Gliosarcoma
Medulloepithelioma
Primitive neuroectodermal tumour (PNETs)
Atypical teratoid/rhabdoid tumour (ATRT)
Malignant peripheral nerve sheath tumour (MPNST)

Source: Kleihues and Cavenee, 2000, *World Health Organisation Classification of Tumours – Pathology and Genetics, Tumours of the Nervous System* (International Agency for Research on Cancer, Lyon).

OVERVIEW OF PRESENT CLINICAL MANAGEMENT

Surgery, radiation therapy and chemotherapy are the three cornerstones of treatment. Several clinical pathological parameters must be considered before a treatment plan is formulated for an individual patient. The age of the patient, preoperative medical condition, presence of other systemic disease and malignant disease and location of the tumour must all be considered. The type of tumour, as determined by pathological examination of biopsy material, dictates the direction of further treatment. Biologically benign CNS and PNS tumours are treated surgically unless they are located in an inoperable location. Malignant tumours are often treated with chemotherapy and radiation therapy in addition to surgery. Most primary brain tumours are candidates for surgical treatment except that haematopoietic tumours are often treated with radiation and chemotherapy alone without bulk tumour resection.

Maximum tumour resection and optimum preservation of neurological functions are the two most important treatment goals for patients with brain tumours that should be surgically treated. Tumours located around or within the brainstem, diencephalon and motor cortex are particularly troublesome because damage to these areas will lead to neurological catastrophe. For these tumours, stereotactic biopsy is the diagnostic procedure of choice for the determination of the nature of the lesion. It is a computer-assisted technique that allows three-dimensional coordinated localization of an intracranial lesion. Based on these coordinates, a needle is inserted to obtain a small amount of tissue for pathological examination without producing excessive damage to the critical surrounding brain structures. Tumours located in these difficult locations are generally treated with radiation therapy and chemotherapy alone.

Since the general principles of radiation therapy are discussed elsewhere, discussion here is limited to issues specific for the CNS. In general, toxic effects produced by irradiating the human brain are categorized temporally and pathologically into three major types. The first type are acute reactions that occur during radiation therapy. They are uncommon in patients receiving conventional daily dose fractionation (1.8–2 Gy per day) but are common in patients treated with 10 Gy or above as a single fraction. Subacute reactions (early-delayed reactions) are related to radiation injury sustained by oligodendrocytes and alterations in capillary permeability and present as transient demyelination. The subacute reactions are characterized by a transient syndrome that includes somnolence, anorexia and irritability. The late-delayed reactions occur within several months or up to many years following treatment. They comprise a spectrum of clinical and pathological conditions involving multiple mechanisms. Clinical manifestations includes asymptomatic changes of the white matter and vasculature, change in cognition, hypothalamic–pituitary dysfunction, cranial neuropathy, disseminated necrotizing leucoencephalopathy, radiation necrosis and second malignancy due to radiation.

REFERENCES

Biegel, J. A., *et al.* (2000). Mutations of the INI1 rhabdoid tumor suppressor gene in medulloblastomas and primitive neuro-ectodermal tumors of the central nervous system. *Clinical Cancer Research*, **6**, 2759–2763.

Cairncross, J. G., *et al.* (1998). Specific genetic predictors of chemotherapeutic response and survival in patients with anaplastic oligodendrogliomas. *Journal of the National Cancer Institute*, **90**, 1473–1479.

Cavenee, W. K., *et al.* (2000). Turcot syndrome. In: Kleihues, P. and Cavenee, W. K. (eds), *World Health Organization Classification of Tumours – Pathology and Genetics, Tumours of the Nervous System.* 238–239 (International Agency for Research on Cancer, Lyon).

Coons, S. W., *et al.* (1997). The prognostic significance of Ki-67 labeling indices for oligodendrogliomas. *Neurosurgery*, **41**, 878–884.

Daumas-Duport, C. (1993). Dysembryoplastic neuroepithelial tumours. *Brain Pathology*, **3**, 283–295.

Dehghani, F., *et al.* (1998). Prognostic implication of histo-pathological, immunohistochemical and clinical features of oligodendrogliomas: a study of 89 cases. *Acta Neuropathologica (Berlin)*, **95**, 493–504.

Dorfman, H. D. and Czerniak, B. (1998). Chordoma and related lesions. In: *Bone Tumors*. 974–1008 (Mosby, St. Louis).

Hahn, H., *et al.* (1996). Mutations of the human homolog of *Drosophila* patched in the nevoid basal cell carcinoma syndrome. *Cell*, **85**, 841–851.

Harris, N. L., *et al.* (1994). A revised European–American classification of lymphoid neoplasms: a proposal from the International Lymphoma Study Group. *Blood*, **84**, 1361–1392.

Hamilton, S. R., *et al.* (1995). The molecular basis of Turcot's syndrome. *New England Journal of Medicine*, **332**, 839–847.

Kandt, R. S., *et al.* (1992). Linkage of an important gene locus for tuberous sclerosis to a chromosome 16 marker for polycystic kidney disease. *Nature Genetics*, **2**, 37–41.

Kleihues, P. and Cavenee, W. K. (2000). *World Health Organization Classification of Tumours – Pathology and Genetics, Tumours of the Nervous System.* (International Agency for Research on Cancer, Lyon).

Lang, F. F., *et al.* (1993). Central nervous system gangliogliomas. Part 2. Clinical outcome. *Journal of Neurosurgery*, **79**, 867–873.

Latif, F., *et al.* (1993). Identification of the von Hippel–Lindau disease tumor suppressor gene. *Science*, **260**, 1317–1320.

Maddock, I. R., *et al.* (1996). A genetic register for von Hippel–Lindau disease. *Journal of Medical Genetics*, **33**, 120–127.

Malkin, D., *et al.* (1990). Germ line p53 mutations in a familial syndrome of breast cancer, sarcomas, and other neoplasms. *Science*, **250**, 1233–1238.

Onda, K., *et al.* (1996). Comparison of bromodeoxyuridine uptake and MIB 1 immunoreactivity in medulloblastomas determined with single and double immunohistochemical staining methods. *Journal of Neurooncology*, **29**, 129–136.

Packer, R. J., *et al.* (1999). Outcome for children with medullo-blastoma treated with radiation and cisplatin, CCNU, and vincristine chemotherapy. *Journal of Neurosurgery*, **81**, 690–698.

Paraf, F., *et al.* (1997). Brain tumor–polyposis syndrome: two genetic diseases? *Journal of Clinical Oncology*, **15**, 2744–2758.

Pollack, I. F. and Mulvihill, J. J. (1997). Neurofibromatosis 1 and 2. *Brain Pathology*, **7**, 823–836.

Pratt, C. B., *et al.* (1994). Outcome for patients with constitutional 13q chromosomal abnormalities and retinoblastoma. *Pediatric Hematology and Oncology*, **11**, 541–547.

Ritter, A. M., *et al.* (1998). Ependymomas: MIB-1 proliferation index and survival. *Journal of Neurooncology*, **40**, 51–57.

Robinson, S. and Cohen, A. R. (2000). Cowden disease and Lhermitte–Duclos disease: characterization of a new phakomatosis. *Neurosurgery*, **46**, 371–378.

Ron, E., *et al.* (1988). Tumors of the brain and nervous system after radiotherapy in childhood. *New England Journal of Medicine*, **319**,1033–1039.

Schiffer, D., *et al.* (1991). Ependymoma: internal correlations among pathological signs: the anaplastic variant. *Neurosurgery*, **29**, 206–210.

Schild, S. E., *et al.* (1996). Histologically confirmed pineal tumors and other germ cell tumors of the brain. *Cancer*, **78**, 2564–2571.

Seizinger, B. R., *et al.* (1987). Genetic linkage of von Recklinghausen neurofibromatosis to the nerve growth factor receptor gene. *Cell*, **49**, 589–594.

Shaw, E. G., *et al.* (1992). Oligodendrogliomas: the Mayo Clinic experience. *Journal of Neurosurgery*, **76**, 428–434

Shaw, E. G., *et al.* (1994). Mixed oligoastrocytomas: a survival and prognostic factor analysis. *Neurosurgery*, **34**, 577–582.

Shimada, H., *et al.* (1999). The International Neuroblastoma Pathology Classification (the Shimada system). *Cancer*, **86**, 364–372.

Sopta, M., *et al.* (1992). The retinoblastoma protein and the cell cycle. *Seminars in Cancer Biology*, **3**, 107–113.

Sutphen, R., *et al.* (1999). Severe Lhermitte–Duclos disease with unique germline mutation of PTEN. *American Journal of Medical Genetics*, **82**, 290–293.

Tachibana, I., *et al.* (2000). Investigation of germline PTEN, p53, p16(INK4A)/p14(ARF), and CDK4 alterations in familial glioma. *American Journal of Medical Genetics*, **92**, 136–141.

Trofatter, J. A., *et al.* (1993). A novel moesin-, ezrin-, radixin-like gene is a candidate for the neurofibromatosis 2 tumor suppressor. *Cell*, **72**, 791–800.

Vajtai, I., *et al.* (1996). MIB-1 immunoreactivity reveals different labelling in low-grade and in malignant epithelial neoplasms of the choroid plexus. *Histopathology*, **29**, 147–151.

van Slegtenhorst, M., *et al.* (1997). Identification of the tuberous sclerosis gene TSC1 on chromosome 9q34. *Science*, **277**, 805–808.

Von Deimling, A., *et al.* (2000). Neurofibromatosis type 1. In: Kleihues, P. and Cavenee, W. K. (eds), *World Health Organization Classification of Tumours – Pathology and Genetics, Tumours of the Nervous System*. 216–218 (International Agency for Research on Cancer, Lyon).

Vorechovsky, I., *et al.* (1999). The patched/hedgehog/smoothened signalling pathway in human breast cancer: no evidence for H133Y SHH, PTCH and SMO mutations. *European Journal of Cancer*, **35**, 711–713.

FURTHER READING

Adams, E. D., *et al.* (1997). Intracranial neoplasms and paraneoplastic disorders. In: *Principles of Neurology*, 6th edn. 642–698 (McGraw-Hill, New York).

Aicardi, J. (1998). Tumors of the central nervous system and other space-occupying lesions. In: *Diseases of the Nervous System in Childhood*, 2nd edn. 491–533. (Cambridge University Press, Cambridge).

Berger, M. S. and Wilson, C. B. (1999). The Gliomas (W. B. Saunders, Philadelphia).

Bigner, D. D., *et al.* (eds) (1998). *Russel and Rubinstein's Pathology of Tumours of the Nervous System*, 6th edn (Arnold, London).

Enzinger, F. M. and Weiss, S. W. (2001). *Soft Tissue Tumors*, 4th edn (Mosby, St. Louis).

Greenberg, H. S., *et al.* (1999). *Brain Tumors* (Oxford University Press, Oxford).

Jacobson, M. (1991). *Developmental Neurobiology*, 3rd edn. (Plenum Press, New York).

Norman, M. G., *et al.* (1995). Embryology of the central nervous system. In: *Congenital Malformations of the Brain*. 9–51 (Oxford University Press, Oxford).

Pannese, E. (1994). *Neurocytology. Fine structure of Neurons, Nerve Processes, and Neuroglial Cells*. 156–168 (George Thieme, Stultgant).

Russell, D. S. and Rubinstein, L. J. (1989). *Pathology of Tumours of the Nervous System* (Williams and Wilkins, Baltimore).

Sidman, R. L. and Rakic, P. (1982). Development of the central nervous system. In: Hayemarker, W. and Adams, R. D. (eds), *Histology and histopathology of the Central Nervous System*, Vol. 1, 3–145 (Charles C. Thomas, Springfield).

Zülch, K. J. (1986). *Brain Tumors. Their Biology and Pathology*, 3rd edn (Springer, Berlin).

Websites

Neuroanatomy and neuropathology on the internet: http://www.neuropat.dote.hu/document.htm

Chapter 52

Eye and Ocular Adnexa

Arun Jain and Frederick A. Jakobiec
Massachusetts Eye and Ear Infirmary, Boston, MA, USA

CONTENTS

- Normal Development and Structure
- Tumour Pathology

NORMAL DEVELOPMENT AND STRUCTURE

The globe and the ocular adnexa represent a unique compartment, where terminal differentiation from all three germinal layers of the embryo has given rise to very specialized structures not found elsewhere in the body. Owing to this extraordinary collection of different tissues, one encounters tumours unique to this location as well as others found more commonly in distant parts of the body.

The eye is a sensory end organ that develops from the interaction of the primordial optic vesicle with the overlying ectoderm during the fourth week of gestation. The optic vesicle, one on each side, is an out pouching from the rostral end of the neural tube. The neural tube originates from the neural plate, which is a derivative of embryonic ectoderm and precursor of the entire central nervous system. The lens and most of the cornea develop from the inductive interaction of the optic vesicle with the surface ectoderm. The neural crest contributes extensively to the connective tissue of the head and neck region, which is due to the absence of paraxial somites in the head and neck

region. These connective tissue contributions of the neural crest are collectively referred to as mesoectoderm or ectomesenchyme. Therefore, in the orbit, the fibrous and fibroadipose tissue, meninges of the optic nerve, sclera and episclera, vascular pericytes and striated extraocular muscle satellite cells, peripheral nerve cellular elements, and osteocytes and cartilaginous elements are all progeny of neural crest anlage. **Table 1** demonstrates the origin of the various structures of the eye from different germinal layers.

The eye is composed of three layers: the outermost sclera with its anterior extension as the cornea, the uveal tract and the innermost layer being the retina. The six extraocular muscles are composed of striated muscle fibres and aid in the fine and gross control of eye movements. Four of these muscles arise from the orbital apex in a concentric fashion surrounding the annulus of Zinn. Intraocularly the iris and ciliary body are composed of smooth muscle and are innervated by autonomic nerve fibres. The retina is a complex multilayered structure, innermost layer of which is formed by the axons of the ganglion cell layer (nerve fibre layer) and the outmost

Table 1 Origin of different structures from germinal layers

Ectoderm		Mesoderm	Endoderm	Neural crest
Surface ectoderm	**Neuroectoderm**			
Anterior cornea	Neurosensory retina	Vascular endothelium	None	Anterior chamber
Eyelids	Retinal pigment epithelium	Extraocular muscles		(Posterior cornea)
(Holocrine glands)	Pars plana epithelium	Corneal stroma		(Trabecular meshwork)
(Apocrine glands)	(Secondary vitreous)			(Iris stroma)
(Eccrine glands)	(Lens zonules)			Uveal tract
(Pilosebaceous units)	Ciliary epithelium			(Dendritic melanocytes)
Conjunctiva	Iris pigment epithelium			Sclera
(Lachrymal glands)	(Dilator muscle)			Meninges
(Mucous glands)	(Sphincter muscle)			Orbital soft tissues
Crystalline lens	Optic nerve			Facial bones
				Trochlea

layer is formed by the photoreceptors. The neuro-sensory retina and the retinal pigment epithelium (RPE) continue anteriorly as the pigmented and non-pigmented epithelium of the ciliary body and iris.

The conjunctiva is lined by non-keratinized stratified squamous epithelium about 4–5 cell layers thick and has numerous goblet cells. Accessory lachrymal glands of Krause and Wolfring are present in the superior fornix of the conjunctiva. At the mucocutaneous junction of the eyelid, where conjunctival epithelium changes into keratinized stratified squamous epithelium of the skin, there are openings for about 30 sebaceous glands known as meibomian glands in the upper lid and 20 in the lower lid. These glands are embedded in a matrix of dense connective tissue known as tarsus. Anterior to this row of meibomian glands is a row of cilia (eye lashes) which have their own associated sebaceous glands known as glands of Zeiss and apocrine glands known as glands of Moll.

The orbit is compartmentalized into intraconal and extraconal spaces by the intermuscular septa of the extraocular muscles. The intraconal space is by far the larger of the two and is further divided by numerous thin fibrous septa into spaces that are all filled with fat. Through these compartments traverse the nerves and vessels supplying the extraocular muscles and the autonomic nerves and vessels to the choroid, ciliary body and iris. The ophthlamic artery, which later becomes the central retina artery, supplies the optic nerve and the retina. The orbit and the intraocular tissues are devoid of lymphatics, which serves to explain the metastatic pattern of some tumours. Conjunctiva and eyelids, on the other hand, are richly supplied with lymphatics.

The lachrymal gland is present in the supero-lateral recess of the orbit and is divided into two lobes by the lateral extension of the levator palpebrae superioris. The fine ductules of the lachrymal gland then open into superior fornix for the egress of tears. The tears then drain though two canaliculi into the lachrymal sac present in the lachrymal fossa formed by the lachrymal bone and frontal process of the maxilla.

TUMOUR PATHOLOGY

Eye and adnexal tumours can be subdivided into intraocular tumours, adnexal tumours of the eyelid, lachrymal sac and conjunctiva and orbital tumours. There is considerable overlap in this classification scheme, since intraocular tumours can sometimes invade the orbit and adnexal tumours on rare occasions can extend intraocularly.

Eyelid and conjunctival tumours have various counterparts in the skin from other parts of the body. Primary acquired melanosis, although analogous to lentigo maligna in the skin, has different prognostic and therapeutic implications. One of the most important malignancies

confined almost exclusively to the skin of the eyelids is sebaceous cell carcinoma.

The differential diagnosis of orbital tumours in children is strikingly different from that of adults. Capillary haemangioma and dermoid cysts are probably the most frequent orbital tumours encountered in children, whereas cavernous haemangioma is more often seen in adults and lymphoproliferative lesions are confined almost exclusively to the sixth and seventh decades of life.

The most important intraocular tumours are retinoblastoma in children and uveal melanoma in adults. However, there is a long list of other intraocular tumours that can arise *de novo* or from metastasis. In the following sections, emphasis will be placed on tumours that are unique to the eye and ocular adnexa.

Epidemiology

Eyelid and conjunctival tumours usually affect the elderly. The median age at diagnosis of sebaceous carcinoma of the eyelid is 64 years and 60–70% of them are females.

Retinoblastoma is the most common intraocular tumour of childhood and the most common tumour of the retina. It is a rare malignant tumour with a prevalence of about 1 in 23 000 live births in the UK, 1 in 16 000 in The Netherlands and 1 in 20 000 in Japan (Albert and Jakobiec, 2000a)

Uveal melanoma is by far the most clinically important intraocular malignancy in adults, owing to its risk of metastasis and subsequent death, even though uveal metastasis has a higher incidence when autopsy eyes are studied for occult intraocular tumours. It is the most common primary intraocular malignancy, occurring in approximately 6–7 cases per million people in the USA.

Aetiology

A variety of known and unknown factors contribute to neoplastic transformation of cells in the eye and ocular adnexa. The risk associated with UV exposure in the development of skin tumours is well established. Conjunctival lesions such as pterygia, pinguecula, and actinic keratosis are also related to prolonged exposure to UV light as documented by their higher frequency in more tropical areas.

Conjunctival papillomas and dysplasias are akin to skin papillomas, and human papillomaviruses 16 and 18 have been implicated in the pathogenesis of some of these lesions.

The presence of genetic mutations is well established in retinoblastoma. The role of specific gene alterations in the pathogenesis of uveal melanoma is less well defined than it is in retinoblastoma (see section on Molecular Genetic Findings).

Certain lesions in the conjunctiva and the uveal tract predispose to the development of malignant melanoma.

These include congenital melanosis and naevi. Congenital melanosis can involve only the sclera (ocular melanocytosis) or it can affect both the sclera and the skin of the lids, in which case it is referred to as Naevus of Ota (oculodermal melanocytosis) (**Figure 1; see colour plate section**). The risk of progression to malignant melanoma in congenital melanosis is primarily in the uveal tract. Naevi, however, in the conjunctiva or the uvea can give rise to malignant melanoma in either location.

The role of racial pigmentation is well established in a variety of skin, conjunctival and uveal malignancies. Individuals with lightly pigmented skin also have less melanin in the RPE and choroid, which leads to less protection from the harmful UV rays of the sun. The incidence of uveal malignant melanoma is 8–9 times higher in whites than in blacks in the USA.

Radiation used for the treatment of childhood retinoblastoma has led to an increase in the development of sarcomas in the field of radiation. Patients with the heritable form of retinoblastoma, however, have an increased incidence of sarcomas within and outside the field of radiation, with osteogenic sarcoma the most prevalent.

Screening and Prevention

Better understanding of the pathophysiology of certain tumours of the eye and ocular adnexa has greatly improved the prognosis of these tumours owing to the increased emphasis on screening and prevention. The risk of development of retinoblastoma in the siblings and progeny of patients with retinoblastoma can be accurately assessed and appropriate screening can be deployed to detect early lesions. Patients with uveal and conjunctival naevi should be evaluated on a yearly basis to detect progression of these lesions to malignant melanoma.

The association of certain tumours of the eye and ocular adnexa with other systemic neoplasms (both benign and malignant) has led to an increased awareness of these genetic syndromes and underscores the importance of the ophthlamologist in making an early diagnosis. Some of these will be discussed in the sections below.

Gross/Histopathology/Preinvasive Lesions/Ultrastructure/Immunohistochemistry

Tumours of the Eyelid and Conjunctiva

Tumours of the eyelid skin are the same as found in other parts of the body and are detailed elsewhere in this book. Basal cell carcinoma of the eyelids is the most frequent of the skin malignancies followed by squamous cell carcinoma (Albert and Jakobiec, 2000b). The lower lid is the most frequently affected area followed by the medial canthus and then the upper lid and lateral canthus. The basal cell naevus (Gorlin–Goltz) syndrome is characterized by the presence of multiple basal cell epitheliomas on the face, and less frequently on the trunk, neck and axilla. The tumours may not become invasive for many years. Associated anomalies include pitted areas in the skin of the palms and soles, odontogenic cysts of the jaw, spina bifida occulta, rib anomalies, skull anomalies, cleft lip and palate and hypogonadism in males. It is inherited in an autosomal dominant fashion with variable penetrance. The specialized glands of Moll, Zeiss, Wolfring and Krause can give rise to adenocarcinoma or a variety of benign lesions such as hydrocystoma, syringoma, eccrine acrospiroma and pleomorphic adenoma. Benign tumours of hair follicle origin include trichoepithelioma, trichofolliculoma, trichilemmoma and pilomatrixoma (calcifying epithelioma of Malherbe). Multiple trichilemmomas are seen in Cowden's syndrome. Melanocytic lesions of the eyelid skin and conjunctiva such as naevi and melanomas are also frequently encountered.

Pinguecula, pterygium and actinic keratosis result from UV damage to the conjunctiva. These lesions are exclusively found in the interpalpebral conjunctiva exposed to sunlight. The characteristic hallmark of all three is the elastotic degeneration present in the substantia propria of the conjunctiva.

Dysplasia and conjunctival intraepithelial neoplasia (carcinoma-*in-situ*) may occur anywhere on the conjunctival surface, but most often starts at the limbus (**Figure 2**). Most lesions have an opalescent papillary rather than a leukoplakic appearance due to lack of keratinization observed microscopically. A benign condition but often confused for malignancy seen in certain Haliwa Indian tribes of North Carolina is benign hereditary intraepithelial dyskeratosis appearing as patches of thickened and injected plaques of conjunctiva on the bulbar surface.

Other rare tumours include choristomas of the conjunctiva and Merkel cell tumours and myxomas of the

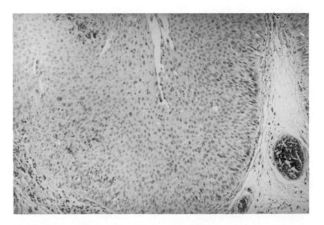

Figure 2 Conjunctival intraepithelial neoplasia demonstrating full thickness involvement of the epithelium with malignant cells.

eyelid. The latter are associated with the Carney complex, a genetic syndrome comprised of cardiac and cutaneous myxomas, spotty skin pigmentation and endocrinopathy. Choristomas such as the limbal dermoid are associated with lid coloboma in the Goldenhar syndrome. Two categories of tumours deserve special focus owing to their exclusive localization to the ocular adnexa and often challenging management. These are the sebaceous cell carcinoma of the eyelid and primary acquired melanosis of the conjunctiva.

Sebaceous Gland Tumours

Sebaceous adenomas are rare and usually solitary lesions not exceeding 1 cm in size. Histologically, they are composed of sebaceous lobules that show an orderly maturation from germinative cells located on the periphery towards the more central sebaceous cells. Muir–Torre syndrome, an autosomal dominant cause of familial cancer, is an association of multiple sebaceous gland neoplasms, other cutaneous neoplasms and multiple visceral carcinomas, especially of the colon. Often, only a single sebaceous adenoma of the eyelid may be associated with internal malignancy.

Most sebaceous carcinomas of the eyelid arise in the meibomian (tarsal) glands, followed by the glands of Zeiss, and, less frequently, sebaceous glands in the caruncle or the skin of the eyebrow. A distinctive clinical feature of many sebaceous gland carcinomas is a persistent unilateral blepharo-conjunctivitis, referred to as the 'masquerade syndrome' (**Figure 3; see colour plate section**). They can also arise in a nodular fashion at the lid margin where they appear as waxy yellowish lesions, sometimes simulating a chalazion. Histologically, the most common pattern is lobular with the degree of differentiation determining the type of cells present. The lobules exhibit basaloid features but lack the peripheral palisading of basal cell carcinoma. Well-differentiated tumours usually have areas of easily identifiable sebaceous cells with the characteristic finely vacuolated cytoplasm. Poorly differentiated neoplasms have anaplastic cells with hyperchromatic nuclei and typical mitotic figures. Frozen section and oil red O stains for lipid may be necessary to establish the diagnosis.

Sebaceous carcinoma can spread by either intraepithelial or direct extension. Intraepithelial spread can occur in a carcinoma-*in-situ* like fashion with the entire epithelium being replaced by neoplastic cells, or individual cells can migrate through intercellular spaces to distant areas in the eyelid skin or conjunctiva (**Figure 4**). This latter phenomenon is termed pagetoid spread, resembling Paget disease of the breast.

Primary Acquired Melanosis (PAM)

PAM is a unilateral neoplastic melanocytic proliferation within the conjunctival epithelium, observed most often in white patients. They appear as flat areas of increased

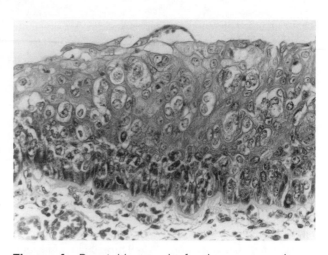

Figure 4 Pagetoid spread of sebaceous carcinoma (cells with clear cytoplasm) in the conjunctival epithelium (courtesy AFIP).

yellow–brown pigmentation in middle age, mostly on the bulbar conjunctiva, which does not fade towards the fornices like racial melanosis (**Figure 5; see colour plate section**). When the palpebral conjunctiva near the lid margin is involved, the melanosis often extends on to the adjacent epidermis. Elevated lesions developing in PAM is usually an indication of malignancy, i.e. melanoma.

Histologically, their appearance can be variable. There may be small polyhedral cells with no atypia, spindle-shaped cells with moderate atypia or large highly atypical epithelioid cells. The pattern of invasion of the conjunctival epithelium can vary from involvement of the basal layers to pagetoid extension or even full thickness replacement by atypical melanocytes resembling melanoma-*in-situ* (**Figure 6**).

Tumours of the Retina

Retinoblastoma

Five growth patterns are recognized for intraocular retinoblastoma: endophytic, exophytic, mixed endophytic–exophytic, diffuse infiltrating and complete spontaneous regression. The tumour can either arise from one location or be multicentric. Endophytic retinoblastomas grow mainly from the inner nuclear layer of the retina into the vitreous. Endophytic tumours can shed tumour cells into the vitreous, as they become large and friable, where they grow into separate tiny spheroidal masses that appear as cotton balls. Tumour cells in the vitreous may seed on to the inner surface and invade into the retina. It is important to distinguish multicentric retinoblastoma from retinal seeding because the presence of multiple tumours indicates a germ-line mutation. This distinction is frequently difficult or impossible to make.

Exophytic retinoblastomas grow from the outer nuclear layer towards the choroid, producing first an elevation and

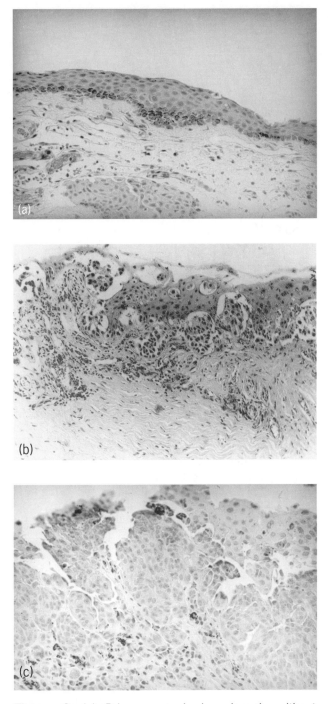

Figure 6 (a) Primary acquired melanosis without atypia. The melanotic hyperplasia is confined to the basilar layer. (b) Primary acquired melanosis with severe atypia. Nests and individual epithelioid melanocytes extend throughout the thickness of the epithelium in a pagetoid fashion (courtesy AFIP). (c) Primary acquired melanosis with invasive melanoma. Besides full thickness involvement of the epithelium with melanoma cells, some have invaded the substantia propria through the basement membrane.

then a detachment of the retina (**Figure 7; see colour plate section**). On ophthalmoscopic examination, the tumour is seen through the retina with vessels coursing over it (**Figure 8; see colour plate section**). Tumour cells can then seed the outer retinal surface or invade into the RPE and Bruch's membrane with subsequent infiltration of the choroid. From the choroid, the tumour cells can escape along the ciliary vessels and nerves into the orbit and conjunctiva and then gain access to blood vessels and lymphatics.

Mixed endophytic–exophytic tumours are the most common form of presentation, especially among larger tumours. They have features of both endophytic and exophytic growth. Diffuse infiltrating retinoblastomas often present the greatest challenge in clinical diagnosis, but fortunately are the least common of all forms. These tumours grow diffusely within the retina without thickening it much. Tumour cells are often shed into the vitreous, which can reach the anterior chamber to create a pseudohypopyon. Because of the absence of a mass, this type of retinoblastoma masquerades as a retinitis, vitritis or Toxocara endophthalmitis.

Complete spontaneous regression is believed to occur more frequently in retinoblastoma than in any other malignant neoplasm. Typically, there is a severe inflammatory reaction followed by phthisis bulbi. The mechanisms by which regression occurs are unknown.

Table 2 illustrates the differential diagnosis of retinoblastoma.

Histologically, retinoblastomas are essentially malignant neuroblastic tumours that may arise in any of the nucleated retinal layers. The predominant cell has a large basophilic nucleus of variable size and shape and scanty cytoplasm. Mitotic figures are typically numerous. The tumour cells have a striking propensity to outgrow their blood supply. Especially in large tumors, cuffs of cells surrounding central dilated vessels form areas of viable tumour that have a characteristic appearance (**Figure 9**). The tumour cells undergo ischaemic necrosis if they are displaced more than 90–110 μm from the vessel. A cuff thickness of approximately 100 μm represents the approximate distance that oxygen can diffuse before it is completely consumed in rapidly growing neoplasms.

The ability of retinoblastomas rapidly to outstrip their blood supply leads to areas of coagulative necrosis. Foci of calcification are frequently seen in these areas. The DNA liberated from necrotic cells can become absorbed preferentially in the walls of blood vessels and by the internal limiting membrane of the retina, giving a deep blue (haematoxylinophilic) or Feulgen-postive stain to these tissues.

Retinoblastomas characteristically form rosettes and flurettes, which are attempts at photoreceptor differentiation. Flexner–Wintersteiner rosettes are highly specific for retinoblastomas, but are also observed in pineoblastoma and medulloepithelioma. Even though these rosettes represent areas of differentiation by the

Table 2 Differential diagnosis of retinoblastoma: conditions simulating retinoblastoma based on clinical diagnoses in a study consisting of 500 patients (From Shields *et al.*, 1996, *Archives of Ophthalmology*, **114**, 1330–1338.)

Condition	%
PHPV	27.8
Coat disease	16.0
Ocular toxocariasis	15.6
Retinopathy of prematurity	4.7
Combined hamartoma	4.2
Coloboma	4.2
Vitreous haemorrhage	3.8
Astrocytic hamartoma	2.8
Familial exudative vitreoretinopathy	2.4
Idiopathic retinal vascular hypoplasia	1.9
Rhegmatogenous retinal detachment	1.9
X-linked retinoschisis	1.9
Medulloepithelioma	1.9
Congenital cataract	1.9
Retinal capillary haemangioma	1.4
Cicumscribed choroidal haemangioma	1.4
Diffuse choroidal haemangioma	1.4
Peripheral uveoretinitis	1.4
Toxoplasmic retinitis	0.9
Idiopathic endophthalmitis	0.9
Norrie disease	0.5
Incongentia pigmenti	0.5
Optic nerve dysplasia	0.5

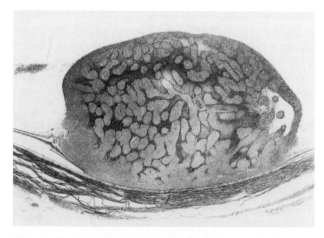

Figure 9 Retinoblastoma. Viable cells forming sleeves around blood vessels with areas of necrosis.

tumour, they are composed of malignant cells and occur in areas of mitotic activity. The typical Flexner–Wintersteiner rosette (**Figure 10**) is composed of tall cuboidal cells that encircle an apical lumen. The apical ends of the cuboidal cells are held together by terminal bars and the cells may have apical cytoplasmic projections into the lumen of the rosette. Electron microscopy has demonstrated that these projections represent primitive inner and

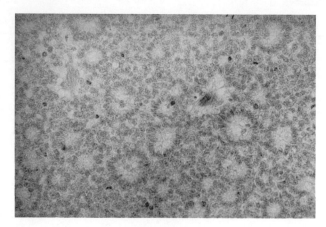

Figure 10 Flexner-Wintersteiner rosettes in retinoblastoma.

outer segments and, therefore, these tumour cells are attempting to form photoreceptor cells. Alcian blue stain reveals the presence of hyaluronidase-resistant glycosaminoglycans in the lumina of the rosettes that have similar staining characteristics to the extracellular matrix of rods and cones. Cells forming Flexner–Wintersteiner rosettes share several other ultrastructural features with retinal photoreceptors: zonula occludens that form a luminal limiting membrane analogous to the external limiting membrane of the retina, cytoplasmic microtubules, cilia with the $9+2$ pattern and lamellated membranous structures resembling the discs of rod outer segments. Immunohistochemical and lectin histochemical studies have also supported the concept that retinoblastomas arise from undifferentiated retinal cells that may differentiate into photoreceptor cells. Homer Wright rosettes are the other type of rosettes found in retinoblastomas, but are less common. They are found in a variety of neuroblastic tumours and are less specific for retinoblastoma. In these rosettes, the cells are not arranged about a lumen but send out cytoplasmic processes that form a tangle in the centre of the rosette. Finally, fleurettes probably represent the highest degree of differentiation of the tumour cells into photoreceptors. Fleurette represents a collection of benign appearing cells with long cytoplasmic processes that stain brightly with eosin. The cytoplasmic processes project through a fenestrated membrane and fan out like a bouquet of flowers (hence the term fleurette).

Extraocular extension and metastasis Retinoblastoma, if left untreated, has a propensity for rapid invasive growth typical of blastic tumours in children. The most common routes for local spread are through the optic nerve (**Figure 11**) and invasion of the choroid. Extraocular extension occurs via scleral canals or by massive replacement of the sclera.

Glial Tumours

Astrocytomas of the retina are rare and almost always benign tumours. The majority of them (over 50%) occur in

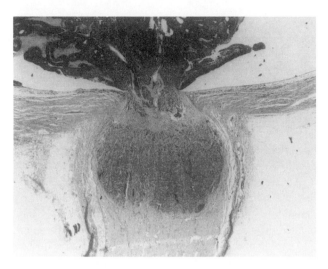

Figure 11   Retinoblastoma. Tumour is invading the optic nerve but not reaching the surgical margin (courtesy AFIP).

patients with tuberous sclerosis and a small proportion develops in patients with neurofibromatosis. They are also described as astrocytic hamartomas. On ophthalmoscopic appearance, early tumours appear flat and translucent. Older lesions tend to calcify and may be confused with retinoblastoma. Histologically, they are composed of elongated fibrous (pilocytic) astrocytes containing small oval nuclei. Rare giant cell (gemistocytic) astrocytomas have also been described.

Vascular Tumours

Retinal capillary haemangiomas are the hallmark of von Hippel–Lindau and are similar to cerebellar haemangioblastomas. Clinically, the tumours progress from small red to greyish appearing lesions with no abnormal vessels, to moderate-sized pink or yellowish lesions with large feeder vessels and retinal haemorrhage and exudation. Fluorescein angiography reveals leakage in the early phase of the angiogram and is diagnostic. Histologically, the tumour is composed of small vascular channels that have the appearance of capillaries. Large foamy cells which are debated to be histocytic, endothelial or astrocytic in origin are present in the stroma. Gliosis of the adjacent retina with massive exudation, haemorrhage and retinal detachment is frequently present.

Cavernous haemangioma of the retina is a rare congenital malformation that differs from capillary haemangiomas in several aspects. The affected retina shows isolated clusters of aneurysmal dilation of retinal vessels with absent feeder vessels. There is no arteriovenous shunting owing to the low flow state of these tumours and there is no disturbance of permeability on clinical examination or fluorescein angiography. Histologically, large vascular channels with normal walls thicken the retina. The inner retinal layers may be discontinuous in the area of the vascular lesions.

Lymphoid Tumours

Retinal involvement may be the initial and only manifestation of primary CNS lymphoma. The retina is usually not involved in a generalized systemic lymphoma and conversely the reticuloendothelial system is not affected by a primary CNS lymphoma. The vitreous is often involved by the presence of lymphoma cells and can masquerade as uveitis. In fact, the the presence of glaucoma, uveitis and neurological symptoms in an elderly individual should raise the suspicion of primary CNS lymphoma and appropriate imaging studies of the brain should be performed. The diagnosis may be confirmed microscopically by cytological examination of cells from the cerebral spinal fluid, vitrectomy, vitreous aspiration, or from biopsy of brain or retina.

The gross findings include placoid or hemispherical mound-like elevations of the retinal pigment epithelium (**Figure 12; see colour plate section**). The optic nerve may be involved with neoplastic cells as opposed to the uvea, which is rarely affected except for the presence of a reactive inflammatory infiltrate. The tumour cells possess varying amounts of cytoplasm with polyhedral or amoeboid outlines. Most of the nuclei exhibit single or multiple nucleoli. Mitotic figures are frequently present along with areas of retinal necrosis.

Neuroepithelial Tumours

Tumours of the neuroepithelium can be divided into congenital and acquired lesions. Congenital lesions usually arise from the medullary epithelium and are called meduloepitheliomas. The medullary epithelium has the capacity to differentiate into retinal pigment epithelium (RPE), non-pigmented and pigmented ciliary epithelium and neurons. They have also been termed diktyomas, since they are composed of a network of neuroepithelial bands. When they contain heterologous tissue elements such as cartilage, skeletal muscle and brain, they are referred to as teratoid.

Clinically, these tumours usually arise from the ciliary body, but on rare occasion may arise from the retina or optic disc. Some ciliary body medulloepitheliomas are cystic and may become detached to be carried into the anterior chamber through the pupil. Histologically, the tumour is composed of cords and sheets of cells ranging from a single layer of columnar epithelium to stratified multilayered structure that resembles embryonic retina. The apical side of the cords has several fenestrations resembling the external limiting membrane of the retina. Malignant medulloepitheliomas contain totally undifferentiated cells and Flexner–Wintersteiner rosettes may occasionally be observed, making differentiation from childhood retinoblastoma difficult.

Acquired lesions arising from the retinal pigment epithelium, non-pigmented and pigmented ciliary pigment epithelium can be categorized either as adenomas or adenocarcinomas. However, a more frequent lesion arising from the non-pigmented ciliary epithelium is a Fuchs adenoma, which is a hyperplasia rather than a true neoplasm. Grossly, Fuchs adenomas are small, white nodules that usually measure less than 1 mm in diameter and are located on the pars plicata. Histologically, the lesion consists of a nodule of hyperplastic, nonpigmented ciliary epithelium arranged in sheets and tubules, embedded in a matrix of PAS-positive basement membrane-like material. Congenital lesions of the RPE include combined hamartoma of the retina and RPE and congenital hypertrophy of the retinal pigment epithelium (CHRPE). Bilateral and multiple CHRPE lesions have been associated with Gardner's syndrome, an autosomal dominant condition characterized by adenomatous polyps of the colon, which may progress to adenocarcinoma and musculoskeletal anomalies.

Tumours of the Uveal-Tract

Melanocytic naevi and malignant melanoma are by far the most frequent and clinically important tumours of the iris, ciliary body and the choroid. In autopsy studies, metastasis is the most frequent tumour observed in the choroid; however, choroidal melanoma is the most frequent primary intraocular malignancy of adults.

Iris

Tumours of the iris can arise from the iris pigment epithelium, smooth muscle or stromal melanocytes. These include cysts and adenomas of the iris pigment epithelium, leiomyomas, naevi and malignant melanomas.

An iris naevus is a benign tumour that arises from the stromal melanocytes. They appear flat to slightly elevated under slit lamp examination and usually remain stationary in size, although they have the potential for malignant transformation (**Figure 13; see colour plate section**). Histologically, they are composed of low-grade spindle-

type cells. Occasionally, when the naevus consists of heavily pigmented, plump polyhedral cells, it is referred to as a melanocytoma (**Figure 14**). In neurofibromatosis type I, the stromal melanocytes undergo a hamartomatous proliferation into small, tan-coloured nodules on the surface of the iris known as Lisch nodules. Juvenile xanthogranuloma, a benign dermatological disorder of children and young adults, can lead to thickening of the iris with neovascularization and haemorrhage. Histologically, it is composed of mildly atypical histiocytes.

An iris melanoma is a malignant neoplasm of the stromal melanocytes. They are nodular, circumscribed and variably pigmented. An iris melanoma can be darkly pigmented or amelanotic or a mixture of the two. An important variant of the nodular type of iris melanoma is diffuse iris melanoma. This type of melanoma presents with diffuse thickening of the iris, acquired hyperchromic heterochromia and glaucoma (**Figure 15**). The histology of

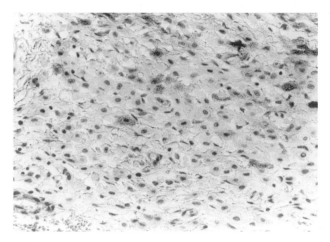

Figure 14 Melanocytoma. Bleached preparation showing plump polyhedral melanocytes with small ovoid nuclei (courtesy AFIP).

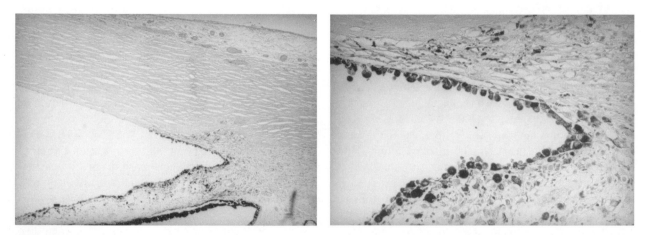

Figure 15 Diffuse iris melanoma. The angle of the eye is well shown in the low-power photomicrograph. The higher power photograph shows discohesive epithelioid melanoma cells studded on the anterior surface of iris and the angle structures.

iris naevus and melanoma will be discussed with their choroidal counterparts.

Ciliary Body

Ciliary body tumours include neoplasms of the pigmented and non-pigmented ciliary epithelium as discussed in the section on retinal tumours. Ciliary body melanomas are less frequent than choroidal melanomas but more frequent than iris malignant melanomas. The growth pattern of ciliary body melanomas differs from that of the choroidal variety. The absence of Bruch's membrane in the ciliary body leads to early endophytic growth of the tumour in the posterior chamber, with occasional subluxation or indentation of the lens. Ciliary body melanoma can grow on to the iris, in which case a small hyperpigmented lesion on the iris might appear on the periphery of the iris, representing the tip of the iceberg. Occasionally, they can erode through the sclera and appear on the surface of the globe near the limbus, simulating a conjunctival melanoma. Diffuse ciliary body melanomas have a tendency to grow in a ring-like fashion.

Choroid

Choroidal naevi are benign melanocytic tumours that can occasionally degenerate into malignant melanomas. Ophthalmoscopically, a choroidal naevus is variably pigmented (it may rarely be amelanotic) and is usually less than 2 mm in height. The surface of the lesion often has small yellowish–white deposits known as drusen. Subretinal fluid is not a hallmark of choroidal naevi as is the case with melanomas. Histologically, choroidal naevi are composed of low-grade spindle cells. The proliferation of benign melanocytes throughout the uvea is associated with certain systemic malignancies such as ovarian and uterine carcinoma (Gass *et al.*, 1990). This is referred to as bilateral diffuse uveal melanocytic proliferation (BDUMP) and is a paraneoplastic syndrome.

Choroidal melanomas are the most frequent of all the uveal (iris, ciliary body and choroid) melanomas. The use of the indirect ophthalmoscope has dramatically improved the detection and diagnosis of small choroidal tumours. The gross pathological features of choroidal melanoma are characteristic. The tough fibrous sclera prevents the outward growth of the melanoma into the orbit. However, the weaker Bruch's membrane on the inner aspect of the tumour can become stretched and eventually rupture from the expanding sub-retinal pigment epithelial mass. The tumour herniates through the rupture and grows into the subretinal space, giving a 'collar button' or mushroom-shaped configuration (**Figure 16; see colour plate section**). The retina overlying the uveal melanoma undergoes atrophy or cystoid degeneration while the retina surrounding the tumour is detached by the accumulation of serous exudate between the retina and the RPE. Some choroidal melanomas can invade the orbit by growing along the course of perforating nerves and vessels.

In 1913, Calender classified uveal malignant melanoma based on cytological and histological features. Since then, this scheme has been widely accepted owing to its prognostic significance, but has also undergone some modification from the original description of cell types. The cells of the uveal malignant melanoma are now divided into spindle and epithelioid cell types. Spindle-type cells are fusiform shaped and usually arranged in a fascicular pattern (**Figure 17**). They have cigar-shaped nuclei, with prominent nucleoli and frequent mitotic figures. The epithelioid-type cells are larger and more pleomorphic than the spindle type cells. They have abundant cytoplasm with distinct cell boundaries (**Figure 18**). Their characteristic loose intercellular cohesion leads to extracellular space between adjacent cells. The nucleus is larger and rounder with irregular indentations when compared with the spindle cell counterpart. Mitotic activity is also greater than in spindle cell tumours. Based on the presence or absence of each cell type, uveal melanomas can be classified as

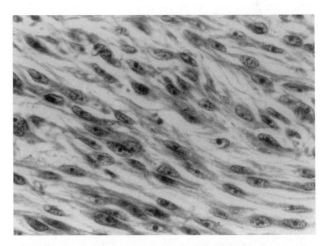

Figure 17 Malignant melanoma. Spindle-type cells (courtesy AFIP).

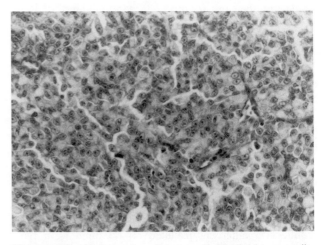

Figure 18 Malignant melanoma. Epithelioid-type cells (courtesy AFIP).

spindle, epithelioid or mixed cell-type tumours, each with different prognostic significance (discussed later).

Since uveal melanocytes are derived from neural crest, they stain positive for HMB-45, S-100 and neuron-specific enolase. Uveal naevi stain with less intensity for all three immunohistochemical markers.

Other tumours of the uvea include leukaemic infiltration, uveal lymphoma with extraocular extension, leiomyosarcoma and neuroepithelial tumours of the ciliary body (discussed under Tumours of the Retina). Choroidal osteoma and haemangioma are relatively rare tumours. The latter when seen in association with the Sturge–Weber syndrome often gives the fundus a 'tomato ketchup' appearance.

Tumours of the Orbit

A variety of benign and malignant tumours of the orbit have been described in adults and children. Capillary haemangioma, lymphangioma, dermoid cysts and rhabdomyosarcoma are most common in children whereas fibrous histiocytoma, cavernous haemangioma, schwannoma and lymphoid neoplasms occur more commonly in adults.

Capillary Haemangioma

In most cases, capillary haemangioma is located in the anterior aspect of the orbit and frequently involves the lid. The appearance of the lesion varies from a striking red 'strawberry naevus' located in the dermis to a more diffuse and light blue discoloration of the skin present in deeper orbital lesions. They have an infiltrative growth pattern and can involve any of the orbital structures. The tumour is composed of plump endothelial cells, which proliferate in solid lobules during the rapid growth phase of the tumour. Although these are benign tumours, they may contain numerous mitotic figures. Electron microscopy has revealed pericytes surrounding the endothelial lobules, indicating the capillary origin of these tumours.

Cavernous Haemangioma

Grossly, cavernous haemangiomas have an intense violaceous hue due to the presence of partially oxygenated venous blood in the vascular spaces. The tumour has a well-formed capsule surrounding vascular channels, which measure 0.5–1 mm in diameter and are filled with blood. Electron microscopy has revealed the vascular spaces to be lined by a monolayer of endothelial cells.

Lymphangioma

Lymphangioma is considered a choristoma since there are no endothelial-lined lymphatic channels in the orbit. In contrast to other encapsulated orbital tumours, a lymphangioma does not possess a capsule and therefore has a tendency to diffusely infiltrate soft tissues of the orbit. It is composed of endothelial lined channels with the ultrastructural features of lymphatics.

Haemangiopericytoma

Haemangiopericytoma is an encapsulated tumour with a grey to red–brown colour on cut section. They are composed of small polyhedral and spindle-shaped cells tightly packed around blood vessels. These vessels range from small capillaries to large sinusoidal spaces, some of which have a typical 'staghorn' configuration. Haemangiopericytoma have been divided into benign and malignant varieties based on histological criteria: cytological atypia, mitotic activity and necrosis.

Fibrous Histiocytoma

Fibrous histiocytoma is one of the most common tumours of the orbit. Grossly, they are encapsulated, rubbery to firm and vary from greyish white to yellow–tan. Microscopically they are composed of a mixture of spindle-shaped fibroblast-like cells and more ovoid, sometimes lipidized histiocytes. Detailed descriptions about the histological variations can be found elsewhere.

Neurofibroma

Of the three types of neurofibromas found in the orbit, plexiform, diffuse and isolated, only the plexiform variant is consistently observed in patients with neurofibromatosis type I. It appears within the first decade of life and grows in an infiltrating fashion that may involve any orbital structure. The enormous overgrowth of the orbital peripheral nerves may sometimes cause excessive redundancy of the lid skin, leading to elephantiasis neuromatosa. This tumour-like lymphangioma is not encapsulated. Histologically, it is composed of numerous proliferating units of the terminal branches of peripheral nerves in a loose stroma of axons, Schwann cells and endoneural fibroblasts.

Schwannoma

Like neurofibroma, schwannoma originates from the peripheral nerves of the orbit, most often the supraorbital nerve. Histopathologically, they are encapsulated by the perineurium of the nerve of origin. The classical feature of a schwannoma is the presence of solid cellular areas, referred to as the Antoni A pattern and other more myxoid areas with stellate or ovoid-appearing cells referred to as Antoni B areas. In Antoni A areas, nuclear palisading is common, which often leads to formation of fascicles of nuclei in a highly regimented fashion known as Verocay bodies.

Rhabdomyosarcoma

Rhabdomyosarcoma is the most common primary malignant tumour of childhood. The average age at time of diagnosis is 7 years. The superonasal aspect of the orbit is the site of predilection for this tumour. When it originates in a submucosal site such as the conjunctival stroma, it is referred to as the botryoid type. The tumour is not encapsulated and usually invades adjacent structures. Based on histological features, rhabdomyosarcomas are divided into embryonal, alveolar and pleomorphic (differentiated) types.

Dermoid Cyst

Dermoid cysts result from congenital arrest of ectoderm within sutures of the orbital bones. The majority of dermoid cysts become symptomatic within the first decade of life. Nasally located dermoids are often lined by conjunctival epithelium, whereas temporal dermoids are lined by skin and have dermal appendages such as hair and sebaceous glands present in the wall of the cyst.

Lymphoid Neoplasms

Lymphoid neoplasms of the orbit are among the most prevalent of orbital tumours. In patients above age 60 years, they represent >50% of all orbital tumours. Clinically and grossly, lymphoid tumours have a fish-flesh ('salmon patch') or creamy to yellow appearance. They are very friable owing to the absence of fibrous stroma. Histologically, lymphoid tumours should be divided into lymphomas and benign lymphoid hyperplasia. However, this distinction is not always possible and tumours exhibiting intermediate characteristics are referred to as atypical lymphoid hyperplasia (Knowles et al., 1990). Benign lymphoid hyperplasia has a follicular organisation with benign-appearing small, dark lymphocytes. However, the follicles can be of irregular size and shape and have high mitotic activity.

Orbital and adnexal lymphomas are almost always of the non-Hodgkins's type. Small cell lymphomas of B cell type originating in the conjunctival substantia propria are referred to as Maltoma (mucosal associated lymphoid tissue).

Other Tumours

Other tumours found in the orbit include teratomas, exclusively in newborns, histiocytic disorders such as unifocal and multifocal eosinophilic granuloma (Langerhans cell histiocytosis), malignant melanoma, blue naevus, fibrous dysplasia, granulocytic sarcoma, osteogenic sarcoma and metastasis. This is by no means an exhaustive list, since other rare tumours in the orbit have been described.

Tumours of the Optic Nerve

Glioma

Most gliomas of the optic nerve are benign pilocytic astrocytomas. They are usually seen in association with neurofibromatosis type I. They are very slow-growing tumours, often enlarging in an episodic fashion and then lying dormant for many years. On imaging studies such as MRI and CT, they appear as fusiform enlargements of the optic nerve. The dura is always intact surrounding the tumour and it is often difficult to determine the margin of the tumour from the normal optic nerve. Histologically, pilocytic astrocytomas of the optic nerve are composed of elongated, spindle-shaped, hair-like astrocytes. They have a benign appearance with the notable exception of mitotic figures. These tumours show positive immunohistochemical staining for glial fibrillary acidic protein (GFAP). Rosenthal fibres, which represent degenerative changes within the astrocytic cell processes, are also frequently seen in these tumours. They appear as cylindrical or spherical eosinophilic bodies. Ultrastructurally, Rosenthal fibres are composed of electron-dense granular material and glial filaments.

Meningioma

Almost all orbital meningiomas either arise from the meninges of the optic nerve or invade the orbit secondarily from an adjacent intracranial site such as the sphenoid wing. The clinical features of meningioma are much different from those of glioma. Meningiomas are associated with type II and not type I neurofibromatosis. The age at diagnosis is considerably greater in patients with meningioma. However, it should be considered in the differential diagnosis of any optic nerve lesion causing exophthalmos and visual loss even in the first few years of life.

Unlike gliomas, meningiomas usually extend through the dura. The tumour does not invade the optic nerve and grows in a sleeve-like manner within the meninges. Meningiomas may infiltrate all of the orbital structures but intraocular invasion through the sclera is rare. Histologically, they are similar to intracranial meningiomas.

Tumours of the Lachrymal Gland and Sac

Lachrymal gland tumours bear a striking resemblance to those of the salivary gland. Approximately half of all lachrymal gland tumours are epithelial and the rest are non-epithelial. Of the epithelial tumours, half are benign and half malignant. They constitute 10% of all orbital lesions in some series.

Pleomorphic Adenoma

Pleomorphic adenomas or benign mixed tumours are the most common tumours of the lachrymal gland. They present as a firm, painless and slowly developing mass in the superolateral orbit. They are pseudoencapsulated and may contain cystic areas. Histological sections reveal an admixture of epithelial and mesenchymal elements that can take a variety of patterns.

Pleomorphic Carcinoma

Also known as malignant mixed tumours, pleomorphic carcinomas arise from malignant transformation of pleomorphic adenomas. Histologically, they can take the appearance of adenocarcinoma, adenoid cystic carcinoma, squamous cell carcinoma, undifferentiated carcinoma or sebaceous carcinoma in which a pre-existing pleomorphic adenoma can be identified.

Other Tumours

Adenoid cystic carcinoma, mucoepidermoid and adeno-carcinoma of the lachrymal gland can arise *de novo* in the lachrymal gland. Their histopathology is similar to that of tumours found in the salivary glands. Lymphomas and benign reactive lymphoid hyperplasia are the most common non-epithelial tumours of the lachrymal gland. **Table 3** lists the different types of tumours that can arise in the lachrymal sac.

Molecular Genetic Findings

Retinoblastoma represents a paradigm in understanding the molecular basis of inherited predisposition to developing malignancy. The retinoblastoma gene, a tumour suppressor gene, is located on the long arm (q14 locus) of chromosome 13 (Dryja *et al.*, 1984). Hence each cell carries two copies of this gene and in normal individuals their gene product serves to inhibit the development of

Table 3   Lachrymal sac tumours

Epithelial tumours
  Benign papillomas—exophytic (grow into lumen of sac) and
  endophytic (inverted).
    Squamous
    Transitional
    Mixed
  Carcinomas—*de novo* or within papillomas
    Squamous
    Transitional
    Mixed
    Mucoepidermoid
Glandular tumours
  Benign
    Pleomorphic adenoma
    Oncocytoma
  Malignant
    Oncocytic adenocarcinoma
    Adenocarcinoma
    Adenoid cystic
Mesenchymal tumours
  Fibrous histiocytoma
  Haemangiopericytoma
  Fibroma/fibromyxoma
  Haemangioma
  Malignant melanoma
  Lymphoid infiltrates (benign, atypical, malignant)
  Inflammatory pseudotumour
  Secondary tumours (extension from nose, paranasal
    sinuses, skin and conjunctiva)
  Metastasis (rare)

retinal tumours. The retinoblastoma gene product (pRB) normally inactivates E2F (a nuclear transcription factor) and halts the normal cell cycle between G1 and S phases. However, in each case of retinoblastoma, an initial mutation inactivates one copy of the gene. The mutation can be caused by a single-base change of DNA, a point mutation, a chromosomal translocation, a small deletion or a large deletion that is observable by karyotyping. The mutation can be germ-line or somatic leading to the hereditary (multiplex) and non-hereditary (simplex) forms of retinoblastoma. The homozygous form of the mutated retinoblastoma gene is probably fatal *in utero*. In the heterozygous form (hereditary form), the individual inherits a mutated gene from one parent and acquires the second mutation sometime after birth. This was Knudson's initial 'two hit hypothesis' and postulates the necessity for both genes to be inactivated for development of retinoblastoma. Loss of all pRB due to homologous deficiency at 13q14 eliminates the 'brakes' and uncontrolled proliferation of retinoblastoma ensues. In the non-hereditary form, the individual acquires both mutations after birth.

The majority of retinoblastomas are of the inherited variety. The defective gene in this instance can be acquired from a parent who is a known carrier or more often they may represent a new germline mutation. Multiple and especially bilateral retinoblastomas almost always signify a germinal mutation. Median age at diagnosis is significantly lower for bilateral retino-blastoma than for unilateral retinoblastoma. An important facet of providing care for patients with retinoblastoma is the assessment of risk of developing the same malignancy in the siblings or progeny of the affected individual. This can be done accurately using modern molecular biology techniques.

Phakomatoses ('birthmarks') are comprised of a group of disparate clinical syndromes, which share certain features in common. These include the presence of multisystem hamartomas, predominantly in ocular, cutaneous and intracranial locations. They may arise at birth or later in life, and can undergo malignant transformation. The term is usually applied to include von Hippel–Lindau (angiomatosis retinae, capillary haemangioma), turberous sclerosis (Bournveille disease), neurofibromatosis (type I and II) and Sturge–Weber sydnromes (encephalo-trigeminal angiomatosis), although some authors also include Wyburn–Mason and ataxia-telangectasia (Louis–Bar syndrome) in this group of diseases. Of the first four conditions, all except Sturge–Weber are inherited in an autosomal dominant fashion. The target locus for von Hippel–Lindau was recently mapped to 3p25–26 and the gene product (pVHL) balances mRNA transcription. The same locus is home to the gene which codes for vascular endothelial growth factor (VEGF). Mutations in 3p25–26 lead to unchecked transcription and upregulation of VEGF. Tuberous sclerosis complex (TSC) has two known disease loci, on chromosomes 9q34 (*TSC1*) and 16p13.3 (*TSC2*). The TSC1 and TSC2 gene products are known as hamartin and tuberin, respectively, and are expressed in neurons and astrocytes where they physically interact. Neurofibromatosis (NFT), the most common of the phakomatoses, has two forms. The gene responsible for NFT type I (peripheral form) is located on chromosome 17 and NFT type II (central form) on chromosome 22.

The majority (85%) of follicular B cell lymphomas, such as primary ocular–CNS lymphoma, harbour a characteristic translocation (t(14;18)) which is felt to represent an error occurring during physiological gene rearrangement. Genes located at the translocation breakpoint (*bcl-2/IgH*) are considered putative oncogenes that are deregulated via juxtaposition with an antigen receptor gene. Southern blot analysis is helpful in confirming both the translocation as well as monoclonal IgH expression.

Prognostic Factors

Mortality from choroidal melanoma depends on a variety of factors but has been reported in larger series to be 35% at 5 years and 50% at 10 years. There have been multiple studies to correlate gross and cytopathological features of uveal melanoma with prognosis. Location of the tumour, largest tumour diameter (LTD), height of tumour have all been found to correlate with future mortality. Patient survival is better for LTD less than 10 mm. On the histological side, optic nerve or scleral invasion, cell type (spindle, mixed or epithelioid), standard deviation of the nucleolar area and mean of the largest nucleoli are positively correlated with death from metastatic melanoma. Spindle cell tumours carry the most favourable prognosis, followed by mixed cell lesions. Pure epithelioid cell malignant melanomas have the poorest prognosis, but fortunately are also the most rare.

Retinoblastoma has a much better prognosis than choroidal melanoma. There has been a remarkable shift in the long-term survival of these patients since the early part of the century, when it was uniformly a fatal disease. The overall long-term survival in retinoblastoma in the USA and UK is now 85%. Even though patients with retinoblastoma survive the initial disease, those that have the genetic abnormality are subject to other tumours, most notably osteosarcoma. About two-thirds of the second tumours are in the radiation field used to treat retinoblastoma and the other third are in areas remote from the radiation field.

Retinoblastomas metastasize in four ways: direct infiltration, dispersion, haematogenous and lymphatic dissemination. Direct infiltrative spread occurs along the optic nerve from the eye to the brain. Once the orbital soft tissues are invaded, the tumour spreads directly into the orbital bones, through the sinuses into the nasopharynx, or via the various foramina into the cranium. Dispersion of tumour cells occurs after cells in the optic nerve have invaded the leptomeninges and gained access to the subarachnoid fluid. Flow of cerebrospinal fluid spreads the tumour cells to the brain and spinal cord. The most common sites for haematogenous spread are lungs, bones, brain and other viscera. Extraocular invasion and, to a lesser degree, choroidal invasion increase the risk of haematogenous spread. Lymphatic spread occurs in those tumours that invade the anterior orbital tissues including the conjunctiva, since the orbit is devoid of lymphatics. The spread of retinoblastoma into the optic nerve and into the orbit through the sclera is associated with less favourable prognosis.

When metastasis occurs, it is generally within the first year or two following treatment. The median time to death in patients with metastatic retinoblastoma is 6.4 months in unilateral cases and 14.2 months in bilateral cases. In contrast, the estimated median time to death in uveal melanoma is 7.2 years. Late death from metastasis, which occurs frequently following enucleation for melanoma, is so rare after treatment for retinoblastoma that when metastasis is suspected, the question of an independent new primary tumour must be considered.

All malignant neoplasms of the lachrymal gland with the possible exception of mucoepidermoid carcinoma carry a poor prognosis. Death usually results within 3–5 years from tumour extension along nerves through the superior orbital fissure and invasion through the orbital bones into the middle cranial fossa. Haematogenous metastasis, particularly to the lungs, is the second most common cause of death.

Overview of Present Clinical Management

Tumours of the Eyelid and Conjunctiva

Local excision is usually curative for the majority of skin and conjunctival tumours. Notable exceptions to this are sebaceous cell carcinoma and primary acquired melanosis. Besides growing locally in a nodular fashion, both of these lesions can spread to distant sites of the conjunctiva and epidermis of the skin intraepithelially termed pagetoid extension, rendering local excision unfeasible. Map biopsies are therefore required to assess the extent of neoplastic involvement of the ocular adnexa. In such cases cryotherapy can be used to treat wider areas, but excessive application can lead to dry eye and symblepharon formation.

Squamous cell carcinoma and to a lesser extent basal cell carcinoma can invade the deeper tissues in the orbit, requiring orbital exenteration. Extensive pagetoid spread of sebaceous cell carcinoma to the cornea, all four quadrants of the conjunctiva and the skin of the eyelid may also necessitate orbital exenteration. A variety of composite and myocutaneous flaps and skin grafting techniques from adjacent areas have been described for repair of large defects of the lids in cases where wide local excision is performed.

Primary lymphoid neoplasms of the ocular adnexa may be observed if they are asymptomatic and without evidence of systemic dissemination. Radiation or cryotherapy can be used if they involve extensive areas of the conjunctival fornices or the patient is symptomatic. A thorough evaluation to rule out a systemic lymphoma is mandatory in every patient in whom a lymphoma is suspected.

Tumours of the Retina

It is imperative to make as accurate a diagnosis as possible when a patient in whom retinoblastoma is suspected is encountered. The long list of benign conditions causing leukocoria, one of the cardinal signs of retinoblastoma (see **Table 2**), can cause confusion and lead to misdiagnosis with disastrous consequences. A variety of modalities are available for the treatment of retinoblastomas; however, the type of treatment depends on many factors, such as age of the patient, unilateral or bilateral disease, size and intraocular location of the tumour, and most importantly local or distant spread of the tumour. Enucleation is probably the most widely employed treatment. Other forms of treatment include external beam radiation, cryotherapy and photocoagulation therapy. Invasion of the optic nerve and extraocular extension significantly alter prognosis and mandate the use of chemotherapy in addition to local treatment (Gallie *et al.*, 1996; Murphree *et al.*, 1996; Shields *et al.*, 1996).

Capillary haemangiomas of the retina are most often treated with cryotherapy or photocoagulation, depending upon the location. Treatment of haemangiomas near the optic disc or macula can be challenging. Intraocular lymphoma is treated with radiation and chemotherapy, but it carries a poor prognosis.

Tumours of the Uveal Tract

Iris melanomas can be locally excised by performing a sectoral iridectomy or iridocyclectomy with good results. Juvenile xanthogranuloma responds dramatically to topical steroids and is a self-limited disorder.

The management of choroidal melanoma is controversial (Zimmerman and McLean, 1979). The collaborative ocular melanoma study (COMS) now in progress is comparing enucleation versus plaque radiotherapy for medium-sized tumours (6–10 mm in height) and enucleation versus pre-enucleation radiotherapy for large tumours (>10 mm in height) with 10-year survival as outcome measure. Initial data suggest no statistical difference between enucleation and plaque radiotherapy for medium-sized choroidal melanomas (Collaborative Ocular Melanoma Study Group 1998). Enucleation is generally recommended for large tumours with little hope of salvageable vision (Gragoudas *et al.*, 1980). Radiotherapy, with either radioactive plaque or charged particles (proton beam), is recommended for medium-sized and large

melanomas when there is a possibility of salvaging some vision. More recently, the use of transpupillary thermotherapy either alone or combined with plaque radiotherapy has been advocated.

Tumours of the Orbit

Capillary haemangiomas grow rapidly after birth and usually appear during the first 6 months of life. They enter a stationary stage during the next 1–2 years followed by spontaneous involution during the next 5–6 years. If the tumour is not judged to be a threat to vision and subsequent amblyopia, it can be observed without treatment. In case of significant functional or cosmetic impairment, intralesional corticosteroid injection is the most common form of treatment.

The surgical management of encapsulated and non-encapsulated tumours of the orbit is different. Encapsulated tumours more easily lend themselves to removal without too much dissection. Even then surgery is usually reserved for progressively enlarging tumours that threaten vision due to compromise of the optic nerve or the ocular surface from progressive proptosis. Lymphangioma and plexiform neurofibroma, on the other hand, are rarely approached surgically with the intent of completely excising the tumour, owing to their infiltrative growth pattern. Rhabdomyosarcoma is essentially treated with systemic chemotherapy.

The mainstay of treatment for ocular and periocular lymphoid tumors is radiotherapy (Char *et al.*, 1998). Cryotherapy is often very effective for localized and low-grade conjunctival lymphomas and has much less morbidity when compared with radiotherapy. Local radiotherapy and systemic chemotherapy are recommended for high clinical grade lymphomas, multifocal processes such as angiotropic large cell lymphoma and systemic leukaemia.

Tumours of the Optic Nerve

Both optic nerve glioma and meningioma are slow-growing tumours. Management of these tumours is again controversial. These can often be observed for many years until such time when they extend intracranially to involve the optic chiasm or the contralateral optic nerve. In these instances the tumour can be surgically resected or radiation can be used to retard its growth.

Tumours of the Lachrymal Gland and Sac

Complete excision of pleomorphic adenomas of the lachrymal gland is absolutely essential and usually curative. However, incomplete resection can lead to local recurrence or even malignant transformation in the future. All malignant neoplasms of the lachrymal gland carry a poor prognosis despite aggressive surgical attempts at complete resection. Adenoid cystic and adenocarcinoma of the lachrymal gland are almost uniformly fatal at 5 years.

REFERENCES

Albert, D. M. and Jakobiec, F. A. (2000a). Ocular oncology. In: *Principles and Practice of Ophthalmology*, Sec. XVIII, Vol. 6. 5003–5178 (W. B. Saunders, Philadelphia).

Albert, D. M. and Jakobiec, F. A. (2000b). Lids and orbit. In: *Principles and Practice of Ophthalmology*, Sec. XIII, Vol. 4. 3045–3571 (W. B. Saunders, Philadelphia).

Char, D. H., *et al*. (1988). Primary intraocular lymphoma (ocular reticulum cell sarcoma) diagnosis and management. *Ophthalmology* **95**, 625.

Collaborative Ocular Melanoma Study Group. (1998). The Collaborative Ocular Melanoma Study (COMS) randomized trial of pre-enucleation radiation of large choroidal melanoma II: Initial mortality findings. COMS Report No. 10. *American Journal of Ophthalmology* **125**, 779–796.

Dryja, T. P., *et al*. (1984). Homozygosity of chromosome 13 in retinoblastoma. *New England Journal of Medicine* **310**, 550–553.

Gallie, B. L., *et al*. (1996). Chemotherapy with focal therapy can cure intraocular retinoblastoma without radiotherapy. *Archives of Ophthalmology* **114**, 1321–1328.

Gass, J., *et al*. (1990). Bilateral diffuse uveal melanocytic proliferation in patients with occult carcinoma. *Archives of Ophthalmology* **108**, 527–533.

Gragoudas, E. S., *et al*. (1980). Proton beam irridiation. An alternative to enucleation for intraocular melanomas. *Ophthalmology*, **87**, 571–581.

Knowles, D. M., *et al*. (1990). Lymphoid hyperplasia and malignant lymphoma occurring in the ocular adnexa (orbit, conjunctiva, and eyelids): a prospective multiparametric analysis of 108 cases during 1977 to 1987. *Human Pathology* **21**, 959.

Murphree, A. L., *et al*. (1996). Chemotherapy plus local treatment in the management of intraocular retinoblastoma. *Archives of Ophthalmology* **114**, 1348–1356.

Shields, C. L., *et al*. (1996). Chemoreduction in the initial management of intraocular retinoblastoma. *Archives of Ophthalmology* **114**, 1330–1338.

Zimmerman, L. E. and McLean I. W. (1979). An evaluation of enucleation in the management of uveal melanomas. *American Journal of Ophthalmology* **87**, 741–760.

FURTHER READING

McLean (1994). *Tumors of the Eye and Ocular Adnexa*, Third Series, Fascicle 12. (Armed Forces Institute of Pathology, Washington, DC).

Shields, J. A. and Shields, C. L. (1999). *Atlas of Eyelid and Conjunctival Tumors*. (Lippincott Williams & Wilkins, Baltimore).

Shields, J. A. and Shields, C. L. (1999). *Atlas of Intraocular Tumors*. (Lippincott Williams & Wilkins, Baltimore).

Shields, J. A. and Shields, C. L. (1999). *Atlas of Orbital Tumors*. (Lippincott Williams & Wilkins, Baltimore).

Spencer (1996). *Ophthalmic Pathology–An Atlas and Textbook*. (W. B. Saunders, Philadelphia).

Chapter 53
Ear

Bruce M. Wenig
The Albert Einstein College of Medicine/Montefiore Medical Center, Bronx, NY, USA

CONTENTS

NORMAL DEVELOPMENT AND STRUCTURE

The ear is represented by three distinct compartments, the external ear, the middle ear and temporal bone, and the inner ear. The external ear develops from the first branchial groove. The external auricle (pinna) forms from the fusion of the auricular hillocks or tubercles, a group of mesenchymal tissue swellings from the first and second branchial arches, that lie around the external portion of the first branchial groove (Moore, 1988). The external auditory canal is considered a normal remnant of the first branchial groove. The tympanic membrane forms from the first and second branchial pouches and the first branchial groove (Moore, 1988). The ectoderm of the first branchial groove gives rise to the epithelium on the external side, the endoderm from the first branchial pouch gives rise to the epithelium on the internal side and the mesoderm of the first and second branchial pouches gives rise to the connective tissue lying between the external and internal epithelia (Moore, 1988). The middle ear space develops from invagination of the first branchial pouch (pharyngotympanic tube) from the primitive pharynx. The eustachian tube and tympanic cavity develop from the endoderm of the first branchial pouch; the malleus and incus develop from the mesoderm of the first branchial arch (Meckel's cartilage) while the incus develops from the mesoderm of the second branchial arch (Reichert's cartilage) (Moore, 1988). The first division of the ear to develop is the inner ear that appears toward the end of the first month of gestation (Dayal *et al.*, 1973; Moore, 1988). The membranous labyrinthe, including the utricle, saccule, semicircular ducts and cochlear duct, arises from the otic vesicle (otocyst). The otic vesicle forms from the invagination of the surface ectoderm, located on either side of the neural plate, into the mesenchyme. This invagination eventually loses its connection with the surface ectoderm. The bony labyrinthe, including the vestibule, semicircular canals and cochlea arises from the mesenchyme around the otic vesicle (Dayal *et al.*, 1973; Moore, 1988).

The outer portion of the external ear includes the auricle or pinna leading into the external auditory canal with its medial limit being the external aspect of the tympanic membrane. Histologically, the auricle is essentially a cutaneous structure composed of keratinizing, stratified squamous epithelium with associated dermal adnexal structures that include hair follicles, sebaceous glands and eccrine sweat glands. The subcutaneous tissue is composed of fibroconnective tissue, fat and elastic-type fibrocartilage which gives the auricle its structural support. In addition to the dermal adnexal structures, the outer third of the external canal is noteworthy for the presence of modified apocrine glands called ceruminal glands that replace the eccrine glands seen in the auricular dermis. Ceruminal glands produce cerumen and are arranged in clusters composed of cuboidal cells with eosinophilic cytoplasm often containing a granular, golden yellow pigment. These cells have secretory droplets along their luminal border. In the inner portion of the external auditory canal, ceruminal glands, and also the other adnexal structures, are absent. Similarly to the auricle, the external auditory canal is lined by keratinizing squamous epithelium that extends to include entire canal and covers the external aspect of the tympanic membrane. The inner two-thirds of the external auditory canal contains bone rather than cartilage.

The middle ear or tympanic cavity contents include the ossicles (malleus, incus and stapes), eustacian tube, tympanic cavity proper, epitympanic recess, mastoid cavity and the chorda tympani of the facial (VII) nerve. The middle ear, and also the external ear, function as conduits for sound conduction for the auditory part of the internal ear. The anatomic limits of the middle ear include (1) lateral or internal aspect made up by the tympanic membrane and squamous portion of the temporal bone, (2) medial aspect bordered by the petrous portion of the temporal bone, (3) superior (roof) delimited by the tegmen tympani, a thin plate of bone which separates the middle ear space from the cranial cavity, (4) inferior (floor) aspect bordered by a thin plate of bone separating the tympanic cavity from the superior bulb of the internal jugular vein,

(5) anterior aspect delimited by a thin plate of bone separating the tympanic cavity from the carotid canal housing the internal carotid artery and (6) posterior aspect delimited by the petrous portion of the temporal bone containing the mastoid antrum and mastoid air cells. Histologically, the lining of the middle ear is a respiratory epithelium varying from ciliated epithelium in the eustacian tube to a flat, single, cuboidal epithelium in the tympanic cavity and mastoid. The epithelial lining the eustacian tube becomes pseudostratified as it approaches the pharyngeal end. Under normal conditions, there are no glandular elements within the middle ear. The eustachian tubes contain a lymphoid component, particularly in children, that is referred to as Gerlach's tubal tonsil. The ossicular articulations are typical synovial joints.

The internal ear is embedded within the petrous portion of the temporal bone and consists of the structures of the membranous and osseous labyrinthe, and the internal auditory canal in which the vestibulocochlear (VIII) nerve runs. The internal ear is the sense organ for hearing and balance. The anatomy and histology of this region is complex and beyond the scope of this chapter and the reader is referred to specific texts detailing the inner ear anatomy and histology.

NEOPLASMS OF THE EAR AND TEMPORAL BONE

The classification of neoplastic lesions of the ear and temporal bone are listed in **Table 1**. Owing to limitations of space, this chapter will detail those lesions unique to the ear. The most common lesions of the external ear are of cutaneous origin. The reader is referred to the chapter on dermatopathology for a more complete discussion of cutaneous pathology. Numerous non-neoplastic lesions occur in the ear and temporal bone. Although this chapter is limited to neoplasms, for completion the classification of non-neoplastic lesions of the ear and temporal bone are listed in **Table 2**. Along this line, no chapter dealing with lesions of the ear would be complete without a discussion on cholesteatomas. The section on cholesteatoma precedes the discussion on the neoplasms of this region.

Cholesteatoma (Keratoma)

Cholesteatoma is a pseudoneoplastic lesion of the middle ear characterized by invasive growth and the presence of stratified squamous epithelium that forms a sac-like accumulation of keratin within the middle ear space. Despite their invasive growth, cholesteatomas are not considered to be true neoplasms. The term cholesteatoma is a misnomer in that it is not a neoplasm and it does not contain cholesterol (Ferlito *et al.*, 1997). Perhaps the designation of keratoma would be more accurate, but the term cholesteatoma is entrenched in the literature.

Table 1   Classification of neoplasms of the ear

External ear
  Benign
  Keratoacanthoma
  Squamous papilloma
  Seborrhaeic keratosis
  Ceruminal gland neoplasms
  Melanocytic nevi
  Dermal adnexal neoplasms
  Neurilemmoma/neurofibroma
  Osteoma
  Chondroma
  Others
  Malignant
  Basal cell carcinoma
  Squamous cell carcinoma
  Verrucous carcinoma
  Ceruminal gland adenocarcinomas
  Malignant melanoma
  Merkel cell carcinoma
  Atypical fibroxanthoma
  Others

Middle and inner ear
  Benign
  Middle ear adenoma
  Epithelial papilloma
  Jugulotympanic paraganglioma
  Meningioma
  Acoustic neuroma
  Indeterminant biological behaviour
  Endolymphatic sac papillary tumour
  Malignant
  Middle ear adenocarcinoma
  Primary squamous cell carcinoma
  Rhabdomyosarcoma
  Osteosarcoma, chondrosarcoma
  Haematolymphoid (e.g. malignant lymphoma)
  Others
Secondary tumours

Cholesteatomas tend to be more common in men than in women and are most common in the third and fourth decades of life. The middle ear space is the most common site of occurrence. Initially, cholesteatomas may remain clinically silent until extensive invasion of the middle ear space and mastoid occurs. Symptoms include hearing loss, malodorous discharge and pain and may be associated with a polyp arising in the attic of the middle ear or perforation of the tympanic membrane. Otoscopic examination may reveal the presence of white debris within the middle ear which is considered diagnostic.

The majority of cholesteatomas are acquired and either arise *de novo* without a prior history of middle ear disease or arise following a middle ear infection; a small percentage of cases are congenital. The latter have also been referred to as epidermoid cysts (Schuknecht, 1993a). The pathogenesis is thought to occur via migration of

Table 2 Classification of non-neoplastic lesions of the ear

External ear
  Developmental (accessory tragi; first branchial
    cleft anomalies, others)
  Infectious diseases
  Keloid
  Epidermal and sebaceous cysts
  Idiopathic cystic chondromalacia
  Chondrodermatitis nodularis helicis chronicus
  Angiolymphoid hyperplasia with eosinophilia/Kimura disease
  Autoimmune/systemic diseases (relapsing
    polychondritis; gout)
  Exostosis
  Others

Middle and inner ear, including temporal bone
  Developmental and congenital anomalies
  Infectious (otitis media)
  Otic or aural polyp
  Cholesteatoma
  Otosclerosis
  Langerhans cell histiocytosis (eosinophilic granuloma)
  Heterotopias (central nervous system tissue; salivary gland)
  Teratoma
  Others

squamous epithelium from the external auditory canal or from the external surface of the tympanic membrane into the middle ear. The mechanism by which the epithelium may enter the middle ear probably is by a combination of events, including perforation of the tympanic membrane (particularly in its superior aspect referred to as the pars flaccida or Shrapnell's membrane following an infection) coupled with invagination or retraction of the tympanic membrane into the middle ear as a result of long-standing negative pressure on the membrane secondary to blockage or obstruction of the eustachian tube. Other theories by which cholesteatomas are thought to occur include traumatic implantation, squamous metaplasia of the middle ear epithelium or congenital.

Cholesteatomas appear as a cystic, white to pearly appearing mass of varying size containing creamy or waxy granular material. The histological diagnosis of cholesteatoma is made in the presence of a stratified keratinizing squamous epithelium, subepithelial fibroconnective or granulation tissue and keratin debris (**Figure 1; see colour plate section**). The essential diagnostic feature is the keratinizing squamous epithelium and the presence of keratin debris alone is not diagnostic of a cholesteatoma. The keratinizing squamous epithelium is cytologically bland and shows cellular maturation without evidence of dysplasia. In spite of its benign histology, cholesteatomas are 'invasive' and have widespread destructive capabilities. The destructive properties of cholesteatomas result from a combination of interrelated reasons, including mass effect with pressure erosion of surrounding structures from the cholesteatoma, the production of

collagenase which has osteodestructive capabilities by its resorption of bony structures and bone resorption (Abramson *et al.*, 1984). Collagenase is produced by both the squamous epithelial and the fibrous tissue components of the cholesteatoma.

The histological diagnosis of cholesteatomas is relatively straightforward in the presence of keratinizing squamous epithelium. In contrast to cholesteatomas, squamous cell carcinoma shows dysplastic or overtly malignant cytological features with a prominent desmoplastic stromal response to its infiltrative growth. Cholesteatomas do not transform into squamous cell carcinomas. DNA analysis on human cholesteatomas showed the majority of cases analysed to be euploid (Desloge *et al.*, 1997). As such, owing to a lack of overt genetic instability, cholesteatomas could not be considered to be malignant neoplasms. Cholesterol granuloma is not synonymous with cholesteatoma. These entities are distinctly different pathological entities and should not be confused with one another.

Complete surgical excision of all histological components of the cholesteatoma is the treatment of choice. If not completely excised, cholesteatomas can have progressive and destructive growth, including widespread bone destruction which may lead to hearing loss, facial nerve paralysis, labrynthitis, meningitis, epidural and/or brain abscess.

Ceruminal Gland Neoplasms

Ceruminal gland tumours arise from the cerumen-secreting modified apocrine glands (ceruminal glands) of the external auditory canal. Ceruminal glands are located in the dermis of the cartilaginous (outer) portion of the external auditory canal. In general, ceruminal gland neoplasms are uncommon but represent one of the more common tumours of the external auditory canal. The generic designation of ceruminoma should be avoided. Ceruminal gland neoplasms should be specifically diagnosed according to tumour type. The classification of ceruminal gland neoplasms includes benign and malignant tumours. The benign ceruminal gland tumours include ceruminal gland adenoma (ceruminoma), pleomorphic adenoma and syringocystadenoma papilliferum (Hyams *et al.*, 1988a). The malignant ceruminal gland tumours include ceruminal gland adenocarcinoma, adenoid cystic carcinoma and mucoepidermoid carcinoma.

Ceruminal gland neoplasms tend to affect men more than women and occur over a wide age range but are most frequently seen in the fourth to sixth decades of life. Symptoms include a slow-growing external auditory canal mass or blockage, hearing difficulty and infrequently otic discharge (Wetli *et al.*, 1972; Pulec, 1977; Hyams *et al.*, 1988a). The gross appearance of ceruminal gland neoplasms includes skin-covered, circumscribed, polypoid or rounded mass ranging in size from 1 to 4 cm in diameter. Ulceration is uncommon and may suggest a malignant neoplasm.

Histologically, ceruminal gland adenomas are unencapsulated but well-demarcated glandular proliferations. The glands vary in size and may have various combinations of growth patterns, including solid, cystic and papillary. A cribriform or back-to-back glandular pattern is commonly seen. The glands are composed of two cell layers, the inner or luminal epithelial cell is cuboidal or columnar appearing with an eosinophilic cytoplasm and a decapitation-type secretion (apical 'snouts') characteristic of apocrine-derived cells; the outer cellular layer is a spindle cell with a hyperchromatic nucleus and represents myoepithelial derivation (**Figure 2; see colour plate section**). A golden yellow–brown granular-appearing pigment can be seen in the inner lining cells and represents cerumen. Cellular pleomorphism and mitoses can be seen but are not prominent. Diastase-resistant, PAS-positive and/or muci-carmine-positive intracytoplasmic and/or intraluminal material may be seen.

Ceruminal gland pleomorphic adenomas are uncommon tumours. The histology is similar to that of pleomorphic adenomas of salivary gland origin. Syringocystadenoma papilliferum is a benign tumour of apocrine gland origin that usually occurs on the scalp and face area. Syringocystadenoma papilliferum may originate in the external auditory canal from ceruminal glands. The histology is similar to that of tumours of the more common cutaneous sites.

The treatment of choice for benign ceruminal gland neoplasms is complete surgical excision, which is curative. Recurrence of the tumour can occur and relates to inadequate surgical excision.

In contrast to ceruminal gland adenoma, patients with ceruminal gland adenocarcinomas more often have associated pain (Wetli *et al.*, 1972; Pulec, 1977; Hyams *et al.*, 1988a). Histologically, features that may assist in differentiating ceruminal gland adenocarcinomas from the adenomas include a loss of the glandular double cell layer with identification of only the inner or luminal epithelial cell, the presence of cellular pleomorphism with nuclear anaplasia, increased mitotic acitvity and invasive growth. However, well-differentiated ceruminal gland adenocarcinomas may appear similar to their benign counterparts and are differentiated only on the basis of invasive growth. At the other end of the spectrum, poorly differentiated ceruminal adenocarcinomas occur and are recognized on the basis of their localization in external auditory canal. Other types of ceruminal gland malignant tumours include adenoid cystic carcinoma and mucoepidermoid carcinoma. These tumours are morphologically similar to their salivary gland counterparts.

For ceruminal gland adenocarcinoma, *en bloc* surgical resection is the treatment of choice. Middle ear or temporal bone involvement necessitates more radical surgery (Hicks, 1983). Supplemental radiotherapy is recommended (Hicks, 1983). Metastases are rare and include regional lymph nodes and the lung (Pulec, 1977; Hicks, 1983). For ceruminal gland adenoid cystic carcinoma and muco-epidermoid carcinoma, wide surgical resection is the recommended treatment with or without supplemental radiotherapy. The prognosis for ceruminal gland adenoid cystic carcinoma generally is similar to that for their salivary gland counterparts, including relatively good short-term (i.e. 5-year) survival but poor long-term (i.e. 10–20 years) survival (Perzin *et al.*, 1982).

NEOPLASMS OF THE MIDDLE EAR AND TEMPORAL BONE

Benign Tumours

Middle Ear Adenomas (MEA)

MEA are benign glandular neoplasms originating from the middle ear mucosa (Hyams *et al.*, 1988b; Batsakis, 1989). MEA occur equally in both genders and occur over a wide age range but are most common in the third to fifth decades of life. MEA are found in any portion of the middle ear including the eustachian tube, mastoid air spaces, ossicles and chorda tympani nerve. The most common symptom is unilateral conductive hearing loss but fullness, tinnitus and dizziness may also occur. Pain, otic discharge and facial nerve paralysis rarely occur and, if present, may be indicative of a malignant process. Otoscopic examination in the majority of cases will identify an intact tympanic membrane with tumour confined to the middle ear space with possible extension to the mastoid. Occasionally, the adenoma will perforate through the tympanic membrane with extension into and presentation as an external auditory canal mass. There are no known aetiological factors related to the development of MEA. MEA are not associated with a prior history of chronic otitis media. Concurrent cholesteatomas may be seen with MEA but there is no known association between these two lesions.

An MEA is a grey–white to red–brown, rubbery to firm mass free of significant bleeding on manipulation. Histologically, MEA are unencapsulated lesions with glandular or tubule formation, as well as solid, sheet-like, trabecular, cystic and cribriform growth patterns (**Figure 3; see colour plate section**). Rarely, MEA may show a predominant papillary growth. The neoplastic glands occur individually or have back-to-back growth. The glands are composed of a single layer of cuboidal to columnar cells with a varying amount of eosinophilic cytoplasm and a round to oval hyperchromatic nucleus. Nucleoli may be seen and are generally eccentrically located. The cells may have a prominant plasmacytoid appearance, particularly evident in the more solid areas of growth but also in the cells forming the glandular structures (**Figure 4; see colour plate section**). A paranuclear clear zone is not present. Often, adjacent to or intimately admixed with the glands is a more solid or sheet-like growth of similar-appearing neoplastic cells. The cells may have a more dispersed or stippled nuclear chromatin with the 'salt and pepper' pattern suggestive of neuroendocrine differentiation. Cellular pleomorphism may be prominent but mitoses are uncommon. The stromal component is sparse and may appear fibrous or myxoid.

Histochemical stains show the presence of intraluminal but not intracytoplasmic mucin-positive material. Periodic acid Schiff (PAS)-positive material is not present. By immunohistohemical evaluation, the neoplastic cells are cytokeratin positive but are not reactive with chromogranin, synaptophysin, S-100 protein, desmin, actin or vimentin. Some MEA may have immunoreactivity with one or more neuroendocrine markers, including chromogranin and synaptophysin. These MEA with neuroendocrine differentiation have been termed carcinoid tumours of the middle ear (Latif et al., 1987; Stanley et al., 1987; Manni et al., 1992). However, these 'carcinoid tumours' are better viewed as part of the histologic spectrum of MEA (El Naggar et al., 1994), albeit one with neuroendocrine differentiation, rather than representing a distinct middle ear neoplasm separate from MEA.

MEA should be differentiated from glandular metaplasia that may occur in the setting of chronic otitis media (COM). These metaplastic glands may be misdiagnosed as neoplastic. In contrast to MEA, the glandular proliferation in COM is focal or haphazardly arrayed and occurs in the presence of histological features of COM, including chronic inflammation with fibrosis and calcifications (tympanosclerosis). MEA may perforate the tympanic membrane and appear to represent a neoplasm of the external auditory canal, such as a ceruminal gland adenoma. The histological features of these two tumour types are distinctly different and should allow for easy distinction. In contrast to the rare middle ear adenocarcinoma, MEA lack marked cellular pleomorphism, increased mitotic activity, necrosis or invasion of bone and other soft tissue structures.

The treatment for all MEA is complete surgical excision. Surgery may be conservative if the lesion is small and confined to the middle ear or more radical (mastoidectomy) for larger lesions associated with more extensive structural involvement. Recurrent tumour may occur and is a function of inadequate excision. Some MEA may be locally aggressive and rarely may invade vital structures causing death, but metastatic disease does not occur. In general, the clinical, radiological and pathological findings are indicative of a benign tumour. Nevertheless, the histological appearance is not always predictive of the clinical behaviour.

Jugulotympanic Paragangliomas (JTP)

JTP are benign neoplasms that arise from the extraadrenal neural crest-derived paraganglia specifically located in the middle ear or temporal bone region. Synonyms include glomus jugulare tumour and glomus tympanicum tumour. JTP are considered the most common tumour of the middle ear (Hyams et al., 1988b). JTP affect women more often than men and are most common in the fifth to seventh decades of life. The majority (85%) of the JTP arise in the jugular bulb resulting in a mass lesion in the middle ear or external auditory canal (Hyams et al., 1988b). Approximately 12% take origin from Jacobson's nerve (tympanic branch of the glossopharyngeal nerve) and present as a middle ear tumour (Hyams et al., 1988b). Approximately 3% arise from Arnold's nerve (posterior auricular branch of the vagus nerve) and arise in the external auditory canal (Hyams et al., 1988b). The most common symptom is conductive hearing loss. Other symptoms include tinnitus, fullness, otic discharge, pain, haemorrhage, facial nerve abnormalities and vertigo. JTP are often locally invasive neoplasms with extension into and destruction of adjacent structures including the temporal bone and mastoid. CT scan will show a soft tissue mass often with evidence of extensive destruction of adjacent structures. JGP are vascularized lesions that are fed by branches of nearby large arteries.

The gross appearance of JTP include a polypoid, red, friable mass identified behind an intact tympanic membrane or within the external auditory canal, measuring from a few millimetres to a large mass completely filling the middle ear space. Irrespective of the site of origin, the histological appearance of all extra-adrenal paragangliomas is the same. The hallmark histological feature is the presence of a cell nest or 'zellballen' pattern (**Figure 5; see colour plate section**). The stroma surrounding and separating the nests is composed of prominent fibrovascular tissue. While this pattern is characteristic of paragangliomas it is not unique to paragangliomas and can be seen in other tumours, including neuroendocrine carcinomas (carcinoid and atypical carcinoid tumours), melanomas and carcinomas. Paragangliomas are predominantly composed of chief cells which are round or oval cells with uniform nuclei, dispersed chromatin pattern and abundant eosinophilic, granular or vacuolated cytoplasm. The sustentacular cells, represent modified Schwann cells, are located at the periphery of the cell nests as spindle-shaped, basophilic appearing cells but are difficult to identify by light microscopy. Cellular and nuclear pleomorphism can be seen but these features are not indicative of malignancy. Mitoses and necrosis are infrequently identified. Paragangliomas lack glandular or alveolar differentiation.

Paragangliomas are often readily identified by light microscopic evaluation. However, in certain instances paragangliomas may be difficult to differentiate from other tumours that have similar histomorphological features. Not infrequently, middle ear and temporal paragangliomas do not show the characteristic cell nest appearance that occurs in other sites. This 'loss' of the organoid growth may be artifactually induced by surgical manipulation ('squeezing') of the tissue during removal. The absence of the typical growth pattern may result in diagnostic confusion with other middle ear tumours.

Histochemical stains may be of assistance in the diagnosis of paragangliomas. Reticulin staining may better delineate the cell nest growth pattern with staining of the fibrovascular cores surrounding the neoplastic nests. In addition, the tumour cells are argyrophilic (Churukian–Schenk). Argentaffin (Fontana), mucicarmine and PAS stains are negative. The diagnosis of JTP is facilitated by immunohistochemical stains. The immunohistochemical antigenic profile of paragangliomas includes chromogranin and synaptophysin positivity in the chief cells and S-100 protein staining localized to the peripheral located sustentacular cells. Vimentin is variably reactive in both the chief cells and sustentacular cells. In general, epithelial markers, including cytokeratin, and also HMB-45 and mesenchymal markers (desmin and other markers of myogenic differentiation), are negative. Ultrastructural evaluation shows the presence of neurosecretory granules (Kliewer et al., 1989). DNA ploidy studies by image analysis are not predictive of the behaviour of paragangliomas (Barnes and Taylor, 1990).

Complete surgical excision is the treatment of choice, but the location and invasive nature of these lesions often preclude the ability to resect JTP completely. In such cases, radiotherapy is a useful adjunct to surgery. Radiotherapy results in a decrease or ablation of vascularity and promotes fibrosis. Preoperative embolization is useful in decreasing the vascularity of the tumour and facilitating surgical resection. Local recurrence of the tumour can be seen in as high as 50% of the cases. The histological appearance of paragangliomas does not correlate with the biological behaviour of the tumour. JTP are slow-growing tumours but may be locally invasive with extension into and destruction of adjacent structures, including the temporal bone and mastoid (Larson et al., 1987). Intracranial extension may occur in up to 15% of cases (Spector et al., 1975). Neurological abnormalities, including cranial nerve palsies, cerebellar dysfunction, dysphagia and hoarseness, may be seen and correlate with the invasive capabilities of this neoplasm. Functioning JTP as evidenced by endocrinopathic manifestations occur, but are extremely uncommon. Malignant JTP occur, are associated with histological criteria of malignancy, including increased mitotic activity, necrosis usually seen within the centre of the cell nests and vascular invasion, and may metastasize to cervical lymph nodes, lungs and liver.

Acoustic Neuroma (AN)

AN is a benign neoplasm that originates from Schwann cells specifically from the VIIIth cranial nerve. Synonyms include neurilemmoma, acoustic Schwannoma and benign peripheral nerve sheath tumour. AN accounts for up to 10% of all intracranial neoplasms and represent up to 90% of all cerebellopontine angle tumours (Hyams et al., 1988b). AN are more common in women than in men and may affect any age but are most common in the fourth to seventh decades of life. The majority of AN involve the superior or vestibular portion of the VIIIth nerve as compared with involvement of the cochlear portion of the VIIIth nerve. Symptoms include progressive (sensorineural) hearing loss, tinnitus and loss of equilibrium; with progression the tumour enlarges and may compress adjacent cranial nerves (V, VII, IX, X, XI), the cerebellum and the brainstem leading to facial paraesthesia and numbness, headaches, nausea, vomiting, diplopia and ataxia. Up to 8% of ANs may be bilateral (Erickson et al., 1965; Kasantikul et al., 1980; Martuza and Ojemann, 1982; Anand et al., 1993; Moffat and Irving, 1995). Bilaterality of ANs may represent a potential indicator of neurofibromatosis type 2 (Moffat and Irving, 1995; Rietz et al., 1983). Symptoms of neurofibromatosis may be seen in up to 16% of patients and those with neurofibromatosis who develop AN generally are symptomatic at an earlier age (second decade). The radiological appearance of AN include flaring, asymmetric widening or erosion of the internal auditory canal by CT or MRI. Tumours as small as 1 cm or less are capable of being detected by CT or MRI analysis.

The gross appearance of AN includes a circumscribed, tan–white, rubbery to firm mass which may appear yellow and have cystic change. Tumour sizes range from a few millimetres up to 4—5 cm in greatest diameter. Histologically, the tumours are unencapsulated and similar in appearance to benign Schwannomas of all other locations (**Figure 6; see colour plate section**). The cellular component includes elongated and twisted nuclei with indistinct cytoplasmic borders. The cells are arranged in short, interlacing fascicles and whorling or palisading of nuclei may be seen. Nuclear palisading with nuclear alignment in rows called Verocay bodies can be seen. The cellularity may vary and some benign Schwannomas can be very cellular (so-called cellular Schwannoma). Mitoses are usually sparse in number, and cellular pleomorphism with hyperchromasia can be identified but are not features of malignancy. Retrogressive changes, including cystic degeneration, necrosis, hyalinization, calcification and haemorrhage may be seen. Schwannomas have prominent vascularity composed of large vessels with thickened (hyalinized) walls.

Immunohistochemistry shows the presence of diffuse and intense S-100 protein reactivity. There is no immunoreactivity with cytokeratin or the neuroendocrine markers chromogranin and synaptophysin.

Complete surgical excision is the treatment of choice. Complete removal usually is curative. AN may result in death secondary to herniation of the brainstem in untreated and/or large neoplasms. Malignant AN are exceedingly rare and, if present, neurofibromatosis should be suspected.

Meningiomas

Meningiomas are benign neoplasms arising from arachnoid cells forming the arachnoid villi seen in relation to the dural sinuses. Meningiomas represent 13–18% of all intracranial tumours and are the second most common tumour to AN of the cerebellopontine angle (Hyams *et al.*, 1988b). Meningiomas are more common in women than in men and are most commonly seen in the fifth decade of life. Meningiomas infrequently occur in children. The occurrence of a meningioma outside the central nervous system is considered ectopic and can be divided into those meningiomas with no identifiable CNS connection (primary) and those with CNS connection (secondary). The development of primary meningiomas in the middle ear and temporal bone results either from direct extension or from the presence of arachnoid cells ectopically located. The most common sites of occurrence of the 'ectopically' located meningiomas is the head and neck region, specifically the middle ear and temporal bone, including the internal auditory canal, jugular foramen, geniculate ganglion, roof of the eustachian tube and sulcus of the greater petrosal nerve (Hyams *et al.*, 1988b). The clinical presentation of middle ear meningiomas includes progressive hearing loss, loss of equilibrium, headaches, cerebellar dysfunction and cranial nerve abnormalities. Patients with neurofibromatosis have an increased incidence of developing a meningioma. In addition, patients with neurofibromatosis also experience increased incidence of multiple, separate occurring meningiomas in intra- and extracranial sites. Radiological findings include a soft tissue mass with variable vascularity. A pathognomonic feature for meningioma in this location is the presence of speckled calcification in a soft tissue mass.

The histological features of middle ear and temporal bone meningioma are similar to those of their intracranial counterparts (**Figure 7; see colour plate section**). The immunohistochemical antigenic profile of meningiomas includes reactivity with epithelial membrane antigen (EMA) and vimentin. In contrast to middle ear adenomas, meningiomas are generally nonreactive with cytokeratin, and in contrast to jugulotympanic paragangliomas, meningiomas are nonreactive with neuroendocrine markers (e.g. chromogranin and synaptophysin).

Complete surgical excision is the treatment of choice and is curative. Local recurrence relates to inadequate excision. Malignant change rarely, if ever, occurs. A diagnosis of middle ear meningioma should be made only after clinical evaluation is made to exclude secondary extension from an intracranial neoplasm (Rietz *et al.*, 1983).

Endolymphatic Sac Papillary Tumour

The endolymphatic sac papillary tumour (ESPT) is an uncommon but distinct neoplasm possibly representing a manifestation of von Hippel–Lindau (VHL) syndrome (Megerian *et al.*, 1995; Manski *et al.*, 1997). ESPT has been referred to by a variety of names, including adenoma of endolymphatic sac, adenoma/adenocarcinoma of temporal bone or mastoid, low-grade adenocarcinoma of probable endolymphatic sac origin, papillary adenoma of temporal bone, aggressive papillary tumour of temporal bone, aggressive papillary middle ear tumour and, more recently, as the Heffner tumour (Batsakis and El-Naggar, 1993; Wenig and Heffner, 1996). An endolymphatic sac origin for these tumours is supported by a combination of findings, including the early clinical manifestations of vestibular disease (e.g. sensorineural hearing loss, tinnitus and episodic vertigo), radiographic features showing the tumour to grow in the region site where the endolymphatic sac is located (i.e. posterior–medial petrous ridge), intraoperative identification of an *in situ* tumour originating from within the endolymphatic sac and morphological similarities and shared immunohistochemical and ultrastructural features of the tumour with the normal endolymphatic sac epithelium (Wenig and Heffner, 1996). The diagnosis of this tumour is based on clinical, radiographic and pathological correlation. A diagnosis of ESPT should prompt the clinician to exclude the possibility that the patient has VHL syndrome (Megerian *et al.*, 1995; Manski *et al.*, 1997).

The histopathological appearance of ESPT is variable. ESPTs are papillary and focally cystic tumours. The papillary structures are generally not complex in their growth. The neoplastic cells vary in appearance from flattened or attenuated appearing cells to columnar appearing cells (**Figure 8; see colour plate section**). Most often there is only a single row of cells. Occasionally, the surface epithelial cells may have the appearance suggesting a double layer of cells (epithelial and myoepithelial); however, the 'outer' row of cells, in all probability, represent a stromal element as they have not been shown to be immunoreactive with epithelial markers (Heffner, 1989). The epithelial cells have uniform nuclei that are usually situated either in the centre of the cells or toward the luminal aspect, and have a pale eosinophilic to clear appearing cytoplasm. The latter may predominate in any given tumour. Cell borders may be seen but, not infrequently, the neoplastic cells lack a distinct cell membrane. In some cases, there are hypercellular areas with crowded, variably sized cystic glandular spaces that contain eosinophilic (colloid-like) material (**Figure 9; see colour plate section**). The latter appear remarkably similar to thyroid tissue. In all cases, pleomorphism is minimal, and mitotic activity and necrosis are rarely present.

A granulation tissue reaction is seen in association with the neoplastic cells and includes small vascular spaces lying in close proximity to the surface epithelium and/or within the stroma of the papillary fronds. Owing to the absence of a distinct cell membrane around the neoplastic cells, a sharp demarcation separating the neoplastic cells from the subjacent granulation tissue is not present. This appearance may create diagnostic confusion so that the neoplastic proliferation is not appreciated, and the entire process is viewed as reactive. This interpretation is further enhanced by the presence in the stroma of a mixed inflammatory cell infiltrate, fibrosis, vascular proliferation, fresh haemorrhage and/or haemosiderin (within the neoplastic cells or within macrophages), cholesterol granulomas and dystrophic calcification. The latter does not include laminated calcific concretions (psammomatoid bodies).

Intracytoplasmic diastase-sensitive, PAS-positive material can be seen. The colloid-like luminal material stains strongly with PAS reagent with and without diastase digestion. Intracytoplasmic and intraluminal mucin staining is rarely positive. Iron stains are positive. ESPTs are diffusely cytokeratin positive and also show variable reactivity with epithelial membrane antigen (EMA), S-100 protein, vimentin, neuron-specific enolase (NSE), glial fibrillary acidic protein (GFAP), Ber-EP4, synaptophysin and Leu-7. Thyroglobulin immunoreactivity is not seen. Ultrastructurally, ESPT shows the presence of intercellular junctional complexes, microvilli, basement membrane material, rough endoplasmic reticulum and intracytoplasmic glycogen and secretory granules (Heffner, 1989).

The differential diagnosis includes middle ear adenoma. However, the clinical, radiographic and pathological features that are unique to ESPT should allow for its distinction from middle ear adenoma. The same would apply for the other common neoplasms of the middle ear and temporal bone. The differential diagnosis also includes choroid plexus papilloma and metastatic carcinoma of thyroid gland or renal origin. Choroid plexus papillomas are intracranial (i.e. intraventricular) tumours with histological features different from those of ESPT (Wenig and Heffner, 1996). The absence of thyroglobulin reactivity would differentiate ESPT from metastatic thyroid papillary carcinoma. Metastatic renal cell carcinoma would not have the immunohistochemical antigenic features seen in ESPT.

Radical surgery, including mastoidectomy and temporal bone resection that may necessitate sacrifice of cranial nerves, is the treatment of choice, and is potentially curative. Local recurrence will result following inadequate surgical removal; operative morbidity may be high. Despite their relatively slow growth, these neoplasms are capable of widespread infiltration and destruction, and may be lethal (Heffner, 1989). The prognosis is dependent on the extent of disease and the adequacy of resection. Earlier detection when the tumours are relatively small and confined may decrease the operative-associated morbidity and be curative.

Malignant Neoplasms of the Middle Ear

Primary malignant neoplasms of the middle ear are extremely rare. **Table 1** lists some of these malignant neoplasms. The discussion of malignant neoplasms of the middle ear will be limited to epithelial malignancies, including squamous cell carcinoma and adenocarcinoma, and a brief discussion on rhabdomyosarcoma of this region.

Middle Ear Squamous Cell Carcinoma (ME-SCC)

Primary malignant neoplasms with squamous differentiation originating from the middle ear mucosal epithelium are rare (Kenyon et al., 1985; Hyams et al., 1988c). ME-SCC is most common in the sixth and seventh decades of life. The majority of patients have a long history of chronic otitis media usually greater than 20 years in duration. The development of ME-SCC is also linked to radiation treatment for intracranial neoplasms and, although no longer used, radiotherapy for middle ear inflammatory conditions. Concomitant cholesteatomas can be seen in up to 25% of cases but there is no correlation between cholesteatomas and the development of a middle ear squamous cell carcinoma (Hyams et al., 1988c). ME-SCC should be suspected in patients with a long-standing chronic otitis media who present with sudden onset of pain out of proportion to the clinical extent of disease, onset or increase of otorrhea which is often haemorrhagic and/or a lack of clinical resolution following therapeutic doses of antibiotics.

The histology of ME-SCC is similar to that of squamous carcinomas of other sites. The tumours vary from well to poorly differentiated and include infiltrative malignant cells with associated keratinization and/or intercellular bridges.

The differential diagnosis includes a cholesteatoma and metastatic squamous cell carcinoma. Cholesteatomas do not have the dysplastic cytological changes seen in squamous carcinoma. Secondary involvement of this area by squamous cell carcinoma may originate from a distant site and metastasize to the middle ear and temporal bone. Alternatively, a cutaneous squamous cell carcinoma from an adjacent site (external ear, nasopharynx, parotid gland or skin) can directly invade into the middle ear or temporal bone. Detailed clinical history or physical examination would assist in identifying a squamous carcinoma that is metastatic to this site or extends to the middle ear from an adjacent primary tumour.

Radical surgery with radiotherapy is the treatment of choice. In advanced disease, chemotherapy may be of benefit. Prognosis is poor with 5- and 10-year survival rates of 39% and 21%, respectively (Hyams et al., 1988c). Metastases may occur but are considered uncommon.

Middle Ear Adenocarcinoma

Middle ear adenocarcinoma is a malignant glandular neoplasm arising from the middle ear mucosa. Middle ear adenocarcinomas are rare (Hyams et al., 1988d). In the presence of a malignant glandular neoplasm of the middle ear and temporal bone, secondary metastasis to this region should be excluded. Middle ear adenocarcinomas may attain large sizes, filling the middle ear space and encasing the ossicles. Symptoms are typically present for many years and include progressive hearing loss and a unilateral draining ear; pain and vestibular manifestations are uncommon. Otoscopic examination in the majority of cases will identify an intact tympanic membrane with tumour confined to the middle ear space with possible extension to the mastoid. Occasionally, the adenocarcinoma will perforate through the tympanic membrane with extension into and presentation as an external auditory canal mass. There is no known association between chronic otitis media and the development of these adenocarcinomas.

Histologically, middle ear adenocarcinomas are in many respects similar to adenomas. In contrast to adenomas, adenocarcinomas have increased cellular pleomorphism, increased mitotic activity and extensive infiltration of surrounding soft tissue structures involving nerves, lymphvascular spaces and bone.

Complete surgical excision is the treatment of choice. In general, these are slow-growing neoplasms that are locally aggressive but do not metastasize. Death may occur as a result of direct intracranial extension. Confinement to the middle ear space and association with the middle ear mucosa are supportive evidence of origin from the middle ear; nevertheless, metastatic adenocarcinoma from a separate site must be excluded prior to treatment.

Rhabdomyosarcoma (RMS)

In the head and neck, RMS is primarily but not exclusively a disease of the paediatric population. In children and adolescents, RMS represents the most common auralrelated malignant neoplasm. There is no gender predilection. RMS of the middle ear and mastoid presents as painless unilateral otitis media unresponsive to antibiotic therapy. According to the WHO classification, RMS is divided into six histological subtypes, including embryonal, botryoid, spindle cell, alveolar, pleomorphic and RMS with ganglionic differentiation (so-called ectomesenchymoma) (Weiss, 1995). The International classification of RMS proposed four groups based on prognosis: I, superior prognosis (botryoid RMS and spindle cell RMS); II, intermediate prognosis (embryonal RMS); III, poor prognosis (alveolar RMS and undifferentiated RMS); and IV, subtypes whose prognosis is not presently evaluable (RMS with rhabdoid features) (Newton et al., 1995).

The majority of RMS of the middle ear and mastoid are of the embryonal type that includes botryoid RMS. The next most common histological type is alveolar RMS. The other histological types may occur in the head and neck but are considered uncommon. RMS of the middle ear and mastoid most often appears as an aural (external or middle ear) polypoid lesion similar in appearance to an aural polyp.

RMS is treated by a combination of surgery, radiation and chemotherapy. This combined therapeutic approach has greatly enhanced survival with an overall 5-year survival of 74% for paediatric head and neck RMS (Kraus et al., 1997). A problem with middle ear and mastoid RMS is the delay in diagnosis due to misinterpretation of the biopsy specimen as inflammatory polyps or as granulation tissue. This delay in diagnosis may result in more advanced stage disease, placing patients at greater risk of treatment failure owing to uncontrollable local disease. Poor prognostic findings include meningeal involvement (Raney et al., 1987). Regional lymph node metastasis and distant haematogenous metastasis to the lungs and bones may also occur.

Secondary Tumours

Metastatic tumours secondarily involving the middle ear and temporal bone originate from virtually every site. The more common malignant tumours to metastasize to this region originate from the breast, lungs and kidneys (Hill and Kohut, 1976; Schuknecht, 1993b). Other tumours that may metastasize to this region include malignant melanoma and prostatic adenocarcinoma. While metastases to the temporal bone often occur late in the disease course, metastatic involvement of the temporal bone may represent the initial presentation of a distant malignant disease. Metastatic disease to the temporal bone occurs via haematogenous spread but may also occur by direct extension from a nearby primary tumour (e.g. squamous cell carcinoma), meningeal carcinomatosis or leptomeningeal extension from an intracranial primary neoplasm (Berlinger et al., 1980).

REFERENCES

Abramson, M., et al. (1984). Histology, pathogenesis, and treatment of cholesteatoma. Otolaryngology, Rhinology and Laryngology, 112, 125–128.

Anand, T., et al. (1993). Bilateral acoustic neuromas. Clinical Otolaryngology, 18, 365–371.

Barnes, L. and Taylor, S. R. (1990). Carotid body paragangliomas: a clinicopathologic and DNA analysis of 13 cases. Archives Otolaryngology and Head and Neck Surgery, 116, 447–453.

Batsakis, J. G. (1989). Adenomatous tumors of the middle ear. Annals of Otolaryngology, Rhinology and Laryngology, 98, 749–752.

Batsakis, J. G., and El-Naggar, A. K. (1993). Papillary neoplasms (Heffner's tumors) of the endolymphatic sac. Annals of Otolaryngology, Rhinology and Laryngology, 102, 648–651.

Berlinger, N. T., et al. (1980). Patterns of involvement of the temporal bone in metastastic and systemic malignancy. Laryngoscope, 90, 619–627.

Dayal, V. S., *et al.* (1973). Embryology of the ear. *Canadian Journal of Otolaryngology*, **2**, 136–142.

Desloge, R. B., *et al.* (1997). DNA analysis of human cholesteatomas. *American Journal of Otolaryngology*, **18**, 155–159.

El-Naggar, A. K., *et al.* (1994). Tumors of the middle ear and endolymphatic sac. *Pathology Annual*, **29**, 199–231.

Erickson, L. S., *et al.* (1965). A review of 140 acoustic neurinomas (neurilemmoma). *Laryngoscope*, **75**, 601–627.

Faverly, D. R. G. S., *et al.* (1992). Adenocarcinoid or amphicrine tumors of the middle ear. *Pathology Research and Practice*, **188**, 162–171.

Ferlito, A., *et al.* (1997). Ear cholesteatoma versus cholesterol granuloma. *Annals of Otolaryngology, Rhinology and Laryngology*, **106**, 79–85.

Heffner, D. K. (1989). Low-grade adenocarcinoma of probable endolymphatic sac origin. A clinicopathologic study of 20 cases. *Cancer*, **64**, 2292–2302.

Hicks, G. W. (1983). Tumors arising from the glandular structures of the external auditory canal. *Laryngoscope*, **93**, 326–340.

Hill, B. A. and Kohut, R. I. (1976). Metastatic adenocarcinoma of the temporal bone. *Archives of Otolaryngology*, **102**, 568–571.

Hyams, V. J., *et al.* (1988a). Adenomatous neoplasms of ceruminal gland origin. In: Hartman, X. X. and Sobin, L. H. (eds), *Tumors of the Upper Respiratory Tract and Ear. Atlas of Tumor Pathology*, Fascicle, 25. 285–291 (Armed Forces Institute of Pathology, Washington, DC).

Hyams, V. J., *et al.* (1988b). Neoplasms of the middle ear. In: Hartman, X. X. and Sobin, L. H. (eds), *Tumors of the Upper Respiratory Tract and Ear. Atlas of Tumor Pathology*, Fascicle 25. 306–330 (Armed Forces Institute of Pathology, Washington, DC).

Hyams, V. J., *et al.* (1988c). Squamous cell carcinoma of the middle ear. In: Hartman, X. X. and Sobin, L. H. (eds), *Tumors of the Upper Respiratory Tract and Ear. Atlas of Tumor Pathology*, Fascicle 25. 326–327 (Armed Forces Institute of Pathology, Washington, DC).

Hyams, V. J., *et al.* (1988d). Adenocarcinoma of the middle ear. In: Hartman, X. X. and Sobin, L. H. (eds), *Tumors of the Upper Respiratory Tract and Ear. Atlas of Tumor Pathology*, Fascicle 25. 302–323 (Armed Forces Institute of Pathology, Washington, DC).

Kasantikul, V., *et al.* (1980). Acoustic neurilemmoma. Clinicoanatomical study of 103 patients. *Journal of Neurosurgery*, **52**, 28–35.

Kenyon, G. S., *et al.* (1985). Squamous cell carcinoma of the middle ear; a 25-year retrospective study. *Annals of Otolaryngology, Rhinology and Laryngology*, **94**, 273–277.

Kliewer, K. E., *et al.* (1989). Paragangliomas: assessment of prognosis by histologic, immunohistochemical, and ultrastructural techniques. *Human Pathology*, **20**, 29–39.

Kraus, D. H., *et al.* (1997). Pediatric rhabdomyosarcoma of the head and neck. *American Journal of Surgery*, **174**, 556–560.

Larson, T. C., *et al.* (1987). Glomus tympanicum chemodectomas: radiographic and clinical characteristics. *Radiology*, **163**, 801–806.

Latif, M. A., *et al.* (1987). Carcinoid tumour of the middle ear associated with systemic symptoms. *Journal of Laryngology and Otolaryngology*, **101**, 480–486.

Manni, J., *et al.* (1992). Primary carcinoid tumor of the middle ear: report of four cases and a review of the literature. *Archives of Otolaryngology and Head and Neck Surgery*, **118**, 1341–1347.

Manski, T. J., *et al.* (1997). Endolymphatic sac tumors: the basis of morbid hearing loss in von Hippel–Lindau disease. *Journal of American Medical Association*, **277**, 1461–1466.

Martuza, R. L. and Ojemann, R. G. (1982). Bilateral acoustic neuromas: clinical aspects, pathogenesis and treatment. *Neurosurgery*, **10**, 1–12.

Megerian, C. A., *et al.* (1995). Endolymphatic sac tumors: histopathologic confirmation, clinical characterization, and implication in von Hippel–Lindau disease. *Laryngoscope*, **105**, 801–808.

Moffat, D. A. and Irving, R. M. (1995). The molecular genetics of vestibular schwannomas. *Journal of Laryngology and Otolaryngology*, **109**, 381–384.

Moore, K. L. (1988). The ear. In: Moore, K. L. (ed.), *The Developing Human: Clinically Oriented Embryology*. 412–440 (W. B. Saunder, Philadelphia).

Newton, W. A., *et al.* (1995). Classification of rhabdomyosarcomas and related sarcomas: pathologic aspects and proposal for a new classification – an intergroup rhabdomyosarcoma study. *Cancer*, **76**, 1073–1085.

Perzin, K. H., *et al.* (1982). Adenoid cystic carcinoma involving the external auditory canal. A clinicopathological study of 16 cases. *Cancer*, **50**, 2873–2883.

Pulec, J. L. (1977). Glandular tumors of the external auditory canal. *Laryngoscope*, **87**, 1601–1612.

Raney, R. B., Jr, *et al.* (1987). Improved prognosis with cranial soft tissue sarcomas arising in nonorbital parameningeal sites. A report from the intergroup rhabdomyosarcoma study. *Cancer*, **59**, 147–155.

Rietz, D. R., *et al.* (1983). Significance of apparent intratympanic meningiomas. *Laryngoscope*, **93**, 1397–1404.

Schuknecht, H. F. (1993a). Cholesteatoma. In: Schuknecht H. F. (ed.), *Pathology of the Ear*. 204–206 (Lea & Febiger, Philadelphia).

Schuknecht, H. F. (1993b). Neoplastic growths. In: Schuknecht, H. F. (ed.), *Pathology of the Ear*. 447–448 (Lea & Febiger, Philadelphia).

Spector, G. J., *et al.* (1975). Glomus tumors in the head and neck. III. Analysis of clinical manifestations. *Annals of Rhinology, Otolaryngology and Laryngology*, **84**, 73–79.

Stanley, M. W., *et al.* (1987). Carcinoid tumors of the middle ear. *American Journal of Clinical Pathology*, **87**, 592–600.

Weiss, S. W. (1995). World Health Organization international histological classification of tumours. In: Weiss, S. W. (ed.), *Histological Typing of Soft Tissue Tumours*. (Springer, Berlin).

Wenig, B. M. and Heffner, D. K. (1996). Endolymphatic sac tumors: fact or fiction ? *Advances in Anatomical Pathology*, **3**, 378–387.

Wetli, C. V., *et al.* (1972). Tumors of ceruminous glands. *Cancer,* **29**, 1169–1178.

FURTHER READING

Hollinshead, W. H. (1982). The ear. In: Hollinshead, W. H. (ed.), *Anatomy for Surgeons*, Vol. 1. 159–221 (Harper and Row, Philadelphia).

Nager, G. T. (1993). *Pathology of the Ear and Temporal Bone* (Williams & Wilkins, Baltimore).

Schuknecht, H. F. (1993). *Pathology of the Ear* (Lea & Febiger, Philadelphia).

Addendum

Blood and Bone Marrow: Myeloid Leukaemias and Related Neoplasms

Lawrence M. Weiss
City of Hope National Medical Center, Duarte, CA, USA

CONTENTS

INTRODUCTION

The leukaemias and related neoplasms are neoplastic proliferations of cells of the haematopoietic (blood-forming) lineage. They can be divided into two main types: myeloid leukaemias, which derive from stem cells that give rise to the granulocytic, erythroid, or megakaryocytic lineages, and lymphoid leukaemia, which derive from cells from the B, T, or NK lymphoid cell lineage. Lymphoid leukaemias are closely related to malignant lymphomas and are further discussed in the chapter Lymph Nodes.

NORMAL DEVELOPMENT AND STRUCTURE

In the developing embryo, clusters of haematopoietic stem cells called blood islands first develop in the yolk sac within the first month (Sieff *et al.*, 1998). By the third month, the liver becomes the primary site of haematopoiesis. By the fourth month, the bone marrow begins haematopoiesis. It becomes the major site of haematopoiesis by birth, and in the normal individual, remains virtually the sole site of haematopoiesis throughout life. During childhood, all of the bone marrow is fully active in haematopoiesis, whereas in adults, only the axial (central) and proximal appendicular (limb) skeleton contains haematopoietic cells. In these areas, the haematopoietic elements usually comprise about 50% of the overall marrow space in these sites, with the rest of the space taken up by fat and other stromal cells (**Figure 1; see colour plate section**).

There is a pluripotential haematopoietic stem cell, which gives rise to cells of both the myeloid and lymphoid lineages. Under the influence of cytokines which include stem cell factor, interleukin (IL)-6 and Flt3 ligand, the pluripotential stem cell gives rise to a trilineage myeloid stem cell (colony forming unit [CFU-S]) as well as a lymphoid stem cell. Under the influence of additional cytokines, such as IL-3, IL-6, and granulocyte/macrophage colony stimulating factor (GM-CSF), as well as specific cytokines which determine specific lineage differentiation, the myeloid stem cell gives rise to committed stem cells of the monocytic (under the specific influence of macrophage colony-stimulating factor [CFU-M]), granulocytic (under the specific influence of granulocyte colony-stimulating factor [CFU-G]), eosinophilic (under the specific influence of IL-5), erythroid (under the specific influence of erythropoietin), and megakaryoblastic (platelet forming), (under the specific influence of thrombopoietin) lineages. These stem cells finally give rise to committed cell types which undergo a series of maturational steps to become mature blood cells, including monocytes (destined to become tissue histiocytes and macrophages), neutrophils, basophils, eosinophils, anucleated red blood cells, and platelets.

CLASSIFICATION

There are four main categories of myeloid neoplasms: acute myeloid leukaemia (AML), chronic myeloproliferative diseases (CMPD), myelodysplastic syndromes (MDS) and neoplasms which combine features of both MDS and CMPD. Briefly, acute leukaemias usually cause death within weeks to months if untreated, CMPD usually cause death within months to years; some may transform to acute leukaemia over time. MDS are peculiar clonal proliferations that are closely related to acute leukaemia. In

Table 1 Summary of 2001 World Health Classification of myeloid leukaemia and related neoplasms (Jaffe *et al.*, 2001)

Acute myeloid leukaemia
  Acute myeloid leukaemia with recurrent cytogenetic abnormalities
  Acute myeloid leukaemia with multilineage dysplasia
  Acute myeloid leukaemia and myelodysplastic syndrome, therapy-related
  Acute myeloid leukaemia, not otherwise categorized
Chronic myeloproliferative diseases
  Chronic myelogenous leukaemia
  Chronic neutrophilic leukaemia
  Chronic eosinophilic leukaemia/hypereosinophilic syndrome
  Polycythemia vera
  Chronic idiopathic myelofibrosis
  Essential thrombocythemia
  Chronic myeloproliferative disease, unclassifiable
Myelodysplastic syndromes
  Refractory anaemia
  Refractory anaemia with ringed sideroblasts
  Refractory cytopenia with multilineage dysplasia
  Refractory anaemia with excess blasts
  Myelodysplastic syndrome, unclassifiable
  Isolated del(5q) chromosome abnormality
Myelodysplastic/myeloproliferative diseases
  Chronic myelomonocytic leukaemia
  Atypical chronic myeloid leukaemia
  Juvenile myelomonocytic leukaemia
  Myelodysplastic/myeloproliferative diseases, unclassifiable

---

some patients, they may precede acute leukaemia, they may lead to death on their own due to failure of effective haematopoiesis, or they may persist unchanged for years. Myelodysplastic/myeloproliferative diseases have features that have components of both myelodysplastic and myeloproliferative diseases. Within each main category, there are various specific subtypes recognized by the recent World Health Organisation (WHO) classification, given in **Table 1** (Jaffe *et al.*, 2001).

ACUTE MYELOID LEUKAEMIA

AML and its subtypes are clonal proliferations of blasts committed to the myeloid lineage. They comprise about 2 cases per 100,000 annually in Western countries. They most often occur in adults, with a median age of about 60 years, although there is a second small peak in the first years of life. There is no strong sex predilection. Aetiologic factors include ionizing radiation, prior cytotoxic chemotherapy, benzene exposure and cigarette smoking. Individuals with genetic diseases that promote genomic instability, such as Bloom syndrome, Fanconi anaemia, and ataxia telangiectasia as well as Down syndrome (trisomy 21) are also at increased risk. Nonetheless, there

is no attributable aetiologic agent in the vast majority of cases. Patients with AML usually present with signs and symptoms of marrow failure, such as anaemia, infections due to low numbers of normal neutrophils (neutropenia), and bleeding from low numbers of platelets (thrombocytopenia). In almost all cases, there is replacement of the normal marrow by blasts, which are immature cells with round to oval nuclei with a fine granular chromatin pattern. The amount of cytoplasm varies, and may contain granules. Often, peculiar rod-like structures called Auer bodies, representing aggregations of abnormal granules, can be observed and are specific for acute myeloid leukaemia. The peripheral blood usually shows similar blasts, often with a marked elevation in the while blood cell count. Typically, at least 20–30% blasts are observed in the marrow or blood to establish the diagnosis. AML is generally treated by multidrug chemotherapy or allogeneic bone marrow transplantation. Although most patients achieve initial remission, less than one-third are alive by five years. Prognosis is dependent on multiple factors, particularly the specific cytogenetic abnormalities present.

Acute Myeloid Leukaemia with Recurrent Cytogenetic Abnormalities

As noted in **Table 1**, there are at least four types of AML recognized in the WHO Classification. In acute myeloid leukaemia with recurrent cytogenetic abnormalities, there are additionally four distinct subgroups, each associated with its own specific genetic abnormality, usually a balanced translocation (**Table 2**) (Caligiuri *et al.*, 1997). Each of the subgroups is associated with a favourable prognosis. AML associated with t(8;21) tends to occur in younger patients. It often presents with extramedullary (outside of the bone marrow) masses, and may have a blast percentage below 20%. Morphologically, the blasts often show evidence of maturation, and may contain very large granules (pseudo-Chediak-Higashi granules) in the cytoplasm. There is usually abnormal coexpression of the lymphoid antigen CD19, in addition to the usual myeloid markers CD13, CD33 and myeloperoxidase. AML associated with inv(16) or t(16;16) also has a predilection for younger patients. The patients tend to present in extramedullary sites. The blasts tend to show features of myeloid and monocytic (myelomonocytic) differentiation, and there are often variable numbers of eosinophils and precursor cells with distinctive large basophilic granules. Patients with t(15;17) and variants, often referred to collectively as acute promyelocytic leukaemia, are usually adults who often present with symptoms relating to diffuse intravascular coagulation (DIC). There are two major morphologic variants, the hypergranular variant and the microgranular (or hypogranular) variant. In the hypergranular variants, the marrow contains large numbers of abnormal promyelocytes (cells at the first stage of maturation of granulocytes after blasts), cells with densely

Table 2   Acute myeloid leukaemia with recurrent cytogenetic abnormalities

Genetic Abnormality	Frequency	Molecular Defect
t(8;21)(q22;q22)	10% of cases	Translocation of *AML1* (*RUNX1*) gene which encodes the core binding factor (CBFα) and the *ETO* gene; the fusion transcript have similarities to the Drosophila segmentation *RUNT* gene
inv(16)(p13q22) or t(1616)(p131q22)	10% of cases	Fusion of the *CBFβ* gene to the smooth muscle myosin heavy chain gene
t(15;17)(q22;q12)	5% of cases	Translocation of retinoic acid receptor *RARα* gene with a nuclear regulatory factor
t(11;17)(q23;q21)	< 0.5% of cases	Translocation of *RARα* with promyelocytic leukaemia zinc finger gene (*PLZXF*)
t(11;17)(q13;q21)	< 0.5% of cases	Translocation of nuclear matrix associated gene (*NuMA*) with *RARα*
t(5;17)(q23;q12)	< 0.5% of cases	Translocation of nucleophosmin (*NPM*) gene with *RARα*
11q23 abnormalities	5%	Structural abnormalities of *MLL* (Dorosophila trithorax gene *HRX*)

packed cytoplasmic granules, often with many Auer rods (**Figure 2; see colour plate section**). In the microgranular variant, the granules are not readily apparent and the nucleus shows a characteristic bilobed shape. In contrast to most cases of AML, HLA-DR expression is usually absent in acute promyelocytic leukaemia. The importance of this subtype is that all cases of acute promyelocytic leukaemia, with the exception of cases with the t(11;17), respond well to treatment regimens which include all trans-retinoic acid (ATRA) (a differentiating agent). AML with 11q23 abnormalities fall into two clinical groups: AML occurring in infants and therapy-related leukaemia after treatment with DNA topoisomerase II inhibitors. These leukaemias often show features of monocytic differentiation.

Acute Myeloid Leukaemia with Multilineage Dysplasia

In AML with multilineage dysplasia, there is dysplasia present in > 50% of the cells of two or more of the myeloid cell lines in addition to the presence of myeloid blasts in the bone marrow or blood. These cases usually occurs in older adults, and there may be a history of a preceding myelodysplastic syndrome. These patients often present with signs and symptoms of marked pancytopenia. Morphologically, dysplasia consists of abnormal features indicating aberrant differentiation of the granulocytic, erythroid, or megakaryocytic lines (see below). Cytogenetic abnormalities are typically seen that are similar to those seen in myelodysplastic syndromes (see below). Clinically, the presence of multilineage dysplasia has an adverse effect on prognosis.

Therapy-Associated Acute Myeloid Leukaemia

Cases of therapy-related AML are usually one of two types: alkylating agent/radiation-related or associated with topoisomerase II inhibitor. Those cases associated with alkylating agents tend to resemble cases of AML with

multilineage dysplasia, although dysplastic changes are usually found in all three cell lineages (granulocytic, erythroid, and megakaryocytic). The cytogenetic abnormalities are also similar to cases of AML with multilineage dysplasia, and the prognosis is poor as well. In contrast, cases of topoisomerase II inhibitor-associated AML tend to be similar to those cases of AML with 11q23 abnormalities, with similar cytogenetic findings and possibly favourable prognosis.

Acute Myeloid Leukaemia, Not Otherwise Categorized

AML, not otherwise categorized, is a large category, comprising the majority of cases of AML. These have been classified in the past using the French-American-British classification, relying primarily on morphologic and cytochemical findings (**Table 3**) (Bennett *et al.*, 1985). Although there are definite morphologic and cytochemical differences between the different subtypes, these do not in general translate to strong clinical differences or to specific cytogenetic abnormalities (**Figure 3; see colour plate section**). Therefore, the current prevailing opinion is that it is not clinically or biologically important to separate out these various morphologic variants, although some have suggested that acute megakaryoblastic leukaemia has features to consider it a distinct clinicopathologic entity (Arber, 2001). These include frequent occurrence in children, particularly patients with Down syndrome, and the occurrence of a t(1;22)(p13;13). Rare cases of acute leukaemia have an ambiguous lineage which lack sufficient evidence to definitively characterize as myeloid or lymphoid or which have characteristics of both myeloid and lymphoid cells; the latter have been termed acute biphenotypic leukaemia.

CHRONIC MYELOPROLIFERATIVE DISEASES

The CMPDs are clonal haematopoietic stem cells disorders characterized by proliferation of one or more of the myeloid

Table 3 French-American-British classification system of acute myeloid leukaemia (Bennett *et al.*, 1985).

M0	Minimal evidence of myeloid differentiation, myeloperoxidase negative by cytochemistry
M1	Definite evidence of myeloid differentiation without evidence of maturation (AML with maturation); reactive for myeloperoxidase or Sudan black B (myeloid markers)
M2	Definite evidence of myeloid differentiation with evidence of maturation towards the granulocytic line
M3	Acute promyelocytic leukaemia (AML with t(15;17) and related translocations)
M4	Definite evidence of granulocytic and monocytic maturation (acute myelomonocytic leukaemia); monocytic cells positive for nonspecific esterase
M5	Definite evidence of monocytic without granulocytic maturation (acute monocytic/monoblastic leukaemia); reactive for nonspecific esterase
M6	AML with predominant erythroid differentiation; reactive with antibodies against haemoglobin A
M7	AML with predominant megakaryocytic maturation (acute megakaryoblastic leukaemia); reactive with antibodies against platelet glycoproteins (CD41 and CD61)

lineages with normal maturation. They comprise about 5–10 cases per 100,000 annually in Western countries. They most often occur in older adults. The aetiology is unknown in the large majority of cases, although some are associated with a history of ionizing radiation. Patients with CMPD usually present with signs and symptoms of increased blood cell formation, including enlargement of the spleen and the liver, due to sequestration of excess blood elements, and abnormalities such as thrombosis due to the increased mass of cells in the blood. In almost all cases, the bone marrow shows a marked increase in cellularity due to a proliferation in one or more of the haematopoietic cell lineages (**Figure 4; see colour plate section**). There is often increased marrow fibrosis as well. The peripheral blood usually shows markedly increased numbers of granulocytes, red blood cells, and/or platelets. One characteristic feature of CMPDs is their tendency to undergo acceleration of the disease process or overt transformation to a blastic or acute phase. The presence of about 10–19% blasts in the bone marrow or blood is usually indicative of acceleration, whereas the presence of 20–30% or more blasts is usually evidence of a blastic transformation.

Chronic Myeloid Leukaemia

As shown in **Table 1**, the WHO Classification recognizes at least seven major types of CMPD. Chronic myelogenous leukaemia (CML) is the most common of the CMPDs (Faderl *et al.*, 1999). It occurs primarily in adults, with a slight male predilection. The bone marrow usually shows marked hypercellularity, due to increased numbers of

granulocytes and their normal precursors. There is sometimes an increase in the amount of fibrosis, usually correlating with increased numbers of megakaryocytes. Increased numbers of macrophages may also be evident, secondary to increased cell turnover. The peripheral blood usually shows a marked leukocytosis (increased white blood cell count) due to an increase in the number of mature neutrophils and immature granulocytic cells. An increase in the number of basophils is also a consistent finding. Other organs such as the spleen and liver may show infiltration of the sinusoids by granulocytes in various stages of maturation (**Figure 5; see colour plate section**).

A consistent finding in CML is the presence of the t(9;22)(q34;q11) (the Philadelphia chromosome), or in a small subset of cases, a variant translocation involving a third chromosome or a cryptic translocation that is difficult to detect by classical cytogenetics. In all of these cases, there is a juxtaposition of sequences from the *BCR* gene with regions of the *ABL* gene, leading to an aberrant *BCR-ABL* transcript (Melo *et al.*, 1997). At a molecular level, the breakpoint on the *BCR* gene may vary. Usually, the breakpoint occurs at the major breakpoint cluster region (M-BCR), resulting in a fusion protein called p210, which has abnormally high tyrosine kinase activity. In rare cases, the breakpoint occurs in the minor breakpoint cluster region (m-BCR; p190), often found in patients with unusually prominent monocytic differentiation (this breakpoint is much more commonly seen in patients with Philadelphia chromosome-positive acute lymphocytic leukaemia).

Survival in CML is usually between 5 and 10 years. A recent novel therapy involves use of an agent that blocks the abnormal tyrosine kinase activity, often resulting in rapid, if not lasting, remission. As noted above, many patients eventually progress to an accelerated phase or frank blastic transformation. The accelerated phase is usually recognized when the blast percentage reaches between 10–19% of the white blood cells in the peripheral blood or nucleated cells of the bone marrow, if the percentage of basophils is > 20%, if there is persistent thrombocytopenia, if there is increasing spleen size and increasing white blood cell count, or there is cytogenetic evidence of a new clonal abnormality. The blastic phase resembles acute leukaemia, and may be myeloid (70% of cases) or lymphoid (30%). It is recognized when the blast percentage is greater than 20% of the white blood cells in the peripheral blood or nucleated cells of the bone marrow, when there is an extramedullary proliferation of blasts, or when blasts form large aggregates in the bone marrow. The prognosis in the accelerated phase is poor, and the prognosis in the blastic phase is even worse.

Chronic Neutrophilic Leukaemia

Chronic neutrophilic leukaemia is a very rare CMPD characterized by a sustained and marked neutrophilia

(Zittoun *et al.*, 1994). Patients often present with hepatosplenomegaly (enlargement of the liver and spleen). Laboratory studies demonstrate a sustained and marked increase in the number of mature neutrophils in the peripheral blood in the absence of blasts. The bone marrow is hypercellular, with an increase in neutrophilic granulocytes, and myeloblasts are normal in number. Before establishing the diagnosis, one must rule out an identifiable cause of a reactive neutrophilia or any evidence of another CMPD, a MDS or a MDS/MPD disorder. Karyotypic studies are usually normal, although clonal cytogenetic abnormalities may be present in a minority of cases. Specifically, the identification of the BCR/ABL translocation would indicate the diagnosis of CML rather than chronic neutrophilic leukaemia. The survival is usually measured in years, although the development of myelodysplastic features may indicate transformation, with a worse prognosis.

Chronic Eosinophilic Leukaemia/Hypereosinophilic Syndrome

Chronic eosinophilic leukaemia and the closely related hypereosinophilic syndrome are rare CMPDs, characterized by a sustained and marked eosinophilia (Weller and Bubley, 1994). The disease occurs in all age groups, with a marked predilection for males. Patients usually present with nonspecific symptoms. The diagnosis of chronic eosinophilic leukaemia is based on the presence of sustained and marked eosinophilia in the blood and bone marrow, 2–20% blasts in the blood or 5–20% blasts in the bone marrow, and the demonstration of a clonal chromosomal abnormality (or demonstration of clonality by other means) in the eosinophilic population. It is important to exclude all causes of reactive eosinophilia (including allergy or another neoplastic disease such as a clonal T cell neoplasm that may secondarily cause eosinophilia), and all neoplasms in which a proliferation of eosinophils is part of the neoplastic process (such as CML). When it is not possible to demonstrate clonality and if there is no increase in blasts in the peripheral blood or the bone marrow, then a diagnosis of hypereosinophilic syndrome is usually made. Survival is variable, although the presence of marked splenomegaly, the presence of increased blasts in the peripheral blood or bone marrow, or the presence of dysplastic features in the other myeloid cell lineages are poor prognostic signs.

Polycythemia Vera

Polycythemia vera is a CMPD characterized by an increase in the red blood cell mass (Bilgrami and Greenberg, 1995). The disease usually occurs in older adults, and there is a slight male predilection. Patients usually present with hypertension or an episode of venous or arterial thrombosis, due to changes in blood viscosity due to the increased red numbers of cells. Typically, there is an increased red blood cell mass $> 25\%$ over the mean normal predicted value. It is important to exclude all causes of a reactive erythrocytosis, such as chronic hypoxia, which can usually be ruled out by the presence of low serum erythropoietin levels. Often, there is also thrombocytosis (increased numbers of platelets) and a leukocytosis. In the early stages, the bone marrow usually shows marked hypercellularity, with prominent erythroid and megakaryocytic proliferation. However, there is no abnormality in the pattern of maturation. Later in the disease process, the red blood cell mass becomes normal or may be less than normal ('spent phase'). At this time, the bone marrow usually shows marked fibrosis, and may even show new bone formation (osteosclerosis), a pattern that has been referred to as post-polycythemic myelofibrosis. The spleen may then become greatly enlarged, containing extramedullary haematopoiesis, with erythroid, granulocytic, and megakaryocytic elements present in the sinuses. In about 20% of patients, transformation to a myelodysplastic syndrome or blast transformation to acute leukaemia may occur. There are no specific cytogenetic abnormalities, and clonal cytogenetic abnormalities are found in only a minority of patients in the early stage of disease. The identification of the *BCR/ABL* translocation would indicate CML rather than polycythemia vera. Clonal chromosomal abnormalities are seen in the majority of patients when progression to a myelodysplastic syndrome or acute leukaemia has occurred. Untreated, most patients die of the vascular complications within a period of months. However, with adequate treatment, long survivals are common.

Chronic Idiopathic Myelofibrosis

Chronic idiopathic myelofibrosis is an uncommon clonal CMPD characterized by the proliferation of the megakaryocytic and granulocytic lines in the bone marrow, associated with a marked fibrosis of the marrow (Tefferi, 2000). It occurs mainly in older adults, with no sex predilection. Clinically, many patients are asymptomatic at diagnosis, with the disease often discovered after routine laboratory work, although there may be nonspecific symptoms. There are usually two stages in the disease course. In the prefibrotic stage, there is usually mild anaemia, with leukocytosis and thrombocytosis. The bone marrow is usually hypercellular due to a neutrophilic and megakaryocytic proliferation, with minimal if any fibrosis. In the fibrotic stage, there is usually a marked anaemia, with variable white blood cell and platelet counts. The bone marrow now usually shows a decrease in cellularity, with a prominent atypical megakaryocytic proliferation. However, the most striking finding is a marked marrow fibrosis, sometimes along with osteosclerosis (**Figures 6 and 7; see colour plate section**). At this stage, the patients often have a marked splenomegaly and hepatomegaly due to the presence of extramedullary haematopoiesis. In a subset of cases, there is progression to an accelerated phase, usually identified by the presence of 10–19% blasts in the blood or bone marrow. Although clonal cytogenetics abnormalities occur in the majority of patients, there have been no specific defects identified; the presence of the *BCR/ABL* translocation would indicate CML. The median survival is about 5 years. Although many patients die of consequences of marrow failure (infection, haemorrhage, etc.), about 20% of patients eventually transform to acute myeloid leukaemia.

Essential Thrombocythemia

Essential thrombocythemia is a rare clonal CMPD that is characterized by the proliferation of the megakaryocyte line (Murphy *et al.*, 1997). It usually occurs in older adults, with no sex predilection, although there is a second smaller peak at about 30 years with a predilection for women. Clinically, about one-half of patients are asymptomatic and present only with an increased platelet count discovered on routine laboratory work. However, one-half of patients present with the complications of increased platelets, namely thromboembolic events or haemorrhage. Essential thrombocythemia is diagnosed when there is a sustained and marked thrombocytosis in the absence of any other possible causes. This means that there must be no evidence of other CMPDs, particularly polycythemia vera, CML, or chronic idiopathic myelofibrosis; no evidence of MDS, and no evidence that the thrombocytosis could be due to a reactive cause. The blood shows marked thrombocytosis, with the platelets exhibiting a variety of sizes and shapes, without other major findings. The bone marrow is usually normocellular or mildly hypercellular, but demonstrates a marked proliferation of large to giant megakaryocytes, without the formation of significant fibrosis. There are no specific cytogenetic abnormalities, and most patients usually have normal studies. Clinically, the patients generally survive longer than 10 years, with the only threats to life from thrombosis or haemorrhage. Transformation to MDS or an acute leukaemia occurs in less than 5% of patients, and often as a consequence of the treatment rather than part of the history of the disease.

Chronic Myeloproliferative Disease: Unclassifiable

Some CMPDs cannot readily be classified into the categories delineated above. This group of cases accounts for about 10–20% of all cases of CMPDs. Some of these cases are identified at too early a stage to recognize as a specific entity, others are identified at too late a stage to recognize as a specific entity, while others seems to have overlapping features of two or more CMPDs. The presence of the *BCR/ABL* translocation would indicate CML, regardless of the morphologic features.

MYELODYSPLASTIC SYNDROMES

MDS (dysmyelopoietic syndromes, preleukaemia) are clonal haematopoietic disorders characterized by dysplasia and ineffective haematopoiesis in one or more of the major myeloid cell lineages (Heaney and Golde, 1999). They have an incidence of about 3 per 100,000 annually in Western countries. They most often occur in older adults. MDS occur either primary or secondary to therapy. Therapies that have been associated with MDS include chemotherapeutic agents, particularly alkalyting agents, as well as radiotherapy. Risk factors for primary MDS include benzene exposure, cigarette smoking, and Fanconi's anaemia. Patients with MDS usually present with symptoms related to bone marrow failure, namely anaemia, neutropenia, or thrombocytopenia. The bone marrow is usually hypercellular or normocellular, and demonstrates dysplasia in one or more of the myeloid cell lines (Bennett *et al.*, 1982). Dysplasia is recognized morphologically by the presence of features not associated with the normal maturation sequence in at least 10% of the cell lineage. Dyserythropoiesis manifests as deviation from the normal circular nuclear outline, multinucleation, an abnormal granular chromatin appearance called megaloblastoid, ringed sideroblasts (erythroid precursors in which one third or more of the nucleus is encirculed by ten or more iron granules representing iron in the cristae of mitochrondria), vacuolization, or cells with an abnormal deposition of a periodic acid-Schiff reactive substance in the cytoplasm. Dysgranulopoiesis manifests as small cell size, nuclear hypolobation or hyposegmentation, and cytoplasmic hypogranularity, or the presence of abnormal ('Chediak-Higashi') granules. Abnormal maturation may also be recognized by the presence of small clusters of blasts and promyelocytes in an abnormal location, in the central part of the marrow away from the bone, a phenomenon called abnormal localization of immature precursors. Megakaryocyte dysplasia manifests as abnormalities in or the loss of lobulation of the nuclei (**Figure 8; see colour plate section**). Common cytogenetic abnormalities include abnormalities of chromosomes 5 or 7, trisomy of chromosome 8, or deletion of chromosome 20q. A del(17p) is typical of therapy-related MDS. Regardless of the specific type of MDS, individual cases can be stratified by the percentage of blasts, the karyotype, and the number of affected cell lineages, into four risk groups of different prognosis (Greenberg *et al.*, 1997). Poor risk karyotypes include those cases with complex (> 3) abnormalities or abnormalities of chromosome 7, while good risk karyotypes include no abnormalities or the presence of an isolated del(5q).

Age at diagnosis also affects prognosis, with patients younger than 60 having a more favourable outcome.

Refractory Anaemia

As seen in **Table 1**, there are at least six subtypes of MDS. Refractory anaemia is a MDS with unilineage dysplasia affecting the erythroid series. It is relatively uncommon, occurring primarily in older adults. By definition, there are < 5% blasts in the bone marrow and less than 15% ringed sideroblasts. Abnormal karyotypes may be present in about one-quarter of patients, but no specific recurrent abnormalities are seen. The prognosis of these cases is good (median survival of about 5 years), with a low rate of progression to acute myeloid leukaemia.

Refractory Anaemia with Ringed Sideroblasts

Refractory anaemia with ringed sideroblasts is morphologically similar to refractory anaemia, except that, by definition, > 15% of the nucleated erythroid cells are ringed sideroblasts. It is relatively common, comprising about 10% of cases of MDS. It occurs primarily in older adults, with a predilection for males. Abnormal cytogenetics are seen in about 10% of cases. There is a good prognosis, with a very low rate of progression to acute leukaemia.

Refractory Anaemia with Multilineage Dysplasia

Refractory anaemia with multilineage dysplasia is a MDS with dysplasia in two or more of the myeloid cell lineages. By definition, there are also < 5% blasts in the bone marrow. There are two subcategories, depending upon whether the percentage of ringed sideroblasts is less than or more than 15%. It is relatively common, comprising about 25% of cases of MDS. Clonal cytogenetic abnormalities are found in up to 50% of patients. The prognosis is intermediate (median survival of about 3 years), with about a 10% rate of progression to acute leukaemia. There is no significant difference in survival between the two subcategories.

Refractory Anaemia with Excess Blasts

Refractory anaemia with excess blasts (RAEB) is defined as a MDS with 5–19% blasts in the bone marrow. This is divided into two categories, with RAEB-1 defined as having 5–9% blasts in the bone marrow and < 5% blasts in the blood; and RAEB-2 defined as having either 10–19% blasts in the bone marrow, 5–19% blasts in the blood and < 10% blasts in the bone marrow, or the presence of Auer rods. Clonal cytogenetic abnormalities are found in up to 50% of cases, and may be complex. The prognosis is generally poor (median survival of about 1 year), with about one-third of patients progressing to acute leukaemia.

Myelodysplastic Syndrome Associated with Isolated del(5q) Chromosome Abnormality

Myelodysplastic syndrome associated with isolated del(5q) chromosome abnormality ('5q syndrome') is a relatively uncommon MDS defined by its cytogenetic abnormality in the presence of < 5% blasts in the blood and bone marrow (Boultwood et al., 1994). It occurs in adults, with a marked predilection for females. Most patients present with anaemia, and the bone marrow is usually hypercellular. The 5q deletion involves bands q31 and q33, and by definition, no other cytogenetic abnormalities are present. The prognosis of these cases is excellent, with median survivals greater than 5 years, and progression to acute leukaemia not commonly seen.

MYELODYSPLASTIC/ MYELOPROLIFERATIVE DISEASES

The myelodysplastic/myeloproliferative diseases (MDS/MPD) are as yet poorly understood clonal haematopoietic diseases that share features of both MDS and CMPD. They are rare, with an annual incidence below 1 per 100,000 in Western countries. Their age distribution varies with the specific disease, although a male predilection is seen in all types. The aetiology in most cases is unknown. Typically, patients have evidence of proliferation of one or more of the myeloid lineages along with evidence of dysplastic or ineffective proliferation in other lineages. By definition, the percentage of blasts is < 20%. Patients with well-defined CMPD who develop dysplasia or whose disease carries the *BCR/ABL* translocation (indicative of CML) are not placed in this disease category but are considered to have CMPD with progression to MDS.

Chronic Myelomonocytic Leukaemia

Chronic myelomonocytic leukaemia (CMML) is a clonal haematopoietic neoplasm in which a mature monocytosis is the dominant feature (Germing et al., 1998). It comprises about 3 cases annually per 100,000 in Western population. It occurs primarily in older adults, with a male predilection. Patients generally present with non-specific symptoms, and are found to have a significant monocytosis on laboratory evaluation. There may be splenomegaly, due to infiltration of the sinuses by monocytes. The diagnosis is based on the presence of a sustained and marked monocytosis, < 20% blasts or immature monocytic cells in the peripheral blood or bone marrow, dysplasia involving one or more of the myeloid lineages, and the absence of the *BCR/ABL* translocation. It is further classified into CMML-1, if the blast count is < 5% in the blood and < 10% in the bone marrow, or CMML-2, if the blast count is above this level (but still

< 20%). Clonal karyotypic abnormalities are seen in about one-third of patients, most frequently +8, −7/del(7q) and t(5;12). Many patients have point mutation of the *RAS* genes. The median survival is about 3 years, with progression to acute leukaemia in about 20% of cases.

Atypical Chronic Myeloid Leukaemia

Atypical chronic myeloid leukaemia (subacute myeloid leukaemia) is a very rare disease characterized by proliferative and dysplastic changes in the neutrophilic lineage (Hernandez *et al.*, 1999). Patients either present with non-specific symptoms and are found to have abnormal blood smear, or they may present with splenomegaly. The diagnosis is based on the presence of a sustained and marked neutrophilia in the peripheral blood with neutrophilic precursors representing > 10% of the white blood cells, a hypercellular bone marrow with dysplasia of the granulocytic line, < 20% blasts in the blood or bone marrow, and the absence of a basophilia, a monocytosis, or the *BCR/ABL* translocation. The bone marrow often shows dysplasia of the erythroid and megakaryocytic lines in addition. Cytogenetic abnormalities are found in a majority of patients. The prognosis is poor, with a median survival less than 2 years.

Juvenile Myelomonocytic Leukaemia

Juvenile myelomonocytic leukaemia is a rare disease of childhood characterized by proliferative changes in the granulocytic and monocytic lineages (Luna-Fineman *et al.*, 1999). It primarily occurs in children under the age of 3, with a predilection for males. About 10% of cases occur in association with neurofibromatosis type 1. Patients generally present with non-specific symptoms or evidence of haemorrhage. The diagnosis is based on the presence of a high white blood cell count with an increase in monocytes and the percentage of immature granulocytes, with < 20% blasts or immature monocytic cells in the blood or bone marrow and absence of the *BCR/ABL* translocation. The bone marrow is hypercellular and may show mild dysplastic features in one or more of the major cell lineages. Cytogenetic abnormalities, particularly monosomy 7, occur in about one-third of patients. The prognosis is generally poor, although some patients survive long periods (even without therapy).

REFERENCES

Arber, D. A. (2001). Realistic pathologic classification of acute myeloid leukemias. *American Journal of Clinical Pathology*, **115**, 552–560.

Bennett, J. M., *et al.* (1982). Proposals for the classification of the myelodysplastic syndromes. *British Journal of Haematology*, **52**, 189–199.

Bennett, J. M., *et al.* (1985). Proposed revised criteria for the classification of acute myeloid leukemia. A report of the French-American-British Cooperative Group. *Annals of Internal Medicine*, **103**, 620–625.

Bilgrami, S. and Greenberg, B. R. (1995). Polycythemia rubra vera. *Seminars in Oncology*, **22**, 307–326.

Boultwood, J., *et al.* (1994). The 5q- syndrome. *Blood*, **84**, 3253–3260.

Caligiuri, M. A., *et al.* (1997). Molecular biology of acute myeloid leukemia. *Seminars in Oncology*, **24**, 32–44.

Faderl, S., *et al.* (1999). Chronic myelogenous leukemia: biology and therapy. *Annals of Internal Medicine*, **131**, 207–219.

Germing, U., *et al.* (1998). Problems in the classification of CMML—dysplastic versus proliferative type. *Leukemia Research*, **22**, 871–878.

Greenberg, P., *et al.* (1997). International scoring system for evaluating prognosis in myelodysplastic syndromes. *Blood*, **89**, 2079–2088.

Heaney, M. L. and Golde, D. W. (1999). Myelodysplasia. *New England Journal of Medicine*, **340**, 1649–1660.

Hernandez, J. M., *et al.* (1999). Clinical, hematological and cytogenetic characteristics of atypical chronic myeloid leukemia. *Annals of Oncology*, **11**, 441–444.

Jaffe, E. S., *et al.* (2001). *Pathology & Genetics. Tumours of Haematopoietic and Lymphoid Tissues.* (IARCPress).

Luna-Fineman, S., *et al.* (1999). Myelodysplastic and myeloproliferative disorders of childhood: a study of 167 patients. *Blood*, **93**, 459–466.

Melnick, A. and Licht, J. D. (1999). Deconstructing a disease: RARalpha, its fusion partners, and their roles in the pathoogenesis of acute promyelocytic leukemia. *Blood*, **93**, 3167–3215.

Melo, J. V. (1996). The diversity of BCR-ABL fusion proteins and their relationship to leukemia phenotype. *Blood*, **88**, 2375–2384.

Murphy, S., *et al.* (1997). Experience of the Polycythemia Vera Study Group with essential thrombocythemia: a final report on diagnostic criteria, survival, and leukemia transition by treatment. *Seminars in Hematology*, **34**, 29–39.

Sieff, C. A., *et al.* (1998). The anatomy and physiology of hematopoiesis. In: Nathan, D. G., *et al.* (Eds), *Nathan and Oski's Hematology of Infancy and Childhood*, 5th ed. (WB Saunders, Philadelphia), 161–236.

Tefferi, A. (2000). Myelofibrosis with myeloid metaplasia. *New England Journal of Medicine*, **342**, 1255–1265.

Weller, P. F. and Bubley, G. J. (1994). The idiopathic hypereosinophilic syndrome. *Blood*, **83**, 2759–2779.

Zittoun, R., *et al.* (1994). Chronic neutrophilic leukemia. A study of four cases. *Annals of Hematology*, **68**, 55–60.

FURTHER READING

Brunning, R. D. and McKenna, R. D. (1994). *Tumors of the Bone Marrow. Atlas of Tumor Pathology.* (Armed Forces Institute of Pathology).